JPN&Co.

D1363946

Volume
1

I.I.T.
MATHEMATICS

For JEE Main & Advanced

and many other Engineering Entrance Examinations

PROF. M.L. KHANNA
Head of Mathematics Department (Retd.)
Meerut College, MEERUT

PROF. J.N. SHARMA
Senior Lecturer, Mathematics Department (Retd.)
Meerut College, MEERUT

Revised by

DR. SUDHIR K. PUNDIR
Associate Professor
Department of Mathematics
S.D. (P.G.) College, MUZAFFARNAGAR

Er. Ajay Khanna | **Er. Atul Khanna**
(I.I.T Roorkee) | (I.I.T Delhi)

Newly Revised & Enlarged Edition

PUBLISHED BY:

JAI PRAKASH NATH & CO.

EDUCATIONAL PUBLISHERS
MEERUT
A Dharmendra Nath Gupta Group

ANNIVERSARY
100 YEARS
of
Celebrations
JAI PRAKASH NATH & CO.

Like us at : facebook.com/jpnco1914 | WEBSITE : www.jpncobooks.com

Published by :

JAI PRAKASH NATH & CO.

Head Office
Gandhi Ashram Crossing, Garh Road
Meerut City - 250 002 (U.P.) INDIA
Tel. : Off. : 0121-4004414, 6549111
Fax : : 0121-2600013
email : jpn1914@gmail.com

Like us at : facebook.com/jpnco1914

WEBSITE : www.jpncobooks.com

A DHARMENDRA NATH GUPTA GROUP

Newly Revised Edition, 2016-17

I.S.B.N. : 978-81-929005-2-0

Price : ₹ ████.00 only

(Combined Price for Vol-1 and Vol-2)
Not to be sold separately.

Typesetted at :

BALAJI Computers
Meerut.

Printed at :

Sunny Offset
Meerut.

Preface to the Revised Edition

We have no words to express our gratitude towards our worthy students on account of whose keen interest and continuous suggestions this book today appearing in its new revised and enlarged edition. The teachers and coaching institute of All India fame have been kind enough to recommend this book to the competitions.

We have been regularly revising the subject matter by replacing the old solutions with better ones and also by adding new and important type questions. In almost all the chapters the exercise have been rearranged topic wise.

This time the book has undergone through revision according to the revised syllabus for **JEE-Main and Advanced 2012 onwards.** It includes the chapter on **Set, Relations and Functions, Height and distance and Mathematical reasoning.** The **concept of mean value theorems** have been added in the chapter of limit, continuity and differentiability. Almost in every chapter, new questions has been added to make the book more exhaustive.

All the necessary results and theorems have been given in the begining of each chapter followed by problem set on these results and theorems. Solution to these problems have been given as well. In the end we have given objective type questions. Our sincere advice to the students is that they should attempt the questions in problem set independently. If they fail to do so then they should look to the solutions given in the book.

We are grateful to M/s Jai Prakash Nath & Co., for publishing this volumnious book and organising its sales throughout this country. We are grateful to Almighty on account of whose blessing the book is appearing into latest edition.

In the end, we invite both the competitors and the teachers to suggest any improvement in this book or to point out any printing mistake or suggest any other new questions which they may like to be incorporated in this book.

—**Authors**

Contents

Volume 1

Algebra

Trigonometry

ACKNOWLEDGEMENT

This is what Chetan Bhagat writes about Prof. M.L. Khanna's I.I.T. Mathematics in his book.

the 3 mistakes of my life
chetan bhagat

(on page 85-86)

'The biggest-selling English-language novelist in India's history' —**New York Times**

- 'Guides are a short cut. They solve a certain number of problems. You need to understand the concepts.'
- The shopkeeper brought out the orange and black cover Resnick and Halliday. Yes, the cover was scary and dull at the same time, something possible only in physics books.
- 'I won't understand it. But if you want to, let's buy it,' Vidya agreed.
- 'Of course, you will understand it. **And uncle, for maths do you have M.L. Khanna ?**'
- I could see his displeasure in me calling him uncle, but someone needed to remind him.
- '**Maths Khanna,**' the shopkeeper shouted. His assistant pulled out the yellow and black tome. Now if Resnick and Halliday is scary, **M.L. Khanna is the Exorcist.** I haven't seen a thicker book and every page is filled with the hardest maths problems in the world. It was amusing that a person with a **friendly name like M.L. Khanna could do this to the students of our country.**
- 'What is this ?' Vidya said and tried to lift the book with her left hand. She couldn't. She used both hands and finally took it six inches off the ground. 'No, seriously, what is this ? **An assault weapon?'**
- '**It covers every topic,**' I said and measured the thickness with the fingers of my right hand, the four fingers fell short.
- She held her hand sideways over mine to assist.
- 'Six, it is six fingers thick,' she said softly.
- I pulled my hand out, lest uncle raise his eyebrows again, or worst case join his hand to ours to check the thickness.

1. `...Bhagat has touched a nerve with young Indian readers acquired almost cult status'

    International Herald Tribune

2. `...a well-constructed book with great characters and a captivating plot. Definitely on the right side of five-point something on the 10-point scale'

    India Today

3. `It's easy to forget that Five Point Someone has been penned by a first time author ... a compelling read...'

    Hindustantimes.com

4. `a rockstar of Indian publishing'

    Times of India

Instructions for Reasoning type Questions

(a) if STATEMENT-1 is True, STATEMENT-2 is True, STATEMENT-2 is a correct explanation for STATEMENT-1.

(b) if STATEMENT-1 is True, STATEMENT-2 is True, STATEMENT-2 is NOT a correct explanation for STATEMENT-1.

(c) STATEMENT-1 is True, STATEMENT-2 is False.

(d) STATEMENT-1 is False. STATEMENT-2 is True.

CHAPTER

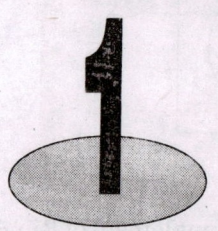

Algebra

SETS, RELATIONS AND FUNCTIONS

Concept of Sets

A set is any well defined collection of definite, distinguishable objects. The elements of a set may be anything *i.e.* numbers, persons, mountains, rivers etc. The sets are generally denoted by $A, B, C, \ldots\ldots$. If an object belongs to A we write it as $a \in A$ and if it does not belong to A we write it as $a \notin A$.

§1 Description of Sets

(A) Tabular Form : We may list the members of the set *i.e.*
$$A = \{a, e, i, o, u\} \quad \text{or} \quad A = \{2, 4, 6, 8, 10\}$$

(B) Property Form :
$A = \{x : P(x)\}$ where $P(x)$ is the property which the element x must satisfy. The sets written in (A) can be written as
$$A = \{x : x \text{ is a vowel in English Alphabet}\}$$
or $\quad A = \{x : x \text{ is an even number} \leq 10\}$

(C) Equality of Sets : *If A, B are sets such that every element of A belongs to B, and every element of B belongs to A, then A and B are the same sets and we write*
$$A = B.$$

(D) Subsets : *If A and B are sets such that every element of A is also an element of B, then A is said to be a **subset** of B. Symbolically, we write*
$$A \subset B,$$
which is read "A is a subset of B" or "A is contained in B". We may also write this relationship as
$$B \supset A,$$
which is read "B is a superset of A" or "B contains A". Two sets A and B are said to be **comparable** if A is a sub-set of B or B is a sub-set of A. The sets are said to be **non-comparable** if A is not a subset of B and B is not a superset of A.

Two sets A and B are said to be **disjoint** if no element of A is in B and no element of B is in A.

(E) Universal Set : In any application of set theory, all the sets under consideration will likely be subsets of a fixed set. We call such a set the "**Universal set**" or '**Universe**' of discourse. Our sets would then be collections of points chosen from the universe. If we choose all real numbers **R** for our universe, we may define many elementary sets from this universe. Thus the set **Q** of all rational numbers, the set **I** of all integers, the set of all even integers, the set **N** of all natural numbers, the set of all real numbers less than or equal to 1, are simple examples of sets in this case.

We shall use the letter U or the letter X for the universal set unless otherwise stated.

(F) The null set. We know that a set may be determined from a fixed universe by stating any property that its elements must satisfy. We frequently write a set as
$$\{x \in U : P(x)\}$$
where U is the universe of discourse. If we take $P(x)$ to be the statement $x \neq x$, it is evident that P is not true for any element of the universe. We must, therefore, agree to take the collection of no elements as a set. We shall call such a set the **empty set** or the **void set** or the **null set** and always denote it by the ϕ. It is easy to see that the empty set is a subset of every set.

(G) Power set : Power set of a set A is the collection of all subsets of A and is denoted by $P(A)$ or $2A$.

It is easy to see that if A has n elements, then $P(A)$ will have 2^n elements.

Let set $A = \{a, b, c\}$ consisting of three elements. Then we will show that $P(A)$ has $2^n = 2^3 = 8$ elements namely $\phi, \{a\}, \{b\}, \{c\}, \{a, b\}, \{b, c\}, \{c, a\}$ and $\{a, b, c\}$. *i.e.*, 8 elements which are subsets of set A.

(H) Venn-Euler Diagrams : A device known as a Venn-Euler diagram or simply Venn Diagram is very often used to assist thinking on the relations which may exist between some subsets of the universal set. A Venn-diagram is a systematic representation of sets by sets of points. The universal set is represented by points within a rectangle and a subset A of the universal set, say U, is represented by the interior of a circle (or some other simple closed curve). Disjoint sets are depicted by non-overlapping regions and set inclusion is depicted by taking one region lying entirely within the other.

§2 Basic operations on Sets

(A) Union of two sets. *If A and B are two sets, then the set of all elements which either belong to A or to B is called the union of the two sets and is denoted by* $A \cup B$.

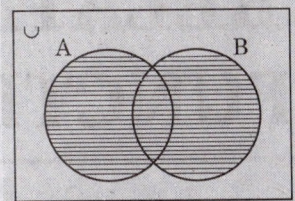

Fig. (1)

It is usually read as "*A* union *B*" or "*A* cup *B*". Union is also known as "join" or "logical sum" of *A* and *B*.

Thus $A \cup B = \{x : x \in A \text{ or } x \in B\}$.

In the following Venn-diagram, the union of *A* and *B* is shown with shaded area.

Note that we have used the word 'or' non-exclusively, as a customary in mathematics so that the points that belong to both *A* and *B* also belong to $A \cup B$.

Union of *n* sets $A_1, A_2, ..., A_n$ is denoted and defined as

$$\overset{n}{\underset{i=1}{\cup}} A_i = \{x : x \in A_i \text{ for at least one } i\}.$$

(B) Intersection of two sets. *If A and B are given sets then the intersection of A and B is the set of all elements which belong to both A and B and is denoted by* $A \cap B$.

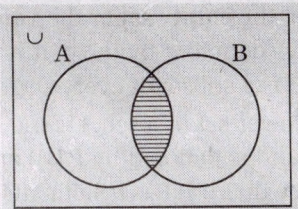

Fig. (2)

Thus $A \cap B = \{x : x \in A \text{ and } x \in B\}$.

It is usually read as "*A* intersection *B*" or "*A* cap *B*". In the adjoining Venn diagram the intersection of *A* and *B* is shown with shaded area.

Intersection of *n* sets $A_1, A_2, ... A_n$ is denoted and defined by

$$\overset{n}{\underset{i=1}{\cap}} A_i = \{x : x \in A_i \text{ for all } i\}$$

(C) Complement. The complement of a set *B* relative to another set *A* is the set of all elements (points) which belong to *A* but which do not belong to *B* and is denoted by $A \sim B$ or by $A - B$. It is sometimes called the **difference** of *A* and *B* in that order and is read as "*A* difference *B*" or "*A* minus *B*". Thus

$$A - B = \{x : x \in A \text{ and } x \notin B\}.$$

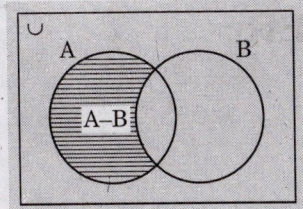

Fig. (3)

If $B \subset A$, then $A - B$ is called the complement of *B* in *A*. The complement of a set *A* relative to universal set *U* is the set of all points which do not belong to *A* and which, of course, belong to *U*. It is denoted by $U - A$ or by $\sim A$ or A^c or by A'. We shall adopt the last notation, that is, A' for the complement of *A*. Thus

$$A' = \{x : x \in U \text{ and } x \notin A\}$$

or simply $A' = \{x : x \notin A\}$.

In future, by a complement of a set we shall understand the complement of the set relative to the universal set unless otherwise stated.

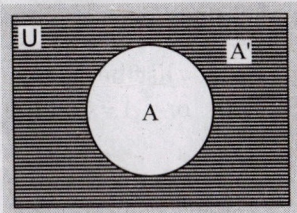

Fig. (4)

In the following Venn diagrams $A - B$ and A' are shown as shaded.

Symmetric difference. $A \triangle B$ of two sets *A* and *B* is defined by

$$A \triangle B = (A - B) \cup (B - A).$$

(D) Cartesian Product of two sets. If $a \in A$ and $b \in B$ where *A* and *B* are sets, then (a, b) denotes what may be called an **ordered pair** whose first member is *a* and second member is *b*. Two ordered pairs (a, b) and (c, d) are said to be equal if and only if $a = c$ and $b = d$. Thus the ordered pairs (1, 2) and (2, 1) are different. Here (a, b) is not the same thing as the set $\{a, b\}$ for we always have $\{a, b\} = \{b, a\}$. The **cartesian product** of two sets *A* and *B* is the set $\{(a, b) : a \in A \text{ and } b \in B\}$ and is denoted by $A \times B$. That is, the cartesian product of two sets *A* and *B* is the set of all ordered pairs whose first member (or co-ordinate) belongs to *A* and whose second member (co-ordinate) belongs to *B*.

If *A* has *m* elements and *B* has *n* elements, then $A \times B$ has *mn* elements.

(E) The cartesian product of n sets. $A_1, A_2, ... A_n$ is the set of all ordered *n* tuples $(a_1, a_2, ... a_n)$, $a_i \in A_i$. $i = 1, 2, ..., n$ and is denoted by $A_1 \times A_2 \times ... \times A_n$ or $\overset{n}{\underset{i=1}{\Pi}} A_i$.

(F) Some elementary results.

(i)	$A \subset A \cup B, B \subset A \cup B$
(ii)	$A \cap B \subset A, A \cap B \subset B$
(iii)	$A \cup A = A, A \cap A = A$
(iv)	$A \subset B \Leftrightarrow A \cup B = B, A \subset B \Leftrightarrow A \cap B = A$
(v)	$A \cup \phi = A, A \cap \phi = \phi$
(vi)	$A \cup U = U, A \cap U = U$
(vii)	$A - A = \phi, A - \phi = A$
(viii)	$\phi' = U, U' = \phi, (A')' = A.$

(G) A notation for number of elements in a set. We shall denote the number of distinct elements in a set A by $n(A)$. We also say that the **cardinal number** of the set A is $n(A)$.

(H) Fundamental Set Operations

1. (i) $[A \subset B$ and $B \subset C] \Rightarrow A \subset C.$
   (ii) $[A \subset B, B \subset C, C \subset A] \Rightarrow B = C$
2. (i) $A \cup B = B \cup A$
   and $A \cap B = B \cap A$ (Commutative law)
   (ii) $A \cup (B \cup C) = (A \cup B) \cup C$
   and $A \cap (B \cap C) = (A \cap B) \cap C$ (Associative Law)
   (iii) $A \cup A = A$ and $A \cap A = A$ (Idempotent Law)
   (iv) $A \cap (B \cup C) = (A \cap B) \cup (A \cap C)$
   and $A \cup (B \cap C) = (A \cup B) \cap (A \cup C)$
                             (Distributive Law)
3. (i) $(A \cup B)' = A' \cap B'$
   and $(A \cap B)' = A' \cup B'$ (De-Morgan's Law)
   (ii) $A - (B \cup C) = (A - B) \cap (A - C)$
   and $A - (B \cap C) = (A - B) \cup (A - C)$
            (Generalized De-Morgan's Law)

§3 Relations and Functions from a Set A to a Set B

(A) Definitions : *A relation between two sets A and B is a sub-set of $A \times B$. Symbolically R is a relation A to B iff $R \subset A \times B$. If $A = B$, we say that R is a **relation on A**. We write aRb iff $(a, b) \in R$ and say that **a is R-related to b** or that **b is a R-relative of a**. We also write $a(\sim R)b$ if a is not R-related to b.*

Total Number of relations from a set A to a set B : If A consists of m elements and B consists of n elements, then $A \times B$ consists of mn elements and so $\mathbf{P}(A \times B)$ will have 2^{mn} elements. Hence the total number of different relations from A to B is 2^{mn}.

Domain and Range of a Relation : If R is a relation from a set A to another set B then the domain of R is the set of all first co-ordinates of the members of R and the range of R is the set of all second co-ordinates of the members of R. Thus

Domain $R = \{a : (a, b) \in R$ for some $b \in B\}$
Range $R = \{b : (a, b) \in R$ for some $a \in A\}.$

Example 1 : Let A be the set of all men living in a certain locality of Delhi and B the set of all women in the same locality. Then the statement "a is the husband of b where $a \in A$ and $b \in B$" defines a relation from A to B. If we denote this relation by R, then R will be the set of all ordered pairs in which the first co-ordinate is a man who is the husband of the second co-ordinate which is a woman. Evidently R is a subset of $A \times B$. Note carefully that the relation is the set R and not the verbal phrase "is the husband of." Here the domain of R is the set of all husbands and the range of R is the set of all wives.

(B) The identity relation : Let A be any set. Then the identity relation I_A (or diagonal relation) on A is denoted by setting $(a, b) \in I_A$ iff $a = b$. The domain and range of I_A are both A.

Example 2. Let $A = \{1, 2, 3, 4\}$. Then the identity relation
$$I_A = \{(1, 1), (2, 2), (3, 3), (4, 4)\}.$$

(C) The inverse relation : Let R be a relation from a set A to another set B. Then the inverse relation R^{-1} of R defined by setting $(b, a) \in R^{-1}$ iff $(a, b) \in R$. Evidently the range of R is the domain of R^{-1} and the domain of R is the range of R^{-1}. If $A = B$, then R and R^{-1} are both relations on A.

Example 3. Let R be the relation on the set $\mathbf{R}$ of real numbers defined by "x is less than y where $x, y \in \mathbf{R}$". Then R^{-1} is the relation defined by "y is greater than x where $x, y \in \mathbf{R}$".

(D) The composition relation : Let R be a relation from A to B and S be the relation from B to C, then the composition relation, denoted as SoR, is the relation from A to C defined by setting $(a, c) \in SoR$ iff there exists a point $b \in B$ such that $(a, b) \in R$ and $(b, c) \in S$.

(E) Reflexive Relation. A relation R on a set A is said to be reflexive iff $aRa \; \forall \; a \in A$, that is, iff $(a, a) \in R \; \forall \; a \in A$.

                                (Note 'for all a')

Evidently a relation S on a set A is reflexive iff $I_A \subset R$.

(F) Symmetric Relation : A relation R on a set A is said to be symmetric iff $aRb \Rightarrow bRa$

It is easy to see that a relation R on a set A is symmetric iff
$$R^{-1} = R.$$

(G) Transitive Relation : A relation R on a set A is said to be transitive iff aRb and $bRc \Rightarrow aRc$. (Not for all a, b, c)

Caution. If a relation R is transitive, then xRy and yRz must imply xRz even when $x = z$.

(H) Anti-symmetric Relation : *Let R be a relation on a set A. Then R is said to be anti-symmetric iff*
$$aRb \text{ and } bRa \Rightarrow a = b.$$
Thus R is anti-symmetric if we never have both aRb and bRa except when $a = b$. It is evident that *a relation R on a set A is anti-symmetric iff*
$$R \cap R^{-1} \subset I_A$$
where I_A denotes the identity relation on A.

Example 4. Let N be the set of all natural numbers. Let a relation R on A be defined by "a is a divisor of b where $a, b \in N$". Then R is reflexive since every natural number is a divisor of itself, R is anti-symmetric since a divides b and b divides a implies $a = b$. R is transitive, since a divides b and b divides c implies a divides c.

(I)   *Equivalence Relation : A relation R on a set A is said to be an equivalence relation iff
(i)   *R is reflexive,*   (ii)   *R is symmetric*
(iii) *R is transitive*

(J)   Equivalence Classes : Let A be a non-empty set and let R be an equivalence relation on A. Further let a be an arbitrary element of A. The elements $x \in A$ satisfying aRx constitute a subset A_a of A, called an *equivalence class of A with respect to R determined by a*. This equivalence class will be denoted by A_a or by $[a]$ or a. Thus, $[a] = \{x : x \in A \text{ and } aRx\}$.

(K)   Partitions : Let X be a non-empty set. Then a **partition (or decomposition)** of X is a collection of non-empty disjoint subsets of X whose union is X.

§4   Functions

(A)   Definition : *Let X and Y be two non-empty sets. A subset f of $X \times Y$ is called a function from X to Y iff to* **each** *$x \in X$, there exists a* **unique** *y in Y such that $(x, y) \in f$.*

The other terms used for functions are "mappings", transformations and "operators". We denote this mapping by
$$f : X \to Y \text{ or } X \to$$
It follows from the above definition that a relation from X to Y is a function from X to Y iff
(i)   to each $x \in X$ there exists a $y \in Y$ such that $(x, y) \in f$,
(ii) $(x, y_1) \in f$ and $(x, y_2) \in f \Rightarrow y_1 = y_2$.
The condition (i) ensures that to each x in X, f **associates** an element y in Y and condition (ii) guarantees that y is unique.
We call X, the domain of f and Y the co-domain of f. The unique element y in Y assigned to $x \in X$ is called the **image** of x under f or the **value** of f at x and is denoted by $f(x)$. Also x is called a **pre-image** (or **inverse image**) of y. Note that there may be more than one pre-images of y. The **graph** of f is the subset of $X \times Y$ defined by $\{(x, f(x)) : x \in X\}$. The **range** of f is the set of all images under f and is denoted by $f[X]$. Thus
$f[X] = \{y \in Y : y = f(x) \text{ for some } x \in X\}$
$\qquad = \{f(x) : x \in X\}$.
If $A \subset X$, then the set $\{f(x) : x \in A\}$ is called the image of A under f and is denoted by $f[A]$. If $B \subset Y$; then the set $\{x \in X : f(x) \in B\}$ is called the inverse image of B under f and is denoted by $f^{-1}[B]$.

(B)   Equal functions : Two functions $f : X \to Y$ and $g : X \to Y$ are said to be equal iff $f(x) = g(x)$ for every $x \in X$ and we write $f = g$.

(C)   Constant functions : A function $f : X \to Y$ is called a constant function if, for some $y_0 \in Y$, we have $f(x) = y_0$ for every $x \in X$.

(D)   Identity mapping : Let $I_x : X \to X$ defined by
$$I_x(x) = x \ \forall \ x \in X$$
Then I_x is called the identity mapping on X.

(E)   Inclusion function : If $B \subset A$, then the function
$$i : B \Rightarrow A : i(b) = b \ \forall \ b \in B$$
is called the inclusion function.

(F)   Many-one, one-one onto and into mappings.
Let $f : X \to Y$.
The mapping f is said to be **many-one** iff two or more different elements in X have the same f-image in Y. The mapping f is said to be **one-one** iff different elements in X have different f-images in Y *i.e.* if $x_1 \neq x_2 \Rightarrow f(x_1) \neq f(x_2)$ or   equivalently, $f(x_1) = f(x_2) \Rightarrow x_1 = x_2$. One-one mappings are also called **injection**. The mapping f is said to be **into** if there is **at least** one element in Y which is not the f-image of any element in X. Note that in this case the range of f is a proper subset of Y, that is, $f[X] \subset Y$ and $f[X] \neq Y$. The mapping f is said to be **onto** if **every** element in Y is the f-image of at least one element in X. In this case, the range of f is equal to Y, that is, $f[X] = Y$. Onto mappings are also called **surjection**. One-one and onto mappings are called **bijection**.

(G)   Real valued functions : *If A is any set, then a function from A into R (the set of reals) is a real valued function on A.*
We denote the collection of all real valued function on A by $\mathbf{R}^A$. The collection $\mathbf{R}^A$ inherits an algebraic structure from $\mathbf{R}$ in as much as we can define **addition, multiplication** and **scalar multiplication** as follows,
If $a \in A, r \in \mathbf{R}, f, g \in \mathbf{R}^A$,
then $(f + g)(a) = f(a) + g(a)$,
          $(fg)(a) = f(a) g(a)$,
          $(rf)(a) = r[f(a)]$.

Example 1. Let $X = \{1, 2, 3\}$ and $Y = \{4, 5\}$. Find whether the following subsets of $X \times Y$ are functions from X to Y or not.
(i) $f_1 = \{(1, 4), (1, 5), (2, 4), (3, 5)\}$,
(ii) $f_2 = \{(1, 4), (2, 4), (3, 4)\}$,
(iii) $f_3 = \{(1, 4), (2, 5), (3, 5)\}$
(iv) $f_4 = \{(1, 4), (2, 5)\}$.

Solution.   (i) No, since $(1, 4)$ and $(1, 5)$ are distinct members of f_1 which have the same first co-ordinate, that is, the element 1 has two distinct images 4 and 5 under f_1.

(ii) Yes, since each member of X has a unique image in Y under f_2. Note that the mapping is **many-one into.** $5 \in Y$ does not have a pre-image.

(iii) Yes. This mapping is **many-one-onto.**

(iv) No, since there is no image of 3 under f_4.

Example 2 : Let **R** be the set of all real numbers and let $A = \{0, 1\}$. Let

$f : \mathbf{R} \to A$ defined by

$$f(x) = \begin{cases} 0 \text{ when x is rational} \\ 1 \text{ when x is irrational} \end{cases}$$

Then f is a many-one into function. Here $f[\mathbf{R}] = A$. Since $\frac{1}{2}$ is rational, we have $f\left(\frac{1}{2}\right) = 0$. Similarly $f(2) = 0, f\left(\frac{4}{5}\right) = 0$ etc.

Since $\pi, e, \sqrt{2}, \sqrt{5}$ etc. are irrational numbers, we have

$f(\pi) = f(e) = f(\sqrt{2}) = f\sqrt{(5)} = 1$ etc.

Example 3 : Let $f : \mathbf{R} \to \mathbf{R}$ be defined by

$f(x) = x^2 \ \forall \ x \in \mathbf{R}.$

Then f is a many-one into mapping.

Here $f(a) = a^2, f(-a) = a^2$

where a is a non-zero real number. Also

$f(0) = 0.$

Hence $f[\mathbf{R}] = R_+ \cup (0)$

i.e. the range of f consists of all the positive real numbers together with zero

$f^{-1}[\{1, 2, 3\}] = \{-1, 1, -\sqrt{2}, \sqrt{2}, -\sqrt{3}, \sqrt{3}\}$

$f^{-1}[\{-1, -2\}] = \phi$ etc.

Example 4 : Let $f : \mathbf{R} \to \mathbf{R}$ be defined by

$f(x) = x^3 \ \forall \ x \in \mathbf{R}.$

Then f is one-one onto. It is one-one since different real numbers have different images under f, that is

$x, y \in \mathbf{R}$ and $x \neq y \to f(x) \neq f(y)$

It is onto since for each y in **R** there exists some x in **R** such that $x^3 = y$.

Thus $f^{-1}[\{2\}] = 2^{1/3}$ etc.

(H) Intervals : An open interval on **R** is any set of the form $\{x \in \mathbf{R} : a < x < b\}$ and is denoted by $]a, b[$. A **closed interval** is any set of the form $\{x \in \mathbf{R} : a \leq x \leq b\}$ and is denoted by $[a, b]$. Similarly the sets $\{x \in \mathbf{R} : a \leq x < b\}$ and $\{x \in \mathbf{R} : a < x \leq b\}$ are called **right half open** and **left half open** intervals and are denoted by $[a, b[$ and $]a, b]$ respectively. The sets of the form $\{x \in \mathbf{R} : x > a\}$, $\{x \in \mathbf{R} : x < a\}$, $\{x \in \mathbf{R} : x \geq a\}$, $\{x \in \mathbf{R} : x \leq a\}$ are called **rays** and are respectively denoted by

$]a, \infty[,]-\infty, a[, [a, \infty[$ and $]-\infty, a]$.

The first two are called **open rays** and the last two rays are said to be **closed rays**.

(I) Inverse Mapping : Let $f : X \to Y$. In general $f^{-1}[\{b\}]$ where $b \in Y$ will consist of more than one element or

might even be the empty set ϕ. Now let f be a one-one mapping and let y be any element of $f[X]$. Then there exists a unique element $x \in X$ such that $y = f(x)$. Thus we define a mapping of $f[X]$ onto X which associates to each $y \in f[X]$ a unique element $x \in X$ such that $y = f(x)$. We denote this mapping of $f[X]$ onto X by f^{-1} and call it **the inverse mapping** of f.

Definition. *Let $f : X \to Y$ be a one-one mapping. Then the map*

$$f^{-1} : f[X] \to X$$

which associates to each element $y \in f[X]$ the element $x \in X$ such that $f(x) = y$ is called the **inverse map** *of f.*

If f is one-one and onto, then f^{-1} is a function from Y onto X.

Note that f^{-1} is always a bijective mapping.

(J) Product or composition of mappings : Let X, Y, Z be three sets and let

$f : X \to Y$ and $g : Y \to Z.$

Then under the map f an element $x \in X$ is mapped to an element $y = f(x) \in Y$ which in turn is mapped by g to an element $z \in Z$ such that $z = g(y) = g[f(x)]$.

Thus we have a rule which assigns to each element $x \in X$ a unique element

$z = g(f(x)) \in Z$. Hence we have a mapping of X onto Z. This new mapping is called the composition of mappings f and g and is denoted by $g \circ f$. It is defined by

$$(g \circ f)(x) = g(f(x))$$

It can be shown that if X, Y, Z, W are four sets f, g, h three mappings

$f : X \to Y, g : Y \to Z, h : Z \to W,$

then $(h \circ g) \circ f = h \circ (g \circ f)$

In other words, **the composition of mappings is associative.**

Further *if f, g are one-one onto then $g \circ f$ is also one-one onto, and $(g \circ f)^{-1} = f^{-1} \circ g^{-1}$.*

Important Points to be Remembered

(1) Basic Difference between Relation and Mapping.

Let A and B be two sets.

$f : A \to B$ or $R : A \to B$

Every element belonging to A must have an image in B in the case of mapping.

Now if R is the relation of being "**Husband of**" i.e. every man belonging to A is husband of some woman belonging to B.

Above is not the necessary condition. A bachelor or widower in A cannot be husband of some woman in B. All these types of persons in set A will not have any image in B. This is basic difference between a relation and a mapping or function.

Every function is a relation but every relation is not a function.

(2) For reflexive relation :

Every element should be related to itself.

(3) For symmetric relation :

The word '**every**' is to be replaced by '**if**' *i.e.* if $(2, 3) \in R$ then $(3, 2)$ must belong to R.

(4) For transitive relation :

This is also conditional *i.e.* if $(1, 3) \in R$ and $(3, 2) \in R$, then $(1, 2)$ must belong to R.

(5) Inverse relation :

In order to get R^{-1} reverse all the ordered pairs of R.

i.e. if $R = \{(2, 3), (2, 5), (3, 4), (7, 5)\}$

then $R^{-1} = \{(3, 2), (5, 2), (4, 3), (5, 7)\}$

(6) Rule to write composite relation RoS

Let $R = \{(4, 5), (4, 6), (7, 6)\}$

$S = \{(5, 7), (3, 7), (6, 4)\}$

In order to find elements of RoS, pick up first any element of S say $(5, 7)$ and then choose any element of R which begins with 7 [the 2nd co-ordinate of $(5, 7)$]

$\therefore \quad \underset{\in S}{(5, 7)} \, o \, \underset{\in R}{(7, 6)} \quad \Rightarrow \quad (5, 6) \in RoS$

Similarly $\underset{\in S}{(3, 7)} \, o \, \underset{\in R}{(7, 6)} \quad \Rightarrow \quad (3, 6) \in RoS$

$\underset{\in S}{(6, 4)} \, o \, \underset{\in R}{(4, 5)} \quad \Rightarrow \quad (6, 5) \in RoS$

$\underset{\in S}{(6, 4)} \, o \, \underset{\in R}{(4, 6)} \quad \Rightarrow \quad (6, 6) \in RoS$

(7) Multiplication of any pair by (a, a) makes no change.

$(3, 2) \, o \, (2, 2) = (3, 2)$

$(5, 4) \, o \, (4, 4) = (5, 4)$

$(1, 1) \, o \, (1, 4) = (1, 4)$

(8) Condition for relation to be symmetric.

$R = R^{-1}$

Problem Set (1)

1. Find the smallest set Y such that

$Y \cup \{1, 2\} = \{1, 2, 3, 5, 9\}$.

2. Let $A = \{1, 2, 3\}, B = \{2, 4, 6, 8\}, C = \{3, 4, 5, 6\}$ then prove the following

$A \cup B = \{1, 2, 3, 4, 6, 8\}, B \cap C = \{4, 6\}, A - B = \{1, 3\}$

$A \cap (B \cup C) = \{2, 3\}$

3. If $U = \{1, 2, 3, 4, 5, 6, 7, 8, 9\}$ and

$A = \{1, 2, 3, 4\}, B = \{2, 4, 6, 8\}, C = \{3, 4, 5, 6\}$

then prove the following

$A' = \{5, 6, 7, 8, 9\}, (A \cup B)' = \{5, 7, 9\}$

$(A \cap C)' = \{1, 2, 5, 6, 7, 8, 9\},$

$(B - C)' = \{2, 8\}' = \{1, 3, 4, 5, 6, 7, 9\}$

4. If $A = \{2, 3, 4, 8, 10\}, B = \{3, 4, 5, 10, 12\}$

and $C = \{4, 5, 6, 12, 14\}$

Find (a) $(A \cup B) \cap (A \cup C)$ and (b) $(A \cap B) \cup (A \cap C)$

5. Prove the following :

1. $A - (A - B) = A \cap B$
2. $A \cap (B - C) = (A \cap B) - (A \cap C)$
3. $A \Delta B = (A \cup B) - (A \cap B)$

6. If A and B are two sets, then prove that

$A \cup B = (A - B) \cup (B - A) \cup (A \cup B)$

7. Let U be the set of all people and

$M = (Meles,), S = (College Students), T = (Teen agers)$

$W = \{People having height more than five feet\}$.

Express each of the following in the notation of set theory.

8. Verify the following identities :

(a) $A \cup (B \cap C) = (A \cup B) \cap (A \cup C)$

(b) $A \cap (B \cup C) = (A \cap B) \cup (A \cap C)$

where $A = \{1, 2, 4, 5\}, B = \{2, 3, 5, 6\}, C = \{4, 5, 6, 7\}$

9. Given $A = \{1, 2, 3\}, B = \{3, 4\}, C = \{4, 5, 6\}$

find : (a) $A \cup (B \cup C)$ and (b) $(A \times B) \cap (B \times C)$

10. Given $A = \{2, 3\}, B = \{4, 5\}, C = \{5, 6\}$, then prove the following :

(a) $A \times (B \cup C) = \{(2, 3), (2, 5), (2, 6), (3, 4), (3, 5), (3, 6)\}$

(b) $A \times (b \cap C) = \{(2, 5), (3, 5)\}$

(c) $(A \times B) \cup (B \times C) = \{(2, 4), (2, 5), (3, 4), (3, 5)\}$

$\cup \{(4, 5), (4, 6), (5, 5), (5, 6)\}$ = All the ordered pairs as they are disjoint.

11. If $A = \{1, 2\}$ and $B = \{1, 3\}$, prove that

$(A \times B) \cup (B \times A)$

$= \{(1, 3), (2, 3), (3, 1), (3, 2), (1, 1), (1, 2), (2, 1)\}$

12. The set A has 3 elements and B has 6 elements. What can be the minimum number of elements of $A \cup B$? **(I.I.T. 1980)**

13. Let $A = \{\theta : 2 \cos^2 \theta + \sin \theta \le 2\}$

and $B = \{\theta : \pi/2 \le \theta \le 3\pi/2\}$. Find $A \cap B$. **(I.I.T. 1976)**

14. If $X = \{4^n - 3n - 1 : n \in \mathbf{N}\}$ and $Y = \{9 (n - 1) : \in \mathbf{N}\}$. Prove that $X \subset Y$. **(I.I.T. 1971)**

15. If $aN = \{ax : x \in N\}$. Describe the set $3N \cap 7N$. **(I.I.T. 1970)**

16. Of the members of three athletic teams in a certain school, 21 are on the Basket ball team (B), 26 on Hockey team (H) and 29 on the Foot ball team (F). 14 play hockey and basket ball, 15 play hockey and foot ball, 12 play foot ball and basket ball and 8 play all the three games. How many members are there in all ? **(I.I.T. 1975)**

17. In a group of 1000 people there are 750 who can speak Hindi and 400 who can speak Bengali. How many can speak Hindi only ? How many can speak Bengali only ? How many can speak both Hindi and Bengali ?

(Roorkee 1978)

18. In a survey of 200 students of a higher secondary school it was found that 120 studied Mathematics (M), 90 studied Physics (P) and 70 studied Chemistry (C), 40 studied M and P, 30 studied P and C, 50 studied C and M, and 20 studied none of these subjects. Find the number of students who studied all the three subjects.

19. An investigator interviewed 100 students to determine their preferences for the three drinks milk (M), coffee (C) and tea (T). He reported the following : 10 students had all the three drinks, M, C, T, 20 had M and C, 30 had C and T, 25 had M and T. 12 had M only, 5 had C only, 8 had T only. Using a Venn diagram find how many did not take any of the three drinks.

(I.I.T. 1978)

20. In a survey of population of 450 people, it is found that 205 can speak English (E), 210 can speak Hindi (H) and 120 people can speak Tamil. If 100 people can speak both E and H, 80 can speak both E and T, 5 can speak both H and T, and 20 can speak all the three languages, find the number of people who can speak E but not H or T. Find also the number of people who can speak neither E nor H nor T.

21. A class has 175 students. The following table shows the number of students studying one or more of the following subjects. Maths (M), Phys. (P), Chem. (C).
$n(M) = 100, n(P) = 70, n(C) = 46.$
$n(M \cap P) = 30, n(M \cap C) = 28, n(P \cap C) = 23,$
$n(M \cap P \cap C) = 18.$
Find how many students are enrolled in Mathematics only, in Physics only, in Chemistry only. Are there students who have not offered any of these three subjects ?

(Roorkee 1984)

22. In pollution study of 1500 Indian rivers the following data were reported.
520 were polluted by sulphur compounds.
335 were polluted by phosphates, 425 were polluted by crude oil. 100 were polluted by both crude oil and sulphur compounds, 180 were polluted by both sulphur compounds and phosphates, 150 were polluted by both phosphates and crude oil and 28 were polluted by sulphur compounds, phosphates and crude oil. How many rivers were polluted by at least one of the three impurities ? How many of the rivers were polluted by exactly one of the three impurities ?

(Roorkee 1987)

23. A survey of 500 television watchers produced the following information : 285 watch foot ball (F), 195 watch hockey (H), 115 watch basket ball (B), 45 watch F and B, 70 watch F and H, 50 watch H and B, 50 do not watch any of the three games. How many watch all the three games ? How many watch exactly one of the three games ?

(Roorkee 1989)

24. A group of 123 workers went to a canteen for cold drinks (C), ice cream (I) and tea (T). 42 workers took I, 36 T, and 30 C. 15 workers purchased I and T, 10 I and C, and 4 C and T, but not ice cream, 11 took I and T but not C. Determine how many workers did not purchase anything.

(M.N.R. 1989)

25. The report of one survey of 100 students stated that the numbers studying the various languages were Sanskrit, Hindi and Tamil. H, T and S, 5; H and S, 10; T and S, 8; H and T, 20; Sanskrit 30, Hindi 23, Tamil 50. The surveyor who prepared the report was fired. Why ?

(Roorkee 1983)

26. At a certain conference of 100 people there are 29 Indian women and 23 Indian men. Of these Indian people 4 are doctors and 24 are either men or doctors. There are no foreign doctors. How many foreigners are attending the conference ? How many women doctors are attending the conference ?

27. What is the distinction between a relation and function and when do you call a relation reflexive, symmetric and transitive ?

28. If $A = \{a, b, c, d\}, B = \{1, 2, 3\}$ find whether or not the following sets of ordered pairs are relations from A to B or not.
$R_1 = \{(a, 1), (a, 3)\}$
$R_2 = \{(a, 1), (c, 2), (d, 1)\}$
$R_3 = \{(a, 1), (b, 2), (3, c)\}.$

29. If $A = \{1, 2, 3, 4\}$, define relations on A which are
(a) R, T but not S (b) S, neither R not T
(c) R, S and T.   **(I.I.T. 1970)**

30. Is it true that every relation which is symmetric and transitive is also reflexive ? Give reasons. **(I.I.T. 1970)**

31. Given a relation $R = \{(1, 2), (2, 3)\}$ on the set of natural numbers, add a minimum number of ordered pairs so that the enlarged relation is R, S and T. **(I.I.T. 1978)**

32. Let $A = \{1, 2, 3\}$ and let

33. Let R be relation on I defined as mRn iff $m \leq n$. Check R for R, S, T and anti-symmetric.

34. An integer m is said to be related to another integer n if m is a multiple of n. Check this relation for R, S, T.

(I.I.T. 1974)

35. (a) Let a relation R be defined by
$R = \{(4, 5), (1, 4), (4, 6), (7, 6), (3, 7)\}$
then find (i) $R \, o \, R$ (ii) $R^{-1} \, o \, R$.
$R^{-1} \equiv \{(5, 4), (4, 1), (6, 4), (6, 7), (7, 3)\}$

(b) Let R be a relation $<$ from $A = \{1, 2, 3, 4\}$ to $B = \{1, 3, 5\}$

i.e. $(a, b) \in R$ if $a < b$ then find $R \circ R^{-1}$ **(M.N.R. 1984)**

36. Let S be the set of all points in a plane. Let R be a relation on S such that for any two points a and b.

37. Consider a non-empty set consisting of children in a family. State giving reasons whether each of the following relations is S and T.
(a) x is a brother $y \neq S, T$ (b) x likes $y \neq S, T$.

38. The following relations are defined on the set of real numbers (a) check them for R, S, T.
(a) $a R b$ iff $|a - b| > 0$ (b) $1 + ab > 0$
(c) $|a| = b$.

39. A relation R on the set of complex numbers is defined by $z_1 R z_2$ if and only if $\dfrac{z_1 - z_2}{z_1 + z_2}$ is real. Show that R is an equivalence relation. **(I.I.T. 1982)**

40. What is the fundamental difference between a function and a relation from a set A to a set B ?

41. Given $A = \{2, 3, 4\}$, $B = \{2, 5, 6, 7\}$. Construct an example of each of the following :
(a) An injective mapping from A to B
$$\{(2, 5), (3, 6), (4, 7)\}$$
You may construct it in any other manner.
(b) A mapping which is not injective from A to B.

42. If $X = \{1, 2, 3, 4, 5\}$, $Y = \{1, 3, 5, 7, 9\}$ determine which of the following sets are mappings, relations or neither from A to B :
(i) $F = \{(x, y) \quad \because \quad y = x + 2, x \in X, y \in Y\}$

43. Suppose f is the collection of all ordered pairs of real numbers and $x = 6$ is the first element of some ordered pair in f. Suppose the vertical line through $x = 6$ cuts the graph of f twice. Is f a function or not ?

44. Is $g = \{(1, 1), (2, 3), (3, 5(, (4, 7)\}$ a function ? If this is described by the formula $g(x) = ax + \beta$ then what values should be assigned to α and β ?

45. Let $A = \{x : -1 \le x \le 1\} = B$

46. Are the following sets of ordered pairs functions ? If so, examine whether the mapping is surjective or injective.
(a) $\{(x, y) : x$ is a person, y is the mother of $x\}$

47. (a) $f : \mathbf{N} \to \mathbf{N}$ s.t. $f(n) = 2n + 3 \ \forall \ n \in \mathbf{N}$.
(b) $g : C \to R$ s.t. $g(z) = |z| \ \forall \ z \in \mathbf{C}$.
Discuss the characteristics of f and g.

48. If the mapping f and g are given by
$f = \{(1, 2), (3, 5), (4, 1)\}$
$g = \{(2, 3), (5, 1), (1, 3)\}$, determine $f \circ g$ and $g \circ f$.

Solutions to Problems Set (1)

1. **Ans.** $\{3, 5, 9\}$
2. **Note :** $A \cap (B \cup C) = (A \cap B) \cup (A \cap C) = \{2, 3\}$
4. By distributive law we have to find

(a) $A \cup (B \cap C) = \{2, 3, 4, 8, 10\} \cup \{4, 5, 12\}$
$$= -\{2, 3, 4, 8, 10, 5, 12\}$$
(b) As above we have to find
$$A \cap (B \cup C) = \{2, 3, 4, 10\}$$

5. We know that $A - B = A \cap B' - B' - A'$
1. L.H.S.
$= A - (A - B) = A - (A \cap B') = A - P = A \cap P'$
$= A \cap (A \cap B') = A \cap (A' \cup B')$.
$\hfill$ By De Morgan's Law
$= A \cap (A' \cup B) = (A \cap A') \cup (A \cap B)$
$= \phi \cup (A \cap B) = A \cap B$.

2. R.H.S. $= (A \cap B) - (A \cap C) = P - Q$ say
$= P \cap Q' = P \cap (A \cap C)'$
$= P \cap (A' \cup C') = (P \cap A') \cup (P \cap C')$
$= \{(A \cap B) \cap A'\} \cup \{(A \cap B) \cap C'\}$
$= \{(B \cap A) \cap A'\} \cup \{A \cap (B \cap C')\}$
$= \{B \cap (A \cap A')\} \cup \{A \cap (B - C)\}$
$= \{B \cap \phi\} \cup \{A \cap (B - C)\}$
$= \phi \cup \{A \cap (B - C)\} = A \cap (B - C)$
We know that

3. $A \Delta B = (A - B) \cup (B - A)$ $\hfill$ ...(1)
Now R.H.S. of given question is
$(A \cup B) - (A \cap B) = P - Q$ say $= P \cap Q'$
$= P \cap (A \cap B)' = P \cap (A' \cup B')$
$= (P \cap A') \cup (P \cap B')$
$= \{(A \cup B) \cap A'\} \cup \{(A \cup B) \cap B'\}$
$= \{(A \cap A') \cup (B \cap A')\} \cup \{(A \cap B') \cup (B \cap B')\}$
$= \{\phi \cup (B \cap A')\} \cup \{(A \cap B') \cup \phi\}$
$= (B \cap A') \cup (A \cap B')$
$= (B - A) \cup (A - B) = A \Delta B$ $\hfill$ by (1)

6. It follows from Venn diagram given as the three sets on the R.H.S. are disjoint and clearly their union is $A \cup B$.
We know that $A - B = A \cap B'$
L.H.S. $= (A \cap B') \cup (B \cap A') \cup (A \cap B)$
Combining first and third we get by distributive law
R.H.S. $= A \cap (B \cup B') \cup (B \cap A')$
$= (A \cap U) \cup (B \cap A')$
$= A \cup (B \cap A') = (A \cup B) \cap (A \cup A')$
$= (A \cup B) \cap U = A \cup B$.

Deduction :
$$n(A \cup B) = n(A) + n(B) - n(A \cap B)$$
where $n(A)$ denotes the number of distinct elements in a set.
From the figure on last page we have
$n(A) = n(A - B) + n(A \cap B)$
$n(B) = n(B - A) + n(A \cap B)$
$\therefore \quad n(A) + n(B) = n(A - B) + n(B - A)$
$\hfill + n(A \cap B) + n(A \cap B)$
$\therefore \quad n(A) + n(B) - n(A \cap B)$
$\hfill - n(A - B) + n(B - A) + n(A \cap B)$
$= n(A \cup B)$

∵ $A - B, B - A$ and $A \cap B$ are disjoint sets.

Some Important Formula

1. $n(A') = n(U) - n(A)$
2. $n(A \cap B') = n(A) - n(A \cap B)$
3. $n(A \cup B) = n(A) + n(B) - n(A \cap B)$

    or $n(A \cap B) = n(A) + n(B) - n(A \cup B)$
4. $n(A \cup B \cup C)$

    $= n(A) + n(B) + n(C) - n(B \cap C) - n(C \cap A)$
    $\qquad\qquad - n(A \cap B) + n(A \cap B \cap C)$

    $= S_1 - S_2 + S_3$ say.
5. If $A_1, A_2, ..., A_n$ are disjoint sets then

    $n(A_1 \cup A_2 \cup A_3 ... A_n)$
    $= n(A_1) + n(A_2) + n(A_3) + ... + n(A_n)$
6. $n(A \cap B' \cap C') = n(A) - n(A \cap B) - n(A \cap C)$
    $\qquad\qquad\qquad\qquad + n(A \cap B \cap C)$

7. (a) College Students having height more than five feet. These boys should belong to both S and W as they have to satisfy both the properties

    ∴ $S \cap W$.

    (b) People who are not teen agers and have their height less than five feet.

    Teen Agers belong to T. Those who are not teen agers belong to T'. Similarly W' and hence $T' \cap W' = \{T \cup W\}'$.

    (c) All people who are neither males nor teen agers nor College Students

    $M' \cap T' \cap S' = \{M \cup T \cup S\}'$

8. Do yourself.
9. (a) $\{1, 2, 3, 4, 5, 6\}$ (b) $\{3, 4\}$.
12. There are two possibilities that either $A \subset B$ or A an B are disjoint.

    If $A \subset B$ then $A \cup B = B$ ∴ $n(A \cup B) = n(B) = 6$.

    If A and B are disjoint i.e. $A \cap B = \phi$ then

    $n(A \cup B) = n(A) + n(B) - n(A \cap B) = 3 + 6 - 0 = 9$.

    Hence the minimum number of elements will be when $A \subset B$ and in that case the number of elements is 6.
13. $A = \{\theta : 2 - 2\sin^2 \theta + \sin \theta \le 2\}$

    $= \{\theta : \sin \theta (1 - 2\sin \theta) \le 0\}$

    $= \{\theta : 2\sin \theta \left(\sin \theta - \frac{1}{2}\right) \ge 0\}$

    Above is possible if $\sin \theta \le 0$ or $\sin \theta \ge \frac{1}{2}$

    $\sin \theta = \frac{1}{2}$ when $\theta = \pi/6$ and is greater than half $\frac{1}{2}$ when $\frac{\pi}{6} \le \theta \le \frac{5\pi}{6}$

    Also $\sin \theta \le 0$ where $\pi \le \theta \le 2\pi$.

    ∴ $A = \{\theta : \pi/6 \le \theta \le 5\pi/6 \text{ or } \pi \le \theta \le 2\pi\}$

    $B = \{\theta : \pi/2 \le \theta \le 3\pi/2\}$

    ∴ $A \cap B = \{\theta : \pi/2 \le \theta \le 5\pi/6 \text{ or } \pi \le \theta \le 3\pi/2\}$
14. Putting $n = 1, 2, 3, ...$

$X = \{0, 9, 54, 243, ...\}, Y = \{0, 9, 18, 27, ...\}$.

Clearly $X \subset Y$.

15. $3N = \{3x : x \in N\} = \{3, 6, 9, 12, 15, ...\}$

    $7N = \{7x : x \in N\} = \{7, 14, 21, 28, ...\}$

    ∴ $3N \cup 7N = \{21, 42, 63, ...\}$
    $\qquad\qquad = \{21(1), 21(2), 21(3), ...\}$
    $\qquad\qquad = \{21x : x \in N\} = 21N$.

16. Given data are as under

    $n(B) = 21, n(H) = 26, n(F) = 29$

    $n(H \cap B) = 14, n(H \cap F) = 15, n(F \cap B) = 12$,

    $n(B \cap H \cap F) = 8$

    We have to find the total number of players

    i.e. $n(B \cup H \cup F) = n(B) + n(H) + n(F)$
    $\qquad\qquad - n(B \cap H) - n(H \cap F) - n(F \cap B)$
    $\qquad\qquad + n(B \cap H \cap F)$ i.e. $S_1 - S_2 + S_3$

    $= (21 + 26 + 29) - (14 + 15 + 12) + 8$

    $= 76 - 41 + 8 = 43$

    Out of the 21 players who are in basket ball team some may also play either foot ball or hockey or also play both the other two games. Similarly those who play both hockey and basket ball, some of them may be playing foot ball also.

Alternative method

Here we shall find the players who play only one game and then the number of players who play only two games and finally those who play all the three games and then add them.

Those who play all the three games

i.e. $n(B \cap H \cap F) = 8$.

Those who play **only** two games for

$14 - 8 = 6$	B and H
$15 - 8 = 7$	H and F
$12 - 8 = 4$	F and B

Those who play only one game

$21 - (6 + 4 + 8) = 21 - 18 = 3$ for B

$26 - (6 + 8 + 7) = 26 - 21 = 5$ for H

$29 - (7 + 8 + 4) = 29 - 19 = 10$ for F

Hence the total number of players

$= (3 + 5 + 10) + (6 + 7 + 4) + 8$

$\quad$ One $\quad$ Two $\quad$ All the three

$= 18 + 17 + 8 = 43$.

17. $n(H \cup B) = 1000, n(H) = 750, n(B) = 400$

    $n(H \cup B) = n(H) + n(B) - n(H \cap B)$

    ∴ $1000 = 750 + 400 - n(H \cap B)$

    ∴ $n(H \cap B) = 150$.

    In other words 150 person can speak both Hindi and Bengali.

    Only Hindi : $n(H) - n(H \cap B)$
    $\qquad\qquad = 750 - 150 = 600$

    Only Bengali : $n(B) - n(H \cap B)$
    $\qquad\qquad = 400 - 150 = 250$.

Another method.

$n(H \cap B) = 150$ = number of those who can speak both Hindi and Bengali.

$n(H \cap B')$ = number of those who can speak Hindi but not Bengali.

$\therefore \quad n(H \cap B') = n(H) - n(H \cap B)$
$$= 750 - 150 = 600 \qquad \text{for only Hindi}$$
$n(B \cap H') = n(B) - n(B \cap H)$
$$= 400 - 150 = 250 \text{ for only Bengali.}$$

Note. You can easily verify the same by Venn diagram.

18. $n(U) = 200, n(M) = 120, n(P) = 90, n(C) = 70$
$n(M \cap P) = 40, n(P \cap C) = 30, n(C \cap M) = 50$
$n(M \cup P \cup C)' = 20$

$x \in A \cup B \Rightarrow x \in A$ or $x \in B$ or $x \in$ both
$x \notin A \cup B \Rightarrow x \notin A$ and $x \notin B$
i.e. $x \in (A \cup B)' \Rightarrow x \notin A$ and $x \notin B$.

Here we have to find the number of students who study the three subjects i.e. $n(M \cap P \cap C)$.

We are given $n(M \cup P \cup C)' = 20$

$\therefore \quad n(U) - n(M \cup P \cup C) = 20$

$\therefore \quad n(M \cup P \cup C) = 200 - 20 = 180$

or $\quad n(M) + n(P) + n(C)$
$$- [n(M \cap P) + n(P \cap C) + n(C \cap M)]$$
$$+ n(M \cap P \cap C) = 180$$

or $(120 + 90 + 70) - [40 + 30 + 50]$
$$+ n(M \cap P \cap C) = 180$$
$$280 - 120 + n(M \cap P \cap C) = 180$$

$\therefore \quad n(M \cap P \cap C) = 180 - 160 = 20.$

Hence 20 studied all the three subjects.

19. Here we have to find $n(M \cup C \cup T)'$
$$= n(U) - n(M \cup C \cup T) \qquad ...(1)$$

We are given that
$$n(U) = 100, n(M \cap T \cap C) = 10$$
$$n(M \cap C) = 20, n(C \cap T) = 30,$$
$$n(M \cap T) = 25$$

12 had only M, 5 had only C, 8 had only T.

It should be noted that we have not written $n(M) = 12$ because this would include all those who take milk and may also be taking some other drink also. We are given the number of students who drink **only milk** as 15

Only one drink $12M + 5C + 8T = 25$

Only two drinks

$n(M \cap C) - n(M \cap C \cap T) = 20 - 10 = 10$ for M and C.

Similarly $30 - 10 = 20$ for C and T, $25 - 10 = 15$ for T and M.

All the three = 10

Hence $n(M \cup C \cup T)$
$$= (12 + 5 + 8) + (10 + 20 + 15) + 10$$
$$= 25 + 45 + 10 = 80.$$

Hence $n(M \cup C \cup T)' = n(U) - n(M \cup C \cup T)$

$$= 100 - 80 = 20.$$

The formula for $n(M \cup C \cup T) = n(M) + n(C) + n(T)$
$$- \{n(M \cap C) + n(C \cap T) + n(T \cap M) + n(M \cap C \cap T)\}$$

is not applicable here because $n(M)$ does not mean the number of persons taking milk **only**. $n(M)$ means the number of person taking milk and some of them may be taking other drinks also.

20. $n(U) = 450, n(E) = 205, n(H) = 210, n(T) = 120$
$n(E \cap H) = 100, n(E \cap T) = 80, n(H \cap T) = 35$
$n(E \cap H \cap T) = 20.$

In the second part we have to find the value of
$n(E' \cap H' \cap T') = n(E \cup H \cup T)'$
$$= n(U) - n(E \cup H \cup T) \qquad ...(1)$$
$$n(U) = 450$$
$$n(E \cup H \cup T) = S_1 - S_2 + S_3$$
$$= (205 - 210 + 120) - (100 + 80 + 35) + 20$$
$$= 535 - 215 + 20 = 555 - 215 = 340$$

Hence from (1)

$n(E' \cap H' \cap T') = 450 - 340 = 110.$

In the first part we have to find
$n(E \cap H' \cap T') = n\{E \cap (H \cup T)'\}$
$$= n(E) - n(E \cap (H \cup T)) \text{ by Ex. 7 (2)}$$
$$= n(E) - n\{(n \cap H) \cup (E \cap T)\}$$
$$= n(E) - [n(E \cap H) + n(E \cap T)$$
$$- n\{(E \cap H) \cap (E \cap T)\}]$$
$$= n(E) - n(E \cap H) - n(E \cap T) + n(E \cap H \cap T)$$
$$= 205 - 100 - 80 + 20$$
$$= 225 - 180 = 45.$$

21. $n(M \cap P' \cap C') = n(M \cap (P \cup C)')$
$$= n(M) - n(M \cap (P \cup C), \text{ Ex. 7. (2)}$$
$$= n(M) - n\{(m \cap P) \cup (M \cap C)\}$$
$$= n(M) - \{n(M \cap P) + n(M \cap C)$$
$$- n\{(M \cap P) \cap (M \cap C)\}$$
$$= n(M) - \{n(M \cap P) + n(M \cap C)$$
$$- n(M \cap P \cap C)\}$$
$$= 100 - 30 - 28 + 18 = 118 - 58 = 60$$

Similarly those studying Physics only is 35 and Chemistry only is 13.

Again $n(M' \cap P' \cap C') = n(M \cup P \cup C)'$
$$= n(U) - n(M \cup P \cup C)$$
$$= 175 - (S_1 - S_2 + S_3)$$
$$= 175 - \{(100 + 70 + 46)$$
$$- (30 + 28 + 23) + 18\}$$
$$= 175 - \{(216 - 81 + 18\}$$
$$= 175 - 153 = 22.$$

22. Polluted by all the three = 28

Polluted by S and $P = 180$ $\qquad ...(1)$

and this includes 28 also.

Hence polluted by S and P only $180 - 28 = 152$

Polluted by P and C only $150 - 28 = 122$

Polluted by C and S only $100 - 28 = 72.$

Polluted by sulphur only $= 520 - (72 + 152) - 28$
$$= 520 - 252 = 268$$

Polluted by Phosphate only $= 335 - (152 + 122) - 28$
$$= 335 - 302 = 33$$

Polluted by crude oil only $= 425 - (122 + 72) - 28.$
$$= 425 - 222 = 203.$$

The rivers polluted by at least one of the impurities
$$n(S \cup P \cup C) = S_1 - S_2 + S_3$$
$$= [520 + 335 + 425] - [100 + 180 + 150] + 28$$
$$= 1280 - 430 + 28$$
$$= 1308 - 430 = 878.$$

By Venn diagram, the rivers polluted by at least one of the impurities = sum of all the digits written in Venn diagram.

$(268 + 33 + 203) + (152 + 122 + 72) + 28 = 878.$

only one   only two   all

23. This is exactly as example 22 done before and we can do it easily by Venn diagram. Another method is given below.

$$n(U) = 500, n(F) = 285, n(H) = 185, n(B) = 115$$
$$n(F \cap B) = 45, n(F \cap H) = 70, n(H \cap B) = 50$$
$$n(F' \cap H' \cap B') = 50$$

We have to find $n(F \cap H \cap B)$ for all the three games and $n(F \cap H' \cap B')$ for football only, similarly for other two games only.

$$50 = n(F' \cap H' \cap B') = n(F \cup H \cup B)' \quad \text{(Given)}$$
$$= n(U) - n(F \cup H \cup B)$$
$$= 500 - [S_1 - S_2 + S_3]$$
$$\therefore \quad 450 = [285 + 195 + 115] - [45 + 70 + 50] + S_3$$
$$S_3 = n(F \cap H \cap B) = 450 - 595 + 165$$
$$= 615 - 595 = 20 \qquad \ldots(1)$$

Again $n(f \cap H' \cap B') = n(F \cap (H \cup B)')$
$$\text{De Morgan's Law}$$
$$= n(F) - n(F \cap (H \cup B))$$
$$= n(F) - n\{(F \cap H) \cup (F \cap B)\}$$
$$= n(F) - \{n(F \cap H) + n(F \cap B)\}$$
$$\qquad - n\{(F \cap H) \cap (F \cap B)\}$$
$$= 285 - [70 + 45 - n\{F \cap H \cap B\}]$$
$$= 285 - [70 + 45 - 20]$$
$$= 285 - 95 = 190$$

i.e. 190 persons play football only.

Similarly 95 play hockey only and 40 play basket ball only.

24. $n(U) = 123, n(I) = 42, n(T) = 35, n(C) = 30$
$$n(I \cap T) = 15, n(I \cap C) = 10, n(C \cap T \cap I') = 4,$$
$$n(I \cap T \cap C') = 11$$
We have to find $n(I' \cap T' \cap C)$.
We know that $n(A \cap B') = n(A) - n(A \cap B)$, Ex. 7 (2)
$$\therefore \quad n(C \cap T \cap I') = n(C \cap T) - n(C \cap T \cap I)$$
$$\text{or} \quad 4 = n(C \cap T) - n(C \cap T \cap I) \qquad \ldots(1)$$
$$n(I \cap T \cap C') = n(I \cap T) - n(I \cap T \cap C)$$

or $11 = 15 - n(I \cap T \cap C)$
$$\therefore \quad n(I \cap T \cap C) = 15 - 11 = 4. \qquad \ldots(2)$$
Putting in (1) we get
$$n(C \cap T) = 4 + 4 = 8 \qquad \ldots(3)$$
Now $n(I' \cap T' \cap C') = n(I \cup T \cup C)'$
$$= n(U) - n(I \cup T \cup C)$$
$$= 123 - [S_1 - S_2 + S_3]$$
$$= 123 - [(42 + 36 + 36)$$
$$\qquad - (15 + 10 + 9) + 4]$$
by given data and (2) and (3)
$$= 123 - [108 - 33 + 4]$$
$$= 123 - 79 = 44$$

25. $n(S \cup H \cup T) = S_1 - S_2 + S_3$
$$= (30 + 23 + 50) - (10 + 8 + 20) + 5$$
$$= 108 - 38 = 70$$
But we are given that $n(S \cup H \cup T) = 100$
Hence he was fired.

26. Let E be the set of Indian people and F the set of foreigners. W stands for Women, M for Men and D for Doctors.
$$E = W \cup M$$
$$\therefore \quad n(E) = n(W \cup M) = n(W) + n(M) + n(W \cap M)$$
$$= 29 + 23 + n(\phi) = 52 + 0 = 52$$
$W \cap M = \phi$ as a man cannot be a woman.
Foreign delegates = Total – Indian $= 100 - 52 = 48$
Again we are given $n(M \cup D) = 24$
or $n(M) + n(D) - n(M \cap D) = 24$
$$23 + 4 - n(M \cap D) = 24 \qquad \therefore \; n(M \cap D) = 3$$
Hence amongst the set of men there are three doctors. Since the total number of doctors (Indian only) is 4 out of which we have shown 3 are men and hence we conclude there is only one woman (Indian) doctor. There are no foreign doctors.

27. Every mapping (function) is a relation but every relation is not a mapping.

The relation R is said to be reflexive
if $a R a \forall \quad a \in A$. (not for all)
The relation R is said to be symmetric
if aRb then bRa. (not for all a and b)
The relation R is said to be transitive.
if $a R b$ and $b R c$ then $a R c$ (not for all a, b, c)
A relation from a set A to the set B is denoted as
$$R = \{(x, y) : x \in A \text{ and } y \in B \text{ and } x R y\}$$
$$\therefore \quad R \subset A \times B.$$

28. Both R_1 and R_2 are subsets of $A \times B$ and hence are relations but R_3 is not a relation because R_3 is not a subset of $A \times B$ because the element $(3, c) \notin (A \times B)$. It belongs to $B \times A$.

29. (a) $\{(1, 1), (2, 2), (3, 3), (4, 4)$ for R
$$(1, 2), (2, 3), (1, 3) \text{ for } T$$
you can add any other set of ordered pairs for T.

Clearly it is not symmetric as $(2,3) \in R$ but $(3,2) \notin R$.

(b) $\{(1,2),(2,1)$ for $S\}$

you can write $\{(3,4),(4,3)\}$ also or any other pair.

(c) $\{(1,1),(2,2),(3,3),(4,4)$ for R

$(1,2),(2,1)$ for S and $T\}$

you may write $\{(3,2),(2,3)\}$ for S and T.

30. Consider the set I of the integers and a relation be defined as aRb if both a and b are odd.

Clearly $aRb \Rightarrow bRa$ i.e. if a and b are both odd then b and a are also both odd. Similarly aRb and bRc implies aRc and hence transitive. But this relation is not reflexive because $2 \in I$ but 2 is not related to 2. In general, any even number is not R-related to itself. Hence it is not reflexive.

31. for R add $\{(1,1),(2,2),(3,3),...\}$

for S add $\{(2,1),(3,2)\}$

for T add $(1,3)$ and also $(3,1)$ for S.

32. $R_1 = \{(1,1),(1,3),(3,1),(2,2),(2,1),(3,3)\}$

$R_2 = \{(2,2),(3,1),(1,3)\}$

$R_3 = \{(1,3),(3,3)\}$

$R_4 = A \times A$.

Note. $R \neq$ means not reflexive, S means symmetric but $\neq S$ means that not symmetric.

Solution. Classify the above relations w.r.t. R, S and T

R_1 is $R, \neq S$ as $(2,1) \in R_1$ but $(1,2) \notin R$,

$\neq T$ as $(2,1) \in R_1$ and $(1,3) \in R$ but $(2,3) \notin R$

$R_2 \neq R$ as $(1,1),(3,3)$ do not belong to R_2

$S, \neq T$ as $(3,1)$ and $(1,3) \in R_2$ but $(3,3) \notin R_2$

$R_3 \neq R, \neq S$ but T.

R_4 Yes. R, S, T all because $A \times A$ contains all possible pairs.

33. Clearly it is reflexive because of the sign of equality. It is not symmetric but it is transitive.

Also if $m \leq n$ and $n \leq m$ then $m = n$ and hence by definition it is anti-symmetric.

34. $m = 1$. $m \forall m \therefore R$ is reflexive.

$6 = 3.2 \therefore 6R2$ but 2 is not related to 6 as 2 is not a multiple of 6.

Again if $= k_1 n$ and $n = k_2 p$ then $m = k_1 k_2 p$

$\therefore \quad mRp$.

Hence T.

35. (a) (i) $RoR : (1,4) \in R, (4,5) \in R \therefore (1,5) \in RoR$

Similarly $(3,6)$ and $(1,6) \in RoR$.

$\therefore \quad RoR = \{(1,5),(3,6),(1,6)\}$.

(ii) $(4,5) \in R, (5,4) \in R^{-1} \quad \therefore \quad (4,4) \in R^{-1}oR$

$(1,4) \in R, (4,1) \in R^{-1} \quad \therefore \quad (1,1) \in R^{-1}oR$

$(7,6) \in R, (6,4) \in R^{-1} \quad \therefore \quad (7,4)R \in R^{-1}oR$.

Similarly $(4,7),(7,7),(3,3)$ also belong to $R^{-1}oR$.

(b) $R = \{(1,3),(1,5),(2,3),(2,5),(3,5),(4,5)\}$

$\therefore \quad R^{-1} = \{(3,1),(5,1),(3,2),(5,2),(5,3),(5,4)\}$

$\therefore \quad RoR^{-1} = (3,1) \in R^{-1}$ and $(1,5) \in R$

$\therefore \quad (3,5) \in RoR^{-1}$ etc.

$RoR^{-1} = \{(3,3),(3,5),(5,3),(5,5)\}$.

36. aRb iff b is within 1 inch from a. Check R for R, S, T.

$aRA = 0 < 1 \qquad \therefore \quad R$

aRb then $bRa \qquad \therefore \quad S$.

Let $\qquad aRb = \dfrac{1}{2}, bRc = \dfrac{3}{4}$

then $\qquad aRc = \dfrac{1}{2} + \dfrac{3}{4} = \dfrac{5}{4} > 1$ and not less than 1.

$\therefore \quad a$ is not related to c.

$\therefore \quad aRb$ and bRc does not imply aRc and hence not transitive.

38. $\neq R, S, \neq T$ [$3R7$ and $7R3$ but $3(\sim R)3$] as $|3-3| = 0$ which is not greater than zero.

(b) R, S both $\because 1 + a^2 > 0$ and $1 + ba > 0$ when $1 + ab > 0 \neq T$. Consider $a = 2, b = -\dfrac{1}{6}, c = -2$.

aRb as $1 + 2\left(-\dfrac{1}{6}\right) = 1 - \dfrac{1}{3} = \dfrac{2}{3} > 0$

bRc as $1 + \left(-\dfrac{1}{6}\right)(-2) = 1 + \dfrac{1}{3} = \dfrac{4}{3} > 0$

but $aRc = 1 + 2(-2) = -3 \not> 0$.

Therefore a is not related to c and hence no transitive.

(c) $|a| \leq b \neq R$. Choose $a = -3$ any real number

$|a| = |-3| = 3$ but 3 is not less than or equal to -3

$\therefore \quad a$ is not related to a.

$\neq S, a = -2, b = 3$

$|a| = 2 < b = 3$ but $|b| = 3$ which is not less than or equal to a i.e. -2.

$\therefore \quad aRb$ does not imply bRa.

$T \quad aRb \Rightarrow |a| \leq b$. $\qquad ...(1)$

Since $|a|$ is $+$ ive $\quad \therefore \quad b$ is certainly $+$ ive.

$bRc \Rightarrow |b| \leq c \qquad \therefore \quad |a| \leq c$. Hence aRc.

39. R and S are obvious.

$z_1 R z_2 \Rightarrow \dfrac{z_1 - z_2}{z_1 + z_2}$ is real.

$\therefore \quad \dfrac{(x_1 + iy_1) - (x_2 + iy_2)}{(x_1 + iy_1) + (x_2 + iy_2)} = \dfrac{(x_1 - x_2) + i(y_1 - y_2)}{(x_1 + x_2) + i(y_1 + y_2)}$

Multiply above and below by conjugate of denominator and it will be real if the imaginary part of numerator is zero because denominator being $z\bar{z} = |z|^2 = $ real.

This will give $x_1 y_2 - x_2 y_1 = 0$ i.e. $\dfrac{x_1}{y_1} = \dfrac{x_2}{y_2}$

Similarly $\qquad z_2 R z_3 \Rightarrow \dfrac{x_2}{y_2} = \dfrac{x_3}{y_3}$

Hence it follows that $\dfrac{x_1}{y_1} = \dfrac{x_3}{y_3} \quad \therefore \quad z_1 R z_3$

Hence the relation R is transitive.

40. For a function every element belonging to A must have an image and that too unique. In a relation a particular element belonging to A may not have an image at all in B or if it has an image, it need not be unique $i.e.$ it can have so many images. Every mapping is a relation but every relation is not a mapping.

41. In other words it is many-one (not one-one)
$$\{(2,5),(3,5),(4,7)\}$$
Hence both 2 and $3 \in A$ have same image in B.

42. Giving x the values given in set X we get
$$\{(1,3),(2,4),(3,5),(4,6),(5,7)\} \quad \because \quad y = x+2$$
Again $y \in Y$ and in the above 4, 6 do not belong to Y.
∴ we exclude the ordered pair $(2, 4)$ and $(4, 6)$
∴ $\{(1,3),(3,5),(5,7)\}$
F is not a mapping because the elements $2, 4 \in X$ do not have any image. $F \subset X \times Y$ and hence F is a relation from X to Y.

(ii) $F = \{(1,1),(2,1),(3,3),(4,3),(5,5)\}$

Each element $\in X$ has a unique image in Y and it is a mapping and since $1, 2 \in x$ have the same image $1 \in Y$ it is many-one. It is into mapping because $7, 9 \in Y$ do not have any pre-image in X and hence it is not onto. Since every mapping is a relation it is therefore a relation also.

(iii) $F = \{(1,1),(1,3),(3,5),(3,7),(5,7)\}$

It is not a mapping because the element $1 \in X$ does not have a unique image in Y and similarly for $3 \in X$. Besides this the elements 2 and $4 \in X$ do not have any image. For a mapping every element belonging to domain must have an image and that image should be unique.
It is a relation as $F \subset X \times Y$.

(iv) $F = \{(1,3),(2,5),(4,7),(5,9),(3,1)\}$

It is clearly a one-one onto mapping $i.e.$ a bijection. It is also a relation.

43. Since $x = 6$ cuts the graph twice which in other words means that we will have two values of y corresponding to $x = 6$. Hence the uniqueness of image of 6 is destroyed.

44. Let $X = \{1,2,3,4\}, Y = \{1,3,5,7\}$

By definition of g we observe that every element in X has a unique image in Y and hence g is a function
$$g(x) = \alpha x + \beta \text{ when } x = 1, g(x) = 1$$
and when $x = 2$, $\qquad g(x) = 3$
∴ $1 = \alpha + \beta$ and $3 = 2\alpha + \beta$. These give $\alpha = 2, \beta = -1$.

∴ $g(x) = 2x - 1$
for $x = 3, g(x) = 5$ and for $x = 4, g(x) = 7$ which are true.

45. For each of the following functions from A to B, find whether it is one-one or onto or bijection (both one-one onto)

(i) $f(x) = x/2$.
$$f(x) = f(y) \Rightarrow \frac{x}{2} = \frac{y}{2} \Rightarrow x = y \qquad \therefore \text{ one-one.}$$
It is not onto because $1 \in B$ and it has no pre-image in A because by definition $f(2) = 2/2 = 1$ but $2 \notin A$.

(ii) $g(x) = |x|$

Here both 1 and -1 in A have the same images as $|1| = 1$ and $|-1| = 1$ and hence it is many-one $i.e.$ not an injective.
It is also not onto because $|x| = +$ive and as such all $-$ive elements in $B(= A)$ do not have any pre-image in A ∴ g is neither one-one nor onto.

(iii) $k(x) = x^2$.

It is clearly many-one because x and $-x \in A$ have the same image x^2. As in (ii) $-$ive element in B do not have any pre-image in A and hence it is not onto.

(iv) $l(x) = \sin \pi x$
$$l(!) = l(-1) = 0 \qquad \therefore \quad \text{Many-one.}$$
Since sin takes all values from -1 to 1 so that it is onto. Hence is many-one onto mapping.

46. Every person must have a mother and that too unique and hence it is a mapping. Since two or more persons can have the same mother and hence it is many-one. Again every mother has a child (person). Hence it is onto $i.e.$ surjective.

(b) $\{(x, y) : x \text{ is person and } y \text{ is ancestor of } x\}$.

No, it is not a mapping because a person have so many ancestors like father, grandfather, grandmother etc.

47. (a) Clearly f is one-one but not onto as even numbers do not have any pre-image.

(b) $z = r(\cos \theta + i \sin \theta) \quad \therefore \quad |z| = r \, \forall \, \theta$.

Hence the mapping is many-one. It is not onto also because negative elements in R do not have any pre-image.

48. $(2,3) \in g$ and $(3,5) \in f \quad \therefore \quad (2,5) \in f \circ g$.
∴ $f \circ g = \{(2,5),(5,2),(1,5)\}$
Similarly $g \circ f = \{(1,3),(3,1),(4,3)\}$.

Problem Set (2)

1. Let A and B be two disjoint subsets of a universal set U. Then $(A \cup B) \cap B' =$
(a) A 　　　　　　(b) B

(c) ϕ 　　　　　　(d) None of these

2. Let $A = \{x : x \in \mathbf{R}, x \geq 2\}$ and $B = \{x : x \in \mathbf{R}, x < 4\}$. Then $A \cap B =$

(a) $\{x : x \in \mathbf{R}, 2 < x < 4\}$ (b) $\{x : x \in \mathbf{R}, 2 \le x < 4\}$

(c) B (d) None of these

3. Let $A = \{x : x \in \mathbf{R}, |x| < 1\}$,
   $\quad B = \{x : x \in \mathbf{R}, |x - 1| \ge 1\}$
   and $A \cup B = \mathbf{R} - D$, then set D is

   (a) $\{x : 1 < x \le 2\}$ (b) $\{x : 1 \le x < 2\}$

   (c) $\{x : 1 \le x \le 2\}$ (d) None of these

4. If X and Y are two sets, then $X \cap (X \cup Y)$ equals

   (a) X (b) Y

   (c) ϕ (d) None of these

5. If $A = \{\phi, \{(\phi)\}\}$, then the power set $P(A)$ of A is

   (a) A (b) $\{\phi, \{\phi\}, A\}$

   (c) $\{\phi, \{\phi\}, \{\{\phi\}\}, A\}$ (d) None of these

6. A set contains n elements. The power set contains

   (a) n elements   (b) 2^n elements

   (c) n^2 elements   (d) none of these

   (C.E.T. 1992)

7. $A - (A - B) = \ldots\ldots\ldots$

8. $(A \cup B) - C = (A - C) \cup \ldots\ldots$

9. $A - (B \cup C \cup D) = (A - B) \cap \ldots\ldots \cap \ldots\ldots$

10. Set $A = \{x : x \in \mathbf{I}, x^4 - x^3 - 2x^2 + 2x = 0\}$
    $\quad B = \{x : x \in \mathbf{N}, 2x^2 - 1 < 7\}$

    Are A and B comparable ?

11. Let $A = \{(x, y) : x, y \in \mathbf{R}, x^2 + y^2 = 1\}$
    and $B = \{(x, 0) : x \in \mathbf{R}, -1 \le x \le 1\}$. Then $A \cap B = \ldots\ldots$

12. $(A - B) \cup (B - A) = (A \cup B) \cap (A' \cup B')$

13. **(i)** $A - (B - C) = (A - B) \cup (A \cap C)$

    (ii) $A - B = (A \cup B) - B = A - (A \cap B)$

    Verify these equalities if
    $A = \{1, 2, 3, 4, 5, 6, 7\}, B = \{3, 5, 6, 7, 9, 11\}$
    and $C = \{2, 5, 6, 9, 20\}$

14. Let U be the set of all people and $M = \{$Males$\}$, $S = \{$College students$\}$, $T = \{$Teenagers$\}$, $W = \{$People having heights more than five feet$\}$. Express each of the following in the notation of set theory.

    (i) College students having heights more than five feet.

    (ii) People who are not teenagers and have their heights less than five feet.

    (iii) All people who are neither males nor teenagers nor college students.

15. Find the smallest set Y such that
    $Y \cup \{1, 2\} = \{1, 2, 3, 5, 9\}$

16. Let $A = \{1, 2, 3\}, B = \{2, 4, 6, 8\}$,
    $C = \{2, 3, 5, 6\}$. Then
    $A \cap (B \cup C), \ldots\ldots\ldots$.

17. Let $A = \{x : x \in \mathbf{R}, -1 \le x \le 1\}$ and
    $\quad B = \{x : x \in \mathbf{R}, |x| \le 1\}$
    Are the sets A and B equal ?

18. If $A = \{2, 3, 4, 8, 10\}, B = \{3, 4, 5, 10, 12\}$
    and $C = \{4, 5, 6, 12, 14\}$,

find $(A \cup B) \cap (A \cup C)$ and $(A \cap B) \cup (A \cap C)$

19. Let $A = \{1, 2, 3\}, B = \{3, 4\}, C = \{4, 5, 6\}$, then $A \cup (B \cap C)$ is

    (a) $\{3\}$ (b) $\{1, 2, 3, 4\}$

    (c) $\{1, 2, 5, 6\}$ (d) $\{1, 2, 3, 4, 5, 6\}$

20. If $aN = \{ax : x \in N\}$, describe the set $3N \cap 7N$.

21. In $aN = \{ax : x \in N\}$ and $bn \cap cN = dN$, where $b, c \in N$ are relatively prime, then

    (a) $d = bc$ (b) $c = bd$

    (c) $b = cd$ (d) none of these

22. Set $A = \{x : x$ is a digit in the number $3591\}$
    $B = \{x : x \in \mathbf{N}, x < 10\}$. Find $A \cup B, A \cap B, A - B$ and $B - A$.

23. Set $U = \{1, 2, 3, 4, 5, 6, 7, 8, 9\}$,
    $\quad A = \{x : x \in \mathbf{N}, 30 \le x^2 \le 70\}$
    $\quad B = \{x : x$ is a prime number $< 10\}$.
    Find $A', B', (A \cup B)', A' \cap B', (A - B)'$

24. Comment on the following statements

    (i) $A - B = A \cap B' = B' - A'$

    (ii) $A - (A - B) = A \cap B$

    (iii) $A \cap (B - C) = (A \cap B) - (A \cap C)$

    (iv) $A \Delta B = (A \cup B) - (A \cap B)$

    (v) $A \times (B \cap C) = (A \times B) \cap (A \times C)$

    (vi) If $A \subset C$, then $A \times B \subset C \times B$.

25. For two sets A and B, $A \cap (A \cup B) =$

    (a) A (b) B

    (c) ϕ (d) None of these

26. Let $U = \mathbf{R}$ (the set of all real numbers)
    If $A = \{x : x \in \mathbf{R}, 0 < x < 2\}$,
    $\quad B = \{x : x \in \mathbf{R}, 1 < x \le 3\}$,
    find $A', B', A \cup B, A \cap B, A - B$.

27. Which of the following is the empty set ?

    (a) $\{x : x$ is a real number and $x^2 - 1 = 0\}$

    (b) $\{x : x$ is a real number and $x^2 + 1 = 0\}$

    (c) $\{x : x$ is a real number and $x^2 - 9 = 0\}$

    (d) $\{x : x$ is a real number and $x^2 = x + 2\}$

28. The number of bijective functions from set A to itself when A contains 106 elements is

    (a) 106 (b) $(106)^2$

    (c) $(106)!$ (d) 2^{106} **(EAMCET 1994)**

29. If X and Y are two sets, then $X \cap (Y \cup X)'$ equals

    (a) X (b) Y

    (c) ϕ (d) None of these

30. If sets A and B are defined as
    $A = \{(x, y) : y = e^x, x \in R\}$
    $B = \{(x, y) : y = x, x \in R\}$, then

    (a) $B \subset A$ (b) $A \subset B$

    (c) $A \cap B = \phi$ (d) $A \cup B = A$

31. Let $A = \{(x, y) : y = e^x, x \in R\}$

$B = \{(x, y) : y = e^{-x}, x \in R\}$. Then

(a) $A \cap B = \phi$ (b) $A \cap B \neq \phi$

(c) $A \cup B = R^2$ (d) none of these

32. Given $A = \{1, 2, 3\}$, $B = \{3, 4\}$, $C = \{4, 5, 6\}$,

the $A \cup (B \cup C) = \{1, 2, 3, 4, 5, 6\}$

$(A \times B) \cap (B \times C) = \{3, 4\}$

33. Given $A = \{2, 3\}$, $B = \{4, 5\}$, $C = \{5, 6\}$, find

(i) $A \times (B \cap C) = \ldots\ldots$

(ii) $A \times (B \cup C) = (A \times B) \cup (A \times C) = \ldots\ldots$

34. If $A = \{2, 3, 5\}$, $B = \{2, 5, 6\}$, then $(A - B) \times (A \cap B)$ is

(a) $\{(3, 2), (3, 3), (3, 5)\}$ (b) $\{(3, 2), (3, 5), (3, 6)\}$

(c) $\{(3, 2), (3, 5)\}$ (d) none of these

35. Let $A = \{1, 2\}$, and $B = \{1, 3\}$, then $(A \times B) \cup (B \times A)$
$= \{(1, 3), (2, 3), (3, 1), (3, 2), (1, 1), (1, 2), (2, 1)\}$

36. If $A = \{2, 4\}$ and $B = \{3, 4, 5\}$, then
$(A \cap B) \times (A \cup B)$ is

(a) $\{(2, 2), (3, 4), (4, 2), (5, 4)\}$

(b) $\{(2, 3), (4, 3), (4, 5)\}$

(c) $\{(2, 4), (3, 4), (4, 4), (4, 5)\}$

(d) $\{(4, 2), (4, 3), (4, 4), (4, 5)\}$

37. If $A = \{1, 2, 3\}$ and $B = \{3, 8\}$, then
$(A \cup B) \times (A \cap B)$ is

(a) $\{(3, 1), (3, 2), (3, 3), (3, 8)\}$

(b) $\{(1, 3), (2, 3), (3, 3), (8, 3)\}$

(c) $\{(1, 2), (2, 2), (3, 3), (8, 8)\}$

(d) $\{(8, 3), (8, 2), (8, 1), (8, 8)\}$

38. Let $A = \{1, 2, 3, 4, 5\}$, $B = \{2, 3, 6, 7\}$. Then the number of elements in $(A \times B) \cap (B \times A)$ is

(a) 18   (b) 6   (c) 4   (d) 0

39. If $A = \{a, b, c\}$, $B = \{c, d, e\}$, $C = \{a, d, f\}$, then $A \times (B \cup C)$ is

(a) $\{(a, d), (a, e), (a, c)\}$ (b) $\{(a, d), (b, d), (c, d)\}$

(c) $\{(d, a), (d, b), (d, c)\}$ (d) none of these

40. A and B are two sets having 3 and 5 elements respectively and having 2 elements in common. Then the number of elements in $A \times B$ is

(a) 6   (b) 36

(c) 15   (d) None of these

41. Let A and B have 3 and 6 elements respectively. What can be the minimum number of elements in $A \cup B$?

(a) 3   (b) 6   (c) 9   (d) 18

42. Suppose $A_1, A_2, \ldots, A_{30}$ are thirty sets each having 5 elements and $B_1, B_2, \ldots, B_n$ are n sets each with 3 elements, let $\bigcup\limits_{i=1}^{30} A_i = \bigcup\limits_{j=1}^{n} B_j = S$ and each element of S belongs to exactly 10 of the A_i's and exactly 9 of the B_j's. Then n is equal to

(a) 15   (b) 3

(c) 45   (d) None of these

43. Consider the set of all determinants of order 3 with entries 0 or 1 only. Let B be the subset of A consisting of

all determinants with value 1. Let C be the subset of the set of all determinants with value -1. Then

(a) C is empty

(b) B has as many elements as C

(c) $A = B \cup C$

(d) B has twice as many elements as C.

44. Two finite sets have m and n elements. The total number of subsets of the first set is 56 more than the total number of subsets of the second set. The values of m and n are

(a) 7, 6   (b) 6, 3   (c) 5, 1   (d) 8, 7

(M.N.R. 1991)

45. Let $A = \{\theta : 2\cos^2\theta + \sin\theta \leq 2\}$ and
$B = \{\theta : \pi/2 \leq \theta \leq 3\pi/2\}$. Then

46. If $X = \{4^n - 3n - 1 : n \in N\}$ and
$Y = \{9(n - 1) : n \in N\}$, then $X \cup Y$ is equal to

(a) X (b) Y

(c) N (d) none of these

47. The set S and E are defined as given below :
$S = \{(x, y) : |x - 3| < 1 \text{ and } |y - 3| < 1\}$
$E = \{(x, y) : 4x^2 + 9y^2 - 32x - 54y + 109 \leq 0\}$
then $S \subset E$

48. If A, B are two sets, prove
$$A \cup B = (A - B) \cup (B - A) \cup (A \cap B)$$
Hence or otherwise prove
$$n(A \cup B) = n(A) + n(B) - n(A \cap B)$$
where $n(A)$ denotes the number of elements in A.

49. Let $n(u) = 700$, $n(A) = 200$, $n(B) = 300$
$n(A \cap B) = 100$, then $n(A' \cap B') =$

(a) 400   (b) 600   (c) 300   (d) None

50. In a group of 1000 people, there are 750 who can speak Hindi and 400 who can speak Bengali. How many can speak Hindi only ? How many can speack Bengali ? How many can speak both Hindi and Bengali ?

51. Of the members of three athletic teams in a certain school, 21 are on the basketball team, 26 on hockey team and 29 on the football team. 14 play hockey and basketball, 15 play hockey and football, 12 play football and basketball and 8 play all the three games. How many members are there in all ?

52. An investigator interviewed 100 students to determine their preferences for the three drinks : milk (M), coffee (C) and tea (T). He reported the following : 10 students had all the three drinks M, C, T; 20 had M and C only; 30 had C and T; 25 had M and T; 12 had M only; 5 had C only, 8 had T only. Using a Venn diagram, find how many did not take any of the three drinks ?

53. In a survey of 200 students of a higher secondary school, it was found that 120 studied mathematics; 90 studied physics; and 70 studied chemistry; 40 studied mathematics and physics; 30 studied physics and chemistry; 50 studied chemistry and mathematics, and

20 studied none of these subjects. Find the number of students who studied all the three subjects.

54. A survey shows that 63% of Indians like mangoes whereas 76% like apples. If x% of the Indians like both mangoes and apples, then

(a) $x = 39$
(b) $x = 63$
(c) $39 \leq x \leq 63$
(d) none of these

55. A class has 175 students. The following table shows the number of students studying one or more of the following subjects in this class :

Subject	Number of students
Mathematics	100
Physics	70
Chemistry	46
Mathematics and Physics	30
Mathematics and Chemistry	28
Physics and Chemistry	23
Mathematics, Physics and Chemistry	18

How many students are enrolled in Mathematics alone, Physics alone and Chemistry alone ? Are there students who have not offered any of these three subjects ?

56. In a pollution study of 1500 Indian rivers the following data were reported. 520 were polluted by sulphur compounds, 335 polluted by phosphate, 425 were polluted by crude oil, 100 were polluted by both crude oil and sulphur compounds, 180 were polluted by both sulphur compunds and phosphates, 150 were polluted by both phosphates and crude oil and 28 were polluted by sulphur compounds, phosphates, and crude oil. How many of the rivers were polluted by at least one of the three impurities ? How many of the rivers were polluted by exactly one of the three impurities ?

57. A group of 123 workers went to a canteen for cold drinks, ice-cream and tea, 42 workers took ice-cream, 36 tea and 30 cold drinks. 15 workers purchased ice cream and tea, 10 ice cream and cold drinks, and 4 cold drinks and tea but not ice cream, 11 took ice cream and tea but not cold drinks. Determine how many workers did not purchase anything ?

58. A survey of 500 television watchers produced the following information; 285 watch foot-ball, 195 watch hockey, 115 watch basketball, 45 watch football and basketball, 70 watch football and hockey, 50 watch hockey and basketball, 50 do not watch any of the three games. How many watch all the three games ? How many watch exactly one of the three games ?

59. In a town of 10,000 families it was found that 40% families buy newspaper A, 20% families buy newspaper B and 10% families buy news- paper C. 5% families buy A and B, 3% buy B and C and 4% buy A and C. If 2% families buy all the three newspapers,

find the number of families which buy (i) A only (ii) B only (iii) none of A, B and C. **(Roorkee 1991)**

60. The report of one survey of 100 students stated that the numbers studying the various languages were : Sanskrit, Hindi and Tamil, 5; Hindi and Sanskrit, 10; Tamil and Sanskrit, 8; Hindi and Tamil, 20; Sanskrit 30; Hindi 23; Tamil 50. The surveyor who prepared the report was fired. Why ?

61. A survey conducted on 600 students of B.A. part I classes of a college gave the following report. "Out of 600 students, 307 took economics, 198 took history, 230 took sociology, 65 took history and economics, 45 took economics and sociology, 31 took sociology and history and 10 took all the three subjects. The report sounded very impressive, but the surveyor was fired. Why ?

62. Let A, B, C be subsets of the universal set U. If $n(U) = 692$, $n(B) = 230$, $n(C) = 370$, $n(B \cap C) = 20$, $n(A \cap B' \cap C') = 10$, find $n(A' \cap B' \cap C')$.

63. The set contains 5 elements, then the number of elements in the power set $P(A)$ is equal to

(a) 32
(b) 36
(c) 25
(d) 40
(Kerela-Eng. 2011)

64. Given $A = \{x : x$ is a root of $x^2 - 1 = 0\}$, $B = \{x : x$ is a root of $x^2 - 2x + 1 = 0\}$ then

(a) $A \cap B = B$
(b) $A \cap B = A$
(c) $A \cup B = A$
(d) $A \cap B = \phi$
(Orissa JEE 2010)

65. Let $S = \{1, 2, 3, 4\}$. The total number of unordered pairs of disjoint subsets of S is equal to

(a) 26
(b) 34
(c) 42
(d) 41
(IIT-JEE 2010)

66. 25 people for program A, 50 people for programme B, 10 people for both. So number of employee employed only A is

(a) 15
(b) 20
(c) 35
(d) 40
(Orissa-JEE 2010)

67. Let $X = \{1, 2, 3, 4, 5\}$. The number of different ordered pair (Y, Z) that can formed such that $Y \subseteq X, Z \subseteq X$ and $Y \cap Z$ is empty us

(a) 5^2
(b) 3^5
(c) 2^5
(d) 5^3
(AIEEE 2012)

Hints/Solutions to Problem Set (2)

1. Ans. (a).
$$(A \cap B') \cup (B \cap B') = A \cup \phi = A$$
Since A and B are disjoint.

2. Ans. (b).
Mark the sets A and B on the number line.

3. Ans. (b).
$$A = \{x : x \in \mathbf{R}, -1 < x < 1\}$$
$$B = \{x : x \in \mathbf{R}, -1 \geq x - 1 \geq 1\}$$

$= \{x : x \in \mathbf{R}, 0 \geq x \geq 2\}$

Now the sets A and B on the number line.

4. **Ans. (a).**

If $X \subset Y$, then $X \cup Y = Y$ and $X \cap Y = X$

If $Y \subset X$, then $X \cup Y = X$ and $X \cap X = X$

5. **Ans. (c).**

$2^2 = 4$

6. **Ans. (b).**

7. **Ans. $(A \cap B)$.**

$A - (A - B) = A - (A \cap B') = A \cap (A \cap B')'$

$\quad = A \cap (A' \cup B) = (A \cap A') \cup (A \cap B)$

$\quad = \phi \cup (A \cap B) = A \cap B$

8. **Ans. $(B - C)$.**

$(A \cup B) - C = (A \cup B) \cap C'$

$\quad = (A \cap C') \cup (B \cap C')$

$\quad = (A - C) \cup (B - C)$

9. **Ans. $(A - C) \cap (A - D)$.**

L.H.S. $= (B \cup C \cup D)'$ w.r.t. 'A'

$\quad = B' \cap C' \cap D'$ w.r.t. A etc.

$\quad = (A - B) \cap (A - C) \cap (A - D)$

10. **Ans. Yes.**

In fact $\quad A = \{-\sqrt{2}, 0, 1, \sqrt{2}\}$

and $\quad\quad B = \{1\}$ so that $B \subset A$.

11. **Ans. $\{(-1, 0), (1, 0)\}$**

12. **Ans. True.**

$(A \cup B) \cap (A' \cup B')$

$= \{(A \cup B) \cap A'\} \cup \{(A \cup B) \cap B'\}$, (Distributive law)

$\quad = \{(A \cap A') \cup (B \cap A')\} \cup \{(A \cap B') \cup (B \cap B')\}$

(Distributive law)

$\quad = \{\phi \cup (B \cap A')\} \cup \{(A \cap B') \cup \phi\}$

$\quad = (B \cap A') \cup (A \cap B') = (B - A) \cup (A - B)$

$\quad = [(A - B) \cup (B - A)]$.

13. **Ans. True.**

(i) $A - (B - C) = A - (B \cap C')$

$\quad = A \cap (B \cap C')'$

$\quad = A \cap (B' \cup C) = A \cap B' \cup (A \cap C)$

$\quad = (A - B) \cup (A \cap C)$

(ii) $(A \cup B) - B = (A \cup B) \cap B'$

$\quad = (A \cap B') \cup (B \cap \bar{B}')$

$\quad = (A \cap B') \cup \phi$

$\quad = A \cap B' = A - B$ etc.

14. **Ans.**

(i) Here we have to write down the set of all those people having both the properties : (1) college students, (2) people having their height more than five feet. Hence it is the set consisting of common elements of the sets S and W, that is, the set $S \cap W$.

(ii) The set of people who are not teenagers is the complement of the set T, that is, it is the set $U - T$ or T'.

Similarly the set of people having height less than

five feet is the complement of W, that is it is the set $U - W$ or W'.

Hence the required set in this case is

$(U - T) \cap (U - W)$ or $T' \cap W'$

(iii) Arguing as in cases (i) and (ii) we see that the required set in this case is

$(U - M) \cap (U - T) \cap (U - S) = M' \cap T' \cap S'$

or using De-Morgan's law, the required set is

$U - (M \cup T \cup S)$ i.e. $(M \cup T \cup S)'$

15. **Ans. $\{3, 5, 9\}$.**

16. **Ans. $\{2, 3\}$.**

$(B \cup C) = \{2, 4, 6, 8, 3, 5\}$

$\therefore \quad \{1, 2, 3\} \cap \{2, 4, 6, 8, 3, 5\} = \{2, 3\}$

17. **Ans. yes.** $\quad |x| \leq 1 \Rightarrow -1 \leq x \leq 1$

18. **Ans.**

(i) $A \cup (B \cap C) = \{2, 3, 4, 8, 10\} \cup \{4, 5, 12\}$

$\quad = \{2, 3, 4, 5, 8, 10, 12\}$

(ii) $A \cap (B \cup C) = \{2, 3, 4, 8, 10\} \cap$

$\{3, 4, 5, 6, 10, 12, 14\}$

$\quad = \{3, 4, 10\}$

19. **Ans. (b).**

20. **Ans. 21 N.**

According to the given notation,

$3\mathbf{N} = \{3x : x \in \mathbf{N}\} = \{3, 6, 9, 12, ...\}$

and $7\mathbf{N} = \{7x : x \in \mathbf{N}\}$

$\quad = \{7, 14, 21, 28, 35, 42, ...\}$

Hence $3\mathbf{N} \cap 7\mathbf{N} = \{21, 42, 63, ...\}$

$\quad = \{21x : x \in \mathbf{N}\} = 21\mathbf{N}$.

21. **Ans. (a).**

Since b and c are relatively prime, therefore $b\mathbf{N} \cap c\mathbf{N} = d\mathbf{N} \Rightarrow (bc)\,\mathbf{N} = d\mathbf{N} \Rightarrow bc = d$.

Note. In case b and c were not relatively prime but any numbers belonging to N, then the corresponding answer would be (d).

22. **Ans.** $\quad A \cup B = B, A \cap B = A, A - B = \phi$,

$B - A = \{2, 4, 6, 7, 8\}$

23. **Ans.** $\quad A' = \{1, 2, 3, 4, 5, 9\}, B' = \{1, 4, 6, 8, 9\}$

$(A \cup B)' = A' \cap B' = \{1, 4, 9\}$

$(A - B)' = \{1, 2, 3, 4, 5, 7, 9\}$

24. **Ans. (i) True.**

$x \in A - B \Leftrightarrow x \in A$

and $x \notin B \Leftrightarrow x \in A$ and $x \in B'$

$\Leftrightarrow x \in A \cap B'$

Hence $A - B = A \cap B'$. Again $\quad\quad\quad ...(1)$

$x \in A \cap B' \Leftrightarrow x \in A$ and $x \in B'$

$\Leftrightarrow \quad x \notin A'$ and $x \in B' \Leftrightarrow x \in B'$ and $x \notin A'$

$\Leftrightarrow \quad x \in (B' - A')$

Hence $A \cap B' = B' - A'$ $\quad\quad\quad ...(2)$

(ii) See Q. 7, P. 16-19.

(iii) We have

$(A \cap B) - (A \cap C) = (A \cap B) \cap (A \cap C)'$ by part (i)

$\quad = (A \cap B) \cap (A' \cup C')$ (De-Morgan Law)

$= \{(A \cap B) \cap A'\} \cup \{(A \cap B) \cap C'\}$

(Distributive law)

$= \phi \cap \{(A \cap B) \cap C'\}$

$[\because (A \cap B) \cap A' = (A \cap A') \cap B = \phi \cap B = \phi]$

$= A \cap (B \cap C') = A \cap (B - C)$

(iv) We have

$(A \cup B) - (A \cap B) = (A \cup B) \cap (A \cap B)'$ by part (i)

$= (A \cup B) \cap (A' \cup B')$ [De-Morgan Law]

$= \{(A \cap A') \cup (A \cap B')\} \cup \{(B \cap A') \cup (B \cap B')\}$

(By Distributive law)

$= \phi \cup (A \cap B') \cup (B \cap A') \cup \phi$

$= (A \cap B') \cup (B \cap A')$

$= (A - B) \cup (B - A) = A \Delta B,$

(by definition of Δ operation)

(v) We have

$(x, y) \in A \times (B \cap C)$

$\Leftrightarrow (x \in A)$ and $(y \in B \cap C)$

(by def. of cross product)

$\Leftrightarrow (x \in A)$ and $(y \in B$ and $y \in C)$

$\Leftrightarrow (x \in A$ and $y \in B)$ and $(x \in A$ and $y \in C)$

$\Leftrightarrow (x, y) \in (A \times B)$ and $(x, y) \in (A \times C)$

$\Leftrightarrow (x, y) \in (A \times B) \cap (A \times C)$

Hence $A \times (B \cap C) = (A \times B) \cap (A \times C)$

(vi) We have

$(x, y) \in A \times B \Rightarrow x \in A$ and $y \in B$

$\Rightarrow x \in C$ and $y \in B$ $[\because A \subset C \therefore x \in A \to x \in C]$

$\Rightarrow (x, y) \in C \times B.$

Hence $A \times B \subset C \times B.$

25. Ans. (a).

$(A \cap A) \cup (A \cap B) = A \cup (A \cap B) = A$

$\because A \cap B \subset A$

26. Ans. We have

$A' = \mathbf{R} - A = \{x : x \in \mathbf{R}$ and $x \notin A\}$

$= \{x : (x \in \mathbf{R}$ and $x \geq 2)$

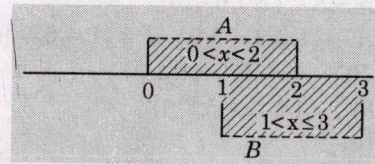

Fig. (5)

or $(x \in \mathbf{R}$ and $x \leq 0)\}$ [See the diagram also]

$= \{x : x \in \mathbf{R}$ and $x \geq 2\} \cup \{x : x \in \mathbf{R}$ and $x \leq 0\}$

$B' = \{x : x \in \mathbf{R}$ and $x \leq 1\} \cup \{x : x \in \mathbf{R}$ and $x > 3\}$

Similarly $A \cup B = \{x : x \in \mathbf{R}$ and $0 < x \leq 3\}$

$A \cap B = \{x : x \in \mathbf{R}$ and $1 < x < 2\}$

$A - B = \{x : x \in \mathbf{R}$ and $0 < x \leq 1\}.$

Note : In such problems use of real number line is useful.

27. Ans. (b).

Only (b) will give $x = \pm i$, rest all give real values of x.

28. Ans. (c).

Bijection means both one-one onto.

$(106)(105)(104)\ldots3.2.1 = (106)!$

29. Ans. (c).

$X \cap (X' \cap Y') = (X \cap X') \cap Y'$

$= \phi \cap Y' = \phi$

30. Ans. (c).

$y = e^x$ represents the exponential curve and $y = x$ represents a line passing through origin and making an angle of $45°$ with x-axis. Draw the figure yourself. Both these curves do not intersect at any point $i.e.$ they are disjoint. Hence $A \cap B = \phi.$

31. Ans. (b).

$y = e^x, y = e^{-x}$ meet where $e^x = e^{-x}$ or $e^{2x} = 1$

$\therefore x = 0$ and hence $y = 1.$ These curves meet at $(0, 1)$ so that $A \cap B = (0, 1).$

In other words $A \cap B \neq \phi.$

32. Ans. True.

Clearly $A \cup (B \cup C) = \{1, 2, 3, 4, 5, 6\}$

Now $A \times B = \{(1, 3), (1, 4), (2, 3), (2, 4), (3, 3), (3, 4)\}$

and $B \times C = \{(3, 4), (3, 5), (3, 6), (4, 4), (4, 5), (4, 6)\}$

Hence $(A \times B) \cap (B \times C) = \{(3, 4)\}.$

33. (i) $A \times (B \cap C) = \{(2, 5), (3, 5)\}$

(ii) $(A \times B) \cup (B \times C) = \{(2, 3), (2, 4), (3, 4),$
$(3, 5), (4, 5), (4, 6), (5, 5), (5, 6)\}$

34. Ans. (c).

$A - B = \{3\}, A \cap B = (2, 5).$

$\therefore (A - B) \times (A \cap B) = \{(3, 2), (3, 5)\}.$

35. Ans. True.

36. Ans. (d).

$A \cap B = \{4\}, (A \cup B) = \{2, 3, 4, 5\}$

$\therefore (A \cap B) \times (A \cup B)$

$= \{(4, 2), (4, 3), (4, 4), (4, 5)\}$

37. Ans. (b).

$(A \cup B) = \{1, 2, 3, 8\}$

$(A \cap B) = \{3\}$

$\therefore (A \cup B) \times (A \cap B)$

$= \{(1, 3), (2, 3), (3, 3), (8, 3)\}$

38. Ans. (c).

Common elements will be

$\{(2, 2), (3, 3), (2, 3), (3, 2)\}$

39. Ans. (d).

$A \times (B \cup C) = \{a, b, c\} \times \{a, c, d, e, f\}$

The above set will consist of 15 ordered pairs and not 3.

40. Ans. (c).

Mind $(a \times b)$ is different from $(b \times a)$

If $A = \{a, b, c\}, B = (a, b, d, e, f)$

41. Ans. (b).

$n(A \cup B) = n(A) + n(B) - n(A \cap B)$ ...(1)

Now A has 3 elements and B has 6 elements.

If they are disjoint, then $n(A \cap B) = 0.$

$\therefore \quad n(A \cup B) = 6 + 3 = 9$

If $A \subset B$ then $A \cup B = B$

$\therefore \quad n(A \cup B) = n(B) = 6$

B cannot be a subset of A and hence the other possibility of $A \cup B = A$ is ruled out.

42. Ans. (c).

Since each A_i has 5 elements, we have

$$\sum_{i=1}^{30} n(A_i) = 5 \times 30 = 150 \qquad \ldots(1)$$

Let S consist of m distinct elements. Since each element of S belongs to exactly 12 of the A_i's, we also have

$$\sum_{i=1}^{30} n(A_i) = 10m \qquad \ldots(2)$$

Hence from (1) and (2), $10m = 150$ or $m = 15$. Again since each B_j has 3 elements and each element of S belongs to exactly 9 of the B_j's we have

$$\sum_{j=1}^{n} n(B_j) = 3n \text{ and } \sum_{j=1}^{n} n(B_j) = 9m$$

It follows that $3n = 9m = 9 \times 15 \qquad [\because m = 15]$

This gives $n = 45$.

43. Ans. (b).

We know that the interchange of two adjacent rows (or columns) changes the value of a determinant only in sign and not in magnitude. Hence corresponding to every element Δ of B there is an element Δ' in C obtained by interchanging two adjacent rows (or columns) in Δ. It follows that

$$n(B) \le n(C).$$

That is, the number of elements in B is less than or equal to the number of elements in C.

Similarly $n(C) \le n(B)$.

Hence $n(B) = n(C)$, that is, B has as many elements as C.

44. Ans. (b).

We are given $2^m - 2^n = 56$.

By trial $m = 6$ and $n = 3$.

Hence (b) is correct.

45. Ans. $\left[\theta : \dfrac{\pi}{2} \le \theta \le \dfrac{5\pi}{6} \text{ or } \pi \le \theta \le \dfrac{3\pi}{2} \right]$

As given set B consists of all values of θ in the interval $\pi/2 \le \theta \le 3\pi/2$ and set A consists of all values of θ which satisfy the inequality

$$2\cos^2 \theta + \sin \theta \le 2. \qquad \ldots(1)$$

Hence $A \cap B$ will consist of all those values of θ in the interval $\pi/2 \le \theta \le 3\pi/2$ which satisfy the inequality (1).

The inequality (1) is equivalent to the inequality

$$2 - 2\sin^2 \theta + \sin \theta \le 2,$$

that is, $\sin \theta (1 - 2\sin \theta) \le 0$

or $2\sin \theta \left(\sin \theta - \dfrac{1}{2} \right) \ge 0 \qquad \ldots(2)$

The inequality (2) is satisfied by all those values of θ which satisfy $\sin \theta \le 0$ or $\sin \theta \ge \dfrac{1}{2}$.

Now the values of θ which lie in the interval $\pi/2 \le \theta \le 3\pi/2$ and satisfy $\sin \theta \le 0$ are given by $\pi \le \theta \le 3\pi/2$. And the values of θ which lie in the interval $\pi/2 \le \theta \le 3\pi/2$ and satisfy $\sin \theta \ge \dfrac{1}{2}$ are given by $\pi/2 \le \theta \le 5\pi/6$.

Thus the solution set of inequality (1) consists of all values of θ in the intervals $\pi/2 \le \theta \le 5\pi/6$ and $\pi \le \theta \le 3\pi/2$. Hence

$A \cap B = \{\theta : \pi/2 \le \theta \le 5\pi/6 \text{ or } \pi \le \theta \le 3\pi/2\}$

46. Ans. (a). Putting $n = 1, 2, 3, \ldots$

$X = \{0, 9, 54, 243, \ldots\}$

$Y = \{0, 9, 18, 27, 36, 45, 54, \ldots\}$

Clearly $X \subset Y$.

47. Ans. True.

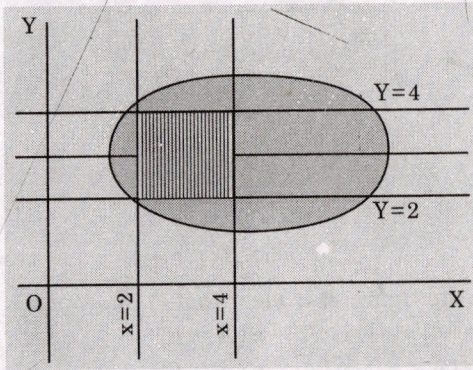

Fig. (6)

We first observe that $|x - 3| < 1$

$\Rightarrow \quad -1 < x - 3 < 1 \qquad \Rightarrow \quad 2 < x < 4$

Similarly $|y - 3| < 1 \rightarrow 2 < y < 4$.

Thus S consists of all points inside the square bounded by the lines $x = 2$, $x = 4$, $y = 2$ and $y = 4$.

This square region is shown in the figure by vertical lines.

Again $4x^2 + 9y^2 - 32x - 54y + 109$

$$= 4(x^2 - 8x + 16) + 9(y^2 - 6y + 9) - 36$$

$$= 4(x - 4)^2 + 9(y - 3)^2 - 36.$$

Hence $4x^2 + 9y^2 - 32x - 54y + 109 \le 0$

$\Rightarrow \quad 4(x - 4)^2 + 9(y - 3)^2 - 36 \le 0$

$\Rightarrow \quad \dfrac{(x - 4)^2}{9} + \dfrac{(y - 3)^2}{4} \le 1.$

Thus the set E consists of all points within and on the ellipse whose centre is $(4, 3)$ and semi major and minor axes are 3 and 2 respectively. This region is shown by dots in the diagram.

We now show that $S \subset E$.

Let (a,b) be any arbitrary element of S. Then by definition of S, we have

$$2 < a < 4 \quad \text{and} \quad 2 < b < 4$$

Now $2 < a < 4 \Rightarrow 2 - 4 < a - 4 < 4 - 4$

$\Rightarrow -2 < a - 4 < 0$

$\Rightarrow -\dfrac{2}{3} < \dfrac{a-4}{3} < 0 \quad \Rightarrow \dfrac{(a-4)^2}{9} < \dfrac{4}{9} \qquad \dots(1)$

and $2 < b < 4$

$\Rightarrow 2 - 3 < b - 3 < 4 - 3 \Rightarrow -1 < b - 3 < 1$

$\Rightarrow -\dfrac{1}{2} < \dfrac{b-3}{2} < \dfrac{1}{2} \quad \Rightarrow \dfrac{(b-3)^2}{4} < \dfrac{1}{4} \qquad \dots(2)$

From (1) and (2), we have

$$\dfrac{(a-4)^2}{9} + \dfrac{(b-3)^2}{4} < \dfrac{4}{9} + \dfrac{1}{4} = \dfrac{25}{36} < 1.$$

$\therefore \quad (a,b) \in E$

$\therefore \quad (a,b) \in S \Rightarrow (a,b) \in E \ \therefore \ S \subset E$

48. Ans. True.

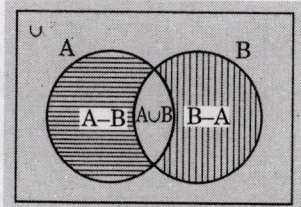

Fig. (7)

From the figure, it is clear that

$n(A) = n(A - B) + n(A \cap B)$

or $\quad n(A - B) = n(A) - n(A \cap B) \qquad \dots(1)$

Also $n(B - A) = n(B) - n(A \cap B) \qquad \dots(2)$

$\quad n(A \cap B) = n(A \cap B) \qquad \dots(3)$

Adding (1), (2) and (3), we get

$n(A - B) + n(B - A) + n(A \cap B)$

$= n(A) + n(B) - n(A \cap B) \qquad \dots(4)$

But $A - B$, $B - A$ and $A \cap B$ are clearly disjoint and hence

L.H.S. $= n(A \cup B)$

$\qquad = n(A - B) + n(B - A) + n(A \cap B)$

or $\quad n(A \cup B) = n(A) + n(B) - n(A \cap B)$ by (4)

(V. Imp.)

Cor. $n(A \triangle B) = n\{(A - B) \cup (B - A)\}$ by def.

$= n(A - B) + n(B - A) - n\{(A - B) \cap (B - A)\}$

$= n(A) - n(A \cap B) + n(B) - n(B \cap A) - 0$

$= n(A) + n(B) - 2n(A \cap B)$

Order of Finite Sets :

$n(A)$ means the total number of elements in A. They may belong to B also. It does not mean the number of elements which **exclusively belong to A.**

We give below certain results which are obvious by the help of Venn diagram. If A, B, C be different sets and U be the universal set, then

(1) $\quad n(A') = n(U) - n(A)$

(2) $\quad n(A \cap B') = n(A - B) = n(A) - n(A \cap B)$

(3) $\quad n(A \cup B) = n(A) + n(B) - n(A \cap B)$

or $\quad n(A \cap B) = n(A) + n(B) - n(A \cup B)$

See Q. 48 for proof of (3).

(4) $\quad n(A \cup B \cup C) = n(A) + n(B) + n(C)$
$\qquad - \{n(A \cap B) - n(B \cap C)$
$\qquad \qquad - n(C \cap A)\} + n(A \cap B \cap C)$

i.e. $S_1 - S_2 + S_3$

Proof. $n(A \cup B \cup C) = n(A \cup P)$

where $P = B \cup C$

$= n(A) + n(P) - n(A \cap P)$. Put for P

$= n(A) + n(B \cup C) - n\{A \cap (B \cup C)\}$

$= n(A) + n(B \cup C) - n\{(A \cap B) \cup (A \cap C)\}$

Dist. Law

$= n(A) + n(B \cup C) - n\{L \cup M\}$

$= n(A) + \{n(B) + n(C) - n(B \cap C)\}$
$\qquad - \{n(L) + n(M) - n(L \cap M)\}$

Now put for L and M and

$L \cap M = (A \cap B) \cap (A \cap C) = A \cap (B \cap C)$

$\therefore \quad n(A \cup B \cup C) = n(A) + n(B) + n(C)$
$\qquad - n(B \cap C) - n(A \cap B) - n(A \cap C)$
$\qquad \qquad + n(A \cap B \cap C)$

$\qquad = S_1 - S_2 + S_3$

Note. If A, B, C are all disjoint, then

$n(A \cup B \cup C) = n(A) + n(B) + n(C)$ only.

This can be extended to any number of disjoint sets.

(5) $\quad n(A' \cap B' \cap C') = n(A \cup B \cup C)'$

$\qquad \qquad = n(U) - n(A \cup B \cup C)$

$\qquad \qquad = n(U) - \{S_1 - S_2 + S_3\}$

Above stands for the number of elements which do not belong to any of the sets A, B and C.

(6) $\quad n(A \cap B' \cap C')$. This stands for the number of elements which belong to **A only** *i.e.* they do not belong to both B and C.

$n(A \cap B' \cap C') = n(A \cap (B \cup C)')$

$\qquad = n(A) - n\{A \cap (B \cup C)\}$

$\qquad = n(A) - n\{(A \cap B) \cup (A \cap C)\}$

$\qquad = n(A) - n(P \cup Q)$

$\qquad = n(A) - \{n(P) + n(Q) - n(P \cap Q)\}$

$\qquad = n(A) - n(A \cap B) - n(A \cap C)$
$\qquad \qquad + n\{(A \cap B) \cap (A \cap C)\}$

$\qquad = n(A) - n(A \cap B) - n(A \cap C)$
$\qquad \qquad + n(A \cap B \cap C)$

$\therefore \quad n(A \cap B' \cap C') = n(A) - n(A \cap B)$
$\qquad \qquad - n(A \cap C) + n\{A \cap B \cap C\}$

(7) $\quad n(A \cap B \cap C')$. This stands for number of elements which belong to both A and B but do not belong to C

$n(A \cap B \cap C') = n(P \cap C')$

$\qquad = n(P) - n(P \cap C) \qquad \text{by (2)}$

$\qquad = n(A \cap B) - n(A \cap B \cap C)$

49. Ans. (c). $n(A' \cap B') = n(A \cup B)'$

$$= n(u) - n(A \cup B)$$
$$= n(u) - \{n(A) + n(B) - n(A \cap B)\}$$
$$= 700 - \{200 + 300 - 100\} = 300$$

50. Ans. Hindi only 600, Bengali only 250, Both 150

Let H and B denote the sets of those people who can speak Hindi and Bengali respectively. Then as given, we have

$$n(H \cup B) = 1000, n(H) = 750, n(B) = 400.$$

Now $n(H \cup B) = n(H) + n(B) - n(H \cap B)$

or $\quad 1000 = 750 + 400 - n(H \cap B)$

∴ $\quad n(H \cap B) = 150.$

Hence 150 people can speak both Hindi and Bengali. We now find those people who can speak Hindi only, that is $n(H \cap B')$

But $n(H \cap B') = n(H) - n(H \cap B)$
$$= 750 - 150 = 600.$$

Hence 600 people can speak Hindi only.

Similarly $n(B \cap H') = n(B) - n(B \cap H)$
$$= 400 - 150 = 250$$

that is, 250 people can speak Bengali only.

51. Ans. 43 only.

Let B, H, F denote the sets of members who are on the basket ball team, hockey team and football team respectively.

Then we are given :
$$n(B) = 21, n(H) = 26, n(F) = 29.$$
$$n(H \cap B) = 14, n(H \cap F) = 15,$$
$$n(F \cap B) = 12$$
and $n(B \cap H \cap F) = 8.$
We have to find $n(B \cup H \cup F).$
To find this, we use the formula
$$n(B \cup H \cup F) = n(B) + n(H) + n(F)$$
$$- n(B \cap H) - n(H \cap F) - n(F \cap B) + n(B \cap H \cap F).$$
i.e. $S_1 - S_2 + S_3$
Hence $n(B \cup H \cup F) = (21 + 26 + 29)$
$$- (14 + 15 + 12) + 8 = 43$$

Thus there are 43 members in all.

Remark. Problems like problem 51 can also be solved by using Venn diagrams. We first write 8 in the region $B \cap H \cap F$.

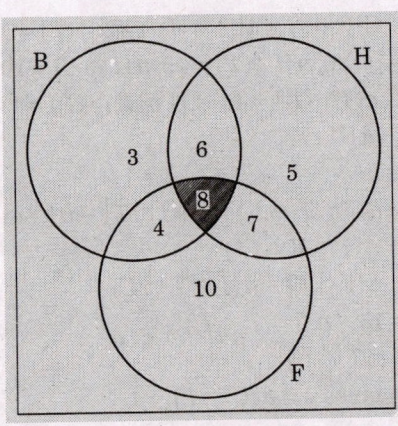

Fig. (8)

Since 14 play hockey and basketball of which 8 are already written in $B \cap H \cap F$. We write 6 in the remaining part of $H \cap B$. Similarly we write 7 and 4 in the remaining parts of $H \cap F$ and $F \cap B$. Finally there are 21 members on the basketball of which $6 + 8 + 4$, that is, 18 have already been written and so we write 3 in the remaining part of B. Similarly we write 5 and 10 in the remaining parts of H and F respectively.

Hence the total number
$$= 3 + 6 + 5 + 4 + 8 + 7 + 10 = 43.$$

52. Ans. 20.

We first draw a Venn-diagram representing the set U of 100 students by a rectangle and its three subsets M, C, T by closed curves inside U.

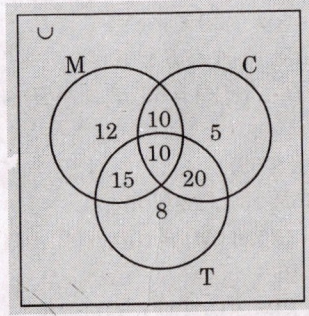

Fig. (10)

We first write 10 in the region $M \cap C \cap T$.

Since $n(M \cap C) = 20$ out of which 10 have already been counted in $M \cap C \cap T$, we write $20 - 10$, that is, 10 in the remaining part of $M \cap C$.

Similarly we write 20 in the remaining part of $C \cap T$ and 15 in $M \cap T$ so that the total numbers in these parts are 30 and 25 respectively as given.

Finally we put 12 in 'M only', 5 in 'C only' and 8 in 'T only'. Thus the total number of students taking drinks M or C or T

$$= n(M \cup C \cup T)$$
$$= 12 + 10 + 5 + 15 + 10 + 20 + 8 = 80.$$

Hence number of students taking none of these drinks
$$= n(M \cup C \cup T)' = n(U) - n(M \cup C \cup T)$$
$$= 100 - 80 = 20.$$

Note. Here $S_1 - S_2 + S_3$ is not applicable as in Q. 43. Here 12 had M **only**, 5 had C **only** and 8 T **only**.

53. Ans. 20. We are given :
$$n(U) = 200, n(M) = 120, n(P) = 90,$$
$$n(C) = 70; n(M \cap P) = 40, n(P \cap C) = 30,$$
$$n(C \cap M) = 50, n(M \cup P \cup C)' = 20.$$
Now $n(M \cup P \cup C)' = n(U) - n(M \cup P \cup C)$
or $\quad 20 = 200 - n(M \cup P \cup C)$
Hence $n(M \cup P \cup C) = 180.$
But $n(M \cup P \cup C) = S_1 - S_2 + S_3$

$$= n(M) + n(P) + n(C) - n(M \cap P) - n(P \cap C)$$
$$- n(C \cap M) + n(M \cap P \cap C)$$
$$\therefore \quad 180 = (120 + 90 + 70) - (40 + 30 + 50)$$
$$+ n(M \cap P \cap C)$$

This gives $\quad n(M \cap P \cap C) = 20$.

Hence 20 students studied all the three subjects.

54. Ans. (c).

Let 100 denote the population of India, then
$$n(A) = 63, n(B) = 76, n(A \cap B) = x$$
$$n(A \cup B) = n(A) + n(B) - n(A \cap B)$$
$$\therefore \quad x = 63 + 76 - n(A \cup B) \qquad \qquad ...(1)$$

If should be noted that $n(A \cup B) \neq 100$ but $n(A \cup B) \leq 100$ because there are Indians who may like other fruits besides mangoes and apples.

Hence from (1), $x = 139 - n(A \cup B)$
$$\therefore \quad x \geq 39 \quad \text{or} \quad 39 \leq x$$

Again $A \cap B \subset A, A \cap B \subset B$
$$\therefore \quad n(A \cap B) \leq n(A) = 63, n(A \cap B) \leq n(B) = 76$$
$$\therefore \quad x \leq 63.$$

Hence $39 \leq x \leq 63$.

55. Ans. $60M, 35P, 13C$, 22 None.

Here $n(U) = 175, n(M) = 100, n(P) = 70,$
$$n(C) = 46$$
$$n(M \cap P) = 30, n(M \cap C) = 28,$$
$$n(P \cap C) = 23$$
and $n(M \cap P \cap C) = 18$

To find $n(M \cap P' \cap C'), n(P \cap M' \cap C'),$
$$n(C \cap M' \cap P')$$
and $n(P' \cap M' \cap C')$.

Now $n(M \cap P' \cap C')$
$$= n(M) - n(M \cap P) - n(M \cap C) + n(M \cap P \cap C)$$
$$= 100 - 30 - 28 + 18 = 60 \qquad \qquad \textbf{[(6) P. 22]}$$

Similarly $n(P \cap M' \cap C') = n(P) - n(P \cap M)$
$$- n(P \cap C) + n(P \cap M \cap C)\}$$
$$= 70 - 30 - 23 + 18 = 35,$$
$$n(C \cap M' \cap P') = n(C) - n(C \cap M)$$
$$- n(C \cap P) + n(C \cap M \cap P)\}$$
$$= 46 - 28 - 23 + 18 = 13$$

and $n(M' \cap P' \cap C') = n(M \cup P \cup C)'$
$$= n(U) - n(M \cup P \cup C)$$
$$= n(U) - \{S_1 - S_2 + S_3\}$$
$$= n(U) - \{n(M) + n(P) + n(C)$$
$$- n[(M \cap P) - n(P \cap C)$$
$$- n(M \cap C) + n(M \cap P \cap C)\}$$
$$= 175 - \{100 + 70 + 46 - 30 - 23 - 28 + 18\}$$
$$= 175 - \{216 - 81 + 18\} = 22.$$

56. Ans. 878, S only 268, P only 33, C only 203.

Here $n(U) = 1500, n(S) = 520, n(P) = 335,$
$$n(C) = 425, n(C \cap S) = 100, n(S \cap P) = 180,$$
$$n(P \cap C) = 150$$
and $n(S \cap P \cap C) = 28,$

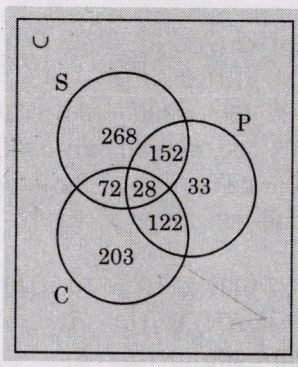

Fig. (11)

where S, P and C denote respectively the set of rivers polluted by sulphur compounds, phos- phates and crude oil.

Now we draw a Venn-diagram representing the set U of 1500 Indian rivers by a rectangle and its three subsets S, P and C by closed curves inside U. We first write 28 in the region
$$S \cap P \cap C.$$

Since $n(C \cap S) = 100$, out of which 28 have already been counted in $S \cap P \cap C$, we write $100 - 28$, that is, 72 in the remaining part of $C \cap S$. Similarly we write 152 and 122 in the remaining parts of $S \cap P$ and $P \cap C$ respecti- vely. Finally we put 268 in 'S only', 33 in 'P only' and 203 in 'C only'.

Now the number of rivers polluted by at least one of the three impurities is given by
$$n(S \cup P \cup C) = 28 + 72 + 152 + 122 + 268 + 33 + 203$$
$$= 878$$
or $\quad S_1 - S_2 + S_3 = (520 + 335 + 425)$
$$- (100 + 180 + 150) + 28$$
$$= 1280 - 430 + 28 = 1308 - 430 = 878$$

Only Sulphur
$$= 520 - (152 + 72 + 28) = 520 - 252 = 268$$

Number of rivers polluted by exactly sulphur compounds $= 268$

Number of rivers polluted by exactly phosphates $= 33$ and the Numb. of rivers polluted by exactly crude oil $= 203$.

57. Ans. 44. Given $N = 123, n(I) = 42, n(T) = 36.$
$$n(C) = 20, n(I \cap T) = 15, n(I \cap C) = 10,$$
$$n(C \cap T \cap I') = 4, \quad n(I \cap T \cap C') = 11$$

To find $\quad n(I' \cap T' \cap C')$

We have
$$4 = n(C \cap T \cap I') = n(C \cap T) - n(C \cap T \cap I) \quad ...(1)$$
and $11 = n(I \cap T \cap C') \qquad \qquad \textbf{[(7) P. 22]}$
$$= n(I \cap T) - n(I \cap T \cap C)$$
$$= 15 - n(I \cap T \cap C)$$
$$\therefore \quad n(I \cap T \cap C) = 4$$

Then (1) gives $4 = n(C \cap T) - 4$
or $\quad n(C \cap T) = 8$

Now $n(I' \cap T' \cup C') = n(I \cup T \cup C)'$

           by De-Morgan law

$= N - n(I \cup T \cup C)$

$= N - \{n(I) + n(T) + n(C) - n(I \cap T)$
$\qquad - n(T \cap C) - n(C \cap I) + n(I \cap T \cap C)\}$

$= 123 - \{42 + 36 + 30 - 15 - 8 - 10 + 4\} = 44$

58. Ans. 20. Only football 190 etc.

Given $N = 500$, $n(F) = 285$,

$\qquad n(H) = 195, n(B) = 115, n(F \cap B) = 45,$

$\qquad n(F \cap H) = 70, n(H \cap B) = 50,$

$\qquad n(F' \cap H' \cap B') = 50.$

To find $n(F \cap H \cap B), n(F \cap H' \cap B'),$

$\qquad n(F' \cap H \cap B')$ and $n(F' \cap H' \cap B)$

we have

$\quad 50 = n(F' \cap H' \cap B') = n(F \cup H \cup B)',$

           By De-Morgan law

$= N - n(F \cup H \cup B) = N - \{S_1 - S_2 + S_3\}$

$= N - \{n(F) + n(H) + n(B) - n(F \cap H)$
$\qquad - n(H \cap B) - n(B \cap F) + n(F \cap H \cap B)\}$

$= 500 - 285 - 195 - 115 + 70 + 50 + 45$
$\qquad\qquad\qquad\qquad - n(F \cap H \cap B)$

$= 665 - 595 - n(F \cap H \cap B)$

$= 70 - n(F \cap H \cap B)$

$\therefore \quad n(F \cap H \cap B) = 20$

Again, $n(F \cap H' \cap B') = n\{F \cap (H \cup B)'\}$

           by De-Morgan law

$= n(F) - n\{F \cap (H \cup B)\}$

$= n(F) - n\{(F \cap H) \cup (F \cap B)\}$

$= n(F) - \{n(F \cap H) + n(F \cap B) - n(F \cap H \cap B)\}$

$= 285 - 70 - 45 + 20 = 190$

59. Ans. 3300, 1400, 4000.

Here we have

$\qquad N = 10,000, n(A) = 40\%$ of $10,000 = 4000,$

$\qquad n(B) = 20\%$ of $10000 = 2000$

$\qquad n(C) = 10\%$ of $10000 = 1000$

$\qquad n(A \cap B) = 5\%$ of $10000 = 500$

$\qquad n(B \cap C) = 3\%$ of $10000 = 300$

$\qquad n(C \cap A) = 4\%$ of $10000 = 400$

$\qquad n(A \cap B \cap C) = 2\%$ of $10000 = 200$

To find

(i) $n(A \cap \overline{B} \cap \overline{C})$ (ii) $n(\overline{A} \cap B \cap \overline{C})$

(iii) $n(\overline{A} \cap \overline{B} \cap \overline{C})$

We have

$n(A \cap \overline{B} \cap \overline{C}) = n[A \cap (\overline{B \cup C})]$

$= n(A) - \overline{n}[A \cap (B \cup C)]$

$= n(A) - \{n(A \cap B) \cup (A \cap C)\}$

$= n(A) - [n(A \cap B) + n(A \cap C)$
$\qquad\qquad\qquad - n(A \cap B) \cap (A \cap C)]$

$= n(A) - \{n(A \cap B) + n(A \cap C) - n(A \cap B \cap C)\}$

You may use the formula **(6) on P. 22** directly

$= 4000 - 500 - 400 + 200 = 3300$

$n(\overline{A} \cap B \cap \overline{C}) = n[B \cap (\overline{A \cup C})]$

$= n(B) - n[B \cap (A \cup C)]$

$= n(B) - n[(B \cap A) \cup (B \cap C)]$

$= n(B) - [n(A \cap B) + n(B \cap C)$
$\qquad\qquad\qquad - n\{(A \cap B) \cap (B \cap C)\}$

$= n(B) - \{n(A \cap B) + n(B \cap C)$
$\qquad\qquad\qquad - n(A \cap B \cap C)\}$

$= 2000 - 500 - 300 + 200 = 1400$

and $n(\overline{A} \cap \overline{B} \cap \overline{C}) = n(\overline{A \cup B \cup C})$

$= N - n(A \cup B \cup C)$

$= N - \{n(A) + n(B) + n(C) - n(A \cap B)$
$\qquad - n(B \cap C) - n(C \cap A) + n(A \cap B \cap C)\}$

$= 10000 - 4000 - 2000 - 1000 + 500$
$\qquad\qquad\qquad\qquad\qquad + 300 + 400 - 200$

$= 4000.$

60. Let S, H and T denote the set of students studying Sanskrit, Hindi and Tamil respectively. Then we are given :

$n(S \cup H \cup T) = 100, n(S) = 30, n(H) = 23,$

$n(T) = 50, n(S \cap H) = 10, n(H \cap T) = 20,$

$\qquad n(T \cap S) = 8, n(S \cap H \cap T) = 5.$

Now $n(S \cup H \cup T) = n(S) + n(H) + n(T)$
$\qquad - n(S \cap H) - n(H \cap T) - n(T \cap S)$
$\qquad\qquad\qquad\qquad\qquad + n(S \cap H \cap T)$

$= S_1 - S_2 + S_3$

$= (30 + 23 + 50) - (10 + 20 + 8) + 5 = 70.$

But we are given $n(S \cup H \cup T) = 100.$

Hence the data is inconsistent. That is why the surveyor was fired.

61. Ans. Data are inconsistent since

$n(E \cup S \cup H) \surd n(E) + n(S) + n(H)$
$\qquad - n(E \cap S) - n(S \cap H)$
$\qquad\qquad\qquad - n(H \cap E) + n(E \cap S \cap H)$

62. Ans. 172. $n(A' \cap B' \cap C') = n\{(B' \cap C') \cap A'\}$

$= n\{(B' \cap C') - n\{(B' \cap C') \cap A\}$

$= n(B \cup C)' - n(A \cap B' \cap C')$

$= n(U) - n(B \cup C) - n(A \cap B' \cap C')$

$= n(U) - n(B) - n(C) + n(B \cap C) - n(A \cap B' \cap C')$

$= 692 - 230 - 370 + 90 - 10 = 172.$

63. Ans. (a). $n(A) = 5 \implies n(P(A)) = 2^5 = 32$

64. $A = \{x : x$ is a root of $x^2 - 1 = 0\} = \{+1, -1\}$

$B = \{x : x$ is a root of $x^2 - 2x + 1 = 0\} = \{1\}$

$\implies \quad A \cup B = \{+1, -1\} = A$

65. Ans. (d).

$S = \{1, 2, 3, 4\}$, clearly each element can be put in 3 ways either in subsets or we don't put in any subset

$\therefore \quad$ Total number of ordered pairs

$\qquad = \dfrac{3 \times 3 \times 3 \times 3 - 1}{2} + 1 = 41$

66. Ans. (a).

$$n(A - B) = n(A) - n(A \cap B) = 25 - 10 - 15$$

67. Ans. (b). Every element has 3 options. Either set Y or set Z or none. Therefore, number of ordered pairs $= 3^5$.

Problem Set (3)

RELATIONS

1. If R is a relation from a finite set A having m elements to a finite set B having n elements, then the number of relations from A to B is

(a) 2^{mn} (b) $2^{mn} - 1$ (c) $2mn$ (d) m^n

2. Let R be a reflexive relation on a finite set A having n elements, and let there be m ordered pairs in R. Then

(a) $m \geq n$ (b) $m \leq n$

(c) $m = n$ (d) none of these

3. Two points A and B in a plane are related if $OA = OB$, where O is a fixed point. This relation is

(a) partial order relation

(b) equivalence relation

(c) reflexive but not symmetric

(d) reflexive but not transitive.

4. Let A and B be two sets such that $A \times B$ consists of 6 elements. If three elements of $A \times B$ are $(1, 4), (2, 6), (3, 6)$, find $A \times B$ and $B \times A$.

5. If $A = \{a, b, c, d\}, B = \{1, 2, 3\}$, find whether or not the following sets of ordered pairs are relations from A to B or not

(a) $R_1 = \{(a, 1), (a, 3)\}$

(b) $R_2 = \{(b, 1), (c, 2), (d, 1)\}$

(c) $R_3 = \{(a, 1), (b, 2), (3, c)\}$

6. If $A = \{1, 2, 3, 4\}$, define relations on A which have properties of being

(a) reflexive, transitive but not symmetric.

(b) symmetric but neither reflexive nor transi- tive.

(c) reflexive, symmetric and transitive.

7. Let $A = \{1, 2, 3\}$ and let

$R_1 = \{(1, 1), (1, 3), (3, 1), (2, 2), (2, 1), (3, 3)\}$

$R_2 = \{(2, 2,), (3, 1), (1, 3)\}$

$R_3 = \{(1, 3), (3, 3)\}, R_4 = A \times A.$

Find whether or not each of the relations $R_1, R_2, R_3, R_4,$ on A is

(a) reflexive   (b) symmetric

(c) transitive

8. Given a relation $R = \{(1, 2), (2, 3)\}$ on the set of natural numbers, add a minimum number of ordered pairs so that the enlarged relation is symmetric, transitive and reflexive.

9. Given the relation $R = \{(1, 2), (2, 3)\}$ on the set $\{1, 2, 3\}$, the minimum number of ordered pairs which when added to R make it an equivalence relation is

(a) 5   (b) 6   (c) 7   (d) 8

10. Let $R = \{(a, a), (b, c), (a, b)\}$ be a relation on a set $A = \{a, b, c\}$. Then the minimum number of ordered pairs which when added to R make it an equivalence relation are ......

11. Is it true that every relation which is symmetric and transitive is also reflexive ? Give reasons.

12. Let a relation R be defined by $R = \{(4, 5), (1, 4), (4, 6), (7, 6), (3, 7)\}$. Find

(i) $R \circ R$ (ii) $R^{-1} \circ R$.

13. If R be a relation $<$ from $A = \{1, 2, 3, 4\}$ to $B = \{1, 3, 5\}$, i.e. $(a, b) \in R$ iff $a < b$, then $R \circ R^{-1}$ is

(a) $\{(1, 3), (1, 5), (2, 3), (2, 5), (3, 5), (4, 5)\}$

(b) $\{(3, 1), (5, 1), (3, 2), (5, 2), (5, 3), (5, 4)\}$

(c) $\{(3, 3), (3, 5), (5, 3), (5, 5)\}$

(d) $\{(3, 3), (3, 4), (4, 5)\}$

14. Let $A = \{1, 2, 3, 4, 5\}, B = \{1, 3, 5, 7, 9, 10, 17, 26, 30\}$. Which of the following sets of ordered pairs are (i) relations (ii) functions (iii) neither, from A to B

(a) $R_1 = \{(1, 3), (3, 3), (5, 17), (1, 2)\}$

(b) $R_2 = \{(3, 7), (4, 5), (5, 30)\}$

(c) $R_3 = \{(x, y) : x \in A, y \in B, x + y = 8\}$

(d) $R_4 = \{(x, y) : x \in A, y \in B, y = x^2 + 1\}$

(e) $R_5 = \{(x, y) : x \in A, y \in B, y = 2x - 1\}$

15. If $X = \{1, 2, 3, 4, 5\}$ and $Y = \{1, 3, 5, 7, 9\}$, determine which of the following sets are (i) mappings (ii) relations (iii) neither of X to Y.

(a) $R_1 = \{(x, y) : y = x + 2, x \in X, y \in Y\}$

(b) $R_2 = \{(1, 1), (2, 1), (3, 3), (4, 3), (5, 5)\}$

(c) $R_3 = \{(1, 1), (1, 3), (3, 5), (3, 7), (5, 7)\}$

(d) $R_4 = \{(1, 3), (2, 5), (4, 7), (5, 9), (3, 1)\}$

16. Let A be the set of first ten natural numbers and let R be relation on A defined by $(x, y) \in R$ ' $x + 2y = 10$, i.e. $R = \{(x, y) : x \in A, y \in A$ and $x + 2y = 10 \}$. Express R and R^{-1} as sets of ordered pairs. Determine also (i) domains of R and R^{-1} (ii) ranges of R and R^{-1}.

17. Three relations R_1, R_2 and R_3 are defined on set $A = \{a, b, c\}$ as follows :

(i) $R_1 = \{(a, a), (a, b), (a, c), (b, c), (c, a), (b, b), (c, b), (c, c)\}$

(ii) $R_2 = \{(a, b), (b, a), (a, c), (c, a)\}$

(iii) $R_3 = \{(a, b), (b, c), (c, a)\}$

Discuss each of them from the point of view of being reflexive, symmetric and transitive.

18. Let R be a relation from a set A to a set B, then

(a) $R = A \cup B$ (b) $R = A \cap B$

(c) $R \subseteq A \times B$ (d) $R \subseteq B \times A$

19. Let $A = \{1, 2, 3, 4\}$, and let $R = \{(2, 2), (3, 3), (4, 4), (1, 2)\}$ be a relation on A. Then R is
    (a) reflexive
    (b) symmetric
    (c) transitive
    (d) none of these

20. If $A = \{a, b, c, d\}, B = \{p, q, r, s\}$, then which of the following are relations from A to B ? Give reasons for your answer :
    (a) $R_1 = \{(a, p), (b, r), (c, s)\}$
    (b) $R_2 = \{q, b), (c, s), (d, r)\}$
    (c) $R_3 = \{(a, p), (a, q), (d, p), (c, r), (b, r)\}$
    (d) $R_4 = \{(a, p), (q, a), (b, s), (s, b)\}$

21. A relation R is defined on the set Z of integers as follows : $(x, y) \in R' x^2 + y^2 = 25$
    Express R and R^{-1} as the sets of ordered pairs and hence find their respective domains.

22. Let R be a relation on I (the set of integers) defined as $mRn(m, n \in I)$ iff $m \le n$. Check R for reflexivity, symmetry, transitivity and anti-symmetry.

23. (a) Let R be a relation defined by $R = \{(a, b), a \ge b\}$ where a and b are real numbers then R is
    (a) Reflexive, symmetric and transitive.
    (b) Reflexive, transitive but not symmetric.
    (c) Symmetric, transitive but not reflexive.
    (d) Neither transitive nor reflexive but symmetric. **(M.N.R. 1994)**

    (b) A relation R defined in N as $aRb \Leftrightarrow b$ is divisible by a is
    (a) reflexive but not symmetric
    (b) symmetric but not transitive
    (c) symmetric and transitive
    (d) none of these **(Karnataka CET 2011)**

24. An integer m is said to be related to another integer n if m is a multiple of n. Then the relation is
    (a) reflexive and symmetric
    (b) reflexive and transitive
    (c) symmetric and transitive
    (d) equivalence relation.

25. If α, β be straight lines in a plane, then check R_1 and R_2 for being reflexive, symmetric and transitive $\alpha R_1 \beta$ if $\alpha \perp \beta$ and $\alpha R_2 \beta$ if $\alpha \| \beta$.

26. Let n be a fixed positive integer. Define a relation R on I (the set of all integers) as follows :
    aRB iff $n / (a - b)$, that is iff $a - b$ is divisible by n. Show that R is an equivalence relation on I.

27. Consider the non-empty set consisting of children in a family. state giving reasons whether each of the following relations is (i) Symmetric (ii) Transitive
    (a) x is a brother of y.
    (b) x likes y

28. Let S be the set of all points in a plane. Let R be a relation on S such that for any two points a and b, $a R b$ iff b is within 1 centimetre from a. Check R for reflexivity, symmetry and transitivity.

29. N is the set of natural numbers. The relation R is defined on $N \times N$ as follows $(a, b) R (c, d)'$ $a + d = b + c$ Prove that R is an equivalence relation.

30. N is the set of positive integers and $\sim$ be a relation on $N \times N$ defined $(a, b) \sim (c, d)$ iff $ad = bc$.
    Check the relation for being an equivalence relation.
    Check the relation in Q. 31, 32 for R, S, T.

31. The following relation is defined on the set of real numbers. $a R b$ iff $|a - b| > 0$.

32. $a R b$ iff $1 + ab > 0$. What about ?

33. A relation R on the set of complex numbers is defined by $z_1 R z_2$ if and only if
    $(z_1 - z_2) / (z_1 + z_2)$ is real. Show that R is an equivalence relation.

34. Let R be a relation defined on the set of natural numbers N as
    $$R = \{(x, y) : x \in N, y \in N, 2x + y = 41\}$$
    Find the domain and range of this relation R. Also, verify whether R is (i) reflexive (ii) symmetric (iii) transitive.

35. On the set of all points in a plane, the relation defined by the phrase 'at the same distance from the origin' is an equivalence relation.
    (a) True
    (b) False

36. A function R on the set N of natural numbers is defined as $R = \{(2n, 2n + 1) : n \in N\}$
    The domain of $R = ...$

37. A relation f on the set N of natural numbers is defined by $f = \{(n, n + 3) : n \in N\}$
    The range of $f = N - ....$

38. Consider the following relations $R = \{(x, y) : x, y \in R\}$ and $x = \omega y$, for some rational no. ω
    $$S = \left\{ \left(\frac{m}{n}, \frac{p}{q} \right) : m, n, p \text{ and } q \text{ are integers such that} \right.$$
    $$\left. n, q, \ne 0 \text{ and } qm = pn \right\}$$
    Then
    (a) R is equivalence but S is not an equivalence
    (b) neither R nor S is an equivalence relation
    (c) S is equivalence but R is not
    (d) R & S both are equivalence **(AIEEE 2010)**

Assertion / Reason

39. Let R be the set of real numbers
    Statement 1 : $A = \{(x, y) \in R \times R : y - x$ is an integer} is an equivalence relation on R
    Statement 2 : $B = \{(x, y) \in R \times R : x = \alpha . y$, for some rational number $\alpha\}$ is an equivalence relation on R **(AIEEE 2011)**

Solutions to Problem Set (3)

1. **Ans. (a).**
   $A \times B$ will have mn ordered pairs. Each subset of $A \times B$ will be relation. The number of subsets of a set consisting of mn elements will be 2^{mn}.

   Note : If $m = n$, then corresponding number will be 2^{n^2}.

2. **Ans. (a).**
   The set consists of n elements and for relation to be reflexive it must have at least n ordered pairs. It has m ordered pairs therefore $m \geq n$.

3. **Ans. (b).**
   $OA = OA, OA = OB \Rightarrow OB = OA$. Now $OA = OB, OB = OC$ $\Rightarrow OA = OC$. Hence R,S,T. *i.e.* equivalence relation.

4. From the given ordered pairs of $A \times B$ we conclude that $A = \{1, 2, 3\}, B = \{4, 6\}$.
   Since $A \times B$ has six elements *i.e.* 3×2 and hence A and B are as stated above.
   ∴ $A \times B = \{(1, 4), (1, 6), (2, 4), (2, 6), (3, 4), (3, 6)\}$
   By reversing the above ordered pairs, we get
   $B \times A = \{(4, 1), (6, 1), (4, 2), (6, 2), (4, 3), (6, 3)\}$.

5. R_1 and R_2 are relations as both are subsets of $A \times B$ but R_3 is not a relation from A to B as the ordered pair $(3, c)$ $\in B \times A$ and $\notin A \times B$.

6. **(i)** We define a relation R_1 as
   $R_1 = \{(1, 1), (2, 2), (3, 3), (4, 4), (1, 2), (2, 3), (1, 3)\}$
   Then it is easy to check that R_1 is reflexive, transitive but not symmetric. Students are advised to write other relations of this type.
   (ii) Define R_2 as : $R_2 = \{(1,2), (2,1)\}$
   It is clear that R_2 is symmetric but neither reflexive nor transitive. Write other relations of this type.
   (iii) We define R_3 as follows :
   $R_3 = \{(1, 1), (2, 2), (3, 3), (4, 4), (1, 2), (2, 1)\}$.
   Then evidently R_3 is reflexive, symmetric and transitive, that is, R_3 is an equivalence relation on A. $(1, 2) \in R_3$, $(2, 1) \in R_3 \Rightarrow (1, 1) \in R_3$

7. **(i)** R but not S as $(2, 1) \in R_1$ but $(1, 2) \notin R_1$ not T as $(2, 1)$ and $(1, 3) \in R_1$ but $(2, 3) \notin R_1$
   (ii) $\neq$ R as all like pairs are not there. It is S but not T as $(3, 1)$ and $(1, 3) \in R_2$ but $(3, 3) \notin R_2$
   (iii) $\neq$ R, $\neq$ S but it is T.
   (iv) R, S, T all as $A \times A$ contains all possible ordered pairs.

8. For the relation R to be reflexive, it is necessary that $(n, n) \in R$ for every $n \in \mathbf{N}$, that is, R must have all pairs $(1, 1), (2, 2), (3, 3), \ldots$
   For R to be symmetric, it must contain the pair $(2, 1)$ and $(3, 2)$ since the pairs $(1, 2)$ and $(2, 3)$ are already present.
   For R to be transitive, it must contain the pair $(1, 3)$ since $(1, 2)$ and $(2, 3)$ are already there. We must then also include the pair $(3, 1)$ for symmetry. Hence the relation

R' obtained from R by adding a minimum number of ordered pairs to R to make it an equivalence relation is
$R' = \{(1, 2), (2, 1), (2, 3), (3, 2), (1, 3), (3, 1),$
$\qquad\qquad (1, 1), (2, 2), (3, 3), \ldots\ldots\}$

9. **Ans. (c).**
   For R add $(1, 1), (2, 2), (3, 3)$ 3
   For S add $(2, 1), (3, 2)$ 2
   For T add $(1, 3), (3, 1)$ 2
   Thus the minimum number of ordered pairs to be added is 7.

10. **Ans.** $\{(b,b), (c,c), (b,a), (c,b), (a,c), (c,a)\}$
    $R = \{(a, a), (b, c), (a, b)\}$
    For reflexive add $(b, b), (c, c)$.
    ∴ $R = \{(a, a), (b, c), (a, b), (b, b), (c, c)\}$
    For symmetric add (c, b) and (b, a)
    ∴ $R = \{(a, a), (b, c), (a, b), (b, b), (c, c), (c, b), (b, a)\}$
    $(a, b) \in R, (b, c) \in R$ so that (a, c) must belong to R.
    Hence we must add (a, c) and for symmetric we must add (c, a) also.
    ∴ $R = \{(a, a), (b, c), (a, b), (b, b), (c, c),$
    $\qquad\qquad (c, b), (b, a), (a, c), (c, a)\}$

11. No. Let $R = \{aRb$ in set I where both a and b are odd$\}$
    Also R is symmetric and transitive
    ∴ $R = \{(1, 3), (3, 1), (1, 1), \ldots\}$
    but R is not reflexive because $(2, 2), (4, 4)$ *i.e.* all even integers belonging to I are not related to each other.

12. **(i)** To obtain the elements of $R \, o \, R$, we proceed as follows. Since $(1, 4) \in R$ and $(4, 5) \in R$ we have $(1, 5) \in R \, o \, R$.
    Again since $(1, 4) \in R$ and $(4, 6) \in R$ we have $(1, 6)$ $\in R \, o \, R$.
    Similarly $(3, 6) \in R \, o \, R$ since $(3, 7) \in R$ and $(7, 6) \in R$
    Hence $R \, o \, R = (1, 5), (1, 6), (3, 6)$
    (ii) We first find R^{-1}. We have
    $R^{-1} = \{(5, 4), (4, 1), (6, 4), (6, 7), (7, 3)\}$
    We now obtain the elements of $R^{-1} o R$. We first pick the element of R and then of R^{-1}
    Since $(4, 5) \in R$ and $(5, 4) \in R^{-1}$, we have $(4, 4)$ $\in R^{-1} o R$.
    Similarly
    $(1, 4) \in R, (4, 1) \in R^{-1} \Rightarrow (1, 1) \in R^{-1} o R,$
    $(4, 6) \in R, (6, 4) \in R^{-1} \Rightarrow (4, 4) \in R^{-1} o R,$
    $(4, 6) \in R, (6, 7) \in R^{-1} \Rightarrow (4, 7) \in R^{-1} o R$
    $(7, 6) \in R, (6, 4) \in R^{-1} \Rightarrow (7, 4) \in R^{-1} o R$
    $(7, 6) \in R, (6, 7) \in R^{-1} \Rightarrow (7, 7) \in R^{-1} o R$
    $(3, 7) \in R, (7, 3) \in R^{-1} \Rightarrow (3, 3) \in R^{-1} o R$
    Hence,
    $R^{-1} o R = \{(1, 1), (4, 4), (4, 7), (7, 4), (7, 7), (3, 3)\}$

13. **Ans. (c).**

$R : A \in B$ under given condition $a < b$ is given by

$R = \{(1, 3), (1, 5), (2, 3), (2, 5), (3, 5), (4, 5)\}$

$R^{-1} = \{(3, 1), (5, 1), (3, 2), (5, 2), (5, 3), (5, 4)\}$

$R\,o\,R^{-1}$: For composing $R\,o\,R^{-1}$ we will pick up an element of R^{-1} first and then of R

$(3, 1) \in R^{-1}\ (1, 3) \in R \rightarrow (3, 3) \in R\,o\,R^{-1}$

∴ $R\,o\,R^{-1} = \{(3, 3), (3, 5), (5, 3), (5, 5)\}$ only.

Elements are not repeated in a set.

14. $R_1 \neq R$ as $(1, 2) \notin A \times B, R_1 \neq f$ as 2 or $4 \in A$ has no image in B, $R_2 = R$ but $R_2 \neq f$ as in R_1

$R_3 = \{(1, 7), (3, 5), (5, 3)\}$

$x + y = 8,\ x \in A,\ y \in B$

∴ $R_3 = R$ being a subset of $A \times B$ but $R_3 \neq f$ as in R_1

$R_4 = \{(2, 5), (3, 10), (4, 17), (5, 26)\}$

∵ $y = x^2 + 1,\ x \in A,\ y \in B$

$R_4 = R$ but $R_4 \neq f$ as in R_1

$R_5 = \{(1, 1), (2, 3), (3, 5), (4, 7), (5, 9)\}$

$y = 2x - 1$

$R_5 = R$ and $R_5 = f$ as each element $\in A$ has a unique image in B.

15. Ans. $R_1 = \{(1, 3), (2, 4), (3, 5), (4, 6), (5, 7)\}$

Since 4 and 6 do not belong to Y

∴ $(2, 4), (4, 6) \notin R_1$

∴ $R_1 = \{(1, 3), (3, 5), (5, 7)\} \subset X \times Y$

Hence R_1 is a relation but not a mapping as the elements 2 and 4 do not have any image.

R_2 : It is certainly a mapping and since every mapping is a relation, it is a relation as well.

R_3 : It is a relation being a subset of $X \times Y$ but the elements 1 and 3 do not have a unique image and hence it is not a mapping

R_4 : It is both a mapping and a relation. Each element in X has a unique image. It is also one-one and onto mapping and hence a bijection.

16. $y = \dfrac{10 - x}{2}$

where both x and y are natural numbers between 1 and 10.

Clearly for $x = 2, 4, 6, 8$ we get values of y as $4, 3, 2, 1$.

∴ $R = \{(2, 4), (4, 3), (6, 2), (8, 1)\}$

∴ $R^{-1} = \{(4, 2), (3, 4), (2, 6), (1, 8)\}$

Domain of R is $\{2, 4, 6, 8\}$ = Range of R^{-1}

Domain of R^{-1} is $\{4, 3, 2, 1\}$ = Range of R

17. (i) R_1 is reflexive as, every element is related to itself

$\neq S$ as $(a, b) \in R$ but $(b, a) \notin R$

$\neq T$ as $(b, c) \in R$ and $(c, a) \in R$ but $(b, a) \notin R$

(ii) $R_2 \neq R$, as every element is not related to itself

sym. as for each pair $(x, y) \in R, (y, x) \in R$

$\neq T$ as $(a, b) \in R_2, (b, a) \in R_2$ but $(a, a) \notin R_2$

(iii) $R_3 \neq R, \neq S, \neq T$.

18. Ans. (c).

19. Ans. (c).

$\neq R$ as every element is not related to itself.

$\neq S$ as $(1, 2) \in R$ but $(2, 1) \notin R$

T $(1, 2) \in R, (2, 2) \in R$

$\Rightarrow$ $(1, 2)\,o\,(2, 2) = (1, 2) \in R$

20. Ans. (a), (c).

If R is a relation from A to B, then $R \subset (A \times B)$ which consists of all ordered pairs of the type (x, y) such that $x \in A, y \in B$.

Clearly R_1 and R_3 are such sets of $A \times B$. The elements (q, b) of $R_2 \in (B \times A)$ and not $A \times B$ and the elements (q, a) and (s, b) of R_4 also do not belong to $A \times B$ and as such R_2 and R_4 are not relations from A to B.

21. $y = \pm \sqrt{25 - x^2}$

where both x and y are integers.

Clearly for $x = 0, \pm 3, \pm 4, \pm 5$, y will be integers as $y = \pm 5, \pm 4, \pm 3, 0$

∴ $R = \{(0, \pm 5), (\pm 3, \pm 4), (\pm 4, \pm 3), (\pm 5, 0)\}$

$R^{-1} = \{(\pm 5, 0), (\pm 4, \pm 3), (\pm 3, \pm 4), (0, \pm 5)\}$

Each R and R^{-1} consists of $2 + 4 + 4 + 2 = 12$ ordered pairs.

Domain of $R = \{0, \pm 3, \pm 4, \pm 5\}$ = domain of R^{-1}.

22. Ans. $R, \neq S, T$, Anti-symmetric.

R is reflexive since $x = x$ for all $x \in I$.

[Note that by definition of R, $x\,R\,y$ iff either $x = y$ or $x < y$] R is not symmetric. For example $1\,R\,2$ since $1 < 2$. But $2\,(\sim R)\,1$ since $2 > 1$.

R is transitive since $m \leq n$ and $n \leq p \rightarrow m \leq p$,

R is anti-symmetric since

$m \leq n$ and $n \leq m \rightarrow m = n$.

23. (A)   Ans. (b). As in last question.

(B)   Ans. (a). For any set $a \in \mathbf{N}$, we have $a\,/\,a$

$\Rightarrow$ R is reflexive, but R is not symmetrix

∵ aRb does not imply bRa.

24. Ans. (b). i.e. $R, \neq S, T$.

Let the relation R be defined on the set $\mathbf{I}$ of integers as mRn iff m is a multiple of n. The relation R is reflexive since $m = 1 . m \,\forall\, m \in I$

R is not symmetric. We have $6R2$ since $6 = 3 \times 2$ so that 6 is a multiple of 2. But $2\,(\sim R)\,6$ since 2 cannot be a multiple of 6.

R is transitive. To prove this, let mRn and nRp. Then by definition of R, $m = k_1\,n$ and $n = k_2\,p$ where $k_1, k_2 \in I$. Then $m = k_1 k_2\,p$. Thus m is a multiple of p and so mRp.

25. Ans. R_1 is $\neq R, S, \neq T$ as $\alpha \perp \beta, \beta \perp \gamma \rightarrow \alpha \parallel$ to γ

R_2 is R, S, T i.e. equivalence relation.

26. Ans. Yes. R is reflexive since for any integer a we have $a - a = 0$ and 0 is divisible by n. Hence $a\,R\,a\ \alpha \in \mathbf{I}$.

R is symmetric. For let $a\,R\,b$. Then by definition of R,

$a - b = nk$ where $k \in \mathbf{I}$.

Hence $b - a = (-k) n$ where $-k \in \mathbf{I}$ and so $b R a$. Thus we have shown that

$$a R b \to b R a$$

R is transitive. For let $a R b$ and $b R c$. Then by definition of R, we have $a - b = k_1 n$ and $b - c = k_2 n$, where $k_1, k_2 \in \mathbf{I}$. It then follows that

$$a - c = (a - b) + (b - c) = k_1 n + k_2 n = (k_1 + k_2) n$$

where $k_1 + k_2 \in \mathbf{I}$.

Hence R is an equivalence relation.

27. Ans. (i) $\neq$ S but T

(ii) $\neq$ S, $\neq$ T

(a) (i) The given relation is not symmetric, since if x is the brother of y, then y may be the sister of x. Thus in this case $x R y$ but $y (\sim R) x$.

(ii) This relation is however transitive, since if x is the brother of y and y is the brother of z, then surely x is the brother of z.

(b) (i) Here the given relation is not symmetric since if x likes y then it is not necessary that y likes x.

(ii) This relation is not transitive since if x likes y and y likes z, then it is not necessary that x likes z.

28. Ans. R, S, $\neq$ T.

R is reflexive since any point is at distance 0 from itself so that it is within 1 centimetre from itself.

R is symmetric since if a point a is within 1 centimetre from another point b, then b is also within 1 centimetre from a.

R is not transitive. Let a, b, c be three points in a straight line in this order such that distance between a and b is $\frac{1}{2}$ centimetre and distance between b and c is $\frac{3}{4}$ centimetre. Then $a R b$ and $b R c$. But $a (\sim R) c$ since the distance between a and c is $\left(\frac{1}{2} + \frac{3}{4}\right) = \frac{5}{4}$ centimetre which is greater than 1 centimetre.

29. Ans. Yes.

We have $(a, b) R (a, b)$ for all $(a, b) \in \mathbf{N} \times \mathbf{N}$ since $a + b = b + a$.

Hence R is reflexive.

R is symmetric. For we have

$$(a, b) R (c, d) \Rightarrow a + d = b + c$$
$$\Rightarrow d + a = c + b$$
$$\Rightarrow c + b = d + a \Rightarrow (c, d) R (a, b)$$

R is transitive. For let

$$(a, b) R (c, d) \text{ and } (c, d) R (e, f).$$

Then by definition of R, we have

$$a + d = b + c \text{ and } c + f = d + e,$$

whence by addition, we get

$$a + d + c + f = b + c + d + e$$

or $a + f = b + e$.

Hence $(a, b) R (e, f)$.

Thus $(a, b) R (c, d)$ and $(c, d) R (e, f) \Rightarrow (a, b) R (e, f)$

30. Ans. Yes. Proceed as in last question.

31. Ans. $\neq$ R, S, $\neq$ T

R is not reflexive since $|a - a| = 0$ and so $|a - a| \not> 0$.

Thus $a (\sim R) a$ for any real number a

R is symmetric since if $|a - b| > 0$, then

$$|b - a| = |a - b| > 0.$$

Thus $a R b \Rightarrow b R a$

R is not transitive. For example.

Consider the numbers 3, 7, 3. Then we have $3 R 7$ since $|3 - 7| = 4 > 0$ and $7 R 3$ since $|7 - 3| = 4 > 0$.

But $3 (\sim R) 3$ since $|3 - 3| = 0$

so that $|3 - 3| \not> 0$

32. Ans. R, S, $\neq$ T.

Here relation R is reflexive since $1 + a \cdot a > 0$ $\square$ real numbers a. It is symmetric since

$1 + ab > 0 \to 1 + ba > 0$. However R is not transitive. For, consider three real numbers $2, -\frac{1}{6}$ and -2. We have

$$1 + 2 \times \left(-\frac{1}{6}\right) = \frac{2}{3} > 0$$

and $1 + \left(-\frac{1}{6}\right)(-2) = \frac{4}{3} > 0$.

Hence $2 R \left(-\frac{1}{6}\right)$ and $\left(-\frac{1}{6}\right) R (-2)$.

But $2 (\sim R) (-2)$ since $1 + 2(-2) = -3 \not> 0$.

33. Ans. Yes.

Here $z_1 R z_1$ for all complex numbers z_1.

For we have $\frac{z_1 - z_1}{z_1 + z_1} = 0$ which is real. Hence R is reflexive. R is symmetric since if $\frac{z_1 - z_2}{z_1 + z_2}$ is real, then

$\frac{z_2 - z_1}{z_2 + z_1}$ is also real.

Hence $z_1 R z_2 \to z_2 R z_1$.

We now show that R is transitive.

Let $z_1 = x_1 + iy_1$, $z_2 = x_2 + iy_2$ and $z_3 = x_3 + iy_3$ be three complex numbers such that $z_1 R z_2$ and $z_2 R z_3$.

Now $z_1 R z_2 \Rightarrow \frac{z_1 - z_2}{z_1 + z_2}$ is real

$$\Rightarrow \frac{(x_1 - x_2) + i(y_1 - y_2)}{(x_1 + x_2) + i(y_1 + y_2)} \text{ is real}$$

$$\Rightarrow \frac{[(x_1 - x_2) + i(y_1 - y_2)][(x_1 + x_2) - i(y_1 - y_2)]}{(x_1 + x_2)^2 + (y + y_2)^2}$$

is real

$$\Rightarrow (y_1 - y_2)(x_1 + x_2) - (x_1 - x_2)(y_1 + y_2) = 0$$

$$\Rightarrow 2x_2 y_1 - 2y_2 x_1 = 0 \Rightarrow (x_1 / y_1) = (x_2 / y_2) \quad \dots(1)$$

Similarly $z_2 R z_3 = \frac{x_2}{y_2} = \frac{x_3}{y_3}$

From (1) and (2), we have $\dfrac{x_1}{y_1} = \dfrac{x_3}{y_3}$

Hence $z_1 \, R \, z_3$.

Thus $z_1 \, R \, z_2$ and $z_2 \, R \, z_3 \Rightarrow z_1 \, R \, z_3$.

Hence R is transitive. It follows that R is an equivalence relation.

Note : If we consider R as a relation on the set of all complex numbers then R is not reflexive since 0 is a complex number but $0\,(\sim R)\,0$ for we have $\dfrac{0-0}{0+0} = \dfrac{0}{0}$

which is indeterminate. Hence in order that R may be an equivalence relation the set on which R is defined must be of non-zero complex numbers.

34. Ans. Neither.

The relation R can be written as

$R = \{(1, 39), (2, 37), (3, 35), ... (10, 21),$
$\qquad\qquad\qquad (11, 19), ... (19, 3), (20, 1)\}$

$\therefore$ Domain of $R = \{1, 2, 3, ... 19, 20\}$

Range of $R = \{39, 37, 35, 9, 7, 5, 3, 1\}$

R is not reflexive since $(x, x) \notin R \; \square \; x \in \mathbf{N}$. For example $(1, 1) \notin R$

R is not symmetric since $(1, 39) \in R$ but $(39, 1) \notin R$.

Note : In order to prove that a relation R is not symmetric, it is enough to produce an ordered pair (x, y) such that $(x, y) \in R$ but $(y, x) \notin R$.

R is not transitive because $(20, 1) \in R$ and $(1, 39) \in R$ but $(20, 39) \notin R$

35. Ans. (a).

36. Ans. $\{2, 4, 6, 8, ...\}$

37. Ans. $\{1, 2, 3\}$. as the second coordinate is $n + 3 : n \in N$ hence 1, 2, 3 can never be 2nd coordinate. They are excluded from N.

38. Ans. (c).

For R $xRy \Rightarrow x = \omega y$, for reflexive $xRx \Rightarrow x = \omega y$ which is true when $\omega = 1$

For symmetric consider $x = 0, y \neq 0$, $xRy \Rightarrow 0Ry \Rightarrow 0 = \omega y$, which is true when $\omega = 0$.

Now $yRx \Rightarrow yR0 \Rightarrow y = \omega . 0$. There is no rational value of ω for which $y = \omega \times 0 \Rightarrow R$ is not symmetric and hence not equivalence.

For S $\qquad \dfrac{m}{n} S \dfrac{m}{n} \Rightarrow mn = nm \Rightarrow$ S is reflexive

For symmetric let $\dfrac{m}{n} S \dfrac{p}{q} \Rightarrow qm = np$

$\dfrac{p}{q} S \dfrac{m}{n} \Rightarrow pn = mq$, which is true.

$\Rightarrow$ S is symmetric

For transitive, let $\dfrac{m}{n} S \dfrac{p}{q} \Rightarrow qm = pn$ ...(i)

$\dfrac{p}{q} S \dfrac{r}{S} \Rightarrow ps = rq$ ...(ii)

From (i) and (ii), we conclude that $ms = nr \Rightarrow \dfrac{m}{n} S \dfrac{r}{s}$

$\Rightarrow$ S is transitive

Hence, S is an equivalence relation.

39. Ans. (c).

Statement-1 :

(i) $x - x$ is an integer $\forall \; x \in \mathbf{R} \Rightarrow A$ is reflexive

(ii) $y - x \in I \Rightarrow x - y \in I \quad \Rightarrow A$ is symmetric

(iii) $y - x \in I$ and $z - y \in I$
$\quad \Rightarrow z - y + y - x = z - x \in I$
$\quad \Rightarrow A$ is transitive.

From (i), (ii) and (iii) A is an equivalence relation.

Statement-2 :

(i) $x = \alpha$ when $\alpha = 1 \Rightarrow B$ is reflexive

(ii) For $x = 0$ and $y = \alpha$, we have $0 = \alpha . (2)$ for $\alpha = 0$
But $2 = \alpha . 0$ for no $\alpha \Rightarrow B$ is not symmetric
$\Rightarrow B$ is not an equivalence relation.

Problem Set (4)

FUNCTIONS AND MAPPING

1. Given $A = \{2, 3, 4\}$, $B = \{2, 5, 6, 7\}$.

Construct an example of each of the following

(i) an injective mapping from A to B.

(ii) a mapping from A to B which is not injective.

(iii) a mapping from B to A.

2. If $A = \{1, 2, 3, 4\}$, then which of the following are functions from A to itself ?

(a) $f_1 = \{(x, y) : y = x + 1\}$

(b) $f_2 = \{(x, y) : x + y > 4\}$

(c) $f_3 = \{(x, y) : y < x\}$

(d) $f_4 = \{(x, y) : x + y = 5\}$

3. Suppose f is the collection of all ordered pairs of real numbers and $x = 6$ is the first element of some ordered pair in f. Suppose the vertical line through $x = 6$ intersects the graph of f twice. Is f a function ? Why or why not ?

4. Is $g = \{(1, 1), (2, 3), (3, 5), (4, 7)\}$ a function ? If this is described by the formula $g(x) = \alpha x + \beta$, then what values should be assigned to α and β ?

5. Is the function $f : \mathbf{N} \to \mathbf{N}$ ($\mathbf{N}$ is set of the natural numbers) defined by $f(n) = 2n + 3$ for all $n \in \mathbf{N}$ surjective ?

6. Are the following sets of ordered pairs functions ? If so, examine whether the mapping is surjective or injective :
   (i) $\{(x, y) : x$ is a person, y is the mother of $x\}$
   (ii) $\{(a, b) : a$ is a person, b is an ancestor of $a\}$

7. If the mappings f and g are given by
   $$f = \{(1, 2), (3, 5), (4, 1)\},$$
   $$g = \{(2, 3), (5, 1), (1, 3)\},$$
   then write down pairs in the mappings $f \circ g$ and $g \circ f$.

8. If the functions $f : \mathbf{R} \to \mathbf{R}$ and $g : \mathbf{R} \to \mathbf{R}$ be defined by $f(x) = 2x + 1, g(x) = x^2 - 2$. Find the formulae for $g \circ f$ and $f \circ g$.

9. If $\mathbf{R}$ is a set of real numbers and $f : \mathbf{R} \to \mathbf{R}$ is given by the relation $f(x) = \sin x, x \in \mathbf{R}$ and mapping $g : \mathbf{R} \to \mathbf{R}$ by the relation $g(x) = x^2, x \in \mathbf{R}$, then prove that $f \circ g \neq g \circ f$.

10. Let $f : \mathbf{R} \to \mathbf{R}, g : \mathbf{R} \to \mathbf{R}$ be two functions given by $f(x) = 2x - 3, g(x) = x^3 + 5$. Then $(f \circ g)^{-1}(x)$ is equal to
    (a) $\left(\dfrac{x+7}{2}\right)^{1/3}$
    (b) $\left(x - \dfrac{7}{2}\right)^{1/3}$
    (c) $\left(\dfrac{x-2}{7}\right)^{1/3}$
    (d) $\left(\dfrac{x-7}{2}\right)^{1/3}$

11. If $f(x) = \dfrac{3x+2}{5x-3}$, then
    (a) $f^{-1}(x) = f(x)$
    (b) $f^{-1}(x) = -f(x)$
    (c) $(f \circ f)(x) = -x$
    (d) $f^{-1}(x) = -\dfrac{1}{19} f(x)$

12. Given $f(x) = \log\left(\dfrac{1+x}{1-x}\right)$ and $g(x) = \dfrac{3x + x^3}{1 + 3x^2}$, then $f \circ g(x)$ equals
    (a) $-f(x)$
    (b) $3f(x)$
    (c) $[f(x)]^3$
    (d) none of these

13. Let $f : \mathbf{R} \to \mathbf{R}$ be defined by $f(x) = \cos(5x + 2)$. Is f invertible ?

14. A mapping is defined as $f : \mathbf{R} \to \mathbf{R}, f(x) = \cos x$. Show that it is neither one-one nor surjective.

15. Let $\mathbf{C}$ be the set of complex numbers. Prove that the mapping $f : \mathbf{C} \to \mathbf{R}$ given by $f(z) = |z|, z \in \mathbf{C}$ is neither one-one nor onto.

16. Let $A = \mathbf{R} - \{3\}, B = \mathbf{R} - \{1\}$. Let $f : A \to B$ be defined by $f(x) = (x - 2)/(x - 3)$. Is f bijective ? Give reasons.

17. Let $f : \mathbf{R} \to \mathbf{R}$ be defined by $f(x) = 3x + 4, x \in \mathbf{R}$. Is f invertible ? If so, give a formula for f^{-1}. **(M.N.R. 1993)**

18. The composite mapping $f \circ g$, of the maps $f : R \to R$, $f(x) = \sin x; g : R \to R, g(x) = x^2$, is
    (a) $\sin x + x^2$
    (b) $(\sin x)^2$
    (c) $\sin x^2$
    (d) $\dfrac{\sin x}{x^2}$

19.

Let A and B be two sets with a finite number of elements. Assume that there is injective mapping from A to B and that there is an injective mapping from B to A. Prove that there is a bijective mapping from A to B.

20. If $f : R \to R$ is defined by $f(x) = x^2 + 1$, then values of $f^{-1}(17)$ and $f^{-1}(-3)$ respectively are
    (a) $\phi, \{4, -4\}$
    (b) $\{3, -3\}, \phi$
    (c) $\phi, \{3, -3\}$
    (d) $\{4, -4\}, \phi$

21. Which of the four statements given below, is different from the other ?
    (a) $f : A \to B$
    (b) $f : x \to f(x)$
    (c) f is a mapping of A into B
    (d) f is a function of A into B

22. Find the domain and range of $f(x) = x^2 / (1 + x^2)$ (x real). Is the function one-to-one ?

23. If $A = \{x : -1 \le x \le 1\} = B$. Discuss the following functions w.r.t. one-one-onto bijective and write their characteristics.
    (a) $f(x) = \dfrac{x}{2}$
    (b) $g(x) = |x|$
    (c) $h(x) = x|x|$
    (d) $k(x) = x^2$
    (e) $l(x) = \sin \pi x$

24. Set A has 3 elements and set B has 4 elements. The number of injections that can be defined from A to B is
    (a) 144
    (b) 12
    (c) 24
    (d) 64
    (EAMCET 1992)

25. The number of surjections from $A = \{1, 2, \ldots n\}$, $n \ge 2$, onto $B = \{a, b\}$ is
    (a) $^nP_2$
    (b) $2^n - 2$
    (c) $2^n - 1$
    (d) none of these
    (EAMCET 1992)

26. Let A and B be two finite sets having m and n elements respectively. Then the total number of mappings from A to B is
    (a) mn
    (b) 2^{mn}
    (c) m^n
    (d) n^m

27. The total number of injective mappings from a set with m elements to a set with n elements, $m \le n$, is
    (a) m^n
    (b) n^m
    (c) $\dfrac{n!}{(n-m)!}$
    (d) $n!$

28. Let A be a set containing 10 distinct elements, then the total number of distinct functions from A to A is
    (a) 101
    (b) 10^{10}
    (c) 2^{10}
    (d) $2^{10} - 1$
    (M.N.R. 1992)

29. If the mappings $f : A \to B$ and $g : B \to C$ are both bijective, then the mapping $g \circ f : A \to C$ is also bijective.
    (a) True
    (b) False

30. Let $E = \{1, 2, 3, 4\}$ and $F \{1, 2\}$. Then the number of onto functions from E to F is
   (a) 14   (b) 16   (c) 6   (d) 4
   (I.I.T. Sc. 2001)

31. Let $A = \{0, 1\}$ and N the set of all natural numbers. Then the mapping $f : N \to A$ defined by
   $$f(2n - 1) = 0, f(2n) = 1 \ \forall \ n \in N$$
   is many-one onto.
   (a) True   (b) False

32. Let f be an injective map with domain $\{x, y, z\}$ and range $\{1, 2, 3\}$ such that exactly one of the following statements is correct and the remaining are false :
   $f(x) = 1, f(y) \sqrt{1}, f(z) \sqrt{2}$. The value of $f^{-1}(1)$ is
   (a) x (b) y
   (c) z (d) none of these
   (Roorkee 1996)

Solutions to Problem Set (4)

1. (i) An injective (*i.e.* one-one) mapping A to B may be defined as
   $$f = \{(2, 5), (3, 7), (4, 6)\}$$
   (ii) A mapping from A to B which is not injective may be defined as
   $$g = \{(2, 2), (3, 5), (4, 2)\}. \text{ It is many-one.}$$
   (iii) A mapping from B to A may be defined as
   $$h = \{(2, 2), (5, 3), (6, 4), (7, 4)\}$$

2. Ans. (d).
   For function **every element** of domain must have a unique image in co-domain   ...(A)
   Let us redefine each function as a set of ordered pairs and see if they satisfy the above condition (A) of a function.
   $f_1 = \{(1, 2), (2, 3), (3, 4)\}$; $(4, 5)$ cannot be an ordered pair as 5 does not belong to co-domain. Thus the element 4 of domain does not have an image.
   $f_2 = \{(1, 4), (2, 3), (2, 4), (3, 2), (3, 3), (3, 4),$
   $$(4, 1), (4, 2), (4, 3), (4, 4)\}$$
   The uniqueness is violated as the elements have not one but many images.
   $f_3 = \{(2, 1), (3, 2), (3, 1), (4, 1), (4, 2), (4, 3)\}$
   Not a function as in f_2 uniqueness is violated.
   $$f_4 = \{(1, 4), (2, 3), (3, 2), (4, 1)\}$$
   It is a function as each element has a unique image.

3. Ans. No.
   First observe that the graph of the function f consists of points represented by the ordered pairs of the form $(x, f(x))$. If the vertical line through $x = 6$ is cut by the graph of f twice, then it means that the element 6 of the domain of f has two images. Hence f is not a function as for f to be a function each element of the domain must have unique image.

4. Ans. $\alpha = 2, \beta = -1$.
   Domain $A = \{1, 2, 3, 4\}$
   Range $B = \{1, 3, 5, 7\}$
   Every element of domain has a unique image in B and hence g is a function. Now $g(x) = \alpha x + \beta$ but $g(2) = 3$, $g(3) = 5$.
   $\therefore \quad 2 = 2\alpha + \beta \quad$ and $\quad 5 = 3\alpha + \beta$
   $\therefore \quad \alpha = 2, \beta = -1$

5. Ans. No. Range will consist of only odd members. Thus even numbers will have no pre-image.

6. (i) not injective (one-one) but surjective (onto)
   (ii) It is not a function.
   (i) Here the given set of ordered pairs is a function since each person has one and only one mother. This function is surjective but not injective, (why ?). Two persons may have the same mother. It is surjective (onto) as every mother must have a child in A. If in place of mother we had a woman then it may not be onto because every woman need not be a mother.
   (ii) Here the given set of ordered pairs is not a function since a person has many ancestors (*e.g.* father, mother, grand father, grand mother, great grand father, great grand mother and so on). So in this case the image $f(a)$ of an element a of the domain is not unique.

7. Ans. $f \circ g = \{(2, 5), (5, 2), (1, 5)\}$,
   $g \circ f = \{(1, 3), (3, 1), (4, 3)\}$

8. Ans. The function $g \circ f : \mathbf{R} \to \mathbf{R}$ is defined by
   $(g \circ f)(x) = g(f(x)) = g(2x + 1)$
   $$= (2x + 1)^2 - 2 = 4x^2 + 4x - 1$$
   and $f \circ g : \mathbf{R} \to \mathbf{R}$ is defined by
   $(f \circ g)(x) = f(g(x)) = f(x^2 - 2)$
   $$= 2(x^2 - 2) + 1 = 2x^2 - 3.$$

9. Ans. $(f \circ g)(x) = f(g(x)) = f(x^2) = \sin x^2$
   and $(g \circ f)(x) = g(f(x)) = g(\sin x) = \sin^2 x$
   Since $\sin x^2 \neq \sin^2 x$ for any $x \in \mathbf{R}$, $g \circ f \neq f \circ g$.

10. Ans. (d).
   $f(x) = 2x - 3, g(x) = x^3 + 5$ are bijections and hence f^{-1} and g^{-1} both exist.
   $y = 2x - 3 \to x = \dfrac{y + 3}{2} \quad \therefore \quad f^{-1}(y) = \dfrac{y + 3}{2}$
   $\therefore \quad f^{-1}(x) = \dfrac{x + 3}{2}$ ...(1)
   $y = x^3 + 5 \quad \therefore \quad x = (y - 5)^{1/3} = g^{-1}(y)$
   $\therefore \quad g^{-1}(x) = (x - 5)^{1/3}$ ...(2)
   $\therefore \quad (f \circ g)^{-1} x = (g^{-1} \circ f^{-1}) x$
   $$= g^{-1}[f^{-1}(x)] = g^{-1}\left[\dfrac{x + 3}{2}\right] \text{ by (1)}$$

$$= \left(\frac{x+3}{2} - 5\right)^{1/3} = \left(\frac{x-7}{2}\right)^{1/3}$$

11. Ans. (a).

$$y = \frac{3x+2}{5x-3} \implies x = \frac{3y+2}{5y-3} = f^{-1}(y)$$

$$\therefore \quad f^{-1}(x) = \frac{3x+2}{5x-3} = f(x).$$

12. Ans. (b).

$$g(x) = \frac{3x + x^3}{1 + 3x^2} = y, \text{ say} \qquad \dots(1)$$

$$\therefore \quad f[g(x)] = f(y) = \log\left(\frac{1+y}{1-y}\right) = \log\left(\frac{1+x}{1-x}\right)^3,$$

on putting for y from (1)

$$= 3\log\left(\frac{1+x}{1-x}\right) = 3f(x)$$

13. Ans. No.

For a function to be invertible it is necessary that it is bijective *i.e.* one-one and onto.

The function given here is neither surjective nor injective as shown below.

Since $-1 \le \cos(5x + 2) \le 1$, the range of f

$$= \{y : y \text{ is real}, -1 \le y \le 1\}.$$

which is a proper subset of the co-domain **R**. Hence f is into so that it is not surjective,

f is many-one since $\cos(5x + 2)$ has the same value for many values of x. Thus

$$f\left(x + \frac{2}{5}n\pi\right) = \cos\left\{5\left(x + \frac{2}{5}n\pi\right) + 2\right\}$$

$$= \cos\{2n\pi + 5x + 2\} = \cos(5x + 2) = f(x),$$

for all $n = 0, \pm 1, \pm 2, \pm 3, \dots$

Since f is not bijective, it is not invertible.

14. Ans. True. Proceed as above.

15. Ans. True. f is many-one into as shown below.

Let $z = \cos\theta + i\sin\theta$, $0 \le \theta \le 2\pi$

Then $f(z) = |z| = +\sqrt{(\cos^2\theta + \sin^2\theta)} = 1$.

Thus all complex numbers $z = \cos\theta + i\sin\theta$ where $0 \le \theta \le 2\pi$ have the same image 1. It follows that f is many-one. Again since the modulus of a complex number is a non-negative number, we see that no negative real number can be the image of a complex number. For example, there is no complex number z such that $f(z) = |z| = -1$.

Hence f is into. Therefore the function f is neither one-one nor onto.

16. Ans. Yes. We have

$$x_1, x_2 \in A, f(x_1) = f(x_2) \implies \frac{x_1 - 2}{x_1 - 3} = \frac{x_2 - 2}{x_2 - 3}$$

$$\implies (x_1 - 2)(x_2 - 3) = (x_1 - 3)(x_2 - 2)$$

$$\implies x_1 x_2 - 2x_2 - 3x_1 + 6 = x_1 x_2 - 2x_1 - 3x_2 + 6$$

$$\implies x_1 = x_2. \text{ Hence one-one}$$

Surjectivity. Let y be any arbitrary element of B and suppose there exists an x such that $f(x) = y$, that is,

$$(x-2)/(x-3) = y \quad \text{or} \quad x - 2 = xy - 3y.$$

This gives $x = (3y - 2)/(y - 1)$. Since $y \sqrt{1}$, x is real. Further $x \sqrt{3}$. For if $x = 3$, then

$3 = (3y - 2)/(y - 1)$ or $3y - 3 = 3y - 2$, which is false. It follows that $x = (3y - 2)/(y - 1) \in A$ such that $f(x) = y$ and so f is surjective. Thus f has been shown to be bijective.

17. Ans. Yes. $f^{-1}(y) = \frac{1}{3}(y - 4)$. $(y \in R)$

(i) f is one-one. For we have

$$x_1, x_2 \in \mathbf{R}, f(x_1) = f(x_2)$$

$$\implies 3x_1 + 4 = 3x_2 + 4 \implies x_1 = x_2 \text{ } f \text{ is onto :}$$

If $y = f(x) = 3x + 4$, then $x = \frac{1}{3}(y - 4)$, which is also a

real number. Thus $f\left\{\frac{1}{3}(y - 4)\right\} = y$. It is therefore

shown that any arbitrary element y in **R** is the f-image

of the element $\frac{1}{3}(y - 4) \in \mathbf{R}$. Hence f is onto. Since f is

one-one onto (*i.e.* bijective), it is invertible.

the inverse mapping $f^{-1} : \mathbf{R} \to \mathbf{R}$ is defined by

$$f^{-1}(y) = \frac{1}{3}(y - 4). \text{ } (y \in \mathbf{R}).$$

18. Ans. (c).

19. Let f be an injective mapping from A to B. Since f is one-one, number of elements in A is less than or equal to the number of elements in B, that, is $n(A) \le n(B)$. Similarly since there exists an injective mapping $g : B \to A$, we have

$$n(B) \le n(A).$$

Hence $n(A) = n(B)$.

Since the number of elements in A and B is the same, we can define a bijective mapping from A to B.

For if $A = \{a_1, a_2, \dots a_n\}$

and $B = \{b_1, b_2, \dots b_n\}$

then one such bijective mapping is

$$h = \{(a_1, b_1), (a_2, b_2), \dots (a_n, b_n)\}$$

In fact, we can define many such bijective mappings from A to B.

20. Ans. (d). Let $y = x^2 + 1$. Then for $y = 17$, we have $x = \pm 4$ and for $y = -3$, x becomes imaginary that is, there is no value of x.

Hence $f(17) = \{-4, 4\}$ and $f^{-1}(-3) = \phi$.

21. Ans. All statements are the same.

22. Since for every real $x, 1 + x^2 \ne 0$, therefore $x^2/(1 + x^2)$ is a real number for all real x. Hence the domain of f is the set **R** of all real numbers. The range of f consists of all real numbers y such that $f(x) = y$ for real x.

Now $f(x) = y \implies x^2/(1 + x^2) = y$

$$\implies x^2 = y + yx^2 \implies x = \sqrt{\{y/(1-y)\}} \qquad \dots(1)$$

Since x is real, we must have $y/(1-y) \geq 0$ $(y \neq 1)$ which is satisfied if $0 \leq y < 1$.

Hence range of f

$= \{y : y \text{ is real and } 0 \leq y < 1\}$

It is not one-one because $f(x)$ and $f(-x)$ are same. Hence it is many-one.

23. **(i)** one-one, $\neq$ onto as $1 \in B$ will have no pre image in A as 1 is the image of 2 by def. and $2 \notin A$.

(ii) $\neq$ one-one as both x and $-x \in A$ have the same image. $\neq$ onto. All $-$ive numbers in B will have no pre-image by definition of $|x|$.

(iii) $h(x) = x^2$ when $x \geq 0$. It is bijection

$= -x^2$ when $x < 0$

(iv) $\neq$ one-one, $\neq$ onto

(v) $\neq$ one-one but onto $l(1) = l(-1) = 0$

By definition $-1 \leq \sin \pi x \leq 1$ as x varies from -1 to 1.

24. **Ans. (c).**

A has 3 elements and B has 4 elements for injective mapping first element of A can go to any of 4 of B, 2nd to 3 of B and 3rd to 2 of B.

∴ $4.3.2 = 24$.

In short $^4P_3$.

25. **Ans. (b).** $f : A \to B$ where A has n elements and B has 2 elements.

Each element of A can go to 2 elements of B.

Hence there will be $2.2.2....n$ times $= 2^n$ mappings.

But if each element of A either goes to a only of B or goes to b only of B then in these two cases the mapping will not be surjective.

Hence the number of surjective mappings are $2^n - 2$.

26. **Ans. (d).** Consider an element $a \in A$, it can be assigned to any of the n elements of B i.e. it has n images. Similarly each of the m elements of A can have n images in B. Hence the number of mappings is $n \times n \times n \times ... m$ times $= n^m$.

27. **Ans. (c).** $a_1 \in A$ can have n images in B, but the element a_2 will have only $(n-1)$ images as the mappings are to be one-one (injective).

Similarly the elements a_3 will have $(n-2)$ images. Hence the total number of mappings will be

$n(n-1)(n-2)...(n-\overline{m-1})$

$= n(n-1)(n-2)...(n-m+1)$

Multiply above and below by

$(n-m)(n-m-1)...3.2.1$

∴ Required number is $\dfrac{n!}{(n-m)!}$

Note : If $m > n$, then for injective mappings n elements of A will have n distinct images and the remaining $m - n$ $(m > n)$ elements of A will have no image in B (for injective).

28. **Ans. (b).** Each element can go to itself and the rest as well. Thus it can have 10 images. Similarly we can argue for other elements. Hence the total number of distinct functions from A to A is 10^{10}.

29. **Ans. (a).**

$g \circ f$ is injective (i.e. one-one). For we have

$(g \circ f)(x) = (g \circ f)(y)$ $(x, y \in A)$

$\Rightarrow$ $g(f(x)) = g(f(y))$

$\Rightarrow$ $f(x) = f(y)$ [∵ g is one-one]

$\Rightarrow$ $x = y$ [∵ f is one-one]

$g \circ f$ is surjective (i.e. onto). For let z be any arbitrary element of C. Then since g is onto there exists an element $y \in B$ such that $g(y) = z$. Again since f is onto there exists an element $x \in A$ such that $f(x) = y$. Thus to each $z \in C$ there exists an element $x \in A$ such that

$z = g(y) = g(f(x)) = (g \circ f)(x)$

Hence gof is both injective and surjective and so it is bijective.

30. **Ans. (a).** Total number of functions form $E \to F$ is $2^4 = 16$. When all the elements of E go to 1 then it will be into as 2 is left out. Similarly when all elements go to 2 then 1 is left out. Hence in two cases the function will be into. This onto functions will be $16 - 2 = 14$.

31. **Ans. (a).**

32. **Ans. (b).**

Note f is injective.

I. Consider $f(x) = 1$ true, then other two are wrong.

∴ $f(y) = 1$, $f(z) = 2$. This is not possible because of injective and in this case it becomes many one.

II. $f(y) \neq 1$ true, then other two are wrong.

∴ $f(x) = 2$ or 3, $f(y) = 2$ or 3

$f(z) = 2$

This also violates the definition of injective.

III. Now consider $f(z) \neq 2$ true, then other two are wrong

∴ $f(x) = 2$ or 3, $f(y) = 1, f(z) = 1$ or 3

∴ $f(z) = 3$ only as $f(y) = 1$.

Hence $f(x) = 2$ only, keeping in view the definition of injective

Since $f(y) = 1$ ∴ $f^{-1}(1) = y$.

FASCINATING FACTS

- The order is not preserved in case of a set. For example $\{1, 2, 3\}$, $\{2, 3, 1\}$ or $\{3, 1, 2\}$ denote the same set.
- The repetition of an element does not change the nature of a set. For example $\{1, 2, 3\}$, $\{1, 2, 2, 3\}$, $\{1, 2, 3, 3, 1\}$ denote the same set.
- $\{0\}$ is not a null set, since it contains 0 as its member. It is a singleton set.
- Equivalent sets are not always equal but equal sets are always equivalent.
- An element can not be a subset of a set only a set can be subset of a set.
- Empty set is a subset of every set and every set is a subset of itself.
- The power set of any set is always non-empty.
- Null set is disjoint from every subset.
- Difference of a set with universal set is known as complimentation.
- (a, b) is not the same as $\{a, b\}$. The former denote an ordered pair whereas the latter denotes a set.
- The void relation ϕ and the universal relation $A \times B$ (respectively called the smallest and largest relation on A) are called trival relation from A to B.

- Some times the inverse of a relation coincides with the relation itself.
- If $f : A \to B$ is a function, then a single element in A can not have more than one image in B. However, two or more elements in A may have the same images in B. Also
  (i) Every element in A must have its image in B, but every element in B may not have its preimage in A.
  (ii) To each element x in A, there exists a unique element y in B such that $y = f(x)$
  (iii) Range of the function is the image of its domain and range is a subset of codomain.
- For one-one into function, Range $\subseteq$ codomain while in case of one-one onto function range = codomain.
- For a finite set A, if $f : A \to A$ is onto function then f is one-one.
- There are function, which are neither even nor odd e.g., $f(x) = x^3 + x^2 + x + c$.
- gof exists if and only if the range of f is a subset of domain of g similarly fog exists if range of g is a subset of domain of f.
- The composition of function is associative but not commutative.
- The inverse of the bijective function is also bijective.

❑

Complex Numbers

§1 Complex Number

A complex number may be defined as an ordered pair of real numbers and may be denoted by the symbol (x, y). If we write $z = (x, y)$, then x is called the real part and y the imaginary part of the complex number z and may be denoted by $\mathbf{R}(z)$ and $\mathbf{I}(z)$ respectively.

It is clear from the definition that two complex numbers (x, y) and (x', y') are equal if and only if $x = x'$ and $y = y'$. We shall denote the set of all complex numbers by the letter **C**.

Sum of two complex numbers. The sum of two complex numbers (x, y) and (x', y') is defined by the equality

$$(x, y) + (x', y') = (x + x', y + y').$$

Product of two complex numbers. The product is defined by the equality

$$(x, y)(x', y') = (xx' - yy', xy' + yx').$$

The symbol i. It is customary to denote the complex number $(0, 1)$ by the symbol i. With this notation

$$i^2 = (0, 1)(0, 1)$$
$$= (0.0 - 1.1, \ 0.1 + 1.0) = (-1, 0)$$

so that i may be regarded as the square root of the real number -1.

Using the symbol i, we may write the complex number (x, y) as $x + iy$. For, we have

$$x + iy = (x, 0) + (0, 1)(y, 0)$$
$$= (x, 0) + (0 \cdot y - 1.0, \ 0.0 + 1 \cdot y)$$
$$= (x, 0) + (0, y) = (x + 0, 0 + y) = (x, y).$$

Remark $\because$ $i = \sqrt{-1}$ and $i^2 = -1$, we have

$$(\sqrt{-1})^2 = \sqrt{-1} \cdot \sqrt{-1} = -1 \qquad \text{...(1)}$$

Again since

$$(\sqrt{a} \cdot \sqrt{-1})^2 = [\sqrt{a} \cdot \sqrt{-1}] \times [\sqrt{a} \cdot \sqrt{-1}]$$
$$= (\sqrt{a})^2 \cdot [\sqrt{-1}]^2 = a(-1) = -a \qquad \text{...(2)}$$

Hence $\sqrt{-a}$ means the product of $\sqrt{a}$ and $\sqrt{-1}$. Thus a pure imaginary number can be expressed as the product of $\sqrt{-1}$ and a real number. Students must note carefully the results (1) and (2). Keeping these results in view following computation is correct.

$$\sqrt{-a} \cdot \sqrt{-b} = \sqrt{a} \cdot \sqrt{-1} \cdot \sqrt{b} \cdot \sqrt{-1}$$
$$= \sqrt{a} \cdot \sqrt{b} (\sqrt{-1})^2 = -\sqrt{ab}$$

But the computation

$$\sqrt{-a} \cdot \sqrt{-b} = \sqrt{(-a)(-b)} = \sqrt{ab} \text{ is wrong.}$$

Difference of two complex numbers.

The difference of two complex numbers $z = (x, y)$ and $z' = (x', y')$ is defined by the equality

$$z - z' = z + (-z') = (x, y) + (-x', -y')$$
$$= (x + (-x'), y + (-y')) = (x - x', y - y').$$

Division. It is defined by the equality

$$z/z' = z(z')^{-1}, \text{ provided}$$
$$z' \neq (0, 0).$$

we have $\dfrac{z}{z'} = (x, y)(x', y')^{-1}$

$$(x, y)\left(\frac{x'}{x'^2 + y'^2}, \frac{-y'}{x'^2 + y'^2} \right)$$

$$= \left(\frac{xx'}{x'^2 + y'^2} + \frac{yy'}{x'^2 + y'^2}, \ -\frac{xy'}{x'^2 + y'^2} + \frac{yx'}{x'^2 + y'^2} \right)$$

$$= \left(\frac{xx' + yy'}{x'^2 + y'^2}, \ \frac{yx' - xy'}{x'^2 + y'^2} \right)$$

provided $x'^2 + y'^2 \neq 0$.

§2 Modulus and argument of a complex number.

Let $z = x + iy$ be any complex number.

If $x = r \cos\theta$, $y = r \sin\theta$, then $r = +\sqrt{x^2 + y^2}$ is called the modulus of the complex number z written as $|z|$ and $\theta = \tan^{-1}(y/x)$ is called the **argument** or **amplitude** of z written as arg z.

It follows that $|z| = 0$ if and only if $x = 0$ and $y = 0$.

Geomterically, $|z|$ is the distance of the point z from the origin.

It can be easily proved that $\hspace{2cm}$ **(V. Imp.)**

* $|z|^2 = |z^2|$, $\hspace{1cm}$ **(See Th IV, P. 69)**

*   Re $z \leq |z|$ and Im $(z) \leq |z|$.

Also argument of a complex number is not unique, since if θ be a value of the argument, so also is $2n\pi + \theta$, where $n = 0, \pm 1, \pm 2, \ldots \ldots$.

The value of argument which satisfies the inequality

$$-\pi \leq \theta \leq \pi$$

is called the **principal value** of the argument. We remark that the argument of 0 is not defined.

Remark. It is evident from the definition of difference and modulus that $|z_1 - z_2|$ is the distance between the points z_1 and z_2. It follows that for fixed complex number z_0 and real number r, the equation $|z - z_0| = r$ represents a circle with centre z_0 and radius r.

§3 Polar Form of a Complex Number

If r is the modulus and θ the argument of a complex number z, then $z = r(\cos \theta + i \sin \theta)$ which is the **polar form** or **trigonometric form** of z.

Since $e^{i\theta} = \cos \theta + i \sin \theta$, we can write $z = re^{i\theta}$. This is known as the **exponential form** of z.

$$\therefore \quad x + iy = z = r(\cos \theta + i \sin \theta) = re^{i\theta}$$

$$\therefore \quad \tan \theta = \frac{y}{x} = \frac{\text{Im } z}{\text{Re } z}, \cos \theta = \frac{\text{Re } z}{|z|}, \sin \theta = \frac{\text{Im } z}{|z|}$$

A complex number whose modulus is unity, *i.e.* $r = 1$ can be written as $z = e^{i\theta}$ **(Imp.)**

§4 The geometrical representation of complex numbers

We represent the complex number $z = x + iy$ by a point P whose Cartesian co-ordinates are (x, y) referred to rectangular axes OX and OY, usually called **real** and **imaginary** axes respectively. Clearly the polar co-ordinates of P are (r, θ) where r is the modulus and θ the argument of complex number z. The plane whose points are represented by complex numbers is called **Argand plane** or **Argand diagram**.

It is also called **Complex plane** or **Gaussian plane**.

Note : The complex number z is known as the **affix** of the point (x, y) which represents it.

Vector representation of complex numbers.

If P is the point (x, y) on the Argand plane corresponding to the complex number $z = x + iy$ referred to OX and OY as co-ordinate axes, the

modulus and argument of z are represented by the magnitude and direction of the vector $\overrightarrow{OP}$ respectively and vice-versa.

The points on the Argand plane representing the sum, and difference of two complex numbers.

Sum. Let the complex numbers z_1 and z_2 be represented by the points P and Q on the Argand plane. (See fig. 2.)

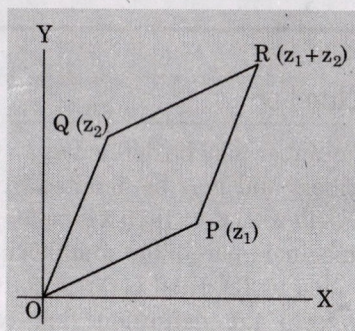

Fig. 2

Complete the parallelogram $OPRQ$. Then the mid-points of PQ and OR are the same. But mid-point of PQ is

$$\left(\frac{x_1 + x_2}{2}, \frac{y_1 + y_2}{2} \right)$$

so that the co-ordinates of R are $(x_1 + x_2, y_1 + y_2)$. Thus the point R corresponds to the sum of the complex numbers z_1 and z_2.

In vector notation we have

$$z_1 + z_2 = \overrightarrow{OP} + \overrightarrow{OQ} = \overrightarrow{OP} + \overrightarrow{PR} = \overrightarrow{OR} \quad \ldots(1)$$

Difference. We first represent $-z_2$ by Q' so that QQ' is bisected at O. Complete the parallelogram $OPRQ'$. Then the point R represents the complex number $z_1 - z_2$ since the mid-point of PQ' and OR are the same.

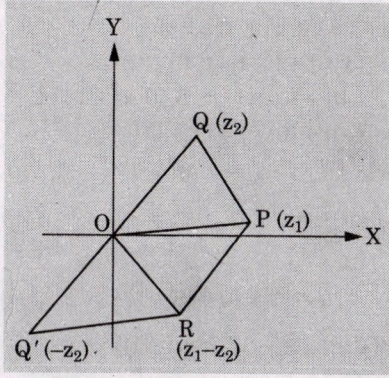

Fig. 3

As OQ is equal and parallel to RP, we see that $ORPQ$ is a parallelogram, so that $\overrightarrow{OR} = \overrightarrow{QP}$.

Thus we have in vectorial notation

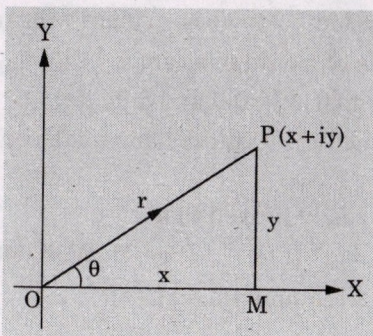

Fig. 1

$$z_1 - z_2 = \overrightarrow{OP} - \overrightarrow{OQ} = \overrightarrow{OP} + \overrightarrow{QO}$$

$$= \overrightarrow{OP} + \overrightarrow{PR} = \overrightarrow{OR} = \overrightarrow{QP} \qquad ...(2)$$

It follows that the complex number $z_1 - z_2$ is represented by vector $\overrightarrow{QP}$, where the points P and Q represent the complex numbers z_1 and z_2 respectively.

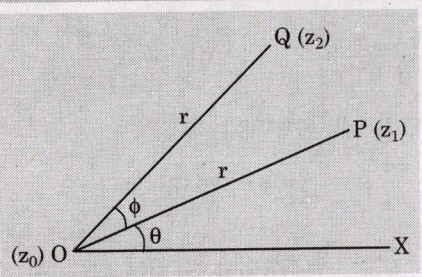

Fig. 4

§5 Conjugate to complex numbers

If $z = x + iy$, then the complex number $x - iy$ is called the **conjugate** of the complex number z and is written as $\bar{z}$. It is easily seen that numbers conjugate to $z_1 + z_2$ and $z_1 z_2$ are $\bar{z}_1 + \bar{z}_2$ and $\bar{z}_1 \bar{z}_2$ respectively. Also we have,

$$|z|^2 = z\bar{z}, \quad 2x = 2\mathbf{R}(z) = z + \bar{z}$$

and $2iy = 2i\,\mathbf{I}(z) = z - \bar{z}$.

It is clear that $|\bar{z}| = |z|$, $(\bar{\bar{z}}) = z$. Geometrically, the conjugate of z is the **reflection** (or image) of z in the **real axis**. If (r, θ) are polar co-ordinates of P, then the polar co-ordinates of its reflection P' are $(r, -\theta)$ so that we have **amp** $z = -$ **amp** $\bar{z}$.

Conjugate of $a + be^{i\theta}$. (V. Imp.)

Conjuagate of $a + be^{i\theta}$ is **not** $a - be^{i\theta}$ but $a + be^{-i\theta}$ as shown below :

$$a + be^{i\theta} = a + b(\cos\theta + i\sin\theta)$$

$$= (a + b\cos\theta) + ib\sin\theta$$

Its conjugate is $(a + b\cos\theta) - ib\sin\theta$

$$= a + b(\cos\theta - i\sin\theta) = a + be^{-i\theta}$$

Note : $\bar{i} = -i, \overline{iz} = \bar{i}\,\bar{z} = -i\,\bar{z}$.

Problem Set (1)

Real and imaginary parts, Powers of i.

1. Under what condition is the sum of two complex numbers $x_1 + iy_1$ and $x_2 + iy_2$
   (a) real number
   (b) a purely imaginary number ?

2. (a) A student writes the formula $\sqrt{ab} = \sqrt{a}\sqrt{b}$.
   Then substitutes $a = -1$ and $b = -1$ and finds $1 = -1$. Explain where he is wrong.
   (b) Is the following computation correct ? If not, give the correct computation :
   "$\sqrt{-2} \cdot \sqrt{-3} = \sqrt{(-2)(-3)} = \sqrt{6}$"

3. If $x + iy = \sqrt{\left(\dfrac{a + ib}{c + id}\right)}$, prove that
   $$(x^2 + y^2)^2 = \frac{a^2 + b^2}{c^2 + d^2}.$$
   (Karnatak C.E.E. 1999)

4. (a)* If $x = -5 + 2\sqrt{-4}$, find the value of $x^4 + 9x^3 + 35x^2 - x + 4$.
   (b) If $x = \dfrac{3 + 5\sqrt{-1}}{2}$, find the value of
   $$2x^3 + 2x^2 - 7x + 72$$
   and show that it will be unaltered if
   $$x = \frac{3 - 5\sqrt{-1}}{2}$$
   (c)* If $x = \dfrac{-5 + i\sqrt{3}}{2}$, prove that
   $$(x^2 + 5x)^2 + x(x + 5) = 42$$

5. (a) If $z = x + iy$ and $z^{1/3} = a - ib$, then show that
   $$\frac{x}{a} - \frac{y}{b} = 4(a^2 - b^2).$$
   (b) If the points on the Argand plane given by $ae^{i\alpha}, be^{i\beta}, ce^{i\gamma}$ are collinear, then show that
   $$\Sigma\, bc\sin(\beta - \gamma) = 0$$

6.* Show that the equation
   $$\frac{A^2}{x - a} + \frac{B^2}{x - b} + \frac{C^2}{x - c} + \ldots + \frac{H^2}{x - h} = k$$
   has no imaginary roots.

7. Prove that $x^4 + 4 = (x + 1 + i)(x + 1 - i)$
   $$(x - 1 + i)(x - 1 - i).$$

(A) **The following relations be committed to memory :**
   $$i^4 = 1, i^{4n} = 1, i^{4n+1} = i,$$
   $$i^{4n+2} = i^2 = -1, i^{4n+3} = i^3 = -i$$
   $$(1 + i)^2 = 1 + i^2 + 2i = 2i$$
   $$\therefore (1 - i)^2 = \text{conj.} = -2i. \quad 1 + i^2 = 0, 1 - i^2 = 2$$
   $$\frac{1 + i}{1 - i} = \frac{(1 + i)^2}{1 - i^2} = \frac{2i}{2} = i \quad \therefore \frac{1 - i}{1 + i} = \frac{1}{i} = -i$$

8. Simplify the following :
   (a) $(i)^{457}$
   (b) $(-\sqrt{-1})^{4n+3}$ (n, a +ive integer)

(c) $\dfrac{1+i}{1-i} - \dfrac{1-i}{1+i}$ (d) $\dfrac{1+2i}{1-(1-i)^2}$

9.   Simplify the following :

(a) $\left(\dfrac{1+i}{1-i}\right)^{4n+1}$ (n, a + ive integer)

(b)   If $\left(\dfrac{1+i}{1-i}\right)^x = 1$, then for any + ive integer n, x is

equal to

(a) $4n$ (b) $4n+1$

(c) $2n$ (d) $2n+1$ **(AIEEE 2003)**

(c) $\dfrac{(1+i)^n}{(1-i)^{n-2}}$ (d) $\dfrac{(1-i)^3}{1-i^3}$

10. Simplify the following :

(a) $\dfrac{3-i}{2+i} + \dfrac{3+i}{2-i}$ (b) $\dfrac{3}{1+i} - \dfrac{2}{2-i} + \dfrac{2}{1-i}$

11. Compute :

(a) $(1+i)^{-1}$ (b) $[(\sqrt{3}+i)(\sqrt{3}-i)]^{-3/2}$

In Q. 12 to 15 put the following in the form $A + iB$:

12. (a) $\dfrac{(1+i)^2}{3-i}$ (b) $\dfrac{5+4i}{4+5i}$

13. (a) $\dfrac{(3-2i)(2+3i)}{(1+2i)(2-i)}$ (b) $\left(\dfrac{1}{1-2i} + \dfrac{3}{1+i}\right)\left(\dfrac{3+4i}{2-4i}\right)$

14. $\dfrac{(a+ib)^2}{(a-ib)} - \dfrac{(a-ib)^2}{(a+ib)}$

15. $\dfrac{1}{1-\cos\theta + 2i\sin\theta}$

16. Find the lengths of the segments connecting the points represented by the following pairs of numbers :

(i) $5, -3$ (ii) $3, -4i$

(iii) $-6i, 3i$ (iv) $-1-i, 2+3i$

(v) $3-2i, 3+5i$.

(B) Method for Square root of a complex number.

Let $z = \sqrt{5+12i} = x + iy$. Squaring,

$$x^2 - y^2 + 2ixy = 5 + 12i$$
$$x^2 - y^2 = 5,\ xy = 6.\ \text{Solve.}$$

*By Inspection : $5 + 12i$

Take half the coefficient of 'i', i.e. $\dfrac{1}{2}(12) = 6$. Now

decompose 6 into two factors, squares of whose difference is 5 i.e. 3 and 2 ... $3^2 - 2^2 = 5$

Hence $\sqrt{(5+12i)} = \pm(3+2i)$

∴ $\sqrt{(5-12i)} = \pm(3-2i)$. Conjugate

and $\sqrt{(-5+12i)} = \pm(2+3i)$

and $\sqrt{(-5-12i)} = \pm(2-3i)$. Conjugate

Here R.P. $= -5 = 2^2 - 3^2$. Hence we choose $2 \pm 3i$ and not $3 \pm 2i$.

In Q. 17 to 20 find the square root of the numbers :

17. (a) $5 + 12i$, $-5 + 12i$ **(J.E.E. W.B. 1993)**

(b)* $\dfrac{\sqrt{5+12i} + \sqrt{5-12i}}{\sqrt{(5+12i)} - \sqrt{(5-12i)}}$.

18. (a) $-8 - 6i$

(b) $-7 - 24i$ (c) $a^2 - 1 + 2a\sqrt{-1}$

19. (a) $4\sqrt{-5} - 1$ (b) $1 + 4\sqrt{-3}$

20. (a) i (b) $-i$

(c) $1 - i$

21. (a)   Find the value of

$$[4 + 3\sqrt{-20}]^{1/2} + [4 - 3\sqrt{-20}]^{1/2}$$

(b) $\sqrt{8+6i} + \sqrt{8-6i}$

(c) $\sqrt{-35+12i} - \sqrt{-35-12i}$

22. Find the square root of the following :

(a) $x + i\sqrt{x^4 + x^2 + 1}$.

(b) $4ab - 2(a^2 - b^2)\sqrt{-1}$.

In Q. 23 to 25 find real values of x and y for which the following equations are satisfied :

23. (a) $(1-i)x + (1+i)y = 1 - 3i$,

(b) $\dfrac{x-1}{3+i} + \dfrac{y-1}{3-i} = i$

24. (a)* $\dfrac{(1+i)x - 2i}{3+i} + \dfrac{(2-3i)y + i}{3-i} = i$

(b) $(x+iy)(2-3i) = 4 + i$

(c) $(1+i)y^2 + 6 + i = (2+i)x$.

25. (a)* $\sqrt{x^2 - 2x + 8} + (x+4)i = y(2+i)$.

(b) $(x^4 + 2xi) - (3x^2 + yi) = (3-5i) + (1+2yi)$

26. (a)*   If $a, b, c, ... k$ are the roots of the equation

$$x^n + p_1 x^{n-1} + p_2 x^{n-2} .... + p_{n-1}x + p_n = 0$$

($p_1, p_2, ... p_n$ are real), then prove that

$$(1+a^2)(1+b^2)...(1+k^2) = (1 - p_2 + p_4 - ...)^2$$
$$+ (p_1 - p_3 + p_5 - ....)^2.$$

(b)   Express $(1+x^2)(1+y^2)(1+z^2)$ as sum of two squares.

27. (a)   Solve the equation $x^4 - 4x^2 + 8x + 35 = 0$

having given that one root is $2 + \sqrt{-3}$.

(b)   Determine the condition that the equation $z^2 + (p+iq)z + r + is = 0$ has real roots only.

28. (a)   Find real θ such that $\dfrac{3 + 2i\sin\theta}{1 - 2i\sin\theta}$ is

(i) real   (ii) purely imaginary.

(b)   If $\dfrac{\tan\theta - i\left(\sin\dfrac{\theta}{2} + \cos\dfrac{\theta}{2}\right)}{1 + 2i\sin\dfrac{\theta}{2}}$

is purely imaginary, then determine the general value of θ.

29. Show that a real value ot x will satisfy the equation

$\dfrac{1-ix}{1+ix} = a - ib$ if $a^2 + b^2 = 1$ $(a, b$ real).

30. Prove the following identities :

(a) $(x^2 + a^2)^4 = (x^4 - 6x^2 a^2 + a^4)^2$

$\qquad\qquad\qquad\qquad + (4x^3 a - 4xa^3)^2.$

(b)* $(x^2 + a^2)^7 = (x^7 - 21x^5 a^2 + 35x^3 a^4 - 7xa^6)^2$

$\qquad\qquad + (7x^6 a - 35x^4 a^3 + 21x^2 a^5 - a^7)^2$

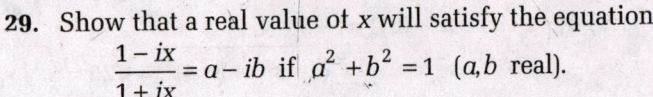

Solutions to Problem Set (1)

1. Sum $= (x_1 + x_2) + i(y_1 + y_2)$

∴ (a) sum is real if $y_1 + y_2 = 0$ and

(b) a purely imaginary number if $x_1 + x_2 = 0$.

2. We first note that the formula $\sqrt{ab} = \sqrt{a}\sqrt{b}$, holds if at least one of a and b is non-negative.

(a) Since here both a and b are negative, we cannot apply the above formula. Thus if $a = -1$ and $b = -1$, we cannot have $\sqrt{(-1)(-1)} = \sqrt{-1}\sqrt{-1}$ which gives the absurd result $1 = -1$.

(b) The computation "$\sqrt{-2}\sqrt{-3} = \sqrt{(-2)(-3)} = \sqrt{6}$" is wrong since here both -2 and -3 are negative. The correct computation is

$\sqrt{-2}\sqrt{-3} = \sqrt{2}\sqrt{-1}\sqrt{3}\sqrt{-1} = \sqrt{2}\sqrt{3}(\sqrt{-1})^2$

$\qquad = \sqrt{6}(-1) = -\sqrt{6}.$

3. $x + iy = \sqrt{\dfrac{a+ib}{c+id}}$ ...(1)

By the property of complex numbers, we have

$x - iy = \sqrt{\dfrac{a-ib}{c-id}}$ by $\overline{\left(\dfrac{z_1}{z_2}\right)} = \left(\dfrac{\bar{z}_1}{\bar{z}_2}\right)$ ...(2)

Multiplying (1) and (2), we get

$x^2 + y^2 = \sqrt{\dfrac{a+ib}{c+id}}\sqrt{\dfrac{a-ib}{c-id}}$

Squaring, we get $(x^2 + y^2)^2 = \dfrac{a^2 + b^2}{c^2 + d^2}$

4. (a) We have, $x + 5 = 2\sqrt{-4}.$

Squaring, $x^2 + 10x + 25 = -16$

or $\qquad x^2 + 10x + 41 = 0$ ...(1)

Now $x^4 + 9x^3 + 35x^2 - x + 4 = (x^2 + 10x + 41)$

$\qquad\qquad\qquad .(x^2 - x + 4) - 160.$

By actual division. Now put $x^2 + 10x + 41 = 0$

∴ Value of $x^4 + 9x^3 + 35x^2 - x + 4 = -160.$

(b) Proceed as in part (a).

$E = (2x^2 - 6x + 17)(x + 4) + 4 = 0 + 4 = 4.$

(c) $x = \dfrac{-5 + i\sqrt{3}}{2}$ ...(1)

$x + 5 = \dfrac{5 + i\sqrt{3}}{2} = -\left(\dfrac{-5 - i\sqrt{3}}{2}\right)$ ...(2)

∴ $\quad x(x + 5) = -\dfrac{1}{4}[(-5)^2 + (\sqrt{3})^2] = -7$

∴ $\quad E = (-7)^2 - 7 = 42.$

5. (a) Cube and equate real and imaginary parts

$x = a^3 - 3ab^2, \; y = b^3 - 3a^2 b$

∴ $\dfrac{x}{a} - \dfrac{y}{b} = a^2 - 3b^2 - (b^2 - 3a^2) = 4(a^2 - b^2)$

(b) $ae^{i\alpha} = a(\cos\alpha + i\sin\alpha) = (a\cos\alpha, a\sin\alpha)$

For collinearity $\begin{vmatrix} a\cos\alpha & a\sin\alpha & 1 \\ b\cos\beta & b\sin\beta & 1 \\ c\cos\gamma & c\sin\gamma & 1 \end{vmatrix} = 0$

$a\cos\alpha(b\sin\beta - c\sin\gamma) - b\cos\beta(a\sin\alpha - c\sin\gamma)$

$\qquad + c\cos\gamma(a\sin\alpha - b\sin\beta) = 0$ etc.

6. If possible let $\alpha + i\beta$ be a root. Then $\alpha - i\beta$ is also a root. Substituting these values for x and subtracting the first result from the second, we get

$\beta\left\{\dfrac{A^2}{(\alpha - a)^2 + \beta^2} + \dfrac{B^2}{(\alpha - b)^2 + \beta^2}\right.$

$\qquad\qquad \left. + \dfrac{C^2}{(\alpha - c)^2 + \beta^2} + ... + \dfrac{H^2}{(\alpha - h)^2 + \beta^2}\right\} = 0$

which is impossible unless $\beta = 0$ as the term inside the bracket is clearly + ive being squares of real numbers.

7. $(x + 1 + i)(x + 1 - i)(x - 1 + i)(x - 1 - i)$

$= [(x + 1)^2 - i^2][(x - 1)^2 - i^2]$

$= (x^2 + 2x + 1 + 1)(x^2 - 2x + 1 + 1)$

$= [(x^2 + 2) + 2x][(x^2 + 2) - 2x]$

$= (x^2 + 2)^2 - 4x^2 = x^4 + 4x^2 + 4 - 4x^2$

$= x^4 + 4.$

8. (a) $i^{456} . i = i$ $\qquad\qquad$ ∵ $i^{4n} = 1$

(b) $(-i)^{4n+3} = (-1)^{\text{odd}}(i)^{4n+3} = -(i^3) = i$

(c) $i - (-i) = 2i$ by result (A) **P. 39**

(d) $\dfrac{1 + 2i}{1 - (-2i)} = 1$ by result (A) **P. 39**

9. (a) $E = i^{4n+1} = i$ by (A)

(b) Ans. (a).

$\dfrac{1+i}{1-i} = \dfrac{\sqrt{2}\, e^{\pi i/4}}{\sqrt{2}\, e^{-\pi i/4}} = e^{\pi i/2} = \cos\dfrac{\pi}{2} + i\sin\dfrac{\pi}{2} = i$

∴ $\quad E = (i)^x = 1.$ Above is possible if $x = 4n$ where n is a + ive integer.

(c) $\left(\dfrac{1+i}{1-i}\right)^{n-2}(1+i)^2 = i^{n-2} . 2i = 2i^{n-1}$ by (A)

(d) Cancel $1 - i$ ∴ $E = \dfrac{(1-i)^2}{1 + i^2 + i} = \dfrac{-2i}{i} = -2$ by (A)

10. (a) $\dfrac{(3-i)(2-i)+(3+i)(2+i)}{4+1}$

$= \dfrac{1}{5}[(6-5i+i^2)+(6+5i+i^2)] = \dfrac{10}{5} = 2.$

(b) $\dfrac{3(1-i)}{2} - \dfrac{2(2+i)}{4+1} + \dfrac{2(1+i)}{2}$

$= \dfrac{1}{10}[15(1-i)-4(2+i)+10(1+i)] = \dfrac{1}{10}(17-9i).$

11. (a) $(1+i)^{-1} = \dfrac{1}{1+i} = \dfrac{1-i}{1-i^2} = \dfrac{1-i}{2}.$

(b) $[(\sqrt{3}+i)(\sqrt{3}-i)]^{-3/2} = (3-i^2)^{-3/2} = 4^{-3/2} = \dfrac{1}{8}.$

12. (a) $\dfrac{(1+i)^2}{3-i} = \dfrac{1+i^2+2i}{3-i} = \dfrac{2i(3+i)}{3^2-i^2}$

$= \dfrac{2(3i+i^2)}{10} = \dfrac{1}{5}(3i-1) = -\dfrac{1}{5} + \dfrac{3}{5}i.$

(b) $\dfrac{(5+4i)(4-5i)}{16+25} = \dfrac{(20+20)+i(16-25)}{41} = \dfrac{40}{41} - \dfrac{9}{41}i.$

13. (a) $\dfrac{(3-2i)(2+3i)(1-2i)(2+i)}{(1+4)(4+1)} = \dfrac{(12+5i)(4-3i)}{25}$

$= \dfrac{(48+15)+i(20-36)}{25} = \dfrac{63}{25} - \dfrac{16}{25}i.$

(b) Ans. $\dfrac{1}{4} + \dfrac{9}{4}i.$

14. $\dfrac{(a+ib)^2}{(a-ib)} - \dfrac{(a-ib)^2}{(a+ib)} = \dfrac{(a+ib)^3-(a-ib)^3}{(a-ib)(a+ib)}$

$= \dfrac{2(3a^2 \cdot ib + i^3 b^3)}{a^2+b^2} = \dfrac{2(3a^2 b - b^3)}{a^2+b^2}i$

$= \dfrac{2b(3a^2-b^2)}{a^2+b^2}i.$

15. $\dfrac{1}{1-\cos\theta+2i\sin\theta} = \dfrac{1}{2\sin^2\frac{\theta}{2}+4i\sin\frac{\theta}{2}\cos\frac{\theta}{2}}$

$= \dfrac{1}{2\sin(\theta/2)} \cdot \dfrac{1}{[\sin(\theta/2)+2i\cos(\theta/2)]}$

$= \dfrac{1}{2\sin(\theta/2)} \cdot \dfrac{\sin(\theta/2)-2i\cos(\theta/2)}{\sin^2(\theta/2)+4\cos^2(\theta/2)}$

$= \dfrac{1-2i\cot(\theta/2)}{2\sin^2(\theta/2)+4[2\cos^2(\theta/2)]}.$

Change to double angle.

$= \dfrac{1-2i\cot(\theta/2)}{5+3\cos\theta}.$

16. First we note that the length of segment joining the points z_1 and z_2 is $|z_1 - z_2|$. Therefore

(i) $|5-(-3)| = |8| = 8.$

(ii) $|3-(-4i)| = |3+4i| = \sqrt{3^2+4^2} = \sqrt{25} = 5.$

(iii) $|-6i-3i| = |-9i| = 9.$

(iv) $|(-1-i)-(2+3i)| = |-3-4i|$

$= \sqrt{(-3)^2+(-4)^2} = \sqrt{25} = 5$

(v) $|(3-2i)-(3+5i)| = |-7i| = 7.$

17. (a) **See (B) Method for square root Page 40.**

(b) $\sqrt{5+12i}$ is easily seen to be equal to $3+2i$.

by part (a).

$\therefore \quad \dfrac{(3+2i)+(3-2i)}{(3+2i)-(3-2i)} = \dfrac{6}{4i} = -\dfrac{3}{2}i \qquad \because \dfrac{1}{i} = -i.$

18. (a) $-8-6i$. Half the coefficient of i is 3 whose factors are 3 and 1 and since the real part is -8, we take the factors as 1 and 3 such that $1^2 - 3^2 = -8$

$\therefore \quad \sqrt{(-8-6i)} = \pm(1-3i)$

$\therefore \quad \sqrt{(-8+6i)} = \pm(1+3i).$

(b) Ans. $\pm(3-4i).$

(c) **1st Method.** $a^2 - 1 + i \cdot 2a$

Half the coefficient of i is a or $a \cdot 1$. Its factors are a, 1 such that $a^2 - 1 = $ R.P.

$\therefore \quad$ Square root is $\pm(a+i).$

Alt. $a^2 - 1 + 2a\sqrt{-1} = a^2 + i^2 + 2ai = (a+i)^2$

Hence $\sqrt{(a^2-1)+2a\sqrt{-1}} = \pm(a+i).$

19. (a) $4\sqrt{-5}-1 = -1+i\,4\sqrt{5}$

Half the coefficient of i is $2\sqrt{5}$ and its factors are $2, \sqrt{5}$ s.t. $2^2 - (\sqrt{5})^2 = -1 = $ Real Part.

$\therefore \quad$ Square root of $-1+i\,4\sqrt{5}$ is $\pm(2+i\sqrt{5}).$

(b) Ans. $\pm(2+\sqrt{3}i)$

20. (a) Let $\sqrt{i} = x+iy$. Then $i = x^2 - y^2 + 2ixy$,

$\therefore \quad x^2 - y^2 = 0$ and $2xy = 1.$

Solving these, we get $x = y = \pm\dfrac{1}{\sqrt{2}}.$

Hence $\sqrt{i} = \pm\left(\dfrac{1}{\sqrt{2}} + \dfrac{1}{\sqrt{2}}i\right) = \pm\dfrac{1}{\sqrt{2}}(1+i).$

(b) Ans. $\sqrt{-i} = \pm\dfrac{1}{\sqrt{2}}(1-i).$

(c) $\sqrt{(1-i)} = \pm(x-iy)$ say. Squaring, we get

$1-i = x^2 - y^2 - i\,2xy$

$\therefore \quad x^2 - y^2 = 1, 2xy = 1 \qquad \qquad \dots(1)$

$\therefore \quad (x^2+y^2)^2 = (x^2-y^2)^2 + 4x^2 y^2 = 1+1 = 2$

$\therefore \quad x^2 + y^2 = \sqrt{2}$ and $x^2 - y^2 = 1,$ by (1)

$\therefore \quad x^2 = \dfrac{\sqrt{2}+1}{2}$ and $y^2 = \dfrac{\sqrt{2}-1}{2}.$

On adding and subtracting, etc.

21. (a) For alternate easier method of Q. 20 (a, b, c) **See Q. 2 (a, b, c) P. 60-62.**

$4+3\sqrt{-20} = 4+i\,6\sqrt{5}$

Half the coefficient of i is $3\sqrt{5}$ and its factors are $3, \sqrt{5}$ such that $3^2 - (\sqrt{5})^2 = 4$

∴ $E = (3 + \sqrt{5}) + (3 - \sqrt{5}) = 6$

(b) $(3 + i) + (3 - i) = 6$

(c) $(1 + 6i) - (1 - 6i) = 12i$

22. (a) $x + i\sqrt{x^4 + x^2 + 1}$

$$= x + i\sqrt{(x^2 - x + 1)(x^2 + x + 1)}$$

         [Factorizing $x^4 + x^2 + 1$]

$$= \frac{1}{2}[2x + 2i\sqrt{(x^2 + x + 1)(x^2 - x + 1)}\ ]$$

$$= \frac{1}{2}[(\sqrt{x^2 + x + 1})^2 - (\sqrt{x^2 - x + 1})^2$$

$$+ 2i\sqrt{(x^2 + x + 1)(x^2 - x + 1)}\ ]$$

$$= \frac{1}{2}[\sqrt{x^2 + x + 1} + i\sqrt{x^2 - x + 1}]^2$$

Hence $[x + i\sqrt{x^4 + x^2 + 1}]^{1/2}$

$$= \pm \frac{1}{\sqrt{2}}[\sqrt{x^2 + x + 1} + i\sqrt{x^2 - x + 1}]$$

(b) $4ab - 2(a^2 - b^2)\sqrt{-1}$

$$= 4ab - 2(a+b)(a-b)i$$

$$= (a+b)^2 - (a-b)^2 - 2(a+b)(a-b)i$$

$$= [(a+b) - (a-b)i]^2$$

Hence $\sqrt{4ab - 2(a^2 - b^2)\sqrt{(-1)}} = \pm[(a+b)$

                            $- (a-b)i]$

23. (a) $(1-i)x + (1+i)y = 1 - 3i$.

Equating real and imaginary parts, we get

     $x + y = 1$ and $-x + y = -3$.

Solving these, we get $x = 2$, $y = -1$.

(b) Ans. $x = -4$, $y = 6$.

24. (a) $\dfrac{(1+i)x - 2i}{3+i} + \dfrac{(2-3i)y + i}{3-i} = i$

or $(1+i)(3-i)x - 2i(3-i)$

      $+ (2-3i)(3+i)y + i(3+i) = i(3+i)(3-i)$

or $(4+2i)x - 6i - 2 + (9-7i)y + 3i - 1 = 10i$

Equating real and imaginary parts,

     $4x + 9y - 3 = 0$ ...(1)

and $2x - 7y - 3 = 10$

or $2x - 7y - 13 = 0$ ...(2)

Solving (1) and (2), we get $x = 3$, $y = -1$.

(b) $(x + iy)(2 - 3i) = 4 + i$

or $(2x + 3y) + i(-3x + 2y) = 4 + i$.

Equating real and imaginary parts,

     $2x + 3y = 4$, $-3x + 2y = 1$.

Solving these, we get

     $x = (5/13)$, $y = (14/13)$.

(c) Ans. $x = 5$, $y = 2$ or $x = 5$, $y = -2$.

25. (a) $\sqrt{x^2 - 2x + 8} + (x+4)i = y(2 + i)$.

Equating real and imaginary parts,

$\sqrt{x^2 - 2x + 8} = 2y$ or $x^2 - 2x + 8 = 4y^2$ ...(1)

and $x + 4 = y$.   ...(2)

Substituting for y from (2) in (1), we get

    $x^2 - 2x + 8 = 4(x+4)^2 = 4x^2 + 32x + 64$

or $3x^2 + 34x + 56 = 0$

or $3x^2 + 28x + 6x + 56 = 0$

or $(3x + 28)(x + 2) = 0$

This gives $x = -2$ or $-(28/3)$.

Then $y = 2$ or $-(16/3)$.

Hence

     $x = -2$, $y = 2$ or $x = -(28/3)$, $y = -(16/3)$.

Of these two solutions $x = -(28/3)$, $y = -(16/3)$ does not satisfy given equation.

Hence the only solution is : $x = -2$, $y = 2$.

Caution : Whenever we square both sides while solving an equation, additional solutions appear which do not satisfy the original equation. Hence we check. A simple example is, say $x = 3$. If we solve it by squaring, then $x^2 = 9 \Rightarrow (x+3)(x-3) = 0$ ∴ $x = -3, 3$.

Check shows that $x = -3$ does not satisfy the original equation $x = 3$.

(b) Ans. $x = 2$, $y = 3$ or $x = -2$, $y = \dfrac{1}{3}$.

26. (a) Since $a, b, c, \ldots k$ are the roots of the given equation, we have the identity

$x^n + p_1 x^{n-1} + p_2 x^{n-2} + \ldots + p_{n-1} x + p_n$

     $\equiv (x-a)(x-b)(x-c)\ldots(x-k)$.   ...(1)

In the identity (1) put $x = i$.

Then $i^n + p_1 i^{n-1} + p_2 i^{n-2} + \ldots + p_{n-1} i + p_n$

     $\equiv (i-a)(i-b)(i-c)\ldots(i-k)$

or $i^n[1 + p_1 i^{-1} + p_2 i^{-2} + p_3 i^{-3} + p_4 i^{-4} \ldots$

                   $+ p_{n-1} i^{-(n-1)} + p_n i^{-n}]$

     $\equiv (i-a)(i-b)(i-c)\ldots(i-k)$

But $i^{-1} = \dfrac{1}{i} = -i$, $i^{-2} = \dfrac{1}{i^2} = -1$,

$i^{-3} = \dfrac{1}{i^3} = i$, $i^{-4} = \dfrac{1}{i^4} = 1$ etc.

∴   The above identity may be written as

$i^n[(1 - p_2 + p_4 - \cdots) - i(p_1 - p_3 + p_5 - \cdots)]$

     $\equiv (-1)^n(a-i)(b-i)(c-i)\ldots(k-i)$ ...(2)

Similarly putting $x = -i$ in (1), we shall obtain

    $(-i)^n[(1 - p_2 + p_4 \ldots) + i(p_1 - p_3 + p_5 \ldots)]$

     $\equiv (-1)^n(a+i)(b+i)(c+i)\cdots(k+i)$.   ...(3)

Multiplying (2) and (3), we get

$(-1)^n \cdot i^{2n}[(1 - p_2 + p_4 \cdots)^2$

                 $- i^2(p_1 - p_3 + p_5 \cdots)^2]$

$$= (-1)^{2n} (a^2 - i^2)(b^2 - i^2)(c^2 - i^2) \cdots (k^2 - i^2)$$

$$\because \quad (-1)^n i^{2n} = (-1)^n (-1)^n = (-1)^{2n} = 1,$$

this gives

$$(1 - p_2 + p_4 \cdots)^2 + (p_1 - p_3 + p_5 \cdots)^2$$

$$= (a^2 + 1)(b^2 + 1)(c^2 + 1) \cdots (k^2 + 1).$$

(b) $E = [(1 + xi)(1 + yi)(1 + zi)]$

$\qquad [(1 - xi)(1 - yi)(1 - zi)]$

$= (1 + iS_1 + i^2 S_2 + i^3 S_3)(1 - iS_1 + i^2 S_2 - i^3 S_3)$

$= [(1 - S_2) + i(S_1 - S_3)][(1 - S_2) - i(S_1 - S_3)]$

$= (1 - S_2)^2 + (S_1 - S_3)^2$

where $S_1 = \Sigma x, S_2 = \Sigma xy, S_3 = xyz$

27. (a) The equation is $x^4 - 4x^2 + 8x + 35 = 0.$ ...(1)

One root of this equation is given as $2 + \sqrt{3}\, i$.

Since the complex roots occur in conjugate pairs, the other root must be $2 - \sqrt{3}i$.

$$\therefore \quad S = 4, P = 7$$

The quadratic factor corresponding to these two roots is $x^2 - Sx + P$ or $x^2 - 4x + 7$.

Then the other quadratic factor of L.H.S. of (1) is of the form $x^2 + px + 5$.

Hence we have the identity

$$x^4 - 4x^2 + 8x + 35 \equiv (x^2 - 4x + 7)(x^2 + px + 5).$$

Equating the coefficient of x on both sides of the above identity, we get $8 = 7p - 20$ or $p = 4$.

[Note that same value of p will be obtained by equating the coefficient of x^2].

Hence the other two roots of the equation are the roots of the equation $x^2 + 4x + 5 = 0$

or $\quad x = \dfrac{-4 \pm \sqrt{16 - 20}}{2} = \dfrac{-4 \pm \sqrt{-4}}{2} = -2 \pm i.$

(b) Suppose $z = x$ (real) is the solution of the given equation, then

$$x^2 + (p + iq)x + r + is = 0$$

$$\therefore \quad x^2 + px + r = 0 \text{ and } qx + s = 0$$

Eliminating x, we get $\dfrac{s^2}{q^2} - \dfrac{ps}{q} + r = 0$

or $\quad s^2 - pqs + rq^2 = 0$

28. (a) $\dfrac{3 + 2i \sin \theta}{1 - 2i \sin \theta} = \dfrac{(3 + 2i \sin \theta)(1 + 2i \sin \theta)}{1 - 4i^2 \sin^2 \theta}$

$$= \dfrac{(3 - 4\sin^2 \theta) + 8i \sin \theta}{1 + 4 \sin^2 \theta} \qquad \text{...(1)}$$

(i) The expression in (1) is real if $\sin \theta = 0$.

This gives $\theta = n\pi$ where n is an integer.

(ii) If the expression in (1) is purely imaginary, then $3 - 4\sin^2 \theta = 0,$

i.e., $\sin^2 \theta = \dfrac{3}{4} = \sin^2 \dfrac{\pi}{3}.$

This gives $\theta = n\pi \pm \dfrac{\pi}{3},$ where n is an integer.

(b) Multiply above and below by conjugate of denominator and put real part equal to zero.

$$\tan \theta - 2 \sin \dfrac{\theta}{2}\left(\sin \dfrac{\theta}{2} + \cos \dfrac{\theta}{2}\right) = 0$$

or $\quad \dfrac{\sin \theta}{\cos \theta} - (1 - \cos \theta) - \sin \theta = 0$

or $\quad \sin \theta \left(\dfrac{1 - \cos \theta}{\cos \theta}\right) - (1 - \cos \theta) = 0$

or $\quad (1 - \cos \theta)(\tan \theta - 1) = 0$

$\therefore \quad \cos \theta = 1 \implies \theta = 2n\pi$

and $\tan \theta = 1 \implies \theta = n\pi + (\pi/4)$

29. $\dfrac{1 - ix}{1 + ix} = \dfrac{a - ib}{1}$

By componendo and dividendo, we have

$$\dfrac{(1 + ix) - (1 - ix)}{(1 + ix) + (1 - ix)} = \dfrac{1 - (a - ib)}{1 + (a - ib)}$$

or $\quad \dfrac{2ix}{2} = \dfrac{1 - a + ib}{1 + a - ib}$

or $\quad ix = \dfrac{(1 - a + ib)(1 + a + ib)}{(1 + a)^2 - i^2 b^2} = \dfrac{1 - a^2 - b^2 + 2ib}{(1 + a)^2 + b^2}$ ...(1)

If $a^2 + b^2 = 1$, the equation (1) reduces to

$$ix = \dfrac{2ib}{(1 + a)^2 + b^2}$$

or $\quad x = \dfrac{2b}{(1 + a)^2 + b^2},$ which is real.

Alternative method.

Let us suppose that x is real, then

$$\dfrac{1 - i\,x}{1 + i\,x} = a - i\,b \text{ (given)} \qquad \text{...(1)}$$

or $\quad \overline{\left(\dfrac{1 - i\,x}{1 + i\,x}\right)} = a + i\,b,$

on taking conjugate of both sides.

or $\quad \dfrac{1 + i\,x}{1 - i\,x} = a + i\,b$ ...(2)

Multiplying (1) and (2), we get

$$\dfrac{1 + x^2}{1 + x^2} = a^2 + b^2 \text{ or } a^2 + b^2 = 1 \text{ which is true by the}$$

given condition. Hence our supposition that x is real is correct.

30. (a) We have $(x^2 + a^2)^4 = (x + ai)^4 (x - ai)^4$

Now $(x + ai)^4 = x^4 + 4x^3 ai + 6x^2 a^2 i^2$

$$+ 4xa^3 i^3 + a^4 i^4$$

$$= (x^4 - 6x^2 a^2 + a^4) + i(4x^3 a - 4xa^3) \qquad \text{...(1)}$$

Similarly,
$$(x - ai)^4 = (x^4 - 6x^2a^2 + a^4) - i(4x^3a - 4xa^3) \qquad ...(2)$$

Multiplying (1) and (2), we get
$$(x + ai)^4 (x - ai)^4 = (x^4 - 6x^2a^2 + a^4)^2$$
$$- i^2(4x^3a - 4xa^3)^2$$
or $(x^2 + a^2)^4 = (x^4 - 6x^2a^2 + a^4)^2$
$$+ (4x^3a - 4xa^3)^2.$$

(b) Similar to part (a). Do yourself.

§6 Cube roots of unity $1, \omega, \omega^2$.

Cube roots of unity are clearly the roots of the equation $x^3 - 1 = 0$, that is, of the equation $(x - 1)(x^2 + x + 1) = 0$ hence we get
$$x = 1, \frac{-1 \pm \sqrt{3}i}{2}.$$

Thus the cube roots of unity are
$$x_1 = 1, \quad x_2 = \frac{-1 + \sqrt{3}i}{2} \text{ and } x_3 = \frac{-1 - \sqrt{3}i}{2}$$

Of these x_1 is real and x_2, x_3 are complex conjugates. Further it is easy to see that $x_2^2 = x_3$ and $x_3^2 = x_2$. That is why we usually denote these complex roots by ω and ω^2. It is easy to see that
$$1 + \omega + \omega^2 = 0 \text{ and } \omega^3 = 1, \omega^{3n} = 1,$$
$$\omega^{3n+1} = \omega, \omega^{3n+2} = \omega^2$$
so that $\omega^4 = \omega^3 \cdot \omega = 1 \cdot \omega = \omega,$
$$\omega^5 = \omega^3 \cdot \omega^2 = \omega^2, \omega^6 = 1,$$
$$1 + \omega - \omega^2 = -\omega^2 - \omega^2 = -2\omega^2,$$
$$1 + \omega^2 - \omega = -2\omega$$

(r, θ) form of ω and ω^2
$$\frac{1}{2} + i\frac{\sqrt{3}}{2} = 1\left(\cos\frac{\pi}{3} + i\sin\frac{\pi}{3}\right) = 1 \cdot e^{\pi i/3},$$
$$r = 1, \theta = \pi/3$$

∴ for $\omega = -\frac{1}{2} + i\frac{\sqrt{3}}{2}, r = 1, \theta = \pi - \frac{\pi}{3} = \frac{2\pi}{3}$

∴ $^*\omega = 1 \cdot e^{2\pi i/3}$

$^*\omega^2 = -\frac{1}{2} - i\frac{\sqrt{3}}{2} = 1 \cdot e^{-2\pi i/3}$ **(conjugate)**
$$= e^{2\pi i} \cdot e^{-2\pi i/3} = e^{4\pi i/3}$$

∵ $e^{2\pi i} = 1$

Note : The following results should be committed to memory.

Roots of $x^2 + x + 1 = 0$ are ω, ω^2.

Replacing x by $-x$ we can say that roots of $x^2 - x + 1 = 0$ are $-\omega, -\omega^2$

Alt. Roots of $x^2 - x + 1 = 0$ are $\frac{1 + i\sqrt{3}}{2}$ and $\frac{1 - i\sqrt{3}}{2}$

which are $-\omega, -\omega^2$

Now $\frac{-1 + i\sqrt{3}}{2} = \omega$ and $\frac{-1 - i\sqrt{3}}{2} = \omega^2$

∴ $\frac{1 + i\sqrt{3}}{2} = \frac{-1 - i\sqrt{3}}{2}(-1) = -\omega^2$

and $\frac{1 - i\sqrt{3}}{2} = \frac{-1 + i\sqrt{3}}{2}(-1) = -\omega$

$^*(a\omega + b\omega^2)(a\omega^2 + b\omega) = a^2 + b^2 - ab$

∵ $\omega^3 = 1, \omega + \omega^2 = -1$

∴ $^*(a + b)(a\omega + b\omega^2)(a\omega^2 + b\omega) = a^3 + b^3 \qquad ...(1)$

Similarly $(a\omega - b\omega^2)(a\omega^2 - b\omega) = a^2 + b^2 + ab$

∴ $(a - b)(a\omega - b\omega^2)(a\omega^2 - b\omega) = a^3 - b^3 \qquad ...(2)$

Again by using $\omega + \omega^2 = -1, \omega^3 = 1$, we can have
$^*(a + b\omega + c\omega^2)(a + b\omega^2 + c\omega) = a^2 + b^2 + c^2$
$$- ab - bc - ca \quad ...(3)$$

*and $(a + b + c)(a + b\omega + c\omega^2)(a + b\omega^2 + c\omega)$
$$= (a + b + c)(a^2 + b^2 + c^2 - ab - bc - ca)$$
$$= a^3 + b^3 + c^3 - 3abc. \qquad \text{(See Q. 4 (c) P. 46-48)}$$

Problem Set (2)

Square root, cube roots of unity

1. If $1, \omega, \omega^2$ are the three cube roots of unity, show that

(a) $(1 - \omega + \omega^2)(1 + \omega - \omega^2) = 4$.

(b) $(1 + \omega)^3 - (1 + \omega^2)^3 = 0$.

(c) $(1 - \omega + \omega^2)^3 = (1 + \omega - \omega^2)^3 = -8$.

2. (a)* If ω is an imaginary cube root of unity, then $(1 + \omega - \omega^2)^7$ equals

(a) 128ω (b) -128ω

(b) $128\omega^2$ (d) $-128\omega^2$ **(I.I.T. 1998)**

(b) $(1 - \omega + \omega^2)^5 + (1 + \omega - \omega^2)^5 = 32$.

(c) $(2 + 5\omega + 2\omega^2)^6 = (2 + 2\omega + 5\omega^2)^6 = 729$.

Prove the following (Q. 3 to 5) :

3. (a) $(1 - \omega)(1 - \omega^2)(1 - \omega^4)(1 - \omega^8) = 9$.

(b) $(1 + \omega)(1 + \omega^2)(1 + \omega^4)(1 + \omega^8) = 1$.

                              (J.E.E. W.B. 1992)

(c)* $(1 - \omega + \omega^2)(1 - \omega^2 + \omega^4)(1 - \omega^4 + \omega^8)...$
$$\text{to } 2n \text{ factors} = 2^{2n}.$$

4. (a) $x^3 + y^3 = (x + y)(\omega x + \omega^2 y)(\omega^2 x + \omega y)$.

(b) $x^3 - y^3 = (x - y)(\omega x - \omega^2 y)(\omega^2 x - \omega y)$.

(c)* $(a+b+c)(a+b\omega+c\omega^2)(a+b\omega^2+c\omega)$

$$= a^3+b^3+c^3-3abc$$

(d) If $a = 1 + \dfrac{x^3}{3!} + \dfrac{x^6}{6!} + \dots\infty$

$$b = x + \frac{x^4}{4!} + \frac{x^7}{7!} + \dots\infty$$

$$c = \frac{x^2}{2!} + \frac{x^5}{5!} + \frac{x^8}{8!} + \dots\infty$$

then find the value of $a^3+b^3+c^3-3abc$.

5. (a) $(x+y)^2 + (x\omega+y\omega^2)^2 + (x\omega^2+y\omega)^2 = 6xy$.

(b)* $(a+b\omega+c\omega^2)^3 + (a+b\omega^2+c\omega)^3$

$$= (2a-b-c)(2b-c-a)(2c-a-b)$$
$$= 27abc \text{ if } a+b+c=0 \qquad \textbf{(J.E.E. W.B. 1992)}$$

6. (a)* If α,β,γ are the cube roots of $p, p<0$, then for any x, y and z, $\dfrac{x\alpha+y\beta+z\gamma}{x\beta+y\gamma+z\alpha} = \dots\dots$

(b) $\dfrac{a+b\omega+c\omega^2}{c+a\omega+b\omega^2} + \dfrac{a+b\omega+c\omega^2}{b+c\omega+a\omega^2} = \dots$

7. (a) If α and β are the complex cube roots of unity, show that $\alpha^4+\beta^4+\alpha^{-1}\beta^{-1}=0$. **(Bihar 1999)**

(b)* Prove that $\dfrac{1}{1+2\omega} + \dfrac{1}{2+\omega} - \dfrac{1}{1+\omega} = 0$, where ω is imaginary cube root of unity.

(c) If $\omega(\neq 1)$ be a cube root of unity and $(1+\omega^2)^n = (1+\omega^4)^n$, then the least +ive value of n is

(a) 2   (b) 3

(c) 4   (d) 5   **(Screening 2004)**

8. If $x=a+b$, $y=a\alpha+b\beta$ and $z=a\beta+b\alpha$ where α and β are complex cube roots of unity, show that

(a) $xyz = a^3+b^3$

(b) $x^3+y^3+z^3 = 3(a^3+b^3)$.

9. Prove that

(a) $\left(\dfrac{-1+\sqrt{-3}}{2}\right)^{100} + \left(\dfrac{-1-\sqrt{-3}}{2}\right)^{100} = -1$

(b)* $\left(\dfrac{-1+\sqrt{-3}}{2}\right)^{3n} + \left(\dfrac{-1-\sqrt{-3}}{2}\right)^{3n} = 2$

(c) If $i = \sqrt{-1}$, then

$$4 + 5\left(-\frac{1}{2} + \frac{i\sqrt{3}}{2}\right)^{334} + 3\left(-\frac{1}{2} + \frac{i\sqrt{3}}{2}\right)^{365}$$

is equal to

(a) $1 - i\sqrt{3}$ (b) $-1 + i\sqrt{3}$

(c) $i\sqrt{3}$ (d) $-i\sqrt{3}$ **(I.I.T. 1999)**

10. (a) If α is a complex number such that $\alpha^2+\alpha+1=0$, then show that α^{31} is equal to α.

(b) If α,β are the roots of $x^2-x+1=0$, then $\alpha^{1030}+\beta^{1030}$ is equal to

(a) 1030   (b) 0

(c) 1   (d) −1

(c) If α,β are the roots of $x^2-2x+4=0$, then $\dfrac{\alpha}{\beta}$ is equal to $\dfrac{1}{2}(-1\pm\sqrt{3}i)$.

11. (a) Prove that the cube roots of unity $1, \omega, \omega^2$ are the vertices of an equilateral triangle.

(b) If $z = \dfrac{\sqrt{3}+i}{2}$ then show that $(z^{101} + i^{103})^{105}$ equals z^3.

(c) Prove that for all odd integral values of n, $\left(\dfrac{\sqrt{3}+i}{\sqrt{3}-i}\right)^{3n} + 1 = 0$.

12. Prove that

(a) $\left(\dfrac{-1+\sqrt{3}i}{2}\right)^n + \left(\dfrac{-1-\sqrt{3}i}{2}\right)^n = -1$

Another form :

$1+\omega^n+\omega^{2n} = 0$ when n is a positive integer but not a multiple of 3.

(b) $1+\omega^n+\omega^{2n} = 3$ when n is a multiple of 3.

(c) If ω is a cube root of unity and $\omega^n+\omega^{2n} = -1$, then prove that the integer n is of the form $km+l$ where $(k, l) = (3, 1), (3, 2)$.

Note : See similar question 13 (a, b) **P. 46-49.**

13. (a)* It is given that n is an odd integer greater than 3 but n is not a multiple of 3. Prove that x^3+x^2+x is a factor of $(x+1)^n - x^n - 1$.

(b) If $f(z)$ be divided by $z-i$ and $z+i$, the remainders are respectively i and $1+i$. Determine the remainder when $f(z)$ is divided by z^2+1.

(c) If $A(x)$ and $B(x)$ be two polynomials and $f(x) = A(x^3) + xB(x^3)$. If $f(x)$ is divisible by x^2+x+1 then show that it is divisible by $x-1$ also.

(d) If $(1+x+x^2)^n$

$$= a_0 + a_1 x + a_2 x^2 + a_3 x^3 + \dots + a_{2n} x^{2n},$$

then prove that

$$(a_0 + a_3 + a_6 + \dots) = (a_1 + a_4 + a_7 + \dots)$$
$$= (a_2 + a_5 + a_8 + \dots) = 3^{n-1}$$

14. Prove that $(x+y)^n - x^n - y^n$ is divisible by

$$xy(x+y)(x^2 + xy + y^2),$$

if n is odd but not a multiple of 3.

15. (a) Show that the polynomial
$$x^{4l} + x^{4m+1} + x^{4n+2} + x^{4p+3}$$
is divisible by $x^3 + x^2 + x + 1$ where l, m, n, p are positive integers.

(b)* Find the common roots of the equations
$$z^3 + 2z^2 + 2z + 1 = 0, \quad z^{1985} + z^{100} + 1 = 0.$$

16. (a) Prove that the value of $\sum_{n=1}^{5} \left(x^n + \frac{1}{x^n}\right)^2$ when $x^2 - x + 1 = 0$ is 8.

(b) If $t^2 + t + 1 = 0$, then prove that the value of

(i) $\left(t + \frac{1}{t}\right)^2 + \left(t^2 + \frac{1}{t^2}\right)^2 + \ldots + \left(t^{27} + \frac{1}{t^{27}}\right)^2 = 54$

(ii) If $z^2 + z + 1 = 0$ where z is a complex number, then the value of
$$\left(z + \frac{1}{z}\right)^2 + \left(z^2 + \frac{1}{z^2}\right)^2 + \ldots + \left(z^6 + \frac{1}{z^6}\right)^2 =$$
(a) 6   (b) 12
(c) 18   (d) 54   **(AIEEE 2006)**

(c) If $t^2 + t + 1 = 0$, then the value of the expression
$$\left(t + \frac{1}{t}\right) + \left(t^2 + \frac{1}{t^2}\right) + \ldots + \left(t^{27} + \frac{1}{t^{27}}\right) \text{ equals}$$
(a) 0   (b) 1
(c) −1   (d) none

(d) If α, β, γ are the roots of $x^3 - 3x^2 + 3x + 7 = 0$ and ω is cube root of unity, then the value of
$$\frac{\alpha - 1}{\beta - 1} + \frac{\beta - 1}{\gamma - 1} + \frac{\gamma - 1}{\alpha - 1} \text{ is}$$
(a) ω^2 (b) $2\omega^2$
(c) $3\omega^2$ (d) $-3\omega^2$

(e) $\sin \frac{\pi}{900} \left\{ \sum_{r=1}^{10} (r - \omega)(r - \omega^2) \right\} =$
(a) −1   (b) 0
(c) 1   (d) $\sqrt{3}/2$

17. If the argument of $(z - a)(\bar{z} - b)$ is equal to that of $\frac{(\sqrt{3} + i)(1 + \sqrt{3}i)}{1 + i}$, where a, b are two real numbers, find the values of a and b so that the locus becomes a circle having its centre at $\frac{1}{2}(3 + i)$.

18. (a)* If $\frac{1}{a+\omega} + \frac{1}{b+\omega} + \frac{1}{c+\omega} + \frac{1}{d+\omega} = 2\omega^2$
and $\frac{1}{a+\omega^2} + \frac{1}{b+\omega^2} + \frac{1}{c+\omega^2} + \frac{1}{d+\omega^2} = 2\omega$
then prove that
$$\frac{1}{a+1} + \frac{1}{b+1} + \frac{1}{c+1} + \frac{1}{d+1} = 2.$$

(b) If ω be complex cube root of unity satisfying the equation
$$\frac{1}{a+\omega} + \frac{1}{b+\omega} + \frac{1}{c+\omega} = 2\omega^2 \text{ and}$$
$$\frac{1}{a+\omega^2} + \frac{1}{b+\omega^2} + \frac{1}{c+\omega^2} = 2\omega, \text{ then}$$
$$\frac{1}{a+1} + \frac{1}{b+1} + \frac{1}{c+1} \text{ is equal to}$$
(a) 2   (b) −2
(c) $-1 + \omega^2$ (d) $-1 + \omega$

19.* If $ax + cy + bz = X$, $cx + by + az = Y$, $bx + ay + cz = Z$, show that:

(a) $(a^2 + b^2 + c^2 - bc - ca - ab)(x^2 + y^2 + z^2 - yz - zx - xy)$
$$= X^2 + Y^2 + Z^2 - YZ - ZX - XY.$$

(b) $(a^3 + b^3 + c^3 - 3abc)(x^3 + y^3 + z^3 - 3xyz)$
$$= X^3 + Y^3 + Z^3 - 3XYZ.$$

20.* Given $z_1 + z_2 + z_3 = A$, $z_1 + z_2\omega + z_3\omega^2 = B$, $z_1 + z_2\omega^2 + z_3\omega = C$.

(a) Express z_1, z_2, z_3 in terms of A, B, C.

(b) Prove:
$$|A|^2 + |B|^2 + |C|^2 = 3(|z_1|^2 + |z_2|^2 + |z_3|^2).$$

21. (a) For positive integers n_1, n_2 the value of the expression
$$(1+i)^{n_1} + (1+i^3)^{n_1} + (1+i^5)^{n_2} + (1+i^7)^{n_2},$$
where $i = \sqrt{-1}$ is a real number if and only if
(a) $n_1 = n_2 + 1$ (b) $n_1 = n_2 - 1$
(c) $n_1 = n_2$ (d) $n_1 > 0, n_2 > 0$
           (I.I.T. 1996)

(b) $z^{14} + 1/z^{14} = -1$, where z is a root of the equation $z + 1/z = 1$.

22. (a) For what real values of x and y are the numbers $-3 + i x^2 y$ and $x^2 + y + 4i$ conjugate complex?

(b) For what real values of x and y are the complex numbers $x^2 - 7x + 9y\,i$ and $y^2 i + 20i - 12$ equal?

(c)* The complex numbers $\sin x + i \cos 2x$ and $\cos x - i \sin 2x$ are conjugate to each other for $x = \ldots$

Solutions to Problem Set (2)

1. (a) Using the relations $1 + \omega + \omega^2 = 0$ and $\omega^3 = 1$, we get
$$(1 - \omega + \omega^2)(1 + \omega - \omega^2) = (-2\omega)(-2\omega^2) = 4\omega^3 = 4.$$

(b) $E = (-\omega^2)^3 - (-\omega)^3 = -1 + 1 = 0.$

(c) Do yourself.

2. (a) Ans. (d).

(b) $(1-\omega+\omega^2)^5+(1+\omega-\omega^2)^5=(-2\omega)^5+(-2\omega^2)^5$

$=-32(\omega^5+\omega^{10})=-32(\omega^3.\omega^2+\omega^9.\omega)$

$=-32(\omega^2+\omega)=-32(-1)=32$.

(c) $E=(5\omega-2\omega)^6=3^6.\omega^6=729$

$E=(5\omega^2-2\omega^2)^6=3^6.\omega^{12}=729$

3. (a) L.H.S. $=(1-\omega)(1-\omega^2)(1-\omega^3\omega)(1-\omega^3\omega^2)$

$=[(1-\omega)(1-\omega^2)]^2$

$=(1-\omega-\omega^2+\omega^3)^2$

$=(1+1+1)^2=9.$ [$\because$ $\omega+\omega^2=-1,\ \omega^3=1$]

(b) Proceed as above.

(c) $(1-\omega+\omega^2)(1-\omega^2+\omega^4)(1-\omega^4+\omega^8)$

$(1-\omega^8+\omega^{16})$....... to $2n$ factors.

$=(1-\omega+\omega^2)(1-\omega^2+\omega)(1-\omega+\omega^2)$

$(1-\omega^2+\omega)$...to $2n$ factors.

[$\because$ $\omega^4=\omega$, $\omega^8=\omega^2$, $\omega^{16}=\omega$ etc.]

$=(-2\omega)(-2\omega^2)(-2\omega)(-2\omega^2)$ .... to $2n$ factors

$=(2^2\omega^3)(2^2\omega^3)$ .... to n factors.

[$\because$ $(-2\omega)(-2\omega^2)=2^2\omega^3=2^2$]

$=(2^2)^n=2^{2n}$.

4. (a) **See § 6 P. 45.**

(b) **See § 6 P. 45.**

(c) $(a+b+c)(a+b\omega+c\omega^2)(a+b\omega^2+c\omega)$

$=(a+b+c)[a^2+b^2\omega^3+c^2\omega^3+ab(\omega+\omega^2)$

$+bc(\omega^2+\omega^4)+ca(\omega+\omega^2)]$

$=(a+b+c)(a^2+b^2+c^2-ab-bc-ca)$

[$\because$ $\omega^4=\omega$ and $\omega+\omega^2=-1$]

$=a^3+b^3+c^3-3abc$.

(d) $E=a^3+b^3+c^3-3abc$

$=(a+b+c)(a+b\omega+c\omega^2)(a+b\omega^2+c\omega)$

where $a+b+c=e^x$ and $\omega^3=1,\omega^4=\omega,\omega^5=\omega^2$

$a+b\omega+c\omega^2=1+\omega x+\dfrac{(\omega x)^2}{2!}+\dfrac{(\omega x)^3}{3!}+\dfrac{(\omega x)^4}{4!}$

$=e^{\omega x}$

and $a+b\omega^2+c\omega=e^{\omega^2 x}$ as above

$\therefore$ $E=e^{x(1+\omega+\omega^2)}=e^0=1$

5. (a) Expanding, we get

L.H.S. $=x^2(1+\omega^2+\omega^4)+y^2(1+\omega^4+\omega^2)$

$+2xy(1+\omega^3+\omega^3)$

$=x^2(1+\omega^2+\omega)+y^2(1+\omega+\omega^2)+2xy(1+1+1)$

$=6xy$ [$\because$ $1+\omega+\omega^2=0$]

(b) Refer § 6 (1) P. 45. We know that

$x^3+y^3=(x+y)(\omega x+\omega^2 y)(\omega^2 x+\omega y)$

Put $x=a+b\omega+c\omega^2,y=a+b\omega^2+c\omega$

$\therefore$ $x+y=2a-b-c$

$\omega x+\omega^2 y=(a\omega+b\omega^2+c)+(a\omega^2+b\omega+c)$

$=2c-a-b$

$\omega^2 x+\omega y=2b-c-a$

Each of the factors corresponds to three given factors. In case $a+b+c=0$, i.e., $b+c=-a$ etc., then the answer is $(3a)(3b)(3c)=27abc$.

6. (a) Ans. ω^2. Since $p<0$

$p=-q$, where q is + ive.

$\therefore$ $p^{1/3}=-q^{1/3}(1)^{1/3}$

$\therefore$ If $1,\omega,\omega^2$ be cube roots of unity, then

$\alpha=-q^{1/3}.1,\ \beta=-q^{1/3}.\omega,\ \gamma=-q^{1/3}.\omega^2$

$\therefore$ Given expression $=\dfrac{x+y\omega+z\omega^2}{x\omega+y\omega^2+z}$

$=\dfrac{1}{\omega}\dfrac{x\omega+y\omega^2+z}{x\omega+y\omega^2+z}=\dfrac{1}{\omega}=\dfrac{\omega^2}{\omega^3}=\omega^2$

(b) Ans. -1.

$\dfrac{1}{\omega}\cdot 1+\dfrac{1}{\omega^2}\cdot 1=\dfrac{\omega+\omega^2}{\omega^3}=-1$

7. (a) Since α,β are the complex roots of unity, we may write $\alpha=\omega$ and $\beta=\omega^2$.

Hence $\alpha^4+\beta^4+\alpha^{-1}\beta^{-1}=\omega^4+\omega^8+\omega^{-1}\omega^{-2}$

$=\omega^3\omega+\omega^6.\omega^2+(\omega^3)^{-1}$

$=\omega+\omega^2+1=0$. [$\because$ $\omega^3=1$]

(b) $1+\omega+\omega^2=0$ $\therefore$ $1+\omega=-\omega^2$

$\therefore$ $1+2\omega=\omega-\omega^2$

$2+\omega=1-\omega^2,1+\omega=-\omega^2$

$\therefore$ L.H.S. $=\dfrac{1}{\omega(1-\omega)}+\dfrac{1}{(1-\omega)(1+\omega)}+\dfrac{1}{\omega^2}$

$=\dfrac{\omega(1+\omega)+\omega^2+1-\omega^2}{\omega^2(1-\omega^2)}=\dfrac{1+\omega+\omega^2}{\omega^2(1-\omega^2)}=0$

(c) Ans. (b) Given $(1+\omega^2)^n=(1+\omega)^n$ $\because$ $\omega^4=\omega$

or $(-\omega)^n=(-\omega^2)^n$ or $\omega^n=\omega^{2n}$.

Clearly $n=3$ is the least value of n satisfying above

$\because$ $\omega^3=\omega^6=1$

8. (a) $\alpha=\omega$ and $\beta=\omega^2$

Then $xyz=(a+b)(a\omega+b\omega^2)(a\omega^2+b\omega)=a^3+b^3$

[§ 5. (1) P. 45].

(b) Here $x+y+z=(a+b)+(a\omega+b\omega^2)+(a\omega^2+b\omega)$

$=a(1+\omega+\omega^2)+b(1+\omega^2+\omega)$

$=a\times 0+b\times 0=0$. ...(1)

Since $x + y + z = 0$, we have
$$x^3 + y^3 + z^3 = 3xyz = 3(a^3 + b^3), \text{ by part (a)}$$

9. (a) $\omega^{100} + (\omega^2)^{100} = \omega^{99}\omega + \omega^{198}.\omega^2 = \omega + \omega^2 = -1.$

(b) $\omega^{3n} + (\omega^2)^{3n} = 1 + 1 = 2.$

(c) Ans. (c). $E = 4 + 5(\omega)^{334} + 3(\omega)^{365}$
$$= 4 + 5\omega + 3\omega^2 = 1 + 2\omega + 3(1 + \omega + \omega^2)$$
$$= 1 + (-1 + i\sqrt{3}) = i\sqrt{3}$$

10. (a) $\alpha = \omega, \omega^2$
$$\therefore \quad \alpha^{31} = \omega^{31} = \omega = \alpha \quad \text{or} \quad \alpha^{31} = \omega^{62} = \omega^2 = \alpha$$

(b) Ans. (d).
$$\alpha = -\omega, \beta = -\omega^2, 1030 = 3(343) + 1$$
$$= 3n + 1, (-1)^{1030} = 1$$
$$\therefore \quad E = \omega^1 + \omega^2 = -1 \qquad \because \quad \omega^{3n} = \omega^{6n} = 1$$

(c) $\alpha + \beta = 2, \alpha\beta = 4 \quad \therefore \quad \dfrac{(\alpha+\beta)^2}{\alpha\beta} = \dfrac{4}{4} = 1$
$$\dfrac{\alpha}{\beta} + \dfrac{\beta}{\alpha} + 2 = 1 \quad \text{or} \quad t + \dfrac{1}{t} + 1 = 0 \qquad \text{where } t = \dfrac{\alpha}{\beta}$$
$$\text{or} \quad t^2 + t + 1 = 0 \quad \therefore \quad t = \omega, \omega^2$$
$$\text{or} \quad \dfrac{-1 \pm i\sqrt{3}}{2}$$

11. (a) A, B, C are $1, \omega, \omega^2$
$$\text{or} \quad A = (1,0), B\left(-\dfrac{1}{2}, \dfrac{\sqrt{3}}{2}\right), C\left(-\dfrac{1}{2}, -\dfrac{\sqrt{3}}{2}\right)$$
Clearly $AB = BC = CA = \sqrt{3}$
$$\therefore \quad \Delta \text{ is equilateral.}$$
Alt. $1 + \omega + \omega^2 = 0$
Hence centroid G is at the origin.
Again if $|1| = |\omega| = |\omega^2| = 1$
Circumcentre is also at origin.
Thus centroid and circumcentre coincide.
$$\therefore \quad \Delta \text{ is equilateral.}$$

(b) $iz = \dfrac{-1 + i\sqrt{3}}{2} = \omega$
$$\Rightarrow \quad z = \dfrac{1}{i}\omega = -i\omega \qquad \qquad \dots(1)$$
Also $\omega^{3n} = 1, i^{4n} = 1, i^3 = -i \qquad \dots(2)$
$$\therefore \quad z^{101} + i^{103} = -i^{101}\omega^{101} + i^{103} = -i\omega^2 - i$$
$$\text{by (2)}$$
$$= -i(1 + \omega^2) = -i(-\omega) = i\omega$$
$$\therefore \quad \text{L.H.S.} = i^{105}\omega^{105} = i.\omega^3 = i(iz)^3 = i^4 z^3 = z^3$$
Note : You may try it by polar form
i.e., $z = 1.e^{\pi i/6}$ and $e^{2n\pi i} = 1, i = e^{\pi i/2}$

(c) $\dfrac{\sqrt{3} + i}{\sqrt{3} - i} = \dfrac{i(\sqrt{3} + i)}{i(\sqrt{3} - i)} = \dfrac{-1 + i\sqrt{3}}{1 + i\sqrt{3}} = \dfrac{2\omega}{-2\omega^2} = -\dfrac{1}{\omega}$

$$\therefore \quad E = \left(-\dfrac{1}{\omega}\right)^{3n} + 1 = (-1).\dfrac{1}{\omega^{3n}} + 1$$
$$= -1 + 1 = 0 \text{ as } n \text{ is odd} \Rightarrow 3n \text{ is odd}$$

12. (a) Since $\dfrac{-1 + \sqrt{3}i}{2} = \omega$ and $\dfrac{-1 - \sqrt{3}i}{2} = \omega^2$.
$$\therefore \quad \text{We have to prove that } \omega^n + \omega^{2n} = -1$$
$$\text{or} \quad 1 + \omega^n + \omega^{2n} = 0,$$
when n is not a multiple of 3.

Another form :
Now $1 + \omega^n + \omega^{2n} = \dfrac{(1 - \omega^n)(1 + \omega^n + \omega^{2n})}{1 - \omega^n} = \dfrac{1 - \omega^{3n}}{1 - \omega^n}.$
[the formula $1 - x^3 = (1 - x)(1 + x + x^2)$ is used here]
$$= \dfrac{1 - 1}{1 - \omega^n} = 0$$
[$\because 1 - \omega^n \neq 0$, since n is not a multiple of 3. $\therefore \omega^n \neq 1$]
We give a second proof of this. Since n is not a multiple of 3, we have
$$n = 3m + 1 \quad \text{or} \quad n = 3m + 2$$
where m is a +ive integer.
When $n = 3m + 1$, we have
$$1 + \omega^n + \omega^{2n} = 1 + \omega^{3m+1} + \omega^{6m+2}$$
$$= 1 + \omega^{3m}.\omega + \omega^{6m}.\omega^2$$
$$= 1 + \omega + \omega^2 \quad [\because \omega^{3n} = \omega^{6m} = 1]$$
$$= 0.$$
Similarly when $n = 3m + 2$, we can prove the result.

(b) Since n is a multiple of 3, we have
$$\omega^n = 1 \text{ and } \omega^{2n} = 1$$
Hence $1 + \omega^n + \omega^{2n} = 1 + 1 + 1 = 3.$

(c) $1 + \omega^n + \omega^{2n} = 0$
$$\Rightarrow \quad \dfrac{1 - \omega^{3n}}{1 - \omega^n} = 0 \text{ if } \omega^n \neq 1 \text{ because if } \omega^n = 1 \text{ then it}$$
takes the indeterminate form $\dfrac{0}{0}$.
Now $\omega^n = 1$ when n is a multiple of 3 say $n = 3m$
Hence $n = 3m + 1, 3m + 2$ (not $3m + 3$ as it is a multiple of 3). This implies $k = 3, l = 1$ or 2.

13. (a) We have $x^3 + x^2 + x = x(x^2 + x + 1)$
$$= x(x - \omega)(x - \omega^2).$$
Let $f(x) = (x + 1)^n - x^n - 1.$
In order to show that $x^3 + x^2 + x$ is factor of $f(x)$, we must show that $f(x) = 0$ when $x = 0$, $x = \omega$ and $x = \omega^2$.
Now $f(0) = (0 + 1)^n - 0 - 1 = 1 - 1 = 0$
$f(\omega) = (\omega + 1)^n - \omega^n - 1 = (-\omega^2)^n - \omega^n - 1$

$= (-1)^n \omega^{2n} - \omega^n - 1 = -\omega^{2n} - \omega^n - 1$

$\qquad [\because (-1)^n = -1 \text{ since } n \text{ is odd integer}]$

$= -(1 + \omega^n + \omega^{2n}) = 0 \quad$ **[Q. 12 (a), P. 46-49]**

Similarly $f(\omega^2) = (\omega^2 + 1)^n - (\omega^2)^n - 1$

$\qquad\qquad = (-\omega)^n - \omega^{2n} - 1$

$\qquad\qquad = -\omega^n - \omega^{2n} - 1 = 0.$

Hence $x(x - \omega)(x - \omega^2)$, that is, $x^3 + x^2 + x$ is a factor of $f(x)$.

(b) If $f(x)$ be divided by $(x - a)$, then the remainder is $f(a)$

$\quad \therefore \quad f(x) = (x - a) Q + R \qquad\qquad \text{...(1)}$

$\quad \therefore \quad f(a) = 0 + R$

Here $f(z)$ is divided by $z^2 + 1$ therefore remainder will be of first degree say $pz + q$

$\quad \therefore \quad f(z) = (z^2 + 1) Q + (pz + q)$

$\quad \therefore \quad f(i) = 0 + pi + q = i \qquad\qquad \text{...(2)}$

$\quad \therefore \quad f(-i) = 0 + p(-i) + q = 1 + i \qquad \text{...(3)}$

Solving (2) and (3), $p = \dfrac{1}{2} i, q = \left(\dfrac{1}{2} + i\right)$

$\quad \therefore \quad$ Remainder $= \dfrac{z}{2} i + \left(\dfrac{1}{2} + i\right)$

(c) We know that $x^2 + x + 1 = 0$

$\Rightarrow (x - \omega)(x - \omega^2) = 0$. By given condition ω, ω^2 will also be roots of $f(x) = 0$ and $\omega^3 = 1$

$\quad \therefore \quad f(\omega) = 0 \quad \Rightarrow \quad A(1) + \omega B(1) = 0 \qquad \text{...(1)}$

$\qquad\quad f(\omega^2) = 0 \quad \Rightarrow \quad A(1) + \omega^2 B(1) = 0 \qquad \text{...(2)}$

Solving (1) and (2), we get $A(1) = 0, B(1) = 0$ showing that both $A(x)$ and $B(x)$ are divisible by $x - 1$

$\quad \therefore \quad f(x) = A(x^3) + x B(x^3)$ is also divisible by $x - 1$

(d) Put $x = \omega$ and note that $1 + \omega + \omega^2 = 0$

where $\omega = -\dfrac{1}{2} + i\dfrac{\sqrt{3}}{2}$ and $\omega^2 = -\dfrac{1}{2} - i\dfrac{\sqrt{3}}{2}$

$\Delta = (a_0 + a_3 + a_6 + \ldots) + \omega(a_1 + a_4 + \ldots)$
$\qquad\qquad\qquad\qquad + \omega^2(a_2 + a_5 + \ldots)$

or $\quad \Delta = A + B\omega + C\omega^2 = 0$

Equating real and imaginary parts on both sides

$\qquad A - \dfrac{B}{2} - \dfrac{C}{2} = 0, \quad \dfrac{\sqrt{3}}{2}(B - C) = 0$

$\quad \therefore \quad B = C$ and hence $A = B \quad \therefore \quad A = B = C$

Again putting $x = 1$ in the given relation, we get

$\qquad 3^n = $ Sum of all the coefficients $= A + B + C$

or $\quad 3^n = 3A \quad \therefore \quad A = 3^{n-1} = B = C.$

14. We have $\quad xy(x + y)(x^2 + xy + y^2)$
$\qquad = xy(x + y)(y - x\omega)(y - x\omega^2)$

Let $f(x, y) = (x + y)^n - x^n - y^n$.

Considering the given expression $f(x, y)$ as a polynomial in y, we put $y = 0$.

We see that at $y = 0$, the polynomial $f(x, y)$ becomes $x^n - x^n = 0$ i.e. it becomes 0 for any x. Thus $f(x, y)$ is divisible by y.

Similarly $f(x, y)$ is divisible by x. Thus $f(x, y)$ is divisible by xy.

To prove that $f(x, y)$ is divisible by $x + y$, we put $y = -x$.

In this case $f(x, y)$ becomes $(x - x)^n - x^n - (-x)^n$

$\qquad\qquad = 0 - x^n + x^n = 0$

$[\because n$ is odd, we have $(-x)^n = -x^n]$

Consequently our polynomial is divisible by $x + y$.

It remains to prove that $f(x, y)$ is divisible by

$\qquad y - x\omega$ and $y - x\omega^2$.

In $f(x, y)$, we put $y = x\omega$. It becomes

$(x + x\omega)^n - x^n - (x\omega)^n = x^n(-\omega^2)^n - x^n - x^n \omega^n$

$\qquad = x^n[(-1)^n \omega^{2n} - \omega^n - 1]$

$\qquad = -x^n[\omega^{2n} + \omega^n + 1] \qquad\qquad [\because n$ is odd$]$

$\qquad = x^n \times 0 = 0$, by **Q. 12 (a), P. 46-49.**

Similarly $f(x, y)$ vanishes when $y = \omega^2 x$.

Hence the polynomial $f(x, y)$ is divisible by

$\qquad xy(x + y)(x^2 + xy + y^2)$.

15. (a) Let $f(x) = x^{4l} + x^{4m+1} + x^{4n+2} + x^{4p+3}$

Also $x^3 + x^2 + x + 1 = (x + 1)(x^2 + 1)$

$\qquad\qquad\qquad\qquad = (x + 1)(x + i)(x - i)$

Then $f(-1) = (-1)^{4l} + (-1)^{4m+1}$

$\qquad\qquad\qquad\qquad + (-1)^{4n+2} + (-1)^{4p+3}$

$\qquad = 1 - 1 + 1 - 1 = 0$

Hence $x + 1$ is a factor of $f(x)$.

Again $f(-i) = (-i)^{4l} + (-i)^{4m+1}$

$\qquad\qquad\qquad\qquad + (-i)^{4n+2} + (-i)^{4p+3}$

$= (-1)^{4l} . i^{4l} + (-1)^{4m+1} . i^{4m} . i$

$\qquad\qquad + (-1)^{4n+2} i^{4n} i^2 + (-1)^{4p+3} i^{4p} i^3$

$= 1.1 + (-1).1.i + 1.1(-1) + (-1).1(-i)$

$= 1 - i - 1 + i = 0.$

Hence $x + i$ is a factor of $f(x)$.

Similarly $x - i$ is a factor of $f(x)$.

Thus $(x + 1)(x + i)(x - i)$, that is,

$x^3 + x^2 + x + 1$ is a factor of $f(x)$, as required.

(b) The first equation may be written as

$\qquad (z + 1)(z^2 + z + 1) = 0;$

its roots are $-1, \omega$ and ω^2. The root $z = -1$ does not satisfy the second equation but $z = w$ and $z = \omega^2$ satisfy it.

Hence ω and ω^2 are the common roots.

$$x = -\omega; -\omega^2 \qquad \text{[§ 6, P. 45]}$$

16. (a) $\left(x^n + \dfrac{1}{x^n}\right)^2 = (-1)^{2n}\left(\omega^n + \dfrac{1}{\omega^n}\right)^2 = (\omega^n + \omega^{2n})^2$

$$\qquad \qquad \qquad \qquad \qquad \qquad \text{...(I)}$$

$\because \quad \dfrac{1}{\omega^n} = \dfrac{\omega^{2n}}{\omega^{3n}} = \omega^{2n}$

Now, $1 + \omega^n + \omega^{2n} = \dfrac{1 - \omega^{3n}}{1 - \omega^n} = 0$ for $n \neq 3p$.

$$= 1 + 1 + 1 = 3 \text{ for } n = 3p$$

$\therefore \quad \omega^n + \omega^{2n} = -1$ for $n \neq 3p = 2$ for $n = 3p$ ...(A)

$\therefore \quad \displaystyle\sum_{n=1}^{5}\left(x^n + \dfrac{1}{x^n}\right)^2 = \sum_{n=1}^{5}(\omega^n + \omega^{2n})^2$

Now $n \neq 3p$ for $n = 1, 2, 4, 5$ and $n = 3p$ for $n = 3$

$\therefore \quad \Sigma = \{(-1)^2 + (-1)^2 + (-1)^2 + (-1)^2\} + \{2\}^2$

$$\text{by (A)}$$

$$= 4 + 4 = 8$$

Same result will be true for $x = -\omega^2$.

(b) (i) Here $x = \omega, \omega^2$. As in last question for $x = \omega$

$$\sum_{n=1}^{27}\left(t^n + \dfrac{1}{t^n}\right)^2 = \sum_{n=1}^{27}(\omega^n + \omega^{2n})^2$$

Now $n \neq 3p$ for 18 numbers from 1 to 27 and $n = 3p$ for 9 numbers from 1 to 27

$\therefore \quad \displaystyle\sum_{n=1}^{27} = 18(-1)^2 + 9(2)^2 = 18 + 36 = 54$

The same result will be true for $x = \omega^2$.

(ii) Ans. (b).

Proceed exactly as in part (a).

Since $z^2 + z + 1 = 0 \quad \therefore \quad z = \omega, \omega^2$

$$n \neq 3p \text{ for } n = 1, 2, 4, 5; \quad n = 3p \text{ for } n = 3, 6$$

$\displaystyle\sum_{n=1}^{6} = [(-1)^2 + (-1)^2 + (-1)^2 + (-1)^2] + (2)^2 + (2)^2$

$$= 4 + 4 + 4 = 12.$$

(c) Ans. (a).

$t = \omega, \omega^2, S_{27}$ of G.P. $= \dfrac{t(1 - t^{27})}{1 - t} = 0$ both for $t = \omega, \omega^2$

(d) Ans. (c). $(x - 1)^3 = -8$

$\therefore \quad \dfrac{x - 1}{-2} = (1)^{1/3} = 1, \omega, \omega^2$

$\therefore \quad \alpha = -1, \beta = 1 - 2\omega, \gamma = 1 - 2\omega^2$

$\therefore \quad E = \dfrac{-2}{-2\omega} + \dfrac{-2\omega}{-2\omega^2} + \dfrac{-2\omega^2}{-2}$

$$= \dfrac{1}{\omega} + \dfrac{1}{\omega} + \dfrac{1}{\omega} = \dfrac{3}{\omega} = 3\omega^2$$

(e) Ans. (c).

$\displaystyle\sum_{r=1}^{10}(r - \omega)(r - \omega^2) = \sum_{r=1}^{10}\{r^2 - r(-1) + 1\}$

$$= \sum_{r=1}^{10}(r^2 + r + 1) = \Sigma r^2 + \Sigma r + \Sigma 1$$

$$= \dfrac{r(r+1)(2r+1)}{6} + \dfrac{r(r+1)}{2} + 10.$$

Put $r = 10$

$$= \dfrac{10 . 11 . 21}{6} + \dfrac{10 . 11}{2} + 10 = 450$$

$\therefore \quad E = \sin\left(450 \cdot \dfrac{\pi}{900}\right) = \sin\dfrac{\pi}{2} = 1.$

17. The given number is $2 . e^{\frac{\pi i}{6}} . 2e^{\frac{\pi i}{3}} \div 2e^{\frac{\pi i}{4}}$

Hence the given number has argument $\dfrac{\pi}{4}$.

Now $(z - a)(\bar{z} - b) = z\bar{z} - a\bar{z} - bz + ab$

$$= (x^2 + y^2) - a(x - iy) - b(x + iy) + ab$$

$$= (x^2 + y^2) - (a + b)x + i(a - b)y + ab$$

$$= X + iY \text{ say}$$

If its argument is $\dfrac{\pi}{4}$ then $\tan\dfrac{\pi}{4} = \dfrac{Y}{X} = 1$ or $Y = X$

or $\quad x^2 + y^2 - (a + b)x + ab = (a - b)y$

or $\quad x^2 + y^2 - (a + b)x - (a - b)y + ab = 0$

Above represents a circle whose centre is $\left[\dfrac{1}{2}(a + b), \dfrac{1}{2}(a - b)\right] = \left(\dfrac{3}{2}, \dfrac{1}{2}\right)$, the number given by complex number $\dfrac{1}{2}(3 + i)$

$\therefore \quad a + b = 3, a - b = 1 \quad \therefore \quad a = 2, b = 1$

18. (a) Because $\omega^2 = \dfrac{1}{\omega}$ and hence the two questions can be written as $\Sigma\dfrac{1}{a + \omega} = \dfrac{2}{\omega}, \Sigma\dfrac{1}{a + \omega^2} = \dfrac{2}{\omega^2}$ and

we have to prove that $\Sigma\dfrac{1}{a + 1} = \dfrac{2}{1}$.

Consider the equation $\Sigma\dfrac{1}{a + x} = \dfrac{2}{x}$ \qquad ...(1)

whose two roots are ω, ω^2 by virtue of given equations and we have to show $x = 1$ is also a root of this equation

$$\dfrac{1}{a + x} + \dfrac{1}{b + x} + \dfrac{1}{c + x} + \dfrac{1}{d + x} = \dfrac{2}{x}$$

$\therefore \quad \Sigma x(x + a)(x + b)(x + c) = 2(x + a)(x + b)(x + c)(x + d)$

or $\quad \Sigma x[x^3 + x^2(a + b + c) + x(ab + bc + ca) + abc]$

$$= 2[x^4 + x^3 . \underset{4}{\Sigma a} + x^2\underset{6}{\Sigma ab} + x\underset{4}{\Sigma abc} + abcd]$$

or $\quad 4x^4 + x^3\underset{12}{(3\Sigma a)} + x^2\underset{12}{2\Sigma ab} + x\underset{4}{\Sigma abc}$

$$= 2[x^4 + x^3\Sigma a + x^2\Sigma ab + x\Sigma abc + abcd]$$

$\therefore \quad 2x^4 + x^3\Sigma a + 0x^2 - x\Sigma abc - 2bacd = 0$

Above is a fourth degree equation two of whose roots are ω and ω^2 and let the other two be α, β then

$$\alpha + \beta + \omega + \omega^2 = -\frac{\Sigma a}{2}$$

or $\quad \alpha + \beta - 1 = -\frac{\Sigma a}{2} \qquad \ldots(2)$

$\because \quad \omega + \omega^2 + 1 = 0, \ \omega^3 = 1$

Products taken two at a time $= 0$ as coefficient of x^2 is zero.

$$(\alpha + \beta)(\omega + \omega^2) + \alpha\beta + \omega \cdot \omega^2 = 0$$

or $\quad (\alpha + \beta)(-1) + \alpha\beta + 1 = 0$

or $\quad \alpha\beta - (\alpha + \beta) + 1 = 0 \quad \therefore \ (\alpha - 1)(\beta - 1) = 0$

$\therefore \quad$ If $\alpha = 1$ then $\beta = -\frac{\Sigma a}{2}$ and if $\beta = 1$ then

$\alpha = -\frac{\Sigma a}{2}$ by (2)

Hence in either case the other two roots are 1 and $-\frac{\Sigma a}{2}$. Putting $x = 1$ in (1), we get the required result.

(b) **Ans. (a).** Given relations show that ω and ω^2 are the roots of $\frac{1}{a+x} + \frac{1}{b+x} + \frac{1}{c+x} = \frac{2}{x}$ which is a cubic in x and we have to prove that 1 is also a root of it. Above equation is simplified to

$$x \Sigma (b+x)(c+x) = 2(a+x)(b+x)(c+x)$$

or $\quad x[\Sigma bc + 2(\Sigma a)x + 3x^2]$

$$= 2[x^3 + x^2 \Sigma a + x \Sigma ab + abc]$$

or $\quad 3x^3 + 2x^2 \Sigma a + x \Sigma bc$

$$= 2x^3 + 2x^2 \Sigma a + 2x \Sigma ab + 2abc$$

or $\quad x^3 + 0\,x^2 - x \Sigma ab - 2abc = 0$

Above is a cubic in x whose two roots, are ω, ω^2. If α be the third root then $\alpha + \omega + \omega^2 =$ sum of the roots $= 0$ as the term of x^2 is missing. Put $\omega + \omega^2 = -1$

$\therefore \quad \alpha - 1 = 0 \quad$ or $\quad \alpha = 1$ is the third root

$\therefore \quad \Sigma \frac{1}{a+1} = \frac{2}{1}$

19. (a) $(a^2 + b^2 + c^2 - bc - ca - ab)$

$$(x^2 + y^2 + z^2 - yz - zx - xy)$$

$= (a + b\omega + c\omega^2)(a + b\omega^2 + c\omega)(x + y\omega + z\omega^2)$

$$(x + y\omega^2 + z\omega)$$

[See Q. 4 (c) P. 46-49]

$= [(a + b\omega + c\omega^2)(x + y\omega + z\omega^2)]$

$$[(a + b\omega^2 + c\omega)(x + y\omega^2 + z\omega)]$$

$= (ax + cy\omega^3 + bz\omega^3 + cx\omega^2 + by\omega^2 + az\omega^2$

$$+ bx\omega + ay\omega + cz\omega^4)$$

$\times (ax + cy\omega^3 + bz\omega^3 + cx\omega + by\omega^4 + az\omega$

$$+ bx\omega^2 + ay\omega^2 + cz\omega^2)$$

$= [(ax + cy + bz) + (cx + by + az)\omega^2$

$$+ (bx + ay + cz)\omega]$$

$\times [(ax + cy + bz) + (cx + by + az)\omega$

$$+ (bx + ay + cz)\omega^2]$$

$= (X + Y\omega^2 + Z\omega)(X + Y\omega + Z\omega^2)$

$= X^2 + Y^2 + Z^2 - YZ - ZX - XY$.

(b) $(a^3 + b^3 + c^3 - 3abc)(x^3 + y^3 + z^3 - 3xyz)$

$= (a + b + c)(a^2 + b^2 + c^2 - bc - ca - ab)$

$$\times (x + y + z)(x^2 + y^2 + z^2 - yz - zx - xy) \ \ldots(1)$$

Now $(a + b + c)(x + y + z) = [(ax + cy + bz)$

$$+ (cx + by + az) + (bx + ay + cz)]$$

$= X + Y + Z \qquad \ldots(2)$

And by part (1) we have

$(a^2 + b^2 + c^2 - bc - ca - ab)$

$$\cdot (x^2 + y^2 + z^2 - yz - zx - xy)$$

$= X^2 + Y^2 + Z^2 - YZ - ZX - XY . \qquad \ldots(3)$

Substituting from (2) and (3) in (1), we get

$(a^3 + b^3 + c^3 - 3abc)(x^3 + y^3 + z^3 - 3xyz)$

$= (X + Y + Z)(X^2 + Y^2 + Z^2 - YZ - ZX - XY)$

$= X^3 + Y^3 + Z^3 - 3XYZ.$

20. We are given

$z_1 + z_2 + z_3 = A \qquad \ldots(1)$

$z_1 + z_2\omega + z_3\omega^2 = B \qquad \ldots(2)$

$z_1 + z_2\omega^2 + z_3\omega = C \qquad \ldots(3)$

(a) Adding (1), (2) and (3), we get

$3z_1 + z_2(1 + \omega + \omega^2) + z_3(1 + \omega^2 + \omega) = A + B + C$

or $\quad z_1 = \frac{A + B + C}{3} \qquad [\because \ 1 + \omega + \omega^2 = 0]$

Now multiplying (1), (2) and (3) by $1, \omega^2, \omega$ respectively and adding, we get

$z_1(1 + \omega^2 + \omega) + z_2(1 + \omega^3 + \omega^3)$

$$+ z_3(1 + \omega^4 + \omega^2)$$

$= A + B\omega^2 + C\omega.$

or $\quad z_2 = \frac{A + B\omega^2 + C\omega}{3}$

$[\because \ 1 + \omega^4 + \omega^2 = 1 + \omega + \omega^2 = 0 \text{ and } \omega^3 = 1]$

Similarly, $\quad z_3 = \frac{A + B\omega + C\omega^2}{3}$

(b) We have

$|A|^2 + |B|^2 + |C|^2 = A\bar{A} + B\bar{B} + C\bar{C} \qquad \ldots(1)$

But $A\bar{A} = (z_1 + z_2 + z_3)(\bar{z_1} + \bar{z_2} + \bar{z_3})$

$$= z_1 \overline{z_1} + z_2 \overline{z_2} + z_3 \overline{z_3} + \overline{z_1} (z_2 + z_3) \ldots$$
$$+ \overline{z_2} (z_3 + z_1) + \overline{z_3} (z_1 + z_2) \ldots$$
$$= |z_1|^2 + |z_2|^2 + |z_3|^2 + \overline{z_1} (z_2 + z_3)$$
$$+ \overline{z_2} (z_3 + z_1) + \overline{z_3} (z_1 + z_2) \ldots$$

$$B\overline{B} = (z_1 + z_2 \omega + z_3 \omega^2)(\overline{z_1} + \overline{z_2} \omega + \overline{z_3} \omega^2)$$
$$= (z_1 + z_2 \omega + z_3 \omega^2)(\overline{z_1} + \overline{z_2} \omega^2 + \overline{z_3} \omega)$$
$$[\because \ \overline{\omega} = \omega^2 \quad \text{and} \quad \overline{(\omega^2)} = \omega]$$
$$= z_1 \overline{z_1} + z_2 \overline{z_2} \omega^3 + z_3 \overline{z_3} \omega^3 + \overline{z_1} (z_2 \omega + z_3 \omega^2)$$
$$+ \overline{z_2} (z_3 \omega^4 + z_1 \omega^2) + \overline{z_3} (z_1 \omega + z_2 \omega^2)$$
$$= |z_1|^2 + |z_2|^2 + |z_3|^2 + \overline{z_1} (z_2 \omega + z_3 \omega^2)$$
$$+ \overline{z_2} (z_3 \omega + z_1 \omega^2) + \overline{z_3} (z_1 \omega + z_2 \omega^2) \quad \ldots(2)$$

Similarly,
$$C\overline{C} = |z_1|^2 + |z_2|^2 + |z_3|^2 + \overline{z_1} (z_2 \omega^2 + z_3 \omega)$$
$$+ \overline{z_2} (z_3 \omega^2 + z_1 \omega) + \overline{z_3} (z_1 \omega^2 + z_2 \omega) \quad \ldots(3)$$

Adding (1), (2) and (3), we get
$$A\overline{A} + B\overline{B} + C\overline{C} = 3[|z_1|^2 + |z_2|^2 + |z_3|^2]$$
$$+ \overline{z_1} [z_2 (1 + \omega + \omega^2) + z_3 (1 + \omega^2 + \omega)]$$
$$+ \overline{z_2} [z_3 (1 + \omega + \omega^2) + z_1 (1 + \omega^2 + \omega)]$$
$$+ \overline{z_3} [z_1 (1 + \omega + \omega^2) + z_2 (1 + \omega^2 + \omega)]$$
$$= 3[|z_1|^2 + |z_2|^2 + |z_3|^2] \quad [\because \ 1 + \omega + \omega^2 = 0]$$

∴ From (1) and (2), we conclude
$$|A|^2 + |B|^2 + |C|^2 = 3[|z_1|^2 + |z_2|^2 + |z_3|^2]$$

21. (a) $i^3 = -i, i^5 = i, i^7 = -i$

The first two and last two brackets are combined
$$(1 + i)^{n_1} + (1 - i)^{n_1} + (1 + i)^{n_2} + (1 - i)^{n_2}$$
$$= 2[1 + {}^{n_1}C_2 i^2 + {}^{n_1}C_4 i^4 + \ldots.$$
$$+ 1 + {}^{n_2}C_2 i^2 + {}^{n_2}C_4 i^4 + \ldots.]$$

Now $i^2, i^4, i^6, \ldots$ are all real. Hence the given expression is real if $n_1 > 0, n_2 > 0$.

${}^nC_r$ is defined when both n and r are +ive.

(b) Hint : Roots of $z + 1/z = 1$ are $-\omega$ and $-\omega^2$.

22. (a) $-3 + ix^2 y$ and $x^2 + y + 4i$ are complex conjugates if $-3 + ix^2 y = \overline{(x^2 + y + 4i)} = x^2 + y - 4i$.

Equating real and imaginary parts, we get
$$x^2 + y = -3, \ x^2 y = -4. \qquad \ldots(1)$$

Eliminating x^2, we get
$$(-4/y) + y = -3 \quad \text{or} \quad y^2 + 3y - 4 = 0$$
or $(y + 4)(y - 1) = 0. \quad \therefore \ y = 1 \ \text{or} \ -4.$
Then $x^2 = -4 / y = 1$, when $y = -4 \ \therefore \ x = \pm 1.$
Hence $x = 1, y = -4$ or $x = -1, y = -4.$
The other value of $y = 1$ gives imaginary values of x as $x^2 = -4 / y = -4$. We therefore reject this case since x and y are real.
Hence $x = 1, y = -4$ or $x = -1, y = -4.$

Note : From (1), Sum of x^2 and $y = -3$ and their product $= -4$, ∴ x^2 and y are the roots of
$$t^2 + 3t - 4 = 0 \quad \therefore \ t = -4, 1$$
∴ $x^2 = -4, y = 1$ or $x^2 = 1, y = -4$
The first set is rejected as it gives imaginary values of x and from second, we get $x = \pm 1, y = -4$.

(b) Equate real and imaginary parts,
Ans. (3, 4), (3, 5), (4, 4), (4, 5)

(c) Ans. No value of x.
∵ $\tan x = 1$ and $\tan 2x = 1$ cannot hold together.

§7 De-Moivre's Theorem.

1. $(\cos \alpha + i \sin \alpha)(\cos \beta + i \sin \beta) = \cos(\alpha + \beta)$
$$+ i \sin(\alpha + \beta)$$
or $e^{i\alpha} \cdot e^{i\beta} = e^{i(\alpha + \beta)}$

2. $\cos \beta - i \sin \beta = \cos(-\beta) + i \sin(-\beta) = e^{-i\beta}$

3. $(\cos \alpha + i \sin \alpha)(\cos \beta - i \sin \beta) = \cos(\alpha - \beta)$
$$+ i \sin(\alpha - \beta)$$

(a) V. Imp. $\sin \alpha + i \cos \alpha$
$$= \cos\left(\frac{\pi}{2} - \alpha\right) + i \sin\left(\frac{\pi}{2} - \alpha\right) = e^{i(\pi/2 - \alpha)}$$

Another Form :
$$\sin \alpha + i \cos \alpha = -i^2 \sin \alpha + i \cos \alpha$$
$$= i(\cos \alpha - i \sin \alpha) = ie^{-i\alpha}$$

Note : $i = e^{i\pi/2}$

4. $x = \cos \theta + i \sin \theta$ then $\dfrac{1}{x} = \cos \theta - i \sin \theta$
$$= e^{i\theta} \qquad\qquad\qquad = e^{-i\theta}$$
∴ $x + \dfrac{1}{x} = 2\cos \theta, \quad x - \dfrac{1}{x} = 2i\sin \theta$
or $x^2 - 2x \cos \theta + 1 = 0$
⇒ $x = \cos \theta \pm i \sin \theta = e^{i\theta}, e^{-i\theta}$

5. If n is any rational number, then De-Moivre's theorem states that
$$(\cos \theta + i \sin \theta)^n = \cos n\theta + i \sin n\theta$$
It is easy to check that
$$(\cos \theta + i \sin \theta)^{-n} = \cos n\theta - i \sin n\theta,$$
$$(\cos \theta - i \sin \theta)^n = \cos n\theta - i \sin n\theta$$
and $(\cos \theta - i \sin \theta)^{-n} = \cos n\theta + i \sin n\theta.$

Another form : $e^{i\theta} = \cos \theta + i \sin \theta$
$$e^{-i\theta} = \cos(-\theta) + i \sin(-\theta) = \cos \theta - i \sin \theta$$
$$\boldsymbol{e^{i\theta} + e^{-i\theta} = 2\cos \theta, e^{i\theta} - e^{-i\theta} = 2i \sin \theta} \qquad \textbf{(V. Imp.)}$$
* $e^{\pi i} = \cos \pi + i \sin \pi = -1$
* $e^{i\pi/2} = \cos \dfrac{\pi}{2} + i \sin \dfrac{\pi}{2} = i$
* $e^{-i\pi/2} = \cos(\pi/2) - i \sin(\pi/2) = -i$
$e^{i\alpha} \cdot e^{i\beta} \cdot e^{i\gamma} \ldots = e^{i(\alpha + \beta + \gamma + \ldots)}$
∴ $(\cos \alpha + i \sin \alpha)(\cos \beta + i \sin \beta)(\cos \gamma + i \sin \gamma) \ldots$
$$= \cos(\alpha + \beta + \gamma + \ldots) + i \sin(\alpha + \beta + \gamma + \ldots.)$$

Problem Set (3)

De Moivre's Theorem

1. Prove the following :

(a) $(\cos 60° + i \sin 60°)^6 = 1$.

(b) $[\sqrt{2}(\cos 56° \ 15' + i \sin 56° \ 15')]^8 = 16i$.

(c) $(\sin \theta + i \cos \theta)^n = \cos n\left(\dfrac{1}{2}\pi - \theta\right)$

$$+ i \sin n\left(\dfrac{1}{2}\pi - \theta\right).$$

2. Compute :

(a) $[(\cos \theta + i \sin \theta)(\cos \theta - i \sin \theta)]^{-1}$

(b) $\dfrac{4(\cos 75° + i \sin 75°)}{0 \cdot 4(\cos 30° + i \sin 30°)}$.

3. Put in the form $A + iB$:

(a)* $\dfrac{(\cos x + i \sin x)(\cos y + i \sin y)}{(\cot u + i)(1 + i \tan v)}$

(b) $\dfrac{(\cos 2\theta - i \sin 2\theta)^7 (\cos 3\theta + i \sin 3\theta)^{-5}}{(\cos 4\theta + i \sin 4\theta)^{12} (\cos 5\theta + i \sin 5\theta)^{-6}}$

(c)* Simplify

$(\cos 2\theta + i \sin 2\theta)^{-5} (\cos 3\theta - i \sin 3\theta)^6$

$$(\sin \theta - i \cos \theta)^3$$

(M.N.R. 1991)

4. (a) Prove the following : $\left(\dfrac{1+i}{\sqrt{(2)}}\right)^8 + \left(\dfrac{1-i}{\sqrt{(2)}}\right)^8 = 2$.

(b) If $z = \left(\dfrac{\sqrt{3}}{2} + \dfrac{i}{2}\right)^5 + \left(\dfrac{\sqrt{3}}{2} - \dfrac{i}{2}\right)^5$, then Im $(z) = 0$.

5. (a) Prove that $\left(\dfrac{\sqrt{3}+i}{2}\right)^6 + \left(\dfrac{\sqrt{3}-i}{2}\right)^6 = -2$.

(b)* If $\left(\dfrac{3}{2} + i\dfrac{\sqrt{3}}{2}\right)^{50} = 3^{25}(a + ib)$, then prove that

$$(a, b) = \left(\dfrac{1}{2}, \dfrac{\sqrt{3}}{2}\right)$$

when n is a positive integer but not a multiple of 3.

6. (a)* Prove that

$$\left(\dfrac{1 + \cos \phi + i \sin \phi}{1 + \cos \phi - i \sin \phi}\right)^n = \cos n\phi + i \sin n\phi.$$

(b)* $\dfrac{(\cos \theta + i \sin \theta)^4}{(\sin \theta + i \cos \theta)^5}$ is equal to ......

(c) If $\left[\dfrac{1 + \cos \theta + i \sin \theta}{\sin \theta + i(1 + \cos \theta)}\right]^4$

$= \cos n\theta + i \sin n\theta$, then $n =$

(a) 2   (b) 3

(c) 4   (d) none

7. (a)* If $x_r = \cos \dfrac{\pi}{2^r} + i \sin \dfrac{\pi}{2^r}$, prove that

$$x_1 \ x_2 \ x_3 \ ... \text{ad inf.} = -1$$

(b)* If $z_r = \cos \dfrac{\pi}{3^r} + i \sin \dfrac{\pi}{3^r}$, $r = 1, 2, 3, ...$ then

prove that $z_1 \ z_2 \ z_3 \ .... \infty = i$

(c) $z_r = \cos \dfrac{r\pi}{10} + i \sin \dfrac{r\pi}{10}$ then $z_1 \ z_2 \ z_3 \ z_4 = -1$

(D.C.E. 1998)

(d) If $z = \cos \dfrac{8\pi}{11} + i \sin \dfrac{8\pi}{11}$, then

Real $(z + z^2 + z^3 + z^4 + z^5)$ is

(a) $-\dfrac{1}{2}$ (b) 0

(c) $\dfrac{1}{2}$ (d) none

8. (a) Let $f_p(\beta) = \left(\cos \dfrac{\beta}{p^2} + i \sin \dfrac{\beta}{p^2}\right)$

$$\left(\cos \dfrac{2\beta}{p^2} + i \sin \dfrac{2\beta}{p^2}\right)... \left(\cos \dfrac{\beta}{p} + i \sin \dfrac{\beta}{p}\right)$$

then $\lim\limits_{n \to \infty} f_n(\pi) = ...$

(b) Given $2^7 \cos^3 \theta \sin^5 \theta = a \sin 8\theta - b \sin 6\theta$

$$+ c \cos 4\theta + d \sin 2\theta$$

Determine the values of a, b, c, d if θ is real and $z = \cos \theta + i \sin \theta$.

9. (a) If α, β are the roots of the equation $x^2 - 2x + 4 = 0$, prove that

$$\alpha^n + \beta^n = 2^{n+1} \cos(n\pi/3).$$

(b) If $x^2 - 2x \cos \theta + 1 = 0$, prove that

$$x^{2n} - 2x^n \cos n\theta + 1 = 0.$$

(c)* Construct an equation whose roots are nth powers of the roots of the equation $x^2 - 2x \cos \theta + 1 = 0$.

In Q. 10 and 11, if $2 \cos \theta = x + \dfrac{1}{x}$ and

$2 \cos \phi = y + \dfrac{1}{y}$ etc., then prove that :

10. (a) $xyz... + \dfrac{1}{xyz .....} = 2 \cos(\theta + \phi + ...)$

(b) $\dfrac{x}{y} + \dfrac{y}{x} = 2 \cos(\theta - \phi)$

11. (a)* $x^m y^n + \dfrac{1}{x^m y^n} = 2 \cos(m\theta + n\phi)$

(b) $\dfrac{x^m}{y^n} + \dfrac{y^n}{x^m} = 2 \cos(m\theta - n\phi)$

In Q. 12 and 13 if $\cos \alpha + \cos \beta + \cos \gamma$
$= \sin \alpha + \sin \beta + \sin \gamma = 0$, prove that :

12. (a)* $\cos 3\alpha + \cos 3\beta + \cos 3\gamma = 3 \cos (\alpha + \beta + \gamma)$.

    (b) $\sin 3\alpha + \sin 3\beta + \sin 3\gamma = 3 \sin (\alpha + \beta + \gamma)$.

13. (a) $\cos 2\alpha + \cos 2\beta + \cos 2\gamma = \sin 2\alpha + \sin 2\beta$
$+ \sin 2\gamma = 0$.

    (b)* $\cos^2 \alpha + \cos^2 \beta + \cos^2 \gamma = \sin^2 \alpha + \sin^2 \beta$
$+ \sin^2 \gamma = 3/2$.

    (c) $\cos (\beta + \gamma) + \cos (\gamma + \alpha) + \cos (\alpha + \beta) = 0$
$\sin (\beta + \gamma) + \sin (\gamma + \alpha) + \sin (\alpha + \beta) = 0$

    (d) If $a \cos \alpha + b \cos \beta + c \sin \gamma = 0$
and $a \sin \alpha + b \sin \beta + c \cos \gamma = 0$
then prove that $a^3 \cos 3\alpha + b^3 \cos 3\beta - c^3 \sin 3\gamma$
$= 3abc \cos (\gamma - \alpha - \beta)$

14. If α, β are the roots of the equation
$t^2 - 2t + 2 = 0$ and
$$\frac{(x + \alpha)^n - (x + \beta)^n}{\alpha - \beta} = \frac{\sin n\theta}{\sin^n \theta}$$
then prove that $x = \cot \theta - 1$.

15. (a) For natural number n, prove that
$\cos n\alpha = \cos^n \alpha - {}^nc_2 \cos^{n-2} \alpha \sin^2 \alpha$
$+ {}^nc_4 \cos^{n-4} \alpha \sin^4 \alpha ...$
$\sin n\alpha = {}^nc_1 \cos^{n-1} \alpha \sin \alpha$
$- {}^nc_3 \cos^{n-3} \alpha \sin^3 \alpha + {}^nc_5 \cos^{n-5} \alpha \sin^5 \alpha - .....$

    (b) Form the equation whose roots are
$$\cot^2 \frac{\pi}{2n + 1}, \cot^2 \frac{2\pi}{2n + 1}, \cot^2 \frac{3\pi}{2n + 1}, ...,$$
$$\cot^2 \frac{n\pi}{2n + 1}$$
Hence find the value of
$$\cot^2 \frac{\pi}{2n + 1} + \cot^2 \frac{2\pi}{2n + 1} + \cot^2 \frac{3\pi}{2n + 1}$$
$$+ ... + \cot^2 \frac{n\pi}{2n + 1}$$

16. Express $\sin 5\theta$ in terms of $\sin \theta$ and hence show that $\sin 36°$ is a root of the equation $16 x^4 + 20 x^2 + 5 = 0$

In Q. 17 to 20 if $(1 + x)^n = p_0 + p_1 x + p_2 x^2 + ... p_n x^n$,
prove that :

17. (a)* $p_0 - p_2 + p_4 - ... = 2^{n/2} \cos (n\pi/4)$

    (b) $p_1 - p_3 + p_5 - ... = 2^{n/2} \sin (n\pi/4)$.

18. (a) $p_0 + p_4 + p_8 + ... = 2^{n/2 - 1} \cos \frac{n\pi}{4} + 2^{n-2}$

    (b)* $p_0 + p_3 + p_6 + ... = \frac{1}{3} \left(2^n + 2 \cos \frac{n\pi}{3} \right)$

19. (a)* $p_1 + p_4 + p_7 + ... = \frac{1}{3} \left[2^n + 2 \cos (n - 2) \frac{\pi}{3} \right]$

    (b)* $p_2 + p_5 + p_8 + ... = \frac{1}{3} \left[2^n + 2 \cos (n + 2) \frac{\pi}{3} \right]$

20. $p_3 + p_7 + p_{11} + ... = \frac{1}{2} \left\{ 2^{n-1} - 2^{n/2} \sin \frac{n\pi}{4} \right\}$

21. Prove that if $\cos \alpha + i \sin \alpha$ is a solution of the equation
$$x^n + p_1 x^{n-1} + p_2 x^{n-2} + ... + p_n = 0,$$
then $p_1 \sin \alpha + p_2 \sin 2\alpha + ... + p_n \sin n\alpha = 0$
$(p_1, p_2, ..., p_n$ are real)

Solutions to Problem Set (3)

1. We shall use De-Moivre's Theorem :
$$(\cos \theta + i \sin \theta)^n = \cos n\theta + i \sin n\theta.$$

    (a) $(\cos 60° + i \sin 60°)^6$
$= \cos (6 \times 60°) + i \sin (6 \times 60°)$
$= \cos 360° + i \sin 360° = 1 + i0 = 1.$

    (b) $[\sqrt{2} (\cos 56° 15' + i \sin 56° 15')^8].$
$= 16 [\cos (8 \times 56° 15') + i \sin (8 \times 56° 15')]$
$= 16 [\cos 450° + i \sin 450°]$
$= 16 [\cos 90° + i \sin 90°]$
$= 16 (0 + i) = 16i.$

    (c) $(\sin \theta + i \cos \theta)^n$
$= [\cos (\pi/2 - \theta) + i \sin (\pi/2 - \theta)]^n$
$= \cos n (\pi/2 - \theta) + i \sin n (\pi/2 - \theta).$

2. (a) $[(\cos \theta + i \sin \theta) (\cos \theta - i \sin \theta)]^{-1}$
$= (\cos^2 \theta - i^2 \sin^2 \theta)^{-1}$
$= (\cos^2 \theta + \sin^2 \theta)^{-1} = 1.$

Alt. $(e^{i\theta} . e^{-i\theta})^{-1} = 1$

    (b) $\dfrac{4 (\cos 75° + i \sin 75°)}{0 \cdot 4 (\cos 30° + i \sin 30°)}$
$= \dfrac{10 (\cos 75° + i \sin 75°) (\cos 30° - i \sin 30°)}{\cos^2 30° - i^2 \sin^2 30°}$
$= \dfrac{10 [\cos (75° - 30°) + i \sin (75° - 30°)]}{\cos^2 30° + \sin^2 30°}$
$= 10 [\cos 45° + i \sin 45°] = \dfrac{10}{\sqrt{(2)}} (1 + i).$

or $10 \dfrac{e^{i\theta}}{e^{i\phi}} = 10e^{i(\theta - \phi)} = 10e^{i\pi/4} = \dfrac{10}{\sqrt{2}} (1 + i).$

3. (a) Given expression
$= \dfrac{(\cos x + i \sin x) (\cos y + i \sin y)}{(\cos u/\sin u + i) (1 + i \sin v/\cos v)}$
$= \dfrac{(\cos x + i \sin x) (\cos y + i \sin y)}{(\cos u + i \sin u) (\cos v + i \sin v)} . \sin u \cos v$
$= \dfrac{\cos (x + y) + i \sin (x + y)}{\cos (u + v) + i \sin (u + v)} . \sin u \cos v$

$$= \frac{e^{i(x+y)}}{e^{i(u+v)}} \sin u \sin v = e^{i(x+y-u-v)} \times \sin u \cos v$$

$$= \sin u \cos v [\cos (x+y-u-v)$$
$$+ i \sin (x+y-u-v)]$$

(b) Using De-Moivre's Theorem, the given expression

$$= \frac{(\cos \theta + i \sin \theta)^{-14} (\cos \theta + i \sin \theta)^{-15}}{(\cos \theta + i \sin \theta)^{48} (\cos \theta + i \sin \theta)^{-30}}$$

$$= \frac{(e^{i\theta})^{-29}}{(e^{i\theta})^{18}} = (e^{i\theta})^{-47}$$

$$= (\cos \theta + i \sin \theta)^{-47} = \cos 47\theta - i \sin 47\theta.$$

(c) $\sin \theta - i \cos \theta = -i^2 \sin \theta - i \cos \theta$

$$= -i (\cos \theta + i \sin \theta)$$

Given expression is

$$(-i)^3 [\cos (-10\theta - 18\theta + 3\theta) + i \sin (-25\theta)]$$

$$= i (\cos 25\theta - i \sin 25\theta)$$

4. (a) $\left(\dfrac{1+i}{\sqrt{2}}\right)^2 = \dfrac{1+i^2+2i}{2} = i$

$$\left(\frac{1-i}{\sqrt{2}}\right)^2 = -i$$

$$\therefore \left(\frac{1+i}{\sqrt{(2)}}\right)^8 + \left(\frac{1-i}{\sqrt{(2)}}\right)^8 = i^4 + (-i)^4 = 2$$

(b) Put $\sqrt{3}/2 = r \cos \theta, \dfrac{1}{2} = r \sin \theta$.

$$\therefore \quad r = 1 \text{ and } \theta = \pi/6.$$

$$\therefore \quad z = (\cos \theta + i \sin \theta)^5 + (\cos \theta - i \sin \theta)^5$$

$$= \cos 5\theta + i \sin 5\theta + \cos 5\theta - i \sin 5\theta,$$

$$= 2 \cos 5\theta. \quad \text{Hence Im} (z) = 0.$$

5. (a) $\dfrac{\sqrt{3}}{2} + \dfrac{i}{2} = (r, \theta) = \left(1, \dfrac{\pi}{6}\right) = e^{\pi i/6}$

$$\left(\frac{\sqrt{3}+i}{2}\right)^6 = e^{\pi i}, \quad \left(\frac{\sqrt{3}-i}{2}\right)^6 = e^{-\pi i} \text{ (conjugate)}$$

$$\therefore \quad \text{Sum} = 2 \cos \pi = -2.$$

(b) $r = \sqrt{3}, \theta = \pi/6,$

$$e^{50\pi i/6} = e^{25\pi i/3} = e^{8\pi i + \pi i/3} = e^{\pi i/3}$$

$$\therefore \quad (\sqrt{3})^{50} \left(\cos \frac{\pi}{3} + i \sin \frac{\pi}{3}\right) = 3^{25} (a + ib)$$

$$\therefore \quad a = \cos 60° = \frac{1}{2}, b = \sin 60° = \frac{\sqrt{3}}{2}$$

6. (a) $\left(\dfrac{1+\cos\phi + i \sin\phi}{1+\cos\phi - i \sin\phi}\right)^n$

$$= \left[\frac{2\cos^2 (\phi/2) + 2i \sin (\phi/2) \cos (\phi/2)}{2\cos^2 (\phi/2) - 2i \sin (\phi/2) \cos (\phi/2)}\right]^n$$

$$= \left[\frac{\cos (\phi/2) + i \sin (\phi/2)}{\cos (\phi/2) - i \sin (\phi/2)}\right]^n$$

$$= [\cos (\phi/2) + i \sin (\phi/2)]^n [\cos (\phi/2) - i \sin (\phi/2)]^{-n}$$

$$= [\cos (\phi/2) + i \sin (\phi/2)]^n [\cos (\phi/2) + i \sin (\phi/2)]^n$$

$$= [\cos (\phi/2) + i \sin (\phi/2)]^{2n}$$

$$= \cos [2n . (\phi/2)] + i \sin [2n . (\phi/2)]$$

$$= \cos n\phi + i \sin n\phi.$$

(b) Ans. $\sin 9\theta - i \cos 9\theta$

$$D^r = (\sin \theta + i \cos \theta)^5 = (-i^2 \sin \theta + i \cos \theta)^5$$

$$= i^5 (\cos \theta - i \sin \theta)^5 = i e^{-5i\theta}$$

$$\therefore \quad \text{L.H.S.} = \frac{e^{4i\theta}}{i e^{-5i\theta}} = -i e^{9i\theta}$$

$$= -i (\cos 9\theta + i \sin 9\theta)$$

$$= \sin 9\theta - i \cos 9\theta$$

(c) Ans. (c).

$$N^r = 1 + \cos \theta + i \sin \theta$$

$$= 2 \cos \frac{\theta}{2} \left[\cos \frac{\theta}{2} + i \sin \frac{\theta}{2}\right] = 2 \cos \frac{\theta}{2} . e^{i\theta/2}$$

$$D^r = -i^2 \sin \theta + i (1 + \cos \theta) = i [\text{conjugate of } N^r]$$

$$= i 2 \cos \frac{\theta}{2} . e^{-i\theta/2}$$

$$\therefore \quad E = \left(\frac{N^r}{D^r}\right)^4 = \left[\frac{1}{i} \frac{e^{i\theta/2}}{e^{-i\theta/2}}\right]^4 = \frac{1}{i^4} . e^{4i\theta}$$

$$= \cos 4\theta + i \sin 4\theta \quad \therefore \quad n = 4$$

7. (a) $x_1 . x_2 . x_3 ....$

$$= [\cos (\pi/2) + i \sin (\pi/2)] . [\cos (\pi/2^2) + i \sin (\pi/2^2)]$$

$$. [\cos (\pi/2^3) + i \sin (\pi/2^3)] ....$$

$$= \cos (\pi/2 + \pi/2^2 + \pi/2^3 + ...)$$

$$+ i \sin (\pi/2 + \pi/2^2 + \pi/2^3 + ...)$$

$$= \cos \left(\frac{\pi/2}{1 - 1/2}\right) + i \sin \left(\frac{\pi/2}{1 - 1/2}\right)$$

(Summing the infinite G.P.)

$$= \cos \pi + i \sin \pi = -1$$

$$[\because \cos \pi = -1 \text{ and } \sin \pi = 0]$$

(b) As in last part,

$$E = \cos \left(\frac{\pi/3}{1 - 1/3}\right) + i \sin \left(\frac{\pi/3}{1 - 1/3}\right)$$

$$= \cos \frac{\pi}{2} + i \sin \frac{\pi}{2} = 0 + i . 1 = i .$$

(c) Proceed as above $\cos \pi + i \sin \pi = -1$

(d) Ans. (a) Real $(z) = \dfrac{z + \bar{z}}{2} = \dfrac{1}{2}\left(z + \dfrac{1}{z}\right)$

$$\because \quad z\bar{z} = \cos^2 \frac{8\pi}{11} + \sin^2 \frac{8\pi}{11} = 1 \quad \therefore \quad \bar{z} = \frac{1}{z}$$

$$\therefore \quad E = \text{Real part of}$$

$$\left(z + z^2 + z^3 + z^4 + z^5 + \frac{1}{z} + \frac{1}{z^2} + \frac{1}{z^3} + \frac{1}{z^4} + \frac{1}{z^5}\right)$$

Now $z^{11} = \cos 8\pi + i \sin 8\pi = 1$ ...(I)

$$\therefore \quad \frac{1}{z^4} = \frac{z^7}{z^{11}} = z^7 \text{ etc.}$$

∴ $E = \frac{1}{2}[z + z^2 + z^3 + z^4 + z^5 + z^{10} + z^9$

$+ z^8 + z^7 + z^6]$

Add and subtract z^{11}.

∴ $E = \frac{1}{2}$ [sum of G.P. of 11 terms $- z^{11}$]

$= \frac{1}{2}\left[\frac{z(1-z^{11})}{1-z} - z^{11}\right] = \frac{1}{2}(0-1) = -\frac{1}{2}$ by (I)

8. (a) Ans. i.

In the last term write $\frac{\beta}{p}$ as $\frac{p\beta}{p^2}$

∴ $f_p(\beta) = e^{i\beta/p^2 + 2i\beta/p^2 + ... + pi\beta/p^2}$

$= e^{(i\beta/p^2)\{1+2+3+...+p\}} = e^{(i\beta/p^2)\left\{\frac{p(p+1)}{2}\right\}}$

$= e^{\frac{i\beta}{2}\left(1+\frac{1}{p}\right)}$

∴ $f_n(\pi) = e^{\frac{i\pi}{2}\left(1+\frac{1}{n}\right)}$

$\lim_{n\to\infty} f_n(\pi) = e^{i\pi/2} = \cos\frac{\pi}{2} + i\sin\frac{\pi}{2} = i$

(b) $(2\cos\theta)^3 = \left(z + \frac{1}{z}\right)^3, (2i\sin\theta)^5 = \left(z - \frac{1}{z}\right)^5$

Multiplying the above relations, we have

$2^8 i\cos^3\theta\sin^5\theta = \left(z^2 - \frac{1}{z^2}\right)^3\left(z - \frac{1}{z}\right)^2$

$= \left(z^6 - 3z^2 + 3\cdot\frac{1}{z^2} - \frac{1}{z^6}\right)\left(z^2 - 2 + \frac{1}{z^2}\right)$

$= \left(z^8 - \frac{1}{z^8}\right) - 2\left(z^6 - \frac{1}{z^6}\right) - (3-1)\left(z^4 - \frac{1}{z^4}\right)$

$+ 6\left(z^2 - \frac{1}{z^2}\right)$

$= (2i\sin 8\theta) - 2(2i\sin 6\theta) - 2(2i\sin 4\theta)$
$+ 6(2i\sin 2\theta)$

∴ $2^7\cos^3\theta\sin^5\theta = \sin 8\theta - 2\sin 6\theta$
$- 2\sin 4\theta + 6\sin 2\theta$

∴ $(a,b,c,d) = (1,-2,-2,6)$

9. (a) $x^2 - 2x + 4 = 0,$

∴ $x = \frac{2 \pm \sqrt{4-16}}{2} = 1 \pm \sqrt{3}i$

∴ $\alpha = re^{i\theta}, \beta = re^{-i\theta}$ where $r = 2$ and $\theta = \pi/3$

∴ $\alpha^n + \beta^n = r^n(e^{in\theta} + e^{-in\theta})$

$= r^n[\cos n\theta + i\sin n\theta + \cos n\theta - i\sin n\theta]$

$= r^n . 2\cos n\theta = 2^{n+1}\cos(n\pi/3)$

(b) **Hint :** From the given relation, $x = \cos\theta \pm i\sin\theta$
Take $x = \cos\theta + i\sin\theta$,
then $x^n = \cos n\theta + i\sin n\theta$

and $1/x^n = \cos n\theta - i\sin n\theta$

∴ $x^n + (1/x^n) = 2\cos n\theta$ ...(1)

Now $x^{2n} - 2x^n\cos n\theta + 1$

$= x^n\left[\left(x^n + \frac{1}{x^n}\right) - 2\cos n\theta\right]$

$= x^n[2\cos n\theta - 2\cos n\theta] = 0,$ by (1),

(c) $\alpha = \cos\theta + i\sin\theta, \ \beta = \cos\theta - i\sin\theta$

$\alpha^n = \cos n\theta + i\sin n\theta,$

$\beta^n = \cos n\theta - i\sin n\theta$

$S = 2\cos n\theta, \ P = 1 \ \therefore \ x^2 - Sx + P = 0$

or $x^2 - 2\cos n\theta\, x + 1 = 0$ is the required equation.

10. From the given relations

$x = \cos\theta + i\sin\theta = e^{i\theta}$

$y = \cos\phi + i\sin\phi = e^{i\phi}$

(a) $xyz... = e^{i(\theta+\phi+\psi+...)}$

$\frac{1}{xyz...} = e^{-i(\theta+\phi+\psi+...)}$

∴ $xyz... + \frac{1}{xyz......} = 2\cos(\theta+\phi+\psi+....)$

(b) $\frac{x}{y} = \frac{e^{i\theta}}{e^{i\phi}} = e^{i(\theta-\phi)}$

∴ $y/x = (x/y)^{-1} = e^{-i(\theta-\phi)}$

$\frac{x}{y} + \frac{y}{x} = 2\cos(\theta-\phi).$

11. (a) $x^m y^n = (e^{i\theta})^m(e^{i\phi})^n = e^{i(m\theta+n\phi)}$

∴ $\frac{1}{x^m y^n} = e^{-i(m\theta+n\phi)}$ etc.

(b) Proceed as above.

12. $\begin{rcases} \cos\alpha + \cos\beta + \cos\gamma = 0 \\ \sin\alpha + \sin\beta + \sin\gamma = 0 \end{rcases}$ given $\begin{matrix}...(1)\\...(2)\end{matrix}$

Multiplying (2) by i and adding to (1), we get

$(\cos\alpha + i\sin\alpha) + (\cos\beta + i\sin\beta)$
$+ (\cos\gamma + i\sin\gamma) = 0$ ...(3)

Let $z_1 = \cos\alpha + i\sin\alpha, \ z_2 = \cos\beta + i\sin\beta,$
$z_3 = \cos\gamma + i\sin\gamma$

Then (3) gives $z_1 + z_2 + z_3 = 0$ ...(4)

∴ $z_1^3 + z_2^3 + z_3^3 = 3z_1 z_2 z_3$

∴ $(\cos\alpha + i\sin\alpha)^3 + (\cos\beta + i\sin\beta)^3$
$+ (\cos\gamma + i\sin\gamma)^3$

$= 3(\cos\alpha + i\sin\alpha)(\cos\beta + i\sin\beta)$
$.(\cos\gamma + i\sin\gamma).$

or $(\cos 3\alpha + i\sin 3\alpha) + (\cos 3\beta + i\sin 3\beta)$
$+ (\cos 3\gamma + i\sin 3\gamma)$

$= 3[\cos(\alpha+\beta+\gamma) + i\sin(\alpha+\beta+\gamma)]$ ...(5)

(a) Equating real parts in (5), we get

$\cos 3\alpha + \cos 3\beta + \cos 3\gamma = 3 \cos (\alpha + \beta + \gamma)$.

(b) Equating imaginary parts in (5), we get

$\sin 3\alpha + \sin 3\beta + \sin 3\gamma = 3 \sin (\alpha + \beta + \gamma)$.

13. (a) To prove this, we observe that

$$\frac{1}{z_1} + \frac{1}{z_2} + \frac{1}{z_3} = (\cos \alpha + i \sin \alpha)^{-1}$$

$$+ (\cos \beta + i \sin \beta)^{-1} + (\cos \gamma + i \sin \gamma)^{-1}$$

$$= \cos \alpha - i \sin \alpha + \cos \beta - i \sin \beta + \cos \gamma - i \sin \gamma$$

$= 0$, by (1) and (2) given

or $z_2 z_3 + z_3 z_1 + z_1 z_2 = 0$. ...(1)

Also $z_1 + z_2 + z_3 = 0$ whence squaring, we get

$$z_1^2 + z_2^2 + z_3^2 + 2z_1 z_2 + 2z_2 z_3 + 2z_3 z_1 = 0$$

or $z_1^2 + z_2^2 + z_3^2 = 0$, by (1).

$\therefore \quad (\cos \alpha + i \sin \alpha)^2 + (\cos \beta + i \sin \beta)^2$

$$+ (\cos \gamma + i \sin \gamma)^2 = 0$$

or $\cos 2\alpha + i \sin 2\alpha + \cos 2\beta + i \sin 2\beta$

$$+ \cos 2\gamma + i \sin 2\gamma = 0$$

In this equating real and imaginary parts to zero, we obtain

$\cos 2\alpha + \cos 2\beta + \cos 2\gamma = 0$ ...(2)

and $\sin 2\alpha + \sin 2\beta + \sin 2\gamma = 0$. ...(3)

(b) Putting $\cos 2\alpha = 2 \cos^2 \alpha - 1$

or $= 1 - 2 \sin^2 \alpha$ in (2),

we get the results.

(c) From (1) $z_2 z_3 + z_3 z_1 + z_1 z_2 = 0$

$\therefore \quad \Sigma [\cos (\beta + \gamma) + i \sin (\beta + \gamma)] = 0$

Equating real and imaginary parts, we get the results.

(d) A careful look at the question will suggest that replace γ by $90° - \lambda$ so that we have $\Sigma a \cos \alpha = 0$ and $\Sigma a \sin \alpha = 0$. Now choose

$$z_1 = ae^{i\alpha}, z_2 = be^{i\beta}, z_3 = ce^{i\lambda}$$

$\therefore \quad z_1 + z_2 + z_3 = 0$ by given condition ...(1)

Hence $z_1^3 + z_2^3 + z_3^3 = 3z_1 z_2 z_3$ by (1)

Now equate real and imaginary parts and replace λ by $90° - \gamma$.

14. $\alpha = 1 + i, \beta = 1 - i$

$x + \alpha = x + 1 + i = re^{i\psi}$ where $\tan \psi = \dfrac{1}{x+1}$ ...(1)

and $r = (x+1)^2 + 1 = \cot^2 \psi + 1 = \text{cosec} \, \psi$ ...(2)

$x + \beta = x + 1 - i = re^{-i\psi}$ conjugate.

Put in the given equation

$$\frac{r^n [e^{in\psi} - e^{-in\psi}]}{2i} = \frac{r^n}{2i} 2i \sin n\psi$$

$$= \frac{\sin n\psi}{\sin^n \psi} = \frac{\sin n\theta}{\sin^n \theta}, \text{ by (2)}$$

$\therefore \quad \psi = \theta \quad \therefore \quad \cot \psi = \cot \theta$

or $x + 1 = \cot \theta \quad \therefore \quad x = \cot \theta - 1$, by (1)

15. (a) We have $\cos n\alpha + i \sin n\alpha = (\cos \alpha + i \sin \alpha)^n$

Now expanding the R.H.S. by the binomial theorem, we get

$\cos n\alpha + i \sin n\alpha = \cos^n \alpha + {}^nC_1 \cos^{n-1} \alpha \, (i \sin \alpha)$

$$+ {}^nC_2 \cos^{n-2} \alpha \, (i \sin \alpha)^2 + {}^nC_3 \cos^{n-3} \alpha (i \sin \alpha)^3$$

$$+ {}^nC_4 \cos^{n-4} \alpha \, (i \sin \alpha)^4$$

$$+ {}^nC_5 \cos^{n-5} \alpha \, (i \sin \alpha)^5 + ...$$

Equating real and imaginary parts, we get

$\cos n\alpha = \cos^n \alpha - {}^nC_2 \cos^{n-2} \alpha \sin^2 \alpha$

$$+ {}^nC_4 \cos^{n-4} \alpha \sin^4 \alpha - ....$$ ...(1)

and $\sin n\alpha = {}^nC_1 \cos^{n-1} \alpha \sin \alpha$

$$- {}^nC_3 \cos^{n-3} \alpha \sin^3 \alpha + {}^nC_5 \cos^{n-5} \alpha \sin^5 \alpha$$

...(2)

(b) In (2) of part (a), replacing n by $2n + 1$, we get

$\sin (2n+1) \alpha = {}^{2n+1}C_1 \cos^{2n} \alpha \sin \alpha$

$$- {}^{2n+1}C_3 \cos^{2n-2} \alpha \sin^3 \alpha$$

$$+ {}^{2n+1}C_5 \cos^{2n-4} \alpha \sin^5 \alpha - ......$$

$$= \sin^{2n+1} \alpha [{}^{2n+1}C_1 \cot^{2n} \alpha - {}^{2n+1}C_3 \cot^{2n-2} \alpha$$

$$+ {}^{2n+1}C_5 \cot^{2n-4} \alpha - .....]$$ ...(3)

Now L.H.S. $= \sin (2n+1) \alpha = 0$

when $(2n+1) \alpha = r\pi$

or $\alpha = \dfrac{\pi}{2n+1}, \dfrac{2\pi}{2n+1}, \dfrac{3\pi}{2n+1}, ...$

Hence R.H.S. of (3) gives

$${}^{2n+1}C_1 \cot^{2n} \alpha - {}^{2n+1}C_3 \cot^{2n-2} \alpha$$

$$+ {}^{2n+1}C_5 \cot^{2n-4} \alpha - ...... = 0$$

Above is an nth degree equation in $\cot^2 \alpha$.

Hence $\cot^2 \dfrac{\pi}{2n+1}, \cot^2 \dfrac{2\pi}{2n+1}, \cot^2 \dfrac{3\pi}{2n+1}, ...$

$\cot^2 \dfrac{n\pi}{2n+1}$ are the n roots of the equation

$${}^{2n+1}C_1 x^n - {}^{2n+1}C_3 x^{n-1} + {}^{2n+1}C_5 x^{n-2} - ..... = 0$$

...(4)

Sum of the roots of (4)

$$= - \frac{\text{coeff. of } x^{n-1}}{\text{coeff. of } x^n} = \frac{{}^{2n+1}C_3}{{}^{2n+1}C_1}$$

$$= \frac{(2n+1).2n(2n-1)}{(1.2.3)(2n+1)} = \frac{n(2n-1)}{3}.$$

16. It is easy to prove as above in Q. 15 (a) that

$\sin 5\theta = 5 \cos^4 \theta \sin \theta - 10 \cos^2 \theta \sin^3 \theta + \sin^5 \theta$

$$= \sin \theta [5 (1 - \sin^2 \theta)^2 - 10 \sin^2 \theta (1 - \sin^2 \theta)$$

$$+ \sin^4 \theta] = 0$$

$$= \sin \theta [16 \sin^4 \theta - 20 \sin^2 \theta + 5] = 0$$

If we choose $\theta = 36^o$ or $5\theta = 180^o$

$\sin\theta \neq 0$ but $\sin 180^o = 0$

$\therefore \quad 0 = s[16s^4 - 20s^2 + 5]$ but $s \neq 0$

$\therefore \quad 16s^4 - 20s^2 + 5 = 0$, where $s = \sin 36^o$

is a root of above.

17. $(1+x)^n = p_0 + p_1 x + p_2 x^2 + p_3 x^3 + p_4 x^4 + \ldots\ldots$

$$+ p_n x^n$$

In this put $x = i$. Then

$(1+i)^n = p_0 + p_1 i - p_2 - p_3 i + p_4 + \ldots + p_n i^n$ ...(1)

$1 + i = \sqrt{2}\left(\cos\dfrac{\pi}{4} + i\sin\dfrac{\pi}{4}\right)$

Hence $(1+i)^n = (\sqrt{2})^n [\cos(\pi/4) + i\sin(\pi/4)]^n$

$\qquad = 2^{n/2}[\cos(n\pi/4) + i\sin(n\pi/4)]$.

Substituting in (1), we get

$2^{n/2}[\cos(n\pi/4) + i\sin(n\pi/4)]$

$$= p_0 + p_1 i - p_2 - p_3 i + p_4 + \ldots$$

Equating real and imaginary parts,

(a) $2^{n/2}\cos(n\pi/4) = p_0 - p_2 + p_4 \ldots$ ...(2)

and (b) $2^{n/2}\sin(n\pi/4) = p_1 - p_3 + p_5 \ldots$

18. (a) Again putting $x = 1$ and -1 in the given equation, we get

$2^n = p_0 + p_1 + p_2 + p_3 + p_4 + \ldots + p_n$

$0 = p_0 - p_1 + p_2 - p_3 + p_4 - \ldots$

Adding, $2^n = 2(p_0 + p_2 + p_4 + p_6 + p_8 + \ldots)$

or $2^{n-1} = p_0 + p_2 + p_4 + p_6 + p_8 + \ldots$ ...(3)

Again adding (2) and (3), we get

$2^{n/2}\cos\dfrac{n\pi}{4} + 2^{n-1} = 2(p_0 + p_4 + p_8 + \ldots)$

$\therefore \quad 2^{n/2-1}\cos\dfrac{n\pi}{4} + 2^{n-2} = p_0 + p_4 + p_8 + \ldots$

(b) Putting $x = 1, \omega, \omega^2$ and adding,

$1 + \omega = -\omega^2, 1 + \omega^2 = -\omega$

$3(p_0 + p_3 + p_6 + \ldots) = 2^n + (-\omega^2)^n + (-\omega)^n$ ...(1)

$\omega = \dfrac{-1+i\sqrt{3}}{2}$

$\therefore -\omega = \dfrac{1}{2} - i\dfrac{\sqrt{3}}{2} = \cos\dfrac{\pi}{3} - i\sin\dfrac{\pi}{3}, \because r = 1, \theta = -\dfrac{\pi}{3}$

$-\omega^2 = \cos\dfrac{\pi}{3} + i\sin\dfrac{\pi}{3}$ **(Conjugate)**

$\therefore (-\omega)^n + (-\omega^2)^n = 2\cos\dfrac{n\pi}{3}$.

(by De-Moivre's Theorem)

Putting in (1), we get the result.

19. (a) $(1+x)^n = p_0 + p_1 x + p_2 x^2 + p_3 x^3 + p_4 x^4 + \ldots$

Keeping in view that we want $3p_1$ in (a), we multiply both sides by x^2.

$\therefore \quad x^2(1+x)^n$

$= p_0 x^2 + p_1 x^3 + p_2 x^4 + p_3 x^5 + p_4 x^6 + \ldots$

Now put $x = 1, \omega, \omega^2$ and add.

$1.2^n + \omega^2(1+\omega)^n + \omega^4(1+\omega^2)^n$

$= 3(p_1 + p_4 + p_7 + \ldots)$ ...(1)

$\omega = -\dfrac{1}{2} + i\dfrac{\sqrt{3}}{2} = e^{2\pi i/3}, \omega^2 = -\dfrac{1}{2} - i\dfrac{\sqrt{3}}{2} = e^{4\pi i/3}$

$1 + \omega = \dfrac{1}{2} + i\dfrac{\sqrt{3}}{2} = e^{i\pi/3}$,

$1 + \omega^2 = \dfrac{1}{2} - i\dfrac{\sqrt{3}}{2} = e^{-i\pi/3}$.

Hence from (1), L.H.S.

$= 2^n + e^{4\pi i/3} \cdot e^{n\pi i/3} + e^{2\pi i/3} \cdot e^{-n\pi i/3}$

$= 2^n + e^{-2\pi i/3} \cdot e^{n\pi i/3} + e^{2\pi i/3} \cdot e^{-n\pi i/3}$

$= 2^n + e^{\frac{(n-2)\pi i}{3}} + e^{-\frac{(n-2)\pi i}{3}}$

$= 2^n + 2\cos\dfrac{n-2}{3}\pi = 3S$ etc.

(b) Similarly multiply both sides by x and then put $x = 1, \omega, \omega^2$ and proceed as above.

20. $(1+x)^n = p_0 + p_1 x + p_2 x^2 + p_3 x^3 + \ldots$

Multiplying both sides by x,

$x(1+x)^n = p_0 x + p_1 x^2 + p_2 x^3 + p_3 x^4 + \ldots$ ...(1)

If $x = 1^{1/4}$ then $x^4 - 1 = 0$

or $(x^2-1)(x^2+1) = 0$

$\therefore \quad x = 1, -1, i, -i$ and $x^4 = 1$

Also $1 + 1 + i - i = 0$

Put $x = 1, -1, i, -i$ in both sides of (1) and add

$2^n + 0 + i(1+i)^n - i(1-i)^n$

$$= 4(p_3 + p_7 + p_{11} + \ldots)$$

$1 + i = \sqrt{2}e^{\pi i/4}, 1 - i = \sqrt{2}e^{-\pi i/4}$

L.H.S. $= 2^n + i.2^{n/2}\left[e^{n\pi i/4} - e^{-n\pi i/4}\right]$

$$= 2^n + i.2^{n/2}.2i\sin\dfrac{n\pi}{4}$$

$= 2^n - 2.2^{n/2}\sin\dfrac{n\pi}{4} = 4E$

$\therefore \quad E = \dfrac{1}{2}\left\{2^{n-1} - 2^{n/2}\sin\dfrac{n\pi}{4}\right\}$.

21. Since $\cos\alpha + i\sin\alpha$ is the root of the given equation, we have

$(\cos\alpha + i\sin\alpha)^n + p_1(\cos\alpha + i\sin\alpha)^{n-1}$

$$+ p_2(\cos\alpha + i\sin\alpha)^{n-2} + \ldots p_n = 0$$

or $(\cos\alpha + i\sin\alpha)^n [1 + p_1 e^{-i\alpha} + p_2 e^{-2i\alpha}$

$$+ p_3 e^{-3i\alpha} + \ldots + p_n e^{-ni\alpha}] = 0$$ ...(1)

Now $\cos\alpha + i\sin\alpha \neq 0$ for any α, we can cancel the factor $(\cos\alpha + i\sin\alpha)^n$ in the equation (1). Hence (1) can be written as

$1 + p_1 (\cos\alpha - i\sin\alpha) + p_2 (\cos 2\alpha - i\sin 2\alpha)$
   $+ p_3 (\cos 3\alpha - i\sin 3\alpha)$
   $+ ..... + p_n (\cos n\alpha - i\sin n\alpha) = 0$ ...(2)

Equating imaginary part to 0 in (2), we get
$p_1 \sin\alpha + p_2 \sin 2\alpha + p_3 \sin 3\alpha + ... + p_n \sin n\alpha = 0.$

Remark. Equating real parts in (2), we shall obtain
$1 + p_1 \cos\alpha + p_2 \cos 2\alpha + ... + p_n \cos n\alpha = 0$

§8 *n*-th roots of a complex number

Put $z = x + iy = r (\cos\theta + i\sin\theta)$

$\therefore z^{1/n} = r^{1/n} [\cos (2p\pi + \theta) + i\sin (2p\pi + \theta)]^{1/n}$

we have generalized the angle. Now apply De-Moivre's theorem

$\therefore \quad z^{1/n} = r^{1/n} \left[\cos \dfrac{2p\pi + \theta}{n} + i\sin \dfrac{2p\pi + \theta}{n} \right]$

Now put $p = 0, 1, 2, 3, ... (n-1)$ and thus you will get n roots.

It has been shown in **Q. 6 (a), P. 61-64** that these n roots are in G.P.

Representation of roots of unity.

- Square roots of unity $x^2 - 1 = 0$

   $\therefore \quad x = 1, -1; 1, e^{\pi i}$

- Cube roots of unity $x^3 - 1 = 0$

   $\therefore \quad x = 1, \omega, \omega^2; 1, e^{2\pi i/3}, e^{4\pi i/3}$

- 4th roots of unity $x^4 - 1 = 0$ or $(x^2 - 1)(x^2 + 1) = 0$

   $\therefore \quad x = 1, i, -1, -i$ or $x = 1, e^{\pi i/2}, e^{\pi i}, e^{3\pi i/2}$

- Similarly 8th roots of unity are given by a G.P. $1, \alpha, \alpha^2, ..., \alpha^7$ where $\alpha = e^{2\pi i/8} = e^{\pi i/4}$.

- Roots of $x^2 - 1 = 0$ are $1, \alpha \quad ; \alpha^2 = 1$

- Roots of $x^3 - 1 = 0$ are $1, \alpha, \alpha^2 \quad ; \alpha^3 = 1$

- Roots of $x^4 - 1 = 0$ are $1, \alpha, \alpha^2, \alpha^3 \quad ; \alpha^4 = 1$

- Roots of $x^8 - 1 = 0$ are $1, \alpha, \alpha^2, ..., \alpha^7 \quad ; \alpha^8 = 1$

Roots of $x^n - 1 = 0$ are $1, \alpha, \alpha^2, ..., \alpha^{n-1}$; $\alpha^n = 1$ and $\alpha \neq 1$ in each case.

***Common properties of roots of unity.**

(a) Sum of the roots of unity in each case is zero, whether square roots, cube roots, 4th roots, 8th roots or nth roots. **See Q. 10 (a), P. 61-65.**

$\therefore \quad 1 + \alpha + \alpha^2 + ... + \alpha^{n+1} = \dfrac{1 - \alpha^n}{1 - \alpha} = \dfrac{1 - 1}{\neq 0} = 0.$

   (Karnatak C.E.E. 1999)

(b) They are in G.P. of common ratio $\alpha = e^{2\pi i/r}$ where $r = 2, 3, 4, ..., n$

(c) Sum of their pth powers   **Q. 13 (a), P. 61-65**

$1 + \alpha^p + \alpha^{2p} + ... \alpha^{(n-1)p} = \dfrac{1 - (\alpha^n)^p}{1 - \alpha^p} = 0$

$\because \quad \alpha^n = 1, \ p \neq kn$

If $p = kn$, then $\alpha^p = \alpha^{kn} = (\alpha^n)^k = 1$

$\therefore \quad$ Each root is 1.

$\therefore \quad$ Sum $= 1 + 1 + 1 + ... + 1 = n$

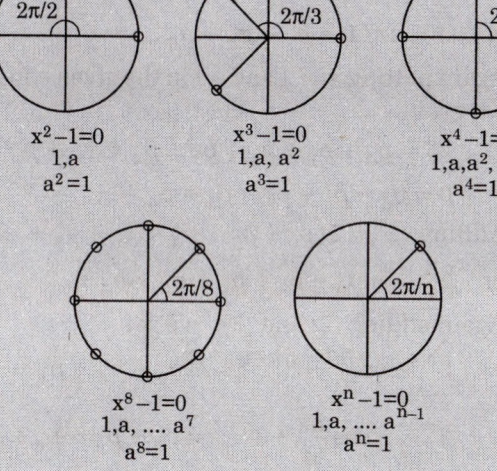

Fig. 5

Problem Set (4)

*n*th roots of unity.

1. Find all the values of the given root :

   (a) $(2 - 2i)^{1/3}$,   (b) $(1 - \sqrt{3}i)^{1/4}$,

   (c) $(-64a^4)^{1/4}$ (a, real).

2. Find all the values of the given root :

   (a)* $\sqrt{i}$ (b) $\sqrt{-i}$

   (c) $\sqrt{1+i}$ (d) $\sqrt{1-i}$

3. (a) Find the roots of the equation $z^{10} - z^5 - 992 = 0$, whose real part is negative.

   (b) Find all those roots of the equation $z^{12} - 56z^6 - 512 = 0$ whose imaginary part is positive.   **(Roorkee 2001)**

4. (a)* The roots of equation $(x - 1)^3 + 8 = 0$ are $-1, 1 - 2\omega, 1 - 2\omega^2$. True or False ?

   (b) Given z is a complex number with modulus 1. Then prove that the equation $\left(\dfrac{1 + ia}{1 - ia} \right)^4 = z$ has all roots real and distinct.

5. (a)* Use De-Moivre's theorem to solve the equation $2\sqrt{2} x^4 = (\sqrt{3} - 1) + i (\sqrt{3} + 1)$.   **(Roorkee 1994)**

   (b)* Find all the roots of the equation
   $(3z - 1)^4 + (z - 2)^4 = 0$
   in the simplified form of $a + ib$.   **(Roorkee 1998)**

(c) Prove that the roots of the equation $(z+1)^6 + (z-1)^6 = 0$ are given by $\pm \cot \dfrac{\pi}{12}, \pm \cot \dfrac{3\pi}{12}, \pm \cot \dfrac{5\pi}{12}$

(d) Solve the equation $(1+z)^8 + z^8 = 0$ and show that real part of each root of the equation is $-1/2$.

6. (a) Prove that n, nth roots of unity form a series in G.P.

(b) Let z_1 and z_2 be nth roots of unity which subtend a right angle at the origin. Then n must be of the form

    (a) $4k+1$ (b) $4k+2$

    (c) $4k+3$ (d) $4k$ **(I.I.T. Sc. 2001)**

(c) If z_1 and z_2 are two nth roots of unity, then $\arg\left(\dfrac{z_1}{z_2}\right)$ is a multiple of

    (a) $n\pi$ (b) $\dfrac{3\pi}{n}$

    (c) $\dfrac{2\pi}{n}$ (d) none of these

7. (a)* If $1, \omega, \omega^2, \ldots, \omega^{n-1}$ are the n, nth roots of unity, then $(1-\omega)(1-\omega^2)\ldots(1-\omega^{n-1})$ equals

    (i) 0 (ii) 1

    (iii) n (iv) n^2 **(M.N.R. 1992)**

(b)* Find all the six sixth roots of unity. Which of these are also cube roots of unity ?   **(M.N.R. 1991)**

8. (a) Prove that the product of any two of the ten, tenth roots of unity is again one of the ten roots.

(b)* If ω is fifth root of unity, then $\log_2 |1 + \omega + \omega^2 + \omega^3 - \omega^{-1}|$ is equal to

    (a) 1 (b) 0

    (c) -1 (d) 2

9. (a)* If $\alpha = \cos \dfrac{2\pi}{7} + i \sin \dfrac{2\pi}{7}$ and $p = \alpha + \alpha^2 + \alpha^4$ and $q = \alpha^3 + \alpha^5 + \alpha^6$, then find the equation whose roots are p and q.

(b) Given $z = \cos \dfrac{2\pi}{2n+1} + i \sin \dfrac{2\pi}{2n+1}$, n a positive integer, find the equation whose roots are $\alpha = z + z^3 + \ldots + z^{2n-1}$ and $\beta = z^2 + z^4 + \ldots + z^{2n}$ **(Roorkee 2000)**

10. (a) Let a complex number $\alpha, \alpha \neq 1$, be a root of the equation $z^{p+q} - z^p - z^q + 1 = 0$, where p, q are distinct primes. Show that either $1 + \alpha + \alpha^2 + \ldots + \alpha^{p-1} = 0$ or $1 + \alpha + \alpha^2 + \ldots + \alpha^{q-1} = 0$, but not both together.   **(I.I.T. 2002)**

(b) If β is an imaginary root of the equation $z^n - 1 = 0$, prove that $1 + \beta + \beta^2 + \ldots + \beta^{n-1} = 0$.

(c)* If $\beta \neq 1$ be any n^{th} root of unity then prove that $1 + 3\beta + 5\beta^2 + \ldots + n$ terms $= -\dfrac{2n}{1-\beta}$

11. If $\omega \neq 1$ and ω is a nth root of unity then find the value of $1 + 4\omega + 9\omega^2 + 16\omega^3 \ldots + n^2 \omega^{n-1}$

12.* Prove that all the complex numbers z which satisfy the equation $z^n = (1+z)^n$ $(n > 1)$ lie on a line parallel to imaginary axis.

13. (a)* Find the n, nth roots of unity and prove that the sum of their pth powers vanishes unless p be a multiple of n, p being an integer, and then the sum is n.

(b) Find the seven seventh roots of unity and prove that sum of their nth powers always vanishes unless n be a multiple of seven, n being an integer and then the sum is seven.

(c) If $\alpha_1, \alpha_2, \ldots, \alpha_{100}$ are all the 100th roots of unity, then $\Sigma \Sigma (\alpha_i \alpha_j)^5$ is $1 \leq i < j \leq 100$

    (a) 20 (b) $(20)^{1/20}$

    (c) 0 (d) none

14. If $\alpha = e^{2\pi i/7}$ and $f(x) = A_0 + \sum_{k=1}^{20} A_k x^k$, then find the value of $f(x) + f(\alpha x) + \ldots + f(\alpha^6 x)$ independent of α.   **(Roorkee 1999)**

15. (a)* The value of $\sum_{k=1}^{6} \left(\sin \dfrac{2\pi k}{7} - i \cos \dfrac{2\pi k}{7} \right)$ is

    (a) -1 (b) 0

    (c) $-i$ (d) None

(b) The value of $\sum_{i=1}^{10} \left(\sin \dfrac{2k\pi}{11} + i \cos \dfrac{2k\pi}{11} \right)$ is

    (a) 1 (b) -1

    (c) i (d) $-i$ **(AIEEE 2006)**

Summation of Series : $C + iS$ method

Sum the following series :

16.* $\sin \theta \cos \theta + \dfrac{\sin 2\theta \cos^2 \theta}{2!} + \dfrac{\sin 3\theta \cos^3 \theta}{3!} + \ldots \infty$

17.* $\cos^n \alpha - n \cos^{n-1} \alpha \cos \alpha$
$+ \dfrac{n(n-1)}{2!} \cos^{n-2} \alpha \cos 2\alpha + \ldots (n+1)$ terms

18. $1 + \dfrac{1}{2} \cos \alpha + \dfrac{1.3}{2.4} \cos 2\alpha + \dfrac{1.3.5}{2.4.6} \cos 3\alpha + \ldots$

19.* $\cos y \sin y + \cos^2 y \sin 2y + \cos^3 y \sin 3y + \ldots n$ terms.

Solutions to Problem Set (4)

1. (a) Put $2 = r \cos \theta; 2 = r \sin \theta$; then $r = 2\sqrt{2}$ and $\theta = \pi/4$

Hence $(2 - 2i)^{1/3} = (r \cos \theta - ri \sin \theta)^{1/3}$
$= r^{1/3} [\cos \theta - i \sin \theta]^{1/3}$
$= r^{1/3} [\cos (2n\pi + \theta) - i \sin (2n\pi + \theta)]^{1/3}$

$$= (2\sqrt{2})^{1/3} \left[\cos(2n\pi + \pi/4)\right.$$
$$\left. - i\sin(2n\pi + \pi/4)\right]^{1/3}$$
$$= \sqrt{2}\left[\cos\frac{1}{3}(2n\pi + \pi/4) - i\sin\frac{1}{3}(2n\pi + \pi/4)\right]$$

Putting $n = 0, 1, 2$, the required roots are
$$\sqrt{2}\left[\cos(\pi/12) - i\sin(\pi/12)\right],$$
$$\sqrt{2}\left[\cos(3\pi/4) - i\sin(3\pi/4)\right]$$
and $\sqrt{2}\left[\cos(17\pi/12) - i\sin(17\pi/12)\right]$.

Now $\cos\dfrac{3\pi}{4} = -\dfrac{1}{\sqrt{(2)}}$, $\sin\dfrac{3\pi}{4} = \dfrac{1}{\sqrt{(2)}}$,
$$\cos\frac{17\pi}{12} = \cos\left(\frac{3\pi}{2} - \frac{\pi}{12}\right) = -\sin\frac{\pi}{12}$$
and $\sin\left(\dfrac{17}{12}\pi\right) = \sin\left(\dfrac{3\pi}{2} - \dfrac{\pi}{12}\right) = -\cos\dfrac{\pi}{12}$.

Hence the roots are :
$$\sqrt{2}\left(\cos\frac{\pi}{12} - i\sin\frac{\pi}{12}\right), \quad -1 - i,$$
$$\sqrt{2}\left(-\sin\frac{\pi}{12} + i\cos\frac{\pi}{12}\right).$$

(b)   Ans. $\pm 2^{1/4}\left[\cos(r\pi/12) - i\sin(r\pi/12)\right]$,
where $r = 1$ or 7.

(c) $(-64a^4)^{1/4} = (2\sqrt{2})\, a(-1)^{1/4}$

We know that $-1 = \cos\pi + i\sin\pi$
Now put $-1 = r\cos\theta$, $0 = r\sin\theta$
$$\therefore \quad (-64a^4)^{1/4} = 2\sqrt{2}a\cdot[\cos\pi + i\sin\pi]^{1/4}$$
$$= 2\sqrt{2}a[\cos(2n\pi + \pi) + i\sin(2n\pi + \pi)]^{1/4}$$
$$= 2\sqrt{2}a\left[\cos\frac{2n\pi + \pi}{4} + i\sin\frac{2n\pi + \pi}{4}\right],$$
where $n = 0, 1, 2$ and 3.
Hence the required roots are
$$2\sqrt{2}a[\cos(\pi/4) + i\sin(\pi/4)],$$
$$2\sqrt{2}a[\cos(3\pi/4) + i\sin(3\pi/4)],$$
$$2\sqrt{2}a[\cos(5\pi/4) + i\sin(5\pi/4)],$$
$$2\sqrt{2}a[\cos(7\pi/4) + i\sin(7\pi/4)].$$
Thus the roots on putting the values are
$$2\sqrt{2}a(1/\sqrt{2} + i/\sqrt{2}), \quad 2\sqrt{2}a(-1/\sqrt{2} + i/\sqrt{2}),$$
$$2\sqrt{2}a(-1/\sqrt{2} - i/\sqrt{2}), \quad 2\sqrt{2}a(1/\sqrt{2} - i/\sqrt{2}).$$
Hence the roots are $\pm 2a(1 \pm i)$.

2.   (a) $i = \cos\dfrac{\pi}{2} + i\sin\dfrac{\pi}{2}$
$$= \cos\left(2n\pi + \frac{\pi}{2}\right) + i\sin\left(2n\pi + \frac{\pi}{2}\right)$$
$$= \cos(4n+1)\frac{\pi}{2} + i\sin(4n+1)\frac{\pi}{2}$$
$$\therefore \quad \sqrt{i} = \cos(4n+1)\frac{\pi}{4} + i\sin(4n+1)\frac{\pi}{4}$$
where $n = 0, 1$
$$\therefore \quad \sqrt{i} = \cos\frac{\pi}{4} + i\sin\frac{\pi}{4} \quad \text{or} \quad \cos\frac{5\pi}{4} + i\sin\frac{5\pi}{4}$$

$$= \frac{1}{\sqrt{2}}(1 + i) \quad \text{or} \quad \frac{1}{\sqrt{2}}(-1 - i)$$
or $\quad \sqrt{i} = \pm\dfrac{1}{\sqrt{2}}(1 + i)$

(b) $\sqrt{-i} = \pm\dfrac{1}{\sqrt{2}}(1 - i)$

(c) & (d) $1 \pm i = \sqrt{2}\left(\cos\dfrac{\pi}{4} \pm i\sin\dfrac{\pi}{4}\right)$
$$= \sqrt{2}\left[\cos\left(2n\pi + \frac{\pi}{4}\right) \pm i\sin\left(2n\pi + \frac{\pi}{4}\right)\right]$$
$$= \sqrt{2}\left[\cos(8n+1)\frac{\pi}{4} \pm i\sin(8n+1)\frac{\pi}{4}\right]$$
$$\therefore \quad \sqrt{(1 \pm i)} = 2^{1/4}\left[\cos(8n+1)\frac{\pi}{8} \pm i\sin(8n+1)\frac{\pi}{8}\right]$$
where $n = 0, 1$
$$= 2^{1/4}\left[\cos\frac{\pi}{8} \pm i\sin\frac{\pi}{8}\right] \qquad \text{for } n = 0$$
$$= 2^{1/4}\left[\cos\left(\pi + \frac{\pi}{8}\right) \pm i\sin\left(\pi + \frac{\pi}{8}\right)\right] \qquad \text{for } n = 1$$
$$= -2^{1/4}\left(\cos\frac{\pi}{8} \pm i\sin\frac{\pi}{8}\right) \text{ where}$$
$$\cos\frac{\pi}{8} = \sqrt{\left(\frac{\sqrt{2}+1}{2\sqrt{2}}\right)}, \sin\frac{\pi}{8} = \sqrt{\left(\frac{\sqrt{2}-1}{2\sqrt{2}}\right)}.$$

Note : We have already done parts (a, b, c, d) in **Set (5), Q. 20 (a, b, c) P. 40-42**. Here we have done them by the help of De-Moivre's Theorem.

3.   (a)   Put $z^5 = t$ $\therefore \quad t^2 - t - 992 = 0$
or $(t - 32)(t + 31) = 0$
$\therefore \quad t = z^5 = 32, -31$
$\therefore \quad z = 2(1)^{1/5}, \sqrt[5]{31}(-1)^{1/5}$
Now calculate $(1)^{1/5}$ and $(-1)^{1/5}$ and choose the answers whose real part is $-$ive.
Ans. $2(\cos 144° + i\sin 144°)$,
$\quad 2(\cos 216° + i\sin 216°)$,
$\quad \sqrt[5]{31}(\cos 108° + i\sin 108°)$,
$\quad -\sqrt[5]{31}, \sqrt[5]{31}(\cos 252° + i\sin 252°)$.

(b)   Put $z^6 = t$ $\therefore \quad t^2 - 56t - 512 = 0$
or $(t - 64)(t + 8) = 0$
$\therefore \quad z = (64)^{1/6}, (-8)^{1/6}$
or $z = 2(1)^{1/6}, \sqrt{2}(-1)^{1/6}$
$\quad z = 2(\cos 0° + i\sin 0°)^{1/6}$
$$= 2\left[\cos\frac{2r\pi}{6} + i\sin\frac{2r\pi}{6}\right]$$
where $r = 0, 1, 2, 3, 4, 5$
The imaginary part corresponding to $r = 4, 5$, will be $-$ive. Hence we choose $r = 0, 1, 2, 3$ only.
Again $z = \sqrt{2}(-1)^{1/6} = \sqrt{2}[\cos\pi + i\sin\pi]^{1/6}$

or $\quad z = \sqrt{2}\left[\cos\dfrac{(2r+1)\,\pi}{6} + i\sin\dfrac{(2r+1)\,\pi}{6}\right]$

The imaginary part corresponding to $r = 3, 4, 5$ will be $-$ive. Hence we choose $r = 0, 1, 2$ only.

4. **(a)** Ans. True.

$(x-1)^3 + 8 = 0 \quad \text{or} \quad (x-1)^3 = -8.$

$\therefore \quad x - 1 = (-8)^{1/3} = -2, -2\omega, -2\omega^2.$

Hence $x = -1, 1 - 2\omega, 1 - 2\omega^2.$

(b) Since z is unimodular

$\therefore \quad z = \cos\theta + i\sin\theta = e^{i\theta}$

$\therefore \quad \dfrac{1+ia}{1-ia} = z^{1/4} = (\cos\theta + i\sin\theta)^{1/4}$

$= \left(\cos\dfrac{2n\pi + \theta}{4} + i\sin\dfrac{2n\pi + \theta}{4}\right)e^{i\alpha} \quad$ say,

$n = 0, 1, 2, 3$

Now $\quad \dfrac{1+ia}{1-ia} = e^{i\alpha} = \dfrac{e^{i\alpha/2}}{e^{-i\alpha/2}}$

Apply Componendo and Dividendo

$\dfrac{2ia}{2} = \dfrac{e^{i\alpha/2} - e^{-i\alpha/2}}{e^{i\alpha/2} + e^{-i\alpha/2}} = \dfrac{2i\sin(\alpha/2)}{\cos(\alpha/2)}$

$\therefore \quad a = \tan\dfrac{\alpha}{2} \quad$ where

$\alpha = \dfrac{2n\pi + \theta}{4}, n = 0, 1, 2, 3.$

Hence all the four values of a are real.

5. **(a)** $r^2 = a^2 + b^2 = 2(3+1)$

$\therefore \quad r = 2\sqrt{2}, \tan\theta = \dfrac{b}{a} = \dfrac{\sqrt{3}+1}{\sqrt{3}-1}$

$= \dfrac{1 + 1/\sqrt{3}}{1 - 1/\sqrt{3}} = \tan(45° + 30°) = \tan 75°$

$\therefore \quad \theta = 5\pi/12$

$\therefore \quad 2\sqrt{2}\,x^4 = 2\sqrt{2}\left(\cos\dfrac{5\pi}{12} + i\sin\dfrac{5\pi}{12}\right)$

$\therefore \quad x^4 = \cos\left(2n\pi + \dfrac{5\pi}{12}\right) + i\sin\left(2n\pi + \dfrac{5\pi}{12}\right)$

$\therefore \quad x = [\cos(24n+5)\,(\pi/12)$

$\qquad\qquad + i\sin(24n+5)\,(\pi/12)]^{1/4}$

$= \cos\dfrac{24n+5}{48}\pi + i\sin\dfrac{24n+5}{48}\pi,$

where $n = 0, 1, 2, 3$

$\therefore \quad x = \cos\dfrac{r\,\pi}{48} + i\sin\dfrac{r\,\pi}{48}$

where $r = 5, 29, 53, 77.$

(b) $\dfrac{3z-1}{z-2} = (-1)^{1/4} = (\cos\pi + i\sin\pi)^{1/4}$

$= \cos(2n+1)\dfrac{\pi}{4} + i\sin(2n+1)\dfrac{\pi}{4},$

where $n = 0, 1, 2, 3$

$= e^{i\theta}, \text{ where } \theta = \dfrac{\pi}{4}, \dfrac{3\pi}{4}, \dfrac{5\pi}{4}, \dfrac{7\pi}{4} \qquad ...(1)$

$\therefore \quad (3z-1) = (z-2)\,e^{i\theta} \quad \text{or} \quad z = \dfrac{1 - 2e^{i\theta}}{3 - e^{i\theta}}$

or $\quad z = \dfrac{(1 - 2e^{i\theta})(3 - e^{-i\theta})}{(3 - e^{i\theta})(3 - e^{-i\theta})} = \dfrac{5 - 6e^{i\theta} - e^{-i\theta}}{9 + 1 - 3(2\cos\theta)}$

or $\quad z = \dfrac{5 - 6(\cos\theta + i\sin\theta) - (\cos\theta - i\sin\theta)}{2(5 - 3\cos\theta)}$

$= \dfrac{5 - 7\cos\theta}{2(5 - 3\cos\theta)} - i\dfrac{5\sin\theta}{2(5 - 3\cos\theta)}$

where θ has four values given in (1).

(c) We have $\dfrac{z+1}{z-1} = (-1)^{1/6} = (\cos\pi \pm i\sin\pi)^{1/6}$

or $\quad \dfrac{z+1}{z-1} = \left[\cos\dfrac{(2n\pi + \pi)}{6} \pm i\sin\dfrac{2n\pi + \pi}{6}\right]$

where $n = 0, 1, 2$

or $\quad \dfrac{z+1}{z-1} = \dfrac{\cos\theta \pm i\sin\theta}{1} \quad$ where $\theta = (2n+1)\dfrac{\pi}{6}$

Apply componendo and dividendo

$\dfrac{2z}{2} = \dfrac{(1 + \cos\theta) \pm i\sin\theta}{(\cos\theta - 1) \pm i\sin\theta}$

or $\quad z = \dfrac{2\cos^2\dfrac{\theta}{2} \pm i\,2\sin\dfrac{\theta}{2}\cos\dfrac{\theta}{2}}{-2\sin^2\dfrac{\theta}{2} \pm i\,2\sin\dfrac{\theta}{2}\cos\dfrac{\theta}{2}}$

or $\quad z = \dfrac{2\cos\dfrac{\theta}{2}\left(\cos\dfrac{\theta}{2} \pm i\sin\dfrac{\theta}{2}\right)}{\pm i\,2\sin\dfrac{\theta}{2}\left(\cos\dfrac{\theta}{2} \pm i\sin\dfrac{\theta}{2}\right)} \quad \because -1 = i^2$

or $\quad z = \pm\,\mathbf{i}\cot\dfrac{\theta}{2} = \pm\cot(2n+1)\dfrac{\pi}{12},$

where $n = 0, 1, 2$

or $\quad z = \pm\cot\dfrac{\pi}{12}, \ \pm\cot\dfrac{3\pi}{12}, \ \pm\cot\dfrac{5\pi}{12}$

(d) $\dfrac{1+z}{z} = (-1)^{1/8} = (\cos\pi + i\sin\pi)^{1/8}$

or $\quad \dfrac{1}{z} + 1 = \cos\dfrac{(2n\pi + \pi)}{8} + i\sin\dfrac{(2n\pi + \pi)}{8}$

or $\quad \dfrac{1}{z} = -1 + \cos\theta + i\sin\theta \quad$ where $\theta = (2n+1)\dfrac{\pi}{8}$

$\dfrac{1}{z} = -2\sin^2\dfrac{\theta}{2} + i\,2\sin\dfrac{\theta}{2}\cos\dfrac{\theta}{2}. \quad$ Put $-1 = i^2$

$= +i\,2\sin\dfrac{\theta}{2}\left(\cos\dfrac{\theta}{2} + i\sin\dfrac{\theta}{2}\right)$

$\therefore \quad z = \dfrac{1}{+2i\sin(\theta/2)}\left(\cos\dfrac{\theta}{2} - i\sin\dfrac{\theta}{2}\right)$

$= \dfrac{1}{2}\left(-1 - i\cot\dfrac{\theta}{2}\right) \qquad \because \dfrac{1}{i} = -i$

where $\dfrac{\theta}{2} = (2n+1)\dfrac{\pi}{16}$ and n varies from 0 to 7.

Clearly real part of every root is $-\dfrac{1}{2}$.

Note : See solution Q. 12, P. 66.

6. (a) We have to find all the values of $1^{1/n}$

We know that $1 = \cos 0^\circ + i \sin 0^\circ$

$\therefore$ $(1)^{1/n} = (\cos 0^\circ + i \sin 0^\circ)^{1/n}$

$= (\cos 2m\pi + i \sin 2m\pi)^{1/n}$

$= \cos (2m\pi/n) + i \sin (2m\pi/n)$,

where, $m = 0, 1, 2, ..., n-1$.

Hence n, n^{th} roots of 1 are :

$1, \cos (2\pi/n) + i \sin (2\pi/n)$,

$\cos (4\pi/n) + i \sin (4\pi/n), ...,$

$\cos \dfrac{2(n-1)\pi}{n} + i \sin \dfrac{2(n-1)\pi}{n}$.

If we put $\alpha = \cos (2\pi/n) + i \sin (2\pi/n)$, then

$\cos (4\pi/n) + i \sin (4\pi/n) = [\cos (2\pi/n)$

$+ i \sin (2\pi/n)]^2 = \alpha^2$

$\cos (6\pi/n) + i (\sin 6\pi/n) = [\cos (2\pi/n)$

$+ i \sin (2\pi/n)]^3 = \alpha^3$

and so on. Hence the roots are $1, \alpha, \alpha^2, \alpha^3, ... \alpha^{n-1}$

where $\alpha = \cos (2\pi/n) + i \sin (2\pi/n)$.

These roots clearly form a G.P.

(b) Ans. (d).

$z = (1)^{1/n} = (\cos 0 + i \sin 0)^{1/n}$

$= \dfrac{\cos 2r\pi}{n} + i \dfrac{\sin 2r\pi}{n}$

or $z = e^{\frac{i 2r\pi}{n}}$ where r varies from 0 to $n-1$

and each root is unimodular as $|e^{i\theta}| = 1$

Let $z_1 = 1$ and $z_2 = e^{i\frac{2k\pi}{n}}$,

where $z_2 - 0 = (z_1 - 0) e^{\frac{\pi}{2} i}$ by given condition.

or $e^{i\frac{2k\pi}{n}} = 1.e^{\frac{\pi}{2} i}$ $\therefore$ $n = 4k$

(c) Ans. (c).

$z = (1)^{1/n} = \left(\cos \dfrac{2r\pi}{n} + i \sin \dfrac{2r\pi}{n}\right) = e^{\frac{2r\pi}{n} i}$

$z_1 = e^{\frac{2p\pi}{n} i}, z_2 = e^{\frac{2q\pi}{n} i}$

$\therefore$ $\arg z_1 = \dfrac{2p\pi}{n}$

$\therefore$ $\arg\left(\dfrac{z_1}{z_2}\right) = \arg z_1 - \arg z_2$

$= (p - q) \dfrac{2\pi}{n} = $ multiple of $\dfrac{2\pi}{n}$.

7. (a) Ans. (iii). If $z = (1)^{1/n}$, then $z^n - 1 = 0$ has roots $1, \alpha,$ $\alpha^2, ... \alpha^{n-1}$. **(See Q. 6 above)**

$\therefore$ $(z^n - 1) = (z-1)(z-\alpha)(z-\alpha^2)...(z-\alpha^{n-1})$

$\therefore$ $\dfrac{z^n - 1}{z - 1} = (z - \alpha)(z - \alpha^2)...(z - \alpha^{n-1})$

L.H.S. $= z^{n-1} + z^{n-2} + ... + z^2 + z + 1$

Putting $z = 1$ in both sides, we get

$n = (1 - \alpha)(1 - \alpha^2)...(1 - \alpha^{n-1})$

(b) $(1)^{1/6} = \cos \dfrac{2m\pi}{6} + i \sin \dfrac{2m\pi}{6}$

where $m = 0, 1, 2, 3, 4, 5$

$= \cos \dfrac{m\pi}{3} + i \sin \dfrac{m\pi}{3}$

where $m = 0, 1, 2, 3, 4, 5$

$(1)^{1/3} = \cos \dfrac{2k\pi}{3} + i \sin \dfrac{2k\pi}{3}$

where $k = 0, 1, 2$

The common values correspond to $m = 0, 2, 4$ or $k = 0, 1, 2$ and they are

$1, \cos \dfrac{2\pi}{3} + i \sin \dfrac{2\pi}{3}, \cos \dfrac{4\pi}{3} + i \sin \dfrac{4\pi}{3}$

or $1, -1/2 + i \sqrt{3}/2, -1/2 - i \sqrt{3}/2$

8. (a) Roots are $1, \alpha, \alpha^2, ... \alpha^9$ where

$\alpha = \cos \dfrac{2\pi}{10} + i \sin \dfrac{2\pi}{10}$ and $\alpha^{10} = 1$

Consider $\alpha^3 . \alpha^8 = \alpha^{11} = \alpha^{10} . \alpha = \alpha$ and α is one of the ten roots.

or $\alpha^4 . \alpha^9 = \alpha^{13} = \alpha^{10} . \alpha^3 = \alpha^3$ which is again a root.

(b) Ans. (a). $\omega^5 = 1, 1 + \omega + \omega^2 + \omega^3 + \omega^4 = 0, |\omega| = 1$

$\log_2 \left| \dfrac{\omega + \omega^2 + \omega^3 + \omega^4 - 1}{\omega} \right| = \log_2 \left| \dfrac{-2}{\omega} \right|$

$= \log_2 \dfrac{|-2|}{|\omega|} = \log_2 \dfrac{2}{1} = 1$

9. (a) $\alpha^7 = \cos 2\pi + i \sin 2\pi = 1$ (De-Moivres)

$S = \alpha + \alpha^2 + \alpha^3 + ... \alpha^6 = \dfrac{\alpha(1 - \alpha^6)}{1 - \alpha}$

$S = \dfrac{\alpha - \alpha^7}{1 - \alpha} = \dfrac{\alpha - 1}{1 - \alpha} = -1$ ...(1)

$P = pq = $ nine terms

$= (\alpha^4 + \alpha^6 + \alpha^7) + (\alpha^5 + \alpha^7 + \alpha^8)$

$+ (\alpha^7 + \alpha^9 + \alpha^{10})$

$= (\alpha^4 + \alpha^6 + 1) + (\alpha^5 + 1 + \alpha) + (1 + \alpha^2 + \alpha^3)$

$= 3 + (\alpha + \alpha^2 + \alpha^3 + ... \alpha^6) = 3 + S$

$= 3 - 1 = 2$ from (1) $\therefore$ $x^2 - Sx + P = 0$

or $x^2 + x + 2 = 0$ is the required equation.

(b) Clearly $z^{2n+1} = \cos 2\pi + i \sin 2\pi = 1$ ...(1)

Both α and β are G.P.s of n terms each with common ratio z^2

$$\alpha = \frac{z[1-(z^2)^n]}{1-z^2} = \frac{z-1}{1-z^2} = -\frac{1}{z+1}$$

$$\beta = \frac{z^2[1-(z^2)^n]}{1-z^2} = \frac{z[z-1]}{1-z^2} = -\frac{z}{z+1}$$

$$\alpha + \beta = -\frac{z+1}{z+1} = -1 = S$$

$$\alpha\beta = \frac{z}{(z+1)^2} = \frac{1}{z + \frac{1}{z} + 2}$$

$z = \cos\theta + i\sin\theta$, where $\theta = \dfrac{2\pi}{2n+1}$ ...(2)

and $\dfrac{1}{z} = \cos\theta - i\sin\theta$ $\therefore z + \dfrac{1}{z} = 2\cos\theta$

$$\therefore \quad \alpha\beta = \frac{1}{2\cos\theta + 2} = \frac{1}{4\cos^2(\theta/2)} = P$$

Hence the equation is $x^2 - Sx + P = 0$

$$x^2 + x + \frac{1}{4\cos^2\dfrac{\pi}{2n+1}} = 0, \quad \text{by (2)}$$

10. (a) The given equation can be written as

$(z^p - 1)(z^q - 1) = 0$ $\therefore$ $z = (1)^{1/p}$ or $(1)^{1/q}$ ...(1)

where p and q are distinct prime numbers. Hence both the equations will have distinct roots and as $z \neq 1$, both will not be simultaneously zero for any value of z given by equations in (1).

$$1 + \alpha + \alpha^2 + \dots \alpha^p = \frac{1-\alpha^p}{1-\alpha} = 0 \ (\alpha \neq 1)$$

or $\quad 1 + \alpha + \alpha^2 + \dots \alpha^q = \dfrac{1-\alpha^q}{1-\alpha} = 0 \ (\alpha \neq 1)$

Because of (1) either $\alpha^p = 1$ or $\alpha^q = 1$ but not both simultaneously as p and q are distinct primes.

(b) As shown in Q.6, the roots of the equation

$z = (1)^{1/n}$ or $z^n - 1 = 0$ are $1, \beta, \beta^2, \dots, \beta^{n-1}$

where $\quad \beta^n - 1 = 0$ ...(1)

and β is one of the complex roots and $\beta \neq 1$

Now $1 + \beta + \beta^2 + \dots + \beta^{n-1}$

$$= \frac{1-\beta^n}{1-\beta}, \qquad \text{sum of a G. P.}$$

$$= \frac{0}{\neq 0} = 0, \qquad \text{by (1).}$$

(c) $\beta = (1)^{1/n} \Rightarrow \beta^n = 1$ ...(1)

If S be the sum of the given series which is arithmetico-geometric series, then

$$S = 1 + 3\beta + 5\beta^2 + \dots (2n-1)\beta^{n-1}$$

$$S = \quad \beta + 3\beta^2 + \dots (2n-3)\beta^{n-1} + (2n-1)\beta^n$$

$$S(1-\beta) = 1 + [2\beta + 2\beta^2 + \dots(n-1) \text{ terms}]$$
$$\qquad\qquad - (2n-1), \text{ by (1)}$$

$$= 2 + 2\beta + 2\beta^2 + \dots n \text{ terms} - 2n \qquad \textbf{(Note)}$$

$$= 2\frac{(1-\beta^n)}{1-\beta} - 2n = 0 - 2n, \text{ by (1)}$$

$$\therefore \quad S = \frac{-2n}{1-\beta}.$$

11. $1 + x + x^2 + \dots + x^n = \dfrac{x^{n+1}-1}{x-1}$ G.P.

Differentiate both sides w.r. to x, we get

$1 + 2x + 3x^2 + \dots + nx^{n-1}$

$$= \frac{(n+1)x^n}{x-1} - \frac{x^{n+1}-1}{(x-1)^2} \qquad \text{...(1)}$$

We have used product formula instead of quotient formula for differentiation keeping in view the form of the question we multiply both sides of (1) by x and then we will differentiate once again by using product formula instead of quotient formula

$$x + 2x^2 + 3x^3 + \dots + nx^n = \frac{(n+1)x^{n+1}}{x-1} - \frac{x^{n+2}-x}{(x-1)^2}$$

Differentiate both sides w.r. to x, we get

$$1 + 4x + 9x^2 + \dots + n^2 x^n = \frac{(n+1)^2 x^n}{x-1}$$
$$- \frac{(2n+3)x^{n+1}-1}{(x-1)^2} + \frac{2(x^{n+2}-x)}{(x-1)^2}$$

or $\quad 1 + 2^2 x + 3^2 \cdot x^2 + \dots + n^2 x^n = \dfrac{(n+1)^2 x^n}{x-1}$
$$- \frac{(2n+3)x^{n+1}-1}{(x-1)^2} + \frac{2(x^{n+2}-x)}{(x-1)^3}$$

Now put $x = \omega$ and $\omega^n = 1$ in both sides and simplify R.H.S.

$$\therefore \quad \text{L.H.S.} = \frac{(n+1)^2}{\omega-1} - \frac{(2n+3)\omega-1}{(\omega-1)^2} + \frac{2\omega(\omega-1)}{(\omega-1)^3}$$

$$= \frac{1}{(\omega-1)^2}[(n+1)^2(\omega-1) - (2n+3)\omega + 1 + 2\omega]$$

$$= \frac{1}{(\omega-1)^2}[\omega\{(n^2+2n+1) - 2n - 3 + 2\}$$
$$- (n^2+2n+1) + 1]$$

$$= \frac{1}{(\omega-1)^2}[n^2\omega - n(n+2)]$$

12. Let $Z = \dfrac{1+z}{z} = 1 + \dfrac{1}{z} \neq 1$

$$\therefore \quad Z^n = \frac{(1+z)^n}{z^n} = 1 \text{ (given)} \quad \text{or} \quad Z = (1)^{1/n},$$

$$\cos\frac{2r\pi}{n} + i\sin\frac{2r\pi}{n}$$

where $r = 0, 1, 2, 3, \ldots (n-1)$

Now for $r = 0$, $Z = 1$ but since $Z \neq 1$, hence we have

$$\therefore \quad Z = \left(\cos\frac{2r\pi}{n} + i\sin\frac{2r\pi}{n}\right)$$

where $r = 1, 2, 3, \ldots (n-1)$

See Q. 5 (d) and Q. 6 P. 61-64.

or $\quad 1 + \dfrac{1}{z} = \cos\dfrac{2r\pi}{n} + i\sin\dfrac{2r\pi}{n}$

$$\therefore \quad \frac{1}{z} = -1 + \cos\frac{2r\pi}{n} + i\sin\frac{2r\pi}{n}$$

$$= -2\sin^2\frac{r\pi}{n} + i.2\sin\frac{r\pi}{n}\cos\frac{r\pi}{n}$$

$$= 2i\sin\frac{r\pi}{n}\left(\cos\frac{r\pi}{n} + i\sin\frac{r\pi}{n}\right) \qquad \text{as } -1 = i^2$$

Taking reciprocal, we get

$$\therefore \quad z = \frac{1}{2i\sin\dfrac{r\pi}{n}}\left(\cos\frac{r\pi}{n} - i\sin\frac{r\pi}{n}\right)$$

De-Moivre's theorem

or $\quad x + iy = -\dfrac{1}{2} - \dfrac{i}{2}\cot\dfrac{r\pi}{n} \quad \because \ \dfrac{1}{i} = -i$

$$\therefore \quad x = -\frac{1}{2}.$$

This represents a line parallel to y-axis.

13. (a) Already proved in § 8 (c), P. 60.

As in Q. 6, the n, n^{th} roots of unity are

$1, \alpha, \alpha^2, \ldots, \alpha^{n-1}$ where

$\alpha = \cos(2\pi/n) + i\sin(2\pi/n)$.

We have to find the sum of the pth powers of these roots.

$$\therefore \quad 1^p + \alpha^p + (\alpha^2)^p + (\alpha^3)^p + \ldots + (\alpha^{n-1})^p$$

$$= 1 + \alpha^p + \alpha^{2p} + \alpha^{3p} + \ldots + \alpha^{(n-1)p} \qquad \ldots(1)$$

$$= \frac{1 - (\alpha^p)^n}{1 - \alpha^p}$$

[Summing the G.P. of common ratio α^p]

$$= \frac{1 - \alpha^{pn}}{1 - \alpha^p}$$

$$= \frac{1 - [\cos(2\pi/n) + i\sin(2\pi/n)]^{pn}}{1 - [\cos(2\pi/n) + i\sin(2\pi/n)]^p}$$

$$= \frac{1 - \cos 2\pi p - i\sin 2\pi p}{1 - \cos(2\pi p/n) - i\sin(2\pi p/n)}$$

$$= \frac{1 - 1 - i.0}{1 - \cos(2\pi p/n) - i\sin(2\pi p/n)}$$

$$= \frac{0}{1 - \cos(2\pi p/n) - i\sin(2\pi p/n)} = 0$$

If p is not a multiple of n and hence $D^r \neq 0$

If p is a multiple of n, say $p = nk$

$$\alpha^{mp} = [\cos(2\pi/n) + i\sin(2\pi/n)]^{mnk}$$

$$= \cos\frac{2\pi mnk}{n} + i\sin\frac{2\pi mnk}{n}, \quad 1 \le m \le n-1$$

$$= \cos 2\pi mk + i\sin 2\pi mk = 1 + i\,0 = 1.$$

So in this case, each term of the series in (1) is 1. Hence the sum of the series (1) is n.

(b) Proceed as in part (a).

(c) Ans. (c).

$$2\Sigma\, ab = (\Sigma\, a)^2 - \Sigma\, a^2$$

$$\therefore \quad 2\Sigma\Sigma(\alpha_i \alpha_j)^5 = (\alpha_1^5 + \alpha_2^5 + \ldots)^2 - (\alpha_1^{10} + \alpha_2^{10} + \ldots)$$

$$= 0 - 0 \text{ by Q. 13 (a) P. 66}$$

$\because \ \Sigma\alpha_i^r = 100$ if $r = 100k = 0$ if $r \neq 100k$

Here both 5 and 10 are not multiple of 100.

14. $\alpha = e^{2\pi i/7} \Rightarrow \alpha^7 = e^{2\pi i} = 1, \alpha \neq 1$

or $\quad \alpha^7 - 1 = 0$, or $(\alpha - 1)(\alpha^6 + \alpha^5 + \alpha^4 + \ldots + 1) = 0$

$$\Rightarrow \quad 1 + \alpha + \alpha^2 + \ldots + \alpha^6 = 0$$

Also $1 + \alpha^k + \alpha^{2k} + \ldots + \alpha^{6k}$

$$= \frac{1 - (\alpha^k)^7}{1 - \alpha^k} = \frac{1 - \alpha^{7k}}{1 - \alpha^k} = \frac{1 - 1}{1 - \alpha^k} = 0 \quad \text{where } k \neq 7m$$

$$f(x) = A_0 + \sum_{k=1}^{20} A_k\, x^k$$

Replace x by $x, \alpha x, \alpha^2 x, \ldots, \alpha^6 x$ in the above and add the seven results thus obtained.

$$\text{L.H.S.} = (A_0 + A_0 + \ldots) + \sum_{k=1}^{20} A_k\, x^k$$

$$\cdot(1 + \alpha^k + \alpha^{2k} + \ldots \alpha^{6k})$$

$$= 7A_0 + 0, \text{ as shown above.}$$

$\therefore$ Given expression $= 7A_0$, which is independent of α.

15. (a) Ans. (d).

$$\sin\frac{2\pi k}{7} - i\cos\frac{2\pi k}{7}$$

$$= -i^2\sin\frac{2\pi k}{7} - i\cos\frac{2\pi k}{7}$$

$$= -i\left(\cos\frac{2\pi k}{7} + i\sin\frac{2\pi k}{7}\right) = -i\,e^{i2\pi k/7} = -iz^k$$

where, $z = \cos\dfrac{2\pi}{7} + i\sin\dfrac{2\pi}{7}$ or $z^7 = 1$

or $\quad z = (1)^{1/7} \ \therefore \ 1 + z + z^2 + \ldots + z^6 = 0 \qquad \ldots(I)$

Above being the sum of seven, seventh roots of unity **(Q. 13 (b) P. 61-66)**

$$\Sigma = -i\sum_{i=1}^{k} z^k = -i(z + z^2 + \ldots + z^6)$$

$$= -i(-1) = i \text{ by (I)}$$

Alternative Method. $\sin\theta - i\cos\theta$

$$= -i^2\sin\theta - i\cos\theta = -i(\cos\theta + i\sin\theta)$$

$$= -i\,e^{i\theta} \quad \text{where } \theta = \frac{2\pi}{7} \text{ or } 7\theta = 2\pi$$

Hence the given sigma is

$$\sum_{k=1}^{6} -ie^{ik\theta} = -i[e^{i\theta} + e^{2i\theta} + \ldots + e^{6i\theta}]$$

$$= -ie^{i\theta}\left[\frac{1-(e^{i\theta})^6}{1-e^{i\theta}}\right] = -i\left[\frac{e^{i\theta}-e^{7i\theta}}{1-e^{i\theta}}\right] \text{(G.P.)}$$

$$= -i\left[\frac{e^{i\theta}-1}{1-e^{i\theta}}\right] = -i(-1) = i$$

$$\because \quad 7i\theta = 2\pi i \quad \therefore \quad e^{7i\theta} = (\cos 2\pi + i\sin 2\pi) = 1.$$

(b) Ans. (c).

Proceed as in Part (a).

16. If the series has sines of multiple angles it will be taken as series S and corresponding C series we will write ourself by replacing $\sin r\theta$ by $\cos r\theta$.

$$\therefore \quad S = a\sin\theta + \frac{a^2}{2!}\sin 2\theta + \frac{a^3}{3!}\sin 3\theta + \ldots \infty$$

$$C = a\cos\theta + \frac{a^2}{2!}\cos 2\theta + \frac{a^3}{3!}\cos 3\theta + \ldots \infty$$

where, $a = \cos\theta$

$$\therefore \quad C + iS = a.e^{i\theta} + \frac{a^2}{2!}e^{2i\theta} + \frac{a^3}{3!}e^{3i\theta} + \ldots \infty$$

It is of the form $x + \dfrac{x^2}{2!} + \dfrac{x^3}{3!} + \ldots = e^x - 1$

$$= e^{ae^{i\theta}} - 1$$

$$= e^{a(\cos\theta + i\sin\theta)} - 1$$

$$= e^{a\cos\theta} . e^{i(a\sin\theta)} - 1$$

$$= e^{a\cos\theta}[\cos(a\sin\theta) + i\sin(a\sin\theta)] - 1$$

Equating real and imaginary parts, we get the sum of both the series.

$$\therefore \quad S = e^{a\cos\theta}\sin(a\sin\theta)$$

$$= e^{\cos^2\theta}\sin(\cos\theta\sin\theta) \quad \because \quad a = \cos\theta$$

Also $C = e^{a\cos\theta}\cos(a\sin\theta) - 1$

$$= e^{\cos^2\theta}\cos(\cos\theta\sin\theta) - 1$$

17. The given series is cosine series as it has multiple angles with cos. For convenience sake put $\cos\alpha = a$

$$\therefore \quad C = a^n - na^{n-1}\cos\alpha + \frac{n(n-1)}{2!}a^{n-2}\cos 2\alpha + \ldots$$

$$S = -na^{n-1}\sin\alpha + \frac{n(n-1)}{2!}a^{n-2}\sin 2\alpha + \ldots$$

Note : We have changed cosines of multiple angles with sines of multiple angles only.

$$\therefore \quad C + iS = a^n - na^{n-1}e^{i\alpha} + \frac{n(n-1)}{2!}a^{n-2}e^{2i\alpha} + \ldots$$

$C + iS$ is of the form of Binomial expansion

$$= (a - e^{i\alpha})^n = [\cos\alpha - (\cos\alpha + i\sin\alpha)]^n$$

$$= (-1)^n i^n \sin^n\alpha = (-1)^{n/2}\sin^n\alpha \text{ if } \textbf{n} \text{ is even.}$$

$$= \text{ purely imaginary } \textbf{if } \textbf{n} \text{ is odd.}$$

Equating real parts,

$$\therefore \quad C = (-1)^{n/2}\sin^n\alpha, \text{ when } n \text{ is even}$$

$$= 0 \qquad \text{when } n \text{ is odd.}$$

18. The given series is C and choose sine series

$$S = \frac{1}{2}\sin\alpha + \frac{1.3}{2.4}\sin 2\alpha + \frac{1.3.5}{2.4.6}\sin 3\alpha + \ldots$$

$$\therefore \quad C + iS = 1 + \frac{1}{2}e^{i\alpha} + \frac{\frac{1}{2}.\frac{3}{2}}{1.2}e^{2i\alpha} + \frac{\frac{1}{2}.\frac{3}{2}.\frac{5}{2}}{1.2.3}e^{3i\alpha} + \ldots$$

$$= 1 + \frac{1}{2}e^{i\alpha} + \frac{\frac{1}{2}\left(\frac{1}{2}+1\right)}{2!}e^{2i\alpha}$$

$$+ \frac{\frac{1}{2}\left(\frac{1}{2}+1\right)\left(\frac{1}{2}+2\right)}{3!}e^{3i\alpha} + \ldots$$

$$= (1-e^{i\alpha})^{-1/2} = (1 - \cos\alpha - i\sin\alpha)^{-1/2}$$

$$= \left(2\sin^2\frac{\alpha}{2} - 2i\sin\frac{\alpha}{2}\cos\frac{\alpha}{2}\right)^{-1/2}$$

$$= \left(2\sin\frac{\alpha}{2}\right)^{-1/2}\left[\sin\frac{\alpha}{2} - i\cos\frac{\alpha}{2}\right]^{-1/2}$$

$$= \left(2\sin\frac{\alpha}{2}\right)^{-1/2}\left[\cos\left(\frac{\pi}{2}-\frac{\alpha}{2}\right) - i\sin\left(\frac{\pi}{2}-\frac{\alpha}{2}\right)\right]^{-1/2}$$

$$= \left(2\sin\frac{\alpha}{2}\right)^{-1/2}\left[\cos\frac{\pi-\alpha}{4} + i\sin\frac{\pi-\alpha}{4}\right]$$

Equate real parts to get C.

19. $\cos y \sin y + \cos^2 y \sin 2y + \cos^3 y \sin 3y + \ldots n$ terms

The above series involves sine of multiple angles and it will be sine series. For convenience sake put $\cos y = a$

$$S = a\sin y + a^2\sin 2y + a^3\sin 3y + \ldots$$

$$C = a\cos y + a^2\cos 2y + a^3\cos 3y + \ldots$$

$$\therefore \quad C + iS = ae^{iy} + a^2 e^{i2y} + a^3 e^{i3y} + \ldots n \text{ terms}$$

$$= \frac{ae^{iy}[1 - a^n e^{iny}]}{1 - ae^{iy}} \text{ Sum of G.P.}$$

$$1 - ae^{iy} = 1 - a(\cos y + i\sin y)$$

$$= 1 - a\cos y - ia\sin y$$

Its conjugate is $1 - a\cos y + ia\sin y = 1 - ae^{-iy}$

Multiplying above and below by the conjugate

$$C + iS = \frac{ae^{iy}[1 - a^n e^{iny}][1 - ae^{-iy}]}{1 - a(e^{iy} + e^{-iy}) + a^2 e^{iy}.e^{-iy}}$$

$$= \frac{(ae^{iy} - a^2)[1 - a^n e^{iny}]}{1 - a(2\cos y) + a^2}$$

Now put $a = \cos y$ and $e^{i\theta} = \cos\theta + i\sin\theta$

$$[\cos y (\cos y + i \sin y) - \cos^2 y]$$

$$C + iS = \frac{\cdot [1 - \cos^n y (\cos ny + i \sin ny)]}{1 - 2\cos^2 y + \cos^2 y}$$

$$= \frac{i \sin y \cos y}{\sin^2 y} \times$$

$$[1 - \cos^n y \cos ny - i \cos^n y \sin ny]$$

$$\therefore \quad S = \text{imaginary part}$$
$$= \cot y (1 - \cos^n y \cos ny)$$

§9 Properties of Moduli.

We now prove some basic results on moduli.

Theorem I. *The modulus of the sum of two complex numbers can never exceed the sum of their moduli.*

Proof. We shall prove that $\quad *|z_1 + z_2| \le |z_1| + |z_2|$.
Writing $\quad z_1 = r_1 (\cos\theta_1 + i \sin\theta_1)$
and $\quad z_2 = r_2 (\cos\theta_2 + i \sin\theta_2)$,
we get $\quad z_1 + z_2 = (r_1 \cos\theta_1 + r_2 \cos\theta_2)$
$$+ i (r_1 \sin\theta_1 + r_2 \sin\theta_2) ;$$
so that $|z_1 + z_2| = \sqrt{r_1^2 + r_2^2 + 2r_1 r_2 \cos(\theta_1 - \theta_2)}$
$$\le \sqrt{r_1^2 + r_2^2 + 2r_1 r_2} \qquad [\because \cos(\theta_1 - \theta_2) \le 1]$$
$$= r_1 + r_2 = |z_1| + |z_2|.$$
Hence $\quad |z_1 + z_2| \le |z_1| + |z_2|$.

Ex. For any two complex numbers z_1, z_2 we have $|z_1 + z_2|^2 = |z_1|^2 + |z_2|^2$. Then show that

$$\text{Re}\left(\frac{z_1}{z_2}\right) = 0.$$

$$|z_1 + z_2|^2 = r_1^2 + r_2^2 + 2r_1 r_2 \cos(\theta_1 - \theta_2)$$
$$= r_1^2 + r_2^2 = |z_1|^2 + |z_2|^2$$
$$\therefore \quad \cos(\theta_1 - \theta_2) = 0 \quad \text{or} \quad \theta_1 - \theta_2 = \pi/2$$
$$\arg\left(\frac{z_1}{z_2}\right) = \frac{\pi}{2} \quad \therefore \quad \text{Re}\left(\frac{z_1}{z_2}\right) = 0 \text{ as } \cos\frac{\pi}{2} = 0$$

Geometrical interpretation.

Let P, Q be the points of affix of z_1 and z_2. Complete the parallelogram $OPRQ$. Then R is the point of affix $(z_1 + z_2)$.

Now $|z_1| = OP$, $|z_2| = OQ = PR$ and $|z_1 + z_2| = OR$
We know that in any triangle sum of any two sides is greater than the third side.

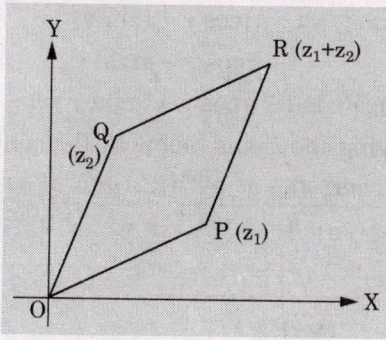

Fig. 6

Hence $\quad OP + PR > OR$
or $\quad |z_1| + |z_2| > |z_1 + z_2|$
or $\quad |z_1 + z_2| < |z_1| + |z_2|$
Equality will hold when O, P, Q are in a straight line.
Hence $\quad |z_1 + z_2| \le |z_1| + |z_2|$
As a special case $|\alpha + i\beta| \le |\alpha| + |\beta|$.
Remark. By the above theorem, we have
$|z_1 + z_2 + z_3| \le |z_1 + z_2| + |z_3| \le |z_1| + |z_2| + |z_3|$
This property can easily be extended, by induction to the form
$$\left| \sum_{k=1}^{n} z_k \right| \le \sum_{k=1}^{n} |z_k| \qquad (n = 1, 2, 3, \ldots\ldots).$$

Theorem II. *The modulus of the difference of two complex numbers can never be less than the difference of their moduli.*
i.e., $|z_1 - z_2| \ge | |z_1| - |z_2| |$.
Proof. We have
$$z_1 - z_2 = (r_1 \cos\theta_1 - r_2 \cos\theta_2)$$
$$+ i (r_1 \sin\theta_1 - r_2 \sin\theta_2)$$
so that
$$|z_1 - z_2| = \sqrt{r_1^2 + r_2^2 - 2r_1 r_2 \cos(\theta_1 - \theta_2)}$$
$$\ge \sqrt{r_1^2 + r_2^2 - 2 r_1 r_2} \qquad [\because \cos(\theta_1 - \theta_2) \le 1]$$
$$= |r_1 - r_2| = | |z_1| - |z_2| |.$$

Geometrical Interpretation.
Here $OP = |z_1|$, $OQ = |z_2|$, $QP = |z_1 - z_2|$
(See figure 6 on P. 68).
Since in a triangle difference of any two sides is less than the third side, we have from $\triangle OPQ$,
$$OP - OQ < QP$$
or $\quad |z_1| - |z_2| < |z_1 - z_2|$
or $\quad |z_1 - z_2| > |z_1| - |z_2|$.
Equality will hold when O, P, Q are in a straight line.
Remark. Theorem II can be derived from theorem I.
We have $\quad |z_1| = |z_1 - z_2 + z_2| \le |z_1 - z_2| + |z_2|$
or $\quad |z_1| - |z_2| \le |z_1 - z_2|$.
Very Imp. Note : $\quad |z_1 - z_2| \ge |z_1| - |z_2|$
Replace z_2 by $- z_2$ and $|- z_2| = |z_2|$
$\therefore \quad |z_1 + z_2| \ge |z_1| - |z_2|$
$*$or $\quad |z_1| - |z_2| \le |z_1 + z_2| \le |z_1| + |z_2|$,
by Th. I. **(Remember)** ...(a)

Another form :
$$|z_1 + z_2| < |z_1| + |z_2|$$
$$|z_1 - z_2| > |z_1| - |z_2|$$
If $x \ge a$, then the least value of x is a and if $x \le b$, then the greatest value of x is b.
I. $\quad |OP - OQ| < QP$.
or $\quad ||z_1| - |z_2|| < |z_1 - z_2|$ ...(b)
II. $\quad |OP - PR| < OR$
or $\quad |OP - OQ| < OR$

or $||z_1|-|z_2||<|z_1+z_2|$ ...(c)

Again $|x|\le a \Rightarrow x^2 < a^2 \Rightarrow x^2 - a^2 < 0$

or $(x+a)(x-a)\le 0$

$\therefore \quad -a < x < a$ ...(d)

Theorem III. *The modulus of the product of two complex numbers is equal to the product of their moduli.*

Proof. We have

$$|z_1 z_2|^2 = z_1 z_2 \bar{z}_1 \bar{z}_2 = z_1 \bar{z}_1 z_2 \bar{z}_2 = |z_1|^2 |z_2|^2$$

so that $\quad |z_1 z_2| = |z_1||z_2|.$

In the same manner it can be proved that

$$\left|\frac{z_1}{z_2}\right| = \frac{|z_1|}{|z_2|} \text{ provided } (z_2 \ne 0).$$

It is easy to see that

$$|z_1 z_2 ...... z_n| = |z_1||z_2|....|z_n|$$

and in particular $|z^n| = |z|^n.$

Theorem IV. *Square of modulus of a complex number is equal to modulus of the square of that complex number.*

i.e., $|z|^2 = |z^2|$

Proof. If $z = x + iy$, then $|z| = \sqrt{(x^2 + y^2)}$

$\therefore \quad |z|^2 = x^2 + y^2$ ...(1)

$z^2 = x^2 - y^2 + i\, 2xy$

$\therefore \quad |z^2| = \sqrt{[(x^2-y^2)^2 + 4x^2 y^2]} = \sqrt{(x^2+y^2)^2}$

$\qquad = x^2 + y^2 = |z|^2$, by (1)

Theorem V. $|z_1 + z_2|^2 = |z_1|^2 + |z_2|^2 + 2\,\text{Re}\,(z_1 \bar{z}_2)$

Proof. L.H.S. $= (z_1 + z_2)\overline{(z_1 + z_2)} = (z_1 + z_2)(\bar{z}_1 + \bar{z}_2)$

$= z_1 \bar{z}_1 + z_2 \bar{z}_2 + z_1 \bar{z}_2 + \bar{z}_1 z_2$

$= |z_1|^2 + |z_2|^2 + z_1 \bar{z}_2 + \overline{(z_1 \bar{z}_2)}$

$= |z_1|^2 + |z_2|^2 + 2\,\text{Re}\,(z_1 \bar{z}_2)$

Important Remark : **The notion of linear ordering, greater than or less than, does not apply to complex numbers. Thus the statement $z_1 > z_2$ and $z_1 < z_2$ have no meaning unless z_1 and z_2 are both real.** Since $|z|$, $\mathbf{R}(z)$ and $\mathbf{I}(z)$ are real numbers, the statements like $|z_1| > |z_2|$, $\mathbf{R}(z_1) < \mathbf{R}(z_2)$ and $\mathbf{I}(z_1) > \mathbf{I}(z_2)$ are meaningful. Also since $|z|^2 = \mathbf{R}^2(z) + \mathbf{I}^2(z)$, it is easy to see that $|z| \ge |\mathbf{R}(z)| \ge \mathbf{R}(z)$ and $|z| \ge |\mathbf{I}(z)| \ge \mathbf{I}(z)$.

§10 Properties of Arguments

We now prove the following theorems on arguments of complex numbers.

Theorem I. *The argument of the product of any number of complex quantities is equal to the sum of their arguments.*

Proof. Let $z_1, z_2, z_3, ..., z_n$ be non-zero complex numbers. Let $r_1, r_2, ..., r_n$ denote their moduli and $\theta_1, \theta_2, ..., \theta_n$ their arguments.

We then have

$z_1 z_2 ... z_n = r_1 (\cos\theta_1 + i\sin\theta_1).$
$\qquad r_2 (\cos\theta_2 + i\sin\theta_2) .... r_n (\cos\theta_n + i\sin\theta_n)$

$= r_1 r_2 ... r_n [\cos(\theta_1 + \theta_2 + ...\theta_n)$
$\qquad\qquad\qquad + i\sin(\theta_1 + \theta_2 + ...+ \theta_n)]$

$\therefore \quad *\text{Arg}\,(z_1 . z_2 ... z_n) = \theta_1 + \theta_2 + ... + \theta_n$
$\qquad\qquad\qquad = \arg z_1 + \arg z_2 + ... + \arg z_n$

which proves the theorem.

In particular, $\arg z^n = n \arg z$.

Note : In particular $\arg\,(z_1 z_2) = \arg z_1 + \arg z_2$ provided the R.H.S. lies in the interval $(-\pi, \pi)$. If it be not true, then we may either add or subtract 2π from R.H.S.

Illustration.

If amp. of $z_1 = \dfrac{2\pi}{7}$ and of z_2 is $\dfrac{6\pi}{7}$ then the amp. of

$$z_1 z_2 = \frac{2\pi}{7} + \frac{6\pi}{7} = \frac{8\pi}{7}$$

But this does not lie in $(-\pi, \pi)$. Hence we will subtract 2π

$\therefore \quad \text{amp } z_1 z_2 = \dfrac{8\pi}{7} - 2\pi = -\dfrac{6\pi}{7}.$

Log of a complex number.

Let $\quad z = a + ib = re^{i\theta}$

where, $r = \sqrt{a^2 + b^2}$ and $\tan\theta = b/a$

or $\quad \theta = \tan^{-1}(b/a)$

$\therefore \quad \log z = \log r + \log e^{i\theta} = \log r + i\theta$

$\qquad\qquad = \dfrac{1}{2}\log(a^2 + b^2) + i\tan^{-1}(b/a)$

Ex. If $\prod\limits_{r=1}^{n} (a_i + b_i) = p + iq$, then prove that

$$\sum_{r=1}^{n} \tan^{-1}\frac{b_i}{a_i} = \tan^{-1}\frac{q}{p} + n\pi$$

Sol. L.H.S. $= r_1 r_2 r_3 .... r_n [\cos(\theta_1 + \theta_2 + ... \theta_n)$
$\qquad\qquad\qquad\qquad + i\sin(\theta_1 + \theta_2 + ... + \theta_n)]$

$\qquad = R(\cos\theta + i\sin\theta)$

Equating real and imaginary parts and dividing, we get $\tan(\theta_1 + \theta_2 + ... + \theta_n) = \tan\theta$

or $\quad \theta_1 + \theta_2 + ... + \theta_n = n\pi + \theta$

or $\quad \tan^{-1}\dfrac{b_1}{a_1} + \tan^{-1}\dfrac{b_2}{a_2} + ... + \tan^{-1}\dfrac{b_n}{a_n}$

$\qquad = n\pi + \tan^{-1}\dfrac{q}{p}$

Theorem II. *The argument of the quotient of two complex numbers is equal to the difference of their arguments.*

Proof. We have $\dfrac{z_1}{z_2} = \dfrac{r_1(\cos\theta_1 + i\sin\theta_1)}{r_2(\cos\theta_2 + i\sin\theta_2)}$

$= (r_1/r_2)(\cos\theta_1 + i\sin\theta_1)(\cos\theta_2 - i\sin\theta_2)$

$= (r_1/r_2)[\cos(\theta_1 - \theta_2) + i\sin(\theta_1 - \theta_2)]$

$\therefore \quad \arg(z_1/z_2) = \theta_1 - \theta_2 = \arg z_1 - \arg z_2.$

Note : The note given in Theorem I is applicable to Theorem II also.

Illustration. amp $z_1 = -\dfrac{2\pi}{7}$, amp $z_2 = \dfrac{6\pi}{7}$

∴ amp $\dfrac{z_1}{z_2} = -\dfrac{2\pi}{7} - \left(\dfrac{6\pi}{7}\right) = -\dfrac{8\pi}{7}$

But this does not lie between $(-\pi, \pi)$ and hence we will add 2π.

∴ amp $\dfrac{z_1}{z_2} = 2\pi - \dfrac{8\pi}{7} = \dfrac{6\pi}{7}$.

Cor. Angle between two lines AB and CD and the condition that the lines be parallel or perpendicular :

Let the points be represented by z_1, z_2, z_3, z_4. If θ be the angle between the lines AB and CD, then

$$\theta = \text{amp } AB - \text{amp } CD = \text{amp } \dfrac{AB}{CD}$$

*or $\theta = \text{amp } \dfrac{z_2 - z_1}{z_4 - z_3} = \text{amp } z$ ...(1)

Condition of Perpendicularity :

If amp $z = \dfrac{\pi}{2}$ then $z = r\left(\cos\dfrac{\pi}{2} + i\sin\dfrac{\pi}{2}\right) = ir$

i.e., z is purely imaginary number.

*Hence from (1) lines AB and CD will be perpendicular if $\dfrac{z_2 - z_1}{z_4 - z_3}$ is **purely imaginary.**

Condition of Parallelism :

If the lines be parallel, then $\theta = 0$ or π

∴ $z = r(\cos 0 + i\sin 0)$ or $r(\cos\pi + i\sin\pi)$

∴ $z = \pm r$ *i.e.* **purely real.**

*Hence from (1) lines AB and CD will be parallel if $\dfrac{z_2 - z_1}{z_4 - z_3}$ is **purely real.**

Theorem III.

(a) Equation of a line.

(1) Passing through origin and making an angle θ with + ive direction of x-axis.

$$\arg(z - 0) = \theta \text{ or } \arg z = \theta \qquad \text{(Fig. I)}$$

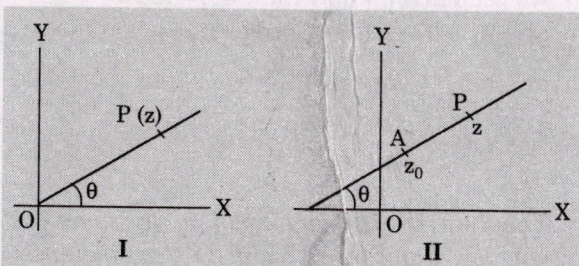

Fig. 7

$\tan^{-1}\dfrac{y}{x} = \theta$ or $\dfrac{y}{x} = \tan\theta = m$ ∴ $y = mx$

(2) Passing through a given point z_0 and making an angle θ with + ive direction of x-axis.

$\arg(z - z_0) = \theta$.

or $y - y_0 = m(x - x_0)$ (Fig. II)

(3) The equation of a line passing through two given points z_1 and z_2

$$\arg\left(\dfrac{z - z_1}{z - z_2}\right) = 0 \text{ (Fig. III), } = \pi \text{ (Fig. IV)}$$

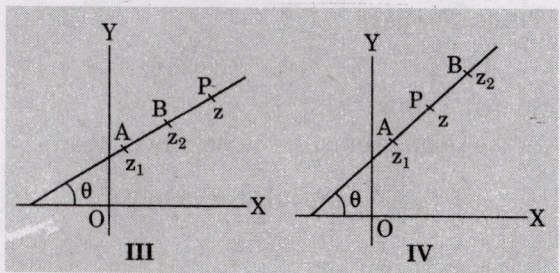

Fig. 8

∴ $\dfrac{z - z_1}{z - z_2} = re^{i0}$ or $re^{i\pi} = r$ or $-r$

or $\dfrac{z - z_1}{z - z_2}$ is purely real.

(4) Arg $AP = $ Arg AB

$\tan^{-1}\dfrac{y - y_1}{x - x_1} = \tan^{-1}\dfrac{y_2 - y_1}{x_2 - x_1}$

or $y - y_1 = \dfrac{y_2 - y_1}{x_2 - x_1}(x - x_1)$

(5)* **Condition for three points z_1, z_2, z_3 to be collinear.**

* $\arg\left(\dfrac{z_3 - z_1}{z_3 - z_2}\right) = 0$ or π.

(b) Circle whose centre is (x_0, y_0) i.e. z_0 and radius r

$(x - x_0)^2 + (y - y_0)^2 = r^2$ or $|z - z_0| = r$

*Another form. $|z - z_0|^2 = r^2$

or $(z - z_0)(\overline{z - z_0}) = r^2$

or $(z - z_0)(\bar{z} - \bar{z}_0) = r^2$

or $z\bar{z} + z_0\bar{z}_0 - (z\bar{z}_0 + \bar{z}z_0) = r^2$

$|z|^2 + |z_0|^2 - (z\bar{z}_0 + \overline{z\bar{z}_0}) = r^2$

∴ $|z|^2 + |z_0|^2 - 2R(z\bar{z}_0) = r^2$

$(z - z_0)^2 = |z|^2 + |z_0|^2 - 2R(z\bar{z}_0) = r^2$

Similarly,

$|z + z_0|^2 = |z|^2 + |z_0|^2 + (z\bar{z}_0 + \bar{z}z_0)$

$= |z|^2 + |z_0|^2 + 2\text{Re}(z\bar{z}_0)$

∴ $|z + z_0|^2 + |z - z_0|^2 = 2|z|^2 + 2|z_0|^2$

Remember the above result.

$|z - z_0| < r$ will represent the **interior** and $|z - z_0| > r$ will represent the **exterior** of the circle centred at z_0 and of radius r.

(c) **Circle on join of $A(x_1, y_1)$ or z_1 and $B(x_2, y_2)$ or z_2 as diameter.**

If $P, z(x, y)$ be a point on the circumference, then PA and PB are perpendicular

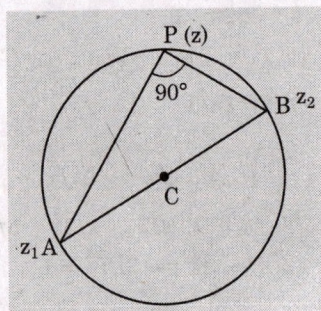

Fig. 9

∴ $\arg PA - \arg PB = \dfrac{\pi}{2}$

or $\arg \dfrac{PA}{PB} = 90^\circ$ or $\arg\left(\dfrac{z - z_1}{z - z_2}\right) = \dfrac{\pi}{2}$.

Another form :

$$\dfrac{z - z_1}{z - z_2} = e^{\pi i/2} = i \quad \therefore \quad (z - z_1)^2 = i^2 (z - z_2)^2$$

Take mod of both sides and $|z^2| = |z|^2$

∴ $|z - z_1|^2 + |z - z_2|^2 = 0$

or $(z - z_1)\overline{(z - z_1)} + (z - z_2)\overline{(z - z_2)} = 0$

* $(z - z_1)(\bar{z} - \bar{z}_1) + (z - z_2)(\bar{z} - \bar{z}_2) = 0$

Cor : If AB be a chord of a circle subtending an angle α at the circumference, then the equation of circle will be

$$\arg\left(\dfrac{z - z_1}{z - z_2}\right) = \alpha.$$

(d) **Equation of ellipse.**

We know that in an ellipse sum of the focal distances of the point on the ellipse is always constant.

If z_1, z_2 be the foci, then

* $|z - z_1| + |z - z_2| = \lambda$ (constant)

represents the equation of an ellipse.

§11 First of all remember the formulae for modulus and amplitude of complex numbers. Reference will be given as § 11.1, § 11.2, ... in the solutions of problems.

Modulus :

1. $|z_1 + z_2| \le |z_1| + |z_2|$
2. $|z_1 - z_2| \ge |z_1| - |z_2|$
3. $|z_1| - |z_2| \le |z_1 + z_2| \le |z_1| + |z_2|$
4. $||z_1| - |z_2|| \le |z_1 - z_2|$
       $||z_1| - |z_2|| \le |z_1 + z_2|$ (by $z_2 \Rightarrow -z_2$)
5.   (a) $|z_1 z_2 \ldots| = |z_1| |z_2| \ldots$
       (b) $\left|\dfrac{z_1}{z_2}\right| = \dfrac{|z_1|}{|z_2|}$
6. $|z| = |iz| = |-z|$

7.   (a) $|z^2| = |z|^2$
       (b) $|z^n| = |z|^n$
8.   (a)   Any **unimodular number** can be written as $e^{i\theta} \, \forall \, \theta$.
       (b) $|e^{a + ib}| = |e^a . e^{ib}| = e^a . 1$
9.   (a) $|1 - e^{i\theta}| = 2\sin\dfrac{\theta}{2}$
       (b) $|1 + e^{i\theta}| = 2\cos\dfrac{\theta}{2}$
       ∵ $(1 \mp \cos\theta)^2 + \sin^2\theta = 2(1 \mp \cos\theta)$
   $$= 4\sin^2\dfrac{\theta}{2} \quad \text{or} \quad 4\cos^2\dfrac{\theta}{2}$$

Amplitude :

10. Amplitude θ is chosen such that $-\pi \le \theta \le \pi$
11. $\text{amp}\left(\dfrac{z_1}{z_2}\right) = \text{amp } z_1 - \text{amp } z_2$
12. $\text{amp}(z_1 z_2) = \text{amp } z_1 + \text{amp } z_2$
13. (a) $\text{amp}(z) = 0$ or $\pi \Rightarrow z$ is purely real
    (b) $\text{amp}(z) = \pi/2 \Rightarrow z$ is purely imaginary
    (c) $\text{amp}(z) = \dfrac{\pi}{4} \Rightarrow \tan^{-1}\left(\dfrac{y}{x}\right) = \dfrac{\pi}{4}$
    $$\therefore \quad x = y \Rightarrow \text{R.P.} = \text{I.P.}$$
14. **Representation of certain complex numbers of the form $a + ib$ in the form $r(\cos\theta + i\sin\theta)$.**
    $r = +\sqrt{a^2 + b^2}$ **always** and $\tan\theta = b/a$
    $= \tan\alpha$ say   ∴ $\theta = \alpha$.

§12 $a + ib$, where both a and b are + ive

(i) $a + ib = (r, \theta) = re^{i\theta}$
    where, $r = \sqrt{(a^2 + b^2)}, \theta = \tan^{-1}(b/a)$

(ii) $-a + ib = (r, \pi - \theta)$
    ∵ $\cos(\pi - \theta) = -\cos\theta, \sin(\pi - \theta) = \sin\theta$

(iii) $-a - ib = \{r, -(\pi - \theta)\}$ conjugate rule as in (i), (ii)
    If $z = a + ib$, then $\arg z = \theta = \tan^{-1}\dfrac{b}{a}$ where z is in

Ist quardant.

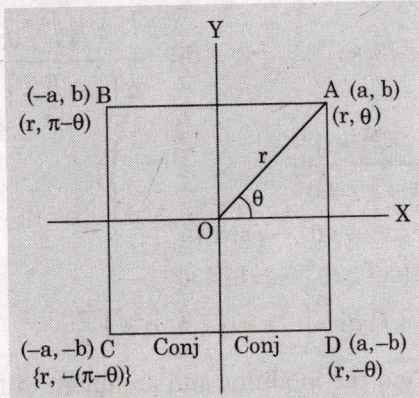

Fig. 10

z in II $\arg z = (\pi - \theta)$

z in III $\arg z = -(\pi - \theta)$

z in IV $\arg z = -\theta$

(iv) $a - ib = (r, -\theta) = re^{-i\theta}$ **conjugate**

(v) $a = a + 0i = (a, 0) = ae^{i0}$

(vi) $-a = -a + 0i = (a, \pi - 0) = (a, \pi) = ae^{i\pi}$

(vii) $ib = 0 + ib = (b, \pi/2) = be^{i\pi/2}$

(viii) $-ib = 0 - ib = (b, -\pi/2) = be^{-i\pi/2}$ **conjugate**

(ix) $1 + i = (\sqrt{2}, \pi/4) = \sqrt{2}\, e^{i\pi/4}$

(x) $(1 - i) = (\sqrt{2}, -\pi/4) = \sqrt{2}\, e^{-i\pi/4}$ **conjugate**

(xi) $-1 + i = (\sqrt{2}, \pi - \pi/4) = (\sqrt{2}, 3\pi/4) = \sqrt{2}\, e^{i3\pi/4}$

(xii) $-1 - i = (\sqrt{2}, -3\pi/4) = \sqrt{2}\, e^{-i3\pi/4}$ **conjugate**

(xiii) $1 + i\sqrt{3} = (2, \pi/3) = 2e^{i\pi/3}$

$(1 - i\sqrt{3}) = (2, -\pi/3) = 2e^{-i\pi/3}$ **conjugate**

$-1 + i\sqrt{3} = (2, 2\pi/3),$

$(-1 - i\sqrt{3}) = (2, -2\pi/3) = 2e^{-i2\pi/3}$ **conjugate**

$\because \quad \pi - \pi/3 = 2\pi/3$

(xiv) If

$\tan\theta = 1$	$1/\sqrt{3}$	$\sqrt{3}$	$2 - \sqrt{3}$	$2 + \sqrt{3}$	0	∞
$\theta = \pi/4$	$\pi/6$	$\pi/3$	$\pi/12$	$5\pi/12$	0	$\pi/2$

(xv) $(1 + i)^2 = 2i, (1 - i)^2 = -2i, i^4 = 1,$

$\dfrac{1}{i} = -i, i^3 = -i, \dfrac{1}{i^3} = i$ **(V. Imp.)**

Problem Set (5)

Solution of equations. Locus. The modulus and argument of a complex number $z = x + iy$.

This excercise contains questions based upon Modulus and Amplitude of complex numbers.

1. Find the modulus and the principal value of the argument of the following numbers :

(a) $1 - i$ (b) $-1 - \sqrt{3}i$

(c) $1 + \sqrt{2} + i$

In Q. 2 to 8 (a), put the numbers in trigonometrical form, i.e., in the form $r(\cos\theta + i\sin\theta)$ **where r is a positive real number and** $-\pi < \theta \le \pi$:

2. (a) 3 (b) -5

3. (a) $6i$ (b) $-2i$

(c) $\dfrac{(1 + i)^{2n+1}}{(1 - i)^{2n-1}}, \quad n \in \mathbf{N}$

4. (a)* $\dfrac{1 + 7i}{(2 - i)^2}$

(b) $2 \cdot 5 (\cos 300° + i\sin 30°)$

5. (a)* $\sin\dfrac{6\pi}{5} + i\left(1 + \cos\dfrac{6\pi}{5}\right)$

(b)* $\dfrac{i - 1}{i\left(1 - \cos\dfrac{2\pi}{5}\right) + \sin\dfrac{2\pi}{5}}$

6. (a) $-\sqrt{3} + i$ (b) $\dfrac{1 + i\sqrt{3}}{2i\left(\cos\dfrac{\pi}{3} + i\sin\dfrac{\pi}{3}\right)}$

(c) $\dfrac{i(\sqrt{3} + i)^6}{4(1 - i\sqrt{3})^2}$

7. (a) $-5(\cos 40° - i\sin 40°)$

(b)* $4(\cos 330° - i\sin 330°)$

8. (a) $1 + i\tan\alpha\left(-\pi < \alpha < \pi, \alpha \ne \pm\dfrac{\pi}{2}\right)$

(b) Find the modulus and argument of the complex number $z_1 = z^2 - z$ if $z = \cos\phi + i\sin\phi$.

9. (a) Show that $-3 - 4i = 5e^{i(\pi + \tan^{-1} 4/3)}$

(b)* Show that $e^{2mi\cot^{-1}p} \cdot \left[\dfrac{pi + 1}{pi - 1}\right]^m = 1.$

10. (a) For any two non-zero complex numbers z_1 and z_2 if $|z_1 + z_2| = |z_1| + |z_2|$, then prove that $\arg z_1 - \arg z_2$ is zero.

(b) Prove the above result if we have

$|z_1 - z_2| = |z_1| - |z_2|$

(c) If $\arg(z) < 0$, then $\arg(-z) - \arg(z) =$

(a) π (b) $-\pi$

(c) $-\dfrac{\pi}{2}$ (d) $\dfrac{\pi}{2}$

(I.I.T. Sc. 2000)

(d) If $|a_i| < 2, i \in \{1, 2, 3 \ldots n\}$. Prove that for no z, $|z| < \dfrac{1}{3}$ and $\sum\limits_{i=1}^{n} a_i z^i = 1$ can occur simultaneously.

(IIT 2003)

11.* Prove the following inequalities :

(a) $\left|\dfrac{z}{|z|} - 1\right| \le \arg z$

(b) $|z - 1| \le ||z| - 1| + |z||\arg z|$

12. (a) If $|z| = 1$, prove that $\dfrac{z - 1}{z + 1}$ $(z \ne -1)$, is a pure imaginary number. What will you conclude if $z = 1$?

(b) The complex number z is such that $|z| = 1, z \ne -1$ and $\omega = \dfrac{z - 1}{z + 1}$. Then real part of ω is

(a) $\dfrac{1}{|z + 1|^2}$ (b) $\dfrac{-1}{|z + 1|^2}$

(c) $\dfrac{\sqrt{2}}{|z + 1|^2}$ (d) 0

(Screening 2003)

(c) If the number $\dfrac{z-1}{z+1}$ is a pure imaginary, then prove that $|z| = 1$.

(d) If P is the affix of z in the Argand diagram and P moves so that $\dfrac{z-i}{z-1}$ is always purely imaginary, then prove that locus of z is a circle of centre $\left(\dfrac{1}{2}, \dfrac{1}{2}\right)$ radius $\dfrac{1}{\sqrt{2}}$.

(e) If $\arg\left(z^{1/3}\right) = \dfrac{1}{2} \arg\left(z^2 + \overline{z} z^{1/3}\right)$, then prove that $|z| = 1$

13. (a) If $\left|\dfrac{z_1 + z_2}{z_1 - z_2}\right| = 1$, then prove that $\dfrac{z_1}{z_2}$ is purely imaginary number. What is the condition that it may be zero ?

(b)* For two complex numbers z_1 and z_2, it is given that $\left|\dfrac{z_1 - z_2}{z_1 + z_2}\right| = 1$. Prove that $i\,\dfrac{z_1}{z_2} = \lambda$, where λ is real. Also determine the angle between the lines drawn from origin to points $z_1 + z_2$ and $z_1 - z_2$.

14. (a) If z be any point on the circle $|z - 1| = 1$ then prove that $\dfrac{z-2}{z} = i \tan(\arg z)$.

(b) Demonstrate that the complex number $x + iy$ whose modulus is unity, $y \neq 0$, can be represented as
$$x + iy = \frac{a+i}{a-i},$$
where a is real number.

(c) If z and ω are two non-zero complex numbers such that $|z\omega| = 1$ and $\text{Arg } z - \text{Arg } \omega = \dfrac{\pi}{2}$, then $\overline{z}\omega =$
(a) 1   (b) -1
(c) i (d) $-i$ **(AIEEE 2003)**

(d) Let z and ω be complex numbers such that $\overline{z} + i\overline{\omega} = 0$ and $\arg z\omega = \pi$, then $\arg z =$
(a) $\pi/4$ (b) $\pi/2$
(c) $3\pi/4$ (d) $5\pi/4$ **(AIEEE 2004)**

15. (a) Prove that for any complex number z,
$$|\text{Re}(z)| + |\text{Im}(z)| \leq |z|\sqrt{2}$$
or $|x| + |y| \leq \sqrt{2}\,|x + iy|$

(b) If z_1, z_2, z_3 are three complex numbers, prove that
$$z_1 \text{ Im}(\overline{z_2}\,z_3) + z_2 \text{ Im}(\overline{z_3}\,z_1) + z_3 \text{ Im}(\overline{z_1}\,z_2) = 0$$
where $\text{Im}(w) = $ imaginary part of w, w being a complex number.

16. (a)* If $iz^3 + z^2 - z + i = 0$, then show that $|z| = 1$.
                        (I.I.T. 1995)

(b) If $27iz^3 + 18z^2 - 12z + 8i = 0$, then $|z| =$

(a) $\dfrac{2}{3}$ (b) $\dfrac{4}{9}$
(c) 1   (d) none

(c) The two complex numbers satisfying the equation $z\overline{z} - (1+i)z - (3+2i)\overline{z} + (1+5i) = 0$ are
(a) $1+i, 3-2i$ (b) $1+i, 3+2i$
(c) $1-i, 3+2i$ (d) $1-i, 3-2i$

(d) Let $z = x + iy$ be a complex number where x and y are integers. Then the area of the rectangle whose vertices are the roots of the equation $\overline{z}z^3 + z\overline{z}^3 = 350$ is
(a) 48   (b) 32
(c) 40   (d) 80   **(I.I.T. 2009)**

17. Prove that the sum and product of two complex numbers are real if and only if they are conjugate of each other.

18. (a) If z_1, z_2 are conjugate complex numbers, and z_3, z_4 are also conjugate, then show that $\arg\dfrac{z_3}{z_2} = \arg\dfrac{z_1}{z_4}$.

(b) If (z_1, z_2) and (z_3, z_4) are two pairs of conjugate complex numbers, then show that $\arg\dfrac{z_1}{z_3} + \arg\dfrac{z_2}{z_4} = 0$.

(c) z_1, z_2, z_3 are three complex numbers whose moduli are a, b, c respectively and are such that
$$\begin{vmatrix} a & b & c \\ b & c & a \\ c & a & b \end{vmatrix} = 0.$$
If $z_1 \neq z_2$, then prove that
$$\arg\left(\frac{z_3 - z_1}{z_2 - z_1}\right)^2 = \arg\left(\frac{z_3}{z_2}\right)$$

19. (a)* Let $z_1 = 10 + 6i$ and $z_2 = 4 + 6i$. If z is a complex number such that the argument of $(z - z_1)/(z - z_2)$ is $\pi/4$, then prove that $|z - 7 - 9i| = 3\sqrt{2}$.   **(I.I.T. 1990)**

(b) If $\arg\dfrac{z-2}{z+2} = \dfrac{\pi}{4}$, then prove that $|z - 2i| = 2\sqrt{2}$.

(c) Find the complex numbers z which simultaneously satisfy the equations
$$\left|\frac{z-12}{z-8i}\right| = \frac{5}{3} \text{ and } \left|\frac{z-4}{z-8}\right| = 1.$$
                         (Roorkee 1993)

(d)* Find all complex numbers z for which
$$\arg\left(\frac{3z-6-3i}{2z-8-6i}\right) = \frac{\pi}{4} \text{ and } |z-3+i| = 3.$$
                         (Roorkee 1995)

20. (a) If $|z^2 - 1| = |z|^2 + 1$, then z lies on
(a) real axis   (b) imag. axis
(c) circle   (d) ellipse   **(AIEEE 2004)**

(b) If $\omega = \dfrac{z}{z - \frac{1}{3}i}$ and $|\omega| = 1$, then z lies on

(a) line   (b) parabola

(c) circle   (d) ellipse   **(AIEEE 2005)**

(c) If z_1, z_2, z_3 be three unimodular complex numbers then $E = |z_1 - z_2|^2 + |z_2 - z_3|^2 + |z_3 - z_1|^2$ cannot exceed

(a) 6   (b) 9

(c) 12   (d) none

(d) For any three numbers z_1, z_2, z_3 if

$$\Delta = \begin{vmatrix} 1 & z_1 & \bar{z}_1 \\ 1 & z_2 & \bar{z}_2 \\ 1 & z_3 & \bar{z}_3 \end{vmatrix}, \text{ then}$$

(a) R.P. of $\Delta = 0$ (b) R.P. of $\Delta = -$ive

(c) R.P. of $\Delta = +$ive   (d) none

(e) If $\Delta = \begin{vmatrix} \arg z_1 & \arg z_2 & \arg z_3 \\ \arg z_2 & \arg z_3 & \arg z_1 \\ \arg z_3 & \arg z_1 & \arg z_2 \end{vmatrix}$

then Δ is divisible by

(a) $\arg (z_1 + z_2 + z_3)$

(b) $\arg z_1 z_2 z_3$

(c) $\arg z_1 + \arg z_2 + \arg z_3$

(d) none

21. (a) The complex numbers $z = x + iy$ which satisfy the equation $\left| \dfrac{z - 5i}{z + 5i} \right| = 1$ lie on the axis of x.

(b) The locus of the point z satisfying the condition $\arg \dfrac{z - 1}{z + 1} = \dfrac{\pi}{3}$ is the circle $x^2 + y^2 - \dfrac{2}{\sqrt{3}} y - 1 = 0$

(c) The region of the z-plane for which $\left| \dfrac{z - a}{z + \bar{a}} \right| = 1$ (Re $a \neq 0$) is y-axis.

(d)* If $z = x + iy$ and $\omega = \dfrac{1 - iz}{z - i}$, then $|\omega| = 1$ implies that, in the complex plane z lies on the real axis.

(e) If $\omega = \left(\dfrac{z - i}{1 + iz} \right)^n$, n integral, then prove that ω lies on the unit circle for all n.

22. (a) If the imaginary part of the expression $\dfrac{z - 1}{e^{i\theta}} + \dfrac{e^{i\theta}}{z - 1}$ be zero, then locus of z is :

(a) st. line   (b) parabola

(c) unit circle   (d) none

(b) Let z be a complex number such that $\left| z + \dfrac{1}{z} \right| = 2$.

If $|z| = r_1$ and r_2 for $\arg z = \dfrac{\pi}{4}$ then

(i) $|r_1 - r_2| =$

(a) $\dfrac{1}{\sqrt{2}}$ (b) 1

(c) $\sqrt{2}$ (d) 2

(ii) As arg z varies $|r_1 - r_2| =$

(a) $[0, 2]$ (b) $[0, 1]$

(c) $\left[\dfrac{1}{\sqrt{2}}, \sqrt{2} \right]$ (d) $[1, 2]$

(c) If ω is a complex number such that $|\omega| = r \neq 1$ then $z = \omega + \dfrac{1}{\omega}$ describes a conic. The distance between the foci is :

(a) 2   (b) $2(\sqrt{2} - 1)$

(c) 3   (d) 4

(d) If $|z| = 1$ and $z \neq \pm 1$, then all the values of $\dfrac{z}{1 - z^2}$ lie on

(a) a line not passing through the origin

(b) $|z| = \sqrt{2}$

(c) the x-axis

(d) the y-axis   **(I.I.T. 2007)**

(e) $\omega = \alpha + i\beta, \beta \neq 0$ and $\dfrac{\omega - \bar{\omega} z}{1 - z}$ is real, then z will satisfy :

(a) $z : |z| \neq 1$ (b) $z : |z| = 1$

(c) $z : z \neq 1$ (d) $z : z = \bar{z}$ **(I.I.T. 2006)**

(f) A man walks a distance of 3 units from the origin towards the north-east (N 45° E) direction. From there, he walks a distance of 4 units towards the north-west (N 45° W) direction to reach a point P. Then the position of P in the Argand plane is

(a) $3e^{i\pi/4} + 4i$ (b) $(3 - 4i) e^{i\pi/4}$

(c) $(4 + 3i) e^{i\pi/4}$ (d) $(3 + 4i) e^{i\pi/4}$ **(I.I.T. 2007)**

(g) A particle P starts from the point $z_0 = 1 + 2i$, where $i = \sqrt{-1}$. It moves first horizontally away from origin by 5 units and then vertically away from origin by 3 units to reach a point z_1. From z_1 the particle moves $\sqrt{2}$ units in the direction of the vector $\hat{i} + \hat{j}$ and then it moves through an angle $\dfrac{\pi}{2}$ in anticlockwise direction on a circle with centre at origin, to reach a point z_2. The point z_2 is given by

(a) $6 + 7i$ (b) $-7 + 6i$

(c) $7 + 6i$ (d) $-6 + 7i$ **(I.I.T. 2008)**

23. Locate the complex numbers $z = x + iy$ such that

(a)* $|z - 1| + |z + 1| \leq 4$

Show that the point z satisfying the above equation represents the interior and boundary of ellipse $\dfrac{x^2}{4} + \dfrac{y^2}{3} = 1$.

(b)* $|z - i| = 1, \arg \dfrac{z}{z + i} = \dfrac{\pi}{2}$.

(c) If the imaginary part of $\dfrac{2z + 1}{iz + 1}$ is -2, then the locus of the point representing z in the complex plane is a straight line $x + 2y - 2 = 0$.

(C.E.T. 1990)

24. (a) If $|z| = \sqrt{2}$, then the points given by $3 + 4z$ will lie on a circle. What is the centre and radius of this circle ?

(b)* Determine the locus of the point z such that

$\dfrac{z^2}{z-1}$ is always real.

(c) Find the centre and radius of the circle formed by all the points represented by $z = x + iy$ satisfying

the relation $\dfrac{|z - \alpha|}{|z - \beta|} = k$ $(k \neq 1)$ where α and β are

constant complex numbers given by $\alpha = \alpha_1 + i\alpha_2$, $\beta = \beta_1 + i\beta_2$. **(I.I.T. 2004)**

25. (a) For complex numbers z and w, prove that $|z|^2 w - |w|^2 z = z - w$ if and only if $z = w$ or $z\overline{w} = 1$. **(I.I.T. 1999)**

(b)* If λ be real, prove that the equation $|z - a|^2 + |z - b|^2 = \lambda$ represents a circle. Determine its centre and radius.

26. (a) If P, A, B represent the complex numbers $x + iy, 6i$ and 3 respectively and P moves in such a manner that $PA = 2PB$, then prove that $z\overline{z} = (4 + 2i)z + (4 - 2i)\overline{z}$. Also prove that the locus of the point P is a circle whose centre is the point $(4 - 2i)$ and radius $\sqrt{20}$.

(b) If $z = 2 + k + i\sqrt{(3 - k^2)}$ where k is real such that $k^2 < 3$, prove that $\left|\dfrac{z+1}{z-1}\right|$ is independent of k. Also prove that the locus of the point z for different values of k is a part of the circle. What is its centre and radius ?

27. (a)* Find all complex numbers satisfying the equation
$$2|z|^2 + z^2 - 5 + i\sqrt{3} = 0. \quad \textbf{(Roorkee 1996)}$$

(b) The number of solutions of the system of equations given by $|z| = 3$ and $|z + 1 - i| = \sqrt{2}$ is equal to

(a) 4   (b) 2
(c) 1   (d) none

28. (a)* If $|z| \leq 1, |w| \leq 1$, show that
$$|z - w|^2 \leq (|z| - |w|)^2 + (\text{Arg } z - \text{Arg } w)^2$$
(I.I.T. 1995)

(b) If $\dfrac{5z_2}{7z_1}$ is a purely imaginary number, then prove

that $\left|\dfrac{2z_1 + 3z_2}{2z_1 - 3z_2}\right|$ is equal to 1.

29. (a) Prove that the roots of the cubic equation $(z + ab)^3 = a^3$, $a \neq 0$ represent the vertices of a triangle of sides of length $\sqrt{3}|a|$.

(b) Show that the triangle with vertices at the points z_1, z_2 and $(1 - i)z_1 + iz_2$ is right angled and isosceles.

(c) Determine the condition so that the equation $z^2 + (a + ib)z + (c + id) = 0$ has (i) one root real (ii) both roots equal.

30. (a) If $z_1 = 1 + 2i, z_2 = 2 + 3i, z_3 = 3 + 4i$, then z_1, z_2 and z_3 are collinear.

(b) Given that e^{iA}, e^{iB}, e^{iC} are in A.P., where A, B, C are the angles of a triangle then the triangle is

(a) isosceles   (b) equilateral
(c) right angled   (d) none

31. Prove that the least value of r for which the two curves $\arg(z) = \dfrac{\pi}{6}$ and $|z - 2\sqrt{3}i| = r$ intersect is 3.

32. (a) Find the equation in complex variables of all the circles which are orthogonal to $|z| = 1$ and $|z - 1| = 4$. **(Roorkee 1992)**

(b) For all complex numbers z_1, z_2 satisfying $|z_1| = 12$ and $|z_2 - 3 - 4i| = 5$, the minimum value of $|z_1 - z_2|$ is

(a) 0   (b) 2
(c) 7   (d) 17   **(I.I.T. Sc. 2002)**

33. (a) Prove that
$$|z_1 + z_2|^2 + |z_1 - z_2|^2 = 2|z_1|^2 + 2|z_2|^2.$$

Interpret the result geometrically and deduce that **(See § 9, P. 68)**
$$\left|\alpha + \sqrt{\alpha^2 - \beta^2}\right| + \left|\alpha - \sqrt{\alpha^2 - \beta^2}\right| = |\alpha + \beta| + |\alpha - \beta|,$$

all numbers involved being complex.

(b) Prove that
$$|z_1| + |z_2| = \left|\frac{1}{2}(z_1 + z_2) + \sqrt{z_1 z_2}\right| + \left|\frac{1}{2}(z_1 + z_2) - \sqrt{z_1 z_2}\right|.$$

(c) For any two complex numbers z_1, z_2 and any real numbers a and b
$$|az_1 - bz_2|^2 + |bz_1 + az_2|^2 = (a^2 + b^2)[|z_1|^2 + |z_2|^2].$$

(a) True   (b) False

34. (a)* If z_1 and z_2 are complex numbers, prove that $|z_1 + z_2|^2 = |z_1|^2 + |z_2|^2$ if and only if $z_1 \overline{z}_2$ is pure imaginary.

(b) Prove the inequality :
$$|z_1 + z_2|^2 \leq (1 + \lambda)|z_1|^2 + \left(1 + \frac{1}{\lambda}\right)|z_2|^2$$

where $\lambda > 0$.

35. (a)* Prove that $\left|\dfrac{z_1 - z_2}{1 - \overline{z}_1 z_2}\right| < 1$ if $|z_1| < 1$ and $|z_2| < 1$.

(b) Prove that $\left| \dfrac{1 - z_1 \bar{z}_2}{z_1 - z_2} \right| < 1$ if $|z_1| < 1 < |z_2|$

(IIT 2003)

(c) If z_1 and z_2 are two complex numbers such that $\left| \dfrac{z_1 - z_2}{1 - z_1 z_2} \right| = 1$, then prove that both z_1 and z_2 are unimodular.

(d) Prove that
$$|1 - \bar{z}_1 z_2|^2 - |z_1 - z_2|^2 = (1 - |z_1|^2)(1 - |z_2|^2)$$

(e) If $\left| \dfrac{az_1 - bz_2}{ab - z_1 \bar{z}_2} \right| = 1$ and $|z_1| \ne b$ then prove that

$|z_2|$ is a, where a, b are real numbers.

(f) Let z_1, z_2 be two complex numbers such that $\dfrac{z_1 - 2z_2}{2 - z_2 \bar{z}_2}$ is unimodular. If z_2 is not unimodular then prove that $|z_1| = 2$.

36. (a) Prove the following inequality
$$[(a_1 + a_2 + \dots a_n)^2 + (b_1 + b_2 + \dots + b_n)^2]^{1/2}$$
$$< \sqrt{a_1^2 + b_1^2} + \sqrt{a_2^2 + b_2^2} + \dots + \sqrt{a_n^2 + b_n^2}.$$
where a_r, b_r ($r = 1, 2, \dots, n$) are real.

(b)* For any two non-zero complex numbers z_1, z_2 prove the inequality
$$(|z_1| + |z_2|) \left| \dfrac{z_1}{|z_1|} + \dfrac{z_2}{|z_2|} \right| \le 2(|z_1| + |z_2|)$$

37. (a)* If $|z_1| = |z_2| = \dots = |z_n| = 1$, prove that
$$|z_1 + z_2 + \dots + z_n| = \left| \dfrac{1}{z_1} + \dfrac{1}{z_2} + \dots + \dfrac{1}{z_n} \right|.$$

(b) If z_1, z_2, z_3 be the complex numbers such that $z_1 + z_2 + z_3 = 0$ and $|z_1| = |z_2| = |z_3| = 1$, prove that $\dfrac{1}{z_1} + \dfrac{1}{z_2} + \dfrac{1}{z_3} = 0$

(T.S. Rajendra 1992)

(c) If z_1, z_2, z_3 are complex numbers such that $|z_1| = |z_2| = |z_3| = \left| \dfrac{1}{z_1} + \dfrac{1}{z_2} + \dfrac{1}{z_3} \right| = 1$, then

$|z_1 + z_2 + z_3|$ is
(a) equal to 1
(b) less than 1
(c) greater than 3
(d) equal to 3

(I.I.T. Sc. 2000)

(d) If z_1, z_2, z_3 be three complex numbers whose moduli are 1, 2, 3 respectively and $|z_1 + z_2 + z_3| = 1$, then find the value of $|9z_1 z_2 + z_2 z_3 + 4z_3 z_1|$.

(e) If z_1, z_2, z_3 are three distinct complex numbers and p, q, r are three positive real numbers such that $\dfrac{p}{|z_2 - z_3|} = \dfrac{q}{|z_3 - z_1|} = \dfrac{r}{|z_1 - z_2|}$ then

$$\dfrac{p^2}{z_2 - z_3} + \dfrac{q^2}{z_3 - z_1} + \dfrac{r^2}{z_1 - z_2} = 0$$

In Q. 38 and 39 locate the points representing the complex number z for which

38. (a) $\arg z = \pi/3$ (b) $\pi/3 < \arg z \le 3\pi/2$
(c)* $|z - i| = 1$ and $\arg z = \pi/2$

39. (a) $|\pi - \arg z| < \pi/4$.   (b)* $\arg\left(\dfrac{z - 1 - i}{z - 2} \right) = \dfrac{\pi}{3}$

In Q. 40 to 42 find all complex numbers z which satisfy the following equations

40. (a) $z = \bar{z}$ (b) $z = -\bar{z}$
(c) $\bar{z} = 2 - z$

41. (a)* $z^2 = -\bar{z}$ (b) $z^2 = \bar{z}$
(c) $z^3 = \bar{z}$

(d) The number of solutions of the equation $z^3 + \bar{z} = 0$ is
(a) 2   (b) 3
(c) 4   (d) 5

42. (a)* $z^2 + |z| = 0$.

(b)* Find all non-zero complex numbers z satisfying $\bar{z} = iz^2$.   **(I.I.T. 1996)**

(c) $(i - z)(1 + 2i) + (1 - zi)(3 - 4i) = 1 + 7i$

43. (a)* Solve the equation $z^2 + z|z| + |z^2| = 0$.

(b) Solve the equation $z^{n-1} = \bar{z}$, $n \in N$.

In Q. 44 to 47 locate the point representing the complex numbers z on the Argand diagram for which

44. (a) $|z| < 1$,   (b) $|z| \ge 3$,
(c) $|z - 3| = 1$

45. (a) $|z - i| < 1$,   (b) $|i - 1 - 2z| > 9$,
(c)* $2 \le |z + i| \le 3$

46. (a) $|z + i| = |z - 2|$,
(b)* $|z| - 4 = |z - i| - |z + 5i| = 0$

47. (a) $|z - 1| = |z - 3| = |z - i|$,
(b) $|z - 1|^2 + |z + 1|^2 = 4$.

48.* If the imaginary part of the expression $\dfrac{z - 1}{e^{i\theta}} + \dfrac{e^{i\theta}}{z - 1}$ be

zero, then determine the locus of the point z.

49. (a) If $z = x + iy$, $r = \sqrt{x^2 + y^2} = \text{const.}$, what is the location of the points corresponding to
(i) $z + 2$ (ii) $z - 1 + i$

(b) If $|z| = 3$, then where are the points representing the numbers
(i) $2 - z$,   (ii) $-1 + 3z$ located?

50. (a) Write the correct letter from column (2) against column (1) :

C_1	C_2
(a) Re $z = 0$	(i) Re $z^2 = 0$
	(ii) Im $z^2 = 0$
(b) Arg $z = \pi/4$	(iii) Re $z^2 = $ Im z^2.

(I.I.T. 1992)

(b)* Write the correct letter from column (2) against column (1) :

C_1 C_2

(a) $|z - (1 + 2i)| = 5$ (i) Straight line

(b) $\text{Re}\left(\dfrac{1}{z}\right) < \dfrac{1}{2}$ (ii) Circle

(c) $\text{Arg}(z - a) = \pi/4$,   (iii) Exterior of a circle

     $a \in R$

51. (a)* The greatest and least values of $|z + 1|$ if $|z + 4| \le 3$ are ... and ...

(a_1) $|z - 2 + i| \le 2$, find the greatest and least values of $|z|$.

(b) The inequality $|z - 4| < |z - 2|$ represents the region given by $\text{Re}(z) > 3$.

(c) If $|z| < \dfrac{1}{2}$, show that $|(1 + i)z^3 + iz| < \dfrac{3}{4}$.

(d) The greatest and least value of $|z_1 + z_2|$ if $z_1 = 24 + 7i$ and $|z_2| = 6$ are respectively

(a) 31, 25   (b) 25, 19

(c) 31, 19   (d) none

52. Locate the complex numbers $z = x + iy$ for which

(a) $\log_{1/2} |z - 2| > \log_{1/2} |z|$

(b) $\log_{\sqrt{3}} \dfrac{|z|^2 - |z| + 1}{2 + |z|} < 2$.

(c) Find all the values of z which satisfy the equation

$$\exp\left| \dfrac{|z|^2 - |z| + 4}{|z|^2 + 1} \log 2 \right| = \log_{\sqrt{2}} |3\sqrt{15} + 11i|$$

53. (a) The complex numbers z which satisfy the inequality $\log_{1/3} |z + 1| > \log_{1/3} |z - 1|$ are such that their real part is $-$ive. Is this statement true ?

(b) Locate the points representing the complex number for which $\log_{1/2} \dfrac{|z - 1| + 4}{|z - 1| - 2} > 1$

54. Find the integral solutions of the equations

(a) $(1 - i)^n = 2^n$ (b) $(1 + i)^n = (1 - i)^n$.

55. (a)* Among the complex numbers z which satisfy the condition $|z - 25i| \le 15$, find the number having the least positive and greatest positive argument.

(b)* Find the complex number z, the least in absolute value which satisfies the condition $|z - 2 + 2i| = 1$.

(c) Let z be a complex number satisfying $|z - 5i| \le 1$ such that amp z is minimum. Prove that $z = \dfrac{2\sqrt{6}}{5} + \dfrac{24i}{5}$.

56. (a) If $\left| z + \dfrac{2}{z} \right| = 2$, then prove that the maximum value of $|z|$ is $\sqrt{3} + 1$.

(b) If $\left| z + \dfrac{1}{z} \right| = a$ where a is real number, then find a so that the greatest and least values of a are equal.

(c) If $|z| \ge 3$, prove that the least value of $\left| z + \dfrac{1}{z} \right|$ is $\dfrac{8}{3}$.

(d) If z is a complex number, then show that the minimum value of

(a) $|z - 1| + |z + 1|$

and (b) $|z| + |z - 1| + |2z - 3|$ is each 2.

(e) If a, b, c are distinct integers and $w \ne 1$ is a cube root of unity, then minimum value of $x = |a + bw + cw^2| + |a + bw^2 + cw|$ is

(a) 2   (b) 3

(c) $4\sqrt{2}$ (d) $6\sqrt{2}$

57. (a)* Find the greatest and least values of the moduli of complex numbers z satisfying the equation $|z - 4/z| = 2$.

(b) If a complex number z lies in the interior or on the boundary of a circle of radius 3 and centre at $(-4, 0)$, then prove that the greatest and least values of $|z + 1|$ are 6, 0.

58. (a)* Prove that the equation of circle in the z plane can be written in the form $\alpha z\bar{z} + \bar{\beta}z + \beta\bar{z} + c = 0$ Deduce the equation of the line.

(b) Prove that the equation of a line through two given points in the Argand plane can be put in the form $z\bar{\beta} + \bar{z}\beta + c = 0$ where β is non-zero complex and c is real.

(c)* Let $\bar{b}z + b\bar{z} = c$, $b \ne 0$, be a line in the complex plane, where $\bar{b}$ is the complex conjugate of b. If a point z_1 is the reflection of a point z_2 through the line, then show that $c = \bar{z}_1 b + z_2\bar{b}$. **(I.I.T. 1997)**

59.* Prove that the points z_1, z_2, z_3, z_4 taken in order are concyclic if and only if $\dfrac{(z_3 - z_1)(z_4 - z_2)}{(z_3 - z_2)(z_4 - z_1)}$ is purely real.

60. If $a^2 + b^2 + c^2 = 1$, $b + ic = (1 + a)z$, prove that

$$\dfrac{a + ib}{1 + c} = \dfrac{1 + iz}{1 - iz},$$

where a, b, c are real numbers and z is a complex number.

61. The complex numbers z_1, z_2, z_3 are the vertices of a triangle. Find all the complex numbers z which make the triangle into a parallelogram.

62. Show that the triangle whose vertices are z_1, z_2, z_3 and z_1', z_2', z_3' are directly similar if

$$\begin{vmatrix} z_1 & z_1' & 1 \\ z_2 & z_2' & 1 \\ z_3 & z_3' & 1 \end{vmatrix} = 0$$

63.* If A, B, C be the angles of a triangle, then prove that

$$\begin{vmatrix} e^{2iA} & e^{-iC} & e^{-iB} \\ e^{-iC} & e^{2iB} & e^{-iA} \\ e^{-iB} & e^{-iA} & e^{2iC} \end{vmatrix}$$ is purely real.

64. (a) Prove that the area of the triangle whose vertices are the points represented by the complex numbers z_1, z_2, z_3 on the Argand diagram is $\Sigma\left[(z_2 - z_3)|z_1|^2/4i\, z_1\right]$ **(D.C.E. 1997)**

(b) The three points z_1, z_2, z_3 are connected by the relation $az_1 + bz_2 + cz_3 = 0$, where $a + b + c = 0$. Prove that three points are collinear.

65. (a) The vertices of a triangle ABC are given by complex numbers z_1, z_2, z_3. If z be the circumcentre of the triangle, then prove that

$$z = \frac{\Sigma |z_1|^2 (z_2 - z_3)}{\Sigma \bar{z}_1 (z_2 - z_3)}$$

(b) Determine the equation of the right bisector of line joining the points z_1, z_2.

Paragraph for Question No. 66 : Let A, B, C be three sets of complex numbers as defined below

$A = \{z : \text{Im } z \geq 1\}$
$B = \{z : |z - 2 - i| = 3\}$
$C = \{z : \text{Re }((1 - i) z) = \sqrt{2}\}$ **(I.I.T. 2008)**

66. (a) The number of elements in the set $A \cap B \cap C$ is :

   (a) 0   (b) 1

   (c) 2   (d) ∞

(b) Let z be any point in $A \cap B \cap C$. Then, $|z + 1 - i|^2 + |z - 5 - i|^2$ lies between

   (a) 25 and 29   (b) 30 and 34

   (c) 35 and 39   (d) 40 and 44

(c) Let z be any point in $A \cap B \cap C$ and let w be any point satisfying $|w - 2 - i| < 3$. Then, $|z| - |w| + 3$ lies between

   (a) -6 and 3   (b) -3 and 6

   (c) -6 and 6   (d) -3 and 9

67. Let $z = \cos\theta + i\sin\theta$. Then the value of $\sum_{m=1}^{15} \text{Im}(z^{2m-1})$ at $\theta = 2°$ is

  (a) $\dfrac{1}{\sin 2°}$ (b) $\dfrac{1}{3\sin 2°}$ (c) $\dfrac{1}{2\sin 2°}$ (d) $\dfrac{1}{4\sin 2°}$

(I.I.T. 2009)

Solutions to Problem Set (5)

1. (a) Let $1 = r\cos\theta$, $-1 = r\sin\theta$.

Squaring and adding these relations, we get

$$r^2(\cos^2\theta + \sin^2\theta) = 1^2 + (-1)^2 = 2$$

or $r^2 = 2$ i.e. $r = \sqrt{2}$.

Then $\cos\theta = 1/\sqrt{2}$, $\sin\theta = -1/\sqrt{2}$,

The value of θ between $-\pi$ and π which satisfies these equations is $-(\pi/4)$

Thus $|1 - i| = r = \sqrt{2}$ and $\arg(1 - i) = -(\pi/4)$.

(b) Ans. $|-1 - \sqrt{3}i| = 2$,

$$\arg(-1 - \sqrt{3}i) = -(2\pi/3)$$

$\because \quad \arg(1 + \sqrt{3}i) = \pi/3$

$\therefore \quad \arg(-1 + \sqrt{3}i) = \pi - \dfrac{\pi}{3} = \dfrac{2\pi}{3}$

or $\quad \arg(-1 - \sqrt{3}i) = -\dfrac{2\pi}{3}$ **(Conj.)**

(c) Let $r\cos\theta = 1 + \sqrt{2}$, $r\sin\theta = 1$.

Then $r^2 = (1 + \sqrt{2})^2 + 1 = 4 + 2\sqrt{2}$,

$\therefore \quad r = \sqrt{4 + 2\sqrt{(2)}}$.

On dividing, $\tan\theta = \dfrac{1}{\sqrt{(2)} + 1} = \dfrac{\sqrt{2} - 1}{2 - 1} = \sqrt{2} - 1$

Hence $\theta = \pi/8$ (Standard result) as proved below.

$\alpha = \dfrac{\pi}{4}$ $\therefore \dfrac{\alpha}{2} = \dfrac{\pi}{8}$ $\therefore \tan\dfrac{\pi}{4} = \dfrac{2t}{1 - t^2} = 1$

when $t = \tan(\alpha/2) = \tan(\pi/8)$

or $1 - t^2 = 2t$

or $t^2 + 2t + 1 = 1 + 1$ or $(t + 1)^2 = (\sqrt{2})^2$

$\therefore \quad t = \pm\sqrt{2} - 1 = \sqrt{2} - 1$

The other value $-\sqrt{2} - 1$ is being rejected as $\tan(\pi/8)$ is $+$ ive.

Hence $|1 + \sqrt{2} + i| = \sqrt{4 + 2\sqrt{(2)}}$

and $\arg(1 + \sqrt{(2)} + i) = \pi/8$.

2. (a) $3 = (r, \theta) = 3, 0$

(b) $-5 = 5(-1) = 5, \pi$

3. (a) $6i = 6(i) = 6, \pi/2$

(b) $-2i = 2(-i) = 2, -\pi/2$

(c) $\dfrac{(1 + i)^{2n+1}}{(1 - i)^{2n-1}} = 2(-1)^n$ **by Q. 9 (b), P. 40-41**

$= 2(n\text{ even}) = 2, 0 = -2(n\text{ odd}) = 2, \pi$

4. (a) $\dfrac{1 + 7i}{(2 - i)^2} = \dfrac{1 + 7i}{4 + i^2 - 4i} = \dfrac{1 + 7i}{4 - 1 - 4i} = \dfrac{1 + 7i}{3 - 4i}$

$= \dfrac{(1 + 7i)(3 + 4i)}{3^2 - 4^2 i^2} = \dfrac{-25 + 25i}{25} = -1 + i$.

$1 + i = (\sqrt{2}, \pi/4)$

$\therefore \quad -1 + i = \left(\sqrt{2}, \pi - \dfrac{\pi}{4}\right) = \sqrt{2}, \dfrac{3\pi}{4}$

(b) First we note that

$2 \cdot 5(\cos 300° + i\sin 30°)$

$= (5/2)[\cos(360° - 60°) + i\sin 30°]$

$= (5/2)[\cos(60°) + i\sin 30°]$

$= \dfrac{5}{2}\left(\dfrac{1}{2} + \dfrac{1}{2}i\right) = \dfrac{5}{4}(1 + i)$

$= \dfrac{5}{4}\sqrt{2}\left(\cos\dfrac{\pi}{4} + i\sin\dfrac{\pi}{4}\right) = \dfrac{5}{2\sqrt{2}}, \dfrac{\pi}{4}$.

5. (a) $2\sin\dfrac{3\pi}{5}\cos\dfrac{3\pi}{5} + i \cdot 2\cos^2\dfrac{3\pi}{5}$

$= 2\cos\dfrac{3\pi}{5}\left[\sin\dfrac{3\pi}{5} + i\cos\dfrac{3\pi}{5}\right]$

But $r = 2\cos\dfrac{3\pi}{5} = -\text{ive}$

Hence we rewrite as under :

$$z = -2\cos\frac{3\pi}{5}\left[-\sin\frac{3\pi}{5} - i\cos\frac{3\pi}{5}\right]$$

$$= -2\cos\frac{3\pi}{5}\left[\cos\left(\frac{3\pi}{2} - \frac{3\pi}{5}\right) + i\sin\left(\frac{3\pi}{2} - \frac{3\pi}{5}\right)\right]$$

$$= -2\cos\frac{3\pi}{5}\left[\cos\frac{9\pi}{10} + i\sin\frac{9\pi}{10}\right]$$

$$\therefore \quad r = -2\cos\frac{3\pi}{5} \quad (+\text{ive})$$

and $\theta = \dfrac{9\pi}{10}$ which lies between $-\pi$ and π.

(b) $N^r = i - 1 = -1 + i = \sqrt{2}\left(\cos\dfrac{3\pi}{4} + i\sin\dfrac{3\pi}{4}\right)$

$$D^r = i \cdot 2\sin^2\frac{\pi}{5} + 2\sin\frac{\pi}{5}\cos\frac{\pi}{5}$$

$$= 2\sin\frac{\pi}{5}\left(\cos\frac{\pi}{5} + i\sin\frac{\pi}{5}\right)$$

$$\therefore \quad \frac{\sqrt{2}\,e^{3\pi i/4}}{2\sin\dfrac{\pi}{5}\,e^{\pi i/5}} = \frac{\operatorname{cosec}\dfrac{\pi}{5}}{\sqrt{2}}\left[e^{i(3\pi/4 - \pi/5)}\right]$$

$$\therefore \quad \theta = \frac{11\pi}{20},\; r = \frac{\operatorname{cosec}36°}{\sqrt{2}}$$

6. (a) $\sqrt{3} + i = r, \theta$ where $r = 2, \theta = \pi/6$

$$\therefore \quad -\sqrt{3} + i = (r, \pi - \theta) = 2, 5\pi/6.$$

(b) $1 + i\sqrt{3} = 2\left(\cos\dfrac{\pi}{3} + i\sin\dfrac{\pi}{3}\right)$

$$\therefore \quad z = \frac{2}{2i} = -i = 1, -\frac{\pi}{2}$$

(c) $z = \dfrac{e^{i\pi/2}\,(2e^{i\pi/6})^6}{4 \cdot (2 \cdot e^{-i\pi/3})^2} = 4 \cdot e^{i(\pi/2 + \pi + 2\pi/3)}$

$$z = 4e^{i13\pi/6}$$

$$\therefore \quad \arg z = \frac{13\pi}{6} = 2\pi + \frac{\pi}{6} = \frac{\pi}{6}$$

$$\therefore \quad r = 4,\; \theta = \frac{\pi}{6}$$

7. (a) $-5(\cos 40° - \sin 40°)$

$$= 5[-\cos 40° + i\sin 40°] \text{ as } r = +\text{ive}$$

$$= 5[\cos(180° - 40°) + i\sin(180° - 40°)]$$

$$= 5[\cos 140° + i\sin 140°] = 5, 140°$$

(b) $\cos(2\pi - \theta) = \cos\theta,$

$\sin(2\pi - \theta) = -\sin\theta$

$4(\cos 30° + i\sin 30°)$ $\therefore r = 4, \theta = 30°$

8. (a) Let $r\cos\theta = 1,\; r\sin\theta = \tan\alpha$

Then $r = \sqrt{1 + \tan^2\alpha} = |\sec\alpha| = \dfrac{1}{|\cos\alpha|}$.

Then $\cos\theta = |\cos\alpha|$ ...(1)

$\sin\theta = \tan\alpha\,|\cos\alpha|$ ...(2)

To solve (1) and (2), we consider two cases :

(i) **$\cos\alpha > 0$**, that is, α lies in the interval $-\pi/2 < \alpha < \pi/2$.

In this case $|\cos\alpha| = \cos\alpha$, and the equations (1) and (2) take the form $\cos\theta = \cos\alpha,\; \sin\theta = \sin\alpha$.

Clearly one of the values of θ is α.

Hence for $-\pi/2 < \alpha < \pi/2$, the trigonometric form is

$$1 + i\tan\alpha = \frac{1}{\cos\alpha}(\cos\alpha + i\sin\alpha)$$

(ii) **$\cos\alpha < 0$**, that is, α lies in the interval $-\pi < \alpha < -\dfrac{\pi}{2}$

or in the interval $\dfrac{\pi}{2} < \alpha < \pi$. In this case, $|\cos\alpha| = -\cos\alpha$ and the equation (1) and (2) take the form $\cos\theta = -\cos\alpha,\; \sin\theta = -\sin\alpha$.

One value of θ from these is, $\theta = \pi + \alpha$.

hence for $-\pi < \alpha < -\dfrac{\pi}{2}$ and $\dfrac{\pi}{2} < \alpha < \pi$ the trigonometric form is

$$1 + i\tan\alpha = \frac{1}{-\cos\alpha}[\cos(\pi + \alpha) + i\sin(\pi + \alpha)]$$

Remark. Students may think that the expression can be written as

$$1 + i\tan\alpha = 1 + \frac{i\sin\alpha}{\cos\alpha} = \frac{1}{\cos\alpha}(\cos\alpha + i\sin\alpha)$$

But this is the trigonometric form only when $\dfrac{1}{\cos\alpha} > 0$.

That is why we considered two separate cases.

(b) Substituting $z = \cos\phi + i\sin\phi$, we get

$$z_1 = (\cos\phi + i\sin\phi)^2 - (\cos\phi + i\sin\phi)$$

$$= \cos 2\phi + i\sin 2\phi - \cos\phi - i\sin\phi$$

$$= (\cos 2\phi - \cos\phi) + i(\sin 2\phi - \sin\phi)$$

$$= 2\sin\frac{3\phi}{2}\sin\left(-\frac{\phi}{2}\right) + 2i\cos\frac{3\phi}{2}\sin\frac{\phi}{2}$$

$$= 2\sin\frac{\phi}{2}\left[-\sin\frac{3\phi}{2} + i\cos\frac{3\phi}{2}\right] \quad \text{...(A)}$$

$$\therefore \quad = 2\sin\frac{\phi}{2}\left[\cos\left(\frac{\pi}{2} + \frac{3\phi}{2}\right) + i\sin\left(\frac{\pi}{2} + \frac{3\phi}{2}\right)\right]$$

$$\therefore \quad |z| = 2\left|\sin\frac{\phi}{2}\right|$$

In view of the definition of modulus, we consider three cases :

Case I. Let $\sin\dfrac{\phi}{2} = 0$, that is, $\phi = 2n\pi, n$ any integer. Then $|z_1| = 0$ which implies that $z_1 = 0$. Thus, for $\phi = 2n\pi$ (n, any integer), $\arg z_1$ is undefined.

Case II. Let $\sin\dfrac{\phi}{2} > 0$ which occurs when

$$0 < \frac{\phi}{2} < \pi, \text{ i.e. I, II Quadrant.}$$

or $\quad 2n\pi < \dfrac{1}{2}\phi < (2n+1)\,\pi$, that is, when

$\qquad 4n\pi < \phi < (4n+2)\,\pi$, n any integer . ...(1)

Then $|z_1| = 2\sin\dfrac{\phi}{2}$ and the trigonometrical form

of z_1 is as

$$z_1 = 2\sin\frac{\phi}{2}\left[\cos\left(\frac{\pi+3\phi}{2}\right) + i\sin\left(\frac{\pi+3\phi}{2}\right)\right]$$

Consequently, if ϕ satisfies the condition (1), then

$$\arg z_1 = \frac{\pi+3\phi}{2}.$$

Case III. Let $\sin\dfrac{\phi}{2} < 0$, that is,

$\qquad \pi < \dfrac{\phi}{2} < 2\pi$ *i.e.* III, IV Quadrant.

or $\quad (2n+1)\,\pi < \dfrac{1}{2}\phi < (2n+2)\,\pi$

or $\quad (4n+2)\,\pi < \phi < (4n+4)\,\pi$, ...(2)
$\quad n$, any integer.

Then $\quad |z_1| = -2\sin\dfrac{\phi}{2}$ and the trigonometrical

form of z_1 is $-2\sin\dfrac{\phi}{2}\left[\sin\dfrac{3\phi}{2} - i\cos\dfrac{3\phi}{2}\right]$ by (A)

$$z_1 = -2\sin\frac{\phi}{2}\left[\cos\left(\frac{3\pi+3\phi}{2}\right) + i\sin\left(\frac{3\pi+3\phi}{2}\right)\right].$$

Hence, when ϕ satisfies (2), we have

$$\arg z_1 = \left(\frac{3\pi+3\phi}{2}\right).$$

9. (a) We know that if $z = (r, \theta)$, then $-z = r, -(\pi - \theta)$

$z = 3 + 4i = 5, \theta \qquad$ where $\theta = \tan^{-1}(4/3)$.

$-z = -3 - 4i = 5, -(\pi - \theta)$

Now adding $2\pi, -(\pi - \theta)$ becomes

$\qquad \pi + \theta = \pi + \tan^{-1}(4/3)$.

(b) $\dfrac{pi+1}{pi-1} = \dfrac{1+pi}{-1+pi} = \dfrac{re^{i\theta}}{re^{i(\pi-\theta)}}$

where $\tan\theta = p$ or $\theta = \tan^{-1}p$

$\therefore \quad \cot^{-1}p = \dfrac{\pi}{2} - \theta$

$\therefore \quad \left[\dfrac{pi+1}{pi-1}\right]^m = e^{im(2\theta-\pi)}$

$\therefore \quad$ L.H.S. $= e^{2mi(\pi/2-\theta)} \cdot e^{im(2\theta-\pi)} = e^0 = 1$.

10. (a) **Refer Alternative proof of Theorem I, II P. 69.**

$|z_1 + z_2| = \sqrt{r_1^2 + r_2^2 + 2r_1 r_2 \cos(\theta_1 - \theta_2)}$

and $|z_1 - z_2| = \sqrt{r_1^2 + r_2^2 - 2r_1 r_2 \cos(\theta_1 - \theta_2)}$

If $\cos(\theta_1 - \theta_2) = 1$ *i.e.* $\theta_1 - \theta_2 = 0$

or $\arg z_1 - \arg z_2 = 0$, then

$|z_1 + z_2| = \sqrt{r_1^2 + r_2^2 + 2r_1 r_2} = r_1 + r_2$
$\qquad\quad = |z_1| + |z_2|$

and $|z_1 - z_1| = r_1 - r_2 = |z_1| - |z_2|$

(b) Do yourself.

(c) Ans. (a). Since $\arg z < 0$, *i.e.* $-$ive, we choose $\arg z = -\theta$, where θ is $+$ive

$\therefore \quad \arg(-z) = -[\pi - (-\theta)] = -\pi - \theta = 2\pi + (-\pi - \theta)$
$\qquad\qquad = \pi + (-\theta) = \pi + \arg z$

$\therefore \quad \arg(-z) - \arg z = \pi$

(d) Given $|a_i| < 2 \;\forall\; i$ ...(1)

$|z| < \dfrac{1}{3}$ ...(2)

$\displaystyle\sum_{i=1}^{n} a_i z^i = 1$ ...(3)

Now we know that modulus of sum $\le$ sum of moduli and modulus of product is equal to product of moduli.

$1 = \left|\displaystyle\sum_{i=1}^{n} a_i z^i\right| \le \Sigma|a_i z^i| = \Sigma|a_i||z^i| < 2\Sigma|z^i|$,

$\qquad\qquad\qquad\qquad\qquad\qquad\qquad$ by (1)

$= 2[|z| + |z|^2 + |z|^3 + ... + |z|^n]$

Divide by 2 and add 1 in both sides

$\therefore \quad \dfrac{1}{2} + 1 < 1 + |z| + |z|^2 + ... |z|^n$

$\therefore \quad 1 + |z| + |z|^2 + ... + |z|^n > \dfrac{3}{2}$ or $S_n > \dfrac{3}{2}$

Case I. If $|z| < 1$, then

$\qquad S_\infty > S_n \Rightarrow \dfrac{1}{1-|z|} > \dfrac{3}{2}$ or $2 > 3 - 3|z|$

$\Rightarrow \quad |z| > \dfrac{1}{3}$

and this violates (2).

Case II. If $|z| \ge 1$, then both (2) and (3) cannot hold simultaneously. Also it violates (2).

11. (a) $\dfrac{z}{|z|}$ is unimodular complex number $= e^{i\theta}$ say

L.H.S. $= |e^{i\theta} - 1| = |(\cos\theta - 1) + i\sin\theta|$

$\qquad = [(\cos\theta - 1)^2 + \sin^2\theta]^{1/2} = [2(1-\cos\theta)]^{1/2}$

$\qquad = \left(4\sin^2\dfrac{\theta}{2}\right)^{1/2} = 2\sin\dfrac{\theta}{2} \le 2 \cdot \dfrac{\theta}{2} = \theta = \arg z$

$\because \quad \sin\theta \le \theta$ if $\theta \ge 0$

(b) $|z - 1| = |(z - |z|) + (|z| - 1)|$

We have subtracted and added $|z|$

Now apply $|z_1 + z_2| \le |z_1| + |z_2|$

L.H.S. is $\le |z - |z|| + ||z| - 1|$

$\qquad = |z|\left|\dfrac{z}{|z|} - 1\right| + ||z| - 1|$

$\qquad = |z|(\arg z) + ||z| - 1|$ by (a).

12. (a) Let $z = x + iy$. Then $|z|^2 = x^2 + y^2$.

Therefore the condition $|z| = 1$ is equivalent to
$\qquad x^2 + y^2 = 1$. ...(1)

Now $\dfrac{z-1}{z+1} = \dfrac{x+iy-1}{x+iy+1}$

$= \dfrac{(x-1+iy)(x+1-iy)}{(x+1+iy)(x+1-iy)}$

$= \dfrac{(x^2+y^2-1)+2iy}{(x+1)^2+y^2} = \dfrac{2iy}{(x+1)^2+y^2}$, by (1)

Hence $\dfrac{z-1}{z+1}$ is purely imaginary when $|z|=1$

provided $z \neq -1$.

When $z=1$, we have $\dfrac{z-1}{z+1}=0$.

Now recall that according to the definition 2 given in § 2, 0 is a pure imaginary number, since the point 0 which corresponds to $z=0$ lies on both real and imaginary axes.

So in this case also, $\dfrac{z-1}{z+1}$ is a pure imaginary

number.

(b) Ans. (d). It follows last part (a).

(c) Let $\dfrac{z-1}{z+1}$ be purely imaginary. Then

$\dfrac{x^2+y^2-1}{(x+1)^2+y^2}=0$,

whence $x^2+y^2-1=0$, that is

$|z| = \sqrt{x^2+y^2} = 1$. This completes the proof.

(d) Put $z=x+iy$. Multiply by conjugate of denominator. Since it is purely imaginary its real part is zero.

$\therefore \quad x(x-1)+y(y-1)=0$

$\quad x^2+y^2-x-y=0$ etc.

(e) Given $2 \arg(z^{1/3}) = \arg(z^2 + \bar{z} z^{1/3})$

or $\arg(z^2+\bar{z}z^{1/3}) - \arg(z^{2/3}) = 0$

$\because \quad n \arg z = \arg z^n$

or $\arg \left(\dfrac{z^2 + \bar{z} z^{1/3}}{z^{2/3}} \right) = 0$

$\therefore \quad z^{4/3} + \bar{z} z^{-1/3}$ is purely real

$\because \quad \arg z = 0 \Rightarrow z$ is real

Now we know that if A is real then $A = \bar{A}$

$\therefore \quad z^{4/3} + \dfrac{\bar{z}}{z^{1/3}} = (\bar{z})^{4/3} + \dfrac{z}{(\bar{z})^{1/3}}$

or $z^{4/3} - (\bar{z})^{4/3} = \dfrac{z}{(\bar{z})^{1/3}} - \dfrac{\bar{z}}{z^{1/3}} = \dfrac{z^{4/3} - (\bar{z})^{4/3}}{(z\bar{z})^{1/3}}$

or $[z^{4/3} - (\bar{z})^{4/3}] \left(1 - \dfrac{1}{|z|^{2/3}} \right) = 0$

Since $z \neq \bar{z}$ therefore we have

$1 - \dfrac{1}{|z|^{2/3}} = 0$ or $|z|^{2/3}=1$ or $|z|=1$

13. (a) Any complex number whose modulus is unity can be written as $\cos\theta + i\sin\theta = e^{i\theta}$

$\therefore \quad \dfrac{z_1+z_2}{z_1-z_2} = e^{i\theta} = \dfrac{e^{i\theta/2}}{e^{-i\theta/2}}$

Apply componendo and dividendo

$\dfrac{2z_1}{2z_2} = \dfrac{e^{i\theta/2}+e^{-i\theta/2}}{e^{i\theta/2}-e^{-i\theta/2}} = \dfrac{2\cos(\theta/2)}{2i\sin(\theta/2)}$

or $\dfrac{z_1}{z_2} = -i \cot \dfrac{\theta}{2}.$ $\quad \because \dfrac{1}{i} = -i.$

It is certainly a purely imaginary number, it will be zero if θ is odd multiple of π, i.e.

$\theta = (2n+1)\pi.$

In this case, $\cot \dfrac{\theta}{2} = \cot \dfrac{\pi}{2} = 0$

Hence the condition is that $\theta = (2n+1)\pi$.

(b) Here $\dfrac{z_1-z_2}{z_1+z_2} = e^{i\theta} = \dfrac{e^{i\theta/2}}{e^{-i\theta/2}}$

Apply comp. and divid.

$\dfrac{2z_1}{-2z_2} = \dfrac{2\cos(\theta/2)}{2i\sin(\theta/2)} = -i \cot \dfrac{\theta}{2}$

$\therefore \quad i \dfrac{z_1}{z_2} = -\cot \dfrac{\theta}{2} = \lambda$ (Real), say $\qquad$ ...(1)

Now angle between the lines joining origin to the points z_1+z_2 and z_1-z_2 is

$\arg \dfrac{z_1+z_2}{z_1-z_2} = \arg Z$

$Z = \dfrac{z_1+z_2}{z_1-z_2} = \dfrac{\dfrac{z_1}{z_2}+1}{\dfrac{z_1}{z_2}-1} = \dfrac{\lambda/i+1}{\lambda/i-1} = \dfrac{\lambda+i}{\lambda-i}$

$= \dfrac{(\lambda+i)^2}{\lambda^2+1} = \dfrac{\lambda^2-1+2\lambda i}{\lambda^2+1} = X + iY$

$\therefore \quad \arg Z = \tan^{-1} \dfrac{Y}{X} = \tan^{-1} \dfrac{2\lambda}{\lambda^2-1}$

or $\theta = \tan^{-1} \dfrac{2\lambda}{\lambda^2-1} = -\tan^{-1} \dfrac{2\lambda}{1-\lambda^2}$

$= -2\tan^{-1}\lambda.$

14. (a) Since $|z-1|=1$ $\therefore z-1 = e^{i\alpha}$ $\qquad$ ...(1)

$\therefore \quad z = 1 + \cos\alpha + i\sin\alpha$

$= 2\cos^2 \dfrac{\alpha}{2} + i \, 2\sin \dfrac{\alpha}{2} \cos \dfrac{\alpha}{2}$

$\therefore \quad z = 2\cos \dfrac{\alpha}{2} \left(\cos \dfrac{\alpha}{2} + i\sin \dfrac{\alpha}{2} \right)$

$\therefore \quad \arg z = \dfrac{\alpha}{2}$ $\qquad$ ...(2)

$\therefore \quad \dfrac{z-2}{z} = \dfrac{e^{i\alpha}-1}{e^{i\alpha}+1} = \dfrac{e^{i\alpha/2}-e^{-i\alpha/2}}{e^{i\alpha/2}+e^{-i\alpha/2}},$ by (1)

$= \dfrac{2i \sin(\alpha/2)}{2 \cos(\alpha/2)} = i \tan \dfrac{\alpha}{2} = i \tan(\arg z),$ by (2)

Note : See alternative method below.

$|z-1| = 1$ represents the equation of a circle of radius 1 and with centre at (1, 0) $\quad \therefore \quad A = (2, 0).$

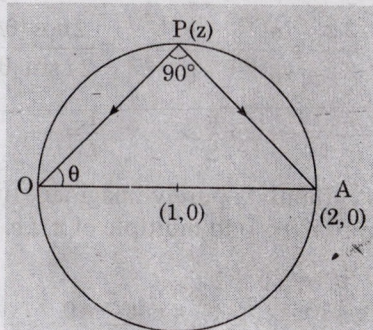

Fig. 10(a)

Also $\angle OPA = 90°.$ Hence by anti-clockwise rotation

$$\dfrac{\overrightarrow{PA}}{\overrightarrow{PO}} = \dfrac{PA}{PO} e^{i\pi/2}$$

or $\dfrac{z-2}{z-0} = (\tan\theta)\, i = i \tan(\arg z)$

(b) Since $|x + iy| = 1,$ therefore

$x + iy = e^{i\alpha} = \cos\alpha + i \sin\alpha$

where $x = \cos\alpha,\ y = \sin\alpha,\ y \neq 0 \Rightarrow \alpha \neq 0$

We have to show that

$x + iy = \dfrac{a+i}{a-i} = \dfrac{e^{i\alpha}}{1},$ where a is real

$\dfrac{a+i}{a-i} = \dfrac{e^{i\alpha/2}}{e^{-i\alpha/2}}$

Apply componendo and dividendo

$\dfrac{2a}{2i} = \dfrac{e^{i\alpha/2}+e^{-i\alpha/2}}{e^{i\alpha/2}-e^{-i\alpha/2}} = \dfrac{2\cos(\alpha/2)}{2i\sin(\alpha/2)}$ $(\alpha \neq 0)$

$\therefore \quad a = \cot(\alpha/2)$ which is real.

(c) Ans. (d).

$|z\omega| = 1 \Rightarrow |z||\omega| = 1$

$\therefore \quad |\omega| = \dfrac{1}{|z|}$ ...(1)

Let $z = r e^{i\theta} \quad \therefore \quad \overline{z} = r e^{-i\theta}$

Given, Arg $\omega = $ Arg $z - \pi/2 = \theta - \pi/2$

$\therefore \quad \overline{\omega} = \dfrac{1}{r} e^{i(\theta - \pi/2)}$ by (1)

$\therefore \quad \overline{z}\omega = (re^{-i\theta}) \cdot \dfrac{1}{r} e^{i(\theta - \pi/2)} = e^{-i\pi/2}$

$= \cos\dfrac{\pi}{2} - i\sin\dfrac{\pi}{2} = -i.$

(d) Ans. (c).

Let $z = r e^{i\theta}.$ Given $\arg z + \arg \omega = \pi$

$\therefore \quad \arg\omega = \pi - \theta \quad \therefore \quad \omega = r_1 e^{i(\pi - \theta)}$

Now $\overline{z} + i\overline{\omega} = 0 \Rightarrow re^{-i\theta} + ir_1 e^{-i(\pi - \theta)} = 0$

or $\quad r(\cos\theta - i\sin\theta) + i r_1 [\cos(\pi - \theta)$
$\hspace{5cm} - i\sin(\pi - \theta)] = 0$

or $\quad r(\cos\theta - i\sin\theta) + r_1(-i\cos\theta + \sin\theta) = 0$

$\therefore \quad$ Equating real and imaginary parts

$r\cos\theta + r_1 \sin\theta = 0$

$-r\sin\theta - r_1 \cos\theta = 0$

$\therefore \quad \dfrac{r}{r_1} = -\tan\theta = \dfrac{r_1}{r}$ or $r^2 = r_1^2 \quad \therefore \quad r = r_1$

$\therefore \quad \tan\theta = -1$ or $\theta = \arg z = 3\pi/4 \Rightarrow$ (c)

15. (a) Let $z = x + iy = r e^{i\theta} = r(\cos\theta + i\sin\theta)$

$|x| + |y| = r[|\cos\theta| + |\sin\theta|]$

Squaring both sides ($r = +$ive always)

$[|x| + |y|]^2 = r^2 [1 + |2\sin\theta\cos\theta|]$

$\hspace{2.8cm} = r^2 [1 + |\sin 2\theta|]$

$\hspace{2.8cm} < r^2 [1 + 1] \quad \because \quad |\sin x| \leq 1$

$\therefore \quad |x| + |y| \leq r\sqrt{2}$

$\therefore \quad |\mathrm{Re}\, z| + |\mathrm{Im}\, z| \leq \sqrt{2}|z| \quad \because \quad |z| = r$

or $\quad |x| + |y| \leq \sqrt{2}|x + iy|$

(b) $z_1 = x_1 + iy_1,\ \overline{z_2}\, z_3 = (x_2 - iy_2)(x_3 + iy_3)$

$\therefore \quad \mathrm{Im}(\overline{z_2}\, z_3) = (x_2 y_3 - x_3 y_2)$

$\therefore \quad z_1 \mathrm{Im}(\overline{z_2}\, z_3) = (x_1 + iy_1)(x_2 y_3 - x_3 y_2)$
$\hspace{2cm} = x_1(x_2 y_3 - x_3 y_2) + iy_1(x_2 y_3 - x_3 y_2)$

$\therefore \quad \Sigma z_1 \mathrm{Im}(\overline{z_2}\, z_3) = 0$

Each sigma will have six terms, three +ive and three –ive which will cancel.

16. (a) Dividing throughout by i and knowing that $\dfrac{1}{i} = -i,$ we get

$z^3 - iz^2 + iz + 1 = 0$

or $z^2(z - i) + i(z - i) = 0$ as $1 = -i^2$

or $(z - i)(z^2 + i) = 0$

$\therefore \quad z = i$ or $z^2 = -i$

$\therefore \quad |z| = |i| = 1$

and $|z^2| = |z|^2 = |-i| = 1$

$\therefore \quad |z| = 1$

Hence in either case $|z| = 1.$

(b) Ans. (a).

$9iz^2(3z - 2i) - 4(3z - 2i) = 0$

$\therefore \quad (3z - 2i)(9iz^2 - 4) = 0$

$\therefore \quad z = \dfrac{2}{3}i$ or $z^2 = \dfrac{4}{9i} = -\dfrac{4}{9}i$

$\therefore$ $|z| = \dfrac{2}{3}$ or $|z^2| = |z|^2 = \dfrac{4}{9}$ $\therefore$ $|z| = \dfrac{2}{3}$.

Hence in either case $|z| = \dfrac{2}{3}$ being a + ive number.

(c) Ans. (c).

Let $a = 1 + i, b = 3 + 2i$ then $ab = 1 + 5i$

$\therefore$ $z\bar{z} - az - b\bar{z} + ab = 0$

or $(\bar{z} - a)(z - b) = 0$

$\therefore$ $\bar{z} = a, z = b$ or $z = \bar{a}, z = b$

or $z = 1 - i, 3 + 2i \Rightarrow$ (c).

17. Let $z_1 = x_1 + iy_1$ and $z_2 = x_2 + iy_2$ be two complex numbers.

First suppose z_1, z_2 are conjugate of each other. Then,

$z_2 = \bar{z}_1 = x_1 - iy_1$

Hence $z_1 + z_2 = z_1 + \bar{z}_1 = 2x_1$, which is real

and $z_1 z_2 = z_1 \bar{z}_1 = (x_1 + iy_1)(x_1 - iy_1) = x_1^2 + y_1^2$,

which is also real.

Thus sum $z_1 + z_2$ and product $z_1 z_2$ are real when z_1 and z_2 are conjugate complex.

Now let the sum $z_1 + z_2$ and product $z_1 z_2$ be real. We have $z_1 + z_2 = (x_1 + x_2) + i(y_1 + y_2)$

and $z_1 z_2 = x_1 x_2 - y_1 y_2 + i(x_1 y_2 + x_2 y_1)$

Since $z_1 + z_2$ and $z_1 z_2$ are both real, we must have

$y_1 + y_2 = 0$ and $x_1 y_2 + x_2 y_1 = 0$

These give $y_2 = -y_1$ and $x_2 = x_1$.

Hence $z_2 = x_2 + iy_2 = x_1 - iy_1 = \bar{z}_1$, that is, z_1 and z_2 are conjugate complex.

18. (a) $z_1 = re^{i\theta}, z_2 = re^{-i\theta}$ **(conjugate)**

$z_3 = Re^{i\phi}, z_4 = Re^{-i\phi}$ **(conjugate)**

$\dfrac{z_3}{z_2} = \dfrac{R}{r} e^{i(\theta + \phi)}$ $\therefore$ $\arg \dfrac{z_3}{z_2} = \theta + \phi$

$\dfrac{z_1}{z_4} = \dfrac{r}{R} e^{i(\theta + \phi)}$ $\therefore$ $\arg \dfrac{z_1}{z_4} = \theta + \phi$

(b) $\arg \dfrac{z_1}{z_3} + \arg \dfrac{z_2}{z_4} = \arg \dfrac{z_1}{z_3} \cdot \dfrac{z_2}{z_4}$

But z_1, z_2 are conjugate $\therefore$ $z_1 z_2 = |z_1|^2$

L.H.S. $= \arg \dfrac{|z_1|^2}{|z_3|^2} = 0$

$(\because$ arg of purely real number is zero)

(c) The given determinant is a circulant which when expanded gives $3abc - a^3 - b^3 - c^3 = 0$

or $(a + b + c)(a^2 + b^2 + c^2 - ab - bc - ca) = 0$

or $\dfrac{1}{2}(a + b + c)[(a - b)^2 + (b - c)^2 + (c - a)^2] = 0$

Since $a + b + c$ being the sum of moduli cannot be zero and hence we must have

$\Sigma(a - b)^2 = 0 \Rightarrow a - b = 0, b - c = 0, c - a = 0$

or $a = b = c$ or $|z_1| = |z_2| = |z_3| = r$ say

$\therefore$ Let $z_1 = re^{i\theta_1}, z_2 = re^{i\theta_2}, z_3 = re^{i\theta_3}$

Now $\dfrac{z_3 - z_1}{z_2 - z_1}$

$= \dfrac{(\cos\theta_3 + i\sin\theta_3) - (\cos\theta_1 + i\sin\theta_1)}{(\cos\theta_2 + i\sin\theta_2) - (\cos\theta_1 + i\sin\theta_1)}$

$= \dfrac{(\cos\theta_3 - \cos\theta_1) + i(\sin\theta_3 - \sin\theta_1)}{(\cos\theta_2 - \cos\theta_1) + i(\sin\theta_2 - \sin\theta_1)}$

$= \dfrac{2\sin\dfrac{\theta_3 + \theta_1}{2}\sin\dfrac{\theta_1 - \theta_3}{2} + i\,2\sin\dfrac{\theta_3 - \theta_1}{2}\cos\dfrac{\theta_3 + \theta_1}{2}}{2\sin\dfrac{\theta_2 + \theta_1}{2}\sin\dfrac{\theta_1 - \theta_2}{2} + i\,2\sin\dfrac{\theta_2 - \theta_1}{2}\cos\dfrac{\theta_2 + \theta_1}{2}}$

Now, $\sin\dfrac{\theta_1 - \theta_3}{2} = -\sin\dfrac{\theta_3 - \theta_1}{2} = i^2\sin\dfrac{\theta_3 - \theta_1}{2}$

$= \dfrac{2\sin\dfrac{\theta_3 - \theta_1}{2}\left[\cos\dfrac{\theta_3 + \theta_1}{2} + i\sin\dfrac{\theta_3 + \theta_1}{2}\right]}{2\sin\dfrac{\theta_2 - \theta_1}{2}\left[\cos\dfrac{\theta_2 + \theta_1}{2} + i\sin\dfrac{\theta_2 + \theta_1}{2}\right]}$

$= \dfrac{\sin\dfrac{\theta_3 - \theta_1}{2}}{\sin\dfrac{\theta_2 - \theta_1}{2}} e^{i\left[\frac{\theta_3 + \theta_1}{2} - \frac{\theta_2 + \theta_1}{2}\right]}$

or $\dfrac{z_3 - z_1}{z_2 - z_1} = k\,e^{i\frac{\theta_3 - \theta_2}{2}}$

$\therefore$ $\left(\dfrac{z_3 - z_1}{z_2 - z_1}\right)^2 = k^2\left[e^{i\left(\frac{\theta_3 - \theta_2}{2}\right)}\right]^2 = k^2 e^{i(\theta_3 - \theta_2)}$

$\because$ $(e^{ix})^2 = e^{i2x}$

$\therefore$ $\arg\left(\dfrac{z_3 - z_1}{z_2 - z_1}\right)^2 = \theta_3 - \theta_2$

$= \arg z_3 - \arg z_2 = \arg\left(\dfrac{z_3}{z_2}\right)$

19. (a) $\dfrac{\pi}{4} = \arg\dfrac{z - z_1}{z - z_2} = \arg\left(\dfrac{x + iy - 10 - 6i}{x + iy - 4 - 6i}\right)$

$\dfrac{\pi}{4} = \arg\dfrac{z - z_1}{z - z_2} = \arg(z - z_1) - \arg(z - z_2)$

or $\pi/4 = \theta_1 - \theta_2$

or $\tan^{-1} 1 = \tan^{-1}\dfrac{y_1}{x_1} - \tan^{-1}\dfrac{y_2}{x_2}$

or $\tan^{-1} 1 = \tan^{-1}\dfrac{y - 6}{x - 10} - \tan^{-1}\dfrac{y - 6}{x - 4}$

or $\tan^{-1} 1 = \tan^{-1} \dfrac{(y-6)\left[\dfrac{1}{x-10} - \dfrac{1}{x-4}\right]}{1 + \dfrac{(y-6)^2}{(x-10)(x-4)}}$

$\therefore \quad 1 = \dfrac{6(y-6)}{x^2 - 14x + 40 + y^2 - 12y + 36}$

or $x^2 - 14x + y^2 - 18y + 112 = 0$

or $(x-7)^2 - 49 + (y-9)^2 - 81 + 112 = 0$

$\therefore \quad (x-7)^2 + (y-9)^2 = 18$ ...(1)

$\therefore \quad |z - 7 - 9i| = |(x-7) + i(y-9)|$

$= [(x-7)^2 + (y-9)^2]^{1/2} = \sqrt{18} = 3\sqrt{2}$ by (1)

(b) $\tan^{-1} \dfrac{y}{x-2} - \tan^{-1} \dfrac{y}{x+2} = \dfrac{\pi}{4}$

or $x^2 + (y-2)^2 = 8$ or $|x + i(y-2)|^2 = 8$

or $|z - 2i| = 2\sqrt{2}$.

(c) Putting $z = x + iy$, the given equations become

$\left|\dfrac{x + iy - 12}{x + iy - 8i}\right| = \dfrac{5}{3}$ and $\left|\dfrac{x + iy - 4}{x + iy - 8}\right| = 1$

or $9|(x-12) + iy|^2 = 25|x + i(y-8)|^2$

and $|(x-4) + iy|^2 = |(x-8) + iy|^2$

or $9[(x-12)^2 + y^2] = 25[x^2 + (y-8)^2]$

and $(x-4)^2 + y^2 = (x-8)^2 + y^2$

The above equations can be written as

$[3(x-12)]^2 - (5x)^2 = [5(y-8)]^2 - (3y)^2$

and $(x-4)^2 - (x-8)^2 = 0$

Apply $a^2 - b^2 = (a+b)(a-b)$

$(8x - 36)(-2x - 36) = (8y - 40)(2y - 40)$ ...(1)

and $(2x - 12)(4) = 0 \quad \therefore \quad x = 6$ ...(2)

and putting in (1), we get

$12(-48) = 8 \times 2(y-5)(y-20)$

or $y^2 - 25y + 136 = 0$ or $(y-8)(y-17) = 0$.

$\therefore \quad y = 8, 17$.

Hence $z_1 = (6, 8)$ and $z_2 = (6, 17)$

i.e. $z_1 = 6 + 8i$ and $z_2 = 6 + 17i$ are two solutions.

(d) $\arg \dfrac{z_1}{z_2} = \arg z_1 - \arg z_2$

Let $z = x + iy$

$\arg \dfrac{3(x-2) + i3(y-1)}{2(x-4) + i2(y-3)} = \dfrac{\pi}{4}$

$\therefore \quad \tan^{-1} \dfrac{y-1}{x-2} - \tan^{-1} \dfrac{y-3}{x-4} = \dfrac{\pi}{4}$

$\therefore \quad \dfrac{\dfrac{y-1}{x-2} - \dfrac{y-3}{x-4}}{1 + \dfrac{(y-1)(y-3)}{(x-2)(x-4)}} = \tan \dfrac{\pi}{4} = 1$

$2x - 2y - 2 = x^2 + y^2 - 6x - 4y + 11$

or $x^2 + y^2 - 8x - 2y + 13 = 0$ ...(1)

and $|z - 3 + i| = 3$

$\Rightarrow \quad (x-3)^2 + (y+1)^2 = 9$

$x^2 + y^2 - 6x + 2y + 1 = 0$ ...(2)

Subtracting (1) and (2), we get

$x + 2y = 6 \quad \therefore \quad x = 6 - 2y$

Putting in (1), $5y^2 - 10y + 1 = 0$

$\therefore \quad y = 1 + \dfrac{2}{\sqrt{5}}, 1 - \dfrac{2}{\sqrt{5}}$

$\therefore \quad x = 4 - \dfrac{4}{\sqrt{5}}, 4 + \dfrac{4}{\sqrt{5}}$

$\therefore \quad z = x + iy$ where (x, y) is $\left(4 - \dfrac{4}{\sqrt{5}}, 1 + \dfrac{2}{\sqrt{5}}\right)$

and $\left(4 + \dfrac{4}{\sqrt{5}}, 1 - \dfrac{2}{\sqrt{5}}\right)$

20. (a) Ans. (b).

If $z = x + iy$, then $z^2 - 1 = (x^2 - y^2 - 1) + i\,2xy$ and $|z|^2 = x^2 + y^2$. The given relation implies

$[(x^2 - y^2 - 1)^2 + 4x^2 y^2]^{1/2} = x^2 + y^2 + 1$. Square

$(x^2 - y^2 - 1)^2 + 4x^2 y^2 = [(x^2 + y^2) + 1]^2$

or $(x^2 - y^2)^2 + 1 - 2(x^2 - y^2) + 4x^2 y^2$

$= (x^2 + y^2)^2 + 1 + 2(x^2 + y^2)$

Cancel 1 and use $(A - B)^2 + 4AB = (A + B)^2$

$\therefore \quad (x^2 + y^2)^2 - 2(x^2 - y^2) = (x^2 + y^2)^2$
$\qquad\qquad\qquad\qquad\qquad + 2(x^2 + y^2)$

or $-4x^2 = 0 \quad \therefore \quad x = 0$, i.e., Imag. axis.

(b) Ans. (a).

$|\omega| = \left|\dfrac{z_1}{z_2}\right| = 1 \Rightarrow |z_1| = |z_2|$.

$|z| = \left|z - \dfrac{1}{3}i\right|$. If $z = x + iy$, then

$\therefore \quad x^2 + y^2 = x^2 + \left(y - \dfrac{1}{3}\right)^2$ or $-\dfrac{2y}{3} + \dfrac{1}{9} = 0$

or $y = \dfrac{1}{6}$, i.e., a line parallel to x-axis.

(c) Ans. (b).

$|z_1 - z_2|^2 = (z_1 - z_2)(\overline{z_1 - z_2}) = (z_1 - z_2)(\overline{z_1} - \overline{z_2})$

$= |z_1|^2 + |z_2|^2 - (z_1 \overline{z_2} + \overline{z_1} z_2)$

$= 1 + 1 - (z_1 \overline{z_2} + \overline{z_1 \overline{z_2}}) = 2 - 2\operatorname{Re}(z_1 \overline{z_2})$

$\therefore \quad E = (2 + 2 + 2) - 2\operatorname{Re}(z_1 \overline{z_2} + z_2 \overline{z_3} + z_3 \overline{z_1})$ ...(1)

Again $|z_1 + z_2 + z_3|^2 \geq 0$

or $1 + 1 + 1 + 2\operatorname{Re}(z_1 \overline{z_2} + z_2 \overline{z_3} + z_3 \overline{z_1}) \geq 0$

or $3 + (6 - E) \geq 0$ by (1) $\quad \therefore \quad E \leq 9$.

(d) Ans. (a).

Apply $R_3 + R_2, R_2 - R_1$

$\therefore \quad \Delta = \begin{vmatrix} 1 & z_1 & \bar{z}_1 \\ 0 & z_2 - z_1 & \bar{z}_2 - \bar{z}_1 \\ 0 & z_3 - z_2 & \bar{z}_3 - \bar{z}_2 \end{vmatrix}$

Put $\bar{z}_2 - \bar{z}_1 = \overline{z_2 - z_1}$

$\Delta = (z_2 - z_1)(\overline{z_3 - z_2}) - (z_3 - z_2)(\overline{z_2 - z_1})$

$= Z - \bar{Z} = $ purely imag.

$\therefore \quad$ R.P. of $\Delta = 0$.

(e) Ans. (b), (c).

Apply $C_1 + C_2 + C_3$ and take Σ arg z_1 common.

$\therefore \quad \Delta = \Sigma (\arg z_1) \begin{vmatrix} 1 & \arg z_2 & \arg z_3 \\ 1 & \arg z_3 & \arg z_1 \\ 1 & \arg z_1 & \arg z_2 \end{vmatrix}$

Hence Δ is divisible by Σ arg z_1

$= \arg z_1 + \arg z_2 + \arg z_3 = \arg(z_1 z_2 z_3)$.

21. (a) $\left|\dfrac{z - 5i}{z + 5i}\right| = 1$

or $\quad |x + iy - 5i|^2 = |x + iy + 5i|^2$

or $\quad x^2 + (y - 5)^2 = x^2 + (y + 5)^2$

or $\quad 20y = 0 \qquad$ or $\quad y = 0$

(b) Putting $z = x + iy$, we have

$\arg \dfrac{z - 1}{z + 1} = \dfrac{\pi}{3}$ or $\arg \dfrac{x + iy - 1}{x + iy + 1} = \dfrac{\pi}{3}$

$\therefore \quad \tan^{-1} \dfrac{y}{x - 1} - \tan^{-1} \dfrac{y}{x + 1} = \dfrac{\pi}{3}$

$\because \quad \text{Arg} \dfrac{z_1}{z_2} = \text{Arg } z_1 - \text{Arg } z_2$

or $\quad \tan^{-1} \dfrac{\dfrac{y}{x-1} - \dfrac{y}{x+1}}{1 + \dfrac{y^2}{x^2 - 1}} = \dfrac{\pi}{3}$

or $\quad \dfrac{2y}{x^2 + y^2 - 1} = \tan \dfrac{\pi}{3} = \sqrt{3}$

or $\quad x^2 + y^2 - (2/\sqrt{3})y - 1 = 0$, i.e. circle.

(c) $\left|\dfrac{z - a}{z + \bar{a}}\right| = 1 \Rightarrow |z - a|^2 = |z + \bar{a}|^2$

If $z = (x, y)$, $a = (p, q)$ then $\bar{a} = (p, -q)$

$\therefore \quad (x - p)^2 + (y - q)^2 = (x + p)^2 + (y - q)^2$

$\therefore \quad (x + p)^2 - (x - p)^2 = 0 \quad$ or $\quad 4px = 0$

$\therefore \quad x = 0$ i.e. y-axis as $p \neq 0$

This is the equation of y-axis.

(d) $|\omega| = 1 \Rightarrow \left|\dfrac{1 - iz}{z - i}\right| = 1$

$\Rightarrow \quad |1 - iz|^2 = |z - i|^2$

$\Rightarrow \quad (1 - iz)(1 + i\bar{z}) = (z - i)(\bar{z} + i)$

$\because \quad \overline{iz} = \bar{i}\,\bar{z} = -i\,\bar{z}$

$\Rightarrow \quad 1 - iz + i\bar{z} + z\bar{z} = z\bar{z} + iz - i\bar{z} + 1$

$\Rightarrow \quad 2i(z - \bar{z}) = 0 \Rightarrow 2i(2iy) = 0 \Rightarrow y = 0$,

which is the equation of real axis.

(e) $z - i = \dfrac{1}{i}(zi - i^2) = -i(1 + iz)$

$\therefore \quad \omega = (-i)^n = \left(\cos \dfrac{\pi}{2} - i \sin \dfrac{\pi}{2}\right)^n$

or $\quad \omega = \cos \dfrac{n\pi}{2} - i \sin \dfrac{n\pi}{2}$

$\therefore \quad |\omega| = 1 \; \forall \; n$.

22. (a) Ans. (c).

Given I.P. of $U + \dfrac{1}{U} = 0$ where $U = \dfrac{z - 1}{e^{i\theta}}$.

Now, I.P. of $Z = 0 \Rightarrow Z - \bar{Z} = 2iY = 0$

$\therefore \quad \left(U + \dfrac{1}{U}\right) - \overline{\left(U + \dfrac{1}{U}\right)} = 0$

or $\quad \left(U + \dfrac{1}{U}\right) - \left(\bar{U} + \dfrac{1}{\bar{U}}\right) = 0$

or $\quad (U - \bar{U}) + \left(\dfrac{1}{U} - \dfrac{1}{\bar{U}}\right) = 0$

or $\quad (U - \bar{U}) - \dfrac{U - \bar{U}}{U\bar{U}} = 0$

or $\quad (U - \bar{U})\left(1 - \dfrac{1}{|U|^2}\right) = 0$

or $\quad |U|^2 = 1 \quad$ as $\quad U \neq \bar{U}$

$\left|\dfrac{z - 1}{e^{i\theta}}\right|^2 = \dfrac{|z - 1|^2}{1} = 1$ as $|e^{i\theta}| = 1$.

$\therefore \quad |z - 1| = 1$ which represents a unit circle.

(b) Ans. (b).

If $z_1 = r_1 e^{i\theta_1}, z_2 = r_2 e^{i\theta_2}$, then

$|z_1 + z_2|^2 = r_1^2 + r_2^2 + 2r_1 r_2 \cos(\theta_1 - \theta_2)$

§ 9 P. 68

If $z = re^{i\theta_1}, \dfrac{1}{z} = \dfrac{1}{r} e^{-i\theta}$

(i) Ans. (c).

$\left|z + \dfrac{1}{z}\right|^2 = r^2 + \dfrac{1}{r^2} + 2r \cdot \dfrac{1}{r} \cos(\theta + \theta) = 4$

or $\quad r^2 + \dfrac{1}{r^2} = 4 - 2\cos 2\theta$

$\therefore \quad \left(r - \dfrac{1}{r}\right)^2 = 2(1 - \cos 2\theta) = 4\sin^2 \theta \qquad \dots(1)$

$|r_1 - r_2| = \left|r - \dfrac{1}{r}\right| = 2 \sin \theta = 2 \sin \dfrac{\pi}{4} = \sqrt{2}$

(ii) Ans. (a).

As θ varies, max. value of $\sin^2 \theta = 1$ and min. is 0.

$\therefore \quad \left(r - \dfrac{1}{r}\right)^2$ varies from 0 to 4.

or $\quad |r_1 - r_2| \in [0, 2]$.

(c) Ans. (d).

If $\omega = re^{i\theta}$ then $\dfrac{1}{\omega} = \dfrac{1}{r} e^{-i\theta}$

$\therefore \quad z = \left(\omega + \dfrac{1}{\omega}\right)$

$= r(\cos\theta + i\sin\theta) + \dfrac{1}{r}(\cos\theta - i\sin\theta)$

$\therefore \quad x = \left(r + \dfrac{1}{r}\right)\cos\theta, \, y = \left(r - \dfrac{1}{r}\right)\sin\theta$

Eliminating θ, $\dfrac{x^2}{\left(r + \dfrac{1}{r}\right)^2} + \dfrac{y^2}{\left(r - \dfrac{1}{r}\right)^2} = 1$

Above represents an ellipse and distance between foci is

$$2ae = 2\sqrt{a^2\left(1 - \dfrac{b^2}{a^2}\right)} = 2\sqrt{a^2 - b^2} = 2\sqrt{4} = 4$$

(d) Ans. (d).

Since $|z| = 1 \quad \therefore z = e^{i\theta}$ as $r = 1$

$\therefore \quad \dfrac{z}{1 - z^2} = \dfrac{1}{z^{-1} - z} = \dfrac{1}{e^{-i\theta} - e^{i\theta}} = \dfrac{-1}{2i\sin\theta}$

$= 0 + i \cdot \dfrac{1}{2\sin\theta} \quad \ldots \dfrac{1}{i} = -i$

$\therefore$ Real part of $\dfrac{z}{1 - z^2}$ is zero. Hence it lies on y-axis.

(e) Ans. (b).

If Z is real then $Z = \bar{Z}$

$\therefore \quad \dfrac{\omega - \bar{\omega}z}{1 - z} = \left[\overline{\dfrac{\omega - \bar{\omega}z}{1 - z}}\right] = \dfrac{\bar{\omega} - \omega\bar{z}}{1 - \bar{z}}$

$\therefore \quad \omega(1 - \bar{z}) - \bar{\omega}z(1 - \bar{z}) = \bar{\omega}(1 - z) - \omega\bar{z}(1 - z)$

or $\quad \omega[1 - \bar{z} + \bar{z} - |z|^2] = \bar{\omega}[1 - z + z - |z|^2]$

or $\quad \omega(1 - |z|^2) - \bar{\omega}(1 - |z|^2) = 0$

or $\quad (1 - |z|^2)(\omega - \bar{\omega}) = 0 \Rightarrow 1 - |z|^2 = 1$

$\therefore \quad |z| = 1$

(f) Ans. (d).

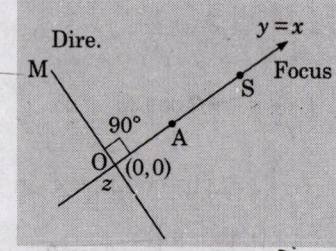

Fig. 10(b)

Let the points A and P be $3e^{i\pi/4}$ and z respectively $AP = 4$ is obtained by rotating $AO = 3$ about A through an angle $\pi/2$ in clockwise sense or an angle $-\pi/2$ in anticlockwise direction to become AP.

$\therefore \quad \widehat{AP} = \widehat{AO}\,e^{-i\pi/2}$ or $\dfrac{AP}{4} = \dfrac{AO}{3} e^{-i\pi/2}$

$\therefore \quad \dfrac{z - 3e^{i\pi/4}}{4} = \dfrac{0 - 3e^{i\pi/4}}{3} e^{-i\pi/2}$ **(by § 12, P. 71)**

$\therefore \quad z = 3e^{i\pi/4} - 4e^{i\pi/4}(-i) = e^{i\pi/4}(3 + 4i) \Rightarrow$ (d)

(g) Ans. (d).

$z_0 = 1 + 2i = (1, 2) = (x_0, y_0)$

$z_1 = (x_0 + 5, y_0 + 3) = (6, 5) = 6 + 5i$

$\sqrt{2}$ in the direction of $\mathbf{i} + \mathbf{j}$

$\therefore \quad x_1 = \sqrt{2}\cos 45°, y_1 = \sqrt{2}\sin 45°$

or $(x_1, y_1) = (1, 1)$

$\therefore \quad z_2 = (7 + 6i)$. Now rotation about origin through an angle of $\dfrac{\pi}{2}$ means multiply z_2 by $e^{(\pi/2)i}$

$= \cos 90° + i\sin 90° = i$

$\therefore \quad z_3 = i(7 + 6i) = -6 + 7i \Rightarrow$ (d)

23. (a) $\sqrt{(x-1)^2 + y^2} + \sqrt{(x+1)^2 + y^2} \le 4$

Consider $L + M = 4$

$L^2 - M^2 = -4x \quad \therefore \quad L - M = -x$

$\therefore \quad 2L = 4 - x$ or $4L^2 = (4 - x)^2$

or $4[x^2 + y^2 - 2x + 1] = 16 + x^2 - 8x$

$3x^2 + 4y^2 = 12.$

Hence the given equation is

$\dfrac{x^2}{4} + \dfrac{y^2}{3} - 1 \le 0$ or $S' \le 0$ ...(1)

$\dfrac{x^2}{4} + \dfrac{y^2}{3} = 1.$

(b) Here are two conditions to be satisfied.

$|z - i| = 1 \Rightarrow x^2 + (y - 1)^2 = 1$ ...(1)

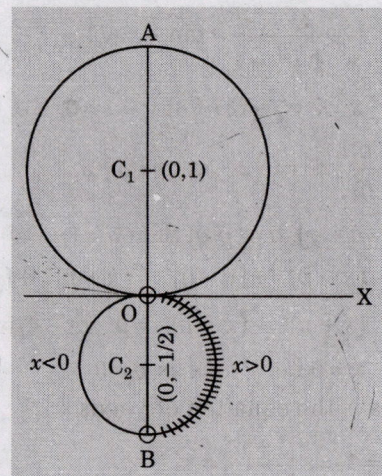

Fig. 11

It represents a circle with centre at $(0, 1)$ and radius 1. It clearly touches x-axis as $r = k = 1$. Hence all points on the boundary of this circle are the solutions of this.

Again arg $\dfrac{z}{z+i} = \dfrac{\pi}{2}$

$\therefore \quad \dfrac{z}{z+i} = r\left(\cos\dfrac{\pi}{2} + i\sin\dfrac{\pi}{2}\right)$

$$0 + ir$$

$\therefore$ R.P. $= 0$, I.P. $= r = +$ive ...(2)

Now $\dfrac{z}{z+i} = \dfrac{x+iy}{x+i(y+1)} \cdot \dfrac{x-i(y+1)}{x-i(y+1)}$

$= \dfrac{x^2 + y^2 + y - ix}{x^2 + (y+1)^2}$

Condition (2) $\Rightarrow x^2 + y^2 + y = 0$

It represents a circle with centre at $\left(0, -\dfrac{1}{2}\right)$ and

radius $\dfrac{1}{2}$, i.e., $x^2 + \left(y+\dfrac{1}{2}\right)^2 = \left(\dfrac{1}{2}\right)^2$

Also I.P. $= -x > 0$ or $x < 0$

Thus we have two circles $x^2 + (y-1)^2 = 1^2$

and $x^2 + \left(y+\dfrac{1}{2}\right)^2 = \left(\dfrac{1}{2}\right)^2$ with $x<0$

Because of the condition $x<0$, only left hand portion of the second circle will be valid except the points P and Q as for both $x=0$. Also $P(0,0)$ does not satisfy 1st circle.

(c) $\dfrac{2z+1}{iz+1} = \dfrac{2(x+iy)+1}{i(x+iy)+1} = \dfrac{2x+1+2iy}{(1-y)+ix}$

$= \dfrac{[(2x+1)+2iy][(1-y)-ix]}{(1-y)^2 + x^2}$

$= \dfrac{(2x+1)(1-y)+2xy + i[-x(2x+1)+2y(1-y)]}{(1-y)^2 + x^2}$

Since $I_m\left(\dfrac{2z+1}{iz+1}\right) = -2$, we have

$\dfrac{-x(2x+1)+2y(1-y)}{(1-y)^2 + x^2} = -2$

or $-2x^2 - 2y^2 - x + 2y = -2(1+y^2 - 2y) - 2x^2$

or $x + 2y - 2 = 0$.

24. (a) Let $Z = 3 + 4z$ $\therefore$ $Z - 3 = 4z$

$\therefore$ $|Z-3|^2 = 16|z|^2 = 32 = (4\sqrt{2})^2$

$\therefore$ Z clearly lies on a circle whose centre is $(3,0)$ and radius $4\sqrt{2}$.

(b) We know that if z is real, then $z = \bar{z}$

If $\dfrac{z^2}{z-1}$ is real then $\dfrac{z^2}{z-1} = \dfrac{\bar{z}^2}{\bar{z}-1}$

Cross multiplying, we get

$(z-\bar{z})\{z\bar{z} - (z+\bar{z})\} = 0$

$\therefore$ $z - \bar{z} = 0$ or $z = \bar{z}$ or z is real $\therefore$ $y = 0$

or $z\bar{z} - (z+\bar{z}) = 0$ or $x^2 + y^2 - 2x = 0$

Hence the locus is either $y = 0$ i.e. x-axis or a circle $x^2 + y^2 - 2x = 0$

Note : You may do it by Cartesian method and put imaginary part equal to zero.

$\therefore$ $y(x^2 + y^2 - 2x) = 0$.

(c) Squaring the given relation, we have

$\overline{(z-\alpha)}\,\overline{(z-\beta)} = k^2\,\overline{(z-\beta)}\,\overline{(z-\beta)}$

or $(z-\alpha)\overline{(z-\bar\alpha)} = k^2(z-\beta)\overline{(z-\bar\beta)}$

or $z\bar{z} - \bar\alpha z - \alpha\bar{z} + \alpha\bar\alpha = k^2(z\bar{z} - \bar\beta z - \beta\bar{z} + \beta\bar\beta)$

or $z\bar{z}(1-k^2) - (\bar\alpha - k^2\bar\beta)z - (\alpha - k^2\beta)\bar{z}$
$\qquad\qquad + \alpha\bar\alpha - k^2\beta\bar\beta = 0$

or $z\bar{z} - \dfrac{\bar\alpha - k^2\bar\beta}{1-k^2}z - \dfrac{(\alpha - k^2\beta)}{1-k^2}\bar{z}$
$\qquad\qquad + \dfrac{|\alpha|^2 - k^2|\beta|^2}{1-k^2} = 0$

or $z\bar{z} - \bar{a}z - a\bar{z} + a\bar{a} - a\bar{a} + \dfrac{|\alpha|^2 - k^2|\beta|^2}{1-k^2} = 0$

or $|z-a|^2 = |a|^2 - \dfrac{|\alpha|^2 - k^2|\beta|^2}{1-k^2} = r^2$ say

Above represents a circle with centre at $a = \dfrac{\alpha - k^2\beta}{1-k^2}$ and $r^2 =$ as written above.

25. (a) Note the following points $|z|^2 = z\bar{z}$, when z is real then $z = \bar{z}$. From the given relation

$z(1 + |w|^2) = w(1 + |z|^2)$

$\therefore$ $\dfrac{z}{w} = \dfrac{1 + |z|^2}{1 + |w|^2} = $ Real

Hence $\dfrac{z}{w} = \overline{\left(\dfrac{z}{w}\right)} = \dfrac{\bar{z}}{\bar{w}}$

or $z\bar{w} = \bar{z}w$ ...(1)

Now $(z\bar{z})w - (w\bar{w})z = z - w$ as given

or $z(\bar{z}w - 1) - w(\bar{w}z - 1) = 0$

or $(z\bar{w} - 1)(z - w) = 0$ by (1)

$\therefore$ $z = w$ or $z\bar{w} = 1$

(b) $|z-a|^2 = (z-a)(\bar{z}-\bar{a})$

$= z\bar{z} + |a|^2 - (z\bar{a} + \bar{z}a)$

$= |z|^2 + |a|^2 - (z\bar{a} + \overline{z\bar{a}})$

$= |z|^2 + |a|^2 - 2\,\text{Re}(z\bar{a})$ ...(1)

$\therefore$ L.H.S. $= 2|z|^2 - 2\,\text{Re}(z\bar{a} + z\bar{b}) + |a|^2$
$\qquad\qquad\qquad\qquad + |b|^2 = \lambda$

or $|z|^2 - 2\,\text{Re}\left[\dfrac{z(\bar{a}+\bar{b})}{2}\right] = \dfrac{1}{2}\{\lambda - |a|^2 - |b|^2\}$

Add $\dfrac{|a+b|^2}{4}$ on both sides, then by (1)

L.H.S. $= \left| z - \dfrac{a+b}{2} \right|^2 = \dfrac{1}{4}\{2\lambda - |a-b|^2\}$

Above represents a circle whose centre is $\dfrac{a+b}{2}$ and radius is $\dfrac{1}{2}\{2\lambda - |a-b|^2\}^{1/2}$.

26. (a) $PA^2 = 4PB^2 \Rightarrow |z - 6i|^2 = 4|z - 3|^2$ ...(1)

Again from (1), we have

$x^2 + (y-6)^2 = 4[(x-3)^2 + y^2]$

or $x^2 + y^2 - 12y + 36 = 4[x^2 + y^2 - 6x + 9]$

or $3(x^2 + y^2) - 24x + 12y = 0$

or $x^2 + y^2 - 8x + 4y = 0$

Above represents a circle with centre at $(4, -2)$ and radius $= \sqrt{g^2 + f^2 - c} = \sqrt{20} = r$

In complex form, centre is $z_0 = 4 - 2i$ and $r = \sqrt{20}$

$\therefore \quad |z - z_0|^2 = r^2$ or $|z - (4 - 2i)|^2 = 20$

Another form : $x^2 + y^2 - 8x + 4y = 0$

$x^2 + y^2 = 4(2x) + 2i(2iy)$

$|z|^2 = 4(z + \bar{z}) + 2i(z - \bar{z})$

or $z\bar{z} = (4 + 2i)z + (4 - 2i)\bar{z}$

(b) $\dfrac{z+1}{z-1} = \dfrac{3 + k + i\sqrt{(3-k^2)}}{1 + k + i\sqrt{(3-k^2)}}$

$\therefore \quad \left| \dfrac{z+1}{z-1} \right| = \dfrac{|z+1|}{|z-1|} = \dfrac{(3+k)^2 + 3 - k^2}{(1+k)^2 + 3 - k^2}$

$= \dfrac{6(k+2)}{2(k+2)} = 3$

From given value of z

$x = 2 + k, \ y = \sqrt{3 - k^2}$

$(x-2)^2 = k^2, \ y^2 = 3 - k^2$

$\therefore \quad (x-2)^2 + (y-0)^2 = 3$

or $(x-2)^2 + y^2 = (\sqrt{3})^2 \quad \therefore \quad (2,0), \sqrt{3}$

27. (a) $2(x^2 + y^2) + (x^2 - y^2 + i\,2xy) = 5 - i\sqrt{3}$.

Equating real and imaginary parts, we get

$3x^2 + y^2 = 5, \ xy = -\dfrac{\sqrt{3}}{2}$

Solving, we get $x = \pm\dfrac{1}{\sqrt{6}}, \pm\sqrt{\dfrac{3}{2}}$ and $y = -\dfrac{\sqrt{3}}{2x}$

$(x, y) = \left(\dfrac{1}{\sqrt{6}}, -\dfrac{3}{\sqrt{2}} \right), \left(-\dfrac{1}{\sqrt{6}}, \dfrac{3}{\sqrt{2}} \right),$

$\left(\sqrt{\dfrac{3}{2}}, -\dfrac{1}{\sqrt{2}} \right), \left(-\sqrt{\dfrac{3}{2}}, \dfrac{1}{\sqrt{2}} \right)$

(b) Ans. (d).

The two equations represent circles

$x^2 + y^2 = 9, (x+1)^2 + (y-1)^2 = 2$

$C_1(0,0), r_1 = 3 \qquad C_2(-1,1), r_2 = \sqrt{2}$

$C_1 C_2 = \sqrt{2} \qquad\qquad r_1 - r_2 = 3 - \sqrt{2}$

Now $\sqrt{2} < 3 - \sqrt{2}$ as $2\sqrt{2} < 3$ i.e. $8 < 9$

$\therefore \quad C_1 C_2 < r_1 - r_2$. Hence the two circles do not intersect but one lies completely within the other. Hence there is no solution.

Note : You may solve for x and y but you will not get any real values of x and y.

28. (a) Let $z = re^{i\theta}, w = Re^{i\phi} \quad \therefore \quad r \le 1, R \le 1,$

Arg $z = \theta$, Arg $w = \phi$

$|z - w|^2 = r^2 + R^2 - 2rR\cos(\theta - \phi)$

Th. II Alt., Page 69.

$= r^2 + R^2 - 2rR + 2rR[1 - \cos(\theta - \phi)]$

$= (r - R)^2 + 2rR \cdot 2\sin^2\left\{ \dfrac{\theta - \phi}{2} \right\}$

$\le (r - R)^2 + 4 \cdot 1 \cdot 1 \left(\dfrac{\theta - \phi}{2} \right)^2$

$= (|z| - |w|)^2 + (\text{Arg } z - \text{Arg } w)^2$

$\psi = \dfrac{\theta - \phi}{2}$ such that $-\psi < \sin\psi < \psi$. Since $r < 1$, $R < 1$, $\sin\psi < \psi$ where ψ is a +ive angle. Also $\sin^2\psi < \psi^2$.

(b) $\dfrac{5z_2}{7z_1} = ki \quad \Rightarrow \quad \dfrac{z_1}{z_2} = \dfrac{5}{7ki}$

or $\dfrac{2z_1}{3z_2} = \dfrac{10}{21ki}$ Apply Comp. and Divi.

$\dfrac{2z_1 + 3z_2}{2z_1 - 3z_2} = \dfrac{10 + 21ki}{10 - 21ki} = \dfrac{p}{\bar{p}}$

Take mod of both sides and $\left| \dfrac{p}{\bar{p}} \right| = 1$.

29. (a) Taking cube root of both sides, we get

$z + ab = a \cdot (1)^{1/3} = a, a\omega, a\omega^2$ where

$\omega = -\dfrac{1}{2} + i\dfrac{\sqrt{3}}{2}, \omega^2 = -\dfrac{1}{2} - i\dfrac{\sqrt{3}}{2}$

$\therefore \quad z_1 = a - ab, z_2 = a\omega - ab, z_3 = a\omega^2 - ab$

The sides are given by $|z_1 - z_2|, |z_2 - z_3|, |z_3 - z_1|$

$\therefore \quad |a||1 - \omega|, |a||\omega - \omega^2|, |a||\omega^2 - 1|$

each is $|a|\sqrt{3}$ as shown below

$\therefore \quad 1 - \omega = \dfrac{3}{2} - i\dfrac{\sqrt{3}}{2}, 1 - \omega^2 = \dfrac{3}{2} + i\dfrac{\sqrt{3}}{2}$

Modulus of each is $\sqrt{3/4 + 9/4} = \sqrt{3}$

Also $|\omega - \omega^2| = |i\,2\sqrt{3}/2| = \sqrt{3}$

(b) If the given points be A, B, C

$|AB| = |z_1 - z_2|,$

$|BC| = |(1 - i)z_1 - (1 - i)z_2|$

$= |1 - i||z_1 - z_2| = \sqrt{2}|z_1 - z_2|$

$|CA| = |i(z_1 - z_2)| = |i||z_1 - z_2| = |z_1 - z_2|$

Clearly $AB = CA$ and also

$$AB^2 + CA^2 = BC^2 = 2|z_1 - z_2|^2$$

$\therefore \quad BC = \sqrt{2}|z_1 - z_2|$

Hence the triangle is right angled isosceles.

(c) (i) Let $z = k$ (k real) be a root, then

$$k^2 + (a + ib)k + (c + id) = 0$$

$\therefore \quad k^2 + ak + c = 0$ and $bk + d = 0$

Eliminating k we have the condition as

$$\frac{d^2}{b^2} - \frac{ad}{b} + c = 0 \quad \text{or} \quad d^2 - adb + b^2 c = 0$$

(ii) Let both the roots be equal and each equal to $p + iq$

$\therefore \quad z^2 + (a + ib)z + (c + id) = [z - (p + iq)]^2$

$$= z^2 - 2z(p + iq) + (p + iq)^2$$

Comparing, $a + ib = -2(p + iq)$

$\therefore \quad a = -2p, b = -2q$ \hfill ...(1)

and $c + id = (p + iq)^2 = p^2 - q^2 + i\,2pq$

$\therefore \quad c = p^2 - q^2, d = 2pq$

or $\quad c = \dfrac{a^2}{4} - \dfrac{b^2}{4}$ and $d = \dfrac{ab}{2}$ by (1)

or $\quad a^2 - b^2 = 4c$ and $ab = 2d$ are the required conditions.

30. (a) The three points are collinear as

$2z_2 = z_1 + z_3$ i.e. z_2 is mid-point of z_1, z_3.

(b) Ans. (a), (b).

$$2e^{iB} = e^{iA} + e^{iC}$$

Equating real and imaginary parts,

$2\cos B = \cos A + \cos C$,

$2\sin B = \sin A + \sin C$

$\therefore \quad \tan B = \dfrac{2\sin \dfrac{A+C}{2} \cos \dfrac{A-C}{2}}{2\cos \dfrac{A+C}{2} \cos \dfrac{A-C}{2}} = \tan \dfrac{A+C}{2}$

or $\quad \tan B = \tan \dfrac{A+C}{2} \Rightarrow \tan B = \cot \dfrac{B}{2}$

$\therefore \quad B = \dfrac{\pi}{2} - \dfrac{B}{2}$ or $\dfrac{3B}{2} = \dfrac{\pi}{2}$

$\therefore \quad B = \dfrac{\pi}{3} = 60° \quad \therefore \quad A + C = 120°$

$\therefore \quad 2\cos 60° = 2\cos \dfrac{A+C}{2} \cos \dfrac{A-C}{2}$ by (I)

$1 = 2\cos 60° \cos \dfrac{A-C}{2} = \cos \dfrac{A-C}{2}$

$\Rightarrow \dfrac{A-C}{2} = 0 \Rightarrow A = C$

$\therefore$ Isosceles, since $A = C$ and $B = 60°$, Δ is equilateral also.

31. Change the two equations to Cartesian form

$\arg z = \dfrac{\pi}{6} \Rightarrow \dfrac{y}{x} = \tan 30° \Rightarrow x - \sqrt{3}y = 0$

$|z - 2\sqrt{3}i| = r$ represents a circle centred at $(0, 2\sqrt{3})$ and radius r

$$x^2 + (y - 2\sqrt{3})^2 = r^2$$

If the two curves touch, then $p = r$ and in case they intersect, then $p \le r$ where p is perpendicular from centre $(0, 2\sqrt{3})$ to line

$\therefore \quad \left| \dfrac{0 - 2\sqrt{3}.\sqrt{3}}{2} \right| \le r$ or $3 \le r \quad \therefore \quad r \ge 3$

Hence the least value of r is 3 for the curves to intersect. (Touching is also intersection at two coincident points).

32. (a) The given circles are $x^2 + y^2 = 1$ and $(x - 1)^2 + y^2 = 16$

or $x^2 + y^2 - 1 = 0$ and $x^2 + y^2 - 2x - 15 = 0$.

Let the equation of the circle which cuts the above circles orthogonally be

$$x^2 + y^2 + 2gx + 2fy + c = 0$$

Apply the condition $2g_1 g_2 + 2f_1 f_2 = c_1 + c_2$ with the given circles we get $c = 1$ and $g = 7$. Hence the family of circles is given by

$$x^2 + y^2 + 14x + 2fy + 1 = 0$$

centre $(-7, -f)$, $r = \sqrt{(48 + f^2)}$

$$(x + 7)^2 + (y + f)^2 = (48 + f^2)$$

or $|z + (7 + if)| = \sqrt{(48 + f^2)}$,

where f is parameter.

(b) Ans. (b). The two circles are $C_1 (0,0), r_1 = 12$

$C_2 (3,4), r_2 = 5$

and it passes through origin, the centre of C_1.

$C_1 C_2 = 5 < r_1 - r_2 = 7$

Hence circle C_2 lies inside circle C_1.

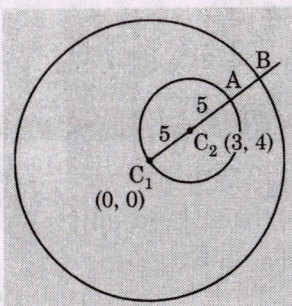

Fig. 12

Therefore minimum distance between them is

$AB = C_1 B - C_1 A = r_1 - 2r_2 = 12 - 10 = 2$.

33. (a) $|z_1 + z_2|^2 + |z_1 - z_2|^2$

$= (z_1 + z_2)\overline{(z_1 + z_2)} + (z_1 - z_2)\overline{(z_1 - z_2)}$

$= (z_1 + z_2)(\bar{z}_1 + \bar{z}_2) + (z_1 - z_2)(\bar{z}_1 - \bar{z}_2)$

$= 2z_1 \bar{z}_1 + 2z_2 \bar{z}_2$ [other terms cancel]

$= 2|z_1|^2 + 2|z_2|^2$ \hfill ...(1)

Geometrical Interpretation.

Let P and Q be the points of affix of z_1 and z_2 respectively.

Complete the parallelogram $OPRQ$. Then R represents the point $z_1 + z_2$.

Hence $|z_1| = OP, |z_2| = OQ, |z_1 + z_2| = OR$, and $|z_1 - z_2| = QP$.

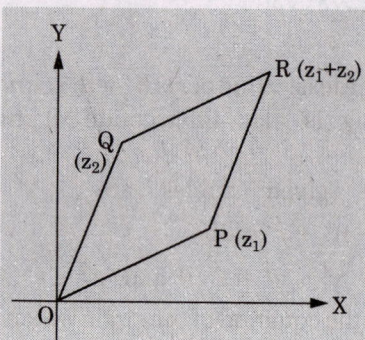

Fig. 13

We know that the sum of squares of the sides of a parallelogram is equal to the sum of squares of its diagonals, that is

$$2OP^2 + 2OQ^2 = OR^2 + QP^2$$

or $\quad 2|z_1|^2 + 2|z_2|^2 = |z_1 + z_2|^2 + |z_1 - z_2|^2$

Deduction : Let $z_1 = \alpha + \sqrt{\alpha^2 - \beta^2}$

and $z_2 = \alpha - \sqrt{\alpha^2 - \beta^2}$.

$\therefore \quad z_1 + z_2 = 2\alpha, z_1 - z_2 = 2\sqrt{\alpha^2 - \beta^2}$ ...(2)

$\quad z_1 z_2 = \alpha^2 - (\alpha^2 - \beta^2) = \beta^2$ ...(3)

Square both sides of the result to be proved.

$|z_1|^2 + |z_2|^2 + 2|z_1 z_2| = [|\alpha + \beta| + |\alpha - \beta|]^2$

L.H.S. $= \dfrac{1}{2}[|z_1 + z_2|^2 + |z_1 - z_2|^2] + 2|z_1 z_2|$

$= \dfrac{1}{2}[|2\alpha|^2 + 2|\overline{\alpha^2 - \beta^2}|^2 + 2|\beta^2|]$, by (2)

$= [2|\alpha|^2 + 2|\beta|^2 + 2|\alpha + \beta||\alpha - \beta|]$

$= |\alpha + \beta|^2 + |\alpha - \beta|^2 + 2|\alpha + \beta||\alpha - \beta|$

$= [|\alpha + \beta| + |\alpha - \beta|]^2$

Proceed as in last part.

(b) R.H.S. $= \dfrac{1}{2}|(\sqrt{z_1} + \sqrt{z_2})^2| + \dfrac{1}{2}|(\sqrt{z_1} - \sqrt{z_2})^2|$

Now $|z^2| = |z|^2$ **Th. IV, P. 69.**

R.H.S. $= \dfrac{1}{2}|\sqrt{z_1} + \sqrt{z_2}|^2 + \dfrac{1}{2}|\sqrt{z_1} - \sqrt{z_2}|^2$

Using the identity (1) of part (a), we get

R.H.S. $= \dfrac{1}{2}.2|\sqrt{z_1}|^2 + \dfrac{1}{2}.2|\sqrt{z_2}|^2 = |z_1| + |z_2|$

$\therefore \quad |z|^2 = |z^2|$ **Th. IV, P. 69.**

(c) Ans. True. Proceed as in Q. 33 (a).

34. (a). $|z_1 + z_2|^2 = |z_1|^2 + |z_2|^2 + 2\operatorname{Re}(z_1 \bar{z}_2)$

Th. I, P. 69.

If $z_1 \bar{z}_2$ is purely imaginary, then $\operatorname{Re}(z_1 \bar{z}_2) = 0$

$\therefore \quad |z_1 + z_2|^2 = |z_1|^2 + |z_2|^2$ ...(2)

Conversely if (1) holds, then $\operatorname{Re}(z_1 \bar{z}_2) = 0$

It means that $z_1 \bar{z}_2$ is purely imaginary.

(b) $|z_1 + z_2|^2 = (z_1 + z_2)\overline{(z_1 + z_2)}$

$= (z_1 + z_2)(\bar{z}_1 + \bar{z}_2)$

$= |z_1|^2 + |z_2|^2 + z_1 \bar{z}_2 + \overline{z_1 \bar{z}_2}$

$= |z_1|^2 + |z_2|^2 + 2R(z_1 \bar{z}_2)$ **(Remember)**

$\leq |z_1|^2 + |z_2|^2 + 2|z_1 \bar{z}_2|$ $\quad \because R(z) \leq |z|$

$= |z_1|^2 + |z_2|^2 + 2|z_1||z_2|$ ...(1)

Now $\lambda > 0 \quad \therefore \sqrt{\lambda}$ is real.

We write the last term in (1) as

$$2\left|\sqrt{\lambda}\, z_1\right|\left|\dfrac{1}{\sqrt{\lambda}}\, z_2\right|.$$

$= 2AB \leq A^2 + B^2$

$= \lambda |z_1|^2 + \dfrac{1}{\lambda}|z_2|^2$. Put in (1) etc.

35. (a) $\left|\dfrac{z_1 - z_2}{1 - \bar{z}_1 z_2}\right| < 1$

$|z_1 - z_2|^2 < |1 - \bar{z}_1 z_2|^2$

or $|z_1|^2 + |z_2|^2 - 2\operatorname{Re}(z_1 \bar{z}_2)$ **Th. I. P. 69**

$< |1|^2 + |\bar{z}_1 z_2|^2 - 2\operatorname{Re}(z_1 \bar{z}_2)$

$= 1 + |\bar{z}_1|^2|z_2|^2 - 2\operatorname{Re}(z_1 \bar{z}_2)$

$\therefore \quad |z_1|^2 + |z_2|^2 - |z_1|^2|z_2|^2 - 1 < 0$

or $(|z_1|^2 - 1)(1 - |z_2|^2) < 0$

Above is true if $|z_1| < 1$ and $|z_2| < 1$, as one factor will be positive and other negative.

(b) Proceeding as in part (a), on squaring

$(1 - |z_1|^2)(1 - |z_2|^2) < 0$ i.e., $-$ ive.

Above will be true if $|z_1| < 1 < |z_2|$.

(c) As in part (a), we get

$(1 - |z_1|^2)(1 - |z_2|^2) = 0$

$\therefore \quad |z_1| = 1, |z_2| = 1$

or $z_1 = e^{i\theta}, z_2 = e^{i\phi}$; $\theta, \phi \in R$

(d) $|z|^2 = z\bar{z}$

L.H.S. $= (1 - \bar{z}_1 z_2)(1 - z_1 \bar{z}_2) - (z_1 - z_2)(\bar{z}_1 - \bar{z}_2)$

$= 1 - |z_1|^2 - |z_2|^2 + |z_1|^2|z_2|^2$

All other terms cancel.

$= (1 - |z_1|^2)(1 - |z_2|^2)$.

(e) Proceeding as in part (a) squaring and writing $|z|^2 = z\bar{z}$, we have

$(a^2 - |z_2|^2)(b^2 - |z_1|^2) = 0$

∴ $|z_2| = a$ as $|z_1| \neq b$ given.

(f) Proceeding exactly as in part (a), we have
$$(1 - |z_2|^2)(|z_1|^2 - 4) = 0$$
Since $|z_2| \neq 1$ therefore, we must have $|z_1|^2 = 4$

∴ $|z_1| = 2$.

36. (a) Let $z_k = a_k + ib_k$, $k = 1, 2, \ldots n$.
Then $z_1 + z_2 + \ldots + z_n = (a_1 + a_2 + \ldots + a_n)$
$$+ i(b_1 + b_2 + \ldots + b_n)$$
Now $|z_1 + z_2 + \ldots + z_n| \leq |z_1| + |z_2| + \ldots + |z_n|$
$$\ldots (1)$$
But $|z_k| = \sqrt{a_k^2 + b_k^2}$ and $|z_1 + z_2 + \ldots + z_n|$
$$= \sqrt{(a_1 + a_2 + \ldots + a_n)^2 + (b_1 + b_2 + \ldots + b_n)^2}$$
Hence substituting in (1), we get the required inequality.

(b) We have
$$(|z_1| + |z_2|)\left|\frac{z_1}{|z_1|} + \frac{z_2}{|z_2|}\right| \leq (|z_1| + |z_2|)$$
$$\cdot \left[\left|\frac{z_1}{|z_1|}\right| + \left|\frac{z_2}{|z_2|}\right|\right]$$
$$= (|z_1| + |z_2|)\left[\frac{|z_1|}{|z_1|} + \frac{|z_2|}{|z_2|}\right]$$
$$= 2(|z_1| + |z_2|).$$

37. (a) Let $z_k = \cos\theta_k + i\sin\theta_k$.
Then
$$\frac{1}{z_k} = (\cos\theta_k + i\sin\theta_k)^{-1} = \cos\theta_k - i\sin\theta_k.$$
Then $|z_k| = \sqrt{\cos^2\theta_k + \sin^2\theta_k} = 1$, $k = 1, 2, \ldots n$.
Now $z_1 + z_2 + \ldots + z_n$
$$= (\cos\theta_1 + \cos\theta_2 + \ldots + \cos\theta_n)$$
$$+ i(\sin\theta_1 + \sin\theta_2 + \ldots + \sin\theta_n).$$
And $1/z_1 + 1/z_2 + \ldots + 1/z_n$
$$= (\cos\theta_1 + \cos\theta_2 + \ldots + \cos\theta_n)$$
$$- i(\sin\theta_1 + \sin\theta_2 + \ldots + \sin\theta_n).$$
Hence $|z_1 + z_2 + \ldots + z_n| = \left|\dfrac{1}{z_1} + \dfrac{1}{z_2} + \ldots + \dfrac{1}{z_n}\right|$

since each side is equal to
$$\sqrt{\begin{array}{l}(\cos\theta_1 + \cos\theta_2 + \ldots + \cos\theta_n)^2 \\ + (\sin\theta_1 + \sin\theta_2 + \ldots + \sin\theta_n)^2\end{array}}.$$

Alternative : $|z_k| = 1 \Rightarrow |z_k|^2 = 1$

$\Rightarrow \quad z_k\bar{z}_k = 1$, $k = 1, 2, \ldots, n$. $\ldots(1)$
Then $|z_1 + z_2 + \ldots + z_n| = |\overline{z_1 + z_2 + \ldots + z_n}|$
$$= |\bar{z}_1 + \bar{z}_2 + \ldots + \bar{z}_n|$$
$$= \left|\frac{1}{z_1} + \frac{1}{z_2} + \ldots + \frac{1}{z_n}\right|, \text{from (1)}.$$

(b) $z_1 = \cos\theta_1 + i\sin\theta_1$ as $|z_1| = 1$
$z_1 + z_2 + z_3 = 0 \Rightarrow \Sigma\cos\theta_1 = 0$ and $\Sigma\sin\theta_1 = 0$

∴ $\dfrac{1}{z_1} + \dfrac{1}{z_2} + \dfrac{1}{z_3} = \Sigma\cos\theta_1 - i\Sigma\sin\theta_1 = 0$

(c) Ans. (a). $|z_1| = 1 \Rightarrow z_1\bar{z}_1 = 1$.
Also $\dfrac{1}{z_1} = \bar{z}_1$

∴ $|\bar{z}_1 + \bar{z}_2 + \bar{z}_3| = 1$ or $|\overline{z_1 + z_2 + z_3}| = 1$
or $|z_1 + z_2 + z_3| = 1 \Rightarrow$ (a).

(d) $|z_1 + z_2 + z_3| = 1$.   Squaring
$(z_1 + z_2 + z_3)(\bar{z}_1 + \bar{z}_2 + \bar{z}_3) = 1$
$|z_1|^2 + |z_2|^2 + |z_3|^2 + z_1(\bar{z}_2 + \bar{z}_3)$
$$+ z_2(\bar{z}_3 + \bar{z}_1) + z_3(\bar{z}_1 + \bar{z}_2) = 1$$
or $\Sigma z_1(\bar{z}_2 + \bar{z}_3) = 1 - (1 + 4 + 9) = -13$ $\ldots(1)$
Now $|9z_1z_2 + z_2z_3 + 4z_3z_1|^2$
$$= (9z_1z_2 + z_2z_3 + 4z_3z_1)$$
$$\overline{(9z_1\,\bar{z}_2 + \bar{z}_2\,\bar{z}_3 + 4\bar{z}_3\,\bar{z}_1)}$$
$$= 81(1.4) + 1(4.9) + 16(9.1)$$
$$+ 9|z_2|^2 \cdot z_1\,\bar{z}_3 + 36|z_1|^2 z_2 \cdot \bar{z}_3$$
$$+ 9|z_2|^2 z_3\,\bar{z}_1 + 4|z_3|^2 z_2\,\bar{z}_1$$
$$+ 36|z_1|^2 z_3\bar{z}_2 + 4|z_3|^2 z_1\,\bar{z}_2$$
Now put $|z_1|^2 = 1, |z_2|^2 = 4$ and $|z_3|^2 = 9$
$$= 324 + 36 + 144 + 36\,\Sigma\,z_1(\bar{z}_2 + \bar{z}_3)$$
$$= 36(9 + 1 + 4) + 36(-13) = 36 \text{ by (1)}$$
∴ $|9z_1z_2 + z_2z_3 + 4z_3z_1| = 6$

(e) $p^2 = k^2|z_2 - z_3|^2 = k^2(z_2 - z_3)(\overline{z_2 - z_3})$
$$= k^2(z_2 - z_3)(\bar{z}_2 - \bar{z}_3)$$
∴ $\dfrac{p^2}{z_2 - z_3} = k^2(\bar{z}_2 - \bar{z}_3)$

∴ $\Sigma\dfrac{p^2}{z_2 - z_3} = k^2\,\Sigma\,(\bar{z}_2 - \bar{z}_3) = 0$

38. (a) The condition arg $z = \pi/3$ is satisfied by all points lying on a ray emanating from the origin at an angle of $\pi/3$ to the x-axis. (See figure)

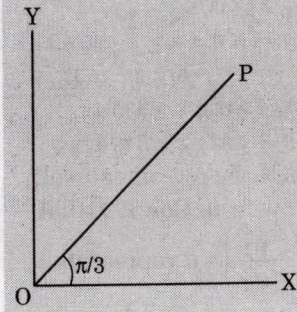

Fig. 14

We emphasize that this condition is not satisfied by the entire straight line but only by one side of the ray (excluding the origin). For on the other side of the line, the arg z is $-(2\pi/3)$ and not $\pi/3$. We also exclude the origin since argument of 0 is undefined.

(b) Here the point z satisfying the condition lie on the portion of the Argand plane containing the second and third quadrants including the entire y-axis except the origin, and a portion of the first quadrant located between rays emerging from origin at angles of $\pi/3$ and $\pi/2$. (See fig. 15)

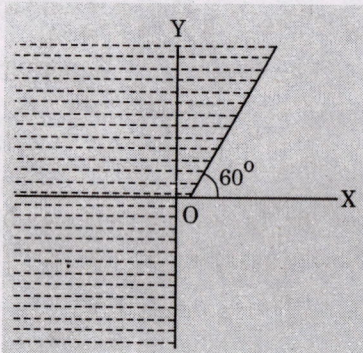

Fig. 15

(c) Here the equation $|z - i| = 1$ represents all points z on the boundary of a circle whose centre is i and radius 1. And the equation $\arg z = \pi/2$ represents all points on the positive side of y-axis excluding the origin. These two regions have only one common point A whose co-ordinates are $(0, 2)$.

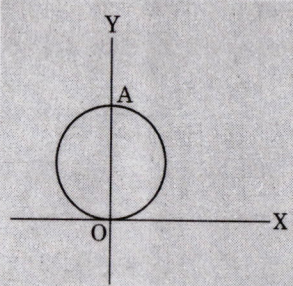

Fig. 16

Hence the two equations $|z - i| = 1$ and $\arg z = \pi/2$ represent only one point $A(0, 2)$.

39. (a) $|\pi - \arg z| < \pi/4$

$\Rightarrow \quad -\pi/4 < \pi - \arg z < \pi/4$

$\Rightarrow \quad -5\pi/4 < -\arg z < -3\pi/4$

$\Rightarrow \quad 5\pi/4 > \arg z > 3\pi/4$

$\Rightarrow \quad 3\pi/4 < \arg z < 5\pi/4$.

Now plot the region yourself.

(b) We know from **Cor. P. 71 that**

$\arg\left(\dfrac{z - z_1}{z - z_2}\right) = \alpha$ **represents a circle whose chord**

AB joining the points z_1 and z_2 subtends an angle α at the circumference. Hence the equation represents a circle whose equation can be shown to be

$\sqrt{3}(x^2 + y^2) - (3\sqrt{3} - 1)x - (\sqrt{3} - 1)y + 2\sqrt{3} - 2 = 0$

$\because \quad \tan^{-1}\dfrac{y - 1}{x - 1} - \tan^{-1}\dfrac{y}{x - 2} = \dfrac{\pi}{3}$ etc.

40. (a) Let $z = x + iy$. Then $\bar{z} = x - iy$.

Hence the equation $z = \bar{z}$ is equivalent to

$x + iy = x - iy$ which gives $2iy = 0$ or $y = 0$.

Hence $z = x$ which means that all real numbers satisfy the given equation.

(b) Ans. All pure imaginary numbers.

(c) $\bar{z} = 2 - z$ or $x - iy = 2 - x - iy$.

This gives $x = 1$.

Hence $z = 1 + iy$.

41. (a) $z^2 = -\bar{z}$ or $(x + iy)^2 = -(x - iy)$

or $x^2 - y^2 + 2ixy = -x + iy$.

Equating real and imaginary parts,

$$x^2 - y^2 = -x \qquad \qquad \text{...(1)}$$

and $2xy = y$ or $y(2x - 1) = 0$. ...(2)

From (2), either $y = 0$ or $x = \dfrac{1}{2}$.

When $y = 0$, (1) gives $x^2 = -x$

or $x(x + 1) = 0$

which gives $x = 0$ or $x = -1$.

Hence we get two sets of solutions $x = 0$, $y = 0$

$x = -1$, $y = 0$.

When $x = \dfrac{1}{2}$, (1) gives $\dfrac{1}{4} - y^2 = -\dfrac{1}{2}$

or $y^2 = \dfrac{3}{4}$ which gives $y = \pm\dfrac{\sqrt{3}}{2}$

Hence we obtain two more sets of solutions :

$x = \dfrac{1}{2}$, $y = \dfrac{\sqrt{3}}{2}$; $x = \dfrac{1}{2}$, $y = -\dfrac{\sqrt{3}}{2}$.

Thus in all we get the following four solutions

$z_1 = 0 + i \, 0 = 0$, $z_2 = -1 + i \cdot 0 = -1$,

$z_3 = \dfrac{1}{2} + \dfrac{i\sqrt{3}}{2}$, $z_4 = \dfrac{1}{2} - \dfrac{i\sqrt{3}}{2}$

(b) Proceed as above $0, 1, \omega, \omega^2$.

(c) $z^3 = \bar{z}$ or $(x + iy)^3 = x - iy$

or $x^3 + 3x^2 \cdot iy + 3xi^2 y^2 + i^3 y^3 = x - iy$

or $(x^3 - 3xy^2) + i(3x^2 y - y^3) = x - iy$.

Equating real and imaginary parts,

$x^3 - 3xy^2 = x \qquad \therefore \quad x(x^2 - 3y^2 - 1) = 0$ ...(1)

$3x^2 y - y^3 = -y \qquad \therefore \quad y(3x^2 - y^2 + 1) = 0$ ...(2)

Putting $x = 0$ from (1) in (2), we get $-y^3 = -y$

or $y(y^2 - 1) = 0 \quad \therefore \quad y = 0, 1, -1$

$\therefore \quad z = 0 + 0 \, i, \; 0 + i, \; 0 - i$

i.e. $z = 0, i, -i$ ...(A)

We may say put $y = 0$ from (2) in (1), then

$x(x^2 - 1) = 0$

$\therefore \quad x = 0, 1, -1$ but these will give real numbers not complex.

Again cancelling x and y from (1) and (2), we get $x^2 - 3y^2 = 1$ and $3x^2 - y^2 = -1$. These when solved give $x^2 = y^2 = -\dfrac{1}{2}$ which is not possible as x and y are real. Hence the values of z are given by (A).

(d) Ans. (d).

You may proceed as in part (c) by taking $z = x + iy$. **Alternative method is given below.**

Given $z^3 = -\bar{z}$ $\therefore |z^3| = |-\bar{z}| \Rightarrow |z|^3 = |z|$

or $|z|[|z|^2 - 1] = 0$ or $|z|[|z| - 1][|z| + 1] = 0$

$\therefore |z| = 0 \Rightarrow z = 0, |z| = 1 \Rightarrow |z|^2 = 1$

$\therefore z\bar{z} = 1 \Rightarrow \bar{z} = \dfrac{1}{z} \quad \therefore z^3 + \bar{z} = 0$

$\Rightarrow z^3 + \dfrac{1}{z} = 0$

$\therefore z^4 + 1 = 0 \Rightarrow z = (-1)^{1/4}$. This will give four solutions and $z = 0$ is the fifth solution.

$|z| + 1 \neq 0$ as $|z| + 1 > 0$.

42. (a) $x^2 - y^2 + i\,2xy + \sqrt{x^2 + y^2} = 0$

$\therefore x^2 - y^2 + \sqrt{x^2 + y^2} = 0$

$2xy = 0 \qquad \therefore x = 0 \text{ or } y = 0$

When $x = 0$ then $-y^2 \pm y = 0 \quad \therefore y = 0, \pm 1$

$\therefore (0, 0), (0, 1), (0, -1)$ or $z = 0, i, -i$

When $y = 0$ then we will get $(0, 0), (1, 0)$ and $(-1, 0)$.

But these are not complex numbers.

Hence $0, i, -i$ are the only three solutions of the given equation.

(b) $x - iy = i(x^2 - y^2 + i \cdot 2xy)$

$\therefore x + 2xy = 0$ and $x^2 - y^2 + y = 0$

$\therefore x(1 + 2y) = 0$

$\therefore x = 0$ and hence $y = 0, 1. \quad \therefore (0, 0), (0, 1)$.

or $y = -\dfrac{1}{2} \quad \therefore x^2 = \dfrac{1}{4} + \dfrac{1}{2} = \dfrac{3}{4}$

or $x = \pm\dfrac{\sqrt{3}}{2} \quad \therefore \left(\pm\dfrac{\sqrt{3}}{2}, -\dfrac{1}{2}\right)$

$\therefore$ Non-zero complex numbers are $\pm\dfrac{\sqrt{3}}{2} - i \cdot \dfrac{1}{2}, i$

(c) Rewriting the given equation, we have

$z(-1 - 2i - 3i - 4) + (i - 2 + 3 - 4i - 1 - 7i) = 0$

or $z = \dfrac{10i}{-5(1+i)} = \dfrac{-2i(1-i)}{1+1} = -1 - i$

43. (a) Clearly $z = 0$ is one obvious solution. When $z \neq 0$ then dividing by $|z|^2$ the equation can be written as $t^2 + t + 1 = 0$ where $t = \dfrac{z}{|z|}$

$\therefore \quad t = \dfrac{-1 \pm i\sqrt{3}}{2}$ or $\dfrac{z}{|z|} = \omega, \omega^2 \quad \therefore z = k\omega, k\omega^2$

where $k = |z|$ is non-negative real number.

(b) If $n = 2$ then $z = \bar{z}$ or $z - \bar{z} = 0$

or $2iy = 0 \quad \therefore y = 0 \quad \therefore z = x$.

Hence any real number x will satisfy the equation. If $n \neq 2$, then

$|z^{n-1}| = |\bar{z}| = |z| \quad \therefore |z|^{n-1} = |z|$

or $|z^{n-2}| = 1 \quad \therefore |z| = 1$

$\therefore z = e^{i\theta}$ and $\bar{z} = e^{-i\theta}$. Putting in $z^{n-1} = \bar{z}$,

we get $e^{i(n-1)\theta} = e^{-i\theta}$ or $e^{in\theta} = 1$

or $\cos n\theta + i \sin n\theta = 1$

$\therefore \cos n\theta = 1, \sin n\theta = 0$

But $\sin n\theta = 0 \Rightarrow \cos n\theta = \pm 1$

but $\cos n\theta = 1$ will imply only $\sin n\theta = 0$

$\therefore \cos n\theta = 1$ or $n\theta = 2m\pi \quad \therefore \theta = \dfrac{2m}{n}\pi$.

$\therefore z = \cos\dfrac{2m\pi}{n} + i \sin\dfrac{2m\pi}{n}$

44. (a) The equation $|z| = 1$ represents a circle with origin as centre and radius unity. Hence all the points z satisfying the condition $|z| < 1$ lie within the circle with origin as centre and radius unity.

(b) Here the points z lie outside and on the circle whose centre is origin and radius 3.

(c) $|z - 3| = 1$ represents all points z on the boundary of a circle with centre *i.e.* $(3, 0)$ and radius 1.

45. (a) $|z - i| < 1$ represents all points z inside the circle with centre i, *i.e.* $(0, 1)$ and radius 1.

(b) The inequality can be written as

$|-2|\left|z - \dfrac{i-1}{2}\right| > 9$ or $\left|z - \dfrac{i-1}{2}\right| > \dfrac{9}{2}$

which represents all points z outside the circle with centre $\dfrac{(i-1)}{2}$ *i.e.* $\left(-\dfrac{1}{2}, \dfrac{1}{2}\right)$ and radius $\dfrac{9}{2}$.

(c) We know that points satisfying $|z + i| \geq 2$ lie outside and on the circle with centre $-i$ *i.e.* $(0, -1)$ and radius 2. Similarly, the points z satisfying

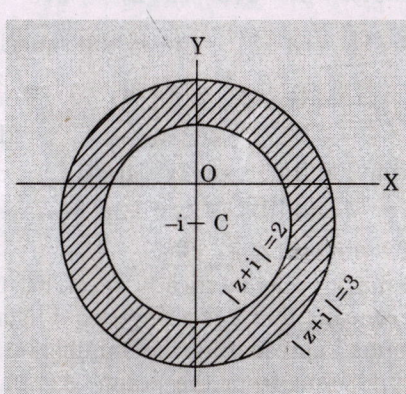

Fig. 17

$|z + i| \le 3$ lie inside and on the circle with centre $-i$ and radius 3.

Hence the points which satisfy $2 \le |z + i| \le 3$ lie on the boundaries and inside a ring shaped region bounded by two concentric circles centred at $-i$, i.e., $(0, -1)$ and having radius $r_1 = 2$ and $r_2 = 3$.

46. (a) $|z + i| = |z - 2|$ or $|z + i|^2 = |z - 2|^2$

or $|x + iy + i|^2 = |x + iy - 2|^2$

or $x^2 + (y + 1)^2 = (x - 2)^2 + y^2$

or $4x + 2y - 3 = 0$ ...(1)

Hence points z satisfying the given equation lie on the straight line (1).

Alternative. We know that $|z + i| = |z - (-i)|$ is the distance from the point z to the point representing the number $-i$ and $|z - 2|$ is the distance from the point z to the point representing the number 2. It is required to find the points for which these distances are equal. The solution will thus be a locus of a point equidistant from two fixed points representing the numbers $-i$ and 2 i.e. from the points $(0, -1)$ and $(2, 0)$.

From geometry we know that this locus is a straight line perpendicular to a line segment connecting the points $(0, -1)$ and $(2, 0)$ and passing through its mid-point. Hence all points z satisfying $|z + i| = |z - 2|$ lie on this line.

(b) We have two equations

$|z| - 4 = 0$ and $|z - i| - |z + 5i| = 0$

Putting $z = x + iy$, these equations become

$|x + iy| = 4$ i.e. $x^2 + y^2 = 16$. ...(1)

and $|x + iy - i| = |x + iy + 5i|$

or $x^2 + (y - 1)^2 = x^2 + (y + 5)^2$

i.e., $y = -2$ ...(2)

Putting $y = -2$ in (1), $x^2 + 4 = 16$ or $x = \pm 2\sqrt{3}$.

Hence the complex numbers z satisfying the given equations are $z_1 = (2\sqrt{3}, -2)$

and $z_2 = (-2\sqrt{3}, -2)$

that is, $z_1 = 2\sqrt{3} - 2i$, $z_2 = -2\sqrt{3} - 2i$.

47. (a) $|z - 1|^2 = |z - 3|^2 = |z - i|^2$ on squaring ...(1)

$\therefore$ $\underset{\text{I}}{(x - 1)^2 + y^2} = \underset{\text{II}}{(x - 3)^2 + y^2} = \underset{\text{III}}{x^2 + (y - 1)^2}$

From I and II, $2(2x - 4) = 0$ $\therefore$ $x = 2$

From I and III, $-2x = -2y$ $\therefore$ $x = y = 2$

$\therefore$ $z = x + iy = 2 + 2i$

Remark : Geometrically speaking, the equation (1) means that z is a point equidistant from the points representing the numbers $1, 3, i$, that is, equidistant from the points $A(1, 0)$, $B(3, 0)$ and $C(0, 1)$. It is therefore the circumcentre of $\triangle ABC$.

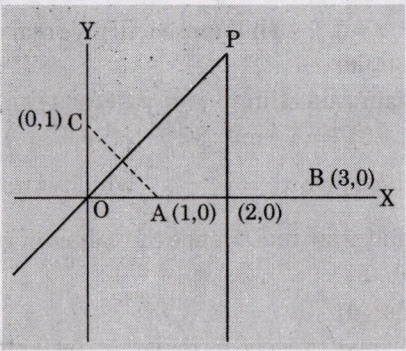

Fig. 18

So it is the intersection of perpendicular bisectors FP and EP of segment AB and AC, that is, the intersection P of the lines represented by the equation $x = 2$ and $y = x$. So we get $x = y = 2$ as before. (See fig.).

(b) $|z - 1|^2 + |z + 1|^2 = 4$ ...(1)

$(x - 1)^2 + y^2 + (x + 1)^2 + y^2 = 4$

or $2(x^2 + y^2 + 1) = 4 \therefore x^2 + y^2 = 1$ or $|z|^2 = 1$

$\therefore$ $|z| = 1$, since $|z|$ cannot be $-$ive.

Thus the equation (1) represents all points z on the circle with centre origin and radius unity.

48. Let $z - 1 = r(\cos \alpha + i \sin \alpha) = re^{i\alpha}$

or $(x - 1) + iy = r \cos \alpha + ir \sin \alpha$

$\therefore$ $r^2 = (x - 1)^2 + y^2$ and $\tan \alpha = \dfrac{y}{x - 1}$

$\therefore$ Given expression, $re^{i(\alpha - \theta)} + \dfrac{1}{r}e^{-i(\alpha - \theta)}$

Its imaginary part is $r \sin(\alpha - \theta) - \dfrac{1}{r} \sin(\alpha - \theta) = 0$

or $\left(r - \dfrac{1}{r}\right) \sin(\alpha - \theta) = 0$

Either $\left(r - \dfrac{1}{r}\right) = 0 \Rightarrow r^2 = 1 \Rightarrow (x - 1)^2 + y^2 = 1$

Above represents a circle centred at $(1, 0)$ and of radius 1.

or $\sin(\alpha - \theta) = 0$ $\therefore$ $\alpha - \theta = 0$

or $\tan \theta = \tan \alpha$

or $\dfrac{y}{(x - 1)} = \tan \alpha$ $\therefore$ $y = (x - 1) \tan \alpha$.

Above represents a straight line passing through the point $(0, 1)$.

49. (a) We are given $z = x + iy$ and $|z| = r = $ const.

(i) Let $Z = z + 2$. Then $Z - 2 = z$

$\therefore$ $|Z - 2| = |z| = r$ ...(1)

(1) shows that points corresponding to $Z = z + 2$ lie on a circle of radius r and centre $(2, 0)$.

(ii) Let $Z = z - 1 + i$ or $Z + 1 - i = z$

Then $|Z + 1 - i| = |z| = r$ ...(2)

(2) shows that the points representing $Z = z - 1 + i$ lie on a circle of radius r and having its centre at the point $-1 + i$, that is, at $(-1, 1)$.

(b) (i) Ans. On a circle of radius 3 and centre $(2,0)$.

(ii) Ans. On a circle of radius 9 and centre $(-1,0)$.

50. (a) Ans. (a) → (ii) (b) → (i).

(a) ⟹ Re $z = 0$ ⟹ $x = 0$ ...(1)

(b) ⟹ Arg $z = \pi/4$ ⟹ $\tan^{-1}(y/x) = \pi/4$

∴ $y = x$ ...(2)

Now $z^2 = x^2 - y^2 + i(2xy) = -y^2 + i \cdot 0$, by (1)

i.e. when $x = 0$ ∴ Im $z^2 = 0 \to$ (ii)

Again $z^2 = 0 + i(2x^2)$, by (2) as $y = x$.

∴ Re $z^2 = 0$ *i.e.* (i)

(b) Ans. (a) → (ii), (b) → (iii), (c) → (i)

(b) $\dfrac{1}{z} = \dfrac{1}{x+iy} = \dfrac{x - iy}{x^2 + y^2}$

∴ Re$\left(\dfrac{1}{z}\right) < \dfrac{1}{2}$ ⟹ $\dfrac{x}{x^2 + y^2} < \dfrac{1}{2}$

or $2x < x^2 + y^2$ or $x^2 + y^2 - 2x > 0$

or $(x-1)^2 + y^2 > 1$

Above represents the exterior of a circle of radius 1 centred at $(1, 0)$.

(a) Clearly represents a circle centred at $(1, 2)$ and of radius 5 as $(x-1)^2 + (y-2)^2 = 25$

(c) $\tan^{-1}\dfrac{y}{x-a} = \dfrac{\pi}{4}$ ∴ $y = (x-a) \cdot \tan \dfrac{\pi}{4}$

or $x - y = a$ *i.e.* a St. line.

51. (a) Ans. 6 and 0.

$|z+1| = |z+4-3| = |(z+4) + (-3)|$

$\leq |z+4| + |-3| = |z+4| + 3$

$\leq 3 + 3 = 6$ $[\because |z+4| \leq 3]$

Hence the greatest value of $|z+1|$ is 6.

Again $|z+1| = |z+4-3|$

$||z+4| - |3|| = 3 - 3 = 0.$

Hence least value is zero.

(a_1) $|z-2+i| = |z-(2-i)| \leq 2$ ...(1)

∴ $|z-2+i| \geq |z| - |2-i| = ||z| - \sqrt{5}|$ ..(2)

∴ $||z| - \sqrt{5}| \leq |z-2+i| \leq 2$ by (1) and (2)

∴ $-2 \leq |z| - \sqrt{5} \leq 2$

or $\sqrt{5} - 2 \leq |z| \leq \sqrt{5} + 2$

Hence the greatest and least values of $|z|$ are $\sqrt{5} + 2$ and $\sqrt{5} - 2$ respectively.

(b) $|z-4| < |z-2| ⟹ |z-4|^2 < |z-2|^2$

⟹ $|x+iy-4|^2 < |x+iy-2|^2$

⟹ $(x-4)^2 + y^2 < (x-2)^2 + y^2$

⟹ $x^2 - 8x + 16 + y^2 < x^2 - 4x + 4 + y^2$

⟹ $-4x < -12$ or $x > 3$ *i.e.* Re $(z) > 3$.

(c) **Hint:** $|(1+i)z^3 + iz| \leq |z^3||1+i| + |i||z|$

$= \sqrt{2}|z|^3 + |z| < \sqrt{2}\dfrac{1}{8} + \dfrac{1}{2} = \dfrac{\sqrt{2}+4}{8} < \dfrac{6}{8} = \dfrac{3}{4}$

$\left[\because |i| = 1 \text{ and } |z| < \dfrac{1}{2}\right]$

(d) Ans. (c).

$|z_2| = 6$ resresents a circle of radius 6 centred at $(0,0)$. $z_1 = 24 + 7i$ represents a point $A(24, 7)$. Let a diameter through A meet the circle in points B and C, then AB is least and AC is greatest distance of A from the circle. Clearly

$AO^2 = 24^2 + 7^2 = 625$ ∴ $AO = 25$

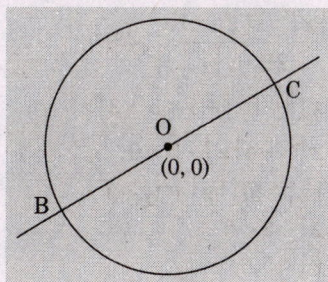

Fig. 18(a)

∴ Greatest distance $= AC = AO + OC$.

$= 25 + 6 = 31$

Least distance $= AB = AO - BO = 25 - 6 = 19$

Alternative Solution.

Since, $|z_2| = 6$ ∴ z_2 may be taken as $z_2 = 6e^{i\theta}$

or $z_2 = 6(\cos\theta + i\sin\theta), z_1 = 24 + 7i$

∴ $z_1 + z_2 = (24 + 6\cos\theta) + i(7 + 6\sin\theta)$

⟹ $[z_1 + z_2]^2 = (24 + 6\cos\theta)^2 + (7 + 6\sin\theta)^2$

$= 576 + 49 + 12(24\cos\theta + 7\sin\theta)$

$+ 36(\cos^2\theta + \sin^2\theta)$

Now put $24 = r\sin\alpha, 7 = r\cos\alpha$

where $r^2 = 24^2 + 7^2 = 625$ ∴ $r = 25$

∴ $d^2 = 625 + 36 + 12r\sin(\theta + \alpha)$

$= 661 + 12(25)(\pm 1)$; $+$ for max, $-$ for min

$= 661 + 300$ or $661 - 300$

$= 961$ or 361 *i.e.*, $(31)^2$ or $(19)^2$

∴ $d = 31$ (max.), $= 19$ (min.)

52. (a) $\log_{1/2}|z-2| > \log_{1/2}|z|$ ...(1)

We first observe that the left hand member of inequality (1) is meaningful for all complex numbers z, except $z = 2$. And the right member is meaningful for all z except $z = 0$. So we seek the solution of the inequality (1) among complex numbers except $z = 0, 2$.

Since here the base of logarithms is 1/2 which is less than 1, inequality (1) implies that

$|z-2| < |z|$

⟹ $|z-2|^2 < |z|^2$

⟹ $(x-2)^2 + y^2 < x^2 + y^2$

$\Rightarrow \quad -4x+4<0 \Rightarrow -4x<-4 \Rightarrow x>1.$

Hence the given inequality is satisfied by all complex numbers z representing the points on the Argand plane to the right of the line $x=1$, *i.e.* to the right of the line Re $(z)=1$ except the point $(2,0)$ represented by $z=2$ as remarked in the beginning.

Note : Similarly $\log_{1/3}|z-3|>\log_{1/3}z$ represents all points to the right of line $x=3/2$ except $(3,0)$ represented by $z=3$.

(b) $\log_{\sqrt{3}}\dfrac{|z|^2-|z|+1}{2+|z|}<2$

$\Rightarrow \quad \dfrac{|z|^2-|z|+1}{2+|z|}<(\sqrt{3})^2$

$\Rightarrow \quad |z|^2-|z|+1<6+3|z|$

$\Rightarrow \quad |z|^2-4|z|-5<0$

$\Rightarrow \quad (|z|-5)(|z|+1)<0$

$\Rightarrow \quad |z|-5<0 \qquad [\because |z|+1>0]$

$\Rightarrow \quad |z|<5.$

Hence the given inequality is satisfied by complex numbers z representing points inside a circle of radius 5 with centre at the origin.

(c) L.H.S. $=\log_{\sqrt{2}}(135+121)$

$=\log_{\sqrt{2}}\sqrt{256}=\log_{\sqrt{2}}16$

$=\log_{\sqrt{2}}(\sqrt{2})^8=8=2^3$

Now exp $[A\log 2]=2^3 \therefore \log e^{A\log 2}=\log 2^3$

$\therefore \quad A\log 2=3\log 2 \quad$ or $\quad A=3$

$|z|^2-|z|+4=3|z|^2+3$

or $\quad 2|z|^2+|z|-1=0$

$\therefore \quad (|z|+1)(2|z|-1)=0$

or $\quad |z|=\dfrac{1}{2} \quad$ as $|z|\neq-1$

$\therefore \quad z=\dfrac{1}{2}(\cos\theta+i\sin\theta)$, where $0\leq\theta\leq2\pi$

53. (a). Yes, true. Since base $1/3$ is less than 1, so given inequality holds if

$|z+1|<|z-1|$

or $\quad (x+1)^2+y^2<(x-1)^2+y^2$

or $\quad 4x<0 \quad$ or $\quad x<0 \quad$ or $\quad$ Re $(z)<0$

(b) Put $|z-1|=t=+$ive

Since its base is less than 1, the given inequality implies that $\dfrac{t+4}{t-2}<\left(\dfrac{1}{2}\right)^1=\dfrac{1}{2}$

or $\quad \dfrac{2t+8}{t-2}<1 \quad$ or $\quad \dfrac{2t+8}{t-2}-1<0 \qquad$ **(Note)**

or $\quad \dfrac{t+10}{t-2}<0$ where t is $+$ive

We cannot multiply by $t-2$ as we do not know whether it is $+$ive or $-$ive.

$\therefore \quad t-2<0 \quad$ or $\quad t<2 \qquad$ ...(1)

Again $\quad \log_{1/2}\left(\dfrac{t+4}{t-2}\right)>1$ (given)

Now order relation occurs only in real numbers and we know that log x is real only when x is $+$ive *i.e.*, >0

$\therefore \quad \dfrac{t+4}{t-2}$ is $+$ive $\Rightarrow t>2 \qquad$ ...(2)

Since results (1) and (2) cannot hold together and hence no such z exists which satisfies the given inequality.

54. (a) Suppose an integer n satisfies the given equation. Then

$(1-i)^n=2^n \qquad$ ...(1)

We know that if two complex numbers are equal, then their moduli are also equal. Hence taking moduli of both sides of (1), we get

$|(1-i)|^n=|2^n|$

or $\quad |1-i|^n=2^n \quad [\because 2^n>0$, we have $|2^n|=2^n]$

or $\quad (\sqrt{2})^n=2^n \qquad$ ...(2)

Now (2) will hold only when $n=0$. Hence the only integral solution of the given equation is $n=0$.

Alternative :

$1-i=\sqrt{2}\left(\cos\dfrac{\pi}{4}-i\sin\dfrac{\pi}{4}\right)$

Then given equation takes the form

$(\sqrt{2})^n[\cos(-\pi/4)+i\sin(-\pi/4)]^n=2^n$

or $\quad 2^{n/2}\left[\cos\dfrac{n\pi}{4}-i\sin\dfrac{n\pi}{4}\right]=2^n$

Equating real and imaginary parts, we get

$\cos(n\pi/4)=2^{n/2}$ and $-\sin(n\pi/4)=0.$

These are satisfied only for $n=0.$

Hence $n=0$ is the only solution.

(b) In this case,

$(\sqrt{2})^n\left[\cos\dfrac{n\pi}{4}+i\sin\dfrac{n\pi}{4}\right]$

$=(\sqrt{2})^n\left[\cos\dfrac{n\pi}{4}-i\sin\dfrac{n\pi}{4}\right]$

$\therefore \quad 2\sin\dfrac{n\pi}{4}=0 \quad$ or $\quad \dfrac{n\pi}{4}=k\pi \quad$ or $\quad n=4k.$

55. (a) The complex numbers z satisfying the condition

$|z-25i|\leq15 \qquad$ ...(1)

are represented by the points inside and on the circle of radius 15 and centre at the point $C(0,25)$.

From the figure, it is clear that the complex number z satisfying (1) and having least positive argument correspond to the point $P(x,y)$ which is the point of contact of a ray issuing from the origin and lying in the first quadrant to the above circle. The positive argument of all other points within and on the circle is greater than the argument of P.

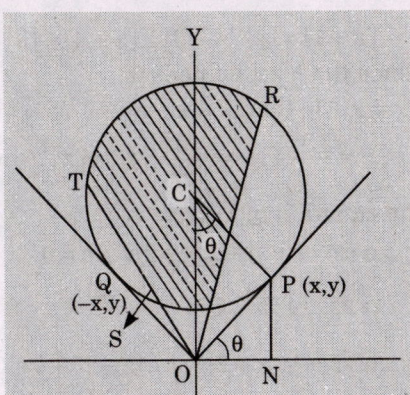

Fig. 19

From figure, we have

$$OC = 25, \ CP = \text{radius} = 15$$

and $\angle CPO = 90°$

Hence $OP = \sqrt{OC^2 - CP^2} = \sqrt{25^2 - 15^2} = 20$.

If $\angle PCO = \theta$, then $\angle PON = \theta$. Also

$$\cos\theta = \frac{PC}{OC} = \frac{15}{25} = \frac{3}{5}.$$

$\therefore \quad x = ON = OP\cos\theta = 20 \times (3/5) = 12$,

and $y = PN = OP\sin\theta = 20 \times (4/5) = 16$.

Hence P represents the complex number $z = x + iy = 12 + 16i$ which is therefore the required value of z satisfying the given conditions. The corresponding point Q on the other tangent from O will have greatest +ive argument. It will be $-12 + 16i$ whose argument is $\pi - \theta$.

(b) The given equation represents points on a circle whose centre is $C(2, -2)$ in 4th quadrant and radius 1 where OC is inclined at an angle of $45°$ to x-axis. Clearly the point P on OC will have least absolute value say r.

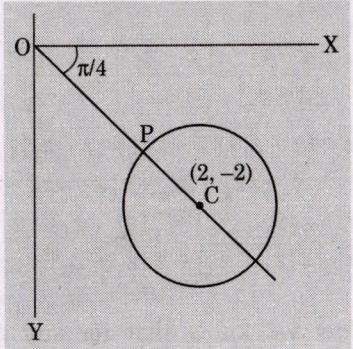

Fig. 20

$$r = OP = OC - PC = \sqrt{4+4} - 1 = 2\sqrt{2} - 1$$

$\therefore$ Point P is $(r\cos 45°, -r\sin 45°)$

$$= \left(\frac{r}{\sqrt{2}}, -\frac{r}{\sqrt{2}}\right) = \frac{r}{\sqrt{2}}(1 - i)$$

$\therefore \quad z = \left(2 - \frac{1}{\sqrt{2}}\right)(1 - i)$.

(c) $|z - 5i| \le 1$ represent all points lying inside and on the circle centred at $(0, 5)$ and of radius 1. Clearly the point A has minimum amplitude $\theta = \angle AOX = \angle ACO$

$$OA^2 = 25 - 1 = 24 \ i.e., \ OA = 2\sqrt{6}.$$

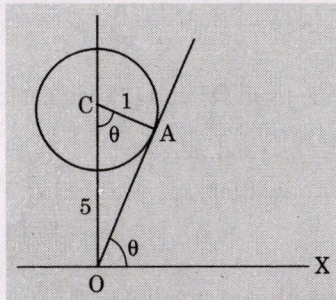

Fig. 21

$\therefore \quad \cos\theta = \frac{1}{5} \quad \Rightarrow \quad \sin\theta = \frac{2\sqrt{6}}{5}$

$$x = OA\cos\theta = 2\sqrt{6} \cdot \frac{1}{5},$$

$$y = OA\sin\theta = 2\sqrt{6} \cdot \frac{2\sqrt{6}}{5}$$

$\therefore \quad A$ is $z = x + iy = \frac{2\sqrt{6}}{5}(1 + 2\sqrt{6}i)$

56. (a) $|z| = \left|z + \frac{2}{z} - \frac{2}{z}\right| = \left|z + \frac{2}{z} + \left(-\frac{2}{z}\right)\right|$

$$\le \left|z + \frac{2}{z}\right| + \left|-\frac{2}{z}\right| = 2 + \left|\frac{2}{z}\right|$$

$\therefore \quad |z| \le 2 + \frac{2}{|z|}$. Put $|z| = t$

$$t^2 - 2t - 2 \le 0$$

$\therefore \quad (t - a)(t - b) \le 0$ where a and b are roots of

$$t^2 - 2t - 2 = 0, a < b$$

$\therefore \quad a = 1 - \sqrt{3}, \ b = 1 + \sqrt{3}, \ a \le t \le b$

or $(1 - \sqrt{3}) \le |z| \le 1 + \sqrt{3}$

Hence the max. value of $|z|$ is $1 + \sqrt{3}$.

(b) $\left|z + \frac{1}{z}\right| \le |z| + \left|\frac{1}{z}\right|$ or $a \le t + \frac{1}{t}$ where $t = |z|$

or $t^2 - at + 1 > 0$ or $(t - \alpha)(t - \beta) > 0, \ \alpha < \beta$

$\therefore \quad t \le \alpha$ or $t \ge \beta$

where α, β are roots of $t^2 - at + 1 = 0$

or $t = \frac{a \pm \sqrt{a^2 - 4}}{2}$

$\therefore \quad \alpha = \frac{a - \sqrt{a^2 - 4}}{2}, \ \beta = \frac{a + \sqrt{a^2 - 4}}{2}$

Hence β is greatest and α the least value of $t = |z|$. In case these values are equal then $a^2 - 4 = 0$

$\therefore \quad a = \pm 2$ and the equal value is $\frac{a}{2} = \pm 1 = 1$ as

$t = |z| = +$ ive.

(c) $\left|z+\dfrac{1}{z}\right|\geq\left|z\right|-\dfrac{1}{\left|z\right|}$ **See P. 71**   ...(1)

Now $\left|z\right|\geq3$ $\therefore$ $\dfrac{1}{\left|z\right|}\leq\dfrac{1}{3}$ or $-\dfrac{1}{\left|z\right|}\geq-\dfrac{1}{3}$.

Adding the two like inequalities

$$\left|z\right|-\dfrac{1}{\left|z\right|}\quad 3-\dfrac{1}{3}=\dfrac{8}{3}\qquad ...(2)$$

Hence from (1) and (2), we get $\left|z+\dfrac{1}{z}\right|\geq\dfrac{8}{3}$

$\therefore$ Least value is 8/3.

(d) We know that $\left|z_1\right|+\left|z_2\right|\geq\left|z_1+z_2\right|$

$\therefore$ $\left|z-1\right|+\left|z+1\right|=\left|1-z\right|+\left|z+1\right|$
$$\geq\left|1-z+z+1\right|=2$$

Hence the least value is 2

Again $E=\left|z\right|+\left|z-1\right|+\left|2z-3\right|$
$$=\left|z\right|+\left|z-1\right|+\left|3-2z\right|$$
$$\geq\left|z+z-1+3-2z\right|=2$$

Hence the least value is 2.

(e) Ans. (d).

Let $z=a+bw+cw^2$

$\therefore$ $\bar{z}=a+bw^2+cw$

$\therefore$ $\left|z\right|=\left|\bar{z}\right|$ ...(1)

and $z\bar{z}=a^2+b^2+c^2-bc-ca-ab$

$$\left|z\right|^2=\dfrac{1}{2}\left[(a-b)^2+(b-c)^2+(c-a)^2\right]$$

$x=\left|z\right|+\left|\bar{z}\right|=2\left|z\right|$ by (1)

$\therefore$ $x^2=4\left|z\right|^2=4\cdot\dfrac{1}{2}\left[\sum(a-b)^2\right]$

$\therefore$ $x=\sqrt{2}\left[(a-b)^2+(b-c)^2+(c-a)^2\right]$ ...(2)

Since, a,b,c are integers, x will be minimum if a,b,c are consecutive integers $p, p+1, p+2$

$\therefore$ $x=\sqrt{2}\left[1+1+4\right]=6\sqrt{2}\Rightarrow$ (d).

57. (a) Here we are to find both max. and min. values and hence we apply

$$\left|\left|z\right|-\dfrac{4}{\left|z\right|}\right|<\left|z-\dfrac{4}{z}\right|=2.$$

$\therefore$ $-2<\left|z\right|-\dfrac{4}{\left|z\right|}<2$ **See Note (b) P. 71**

Put $\left|z\right|=t$ $\therefore$ $t^2-2t-4<0$

and $0<t^2+2t-4$ or $t^2+2t-4>0$

or $(t-1)^2<5$ and $(t+1)^2-5>0$

or $t\leq1\pm\sqrt{5}$ and $t\geq-1\pm\sqrt{5}$

$\therefore$ $\left|z\right|\leq1+\sqrt{5}$ or $\left|z\right|\geq\sqrt{5}-1$

$\therefore$ Max. value of $\left|z\right|=1+\sqrt{5}$.

Least value is $\sqrt{5}-1$.

(b) $\left|z+1\right|=\left|z+4-3\right|=\left|(z+4)+(-3)\right|$
$$\leq\left|z+4\right|+\left|-3\right|=\left|z+4\right|+3$$
$$\leq3+3=6\qquad\left[\because\left|z+4\right|\leq3\right]$$

Hence the greatest value of $\left|z+1\right|$ is 6.

$\left|z+1\right|=\left|z+4-3\right|\geq\left|z+4\right|-\left|3\right|=0$

Hence the least value is 0.

58. (a) If $z=x+iy$ then $\bar{z}=x-iy$

$\therefore$ $x=\dfrac{z+\bar{z}}{2},y=\dfrac{z-\bar{z}}{2i},z\bar{z}=\left|z\right|^2=x^2+y^2$

The equation of a circle is

$\alpha(x^2+y^2)+2gx+2fy+c=0$ ...(1)

$\alpha z\bar{z}+g(z+\bar{z})+f\dfrac{(z-\bar{z})}{i}+c=0$

or $\alpha z\bar{z}+g(z+\bar{z})-if(z-\bar{z})+c=0$

or $\alpha z\bar{z}+(g-if)z+(g+if)\bar{z}+c=0$

Now if $g+if=\beta$ then $g-if=\bar{\beta}$

$\therefore$ $\alpha z\bar{z}+\bar{\beta}z+\beta\bar{z}+c=0$ ...(2)

It is of the same form as given.

Deduction : Circle (1) will reduce to a straight line if $\alpha=0$ in (1). Hence putting $\alpha=0$ in (2) the equation of the line can be put in the form

$$\bar{\beta}z+\beta\bar{z}+c=0.$$

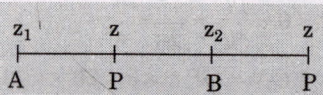

Fig. 22

(b) Let $P(z)$ be any point on the line AB.

$\arg(z-z_1)-\arg(z-z_2)=0$ or π according as P is outside or inside AB.

or $\arg\dfrac{z-z_1}{z-z_2}=0$ or π ...(1)

or $\tan^{-1}\dfrac{Y}{X}=0$ or π or $\dfrac{Y}{X}=0$ $\therefore$ $Y=0$

Hence from (1) we conclude that

$$\dfrac{z-z_1}{z-z_2}=\text{purely real}$$

$\therefore$ $\dfrac{z-z_1}{z-z_2}=\left(\overline{\dfrac{z-z_1}{z-z_2}}\right)=\dfrac{\bar{z}-\bar{z}_1}{\bar{z}-\bar{z}_2}$

or $(z-z_1)(\bar{z}-\bar{z}_2)=(z-z_2)(\bar{z}-\bar{z}_1)$

or $z\bar{z}-\bar{z}z_1-z\bar{z}_2+z_1\bar{z}_2=z\bar{z}-\bar{z}z_2-z\bar{z}_1+z_2\bar{z}_1$

or $z(\bar{z}_1-\bar{z}_2)+\bar{z}(z_2-z_1)+z_1\bar{z}_2-z_2\bar{z}_1=0$

or $z(\bar{z}_1-\bar{z}_2)-\bar{z}(z_1-z_2)+(z_1\bar{z}_2-z_1\overline{z_2})=0$

    ...(2)

Now we know that for any complex number $z=a+ib$, $z-\bar{z}=2i\,\text{Im}\,z=2ib=p.i$

Let $z_1-z_2=\beta$, then $\overline{z_1-z_2}=\bar{\beta}$

Hence from (2), $z\bar{\beta}-\bar{z}\beta+ic=0$

Now $\dfrac{1}{i}=-i,\bar{i}=-i$

Divide by i

$-zi\bar{\beta}+\bar{z}i\beta+c=0.$ If $i\beta=p$ then $\overline{i\beta}=\bar{p}$

or $\bar{i}\bar{\beta}=\bar{p}$ or $-i\bar{\beta}=\bar{p}$

$\therefore$ $z\bar{p}+p\bar{z}+c=0.$

(c) Let Q be z_2 and its reflection be the point $P(z_1)$ in the given line. If $O(z)$ be any point on the given line then by definition OR is right bisector of QP.

$\therefore \quad OP = OQ \quad$ or $\quad |z - z_1| = |z - z_2|$

or $\quad |z - z_1|^2 = |z - z_2|^2$

or $\quad (z - z_1)(\bar{z} - \bar{z}_1) = (z - z_2)(\bar{z} - \bar{z}_2)$

or $\quad z(\bar{z}_1 - \bar{z}_2) + \bar{z}(z_1 - z_2) = z_1\bar{z}_1 - z_2\bar{z}_2$

Comparing with given line $z\bar{b} + \bar{z}b = c$

$$\frac{\bar{z}_1 - \bar{z}_2}{\bar{b}} = \frac{z_1 - z_2}{b} = \frac{z_1\bar{z}_1 - z_2\bar{z}_2}{c} = \lambda, \text{ say}$$

$$\frac{\bar{z}_1 - \bar{z}_2}{\lambda} = \bar{b}, \frac{z_1 - z_2}{\lambda} = b, \frac{z_1\bar{z}_1 - z_2\bar{z}_2}{\lambda} = c \ldots(1)$$

Also $\bar{z}_1 b + z_2\bar{b} = \bar{z}_1 \dfrac{(z_1 - z_2)}{\lambda} + z_2 \dfrac{(\bar{z}_1 - \bar{z}_2)}{\lambda}$

$$= \frac{z_1\bar{z}_1 - z_2\bar{z}_2}{\lambda} = c \quad \text{by (1)}$$

59. If $ABCD$ be concyclic then angle subtended by AB both at C and D are same.

$$\frac{z_2 - z_3}{z_1 - z_3} = \frac{BC}{AC}e^{i\theta}$$

$$\frac{z_2 - z_4}{z_1 - z_4} = \frac{BD}{AD}e^{i\theta}$$

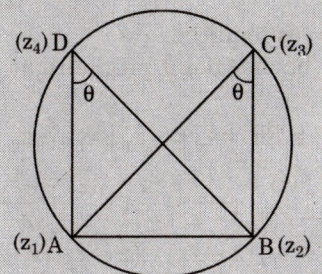

Fig. 23

Dividing, we get

$$\left(\frac{z_2 - z_3}{z_1 - z_3}\right)\left/\left(\frac{z_1 - z_4}{z_2 - z_4}\right)\right. = \frac{BC \cdot AD}{AC \cdot BD} = \text{real}$$

Conversely $\dfrac{(z_2 - z_3)(z_1 - z_4)}{(z_1 - z_3)(z_2 - z_4)} = \text{real} = k$, say

then $\quad \dfrac{z_2 - z_3}{z_1 - z_3} = k\dfrac{z_2 - z_4}{z_1 - z_4}$

$\therefore \quad \arg\dfrac{z_2 - z_3}{z_1 - z_3} = \arg\dfrac{z_2 - z_4}{z_1 - z_4}$

$\therefore \quad \angle ACB = \angle ADB$

Hence the points are concyclic.

Note : If $\arg z = \theta$ then $\arg kz = \theta$, where k is real.

60. $\dfrac{b + ic}{1 + a} = z \quad \therefore \quad \dfrac{b - ic}{1 + a} = \bar{z}$

$$z + \bar{z} = \frac{2b}{1 + a}, \quad z - \bar{z} = \frac{2ic}{1 + a} \qquad \ldots(1)$$

and $z\bar{z} = \dfrac{b^2 + c^2}{(1 + a)^2} = \dfrac{1 - a^2}{(1 + a)^2} = \dfrac{1 - a}{1 + a} \qquad \ldots(2)$

$$\frac{1 + iz}{1 - iz} = \frac{1 + iz}{1 - iz} \times \frac{1 + i\bar{z}}{1 + i\bar{z}} = \frac{1 + i(z + \bar{z}) - z\bar{z}}{1 - i(z - \bar{z}) + z\bar{z}} \qquad \ldots(3)$$

$$\frac{1 + iz}{1 - iz} = \left[1 + i\frac{2b}{1 + a} - \frac{1 - a}{1 + a}\right] \div \left[1 + \frac{2c}{1 + a} + \frac{1 - a}{1 + a}\right]$$

$$= \frac{2(a + ib)}{2(1 + c)} = \frac{(a + ib)}{(1 + c)}$$

61. Let A, B, C be the points represented by the numbers z_1, z_2, z_3 and P be the point represented by z.

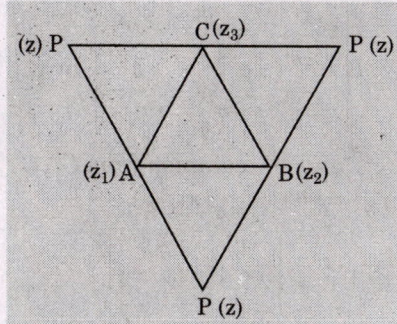

Fig. 24

Now the four points A, B, C, P form a parallelogram in the following three orders :

(i) A, B, P, C

(ii) B, C, P, A and

(iii) C, A, P, B. (See the figure)

In case (i), the condition for A, B, P, C to form a parallelogram is

$$\vec{AB} = \vec{CP} \quad i.e., \quad z_2 - z_1 = z - z_3$$

or $\quad z = z_2 + z_3 - z_1$

Similarly, in case (ii) and (iii), the required conditions are

$$\vec{BC} = \vec{AP} \quad \text{or} \quad z_3 - z_2 = z - z_1 \quad i.e. \quad z = z_3 + z_1 - z_2$$

and $\vec{CA} = \vec{BP} \quad$ or $\quad z_1 - z_3 = z - z_2 \quad i.e. \quad z = z_1 + z_2 - z_3$.

62. Let A, B, C be the points of affix z_1, z_2, z_3 and A', B', C', the points of affix z_1', z_2', z_3'. Then the $\triangle ABC$ and $\triangle A'B'C'$ are similar if

$$\vec{AB} = \lambda \vec{A'B'} \quad i.e. \quad z_2 - z_1 = \lambda(z_2' - z_1')$$

and $\vec{BC} = \lambda \vec{B'C'} \quad i.e. \quad z_3 - z_2 = \lambda(z_3' - z_2')$.

$\therefore \quad \dfrac{z_2 - z_1}{z_3 - z_2} = \dfrac{z_2' - z_1'}{z_3' - z_2'}$

or $z_2(z_3' - z_2') - z_1(z_3' - z_2') = z_3(z_2' - z_1')$
$\qquad\qquad\qquad\qquad\qquad\qquad - z_2(z_2' - z_1')$

or $z_1(z_2' - z_3') + z_2(z_3' - z_1') + z_3(z_1' - z_2') = 0$

or $\begin{vmatrix} z_1 & z_1' & 1 \\ z_2 & z_2' & 1 \\ z_3 & z_3' & 1 \end{vmatrix} = 0$

63. This question is based on the following :

$A + B + C = \pi$, $e^{\pi i} = \cos \pi + i \sin \pi = -1$, $e^{-\pi i} = -1$

...(1)

$$e^{i(B+C)} = e^{i(\pi - A)} = e^{\pi i} \cdot e^{-iA} = -e^{-iA}$$

$$\therefore \quad e^{-i(B+C)} = -e^{iA} \qquad ...(2)$$

Take e^{iA}, e^{iB} and e^{iC} common from R_1, R_2 and R_3 respectively.

$$\therefore \quad \Delta = e^{i(A+B+C)} \begin{vmatrix} e^{iA} & e^{-i(A+C)} & e^{-i(A+B)} \\ e^{-i(B+C)} & e^{iB} & e^{-i(B+A)} \\ e^{-i(B+C)} & e^{-i(C+A)} & e^{iC} \end{vmatrix}$$

$$= -1 \begin{vmatrix} e^{iA} & -e^{iB} & -e^{iC} \\ -e^{iA} & e^{iB} & -e^{iC} \\ -e^{iA} & -e^{iB} & e^{iC} \end{vmatrix}, \text{ by (2)}$$

Take e^{iA}, e^{iB} and e^{iC} common from C_1, C_2 and C_3 and again put $e^{i(A+B+C)} = e^{i\pi} = -1$.

$$\therefore \quad \Delta = (-1)(-1) \begin{vmatrix} 1 & -1 & -1 \\ -1 & 1 & -1 \\ -1 & -1 & 1 \end{vmatrix}$$

Now make two zeros and expand $\Delta = -4$ which is purely real.

64. (a) Let $z_1 = x_1 + iy_1 = (x_1, y_1)$.

$z_2 = x_2 + iy_2 = (x_2, y_2)$,

$z_3 = x_3 + iy_3 = (x_3, y_3)$.

∴ The required area

$$= \frac{1}{2} \begin{vmatrix} x_1 & y_1 & 1 \\ x_2 & y_2 & 1 \\ x_3 & y_3 & 1 \end{vmatrix} = \frac{1}{2i} \begin{vmatrix} x_1 & iy_1 & 1 \\ x_2 & iy_2 & 1 \\ x_3 & iy_3 & 1 \end{vmatrix}$$

$$= \frac{1}{2i} \begin{vmatrix} x_1 & x_1 + iy_1 & 1 \\ x_2 & x_2 + iy_2 & 1 \\ x_3 & x_3 + iy_3 & 1 \end{vmatrix} \text{ by } C_2 + C_1$$

$$= \frac{1}{2i} \begin{vmatrix} x_1 & z_1 & 1 \\ x_2 & z_2 & 1 \\ x_3 & z_3 & 1 \end{vmatrix} = \frac{1}{4i} \begin{vmatrix} 2x_1 & z_1 & 1 \\ 2x_2 & z_2 & 1 \\ 2x_3 & z_3 & 1 \end{vmatrix}$$

$$= \frac{1}{4i} \begin{vmatrix} z_1 + \bar{z}_1 & z_1 & 1 \\ z_2 + \bar{z}_2 & z_2 & 1 \\ z_3 + \bar{z}_3 & z_3 & 1 \end{vmatrix} = \frac{1}{4i} \begin{vmatrix} \bar{z}_1 & z_1 & 1 \\ \bar{z}_2 & z_2 & 1 \\ \bar{z}_3 & z_3 & 1 \end{vmatrix},$$

by $C_1 - C_2$

$$= \frac{1}{4i} \Sigma \bar{z}_1 (z_2 - z_3) = \frac{1}{4i} \frac{\Sigma \bar{z}_1 z_1 (z_2 - z_3)}{z_1}$$

$$= \frac{1}{4i} \Sigma \frac{|z_1|^2}{z_1} (z_2 - z_3) = \Sigma \frac{|z_1|^2 (z_2 - z_3)}{4iz_1}$$

(b) $z_1 = (x_1 + iy_1) = (x_1, y_1)$

$az_1 + bz_2 + cz_3 = (ax_1 + bx_2 + cx_3)$

$\qquad\qquad\qquad + i(ay_1 + by_2 + cy_3) = 0$

Above relation implies that

$ax_1 + bx_2 + cx_3 = 0$ ...(1)

$ay_1 + by_2 + cy_3 = 0$ ...(2)

$a + b + c = 0$ (given) ...(3)

Eliminating a, b, c we get

$$\begin{vmatrix} x_1 & x_2 & x_3 \\ y_1 & y_2 & y_3 \\ 1 & 1 & 1 \end{vmatrix} = 0 \text{ or } \frac{1}{2} \begin{vmatrix} x_1 & y_1 & 1 \\ x_2 & y_2 & 1 \\ x_3 & y_3 & 1 \end{vmatrix} = 0$$

∴ $\Delta = 0$ *i.e.*, the points are collinear.

65. (a) Let the circumcentre O be represented by the complex number z. Now $OA = OB = OC$.

$|z - z_1| = |z - z_2| = |z - z_3|$. Square

$(z - z_1)(\bar{z} - \bar{z}_1) = (\ )(\ ) = (\ )(\ )$

or $z\bar{z} - z\bar{z}_1 - \bar{z}z_1 + z_1\bar{z}_1 = ... = ...$

or $|z|^2 - z\bar{z}_1 - \bar{z}z_1 + |z_1|^2 = ... = ...$

Cancel $|z|^2$ from all the three terms and multiply by (-1). From 1st two equalities

$z(\bar{z}_1 - \bar{z}_2) + \bar{z}(z_1 - z_2) = |z_1|^2 - |z_2|^2$ ...(1)

Similarly from 2nd and 3rd,

$z(\bar{z}_2 - \bar{z}_3) + \bar{z}(z_2 - z_3) = |z_2|^2 - |z_3|^2$ ...(2)

We have to find z and hence we will eliminate $\bar{z}$ for which multiply (1) by $(z_2 - z_3)$ and (2) by $(z_1 - z_2)$ and subtract

$z[(\bar{z}_1 - \bar{z}_2)(z_2 - z_3) - (\bar{z}_2 - \bar{z}_3)(z_1 - z_2)]$

$\quad = (z_2 - z_3)(|z_1|^2 - |z_2|^2)$

$\qquad\qquad - (z_1 - z_2)(|z_2|^2 - |z_3|^2)$

or $z[\Sigma \bar{z}_1(z_2 - z_3)] = \Sigma |z_1|^2(z_2 - z_3)$

∴ $z =$ as required.

(b) If $P(z)$ be any point on the right bisector of AB, then

$PA = PB \Rightarrow |z - z_1| = |z - z_2|$

∴ $|z - z_1|^2 = |z - z_2|^2$

or $(z - z_1)(\overline{z - z_1}) = (z - z_2) \cdot (\overline{z - z_2})$

or $(z - z_1)(\bar{z} - \bar{z}_1) - (z - z_2)(\bar{z} - \bar{z}_2) = 0$

or $z(\bar{z}_2 - \bar{z}_1) + \bar{z}(z_1 - z_2) = z_2\bar{z}_2 - z_1\bar{z}_1$

66. (a) Ans. (b).

Set A represents all points above the line $y = 1$, as Imaginary $z \geq 1$ or $y \geq 1$. Set B represents all points on the circle $(x - 2)^2 + (y - 1)^2 = 9$

Set C represents all points such that R.P. of $(1 - i)(x + iy) = \sqrt{2}$ or line $x + y = \sqrt{2}$. From the figure, it is clear that P is the only point which lies on A, B and C all.

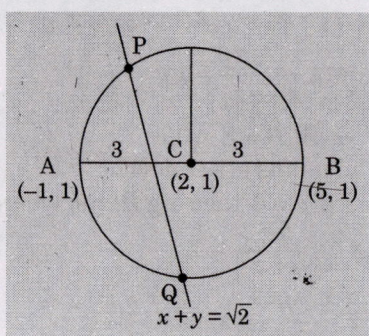

Fig. 24(a)

(b) Ans. (c).

$$|z+1-i|^2 + |z-5-i|^2$$

The points $(-1, 1)$ and $(5, 1)$ are the extremities of the diameter of the given circle of radius 3.

Hence $PA^2 + PB^2 = AB^2 = 36$.

(c) Ans. (d). $|w - 2 - i| < 3$

$$||z| - |w|| < |z - w|$$

$|z - w| =$ distance between z and w, z is fixed. It will be maximum for diametrically opposite points.

$$\therefore \quad |z - w| < 6 \quad \therefore \quad -6 < |z| - |w| < 6$$

Add 3 in all.

$$\therefore \quad -3 < |z| - |w| + 3 < 9 \Rightarrow \text{(d)}$$

67. Ans. (d). $z = \cos\theta + i\sin\theta$

$$\therefore \quad z^m = \cos m\theta + i \sin m\theta$$

$$\therefore \quad \text{Im}(z^{2m-1}) = \sin(2m-1)\theta$$

$$\therefore \quad E = \sum_{m=1}^{15} \sin(2m-1)\theta$$

$$= \sin\theta + \sin 3\theta + \sin 5\theta + \ldots + \sin 29\theta$$

$$= \frac{\sin m \cdot \dfrac{2\theta}{2}}{\sin \dfrac{2\theta}{2}} \sin\left[\frac{\theta + 29\theta}{2}\right]$$

$$= \frac{\sin 15\theta}{\sin\theta} \sin 15\theta = \frac{\sin 30° \sin 30°}{\sin 2°} \quad (\because m = 15)$$

$$= \frac{1}{4\sin 2°}$$

Alternate Solution

$$\text{Im}[z + z^3 + z^5 + \ldots 15 \text{ terms}]$$

$$= \text{Im} \frac{z[1 - (z^2)^{15}]}{1 - z^2} \quad \text{Sum of a G.P.}$$

$$= \text{Im} \frac{[1 - z^{30}]}{\dfrac{1}{z} - z} = \text{Im} \frac{[1 - \cos 30\theta - i \sin 30\theta]}{-\left(z - \dfrac{1}{z}\right)}$$

$$= \text{Im} \frac{[1 - \cos 30\theta - i \sin 30\theta]}{-2 i \sin\theta}$$

$$= \text{Im} \frac{i[1 - \cos 30\theta - i \sin 30\theta]}{2 \sin\theta}$$

$$= \frac{1 - \cos 30\theta}{2\sin\theta}, \text{ taking imaginary part}$$

$$= \frac{1 - \cos 60°}{2\sin 2°} = \frac{1}{4\sin 2°}, \text{ as } \theta = 2°$$

§13 Anti-clockwise rotation.

(i) Let $OP = |z_1 - z_0| = r$ where OP is inclined to OX at an angle θ.

$$\therefore \quad z_1 - z_0 = r(\cos\theta + i\sin\theta) = re^{i\theta}$$

Now let OP rotate about $O(z_0)$ through an angle φ in anti-clockwise direction and OP takes the position OQ where $OP = OQ = r$

Now $OQ = r = |z_2 - z_0|$.

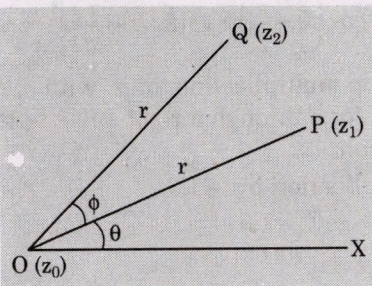

Fig. 25

Also $z_2 - z_0 = r e^{i(\theta + \varphi)} = re^{i\theta} \cdot e^{i\varphi} = OP e^{i\varphi}$

*or $z_2 - z_0 = (z_1 - z_0)e^{i\varphi}$ **(V. Imp.)**

In the above z_0 is the point about which rotation is made and φ is the angle of rotation in **anticlock-wise** direction. In case the rotation is **clock-wise**, then

$$z_2 - z_0 = (z_1 - z_0)e^{-i\varphi} \quad \textbf{(Note this). (V. Imp.)}$$

General formula for rotation.

Earlier $OP = PQ = r$

But now we will discuss when AB is rotated to AC but $AB \neq AC$.

Cor. If z_1, z_2, z_3 be the vertices of a triangle ABC described in anticlockwise sense, then

$$\frac{z_3 - z_1}{z_2 - z_1} = \frac{AC}{AB} e^{i\phi} = \frac{r_3}{r_2} e^{i\phi}$$

or $\dfrac{z_3 - z_1}{r_3} = \dfrac{z_2 - z_1}{r_2} e^{i\phi}$ **(Remember)**

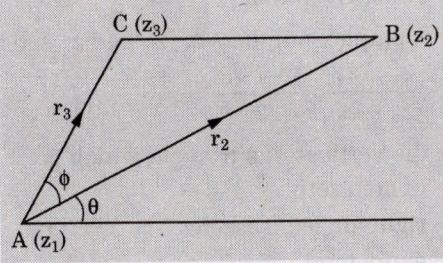

Fig. 26

Proof. $z_2 - z_1 = r_2 e^{i\theta}$

$$z_3 - z_1 = r_3 e^{i(\theta + \phi)} = r_3 e^{i\theta} \cdot e^{i\phi}$$

or $\dfrac{z_3 - z_1}{z_2 - z_1} = \dfrac{r_3}{r_2} e^{i\phi} = \dfrac{AC}{AB} e^{i\phi}$

or $\dfrac{z_3 - z_1}{AC} = \dfrac{z_2 - z_1}{AB} e^{i\phi}$ or $\hat{AC} = \hat{AB} e^{i\phi}$

*or $\dfrac{z_3 - z_1}{|z_3 - z_1|} = \dfrac{z_2 - z_1}{|z_2 - z_1|} e^{i\phi}$

When r is different we apply rotation on unit vectors.

(ii) **Multiplication by i.**

Since $z = r(\cos\theta + i\sin\theta) = re^{i\theta}$ and

$$i = \left(\cos\frac{1}{2}\pi + i\sin\frac{1}{2}\pi\right) = e^{i\pi/2}, \text{ we get}$$

$$iz = r\left[\cos\left(\theta + \frac{\pi}{2}\right) + i\sin\left(\theta + \frac{\pi}{2}\right)\right] = re^{i(\theta + \pi/2)}.$$

*Hence multiplication of z with i rotates the vector for z through a right angle in the positive direction.

(iii) Multiplication by '−1'.

$$z = re^{i\theta}, -1 = e^{\pi i}$$
$$\therefore \quad -z = re^{i(\theta + \pi)}$$

Hence multiplication by −1 rotates the vector z through an angle of $180°$ in the +ive direction.

(iv) Multiplication by $\omega = e^{2\pi i/3}$ will rotate the vector z by an angle of $120°$.

Also $\omega^2 = e^{4\pi i/3} = e^{-2\pi i/3}$ (as ω, ω^2 are conjugate).

(v) Let the lines AB and CD intersect at the point P_0 represented by the complex number z_0 and let P_1, P_2 be any two points on AB and CD

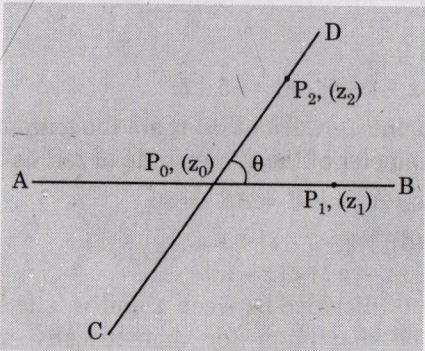

Fig. 27

AB and CD represented by z_1 and z_2 respectively. Then the angle θ between the lines is given by

$$\theta = \arg(z_2 - z_0) - \arg(z_1 - z_0)$$
$$= \arg\left(\frac{z_2 - z_0}{z_1 - z_0}\right)$$

[Note that here only principal values of the arguments are considered].

Problem Set (6)

Rotation, Area and nature of triangles in complex plane and locus.

1. (a)* Show that area of the triangle on the Argand diagram formed by the complex numbers z, iz and $z + iz$ is $\frac{1}{2}|z|^2$.

    (D.C.E. 1997)

   (b) Prove that the area of the triangle formed by complex numbers $z, \omega z$ and $z + \omega z$ as its sides is $\sqrt{3}$ sq. units, given that $|z|^2 = 4$.

2. (a) The complex numbers z_1, z_2 and z_3 satisfying
   $$\frac{z_1 - z_3}{z_2 - z_3} = \frac{1 - i\sqrt{3}}{2}$$
   are the vertices of a triangle which is
   (a) of area zero
   (b) right-angled isosceles
   (c) equilateral
   (d) obtuse-angled isosceles   **(I.I.T. Sc. 2001)**

   (b)* Determine the equation of the line joining the points whose affixes are z_1 and z_2 in argand plane. Hence prove that the equation of the line joining the point α and $i\beta$ where $\alpha, \beta \in R$ and $\alpha, \beta \neq 0$ is $\dfrac{z}{2}\left(\dfrac{1}{\alpha} - \dfrac{i}{\beta}\right) + \dfrac{\bar{z}}{2}\left(\dfrac{1}{\alpha} + \dfrac{i}{\beta}\right).$

3. (a) Let a and b be two non-zero complex numbers. If the lines $a\bar{z} + \bar{a}z + 1 = 0$ and $b\bar{z} + \bar{b}z - 1 = 0$ are mutually perpendicular, then a, b are connected by the relation
   (a) $ab + \bar{a}\bar{b} = 0$ (b) $ab - \bar{a}\bar{b} = 0$
   (c) $\bar{a}b - a\bar{b} = 0$ (d) $a\bar{b} + \bar{a}b = 0$

   (b) The closest distance of origin from the curve given by $b\bar{z} + \bar{b}z + b\bar{b} = 0$ (b is also a complex number) is

(a) 1 unit   (b) $\dfrac{\text{Re}(b)}{|b|}$

(c) $\dfrac{\text{Im}(b)}{|b|}$ (d) $\dfrac{1}{2}|b|$

4. (a) Find the vertices of a regular polygon of n sides if its centre is located at $z = 0$ and one of its vertices z_1 is known.

   (b)* Let $A_0 A_1 A_2 A_3 A_4 A_5$ be a regular hexagon inscribed in a circle of unit radius. Then the product of the lengths of the line segments $A_0 A_1, A_0 A_2$ and $A_0 A_4$ is

   (A) $\dfrac{3}{4}$ (B) $3\sqrt{3}$

   (C) 3 (D) $\dfrac{3\sqrt{3}}{2}$

   (I.I.T. 1998)

5. (a) The adjacent vertices of a regular polygon of n sides are the points z and its conjugate $\bar{z}$. If $\dfrac{\text{Im}(z)}{\text{Re}(z)} = \sqrt{2} - 1$, then the value of n is
   (a) 24   (b) 18
   (c) 16   (d) 8

   (b) Points z_1 and z_2 are adjacent vertices of a regular polygon of n sides. Find the vertex z_3 adjacent to z_2 $(z_3 \neq z_1)$.

6. Assume that A_i $(i = 1, 2, ... n)$ are the vertices of a regular n-gon inscribed in a circle of radius unity. Find (a) $|A_1 A_2|^2 + |A_1 A_3|^2 + ... + |A_1 A_n|^2$.

   (b) $|A_1 A_2| |A_1 A_3| ....|A_1 A_n|$.

7. (a)* Let $A_1, A_2, ... A_n$ be vertices of an n sided regular polygon such that

$$\frac{1}{A_1 A_2} = \frac{1}{A_1 A_3} + \frac{1}{A_1 A_4}.$$

Find the value of n. **(I.I.T. 1994)**

(b)* Prove that $\displaystyle\sum_{k=1}^{n-1} (n-k)\cos\frac{2k\pi}{n} = -\frac{n}{2}$,

where $n \geq 3$ is an integer. **(I.I.T. Re-ex. 1997)**

8. (a)* $ABCD$ is a rhombus. Its diagonals AC and BD intersect at the point M and satisfy $BD = 2AC$. If the points D and M represent the complex numbers $1+i$ and $2-i$ repectively, then A represents the complex number .... or .... **(I.I.T. 1993)**

(b) The complex numbers $1+i, -4+4i, 4+6i$ are the vertices A, B, C of a triangle on the Argand plane. Prove that the triangle is isosceles. If the triangle be converted into a rhombus then determine the point D.

9. Show that the triangle whose vertices are the points represented by the complex numbers z_1, z_2, z_3 on the Argand diagram is equilateral if and only if

$$\frac{1}{z_2 - z_3} + \frac{1}{z_3 - z_1} + \frac{1}{z_1 - z_2} = 0$$

that is, iff $\quad z_1^2 + z_2^2 + z_3^2 = z_1 z_2 + z_2 z_3 + z_3 z_1$;

10. (a)* Let the complex numbers z_1, z_2 and z_3 be the vertices of an equilateral triangle. Let z_0 be the circumcentre of the triangle. Prove that $z_1^2 + z_2^2 + z_3^2 = 3z_0^2$.

(b) The roots of the equation $t^3 + 3at^2 + 3bt + c = 0$ are z_1, z_2, z_3 which represent the vertices of a triangle ABC on the Gaussian plane. Determine the centroid of the triangle. In case the triangle be equilateral then prove that $a^2 = b$.

(c) If $z_1 = 10 + 6i, z_2 = 4 + 2i$ such that $\arg\left(\dfrac{z - z_1}{z - z_2}\right)$

$= \dfrac{\pi}{4}$, then find the centre and radius of the locus of complex number z.

11. (a) If $|z_1| = |z_2| = |z_3| = 1$ and $z_1 + z_2 + z_3 = 0$, show that z_1, z_2, z_3 are the vertices of an equilateral triangle inscribed in a unit circle.

(b)* Complex numbers z_1, z_2, z_3 are the vertices A, B, C respectively of an isosceles right angled triangle with right angle at C show that $(z_1 - z_2)^2 = 2(z_1 - z_3)(z_3 - z_2)$
(J.E.E.W.B. 1998; D.C.E. 1998)

12. (a)* ABC is an isosceles triangle with angle at A being θ. If the vertices be the complex numbers z_1, z_2, z_3 then prove that

$$(z_3 - z_2)^2 = 4(z_3 - z_1)(z_1 - z_2)\sin^2\frac{\theta}{2}$$

(b) If A, B, C are the points z_1, z_2, z_3 and the angles B and C are each $\dfrac{\pi - \alpha}{2}$ then

$$(z_2 - z_3)^2 = 4(z_3 - z_1)(z_1 - z_2)\sin^2\frac{\alpha}{2}$$

Is this statement true or false ? **(I.I.T. Re-ex. 1997)**

13. (a) Let z_1 and z_2 be roots of the equation $z^2 + pz + q = 0$, where the co-efficients p and q may be complex numbers. Let A and B represent z_1 and z_2 in the complex plane. If $\angle AOB = \alpha \neq 0$ and $OA = OB$, where O is the origin, prove that $p^2 = 4q\cos^2\left(\dfrac{\alpha}{2}\right)$.
(I.I.T. Re-ex. 1997)

(b)* The cube roots of unity when represented on the Argand diagram form the vertices of an equilateral triangle
(a) True   (b) False

14. (a) If $z_1^2 + z_2^2 \pm 2z_1 z_2 \cos\theta = 0$, prove that the points represented by z_1, z_2 and the origin form an isosceles triangle, θ being real.

(b)* If $z_1^2 + z_2^2 + z_1 z_2 = 0$, prove that the points represented by z_1, z_2 and the origin form an isosceles triangle with vertical angle $2\pi/3$.

15. (a)* Let A and B be complex numbers such that $\dfrac{A}{B} + \dfrac{B}{A} = 1$.

Prove that the origin and the two points represented by A and B form vertices of an equilateral triangle.

(b) If z_1 and z_2 be the roots of $z^2 + az + b = 0$ then triangle OAB will be equilateral if $a^2 = 3b$ where O is the origin.

16. If z_1, z_2, z_3 are complex numbers such that $\dfrac{2}{z_2} = \dfrac{1}{z_1} + \dfrac{1}{z_3}$ then the points z_1, z_2, z_3 lie on a circle passing through origin. Is this statement true or false ?

17. (a) If z_1, z_2, z_3 are non-zero complex numbers such that $z_1 + z_2 + z_3 = 0$, and $z_1^{-1} + z_2^{-1} + z_3^{-1} = 0$, then prove that the given points are the vertices of an equilateral triangle. Also show that $|z_1| = |z_2| = |z_3|$

(b)* If the complex numbers z_1, z_2, z_3 represent the vertices of an equilateral triangle such that $|z_1| = |z_2| = |z_3|$, then prove that $z_1 + z_2 + z_3 = 0$.

18. (a)* Suppose z_1, z_2, z_3 are the vertices of an equilateral triangle inscribed in the circle $|z| = 2$. If $z_1 = 1 + i\sqrt{3}$, then $z_2 = ..., z_3 = ...$ **(I.I.T. 1994)**

(b) If a and b are real numbers between 0 and 1 such that the points $z_1 = a + i, z_2 = 1 + bi$ and $z_3 = 0$ form an equilateral triangle, then $a = ...$ and $b = ...$

(c) Find the three vertices of the square that circumscribes the circle $|z - 1| = \sqrt{2}$, if one of the vertices is $2 + i\sqrt{3}$. **(I.I.T. 2005)**

19. (a)* If z_1, z_2, z_3, z_4 be the vertices of a square in Argand plane, then prove that
$$2z_2 = (1+i)z_1 + (1-i)z_3$$
and $2z_4 = (1-i)z_1 + (1+i)z_3$.

(b) If z_1, z_2, z_3, z_4 be the vertices of rhombus in argand plane and $\angle CBA = \pi/3$, then prove that
$$2z_2 = z_1(1 + i\sqrt{3}) + z_3(1 - i\sqrt{3})$$
and $2z_4 = z_1(1 - i\sqrt{3}) + z_3(1 + i\sqrt{3})$.

(c) If one vertex of a square whose diagonals intersect at origin is $3(\cos\theta + i\sin\theta)$ then prove that the two adjacent vertices are $\pm 3(\sin\theta - i\cos\theta)$.

(d) The centre of a square is at the point $z_0 = 1 + i$ and one of its vertices is at the point $z_1 = 1 - i$. Find the other vertices.

20. (a) The points A, B, C are z_1, z_2, z_3 on the circumference of the circle drawn on OA as diameter, O being the origin. If $\angle AOB = \angle BOC$ then prove that $z_2^2 \cos 2\theta = z_1 z_3 \cos^2 \theta$

Passage : Angle subtended by chord of a circle at the centre is twice the angle subtended at the circumference. If OP is rotated through an angle ϕ in anti-clockwise direction to become OQ, then $OQ = OP\, e^{i\phi}$

(b) If $|z - 3| = 3$, then $\dfrac{z-6}{z}$ is equal to

(a) $i \tan(\arg z)$ (b) $i \cot(\arg z)$

(c) $\cot(\arg z)$ (d) $\tan[\arg(z-3)]$

21. For every real number $c \geq 0$, find all the complex numbers z which satisfy the equation $|z|^2 - 2iz + 2c(1+i) = 0$.

22. (a)* For every real number $c \geq 1$, find all the complex numbers z that satisfy the equation $z + c|z+1| + i = 0$.

(b)* Find the range of real number α for which the equation $z + \alpha|z-1| + 2i = 0$; $z = x + iy$ has a solution. And find the solution.   **(Roorkee 1991)**

23. (a) For every real number $c \geq 0$, find all the complex numbers z which satisfy the equation $2|z| - 4cz + 1 + ic = 0$.

(b) For every real number $c > 0$, find all complex numbers z, satisfying the equation $z|z| + cz + i = 0$.

24. If A, B, C, D are four points in a plane, prove that $AD \cdot BC \leq BD \cdot CA + CD \cdot AB$.

25. It is known that $\left| z + \dfrac{1}{z} \right| = a$, where z is a complex number. What are the greatest and the least possible values of $|z|$?

26. Let z_1, z_2 be any two complex numbers and a, b real numbers $(a^2 + b^2 \neq 0)$. Prove the inequalities
$$|z_1|^2 + |z_2|^2 - |z_1^2 + z_2^2| \leq \frac{2|az_1 + bz_2|^2}{a^2 + b^2}$$

$$\leq |z_1|^2 + |z_2|^2 + |z_1^2 + z_2^2|.$$

Solutions to Problem Set (6)

1. (a) We have $z = x + iy = (x, y)$, $iz = ix - y = (-y, x)$
and so $z + iz = (x - y, x + y)$
Hence area of triangle
$$= \frac{1}{2} \begin{vmatrix} x & y & 1 \\ -y & x & 1 \\ x-y & x+y & 1 \end{vmatrix}$$
$$= \frac{1}{2} \begin{vmatrix} x & y & 1 \\ -y-x & x-y & 0 \\ -y & x & 0 \end{vmatrix}$$
$$= \frac{1}{2}[(-y - x)x + y(x - y)]$$
$$= \frac{1}{2}(-x^2 - y^2) = \frac{1}{2}(x^2 + y^2), \text{ numerically}$$
$$= \frac{1}{2}|z|^2.$$

Alternative easier method :
$$\vec{CA} = z - (z + iz) = -iz$$
$$\vec{CB} = iz - (z + iz) = -z$$
$$|\vec{CA}| = |\vec{CB}| = |z|$$
Also $\vec{CA} = i\vec{CB}$

Multiplication of a complex number by $i = e^{i\pi/2}$ means rotation by $\pi/2$. Thus CA is perpendicular to CB.

$\triangle ABC$ is right angled and hence its area
$$= \frac{1}{2} CA \cdot CB = \frac{1}{2}|z||z| = \frac{1}{2}|z|^2 \text{ [See fig. 49(a)]}$$

Another method :

If $\vec{OA} = z$, then $\vec{AB} = iz$ by rotation of $\vec{OA}$ through $90°$ about $\vec{OA}$.

Hence $\vec{OB} = \vec{OA} + \vec{AB} = z + iz$

$\triangle OAB$ is right angled and hence its area is
$$\frac{1}{2} OA \cdot OB = \frac{1}{2}|z||iz| = \frac{1}{2}|z||z| = \frac{1}{2}|z|^2$$

(See fig. 29)

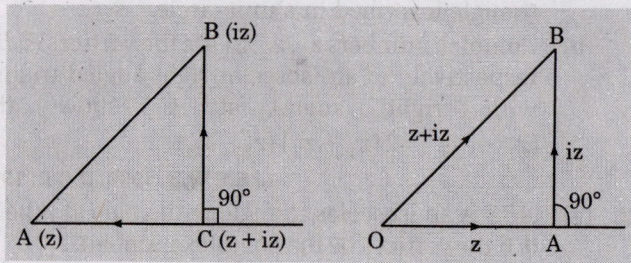

Fig. 28   Fig. 29

(b) $|z| = 2$
$$\vec{AC} = (z + \omega z) - z = \omega z$$
$$\vec{BC} = (z + \omega z) - \omega z = z$$

$|\vec{AC}| = |\omega z| = |\omega||z| = |z|$ as $|\omega| = 1$

$|\vec{BC}| = |z|$. Also $\vec{AC} = \omega \vec{BC}$.

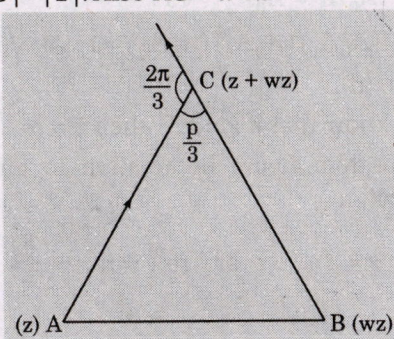

Fig. 30

Also we know that multiplication of a complex number by $\omega = e^{2\pi i/3}$ means rotation by $2\pi/3$. Hence angle between AC and BC is $2\pi/3$ so that the vertical angle $\angle C$ is $\pi - \dfrac{2\pi}{3} = \dfrac{\pi}{3}$. Since $AC = BC$, we conclude that triangle ABC is equilateral whose side is $|z| = 2$. Hence its area is $\dfrac{1}{2} 2 \cdot 2 \sin 60^\circ = 2 \cdot \dfrac{\sqrt{3}}{2} = \sqrt{3}$.

2. (a) Ans. (c).

Taking mod of both sides of given relation,

$$\left|\frac{z_1 - z_3}{z_2 - z_3}\right| = \frac{1}{4} + \frac{3}{4} = 1 \quad \therefore \ AC = BC$$

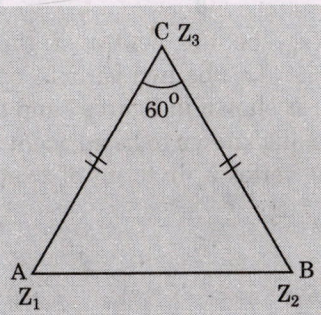

Fig. 31

Hence Δ is isosceles.

Also $\dfrac{z_1 - z_3}{z_2 - z_3} = \cos\dfrac{\pi}{3} - i \sin\dfrac{\pi}{3} = e^{-\frac{\pi}{3}i}$

or $(z_2 - z_3) = (z_1 - z_3) e^{\frac{\pi}{3}i}$

Anticlockwise rotation implies that $\angle ACB = 60^\circ$.

Hence isosceles Δ is equilateral.

(b) 1st Method : If z be any point on the line joining z_1 and z_2 then

$\arg\left(\dfrac{z - z_1}{z - z_2}\right) = 0$ or π **See Theorem III P. 70**

$\therefore \ \dfrac{z - z_1}{z - z_2} = e^{i.0}$ or $e^{i\pi}$ *i.e.* purely real

$\therefore \ \dfrac{z - z_1}{z - z_2} = \overline{\left(\dfrac{z - z_1}{z - z_2}\right)} = \dfrac{\bar{z} - \bar{z}_1}{\bar{z} - \bar{z}_2}$

Cross-multiply and cancel $z\bar{z}$ from both sides and we have

$$z(\bar{z}_1 - \bar{z}_2) - \bar{z}(z_1 - z_2) + z_1 \bar{z}_2 - \bar{z}_1 z_2 = 0$$

or $\begin{vmatrix} z & \bar{z} & 1 \\ z_1 & \bar{z}_1 & 1 \\ z_2 & \bar{z}_2 & 1 \end{vmatrix} = 0$

2nd Method : If $z_1 = x_1 + iy_1$ and $z_2 = x_2 + iy_2$ then equation of line is

$\begin{vmatrix} x & y & 1 \\ x_1 & y_1 & 1 \\ x_2 & y_2 & 1 \end{vmatrix} = 0$

Apply $C_1 + iC_2$ and then multiply C_2 by $2i$.

$\begin{vmatrix} z & 2iy & 1 \\ z_1 & 2iy_1 & 1 \\ z_2 & 2iy_2 & 1 \end{vmatrix} = 0$ or $\begin{vmatrix} z & z - \bar{z} & 1 \\ z_1 & z_1 - \bar{z}_1 & 1 \\ z_2 & z_2 - \bar{z}_2 & 1 \end{vmatrix} = 0$

Apply $C_2 - C_1$ and take -1 common.

$\therefore \ \begin{vmatrix} z & \bar{z} & 1 \\ z_1 & \bar{z}_1 & 1 \\ z_2 & \bar{z}_2 & 1 \end{vmatrix} = 0$

Deduction :

Here $z_1 = \alpha$, $\bar{z}_1 = \alpha$, $z_2 = i\beta$ $\therefore \ \bar{z}_2 = -i\beta$

$\therefore$ Line is $\begin{vmatrix} z & \bar{z} & 1 \\ \alpha & \alpha & 1 \\ i\beta & -i\beta & 1 \end{vmatrix} = 0$

or $z(\alpha + i\beta) - \bar{z}(\alpha - i\beta) - 2i\alpha\beta = 0$

Dividing throughout by $2i\alpha\beta$ and putting $\dfrac{1}{i} = -i$

$$\frac{z}{2}\left(\frac{1}{\alpha} - \frac{i}{\beta}\right) + \frac{\bar{z}}{2}\left(\frac{1}{\alpha} + \frac{i}{\beta}\right) = 1.$$

3. (a) Ans. (d).

We know that multiplication of a complex number by i means rotation through an angle 90°. Replacing z by iz or $\bar{z}$ by $\overline{iz} = \bar{i}\,\bar{z} = -i\,\bar{z}$ in one line should give the other perpendicular line.

$\therefore \ a(\overline{iz}) + \bar{a}(iz) + 1 = 0$

or $-ai\bar{z} + \bar{a}\,iz + 1 = 0$

$ai\bar{z} - \bar{a}\,iz - 1 = 0$ is same as

$b\bar{z} + \bar{b}\,z - 1 = 0$

Comparing $\dfrac{ai}{b} = -\dfrac{\bar{a}i}{\bar{b}}$

or $a\bar{b} + \bar{a}b = 0 \implies$ **(d)**

(b) Ans. (d).

The given equation when converted to Cartesian represents the line

$$(b + \bar{b})x + (\bar{b} - b)iy + b\bar{b} = 0$$

By closest distance of origin from the line is perpendicular distance from $(0, 0)$

$\therefore \ p = \dfrac{b\bar{b}}{\sqrt{(b + \bar{b})^2 + i^2(\bar{b} - b)^2}} = \dfrac{|b|^2}{\sqrt{4b\bar{b}}}$

$$p = \frac{1}{2}|b| \quad \because \sqrt{b\,\bar{b}} = \sqrt{|b|^2} = |b|$$

4. (a) Let O be the origin and A_1 the vertex z_1. Let the vertex adjacent to A_1 be A_2.
Then $z_2 = z_1 e^{2\pi i/n}$ since $\angle A_2 O A_1 = 2\pi/n$.

(See § 13 (i), P. 101).

Similarly if $z_3, z_4, \ldots z_n$ are the other vertices in order, then $z_3 = z_1 e^{4\pi i/n}$, $z_4 = z_1 e^{6\pi i/n}$ etc. Thus all the vertices are given by

$$z_{k+1} = z_1 \, e^{2\pi k i/n} = z_1 \, (\cos 2\pi k/n + i \sin 2\pi k/n),$$

$k = 1, 2, \cdots, n-1$.

(b) Ans. (c).

Let the vertices be $z_0, z_1, \ldots z_5$ w.r.t. centre O as origin $|z_0| = 1$, $A_0 A_1 = |z_1 - z_0| = |z_0 e^{i\theta} - z_0|$

$$\therefore \quad A_0 A_1 = |z_0||\cos\theta + i\sin\theta - 1|$$

$$= 1 \cdot \sqrt{(\cos\theta - 1)^2 + \sin^2\theta} = \sqrt{2(1 - \cos\theta)}.$$

$$\therefore \quad A_0 A_1 = \sqrt{2 \cdot 2\sin^2\frac{\theta}{2}} = 2\sin\frac{\theta}{2}$$

where $\theta = \frac{2\pi}{6} = \frac{\pi}{3}$

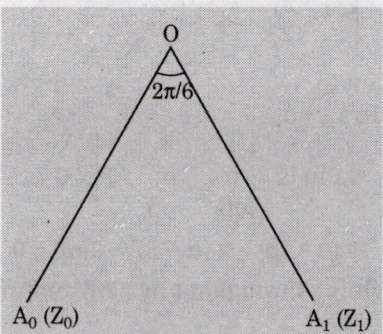

Fig. 32

Replacing θ by 2θ and 4θ we get

$$A_0 A_2 = 2\sin\frac{2\theta}{2} = 2\sin\theta,$$

$$A_0 A_4 = 2\sin\frac{4\theta}{2} = 2\sin 2\theta$$

$$\therefore \quad (A_0 A_1)(A_0 A_2)(A_0 A_4) = 8\sin\frac{\pi}{6}\sin\frac{\pi}{3}\sin\frac{2\pi}{3}$$

$$= 8 \cdot \frac{1}{2} \cdot \frac{\sqrt{3}}{2} \cdot \frac{\sqrt{3}}{2} = 3.$$

Alt. $OA_0 = OA_1 = 1$ and $\Delta OA_0 A_1$ is equilateral.

$$\therefore \quad A_0 A_1 = 1$$

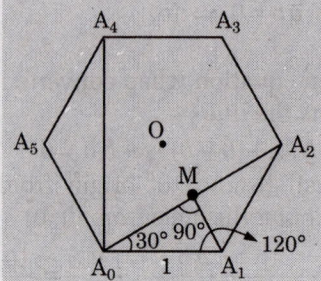

Fig. 33

$$A_0 A_2 = 2 A_0 M = 2 A_0 A_1 \cos 30° = 2 \cdot \frac{\sqrt{3}}{2} = \sqrt{3}$$

$$A_0 A_4 = A_0 A_2 = \sqrt{3}$$

$$\therefore \quad (A_0 A_1)(A_0 A_2)(A_0 A_4) = 1 \cdot \sqrt{3} \cdot \sqrt{3} = 3$$

5. (a) Ans. (d).

We know that if $z = re^{i\theta}$ then $\bar{z} = re^{-i\theta}$. ...(1)

Also from figure by rotation in anticlockwise direction

$$z = \bar{z} e^{\frac{2\pi}{n} i} \quad \text{or} \quad re^{i\theta} = re^{\left(\frac{2\pi}{n} - \theta\right)i} \quad \text{by (1)}$$

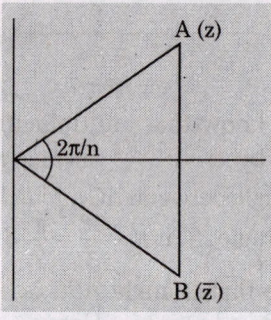

Fig. 34

$$\therefore \quad \theta = \frac{2\pi}{n} - \theta \quad \text{or} \quad 2\theta = \frac{2\pi}{n} \quad i.e. \quad \theta = \frac{\pi}{n}$$

$$\therefore \quad \frac{\text{Im}(z)}{\text{Re}(z)} = \frac{r\sin\theta}{r\cos\theta} = \tan\theta = \tan\frac{\pi}{n} = \sqrt{2} - 1$$

$$\tan\frac{\pi}{n} = \tan\frac{\pi}{8} \Rightarrow n = 8$$

(b) Let $C(z_0)$ be the centre of the polygon and $A_1(z_1)$, $A_3(z_3)$ be two vertices on either side of $A_2(z_2)$ as shown in figures I and II.
z_1, z_2 being known to be adjacent and we have to find the vertex z_3 in terms of z_1 and z_2.

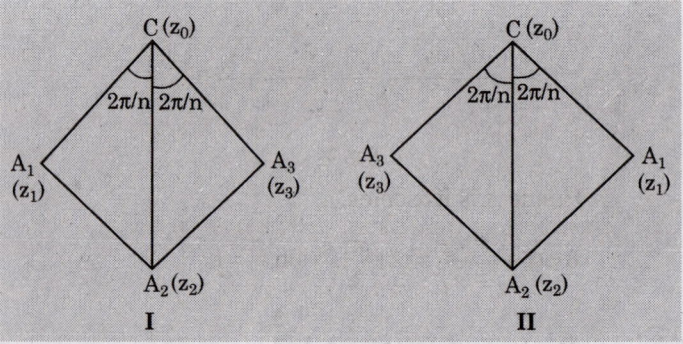

Fig. 35

From fig. (1), rotation being anticlockwise, we have

$$z_2 - z_0 = (z_1 - z_0) e^{2\pi i/n}$$

$$z_3 - z_0 = (z_2 - z_0) e^{2\pi i/n}. \text{ Subtracting we get}$$

$$z_3 - z_2 = (z_2 - z_1) e^{2\pi i/n}$$

$$\therefore \quad z_3 = z_2 + (z_2 - z_1) e^{2\pi i/n} \quad \text{...(1)}$$

Similarly, proceeding as above for the second figure in which the rotation is clockwise, we have

$$z_3 = z_2 + (z_2 - z_1) e^{-2\pi i/n} \qquad ...(2)$$

$$\therefore \quad z_3 = z_2 + (z_2 - z_1) e^{\pm 2\pi i/n}$$

$$= z_2 + (z_2 - z_1) \left[\cos \frac{2\pi}{n} \pm i \sin \frac{2\pi}{n} \right].$$

6. (a) With origin as the centre of the circle of radius unity, let $z_1, z_2, ..., z_n$ represent the vertices $A_1, A_2, ..., A_n$ of the n-gon.

Then we easily get

$$z_2 = z_1 e^{2\pi i/n}, \; z_3 = z_1 e^{4\pi i/n}, ...,$$

$$z_n = z_1 e^{2(n-1)\pi i/2n}$$

Now $|A_1 A_r|^2 = |z_1 - z_r|^2$

$$= |z_1 - z_1 e^{2(r-1)\pi i/n}|^2$$

$$= |z_1|^2 \; |1 - e^{2(r-1)\pi i/n}|^2$$

$$= \left| 1 - \cos \frac{2(r-1)\pi}{n} - i \sin \frac{2(r-1)\pi}{n} \right|^2$$

$$[\because \; |z_1| = \text{radius of the circle} = 1]$$

$$= \left(1 - \cos \frac{2(r-1)\pi}{n} \right)^2 + \sin^2 \frac{2(r-1)\pi}{n}$$

$$= 2 - 2\cos \frac{2(r-1)\pi}{n} \qquad ...(A)$$

Hence $\sum_{r=2}^{n} |A_1 A_r|^2 = 2(n-1)$

$$- 2 \sum_{r=2}^{n} \left[\cos \frac{2(r-1)\pi}{n} \right] \quad ...(1)$$

Let $S = \sum_{r=2}^{n} \cos \frac{2(r-1)\pi}{n} \qquad ...(2)$

$$= \cos \frac{2\pi}{n} + \cos \frac{4\pi}{n} + \cos \frac{6\pi}{n} + ... + ... + \cos \frac{2(n-1)}{n}\pi$$

Formula :

$$\cos A + \cos(A+B) + \cos(A+2B)$$
$$+ ...... + \cos(A + \overline{n-1} \; B)$$

$$\sin A + \sin(A+B) + \sin(A+2B)$$
$$+ .... + \sin(A + \overline{n-1} \; B)$$

There are n angles in A.P. of common diff. B.

$$S = \frac{\sin n \cdot \frac{B}{2}}{\sin \frac{B}{2}} \cos \text{ or } \sin \left\{ \frac{\text{1st ang.} + \text{last ang.}}{2} \right\}$$

In (2) there are $(n-1)$ terms and angles are in A.P. of common difference $\frac{2\pi}{n}$.

$$S = \frac{\sin[(n-1)\cdot \pi/n]}{\sin(\pi/n)} \cos \left\{ \frac{\frac{2\pi}{n} + \frac{2(n-1)\pi}{n}}{2} \right\}$$

$$= \frac{\sin(\pi - \pi/n)}{\sin(\pi/n)} \cos \pi$$

$$= \frac{\sin(\pi/n)}{\sin(\pi/n)}(-1) = -1$$

Hence $\sum_{r=2}^{n} |A_1 A_r|^2 = 2(n-1) - 2S$, by (1)

$$= 2n - 2 + 2 = 2n \quad \text{as } S = -1$$

(b) From part (i), $|A_1 A_r| = |z_1| \; |1 - e^{2(r-1)\pi i/n}|$

$$= |1 - e^{2(r-1)\pi i/n}| \qquad [\because \; |z_1| = 1]$$

Hence $|A_1 A_2| \cdot |A_1 A_3| ...... |A_1 A_n|$

$$= |1 - e^{2\pi i/n}| |1 - e^{4\pi i/n}| .... |1 - e^{2(n-1)\pi i/n}| \qquad ...(1)$$

Since $e^{2\pi i/n}, e^{4\pi i/n}, ..., e^{2(n-1)\pi i/n}$ are the $n-1$ imaginary, n^{th} roots of unity, we have the identity

$$z^n - 1 \equiv (z-1)(z - e^{2\pi i/n})(z - e^{4\pi i/n}) ......(z - e^{2(n-1)\pi i/n})$$

or $\dfrac{z^n - 1}{z-1} \equiv (z - e^{2\pi i/n})(z - e^{4\pi i/n}) ....(z - e^{2(n-1)\pi i/n})$

or $1 + z + z^2 + ... + z^{n-1} \equiv (z - e^{2\pi i/n}) ....(z - e^{2(n-1)\pi i/n})$

Putting $z = 1$ in the above identity, we get

$$n = (1 - e^{2\pi i/n})(1 - e^{4\pi i/n}) ..... (1 - e^{2(n-1)\pi i/n})$$

Hence $n = |n| = |1 - e^{2\pi i/n}| |1 - e^{4\pi i/n}| ...... |1 - e^{2(n-1)\pi i/n}| \quad ...(2)$

$\therefore$ From (1) and (2), we get

$\therefore \quad |A_1 A_2| \cdot |A_2 A_3| ... |A_1 A_n| = n.$

7. (a) $A_1 A_2 = \text{mod of } A_1 A_2 = |A_1 A_2|$

$$|A_1 A_r|^2 = |z_1|^2 \left[2 - 2\cos \frac{2(r-1)\pi}{n} \right]$$

$$= a^2 \cdot 4 \sin^2 \frac{2(r-1)\pi}{2n} \text{ by (A) of col I Q. 6 P. 107}$$

$$\therefore \quad |A_1 A_r| = 2a \sin(r-1)\frac{\pi}{n}$$

$\because \quad 1 - \cos\theta = 2\sin^2(\theta/2)$

Putting $r = 2, 3, 4$ we have from the given relation,

$$\frac{1}{\sin \frac{\pi}{n}} = \frac{1}{\sin \frac{2\pi}{n}} + \frac{1}{\sin \frac{3\pi}{n}}.$$

$$2\sin \frac{\pi}{n} \cos \frac{\pi}{n} \sin \frac{3\pi}{n} = \sin \frac{\pi}{n} \left[\sin \frac{3\pi}{n} + \sin \frac{2\pi}{n} \right]$$

Cancel $\sin \frac{\pi}{n}$ as $\sin \frac{\pi}{n} \neq 0$ as $n \neq 1$

$$\therefore \quad \sin \frac{4\pi}{n} + \sin \frac{2\pi}{n} = \sin \frac{3\pi}{n} + \sin \frac{2\pi}{n}$$

or $\sin \frac{4\pi}{n} = \sin \frac{3\pi}{n} \quad \therefore \quad \frac{4\pi}{n} = \pi - \frac{3\pi}{n}$

or $\frac{7\pi}{n} = \pi \quad$ or $\quad n = 7.$

(b) Expanding the sigma on putting $k = 1, 2, 3, ..., n$

$$S = (n-1)\cos \frac{2\pi}{n} + (n-2)\cos \frac{4\pi}{n} + ...$$

$$+ 1.\cos(n-1)\frac{2\pi}{n} \quad ...(1)$$

We know that $\cos\theta = \cos(2\pi - \theta)$

Replacing each angle θ by $2\pi - \theta$ in (1), we get

$$S = (n-1)\cos(n-1)\frac{2\pi}{n} + (n-2)\cos(n-2)\frac{2\pi}{n} +$$
$$..... + 1.\cos\frac{2\pi}{n} \quad \text{by (I)}$$

Add terms having the same angle and take n common

$$\therefore \quad 2S = n\left[\cos\frac{2\pi}{n} + \cos\frac{4\pi}{n} + \cos\frac{6\pi}{n} + ...\right.$$
$$\left.+ \cos(n-1)\frac{2\pi}{n}\right]$$

Angles are in A.P. of $d = \dfrac{2\pi}{n}$

$$= n\left[\frac{\sin(n-1)\dfrac{\pi}{n}}{\sin\dfrac{\pi}{n}}\cos\frac{\dfrac{2\pi}{n} + (n-1)\dfrac{2\pi}{n}}{2}\right]$$

(Rule 38)

$$= n.1\cos\pi = -n \qquad \because \sin(\pi-\theta) = \sin\theta$$

$$\therefore \quad S = -n/2.$$

8. (a) $BD = 2AC \Rightarrow 2DM = 2(2AM)$

or $\quad DM = 2AM$ or $DM^2 = 4AM^2$

or $\quad 5 = 4[(x-2)^2 + (y+1)^2]$ ...(1)

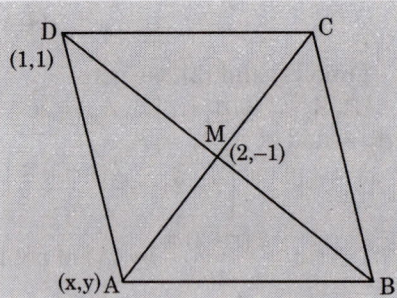

Fig. 36

Again slope of $DM = -2$ and slope of AM is $\dfrac{y+1}{x-2}$.

AM is perpendicular to DM.

$$\therefore \quad -2\left(\frac{y+1}{x-2}\right) = -1$$

or $\quad x - 2 = 2(y+1)$ ...(2)

Hence from (1) and (2), we get

$$5 = 4[(2y+2)^2 + (y+1)^2] = 4.5(y+1)^2$$

or $\quad 4y^2 + 8y + 3 = 0$ or $(2y+3)(2y+1) = 0$

$$\therefore \quad y = -\frac{1}{2}, -\frac{3}{2} \quad \therefore \quad x = 3, 1.$$

Hence point A represents the complex number $x + iy$

i.e. $\quad 3 - \dfrac{1}{2}i, 1 - \dfrac{3}{2}i.$

(b) It is easy to observe that $AB = AC = \sqrt{34}$.

If it be converted into a rhombus then $BC = \sqrt{68}$ must be the diagonal. Hence if D be (x, y) then diagonals bisect.

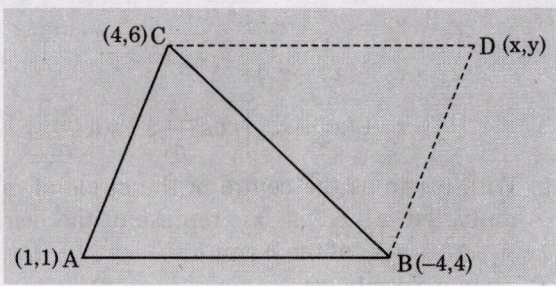

Fig. 37

$$\therefore \quad \frac{x+1}{2} = 0, \frac{y+1}{2} = 5$$

$$\therefore \quad (x, y) \text{ is } (-1, 9) \text{ or } D \text{ is } -1 + 9i.$$

9. Let the vertices A, B, C of a ΔABC be represented by z_1, z_2, z_3 respectively.

Suppose $z_2 - z_3 = \alpha$, $z_3 - z_1 = \beta$, $z_1 - z_2 = \gamma$.

Then $\quad \alpha + \beta + \gamma = 0$ ...(1)

$$\therefore \quad \overline{\alpha + \beta + \gamma} = 0 \text{ or } \overline{\alpha} + \overline{\beta} + \overline{\gamma} = 0 \quad ...(2)$$

We first assume that ΔABC is equilateral.

Then $BC = CA = AB$

or $\quad |z_2 - z_3| = |z_3 - z_1| = |z_1 - z_2|$

or $\quad |\alpha| = |\beta| = |\gamma|$ or $|\alpha|^2 = |\beta|^2 = |\gamma|^2$

or $\quad \alpha\overline{\alpha} = \beta\overline{\beta} = \gamma\overline{\gamma} = k$, say. ...(3)

$\therefore$ From (2) and (3), we have

$$k/\alpha + k/\beta + k/\gamma = 0 \Rightarrow 1/\alpha + 1/\beta + 1/\gamma = 0 \quad ...(4)$$

or $\quad \dfrac{1}{z_2 - z_3} + \dfrac{1}{z_3 - z_1} + \dfrac{1}{z_1 - z_2} = 0.$

or $\quad \Sigma (z_3 - z_1)(z_1 - z_2) = 0$

or $\quad \Sigma z_3(z_1 - z_2) - \Sigma z_1(z_1 - z_2) = 0$

or $\quad 0 - \Sigma z_1^2 + \Sigma z_1 z_2 = 0$

i.e. $z_1^2 + z_2^2 + z_3^2 = z_1 z_2 + z_2 z_3 + z_3 z_1.$

Note : $\quad \dfrac{1}{z_2 - z_3} = \dfrac{\overline{(z_2 - z_3)}}{(z_2 - z_3)(\overline{z_2 - z_3})}$

$$= \frac{1}{|z_2 - z_3|^2}[\overline{z}_2 - \overline{z}_3]$$

$$\therefore \quad \Sigma \frac{1}{z_2 - z_3} = \frac{1}{k^2}[\overline{z}_2 - \overline{z}_3 + \overline{z}_3 - \overline{z}_1 + \overline{z}_1 - \overline{z}_2] = 0$$

$$\therefore \quad \frac{1}{z_2 - z_3} + \frac{1}{z_3 - z_1} + \frac{1}{z_1 - z_2} = 0.$$

Alternative Easier Method :

See Q. 10 (a), P. 102-108.

Conversely $z_1^2 + z_2^2 + z_3^2 - z_1 z_2 - z_2 z_3 - z_3 z_1 = 0$

$$\therefore \quad (z_1 + z_2\omega + z_3\omega^2)(z_1 + z_2\omega^2 + z_3\omega) = 0$$

See 3 P. 45

$$\therefore \quad z_1 + z_2\omega + z_3\omega^2 = 0 \quad ...(1)$$

or $\quad z_1 + z_2\omega^2 + z_3\omega = 0$ ...(2)

From (1), $z_1 + z_2\omega - z_3(1+\omega) = 0,$

$$\therefore \quad 1 + \omega + \omega^2 = 0$$

$$z_1 - z_3 = (z_3 - z_2)\omega$$

$$|z_1 - z_3| = |z_3 - z_2||\omega|$$

or $\quad CA = BC \cdot 1 \quad \because \quad |\omega| = 1$

Similarly from the other factor, by (2) we can prove that

$AB = BC$.

Hence $AB = BC = CA \quad \therefore \quad \Delta$ is equilateral.

10. (a) Let the vertices of the ΔABC be represented by z_1, z_2 and z_3. Then by rotation in anticlock-wise sense about A and B, we get

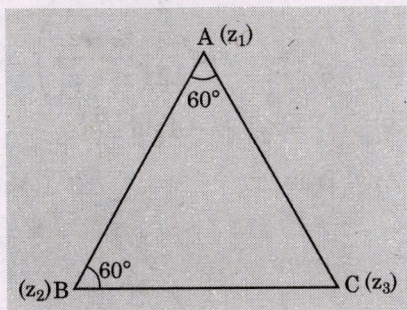

Fig. 38

$$AC = AB \, e^{\pi i/3}, \; BA = BC \, e^{\pi i/3}$$

or $\quad (z_3 - z_1) = (z_2 - z_1) \, e^{i\pi/3}$

and $\quad (z_1 - z_2) = (z_3 - z_2) \, e^{i\pi/3}$

whence on dividing, we get

$$\frac{z_3 - z_1}{z_1 - z_2} = \frac{z_2 - z_1}{z_3 - z_2}$$

or $\quad (z_3 - z_1)(z_3 - z_2) = -(z_2 - z_1)^2$

or $\quad z_1^2 + z_2^2 + z_3^2 = z_1 z_2 + z_2 z_3 + z_3 z_1. \quad \dots(1)$

Now for an equilateral triangle, circumcentre is the same as the centroid so that

$$z_0 = (z_1 + z_2 + z_3)/3.$$

or $\quad 9z_0^2 = z_1^2 + z_2^2 + z_3^2 + 2z_1 z_2 + 2z_2 z_3 + 2z_3 z_1$

$$= 3z_1^2 + 3z_2^2 + 3z_3^2, \quad \text{from (1)}$$

or $\quad 3z_0^2 = z_1^2 + z_2^2 + z_3^2$

(b) $z_1 + z_2 + z_3 = -3a$

$\therefore \quad G$ is $\dfrac{\Sigma z_1}{3} = -a$

In case triangle be equilateral then we know that

$$z_1^2 + z_2^2 + z_3^2 = z_1 z_2 + z_2 z_3 + z_3 z_1$$

(You have to prove the result as in **Q. 10 (a) P. 102-108** or as in part (i) above)

or $\quad (\Sigma z_1)^2 - 2\Sigma z_1 z_2 = \Sigma z_1 z_2$

or $\quad (\Sigma z_1)^2 = 3\Sigma z_1 z_2$

or $\quad (-3a)^2 = 3(3b) \quad \text{or} \quad a^2 = b.$

(c) Ans. $r = \sqrt{26}, \; C \, (5 + 7i).$

$\vec{AB} = 6 + 4i \quad \therefore \quad |AB| = \sqrt{36 + 16} = \sqrt{52}$

If $C(z_0)$ be the centre, then angle at $C = 2\left(\dfrac{\pi}{4}\right) = \dfrac{\pi}{2}.$

If r be the radius then $r^2 + r^2 = \sqrt{52}$

$\therefore \quad r = \sqrt{26}.$

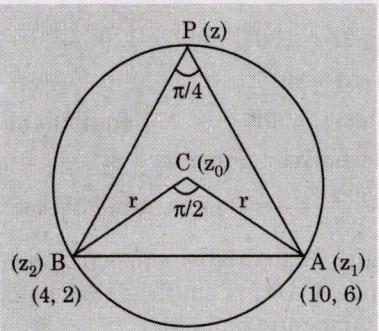

Fig. 39

Again by rotation through an angle of $\pi/2$ in anti-clockwise direction,

$$z_1 - z_0 = (z_2 - z_0) \, e^{i\pi/2} = i(z_2 - z_0)$$

$\therefore \quad z_1 - iz_2 = z_0(1 - i)$

$$z_0 = \frac{z_1 - iz_2}{1 - i} = \frac{(1 + i)(z_1 - iz_2)}{2}$$

$$= \frac{1 + i}{2}[(10 + 6i) - i(4 + 2i)]$$

$$= (1 + i)[6 + i] = (6 - 1) + i(6 + 1) = 5 + 7i$$

11. (a) $\because |z_1| = |z_2| = |z_3| = 1$, the origin is the circumcentre of the triangle and circum-radius is 1.

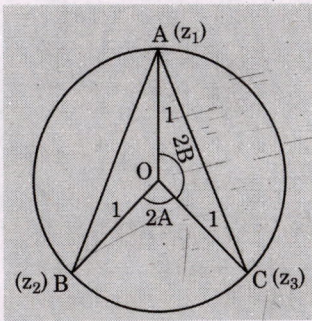

Fig. 40

Hence by rotating in anti-clockwise direction about O,

$$OC = OB \, e^{i2A}, \quad OA = OB \, e^{i(2A + 2B)}$$

or $\quad z_3 = z_2 e^{2Ai} \quad$ and $\quad z_1 = z_2 \, e^{(2A + 2B)i}$

Hence $z_1 + z_2 + z_3 = 0$

$\Rightarrow \quad z_2 \, e^{(2A + 2B)i} + z_2 + z_2 \, e^{2Ai} = 0$

$\Rightarrow \quad \cos(2A + 2B) + i \sin(2A + 2B) + 1$

$$+ \cos 2A + i \sin 2A = 0$$

$\Rightarrow \quad \cos 2A + \cos(2A + 2B) = -1$

and $\sin 2A + \sin(2A + 2B) = 0 \quad \dots(1)$

Squaring and adding, $2 + 2\cos 2B = 1$

or $\quad \cos 2B = -1/2.$

Hence $2B = 120° \quad$ or $\quad B = 60°.$

Putting in (1), we get

$$\sin 2A + \sin(2A + 120°) = 0$$

or $\quad 2 \sin(2A + 60°) \cos 60° = 0$

$\therefore \quad \sin(2A + 60°) = 0 = \sin \pi$

$$\therefore \quad 2A = 180^\circ - 60^\circ = 120^\circ$$

$$\therefore \quad A = 60^\circ$$

Hence $C = 60^\circ$ $\therefore$ Δ is equilateral.

Alternative : Since $z_1 + z_2 + z_3 = 0$, we have
$\dfrac{z_1 + z_2 + z_3}{3} = 0$ *i.e.* centroid of the Δ ABC is at the origin. Also origin is the circum-centre. Hence Δ ABC is equilateral as both centroid and circumcentre coincide.

(b) $\because$ $BC = AC$ and $\angle C = \dfrac{1}{2}\pi$, we have by rotation

about C in anti-clockwise sense $CB = CA\, e^{i\,\pi/2}$

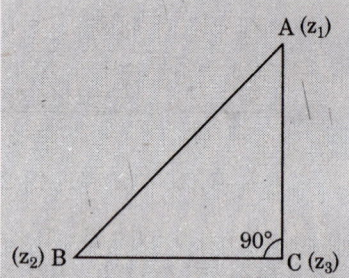

Fig. 41

$$(z_2 - z_3) = (z_1 - z_3)\, e^{\frac{1}{2}\pi i} = i(z_1 - z_3)$$

or $\quad (z_2 - z_3)^2 = -(z_1 - z_3)^2$

or $\quad z_2^2 + z_3^2 - 2z_2 z_3 = -z_1^2 - z_3^2 + 2z_1 z_3$

or $\quad z_1^2 + z_2^2 - 2z_1 z_2 = 2z_1 z_3 + 2z_2 z_3 - 2z_3^2$
$$- 2z_1 z_2$$

or $\quad (z_1 - z_2)^2 = 2[(z_1 z_3 - z_3^2) - (z_1 z_2 - z_2 z_3)]$
$$= 2(z_1 - z_3)(z_3 - z_2).$$

12. (a) Here $AB = AC$. By rotation we have
$$z_3 - z_1 = (z_2 - z_1)\, e^{i\theta}$$

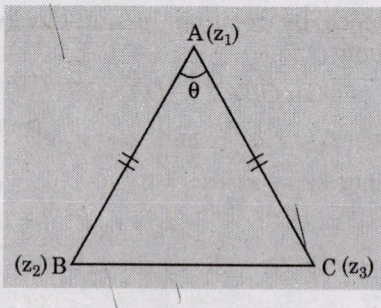

Fig. 42

or $\quad \dfrac{z_3 - z_1}{z_2 - z_1} = \cos\theta + i\sin\theta$ ...(1)

Subtract 1 from both sides in order to get the term $z_3 - z_2$.

$\therefore \quad \dfrac{z_3 - z_1}{z_2 - z_1} - 1 = (\cos\theta - 1) + i\sin\theta$

or $\quad \dfrac{z_3 - z_2}{z_2 - z_1} = 2i\sin\dfrac{\theta}{2}\cos\dfrac{\theta}{2} - 2\sin^2\dfrac{\theta}{2}$

$$= 2i\sin\dfrac{\theta}{2}\left(\cos\dfrac{\theta}{2} + i\sin\dfrac{\theta}{2}\right) \qquad \because -1 = i^2$$

Square both sides

$$\dfrac{(z_3 - z_2)^2}{(z_2 - z_1)^2} = -4\sin^2\dfrac{\theta}{2}\left(\cos\dfrac{\theta}{2} + i\sin\dfrac{\theta}{2}\right)^2$$

$$= -4\sin^2\dfrac{\theta}{2}(\cos\theta + i\sin\theta)\ \text{De-Moivres}$$

$$= -4\sin^2\dfrac{\theta}{2}\left(\dfrac{z_3 - z_1}{z_2 - z_1}\right),\ \text{by (1)}$$

$\therefore \quad (z_3 - z_2)^2 = -4\sin^2\dfrac{\theta}{2}(z_3 - z_1)(z_2 - z_1)$ etc.

(b) **Ans. True.** **Also see Part (a).**

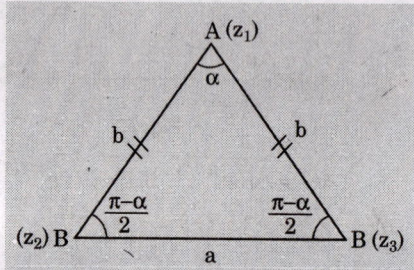

Fig. 43

Rotation about B gives $\dfrac{BA}{|BA|} = \dfrac{BC}{|BC|}\, e^{i\left(\frac{\pi - \alpha}{2}\right)}$

or $\quad \dfrac{z_1 - z_2}{z_3 - z_2} = \dfrac{b}{a}\, e^{i\frac{\pi - \alpha}{2}}$

Rotation about C gives in anti-clockwise sense

$$\dfrac{z_2 - z_3}{z_1 - z_3} = \dfrac{a}{b}\, e^{i\frac{\pi - \alpha}{2}}$$

Dividing, we get

$$(z_1 - z_2)(z_1 - z_3) = -(z_2 - z_3)^2\left(\dfrac{b}{a}\right)^2$$

or $\quad (z_1 - z_2)(z_3 - z_1) = (z_2 - z_3)^2\left[\dfrac{\sin\left(\frac{\pi - \alpha}{2}\right)}{\sin\alpha}\right]^2$

$$= (z_2 - z_3)^2\left[\dfrac{\cos(\alpha/2)}{2\sin(\alpha/2)\cos(\alpha/2)}\right]^2$$

or $\quad 4(z_1 - z_2)(z_3 - z_1)\sin^2(\alpha/2) = (z_2 - z_3)^2$

13. (a) $z^2 + pz + q = 0,\quad z_1 + z_2 = -p,\quad z_1 z_2 = q$

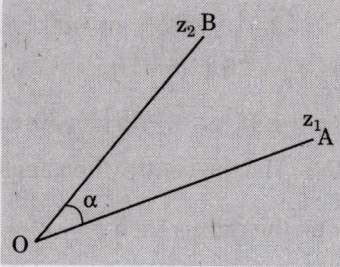

Fig. 44

By rotation through α in anti-clockwise direction,

$$z_2 = z_1 e^{i\alpha} \qquad \qquad ...(I)$$

$$\frac{z_2}{z_1} = \frac{e^{i\alpha}}{1} = \frac{\cos\alpha + i\sin\alpha}{1}$$

Add 1 in both sides to get $z_1 + z_2 = -p$

$$\therefore \quad \frac{z_1 + z_2}{z_1} = \frac{1 + \cos\alpha + i\sin\alpha}{1}$$

$$= 2\cos\frac{\alpha}{2}\left[\cos\frac{\alpha}{2} + i\sin\frac{\alpha}{2}\right]$$

or $\quad \dfrac{z_2 + z_1}{z_1} = 2\cos\dfrac{\alpha}{2} \cdot e^{i\alpha/2}$ Square.

$$(z_2 + z_1)^2 = 4\cos^2(\alpha/2)\, z_1^2 \cdot e^{i\alpha}$$

$$= 4\cos^2\frac{\alpha}{2} \cdot z_1^2 \cdot \frac{z_2}{z_1} = 4\cos^2\frac{\alpha}{2} \cdot z_1 z_2$$

or $\quad p^2 = 4q\cos^2\dfrac{\alpha}{2}$

(b) Ans. (a). $1, \omega, \omega^2$ are the cube roots of unity and they satisfy the condition

$$z_1^2 + z_2^2 + z_3^2 = z_1 z_2 + z_2 z_3 + z_3 z_1$$

for the three points z_1, z_2, z_3 to form an equilateral triangle by part (a).

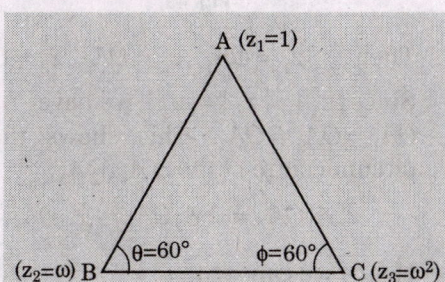

Fig. 45

Alternative Direct Method :

$$z_1 = 1$$

$$z_2 = \omega = -\frac{1}{2} + i\frac{\sqrt{3}}{2}$$

$$z_3 = \omega^2 = -\frac{1}{2} - i\frac{\sqrt{3}}{2}$$

Rotation about B,

$$1 - \omega = (\omega^2 - \omega)\, e^{iB}$$

$$\therefore \quad e^{iB} = \frac{1 - \omega}{\omega(\omega - 1)} = -\frac{1}{\omega} = -\frac{\omega^2}{1} = \frac{1}{2} + i\frac{\sqrt{3}}{2}$$

$$\therefore \quad e^{iB} = 1.(\cos 60^\circ + i\sin 60^\circ) = e^{i\pi/3}$$

$\therefore \quad B = \pi/3$. Similarly considering rotation about C we can prove $\angle C = \pi/3$.

3rd Method :

Converting to Cartesian, the vertices are

$$A(1, 0), \quad B\left(-\frac{1}{2}, \frac{\sqrt{3}}{2}\right), \quad C\left(-\frac{1}{2}, -\frac{\sqrt{3}}{2}\right)$$

$\therefore \quad AB = BC = CA = \sqrt{3}$

$\therefore \quad \Delta$ is equilateral.

14. (a) Let z_1, z_2 represent the points A and B on the Argand plane and let O be origin.

Now $z_1^2 + z_2^2 + 2z_1 z_2 \cos\theta = 0$

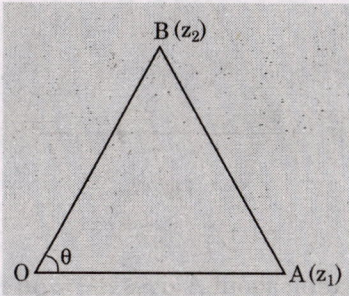

Fig. 46

$\Rightarrow \quad z_1^2 + z_2^2 + z_1 z_2 (e^{i\theta} + e^{-i\theta}) = 0$

$\Rightarrow \quad z_1^2 + z_1 z_2 e^{i\theta} + z_2^2 + z_1 z_2 e^{-i\theta} = 0$

$\Rightarrow \quad z_1(z_1 + z_2 e^{i\theta}) + z_2 e^{-i\theta}(z_1 + z_2 e^{i\theta}) = 0$

$\Rightarrow \quad (z_1 + z_2 e^{i\theta})(z_1 + z_2 e^{-i\theta}) = 0$

$\Rightarrow \quad$ either $z_1 = -z_2 e^{-i\theta}$ or $z_1 = -z_2 e^{i\theta}$

$\Rightarrow \quad |z_1| = |-z_2||e^{-i\theta}|$ or $|z_1| = |-z_2||e^{i\theta}|$

$\Rightarrow \quad |z_1| = |z_2| \qquad [\because |e^{-i\theta}| = |e^{i\theta}| = 1]$

$\Rightarrow \quad OA = OB.$

$\therefore \quad OAB$ is an isosceles triangle.

In the second case,

$$z_1^2 + z_2^2 - 2z_1 z_2 \cos\theta$$
$$= (z_1 - z_2 e^{i\theta})(z_1 - z_2 e^{-i\theta}) = 0$$

As above we prove that $|z_1| = |z_2|$.

$\therefore \quad \Delta$ is isosceles.

Alternative Rotation Method :

$z_2 - 0 = (z_1 - 0)e^{i\theta}$. Putting in the given expression, we get

$$z_1^2(1 + e^{2i\theta} - 2\cos\theta \cdot e^{i\theta}) = z_1^2\{1 + \cos 2\theta$$
$$+ i\sin 2\theta - 2\cos\theta(\cos\theta + i\sin\theta)\}$$

$$= z_1^2\{2\cos^2\theta + i\cdot 2\sin\theta\cos\theta - 2\cos^2\theta$$
$$- i\cdot 2\sin\theta\cos\theta\}$$

$$= z_1^2 \cdot 0 = 0$$

(b) Proceed as above in alternative method of part (a). $z_2 - 0 = (z_1 - 0)e^{2\pi i/3}$

or $\quad z_2 = z_1\left(-\frac{1}{2} + i\frac{\sqrt{3}}{2}\right) = z_1\omega$.

Put in the given relation, we get

$$z_1^2(1 + \omega + \omega^2) = 0 \text{ as } 1 + \omega + \omega^2 = 0$$

15. (a) Refer figure 47. z_3 is origin and Δ being equilateral we have angle at $O = 60^\circ$.

Hence rotation about O gives

$$OB = OA\, e^{\pi i/3}$$

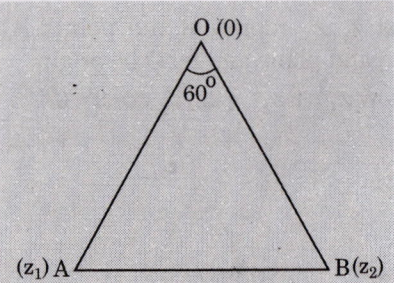

Fig. 47

or $z_2 - 0 = (z_1 - 0) e^{\pi i/3}$ ...(1)

Rotation about A gives $AO = AB\, e^{\pi i/3}$

or $0 - z_1 = (z_2 - z_1) e^{\pi i/3}$ ...(2)

Dividing (1) by (2), we get $\dfrac{z_2}{-z_1} = \dfrac{z_1}{z_2 - z_1}$

or $z_2^2 - z_1 z_2 = -z_1^2$ or $z_1^2 + z_2^2 = z_1 z_2$

or $\dfrac{z_1}{z_2} + \dfrac{z_2}{z_1} = 1$ or $\dfrac{A}{B} + \dfrac{B}{A} = 1$

(b) $z_1 + z_2 = -a, \quad z_1 z_2 = b$

As in last part, we have $z_1^2 + z_2^2 = z_1 z_2$

or $(z_1 + z_2)^2 = 3 z_1 z_2$ or $a^2 = 3b$.

16. Ans. True.

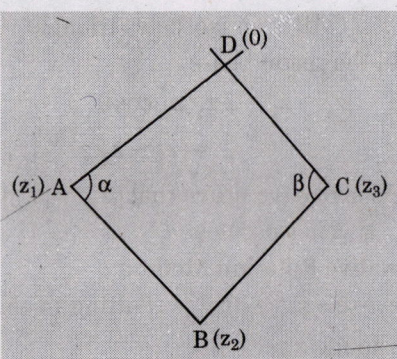

Fig. 48

Let angles at A and C be α and β. Anticlockwise rotation about A and C gives

$-z_1 = (z_2 - z_1) e^{i\alpha}$

$(z_2 - z_3) = -z_3 e^{i\beta}$

Multiplying $z_1 z_2 - z_1 z_3 = (z_2 z_3 - z_1 z_3) e^{i(\alpha+\beta)}$

If the points are concylic, then $\alpha + \beta = \pi$ and

$e^{i\pi} = \cos\pi + i\sin\pi = -1$

$\therefore \quad z_1 z_2 - z_1 z_3 = -z_2 z_3 + z_1 z_3$

or $z_1 z_2 + z_2 z_3 = 2 z_1 z_3$

Dividing both sides by $z_1 z_2 z_3$, we get

$\dfrac{2}{z_2} = \dfrac{1}{z_1} + \dfrac{1}{z_3}$ which is given.

Hence the given statement is true.

17. (a) Given $z_1 + z_2 + z_3 = 0,$ and from 2nd relation

$z_2 z_3 + z_3 z_1 + z_1 z_2 = 0$

$\therefore \quad z_2 z_3 = -z_1 (z_2 + z_3) = -z_1(-z_1) = z_1^2$

$\therefore \quad z_1^3 = z_1 z_2 z_3 = z_2^3 = z_3^3$

$|z_1|^3 = |z_2|^3 = |z_3|^3$

Above shows that distance of origin from A, B, C is same.

$\therefore$ Origin is circumcentre, but $z_1 + z_2 + z_3 = 0 \Rightarrow$ that centroid is also at the origin. Hence circumcentre and centroid coincide so that the triangle must be equilateral.

(b) Let z_1, z_2, z_3 represent the vertices A_1, A_2, A_3 of $\Delta A_1 A_2 A_3$ respectively and let O be the origin. **(See also Q. 11 (a) P. 102-108)**

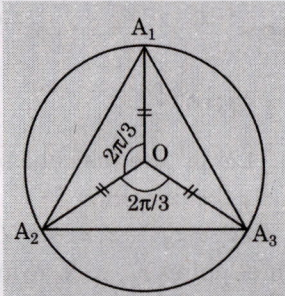

Fig. 49

Then $z_1 = \overrightarrow{OA_1}, \; z_2 = \overrightarrow{OA_2}, \; z_3 = \overrightarrow{OA_3}.$

Since $|z_1| = |z_2| = |z_3|$, we have $OA_1 = OA_2 = OA_3$. This shows that O is the circum-centre of the $\Delta A_1 A_2 A_3$.

$\angle A_1 O A_2 = \angle A_2 O A_3 = A_3 O A_1 = \dfrac{2\pi}{3}.$

Hence we can write

$z_2 = z_1 e^{2\pi i/3} = z_1 \omega$ and $z_3 = z_1 e^{4\pi i/3} = z_1 \omega^2$

(See remark (i), §3)

Hence $z_1 + z_2 + z_3 = z_1 (1 + \omega + \omega^2) = 0$

18. (a) $z_1 = 1 + i\sqrt{3} = 2\left(\cos\dfrac{\pi}{3} + i\sin\dfrac{\pi}{3}\right) = 2e^{\pi i/3}$

Rotating through $\dfrac{2\pi}{3}$ about the centre O,

$z_2 = z_1 e^{2\pi i/3} = 2e^{\pi i} = 2(\cos\pi + i\sin\pi)$

$z_3 = z_1 e^{4\pi i/3} = 2e^{5\pi i/3} = 2\cos\left(\dfrac{5\pi}{3} + i\sin\dfrac{5\pi}{3}\right)$

$\therefore \quad z_2 = -2, z_3 = 1 - i\sqrt{3}.$

(b) Ans. $a = b = 2 - \sqrt{3}.$

If z_1, z_2 and $z_3 = 0$ be the three sides, then the sides are given by $|z_1 - z_2|, |z_1 - 0|$ and $|z_2 - 0|$

Since the triangle is equilateral the sides are of equal length

$\therefore \quad (a-1)^2 + (b-1)^2 = a^2 + 1 = b^2 + 1$

From last two, we have $a = b$

and from first two, we have

$\therefore \quad a^2 - 4a + 1 = 0 \quad \therefore a = b$

∴ $a = 2 + \sqrt{3}, 2 - \sqrt{3}$. Since $0 < a < 1$

∴ $a = 2 - \sqrt{3} = b$.

(c)   The centre $z_0 = 1 + 0i$, A is $z_1 = 2 + i\sqrt{3}$

If B be the vertex z_2, then by rotation formula

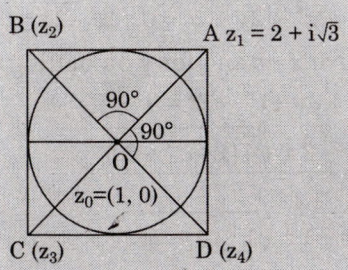

Fig. 49(a)

$z_2 - z_0 = (z_1 - z_0) e^{\pi i/2} = (2 + i\sqrt{3} - 1) i$

∴ $z_2 = z_0 + (i - \sqrt{3}) = (1 + 0i) + (i - \sqrt{3})$

         $= (1 - \sqrt{3}) + i$

For vertex D, we rotate in clockwise direction. If D be z_3, then

$z_4 - z_0 = (z_1 - z_0) e^{-\pi i/2} = (2 + i\sqrt{3} - 1)(-i)$

∴ $z_4 = z_0 + (-i + \sqrt{3}) = (1 + 0i) + (-i + \sqrt{3})$

         $= (\sqrt{3} + 1) - i$

For vertex C you may use that O is mid-point of AC.

∴ C is $0 - i\sqrt{3}$. Alternately you can say that

$z_3 - z_0 = (z_1 - z_0) e^{\pi i} = (2 + i\sqrt{3} - 1)(-1)$

                       $= -1 - i\sqrt{3}$

∴ $z_3 = z_0 + (-1 - i\sqrt{3}) = 1 + 0i - 1 - i\sqrt{3} = -i\sqrt{3}$.

19. (a)   We want the values of z_2 and z_4 in terms of z_1 and z_3

Hence we rotate about B and D.

Rotation about B in anti-clockwise sense

$z_1 - z_2 = (z_3 - z_2) e^{\pi i/2} = i(z_3 - z_2)$

$z_1 - i z_3 = z_2(1 - i) = \dfrac{z_2 \cdot 2}{1 + i}$

$2 z_2 = (1 + i) z_1 - i(1 + i) z_3$

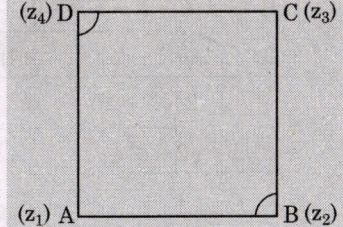

Fig. 50

or $2z_2 = (1 + i) z_1 + (1 - i) z_3$

Similarly rotation about D will give z_4 in terms of z_1 and z_3.

(b)   Rotation about B in anti-clockwise sense

$z_1 - z_2 = (z_3 - z_2) e^{i\pi/3}$

or $z_1 - z_2 = (z_3 - z_2) \dfrac{(1 + i\sqrt{3})}{2}$

$z_1 - z_3 \cdot \dfrac{1 + i\sqrt{3}}{2} = z_2 \left(1 - \dfrac{1 + i\sqrt{3}}{2}\right)$

or $z_1 - \dfrac{z_3}{2}(1 + i\sqrt{3}) = \dfrac{z_2}{2}(1 - i\sqrt{3})$

Multiply by $\dfrac{4}{1 - i\sqrt{3}} = \dfrac{4(1 + i\sqrt{3})}{4} = 1 + i\sqrt{3}$ to get $2z_2$

∴ $z_1(1 + i\sqrt{3}) - \dfrac{z_3}{2}(-2 + 2i\sqrt{3}) = 2z_2$

or $z_1(1 + i\sqrt{3}) + z_3(1 - i\sqrt{3}) = 2z_2$

Similarly we get $2z_4$ by rotation about D.

(c) $\overrightarrow{OA} = 3(\cos\theta + i\sin\theta)$

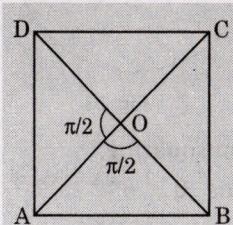

Fig. 51

$\overrightarrow{OB} = \overrightarrow{OA} e^{i\pi/2}$ by anti-clockwise rotation

      $= 3(\cos\theta + i\sin\theta) i = 3(-\sin\theta + i\cos\theta)$

$\overrightarrow{OD} = OA e^{-i\pi/2}$ by clockwise rotation

      $= 3(\cos\theta + i\sin\theta)(-i) = 3(\sin\theta - i\sin\theta)$

∴ B and D vertices are $\pm 3(\sin\theta - i\cos\theta)$

(d)   If D be (x, y) then $O(1, 1)$ is mid-point of $B(1, -1)$ and D

$$1 = \dfrac{x + 1}{2}, \quad 1 = \dfrac{y - 1}{2}$$

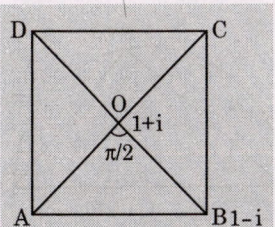

Fig. 52

∴ $D(x, y) = 1, 3 = 1 + 3i$

Again rotation in anti-clockwise direction about O gives $OC = OBe^{i\pi/2} = -2i(i) = 2$

∴ $(x - 1) + i(y - 1) = 2 + 0i$

∴ $x = 3, y = 1$ or $C = 3 + i$.

Hence by mid-point formula A is $-1 + i$.

20. (a)   It is a simple question of rotation but $OA \neq OB \neq OC$. Hence we shall apply the principle of rotation on unit lengths

$$\frac{z_2}{|z_2|} = \frac{z_1}{|z_1|}e^{i\theta} \qquad \ldots(1)$$

$$\frac{z_3}{|z_3|} = \frac{z_1}{|z_1|}e^{2i\theta} \qquad \ldots(2)$$

Since angles at B and C are $90°$ as OA is a diameter.

$$\therefore \quad \frac{OC}{OA} = \frac{|z_3|}{|z_1|} = \cos 2\theta \qquad \ldots(3)$$

$$\frac{OB}{OA} = \frac{|z_2|}{|z_1|} = \cos\theta \qquad \ldots(4)$$

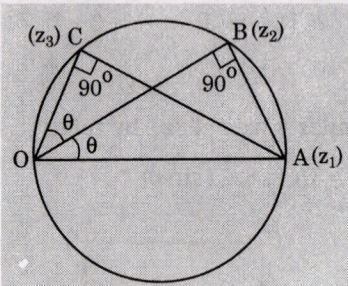

Fig. 53

From 1st on squaring,

$$z_2^2 = \cos^2\theta\, z_1^2\, e^{2i\theta} \qquad \text{by (4)}$$

and $z_3 = \cos 2\theta\, z_1\, e^{2i\theta} \qquad$ by (3) and (2)

Dividing, $\dfrac{z_2^2}{z_3} = \dfrac{\cos^2\theta}{\cos 2\theta}\cdot z_1$

or $\quad z_2^2\cos 2\theta = z_1 z_3 \cos^2\theta$.

(b) Ans. (a).

$|z - 3| = 3$ is a circle centred at the point $(3, 0)$ and of radius 3. Hence A is $(6, 0)$.

$$AP = z - 6, OP = z$$

OA subtends an angle of $\dfrac{\pi}{2}$ at P. Now PA and PO are of different lengths.

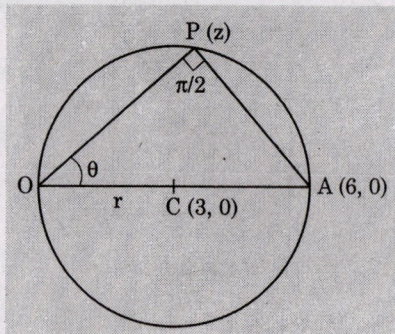

Fig. 54

Hence we take unit vectors and apply anticlockwise rotation.

$$\frac{\vec{AP}}{AP} = \frac{\vec{OP}}{OP}e^{i\pi/2}$$

$$\frac{z - 6}{z} = \frac{AP}{OP}\cdot i = i\tan\theta = i\tan(\arg z)$$

21. Put $z = x + iy$. Then equation takes the form

$$x^2 + y^2 - 2i(x + iy) + 2c(1 + i) = 0$$

or $\quad (x^2 + y^2 + 2y + 2c) + 2i(c - x) = 0$

Equating real and imaginary parts to zero, we get

$$x^2 + y^2 + 2y + 2c = 0, \quad 2c - 2x = 0 \quad \therefore \quad x = c. \ldots(1)$$

These give $x = c$ and for y on putting for x, we get

$$y^2 + 2y + c^2 + 2c = 0$$

or $\quad y = \dfrac{-2 \pm \sqrt{4(1 - c^2 - 2c)}}{2} \qquad \ldots(2)$

$$= -1 \pm \sqrt{1 - c^2 - 2c}.$$

where $1 - c^2 - 2c \geq 0$ for real y

or $\quad 2 \geq c^2 + 2c + 1$ or $(c + 1)^2 - (\sqrt{2})^2 \leq 0$

$\therefore \quad -\sqrt{2} \leq (c + 1) \leq \sqrt{2}$

or $\quad -\sqrt{2} - 1 \leq c \leq \sqrt{2} - 1$

Since $c \geq 0$ we contract the above interval to $0 \leq c \leq \sqrt{2} - 1$

I. $\quad c = 0 \quad (x, y) = (0, -1 \pm 1)$ or $(0, 0), (0, -2)$

II. $\quad 0 < c < (\sqrt{2} - 1)$.

There are two solutions x, y given by (1) and (2).

III. $\quad c = \sqrt{2} - 1$ i.e. $1 - c^2 - 2c = 0$, then from (1) and (2) there is only one solution from (1) and (2), $(x, y) = (c, -1)$.

IV. For $c > \sqrt{2} - 1, \Delta < 0$ and hence there is no solution.

22. (a) Putting $z = x + iy$, the given equation becomes

$$x + iy + c|x + iy + 1| + i = 0$$

or $\quad x + iy + c\sqrt{(x + 1)^2 + y^2} + i = 0$.

Equating real and imaginary parts to zero, we get

$$c\sqrt{(x + 1)^2 + y^2} + x = 0, \quad y + 1 = 0$$

whence $\quad y = -1 \qquad \ldots(1)$

and for x, we get the eq.

$$c\sqrt{(x + 1)^2 + (-1)^2} + x = 0$$

or $\quad c^2[(x + 1)^2 + 1] = x^2$

or $\quad (c^2 - 1)x^2 + 2c^2 x + 2c^2 = 0 \qquad \ldots(2)$

$\therefore \quad x = \dfrac{-2c^2 \pm 2\sqrt{c^4 - 2c^2(c^2 - 1)}}{2(c^2 - 1)}$

$$x = \dfrac{-c^2 \pm c\sqrt{2 - c^2}}{c^2 - 1} \qquad \ldots(3)$$

For real x, we must have $2 - c^2 \geq 0$

or $\quad c^2 - \sqrt{2} \leq 0 \quad \therefore \quad -\sqrt{2} \leq c \leq \sqrt{2}$

Since $c \geq 1$ we must contract to $1 \leq c \leq \sqrt{2}$

I. If $c = 1$ then from (2), $x = -1$

and from (1), $\qquad y = -1$

$\therefore \quad (x, y) = (-1, -1)$

II. If $1 < c < \sqrt{2}$ then the values of x, y are given by (1) and (3)

III. If $c = \sqrt{2}$ or $c^2 = 2$ then from (3),

$$x = \frac{-2}{2-1} = -2$$

$$\therefore \quad (x, y) = (-2, -1)$$

(b) $x + i(y + 2) + \alpha\sqrt{(x-1)^2 + y^2} = 0$

Equating real and imaginary parts,

$$y + 2 = 0 \quad \therefore \quad y = -2 \qquad \ldots(1)$$

and $x + \alpha\sqrt{(x-1)^2 + 4} = 0$

$$\therefore \quad x^2 = \alpha^2(x^2 - 2x + 5)$$

or $(1 - \alpha^2)x^2 + 2\alpha^2 x - 5\alpha^2 = 0 \qquad \ldots(2)$

$$\therefore \quad x = \frac{-\alpha^2 \pm \alpha\sqrt{5 - 4\alpha^2}}{1 - \alpha^2} \qquad \ldots(3)$$

Since x is real, we must have

$$5 - 4\alpha^2 \geq 0 \quad \text{or} \quad \alpha^2 - \frac{5}{4} \leq 0$$

$$\therefore \quad -\frac{1}{2}\sqrt{5} \leq \alpha \leq \frac{1}{2}\sqrt{5}$$

$$\therefore \quad \alpha \in \left[-\frac{1}{2}\sqrt{5}, \frac{1}{2}\sqrt{5}\right]$$

$z = (x, y)$ is given by (1) and (3).

23. (a) $2\sqrt{x^2 + y^2} - 4c(x + iy) + 1 + ic = 0$

$$\therefore \quad -4cy + c = 0 \implies y = 1/4 \qquad \ldots(1)$$

$$2\sqrt{x^2 + \frac{1}{16}} - 4cx + 1 = 0$$

or $4\left(x^2 + \frac{1}{16}\right) = (4cx - 1)^2$

or $4x^2(4c^2 - 1) - 8cx + \frac{3}{4} = 0$

$$\therefore \quad x = \frac{8c \pm \sqrt{64c^2 - 12(4c^2 - 1)}}{8(4c^2 - 1)}$$

or $x = \frac{4c \pm \sqrt{4c^2 + 3}}{4(4c^2 - 1)} \qquad \ldots(2)$

x is real as $c \geq 0$.

$z = (x, y)$ as given by (1) and (2), $c \geq 0$

(b) Equating real and imaginary parts,

$x\sqrt{x^2 + y^2} + cx = 0 \quad \therefore \quad x = 0 \qquad \ldots(1)$

$y\sqrt{x^2 + y^2} + cy + 1 = 0 \quad \therefore \quad y^2 + cy + 1 = 0$

$$y = \frac{-c \pm \sqrt{c^2 - 4}}{2} \qquad \ldots(2)$$

provided $c^2 - 4 \geq 0$ or $(c + 2)(c - 2) \geq 0$

$\therefore \quad c \leq -2$ or $c \geq 2$. Since $c > 0$

we choose $c \geq 2$

$c > 2$, $z = (x, y)$ as given by (1) and (2)

$c = 2$, $z = (x, y) = (0, -1)$

24. Let z_1, z_2, z_3, z_4 be the affixes of the points A, B, C, D, we have the identity

$$(z_1 - z_4)(z_2 - z_3) + (z_2 - z_4)(z_3 - z_1)$$
$$+ (z_3 - z_4)(z_1 - z_2) = 0$$

or $|-(z_1 - z_4)(z_2 - z_3)| = |(z_2 - z_4)(z_3 - z_1)$
$$+ (z_3 - z_4)(z_1 - z_2)|$$

or $|(z_1 - z_4)(z_2 - z_3)| \leq |(z_2 - z_4)(z_3 - z_1)|$
$$+ |(z_3 - z_4)(z_1 - z_2)|$$

or $|(z_1 - z_4)||(z_2 - z_3)| \leq |(z_2 - z_4)||(z_3 - z_1)|$
$$+ |(z_3 - z_4)||(z_1 - z_2)|$$

i.e. $AD \cdot BC \leq BD \cdot CA + CD \cdot AB$

25. We know from **§ 11 (4), P. 71** that

$$\left||z| - \left|\frac{1}{z}\right|\right| \leq \left|z + \frac{1}{z}\right| = a \text{ (given)}$$

$$\therefore \quad -a < \left(t - \frac{1}{t}\right) < a, \text{ where } t = |z|$$

$$\therefore \quad t^2 - at - 1 < 0 \quad \text{--ive} \qquad \ldots(1)$$

$$t^2 + at - 1 > 0 \quad \text{+ive} \qquad \ldots(2)$$

$$t = \frac{1}{2}[a \pm \sqrt{(a^2 + 4)}] \text{ say } p, q; p < q$$

$$\therefore \quad p \leq |z| \leq q, \text{ by (1)}$$

$$\frac{1}{2}[a - \sqrt{a^2 + 4}] \leq |z| \leq \frac{1}{2}[a + \sqrt{(a^2 + 4)}]$$

Hence max. value of $|z|$ is $\frac{1}{2}[a + \sqrt{(a^2 + 4)}]$. From (2)

$$t = \frac{1}{2}[-a \pm \sqrt{(a^2 + 4)}] \text{ say } p, q; p < q$$

$$t \leq \frac{1}{2}[-a - \sqrt{a^2 + 4}]$$

or $t \geq \frac{1}{2}[-a + \sqrt{(a^2 + 4)}]$

Hence min. value of $|z|$ is $\frac{1}{2}[-a + \sqrt{(a^2 + 4)}]$

Note : If $a = 1$, i.e. $\left|z + \frac{1}{z}\right| = 1$

then max. value of $|z| = \frac{1}{2}[1 + \sqrt{5}] = r$, say

and min. value of $|z| = \frac{1}{2}[\sqrt{5} - 1]$

When $|z| = r$ $\therefore$ z is $r(\cos\theta + i\sin\theta)$

and $\frac{1}{z} = \frac{1}{r}(\cos\theta - i\sin\theta)$

$$z + \frac{1}{z} = \left(r + \frac{1}{r}\right)\cos\theta + i\left(r - \frac{1}{r}\right)\sin\theta \qquad \ldots(3)$$

When $|z|$ is max., $r = \frac{1}{2}(1 + \sqrt{5})$

$$\therefore \quad \frac{1}{r} = \frac{2}{1 + \sqrt{5}} = \frac{2(1 - \sqrt{5})}{-4} = -\frac{1}{2}(1 - \sqrt{5})$$

$\therefore \quad r + \dfrac{1}{r} = \sqrt{5}, r - \dfrac{1}{r} = 1$

$\therefore \quad z + \dfrac{1}{z} = \sqrt{5} \cos \theta + i \sin \theta$

Now $\left| z + \dfrac{1}{z} \right| = 1$ $\therefore \quad 5 \cos^2 \theta + \sin^2 \theta = 1$

or $\quad 4 \cos^2 \theta = 0 \qquad \therefore \quad \cos \theta = 0$

$\therefore \quad z = r (\cos \theta + i \sin \theta) = r \, i \sin \theta$

or $\quad \mathrm{Re}\, z = 0.$

Note : See Q. 57 (a), P. 77-96 also.

26. Put $a = r \cos \alpha, \ b = r \sin \alpha,$

$z_1 = r_1 (\cos \theta_1 + i \sin \theta_1)$

and $z_2 = r_2 (\cos \theta_2 + i \sin \theta_2).$ Then

$|z_1| = r_1, \ |z_2| = r_2$

and $|z_1^2 + z_2^2| = |r_1^2 (\cos \theta_1 + i \sin \theta_1)^2$

$\qquad\qquad + r_2^2 (\cos \theta_2 + i \sin \theta_2)^2 |$

$= |r_1^2 (\cos 2\theta_1 + i \sin 2\theta_1) + r_2^2 (\cos 2\theta_2 + i \sin 2\theta_2)|$

$= \sqrt{\begin{array}{l}(r_1^2 \cos 2\theta_1 + r_2^2 \cos 2\theta_2)^2 \\ \quad + (r_1^2 \sin 2\theta_1 + r_2^2 \sin 2\theta_2)^2\end{array}}$

$= \sqrt{r_1^4 + r_2^4 + 2 r_1^2 r_2^2 \cos 2(\theta_1 - \theta_2)}$

Hence $\dfrac{2|az_1 + bz_2|^2}{a^2 + b^2}$

$= \dfrac{2|r \cos \alpha \, r_1 (\cos \theta_1 + i \sin \theta_1)}{}$
$\dfrac{\qquad + r \sin \alpha . r_2 (\cos \theta_2 + i \sin \theta_2)|^2}{r^2}$

$= 2 | (r_1 \cos \alpha \cos \theta_1 + r_2 \sin \alpha \cos \theta_2)^2$

$\qquad + i (r_1 \cos \alpha \sin \theta_1 + r_2 \sin \alpha \sin \theta_2)^2 |$

$= 2 [(r_1 \cos \alpha \cos \theta_1 + r_2 \sin \alpha \cos \theta_2)^2$

$\qquad + (r_1 \cos \alpha \sin \theta_1 + r_2 \sin \alpha \sin \theta_2)^2]$

$= 2 [r_1^2 \cos^2 \alpha + r_2^2 \sin^2 \alpha$

$\qquad + 2 r_1 r_2 \sin \alpha \cos \alpha \cos (\theta_1 - \theta_2)]$

$= [r_1^2 (1 + \cos 2\alpha) + r_2^2 (1 - \cos 2\alpha)$

$\qquad + 2 r_1 r_2 \sin 2\alpha \cos (\theta_1 - \theta_2)]$

$= [A + B \cos 2\alpha + C \sin 2\alpha]$

where $A = r_1^2 + r_2^2, \ B = r_1^2 - r_2^2,$

$\qquad C = 2 r_1 r_2 \cos (\theta_1 - \theta_2).$

$= [A + R \sin (2\alpha + \phi)]$ where $B = R \sin \phi,$

$\qquad C = R \cos \phi.$

Hence max. and min. values of $\dfrac{2|az_1 + bz_2|^2}{a^2 + b^2}$ are

respectively $[A + R]$ and $[A - R]$

i.e. $[A + \sqrt{B^2 + C^2}]$ and $[A - \sqrt{B^2 + C^2}]$

so that

$A - \sqrt{B^2 + C^2} \leq \dfrac{2|az_1 + bz_2|^2}{a^2 + b^2}$

$\qquad\qquad \leq A + \sqrt{B^2 + C^2}.$

But $\quad A = r_1^2 + r_2^2 = |z_1|^2 + |z_2|^2$ etc.

Problem Set (7)

▶ MULTIPLE CHOICE QUESTIONS

1. $z + \bar{z} = 0$ if and only if

(a) $\mathrm{Re}\,(z) = 0$ \qquad (b) $I_m (z) = 0$

(c) none of these.

2. $z \bar{z} = 0$ if and only if

(a) $\mathrm{Re}\,(z) = 0$ \qquad (b) $\mathrm{Im}\,(z) = 0$

(c) $z = 0$ \qquad (d) none of these.

3. $\arg bi \ \ (b > 0)$ is

(a) π \quad (b) $\dfrac{\pi}{2}$ \quad (c) $-\dfrac{\pi}{2}$ \quad (d) 0

4. $\arg a \ (a < 0)$ is

(a) 0 \qquad (b) $\dfrac{\pi}{2}$

(c) π \qquad (d) none of these.

5. $\arg z + \arg \bar{z} \ (z \neq 0)$

(a) 0 \qquad (b) π

(c) $\dfrac{\pi}{2}$ \qquad (d) none of these.

6. $\overline{(z^{-1})} = (\bar{z})^{-1}$

(a) True \qquad (b) False

7. Which of the following statements is false

(a) $|z^2| = |z|^2$ \qquad (b) $|z|^2 = z^2$

8. $(3 + \omega + 3\omega^2)^4$ equals

(a) 16 \qquad (b) 16ω

(c) $16\omega^2$ \qquad (d) none of these.

9. $\left(-\dfrac{1}{2} + \dfrac{\sqrt{3}}{2} i \right)^{1000} = -\dfrac{1}{2} + \dfrac{\sqrt{3}}{2} i$

(a) True \qquad (b) False

10. Which of the following is correct ?

(a) $2 + 3i > 1 + 4i$ \qquad (b) $6 + 2i > 3 + 3i,$

(c) $5 + 8i > 5 + 7i$ \qquad (d) none of these.

11. The real part of $(1 + i)^2 / (3 - i)$ is

(a) $\dfrac{1}{5}$ \qquad (b) $\dfrac{1}{3}$

(c) $-\dfrac{1}{3}$ \qquad (d) none of these.

12. $\left(\dfrac{2i}{1+i}\right)^2 =$

    (a) i (b) $2i$

    (c) $1-i$ (d) $1-2i$ **(B.I.T.S. 1992)**

13.* The smallest integer for which $\left(\dfrac{1+i}{1-i}\right)^n = 1$ is

    (a) $n=8$ (b) $n=12$

    (c) $n=16$ (d) none of these.

14. A square root of $3+4i$ is

    (a) $\sqrt{3}+i$ (b) $2-i$

    (c) $2+i$ (d) none of these.

15. $(-64)^{1/4}$ equals

    (a) $\pm 2(1+i)$ (b) $\pm 2(1-i)$

    (c) $\pm 2(1\pm i)$ (d) none of these.

16. Multiplying a complex number by i rotates the vector representing the complex number through $180°$.

    (a) True   (b) False

17. The vector $z=3-4i$ is turned anticlockwise through an angle of $180°$ and stretched $2\cdot5$ times. The complex number corresponding to the newly obtained vector is ......

18. If $z=re^{i\theta}$, then $|e^{iz}|=$ ....

19. In a geometrical progression first term and common ratio are both $\dfrac{1}{2}(\sqrt{3}+i)$. Then the absolute value of the nth term of the progression is

    (a) 2^n (b) 4^n

    (c) 1 (d) none of these.

20.* If three complex numbers are in A.P., then they lie on a circle in the complex plane.

    (a) True   (b) False.

21. Given that the equation $z^2+(p+iq)z+r+is=0$, where p,q,r,s are non-zero has a real root. Then

    (a) $pqr=r^2+p^2s$ (b) $prs=q^2+r^2p$

    (c) $qrs=p^2+s^2q$ (d) $pqs=s^2+q^2r$.

22. (a) If $2+i\sqrt{3}$ is a root of the equation $x^2+px+q=0$ where p and q are real, then $(p,q)=(...,...)$

    (b) The solution of the equation $|z|-z=1+2i$ is

    (a) $\dfrac{3}{2}-2i,$ (b) $\dfrac{3}{2}+2i$

    (c) $2-\dfrac{3}{2}i$ (d) none of these.

23. The equation $a^2-2a\sin x+1=0$ has only two possible real solutions for a

    (a) True   (b) False

24. There exist no real numbers x and y such that
       $(2-i)x+(1+3i)y+2=0$

    (a) True   (b) False

25. Let z be a complex number. Then the equation $z^4+z+2=0$ cannot have a root such that $|z|<1$.

    (a) True   (b) False

26.* Among the complex numbers z satisfying the condition $|z+1-i|\le 1$, the number having the least positive argument is

    (a) $1-i$ (b) $-1+i$

    (c) $-i$ (d) none of these.

27. If $|a_i|<1$, $\lambda_i \ge 0$ for $i=1,2,...n$ and
    $\lambda_1+\lambda_2+....+\lambda_n=1$, then
    $|\lambda_1 a_1+\lambda_2 a_2+...+\lambda_n a_n|<1$.

    (a) True   (b) False

28. The equation $\bar{b}z+b\bar{z}=c$, where b is a non-zero complex constant and c is real, represents

    (a) a circle   (b) a straight line

    (c) none of these

29.* If the complex numbers z_1 and z_2 are such that the sum z_1+z_2 is a real number, then they are necessarily conjugate complexes

    (a) True   (b) False

30. If the complex numbers z_1 and z_2 are such that the product $z_1 z_2$ is a real number, then they are necessarily conjugate complexes

    (a) True   (b) False

31. Let z be a complex number such that the imaginary part of z is non-zero and $a=z^2+z+1$ is real. Then a cannot take the value.

    (a) -1 (b) $\dfrac{1}{3}$ (c) $\dfrac{1}{2}$ (d) $\dfrac{3}{4}$

    (IIT-JEE 2012)

32. If $z\ne 1$ and $\dfrac{z^1}{z-1}$ is real, then the point represented by the complex number z lies.

    (a) either on the real axis or on a circle passing through the origin

    (b) on a circle with centre at origin

    (c) either on the real axis or on a circle not passing through the origin

    (d) on the imaginary axis.   **(AIEEE 2012)**

33. If $\omega(\ne 1)$ is a case root of unity and $(1+\omega)^7=A+B\omega$ then A and B are respectively given by

    (a) $0,1$ (b) $1,0$ (c) $1,1$ (d) $-1,1$

    (AIEEE 2011; IIT 1995)

34. If α and β are the roots of the equation $x^2-x+1=0$, then $\alpha^{2009}+\beta^{2009}=$

    (a) -2 (b) -1 (c) 1 (d) 2

    (AIEEE 2010)

35. If z_1,z_2 be two distinct complex numbers and let $z=(1-t)z_1+tz_2$ for some real number t with $0<t<1$. If $\arg(\omega)$ denotes the principal argument of a non-zero complex number ω, then

(a) $|z - z_1| + |z - z_2| = |z_1 - z_2|$

(b) $\arg(z - z_1) = \arg(z - z_2)$

(c) $\begin{vmatrix} z - z_1 & \bar{z} - \bar{z}_1 \\ z_2 - z_1 & \bar{z}_2 - \bar{z}_1 \end{vmatrix} = 0$

(d) $\arg(z - z_1) = \arg(z_2 - z_1)$ **(IIT-JEE 2010)**

36. If z is any complex number satisfying $|z - 3 - 2i| \le 2$ then the minimum value of $|2z - 6 + 5i|$ is

(a) 5   (b) 6   (c) 7   (d) 0

(IIT-JEE 2011)

37. Let $\omega = e^{\frac{i\pi}{3}}$ and a, b, c, x, y, z be non-zero complex numbers such that $a + b + c = x$, $a + b\omega + c\omega^2 = y$, $a + b\omega^2 + c\omega = z$.

Then the value of $\dfrac{|x|^2 + |y|^2 + |z|^2}{|a|^2 + |b|^2 + |c|^2}$ is

(a) 3   (b) 4   (c) 0   (d) 5

(IIT-JEE 2011)

38. The number of complex numbers z such that $|z - 1| = |z + 1| = |z - i|$ equals

(a) 10   (b) 1   (c) 2   (d) ∞

(AIEEE 2010)

Solutions to Problem Set (7)

1. Ans. (a).   2. Ans. (c).

3. Ans. (b).

Since $b > 0$, bi represents a point on the positive side of the imaginary axis on which the argument of every point is $\pi/2$.

4. Ans. (c).

Here a will represent a point on the negative side of real axis where the argument of each point is π.

5. Ans. (a).

$$\arg z + \arg \bar{z} = \arg z\bar{z} = \arg |z|^2.$$

Since $|z|^2$ is a positive real number, we have $\arg |z|^2 = 0$.

6. Ans. (a).

Put $z = x + iy$.

Then $z^{-1} = \dfrac{1}{x + iy} = \dfrac{x - iy}{x^2 + y^2}$

so that $\overline{(z^{-1})} = \dfrac{x + iy}{x^2 + y^2}$

Again $\bar{z} = x - iy$ and so $(\bar{z})^{-1} = \dfrac{1}{x - iy} = \dfrac{x + iy}{x^2 + y^2}$.

7. Ans. (b), as L.H.S. is real and R.H.S. is complex.

8. Ans. (b).

9. Ans. (a).

$\because -\dfrac{1}{2} + \dfrac{\sqrt{3}}{2} i = \omega$,   we have $\omega^{1000} = \omega^{999} \cdot \omega = \omega$.

10. Ans. (d), since there exists no relation of $>$ and $<$ in complex numbers.

11. Ans. (d).

$$\dfrac{(1 + i)^2}{3 - i} = \dfrac{1 + i^2 + 2i}{3 - i} = \dfrac{2i(3 + i)}{3^2 - i^2} = \dfrac{6i - 2}{10}$$

$$\therefore \quad \text{Re}\left(\dfrac{(1 + i)^2}{3 - i}\right) = -\dfrac{2}{10} = -\dfrac{1}{5}.$$

12. Ans. (b).

$$\dfrac{4i^2}{2i} = 2i$$

13. Ans. (d).

$$\because \quad \dfrac{1 + i}{1 - i} = \dfrac{(1 + i)^2}{1 - i^2} = \dfrac{1 + i^2 + 2i}{2} = \dfrac{1 - 1 + 2i}{2} = i$$

we have $\left(\dfrac{1 + i}{1 - i}\right)^n = 1 \Rightarrow i^n = 1.$ ...(1)

The smallest positive integer n satisfying (1) is 4. Hence (d) is true.

14. Ans. (c).

15. Ans. (c).

See solution Q. **1 (c), P. 60-62** and put $a = 1$.

16. Ans. (b). [See (ii), P. 101].

17. Ans. $-\dfrac{15}{2} + 10i$

18. $z = re^{i\theta}$, $i = e^{i\pi/2}$

$$\therefore \quad iz = re^{i(\theta + \pi/2)} = r(-\sin\theta + i\cos\theta)$$

$$= r(a + ib) \text{ where } a = -\sin\theta, b = \cos\theta$$

$$\therefore \quad e^{iz} = e^{ra} \cdot e^{ibr}$$

$$\therefore \quad |e^{iz}| = |e^{ra}||e^{ibr}| = e^{-r\sin\theta} \cdot 1$$

$\because$ exponential function is always $+$ive and $|e^{i\theta}| = 1 \ \forall \ \theta$.

19. Ans. (c).

Here $a = \dfrac{1}{2}(\sqrt{3} + i)$, $r = \dfrac{1}{2}(\sqrt{3} + i)$

$$\therefore \quad T_n = ar^{n-1} = \left[\dfrac{1}{2}(\sqrt{3} + i)\right]^n = (re^{i\theta})^n$$

where $r = 1$ and $\theta = \pi/6$,

$$\therefore \quad T_n = e^{in\theta} \quad \therefore \ |T_n| = |e^{in\theta}| = 1$$

20. Ans. (b). For, consider the complex numbers $e^{i\pi/3}$, $3e^{i\pi/3}$ and $5e^{i\pi/3}$ which are in A.P. But they do not lie on a circle. In fact, they lie on the straight line $\theta = \pi/3$.

21. Ans. (d).

Since the equation has real solution

$$\therefore \quad z = x + iy = x$$

$$\therefore \quad x^2 + (p + iq)x + r + is = 0$$

$$\therefore \quad x^2 + px + r = 0 \text{ and } qx + s = 0$$

From 2nd $x = -\dfrac{s}{q}$ and putting in first, we get

$pqs = s^2 + q^2 r$ which is the required condition.

22. (a) Ans. $(-4, 7)$.

Since complex roots occur in conjugate pairs, the roots of the equation are

$\alpha = 2 + i\sqrt{3}$ and $\beta = 2 - i\sqrt{3}$

$\therefore \quad \alpha + \beta = -p$ and $\alpha\beta = q$,

i.e. $4 = -p$ and $7 = q$.

Thus $p = -4$ and $q = 7$.

(b) Ans. (a).

$\sqrt{x^2 + y^2} - x = 1, y = -2 \quad \therefore \quad x = 3/2$

23. Ans. (a).

Solving the given equation for a, we get

$$a = \frac{2\sin x \pm \sqrt{4\sin^2 x - 4}}{2} = \sin x \pm i\cos x.$$

Now a will be real if $\cos x = 0$, which gives $x = n\pi + \pi/2$. For these values of x, we have

$$a = \sin\left(n\pi + \frac{\pi}{2}\right) = \pm 1$$

Hence $a = 1$ and $a = -1$ are only two possible real solutions.

24. Ans. (b).

$$x = -\frac{6}{7}, \quad y = -\frac{2}{7}.$$

25. Ans. (a).

From the equation, we have $2 = -z - z^4$

$\therefore \quad |2| = |-z - z^4| = |z + z^4| \le |z| + |z^4|$

Thus $\quad |2| \le |z| + |z|^4 < 2 \qquad [\because |z| < 1]$

or $\quad 2 < 2$ which is impossible.

Hence if $|z| < 1$, the equation $z^4 + z + 2 = 0$ cannot have a root.

26. Ans. (d).

The required complex number is i. Draw figure on the Argand plane to verify it.

27. Ans. (a).

$|\lambda_1 a_1 + \lambda_2 a_2 + \ldots + \lambda_n a_n|$

$\qquad\qquad \le |\lambda_1 a_1| + |\lambda_2 a_2| + \ldots + |\lambda_n a_n|$

$= |\lambda_1||a_1| + |\lambda_2||a_2| + \ldots + |\lambda_n||a_n|$

$= \lambda_1|a_1| + \lambda_2|a_2| + \ldots + \lambda_n|a_n| \qquad [\because \lambda_i \ge 0]$

$< \lambda_1 + \lambda_2 + \lambda_3 + \ldots + \lambda_n \qquad [\because |a_i| < 1]$

$= 1$

Thus $|\lambda_1 a_1 + \lambda_2 a_2 + \ldots + \lambda_n a_n| < 1$.

28. Ans. (b).

Put $z = x + iy$, $b = b_1 + ib_2$ where x, y, b_1, b_2 are real. Then the equation may be written as

$(b_1 - ib_2)(x + iy) + (b_1 + ib_2)(x - iy) = c$

or $2b_1 x + 2b_2 y = c$, which is a straight line.

29. Ans. (b).

For example take $z_1 = 2 + i$ and $z_2 = 5 - i$.

30. Ans. (b).

For example take $z_1 = 2i$ and $z_2 = 5i$.

31. Ans. (d).

$z^2 + z + 1 - a = 0$

$\Rightarrow \quad z = \frac{-1 \pm \sqrt{4a - 3}}{2}, a \ne \frac{3}{4}$, otherwise z will be purely real.

32. Ans. (a).

$$\frac{z^2}{z - 1} = \frac{\bar{z}^2}{\bar{z} - 1}$$

$\Rightarrow \quad z\bar{z}z - z^2 = z\bar{z}\bar{z} - \bar{z}^2$

$\Rightarrow \quad |z|^2 (z - \bar{z}) - (z - \bar{z})(z + \bar{z}) = 0$

$\Rightarrow \quad (z - \bar{z})[|z|^2 - (z + \bar{z})] = 0$

$\Rightarrow \quad$ either $z = \bar{z}$ so real axis.

or $\quad |z|^2 = z + \bar{z}$

$\Rightarrow \quad z\bar{z} - z - \bar{z} = 0$,

which represent a circle passing through origin.

33. Ans. (c).

$(1 + \omega)^7 = A + B\omega \quad \Rightarrow \quad (-\omega^2)^7 = A + B\omega$

$\Rightarrow \quad \omega^{14} = -A - B\omega$

$\Rightarrow \quad \omega^2 \cdot \omega^{12} = -A - B\omega$

$\Rightarrow \quad A + B\omega + \omega^2 = 0 \qquad (\because 1 + \omega + \omega^2 = 0)$

$\Rightarrow \quad A = 1, B = 1$

34. Ans. (c).

Roots of equation $x^2 - x + 1 = 0$ are $\alpha = -\omega$, $\beta = -\omega^2$

$\alpha^{2009} + \beta^{2009} = (-\omega)^{2009} + (-\omega^2)^{2009}$

$\qquad\qquad = -(\omega^2 + \omega) = 1$

35. Ans. (a), (c) and (d)

(a) $|z - z_1| + |z - z_2| = |z_1 - z_2|$

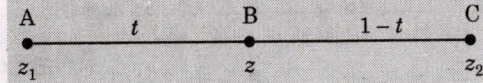

Fig. 55 (a)

$\Rightarrow \quad AB + BC = AC$

(b) $\arg(z - z_1) - \arg(z - z_2) = \pi$

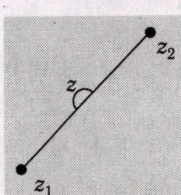

Fig. 55 (b)

(c) $\begin{vmatrix} z & \bar{z} & 1 \\ z_1 & \bar{z}_1 & 1 \\ z_2 & \bar{z}_2 & 1 \end{vmatrix} = 0$

$$\Rightarrow \begin{vmatrix} z - z_1 & \bar{z} - \bar{z}_1 & 0 \\ z_1 - z_2 & \bar{z}_1 - \bar{z}_2 & 0 \\ z_2 & \bar{z}_2 & 1 \end{vmatrix} = 0$$

$$\Rightarrow \begin{vmatrix} z - z_1 & \bar{z} - \bar{z}_1 \\ z_1 - z_2 & \bar{z}_1 - \bar{z}_2 \end{vmatrix} = 0$$

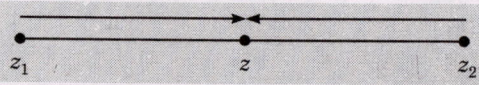

Fig. 55(c)

(d) $\arg(z - z_1) = \arg(z_2 - z_1)$

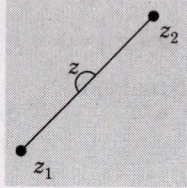

Fig. 55(d)

36. Ans. (a).

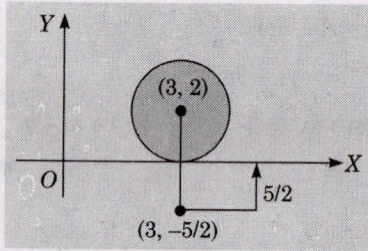

Fig. 55(e)

$$|2z - 6 + 5i| = 2\left| z - \left(3 - \frac{5i}{2} \right) \right|$$

for minima, $= 2 \times \dfrac{5}{2} = 5$

37. Ans. (a).

On taking $\omega = e^{i\pi/3}$

Expression is in terms of a, b, c. So let us assume $\omega = e^{2\pi i/3}$

Then the solution is following.

$$a + b + c = x, \ a + b\omega + c\omega^2 = y, \ a + b\omega^2 + c\omega = z$$

$$\therefore \quad \frac{|x|^2 + |y|^2 + |z|^2}{|a|^2 + |b|^2 + |c|^2} = \frac{x\bar{x} + y\bar{y} + z\bar{z}}{|a|^2 + |b|^2 + |c|^2}$$

$$= \frac{(a+b+c)(\bar{a}+\bar{b}+\bar{c}) + (a+b\omega+c\omega^2)(\bar{a}+\bar{b}\omega^2+\bar{c}\omega)}{|a|^2 + |b|^2 + |c|^2}$$
$$ + \frac{(a+b\omega^2+c\omega).(\bar{a}+\bar{b}\omega+\bar{c}\omega^2)}{|a|^2 + |b|^2 + |c|^2}$$

$$= \frac{3(|a|^2 + |b|^2 + |c|^2)}{|a|^2 + |b|^2 + |c|^2} = 3$$

38. Ans. (b).

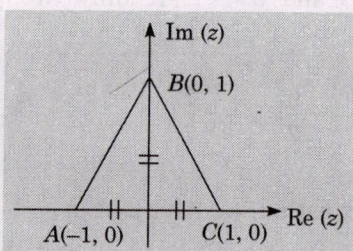

Fig. 55(f)

z is the circum-centre $(0, 0)$ of triangle ABC

$\therefore$ there exist only one complex number.

MISCELLANEOUS EXERCISE

Matching Entries

◆ *Match the entries of List-A and List-B :*

1. **List-A**

(a) $\arg \dfrac{i(\sqrt{3}+i)^6}{4(1 - i\sqrt{3})^2} =$

(b) If $|z_1 + z_2| = |z_1| + |z_2|$, then $\arg\left(\dfrac{z_1}{z_2}\right) =$

(c) If $\arg z < 0$, then $\arg(-z) - \arg(z) =$

(d) If $\arg z = \dfrac{\pi}{4}$, then Im $z^2 =$

List-B

1. 0

2. $2(\operatorname{Re} z)^2 = 2x^2$

3. $\pi/6$

4. π

2. **List-A**

(a) $\sin \dfrac{\pi}{900}\left\{ \displaystyle\sum_{r=1}^{10} (r - \omega)(r - \omega^2) \right\} =$

List-B

1. 0

(b) If roots of $t^2 + t + 1 = 0$ be α, β then $\alpha^4 + \beta^4 + \alpha^{-1}\beta^{-1} =$ 2. 4

(c) If $\left[\dfrac{1 + \cos\theta + i\sin\theta}{\sin\theta + i(1 + \cos\theta)}\right]^4 = \cos n\theta + i\sin n\theta$, then $n =$ 3. i

(d) If $z_r = \cos\dfrac{\pi}{3^r} + i\sin\dfrac{\pi}{3^r}, r = 1, 2, 3, \ldots$, then value of $z_1 z_2 z_3 \ldots \infty =$ 4. 1

3. **List-A** **List-B**

(a) If $\left(\dfrac{1+i}{1-i}\right)^n = 1$, then the least value of n is 1. $1 + \sqrt{3}$

(b) If $\left|z + \dfrac{2}{z}\right| = 2$, then max. value of $|z|$ is 2. circle

(c) If $\arg\dfrac{z-1}{z+1} = \dfrac{\pi}{3}$, then locus of the point z is 3. $|z| < 5$

(d) If $\log_{\sqrt{3}}\left[\dfrac{|z|^2 - |z| + 1}{2 + |z|}\right] < 2$, then locus of z is 4. 4

4. **List-A** **List-B**

(a) If z_1 and z_2 be two nth roots of unity then $\arg\left(\dfrac{z_1}{z_2}\right)$ is a multiple of 1. $-\dfrac{1}{\omega_1 \omega_2}$

(b) If $\omega \neq 1$ be nth root of unity, then $\omega + \omega^2 + \omega^3 + \ldots + \omega^{n-1} =$ 2. $-\dfrac{2n}{1-\omega}$

(c) $1 + 3\omega + 5\omega^2 + \ldots n$ terms $=$ 3. -1

(d) $(1-\omega)(1-\omega^2)\ldots(1-\omega^{n-1}) =$ 4. $\dfrac{2\pi}{n}$

(e) If ω_1, ω_2 be complex cube roots of unity then $\omega_1^4 + \omega_2^4 =$ 5. n

5. Given $z_1 + z_2 + z_3 = A$, $z_1 + z_2 w + z_3 w^2 = B$ and $z_1 + z_2 w^2 + z_3 w = C$ where w is cube root of unity.

List-A **List-B**

(a) $|A|^2$ 1. $\Sigma|z_1|^2 + \overline{z}_1(z_2 w + z_3 w^2) +$
$\overline{z}_2(z_3 w + z_1 w^2) + \overline{z}_3(z_1 w + z_2 w^2)$

(b) $|B|^2$ 2. $\Sigma|z_1|^2 + \overline{z}_1(z_2 w^2 + z_3 w) +$
$\overline{z}_2(z_3 w^2 + z_1 w) + \overline{z}_3(z_1 w^2 + z_2 w)$

(c) $|C|^2$ 3. $3\Sigma|z_1|^2$

(d) $\Sigma|A|^2$ 4. $\Sigma|z_1|^2 + \overline{z}_1(z_2 + z_3) + \overline{z}_2(z_3 + z_1) + \overline{z}_3(z_1 + z_2)$

(e) Express z_1, z_2, z_3 in terms of A, B, C.

(f) Prove : $|A|^2 + |B|^2 + |C|^2 = 3(|z_1|^2 + |z_2|^2 + |z_3|^2)$.

6. If a, b, c are distinct integers and $w \neq 1$ is a cube root of unity, then

Column-I **Column-II**

(a) $|a + bw + cw^2|^2$ (p) 1

(b) $|a + bw + cw^2|^2 + |a + bw^2 + cw|^2$ (q) ≥ 1

(c) $\left|\dfrac{a + bw + cw^2}{a + bw^2 + cw}\right|$ (r) ≥ 2

(d) $|a + bw^2 + cw|$ (s) 2

7. Number of solutions of

	Column-I		Column-II
(a)	$z^2 + |z| = 0$	(p)	1
(b)	$z^2 + \bar{z}^2 = 0$	(q)	3
(c)	$z^2 + 8\bar{z} = 0$	(r)	4
(d)	$|z - 2| = 1$ and $|z - 1| = 2$	(s)	Infinite

8. Centres of the following circles are :

	Column-I		Column-II
(a)	$|z - 2|^2 + |z - 4i|^2 = 20$	(p)	$(1, -1)$
(b)	$\left|\dfrac{z-1}{z+1}\right| = \dfrac{1}{2}$	(q)	$\left(\dfrac{5}{3}, 0\right)$
(c)	$z\bar{z} - (1 + i)z - (1 - i)\bar{z} + 7 = 0$	(r)	$(-4, -1)$
(d)	$\arg\dfrac{(z + 3 + 4i)}{(z + 5 - 2i)} = \dfrac{\pi}{2}$	(s)	$(1, 2)$

9. The following curves represents the equations of

	Column-I		Column-II
(a)	$|z - 3| + |z - i| = 10$	(p)	Circle
(b)	$\left|\dfrac{2z - 3}{z - i}\right| = 2$	(q)	Hyperbola
(c)	$z^2 + \bar{z}^2 = 5$	(r)	St. line
(d)	$\left|\dfrac{z - 6}{z - 2i}\right| = 3$	(s)	Ellipse

10.

	Column-I		Column-II
(a)	The set of points z satisfying $|z - i|z|| = ||z + i|z||$ is contained in or equal to	(p)	An ellipse with eccentricity $\dfrac{4}{5}$
(b)	The set of points z satisfying $|z + 4| + |z - 4| = 1$ is contained in or equal to	(q)	The set of points z satisfying $\mathrm{Im}(z) = 0$
(c)	If $|\omega| = 2$ then the set of points $z = \omega - \dfrac{1}{\omega}$ is contained in or equal to	(r)	The set of points z satisfying $|\mathrm{Im}(z)| \le 2$
(d)	If $|\omega| = 1$ then the set of points $z = \omega + \dfrac{1}{\omega}$ is contained in or equal to	(s)	The set of a points z satisfying $|\mathrm{Re}(z)| \le 2$
		(t)	The set of a points z satisfying $|z| \le 3$

(IIT-JEE 2010)

Hints/Solutions

1. (a) → 3 **Q. 6 (c) P. 72**
(b) → 1. **Q. 10 (a) P. 72**
(c) → 4 **Q. 10 (c) P. 72**
(d) → 2. **Q. 50 (a) P. 76**
2. (a) → 4. **Q. 16 (e) P. 47**
(b) → 1 **Q. 7 (a) P. 46**
(c) → 2. **Q. 6 (c) P. 54**
(d) → 3 **Q. 7 (b) P. 54**
3. (a) → 4. **Q. 5. P. 40**

(b) → 1 **Q. 56 (a) P. 77**
(c) → 2. **Q. 21 (b) P. 74**
(d) → 3 **Q. 52 (b) P. 77**
4. (a) → 4. **Q. 6 (c) P. 61**
(b) → 3 **Q. 10 (b) P. 61**
(c) → 2. **Q. 10 (c) P. 61**
(d) → 5 **Q. 7 P. 61**
(e) → 1

Explanation for (a) and (e)

$$\omega_1 = \omega, \omega_2 = \omega^2, \qquad \text{where } \omega^3 = 1$$

$$\therefore \quad \omega_1^4 + \omega_2^4 = \omega^4 + \omega^8 = \omega + \omega^2 = -1 = -\frac{1}{\omega^3}$$

$$= -\frac{1}{\omega \cdot \omega^2} = -\frac{1}{\omega_1 \omega_2}$$

5. (a) $\to 4$, (b) $\to 1$, (c) $\to 2$, (d) $\to 3$

(e) We are given

$$z_1 + z_2 + z_3 = A \qquad \qquad \dots(1)$$

$$z_1 + z_2\omega + z_3\omega^2 = B \qquad \qquad \dots(2)$$

$$z_1 + z_2\omega^2 + z_3\omega = C \qquad \qquad \dots(3)$$

(a) Adding (1), (2) and (3), we get

$$3z_1 + z_2(1 + \omega + \omega^2) + z_3(1 + \omega^2 + \omega)$$

$$= A + B + C$$

or $\quad z_1 = \dfrac{A + B + C}{3} \qquad [\because \ 1 + \omega + \omega^2 = 0]$

Now multiplying (1), (2) and (3) by $1, \omega^2, \omega$ respectively and adding, we get

$$z_1(1 + \omega^2 + \omega) + z_2(1 + \omega^3 + \omega^3) + z_3(1 + \omega^4 + \omega^2)$$

$$= A + B\omega^2 + C\omega.$$

or $\quad z_2 = \dfrac{A + B\omega^2 + C\omega}{3}$

$[\because \ 1 + \omega^4 + \omega^2 = 1 + \omega + \omega^2 = 0 \ \text{and} \ \omega^3 = 1]$

Similarly, $\quad z_3 = \dfrac{A + B\omega + C\omega^2}{3}$

This proves (e).

(f) We have for (a), (b), (c), (d)

$$|A|^2 + |B|^2 + |C|^2 = A\overline{A} + B\overline{B} + C\overline{C} \qquad \dots(1)$$

But $A\overline{A} = (z_1 + z_2 + z_3)(\overline{z_1} + \overline{z_2} + \overline{z_3})$

$$= z_1\overline{z_1} + z_2\overline{z_2} + z_3\overline{z_3} + \overline{z_1}(z_2 + z_3)$$

$$\qquad + \overline{z_2}(z_3 + z_1) + \overline{z_3}(z_1 + z_2) \dots$$

$$= |z_1|^2 + |z_2|^2 + |z_3|^2 + \overline{z_1}(z_2 + z_3)$$

$$\qquad + \overline{z_2}(z_3 + z_1) + \overline{z_3}(z_1 + z_2) \dots$$

$B\overline{B} = (z_1 + z_2\omega + z_3\omega^2)(\overline{z_1} + \overline{z_2\omega} + \overline{z_3\omega^2})$

$$= (z_1 + z_2\omega + z_3\omega^2)(\overline{z_1} + \overline{z_2}\omega^2 + \overline{z_3}\omega)$$

$$[\because \ \overline{\omega} = \omega^2 \ \text{and} \ \overline{(\omega^2)} = \omega]$$

$$= z_1\overline{z_1} + z_2\overline{z_2}\omega^3 + z_3\overline{z_3}\omega^3 + \overline{z_1}(z_2\omega + z_3\omega^2)$$

$$\qquad + \overline{z_2}(z_3\omega^4 + z_1\omega^2) + \overline{z_3}(z_1\omega + z_2\omega^2)$$

$$= |z_1|^2 + |z_2|^2 + |z_3|^2 + \overline{z_1}(z_2\omega + z_3\omega^2)$$

$$\qquad + \overline{z_2}(z_3\omega + z_1\omega^2) + \overline{z_3}(z_1\omega + z_2\omega^2) \quad \dots(2)$$

Similarly

$$C\overline{C} = |z_1|^2 + |z_2|^2 + |z_3|^2 + \overline{z_1}(z_2\omega^2 + z_3\omega)$$

$$\qquad + \overline{z_2}(z_3\omega^2 + z_1\omega) + \overline{z_3}(z_1\omega^2 + z_2\omega) \quad \dots(3)$$

Adding (1), (2) and (3), we get

$$A\overline{A} + B\overline{B} + C\overline{C} = 3[|z_1|^2 + |z_2|^2 + |z_3|^2]$$

$$+ \overline{z_1}[z_2(1 + \omega + \omega^2) + z_3(1 + \omega^2 + \omega)]$$

$$+ \overline{z_2}[z_3(1 + \omega + \omega^2) + z_1(1 + \omega^2 + \omega)]$$

$$+ \overline{z_3}[z_1(1 + \omega + \omega^2) + z_2(1 + \omega^2 + \omega)]$$

$$= 3[|z_1|^2 + |z_2|^2 + |z_3|^2]^2 \qquad [\because \ 1 + \omega + \omega^2 = 0]$$

$\therefore$ From (1) and (2), we conclude

$$|A|^2 + |B|^2 + |C|^2$$

$$= 3[|z_1|^2 + |z_2|^2 + |z_3|^2]$$

Above proves (f).

6. Ans. (a) $\to$ (q, r), (b) $\to$ (r), (c) $\to$ (p), (d) $\to$ (q, r)

(a) **Refer § 6, P. 61**

If $\quad z = a + bw + cw^2$, then

$$\overline{z} = a + bw^2 + cw, |z| = |\overline{z}|$$

and $\quad z\overline{z} = a^2 + b^2 + c^2 - ab - bc - ca$

$$= \frac{1}{2}[(a - b)^2 + (b - c)^2 + (c - a)^2]$$

$$= |z|^2 \geq 0$$

$\therefore$ (a), (d) $\to$ (q, r)

(b) $\because \quad a, b, c$ are distinct integers.

$\therefore \quad |z|^2 + |\overline{z}|^2 = 2|z|^2$

$$= |(a - b)^2 + (b - c)^2 + (c - a)^2| \geq 2$$

(c) $\left|\dfrac{z}{\overline{z}}\right| = \dfrac{|z|}{|\overline{z}|} = 1$

7. Ans. (a) $\to$ (q), (b) $\to$ (s), (c) $\to$ (r), (d) $\to$ (p)

(a) $z^2 = -|z|$

$\therefore \quad |z^2| = |z| \qquad$ or $\quad |z|^2 - |z| = 0$

$\therefore \quad |z|(|z| - 1) = 0 \ \therefore \ |z| = 0 \ \Rightarrow \ z = 0$

$|z| = 1 \ \Rightarrow \ z^2 + 1 = 0$ by (a)

$\Rightarrow \quad z^2 = -1 \qquad \therefore \quad z = 0 \pm i$

Hence, (a) has got 3 solutions $0, \pm i$.

(b) $z = x + iy$

$\therefore \quad \overline{z} = x - iy$

$\therefore \quad z^2 + \overline{z}^2 = 0 \ \Rightarrow \ 2(x^2 - y^2) = 0$

$\therefore \quad y = \pm x$

$\therefore \quad z = x(1 \pm i)$ where $x \in R$

Hence there will be infinite solutions.

(c) $z^2 + 8\overline{z} = 0 \ \Rightarrow \ z^2 = -8\overline{z}$

$\therefore \quad |z^2| = |-8\overline{z}| \qquad$ or $\quad |z|^2 = 8|z|$

$\therefore \quad |z| = 0 \quad$ or $\quad |z| = 8$

$\therefore \quad z = 0$ is one solution.

Now $|z| = 8 \ \Rightarrow \ |z|^2 = 64 \ \Rightarrow \ z\overline{z} = 64$

$\therefore \quad z^2 = -8\overline{z} = -8 \cdot \dfrac{64}{z}$

$\therefore \quad z^3 = -(8)^3 \ \therefore \ z = -8(1, w, w^2)$

$$= -(8, 8w, 8w^2)$$

Thus, there are $1 + 3 = 4$ solutions.

(d) $(x-2)^2 + (y-0)^2 = 1$

and $(x-1)^2 + y^2 = 2$

$C_1(2,0), r_1 = 1; C_2(1,0), r_2 = 2$

$\therefore \quad C_1C_2 = 1 = r_2 - r_1$

Hence, the two circles touch internally at the point $(3,1)$. Thus there is only one solution.

$\therefore \quad$ (d)$\rightarrow$ (p)

8. Ans. (a)$\rightarrow$ (s), (b)$\rightarrow$ (q), (c)$\rightarrow$ (p), (d)$\rightarrow$ (r)

(a) $(x-2)^2 + y^2 + x^2 + (y-4)^2 = 20$

or $2[x^2 + y^2 - 2x - 4y] = 0$

Above represents a circle with centre at $(1,2)$.

(b) $4[(x-1)^2 + y^2] - [(x+1)^2 + y^2] = 0$

$3x^2 + 3y^2 - 10x + 3 = 0$

or $x^2 + y^2 - \dfrac{10}{3}x + 1 = 0$

$\therefore$ Centre is $\left(\dfrac{5}{3}, 0\right)$. $\quad \therefore \quad$ (b)$\rightarrow$ (q)

(c) $z\bar{z} - (z+\bar{z}) - i(z-\bar{z}) + 7 = 0$

$(x^2 + y^2) - 2x - i(2iy) + 7 = 0$

$x^2 + y^2 - 2x + 2y + 7 = 0$

$\therefore$ Centre is $(1,-1)$. $\quad \therefore \quad$ (c)$\rightarrow$ (p)

(d) $\tan^{-1}\left(\dfrac{y+4}{x+3}\right) - \tan^{-1}\left(\dfrac{y-2}{x+5}\right) = \dfrac{\pi}{2}$

$\tan^{-1}\dfrac{A-B}{1+AB} = \dfrac{\pi}{2} \Rightarrow \dfrac{A-B}{1+AB} = \tan\dfrac{\pi}{2} = \infty$

$\therefore \quad AB + 1 = 0$ or $(y+4)(y-2) + (x+3)(x+5) = 0$

or $x^2 + y^2 + 8x + 2y + 7 = 0$

$\therefore$ Centre is $(-4,-1)$. $\quad \therefore \quad$ (d)$\rightarrow$ (r)

9. Ans. (a)$\rightarrow$ (s), (b)$\rightarrow$ (r), (c)$\rightarrow$ (q), (d)$\rightarrow$ (p)

(a) The given equation states that the sum of the distances of a point $z(x,y)$ from the points $(3,0)$ and $(0,1)$ is constant and hence, by definition, it represents the equation of ellipse

$\therefore \quad$ (a)$\rightarrow$ (s)

(b) The given equation can be written as

$2\left|z - \dfrac{3}{2}\right| = 2|z - i|$

Distance of any point (x,y) from $\left(\dfrac{3}{2}, 0\right)$ is equal to its distance from the point $(0,1)$. Hence, locus of (x,y) is a straight line which is the right bisector of the line joining the points $\left(\dfrac{3}{2}, 0\right)$ and $(0,1)$

$\therefore \quad$ (b)$\rightarrow$ (r)

(c) $(x^2 - y^2 + 2ixy) + (x^2 - y^2 - 2ixy) = 5$

$\therefore \quad x^2 - y^2 = \dfrac{5}{2}$, i.e., hyperbola, i.e., (c)$\rightarrow$ (q)

(d) $(x-6)^2 + y^2 = 9[x^2 + (y-2)^2]$

or $8(x^2 + y^2) + 12x - 36y = 0$

or $x^2 + y^2 + \dfrac{3}{2}x - \dfrac{9}{2}y = 0$ i.e., circle

$\therefore \quad$ (d)$\rightarrow$ (p)

10. Ans. (a) $\rightarrow$ (q, r); (b)$\rightarrow$ (p);

(c)$\rightarrow$ (p, s, t); (d)$\rightarrow$ (q, r, s, t)

(a) $|z - i|z|| = |z + i\,z||$

$\Rightarrow \left|x + iy - i\sqrt{x^2 + y^2}\right| = \left|x + iy + i\sqrt{x^2 + y^2}\right|$

$\Rightarrow x^2 + \left(y - \sqrt{x^2 + y^2}\right)^2 = x^2 + \left(y + \sqrt{x^2 + y^2}\right)^2$

$\Rightarrow 4y\sqrt{x^2 + y^2} = 0$

$\Rightarrow y = 0 \quad \Rightarrow I_m(z) = 0$

(b) $|z + 4| + |z - 4| = 10$

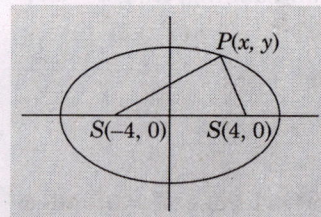

Fig. 55(g)

ellipse with $2a = 10 \Rightarrow a = 5$

$ae = 4 \Rightarrow e = \dfrac{4}{5}$

(c) Let $\omega = 2(\cos + i\sin\theta)$

$z = 2(\cos\theta + i\sin\theta) - \dfrac{(\cos\theta - i\sin\theta)}{2}$

$= \dfrac{3\cos\theta + 5i\sin\theta}{2} \Rightarrow x = \dfrac{3\cos\theta}{2}, y = \dfrac{5\sin\theta}{2}$

$\Rightarrow \dfrac{x^2}{\dfrac{9}{4}} + \dfrac{y^2}{\dfrac{25}{4}} = 1 \Rightarrow e = \dfrac{4}{5}$

$|z| = \sqrt{\dfrac{9\cos^2\theta}{4} + \dfrac{25\sin^2\theta}{4}} = \sqrt{\dfrac{9 + 16\sin^2\theta}{4}}$

$= \sqrt{\dfrac{9}{4} + 4\sin^2\theta} \le \dfrac{5}{2}$

$|Re(z)| = \left|\dfrac{3}{2}\cos\theta\right| \le \dfrac{3}{2}$

(d) $z = \cos\theta + i\sin\theta + \cos\theta - i\sin\theta = 2\cos\theta$

$\therefore \quad |z| \le 2 \Rightarrow Im(z) = 0$

$Re(z) = |2\cos\theta| \le 2$

$|z| \le 2$

Assertion / Reason

1. **Statement-1.** a, b, c are three distinct real numbers and $w \neq 1$ is a cube root of unity, then $\left| \dfrac{a + bw + cw^2}{aw^2 + b + cw} \right| = 1$

Statement-2. $z \neq 0, \left| \dfrac{z}{\bar{z}} \right| = 1$

Sol. Ans. (b). Both are true.

$$|N^r| = |a + bw + cw^2| = |w(aw^2 + b + cw)|$$

$$(\because w^3 = 1)$$

$$= |w| \cdot |D^r| = 1(D^r)$$

$$\therefore \quad \left| \dfrac{N^r}{D^r} \right| = |w| = 1$$

2. **Statement-1.** a, b, c are three non-zero real numbers such that $a + b + c = 0$ and z_1, z_2, z_3 are three complex numbers such that $az_1 + bz_2 + cz_3 = 0$, then z_1, z_2, z_3 lie on a circle.

Statement-2. If z_1, z_2, z_3 are collinear, then

$$\begin{vmatrix} z_1 & \bar{z}_1 & 1 \\ z_2 & \bar{z}_2 & 1 \\ z_3 & \bar{z}_3 & 1 \end{vmatrix} = 0$$

Sol. Ans. (d).

Statement-1 is false but statement-2 is true.

$$az_1 + bz_2 + cz_3 = 0 \Rightarrow az_1 + bz_2 - (a+b)z_3 = 0$$

$$\therefore \quad z_3 = \dfrac{az_1 + bz_2}{a + b}$$

$\therefore$ z_3 divides the join of z_1 and z_2 in the ratio $b : a$. Hence, they are collinear.

Fascinating Facts

- If a and b are positive real numbers then
$$\sqrt{-a} \times \sqrt{-b} = -\sqrt{ab}$$
- For any two real number a and b, $\sqrt{a} \times \sqrt{b} = \sqrt{ab}$ is true only when at least one of a and b is either positive or zero i.e., $\sqrt{a} \times \sqrt{b} = \sqrt{ab}$ is not valid if a and b both are negative.
- For any positive real number a, we have
$$\sqrt{-a} = \sqrt{-1 \times a} = \sqrt{-1} \times \sqrt{a} = i\sqrt{a}$$
- A complex number is zero if $a = 0$ and $b = 0$
- The value i^n for $n > 4$ is i^k, where k is the remainder when n is divided by 4.
- The value of i^{-n} for $n > 4$ is i^{-k} where k is the remainder when n is divided by 4.
- The argument of a complex number is not unique.
- The argument of 0 is not defined.
- The zero complex number is not included in the polar representation of a complex number, because in that case

$r = 0$, where as r must be greater then 0 and $\tan \theta$ becomes indeterminate.
- Every non-zero complex number has two square roots which are opposite to each other in sign.
- If the complex numbers z_1 and z_2 are such that the sum $z_1 + z_2$ is a real number then they are not necessarily conjugate numbers.
- If z_1, z_2 are complex numbers such that the product $z_1 z_2$ is a real number then they are not necessarily conjugate numbers.
- The sum and product of two complex numbers are real simultaneously if and only if they are conjugate to each other.
- If z is a complex number then e^z is periodic.
- If three complex numbers are in A.P. then they lie on a straight line in the complex plane.

❏

CHAPTER 3

Algebra

Progressions

§1. Arithmetical Progression.

(a) Definition. If certain quantities increase or decrease by the same constant, then such quantities form a series which is called an arithmetical progression. This constant is called commom difference. For example :

(i) $1, 4, 7, 10, \ldots$

(ii) $9, 6, 3, 0, -3, \ldots$

(iii) $a, a+d, a+2d, \ldots$

The common difference in the above three series are $3, -3$ and d respectively.

(b) Notation. The first term of the series is denoted by a, common difference by d, the last term by l, the number of terms by n, sum of its n terms by S_n, and the nth term by T_n.

Standard Results : $T_n = a + (n-1)d = l$.

$$S_n = \frac{n}{2}(a+l) = \frac{n}{2}[2a + (n-1)d].$$

(c) (i) Arithmetic Mean (A. M.)

The arithmetic mean between two given quantities a and b is x so that

a, x, b are in A.P. *i.e.,* $x - a = b - x$

or $2x = a + b$ ∴ $x = \dfrac{a+b}{2} = A$ **(Notation)**

Similarly A.M. of n numbers $a_1, a_2, \ldots, a_n$ is

$$A = \frac{\Sigma a_i}{n} \ i.e., \ \frac{S}{n}$$

(ii) n arithmetic means between two quantities a and b .

If between two given quantities a and b we have to insert n arithmetic means $x_1, x_2, \ldots x_n$, then $a, x_1, x_2, \ldots x_n, b$ will be in A.P. In order to find the values of these means we require the common difference. The above series consists of $(n+2)$ terms and the last term is b and first term is a.

∴ $b = T_{n+2} = a + (n+2-1)d$

∴ $d = \dfrac{b-a}{n+1}$.

∴ $x_1 = T_2 = a + d,$
$x_2 = T_3 = a + 2d, \ldots,$

$x_n = T_{n+1} = a + nd.$

On putting for d, we get

* $x_1 = a + \dfrac{b-a}{n+1} = \dfrac{na+b}{n+1}$ ...(1)

Interchanging a and b, we get

* $x_n = \dfrac{nb+a}{n+1}$ ...(2)

If we interchange a and b in x_1 we get x_n because x_1 is first of n means from begining and x_n is first of n means from the end.

*Sum of n arithmetic means $= n$ [single A. M.]

$x_1 + x_2 + \ldots + x_n = \dfrac{n}{2}[x_1 + x_n]$ (Sum of A.P.)

$= \dfrac{n}{2}[a+d+b-d] = n\left(\dfrac{a+b}{2}\right).$

$= n$ (A.M. of a and b)

(d) An important note.

(1) If each term of a given arithmetical progression be **increased, decreased, multiplied or divided by the same non-zero quantity**, then the resulting series thus obtained will also be in A.P.

Further $a_1, a_3, a_5, a_7, \ldots$ or $a_2, a_4, a_6, \ldots$ will also form an A.P. of common difference $2d$.

Also $a_m, a_{m+n}, a_{m+2n}, a_{m+3n}, \ldots$ will also form an A.P. of common difference nd.

(2) **Any three numbers in A.P. be taken as $a-d, a, a+d$. Any four numbers in A.P. be taken as $a-3d, a-d, a+d, a+3d$.**

Similarly five terms in A.P. should be taken as $a-2d, a-d, a, a+d, a+2d$ and six terms as $a-5d, a-3d, a-d, a+d, a+3d, a+5d$ etc.

(e) Two important Properties of A.P.

(1)* In an A.P. the sum of terms equidistant from the beginning and end is constant and equal to the sum of first and last terms.

(2)* Any term of an A.P. (except the first) is equal to half the sum of terms which are equidistant from it :

$$a_n = \frac{1}{2}(a_{n-k} + a_{n+k}), k < n, \text{ and for } k = 1,$$

$$a_n = \frac{1}{2}(a_{n-1} + a_{n+1})$$

(f)* $T_n = S_n - S_{n-1}$ $(n \geq 2)$.

(g) Sum and difference of corresponding terms of two A.P.'s will form a series in A.P.

(h)* If $T_n = pn + q$, i.e. a linear expression in n then it will form an A.P. of common difference $p = (T_n - T_{n-1})$ and first term $p + q$ $(n = 1)$ i.e. if $T_n = 3n + 4$, then it is an A.P. of common difference 3 and first term as $3.1 + 4 = 7$.

(i) If $S_n = an^2 + bn + c$ i.e. quadratic function in n then the series is A.P. where $d = 2a = $ Twice the coefficient of n^2

$$\therefore \quad T_n = S_n - S_{n-1} = (an^2 + bn + c)$$
$$- [a(n-1)^2 + b(n-1) + c]$$
$$= 2an - (a+b) = \text{linear in } n$$

$$\therefore \quad d = 2a$$

Hence an A.P. of $d = 2a$, by (h).

(j) **mth term of an A.P. from end**

Let the first and last terms of an A.P. of n terms be a and b respectively, then

T_m from beginning $= a + (m-1)d$ ...(1)

where $b = a + (n-1)d$ or $d = \dfrac{b-a}{n-1}$

Now T_m from end of above
$$= T_m \text{ of A.P. } b \ldots a \text{ of common difference } -d$$
$$= b + (m-1)(-d)$$
$$= b - (m-1)d \qquad \ldots(2)$$

Alt. T_m from end $= T_{n-m+1}$ from beginning

If there be 10 terms, then T_4 from end is $T_{10-4+1} = T_7$ from beginning.

Problem Set (1)

Arithmetical progression, nth term, S_n of an A.P. and Arithmetic means.

1. **(a)** The fifth term of an A.P. is 1 whereas its 31st term is -77. Find its 20th term and sum of its first fifteen terms. Also find which term of the series will be -17 and sum of how many terms will be 20.

   (b) The third term of an A.P. is 7 and its 7th term is 2 more than thrice of its 3rd term. Find the first term, common difference and the sum of its first 20 terms.

2. **(a)** Find the number of terms in the series $20, 19\frac{1}{3}, 18\frac{2}{3}, \ldots\ldots$ of which the sum is 300, explain the double answer.

   (b) Prove that the maximum value of the sum of the series $20 + 19\frac{1}{3} + 18\frac{2}{3} + \ldots$ is 310.

   (c)* How many terms of the series 54, 51, 48, ... be taken so that their sum is 513 ? Explain the double answer.

   (d) The sum of the series $\frac{1}{2} + \frac{1}{3} + \frac{1}{6} + \ldots\ldots$ to 9 terms is $-\frac{3}{2}$.

   (e) There are only sixteen A.P.'s having 3, 8, 14 as three of its terms. Is this statement true ?

3. **(a)** The nth term of a series is given to be $\frac{3+n}{4}$, find the sum of 105 terms of this series.

   (b)* Find the sum of first 24 terms of the A.P. $a_1, a_2, a_3, \ldots\ldots$ if it is known that $a_1 + a_5 + a_{10} + a_{15} + a_{20} + a_{24} = 225$.

   (M.P. C.E.E. 1999)

   (c) Find $a_1 + a_6 + a_{11} + a_{16}$ if it is known that $a_1, a_2, \ldots$ is an A.P. and

   $a_1 + a_4 + a_7 + \ldots + a_{16} = 147$.

4. If the sum of first 8 and 19 terms of an A.P. are 64 and 361 respectively, find the common difference and sum of its n terms.

5. **(a)** A man arranges to pay off a debt of Rs. 3600 in 40 annual instalments which form an arithmetic series. When 30 of the instalments are paid he dies leaving one-third of the debt unpaid. Find the value of the first instalment.

   (b) A class consists of a number of boys whose ages are in A.P. the common difference being four months. If the youngest boy is just eight years old and if the sum of the ages is 168 years, find the number of boys.

6. **(a)*** The interior angles of a polygon are in arithmetic progression. The smallest angle is $120°$ and the common difference is 5. Find the number of sides of the polygon.

   (b) Find the least value of n for which $3 + 6 + 9 + \ldots n$ terms exceeds 1000.

7. Find the sum of n terms of the series

   $$\log a + \log \frac{a^2}{b} + \log \frac{a^3}{b^2} + \log \frac{a^4}{b^3} + \ldots \text{to } n \text{ terms.}$$

8. **(a)*** The mth term of an A.P. is n and its nth term is m. Prove that its pth term is $m + n - p$. Also show that its $(m+n)$th term is zero.

   (b)* Let T_r be the rth term of an A.P., for $r = 1, 2, 3, \ldots$. If for some positive integers m, n we have $T_m = \frac{1}{n}$ and $T_n = \frac{1}{m}$, then T_{mn} equals

(a) $\dfrac{1}{mn}$ (b) $\dfrac{1}{m} + \dfrac{1}{n}$

(c) 1 (d) 0 **(I.I.T. 1998)**

(c) a, b, c, d are four distinct real numbers and they are in A.P. If $2(a-b) + x(b-c)^2 + (c-a)^3$

$$= 2(a-d) + (b-d)^2 + (c-d)^3$$

then prove that $x \geq 16$ or $x \leq -8$.

(d) If a, b, c, d, e are in A.P. then find the value of $a - 4b + 6c - 4d + e$.

9. The first and last term of an A.P., are a and l respectively. If S be the sum of all the terms of the A.P., show that the common difference is $\dfrac{l^2 - a^2}{2S - (l + a)}$.

10. Show that the sum of an A.P. whose first term is a, second term is b and the last term is c is equal to $\dfrac{(a+c)(b+c-2a)}{2(b-a)}$.

11. (a) The sum of n terms of a series is $3n^2 + 4n$. Show that the series is an A.P. and find the first term and common difference. What will be its nth term ?

(b) Find an A.P. in which sum of any number of terms is always three times the squared number of these terms.

(c)* If $s_n = an^2 + bn$, prove that series is an A.P.

12. (a) The number of terms of an A.P. is even ; the sum of the odd terms is 24, of the even terms 30, and the last term exceeds the first by $10\frac{1}{2}$, find the number of terms and the series.

(b) Find the sum of all two digit numbers which when divided by 4, yield unity as remainder.

13. (a) 150 workers were engaged to finish a piece of work in a certain number of days. Four workers dropped the second day, four more workers dropped the third day and so on. It takes 8 more days to finish the work now. Find the number of days in which the work was completed.

(b)* Along a road lie an odd number of stones placed at intervals of 10 metres. These stones have to be assembled around the middle stone. A person can carry only one stone at a time. A man carried the job with one of the end stones by carrying them in succession. In carrying all the stones he covered a distance of 3 km. Find the number of stones.

(c) Ram starts travelling from a certain point O and in successive days travels distances which are in A.P. ($a = 1, d = 2$). Shyam starts from the point after three days and in successive days travels distances which too are in A.P. ($a = 12, d = 1$). Prove that Shyam will be ahead of Ram for 7 days.

14. (a) Prove that square of any even natural number i.e. $(2n)^2$ is equal to sum of n terms of a certain series of integers in A.P.

(b) Any odd square i.e. $(2n+1)^2$ is equal to sum of n terms of an A.P. increased by unity.

(c) The fourth power of the common difference of an arithmetic progression with integer entries is added to the product of any four consecutive terms of it. Prove that the resulting sum is the square of an integer. **(I.I.T. 2000)**

15.* If the ratio of the sum of m terms and n terms of an A.P. be $m^2 : n^2$, prove that the ratio of its mth and nth terms will be $2m - 1 : 2n - 1$.

16. (a) The ratio between the sum of n terms of two A.P.'s is $3n + 8 : 7n + 15$. Find the ratio between their 12th terms.

(b)* The ratio between the sum of n terms of two A.P.'s is $7n + 1 : 4n + 27$. Find the ratio between their nth terms.

(c) The sum of the first n terms of two A.P.'s are as $3n + 5 : 5n - 9$. Prove that their 4th terms are equal.

(d) In an A.P. if $\dfrac{S_m}{S_n} = \dfrac{m^4}{n^4}$ then prove that

$$\dfrac{T_{m+1}}{T_{n+1}} = \dfrac{(2m+1)^3}{(2n+1)^3}.$$

(e) If S_n be the sum of first n terms of an A.P. and if $\dfrac{S_{pn}}{S_n}$ is independent of n, then find the ratio $\dfrac{a}{d}$.

17. There are two A.P.'s whose common differences differ by unity, but sum of the three consecutive terms in each is 15. If P and P_1 be the products of these terms such that $\dfrac{P}{P_1} = \dfrac{7}{8}$, then find the two A.P.'s.

18. (a) Find the sum of all natural numbers between 250 and 1000 which are exactly divisible by 3.

(b) The sum of integers from 1 to 100 which are divisible by 2 or 5 is

(a) 3000 (b) 3050
(c) 3200 (d) 3250

19. (a) Show that the sum of all odd numbers between 1 and 1000 which are divisible by 3 is 83667.

(b) Find the sum of first n odd natural numbers.

(c) Find the sum of all odd integers between 2 and 100 divisible by 3.

(d) Sum of certain consecutive odd positive integers is $57^2 - 13^2$. Find them.

20. Find the sum of all natural numbers which are multiples of 7 or 3 or both and lie between 200 and 500.

21.* The pth term of an A.P. is a and qth term is b. Prove that sum of its $(p + q)$ terms is

$$\dfrac{p+q}{2}\left[a + b + \dfrac{a-b}{p-q}\right].$$

22. If the pth, qth and rth terms of an A.P. be a, b and c respectively, then prove that
$$a(q - r) + b(r - p) + c(p - q) = 0.$$

23.* If the sums of p, q and r terms of an A.P. be a, b and c respectively, then prove that
$$\frac{a}{p}(q - r) + \frac{b}{q}(r - p) + \frac{c}{r}(p - q) = 0.$$

24. (a) If in an A.P. the sum of p terms is equal to sum of q terms, then prove that the sum of $p + q$ terms is zero.

   (b) In an A.P., of which a is the first term, if the sum of the first p terms is zero, show that the sum of the next q terms is $-\dfrac{a(p + q)q}{p - 1}$.

25. (a)* The sum of first p terms of an A.P. is q and the sum of the first q terms is p. Find the sum of the first $(p + q)$ terms. **(J.E.E. W.B. 1993)**

   (b) Prove that the sum of the latter half of $2n$ terms of any A.P. is one-third the sum of $3n$ terms of the same A.P.

   (c) An A.P. has even number of terms, the first term of which is unity. S_1 and S_2 stand for the sum of its first n terms and sum of its last n terms such that $S_1 / S_2 = \lambda$. What is the common difference of A.P.?

26. (a) The sums of n terms of three arithmetical progressions are S_1, S_2 and S_3. The first term of each is unity and the common differences are 1, 2 and 3 respectively. Prove that $S_1 + S_3 = 2S_2$.

   (b)* There are two A.P.'s each of n terms.
$$a, a + d, a + 2d, \dots L$$
$$p, p + q, p + 2q, \dots L'$$
   These A.P.'s satisfy the following conditions :
$$\frac{L}{p} = \frac{L'}{a} = 4, \frac{S_n}{S_n'} = 2 ; \text{find out } \frac{d}{q} \text{ and } \frac{L}{L'}.$$

27. (a) The sums of $n, 2n, 3n$ terms of an A.P. are S_1, S_2, S_3 respectively. Prove that $S_3 = 3(S_2 - S_1)$.

   (b)* If $S_n = n^2 p$ and $S_m = m^2 p$, $m \neq n$, in an A.P., prove that $S_p = p^3$.

28. (a) If s_n be the sum of n terms of an A.P. and if $\dfrac{s_{pn}}{s_n}$ is independent of n, then prove that $d = 2a$ in usual notation.

   (b)* Let S_n denote the sum of first n terms of an A.P. If $S_{2n} = 3S_n$, then the ratio S_{3n} / S_n is equal to 6. **(M.N.R. 1993)**

   (c) If the sum of first $2n$ terms of the A.P. $2, 5, 8, \dots$ is equal to the sum of the first n terms of the A.P. $57, 59, 61, \dots$, then n equals

   (a) 10   (b) 12

   (c) 11   (d) 13   **(I.I.T. Sc. 2001)**

29. (a) There are n A.P.'s whose common differences are $1, 2, 3, \dots n$ respectively, the first term of each being

unity. Prove that sum of their nth terms is $\dfrac{1}{2}n(n^2 + 1)$.

   (b) If there be m A.P.'s beginning with unity whose common differences are $1, 2, 3, \dots m$ respectively, show that the sum of their nth terms is $\dfrac{1}{2}m[mn - m + n + 1]$.

   (c) The sum of n terms of m arithmetical progressions are $S_1, S_2, S_3, \dots S_m$. The first term and common differences are $1, 2, 3, \dots, m$ respectively. Prove that
$$S_1 + S_2 + S_3 + \dots + S_m = \frac{1}{4}mn(m + 1)(n + 1).$$

30. (a) If $S_1, S_2, S_3, \dots, S_m$ are the sums of n terms of m A.P.'s whose first terms are $1, 2, 3, \dots, m$ and common differences are $1, 3, 5, \dots, 2m - 1$ respectively. Show that
$$S_1 + S_2 + S_3 + \dots + S_m = \frac{1}{2}mn(mn + 1).$$

   (b) In an A.P. if
$$S_1 = T_1 + T_2 + T_3 + \dots + T_n \ (n \text{ odd})$$
$$S_2 = T_1 + T_3 + T_5 + \dots + T_n, \text{then} \quad S_1 / S_2 =$$
   (a) $\dfrac{2n}{n + 1}$ (b) $\dfrac{n}{n + 1}$

   (c) $\dfrac{n + 1}{2n}$ (d) $\dfrac{n + 1}{n}$

31. (a) The series of natural numbers is divided into groups (1) ; $(2, 3, 4)$; $(5, 6, 7, 8, 9)$; ..... and so on. Show that the sum of the numbers in the nth group is $(n - 1)^3 + n^3$. **(I.I.T. 1983)**

   (b)* The series of natural numbers is divided into groups $(1), (2, 3, 4), (3, 4, 5, 6, 7), (4, 5, 6, 7, 8, 9, 10), \dots$ Find the sum of the numbers in nth group.

32.* N, the set of natural numbers, is partitioned into subsets
$$S_1 = \{1\}, S_2 = \{2, 3\}, S_3 = \{4, 5, 6\}, S_4 = \{7, 8, 9, 10\}.$$
The last term of these groups is
$$1, 1 + 2, 1 + 2 + 3, 1 + 2 + 3 + 4,$$
so on. Find the sum of the elements in the subset S_{50}.

33. (a) Show that sum of the terms in the nth bracket $(1); (3, 5); (7, 9, 11); \dots$ is n^3.

   (b) The odd natural numbers are arranged in groups as $(1); (3, 5, 7); (9, 11, 13, 15, 17) \dots$ prove that the sum of terms in nth group is $(2n - 1)[n^2 + (n - 1)^2]$.

34. (a) The sum of three numbers in A.P. is 15 whereas sum of their squares is 83. Find the numbers.

   (b) If the roots of the equation $x^3 - 12x^2 + 39x - 28 = 0$ are in A.P., then their common difference will be ...... **(M.N.R. 1994)**

   (c)* If a, b, c are real numbers satisfying the equation $25(9a^2 + b^2) + 9c^2 - 15(5ab + bc + 3ca) = 0$ then prove that a, b, c are in A.P.

35. (a)* The sum of three numbers in A.P. is 12 and the sum of their cubes is 288. Find the numbers.

(b) There are two sets A and B of three numbers in A.P. whose sum is 15 and where D and d are the common differences such that $D - d = 1$. Find the numbers if $\dfrac{P}{p} = \dfrac{7}{8}$ where P and p are the products of the numbers in the two sets.

36. Find four numbers in A.P. whose

(a) sum is 20 and sum of their squares is 120,

(b) sum is 32 and sum of squares is 276.

37.* Divide 28 into four parts in A.P. so that ratio of the product of first and third with the product of second and fourth is 8 : 15.

38.* Between 1 and 31 are inserted m arithmetic means so that the ratio of the 7th and $(m-1)$th means is 5 : 9. Find the value of m.

39. Prove that the sum of the n arithmetic means inserted between two quantities is n times the single arithmetic mean between them. **(CET 1992)**

40. For what value of n, $\dfrac{a^{n+1} + b^{n+1}}{a^n + b^n}$ is the arithmetic mean of a and b ?

41. (a)* The sum of two numbers is $2\dfrac{1}{6}$. An even number of arithmetic means are being inserted between them and their sum exceeds their number by 1. Find the number of means inserted.

(b)* n arithmetic means are inserted in between x and $2y$ and then between $2x$ and y. In case the rth means in each case be equal, then find the ratio x / y.

42. (a) If a, b, c are in A.P., prove that the following are also in A.P.

(i) $b + c,\ c + a,\ a + b$.

(ii) $\dfrac{1}{bc},\ \dfrac{1}{ca},\ \dfrac{1}{ab}$.

(iii)* $a^2 (b + c),\ b^2 (c + a),\ c^2 (a + b)$ provided $\Sigma\, ab \neq 0$.

(iv) $a\left(\dfrac{1}{b} + \dfrac{1}{c}\right),\ b\left(\dfrac{1}{c} + \dfrac{1}{a}\right),\ c\left(\dfrac{1}{a} + \dfrac{1}{b}\right)$. **(D.C.E. 1997)**

(v)* $\dfrac{1}{\sqrt{(b)} + \sqrt{(c)}},\ \dfrac{1}{\sqrt{(c)} + \sqrt{(a)}},\ \dfrac{1}{\sqrt{(a)} + \sqrt{(b)}}$. **(D.C.E. 1998)**

(b) If a, b, c are in A.P., then prove that $(a - c)^2 = 4(b^2 - ac)$.

43. If a^2, b^2, c^2 are in A.P., then the following are also in A.P.

(i) $\dfrac{1}{b+c},\ \dfrac{1}{c+a},\ \dfrac{1}{a+b}$. (ii) * $\dfrac{a}{b+c},\ \dfrac{b}{c+a},\ \dfrac{c}{a+b}$.

44. If $\dfrac{b+c-a}{a},\ \dfrac{c+a-b}{b},\ \dfrac{a+b-c}{c}$ are in A.P., then $\dfrac{1}{a}, \dfrac{1}{b}, \dfrac{1}{c}$ are also in A.P.

45. If $(b - c)^2,\ (c - a)^2,\ (a - b)^2$ are in A.P. then prove that $\dfrac{1}{b-c}, \dfrac{1}{c-a}, \dfrac{1}{a-b}$ are also in A.P.

46.* If $a_1, a_2, \ldots a_n$ are in A.P. where $a_i > 0$ for all i, show that

$$\dfrac{1}{\sqrt{(a_1)} + \sqrt{(a_2)}} + \dfrac{1}{\sqrt{(a_2)} + \sqrt{(a_3)}}$$

$$+ \ldots + \dfrac{1}{\sqrt{(a_{n-1})} + \sqrt{(a_n)}} = \dfrac{n-1}{\sqrt{(a_1)} + \sqrt{(a_n)}}$$

47. (a)* If $\log_{10} 2$, $\log_{10} (2^x - 1)$ and $\log_{10} (2^x + 3)$ be three consecutive terms of an A.P., then

(i) $x = 0$ (ii) $x = 1$

(iii) $x = \log_2 5$ (iv) $x = \log_{10} 2$

(b) For what values of the parameter a are there values of x such that $5^{1+x} + 5^{1-x}$, $a/2$, $25^x + 25^{-x}$ are three consecutive terms of an A.P. ?

(c) Show that the value of x for which $\log_3 (2^{1-x} + 3), \log_9 4$ and $\log_{27} (2^x - 1)^3$ form an A. P. is 1.

48. (a)* If $x^{18} = y^{21} = z^{28}$, prove that 3, $3 \log_y x$, $3 \log_z y, 7 \log_x z$ form an A.P.

(b) If $3, 3 \log_y x, 3 \log_z y, 7 \log_x z$ be in A.P. the prove that $x^{18} = y^{21} = z^{28}$.

(c) The numbers $3^{2 \sin 2\theta - 1}$, 14, $3^{4 - 2 \sin 2\theta}$ form first three terms of an A.P. Show that its fifth term is equal to 53.

(d) If the non-zero numbers a, b, c are in A.P. and $\tan^{-1} a, \tan^{-1} b, \tan^{-1} c$ are also in A.P., then prove that $a = b = c$ and $b^2 = ac$.

49. (a) Prove that if p, q, r $(p \neq q)$ are terms (not necessarily consecutive) of an A.P., then there exists a rational number k such that $(r - q) / (q - p) = k$.

(b) Prove that the numbers $\sqrt{2}, \sqrt{3}, \sqrt{5}$ cannot be the terms of a single A.P. with non-zero common difference.

50. (a) Determine the relations in x, y and z if $1, \log_y x, \log_z y, -15 \log_x z$ are in A.P.

(b) Can there be an A.P. which consists of only prime numbers ?

51.* If the sum of m terms of an A.P. is equal to sum of either the next n terms or the next p terms, prove that

$$(m + n) \left(\dfrac{1}{m} - \dfrac{1}{p}\right) = (m + p) \left(\dfrac{1}{m} - \dfrac{1}{n}\right).$$

52. (a)* Show that in an arithmetical progression $a_1, a_2, a_3, \ldots,$

$$S = a_1^2 - a_2^2 + a_3^2 - a_4^2 + \ldots - a_{2k}^2$$

$$= \dfrac{k}{2k - 1} (a_1^2 - a_{2k}^2).$$

(b) If $a_1, a_2, \ldots a_n$ be an A.P. of +ive terms, then
$\sum\limits_{k=1}^{n} a_k \geq n\sqrt{a_1^2 + (n-1)\,da_1}$ where d is the common difference of A.P.

(c) $\dfrac{1}{a_1 a_n} + \dfrac{1}{a_2 a_{n-1}} + \dfrac{1}{a_3 a_{n-2}} + \ldots + \dfrac{1}{a_n a_1}$

$= \dfrac{2}{a_1 + a_n}\left(\dfrac{1}{a_1} + \dfrac{1}{a_2} + \ldots + \dfrac{1}{a_n}\right),$

(d) $\dfrac{1}{a_1 a_2} + \dfrac{1}{a_2 a_3} + \ldots + \dfrac{1}{a_{n-1}a_n} = \dfrac{n-1}{a_1 a_n}.$

53.* If $a_1, a_2, a_3, \ldots$ are in A.P. of common difference d, then prove that

$S = \tan^{-1}\dfrac{d}{1+a_1 a_2} + \tan^{-1}\dfrac{d}{1+a_2 a_3} + \ldots$

$\hspace{3cm} + \tan^{-1}\dfrac{d}{1+a_n a_{n+1}}$

$= \tan^{-1}\dfrac{nd}{1+a_1 a_{n+1}}$

54. If $\alpha_1, \alpha_2, \alpha_3, \ldots \alpha_n$ are in A.P. of common difference d, then prove that

(a)* $\sec\alpha_1\sec\alpha_2 + \sec\alpha_2\sec\alpha_3 + \ldots n$ terms

$= \dfrac{\tan\alpha_{n+1} - \tan\alpha_1}{\sin d}$

(b) $\csc\alpha_1\csc\alpha_2 + \csc\alpha_2\csc\alpha_3$

$\hspace{3cm} + \ldots n$ terms

$= \dfrac{\cot\alpha_1 - \cot\alpha_{n+1}}{\sin d}$

55. Let the sequence $a_1, a_2, \ldots a_n$ form an A.P. and let $a_1 = 0$, prove that

$\dfrac{a_3}{a_2} + \dfrac{a_4}{a_3} + \dfrac{a_5}{a_4} + \ldots + \dfrac{a_n}{a_{n-1}} - a_2\left(\dfrac{1}{a_2} + \dfrac{1}{a_3} + \ldots + \dfrac{1}{a_{n-2}}\right)$

$= \dfrac{a_{n-1}}{a_2} + \dfrac{a_2}{a_{n-1}}.$

56. A sequence of real numbers $a_1, a_2, \ldots a_n$ is such that $a_1 = 0, |a_2| = |a_1 + 1|, |a_3| = |a_2 + 1|, \ldots$ $|a_n| = |a_{n-1} + 1|$. Show that A.M. of these numbers is always greater or equal to $-1/2$.

57. Find the number of terms common to the two A.P.'s $3, 7, 11, \ldots 407$ and $2, 9, 16, \ldots 709$.

58. Prove that there are 17 identical terms in the two A.P.'s $2, 5, 8, 11, \ldots 60$ terms and $3, 5, 7, 9, \ldots 50$ terms.

59. Certain numbers appear in both arithmetic progressions $17, 21, 25, \ldots$ and $16, 21, 26, \ldots$. Find the sum of first hundred numbers appearing in both progressions.

60. Each of the two triplets of numbers $\log a, \log b, \log c$ and $\log a - \log 2b, \log 2b - \log 3c, \log 3c - \log a$ are in A.P. Can the numbers a, b, c be the lengths of the sides of a triangle? If they can, what kind of triangle is it? Find the angles of the triangle provided that it exists.

Solutions to Problem Set (1)

1. (a) $T_5 = a + 4d = 1$, $T_{31} = a + 30d = -77$,
Solving the above two, we get
$a = 13$ and $d = -3$. $\hspace{1.5cm}$ ...(1)
$S_{15} = (n/2)[2a + (n-1)d]$
$\hspace{1cm} = (15/2)[26 + 14(-3)] = -120$.
Let $T_n = -17$. Then $a + (n-1)d = -17$.
$13 + (n-1)(-3) = 17$
$\therefore \quad 3n = 33$ or $n = 11$.
Let $S_n = 20$. Then $(n/2)[2a + (n-1)d] = 20$.
$n[2 \times 13 + (n-1)(-3)] = 40$, by (1).
$3n^2 - 29n + 40 = 0$
$\therefore \quad (n-8)(3n-5) = 0, \ \therefore \ n = 8$.
The value of n cannot be fractional.

(b) Ans. $a = -1, d = 4, S_{20} = 740$.

2. (a) $a = 20, d = -\dfrac{2}{3}$ and let $S_n = 300$.
$\therefore \quad (n/2)[2 \cdot 20 + (n-1)(-2/3)] = 300$.
Simplifying $n^2 - 61n + 900 = 0$
or $(n-25)(n-36) = 0$
$n = 25$ or 36.
Since common ratio is negative and $S_{25} = S_{36} = 300$, it shows that the sum of last eleven terms i.e., $T_{26}, T_{27}, \ldots T_{36}$ is zero.

(b) Given series is an A.P. of common difference $-\dfrac{2}{3}$.
Hence the sum will be maximum when all the terms taken are +ive. $T_n = 20 + (n-1)\left(-\dfrac{2}{3}\right) \geq 0$
if $62 - 2n > 0$ or $n \leq 31$ $\therefore$ S_{31} is max.
Hence $S_{31} = \dfrac{31}{2}\left\{2 \cdot 20 + 30\left(-\dfrac{2}{3}\right)\right\} = 310$

(c) Ans. $n = 18, 19$.

(d) This is an A.P. of common difference $-\dfrac{1}{6}$.
Sum $= \dfrac{9}{2}\left[2 \times \dfrac{1}{2} + (9-1)\left(-\dfrac{1}{6}\right)\right] = -\dfrac{3}{2}$.

(e) Ans. False.
Choose $a = 3, d = \alpha, T_p = 8, T_q = 14$
$\Rightarrow \quad 11p - 5q = 6$
Only one equation in two variables. It will have infinite number of solutions.

3. (a) Putting $n = 1, 2, 3, \ldots$ in $T_n = (3 + n)/4$
we get the series as
$1, \dfrac{5}{4}, \dfrac{3}{2}, \ldots$ $\therefore$ $a = 1, d = \dfrac{1}{4}$.
$S_{105} = \dfrac{105}{2}\left[2 \cdot 1 + (104)\dfrac{1}{4}\right]$
$= (105/2) \times 28 = 1470$.

(b) Using the **property e (1) of P. 126**, we get
$$a_5 + a_{20} = a_1 + a_{24}, \quad a_{10} + a_{15} = a_1 + a_{24}.$$
Hence the given relations reduce to
$$3(a_1 + a_{24}) = 225, \text{ giving } a_1 + a_{24} = 75,$$
Hence $S_{24} = (24/2)(a_1 + a_{24}) = 12 \times 75 = 900.$

(c) Ans.   98.

4. $S_8 = 64.$ ∴ $2a + 7d = 16$
$S_{19} = 361$ ∴ $2a + 18d = 38.$
Solving, $a = 1, d = 2$
$$S_n = (n/2)[2 \cdot 1 + (n-1)2] = n^2.$$

5.   (a) $S_{40} = 3600, \quad S_{30} = 3600 - \frac{1}{3}(3600) = 2400,$

because after paying 30 instalments $\frac{1}{3}$rd of debt is

still left. The above two equations give
$$2a + 39d = 180 \text{ and } 2a + 29d = 160.$$
Solving them, we get $d = 2$ and $a = 51,$
i.e., the value of first instalment is Rs. 51.

(b) Do yourself. Ans. 16.

6.   (a) Sum of the interior angles of a polygon of n sides.
$$= (2n - 4)\pi/2 = (n-2)\pi = (n-2) \cdot 180°.$$
Also $a = 120°, d = 5°.$

∴ $\frac{n}{2}[2 \cdot 120° + (n-1)5°] = (n-2) \cdot 180°$

Cancel 5 and simplify.

∴ $n^2 - 25n + 144 = 0$ ∴ $(n-9)(n-16) = 0.$

∴ $n = 9, 16.$

But when $n = 16$, $T_n = a + (16-1)d$
$$= 120° + 15 \times 5° = 195°$$
This is not possible as interior angle cannot be greater than $180°.$

∴ $n = 9$ is the correct answer.

(b) $S_n = 3 \cdot \sum N = \frac{3n(n+1)}{2} > 1000$

or $n^2 + n > \frac{2}{3} 1000$

or $\left(n + \frac{1}{2}\right)^2 \geq 666.9 \Rightarrow n + \frac{1}{2} > 25.8$

or $n > 25.8 - 0.5 = 25.3$

Since $n > 25.3$ and n is an integer, therefore least value of n is 26 .

7. $T_n - T_{n-1} = \log \frac{a^n}{b^{n-1}} - \log \frac{a^{n-1}}{b^{n-2}}$

$= \log \frac{a^n}{b^{n-1}} \cdot \frac{b^{n-2}}{a^{n-1}} = \log \frac{a}{b} = \text{constant}$ as   it   is

independent of n. Hence the given series is an A.P. whose $A = \log a$ and $D = \log \frac{a}{b}$.

∴ $S = \frac{n}{2}\left[2\log a + (n-1)\log \frac{a}{b}\right]$

$= \frac{n}{2}\left[n\log \frac{a}{b} + 2\log a - (\log a - \log b)\right]$

$= \frac{n}{2}\left[n\log \frac{a}{b} + \log ab\right]$

8.   (a) $T_m = a + (m-1)d = n, \quad T_n = a + (n-1)d = m$
Solving, we get
$$d = -1 \text{ and } a = m + n - 1.$$
∴ $T_p = a + (p-1)d$
$$= m + n - 1 + (p-1)(-1) = m + n - p.$$
$T_{m+n} = a + (m+n-1)d$
$$= (m+n-1) + (m+n-1)(-1) = 0.$$

(b) Ans. (c). Proceed as in part (a).
$$a = d = \frac{1}{mn} \quad \therefore \quad T_{mn} = a + (mn-1)d = 1$$

(c) Let D be common difference of A.P. where $D \neq 0$ then $b - a = D, c - a = 2D, c - d = -D, b - d = -2D$ etc.

Thus the given equation can be written as
$$-2D + xD^2 + (2D)^3 = 2(-3D) + (-2D)^2 + (-D)^3$$
Since $D \neq 0$, we can cancel D and arranging as a quardratic in D, we have
$$9D^2 + (x-4)D + 4 = 0$$
Since D is real ∴ $\Delta \geq 0$ or $(x-4)^2 - 144 \geq 0$
or $(x-16)(x+8) \geq 0$
$$[\because P^2 - Q^2 = (P+Q)(P-Q)]$$
∴ $x \leq -8$ or $x \geq 16$

(d) $E = (a+e) - 4(b+d) + 6c$
Now b, c, d in A.P. $\rightarrow b + d = 2c$
Again a, c, e are also in A.P. ∴ $a + e = 2c$
∴ $E = 2c - 4(2c) + 6c = 0$

9. $S = \frac{n}{2}(a+l)$ or $\frac{2S}{a+l} = n$ ...(1)

$l = a + (n-1)d$ so that $d = \frac{l-a}{n-1}$ ...(2)

Now put for n from (1) in (2).

Alt. $\frac{l^2 - a^2}{2S - (l+a)} = \frac{l^2 - a^2}{n(l+a) - (l+a)}$, by (1)

$= \frac{l-a}{n-1} = d$, by (2)

10. $T_1 = a, T_2 = a + d = b$ ∴ $d = b - a$
$T_n = a + (n-1)d = c$
$$n - 1 = \frac{c-a}{d} = \frac{c-a}{b-a}$$
∴ $n = \frac{c-a}{b-a} + 1 = \frac{c+b-2a}{b-a}$ ...(1)

$S_n = \frac{n}{2}[a + T_n] = \frac{(c+b-2a)}{2(b-a)}(a+c),$ by (1).

11.   (a) $T_n = S_n - S_{n-1}$ ...(I)
Now $S_n = 3n^2 + 4n$

$$\therefore \quad S_{n-1} = 3(n-1)^2 + 4(n-1) = 3n^2 - 2n - 1$$

$$\therefore \quad T_n = (3n^2 + 4n) - (3n^2 - 2n - 1), \quad \text{by (1)}$$

$$= 6n + 1$$

$$\therefore \quad T_1 = 7, \ T_2 = 13, \ T_3 = 19, \ldots$$

$$\therefore \quad a = 7, \ d = 6.$$

(b) $S_n = 3n^2$ by given condition.

$$\therefore \quad T_n = S_n - S_{n-1} = 3n^2 - 3(n-1)^2 = 6n - 3.$$

Putting $n = 1, 2, 3, \ldots$ the series is 3, 9, 15, 21, ...

(A.P.)

(c) $T_n = S_n - S_{n-1} = a(2n-1) + b$

Also $T_1 = S_1 = a + b$

$$T_2 = 3a + b, \ T_3 = 5a + b \ \ldots..$$

Hence A.P. whose $d = 2a.$

12. (a) Ans. 8 terms, series is $1\frac{1}{2}, 3, 4\frac{1}{2}, \ldots\ldots$

(b) The first two digit number which when divided by 4 leaves remainder 1 is $4.3 + 1 = 13$ and last is $4.24 + 1 = 97$; form $(4k + 1)$.

Thus we have to find the sum of

$$13 + 17 + 21 + \ldots. + 97,$$

which is an A.P. $\therefore 97 = 13 + (n-1).4 \therefore n = 22$

$$\therefore \quad S = (n/2)[a + l] = 11(13 + 97)$$

$$= 11 \times 110 = 1210.$$

13. (a) Let the work finish in n days when the workers started dropping so that the total number of workers who worked all these days is the sum of A.P.

$150 + 146 + 142 + \ldots. n$ terms

$$= (n/2)[2(150) + (n-1)(-4)] = n(152 - 2n) \quad \ldots(1)$$

Had the workers not dropped, then the work would have finished in $(n - 8)$ days with 150 workers working on each day.

i.e., $150(n-8)$ \hfill ...(2)

$$\therefore \quad n(152 - 2n) = 150(n-8), \quad \text{by (1) and (2)}$$

or $n^2 - n - 600 = 0$

or $(n - 25)(n + 24) = 0 \therefore n = 25$.

(b) Let the number of stones be $2n + 1$ so that there is one mid-stone and n stones each on either side of it. If P be mid-stone and A, B be last stones on the left and right of P respectively.

There will be $(n + 1)$ stones on the left and $(n + 1)$ stones on right side of P (P being common to both sides) or n intervals each of 10 metres both on the right and left side of mid-stone. Now he starts from one of the end stones, picks it up, goes to mid-stone, drops it and goes to last stone on the other side, picks it and comes back to mid-stone. In all he travels n intervals of 10 metres each 3 times. Now from centre he will go to 2nd stone on L.H.S. then come back and then go to 2nd last on

R.H.S. and again come back. Thus he will travel $(n - 1)$ intervals of 10 metres each 4 times. Similarly $(n - 2)$ intervals of 10 metres each 4 times for 3rd and so on for the last.

Hence the total distance covered as given = 3 k.m. = 3000 m.

or $3.10 \, n + 4[10(n-1) + 10(n-2) + \ldots. + 10]$

$$= 30n + 40[1 + 2 + 3 + \ldots + (n-1)] = 3000$$

or $30n + 40[(n-1)/2][1 + n - 1] = 3000$

or $2n^2 + n - 300 = 0$

or $(n - 12)(2n + 25) = 0, \quad \therefore \ n = 12.$

Hence the number of stones = $2n + 1 = 25$.

(c) **Hint.** Suppose Shyam is ahead of Ram on nth day of his start then $S_n - R_{n+3} > 0$

$\Rightarrow \quad (n-2)(n-9) < 0 \Rightarrow 2 < n < 9$

i.e., from 3rd to 9th day i.e., 7 days.

14. (a) $S_n = (2n)^2$

$$\therefore \quad T_n = S_n - S_{n-1} = (2n)^2 - (2n-2)^2$$

or $T_n = (4n - 2).2 = 8n - 4.$

On putting $n = 1, 2, 3, \ldots$ we get the A.P. as 4, 12, 20, 28, $\ldots$

(b) $S_n + 1 = (2n+1)^2$ as above $T_n = S_n - S_{n-1} = 8n$

$$\therefore \quad 8, 16, 24, \ldots$$

(c) Any four consecutive integers in A.P. be taken as $(a - 3d), (a - d), (a + d), (a + 3d)$ so that common difference is $2d$ and their product is $(a^2 - 9d^2)(a^2 - d^2)$.

We have to evaluate

$$(2d)^4 + (a^2 - 9d^2)(a^2 - d^2)$$

or $a^4 - 10a^2d^2 + 25d^4 = (a^2 - 5d^2)^2$

Since a and d are given to be integers therefore $(a^2 - 5d^2)^2$ is also an integer.

15. $\dfrac{S_m}{S_n} = \dfrac{m^2}{n^2} \quad \therefore \ \dfrac{S_m}{m^2} = \dfrac{S_n}{n^2} = k,$ say

Now $\dfrac{T_m}{T_n} = \dfrac{S_m - S_{m-1}}{S_n - S_{n-1}} = \dfrac{k\{m^2 - (m-1)^2\}}{k\{n^2 - (n-1)^2\}} = \dfrac{2m-1}{2n-1}.$

16. (a) $\dfrac{S_n}{S_n{}'} = \dfrac{(n/2)[2a + (n-1)d]}{(n/2)[2d + (n-1)d']} = \dfrac{3n+8}{7n+15}$

or $\dfrac{a + [(n-1)/2]d}{d + [(n-1)/2]d'} = \dfrac{3n+8}{7n+15}$ \hfill ...(1)

We have to find $\dfrac{T_{12}}{T_{12}{}'} = \dfrac{a + 11d}{d + 11d'}$

Choosing $(n-1)/2 = 11$ or $n = 23$ in (1), we get

$$\dfrac{T_{12}}{T_{12}{}'} = \dfrac{a + 11d}{d + 11d'} = \dfrac{3(23) + 8}{7(23) + 15} = \dfrac{77}{176} = \dfrac{7}{16}.$$

(b) $\dfrac{S_n}{S_n{'}} = \dfrac{a + [(n-1)/2]\,d}{d' + [(n-1)/2]\,d'} = \dfrac{7n+1}{4n+27}$ ...(1)

$\therefore \quad \dfrac{T_p}{T_p{'}} = \dfrac{a + (p-1)\,d}{d' + (p-1)\,d'}$.

Put $\dfrac{n-1}{2} = p - 1 \quad$ or $\quad n = 2p - 1$ in (1)

$\therefore \quad \dfrac{T_p}{T_p{'}} = \dfrac{7(2p-1)+1}{4(2p-1)+27} = \dfrac{14p-6}{8p+23}$

Now replace p by n in the above.

(c) Proceed as above.

(d) Given relation implies that

$$\dfrac{\dfrac{m}{2}[2a + (m-1)\,d]}{\dfrac{n}{2}[2a + (n-1)\,d]} = \dfrac{m^4}{n^4}$$

or $\quad \dfrac{a + \dfrac{m-1}{2}d}{a + \dfrac{n-1}{2}d} = \dfrac{m^3}{n^3}$ ...(1)

Now $\dfrac{T_{M+1}}{T_{N+1}} = \dfrac{a + Md}{a + Nd}$ where

$M = \dfrac{m-1}{2} ; N = \dfrac{n-1}{2}$

or $m = 2M + 1, n = 2N + 1$

$\therefore \quad \dfrac{T_{M+1}}{T_{N+1}} = \dfrac{(2M+1)^3}{(2N+1)^3}$ or $\dfrac{T_{m+1}}{T_{n+1}} = \dfrac{(2m+1)^3}{(2n+1)^3}$

(e) $\dfrac{S_{pn}}{S_n} = \dfrac{\dfrac{pn}{2}[2a + (pn-1)\,d]}{\dfrac{n}{2}[2a + (n-1)\,d]} = \dfrac{p[(2a-d)+npd]}{(2a-d)+nd}$

Above will be independent of n only when $2a - d = 0$ as in that case n will cancel from both N^r and D^r. $\quad \therefore \quad \dfrac{a}{d} = \dfrac{1}{2}$.

17. $a - d, a, a + d$

and $A - p, A, A + p \quad$ where $p = d + 1$ ...(1)

$S = 3a = 3A = 15 \quad \therefore \quad a = A = 5$

Also $\dfrac{P}{P_1} = \dfrac{a(a^2 - d^2)}{A(A^2 - p^2)} = \dfrac{7}{8}$

$8(25 - d^2) = 7[25 - (d+1)^2]$, by (1)

or $200 - 175 = 8d^2 - 7(d^2 + 2d + 1)$.

$\therefore \quad d^2 - 14d - 32 = 0 \quad$ or $\quad d = -2, 16$

and hence $p = d + 1 = -1, 17$. Also $a = A = 5$

Hence the two A.P.'s are given by 7, 5, 3 ... and 6, 5, 4 ... or ... -11, 5, 21 ... and .... -12, 5, 22 ... whose three consecutive terms written above satisfy Algebra the given conditions.

18. (a) Clearly the numbers between 250 and 1000 which are divisible by 3 are 252, 255, 258, ... 999.

$\therefore \quad T_n = 999 = a + (n-1)\,d = 252 + (n-1)\,3$

$333 = 84 + n - 1 \quad \therefore \quad n = 333 - 83 = 250$

$\therefore \quad S = \dfrac{n}{2}[a + l] = (250/2)\,[252 + 999]$

$\qquad = 125 \times 1251 = 156375.$

(b) Ans. (b).

L.C.M. of 2 and 5 is 10.

Numbers divisible by 2 will contain numbers which are also divisible by 10. Similarly numbers divisible by 5 will contain numbers which are also divisible by 10. Thus the number divisible by 10 will occur twice. Hence we can write $S = S_2 + S_5 - S_{10}$

By Formula :

$n(A \cup B) = n(A) + n(B) - n(A \cap B)$

$S_2 = n(A) = 2 + 4 + 6 + \ldots 100$

$\qquad = 2(1 + 2 + 3 + \ldots 50)$

$\qquad = \dfrac{2.50.51}{2} = 2550$ by $\Sigma n = \dfrac{n(n+1)}{2}$

$S_5 = n(B) = 5 + 10 + 15 + \ldots 100$

$\qquad = 5(1 + 2 + 3 + \ldots 20)$

$\qquad = \dfrac{5.20.21}{2} = 1050$

$S_{10} = n(A \cap B) = 10 + 20 + 30 + \ldots 100$

$\qquad = 10(1 + 2 + 3 + \ldots 10)$

$\qquad = \dfrac{10.10.11}{2} = 550$

$\therefore \quad S = S_2 + S_5 - S_{10}$

$\qquad = 2550 + 1050 - 550 = 3050 \Rightarrow$ (b).

19. (a) Odd numbers between 1 and 1000 are 3, 5, 7, 9, 11, 13, 15, ... 993, 995, 997, 999.

Those odd numbers which are divisible by 3 are 3, 9, 15, 21, ..., 993, 999.

They form an A.P. of which $a = 3, d = 6, l = 999$

$l = T_n = a + (n-1)\,d$

$\therefore \quad 999 = 3 + (n-1)\,6. \quad \therefore \quad 333 = 1 + 2n - 2$

or $334 = 2n \quad \therefore \quad n = 167.$

$S = \dfrac{n}{2}[a + l] = \dfrac{167}{2}[3 + 999]$

$\qquad = \dfrac{167}{2} \times 1002 = 167 \times 501$

$\qquad = 167 \times 500 + 167 = 83500 + 167 = 83667.$

(b) Ans. n^2.

(c) Ans. 867.

(d) Let the odd integers be $2m + 1, 2m + 3, 2m + 5, \ldots$ and let their number be n. Then

$57^2 - 13^2 = (n/2)[2(2m+1) + (n-1).2]$

$\qquad = n(2m + n) = 2mn + n^2$

or $\quad 57^2 - 13^2 = (n + m)^2 - m^2$

Hence $\quad m = 13$ and $n + m = 57$

or $n = 57 - 13 = 44$.

Hence the required odd integers are 27, 29, 31, ...,
113.

20. Proceeding as in Q. 18 (b), we have

$S = S_3 + S_7 - S_{21}$

S_3 = sum of all those number between 200 and 500 which are divisible by 3

$\quad = 201 + 204 + ... + 498$

$498 = 201 + (n-1).3 \quad$ by $l = a + (n-1)d$

$\therefore \quad n = 100$

$\therefore \quad S_3 = \dfrac{100}{2}[201 + 498] = 50 \times 699 = 34950$

$S_7 = 203 + 210 + ... + 497$

$497 = 203 + (n-1)7 \quad$ or $\quad \dfrac{294}{7} = n = 1 \Rightarrow n = 43$

$S_7 = \dfrac{43}{2}[201 + 497] = 15050$

$S_{21} = 210 + 231 + ... + 483$

$483 = 210 + (n-1)21 \therefore \dfrac{273}{21} = n - 1 \Rightarrow n = 14$

$\therefore \quad S_{21} = \dfrac{14}{2}[210 + 483] = 4851$

$\therefore \quad S = S_3 + S_7 - S_{21} = 34950 + 15050 - 4851$

$\qquad = 50000 - 4851 = 45149$

21. Let the first term be A and common difference D.

$S_{p+q} = \dfrac{p+q}{2}[2A + (p+q-1)D] \qquad ...(1)$

It is given that $T_p = a$ and $T_q = b$

$\therefore \quad \begin{cases} A + (p-1)D = a \\ A + (q-1)D = b \end{cases}$

Subtracting, $(p-q)D = a - b$

$\therefore \quad D = \dfrac{a-b}{p-q} \qquad\qquad ...(2)$

Adding, $2A + (p+q-2)D = a + b$

or $\quad 2A + (p+q-1)D = a + b + D$

$\quad = a + b + \dfrac{a-b}{p-q}, \qquad$ by (2) $\qquad ...(3)$

Hence from (1) and (3),

$S_{p+q} = \dfrac{p+q}{2}\left[a + b + \dfrac{a-b}{p-q}\right]$.

22. Let A be the first term and D the common difference of A.P.

$T_p = a = A + (p-1)D = (A-D) + pD \qquad ...(1)$

$T_q = b = A + (q-1)D = (A-D) + qD \qquad ...(2)$

$T_r = c = A + (r-1)D = (A-D) + rD \qquad ...(3)$

Here we have got two unknowns A and D which are to be eliminated.

We multiply (1), (2) and (3) by $q-r, r-p$ and $p-q$ respectively and add :

$\quad a(q-r) + b(r-p) + c(p-q)$

$= (A-D)[q-r+r-p+p-q] + D[p(q-r)$
$\qquad\qquad\qquad\qquad\qquad + q(r-p) + r(p-q)] = 0$

23. $S_p = \dfrac{p}{2}[2A + (p-1)d] = a$

$\therefore \quad \dfrac{2a}{p} = 2A + (p-1)d \qquad\qquad ...(1)$

$\quad \dfrac{2b}{q} = 2A + (q-1)d \qquad\qquad ...(2)$

$\quad \dfrac{2c}{r} = 2A + (r-1)d \qquad\qquad ...(3)$

Multiply (1), (2) and (3) by $q-r, r-p$ and $p-q$ respectively and add

$\therefore \quad \Sigma \dfrac{a}{p}(q-r) = 0$.

24. (a) We are given that $S_p = S_q$.

$\therefore \quad \dfrac{p}{2}[2a + (p-1)d] = \dfrac{q}{2}[2a + (q-1)d]$

or $\quad (2a-d)(p-q) + (p^2 - q^2)d = 0$,

cancel $p - q$ as $p \neq q$

or $\quad 2a - d + (p+q)d = 0$

or $\quad 2a + (p+q-1)d = 0 \qquad\qquad ...(1)$

$\therefore \quad S_{p+q} = \dfrac{p+q}{2}[2a + (p+q-1)d]$

$\qquad = \dfrac{p+q}{2}.0 = 0, \qquad$ by (1)

(b) $S_p = 0 \therefore \dfrac{p}{2}[2a + (p-1)d] = 0$

$\therefore \quad d = \dfrac{-2a}{p-1} \qquad\qquad\qquad ...(1)$

Sum of next q terms = sum of an A.P. whose first term will be $T_{p+1} = a + pd$

$\therefore \quad S = \dfrac{q}{2}[2(a+pd) + (q-1)d]$

$\qquad = \dfrac{q}{2}[2a + (p-1)d + (p+q)d]$

$\qquad = \dfrac{q}{2}\left[0 - (p+q)\dfrac{2a}{p-1}\right] = -a\dfrac{(p+q)q}{p-1},$ by (1)

25. (a) $S_p = q$ and $S_q = p$

$\quad \dfrac{p}{2}[2a + (p-1)d] = q$

$\quad \dfrac{q}{2}[2a + (q-1)d] = p$

$\quad 2a(p-q) + d\{(p^2 - q^2) - (p-q)\} = 2(q-p)$

$\quad 2a + d(p+q-1) = -2$

$\therefore \quad S_{p+q} = \dfrac{p+q}{2}[2a + (p+q-1)d]$

$\qquad = \dfrac{p+q}{2}(-2) = -(p+q)$.

(b) Show $S_{3n} - S_n = \dfrac{1}{3}S_{3n}$.

(c) Ans. 2 ; $\dfrac{S_1}{S_2} = \dfrac{S_n}{S_{2n} - S_n} = \lambda$. Put $n = 1, 2$.

26. (a) Here $a = 1$ for all and $d = 1, 2, 3$ respectively for S_1, S_2, S_3, and $n = n$ for all.

$S_1 + S_3 = (n/2)[2.1 + (n-1).1]$
$\qquad\qquad\qquad + (n/2)[2.1 + (n-1).3]$
$\qquad = (n/2)[n+1] + (n/2)[3n-1]$
$\qquad = (n/2) 4n = 2n^2$

$2S_2 = 2.(n/2)[2.1+(n-1).2] = n.(2n) = 2n^2$.

∴ $S_1 + S_3 = 2.S_2$.

(b) $\dfrac{L}{p} = \dfrac{L'}{a} = 4$ (given) ...(1)

∴ $a + (n-1)d = 4p$
$p + (n-1)q = 4a$

∴ $\dfrac{4p - a}{4a - p} = \dfrac{d}{q}$ ...(2)

$\dfrac{S_n}{S_n'} = \dfrac{\frac{n}{2}(a+L)}{\frac{n}{2}(p+L')} = \dfrac{a+4p}{p+4a} = 2$, given by (1)

∴ $2p = 7a$ or $\dfrac{a}{2} = \dfrac{p}{7} = \lambda$, say ...(3)

Putting in (2), $\dfrac{d}{q} = \dfrac{28\lambda - 2\lambda}{8\lambda - 7\lambda} = 26$

and $\dfrac{L}{L'} = \dfrac{p}{a} = \dfrac{7}{2}$, by (1) and (3)

27. (a) Here a and d are same as there is same A.P. and N is equal to $n, 2n, 3n$ for S_1, S_2 and S_3 respectively :
$3(S_2 - S_1) = 3[(2n/2)\{2a + (2n-1)d\}$
$\qquad\qquad\qquad - (n/2)\{2a + (n-1)d\}]$
$\qquad = (3n/2)[(4a - 2a) + (4n - 2 - n + 1)d]$
$\qquad = (3n/2)[2a + (3n-1)d] = S_3$

i.e., sum of $3n$ terms.

(b) Solving the given relations for a and d, we get
$a = p$ and $d = 2p$ ...(1)
Putting for a and d from (1), we get
$S_p = \dfrac{p}{2}[2a + (p-1)d] = p^3$.

28. (a) $\dfrac{s_{pn}}{s_n} = \dfrac{\frac{pn}{2}[2a + (pn-1)d]}{\frac{n}{2}[2a+(n-1)d]} = \dfrac{p[2a - d + pnd]}{[2a - d + nd]}$

Above will be independent of n if $2a - d = 0$ and in that case the ratio will be p^2 as nd cancels.

(b) 1st relation implies $2a = (n+1)d$ and putting for a in S_{3n}/S_n, we get it equal to 6.

(c) Ans. (c). $S_{2n} = S_n'$

∴ $\dfrac{2n}{2}[2.2 + (2n-1)3] = \dfrac{n}{2}[2.57 + (n-1)2]$

∴ $6n + 1 = n + 56$

⇒ $5n = 55$ or $n = 11$ ⇒ (c).

29. (a) Here $a = 1$ for all, and $d = 1, 2, 3, ... n$ respectively for the n A.P.'s
We have to find sum of their nth terms.
$\sum T_n = [1 + (n-1).1] + [1 + (n-1).2]$
$\qquad\qquad + ... + [1 + (n-1).n]$
$\qquad = [1 + 1 + 1 + ...n \text{ terms}] + (n-1)$
$\qquad\qquad .[1 + 2 + 3 + ...n \text{ terms}]$
$\qquad = n + (n-1)\dfrac{n}{2}[1+n] = \dfrac{n}{2}(2 + n^2 - 1)$
$\qquad = \dfrac{n}{2}[n^2 + 1]$.

(b) Do yourself.

(c) $S_1 = (n/2)[2.1 + (n-1)1]$,
$S_2 = (n/2)[2.2 + (n-1).2]$,...
$S_m = (n/2)[2.m + (n-1).m]$.

∴ $S_1 + S_2 + ... + S_m$
$= n(1 + 2 + 3 + ...m) + \dfrac{n(n-1)}{2}.(1 + 2 + 3 + ...m)$.
$= \dfrac{m(m+1)}{2}\left[n + \dfrac{n^2 - n}{2}\right]$
$= \dfrac{m(m+1)}{2}.\dfrac{n(n+1)}{2} = \dfrac{1}{4}mn(m+1)(n+1)$.

Here we have used
$1 + 2 + 3 + ... + m = (m/2)[1+m]$
i.e., $S = (n/2)[a+l]$

30. (a) Here $a = 1, 2, 3, ..., m$ respectively
and $d = 1, 3, 5, ...2m - 1$, and $n = n$.
To find $S_1 + S_2 + S_3 + ... + S_m$.
$S_1 = (n/2)[2.1 + (n-1).1]$,
$S_2 = (n/2)[2.2 + (n-1).3]$
$S_m = (n/2)[2.m + (n-1)(2m-1)]$
∴ $S_1 + S_2 + S_3 + ... + S_m$.
$= n(1 + 2 + 3 + ...m) + \dfrac{n(n-1)}{2}$
$\qquad\qquad [1 + 3 + 5 + ... + (2m-1)]$
$= n.\dfrac{m(m+1)}{2} + \dfrac{n(n-1)}{2}.\dfrac{m}{2}[1 + 2m - 1]$,
$\qquad\qquad\qquad \text{using } S = \dfrac{n}{2}[a+l]$
$= \dfrac{1}{2}mn[m + 1 + m(n-1)] = \dfrac{1}{2}mn(mn+1)$.

(b) Ans. (a).
If there are 9 odd terms then T_2, T_4, T_6, T_8 will be $\dfrac{9-1}{2} = 4$ in number and $T_1 + T_3 + T_5 + T_7 + T_9$ will be $\dfrac{9+1}{2} = 5$ in number. Hence S_1 is an A.P. of n terms, but S_2 is an A.P. of $\dfrac{n+1}{2}$ terms with common difference $2d$.

$$S_1 = \frac{n}{2}[2a + (n-1)d] \qquad \ldots(1)$$

$$S_2 = \frac{1}{2}\left(\frac{n+1}{2}\right)\left[2a + \left(\frac{n+1}{2}-1\right)2d\right]$$

$$= \frac{n+1}{4}[2a + (n-1)d] \qquad \ldots(2)$$

$$\therefore \quad \frac{S_1}{S_2} = \frac{2n}{n+1}.$$

31. (a) The number of terms in successive groups are 1, 3, 5, ... and hence in nth group will be nth term of this A.P. *i.e.* $2n - 1 = N$

The last term of successive groups are $1^2, 2^2, 3^2, \ldots$ and hence of nth group is n^2 and of $(n-1)$th group is $(n-1)^2$. Hence 1st term of nth group is one more than the last term of $(n-1)$th group

$$\therefore \quad A = (n-1)^2 + 1 = n^2 - 2n + 2$$

Also terms in each group are in A.P. whose $D = 1$.

$\therefore$ Sum of terms in nth group is sum of an A. P.

$$= \frac{N}{2}[2A + (N-1)D]$$

$$= \frac{2n-1}{2}[2n^2 - 4n + 4 + (2n-2).1]$$

$$= (2n-1)(n^2 - n + 1)$$

$$= 2n^3 - 3n^2 + 3n - 1 = n^3 + (n-1)^3$$

(b) As in part (a) the number of terms in nth group is $2n - 1$ which are in A.P. of common difference 1 and first term of successive groups are 1, 2, 3...., and hence of nth group is n. Sum of terms of nth group

$$= [(2n-1)/2][2.n + (2n-1-1).1]$$

$$= [(2n-1)/2](4n-2) = (2n-1)^2.$$

32. Last term of nth group $= 1 + 2 + 3 + \ldots n$

$$= \frac{n(n+1)}{2}$$

The terms in nth group will be n and in A.P. of common difference -1 and first term being $\frac{n(n+1)}{2}$ (*i.e.* last term as first term and $d = -1$ intead of $+1$)

$$\therefore \quad S_n = \frac{n}{2}\left[2.\frac{n(n+1)}{2} + (n-1)(-1)\right] = \frac{n}{2}(n^2 + 1)$$

$$\therefore \quad S_{50} = 25(2501) = 62525$$

33. (a) The number of terms in successive groups are 1, 2, 3, ... and hence in nth there will be n terms in A.P. of common difference 2.

The only thing we have to find is the first term.

The successive first terms are 1, 3, 7, 13, ... whose successive differnces 2, 4, 6, ... are in A.P.

$$S = 1 + 3 + 7 + 13 + \ldots + T_n$$

$$S = \quad 1 + 3 + 7 + \ldots + T_{n-1} + T_n.$$

Subtract

$$0 = 1 + (2 + 4 + 6 + \ldots (n-1) \text{ terms}) - T_n$$

$$\therefore \quad T_n = 1 + [(n-1)/2][2.2 + (n-2).2]$$

$$= 1 + (n-1)n = n^2 - n + 1.$$

The terms in nth group form an A.P.

for which $\quad a = n^2 - n + 1, \ d = 2, \ n = n.$

$$\therefore \quad S_n = (n/2)[2(n^2 - n + 1) + (n-1).2]$$

$$= n[n^2 - n + 1 + n - 1] = n.n^2 = n^3.$$

(b) **Hint :** The first term in nth group is $2(n-1)^2 + 1$ whereas the last term is $2n^2 - 1$ and the number of term is $2n - 1$ which are in A.P.

$$\therefore \quad S = \frac{N}{2}[A + L]$$

34. (a) Let the three numbers in A.P. be $a - d, a, a + d$

Sum $= 3a = 15 \quad \therefore \quad a = 5.$

Sum of their squares

$$= (a-d)^2 + a^2 + (a+d)^2 = 83$$

or $\quad 3a^2 + 2d^2 = 83$ or $2d^2 = 83 - 3.25$

$$\therefore \quad d^2 = 4 \quad \text{or} \quad d = \pm 2.$$

Hence the numbers are 3, 5, 7 or 7, 5, 3.

(b) Ans. ± 3. Sum of three numbers in A.P.

$$= 3a = 12 \qquad \therefore \quad a = 4 \text{ is a root.}$$

$$\therefore \quad (x - 4)(x^2 - 8x + 7) = 0$$

$$\therefore \quad x = 1, 4, 7 \quad \text{or} \quad 7, 4, 1 \quad \therefore \quad d = \pm 3$$

(c) Let $x = 5.3a, \ y = 5b, \ z = 3c$

then $x^2 + y^2 + z^2 - xy - yz - zx = 0$

$$\Rightarrow \quad \frac{1}{2}[(x-y)^2 + (y-z)^2 + (z-x)^2] = 0$$

$$\Rightarrow \quad x - y = 0, \ y - z = 0, \ z - x = 0$$

$$\Rightarrow \quad x = y = z = \lambda, \text{ say}$$

$$15a = 5b = 3c = 15k, \text{ say}$$

$$\therefore \quad a = k, \ b = 3k, \ c = 5k.$$

Clearly they are in A.P.

35. (a) Here $3a = 12 \ \therefore \ a = 4.$

Also $\quad (a-d)^3 + a^3 + (a+d)^3 = 288,$

or $\quad 3a^3 + 6ad^2 = 288$

or $\quad 24d^2 = 288 - 3 \times 64 = 96$

$$\therefore \quad d^2 = 4 \quad \text{or} \quad d = \pm 2$$

Hence the numbers are 2, 4, 6 or 6, 4, 2.

(b) $(A - D) + A + (A + D) = 15 \ \therefore \ A = 5$

Set $A = 5 - D, 5, 5 + D$

and set $B = 5 - d, 5, 5 + d$, where $D = d + 1$

$$\frac{P}{p} = \frac{5(25 - D^2)}{5(25 - d^2)} = \frac{7}{8}$$

$$\therefore \quad 25(8 - 7) = 8(d+1)^2 - 7d^2$$

or $\quad 25 = d^2 + 16d + 8$

or $d^2 + 16d - 17 = 0$ or $(d + 17)(d - 1) = 0$

∴ $d = -17, 1$ and hence $D = -16, 2$

Hence the numbers of the sets A and B are 21, 5, −11 and 22, 5, −12 respectively or 3, 5, 7 and 4, 5, 6 respectively.

36. (a) Let the four numbers in A.P. be

$$a - 3d, \ a - d, \ a + d, \ a + 3d.$$

Sum $= 4a = 20$ ∴ $a = 5$.

Sum of their squares $= 4a^2 + 20d^2 = 120$.

∴ $20d^2 = 120 - 4 \times 25 = 20$

∴ $d^2 = 1$ or $d = \pm 1$.

Hence the numbers are 2, 4, 6, 8 or 8, 6, 4, 2.

(b) $a = 8, \ d = \pm 1$. Numbers are 5, 7, 9, 11 or 11, 9, 7, 5.

37. Here $4a = 28$ ∴ $a = 7$.

Also $\dfrac{(a - 3d)(a + d)}{(a - d)(a + 3d)} = \dfrac{8}{15}$

or $15[a^2 - 3d^2 - 2ad] = 8[a^2 - 3d^2 + 2ad]$

or $7(a^2 - 3d^2) = 46ad$

or $7(49 - 3d^2) = 46 \times 7 \cdot d$

or $49 - 3d^2 = 46d$ or $3d^2 + 46d - 49 = 0$

$(d - 1)(3d + 49) = 0$ ∴ $d = 1$.

∴ Required numbers are 4, 6, 8, 10.

38. Let the means be $x_1, x_2, \ldots \ldots x_m$ so that $1, x_1, x_2, \ldots \ldots x_m, 31$ is an A.P. of $(m + 2)$ terms.

$31 = T_{m+2} = a + (m + 1)d = 1 + (m + 1)d$

∴ $d = \dfrac{30}{m + 1}$ ...(1)

We are given that

$\dfrac{x_7}{x_{m-1}} = \dfrac{5}{9}$ ∴ $\dfrac{T_8}{T_m} = \dfrac{a + 7d}{a + (m - 1)d} = \dfrac{5}{9}$

or $9a + 63d = 5a + (5m - 5)d$

or $4.1 = (5m - 68) \dfrac{30}{m + 1}$. by (1)

or $2m + 2 = 75m - 1020$

∴ $73m = 1022$ ∴ $m = \dfrac{1022}{73} = 14$.

39. $a, x_1, x_2, \ldots \ldots x_n, b$ is an A.P. of $n + 2$ terms where $x_1, x_2, \ldots x_n$ are n A.M.'s between a and b

Now $x_1 + x_2 + x_3 + \ldots + x_n$.

$= \dfrac{n}{2}(x_1 + x_n) = \dfrac{n}{2}(T_2 + T_{n+1})$

$= \dfrac{n}{2}(a + d + b - d) = n\left(\dfrac{a + b}{2}\right)$

$= n$ (single A.M. of a and b)

40. By the given condition

$\dfrac{a^{n+1} + b^{n+1}}{a^n + b^n} = \dfrac{a + b}{2}$

or $2a^{n+1} + 2b^{n+1} = a^{n+1} + b^{n+1} + ab^n + ba^n$

or $a^{n+1} - a^n b = b^n a - b^{n+1}$

or $a^n(a - b) = b^n(a - b)$

∴ $a^n = b^n$. Above is possible only when $n = 0$

∵ $a^0 = b^0 = 1$.

41. (a) Let a and b be the two numbers so that

$a + b = \dfrac{13}{6}$, given ...(1)

Let $2n$ (even) means be inserted between them whose sum $= (2n + 1)$ given ...(2)

Now we know that in an A.P., sum of $2n$ means $= 2n \times$ (single A.M.) by Q. 39

or $2n + 1 = 2n\left(\dfrac{a + b}{2}\right)$ by (2)

or $2n + 1 = n \cdot \dfrac{13}{6}$, by (1)

or $12n + 6 = 13n$, ∴ $n = 6$.

Hence the number of means inserted $= 2n = 12$.

(b) $a, x_1, x_2, \ldots x_n, b$

$b = T_{n+2} = a + (n + 1)d$

∴ $\dfrac{b - a}{n + 1} = d$

∴ $x_r = T_{r+1} = a + rd = a + \dfrac{r(b - a)}{n + 1}$

$= \dfrac{a(n - r + 1) + rb}{n + 1}$ ...(1)

Put $a = x$ and $b = 2y$ and then again put $a = 2x$ and $b = y$ and equate the results as the two means are equal.

∴ $\dfrac{x(n - r + 1) + 2yr}{n + 1} = \dfrac{2x(n - r + 1) + yr}{n + 1}$

∴ $x(n - r + 1) = yr$ or $\dfrac{x}{y} = \dfrac{r}{n - r + 1}$

42. (a) (i) Subtract $a + b + c$ from each.

∴ $-a, -b, -c$ are in A.P. or a, b, c in A.P.

(ii) Multiply by abc.

(iii) $T_2 - T_1 = b^2(c + a) - a^2(b + c)$

$= c(b^2 - a^2) + ab(b - a) = (b - a)(\Sigma ab)$

and $T_3 - T_2 = c^2(a + b) - b^2(c + a) = (c - b)(\Sigma ab)$

∴ $b - a = c - b$ or $2b = a + c$, which is true.

(iv) Multiply by abc and it reduces to part (iii).

(v) $\dfrac{1}{\sqrt{(c)} + \sqrt{(a)}} - \dfrac{1}{\sqrt{(b)} + \sqrt{(c)}} = \dfrac{1}{\sqrt{(a)} + \sqrt{(b)}}$

$- \dfrac{1}{\sqrt{(c)} + \sqrt{(a)}}$

or $\dfrac{\sqrt{b} - \sqrt{a}}{\sqrt{(b)} + \sqrt{(c)}} = \dfrac{\sqrt{c} - \sqrt{b}}{\sqrt{(a)} + \sqrt{(b)}}$

or $b-a=c-b$ or $2b=a+c$ True.

(b) Put $b=\dfrac{a+c}{2}$ in R.H.S.

43. (i) $\dfrac{1}{c+a}-\dfrac{1}{b+c}=\dfrac{1}{a+b}-\dfrac{1}{c+a}$ or $\dfrac{b-a}{b+c}=\dfrac{c-b}{a+b}$

or $b^2-a^2=c^2-b^2$ or $2b^2=a^2+c^2$ True.

(ii) Add 1 to each and divide by $a+b+c$ and it reduces to part (a).

44. Add 2 to each and divide by $a+b+c$.

45. $\dfrac{1}{c-a}-\dfrac{1}{b-c}=\dfrac{1}{a-b}-\dfrac{1}{c-a}$ $\quad\dfrac{(a+b-2c)}{b-c}=\dfrac{(c+b-2a)}{a-b}$

or $(a-b)(a+b-2c)=(b-c)(b+c-2a)$ ...(1)

Above is true by given condition as shown below by (2).

We are given that

$(c-a)^2-(b-c)^2=(a-b)^2-(c-a)^2$

or $(c-a+b-c)(c-a-b+c)$
$\qquad =(a-b+c-a)(a-b-c+a)$

or $(b-a)(2c-a-b)=(c-b)(2a-b-c)$

or $(b-c)(b+c-2a)=(a-b)(a+b-2c)$ ...(2)

46. $T_1=\dfrac{1}{\sqrt{a_1}+\sqrt{a_2}}=\dfrac{\sqrt{a_1}-\sqrt{a_2}}{-d}$.

$\therefore\ S_n=\Sigma\,T_1=-\dfrac{1}{d}[\sqrt{a_1}-\sqrt{a_n}]$

$\because$ The terms will cancel diagonally

$\therefore\ S_n=-\dfrac{1}{d}\dfrac{a_1-a_n}{\sqrt{a_1}+\sqrt{a_n}}$

$\qquad =-\dfrac{1}{d}\left[\dfrac{-(n-1)d}{\sqrt{a_1}+\sqrt{a_n}}\right]=\dfrac{n-1}{\sqrt{a_1}+\sqrt{a_n}}$

47. (a) Ans. (iii) Since the three terms are in A.P.

$\therefore\ 2\log_{10}(2^x-1)=\log_{10}2+\log_{10}(2^x+3)$

or $(2^x-1)^2=2(2^x+3)$

or $(y-1)^2=2(y+3)$ where $y=2^x$

or $y^2-4y-5=0$

$\therefore\ (y-5)(y+1)=0$ or $y=5$,

$\because\ 2^x=y\neq-1$. Exponential f^n is not $-$ive

or $2^x=5$ $\therefore\ x=\log_2 5$.

(b) Since $5^{1+x}+5^{1-x}$, $a/2$, 25^x+25^{-x} are in A.P., we have

$2a/2=5^{1+x}+5^{1-x}+25^x+25^{-x}$,

Now put $5^x=t$ so that $t>0$, we then have

$a=5t+5/t+t^2+1/t^2=+$ive ...(1)

$\qquad =(t^2+1/t^2)+5(t+1/t)\geq 2+5.2=12$

because A.M.$\geq$G.M.

Also when $a\geq 12$ then (1) becomes

$a=\left(t+\dfrac{1}{t}\right)^2-2+5\left(t+\dfrac{1}{t}\right)$

or $y^2+5y-(a+2)=0$

where $y=t+\dfrac{1}{t}\geq 2$ as A.M.$\geq$G.M.

$\therefore\quad y=\dfrac{-5\pm\sqrt{25+4a+8}}{2}$

$y=\dfrac{-5\pm\sqrt{33+4a}}{2}\geq\dfrac{-5\pm\sqrt{33+48}}{2}$

$\qquad =\dfrac{-5\pm 9}{2}=\dfrac{9-5}{2}=2$ $\therefore\ y\geq 2$

$\therefore\quad y=t+\dfrac{1}{t}=5^x+5^{-x}\geq 2$

which we know is true and will give a solution for x.

(c) Condition for A.P., i.e., $2b=a+c$

$\Rightarrow\ 2\log_9 4=\log_3(2^{1-x}+3)+\log_{27}(2^x-1)^3$

Make base 3.

$\dfrac{2}{2}\log 4=\log(2^{1-x}+3)+\dfrac{3}{3}\log(2^x-1)$

$\therefore\ 4=\left(\dfrac{2}{y}+3\right)(y-1)$ where $y=2^x$

$\therefore\ 4y=(3y+2)(y-1)$ or $3y^2-5y-2=0$

$\therefore\ y=2,-1/3=2^x$

Since exponential function cannot be $-$ive

$\therefore\ 2^x=-1/3$ is rejected.

$\therefore\ 2^x=2\Rightarrow x=1$.

48. (a) Let $x^{18}=y^{21}=z^{28}=k$, say then on taking log we get

$18\log x=21\log y=28\log z=\log k$ ...(1)

If the given terms are a,b,c,d then

$a=3$, $b=3\log_y x=3\left(\dfrac{\log x}{\log y}\right)=3\cdot\dfrac{21}{18}$

$\qquad =\dfrac{21}{6}=\dfrac{7}{2}=3\dfrac{1}{2}$

Similarly, $c=3\cdot\dfrac{28}{21}=4$ and $d=7\cdot\dfrac{18}{28}=\dfrac{9}{2}=4\dfrac{1}{2}$.

Hence the four numbers are $3,3\dfrac{1}{2},4,4\dfrac{1}{2}$ which are clearly in A.P. of common difference $\dfrac{1}{2}$.

(b) $3,\dfrac{3\log x}{\log y},3\dfrac{\log y}{\log z},7\dfrac{\log z}{\log x}$ are in A.P.

where common difference is say d

Let $\log x=p,\log y=q,\log z=r$ then

$\dfrac{3p}{q}=T_2=3+d$, $\dfrac{3q}{r}=T_3=3+2d$, $\dfrac{7r}{p}=T_4=3+3d$

Multiplying the above relation, we get

$$3\frac{3p}{q}\cdot\frac{3q}{r}\cdot\frac{7r}{p}=3\,(3+d)\,(3+2d)\,(3+3d)$$

or $\quad 21=(3+d)(3+2d)(1+d)$

or $\quad 21=(9+9d+2d^2)(1+d)$

or $\quad 21=(9+18d+11d^2+2d^3)$

or $\quad 2d^3+11d^2+18d-12=0$

Clearly $d=\dfrac{1}{2}$ satisfies above as

$$\frac{1}{4}+\frac{11}{4}+9-12=3-3=0$$

$\therefore\quad (2d-1)(d^2+6d+12)=0$ by division

Δ for quadratic factor is $-$ive and hence it gives imaginary values of d. Hence we choose $d=1/2$

$\therefore\quad \dfrac{3p}{q}=3+\dfrac{1}{2}=\dfrac{7}{2}\quad$ or $\quad\dfrac{p}{q}=\dfrac{7}{6}$

Similarly $\dfrac{3q}{r}=3+1\quad$ or $\quad\dfrac{q}{4}=\dfrac{r}{3}\quad$ and $\quad\dfrac{r}{p}=\dfrac{9}{14}$

$\therefore\quad \dfrac{p}{14}=\dfrac{q}{12},\dfrac{q}{12}=\dfrac{r}{9},\dfrac{r}{9}=\dfrac{p}{14}$

$\therefore\quad \dfrac{p}{14}=\dfrac{q}{12}=\dfrac{r}{9}\qquad\qquad\ldots(1)$

or L.C.M. of 14, 12, 9 is 14×18.

Multiplying by 14×18, we get

$\quad 18\,p=21\,q=28\,r$

or $\quad 18\log x=21\log y=28\log r$

or $\quad \log x^{18}=\log y^{21}=\log r^{28}$

or $\quad x^{18}=y^{21}=r^{28}$

(c) Since the numbers are in A.P.

$\therefore\quad 28=3^{2\sin 2\theta-1}+3^{4-2\sin 2\theta}$

or $\quad 28=\dfrac{9^{\sin 2\theta}}{3}+\dfrac{81}{9^{\sin 2\theta}}$

or $\quad 28=\dfrac{x}{3}+\dfrac{81}{x}\quad$ where $x=9^{\sin 2\theta}$

or $\quad x^2-84x+243=0$

or $\quad (x-81)(x-3)=0\quad\therefore\quad x=81\text{ or }3.$

$\therefore\quad x=9^{\sin 2\theta}=81,3\text{ or }9^2,9^{1/2}$

$\therefore\quad \sin 2\theta=2\quad$ or $\quad 1/2$

since $\sin 2\theta$ cannot be greater than 1 so we choose $\sin 2\theta=\dfrac{1}{2}$

Hence the terms in A.P. are

$\quad 3^0,\,14,\,27\quad i.e.\quad 1,\,14,\,27.$

$\therefore\quad T_5=a+4d=1+4.13=53$

(d) $\quad 2b=a+c\qquad\qquad\ldots(1)$

and $2\tan^{-1}b=\tan^{-1}a+\tan^{-1}c$

or $\quad \dfrac{2b}{1-b^2}=\dfrac{a+c}{1-ac}\qquad$ Put $2b=a+c$

$\Rightarrow\quad b^2=ac$ by (1) $i.e.\,a,b,c$ are in G.P.

Also $\quad\Rightarrow\quad 4b^2=4ac$

or $\quad (a+c)^2-4ac=0$, by (1)

$\quad (a-c)^2=0\quad\therefore\quad a=c=b$, by (1)

49. (a) Let p,q,r be the lth, mth and nth terms of an A.P., then $p=a+(l-1)\,d$, $q=a+(m-1)\,d$ and $r=a+(n-1)\,d$

whence $r-q=(n-m)\,d$

and $q-p=(m-l)\,d$

so that $\quad\dfrac{r-q}{q-p}=\dfrac{(n-m)\,d}{(m-l)\,d}=\dfrac{n-m}{m-l}\qquad(\because d\neq 0)$

Since l,m,n are $+$ive integers and $m\neq l$, $(n-m)/(m-l)$ is a rational number.

(b) $T_p=\sqrt{2}$, $T_q=\sqrt{3}$, $T_r=\sqrt{5}$

$\therefore\quad \sqrt{3}-\sqrt{2}=T_q-T_p=(q-p)\,d,$

$\quad \sqrt{5}-\sqrt{3}=(r-p)\,d$

$\therefore\quad \dfrac{\sqrt{3}-\sqrt{2}}{\sqrt{(5)}-\sqrt{(3)}}=\dfrac{q-p}{r-p}=k\,,\text{say}.\qquad\ldots(1)$

As p,q,r are $+$ive integers so k is a rational number in (1).

Squaring (1), we get $5-2\sqrt{6}=k^2\,(8-2\sqrt{15})$

or $\quad \sqrt{15}\,k^2-\sqrt{6}=(8k^2-5)/2=s\text{ say}\qquad\ldots(2)$

Here s is again a rational number. Squaring again

$\therefore\quad 15k^4+6-2\sqrt{90}\,k^2=s^2$

or $\quad 15k^4+6-s^2=6\sqrt{10}\,k^2$

or $\quad (15k^4-s^2+6)/6k^2=\sqrt{10}\qquad\ldots(3)$

L.H.S. of (3) is rational whereas R.H.S. $\sqrt{10}$ is irrational which is not possible. Hence $\sqrt{2},\sqrt{3},\sqrt{5}$ cannot be three terms of an A.P.

50. (a) If d be the common difference of A.P., then $\log_y x=1+d, \log_z y=1+2d, -15\log_x z=1+3d.$

$\therefore\quad x=y^{1+d}\,,\,y=z^{1+2d}\,,\,z=x^{-\frac{1+3d}{15}}$

Eliminating y and z, we get

$\quad x=z^{(1+d)(1+2d)}=x^{-\frac{(1+3d)(1+d)(1+2d)}{15}}$

$\therefore\quad (1+d)\,(1+2d)\,(1+3d)=-15$

or $\quad 6d^3+11d^2+6d+16=0$

$\quad (d+2)\,(6d^2-d+8)=0\quad\therefore\quad d=-2$

The other factor gives imaginary values of d.

$\therefore\quad x=y^{-1}\,,\,y=z^{-3}\,,\,z=x^{1/3}.$

or $\quad x=y^{-1}=z^3\,,\,y=z^{-3}$

(b) Let the A.P. $a,a+d,a+2d\ldots$ be of prime numbers only. If it be possible then we will establish that each term of this series is a prime number only and not composite.

Consider T_{a+1} (**Note**) where a is first term which is prime

$$T_{a+1} = a + (a+1-1)d = a(1+d).$$

Above shows that a term namely T_{a+1} of this series is a composite number $a(1+d)$. Hence our assumption is wrong. Such a series therefore does not exist.

51. $T_1 + T_2 + T_3 + \ldots T_m = T_{m+1} + T_{m+2} + \ldots n$ terms

i.e., $S_m = $ Sum of next n terms

Add S_m to both sides

$\therefore \quad 2S_m = $ Sum of first $(m+n)$ terms

or $\quad 2S_m = S_{m+n}$ ...(1)

Similarly replacing n by p

$$2S_m = S_{m+p} \qquad \ldots(2)$$

Also from the result to be proved on little simplification, we have to prove

$$\frac{m+n}{m-n} = \frac{m+p}{m-p} \cdot \frac{p}{n} \qquad \ldots(3)$$

Now from (1) on using the formula for S,

$$2 \cdot \frac{m}{2}[2a + (m-1)d] = \frac{m+n}{2}[2a + (m+n-1)d]$$

or $\quad \dfrac{2m}{m+n} = \dfrac{2a + (m+n-1)d}{2a + (m-1)d}$ ...(4)

To get the desired form (3), subtract 1 from both sides of (4)

$\therefore \quad \dfrac{m-n}{m+n} = \dfrac{nd}{2a + (m-1)d}$ ...(5)

Replace n by p in (5), we get

$$\frac{m-p}{m+p} = \frac{pd}{2a + (m-1)d} \qquad \ldots(6)$$

Now divide (5) and (6) thereby eliminating the unknown quantities a and d, we get the desired result (3).

52. (a) $a_1^2 - a_2^2 = (a_1 - a_2)(a_1 + a_2) = -d(a_1 + a_2)$

Similarly for each of k brackets formed out of $2k$ given terms.

$$\therefore \quad S = -dS_{2k} = -d \cdot \frac{2k}{2}[a_1 + a_{2k}]$$

$$= -dk\left[\frac{a_1^2 - a_{2k}^2}{a_1 - a_{2k}}\right] = -dk\frac{(a_1^2 - a_{2k}^2)}{a_1 - \{a_1 + (2k-1)d\}}$$

$$= \frac{k}{2k-1}(a_1^2 - a_{2k}^2).$$

(b) $S_n = \dfrac{n}{2}[a_1 + a_n] \geq n\sqrt{a_1 \cdot a_n} \qquad \because \quad$ A.M. $\geq$ G.M.

or $\quad S_n \geq n\sqrt{a_1[a_1 + (n-1)d]}$

$$= n\sqrt{a_1^2 + (n-1)da_1}$$

(c) $\dfrac{1}{a_1} + \dfrac{1}{a_n} = \dfrac{a_n + a_1}{a_1 \cdot a_n}$

$$\frac{1}{a_2} + \frac{1}{a_{n-1}} = \frac{a_{n-1} + a_2}{a_2 \cdot a_{n-1}} = \frac{a_n - d + a_1 + d}{a_2 \cdot a_{n-1}}$$

$$= \frac{a_n + a_1}{a_2 \cdot a_{n-1}}$$

$$\ldots\ldots\ldots\ldots\ldots\ldots\ldots\ldots\ldots\ldots\ldots$$
$$\ldots\ldots\ldots\ldots\ldots\ldots\ldots\ldots\ldots\ldots\ldots$$

$$\frac{1}{a_n} + \frac{1}{a_1} = \frac{a_1 + a_n}{a_n \cdot a_1} = \frac{a_1 + a_n}{a_n \cdot a_1}$$

Adding, $2\left(\dfrac{1}{a_1} + \dfrac{1}{a_2} + \ldots \dfrac{1}{a_n}\right)$

$$= (a_n + a_1)\left[\frac{1}{a_1 \cdot a_n} + \frac{1}{a_2 \cdot a_{n-1}} + \ldots + \frac{1}{a_n \cdot a_1}\right]$$

or $\quad \dfrac{2}{a_n + a_1}\left(\dfrac{1}{a_1} + \dfrac{1}{a_2} + \ldots \dfrac{1}{a_n}\right)$

$$= \left[\frac{1}{a_1 \cdot a_n} + \frac{1}{a_2 \cdot a_{n-1}} + \ldots + \frac{1}{a_n \cdot a_1}\right]$$

(d) $\dfrac{1}{a_1} - \dfrac{1}{a_2} = \dfrac{a_2 - a_1}{a_1 a_2} = \dfrac{d}{a_1 a_2}$

$$\therefore \quad d \sum \frac{1}{a_1 a_2} = \sum\left(\frac{1}{a_1} - \frac{1}{a_2}\right)$$

The terms will cancel diagonally

$$= \frac{1}{a_1} - \frac{1}{a_n} = \frac{a_n - a_1}{a_1 a_n}$$

$$d \sum \frac{1}{a_1 a_2} = \frac{(n-1)d}{a_1 a_n}$$

$$\therefore \quad \sum \frac{1}{a_1 a_2} = \frac{n-1}{a_1 a_n}$$

53. $d = a_2 - a_1 = a_3 - a_2 \ldots = a_n - a_{n-1} = a_{n+1} - a_n$

$\therefore \quad T_1 = \tan^{-1} a_2 - \tan^{-1} a_1$

$\quad T_2 = \tan^{-1} a_3 - \tan^{-1} a_2$

$$\ldots\ldots\ldots\ldots\ldots\ldots\ldots\ldots\ldots\ldots\ldots$$

$T_{n+1} = \tan^{-1} a_{n+1} - \tan^{-1} a_n$

$\therefore \quad S_n = \tan^{-1} a_{n+1} - \tan^{-1} a_1$

$$= \tan^{-1}\frac{a_{n+1} - a_1}{1 + a_1 a_{n+1}} = \tan^{-1}\frac{nd}{1 + a_1 a_{n+1}}$$

54. (a) $\alpha_2 - \alpha_1 = \alpha_3 - \alpha_2 = \alpha_4 - \alpha_3 \ldots = d.$

$$T_1 = \frac{1}{\cos \alpha_1 \cos \alpha_2} = \frac{\sin(\alpha_2 - \alpha_1)}{\cos \alpha_1 \cos \alpha_2} \cdot \frac{1}{\sin d}$$

or $\quad T_1 = \dfrac{1}{\sin d}\left[\dfrac{\sin \alpha_2 \cos \alpha_1 - \cos \alpha_2 \sin \alpha_1}{\cos \alpha_1 \cos \alpha_2}\right]$

$$T_1 = \frac{1}{\sin d}[\tan \alpha_2 - \tan \alpha_1]$$

$$T_2 = \frac{1}{\sin d}[\tan \alpha_3 - \tan \alpha_2]$$

$$\ldots\ldots\ldots\ldots\ldots\ldots\ldots\ldots\ldots\ldots\ldots$$

$$T_n = \frac{1}{\sin d}[\tan\alpha_{n+1} - \tan\alpha_n]$$

$$\therefore\quad S_n = \frac{1}{\sin d}[\tan\alpha_{n+1} - \tan\alpha_1]$$

(b) Proceed exactly as in (a).

55. Let d be the common difference of the given A.P. Then since $a_1 = 0$, we have $a_2 = d$,
$a_3 = 2d, \ldots a_n = (n-1)d$.

Hence L.H.S. $= \dfrac{2d}{d} + \dfrac{3d}{2d} + \dfrac{4d}{3d} + \ldots + \dfrac{(n-1)d}{(n-2)d}$

$$-d\left(\frac{1}{d} + \frac{1}{2d} + \frac{1}{3d} + \ldots + \frac{1}{(n-3)d}\right)$$

$$= (1+1) + \left(1+\frac{1}{2}\right) + \left(1+\frac{1}{3}\right) + \ldots + \left(1+\frac{1}{n-3}\right)$$

$$+ \left(1 + \frac{1}{n-2}\right) - \left(1 + \frac{1}{2} + \frac{1}{3} + \ldots + \frac{1}{n-3}\right)$$

$$= 1 + 1 + 1 + \ldots \text{to } (n-2) \text{ terms} + \frac{1}{n-2}$$

$$= (n-2) + \frac{1}{n-2} = \frac{a_{n-1}}{a_2} + \frac{a_2}{a_{n-1}}.$$

56. Squaring the given relations, we get
$$a_1^2 = 0$$
$$a_2^2 = a_1^2 + 2a_1 + 1$$
$$a_3^2 = a_2^2 + 2a_2 + 1$$
$$\ldots\quad \ldots\quad \ldots$$
$$a_n^2 = a_{n-1}^2 + 2a_{n-1} + 1$$

and $a_{n+1}^2 = a_n^2 + 2a_n + 1$. This last relation we have

written of our own to get the desired result of $\frac{1}{n}\Sigma\, a_n$.

Adding them columnswise and cancelling, we get
$$a_{n+1}^2 = 2\Sigma a_n + n.$$

$$\therefore\quad 2\Sigma a_n = a_{n+1}^2 - n \geq -n$$

$$\therefore\quad \Sigma\frac{a_n}{n} \geq -\frac{1}{2} \quad \text{or} \quad \text{A.M.} \geq -\frac{1}{2}$$

57. It is easy to observe that both the series consist of 102 terms. Let
$T_p = 3 + 4(p-1) = 4p-1$ and $T_q = 2 + 7(q-1) = 7q-5$
be the general terms of the two series where both p and q lie between 1 and 102. We have to find the values of p and q for which $T_p = T_q$
i.e., $4p-1 = 7q-5$ or $4(p+1) = 7q$ ...(1)
Now p and q are +ive integers and hence from (1) we conclude that q is multiple of 4 and so let $q = 4s$ and as q lies between 1 and 102, therefore s lies between 1 and 25.

$$\therefore\quad \frac{p+1}{7} = \frac{q}{4} = \lambda$$

$$p+1 = 7\lambda \quad \text{and} \quad q = 4\lambda$$

both p and q vary from 1 to 102

$\therefore$ λ varies from 1 to 14 or from 1 to 25
Hence we choose λ to vary from 1 to 14.
Thus there are only 14 common terms.
$$T_p = 4p-1 = 4(7\lambda - 1) - 1 = 28\lambda - 5$$
Put $\lambda = 1,2,3,\ldots,14$ and common terms are $23, 51, 79, \ldots$

58. Let $T_p = T_q \Rightarrow 3p-1 = 2q+1$.
Subtract 5 from both sides
$$\therefore\quad 3(p-2) = 2(q-2)$$
or $\dfrac{p-2}{2} = \dfrac{q-2}{3} = k$, say.
$$\therefore\quad p = 2k+2 \quad \text{and} \quad q = 3k+2$$
Now p varies from 1 to 60 and q varies from 1 to 50. Hence we have the following
$1 \leq 2k+2 \leq 60$ and $1 \leq 3k+2 \leq 50$.
$$\therefore\quad -\frac{1}{2} \leq k \leq 29 \quad \text{and} \quad -\frac{1}{3} \leq k \leq 16.$$
Clearly $k = 0,1,2,3,\ldots,16$ for common values and hence there will be 17 common terms.

59. Denoting the nth and mth terms of the two progressions by T_n and T_m', we have
$$T_n = 17 + (n-1).4 = 4n+13$$
and $T_m' = 16 + (m-1).5 = 5m+11$.
For common terms, we must have
$$T_n = T_m' \Rightarrow 4n+13 = 5m+11$$
$$\Rightarrow 5m = 2(2n+1).$$
This shows that $2n+1 = 5k$, $k = 1,3,5,\ldots$
Hence the common terms are given by
$T_{2k}' = 5.2k + 11 = 10k+11$, $k = 1,3,5,\ldots$
$\therefore$ Sum of first 100 common terms
$$= 21 + 41 + 61 + \ldots \text{to 100 terms}$$
$$= \frac{100}{2}[2\times 21 + (100-1).20] = 101100.$$

60. We have $2\log b = \log a + \log c$
or $b^2 = ac$ ...(1)
and $2[\log 2b - \log 3c] = \log 3c - \log 2b$
or $3(\log 2b - \log 3c) = 0$ $\therefore$ $2b = 3c$ ...(2)
Solving (1) and (2) for a and b, we get $a = 9c/4$, $b = 3c/2$.
Thus the triple of numbers that satisfies the given conditions is $9c/4, 3c/2, c$ $(c \neq 0)$. Now $a = 9c/4, b = 3c/2$ and c will form a triangle if
(i) $a+b > c$ (ii) $b+c > a$ and (iii) $c+a > b$.
But since $a+b = 15c/4 > c$,
$b+c = 5c/2 > 9c/4 = a$,
and $a+c = 13c/4 > 3c/2 = b$ $(c > 0)$: a triangle with sides a, b and c exists and since $a^2 > b^2 + c^2$, it is obtuse. To find the angles, we use the cosine formula.
Thus $\cos A = \dfrac{b^2 + c^2 - a^2}{2bc} = -\dfrac{29}{48}$,
$$\cos B = \frac{a^2 + c^2 - b^2}{2ac} = \frac{61}{72}$$

and $\cos C = \dfrac{a^2 + b^2 - c^2}{2ab} = \dfrac{101}{108}$.

Thus, bearing in mind that A, B, C are the angles of a triangle, we get

$$A = \cos^{-1}\left(-\frac{29}{48}\right) = \pi - \cos^{-1}\frac{29}{48}.$$

$$B = \cos^{-1}\left(\frac{61}{72}\right) \quad \text{and} \quad C = \cos^{-1}\left(\frac{101}{108}\right).$$

§2. Geometrical Progression.

Definition. A series in which each term is same multiple of the preceeding term is called a geomertrical progression. In other words, a series in which the ratio of successive terms is constant is called a G.P. This constant ratio is called **common ratio** and is denoted by r. *e.g.*

(i) 1, 4, 16, ... (ii) 9, 6, 4,...

(iii) $a, ar, ar^2,...$

All the above series are geometrical progressions in which common ratios are $4, \dfrac{2}{3}$ and r respectively.

nth term of a G.P.

Let the series be $a, ar, ar^2, ar^3, ...$

$$T_1 = a = ar^{1-1}, \quad T_2 = ar = ar^{2-1},$$

$$T_3 = ar^2 = ar^{3-1}, ...$$

$$\therefore \quad T_n = ar^{n-1}. \qquad ...(1)$$

Sum of n terms of a G.P.

Let $S = a + ar + ar^2 + ... + ar^{n-1}$

$\therefore r.S = [\quad ar + ar^2 + ... + ar^{n-1}] + ar^n.$

Subtracting, we get

$$S(1 - r) = a - ar^n$$

$$\therefore \qquad S = \frac{a(1 - r^n)}{1 - r} \qquad ...(2)$$

Sum of an infinite number of terms of a G.P. when $|r| < 1$.

Since $|r| < 1$ and the number of terms is infinite,

$\therefore \displaystyle\lim_{n \to \infty} r^n = 0$ and hence in this case

$$S_\infty = \frac{a}{1 - r}, \quad \text{from (2)}. \qquad ...(3)$$

Common ratio $= \dfrac{T_n}{T_{n-1}}$

i.e. divide any term by the term which precedes it.

Single geometric mean between a and b.

Let x be the single geometric mean between two given quantities a and b, then a, x, b are in G.P.

$\therefore \quad \dfrac{x}{a} = \dfrac{b}{x} = $ common ratio of the G.P.

$\therefore \quad x^2 = ab \quad \text{or} \quad x = \sqrt{ab} \qquad ...(4)$

n geometric means between two quantities a and b.

Let $x_1, x_2, ... x_n$ be n geometric means between a and b, then $a, x_1, x_2, ... x_n, b$ will be a G.P. of $(n + 2)$ terms, whose last term is b and first term is a.

$\therefore \quad b = T_{n+2} = ar^{n+1}, \quad \therefore \quad r = (b/a)^{1/(n+1)}$

$\therefore \quad x_1 = T_2 = ar,$

$x_2 = T_3 = ar^2 \; ..... \; x_n = T_{n+1} = ar^n$

On putting the value of r, we shall find the n geometric means.

*Product of n geometric means $= G^n$

$a, x_1, x_2, ... x_n, b$ is a G.P. of $n + 2$ terms.

$\therefore \quad b = T_{n+2} = ar^{n+1} \quad \text{or} \quad r = \left(\dfrac{b}{a}\right)^{1/n+1} \qquad ...(1)$

Now product of n means $= x_1 x_2 ..... x_n$

$= (ar)(ar^2)(ar^3)....(ar^n)$

$= a^n r^{1+2+3+......n} = a^n r^{n(n+1)/2}$

$= a^n \left(\dfrac{b}{a}\right)^{n/2}$ by (1) $= a^{n/2} b^{n/2} = (ab)^{n/2} = (\sqrt{ab})^n = G^n$

where G is single G.M. of a and b.

▶ **Important Notes.**

1. (a) If each term of a geometric progression **be multiplied** or **divided by the same non-zero quantity**, then the resulting series is also a G.P.

   (b) In a G.P. the product of terms equidistant from the beginning and end is constant and equal to the product of the first and last terms.

2. * Odd number of terms in G.P. must be taken as

   $......, ar^3, ar^2, ar, a, \dfrac{a}{r}, \dfrac{a}{r^2}, \dfrac{a}{r^3}, ...$

   *An even number of terms in a G.P. must be taken as

   $...., ar^5, ar^3, ar, \dfrac{a}{r}, \dfrac{a}{r^3}, \dfrac{a}{r^5}, ...$

   In particular three terms as $ar, a, \dfrac{a}{r}$ and four terms

   as $ar^3, ar, \dfrac{a}{r}, \dfrac{a}{r^3}$.

3. If $a_1, a_2, a_3, ...$ and $b_1, b_2, b_3, ...$ be two G.P.'s of common ratio r_1 and r_2 respectively, then $a_1 b_1, a_2 b_2, a_3 b_3, ...$ and $\dfrac{a_1}{b_1}, \dfrac{a_2}{b_2}, \dfrac{a_3}{b_3}, ...$ will also form G.P. whose common ratio will be $r_1 r_2$ and $\dfrac{r_1}{r_2}$ respectively.

4. If $a_1, a_2, a_3, ...$ be a G.P. of +ive terms, then $\log a_1, \log a_2, \log a_3, ...$ will be an A.P. and conversely. (Important)

5. **Increasing and decreasing G.P.**

   Case I. Let the first term a be +ive. Then if $r > 1$, then it is an increasing G.P. but if r is +ive and less than 1 *i.e.* $0 < r < 1$ then it is a decreasing G.P.

   Case II. Let the first term a be $-$ive, then if $r > 1$, then it is a decreasing G.P. but if $0 < r < 1$, then it is an increasing G.P.

Problem Set (2)

Geometrical Progression, nth term, and S and S_∞ and Geometric means.

1. (a) The fifth term of a G.P. is 81 whereas its second term is 24. Find the series and sum of its first eight terms.

   (b) The sum of first three terms of a G.P. is to the sum of the first six terms as 125 : 152. Find the common ratio of the G.P.

   (c) In a G.P. if $T_{p-1} + T_{p+1} = 3T_p$ then prove that the common ratio of G.P. is an irrational number.

2. Sum the series

   (a) $(a+b) + (a^2 + 2b) + (a^3 + 3b) + \ldots$ to n terms.

   (b) $\left(x + \dfrac{1}{x}\right)^2 + \left(x^2 + \dfrac{1}{x^2}\right)^2 + \left(x^3 + \dfrac{1}{x^3}\right)^2$
   $$+ \ldots \left(x^n + \dfrac{1}{x^n}\right)^2.$$

3. (a)* $1 + (1+x) + (1+x+x^2) + (1+x+x^2+x^3)$
   $$+ \ldots \text{ to } n \text{ terms.}$$

   (b) If $1 + x + x^2 + \ldots x^p$
   $$= (1+x)(1+x^2)(1+x^4)(1+x^8),$$
   then find the value of p.

4. (a) $x(x+y) + x^2(x^2+y^2) + x^3(x^3+y^3)$
   $$+ \ldots \text{to } n \text{ terms.}$$

   (b) $(x+y) + (x^2 + xy + y^2) + (x^3 + x^2y + xy^2 + y^3)$
   $$+ \ldots n \text{ terms}$$

5. (a)* If $x = 1 + a + a^2 + a^3 + \ldots$ to ∞ $(|a| < 1)$ and
   $y = 1 + b + b^2 + b^3 + \ldots$ to ∞ $(|b| < 1)$ prove that
   $$1 + ab + a^2 b^2 + a^3 b^3 + \ldots \text{ to } \infty = \dfrac{xy}{x+y-1}$$

   (b) If $x = \sum\limits_{n=0}^{\infty} a^n, y = \sum\limits_{n=0}^{\infty} b^n, z = \sum\limits_{n=0}^{\infty} (ab)^n$,
   where $a, b < 1$, then prove that $xz + yz = xy + z$.

   Another form :

   For $0 < \theta, \phi < \dfrac{\pi}{2}$ if $x = \sum\limits_{n=0}^{\infty} \cos^{2n} \theta$

   $y = \sum\limits_{n=0}^{\infty} \sin^{2n} \phi, z = \sum\limits_{n=0}^{\infty} \cos^{2n} \theta \sin^{2n} \phi$ then prove that
   $xz + yz - z = xy$.

   (c) If x is the first term of a G.P. with infinite number of terms and $S_\infty = 5$, then x is

   (a) $0 < x < 10$ (b) $x \geq 10$

   (c) $x < -10$ (d) $-10 < x < 0$

   (IIT-Screening 2004)

   (d) If $3^x + 3^{x-1} + 3^{x-2} + \ldots + 3^{x-100}$
   $$= 5^x + 5^{x-1} + 5^{x-2} + \ldots + 5^{x-100} \text{ then prove that}$$
   $$(x-100) \log \dfrac{5}{3} = \log 2(3^{101} - 1) - \log(5^{101} - 1)$$

6. (a)* $1 + \dfrac{\sqrt{2}-1}{2\sqrt{3}} + \dfrac{3-2\sqrt{2}}{12} + \dfrac{5\sqrt{2}-7}{24\sqrt{3}} + \dfrac{17-12\sqrt{2}}{144} + \ldots \infty$

   (b)* $1 + \dfrac{\sqrt{2}-1}{2\sqrt{2}} + \dfrac{3-2\sqrt{2}}{12} + \dfrac{5\sqrt{2}-7}{24\sqrt{2}} + \dfrac{17-12\sqrt{2}}{80} + \ldots \infty$

   (Roorkee 1991)

7. (a) If $S = 1 + 2 + 4 + 8 + 16 + 32 + \ldots \infty$.
   then S is a $+$ive number. Multiply both sides by 2, then it is found that $2S = S - 1$ which leads to conclusion $S = -1$ which is certainly negative. Do you agree with the conclusion ? Your answer should be supported by explanation.

   (b)* The value of the sum $\sum\limits_{n=1}^{13} (i^n + i^{n+1})$, where $i = \sqrt{-1}$, equals

   (a) i (b) $i - 1$

   (c) $-i$ (d) 0 **(I.I.T. 1998)**

8. (a) If S denotes the sum to infinity and S_n the sum of n terms of the series $1 + \dfrac{1}{2} + \dfrac{1}{4} + \dfrac{1}{8} + \ldots$, such that
   $S - S_n < \dfrac{1}{1000}$, then show that the least value of n is 11.

   (b) Find the sum of the following infinite series :
   $$\sum\limits_{n=0}^{\infty} \dfrac{1}{n!} \left[\sum\limits_{k=0}^{n} (k+1) \int_0^1 2^{-(k+1)x} \, dx \right]$$

   (Roorkee 1999)

9. (a) The first term of an infinite G.P. is 1 and any term is equal to the sum of all the succeeding terms. Find the series.

   (b) Show that the sum of n terms of a G.P. of common ratio r beginning with the pth term is r^{p-q} times the sum of an equal number of terms of the same series beginning with q^{th} term.

   (c) If the common ratio of an infinite G.P. be less than $\dfrac{1}{2}$, show that each term will be greater than the sum of all the terms that follow it.

10. (a) The sum of first two terms of an infinite G.P. is 5 and each term is three times the sum of succeeding terms. Find the series.

   (b) If T_1, T_2, T_7 of an A.P. constitute a G.P. whose sum is 93, then find the numbers.

(c) If T_1, T_2, T_8 of a certain G.P. be x^{-4}, x^k and x^{52} respectively, then prove that $k = 4$.

(d) Consider an infinite geometric series with first term a and common ratio r. If its sum is 4 and the second term is $\frac{3}{4}$, then

(a) $a = \frac{7}{4}, r = \frac{3}{7}$ (b) $a = 2, r = \frac{3}{8}$

(c) $a = \frac{3}{2}, r = \frac{1}{2}$ (d) $a = 3, r = \frac{1}{4}$

(I.I.T. Sc. 2000)

11. (a) Sum of a certain number of terms of the series $\frac{2}{9}, -\frac{1}{3}, \frac{1}{2}, ...$ is $\frac{55}{72}$; Find the number.

(b) How many terms of the series 1, 4, 16, ... must be taken to have their sum equal to 341 ?

(c) In a G.P. sum of n terms is 255, the last term is 128 and the common ratio is 2. Find n.

12. (a)* In an increasing G.P., the sum of the first and the last term is 66, the product of the second and the last but one term is 128, and the sum of all the term is 126. How many terms are there in the progression ? **(M.N.R. 1993)**

(b) If $x, 2x + 2, 3x + 3, ...$ are in G.P., then the fourth term is $-13 \cdot 5$.

(c) Find four + ive numbers G_1, G_2, G_3, G_4 in G.P. which satisfy the following conditions :

(i) $G_2^2 + G_3^2 = 250$

(ii) $G_1 G_4 = \alpha$ where α is greater root of the equation $x^{2 + \log_{10} x} = (0 \cdot 001)^{-8/3}$

13. (a)* If the fourth, seventh and tenth terms of a G.P. are p, q, r respectively then $q^2 = pr$. **(M.N.R. 1995)**

(b) If α, β are the roots of the equation $x^2 - 4x + \lambda = 0$ and γ, δ are the roots of the equation $x^2 - 64x + \mu = 0$ and $\alpha, \beta, \gamma \delta$ are given to be in increasing G.P., find the values of λ and μ.

14. Sum upto n terms the series

(a) $\cdot 7 + \cdot 77 + \cdot 777 + ...$

(b) $6 + 66 + 666 + ...$

(c) $8 + 88 + 888 + ...$

15. (a)* Prove the equality :

$$\underbrace{(666.........6)^2}_{n \text{ digits}} + \underbrace{888........8}_{n \text{ digits}} = \underbrace{444..........4}_{2n \text{ digits}}$$

(b) $\dfrac{\sqrt{\underbrace{(11...1)}_{2n \text{ digits}} - \underbrace{(22...2)}_{n \text{ digits}}}}{} = \underbrace{333...3}_{n \text{ digits}}$

In this true or false ?

16. (a)* Determine whether the number $1111...1$ of 91 digits is prime or composite.

(b)* The numbers 49, 4489, 444889, ... obtained by inserting 48 into the middle of the preceding numbers are square of integers.

(a) True   (b) False.

17. (a) Express the recurring decimal $0 \cdot 125\,125\,125 ....$ as a rational number.

(b)* Prove that the rational number which equals to the number $2 \cdot \overline{357}$ with recurring decimal is $\frac{2355}{999}$.

18. (a) Find the value of $\cdot 1\dot{2}\dot{3}$ regarding it as a geometric series.

(b) Find the value of $\cdot 4\dot{2}\,\dot{3}$.

19. (a) A ball is dropped from a height of 48 ft. and rebounds two-thirds of the distance it falls. If it continues to fall and rebound in this way, how far will it travel before coming to rest ?

(b) After striking a floor a certain ball rebounds 4/5th of the height from which it has fallen. Find the total distance that it travels before coming to rest, if it is gently dropped from a height of 120 metres.

20. (a) The length of a side of a square is a metres. A second square is formed by joining the middle points of this square. Then a third square is formed by joining the middle points of the second square and so on. The process is carried on ad-infinitum. Find the sum of the areas of the squares.

(b) Doctor prescribed an old man to go regularly for a walk. He goes for some distance on first day but being old next day he goes half the distance. Similarly on each subsequent day he continues but goes only half the distances of previous day. Prove that the total distance moved by him can never exceed twice the distance moved by him on first day.

(c) One side of an equilateral triangle is 24 cm. The mid-points of its sides are joined to form another triangle. Again another triangle is formed by joining the mid-points of this triangle and the process is continued indefinitely. Determine the sum of the perimeters of all such triangles.

21. (a) In a G.P. if the $(m + n)$th term be p and $(m - n)$th term be q, then prove that its mth term is $\sqrt{pq}$.

(b)* In a G.P. if $T_l = l$ and $T_m = m$, then prove that its nth term is $\left[\dfrac{l^{n-m}}{m^{n-l}} \right]^{1/(l-m)}$

22. Find the sum of $2n$ terms of a series of which every even term is a times the term before it, and every odd term c times the term before it, the first term being unity.

23. (a)* The rth, sth and tth terms of a certain G.P. are R, S and T respectively. Prove that $R^{s-t} \cdot S^{t-r} \cdot T^{r-s} = 1$.

(b) If S be the sum, P the product and R the sum of the reciprocals of n terms of a G.P., prove that $(S/R)^n = P^2$.

Another form. $S = R(T_1 \cdot T_n)$

(c) If $A = 1 + r^a + r^{2a} + \ldots\ldots\ldots$ to ∞ and

$B = 1 + r^b + r^{2b} + \ldots\ldots\ldots$ to ∞ , prove that

$$r = \left(\frac{A-1}{A}\right)^{1/a} = \left(\frac{B-1}{B}\right)^{1/b}.$$

24. (a) If x, y, z be respectively the pth, qth and rth terms of a G.P., then prove that
$(q-r)\log x + (r-p)\log y + (p-q)\log z = 0$

(b) If the pth , qth , rth terms of an A.P. are in G.P. show that common ratio of the G.P. is $\dfrac{q-r}{p-q}$.

(c) If the pth, qth, rth and sth terms of an A.P. are in G.P. then $p-q, q-r, r-s$ are in G. P.

25.* If S_1, S_2, S_3 be respectively the sums of n, $2n$, $3n$ terms of a G.P. , then prove that

(a) $S_1(S_3 - S_2) = (S_2 - S_1)^2$

(b) $S_1^2 + S_2^2 = S_1(S_2 + S_3)$.

Another form :

If a, b, c be the respective sums of the first n terms, next n terms, and the next n terms of a G.P. then prove that a, b, c are in G.P.

(c) If the series $a_1, a_2, a_3, \ldots a_n$ be a G.P. of common ratio r, then prove that

$$\frac{1}{a_1^m + a_2^m} + \frac{1}{a_2^m + a_3^m} + \ldots + \frac{1}{a_{n-1}^m + a_n^m}$$

$$= \frac{1 - r^{m(1-n)}}{a_1^m(r^m - r^{-m})}$$

26. (a) If $S_1, S_2, \ldots\ldots S_n$ are the sums of infinite geometric series whose first terms are $1, 2, 3, \ldots\ldots n$ and common ratios are $\dfrac{1}{2}, \dfrac{1}{3}, \dfrac{1}{4}, \ldots, \dfrac{1}{n+1}$ respectively then prove that

$$S_1 + S_2 + S_3 + \ldots + S_n = \frac{1}{2}n(n+3).$$

(b)* If $S_1, S_2, S_3, \ldots S_n$ are the sums of infinite geometric series whose first terms are $1, 2, 3, \ldots, n$ and whose common ratios are $\dfrac{1}{2}, \dfrac{1}{3}, \dfrac{1}{4}, \ldots, \dfrac{1}{n+1}$ respectively, then find the value of

$$S_1^2 + S_2^2 + S_3^2 + \ldots + S_{2n-1}^2.$$ **(I.I.T. 1991)**

(c) If S_p denotes the sum of series $1 + r^p + r^{2p} + \ldots\ldots$ to ∞ and s_p the sum of the series $1 - r^p + r^{2p} - \ldots\ldots\ldots$ to ∞, prove that

If $S_n = 1 + R + R^2 + \ldots R^{n-1}$

and $s_n = 1 + r + r^2 + \ldots r^{n-1}$

and R, r are both + ive and $R > r$ then prove that

$$\frac{S_{n+1}}{S_n} > \frac{s_{n+1}}{s_n}$$

27. If S_n represents the sum of n terms of a G.P. whose first term and common ratio are a and r respectively, then prove that

(a) $S_1 + S_2 + S_3 + \ldots + S_n = \dfrac{na}{1-r} - \dfrac{ar(1 - r^n)}{(1-r)^2}$

(b) $S_1 + S_3 + S_5 + \ldots + S_{2n-1} = \dfrac{an}{1-r} - \dfrac{ar(1 - r^{2n})}{(1-r)^2(1+r)}$

In Q. 28 and 29 if a, b, c, d be in G.P., prove that

28. (a) $(a^2 + ac + c^2)(b^2 + bd + d^2) = (ab + bc + cd)^2$.

(b) $(a^2 + b^2 + c^2)(b^2 + c^2 + d^2) = (ab + bc + cd)^2$.

29. (a) $(a-d)^2 = (b-c)^2 + (c-a)^2 + (d-b)^2$

(b) $a^2 - b^2, b^2 - c^2, c^2 - d^2$ are in G. P.

30. (a) If $21(a^2 + b^2 + c^2) = (a + 2b + 4c)^2$ then a, b, c are in G.P.

Is this statement true ?

(b)* If $x_1, x_2, \ldots x_n$ are n non-zero real numbers such that

$$(x_1^2 + x_2^2 + x_3^2 + \ldots x_{n+1}^2)(x_2^2 + x_3^2 + x_4^2 + \ldots x_n^2)$$

$$\leq (x_1 x_2 + x_2 x_3 + \ldots x_{n-1} x_n)^2$$

then prove that $x_1, x_2, \ldots x_n$ are in G.P.

(c)* If a, b, c, d and p are distinct real numbers such that

$$(a^2 + b^2 + c^2) p^2 - 2 (ab + bc + cd) p$$

$$+ (b^2 + c^2 + d^2) \leq 0,$$

then a, b, c, d are in G.P.

31. (a) If a, b, c be in G.P., then prove that $\dfrac{a^2 + ab + b^2}{bc + ca + ab} = \dfrac{b+a}{c+b}$.

(b)* If $\log_t a, a^{t/2}, \log_b t$ be in G.P., then $t = \log_a(\log_b a) = \log_a(\log a) - \log_a(\log b)$

32. (a) If a, b, c are three distinct real numbers in G.P. and $a + b + c = xb$, then prove that either $x < -1$ or $x > 3$. **(J.E.E.W.B. 1992)**

(b) If a, b, c be three consecutive terms of a G.P. with common ratio r, which satisfies the inequality $c > 4b - 3a$ then prove that either $r < 1$ or $r > 3$.

33. (a)* Find three numbers in G.P. whose sum is 65 and whose product is 3375.

(b) The product of three numbers in G.P. is 125 and sum of their products taken in pairs is $87\dfrac{1}{2}$. Find them.

(c)* If the continued product of three numbers in G.P. is 216 and the sum of the products taken in pairs is 156, find the numbers.

34. (a) Three numbers are in G.P. whose sum is 70. If the extremes be each multiplied by 4 and the means by 5, they will be in A.P. Find the numbers.

(b) If a, b, c are in A.P. as well as in G.P. then prove that $a = b = c$.

35. (a) The sum of three numbers in G.P. is 14. If the first two terms are each increased by 1 and the third term decreased by 1, the resulting numbers are in A.P. Find the numbers.

(b) The sum of three numbers in G.P. is 42. If the first two numbers are increased by 2 and third is decreased by 4, the resulting numbers form an A.P. Find the numbers of G.P.   **(Roorkee 2001)**

36. (a) Three numbers whose sum is 15 are in A.P. If 1, 4, 19 be added to them respectively, then they are in G.P. Find the numbers.

(b)* In a set of four numbers the first three are in G.P. and the last three in A.P. with common difference 6. If the first number is the same as the fourth, find the four numbers.

37. (a)* Find four numbers in G.P. whose sum is 85 and product is 4096.

(b) Insert five geometric means between 486 and 2/3.

38. (a) If A and G be the A.M. and G.M. between two numbers, prove that the numbers are $A \pm \sqrt{(A + G)(A - G)}$.

(b) Construct a quadratic in x such that A.M. of its roots is A and G.M. is G.

39. (a)* If one G.M. G and two arithmetic means p and q be inserted between any two given numbers, then show that $G^2 = (2p - q)(2q - p)$.

(b)* If one A.M., A and two geometric means p and q be inserted between any two given numbers, then show that $p^3 + q^3 = 2Apq$.   **(I.I.T. 1997)**

(c)* The A.M. between m and n and the G.M. between a and b are each equal to $(ma + nb)/(m + n)$. Find m and n in terms of a and b.

40. (a)* If n geometric means be inserted between a and b, then prove that their product is $(ab)^{n/2}$.

(b)* For what value of n, $\dfrac{a^{n+1} + b^{n+1}}{a^n + b^n}$ is the geometric mean of a and b?

41. (a)* Does there exist a geometric progression containing 27, 8 and 12 as three of its terms? If it exists, how many such progressions are possible?

(b) Show that the numbers 10, 11, 12 cannot be the terms of a single G.P. with common ratio not equal to 1.

42. (a) The third term of a G.P. is 4. The product of first five terms is
  (i) 4^3 (ii) 4^5
  (iii) 4^4 (iv) None of these.

(b)* Given x^3, y^3, z^3 are in A.P. and $\log_x y$, $\log_z x$, $\log_y z$ are in G.P.

If $xyz = 64$, then prove that $x = y = z = 4$.

(c) If the equation $x^4 - 4x^3 + ax^2 + bx + 1 = 0$ has four positive roots then (a, b) is
  (a) $(-4, 6)$ (b) $(6, -4)$
  (c) $(-4, -6)$ (d) $(4, -6)$

43. (a) If $2x^4 = y^4 + z^4$, $xyz = 8$ and $\log_y x$, $\log_z y$, $\log_x z$ are in G.P., then find the values of x, y, z belonging to R.

(b) The first and second terms of both an A.P. and a G.P. are same x and y respectively where both x and y are +ive and x is greater than y. If S be the sum of infinite G.P., then prove that sum of first n terms of A.P. is given by $nx - \dfrac{n(n-1)x^2}{2S}$.

44. (a) A G.P. consists of an even number of terms. The sum of all the terms is three times that of the odd terms. Determine the common ratio of the G.P.

(b) In a G.P. of real numbers, it is given that
$$T_1 + T_2 + T_3 + T_4 = 30$$
$$\text{and } T_1^2 + T_2^2 + T_3^2 + T_4^2 = 340$$
Determine the G.P.

(c) The set $\{a_1, a_2 \ldots a_n\}$ form a G.P. with first term as a and common ratio r. Prove that
$$\Sigma a_i a_j = \frac{a^2 r(1 - r^{n-1})(1 - r^n)}{(1 - r)^2(1 + r)}$$

(d) If $0 < r < 1$ and n is a +ive integer then prove that $(2n + 1)r^n(1 - r) < 1 - r^{2n+1}$.

45. Determine two G.P.'s which satisfy the following conditions :
$$T_1 + T_2 + T_3 + T_4 = 30 \text{ and } T_5 + T_6 + T_7 + T_8 = 480$$
Also prove the following for both :
  (i) $S_6 - S_4 = 96$ (ii) $\dfrac{T_n}{T_n'} = \dfrac{1}{3}(-1)^n$

46. (a) Find the sum of the terms of an infinitely decreasing G.P. in which all the terms are positive, the first term is 4, and the difference between the third and fifth term is equal to 32/81.

(b)* The sum of an infinite geometric progression is 2 and the sum of the geometric prgression made from the cubes of this infinite series is 24. Then find the series.

(c) The sum of an infinite geometric series is 162 and the sum of its first n terms is 160. If the inverse of its common ratio is an integer, find all possible values of the common ratio, n and the first term of the series.   **(Roorkee 1999)**

47. (a)* In a G.P. the first, third and fifth terms may be considered as the first, fourth and sixteenth terms of an A.P. Determine the fourth term of the A.P., knowing that its first term is 5 and determine T_1, T_3, T_5 of G.P.

(b)* The sum of first ten terms of an A.P. is equal to 155, and the sum of the first two terms of a G.P. is 9, find these progressions if the first term of A.P. is equal to common ratio of G.P. and the first term of G.P. is equal to common difference of A.P.

(Roorkee 1993)

48. (a)* The sum of the squares of three distinct real numbers, which are in G.P. is S^2. If their sum is αS, show that $\alpha^2 \in \left(\frac{1}{3}, 1\right) \cup (1, 3)$

(b) Find all the numbers x and y such that $x, x + 2y, 2x + y$ form an A.P. while the numbers $(y+1)^2, xy + 5, (x+1)^2$ form a G.P. Write down the progressions.

49. (a) Find the three numbers constituting a G.P. if it is known that the sum of the numbers is equal to 26 and that when 1, 6 and 3 are added to them respectively, the new numbers are obtained which form an A.P.

(b)* Three numbers form a G.P. If the 3rd term is decreased by 64, then the three numbers thus obtained will constitute an A.P. If the second term of this A.P. is decreased by 8, a G.P. will be formed again. Determine the numbers. (D.C.E. 1997)

50. The consecutive digits of a three digit number are in G.P. If the middle digit be increased by 2 then they form an A.P. If 792 is subtracted from this number then we get the number consisting of same three digits but in reverse order. Find the number.

51.* If a, b, c, x are all real numbers, and
$$(a^2 + b^2) x^2 - 2b(a+c) x + (b^2 + c^2) = 0$$
then a, b, c are in G.P., and x is their common ratio.

52.* Find the natural number a for which $\sum_{k=1}^{n} f(a+k) = 16(2^n - 1)$, where the function f satisfies the relation $f(x+y) = f(x) \cdot f(y)$ for all natural numbers x, y and further $f(1) = 2$ (I.I.T. 1992)

Solutions to Problem Set (2)

1. (a) $T_5 = ar^4 = 81$, $T_2 = ar = 24$.

Dividing, $r^3 = \frac{81}{24} = \frac{27}{8}$

∴ $r = \frac{3}{2} > 1$ and hence $a = 16$.

∴ $S_8 = \frac{a(r^n - 1)}{r - 1} = \frac{16}{3/2 - 1}[(3/2)^8 - 1]$

$= 32 \cdot \frac{(3^8 - 2^8)}{2^8} = \frac{1}{8}(3^4 - 2^4)(3^4 + 2^4) = \frac{1}{8}(65 \times 97)$.

(b) $\frac{S_3}{S_6} = \frac{125}{152}$ ∴ $\frac{a(r^3 - 1)/(r-1)}{a(r^6 - 1)/(r-1)} = \frac{125}{152}$

∴ $\frac{1}{r^3 + 1} = \frac{125}{152}$ or $152 = 125r^3 + 125$

or $125r^3 = 27$ ∴ $r = \frac{3}{5}$.

(c) $\frac{T_{p-1}}{T_p} + \frac{T_{p+1}}{T_p} = 3$ ∴ $\frac{1}{r} + r = 3$

or $r^2 - 3r + 1 = 0$

∴ $r = \frac{3 \pm \sqrt{5}}{2}$ i.e. irrational.

2. (a) Split into two series one of which is G.P. and the other A.P.

Ans. $a \frac{(a^n - 1)}{a - 1} + b \cdot \frac{n(n+1)}{2}$.

(b) Open the brackets and split into three series

$$(x^2 + x^4 + x^6 + \ldots) + \left(\frac{1}{x^2} + \frac{1}{x^4} + \frac{1}{x^6} + \ldots\right)$$
$$+ (2 + 2 + 2 + \ldots)$$

$$= x^2 \frac{(x^{2n} - 1)}{x^2 - 1} + \frac{1}{x^2} \frac{\left(\frac{1}{x^{2n}} - 1\right)}{\frac{1}{x^2} - 1} + 2n$$

$$= \frac{x^2 (x^{2n} - 1)}{x^2 - 1} + \frac{x^{2n} - 1}{x^{2n} \cdot (x^2 - 1)} + 2n$$

$$= \frac{x^{2n} - 1}{x^2 - 1}\left[x^2 + \frac{1}{x^{2n}}\right] + 2n$$

$$= \frac{x^{2n} - 1}{x^2 - 1} \cdot \left[\frac{x^{2n+2} + 1}{x^{2n}}\right] + 2n.$$

3. (a) nth term of the series is
$$T_n = 1 + x + x^2 + x^3 + \ldots n \text{ terms}$$

∴ $T_n = \frac{1 \cdot (1 - x^n)}{1 - x}$.

Putting $n = 1, 2, 3, \ldots, n$ and adding, we get
$$S_n = \frac{1}{1 - x}[(1 + 1 + 1 + \ldots) - (x + x^2 + x^3 + \ldots)]$$

$$= \frac{1}{1 - x}\left[n - \frac{x \cdot (1 - x^n)}{1 - x}\right]$$

$$= \frac{1}{(1-x)^2}[n(1-x) - x(1 - x^n)]$$

(b) L.H.S. $= \frac{1 - x^{p+1}}{1 - x} =$ R.H.S.

∴ $1 - x^{p+1} = (1 - x)(1 + x)(1 + x^2)$
$$(1 + x^4)(1 + x^8)$$

$= (1 - x^2)(1 + x^2)(1 + x^4)(1 + x^8) = 1 - x^{16}$

∴ $p + 1 = 16$ ∴ $p = 15$.

4. (a) Ans. $x^2 \frac{(1 - x^{2n})}{1 - x^2} + xy \frac{(1 - x^n y^n)}{1 - xy}$.

(b) It is easy to observe that

$$\frac{x^2 - y^2}{x - y} = x + y, \quad \frac{x^3 - y^3}{x - y} = x^2 + xy + y^2, \text{ etc.}$$

$$\frac{x^n - y^n}{x - y} = x^{n-1} + x^{n-2}y + \dots + xy^{n-2} + y^{n-1}$$

L.H.S. $= \frac{1}{x - y}[(x^2 - y^2) + (x^3 - y^3) + \dots n \text{ terms}]$

$$= \frac{1}{x - y}[S_1 + S_2] \text{ of a G.P of } n \text{ terms}$$

$$= \frac{1}{x - y}\left[\frac{x^2(1 - x^n)}{1 - x} - \frac{y^2(1 - y^n)}{1 - y}\right]$$

Note. It may also be noted that

$$\frac{x^3 + y^3}{x + y} = x^2 - xy + y^2$$

$$\frac{x^5 + y^5}{x + y} = x^4 - x^3 y + x^2 y^2 - xy^3 + y^4$$

and $\dfrac{x^n + y^n}{x + y} = x^{n-1} - x^{n-2}y + \dots$

$$- xy^{n-2} + y^{n-1}$$

where n is $3, 5, \dots$ i.e. odd.

5. (a) $x = \dfrac{1}{1 - a}, \quad y = \dfrac{1}{1 - b}$ [summing infinite G.P.'s].

$$\therefore \quad a = \frac{x - 1}{x}, \quad b = \frac{y - 1}{y}$$

$$\therefore \quad 1 + ab + a^2 b^2 + \dots \infty$$

$$= \frac{1}{1 - ab} = \frac{1}{1 - \dfrac{(x - 1)(y - 1)}{xy}} = \frac{xy}{x + y - 1}.$$

(b) $x = \dfrac{1}{1 - a} \Rightarrow a = \dfrac{x - 1}{x}.$

Similarly $b = \dfrac{y - 1}{y}, \quad ab = \dfrac{z - 1}{z}$

$$\therefore \quad \frac{z - 1}{z} = \frac{x - 1}{x} \cdot \frac{y - 1}{y}$$

or $\quad xyz - xy = z(xy - x - y + 1)$

$$\therefore \quad xz + yz = xy + z$$

(c) Ans. (a)

Given $S_\infty = 5 = \dfrac{x}{1 - r} \quad \therefore \quad r = 1 - \dfrac{x}{5}$

$$|r| < 1 \quad \Rightarrow \quad -1 < r < 1$$

or $\quad -1 < 1 - \dfrac{x}{5} < 1 \quad$ or $\quad 1 > -1 + \dfrac{x}{5} > -1$

We have multiplied by – ive sign and changed the sign of inequality

or $\quad 2 > \dfrac{x}{5} > 0$

or $\quad 0 < \dfrac{x}{5} < 2 \quad$ or $\quad 0 < x < 10$

(d) **Hint :** $3^{x-100}[1 + 3 + 3^2 \dots 5^{100}]$

$$= 5^{x-100}[1 + 5 + 5^2 + \dots 3^{100}]$$

Take log of both sides after summing the G.P. series.

(e) Ans. (c).

$$z = \log_2[x \cdot x^{1/2} \cdot x^{1/4} \cdot x^{1/8} \dots \infty]$$

$$= \log_2[x^{1 + \frac{1}{2} + \frac{1}{4} + \frac{1}{8} + \dots \infty}]$$

$$= \log_2 x^{\frac{1}{1 - (1/2)}} = \log_2(x^2) = 4 \quad \text{(given)}$$

$$\therefore \quad x^2 = 2^4 = 16 \quad \therefore \quad x = 4$$

6. (a) $(\sqrt{2} - 1)^2 = 3 - 2\sqrt{2}, \quad (\sqrt{2} - 1)^3 = 5\sqrt{2} - 7$

$$(\sqrt{2} - 1)^4 = (3 - 2\sqrt{2})^2 = 17 - 12\sqrt{2}$$

Also $(2\sqrt{3})^2 = 12, \quad (2\sqrt{3})^3 = 24\sqrt{3},$

$$(2\sqrt{3})^4 = 144 \quad \text{etc.}$$

Hence the given series is a G.P. of infinite number of terms whose first term is 1 and $r = \dfrac{\sqrt{2} - 1}{2\sqrt{3}} < 1$

$$\therefore \quad S_\infty = \frac{a}{1 - r} = \frac{1}{1 - \dfrac{\sqrt{2} - 1}{2\sqrt{3}}} = \frac{2\sqrt{3}}{2\sqrt{3} - \sqrt{2} + 1}$$

(b) Put $\dfrac{\sqrt{2} - 1}{\sqrt{2}} = x$

$$\therefore \quad S = 1 + \frac{x}{2} + \frac{x^2}{6} + \frac{x^3}{12} + \frac{x^4}{20} + \dots$$

$$= 1 + \frac{x}{1.2} + \frac{x^2}{2.3} + \frac{x^3}{3.4} + \frac{x^4}{4.5} + \dots$$

$$= 1 + \left(1 - \frac{1}{2}\right)x + \left(\frac{1}{2} - \frac{1}{3}\right)x^2 + \left(\frac{1}{3} - \frac{1}{4}\right)x^3$$

$$+ \left(\frac{1}{4} - \frac{1}{5}\right)x^4 + \dots$$

$$= \left(1 + x + \frac{x^2}{2} + \frac{x^3}{3} + \dots\right) - \left(\frac{x}{2} + \frac{x^2}{3} + \frac{x^3}{4} + \dots\right)$$

$$= 1 - \log(1 - x) - \frac{1}{x}\left(\frac{x^2}{2} + \frac{x^3}{3} + \frac{x^4}{4} + \dots\right)$$

$$= 1 - \log(1 - x) - \frac{1}{x}\{-\log(1 - x) - x\}$$

$$= 2 + \left(\frac{1}{x} - 1\right)\log(1 - x) . \text{ Put the value of } x.$$

$$\therefore \quad S = 2 + \left(\frac{\sqrt{2}}{\sqrt{2} - 1} - 1\right)\log\left(1 - \frac{\sqrt{2} - 1}{\sqrt{2}}\right)$$

$$= 2 + \frac{1}{\sqrt{2} - 1}\log\frac{1}{\sqrt{2}}$$

$$= 2 + \frac{(\sqrt{2} + 1)}{2 - 1}\left(-\frac{1}{2}\log 2\right)$$

$$= 2 - \frac{1}{2}(\sqrt{2} + 1)\log 2.$$

7. (a) Since here common ratio is 2 which is greater than 1, hence S is infinite so the first step *i.e.* $2S = S - 1$ is correct but conclusion from this that $S = -1$ is false since we cannot cancel S *i.e.* ∞ from both sides.

(b) Ans. (b). Sum of a G.P.

$$(i + i^2)\frac{(1 - i^{13})}{1 - i} = i - 1 \text{ as } i^{13} = i$$

8. (a) $S = \dfrac{1}{1 - (1/2)} = 2,$

$$S_n = \frac{1 - (1/2)^n}{1 - (1/2)} = 2 - \frac{1}{2^{n-1}}$$

$$S - S_n = \frac{1}{2^{n-1}} < \frac{1}{1000} \quad \text{or} \quad 2^{n-1} \geq 1000$$

Now $2^{10} = 32 \times 32 = 1024$

$\therefore \quad n - 1 \geq 10 \quad \text{or} \quad n \geq 11$

Hence the least value is 11.

(b) $\displaystyle\int_0^1 2^{-(k+1)x} dx = \left[\frac{2^{-(k+1)x}}{-(k+1)\log a}\right]_0^1 = \frac{2^{-(k+1)} - 1}{-(k+1)\log a}$

$\therefore \displaystyle\sum_{k=0}^n (k+1) \cdot \left\{\frac{2^{-(k+1)} - 1}{-(k+1)\log a}\right\}$

$= \dfrac{1}{\log a} \displaystyle\sum_{k=0}^n \left\{1 - \frac{1}{2^{k+1}}\right\}$

$= \dfrac{1}{\log a}\left[(n+1) - \left\{\frac{1}{2} + \frac{1}{2^2} + \frac{1}{2^3} + \dots(n+1) \text{ terms}\right\}\right]$

$= \dfrac{1}{\log a}\left[(n+1) - \dfrac{\frac{1}{2}\left\{1 - \left(\frac{1}{2}\right)^{n+1}\right\}}{\left(1 - \frac{1}{2}\right)}\right]$

$= \dfrac{1}{\log a}[(n+1) - (1 - 2^{-(n+1)})]$

$= \dfrac{1}{\log a}\left[n + \left(\frac{1}{2}\right)^{n+1}\right]$

$\therefore S = \dfrac{1}{\log a} \displaystyle\sum_{n=0}^\infty \left[\frac{n}{n!} + \frac{1}{2} \cdot \frac{\left(\frac{1}{2}\right)^n}{n!}\right]$

$= \dfrac{1}{\log a} \displaystyle\sum_{n=0}^\infty \left[\frac{1}{(n-1)!} + \frac{1}{2} \cdot \frac{x^n}{n!}\right],$

where $x = \dfrac{1}{2}$

$= \dfrac{1}{\log a}\left[e + \frac{1}{2}e^x\right] = \dfrac{1}{\log a}\left(e + \frac{1}{2}\sqrt{e}\right)$

9. (a) Given that $T_p = (T_{p+1} + T_{p+2} + \dots\infty)$

or $\quad ar^{p-1} = ar^p + ar^{p+1} \dots\infty$. But $a = 1$

$\therefore \quad r^{p-1} = \dfrac{r^p}{1 - r}$. Sum of an infinite G.P.

$\therefore \quad 1 - r = r \quad \text{or} \quad r = \dfrac{1}{2}.$

Hence the series is $1, \dfrac{1}{2}, \dfrac{1}{4}, \dfrac{1}{8}, \dfrac{1}{16} + \dots\infty$

(b) Do yourself.

(c) $T_p > T_{p+1} + T_{p+2} + \dots\infty$

$\therefore \quad ar^{p-1} > \dfrac{ar^p}{1 - r}$ ...(1)

where $r < 1$ or $1 - r = +$ive

Multiply the inequality (1) by $+$ive quantity $1 - r$ and cancel ar^{p-1}.

$\therefore \quad 1 - r > r \quad \text{or} \quad 1 > 2r \quad i.e. \quad \text{if } r < \dfrac{1}{2}.$

10. (a) Here $a + ar = 5$

$T_p = 3(T_{p+1} + T_{p+2} + \dots\infty)$

$\therefore \quad ar^{p-1} = 3 \cdot \dfrac{ar^p}{1 - r} \quad \therefore \quad 1 - r = 3r$

or $\quad r = \dfrac{1}{4}$ hence $a = 4$, etc.

(b) $a, a + d, a + 6d$ are in G.P.

$\therefore \quad (a + d)^2 = a(a + 6d) \quad \therefore \quad d^2 - 4ad = 0$

$d(d - 4a) = 0 \quad \therefore \quad d = 0 \quad \text{or} \quad d = 4a$

Since d cannot be zero, therefore we take $d = 4a$.

$\therefore \quad$ Numbers are $a, 5a, 25a$ where $a + 5a + 25a = 31a = 93$ given $\therefore a = 3, d = 12$.

Hence the numbers are $3, 15, 75$, which are clearly in G.P.

(c) If r be the common ratio, then $r = \dfrac{T_2}{T_1} = x^{k+4}$

$T_8 = ar^7 = x^{-4} x^{7(k+4)} = x^{52}$

$\therefore \quad 7k + 28 - 4 = 52$

$\therefore \quad 7k = 28 \quad \text{or} \quad k = 4$

(d) Ans. (d). Given $\dfrac{a}{1-r} = 4$ and $ar = \dfrac{3}{4}$.

Eliminating a, we have $16r^2 - 16r + 3 = 0$

or $(4r - 3)(4r - 1) = 0$

$\therefore \quad r = 3/4, 1/4$. Hence $r = 1/4$ so that $a = 3$, $r = 3/4$ is not given in any of the four choices so we choose only $r = 1/4$.

11. (a) Here $a = \dfrac{2}{9}$ and $r = -\dfrac{1}{3} \cdot \dfrac{9}{2} = -\dfrac{3}{2}$.

Let the number of terms be n.

Also $\quad S_n = \dfrac{a(1 - r^n)}{1 - r} = \dfrac{55}{72}$

$\therefore \quad \dfrac{2}{9} \cdot \dfrac{[1 - (-3/2)^n]}{1 - (-3/2)} = \dfrac{55}{72}$

or $1 - \left(-\dfrac{3}{2}\right)^n = \dfrac{55}{72} \times \dfrac{9}{2} \times \dfrac{5}{2} = \dfrac{275}{32}$

$1 - \dfrac{275}{32} = \left(-\dfrac{3}{2}\right)^n \quad \text{or} \quad -\dfrac{243}{32} = \left(-\dfrac{3}{2}\right)^n$

or $\left(-\dfrac{3}{2}\right)^5 = \left(-\dfrac{3}{2}\right)^n \quad \therefore \quad n = 5.$

(b) $a = 1, r = 4$ and $S_n = 341$

$\therefore \dfrac{a(r^n - 1)}{r - 1} = 341$ or $\dfrac{1 \cdot (4^n - 1)}{4 - 1} = 341$

$\therefore \quad 4^n = 341 \times 3 + 1 = 1024 = 16 \times 64 = 4^5$

$\therefore \quad n = 5$

(c) $l = T_n = ar^{n-1} = 128, r = 2$

$S_n = \dfrac{a(r^n - 1)}{r - 1} = 255$

or $\dfrac{ar^{n-1} \cdot r - a}{r - 1} = 255$ or $\dfrac{128 \cdot 2 - a}{2 - 1} = 255$

$\therefore \quad 256 - 255 = a$ or $a = 1$.

Now $ar^{n-1} = 128$ $\therefore$ $1 \cdot (2)^{n-1} = 2^7$

$\therefore \quad n - 1 = 7$ or $n = 8$.

12. (a) $n = 6$. G.P. is increasing $r > 1$,

$a + ar^{n-1} = 66,$ ...(1)

$ar \cdot ar^{n-2} = a^2 r^{n-1} = 128,$

$\therefore \quad ar^{n-1} = \dfrac{128}{a}$

Putting in (1), we get $a + \dfrac{128}{a} = 66$

$\therefore \quad a^2 - 66a + 128 = 0$

or $(a - 2)(a - 64) = 0$

$\therefore \quad a = 2, 64, r^{n-1} = 32, 1/32$

We reject the second value as $r > 1$ $\therefore$ $r^{n-1} = 32$

Sum $= \dfrac{a(r^n - 1)}{r - 1} = 126$ or $\dfrac{2(32r - 1)}{r - 1} = 126$

$\therefore \quad r^{n-1} = 32$

$\therefore \quad 32r - 1 = 63r - 63$

$\therefore \quad r = 2$ and $r^{n-1} = 32$ gives

$2^{n-1} = 2^5$ $\therefore$ $n - 1 = 5$ or $n = 6$

(b) $b^2 = ac$ gives

$x = -4; -4, -6, -9$ $\therefore$ $r = 3/2$

$\therefore \quad T_4 = -9(3/2) = -13 \cdot 5$

(c) Let the numbers be a, ar, ar^2, ar^3

$\therefore \quad a^2(r^2 + r^4) = 250$ or $a^2 r^2 (1 + r^2) = 250$ ...(1)

and $G_1 G_4 = a^2 r^3 = \alpha$ where α is greater root of

$(2 + \log_{10} x) \log_{10} x$
$= \log_{10} (10^{-3})^{-8/3} = \log_{10} (10^8) = 8$

or If $\log_{10} x = t$ then $t^2 + 2t - 8 = 0$

$\therefore \quad t = -4, 2$

$\log_{10} x = -4, 2$ or $x = 10^{-4}, 10^2 = \dfrac{1}{10^4}, 100$

$\therefore \quad \alpha = 100$ being greater root.

$\therefore \quad a^2 r^3 = 100$ and $a^2 r^2 (1 + r^2) = 250$

Dividing, $\dfrac{1 + r^2}{r} = \dfrac{5}{2}$ or $2r^2 - 5r + 2 = 0$

$\therefore \quad r = 2, \dfrac{1}{2}$

Choosing $r = 2$ we get from (1), $a^2 \cdot 4 \times 5 = 250$

$\therefore \quad a^2 = 25/2$ and $r^2 = 2$.

Hence the four numbers are

a, ar, ar^2, ar^3 i.e., $\dfrac{5}{\sqrt{2}}, 5\sqrt{2}, 10\sqrt{2}, 20\sqrt{2}$.

Choosing $r = \dfrac{1}{2}$, we will get the same numbers in reverse order.

13. (a) T_4, T_7 and T_{10} are also in G.P. $\therefore$ $q^2 = pr$

(b) $\alpha + \beta = 4, \alpha\beta = \lambda, \gamma + \delta = 64, \gamma\delta = \mu$

$\alpha, \beta, \gamma, \delta$ are in increasing G.P. $\therefore$ $r > 1$

$\beta = \alpha r, \gamma = \alpha r^2, \delta = \alpha r^3$

$\alpha(1 + r) = 4, \alpha^2 r = \lambda$

$\alpha r^2 (1 + r) = 64, \alpha^2 r^5 = \mu$

Dividing $r^2 = 16$ $\therefore$ $r = 4$ only as $r > 1$

$\therefore \quad \alpha = \dfrac{4}{5}$, $\therefore$ $\lambda = \alpha^2 r = \dfrac{16}{25} \cdot 4 = \dfrac{64}{25}$

$\mu = \alpha^2 \cdot r^5 = \left(\dfrac{4}{5}\right)^2 \cdot 4^5 = \dfrac{4^2 \cdot 4^5}{5 \times 5} = \dfrac{4^7}{25}$

Hence $\lambda = \dfrac{64}{25}, \mu = \dfrac{4^7}{25}$

14. (a) $S = \cdot 7 + \cdot 77 + \cdot 777 + \dots\dots n$ terms

$= \dfrac{7}{9} [\cdot 9 + \cdot 99 + \cdot 999 + \dots]$

$= \dfrac{7}{9} \left[\left(1 - \dfrac{1}{10}\right) + \left(1 - \dfrac{1}{100}\right) + \left(1 - \dfrac{1}{1000}\right) + \dots\dots\right]$

$= \dfrac{7}{9} \left[(1 + 1 + 1 + \dots) - \left(\dfrac{1}{10} + \dfrac{1}{10^2} + \dfrac{1}{10^3} + \dots\right)\right]$

$= \dfrac{7}{9} \left[n - \dfrac{1}{10} \cdot \dfrac{1 - (1/10^n)}{1 - (1/10)}\right] = \dfrac{7n}{9} - \dfrac{7}{81}\left(1 - \dfrac{1}{10^n}\right)$.

(b) $S = 6 + 66 + 666 + \dots\dots$

$= \dfrac{6}{9} [9 + 99 + 999 + \dots\dots]$

$= \dfrac{6}{9} [(10 - 1) + (10^2 - 1) + (10^3 - 1) + \dots\dots]$

$= \dfrac{6}{9} [(10 + 10^2 + 10^3 + \dots\dots) - (1 + 1 + 1 + \dots)]$

$= \dfrac{6}{9} \left[10 \cdot \dfrac{10^n - 1}{10 - 1} - n\right] = \dfrac{6}{81} [10^{n+1} - 9n - 10]$

(c) Ans. $\dfrac{8}{81} [10^{n+1} - 9n - 10]$

15. (a) **Hint :** Represent each number as a G.P. e.g., we write 666...6 as

$6 + 6.10 + 6.10^2 + \ldots + 6.10^{n-1}$

$$= \frac{6(10^n - 1)}{10 - 1} = \frac{2}{3}(10^n - 1) \text{ etc.}$$

Hence we have to prove that

$$\left[\frac{2}{3}(10^n - 1)\right]^2 + \frac{8}{9}(10^n - 1) = \frac{4}{9}(10^{2n} - 1)$$

Now cancel $\frac{1}{9}(10^n - 1)$

$\therefore \quad 4(10^n - 1) + 8 = 4(10^n + 1)$

Above is clearly true.

(b) Ans. True.

$$\text{L.H.S.} = \begin{bmatrix} 1 + 1.10 + 1.10^2 + \ldots 2n \text{ terms} \\ - (2 + 2.10 + 2.10^2 + \ldots n \text{ terms}) \end{bmatrix}^{1/2}$$

$$= \left[1 \cdot \frac{10^{2n} - 1}{10 - 1} - 2 \cdot \frac{10^n - 1}{10 - 1} \right]^{1/2}$$

$$= \frac{1}{3}[10^{2n} - 2(10^n) + 1]^{1/2}$$

$$= \frac{1}{3}(10^n - 1) = 3\left\{ \frac{10^n - 1}{10 - 1} \right\}$$

$$= 3[1 + 10 + 10^2 + \ldots n \text{ terms}] \quad \text{by G.P. Sum}$$

$$= 3\,3\,3\ldots n \text{ digits.}$$

16. (a) $1 = 1, 11 = 1 + 10, 111 = 1 + 10 + 100, \ldots$

$\therefore$ Given number of 91 digits is expressible as

$1 + 10 + 10^2 + 10^3 + \ldots 10^{90}$

$$= \frac{10^{91} - 1}{10 - 1}. \quad \text{(Sum of a G.P.)}$$

$$= \frac{10^{91} - 1}{10^7 - 1} \times \frac{10^7 - 1}{10 - 1} = \frac{t^{13} - 1}{t - 1} \cdot \frac{10^7 - 1}{10 - 1}$$

$$\text{where } t = 10^7$$

$$= (t^{12} + t^{11} + t^{10} + \ldots + 1)$$

$$(10^6 + 10^5 + 10^4 + \ldots + 1)$$

Hence the given number is expressible as the product of two numbers and as such it is a composite number and not prime.

(b) Ans. (a). True.

$T_3 = 444889$, 4 is 3 times, 8 is 2 times and 9 only once at unit place always.

We have, $T_n = 444\ldots\ldots 4888\ldots89$.

It is evident that 4 is repeated n times and 8 is repeated $(n-1)$ times and 9 is in unit place.

We can write T_n as

$T_n = 9 + (8 \times 10 + 8 \times 10^2 + 8 \times 10^3 + \ldots\ldots$

$\qquad + 8 \times 10^{n-1}) + (4 \times 10^n + 4 \times 10^{n+1}$

$\qquad + 4 \times 10^{n+2} + \ldots\ldots\ldots + 4 \times 10^{2n-1})$

$$= 9 + \frac{80(10^{n-1} - 1)}{10 - 1} + \frac{4 \times 10^n (10^n - 1)}{10 - 1}$$

$$= \frac{1}{9}[81 + 80 \times 10^{n-1} - 80 + 4 \times 10^{2n} - 4 \times 10^n]$$

$$= \frac{1}{9}[1 + 2 \times 4 \times 10^n - 4 \times 10^n + 4 \times 10^{2n}]$$

$$= \frac{1}{9}[1 + 4 \times 10^n + 4 \times 10^{2n}] = \left(\frac{1 + 2 \times 10^n}{3}\right)^2.$$

Hence each T_n is the square of an integer since $2 \times 10^n + 1$ is divisible by 3 as sum of digits in N^r is always divisible by 3. e.g. for $n = 1, 2, 3, \ldots$ $N^r = 21, 201, 2001, 20001, \ldots$ each of which is divisible by 3 and gives 7, 67, 667, 6667, ...

17. (a) Let $x = 0 \cdot 125125125\ldots$

$\therefore \quad 1000\,x = 125 \cdot 125125125\ldots$

Subtract $999\,x = 125 \cdot 0000000 = 125$

$\therefore \quad x = \dfrac{125}{999}.$

(b) $\quad x = 2 \cdot 357357357\ldots$

$\therefore \quad 1000\,x = 2357 \cdot 357357\ldots$

Subtracting, $999\,x = 2355 \quad \therefore \quad x = \text{etc.}$

18. (a) $\cdot 12\dot{3} = \cdot 123232323\ldots$

$$= \frac{1}{10} + \frac{23}{1000} + \frac{23}{100000} + \ldots$$

$$= \frac{1}{10} + 23\left[\frac{1}{10^3} + \frac{1}{10^5} + \frac{1}{10^7} + \ldots\ldots\infty\right]$$

$$= \frac{1}{10} + 23 \cdot \frac{(1/10^3)}{1 - (1/10^2)} = \frac{1}{10} + \frac{23}{990}, \quad \because \; S = \frac{a}{1 - r}$$

$$= \frac{99 + 23}{990} = \frac{122}{990} = \frac{61}{495}.$$

(b) Proceed as above. Ans. $\dfrac{419}{990}$.

19. (a) After striking the floor falling from a distance of 48 ft. it rebounds to a height of $\frac{2}{3}(48)$. Again it falls the same distance i.e. $\frac{2}{3}(48)$ and after rebounding it goes to a height of $\frac{2}{3}\left(\frac{2}{3}\right)(48) = \left(\frac{2}{3}\right)^2 \cdot 48$.

It falls the same distance and after rebounding goes to a height of $\frac{2}{3}[(\frac{2}{3})^2 \cdot 48] = (\frac{2}{3})^3 \cdot 48$ and so on.

Hence the total distance travelled is

$48 + 2[\frac{2}{3}(48) + (\frac{2}{3})^2\, 48 + (\frac{2}{3})^3\, 48 + \ldots\infty]$.

We have taken twice as it goes to particular height, and then falls the same distance.

$\therefore \quad S = 48 + 2 \cdot \dfrac{\frac{2}{3} \cdot 48}{1 - \frac{2}{3}}, \quad \text{using } S = \dfrac{a}{1 - r}$

$\qquad = 48 + 2(96) = 48 + 192 = 240 \text{ ft.}$

(b) Ans. $120 + 960 = 1080$.

20. (a) Sides are $a, \dfrac{a}{\sqrt{2}}, \dfrac{a}{2}, \dfrac{a}{2\sqrt{2}}, \ldots,$

Areas are $a^2, \dfrac{a^2}{2}, \dfrac{a^2}{4}, \dfrac{a^2}{8}$, etc. Ans. $2a^2$.

(b) $S = s + \dfrac{s}{2} + \dfrac{s}{2^2} + \dfrac{s}{2^3} + \ldots \infty$

$= \dfrac{s}{1 - \dfrac{1}{2}} = 2s.$

(c) We know that the line joining the mid-points of the sides of a triangle is half the opposite side. The triangle being equilateral.

Sides are $a, \dfrac{a}{2}, \dfrac{a}{4}, \dfrac{a}{8}, \ldots$ G.P.

Perimeters are $3a, \dfrac{3a}{2}, \dfrac{3a}{4}, \ldots$

Sum of perimeters $= \dfrac{3a}{1 - \dfrac{1}{2}} = 6a = 6 \times 24 = 144.$

21. (a) $T_{m+n} = ar^{m+n-1} = p.$

$T_{m-n} = ar^{m-n-1} = q$ and $T_m = ar^{m-1}$

Multiplying $a^2 r^{2m-2} = pq$

$\therefore \quad T_m = ar^{m-1} = \sqrt{pq}.$

(b) $\dfrac{T_l}{T_m} = \dfrac{l}{m} \Rightarrow \dfrac{ar^{l-1}}{ar^{m-1}} = \dfrac{l}{m} \Rightarrow r^{l-m} = \dfrac{l}{m}$

$\therefore \quad r = \left(\dfrac{l}{m}\right)^{1/(l-m)}$

$\therefore \quad a = \dfrac{l}{r^{l-1}} = l\left(\dfrac{m}{l}\right)^{\frac{l-1}{l-m}} = \dfrac{(m)^{(l-1)/(l-m)}}{(l)^{(m-1)/(l-m)}}$

$\therefore \quad T_n = ar^{n-1}$ etc. Now put for a and r.

22. The series is

$1 + a + ac + a^2c + a^2c^2 + a^3c^2 + \ldots$ to $2n$ terms

$= (1 + ac + a^2c^2 + \ldots \ldots \text{to } n \text{ terms})$

$\qquad + (a + a^2c + a^3c^2 + \ldots \text{to } n \text{ terms})$

$= \dfrac{1(1 - a^n c^n)}{1 - ac} + \dfrac{a(1 - a^n c^n)}{1 - ac}$

$= \left(\dfrac{1 + a}{1 - ac}\right)(1 - a^n c^n).$

23. (a) Let the common ratio be taken as k and a be the first term.

$\therefore \quad R = T_r = ak^{r-1}$

$\therefore \quad R^{s-t} = a^{s-t} k^{(r-1)(s-t)}$ Similarly,

$\qquad S^{t-r} = a^{t-r} k^{(s-1)(t-r)}.$

$\qquad T^{r-s} = a^{r-s} k^{(t-1)(r-s)}$

Multiplying the above three and knowing that

$\qquad A^m . A^n . A^p = A^{m+n+p}$

$\therefore \quad R^{s-t} S^{t-r} T^{r-s} = a^0 . k^0 = 1.$

$\because \quad \Sigma(a - b) = 0, \ \Sigma(a + \lambda)(b - c) = 0$

(b) $S = a + ar + ar^2 + ar^3 + \ldots + ar^{n-1}$ i.e. n terms

$S = \dfrac{a(1 - r^n)}{1 - r} \qquad \ldots(1)$

$\therefore \quad P = \text{Product} = a . ar . ar^2 \ldots \ldots ar^{n-1}$

$\qquad = a^n r^{1+2+3+\ldots\ldots n-1} = a^n r^{(n-1)n/2}$

$\therefore \quad P^2 = a^{2n} r^{n(n-1)} \qquad \ldots(2)$

$R = \dfrac{1}{a} + \dfrac{1}{ar} + \dfrac{1}{ar^2} + \ldots + \dfrac{1}{ar^{n-1}}$ (n terms)

$\therefore \quad R = \dfrac{1}{a} . \dfrac{\left(1 - \dfrac{1}{r^n}\right)}{\left(1 - \dfrac{1}{r}\right)} = \dfrac{(r^n - 1)}{r - 1} . \dfrac{1}{ar^{n-1}} \qquad \ldots(3)$

$\therefore \quad \dfrac{S}{R} = a\dfrac{(1 - r^n)}{1 - r} . \dfrac{r - 1}{r^n - 1} a . r^{n-1}$

$\qquad = a^2 . r^{(n-1)}$, by (1) and (3) $\qquad \ldots(4)$

$\therefore \quad \left(\dfrac{S}{R}\right)^n = a^{2n} r^{n(n-1)} = P^2$, by (2).

Another form :

From (4), $\quad \dfrac{S}{R} = a . ar^{n-1} = T_1 . T_n$ etc.

(c) Do yourself.

24. (a) $T_p = AR^{p-1} = x, \ T_q = AR^{q-1} = y, \ T_r = AR^{r-1} = z$

$\therefore \quad \log x = \log A + (p - 1) \log R \qquad \ldots(1)$

$\qquad \log y = \log A + (q - 1) \log R \qquad \ldots(2)$

$\qquad \log z = \log A + (r - 1) \log R \qquad \ldots(3)$

Multiply (1), (2) and (3) by $q - r, r - p$ and $p - q$ respectively and add.

$\therefore \quad (q - r) \log x + (r - p) \log y + (p - q) \log z$

$\qquad = 0 \log A + 0 \log R = 0$

$\because \quad \Sigma(q - r) = 0, \ \Sigma(p - 1)(q - r) = 0$

(b) We are given that T_p, T_q and T_r of an A.P. are in G.P.

$\therefore \quad \dfrac{T_q}{T_p} = \dfrac{T_r}{T_q} = R = \dfrac{T_q - T_r}{T_p - T_q}$ (Ratio Prop.)

$\therefore \quad R = \dfrac{[a + (q - 1)d] - [a + (r - 1)d]}{[a + (p - 1)d] - [a + (q - 1)d]}$

$\qquad = \dfrac{(q - r)d}{(p - q)d} = \dfrac{q - r}{p - q}$

(c) As in part (b).

$\qquad R = \dfrac{r - s}{q - r} = \dfrac{q - r}{p - q}$, by (b)

$\therefore \quad (q - r)^2 = (p - q)(r - s)$. Hence G.P.

25. (a) $S_1 = \dfrac{a(r^n - 1)}{r - 1}, \ S_2 = \dfrac{a(r^{2n} - 1)}{r - 1}, \ S_3 = \dfrac{a(r^{3n} - 1)}{r - 1}$

$\therefore \quad S_3 - S_2 = \dfrac{a}{r-1}(r^{3n} - r^{2n}) = \dfrac{a(r^n - 1)}{r-1} \cdot r^{2n}$

$\therefore \quad S_1(S_3 - S_2) = \dfrac{a(r^n - 1)}{r-1} \cdot \dfrac{a(r^n - 1)}{r-1} r^{2n}$

$$= \left[\dfrac{a(r^n - 1)}{r-1} r^n\right]^2 \qquad \ldots(1)$$

$S_2 - S_1 = \dfrac{a}{r-1}(r^{2n} - r^n) = \dfrac{a(r^n - 1)}{r-1} r^n \ \ldots(2)$

$\therefore \quad S_1(S_3 - S_2) = (S_2 - S_1)^2$, by (1) and (2).

(b) Subtracting $2S_1 S_2$ form both sides of given relation, we get

$$(S_2 - S_1)^2 = S_1(S_2 + S_3 - 2S_2)$$

or $(S_2 - S_1)^2 = S_1(S_3 - S_2)$.

This we have proved in part (i).

Another Form :

$a = S_1, b = S_2 - S_1, c = S_3 - S_2$ and we have proved above that $S_1(S_3 - S_2) = (S_2 - S_1)^2$ i.e., $ac = b^2$

$\therefore \quad a, b, c$ are in G.P.

(c) $a_2 = a_1 r, a_3 = a_2 r, \ldots, a_n = a_{n-1} r$

$S = \dfrac{1}{1 + r^m}\left[\dfrac{1}{a_1^m} + \dfrac{1}{a_2^m} + \ldots \dfrac{1}{a_{n-1}^m}\right] = \dfrac{1}{1 + r^m} \cdot S_1 \ \ldots(1)$

Now

$S_1 = \left[\dfrac{1}{a_1^m} + \dfrac{1}{(a_1 \cdot r)^m} + \dfrac{1}{(a_1 \cdot r^2)^m} + \ldots \dfrac{1}{(a_1 \cdot r^{n-2})^m}\right]$

$= \dfrac{1}{a_1^m}$ [Sum of G.P. of $(n-1)$ terms whose first term

is 1 and common ratio is $\dfrac{1}{r^m}$]

$\therefore \quad S_1 = \dfrac{1}{a_1^m}\left[\dfrac{1 \cdot \left[1 - \left(\dfrac{1}{r^m}\right)^{n-1}\right]}{1 - \dfrac{1}{r^m}}\right] = \dfrac{1}{a_1^m}\left[\dfrac{1 - r^{-m(n-1)}}{1 - r^{-m}}\right]$

$\therefore \quad S = \dfrac{1}{1 + r^m} \cdot S_1 = \dfrac{1}{a_1^m}\left[\dfrac{1 - r^{m(1-n)}}{(1 + r^m)(1 - r^{-m})}\right]$

26. (a) $S_n =$ sum of an infinite G.P. whose first term is n and common ratio $r = 1/(n+1)$

$S_n = \dfrac{a}{1-r} = \dfrac{n}{1 - [1/(n+1)]} = n + 1$.

Putting $n = 1, 2, 3, \ldots, n$

$S_1 + S_2 + S_3 + \ldots + S_n = 2 + 3 + 4 + \ldots + n + 1$

$= (n/2)[2 \cdot 2 + (n-1) \cdot 1] = \dfrac{1}{2} n(n+3)$.

(b) Refer part (i).

$S_r = r + 1 \quad \therefore \quad S_r^2 = (r+1)^2$

$\therefore \quad S_1^2 + S_2^2 + \ldots S_{2n-1}^2 = \displaystyle\sum_{r=1}^{2n-1} S_r^2$

$= 2^2 + 3^2 + 4^2 + \ldots (2n)^2$

$= [1^2 + 2^2 + 3^2 + \ldots N^2] - 1$

where $N = 2n$

$= \dfrac{1}{6} N(N+1)(2N+1) - 1$

$= \dfrac{1}{3} n(2n+1)(4n+1) - 1$

(c) Do yourself.

(d) **Hint.** Since s_n and S_n are both + ive we establish that $s_n S_{n+1} - s_{n+1} S_n > 0$. Put values and cancel

$\Rightarrow \quad (R^n - r^n) + Rr(R^{n-1} - r^{n-1}) + \ldots$

$\qquad\qquad R^{n-1} r^{n-1}(R - r) > 0$

27. $S_n = \dfrac{a(1 - r^n)}{1 - r} = \dfrac{a}{1-r} - a \cdot \dfrac{r^n}{1-r}. \qquad \ldots(1)$

Putting $n = 1, 2, 3, \ldots, n$ and adding, we get

(a) $S_1 + S_2 + S_3 + \ldots + S_n$

$= n \cdot \left(\dfrac{a}{1-r}\right) - \dfrac{a}{1-r}(r + r^2 + r^3 + \ldots + r^n)$

$= \dfrac{na}{1-r} - \dfrac{a}{1-r} \cdot r \cdot \dfrac{(1 - r^n)}{1 - r}$

$= \dfrac{na}{1-r} - \dfrac{ar}{(1-r)^2}(1 - r^n)$.

(b) $S_1 + S_3 + S_5 + \ldots + S_{2n-1}$ i.e. n terms

Putting $n = 1, 3, 5, \ldots$ in (1) and adding,

$= n \cdot \dfrac{a}{1-r} - \dfrac{a}{1-r}[r + r^3 + r^5 + \ldots + r^{2n-1}]$

$= n \cdot \dfrac{a}{1-r} - \dfrac{a}{1-r} \cdot \dfrac{r(1 - r^{2n})}{1 - r^2}$

$= \dfrac{na}{1-r} - \dfrac{ar}{(1-r)^2(1+r)} \cdot (1 - r^{2n})$

28. (a) Since a, b, c, d are in G.P.

$\therefore \quad b = ar, c = ar^2, d = ar^3$

L.H.S. $= a^2(1 + r^2 + r^4) a^2(r^2 + r^4 + r^6)$

$= a^4 r^2(1 + r^2 + r^4)^2$

R.H.S. $= [a^2(r + r^3 + r^5)]^2$

$= a^4 r^2(1 + r^2 + r^4)^2 =$ L.H.S.

(b) Proceed as in (i).

29. (a) R.H.S. $= 2(b^2 - ac) + 2(c^2 - bd) + (d^2 + a^2 - 2bc)$

a, b, c, d being in G.P., we have

$\dfrac{b}{a} = \dfrac{c}{b} = \dfrac{d}{c} \Rightarrow b^2 = ac, c^2 = bd$ and $bc = ad \ \ldots(1)$

$\therefore \quad$ R.H.S. $= 0 + 0 + (d^2 + a^2 - 2ad) = (d-a)^2$

(b) We have to prove that

$(a^2 - b^2)(c^2 - d^2) = (b^2 - c^2)^2 \qquad \ldots(2)$

L.H.S. $= a^2 c^2 + b^2 d^2 - (b^2 c^2 + a^2 d^2)$

$= b^4 + c^4 - 2b^2 c^2 = (b^2 - c^2)^2$, by (1) of (a)

30. (a) Ans. True.

$$21 = 1^2 + 2^2 + 4^2 \text{ and we know that}$$

$$(l_1^2 + m_1^2 + n_1^2)(l_2^2 + m_2^2 + n_2^2)$$
$$- (l_1 l_2 + m_1 m_2 + n_1 n_2)^2$$

$$= \begin{vmatrix} l_1 & m_1 \\ l_2 & m_2 \end{vmatrix}^2 + \begin{vmatrix} m_1 & n_1 \\ m_2 & n_2 \end{vmatrix}^2 + \begin{vmatrix} n_1 & l_1 \\ n_2 & l_2 \end{vmatrix}^2$$

Above is Lagrange's Identity

$$(1^2 + 2^2 + 4^2)(a^2 + b^2 + c^2) - (1.a + 2.b + 4.c)^2$$

$$= \begin{vmatrix} 1 & 2 \\ a & b \end{vmatrix}^2 + \begin{vmatrix} 2 & 4 \\ b & c \end{vmatrix}^2 + \begin{vmatrix} 4 & 1 \\ c & a \end{vmatrix}^2$$

or $0 = (b - 2a)^2 + 4(c - 2b)^2 + (4a - c)^2$

Hence each bracket is zero.

$\therefore \quad b = 2a, 2b = c, c = 4a$ or $a = \dfrac{b}{2} = \dfrac{c}{4} = k$

$\therefore \quad a, b, c$ are $k, 2k, 4k$ which are in G.P. of common ratio 2.

(b) We have $(\ )^2 (\ )^2 - (\ )^2 \le 0$

$$(x_1^2 x_2^2 + x_1^2 x_3^2 + x_2^2 x_2^2 + \ldots)$$
$$- (x_1^2 x_2^2 + 2x_1 x_3 x_2^2 + \ldots) \le 0$$
$$(x_1 x_3 - x_2^2)^2 + (x_2 x_4 - x_3^2)^2 + (x_3 x_5 - x_4^2)^2 + \ldots \le 0$$

Above is possible only when each term is zero.

$\therefore \quad x_1 x_3 = x_2^2, x_2 x_4 = x_3^2, x_3 x_5 = x_4^2 \ldots$

$\Rightarrow \quad x_1, x_2, x_3, x_4, x_5, \ldots x_n$ are in G.P.

(c) The given relation can be written as

$$(a^2 p^2 - 2abp + b^2) + (\quad) + (\quad) \le 0$$

or $(ap - b)^2 + (bp - c)^2 + (cp - d)^2 \le 0$ ...(1)

Since a, b, c, d and p are all real, the inequality (1) is possible only when each of the factors is zero i.e. $ap - b = 0, bp - c = 0, cp - d = 0$

or $p = \dfrac{b}{a} = \dfrac{c}{b} = \dfrac{d}{c}$ or a, b, c, d are in G.P.

31. (a) Just as in Q. 28.

$$\text{L.H.S.} = \frac{a^2[1 + r + r^2]}{a^2[r^3 + r^2 + r]} = \frac{1}{r}$$

$$\text{R.H.S.} = \frac{a(r + 1)}{a(r^2 + r)} = \frac{1}{r} = \text{L.H.S.}$$

(b) Apply $y^2 = zx$

$\therefore \quad a^t = \log_t a . \log_b t = \log_b a$ or $\dfrac{\log a}{\log b}$

$\therefore \quad t = \log_a(\log_b a) = -\log_a(\log_a b)$
$= \log_a(\log a) - \log_a(\log b)$

32. (a) The given relation implies $a(1 + r + r^2) = x(ar)$

or $r^2 + (1 - x)r + 1 = 0, r$ is real

$\therefore \quad (1 - x)^2 - 4 \ge 0$ or $x^2 - 2x - 3 = +\text{ive}$

or $(x + 1)(x - 3)$ is +ive.

$\therefore \quad$ either $x < -1$ or $x > 3$.

(b) $ar^2 - 4ar + 3a > 0$ as $b = ar, c = ar^2$

or $(r - 1)(r - 3) = +\text{ive}$.

$\therefore \quad r < 1$ or $r > 3$

33. (a) Let the three numbers in G.P. be $ar, a, \dfrac{a}{r}$.

$$\text{Sum} = a\left(r + 1 + \frac{1}{r}\right) = 65$$

$\therefore \quad a(r^2 + r + 1) = 65r.$ ...(1)

Product $ar . a . \dfrac{a}{r} = 3375$

or $a^3 = (15)^3 \quad \therefore \quad a = 15$.

Putting for a in (1), we get $15(r^2 + r + 1) = 65r$

or $3r^2 + 3r + 3 = 13r$ or $3r^2 - 10r + 3 = 0$

$(r - 3)(3r - 1) = 0 \quad \therefore \quad r = 3$, or $\dfrac{1}{3}$.

Hence the numbers are 45, 15, 5 or 5, 15, 45.

(b) Here as above $a = 5$.

Also $a^2\left(r.1 + 1.\dfrac{1}{r} + r.\dfrac{1}{r}\right) = \dfrac{175}{2}$

or $25(r^2 + r + 1) = \dfrac{175}{2} r$

or $2(r^2 + r + 1) = 7r$

or $2r^2 - 5r + 2 = 0$ or $(r - 2)(2r - 1) = 0$

$\therefore \quad r = 2, \dfrac{1}{2}$. Hence the numbers are

10, 5, 5 / 2 or 5 / 2, 5, 10.

(c) 18, 6, 2 or 2, 6, 18.

34. (a) Let the numbers be a, ar, ar^2.

$\therefore \quad \text{Sum} = a(1 + r + r^2) = 70$ ...(1)

Also $4a, 5ar, 4ar^2$ are in A.P. by given condition

$\therefore \quad 2(5ar) = 4a + 4ar^2$ or $\dfrac{5}{2}r = 1 + r^2$ ...(2)

or $2r^2 - 5r + 2 = 0$ or $(r - 2)(2r - 1) = 0$

$\therefore \quad r = 2$ or $1/2$

Hence from (1), $a = 10, 40$

Hence the numbers are 10, 20, 40 or 40, 20, 10.

(b) $2b = a + c, b^2 = ac$

Eliminating b, we get $(a + c)^2 = 4ac$

$\therefore \quad (a - c)^2 = 0 \therefore \quad a = c$ and hence $b = a$

35. (a) Proceeding as above in Q. 34 (a),

$$a(1 + r + r^2) = 14$$ ...(1)

and $2(ar + 1) = (a + 1) + (ar^2 - 1)$

or $a(r^2 - 2r + 1) = 2$ ...(2)

Divide (1) and (2) and simplifying,

$2r^2 - 5r + 2 = 0 \quad \therefore \quad r = 2, \dfrac{1}{2}$ and hence $a = 2, 8$.

$\therefore \quad$ Numbers are 2, 4, 8, or 8, 4, 2.

(b) Proceed as in part (a)

$$2r^2 - 5r + 2 = 0 \implies r = 2, \frac{1}{2}$$

and corresponding values of a are 6, 24. Hence the numbers are 6, 12, 24, or 24, 12, 6.

36. (a) The three numbers in A.P. are $a-d$, a, $a+d$. Sum $= 3a = 15 \therefore a = 5$

∴   The numbers are $5-d$, 5, $5+d$.

Adding 1, 4, 19 respectively to these they become $6-d$, 9, $24+d$, and these are given to be in G.P.

∴ $9^2 = (6-d)(24+d)$ or $d^2 + 18d - 63 = 0$

$(d+21)(d-3) = 0 \therefore d = -21$ or 3.

Hence the numbers are 26, 5, −16 or 2, 5, 8.

(b) Last three of the four numbers are in A.P. and hence they may be chosen as $a-d$, a, $a+d$

Also the first number is same as the last one i.e. $a+d$.

Therefore the four numbers are $a+d$, $a-d$, a, $a+d$.

The first three of the above four are in G.P.

∴ $(a-d)^2 = a(a+d)$. But $d = 6$ given

∴ $(a-6)^2 = a(a+6)$

or $a^2 - 12a + 36 = a^2 + 6a$

or $18a = 36 \therefore a = 2$.

Putting for a and d the four numbers are 8, −4, 2, 8, which satisfy the given conditions.

37. (a) Let the four numbers in G.P. be $\frac{a}{r^3}$, $\frac{a}{r}$, ar, ar^3.

Product $= a^4 = 4096 = 8 \times 512$

$= 8 \times 8 \times 64 = 8^4 \therefore a = 8$.

Sum $= 8\left(\frac{1}{r^3} + \frac{1}{r} + r + r^3\right) = 85$

$8\left(r^3 + \frac{1}{r^3}\right) + 8\left(r + \frac{1}{r}\right) - 85 = 0.$ ...(1)

Let $r + \frac{1}{r} = z \therefore \left(r + \frac{1}{r}\right)^3 = z^3$

or $r^3 + \frac{1}{r^3} + 3r \cdot \frac{1}{r}\left(r + \frac{1}{r}\right) = z^3$

∴ $r^3 + \frac{1}{r^3} = z^3 - 3z.$

Hence (1) becomes $8(z^3 - 3z) + 8z - 85 = 0$

or $8z^3 - 16z - 85 = 0.$ ...(2)

Put $2z = t$ ∴ $t^3 - 8t - 85 = 0$

or $(t-5)(t^2 + 5t + 17) = 0$

∴ $t = 2z = 5$ or $2z = 2\left(r + \frac{1}{r}\right) = 5$ ...(3)

The other factor gives inaginary values.

∴   From (3), $2r^2 - 5r + 2 = 0.$

$(r-2)(2r-1) = 0 \therefore r = 2, \frac{1}{2}$, and $a = 8$.

Hence the four numbers are

1, 4, 16, 64 or 64, 16, 4, 1.

(b) $486, x_1, x_2, x_3, x_4, x_5, \frac{2}{3}$ will be a G.P. of 7 terms

∴ $\frac{2}{3} = T_7 = ar^6 = (486) r^6.$

∴ $r^6 = \frac{1}{729} = \frac{1}{3^6} \therefore r = \pm\frac{1}{3}$, take $r = \frac{1}{3}$.

∴ $x_1 = T_2 = ar = 486 \cdot \left(\frac{1}{3}\right) = 162$

$x_2 = T_3 = ar^2 = 486\left(\frac{1}{9}\right) = 54,$

$x_3 = 18$, $x_4 = 6$, $x_5 = 2.$

Hence the five geometric means are 162, 54, 18, 6, 2.

38. (a) Let the numbers be a and b

then $A = \text{A.M.} = \frac{a+b}{2}$ or $a+b = 2A$ ...(1)

$G = \text{G.M.} = \sqrt{ab} \therefore ab = G^2$ ...(2)

From (1) and (2) we find that a and b are the roots of $t^2 - 2At + G^2 = 0$

∴ $t = \frac{2A \pm \sqrt{4A^2 - 4G^2}}{2} = A \pm \sqrt{(A-G)(A+G)}$

(b) It is same as part (a). $t^2 - 2At + G^2 = 0.$

39. (a) Let G be the geometric mean of a and b, then

$G^2 = ab$ ...(1)

Let p and q be two arithmetic means between a and b, then a, p, q, b are in A.P.

∴ $2p = a+q$ and $2q = p+b$

or $a = 2p-q$ and $2q-p = b$

Hence from (1), $G^2 = ab = (2p-q)(2q-p).$

(b) Let the numbers be x and y.

A is their A.M. $2A = x+y$ ...(1)

Also p, q are two geometric means between x and y

∴ x, p, q, y are in G.P.

Since x, p, q are in G.P. ∴ $p^2 = xq$ or $p^3 = xpq$

Since p, q, y are in G.P. ∴ $q^2 = py$ or $q^3 = ypq$

Adding, $p^3 + q^3 = pq(x+y) = 2Apq$, by (1)

∴ $p^3 + q^3 = 2Apq.$

(c) $m = \frac{2b\sqrt{a}}{\sqrt{a} + \sqrt{b}}, n = \frac{2a\sqrt{b}}{\sqrt{a} + \sqrt{b}}$

$\frac{m+n}{2} = \sqrt{ab} = \frac{ma+nb}{m+n}$

∴ $m+n = 2\sqrt{ab}.$ ...(1)

and $ma + nb = (m+n)\sqrt{ab} = 2ab$ by (1)   ...(2)

Solve (1) and (2) for m and n

$$\therefore \quad m = \frac{2\sqrt{ab}}{\sqrt{a}+\sqrt{b}} \cdot \sqrt{b}, n = \frac{2\sqrt{ab}}{\sqrt{a}+\sqrt{b}} \cdot \sqrt{a}$$

40. (a) **See Page 143 col II**.

(b) $\dfrac{a^{n+1}+b^{n+1}}{a^n+b^n} = \sqrt{ab} = a^{1/2} b^{1/2}$

$\qquad\qquad\qquad$ **by given condition**

$\therefore \quad a^{n+1}+b^{n+1} = a^n a^{1/2} b^{1/2} + b^n b^{1/2} a^{1/2}$

$\qquad\qquad = a^{n+1/2} \cdot \sqrt{b} + b^{n+1/2} \sqrt{a}$

$\therefore \quad a^{n+1/2}(\sqrt{a}-\sqrt{b}) = b^{n+1/2}(\sqrt{a}-\sqrt{b})$

$\therefore \quad a^{n+1/2} = b^{n+1/2}$.

Above is possible only when $n+\dfrac{1}{2}=0$

$\therefore \quad n = -\dfrac{1}{2}$.

41. (a) Let if possible 8 be the first term and 12 and 27 be mth and nth terms respectively.

$\therefore \quad 12 = ar^{m-1} = 8r^{m-1}, 27 = 8r^{n-1}$

$\therefore \quad \dfrac{3}{2} = r^{m-1}, \left(\dfrac{3}{2}\right)^3 = r^{n-1} = r^{3(m-1)}$

$\therefore \quad n-1 = 3m-3 \quad \text{or} \quad 3m = n+2$

or $\quad \dfrac{m}{1} = \dfrac{n+2}{3} = k$ say $\quad \therefore \quad m = k, n = 3k-2$.

By giving k different values we get integral values of m and n. Hence there can be infinite number of G.P.'s whose any three terms will be 8, 12, 27 (not consecutive).

(b) Let $T_p = 10, T_q = 11, T_r = 12$

$\therefore \quad AR^{p-1} = 10, AR^{q-1} = 11, AR^{r-1} = 12$

$\therefore \quad R^{p-q} = \dfrac{10}{11}, R^{q-r} = \dfrac{11}{12}$

or $\quad \left(\dfrac{10}{11}\right)^{1/(p-q)} = \left(\dfrac{11}{12}\right)^{1/(q-r)} = R$

or $\quad \left(\dfrac{10}{11}\right)^{q-r} = \left(\dfrac{11}{12}\right)^{p-q}$

or $\quad (10)^{q-r}(12)^{p-q} = (11)^{p-q+q-r} = 11^{p-r}$

Now L.H.S. of above is clearly even whereas R.H.S. is an odd number which is not possible. Hence 10, 11, 12 cannot be the terms of a single G.P.

42. (a) Ans. (ii).

Let the G.P. be $a + ar + ar^2 + ar^3 + \ldots$

Then as given $T_3 = ar^2 = 4$. $\qquad$ ...(1)

$\therefore \quad T_1 T_2 T_3 T_4 T_5 = a \cdot ar \cdot ar^2 \cdot ar^3 \cdot ar^4 = a^5 \cdot r^{10}$

$\qquad = (ar^2)^5 = 4^5,$ $\qquad$ by (1)

(b) $2y^3 = x^3 + z^3 \quad$ or $\quad \left(\dfrac{x}{y}\right)^3 + \left(\dfrac{z}{y}\right)^3 = 2 \quad$ ...(1)

$(\log_z x)^2 = \log_x y \cdot \log_y z$

or $\quad \left(\dfrac{\log x}{\log z}\right)^2 = \dfrac{\log y}{\log x} \cdot \dfrac{\log z}{\log y} = \dfrac{\log z}{\log x}$

$\therefore \quad (\log x)^3 = (\log z)^3 \quad$ or $\quad \log x = \log z$

$\therefore \quad x = z$

Hence from (1), $2y^3 = 2z^3 \quad \therefore \quad y = z = x$

But $xyz = 64 \quad \therefore \quad x^3 = 64$

$\therefore \quad x = y = z = 4$

(c) Ans. (b). If $\alpha, \beta, \gamma, \delta$ be the four + ive roots then

$$\frac{\alpha+\beta+\gamma+\delta}{4} = \frac{4}{4} = (\alpha\beta\gamma\delta)^{1/4}$$

Above shows that A.M. of the four roots is equal to their G.M. Hence $\alpha, \beta, \gamma, \delta$ are all equal and each equal to 1.

$\therefore \quad E = (x-1)^4 = x^4 - 4x^3 + 6x^2 - 4x + 1$

Comparing, $a = 6, b = -4$.

43. (a) $(\log_z y)^2 = (\log_y x)(\log_x z)$

or $\quad \left(\dfrac{\log y}{\log z}\right)^2 = \dfrac{\log x}{\log y} \cdot \dfrac{\log z}{\log x}$

or $\quad (\log y)^3 = (\log z)^3 \quad \therefore \quad y = z$.

$\therefore \quad 2x^4 = 2y^4 \quad \therefore \quad x = y = z$

Also $xyz = 8 \Rightarrow x^3 = 8$

$\therefore \quad x = 2 = y = z$.

(b) $d = y - x$ for A.P.

$r = \dfrac{y}{x} < 1$ for G.P. as $x > y$

$S = \dfrac{a}{1-r} = \dfrac{x}{1-y/x} = \dfrac{x^2}{x-y} \qquad$ ...(1)

$S_n = \dfrac{n}{2}[2a+(n-1)d] = \dfrac{n}{2}[2x+(n-1)(y-x)]$

$\qquad = nx - \dfrac{n(n-1)x^2}{2S}$ by (1)

44. (a) By given condition, we have

$S_{2n} = 3[T_1 + T_3 + T_5 + \ldots + T_{2n-1}]$

$\qquad = 3[a + ar^2 + ar^4 + \ldots n \text{ terms}]$

$\therefore \quad \dfrac{a}{1-r}(1-r^{2n}) = 3 \cdot \dfrac{a}{1-r^2}[1-(r^2)^n]$

or $\quad 1 = \dfrac{3}{1+r} \quad \therefore \quad r = 2$.

(b) $a(1+r+r^2+r^3) = 30 \qquad$ ...(1)

$\qquad a^2(1+r^2+r^4+r^6) = 340$

or $\quad \dfrac{a(1-r^4)}{1-r} = 30, \dfrac{a^2(1-r^8)}{1-r^2} = 340$

Eliminate a by squaring 1st and dividing by 2nd.

$\therefore \quad \dfrac{a^2(1-r^4)^2}{(1-r)^2} \cdot \dfrac{1-r^2}{a^2(1-r^8)} = \dfrac{900}{340} = \dfrac{45}{17}$

$\dfrac{1-r^4}{1+r^4} \cdot \dfrac{1+r}{1-r} = \dfrac{45}{17}$

or $17(1+r+r^2+r^3)(1+r) = 45(1+r^4)$

or $17(r^4+2r^3+2r^2+2r+1) = 45+45r^4$

or $14r^4-17r^3-17r^2-17r+14 = 0$

Divide by r^2

$14\left(r^2+\dfrac{1}{r^2}\right)-17\left(r+\dfrac{1}{r}\right)-17 = 0$

Put $r+\dfrac{1}{r} = t$

$14(t^2-2)-17t-17 = 0$

or $14t^2-17t-45 = 0$

$\therefore t = \dfrac{17 \pm \sqrt{289+2520}}{28}$

or $r+\dfrac{1}{r} = \dfrac{17 \pm 53}{28} = \dfrac{5}{2}$ or $-\dfrac{9}{7}$

or $2r^2-5r+2 = 0$ and $7r^2+9r+7 = 0$

$\therefore r = 2, \dfrac{1}{2}$ from 1st and r is imaginary from 2nd

When $r = 2$ then from (1), $a = 2$; when $r = \dfrac{1}{2}$ then

$a = 16$.

Hence the required G.P.'s are 2, 4, 8, 16, 32, ... and 16, 8, 4, 2, 1, ...

(c) $\Sigma a_i = S = \dfrac{a(1-r^n)}{1-r}$ ...(1)

$\Sigma a_i^2 = a^2+a^2r^2+a^2r^4+...... = \dfrac{a^2(1-r^{2n})}{1-r^2}$ ...(2)

Now $(\Sigma a_i)^2 = \Sigma a_i^2 + 2\Sigma a_i a_j$

$\therefore 2\Sigma a_i a_j = (\Sigma a_i)^2 - \Sigma a_i^2$

$= \dfrac{a^2(1-r^n)^2}{(1-r)^2} - \dfrac{a^2(1-r^{2n})}{1-r^2}$ by (1) and (2)

$= \dfrac{a^2(1-r^n)}{(1-r)}\left[\dfrac{1-r^n}{1-r} - \dfrac{1+r^n}{1+r}\right]$

$= \dfrac{a^2(1-r^n)}{(1-r)} \cdot \dfrac{(2r-2r^n)}{(1-r)(1+r)}$

$\therefore \Sigma a_i a_j = \dfrac{1}{2}\dfrac{a^2r(1-r^{n-1})(1-r^n)}{(1-r)^2(1+r)}$

(d) We have to prove that $\dfrac{1-r^{2n+1}}{1-r} > (2n+1)r^n$

L.H.S. = Sum of a G.P. of $2n+1$ terms whose first term is 1, and common ratio r.

L.H.S. $= 1+r+r^2+...+r^{2n}$

$= (1+r^{2n})+(r+r^{2n-1})+(r^2+r^{2n-2})+... n$ pairs $+r^n$

Apply A.M. > G.M. on each pair

$\therefore$ L.H.S. $> \underbrace{(2r^n+2r^n+...+2r^n)}_{n \text{ terms}} + r^n$

$= 2n \cdot r^n + r^n = (2n+1)r^n$

45. $S_4 = 30$ $\therefore \dfrac{a(1-r^4)}{1-r} = 30$ ...(1)

$T_5+T_6+T_7+T_8 = 480$

$\therefore ar^4\dfrac{(1-r^4)}{1-r} = 480$ ...(2)

Dividing (2) by (1),

$\therefore r^4 = 16$ or $r^2 = 4$ or $r = 2, -2$

Putting in (1), $a = 2, -6$

The G.P.'s are $a = 2, r = 2$ and $a = -6, r = -2$

2nd part :

$\dfrac{T_n}{T_n'} = \dfrac{ar^{n-1}}{a'r'^{n-1}} = \dfrac{2}{-6}\left(\dfrac{2}{-2}\right)^{n-1}$

$= -\dfrac{1}{3}(-1)^{n-1} = \dfrac{1}{3}(-1)^n$

$S_6 = \dfrac{a(r^6-1)}{r-1} = \dfrac{2(64-1)}{2-1} = 126$

$\therefore S_6 - S_4 = 126 - 30 = 96$

Similarly, $S_6' - S_4' = 96$.

46. (a) $a = 4, T_3-T_5 = \dfrac{32}{81}$ or $a(r^2-r^4) = \dfrac{32}{81}$

or $r^4-r^2+\dfrac{8}{81} = 0$ or $81r^4-81r^2+8 = 0$

or $(9r^2-8)(9r^2-1) = 0$

$\therefore r^2 = 8/9, 1/9.$ $\therefore$ The value of r is to be +ive since all the terms are +ive. Out of the two we shall first choose $r = \dfrac{1}{3}$.

$\therefore S_\infty = \dfrac{a}{1-r} = \dfrac{4}{1-\dfrac{1}{3}} = \dfrac{4 \cdot 3}{2} = 6.$

Now find S_∞ when $r = 2\sqrt{2}/3$ yourself.

(b) $\dfrac{a}{1-r} = 2$ and $\dfrac{a^3}{1-r^3} = 24$ where $r < 1$

Eliminating a, we get $\dfrac{1-r^3}{(1-r)^3} = \dfrac{8}{24}$

or $3(1+r+r^2) = (1-r)^2 = 1-2r+r^2$

or $2r^2+5r+2 = 0$

$(2r+1)(r+2) = 0$ $\therefore r = -\dfrac{1}{2}$

Putting the value of r, we get $a = 3$

$\therefore 3-\dfrac{3}{2}+\dfrac{3}{4}-\dfrac{3}{8}+......$ is the series.

(c) $S_\infty = \dfrac{a}{1-r} = 162$

$S_n = \dfrac{a(1-r^n)}{1-r} = 160$

Dividing $1 - r^n = \dfrac{160}{162} = \dfrac{80}{81}$

$\therefore \quad 1 - \dfrac{80}{81} = r^n$

or $\quad r^n = \dfrac{1}{81}$ or $\left(\dfrac{1}{r}\right)^n = 81$ ...(1)

Now it is given that $\dfrac{1}{r}$ is an integer and n is also an integer. Hence the relation (1) implies that $\dfrac{1}{r}$ $= 3, 9,$ or 81 so that $n = 4, 2$ or 1

$\therefore \quad a = 162\left(1 - \dfrac{1}{3}\right)$ or $162\left(1 - \dfrac{1}{9}\right)$

or $\quad 162\left(1 - \dfrac{1}{81}\right) = 108$ or 144 or 160.

47. (a) $\quad a = 5,\ ar^2 = a + 3d,\ ar^4 = a + 15d$

$\therefore \quad 5r^2 = 5 + 3d,\ 5r^4 = 5 + 15d$

or $\quad r^4 = 1 + 3d \qquad$ Multiply by 25

$\quad 25r^4 = 25 + 75d$

or $\quad (5 + 3d)^2 = 25 + 75d$

or $\quad 25 + 30d + 9d^2 = 25 + 75d$

$\therefore \quad 9d^2 - 45d = 0 \quad \therefore \quad d = 5, 0.$

$\therefore \quad T_4 = a + 3d = 5 + 15 = 20 = ar^2 = 5r^2$

$\therefore \quad r = 2, -2$

$\therefore \quad 5, 20, 80$ are the 1st, 3rd and 5th terms of G.P. and T_4 of A.P. = 20

(b) Let the A.P. be $a + (a + d) + (a + 2d) + \ldots$

By given condition G.P. is $d + da + da^2 + \ldots$

S_{10} of A.P. $= 155,\quad S_2$ of G.P. $= 9$

$\therefore \quad 2a + 9d = 31 \quad$ and $\quad d + da = 9$

Solving, we get

$\quad a = 2, d = 3$ or $a = \dfrac{25}{2}$ and $d = \dfrac{2}{3}$

$\therefore$ A.P. is $2 + 5 + 8 + 11 + \ldots$ and

G.P. is $3 + 6 + 12 + 24 + \ldots$

or A.P. $\dfrac{25}{2} + \dfrac{79}{6} + \dfrac{83}{6} + \ldots$ and

G.P. is $\dfrac{2}{3} + \dfrac{25}{3} + \dfrac{625}{6} + \ldots$

48. (a) Let the numbers be $ar, a, a/r$ such that

$a\left(r + 1 + \dfrac{1}{r}\right) = \alpha S$ and $a^2\left(r^2 + 1 + \dfrac{1}{r^2}\right) = S^2$

Put $r + \dfrac{1}{r} = t \quad \therefore \quad r^2 + \dfrac{1}{r^2} = t^2 - 2$

$\therefore \quad a(t + 1) = \alpha S$ and $a^2(t^2 - 1) = S^2$

Eliminating S, we get $a^2(t^2 - 1) = \dfrac{a^2(t + 1)^2}{\alpha^2}$

$\therefore \quad (t - 1)\alpha^2 = (t + 1)$ or $t = \dfrac{\alpha^2 + 1}{\alpha^2 - 1}$ ...(1)

Now $\quad t = r + \dfrac{1}{r} \quad \therefore \quad r^2 - rt + 1 = 0$

For t to be real $t^2 - 4 > 0 \quad \therefore \quad (t + 2)(t - 2) > 0$

$\therefore \quad t < -2 \text{ or } t > 2$

Hence from (1), we get

$\quad \dfrac{\alpha^2 + 1}{\alpha^2 - 1} < -2 \quad$ or $\quad \dfrac{\alpha^2 + 1}{\alpha^2 - 1} > 2$

or $\quad \dfrac{\alpha^2 + 1}{\alpha^2 - 1} + 2 < 0 \quad$ or $\quad \dfrac{\alpha^2 + 1}{\alpha^2 - 1} - 2 > 0$

Note : In an inequality we can multiply only by a + ive quantity. Here we do not know whether $(\alpha^2 - 1)$ is + ive or – ive

or $\quad \dfrac{3\alpha^2 - 1}{\alpha^2 - 1} < 0$ or $\dfrac{3 - \alpha^2}{\alpha^2 - 1} > 0 \ \Rightarrow\ \dfrac{\alpha^2 - 3}{\alpha^2 - 1} < 0$

$\therefore \quad \dfrac{3\left(\alpha^2 - \dfrac{1}{3}\right)(\alpha^2 - 1)}{(\alpha^2 - 1)^2} < 0$ ...(1)

and $\quad \dfrac{(\alpha^2 - 1)(\alpha^2 - 3)}{(\alpha^2 - 1)^2} < 0$ ...(2)

The second implies that α^2 lies between 1 and 3 and first implies that α^2 lies between 1/3 and 1.

$\therefore \quad \alpha^2 \in \left(\dfrac{1}{3}, 1\right) \cup (1, 3)$.

(b) The condition for A.P. $\Rightarrow x = 3y$ ...(1)

The condition for G.P.

$\Rightarrow \quad (xy + 5)^2 = (x + 1)^2(y + 1)^2$

$\Rightarrow \quad (3y^2 + 5)^2 - [(3y + 1)(y + 1)]^2 = 0,\qquad$ by (1)

$\Rightarrow \quad (y - 1)(3y^2 + 2y + 3) = 0,$

$\therefore \quad y = 1, -1 + 2\sqrt{2}i, -1 - 2\sqrt{2}i$

$\therefore \quad y = 1$ and $x = 3$

Ans. (i) A.P. 3, 5, 7, G.P. 4, 8, 16.

(ii) A.P. $-1 + 2\sqrt{2}i, \dfrac{-5 + 10\sqrt{2}i}{3}, \dfrac{-7 + 14\sqrt{2}i}{3}$

G.P. $\dfrac{-4 + 8\sqrt{2}i}{9}, \dfrac{8 - 4\sqrt{2}i}{3}, -8$

(iii) A.P. $-1 - 2\sqrt{2}i, \dfrac{-5 - 10\sqrt{2}i}{3}, \dfrac{-7 - 14\sqrt{2}i}{3}$

G.P. $\dfrac{-4 - 8\sqrt{2}i}{9}, \dfrac{8 + 4\sqrt{2}i}{3}, -8$

Note : Answers (ii) and (iii) are conjugates.

49. (a) Let a, ar, ar^2 be in G.P., where

$\quad a(1 + r + r^2) = 26$ ...(1)

Also $\quad a + 1, ar + 6, ar^2 + 3$ are in A.P.

$\therefore \quad 2(ar+6) = (a+1)+(ar^2+3)$

or $\quad a(r^2-2r+1) = 8$ ...(2)

Dividing (1) and (2) and simplifying, we get

$\quad 18(r^2+1) = 60r \quad$ or $\quad 3r^2-10r+3 = 0$

$\therefore \quad (r-3)(3r-1) = 0 \quad \therefore \quad r = 3, \dfrac{1}{3}$.

Putting in (1), $a = 2, 18$.

$\therefore \quad$ The numbers are 2, 6, 18 or 18, 6, 2.

(b) $\quad a, ar, ar^2$ are in G.P.

$\quad\quad a, ar, ar^2-64$ are in A.P.

$\therefore \quad 2ar = a+ar^2-64$.

or $\quad a(r^2-2r+1) = 64$ ...(1)

Again $\quad a, ar-8, ar^2-64$ are in G.P.

$\therefore \quad (ar-8)^2 = a(ar^2-64) \quad$ or $\quad -16ar+64 = -64a$

or $\quad a(16r-64) = 64$ ...(2)

$\therefore \quad r^2-2r+1 = 16r-64 \quad$ by (1) and (2)

or $\quad r^2-18r+65 = 0$

$\therefore \quad (r-5)(r-13) = 0 \quad \therefore \quad r = 5$, hence $a = 4$.

$\therefore \quad$ Numbers are 4, 20, 100 G.P. and 4, 20, 36 A.P. and 4, 12, 36, again G.P.

50. You must know that

$\quad 528 = 500+20+8$

$\quad xyz = 100x+10y+z$

Choose three numbers in G.P. to be a, ar, ar^2

By given condition,

$\quad a(ar)(ar^2)-792 = (ar^2)(ar)a$ ...(1)

Also $(a), (ar+2), (ar^2)$ constitute an A.P.

$\therefore \quad 2(ar+2) = a+ar^2$

or $\quad a(r^2-2r+1) = 4$

or $\quad a(r-1)^2 = 4$ ...(2)

Again from (1), we have

$\quad 100a+10ar+ar^2-792 = 100ar^2+10ar+a$

or $\quad 99(r^2-1)a = -792$

$\therefore \quad (r-1)(r+1)a = -8$ ...(3)

Dividing (3) by (2), we get

$\quad \dfrac{r+1}{r-1} = -2 \quad$ or $\quad r = \dfrac{1}{3} \quad \therefore \quad a = 9$

Hence the numbers are 9, 3, 1 or 931

Also $931-792 = 139$ i.e., reverse of 931.

Again $9, 3+2, 1$ i.e. $9, 5, 1$ are in A.P.

51. Discriminant of the equation in x will be found to be $-4(b^2-ac)^2$ which is ≤ 0. But for real x, it cannot be negative and so we must have $b^2-ac = 0$, showing that a, b, c are in G.P. Under this condition the equation has equal roots say x, x.

Sum $= x+x = \dfrac{2b(a+c)}{(a^2+b^2)}$

$\therefore \quad \dfrac{b(a+c)}{a^2+ac} = \dfrac{b}{a} = \dfrac{c}{b} \quad \because \quad b^2 = ac$

which is the common ratio.

52. We are given that

$\quad f(x+y) = f(x)f(y)$ and $f(1) = 2$

$\therefore \quad f(2) = f(1+1) = f(1).f(1) = 2 \cdot 2 = 2^2$

$\quad f(3) = f(2+1) = f(2).f(1) = 2^2 \cdot 2 = 2^3$,

$\quad f(4) = 2^4$ etc.

Now $\displaystyle\sum_{k=1}^{n} f(a+k) = \sum_{k=1}^{n} f(a)f(k) = 2^a \sum_{k=1}^{n} f(k)$

$\quad = 2^a [2+2^2+2^3+....+2^n]$

$\quad = 2^{a+1} [1+2+2^2+......n \text{ terms}]$

$\quad = 2^{a+1} \dfrac{1 \cdot (2^n-1)}{2-1} = 2^{a+1} (2^n-1)$

$\quad = 16 \cdot (2^n-1)$

$\therefore \quad 2^{a+1} = 16 = 2^4 \quad \therefore \quad a+1 = 4$ or $a = 3$.

§ 3. Arithmetico-geometric series

Definition. A type of series in which each term is the product of the corresponding terms of an A.P. and a G.P. is called arithmetico-geometric series. For example :

$\quad 1+3x+5x^2+7x^3+...$

$\quad a+(a+d)r+(a+2d)r^2+(a+3d)r^3+...$

In the above series $1, 3, 5, 7, ..., a, a+d, a+2d, ...$ are in A.P. and $1, x, x^2, x^3, ...$ and $1, r, r^2, r^3, ...$ are in G.P.

In general if $x_1, x_2, x_3, ...$ be an A.P. and $y_1, y_2, y_3, ...$ be a G.P. then the series

$x_1 y_1, x_2 y_2, x_3 y_3, ...$ will form an arithmetico-geometric series (A.G.S.)

Sum of n terms of an arithmetico-geometric series.

(Ist term of G.P. $= 1$)

Let $\quad S = a+(a+d)r+(a+2d)r^2+...$

$\quad\quad\quad\quad\quad +[a+(n-1)d]r^{n-1}$ ...(1)

Multiply both sides of (1) by common ratio r and writing as below i.e. starting the value of rS by writing its first term below 2nd term of S etc.,

$\therefore \quad rS = ar \quad\quad +(a+d)r^2+...$

$\quad\quad\quad\quad +[a+(n-2)d]r^{n-1}+[a+(n-1)d]r^n$

Subtracting, we get

$S(1-r) = a+[dr+dr^2+...+dr^{n-1} \quad$ i.e. $(n-1)$ terms$]$

$\quad\quad\quad\quad\quad\quad\quad -[a+(n-1)d]r^n$

The middle bracket is a G.P. of $(n-1)$ terms.

$\therefore \quad S(1-r) = a+\dfrac{dr(1-r^{n-1})}{1-r}-[a+(n-1)d]r^n$

$\therefore \quad S = \dfrac{a}{1-r} + \dfrac{dr(1-r^{n-1})}{(1-r)^2} - \dfrac{[a+(n-1)d]r^n}{1-r}.$ ...(2)

Sum upto infinity.

If $|r| < 1$ and $n \to \infty$, then $\lim\limits_{n \to \infty} r^n = 0$.

$*\therefore \quad S = \dfrac{a}{1-r} + \dfrac{dr}{(1-r)^2}.$ **(Remember)** ...(3)

In the above formula the first term of G.P. was 1. If however first term of G.P. be b then proceeding as above

$$S_n = \dfrac{ab}{1-r} + \dfrac{dbr(1-r^{n-1})}{(1-r)^2} + \dfrac{[a+(n-1)d]br^n}{1-r}$$

If $r < 1$, then $\quad S_\infty = \dfrac{ab}{1-r} + \dfrac{dbr}{(1-r)^2}.$ ...(4)

(See Q. 31 P. 164-172)

§ 4. Use of Natural Numbers.

We shall use capital Greek letter Σ (sigma) to denote the sum of a series.

$$\Sigma\, n = 1 + 2 + 3 + \ldots + n = \dfrac{n(n+1)}{2}$$

$$\Sigma\, n^2 = 1^2 + 2^2 + 3^2 + \ldots + n^2 = \dfrac{n(n+1)(2n+1)}{6}$$

$$\Sigma\, n^3 = 1^3 + 2^3 + 3^3 + \ldots + n^3 = \left[\dfrac{n(n+1)}{2}\right]^2$$

$$\Sigma\, a = a + a + a + a + \ldots n \text{ terms} = na.$$

Application :

Let the nth term of a series be given as
$$T_n = an^2 + bn + c.$$

In order to find the sum of n terms, we put $n = 1, 2, 3, \ldots n$ and then add them

$T_1 = a.1^2 + b.1 + c \;;\quad T_2 = a.2^2 + b.2 + c$

$T_3 = a.3^2 + b.3 + c \ldots$ and so on.

$\therefore\quad S_n = a(1^2 + 2^2 + 3^2 + \ldots n^2)$

$\qquad\qquad + b(1 + 2 + 3 + \ldots n) + (c + c + c + \ldots n \text{ terms})$

$\qquad = a\Sigma\, n^2 + b\Sigma\, n + c.n.$

Now putting the values of $\Sigma\, n^2$ and $\Sigma\, n$ in the above we shall have the value of S_n.

*Alternative Method :

If T_n is expressible as product of m consecutive numbers beginning with n.

$T_n = [n(n+1)(n+2)\ldots(n+m-1)]$ then

$S_n = [n(n+1)(n+2)\ldots(n+m-1)]\dfrac{(n+m)}{m+1}$

Illustration :

If $\quad T_n = n$, then $S_n = n.\dfrac{(n+1)}{2}$

If $\quad T_n = n(n+1) = n^2 + n$

$\therefore \quad S_n = \Sigma\, n^2 + \Sigma\, n$

$\qquad = \dfrac{n}{6}(n+1)(2n+1) + \dfrac{n}{2}(n+1)$

$\qquad = \dfrac{n}{3}(n+1)(n+2) = n(n+1).\dfrac{(n+2)}{3}$

*§ 5. Method of difference.

Consider the series $3 + 7 + 14 + 24 + 37 + \ldots n$ terms

Here the differences between the successive terms are

$7 - 3, \quad 14 - 7, \quad 24 - 14, \quad 37 - 24, \ldots$

i.e., $\quad 4, 7, 10, 13 \ldots$ which are in A.P.

The above differences could be in G.P. also.

In order to find its sum we follow the method given below.

Let $S = 3 + 7 + 14 + 24 + 37 + \ldots + T_n$

$\quad S = \qquad 3 + 7 + 14 + 24 + \ldots + T_{n-1} + T_n.$ **(Note)**

Subtracting, we get

$\quad 0 = 3 + [4 + 7 + 10 + 13 + \ldots(n-1) \text{ terms}] - T_n$

$\therefore \quad T_n = 3 + S_{n-1}$ of an A.P. whose $a = 4$ and $d = 3$.

$\therefore \quad T_n = 3 + \dfrac{n-1}{2}[2.4 + (n-2).3]$

$\qquad = \dfrac{6 + (n-1)(3n+2)}{4}$

or $\quad T_n = \dfrac{1}{2}(3n^2 - n + 4).$ ...(A)

Now putting $n = 1, 2, 3, \ldots n$ and adding,

$\therefore \quad S_n = \dfrac{1}{2}[3\Sigma\, n^2 - \Sigma\, n + 4n]$

$\qquad = \dfrac{1}{2}\left[3.\dfrac{n(n+1)(2n+1)}{6} - \dfrac{n(n+1)}{2} + 4n\right]$

$\qquad = \dfrac{n}{2}(n^2 + n + 4).$

*Alternative Method :

The successive terms are

$\qquad 3, 7, 14, 24, 37, \ldots.$

Successive differences are :

$\qquad 4, 7, 10, 13, \ldots.$ 1st difference

$\qquad 3, 3, 3, \ldots$ (equal) 2nd difference

Hence T_n of this series will be a quadratic function of n.

$\therefore \quad T_n = an^2 + bn + c$ ...(1)

In order to find a, b, c put $n = 1, 2, 3$ and we get

$T_1 = 3 = a + b + c$

$T_2 = 7 = 4a + 2b + c$

$T_3 = 14 = 9a + 3b + c$

Subtracting in pairs, we get

$4 = 3a + b, 7 = 5a + b$

$\therefore \quad a = \dfrac{3}{2}, b = -\dfrac{1}{2} \quad \therefore \quad c = 2$

$T_n = \dfrac{3}{2}n^2 - \dfrac{1}{2}n + 2 = \dfrac{1}{2}(3n^2 - n + 4)$

Same as in (A).

Problem Set (3)

Arithmetico-geometric series, Sum of natural numbers, Sum of their squares and cubes, Method of difference.

Sum the series :

1. (a) $1 + \dfrac{4}{5} + \dfrac{7}{5^2} + \dfrac{10}{5^3} + \dots$ to n terms and to ∞.

   (b) Sum the series
   $1 \cdot 1 + 3 \cdot 01 + 5 \cdot 001 + 7 \cdot 0001 \dots n$ terms.

   (c)* $2^{1/4} \cdot 4^{1/8} \cdot 8^{1/16} \cdot 16^{1/32} \dots$ is equal to 2.

2. $1 + \dfrac{1}{5} + \dfrac{3}{5^2} + \dfrac{5}{5^3} + \dots$ to ∞.

3. (a) $1 + \dfrac{3}{2} + \dfrac{5}{4} + \dfrac{7}{8} + \dots n$ terms.

   (b)* $1 + 2.2 + 3.2^2 + 4.2^3 + \dots + 100 . 2^{99}$.

4. $1 + (1+2) + (1+2+3) + (1+2+3+4) + \dots$ to n terms.

5. (a) $1^2 + (1^2 + 2^2) + (1^2 + 2^2 + 3^2) + \dots$ to n terms.

   (b) If $S_n = \lambda n (n-1)$ is an A.P. where $\lambda \neq 0$ then prove that the sum of the squares of the n terms of the A.P. is $\dfrac{2}{3} \lambda^2 n (n-1) (2n-1)$

   (c) Prove that the sum of n terms of the series $1^2 + (1^2 + 3^2) + (1^2 + 3^2 + 5^2) + \dots$ is
   $\dfrac{1}{6} n (n+1) (2n^2 + 2n - 1)$

6. (a) $1 . 2^2 + 2 . 3^2 + 3 . 4^2 + \dots$ to n terms.

   (b) $1 . 2 . 3 + 2 . 3 . 4 + 3 . 4 . 5 + \dots$ to n terms.

   (c) $1 . 2 . 5 + 2 . 3 . 6 + 3 . 4 . 7 + \dots n$ terms.

   (d) Determine the fourth degree expression in n which is equal to $\sum\limits_{r=1}^{n} r (r+1) (2r+3)$.

   (e) Sum the series
   $199.1 + 197.3 + 195.5 + \dots 3.197 + 1.199$

7. (a) $1 . 3^2 + 2 . 5^2 + 3 . 7^2 + \dots$ to 20 terms.

   (b) Prove that the sum of n terms of series $1.3.5 + 3.5.7 + 5.7.9 + \dots$ is equal to
   $n (2n^3 + 8n^2 + 7n - 2)$.

8. (i)* $\dfrac{1^3}{1} + \dfrac{1^3 + 2^3}{1+3} + \dfrac{1^3 + 2^3 + 3^3}{1+3+5} + \dots 16$ terms.

   (ii) $\dfrac{3}{1^2 . 2^2} + \dfrac{5}{2^2 . 3^2} + \dfrac{7}{3^2 . 4^2} + \dots n$ terms and
   deduce the sum upto infinity.

9. $1 + 3 + 7 + 15 + 31 + \dots$ to n terms.

10. (a) $1 + 3 + 6 + 10 + 15 + \dots$ to n terms.

    (b) Prove that the next term of the sequence $1, 5, 14, 30, 55, \dots$ is 91.

11. (i) $4 + 6 + 9 + 13 + 18 + \dots$ to n terms.

    (ii) $2 + 4 + 7 + 11 + 16 + \dots$ to n terms.

(iii)* Find the sum of the series
$\dfrac{3}{1!} + \dfrac{5}{2!} + \dfrac{9}{3!} + \dfrac{15}{4!} + \dfrac{23}{5!} + \dots \infty$.

(Roorkee 1998)

12. (a)* The natural numbers are written in the form of a triangle as shown below :

			1				1st
		2		3			2nd
	4		5		6		3rd
7		8		9		10	4th
11	12	13	14	15			5th

....

.... nth

(i) Find the sum of the numbers in the nth row.

(ii) The sum of numbers in all the n rows.

(b) The odd + ive integers are written in the form of a triangle as shown below :

$$
\begin{array}{ccccccccc}
 & & & & 1 & & & & \\
 & & & 3 & & 5 & & & \\
 & & 7 & & 9 & & 11 & & \\
 & 13 & & 15 & & 17 & & 19 & \\
21 & & 23 & & 25 & & 27 & & 29
\end{array}
$$

Prove that the sum of the numbers in the nth row is n^3.

(c) If $(1^2 - t_1) + (2^2 - t_2) + \dots + (n^2 - t_n)$
$$= \dfrac{1}{3} n (n^2 - 1),$$
then prove that t_n is n.

(d) The sequence n of natural numbers is divided into classes as follows

$$
\begin{array}{cccccc}
 & 1 & 2 & & & \\
3 & 4 & 5 & 6 & & \\
7 & 8 & 9 & 10 & 11 & 12
\end{array}
$$

....

....

Prove that the sum of the numbers in the nth row is $n (2n^2 + 1)$.

(e) The cubes of the natural numbers are grouped as $1^3, (2^3, 3^3), (4^3, 5^3, 6^3), \dots$ then prove that the sum of terms in the nth group is $\dfrac{1}{8} n^3 (n^2 + 1) (n^2 + 3)$.

13. (a)* Find the sum of n terms of the series
$3 + 8 + 22 + 72 + 266 + 1036 + \dots$

    (b) Find the sum of n terms of the series
$2 + 5 + 12 + 31 + 86 + \dots$

14. (a) Find the sum of all possible products of the first n natural numbers taken two by two.

Another Form :

*Find the sum of the products of the integers $1, 2, 3, ..., n$ taken two at a time, and hence show that it is equal to half the excess of the cubes of the given integers over the sum of their squares.

Another form :

Find the coefficient of x^{n-2} in the polynomial
$$(x-1)(x-2)(x-3) ...... (x-n).$$

(b) Coefficient of x^{99} in the polynomial
$(x-1)(x-2)(x-3) ... (x-100)$ is .....

(c) If s_n denotes the sum of n terms of a G.P. whose common ratio is r, then prove that sum of the products taken two and two together of this series is $\dfrac{r}{r+1} s_n \cdot s_{n-1}$.

(d) If the mean deviation of the numbers $1, 1+d, 1+2d, ..., 1+100d$ from their mean is 255, then the d is equal to
  (a) 20.2   (b) 10.0
  (c) 20.0   (d) 10.1   **(AIEEE 2009)**

15. (a)* Sum to n terms the series
$$1^2 - 2^2 + 3^2 - 4^2 + 5^2 - 6^2 + ...$$

(b) Find the sum of the series
$$S = 1^2 - 2^2 + 3^2 - 4^2 + ... + 29^2 - 30^2$$
and $S = 1^2 - 2^2 + 3^2 - 4^2 + ... + 31^2$

16. (a) Find the sum of the series $31^3 + 32^3 + ... + 50^3$.

(b)* Prove that the sum of all the numbers of the form n^3 which lie between 100 and 10,000 is 53261.

17. If s and t are respectively the sum and the sum of the squares of n successive positive integers beginning with a, then show that $nt - s^2$ is independent of a.

18. * Balls are arranged in rows to form an equilateral triangle. The first row consists of one ball, the second row of two balls and so on. If 669 more balls are added then all the balls can be arranged in the shape of a square and each of the sides then contains 8 balls less than each side of the triangle did. Determine the initial numbers of balls.   **(Bihar C.E. 1999)**

19. Sum the series $n.1 + (n-1).2 + (n-2).3 + ... 1.n$.

20. On the ground are placed n stones, the distance between the first and second is one yard, between the 2nd and 3rd is 3 yds, between the 3rd and 4th, 5 yds, and so on. How far will a person have to travel who shall bring them one by one to a basket placed at the first stone ?

21. Find the sum of the infinite series
$$1 + (1+a)b + (1+a+a^2)b^2$$
$$+ (1+a+a^2+a^3)b^3 + ..., b \text{ and } a$$
being proper fractions.

22. (a)* Find the sum of n terms of the series the rth term of which is $(2r+1)2^r$.

(b)* Evaluate :
$$\sum_{p=1}^{32} (3p+2)\left[\sum_{q=1}^{10}\left(\sin\frac{2q\pi}{11} - i\cos\frac{2q\pi}{11}\right)\right]^p$$
                           (Roorkee 1997)

23. * Find the sum S_n of the cubes of the first n terms of an A.P. and show that the sum of first n terms of the A.P. is a factor of S_n.   **(Roorkee 1992)**

24. (a) Sum the series
$$\frac{1^4}{1.3} + \frac{2^4}{3.5} + \frac{3^4}{5.7} + ... + \frac{n^4}{(2n-1)(2n+1)}.$$

(b) Evaluate $\displaystyle\sum_{r=1}^{n}\left(\frac{1}{4r^2-1}\right)$.

(c) Find the sum of first n terms of the series
$$1.(1!) + 2.(2!) + 3.(3!) + ...$$

25. (a) What is the sum of n terms of the series
$$\frac{1}{1.3.5} + \frac{1}{3.5.7} + \frac{1}{5.7.9} + ...$$
Deduce the sum upto infinity.

(b)* Show that the sum of n terms of the series
$$\frac{3}{1^2} + \frac{5}{1^2+2^2} + \frac{7}{1^2+2^2+3^2}$$
$$+ \frac{9}{1^2+2^2+3^2+4^2} + ... = \frac{6n}{n+1}$$

(c) In a certain series if $S_n = \dfrac{1}{6}n(n+1)(n+2)$, then prove that $\displaystyle\operatorname*{Lt}_{n\to\infty}\sum_{r=1}^{n}\frac{1}{t_n} = 2$

26. (a) If $S_n = \dfrac{n(n+1)(n+2)(n+3)}{12}$ then prove that
$$\operatorname*{Lt}_{n\to\infty}\sum_{r=1}^{n}\frac{1}{t_r} = \frac{3}{4}$$

(b) Prove that $\displaystyle\operatorname*{Lt}_{n\to\infty}\frac{1.2.3 + 2.3.4 + ... n \text{ terms}}{n(1.2 + 2.3 + ... n \text{ terms})} = \frac{3}{4}$

(c) Let $H_n = 1 + \dfrac{1}{2} + \dfrac{1}{3} + ... + \dfrac{1}{n}$, then the sum of n terms of the series
$$\frac{1^2}{1^3} + \frac{1^2+2^2}{1^3+2^3} + \frac{1^2+2^2+3^2}{1^3+2^3+3^3} + ... \text{ is}$$
  (a) $\dfrac{4}{3}H_n - 1$ (b) $\dfrac{4}{3}H_n + 1$
  (c) $\dfrac{4}{3}H_n$ (d) $\dfrac{4}{3}H_n - \dfrac{2}{3}\dfrac{n}{n+1}$

27. (a)* The sum of first n terms of the series $1^2 + 2.2^2 + 3^2 + 2.4^2 + 5^2 + 2.6^2 + ...$ is $n(n+1)^2/2$ where n is even. When n is odd, the sum is .....

(b)* Find the sum of first n terms of the series $1^3 + 3.2^2 + 3^3 + 3.4^2 + 5^3 + 3.6^2 + ...$ where (a) n is even (b) n is odd.

(c) Find the sum of n terms of the series
$$\frac{1}{3.5} + \frac{16}{3^2.5^2} + \frac{1}{5.7} + \frac{24}{5^2.7^2} + \frac{1}{7.9} + \frac{32}{7^2.8^2} + \dots$$

(d) Find the sum of $2n$ terms of the series
$$5^3 + 4.6^3 + 7^3 + 4.8^3 + 9^3 + 4.10^3 + \dots$$

28.* For any odd integer $n \geq 1$,
$$n^3 - (n-1)^3 + \dots + (-1)^{n-1} 1^3 = \dots \quad \textbf{(I.I.T. 1996)}$$

29.* The value of the expression
$$1.(2-\omega)(2-\omega^2) + 2.(3-\omega)(3-\omega^2) + \dots +$$
$$(n-1).(n-\omega)(n-\omega^2)$$

where ω is an imaginary cube root of unity, is ......
(I.I.T. 1996)

30.* Let $x = 1 + 3a + 6a^2 + 10a^3 + \dots, |a| < 1,$
$y = 1 + 4b + 10b^2 + 20b^3 + \dots, |b| < 1.$

Find $S = 1 + 3(ab) + 5(ab)^2 + \dots$

in terms of x and y. **(Roorkee 1996)**

31. If $a_1, a_2, a_3 \dots a_n$ form an A.P. with common difference d and $b_1, b_2, b_3 \dots b_n$ form a G.P. with common ratio $r \neq 1$ show that
$$a_1 b_1 + a_2 b_2 + \dots + a_n b_n$$
$$= \frac{a_n b_{n+1} - a_1 b_1}{r-1} - d\left[\frac{b_{n+1} - b}{(r-1)^2}\right].$$

32. If $S_1 = \Sigma n, S_2 = \Sigma n^2, S_3 = \Sigma n^3$ then prove that $9S_2^2 = S_3(1 + 8S_1)$

Solutions to Problem Set (3)

1. (a) $1 + \frac{4}{5} + \frac{7}{5^2} + \frac{10}{5^3} + \dots + T_n$.

Above series is an arithmetico-geometric series as $1, 4, 7, 10, \dots$ are in A.P. and $1, \frac{1}{5}, \frac{1}{5^2}, \frac{1}{5^3}, \dots$ are in G.P.

nth term of A.P. $= a + (n-1)d$
$$= 1 + (n-1)3 = 3n - 2$$

nth term of G.P. $= ar^{n-1} = 1.\frac{1}{5^{n-1}}$.

Let S be the sum of the series.

$\therefore \quad S = 1 + \frac{4}{5} + \frac{7}{5^2} + \frac{10}{5^3} + \dots + \frac{(3n-2)}{5^{n-1}}$.

Multiply both sides by $r = \frac{1}{5}$.

$\therefore \quad \frac{1}{5}S = \frac{1}{5} + \frac{4}{5^2} + \frac{7}{5^3} + \dots + \frac{3n-5}{5^{n-1}} + \frac{3n-2}{5^n}$

Subtract

$$\left(1 - \frac{1}{5}\right)S = 1 + 3\left[\frac{1}{5} + \frac{1}{5^2} + \frac{1}{5^3} + \dots (n-1) \text{ terms}\right]$$
$$- \frac{3n-2}{5^n}$$

or $\frac{4}{5}S = 1 + 3.\frac{1}{5}\frac{[1-(1/5)^{n-1}]}{1-(1/5)} - \frac{3n-2}{5^n}$

$$= 1 + \frac{3}{4} - \frac{3}{4}.\frac{1}{5^{n-1}} - \frac{3n-2}{5.5^{n-1}}$$

or $\frac{4}{5}S = \frac{7}{4} - \frac{1}{5^{n-1}}\left[\frac{3}{4} + \frac{3n-2}{5}\right]$

or $\frac{4}{5}S = \frac{7}{4} - \frac{1}{5^{n-1}}.\frac{7+12n}{20}$

$\therefore \quad S = \frac{35}{16} - \frac{12n+7}{16.5^{n-1}}$.

To find the sum to infinity, we proceed as below :

Let $S = 1 + \frac{4}{5} + \frac{7}{5^2} + \frac{10}{5^3} + \dots \infty$, then

$\frac{1}{5}S = \frac{1}{5} + \frac{4}{5^2} + \frac{7}{5^3} + \dots \infty$

$\therefore \quad S\left(1 - \frac{1}{5}\right) = 1 + 3\left[\frac{1}{5} + \frac{1}{5^2} + \frac{1}{5^3} + \dots \infty\right]$

or $\frac{4}{5}S = 1 + 3.\frac{1/5}{1-(1/5)} = 1 + \frac{3}{4} = \frac{7}{4} \quad \therefore \quad S = \frac{35}{16}$.

(b) $5.001 = 5.\frac{1}{10^3}$

The given series is A.G.S. in which d of A.P. is 2 and r of G.P. $\frac{1}{10}, \frac{1}{10^2}, \frac{1}{10^3}, \dots$ is $\frac{1}{10}$.

Ans. $n^2 + \frac{1}{9}\left(1 - \frac{1}{10^n}\right)$. **Refer Q. 1, 2, 3 P. 162-64**

(c) The given expression $= 2^{1/4 + 2/8 + 3/16 + 4/32 \dots}$

Now let $S = \frac{1}{4} + \frac{2}{8} + \frac{3}{16} + \frac{4}{32} + \dots$ A.G.S.

$\therefore \quad \frac{1}{2}S = \frac{1}{8} + \frac{2}{16} + \frac{3}{32} + \dots$

Subtracting,

$$\frac{1}{2}S = \frac{1}{4} + \frac{1}{8} + \frac{1}{16} + \frac{1}{32} + \dots = \frac{\frac{1}{4}}{1-\frac{1}{2}} = \frac{1}{2}$$

$\therefore \quad S = 1.$

Hence the given expression $= 2^1 = 2$.

Using the direct formula **(4), P. 161**

$$S_\infty = \frac{ab}{1-r} + \frac{d(br)}{(1-r)^2}$$

where $a = 1, d = 1, b = \frac{1}{4}, r = \frac{1}{2}$

$$S_\infty = \frac{1/4}{1-1/2} + \frac{1.\left(\frac{1}{4}.\frac{1}{2}\right)}{\left(1-\frac{1}{2}\right)^2} = \frac{1}{2} + \frac{1}{2} = 1$$

2. The given series is $1 + S$ where S is an infinite arithmetico-geometric series whose sum as in Q. 1 is $3/8$.

$\therefore$ Required sum $= 1 + \dfrac{3}{8} = \dfrac{11}{8}$.

3. (a) Proceed as in Ex. 1.
$$S = 6 - \frac{2n+3}{2^{n-1}}.$$

(b) $2^n (n-1) + 1 = 99 \cdot 2^{100} + 1$ as $n = 100$

4. $T_n = (1 + 2 + 3 + \ldots .n) = \dfrac{n(n+1)}{2} = \dfrac{1}{2}(n^2 + n)$

Putting $n = 1, 2, 3 \ldots, \ldots n$ and adding, we get
$$S_n = \frac{1}{2} (\Sigma n^2 + \Sigma n)$$
$$= \frac{1}{2}\left[\frac{n(n+1)(2n+1)}{6} + \frac{n(n+1)}{2}\right]$$
$$= \frac{1}{4} n(n+1)\left[\frac{2n+1}{3} + 1\right] = \frac{n(n+1)(n+2)}{6}$$

5. (a) $T_n = 1^2 + 2^2 + 3^2 + \ldots + n^2 = \dfrac{n(n+1)(2n+1)}{6}$
$$= \frac{1}{6}[2n^3 + 3n^2 + n]$$

Putting $n = 1, 2, 3, \ldots n$ and adding,
$$S_n = \frac{1}{6}[2\Sigma n^3 + 3\Sigma n^2 + \Sigma n]$$
$$= \frac{1}{6}\left[2 \cdot \left(\frac{n(n+1)}{2}\right)^2 + 3 \cdot \frac{n(n+1)(2n+1)}{6}\right.$$
$$\left. + \frac{n(n+1)}{2}\right]$$
$$= \frac{1}{12} n(n+1)[n(n+1) + (2n+1) + 1]$$
$$= \frac{1}{12} n(n+1)[n^2 + 3n + 2]$$
$$= \frac{1}{12} n(n+1)(n+1)(n+2)$$
$$= \frac{1}{12} n(n+1)^2 (n+2).$$

Alternative Method : by § 4 P. 161
$$T_n = \frac{n}{6}(n+1)(2n+1)$$

Expressing this as the product of consecutive factors,
$$T_n = \frac{1}{3} n(n+1)\left(n + \frac{1}{2}\right) = \frac{1}{3}\left[n(n+1)\left(n + 2 - \frac{3}{2}\right)\right]$$
$$= \frac{1}{3}\left[n(n+1)(n+2) - \frac{3}{2}n(n+1)\right]$$
$$S_n = \frac{1}{3}\left[n(n+1)(n+2)\frac{(n+3)}{4} - \frac{3}{2}n(n+1)\frac{(n+2)}{3}\right]$$
$$= \frac{1}{3} n(n+1)(n+2)\left[\frac{n+3}{4} - \frac{1}{2}\right]$$
$$= \frac{1}{3} n(n+1)(n+2)\frac{(n+1)}{4} = \frac{1}{12} n(n+1)^2 (n+2).$$

(b) $S_n = \lambda n(n-1) \quad \therefore T_n = S_n - S_{n-1}$
or $T_n = \lambda n(n-1) - \lambda(n-1)(n-2)$
or $T_n = \lambda(n-1) \cdot 2$

$$\Sigma T_n^2 = 4\lambda^2 \sum_{n=1}^{n}(n-1)^2$$
$$= 4\lambda^2[0^2 + 1^2 + 2^2 + 3^2 + \ldots(n-1)^2]$$
$$= 4\lambda^2 \Sigma N^2 = \frac{4\lambda^2 N(N+1)(2N+1)}{6}$$
where $N = n - 1$
$$= \frac{4\lambda^2 \cdot (n-1)n(2n-1)}{6} = \frac{2}{3}\lambda^2 n(n-1)(2n-1)$$

6. (a) Here $T_n = n(n+1)^2 = n^3 + 2n^2 + n$
Proceeding as in Q. 5,
$$S_n = \frac{1}{12} n(n+1)(n+2)(3n+5).$$

Alternative Solution :
You may write $T_n = n(n+1)^2$
as $T_n = n(n+1)(n+2-1)$
$$= n(n+1)(n+2) - n(n+1)$$
$\therefore S_n = n(n+1)(n+2)\dfrac{(n+3)}{4} - n(n+1)\dfrac{(n+2)}{3}$
$$= \frac{n(n+1)(n+2)}{12}[3(n+3) - 4]$$
$$= \frac{1}{12} n(n+1)(n+2)(3n+5).$$

(b) Ans. $\dfrac{1}{4} n(n+1)(n+2)(n+3).$

(c) Ans. $S = \dfrac{1}{12} n(n+1)(3n^2 + 23n + 34).$

(d) Ans. $\dfrac{1}{6}(3n^4 + 16n^3 + 27n^2 + 14n).$

(e) Ans. 666700
The series consists of 100 odd terms of the type $a.b$ where $a + b = 200$ or $a = 200 - b$
$\therefore T_r = [200 - (2r-1)](2r-1)$ etc.
$T_r = 404r - 4r^2 - 201 \quad \therefore \sum_{r=1}^{100} T_r$ etc.

7. (a) T_n of A.P. 1, 2, 3... is n
T_n of A.P. 3, 5, 7... is $3 + (n-1)2 = 2n + 1$
$\therefore T_n$ of given series is $n(2n+1)^2$
or $T_n = 4n^3 + 4n^2 + n.$
Put $n = 1, 2, 3 \ldots n$, and add
$\therefore S_n = 4\Sigma n^3 + 4\Sigma n^2 + \Sigma n$
$$S_n = 4\left[\frac{n(n+1)}{2}\right]^2 + 4\frac{n(n+1)(2n+1)}{6} + \frac{n(n+1)}{2}$$
$$= \frac{1}{6} n(n+1)(6n^2 + 14n + 7)$$

Putting $n = 20$, we get
$$S_{20} = \frac{1}{6}(20)(21)(6 \cdot 20^2 + 14 \cdot 20 + 7) = 188090.$$

(b) t_n of Ist factor of terms in the series
$= 1, 3, 5, \ldots = 1 + (n-1)2 = 2n - 1$

$\therefore \quad T_n = (2n-1)(2n+1)(2n+3)$

$\qquad = (4n^2 - 1)(2n+3) = 8n^3 + 12n^2 - 2n - 3$

$\therefore \quad S_n = 8 \sum n^3 - 12 \sum n^2 - 2 \sum n - 3n$

$\qquad = 8\left[\frac{n(n+1)}{2}\right]^2 + 12\frac{n(n+1)(2n+1)}{6}$

$\qquad \qquad \qquad - 2\frac{n(n+1)}{2} - 3n$

$\qquad = 2n^2(n+1)^2 - 2n(2n^2 + 3n + 1) - n(n+1) - 3n$

$\qquad = n[2n^3 + 4n^2 + 2n + 4n^2 + 6n + 2 - n - 1 - 3]$

$\qquad = n[2n^3 + 8n^2 + 7n - 2]$

8. (i) $T_n = \dfrac{1^3 + 2^3 + 3^3 + \ldots + n^3}{1 + 3 + 5 + \ldots n \text{ terms}} = \dfrac{\sum n^3}{\frac{n}{2}[2 \cdot 1 + (n-1)2]}$

$\quad$ or $\quad T_n = \dfrac{1}{4} \cdot \dfrac{n^2(n+1)^2}{n^2} = \dfrac{1}{4}(n^2 + 2n + 1) \qquad \ldots(1)$

Putting $n = 1, 2, 3, \ldots$ and adding, we get

$S_n = \dfrac{1}{4}(\sum n^2 + 2\sum n + n)$

$\qquad = \dfrac{1}{4}\left[\dfrac{n(n+1)(2n+1)}{6} + 2 \cdot \dfrac{n(n+1)}{2} + n\right]$

$\qquad = \dfrac{n}{24}[2n^2 + 3n + 1 + 6n + 6 + 6]$

$\qquad = \dfrac{n}{24}[2n^2 + 9n + 13].$

Putting $n = 16$, we get

$S_{16} = \dfrac{16}{24}[2(256) + 144 + 13] = \dfrac{2}{3}(669) = 446.$

Alternative Method :

$T_n = \dfrac{1}{4}(n+1)^2$ as shown above in (1)

$S_n = \dfrac{1}{4}\sum_{n=1}^{n}(n+1)^2 = \dfrac{1}{4}\sum_{2}^{N}N^2$

where $N = n + 1$

$\qquad = \dfrac{1}{4}\left[\sum_{1}^{N}N^2 - 1^2\right]$ for $N = 1$

$\qquad = \dfrac{1}{4}\left[\dfrac{N(N+1)(2N+1)}{6} - 1\right]$

$\qquad = \dfrac{1}{4}\left[\dfrac{(n+1)(n+2)(2n+3) - 6}{6}\right]$

$\qquad = \dfrac{1}{24}[(n^2 + 3n + 2)(2n+3) - 6]$

$\qquad = \dfrac{1}{24}[2n^3 + 9n^2 + 13n + 0]$

$\qquad = \dfrac{n}{24}(2n^2 + 9n + 13)$ Now put $n = 16$.

(ii) $T_n = \dfrac{2n+1}{n^2(n+1)^2} = \dfrac{1}{n^2} - \dfrac{1}{(n+1)^2}$

Putting $n = 1, 2, 3, \ldots, n$ and adding, we get

$S_n = 1 - \dfrac{1}{(n+1)^2} = \dfrac{n^2 + 2n}{n^2 + 2n + 1}$

$S_\infty = \underset{n \to \infty}{\text{Lt}} \dfrac{n^2(1 + 2/n)}{n^2(1 + 2/n + 1/n^2)} = 1$

9. Here the successive differences are 2, 4, 8, 16, ... which are in G.P.

$S = 1 + 3 + 7 + 15 + 31 + \ldots + T_n$

$S = \qquad 1 + 3 + 7 + 15 + \ldots + T_{n-1} + T_n$

Subtracting, we get

$0 = 1 + [2 + 4 + 8 + 16 \ldots \text{to } (n-1) \text{ terms}] - T_n$

$\therefore \quad T_n = 1 + 2 + 2^2 + 2^3 + 2^4 + \ldots \text{to } n \text{ terms}$

or $\quad T_n = 1 \cdot \dfrac{2^n - 1}{2 - 1} = 2^n - 1.$

Now putting $n = 1, 2, 3 \ldots n$ and adding,

$S_n = (2 + 2^2 + 2^3 + \ldots + 2^n) - n$

$\qquad = 2 \cdot \dfrac{(2^n - 1)}{2 - 1} - n = 2^{n+1} - 2 - n.$

10. (a) Do yourself. Ans. $\dfrac{n(n+1)(n+2)}{6}$

(b) $T_1 = 1 = 1^2 + 0, T_2 = 5 = 2^2 + 1 = 2^2 + T_1$

$T_3 = 14 = 3^2 + 5 = 3^2 + T_2$

$T_4 = 30 = 4^2 + 14 = 4^2 + T_3$

$T_5 = 55 = 5^2 + 30 = 5^2 + T_4$

$\therefore \quad T_6 = 6^2 + T_5 = 36 + 55 = 91$

11. (i) Here as above $T_n = \dfrac{1}{2}(n^2 + n + 6)$

$T_n = \dfrac{1}{2}n(n+1) + 3$

$\therefore \quad S_n = \dfrac{1}{2} \cdot n(n+1)\dfrac{(n+2)}{3} + 3n$

$\qquad = \dfrac{n}{6}(n^2 + 3n + 20)$

(ii) Ans. $\dfrac{1}{6}n(n^2 + 3n + 8).$

(iii) By method of difference **P. 161.**

$T_n = \dfrac{n^2 - n + 3}{n!} = \dfrac{n(n-1)}{n!} + \dfrac{3}{n!}$

or $\quad T_n = \dfrac{1}{(n-2)!} + \dfrac{3}{n!}$

$\therefore \quad S_n = e + 3(e - 1) = 4e - 3.$

12. (a) (i) **Refer §5 Page 161 Alt.**

n^{th} row will have n elements which will form an A.P. of common difference 1, we have to determine only its 1st term.

Successive first terms are 1, 2, 4, 7, 11 ....

1st differences are 1, 2, 3, 4...

2nd differences 1, 1, 1, ... equal. Hence n^{th} term will be of the form

$$T_n = an^2 + bn + c$$
$$T_1 = a + b + c = 1$$
$$T_2 = 4a + 2b + c = 2$$
$$T_3 = 9a + 3b + c = 4$$
$$\therefore \quad 3a + b = 1, \ 5a + b = 2$$
$$\therefore \quad a = \frac{1}{2}, b = -\frac{1}{2}, c = 1$$
$$\therefore \quad T_n = \frac{1}{2}(n^2 - n + 2)$$

Note : T_n can be found by method of differences as explained on **Page 161 Alt.**

$$\therefore \quad \text{Now } a = \frac{1}{2}(n^2 - n + 2), d = 1, n = n$$

$$\therefore \quad S = \frac{n}{2}[2a + (n - 1)d]$$

$$= \frac{n}{2}[n^2 - n + 2 + n - 1] = \frac{n}{2}(n^2 + 1)$$

(ii) All the numbers are natural numbers and if N be their number, then

$$N = 1 + 2 + 3 + 4 + \ldots n = \frac{n(n+1)}{2}$$

$$\therefore \quad S_N = \frac{N(N+1)}{2} = \frac{1}{2}\frac{n(n+1)}{2}\left[\frac{n(n+1)}{2} + 1\right]$$

$$= \frac{1}{8}n(n+1)(n^2 + n + 2).$$

(b) 1st term of nth row by method of differences or as done above is $a = n^2 - n + 1, d = 2, n = n$

$$\therefore \quad S_n = n^3$$

(c) $\Sigma n^2 - S_n = \frac{1}{3}n(n^2 - 1)$

$$\therefore \quad S_n = \frac{1}{6}n(n+1)(2n+1) - \frac{1}{3}n(n+1)(n-1)$$

$$\text{or} \quad S_n = \frac{1}{6}n(n+1).(3) = \frac{1}{2}n(n+1) = \Sigma n$$

$$= 1 + 2 + 3 \ldots n \quad \therefore \quad t_n = n$$

Alt. $t_n = S_n - S_{n-1} = \frac{1}{2}[n(n+1) - (n-1)n]$

$$= \frac{1}{2}n.2 = n.$$

(d) The number of numbers in successive rows are 2, 4, 6 and hence there will be $2n$ numbers in nth row which will be in A.P. of common difference 1. The first term in successive rows are

$$S = \quad 1 + 3 + 7 + 13 \ldots + t_n$$
$$S = \quad \quad 1 + 3 + 7 + \ldots + t_{n-1} - t_n$$

Subtracting,

$$\therefore \quad 0 = 1 + [2 + 4 + 6 + (n - 1) \text{ terms}] - t_n$$

$$\therefore \quad t_n = 1 + \frac{2(n-1)n}{2} = n^2 - n + 1$$

$$\therefore \quad S_n = \text{ sum of an A.P. in which}$$
$$A = n^2 - n + 1, D = 1, N = 2n.$$

$$\therefore \quad S_n = \frac{2n}{2}[2(n^2 - n + 1) + (2n - 1).1]$$

$$= n(2n^2 + 1)$$

(e) We know that $\sum\limits_{n=1}^{n} n^3 = \left[\frac{n(n+1)}{2}\right]^2$

Now suppose we want to find the sum of terms in 3rd group $= 4^3 + 5^3 + 6^3$

$$= [1^3 + (2^3 + 3^3) + (4^3 + 5^3 + 6^3)] - (1^3 + (2^3 + 3^3))]$$

i.e., sum $\sum\limits_{n=1}^{6} n^3 - \sum\limits_{N=1}^{3} N^3$

Hence sum of terms in nth group
= sum of terms in the first n groups – sum of terms in the first $(n - 1)$ groups
Number of terms in the first n groups will be

$$1 + 2 + 3 + \ldots + n = \frac{n(n+1)}{2} = N_1$$

Similarly number of terms in first $(n - 1)$ groups is

$$1 + 2 + 3 + \ldots + (n - 1) = \frac{n(n-1)}{2} = N_2$$

$$S = \sum\limits_{n=1}^{N_1} n^3 - \sum\limits_{N=1}^{N_2} N^3$$

$$= \left[\frac{N_1(N_1 + 1)}{2}\right]^2 + \left[\frac{N_2(N_2 + 1)}{2}\right]^2$$

$$= \frac{1}{4}\left[\frac{n(n+1)}{2}\frac{n^2 + n + 2}{2}\right]^2$$

$$\quad\quad\quad - \left[\frac{n(n-1)}{2}\frac{n^2 - n + 2}{2}\right]^2$$

$$= \frac{n^2}{64}[(n+1)^2(n^2 + n + 2)^2 - (n-1)^2(n^2 - n + 2)^2]$$

$$= \frac{n^2}{64}[(A + B)(A - B)] \quad\quad \ldots(I)$$

$$A + B = [n(2n^2 + 4) + 2n] = n.2(n^2 + 3)$$
$$A - B = [n.2n + 1(2n^2 + 4)] = 4(n^2 + 1)$$

Hence from (I),

$$S = \frac{n^2}{64}8n(n^2 + 1)(n^2 + 3)$$

$$= \frac{1}{8}n^3(n^2 + 1)(n^2 + 3)$$

13. (a) $3 + 8 + 22 + 72 + 266 + 1036 + \ldots$

1st diff. $5, 14, 50, 194, 770, \ldots$

2nd diff. $9, 36, 144, 576, \ldots$

They are in G.P. whose n^{th} term is $ar^{n-1} = a.4^{n-1}$

$$\therefore \quad T_n \text{ of the given series will be of the form}$$
$$T_n = a.4^{n-1} + bn + c$$

$$T_1 = a + b + c = 3$$
$$T_2 = 4a + 2b + c = 8$$
$$T_3 = 16a + 3b + c = 22$$

Solving them as in 1st question, we get

$$a = 1, b = 2, c = 0$$

$$\therefore \quad T_n = 4^{n-1} + 2n$$

$$\therefore \quad S_n = \Sigma\, 4^{n-1} + 2\,\Sigma\, n$$

1st sigma is a G.P. in which $a = 1, r = 4$

$$\therefore \quad S_n = 1 \cdot \frac{4^n - 1}{4 - 1} + 2 \cdot \frac{n(n+1)}{2}$$

$$= \frac{1}{3}(4^n - 1) + n(n+1)$$

(b) $\quad 2 + 5 + 12 + 31 + 86 + \ldots$

1st diff. $\qquad$ 3, 7, 19, 55

2nd $\qquad\qquad$ 4, 12, 36 ... G.P.

Above is a G.P. whose nth term is $ar^{n-1} = 4 \cdot 3^{n-1}$

$\therefore \quad T_n$ of the given series will be of the form

$$T_n = a \cdot 3^{n-1} + bn + c$$

$$T_1 = a + b + c = 2$$

$$T_2 = 3a + 2b + c = 5$$

$$T_3 = 9a + 3b + c = 12$$

Solving, we get $a = 1, \quad b = 1, \quad c = 0$

$$\therefore \quad T_n = 3^{n-1} + n$$

$$\therefore \quad S_n = \Sigma\, 3^{n-1} + \Sigma\, n$$

$$= 1 \cdot \frac{3^n - 1}{3 - 1} + \frac{n(n+1)}{2} = \frac{1}{2}[n(n+1) + 3^n - 1]$$

14. (a) We know that

$$(a_1 + a_2 + \ldots + a_n)^2 = \Sigma\, a_i^2 + 2\Sigma\, a_i a_j.$$

Now put $a_1 = 1, \ a_2 = 2, \ \ldots a_n = n.$

$$\therefore \quad (1 + 2 + 3 + \ldots + n)^2 = (1^2 + 2^2 + 3^2 + \ldots + n^2) + 2\Sigma\, a_i\, a_j$$

$$(\Sigma\, n)^2 - \Sigma\, n^2 = 2S$$

$$\therefore \quad S = \frac{1}{2}\left[\frac{n^2(n+1)^2}{4} - \frac{n(n+1)(2n+1)}{6} \right]$$

$$= \frac{1}{24} n(n+1)[3n^2 + 3n - 4n - 2]$$

$$= \frac{1}{24} n(n+1)(3n^2 - n - 2)$$

$$= \frac{1}{24} n(n+1)(n-1)(3n+2).$$

Another form :

$$S = \frac{1}{2}[(\Sigma\, n)^2 - \Sigma\, n^2] = \frac{1}{2}[\Sigma\, n^3 - \Sigma\, n^2]$$

$$\therefore \quad (\Sigma\, n^3) = (\Sigma\, n)^2$$

Another form :

$$(x-1)(x-2)(x-3)\ldots(x-n)$$

$$= x^n - x^{n-1}(1 + 2 + 3 + \ldots n) + x^{n-2}\,\Sigma\, ab \ldots$$

where a and b are natural numbers such that $a \neq b$.

(b) From above coefficient of x^{n-1} is

$$-\Sigma\, n = -\frac{n(n+1)}{2}. \ \text{Fat } n = 100$$

$$= -\frac{100 \times 101}{2} = -5050.$$

(c) $\quad s_n = \dfrac{a(1 - r^n)}{1 - r}, s_{n-1} = \dfrac{a(1 - r^{n-1})}{1 - r}$

Now we know that

$$(x + y + z + \ldots)^2 = \Sigma\, x^2 + 2\,\Sigma\, xy$$

$$\therefore \quad 2\,\Sigma\, xy = (\Sigma\, x)^2 - \Sigma\, x^2 \qquad \ldots(1)$$

$$\Sigma\, x^2 = a^2 + a^2 r^2 + a^2 r^4 + \ldots n \text{ terms}$$

$$= \frac{a^2(1 - r^{2n})}{1 - r^2}$$

$$2\,\Sigma\, xy = \frac{a^2(1 - r^n)^2}{(1 - r)^2} - \frac{a^2(1 - r^{2n})}{1 - r^2} \text{ from (1)}$$

$$= \frac{a^2(1 - r^n)}{(1 - r)}\left[\frac{1 - r^n}{1 - r} - \frac{1 + r^n}{1 + r} \right]$$

$$= \frac{a^2(1 - r^n)}{1 - r} \cdot \frac{2(r - r^n)}{(1 - r)(1 + r)}$$

$$= \frac{2r}{1 + r} \cdot \frac{a(1 - r^n)}{1 - r} \cdot \frac{a(1 - r^{n-1})}{1 - r}$$

$$= \frac{2r}{1 + r} s_n \cdot s_{n-1}$$

$$\therefore \quad \Sigma\, xy = \frac{r}{1 + r} s_n \cdot s_{n-1}$$

(d) Ans. (d).

Mean of given numbers $= \bar{x}$

$$= \frac{\displaystyle\sum_{r=0}^{100} 1 + rd}{101}$$

or $\quad \bar{x} = \dfrac{101 + \dfrac{100(100+1)}{2}d}{101}$ by $\Sigma n = \dfrac{n(n+1)}{2}$

$$\therefore \quad \bar{x} = 1 + 50d$$

Mean deviation

$$= \frac{\Sigma(x_i - \bar{x})}{n} = \sum_{r=0}^{100} \frac{[1 + rd - (1 + 50d)]}{101}$$

$$= \sum_{r=0}^{100} \frac{(r - 50)d}{101} = \frac{d \cdot 50 \times 51}{101}$$

$$\therefore \quad \frac{d \cdot 50 \times 51}{101} = 255 \quad \therefore \quad d = \frac{255 \times 10}{50 \times 51}$$

or $\quad d = \dfrac{5 \times 101}{50} = \dfrac{101}{10} = 10 + \dfrac{1}{10} = 10 + 0 \cdot 1 = 10 \cdot 1$

15. (a) We consider two cases

(i) **Let n be even.** Then

$$(1^2 - 2^2) + (3^2 - 4^2) + (5^2 - 6^2) + \ldots$$

$$+ [(n-1)^2 - n^2]$$

$$= (1-2)(1+2) + (3-4)(3+4)$$
$$+ (5-6)(5+6) + \ldots + [(n-1)-n].[(n-1)+n]$$
$$= -1(1+2+3+\ldots+n) = -n.\frac{(n+1)}{2}.$$

(ii) **Let n be odd.** In this case

The series $= (1^2 - 2^2) + (3^2 - 4^2) + \ldots$
$$+ [(n-2)^2 - (n-1)^2] + n^2$$
$$= -1[1+2+3+\ldots+(n-1)] + n^2$$
$$= -\frac{(n-1)n}{2} + n^2 = \frac{n(n+1)}{2}.$$

(b) Proceeding as in part (a) when $n = $ even $= 30$

then, $S = -\dfrac{n(n+1)}{2} = \dfrac{-30 \times 31}{2} = 465$

In the 2nd case, $S = S_n + 31^2$
$$= 465 + 31^2 = 465 + 961$$
$$= 1426$$

16. (a) $S = (1^3 + 2^3 + \ldots + 50^3) - (1^3 + 2^3 + \ldots + 30^3)$

$$= \left(\frac{50 \times 51}{2}\right)^2 - \left(\frac{30 \times 31}{2}\right)^2$$

$$\left[\text{using } \Sigma n^3 = \left(\frac{n(n+1)}{2}\right)^2\right]$$

$$= \frac{1}{4}(50 \times 51 - 30 \times 31)(50 \times 51 + 30 \times 31)$$

$$= 1409400.$$

(b) The first number will be $5^3 = 125$

Now $20^3 = 400 \times 20 = 8000, 21^3 = 441 \times 21 = 9261$

It is evident that 22^3 will be greater than 10,000.
Hence we have to find
$$5^3 + 6^3 + 7^3 + \ldots + 21^3$$
$$= (1^3 + 2^3 + \ldots 21^3) - (1^3 + 2^3 + 3^3 + 4^3)$$
$$= \Sigma n^3 \text{ for } n = 21 - \Sigma k^3 \text{ for } k = 4$$
$$\left[\frac{n(n+1)}{2}\right]^2 - \left[\frac{k(k+1)}{2}\right]^2 = (21 \times 11)^2 - (2 \times 5)^2$$
$$= (231 - 10)(231 + 10) = 221 \times 241 = 53261$$

17. $a, a+1, a+2, \ldots, (a+n-1)$

$$s = na + \frac{n(n-1)}{2} \qquad \ldots(1)$$

$$t = a^2 + (a+1)^2 + \ldots + (a+n-1)^2$$

$$= na^2 + 2a.\frac{n(n-1)}{2} + \sum_{N=1}^{n-1} N^2$$

or $nt = n^2 a^2 + an^2(n-1) + n\Sigma N^2$

and $s^2 = n^2 a^2 + an^2(n-1) + \dfrac{n^2(n-1)^2}{4}$, by (1)

$nt - s^2$ is clearly independent of a.

18. $S = 1 + 2 + 3 + 4 + \ldots + n = \Sigma n = \dfrac{n(n+1)}{2}$

$$S + 669 = (n-8)^2$$

or $\dfrac{n(n+1)}{2} + 669 = n^2 - 16n + 64$

or $n^2 - 33n - 1210 = 0$

or $n^2 - 55n + 22n - 1210 = 0$

$(n-55)(n+22) = 0 \quad \therefore \quad n = 55.$

$\therefore$ Number of balls is $\dfrac{55.56}{2} = 1540.$

Check : $1540 + 669 = 2209 = (55-8)^2 = 47^2.$

19. Ans. $\dfrac{n(n+1)(n+2)}{6}.$

$$T_r = (n-r+1)r = (n+1)r - r^2$$

$\therefore \quad S_n = (n+1)\sum_{r=1}^{n} r - \sum_{r=1}^{n} r^2$ etc.

20. Ans. $\dfrac{1}{3}(n-1)n(2n-1)$ yds.

21. $T_n = (1 + a + a^2 + \ldots + a^{n-1})b^{n-1} = \dfrac{1-a^n}{1-a}.b^{n-1}$

$\therefore \quad S_\infty = \sum_{n=1}^{\infty} T_n$

$$= \frac{1}{1-a}\left[\sum_{n=1}^{\infty} b^{n-1} - a \sum_{n=1}^{\infty} (ab)^{n-1}\right]$$

$$= \frac{1}{1-a}\left[\frac{1}{1-b} - a.\frac{1}{1-ab}\right] \text{ by } S_\infty = \frac{A}{1-R}$$

$$= \frac{1}{(1-a)}\left[\frac{1-ab-a+ab}{(1-b)(1-ab)}\right]$$

$$S_\infty = \frac{1}{(1-a)}\frac{(1-a)}{(1-b)(1-ab)} = \frac{1}{(1-b)(1-ab)}$$

22. (a) Ans. $n.2^{n+2} - 2^{n+1} + 2.$

(b) We have

$$\left(\sin\frac{2\pi}{11} + \sin\frac{4\pi}{11} + \ldots 10 \text{ terms}\right) - i \text{ (cosine)}$$

$$= \frac{\sin 10.\frac{\pi}{11}}{\sin\frac{\pi}{11}}$$

$$\times \left[\sin\frac{\left(\frac{2\pi}{11} + \frac{20\pi}{11}\right)}{2} - i\cos\frac{\left(\frac{2\pi}{11} + \frac{20\pi}{11}\right)}{2}\right]$$

$$= 1.[\sin\pi - i\cos\pi]^p \text{ by Supp. Rule} = i^p$$

L.H.S. $= \sum_{p=1}^{32}(3p+2)(i)^p = 3\sum_{p=1}^{32} p(i)^p + 2\left|\sum_{p=1}^{32} i^p\right.$

The first is an A.G.S. and 2nd is a G.P. whose sum

is $\dfrac{2i(1-i^{32})}{1-i} = 0 \quad \because \quad i^{32} = 1$

The sum of A.G.S. as usual is

$$3\left[\frac{i(1-i^{32})}{(1-i)^2}-\frac{32i^{33}}{1-i}\right] \qquad (\S\ 3,\ P.\ 161)$$

$$=3\left[0-\frac{32i(1+i)}{2}\right]=-48i(1+i)$$

23. Let the A.P. be $(a+d)+(a+2d)+......+(a+nd)$.

$$P_n=\text{Sum}=\frac{n}{2}\left[(a+d)+(a+nd)\right]=\frac{n}{2}[2a+(n+1)d]$$

$$\qquad\qquad\qquad\qquad\qquad\qquad ...(1)$$

$$S_n=(a+d)^3+(a+2d)^3+......+(a+nd)^3$$

$$=na^3+3a^2d\sum n+3ad^2\sum n^2+d^3\sum n^3.$$

$$=na^3+3a^2d\cdot\frac{n(n+1)}{2}$$

$$+3ad^2\cdot\frac{n(n+1)(2n+1)}{6}+d^3\cdot\frac{n^2(n+1)^2}{4}$$

$$=\frac{n}{4}[4a^3+6a^2d(n+1)+2ad^2(n+1)(2n+1)$$

$$+d^3n(n+1)^2]$$

$$=\frac{1}{2}\cdot\frac{n}{2}[2a+(n+1)d][2a^2+2ad(n+1)$$

$$+d^2n(n+1)] \qquad ...(2)$$

$$=\frac{1}{2}P_n[2a^2+2ad(n+1)+d^2\cdot n(n+1)]\ \text{by (1)} ...(3)$$

$$=P_n[a^2+ad(n+1)+d^2\lambda]$$

$\because\ n(n+1)=$ product of two consecutive numbers is even $=2\lambda$, say.

By actual division (2) gives S_n and (3) shows that P_n is a factor of S_n.

Note : We have chosen the A.P. as above *i.e.* starting with $a+d$ instead of a so that the formulae for $\Sigma\,n$ and $\Sigma\,n^2$ are applied instead of $\Sigma\,(n-1)$ and $\Sigma\,(n-1)^2$.

24. (a) $T_n=\dfrac{1}{16}\dfrac{16n^4-1+1}{(4n^2-1)}$

$$=\frac{1}{16}\left[4n^2+1+\frac{1}{(2n-1)(2n+1)}\right]$$

Splitting the 2nd term into partial fractions by the method of suppression by putting $2n=1$ and then -1, it becomes

$$\frac{1}{2}\left[\frac{1}{2n-1}-\frac{1}{2n+1}\right]$$

$$\therefore\ T_n=\frac{1}{16}[4n^2+1]+\frac{1}{32}\left[\frac{1}{2n-1}-\frac{1}{2n+1}\right]$$

Now put $n=1,2,3,...n$ and add

$$\therefore\ S_n=\frac{1}{16}[4\Sigma n^2+n]$$

$$+\frac{1}{32}\left[\left(1-\frac{1}{3}\right)+\left(\frac{1}{3}-\frac{1}{5}\right)...+\left(\frac{1}{2n-1}-\frac{1}{2n+1}\right)\right]$$

$$=\frac{1}{16}\cdot4\frac{n(n+1)(2n+1)}{6}+\frac{1}{16}n+\frac{1}{32}\left(1-\frac{1}{2n+1}\right)$$

$$=\frac{1}{16}\left[\frac{2}{3}\cdot n(n+1)(2n+1)+n+\frac{n}{2n+1}\right]$$

$$=\frac{1}{16}\left[\frac{2}{3}n(n+1)(2n+1)+\frac{n\cdot2(n+1)}{2n+1}\right]$$

$$=\frac{1}{16}2n(n+1)\left[\frac{(2n+1)^2+3}{3(2n+1)}\right]$$

$$=\frac{n(n+1)}{8}\cdot\frac{4n^2+4n+4}{3(2n+1)}$$

$$=\frac{n(n+1)(n^2+n+1)}{6(2n+1)}$$

(b) It has already been done in (i),

$$T_n=\frac{1}{2}\left(\frac{1}{2n-1}-\frac{1}{2n+1}\right)$$

$$\therefore\ S_n=\frac{1}{2}\left(1-\frac{1}{(2n+1)}\right)=\frac{n}{2n+1}.$$

(c) $T_n=n(n!)=[(n+1)-1]\,n!=(n+1)!-n!$

$$\therefore\ S_n=(n+1)!-1$$

25. (a) $T_n=\dfrac{1}{(2n-1)(2n+1)(2n+3)}$

Split into partial fractions by the method of suppression by putting $2n=1,-1,-3$ successively.

$$\therefore\ T_n=\frac{1}{8(2n-1)}-\frac{2}{8(2n+1)}+\frac{1}{8(2n+3)}$$

$$T_n=\frac{1}{8}\left[\left(\frac{1}{2n-1}-\frac{1}{2n+1}\right)-\left(\frac{1}{2n+1}-\frac{1}{2n+3}\right)\right]$$

Now putting $n=1,2,3,...n$ and adding

$$S_n=\frac{1}{8}\left[\left(1-\frac{1}{2n+1}\right)-\left(\frac{1}{3}-\frac{1}{2n+3}\right)\right]$$

$$=\frac{1}{8}\left[\frac{2n}{2n+1}-\frac{2n}{3(2n+3)}\right]=\frac{n}{4}\left[\frac{4n+8}{3(2n+1)(2n+3)}\right]$$

$$=\frac{n(n+2)}{3(2n+1)(2n+3)}$$

In order to find S_∞ we re-write the above

$$S_n=\frac{n^2\left(1+\dfrac{2}{n}\right)}{3\cdot4n^2\left(1+\dfrac{1}{2n}\right)\left(1+\dfrac{3}{2n}\right)}$$

when $n\to\infty$

$$S_n\to\frac{1}{12}\cdot\frac{1}{1}=\frac{1}{12}.$$

(b) $T_n=\dfrac{2n+1}{n(n+1)(2n+1)/6}=\dfrac{6}{n(n+1)}$

or $T_n=6\left[\dfrac{1}{n}-\dfrac{1}{n+1}\right]$

$$\therefore\ S_n=\Sigma\,T_n=6\left[1-\frac{1}{n+1}\right]=\frac{6n}{n+1}$$

$$S_\infty=6[1-0]=6$$

(c) **Hint :** $T_n = S_n - S_{n-1} = \frac{1}{2}n(n+1)$

$$\therefore \quad \frac{1}{t_r} = 2\left[\frac{1}{r} - \frac{1}{r+1}\right] \quad \therefore \sum_{r=1}^{n} \frac{1}{t_r} \text{ etc.}$$

26. (a) $t_n = S_n - S_{n-1} = \frac{1}{3}n(n+1)(n+2)$

$$\therefore \quad \frac{1}{t_n} = 3\frac{1}{n(n+1)(n+2)}$$

$$= 3\left[\frac{1}{2n} - \frac{1}{n+1} + \frac{1}{2(n+2)}\right]$$

Partial fractions

$$= \frac{3}{2}\left[\frac{1}{n} - \frac{2}{n+1} + \frac{1}{n+2}\right]$$

$$= \frac{3}{2}\left[\left(\frac{1}{n} - \frac{1}{n+1}\right) - \left(\frac{1}{n+1} - \frac{1}{n+2}\right)\right]$$

Putting $n = 1, 2, 3, \ldots n$ and adding

$$\therefore \quad \sum_{r=1}^{n} \frac{1}{t_r} = \frac{3}{2}\left[\left(1 - \frac{1}{n+1}\right) - \left(\frac{1}{2} - \frac{1}{n+2}\right)\right]$$

$$\therefore \quad \underset{n \to \infty}{Lt} \sum_{r=1}^{n} \frac{1}{t_r} = \frac{3}{2}\left[(1-0) - \left(\frac{1}{2} - 0\right)\right] = \frac{3}{2} \cdot \frac{1}{2} = \frac{3}{4}$$

(b) $N^r = n(n+1)(n+2) \cdot \dfrac{(n+3)}{4}$

$$D^r = n\left[n(n+1)\frac{(n+2)}{3}\right]$$

$$\therefore \quad \frac{N^r}{D^r} = \frac{3}{4}\frac{n+3}{n} = \frac{3}{4}\left(1 + \frac{3}{n}\right)$$

$$\therefore \quad \underset{n \to \infty}{Lt} \frac{N^r}{D^r} = \frac{3}{4}(1+0) = \frac{3}{4}$$

(c) **Ans. (d).**

$$T_n = \frac{\sum n^2}{\sum n^3} = \frac{\frac{1}{6}n(n+1)(2n+1)}{\frac{1}{4}n^2(n+1)^2}$$

$$= \frac{2(2n+1)}{3n(n+1)} = \frac{2}{3}\left[\frac{1}{n} + \frac{1}{n+1}\right] \text{ Partial Fractions.}$$

$$\therefore \quad \sum T_n = \frac{2}{3}\left[\left(1 + \frac{1}{2}\right) + \left(\frac{1}{2} + \frac{1}{3}\right) + \ldots + \frac{1}{n} + \frac{1}{n+1}\right]$$

$$= \frac{2}{3}\left[1 + 2\left(\frac{1}{2} + \frac{1}{3} + \ldots + \frac{1}{n}\right) + \frac{1}{n+1}\right]$$

$$= \frac{2}{3}\left[\left(1 + \frac{1}{n+1}\right) + 2(H_n - 1)\right]$$

$$= \frac{2}{3}\left[\frac{1}{n+1} - 1 + 2H_n\right]$$

$$= \frac{4}{3}H_n - \frac{2}{3} \cdot \frac{n}{n+1}$$

27. (a) **Ans.** $\dfrac{(n-1)n^2}{2} + n^2 = \dfrac{(n+1)n^2}{2}$.

$$T_1 = 1^2, T_3 = 3^2, T_5 = 5^2$$

Hence **when n is odd**, the last term will be n^2 and the sum of first $(n-1)$ i.e. even number of terms is obtained by replacing n by $n-1$ in the given formula.

(b) **Case I. n even = $2m$, say**

T_r of $1, 3, 5, \ldots = 2r - 1$

T_r of $2, 4, 6, \ldots = 2r$

$$S_n = S_{2m} = \sum_{r=1}^{m}(2r-1)^3 + 3\sum_{r=1}^{m}(2r)^2$$

$$= \sum_{r=1}^{m}[8r^3 - 3(2r)^2 + 3(2r) - 1] + 12\sum_{r=1}^{m}r^2$$

$$= 8\sum_{r=1}^{m}r^3 + 6\sum_{r=1}^{m}r - \sum_{r=1}^{m}1$$

$$= 8\left[\frac{m(m+1)}{2}\right]^2 + 6 \cdot \frac{m(m+1)}{2} - m$$

$$= 2m^2(m+1)^2 + 3m(m+1) - m$$

$$= m[2m^3 + 4m^2 + 5m + 2]$$

Put $2m = n$ or $m = \dfrac{n}{2}$

$$\therefore \quad S_n = \frac{n}{8}[n^3 + 4n^2 + 10n + 8] \qquad \ldots(1)$$

Case II. n odd, then $n + 1 = $ even

$$\therefore \quad S_n = S_{n+1} - T_{n+1} \qquad \ldots(2)$$

S_{n+1} is obtained by (1) by replacing n by $n+1$ and $T_{n+1} = (n+1)$th even term $= 3(n+1)^2$

as $T_2 = 3.2^2$, $T_4 = 3.4^2$, $T_6 = 3.6^2$

Hence from (2)

$$S_n(n \text{ odd}) = \frac{n+1}{8}[(n+1)^3 + 4(n+1)^2$$

$$+ 10(n+1) + 8] - 3(n+1)^2$$

$$= \frac{n+1}{8}[n^3 + 7n^2 - 3n - 1] \qquad \ldots(3)$$

(1) and (3) give the required results.

(c) **$n = $ even = $2m$**

$$S_{2m} = \frac{1}{2}\left[\frac{1}{3} - \frac{1}{2m+3}\right] + \frac{1}{3^2} - \frac{1}{(2m+3)^2}$$

$n = $ odd = $2m + 1$

$$S_{2m+1} = S_{2m} + T_{2m+1} = S_{2m} + \frac{1}{(2m+3)(2m+5)}$$

(d) $S_{2n} = (n \text{ odd terms}) + (n \text{ even terms})$

$$= (5^3 + 7^3 + 9^3 + \ldots n \text{ term})$$

$$+ 4(6^3 + 8^3 + 10^3 + \ldots n \text{ terms}]$$

$$= \sum_{r=1}^{n}(2r+3)^3 + 4\sum(2r+4)^3$$

$$= \sum_{r=1}^{n}[8r^3 + 36r^2 + 54r + 27]$$

$$+ 4.8[r^3 + 2r^2 + 4r + 8]$$

$$= \sum_{r=1}^{n}[40r^3 + 228r^2 + 438r + 283]$$

Now put $r = 1, 2, 3, \ldots n$ and add and use the formula for $\Sigma n, \Sigma n^2, \Sigma n^3$ and $\Sigma 1 = n$

Ans. $n[10n^3 + 96n^2 + 343n + 540]$

28. $\frac{1}{4}(2n-1)(n+1)^2$

n is odd so $n-1, n-3, \ldots$ are all even

$S = \Sigma n^3 - 2[(n-1)^3 + (n-3)^3 + \ldots + 4^3 + 2^3]$

$= \Sigma n^3 - 2 \cdot 2^3 \left[1^3 + 2^3 + \ldots \left(\frac{n-1}{2}\right)^3\right]$

$= \Sigma n^3 - 16 \Sigma N^3$ when $N = \frac{n-1}{2}$ = integer as n is odd

$= \left[\frac{1}{2}n(n+1)\right]^2 - 16\left[\frac{1}{2} \cdot \frac{n-1}{2} \cdot \frac{n+1}{2}\right]^2$

$= \frac{1}{4}(n+1)^2[n^2 - (n-1)^2] = \frac{1}{4}(2n-1)(n+1)^2$

29. Ans. $\frac{1}{4}n^2(n+1)^2 - n$

$S = \sum_{n=2}^{n}(n-1)(n-\omega)(n-\omega^2)$

$= \sum_{n=1}^{n}(n-1)\{n^2 - n(\omega+\omega^2) + \omega^3\}$

The term for $n = 1$ is 0 so that S is same.

$= \Sigma(n-1)(n^2 - n(-1) + 1)$

$= \Sigma(n-1)(n^2 + n + 1) = \Sigma(n^3 - 1)$

$= \Sigma n^3 - \Sigma 1 = \frac{1}{4}n^2(n+1)^2 - n.$

30. $\qquad x = 1 + 3a + 6a^2 + 10a^3 + \ldots$

$\therefore \qquad ax = \qquad a + 3a^2 + 6a^3 + \ldots$

$\therefore \quad x(1-a) = 1 + 2a + 3a^2 + 4a^3 + \ldots$

Above is A.G.S. whose $S_\infty = \dfrac{A}{1-R} + \dfrac{dR}{(1-R)^2}$

(See § 3, P. 161)

$\therefore \quad x(1-a) = \dfrac{1}{1-a} + \dfrac{a}{(1-a)^2} = \dfrac{1}{(1-a)^2}$

$\therefore \quad x = \dfrac{1}{(1-a)^3} \qquad \therefore \quad (1-a)^3 = x^{-1}$

or $\quad a = 1 - x^{-1/3}$

Similarly, $\quad b = 1 - y^{-1/4}$

$\therefore \quad S = \dfrac{1}{1-ab} + \dfrac{2ab}{(1-ab)^2}$, as above for A.G.S.

$= \dfrac{1+ab}{(1-ab)^2}.$

Now put the values of a and b from above in terms of x and y.

31. For A.P. $a_n - a_{n-1} = d$ i.e. $a_4 - a_3 = d, a_2 - a_1 = d$ etc.

For G.P. $b_n = rb_{n-1}$ i.e. $b_4 = rb_3, b_2 = rb_1$ etc.

and $b_{n+1} = b_1 r^n$

Let $S = a_1 b_1 + a_2 b_2 + a_3 b_3 + \ldots + a_n b_n$

$rS = a_1 b_1 r + a_2 b_2 r + \ldots + a_{n-1} rb_{n-1} + a_n b_n r$

or $\quad rS = a_1 b_2 + a_2 b_3 + \ldots a_{n-1} b_n + a_n b_{n+1}$

$\therefore \quad S(1-r) = a_1 b_1 + (a_2 - a_1)b_2 + (a_3 - a_2)b_3$
$\qquad\qquad + (a_n - a_{n-1})b_n - a_n b_{n+1}$
$\qquad = (a_1 b_1 - a_n b_{n+1}) + d[b_2 + b_3 + \ldots + b_n] \quad \ldots(1)$

The second bracket is the sum of a G.P. of $n-1$ terms with first term as b_2 and its sum is

$\dfrac{b_2(1-r^{n-1})}{1-r} = \dfrac{b_2 - (b_1 r)r^{n-1}}{1-r} = \dfrac{b_2 - b_1 r^n}{1-r}$

$= \dfrac{b_2 - b_{n+1}}{1-r}.$ Put in (1)

$\therefore \quad S$ is etc. on dividing by $1-r$.

32. $S_1 = \dfrac{n(n+1)}{2}, S_3 = \left[\dfrac{n(n+1)}{2}\right]^2$

$S_2 = \dfrac{n(n+1)(2n+1)}{6}$

$S_3(1 + 8S_1) = \left[\dfrac{n(n+1)}{2}\right]^2 \left[1 + \dfrac{8n(n+1)}{2}\right]$

$= \left[\dfrac{n(n+1)}{2}\right]^2 (4n^2 + 4n + 1)$

$= \dfrac{1}{4}[n(n+1)(2n+1)]^2 = \dfrac{1}{4}(6S_2)^2 = 9S_2^2$

§6. Harmonical Progression (H.P.)

Definition. A series of quantities is said to be in harmonical progression when their reciprocals are in arithmetical progression.

e.g. $\quad \dfrac{1}{3}, \dfrac{1}{5}, \dfrac{1}{7}, \ldots$ and $\dfrac{1}{a}, \dfrac{1}{a+d}, \dfrac{1}{a+2d}, \ldots$ are H.P's as

their reciprocals $3, 5, 7, \ldots$, and $a, a+d, a+2d, \ldots$ are in A.P.

nth term of H.P.

Find the nth term of the corresponding A.P. and then take its reciprocal.

If the H.P. be as $\dfrac{1}{a}, \dfrac{1}{a+d}, \dfrac{1}{a+2d}, \ldots$

then corresponding A.P. is $a, a+d, a+2d, \ldots$

T_n of A.P. is $a + (n-1)d$

$\therefore \quad T_n$ of H.P. is $\dfrac{1}{a + (n-1)d}$.

In order to solve the question on H.P., we should form the corresponding A.P.

Harmonic mean (Single)

The harmonic mean between two quantities a and b will be x if a, x, b be in harmonical progression.

$\therefore \quad \dfrac{1}{a}, \dfrac{1}{x}, \dfrac{1}{b}$ will be in A.P. $\therefore \quad 2 \cdot \dfrac{1}{x} = \dfrac{1}{a} + \dfrac{1}{b} = \dfrac{a+b}{ab}$

$\therefore \quad \boldsymbol{x = \dfrac{2ab}{a+b} = \text{H.M.}}$

n harmonic means between a and b.

Let $x_1, x_2, \ldots x_n$, be n harmonic means between a and b.

$\therefore$ $a, x_1, x_2, \ldots x_n, b$ are in H.P.

or $\dfrac{1}{a}, \dfrac{1}{x_1}, \dfrac{1}{x_2}, \ldots \dfrac{1}{x_n}, \dfrac{1}{b}$ are in A.P.

$\therefore$ $\dfrac{1}{b} = T_{n+2}$ of A.P. $= \dfrac{1}{a} + (n+1)d$

$\therefore$ $(n+1)d = \dfrac{1}{b} - \dfrac{1}{a} = \dfrac{a-b}{ab}$ or $d = \dfrac{a-b}{ab} \cdot \dfrac{1}{n+1}$

$\therefore$ $\dfrac{1}{x_1} = T_2 = \dfrac{1}{a} + d, \dfrac{1}{x_2} = T_3 = \dfrac{1}{a} + 2d,$

$\dfrac{1}{x_n} = T_{n+1} = \dfrac{1}{a} + nd.$

On putting for d, we get

$\dfrac{1}{x_1} = \dfrac{1}{a} + \dfrac{a-b}{ab} \cdot \dfrac{1}{n+1} = \dfrac{nb+a}{(n+1)ab}$

$\therefore$ * $x_1 = \dfrac{(n+1)ab}{nb+a}$ ...(1)

Interchanging a and b, we get

* $x_n = \dfrac{(n+1)ab}{na+b}$ ...(2)

Note : Result (1) or (2) above are obtained by replacing a and b by $\dfrac{1}{a}$ and $\dfrac{1}{b}$ in results (1) and (2) of **Page 126** and then taking reciprocal.

Relations between A, G and H.

$$A = \dfrac{a+b}{2}, G = \sqrt{ab}, H = \dfrac{2ab}{a+b}$$

$$AH = ab = G^2 \quad \text{or} \quad \dfrac{A}{G} = \dfrac{G}{H} \qquad \ldots(3)$$

*(1) A, G, H are in G.P.

$$A - G = \dfrac{a+b}{2} - \sqrt{ab} = \dfrac{1}{2}(\sqrt{a} - \sqrt{b})^2$$

or $A - G > 0$ $\therefore$ $A > G$

or $\dfrac{A}{G} > 1$ $\therefore$ $\dfrac{G}{H} > 1$ or $G > H$ by (3)

$\therefore$ $A > G > H$

*(2) A, G, H are in descending order of magnitude

Classification of given series

If for $n \geq 2$

$t_n - t_{n-1} = \text{constant, then A.P.}$

$\dfrac{t_n}{t_{n-1}} = \text{constant, then G.P.}$

$\dfrac{1}{t_n} - \dfrac{1}{t_{n-1}} = \text{constant, then H.P.}$

Problem Set (4)

Harmonical progression, Harmonic means.

1. (a) If H be the harmonic mean between a and b, then prove that $\dfrac{1}{H-a} + \dfrac{1}{H-b} = \dfrac{1}{a} + \dfrac{1}{b}$.

(b) The sum of three numbers in H.P. is 26 and sum of their reciprocals is 3/8. Find the numbers.

2. If a, b, c be in H.P., prove that

(a) $\dfrac{1}{b-a} + \dfrac{1}{b-c} = \dfrac{2}{b}$ (b) $\dfrac{b+a}{b-a} + \dfrac{b+c}{b-c} = 2.$

(c)* $\left(\dfrac{1}{a} + \dfrac{1}{b} - \dfrac{1}{c}\right)\left(\dfrac{1}{b} + \dfrac{1}{c} - \dfrac{1}{a}\right) = \dfrac{4}{ac} - \dfrac{3}{b^2}.$

Another form :

$*(bc + ca - ab)(ca + ab - bc) = ac(4b^2 - 3ac)$

3. (a) If $\dfrac{1}{b-a} + \dfrac{1}{b-c} = \dfrac{1}{a} + \dfrac{1}{c}$, then prove that a, b, c are in H.P. unless $b = a + c$.

(b) If $\cos(x-y), \cos x$ and $\cos(x+y)$ are in H.P., then $\cos x \sec\left(\dfrac{y}{2}\right) = \ldots\ldots$ **(I.I.T. 1997)**

4. (a) The harmonic mean of the roots of the equation $(5 + \sqrt{2})x^2 - (4 + \sqrt{5})x + 8 + 2\sqrt{5} = 0$ is

(a) 2 (b) 4
(c) 6 (d) 8 **(I.I.T. 1999)**

(b) If a, b, c, d are in H. P., then show that $ab + bc + cd = 3ad.$

5. (a) If the harmonic mean of two numbers is to their geometric mean as 12 : 13, prove that the numbers are in the ratio of 4 : 9.

(b)* Let the harmonic mean and geometric mean of two positive numbers be in the ratio 4 : 5, then the two numbers are in the ratio .... **(I.I.T. 1992)**

6. (a) If x, y, z are in H.P., prove that $\log(x+z) + \log(x+z-2y) = 2\log(x-z).$

(b)* If $x > 1, y > 1, z > 1$ are in G.P., then $\dfrac{1}{1+\ln x}, \dfrac{1}{1+\ln y}, \dfrac{1}{1+\ln z}$ are in

(a) A.P. (b) H.P.
(b) G.P. (d) None of the above
(I.I.T. 1998)

7. (a) Solve the equation $6x^3 - 11x^2 + 6x - 1 = 0$ if its roots are in harmonical progression.

(b)* If the roots of $10x^3 - cx^2 - 54x - 27 = 0$ are in harmonic progression, then find c and all the roots. **(Roorkee 1995)**

(c) If $a^2 + 9b^2 + 25c^2 = abc\left(\dfrac{15}{a} + \dfrac{5}{b} + \dfrac{3}{c}\right)$, then a, b, c are in

(a) A.P. (b) G.P.
(c) H.P. (d) None

8. (a) If the A.M. between a and b is twice as great as their G.M. show that $a:b = (2+\sqrt{3}):(2-\sqrt{3})$.

(b)* The A.M. of a and b is to their G.M. as m to n, show $a:b = m+\sqrt{m^2-n^2}:m-\sqrt{m^2-n^2}$.

9. Prove that a,b,c are in A.P., G.P. or H.P. according as the value of $\dfrac{a-b}{b-c}$ is equal to $\dfrac{a}{a},\dfrac{a}{b}$ or $\dfrac{a}{c}$ respectively.

10. If A,G,H be respectively the A.M., G.M. and H.M. between two given quantities a and b, then prove that
(a) A,G,H are in G.P.
(b) $A > G > H$.

11. (a)* If the first and $(2n-1)$th terms of an A.P., a G.P. and H.P., are equal and their nth terms are $a,b,$ and c respectively, then
(i) $a=b=c$ (ii) $a+c=b$
(iii) $a>b>c$ (iv) $ac-b^2=0$

(b) The A.M., H.M. and G.M. between two numbers are $\dfrac{144}{15}, 15$ and 12, but not necessarily in this order. Then show that H.M., G.M. and A.M. respectively are $\dfrac{144}{15}, 12, 15$

12. (a) If a,b,c are in G. P. and $a-b, c-a$ and $b-c$ are in H.P., then prove that $a+4b+c$ is equal to 0.

(b) If $x = \sum\limits_{n=0}^{\infty} a^n, y = \sum\limits_{n=0}^{\infty} b^n, z = \sum\limits_{n=0}^{\infty} c^n$ where a,b,c are in A.P. such that $|a|<1, |b|<1$ and $|c|<1$, then x,y,z are in H.P.

13. (a) A.M. and H.M. between two quantities are 27 and 12 respectively, find their G.M.

(b)* The harmonic mean of two numbers is 4, their A.M. A, and G.M. G. satisfy the relation $2A + G^2 = 27$. Find the two numbers.

14. (a)* If $I_n = \int_0^{\pi/4} \tan^n x \sec^2 x\, dx$, then $I_1, I_2, I_3 \ldots$ are in
(a) A.P. (b) G.P.
(c) H.P. (d) none

(b) If $I_n = \int_0^{\pi/4} \tan^n x\, dx$, then $\dfrac{1}{I_2+I_4}, \dfrac{1}{I_3+I_5}, \dfrac{1}{I_4+I_6}, \ldots$ are in
(a) A.P. (b) G.P.
(c) H.P. (d) none

(c) If $I_n = \int_0^{\pi/2} \dfrac{\sin^2 nx}{\sin^2 x}\, dx$, then $I_1, I_2, I_3, \ldots$ are in
(a) A.P. (b) G.P.
(c) H.P. (d) none

15. If a,b,c,d are in H.P. show that
(a) $ad > bc$.
(b) $a+d > b+c$ where a,b,c,d are given real numbers.

16.* If a,b,c are all distinct and positive and are either in A.P. or in G.P. or H.P. and n be a positive integer, prove that $a^n + c^n > 2b^n$.

17. (a)* The value of $x+y+z$ is 15 if a,x,y,z,b are in A.P. while the value of $\dfrac{1}{x}+\dfrac{1}{y}+\dfrac{1}{z}$ is $\dfrac{5}{3}$ if a,x,y,z,b are in H.P.; find a and b.

(b)* Find the numbers a,b,c between 2 and 18 such that (i) their sum is 25 (ii) the numbers $2,a,b$ are consecutive terms of an A.P. and (iii) the numbers $b,c,18$ are consecutive terms of a G.P.

(c)* a,b,c are the first three terms of a geometric series. If the harmonic mean of a and b is 12 and that of b and c is 36, find the first five terms of the series.
(Roorkee 1998)

18. (a) The A.M. of two numbers exceeds their G.M. by 15 and H.M. by 27, find the numbers.

(b) If the A.M. between two numbers exceeds their G.M. by 2 and the G.M. exceeds their H.M. by 8/5, find the numbers.

19. (a) If A be the A.M. and H the H.M. between two numbers a and b, then
$$\dfrac{a-A}{a-H} \times \dfrac{b-A}{b-H} = \dfrac{A}{H}.$$

(b)* If 9 arithmetic and harmonic means be inserted between 2 and 3, prove that $A + 6/H = 5$ where A is any of the A.M.'s and H the corresponding H.M.

(c) Let $a_1, a_2, \ldots a_{10}$ be in A.P. and $h_1, h_2, \ldots, h_{10}$ be in H.P. If $a_1 = h_1 = 2$ and $a_{10} = h_{10} = 3$ then $a_4 h_7$ is
(a) 2 (b) 3
(c) 5 (d) 6 **(I.I.T. 1999)**

20. (a) If $A_1, A_2; G_1, G_2$; and H_1, H_2 be two A.M.'s and G.M.'s and H.M.'s between two quantities, then prove that $\dfrac{G_1 G_2}{H_1 H_2} = \dfrac{A_1 + A_2}{H_1 + H_2}$.

(b)* If $A_1, A_2; G_1, G_2$ and H_1, H_2 be two A.M.s, G.M.s and H.M.s between two quantities 'a' and 'b', then
$$A_1 H_2 = A_2 H_1 = G_1 G_2 = ab$$

(c) Let a,b be positive real numbers. If a, A_1, A_2, b are in arithmetic progression, a, G_1, G_2, b are in geometric progression and a, H_1, H_2, b are in harmonic progression, show that
$$\dfrac{G_1 G_2}{H_1 H_2} = \dfrac{A_1 + A_2}{H_1 + H_2} = \dfrac{(2a+b)(a+2b)}{9ab}$$
(I.I.T. 2002)

21.* If $a_1, a_2, a_3, \ldots a_n$ are in harmonic progression, prove that $a_1 a_2 + a_2 a_3 + \ldots + a_{n-1} a_n = (n-1) a_1 a_n$

22.* If p be the first of n arithmetic means between two numbers and q be the first of n harmonic means between the same two numbers, prove that the value of q cannot be between p and $\left(\dfrac{n+1}{n-1}\right)^2 p$.
(I.I.T. 1991)

23. If n harmonic means are inserted between 1 and r, then show that $\dfrac{\text{1st mean}}{n\text{th mean}} = \dfrac{n+r}{nr+1}$.

24. Let $a_1, a_2, ...$ be positive real numbers in geometric progression. For each n, let A_n, G_n, H_n be respectively, the arithmetic mean, geometric mean and harmonic mean of $a_1, a_2, ..., a_n$. Find an expression for the geometric mean of $G_1, G_2, ..., G_n$ in terms of $A_1, A_2, ..., A_n, H_1, H_2, ..., H_n$. **(I.I.T. 2001)**

25. (a)* If $H_1, H_2, ... H_n$ be n harmonic means between a and b, show that $\dfrac{H_1+a}{H_1-a} + \dfrac{H_n+b}{H_n-b} = 2n$.

(b)* If n be a root of the equation
$$x^2(1-ab) - x(a^2+b^2) - (1+ab) = 0,$$
prove that $H_1 - H_n = ab\,(a=b)$.

(c) Between two quantities a and b are inserted n arithmetic means and also n harmonic means. If x and y be the rth terms of A.P. and H.P. respectively, then prove that $\dfrac{x}{a} + \dfrac{b}{y}$ is independent of r and n.

26. Insert six harmonic means between 3 and $6/23$.

27. For what value of n, $\dfrac{a^{n+1}+b^{n+1}}{a^n+b^n}$ is the harmonic mean of a and b?

28. (a) If a, b, c be respectively the pth, qth, and rth terms of an H.P., then prove that $bc(q-r) + ca(r-p) + ab(p-q) = 0$

(b) If pth term of an H.P. is qr and qth term is rp, prove that rth term is pq.

29.* If the roots of the equation
$$a(b-c)x^2 + b(c-a)x + c(a-b) = 0$$
be equal, then prove that a, b, c are in H.P.

30. (a) If the mth term of an H.P. is n and nth term be m, then prove that $(m+n)$th term is $\dfrac{mn}{m+n}$.

(b) The 7th term of a H.P. is $1/10$ and 12th term is $1/25$, find the 20th term.

31. (a) If $\dfrac{1}{a(b+c)}, \dfrac{1}{b(c+a)}, \dfrac{1}{c(a+b)}$ be in H.P., then a, b, c are also in H.P.

(b) If $b+c, c+a, a+b$ are in H.P., then prove that $\dfrac{a}{b+c}, \dfrac{b}{c+a}, \dfrac{c}{a+b}$ are in A.P.

32. If a, b, c be in H.P., prove that

(a) $\dfrac{a}{b+c}, \dfrac{b}{c+a}, \dfrac{c}{a+b}$ are in H.P.

(b) $\dfrac{a}{b+c-a}, \dfrac{b}{c+a-b}, \dfrac{c}{a+b-c}$ are in H.P.

33. If a, b, c be in H.P., then prove that

(a)* $\dfrac{1}{a} + \dfrac{1}{b+c}, \dfrac{1}{b} + \dfrac{1}{c+a}, \dfrac{1}{c} + \dfrac{1}{a+b}$ are in H.P.

(b) $\dfrac{\sqrt{bc}}{\sqrt{b}+\sqrt{c}}, \dfrac{\sqrt{ca}}{\sqrt{c}+\sqrt{a}}, \dfrac{\sqrt{ab}}{\sqrt{a}+\sqrt{b}}$ are in A.P.

34. (a)* If a, b, c are in A.P., prove that $\dfrac{bc}{ca+ab}, \dfrac{ca}{bc+ab}, \dfrac{ab}{bc+ca}$ are in H.P.

(b) Let the positive numbers a, b, c, d be in A.P. Then abc, abd, acd, bcd are

(a) not in A.P./G.P./H.P.

(b) in A.P.

(c) in G.P.

(d) in H.P. **(I.I.T. Sc. 2001)**

(c) If $a_1, a_2, a_3, ... a_n$ are in H.P., then prove that
$$\dfrac{a_1}{a_2+a_3+...+a_n}, \dfrac{a_2}{a_1+a_3+...+a_n},$$
$$\dfrac{a_3}{a_1+a_2+...+a_n} \,......\, \text{are in H.P.}$$

35. (a) If $b+c, c+a, a+b$ are in H.P., then prove that a^2, b^2, c^2 are in A.P.

(b) If $\dfrac{a+b}{1-ab}, b, \dfrac{b+c}{1-bc}$ be in A.P., then prove that a, b^{-1}, c are in H.P.

36. (a) If a be A.M. of b and c, b the G.M. of c and a, then prove that c is the H.M. of a and b.

(b) If a, b, c be in A.P. b, c, a be in H.P., then prove that c, a, b are in G.P.

37. (a)* First three of the four numbers are in A.P., the last three in H.P. prove that the four numbers are proportional.

(b) If x, y, z are in A.P., ax, by, cz in G.P. and a, b, c in H.P., prove that $\dfrac{x}{z} + \dfrac{z}{x} = \dfrac{a}{c} + \dfrac{c}{a}$.

(c) Suppose a, b, c are in A.P. and a^2, b^2, c^2 are in G.P. If $a < b < c$ and $a+b+c = \dfrac{3}{2}$, then the value of a is

(a) $\dfrac{1}{2\sqrt{2}}$ (b) $\dfrac{1}{2\sqrt{3}}$

(c) $\dfrac{1}{2} - \dfrac{1}{\sqrt{3}}$ (d) $\dfrac{1}{2} - \dfrac{1}{\sqrt{2}}$ **(I.I.T. Sc. 2002)**

38. (a) If $a^x = b^y = c^z$ and a, b, c be in G.P., then prove that x, y, z are in H.P.

(b)* If $a^{1/x} = b^{1/y} = c^{1/z}$ and a, b, c be in G.P., then prove that x, y, z are in A.P.

(c) If $a^x = b^y = c^z$ and x, y, z are in G.P. (**Note**), then prove that $\log_b a = \log_c b$.

39. (a) If a, b, c be in G.P., then prove that $\log_a n$, $\log_b n$, $\log_c n$ are in H.P.

(b) If a, b, c be in G.P., then prove that $\log a^n$, $\log b^n$, $\log c^n$ are in A.P.

40. (a)* Given $a^x = b^y = c^z = d^u$ and a, b, c, d are in G.P., then x, y, z, u are in

(a) A.P.   (b) G.P.
(c) H.P.   (d) none

(b) If for an exponential function
$y = a^x$ $(a > 0, \neq 1)$ $x_1, x_2, \ldots x_n$ form an A.P.,
then $y_1, y_2, \ldots y_n$ form a
(a) A.P.   (b) G.P.
(c) H.P.   (d) A.G.P.

41. (a)* If the mth, nth, and pth terms of an A.P. and G.P. be equal and be respectively x, y and z, then prove that $x^{y-z} \cdot y^{z-x} \cdot z^{x-y} = 1$.

Another form :

$x^{y-z} y^{z-x} z^{x-y} = 1 \Rightarrow \dfrac{x^y}{x^z} \cdot \dfrac{y^z}{y^x} \cdot \dfrac{z^x}{z^y} = 1$

or $x^y y^z z^x = x^z y^x z^y$ **(D.C.E. 1998)**

(b)* A G.P. and H.P. have the same pth, qth, and rth terms as a, b, c respectively. Show that
$a(b-c)\log a + b(c-a)\log b + c(a-b)\log c = 0$

42.* If a, b, c, d, e be five numbers such that a, b, c are in A.P. b, c, d are in G.P. and c, d, e are in H.P. prove that
(a) a, c, e are in G.P. and

(b) $e = \dfrac{(2b-a)^2}{a}$.

(c) If $a = 2$ and $e = 18$, find all possible values of b, c and d.

43. If $a = 2$ and $e = 18$, then find three numbers b, c, d between a and e such that
(a) their sum is 25
(b) $2, b, c$ are in A.P.
(c) $c, d, 18$ are in G.P.

44. a, b, c are in H.P., b, c, d are in G.P. and c, d, e are in A.P. show that $e = \dfrac{ab^2}{(2a-b)^2}$.

45. If a, b, c are in G.P. and x, y respectively be arithmetic means between a, b and b, c, then prove that
$\dfrac{a}{x} + \dfrac{c}{y} = 2$ and $\dfrac{1}{x} + \dfrac{1}{y} = \dfrac{2}{b}$.

46. (a) If $\dfrac{a-x}{px} = \dfrac{a-y}{qy} = \dfrac{a-z}{rz}$ and p, q, r be in A.P., then prove that x, y, z are in H.P.

(b) If $\dfrac{a+bx}{a-bx} = \dfrac{b+cx}{b-cx} = \dfrac{c+dx}{c-dx}$ $(x \neq 0)$, then a, b, c, d are in
(a) A.P.   (b) G.P.
(c) H.P.   (d) none of these

47. (a)* If a, b, c be in A.P. and a^2, b^2, c^2 in H.P. then prove that either $-a/2, b, c$ are in G.P. or $a = b = c$.
(I.I.T. 2003)

(b)* If a, b, c be in G.P. whereas $b-c, c-a, a-b$ are in H.P., then prove that $a + b + c = -3\sqrt{(ac)}$

(c) If a, b and c are in arithmetic progression and a^2, b^2 and c^2 are in Harmonic progression, then

prove that either $a = b = c$ or a, b and $-c/2$ are in Geometric Progression.   **(I.I.T. 2003)**

48.* p, q, r are three numbers in G.P. Prove that the first term of an A.P. whose pth, qth, and rth terms are in H.P. is to the common difference as $q + 1 : 1$.

49.* An A.P., a G.P. and a H.P. have a and b for their first two terms. Show that their $(n+2)$th terms will be in G.P. if $\dfrac{b^{2n+2} - a^{2n+2}}{ab(b^{2n} - a^{2n})} = \dfrac{n+1}{n}$.

50. (a)* An A.P. and a H.P., have the same first term, the same last term, and the same number of terms; prove that the product of the rth term from the beginning in one series and the rth term from the end in the other is independent of r.

(b) First two terms of an A.P. as well as an H.P. are a and b. If x be any term of the A.P. and y the corresponding term of H.P., then will $\dfrac{x-a}{y-a} = \dfrac{b}{y}$?

51. Three unequal numbers are in H.P. and their squares are in A.P. prove that the numbers are in the ratio $1-\sqrt{3} : -2 : 1+\sqrt{3}$ or $1+\sqrt{3} : -2 : 1-\sqrt{3}$.

52.* α, β, γ are the geometric means between $ca, ab; ab, bc; bc, ca$ respectively. Prove that if a, b, c are in A.P., then $\alpha^2, \beta^2, \gamma^2$ are also in A.P., and $\beta + \gamma, \gamma + \alpha, \alpha + \beta$ are in H.P.

53. (a)* If the $(m+1)^{th}$, $(n+1)^{th}$ and $(r+1)^{th}$ terms of an A.P. are in G.P., m, n, r are in H.P. show that the ratio of the common difference to the first term in the A.P. is $\left(-\dfrac{2}{n}\right)$.
(Roorkee 1994)

(b) The three A.P.'s, have unity as the first term and common differences are d_1, d_2, d_3 which are in H.P. If S_1, S_2, S_3 be the sum of n terms of these three A.P.'s, then prove that
$n = \dfrac{2S_3 S_1 - S_1 S_2 - S_2 S_3}{S_1 - 2S_2 + S_3}$

54. If $2(y-a)$ is the H.M. between $y-x$ and $y-z$, then show that $x-a, y-a, z-a$ are in G.P.

55. (a) If A, G, H are respectively the A.M., G.M. and H.M. of three +ive numbers p, q, r then prove that
$(x-p)(x-q)(x-r) = x^3 - 3Ax^2 + 3\dfrac{G^3}{H}x - G^3 = 0$

(b) Find the condition that the roots of the equation with binomial coefficients, $i.e.$
$a_0 x^3 + 3a_1 x^2 + 3a_2 x + a_3 = 0$ be in :
(i) A.P.   (ii) G.P.
(iii) H.P.

56.* If S_1, S_2, S_3 denote the sums of n terms of three A.P.'s whose first terms are unity and common differences in H.P., prove that $n = \dfrac{2S_3 S_1 - S_1 S_2 - S_2 S_3}{S_1 - 2S_2 + S_3}$

57. Prove that $a_2 a_3 - a_1 a_4$ is positive, zero or negative according as a_1, a_2, a_3, a_4 are in A.P., G.P. or H.P.

58. (a) If a,b,c are in A.P., α,β,γ in H.P., $a\alpha,b\beta,c\gamma$ in G.P., (with common ratio not equal to 1.), then prove that $a:b:c=\dfrac{1}{\gamma}:\dfrac{1}{\beta}:\dfrac{1}{\alpha}$.

(b) If a,b,c be distinct positive and in G.P. and $\log_c a,\log_b c,\log_a b$ be in A.P. then show that the common difference of this A.P. is 3/2.

Solutions to Problem Set (4)

1. (a) $H=\dfrac{2ab}{a+b}$ ∴ $H-a=\dfrac{2ab}{a+b}-a=\dfrac{ab-a^2}{a+b}$

$H-b=\dfrac{2ab}{a+b}-b=\dfrac{ab-b^2}{a+b}$

∴ $\dfrac{1}{H-a}+\dfrac{1}{H-b}=(a+b)\left[\dfrac{1}{a(b-a)}+\dfrac{1}{b(a-b)}\right]$

$=(a+b)\dfrac{(b-a)}{ab(b-a)}=\dfrac{a+b}{ab}=\dfrac{1}{a}+\dfrac{1}{b}$.

(b) Any three numbers in H.P. be taken as $\dfrac{1}{a-d},\dfrac{1}{a},\dfrac{1}{a+d}$ as their reciprocals are in A.P. given

$\dfrac{1}{a-d}+\dfrac{1}{a}+\dfrac{1}{a+d}=26$ ...(1)

Also $a-d+a+a+d=\dfrac{3}{8}$ ∴ $a=\dfrac{1}{8}$

From (1),

$\dfrac{a(a+d)+(a+d)(a-d)+a(a-d)}{a(a^2-d^2)}=26$

or $3a^2-d^2=26a(a^2-d^2)=\dfrac{13}{4}(a^2-d^2)$

by (1)

$a^2=9d^2$ ∴ $d=\pm\dfrac{a}{3}=\pm\dfrac{1}{24}$

∴ Numbers are 12, 8, 6 or 6, 8, 12.

2. (a) Prove yourself.

(b) $b=\dfrac{2ac}{a+c}$ or $\dfrac{b}{a}=\dfrac{2c}{a+c}$ ∴ $\dfrac{b+a}{b-a}=\dfrac{3c+a}{c-a}$,

by componendo and dividendo

and $\dfrac{b+c}{b-c}=\dfrac{3a+c}{a-c}$, as above.

Adding the above, we get

L.H.S. $=\dfrac{(3c+a)-(3a+c)}{c-a}=2$.

(c) ∵ a,b,c are in H.P., we have $2/b=(1/a)+(1/c)$ ...(1)

Now $\left(\dfrac{1}{a}+\dfrac{1}{b}-\dfrac{1}{c}\right)\left(\dfrac{1}{b}+\dfrac{1}{c}-\dfrac{1}{a}\right)$

$=\left(\dfrac{1}{b}+\dfrac{1}{a}-\dfrac{1}{c}\right)\left\{\dfrac{1}{b}-\left(\dfrac{1}{a}-\dfrac{1}{c}\right)\right\}$

$=\dfrac{1}{b^2}-\left(\dfrac{1}{a}-\dfrac{1}{c}\right)^2=\dfrac{1}{b^2}-\left\{\left(\dfrac{1}{a}+\dfrac{1}{c}\right)^2-\dfrac{4}{ac}\right\}$

$=\dfrac{1}{b^2}-\left\{\left(\dfrac{2}{b}\right)^2-\dfrac{4}{ac}\right\}=\dfrac{4}{ac}-\dfrac{3}{b^2}$, by (1)

3. (a) From the given relation $\dfrac{1}{b-a}-\dfrac{1}{c}=\dfrac{1}{a}-\dfrac{1}{b-c}$

or $\dfrac{c-b+a}{c(b-a)}=\dfrac{b-c-a}{a(b-c)}$

$-\dfrac{1}{c(b-a)}=\dfrac{1}{a(b-c)}$ or $ac-bc=ab-ac$

or $b=\dfrac{2ac}{a+c}$. Hence a,b,c are in H.P.

(b) Ans. $\pm\sqrt2$;

$\dfrac{2}{\cos x}=\dfrac{1}{\cos(x-y)}+\dfrac{1}{\cos(x+y)}=\dfrac{2\cos x\cos y}{\cos^2 x-\sin^2 y}$

∴ $\cos^2 x-\sin^2 y=\cos^2 x\cos y$

$\cos^2 x(1-\cos y)=\sin^2 y=1-\cos^2 y$

∴ $\cos^2 x=1+\cos y=2\cos^2(y/2)$

∴ $\cos x\sec(y/2)=\pm\sqrt2$

4. (a) Ans. (b).

H.M. $=\dfrac{2\alpha\beta}{\alpha+\beta}=2\dfrac{P}{S}=\dfrac{2(8+2\sqrt5)}{4+\sqrt5}=4$

(b) $b=\dfrac{2ac}{a+c},c=\dfrac{2bd}{b+d}$, $(a+c)(b+d)=\dfrac{2ac}{b}\cdot\dfrac{2bd}{c}$

or $ab+bc+cd+ad=4ad$

or $ab+bc+cd=3ad$

5. (a) By the given condition if the numbers be a and b, then

$\dfrac{2ab}{a+b}:\sqrt{ab}=12:13$ or $2\dfrac{\sqrt{ab}}{a+b}=\dfrac{12}{13}$

or $26\sqrt{ab}=12(a+b)$. Divide by $2b$.

∴ $13\sqrt{\dfrac{a}{b}}=6\left(\dfrac{a}{b}+1\right)$ Put $\sqrt{\dfrac{a}{b}}=x$

∴ $6x^2-13x+6=0$, ∴ $(2x-3)(3x-2)=0$

∴ $x=\dfrac{3}{2}$ or $\dfrac{2}{3}=\sqrt{\dfrac{a}{b}}$ ∴ $\dfrac{a}{b}=\dfrac{9}{4}$ or $\dfrac{4}{9}$.

Hence the numbers are in the ratio 4 : 9.

(b) Proceed as above. $a:b::1:4$

6. (a) Since x,y,z are in H.P. ∴ $y=\dfrac{2xz}{x+z}$

∴ $x-2y+z=x+z-\dfrac{4xz}{x+z}$

$=\dfrac{(x+z)^2-4xz}{x+z}=\dfrac{(x-z)^2}{x+z}$

∴ $\log(x-2y+z)=2\log(x-z)-\log(x+z)$

or $\log(x+z)+\log(x-2y+z)=2\log(x-z)$

(b) Ans. (b). $y^2=xz,1+\log x,1+\log y$, $1+\log z$ are in A.P. if $2\log y=\log x+\log z$

or $y^2=xz$, which is true.

7. (a) Replacing x by $1/x$, we get $6/x^3-11/x^2+6/x-1=0$

or $x^3 - 6x^2 + 11x - 6 = 0$

Its roots are in A.P. say α, β, γ.

$\therefore \quad 2\beta = \alpha + \gamma$ or $3\beta = \alpha + \beta + \gamma = 6$

or $\beta = 2$

Hence $(x - 2)$ is a factor of above.

$\therefore \quad x^3 - 6x^2 + 11x - 6 = (x - 2)(x^2 - 4x + 3)$
$$= (x - 2)(x - 3)(x - 1).$$

$\therefore$ Roots $1, 2, 3$ are in A.P.

or $1, \dfrac{1}{2}, \dfrac{1}{3}$ are in H.P.

(b) If α, β, γ be the roots of the given equation in H.P. then p, q, r will be the roots of the equation

$$\dfrac{10}{x^3} - \dfrac{c}{x^2} - \dfrac{54}{x} - 27 = 0$$

or $27x^3 + 54x^2 + cx - 10 = 0$ are in A.P. ...(1)

$\therefore \quad 2q = p + r$

or $3q = p + q + r = -\dfrac{54}{27} = -2$

$\therefore \quad q = -\dfrac{2}{3}$. Hence $\left(-\dfrac{2}{3}\right)$ is a root of (1).

Putting in (1), we get $c = 9$

$\therefore \quad 27x^3 + 54x^2 + 9x - 10 = 0$

has a root $-\dfrac{2}{3}$ or $3x + 2$ is its factor.

$\therefore \quad (3x + 2)(9x^2 + 12x - 5) = 0$

or $(3x + 2)(3x + 5)(3x - 1) = 0$

$\therefore \quad x = \dfrac{1}{3}, -\dfrac{2}{3}, -\dfrac{5}{3}$ which are in A.P.

Hence the roots of the given equation in H.P. are $3, -\dfrac{3}{2}, -\dfrac{3}{5}$

(b) Ans. (c).

$(a)^2 + (3b)^2 + (5c)^2 - (a)(3b) - (3b)(5c) - (5c)(a) = 0$

$x^2 + y^2 + z^2 - xy - yz - zx = \dfrac{1}{2}\Sigma(x - y)^2 = 0$

$\Rightarrow \quad x - y = 0, y - z = 0, z - x = 0$ or $x = y = z$

$\therefore \quad \dfrac{1}{2}[(a - 3b)^2 + (3b - 5c)^2 + (5c - a)^2] = 0$

$\therefore \quad a = 3b = 5c$ or $\dfrac{a}{1/1} = \dfrac{b}{1/3} = \dfrac{c}{1/5} = k,$ say

$\therefore \quad a : b : c = \dfrac{k}{1}, \dfrac{k}{3}, \dfrac{k}{5}$

or $\dfrac{1}{a}, \dfrac{1}{b}, \dfrac{1}{c} = \dfrac{1}{k}, \dfrac{3}{k}, \dfrac{5}{k}$ respectively.

$\therefore \quad \dfrac{1}{a}, \dfrac{1}{b}, \dfrac{1}{c}$ are in A.P. or a, b, c are in H.P.

8. (a) We are given that $A = 2G$ ...(1)
$2A = a + b, G^2 = ab$

Thus a, b are the roots of $x^2 - 2Ax + G^2 = 0$

or $x^2 - 4Gx + G^2 = 0$

$\therefore \quad x = \dfrac{4G \pm \sqrt{16G^2 - 4G^2}}{2} = 2 \pm \sqrt{3}$

$\therefore \quad \dfrac{a}{b} = \dfrac{2 + \sqrt{3}}{2 - \sqrt{3}}$

(b) $\dfrac{A}{G} = \dfrac{m}{n}$ ...(1)

or $\dfrac{A}{m} = \dfrac{G}{n} = \lambda$ say

$\therefore \quad a + b = 2A = 2m\lambda, ab = G^2 = n^2\lambda^2$

Hence a, b are roots of $x^2 - 2m\lambda x + n^2\lambda^2 = 0$

$\therefore \quad x = 2m\lambda \pm 2\lambda\sqrt{m^2 - n^2}$

$\therefore \quad \dfrac{a}{b} = \dfrac{m + \sqrt{m^2 - n^2}}{m - \sqrt{m^2 - n^2}}$

9. $\dfrac{a - b}{b - c} = \dfrac{a}{a}$ gives $b = \dfrac{a + c}{2}$ $\therefore$ in A.P.

$\dfrac{a - b}{b - c} = \dfrac{a}{b}$ gives $b^2 = ac$ $\therefore$ in G.P.

$\dfrac{a - b}{b - c} = \dfrac{a}{c}$ gives $b = \dfrac{2ac}{a + c}$ $\therefore$ in H.P.

10. See (1), (2) Page 173.

11. (a) Ans. (iii) and (iv).

There are odd i.e. $(2n - 1)$ terms and hence the middle term will be nth. If α, β be the first and last terms of each series then $T_n = a$ for A.P., $= b$ for G.P., $= c$ for H.P.

$\therefore \quad \alpha, a, \beta$ is an A.P.; α, b, β is a G.P. and α, c, β is H.P. In other words, a, b, c are A.M., G.M. and H.M. of same two numbers α and β. We know from result (1), (2) of **P. 173** that $a > b > c$ and that $b^2 = ac$ i.e. they are in G.P.

(b) $A > G > H$ $\therefore$ $15, 12, \dfrac{144}{15}$

$H < G < A$ $\therefore$ $\dfrac{144}{15}, 12, 15$

12. (a) a, b, c in G. P. $\Rightarrow b = ar, c = ar^2$

$\dfrac{1}{a - b}, \dfrac{1}{c - a}, \dfrac{1}{b - c}$ in A. P.

$\Rightarrow \dfrac{2}{a(r^2 - 1)} = \dfrac{1}{a(1 - r)} + \dfrac{1}{ar(1 - r)} = \dfrac{1 + r}{ar(1 - r)}$

$\therefore \quad -2r = (r + 1)^2$ or $r^2 + 4r + 1 = 0$ ...(1)

Now $c + 4b + a = a(r^2 + 4r + 1) = 0$, by (1)

(b) $x = \dfrac{1}{1 - a} \Rightarrow a = 1 - \dfrac{1}{x}$ by S_∞ for G.P.

$\therefore \quad a, b, c$ are in A.P. $\Rightarrow 2b = a + c$

$\therefore \quad 2\left(1 - \dfrac{1}{y}\right) = 1 - \dfrac{1}{x} + 1 - \dfrac{1}{z}$

$\Rightarrow \dfrac{2}{y} = \dfrac{1}{x} + \dfrac{1}{z}$

$\Rightarrow \dfrac{1}{x}, \dfrac{1}{y}, \dfrac{1}{z}$ are in A.P. or x, y, z are in H.P.

13. (a) $A = 27$ and $H = 12$.

But we know that A, G, H are in G.P.

$\therefore \quad G^2 = A \cdot H = 27 \times 12 = 9 \times 36$

$\therefore \quad G = 3 \times 6 = 18.$

(b) $A = \dfrac{a+b}{2}$ or $a+b = 2A$,

$G = \sqrt{ab} \quad \therefore \qquad G^2 = ab$

or $H = \dfrac{2ab}{a+b} = 4$, $\therefore \ G^2 = AH$ gives $G^2 = 4A$.

Also $\quad 2A + G^2 = 27$ or $2A + 4A = 27$

$\therefore \quad A = \dfrac{27}{6} = \dfrac{9}{2}$

$\therefore \quad \dfrac{a+b}{2} = \dfrac{9}{2}$ or $a+b = 9$ ...(1)

Also $G^2 = 4A = 4 \cdot \dfrac{9}{2} = 18$ or $ab = 18$ ...(2)

From (1) and (2) we conclude that a and b are the roots of

$t^2 - 9t + 18 = 0$ or $(t-6)(t-3) = 0$

$\therefore \quad t = 6, 3$

Hence the numbers are 6 and 3.

14. (a) Ans. (c). $I_n = \left[\dfrac{\tan^{n+1} x}{n+1} \right]_0^{\pi/4} = \dfrac{1}{n+1}$

$I_1, I_2, I_3 \ldots$ are $\dfrac{1}{2}, \dfrac{1}{3}, \dfrac{1}{4}, \ldots$ which are in H.P. as their reciprocals are in A.P.

(b) Ans. (a). $I_n = \int_0^{\pi/4} \tan^{n-2} x \tan^2 x \, dx$

$= \int_0^{\pi/4} \tan^{n-2} x (\sec^2 x - 1) \, dx$

$I_n = \left[\dfrac{\tan^{n-1} x}{n-1} \right]_0^{\pi/4} - I_{n-2}$

$\therefore \quad I_n + I_{n-2} = \dfrac{1}{n-1}$

Putting $n = 4, 5, 6, \ldots$ we get

$I_4 + I_2, I_5 + I_3, I_6 + I_4, \ldots$ are respectively $\dfrac{1}{3}, \dfrac{1}{4},$

$\dfrac{1}{5} \ldots$ which are in H.P. and hence their reciprocals are in A.P.

(c) Ans. (a). $I_{n+2} + I_n - 2I_{n+1}$

$= \int_0^{\pi/2} \dfrac{\sin^2 (n+2) + \sin^2 nx - 2\sin^2 (n+1) x \, dx}{\sin^2 x}$

$= \int_0^{\pi/2} \dfrac{\begin{array}{c}[\sin^2 (n+2) x - \sin^2 (n+1) x] \\ + [\sin^2 nx - \sin^2 (n+1) x] \, dx\end{array}}{\sin^2 x}$

Use $\sin^2 A - \sin^2 B = \sin (A+B) \sin (A-B)$

$= \int_0^{\pi/2} \dfrac{\sin (2n+3) x \cdot \sin x + \sin (2n+1) x}{\sin^2 x} \cdot \sin (-x) \, dx$

$= \int_0^{\pi/2} \dfrac{\sin (2n+3) x - \sin (2n+1) x}{\sin x} \, dx$

$= \int_0^{\pi/2} \dfrac{2 \sin x \cos (2n+2) x}{\sin x} \, dx$

$= \int_0^{\pi/2} 2 \cos (2n+2) x \, dx$

$= 2 \left(\dfrac{\sin (2n+2) x}{2n+2} \right)_0^{\pi/2} = 0$

$\therefore \quad I_n, I_{n+1}, I_{n+2}$ are in A.P.

Now put $n = 1, 2, 3, \ldots$

$\therefore \quad I_1, I_2, I_3, I_4 \ldots$ are in A.P.

15. (a), (b) a, b, c, d are in H.P.

b is H.M. of a and c and their A.M. is $\dfrac{a+c}{2}$

and G.M. is $\sqrt{ac}$.

c is H.M. of b and d and their A.M. is $\dfrac{b+d}{2}$ and

G.M. is $\sqrt{bd}$

Also $A > G > H$ where A, G, H are resspective means.

$\therefore \quad \dfrac{a+c}{2} > b$ and $\dfrac{b+d}{2} > c \quad \because \quad A > H$

Add $\quad \dfrac{a+c}{2} + \dfrac{b+d}{2} > b + c$

or $\quad a+b+c+d > 2b + 2c$

or $\quad a+d > b+c$. This is (b).

$\sqrt{ac} > b$ and $\sqrt{bd} > c \quad \because \quad G > H$

Multiply $\therefore \ \sqrt{ac} \sqrt{bd} > bc$ or $acbd > b^2 c^2$

or $\quad ad > bc$ This is (a).

(c) We know that $\dfrac{a^n + c^n}{2} > \left(\dfrac{a+c}{2} \right)^n$. ...(1)

Now since a, b, c are in H.P., b is the H.M. between a and c. Also $\dfrac{a+c}{2}$ is the A.M. between a and c and $A > H$.

Hence $\dfrac{a+c}{2} > b$ and so $\left(\dfrac{a+c}{2} \right)^n > b^n$ ...(2)

$\therefore \quad$ From (1) and (2), we get

$\dfrac{a^n + c^n}{2} > b^n$ i.e. $a^n + c^n > 2b^n$.

16. (i) Let a, b, c be in A.P. so that $b = \dfrac{a+c}{2}$

Then $\dfrac{a^n + c^n}{2} > \left[\dfrac{a+c}{2} \right]^n = b^n$ (Inequality)

or $\quad a^n + c^n > 2b^n$.

(ii) Let a, b, c be in G.P. so that $b^2 = ac$.

Then $\dfrac{a^n + c^n}{2} > (a^n c^n)^{1/2} = (\sqrt{ac})^n = b^n$

or $\quad a^n + c^n > 2b^n$.

(iii) Let a, b, c be in H.P. so that $\sqrt{ac} = G$ of a, c and b is H of a, c

Since $G > H$ $\therefore$ $\sqrt{ac} > b$ ...(1)

Now $\dfrac{a^n + c^n}{2} > (a^n c^n)^{1/2} = (\sqrt{ac})^n > b^n$ by (1)

or $a^n + c^n > 2 b^n$.

17. (a) We know that sum of n A.M.'s between two quantities is equal to n times their single mean. Now x, y, z are three A.M.'s between a and b

$$x + y + z = 3 \left(\frac{a+b}{2} \right) = 15$$

or $a + b = 10$ ...(1)

a, x, y, z, b are in H.P.

$\therefore$ $\dfrac{1}{a}, \dfrac{1}{x}, \dfrac{1}{y}, \dfrac{1}{z}, \dfrac{1}{b}$ are in A.P.

$\therefore$ $\dfrac{1}{x} + \dfrac{1}{y} + \dfrac{1}{z} = \dfrac{3}{2}\left(\dfrac{1}{a} + \dfrac{1}{b} \right) = 3 \left(\dfrac{a+b}{2ab} \right)$

or $\dfrac{5}{3} = \dfrac{3}{2ab} \cdot 10$, by (1) $\therefore$ $ab = 9$ ...(2)

Hence a and b are the roots of

$t^2 - 10t + 9 = 0$, by (1) and (2)

$\therefore$ $t = 9, 1$ are the required values of a and b.

(b) We have $a + b + c = 25$ ...(1)

$2a = b + 2$ ...(2)

and $c^2 = 18b$ ...(3)

Eliminating a from (1) and (2),

$b = 16 - \dfrac{2c}{3}$.

Then from (3), $c^2 = 18 \left(16 - \dfrac{2c}{3} \right)$

or $c^2 + 12c - 18 \times 16 = 0$

or $(c - 12)(c + 24) = 0$

$c = -24$ is rejected since it does not lie between 2 and 18. Hence $c = 12$. Then (3) gives $b = 8$ and finally (2) gives $a = 5$. Thus $a = 5$, $b = 8$ and $c = 12$.

(c) Since a, b, c are in G.P., we may choose them to be $br, b, b/r$.

$\therefore$ $12 = \dfrac{2br \cdot b}{b(1+r)} = \dfrac{2br}{1+r}$.

$36 = \dfrac{2b \cdot b/r}{b(1+1/r)} = \dfrac{2b}{1+r}$.

Dividing, $r = \dfrac{1}{3}$ and hence from any $b = 24$

$\therefore$ Five numbers are 8, 24, 72, 216, 648.

18. (a) Let the numbers be a, b and their A.M., G.M., and H.M. be denoted by $A, G,$ and H respectively. Also we know that A, G, H are in G.P.

or $G^2 = AH$ ...(1)

Since $A - G = 15$ and $A - H = 27$

$(A - 15)^2 = G^2 = AH$ by (1) $= A(A - 27)$

or $-30A + 225 = -27A$ or $3A = 225$

$\therefore$ $A = 75 = \dfrac{a+b}{2}$ $\therefore$ $a + b = 150$ ...(2)

Since $A - G = 15$ $\therefore$ $75 - G = 15$

or $G = 60 = \sqrt{ab}$

$ab = 3600$ ...(3)

Hence from (2) and (3) we conclude that a and b are the roots of $t^2 - 150t + 3600 = 0$

or $(t - 120)(t - 30) = 0$ $\therefore$ $t = 120, 30$

Hence the two numbers are 120 and 30.

(b) If the numbers be a and b, then

$A - G = 2$ $\therefore$ $(a+b)/2 - \sqrt{ab} = 2$

or $(\sqrt{a} - \sqrt{b})^2 = 4$ ...(1)

$G - H = \dfrac{8}{5}$ $\therefore$ $\sqrt{ab} - \dfrac{2ab}{a+b} = \dfrac{8}{5}$

or $\sqrt{ab} \dfrac{[a+b - 2\sqrt{ab}]}{a+b} = \dfrac{8}{5}$

or $5\sqrt{ab}(\sqrt{a} - \sqrt{b})^2 = 8(a+b)$

or $5\sqrt{ab} \cdot 4 = 8(a+b)$, by (1)

$\therefore$ $2a - 5\sqrt{ab} + 2b + 0$

or $(2\sqrt{a} - \sqrt{b})(\sqrt{a} - 2\sqrt{b}) = 0$

$\therefore$ $\sqrt{a} = 2\sqrt{b}$ or $(\sqrt{b}/2)$ $\therefore$ $a = 4b$ or $(b/4)$

From (1), $(2\sqrt{b} - \sqrt{b})^2 = 4$ or $b = 4$

$\therefore$ $\sqrt{a} = 2\sqrt{b} = 4$ or $a = 16$

Hence the numbers are 16 and 4. The other factor will give numbers as 4 and 16.

19. (a) Substitute $A = \dfrac{a+b}{2}$ and $H = \dfrac{2ab}{a+b}$ and simplify.

(b) Let A_i, H_i $(i = 1, 2, \ldots 9)$ denote the 9 A.M.'s and 9 H.M.'s between 2 and 3. If d denote the common difference of A.P., then

$3 = T_{11} = 2 + 10d$ or $d = 1/10$.

Let A denote the ith mean, then

$A = T_{i+1} = 2 + di = 2 + i/10$

Again Let $2, H_1, H_2 \ldots \ldots, H_9, 3$ be in H.P.

or $\dfrac{1}{2}, \dfrac{1}{H_1}, \dfrac{1}{H_2}, \ldots \ldots, \dfrac{1}{H_9}, \dfrac{1}{3}$ are in A.P. If d_1

is the common difference of this A.P., then

$\dfrac{1}{3} = T_{11} = \dfrac{1}{2} + 10d_1$ or $d_1 = -\dfrac{1}{60}$

If H is the ith H.M., then $\dfrac{1}{H} = \dfrac{1}{2} + d_1 i = \dfrac{1}{2} - \dfrac{i}{60}$

Now $A + \dfrac{6}{H} = \left(2 + \dfrac{i}{10} \right) + 6 \left(\dfrac{1}{2} - \dfrac{i}{60} \right)$

$= 5 + \dfrac{i}{10} - \dfrac{i}{10} = 5$.

(c) Ans. (d). $a_1 = h_1 = 2, a_{10} = h_{10} = 3$

$3 = a_{10} = 2 + 9d \Rightarrow d = 1/9$

$\therefore$ $a_4 = 2 + 3d = 7/3$

$3 = h_{10} \Rightarrow \dfrac{1}{3} = \dfrac{1}{h_{10}} = \dfrac{1}{2} + 9D$

$\therefore \quad D = -\dfrac{1}{54}$

$\dfrac{1}{h_7} = \dfrac{1}{2} + 6D = \dfrac{1}{2} - \dfrac{1}{9} = \dfrac{7}{18}$

$\therefore \quad a_4 h_7 = \dfrac{7}{3} \times \dfrac{18}{7} = 6.$

20. (a) Sum of n A.Ms. $= n \times$ single A.M. **Page 126.**

$A_1 + A_2 = 2\left(\dfrac{a+b}{2}\right) = a+b$ formulae.

Product of n G.Ms. $= (\text{single G.M.})^n$ **Page 143.**

$G_1 G_2 = (\sqrt{ab})^2 = ab$ formulae

$\dfrac{1}{a}, \dfrac{1}{H_1}, \dfrac{1}{H_2}, \dfrac{1}{b}$ are in A.P.

$\therefore \quad \dfrac{1}{H_1} + \dfrac{1}{H_2} = \dfrac{1}{a} + \dfrac{1}{b} = \dfrac{a+b}{ab}$

or $\quad \dfrac{H_1 + H_2}{H_1 H_2} = \dfrac{A_1 + A_2}{G_1 G_2}$ etc.

(b) a, A_1, A_2, b are in A.P. $\qquad$ ...(1)

a, H_1, H_2, b are in H.P.

$\therefore \quad \dfrac{1}{a}, \dfrac{1}{H_1}, \dfrac{1}{H_2}, \dfrac{1}{b}$ are in A.P.

Multiply by ab.

$\therefore \quad b, \dfrac{ab}{H_1}, \dfrac{ab}{H_2}, a$ are in A.P.

Take in reverse order.

or $\quad a, \dfrac{ab}{H_2}, \dfrac{ab}{H_1}, b$ are in A.P. $\quad$ ..(2)

Compare (1) and (2)

$\therefore \quad A_1 = \dfrac{ab}{H_2}$ and $A_2 = \dfrac{ab}{H_1}$

$\therefore \quad A_1 H_2 = A_2 H_1 = ab = G_1 G_2$

(c) Now a, H_1, H_2, b are in H.P.

$\therefore \quad \dfrac{1}{a}, \dfrac{1}{H_1}, \dfrac{1}{H_2}, \dfrac{1}{b}$ are in A.P.

$\therefore \quad \dfrac{1}{b} = \dfrac{1}{a} + 3D \quad \therefore \quad D = \dfrac{1}{3}\left(\dfrac{1}{b} - \dfrac{1}{a}\right)$

$\therefore \quad \dfrac{1}{H_1} = \dfrac{1}{a} + D = \dfrac{1}{a} + \dfrac{1}{3}\left(\dfrac{1}{b} - \dfrac{1}{a}\right) = \dfrac{2b+a}{3ab}$

$\dfrac{1}{H_2} = \dfrac{1}{a} + 2D = \dfrac{1}{a} + \dfrac{2}{3}\left(\dfrac{1}{b} - \dfrac{1}{a}\right) = \dfrac{2a+b}{3ab}$

$\therefore \quad \dfrac{G_1 G_2}{H_1 H_2} = \dfrac{ab(2b+a)(2a+b)}{9a^2 b^2}$

$= \dfrac{(2b+a)(2a+b)}{9ab}.$

Note : The value of H_2 can be obtained from the value of H_1 if we interchange a and b.

21. Since $a_1, a_2, \ldots, a_n$ are in H.P.

$\therefore \quad \dfrac{1}{a_1}, \dfrac{1}{a_2}, \dfrac{1}{a_3}, \ldots, \dfrac{1}{a_n}$ are in A.P. of common difference say d.

$\therefore \quad \dfrac{1}{a_2} - \dfrac{1}{a_1} = d, \dfrac{1}{a_3} - \dfrac{1}{a_2} = d, \ldots \dfrac{1}{a_n} - \dfrac{1}{a_{n-1}} = d$

or $\quad a_1 - a_2 = d(a_1 a_2), a_2 - a_3 = d(a_2 a_3),$

$\ldots, (a_{n-1} - a_n) = d(a_{n-1} a_n)$

Adding the above relations, we get

$a_1 - a_n = d(a_1 a_2 + a_2 a_3 + \ldots + a_{n-1} a_n) \qquad$ ...(1)

Now we have to find the value of d

$\dfrac{1}{a_n} = T_n$ of A.P. $= \dfrac{1}{a_1} + (n-1)d$.

$\therefore \quad \dfrac{1}{a_n} - \dfrac{1}{a_1} = (n-1)d$

or $\quad (a_1 - a_n) = (n-1)d\, a_n a_1 \qquad$ ...(2)

Putting the value of $a_1 - a_n$ from (2) in (1), we get

$(n-1)a_n a_1 d = d(a_1 a_2 + a_2 a_3 + \ldots + a_{n-1} a_n)$

$\therefore \quad (n-1)a_n a_1 = a_1 a_2 + a_2 a_3 + \ldots + a_{n-1} a_n.$

22. If a and b be two quantities and p be the first of n A.M.'s between them, then as calculated on **Page 126.**

$$p = \dfrac{na+b}{n+1} \qquad \text{...(1)}$$

Again if q be the first of H.M. between them, then as calculated on **Page 173.**

$$q = \dfrac{(n+1)ab}{nb+a} \qquad \text{...(2)}$$

The result (2) can also be obtained by replacing a by $\dfrac{1}{a}$ and b by $\dfrac{1}{b}$ in (1) and then taking reciprocal.

Note : For obtaining nth A.M. and H.M. interchange a and b in (1) and (2) above.

We have to prove that q cannot lie between p and $\dfrac{(n+1)^2}{(n-1)^2}\, p$.

Now $n+1 > n-1$ or $\left(\dfrac{n+1}{n-1}\right)^2 > 1$

$\therefore \quad \left(\dfrac{n+1}{n-1}\right)^2 p > p$ or $p < \left(\dfrac{n+1}{n-1}\right)^2 p \qquad$ ...(3)

$q - p = \dfrac{(n+1)ab}{nb+a} - \dfrac{na+b}{n+1}$, by (1) and (2)

$= \dfrac{(n+1)^2 ab - (na+b)(nb+a)}{(nb+a)(n+1)}$

$= \dfrac{(n+1)^2 ab - [(n^2+1)ab + n(a^2+b^2)]}{(nb+a)(n+1)}$

$= \dfrac{2abn - n(a^2+b^2)}{(nb+a)(n+1)}$

$= -\dfrac{n}{(nb+a)(n+1)}(a-b)^2 = -\text{ive} < 0$

$\therefore \quad q < p < \left(\dfrac{n+1}{n-1}\right)^2 p$

Note : n, a, b are all +ive quantities.

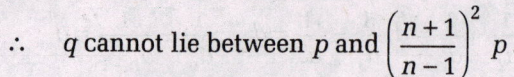

$\therefore$ q cannot lie between p and $\left(\dfrac{n+1}{n-1}\right)^2 p$.

23. We have calculated 1st harmonic mean in (2) of last question

$$y_1 = \frac{(n+1)\,ab}{nb+a} \qquad \qquad \ldots(1)$$

$\therefore$ $y_n = n$th H.M. $= \dfrac{(n+1)\,ab}{na+b}$

[Interchange a and b in (1)]

$\therefore$ $\dfrac{\text{1st Mean}}{n\text{th Mean}} = \dfrac{y_1}{y_n} = \dfrac{b+na}{nb+a}$

$$= \frac{r+n.1}{nr+1} = \frac{n+r}{nr+1} \quad [\because a=1, b=r]$$

24. $a_1, a_2, \ldots, a_n$ are in G.P.

$\therefore$ $a_2 = a_1 r, a_3 = a_1 r^2, \ldots a_n = a_1 r^{n-1}$ ...(1)

$$A_n = \frac{\sum a_1}{n} = \frac{a_1}{n}(1+r+r^2+\ldots r^{n-1}) \qquad \text{by (1)}$$

or $A_n = \dfrac{a_1}{n}\left(\dfrac{r^n-1}{r-1}\right)$ ...(2)

$$G_n = (a_1 a_2 \ldots a_n)^{1/n} = a_1 (1.r.r^2 \ldots r^{n-1})^{1/n}$$

or $G_n = a_1 [r^{(1/2)(n-1)n}]^{1/n} = a_1 r^{(1/2)(n-1)}$ ...(3)

$$\frac{1}{H_n} = \frac{1}{n}\sum \frac{1}{a_1} = \frac{1}{n}\cdot\frac{1}{a_1}\left[1+\frac{1}{r}+\frac{1}{r^2}+\ldots\frac{1}{r^{n-1}}\right]$$

$$= \frac{1}{n.a_1}\cdot\frac{1-(1/r)^n}{1-1/r} = \frac{1}{n.a_1}\cdot\frac{r^n-1}{r-1}\cdot\frac{1}{r^{n-1}}$$

$\therefore$ $H_n = \dfrac{na_1 r^{n-1}(r-1)}{r^n-1}$ ...(4)

From (2), (3) and (4) we observe that

$$G_n^2 = A_n H_n = a_1^2 r^{(n-1)}$$

Above is true for each n, hence

$$G_1^2 G_2^2 \ldots G_n^2 = (A_1 A_2 \ldots A_n)(H_1 H_2 \ldots H_n)$$

$\therefore$ $(G_1 G_2 \ldots G_n)^{1/n} = [(A_1 A_2 \ldots A_n)$

$$(H_1 H_2 \ldots H_n)]^{1/2n}$$

L.H.S. is G.M. of $G_1, G_2, \ldots, G_n$ whose value we have determined in terms of $A_1, A_2, \ldots A_n$ and $H_1, H_2, \ldots H_n$.

25. (a)   We have calculated H_1 and H_n in Q. 23.

$$H_1 = \frac{(n+1)\,ab}{nb+a}, \quad H_n = \frac{(n+1)\,ab}{na+b}$$

$\therefore$ $\dfrac{H_1}{a} = \dfrac{(n+1)\,b}{nb+a}, \quad \dfrac{H_n}{b} = \dfrac{(n+1)\,a}{na+b}.$

Apply Componendo and Dividendo

$\therefore$ $\dfrac{H_1+a}{H_1-a} = \dfrac{(2n+1)\,b+a}{b-a},$

$$\frac{H_n+b}{H_n-b} = \frac{(2n+1)\,a+b}{a-b}$$

$\therefore$ $\dfrac{H_1+a}{H_1-a}+\dfrac{H_n+b}{H_n-b} = \dfrac{1}{b-a}[(2n+1)\,b+a$

$$-(2n+1)\,a-b]$$

$$= \frac{1}{b-a}[2nb-2na] = 2n\frac{(b-a)}{(b-a)} = 2n.$$

(b) $H_n - H_1 = \dfrac{(n+1)\,ab}{na+b} - \dfrac{(n+1)\,ab}{(nb+a)}$

$$= \frac{(n+1)\,ab\,[nb+a-na-b]}{n^2 ab+n(a^2+b^2)+ab}$$

$$= \frac{(n+1)\,ab\,(1-n)\,(a-b)}{n^2-1}$$

$$= -ab\,(a-b), \text{ by (1) below}$$

$\therefore$ $H_1 - H_n = ab\,(a-b).$

Since n is a root of the given equation

$\therefore$ $n^2(1-ab)-n(a^2+b^2)-(1+ab)=0$

or $n^2-1 = n^2 ab+n(a^2+b^2)+ab$ ...(1)

(c) $A_n = n$th A.M. between a and b, $A_n = \dfrac{nb+a}{n+1}$ ...(1)

$H_n = n$th H.M. between a and b,

$$H_n = \frac{(n+1)\,ab}{na+b} \qquad \ldots(2)$$

T_r of A.P. is A_{r-1} (mean) of A.P. $= x$

T_r of H.P. is H_{r-1} (mean) of H.P. $= y$

Hence putting $n = r-1$ or $n+1 = r$ in (1) and (2), we get

$$x = \frac{(r-1)\,b+a}{r}, \quad y = \frac{rab}{(r-1)\,a+b}$$

$\therefore$ $\dfrac{x}{a}+\dfrac{b}{y} = \left[\dfrac{(r-1)\,b+a}{ar}\right]+\left[\dfrac{(r-1)\,a+b}{ra}\right]$

$$= \frac{(r-1)\,(a+b)+(a+b)}{ar} = \frac{r\,(a+b)}{ar} = \frac{a+b}{a}$$

Hence it is independent of r and n.

26. $\dfrac{6}{5}, \dfrac{3}{4}, \dfrac{6}{11}, \dfrac{3}{7}, \dfrac{6}{17}, \dfrac{3}{10}$.

27. $\dfrac{a^{n+1}+b^{n+1}}{a^n+b^n} = $ H.M. of a and $b = \dfrac{2ab}{a+b}$

$\therefore$ $a.a^{n+1}+ab^{n+1}+ba^{n+1}+b.b^{n+1}$

$$= 2a^{n+1} b+2b^{n+1} a$$

$\therefore$ $a.a^{n+1}+b.b^{n+1} = a^{n+1} b+b^{n+1} a$

or $a^{n+1}(a-b) = b^{n+1}(a-b)$

or $a^{n+1} = b^{n+1}$

or $\left(\dfrac{a}{b}\right)^{n+1} = 1$ $\therefore$ $n+1 = 0$ or $n = -1$

28. (a)   Convert into A.P. and proceed as in **Q. 22 P. 129-135.**

(b) T_p of A.P. $= \dfrac{1}{qr}$, T_q of A.P. is $\dfrac{1}{rp}$,

$$A+(p-1)\,D = \frac{1}{qr}; \quad A+(q-1)\,D = \frac{1}{rp}.$$

Subtract $(p-q)\,D = \dfrac{1}{qr}-\dfrac{1}{rp} = \dfrac{p-q}{pqr}$ $\therefore$ $D = \dfrac{1}{pqr}.$

Putting for D, we get

$$A = \frac{1}{qr} - \frac{p-1}{pqr} = \frac{p-p+1}{pqr} = \frac{1}{pqr}$$

$$\therefore \quad T_r \text{ of A.P.} = A + (r-1)D$$
$$= \frac{1+(r-1)}{pqr} = \frac{r}{pqr} = \frac{1}{pq}$$

$$\therefore \quad T_r \text{ of H.P.} = pq.$$

29. We know that $\Sigma\, a(b-c) = 0$, therefore $x = 1$ is a root. Since both the roots are equal therefore the other root should also be 1.

Their sum $S = 1 + 1 = 2$

or $\quad S = \dfrac{-b(c-a)}{a(b-c)} = 2 \quad$ or $\quad -bc + ab = 2ab - 2ac$

or $\quad 2ac = b(a+c) \quad \therefore \quad b = \dfrac{2ac}{a+c}.$

Hence a, b, c are in H.P.

Note : You can also prove by $P = $ Product $= 1$.

30. (a) T_m of A.P. $= \dfrac{1}{n}$ and T_n of A.P. $= \dfrac{1}{m}$

$$\therefore \quad A + (m-1)D = \frac{1}{n} \text{ and } A + (n-1)D = \frac{1}{m}$$

Solving as in Q. 28 (b), $A = D = \dfrac{1}{mn}$

$$T_{m+n} \text{ of A.P.} = A + (m+n-1)D$$
$$= \frac{1+m+n-1}{mn} = \frac{m+n}{mn}$$

$$\therefore \quad T_{m+n} \text{ of H.P. is } \frac{mn}{m+n}.$$

(b) Proceed as in part (a).

$d = 3,\ a = -8,\ T_{20} = \dfrac{1}{49}$

31. (a) Taking reciprocals we are given that

$a(b+c),\ b(c+a),\ c(a+b)$ are in A.P.

Subtract $ab + bc + ca$ from each

$-bc, -ca, -ab$ are in A.P.

Divide by $-abc$,

or $\quad \dfrac{1}{a}, \dfrac{1}{b}, \dfrac{1}{c}$ are in A.P. or a, b, c are in H.P.

(b) $\dfrac{a}{b+c}, \dfrac{b}{c+a}, \dfrac{c}{a+b}$ will be in A.P. if on adding

1 to each

i.e., $\dfrac{a+b+c}{b+c}, \dfrac{b+c+a}{c+a}, \dfrac{c+a+b}{a+b}$ are in A.P.

or $\dfrac{1}{b+c}, \dfrac{1}{c+a}, \dfrac{1}{a+b}$ are in A.P. on dividing by $a+b+c$.

or $b+c,\ c+a,\ a+b$ are in H.P. on taking reciprocal.

But this is given to us.

32. (a) $\dfrac{a}{b+c}, \dfrac{b}{c+a}, \dfrac{c}{a+b}$ will be in H.P.

if $\dfrac{b+c}{a}, \dfrac{c+a}{b}, \dfrac{a+b}{c}$ are in A.P.

Add 1 and cancel $a+b+c$.

that is, if $\dfrac{1}{a}, \dfrac{1}{b}, \dfrac{1}{c}$ are in A.P.

or if a, b, c are in H.P. which is given.

(b) Take reciprocals and add 2 and cancel $a+b+c$ etc. as in (a).

33. (a) We have to prove that

$\dfrac{a+b+c}{a(b+c)}, \dfrac{a+b+c}{b(c+a)}, \dfrac{a+b+c}{c(a+b)}$ to be in H.P.

Taking reciprocal and cancel $a+b+c$.

Thus we have to prove that

$a(b+c),\ b(c+a),\ c(a+b)$ to be in A.P.

or $(ab + bc + ca) - bc, \Sigma ab - ca, \Sigma ab - ab$ to be in A.P.

or $-bc, -ca, -ab$ to be in A.P. Divide by $-abc$

or $\dfrac{1}{a}, \dfrac{1}{b}, \dfrac{1}{c}$ to be in A.P.

or a, b, c to be in H.P., which is true.

(b) $\dfrac{1}{b} - \dfrac{1}{a} = \dfrac{1}{c} - \dfrac{1}{b}$

or $(a-b)c = (b-c)a$ ...(1)

Let the given numbers be x, y, z

then $y - x = \dfrac{\sqrt{ca}}{\sqrt{c} + \sqrt{a}} - \dfrac{\sqrt{bc}}{\sqrt{b} + \sqrt{c}}$

$$= \frac{\sqrt{c}\,[\sqrt{a}(\sqrt{b} + \sqrt{c}) - \sqrt{b}(\sqrt{c} + \sqrt{a})]}{(\sqrt{c} + \sqrt{a})(\sqrt{b} + \sqrt{c})}$$

or $\dfrac{\sqrt{c}\,[\sqrt{c}(\sqrt{a} - \sqrt{b})]}{(\sqrt{c} + \sqrt{a})(\sqrt{b} + \sqrt{c})} = \dfrac{c(a-b)}{(\ )(\ )(\ )}$ ...(2)

Similarly,

$z - y = \dfrac{\sqrt{ab}}{\sqrt{a} + \sqrt{b}} - \dfrac{\sqrt{ca}}{\sqrt{c} + \sqrt{a}} = \dfrac{a(b-c)}{(\ )(\ )(\ )}$ ...(3)

From (2) and (3), by the help of (1) we get

$y - x = z - y \quad \therefore \quad x, y, z$ are in A.P.

34. (a) Take reciprocals, add 1, cancel $a+b+c$, multiply by abc etc.

(b) Ans. (d).

a, b, c, d are in A.P.

Dividing each by $abcd$

$\dfrac{1}{bcd}, \dfrac{1}{acd}, \dfrac{1}{abd}, \dfrac{1}{abc}$ are also in A.P.

Hence their reciprocals are in H.P.

(c) We are given that $\dfrac{1}{a_1}, \dfrac{1}{a_2}, \dfrac{1}{a_3}, \dots \dfrac{1}{a_n}$ are in A.P.

$\therefore \quad \dfrac{\Sigma a_n}{a_1}, \dfrac{\Sigma a_n}{a_2}, \dfrac{\Sigma a_n}{a_3}, \dots$ are also in A.P.

or $1 + \dfrac{a_2 + a_3 + \dots a_n}{a_1}, 1 + \dfrac{a_1 + a_3 + \dots a_n}{a_2}, \dots$

are in A.P.

$\therefore \quad \dfrac{a_2 + a_3 + \dots a_n}{a_1}, \dfrac{a_1 + a_3 + \dots a_n}{a_2}, \dots$ are in A.P.

Take their reciprocals and hence given numbers are in H.P.

35. (a) Taking reciprocals we are given that
$$\frac{1}{b+c}, \frac{1}{c+a}, \frac{1}{a+b} \text{ are in A.P.}$$

$$\therefore \quad \frac{1}{c+a} - \frac{1}{b+c} = \frac{1}{a+b} - \frac{1}{c+a}$$

or $$\frac{b-a}{(c+a)(b+c)} = \frac{c-b}{(a+b)(c+a)}$$

Cancel $c+a$ and cross-multiply
$$b^2 - a^2 = c^2 - b^2$$
$$\therefore \quad a^2, b^2, c^2 \text{ are in A.P.}$$

(b) We have to prove that
$$b^{-1} = \frac{2ac}{a+c} \quad \text{or} \quad a+c = 2abc \qquad \dots(1)$$

We are given that
$$b - \frac{a+b}{1-ab} = \frac{b+c}{1-bc} - b$$

or $$\frac{-a(b^2+1)}{1-ab} = \frac{c(1+b^2)}{1-bc}$$

or $$-a + abc = c - abc \quad \text{or} \quad a+c = 2abc.$$

36. (a) We are given that $a = (b+c)/2$, $b^2 = ca$
and we have to prove that
$$c = 2ab/(a+b) \quad \text{or} \quad ca+bc = 2ab. \qquad \dots(1)$$
L.H.S. of (1)
$$b^2 + bc = b(b+c) \quad \because \quad ca = b^2$$
R.H.S. of (1)
$$(b+c)b = \text{L.H.S.} \quad \because \quad 2a = b+c.$$

(b) $\because$ a,b,c are in A.P., we have $2b = a+c$ $\dots(1)$
$\because$ b,c,a are in H.P., we get
$$c = 2ab/(a+b) \qquad \dots(2)$$
$$\therefore \quad c(a+b) = a(a+c), \text{ by (1) and (2)}$$
$$ac + bc = a^2 + ac \quad \text{or} \quad a^2 = bc$$
$$\therefore \quad c, a, b \text{ are in G.P.}$$

37. (a) Let the four numbers be a, b, c, d.
$$\therefore \quad 2b = a+c \qquad \dots(1)$$
as a,b,c are in A.P.
$$c = 2bd/(b+d) \qquad \dots(2)$$
$\because$ b,c,d are in H.P.
$$c(b+d) = d(a+c), \text{ by (1) and (2)}$$
$$bc + cd = da + cd \quad \therefore \quad bc = ad$$
or $\frac{a}{b} = \frac{c}{d}$ i.e. four numbers are proportional.

(b) By given conditions, we have
$$2y = x + z \qquad \dots(1)$$
$$b^2 y^2 = ax \cdot cz \qquad \dots(2)$$
$$b = 2ac/(a+c) \qquad \dots(3)$$
Substituting for y and b from (1) and (3) in (2), we get
$$\frac{4a^2 c^2}{(a+c)^2} \cdot \frac{(x+z)^2}{4} = axcz$$

or $$\frac{(x+z)^2}{xz} = \frac{(a+c)^2}{ac}$$

or $$\frac{x^2 + z^2 + 2xz}{xz} = \frac{a^2 + c^2 + 2ac}{ac}$$

or $$\frac{x}{z} + \frac{z}{x} + 2 = \frac{a}{c} + \frac{c}{a} + 2$$

or $$\frac{x}{z} + \frac{z}{x} = \frac{a}{c} + \frac{c}{a}.$$

(c) Ans. (d). $2b = a+c$ and $a+b+c = 3/2$
$$\Rightarrow \quad 3b = 3/2 \quad \text{or} \quad b = 1/2$$

Also $b^4 = a^2 c^2 = \left(\frac{1}{2}\right)^4 = \frac{1}{16} \Rightarrow ac = \pm\frac{1}{4}$

Also $a + c = 2b = 1$
$\therefore$ a and c are the roots of $x^2 - x \pm \frac{1}{4} = 0$

$$\therefore \quad x = \frac{1 \pm \sqrt{1 \pm 1}}{2} = \frac{1}{2}, \frac{1}{2} \text{ or } \frac{1}{2} \pm \frac{1}{\sqrt{2}}$$

The first solution is rejected as $a < c$ and from 2nd solution, we have
$$a = \frac{1}{2} - \frac{1}{\sqrt{2}}, c = \frac{1}{2} + \frac{1}{\sqrt{2}}.$$

38. (a) $\because$ a, b, c are in G.P.,
$$\therefore \quad b^2 = ac \qquad \dots(1)$$
Also $\quad a^x = b^y = c^z = k$, say.
$$\therefore \quad a = k^{1/x}, b = k^{1/y}, c = k^{1/z}.$$
Put the values of a, b, c in (1)
$$\therefore \quad k^{2/y} = k^{1/x} \cdot k^{1/z} = k^{1/x + 1/z}$$
$$\therefore \quad \frac{2}{y} = \frac{1}{x} + \frac{1}{z}$$

Hence $\frac{1}{x}, \frac{1}{y}, \frac{1}{z}$ are in A.P.

or x, y, z are in H.P.

(b) Proceed exactly as above and you will have $2y = x + z$ i.e. x, y, z are in A.P.

(c) If each is k then $x = \log_a k$,
$$y = \log_b k, z = \log_c k$$
Also x, y, z are in G.P. $\Rightarrow \frac{y}{x} = \frac{z}{y}$

$$\therefore \quad \frac{\log_b k}{\log_a k} = \frac{\log_c k}{\log_b k} \quad \text{or} \quad \frac{\log a}{\log b} = \frac{\log b}{\log c}$$

$$\because \quad \log_b k = \frac{1}{\log_k b}$$

or $\log_b a = \log_c b.$

39. (a) a, b, c are in G.P.
$$\therefore \quad b^2 = ac \qquad \dots(1)$$
Let $\log_a n = x \quad \therefore \quad n = a^x$ and similarly $n = b^y$, and $n = c^z$.

Determine a, b, c as in Q. 38 (a) and put in (1).

(b) Given a, b, c are in G.P. $\therefore b^2 = ac$ $\dots(1)$
We have to prove that $\log a^n$, $\log b^n$, $\log c^n$ to be in A.P.
or $n \log a, n \log b, n \log c$ to be in A.P.

or $\quad 2\log b = \log a + \log c.$
We have cancelled n.
or $\quad \log b^2 = \log ac \quad$ or $\quad b^2 = ac$
which is true by (1).

40. (a) Proceeding as in Q. 38 (a) we can say that x, y, z are in H.P. y, z, u are in H.P. $\therefore \quad x, y, z, u$ are in H.P.

(b) Ans. (b).
$$x_2 - x_1 = x_3 - x_2 = x_4 - x_3 \ldots = d \text{ given}$$
$$\frac{y_1}{y_2} = \frac{a^{x_1}}{a^{x_2}} = a^{x_1 - x_2} = a^{-d}$$
$$\frac{y_2}{y_3} = \frac{a^{x_2}}{a^{x_3}} = a^{x_2 - x_3} = a^{-d}$$
$$\therefore \quad \frac{y_1}{y_2} = \frac{y_2}{y_3} \quad \text{or} \quad y_1 y_3 = y_2^2$$
Hence $y_1, y_2, y_3, \ldots$ form a G.P.

41. (a) By given conditions,
$$x = a + (m-1)d = AR^{m-1} \text{ for } T_m$$
$$y = a + (n-1)d = AR^{n-1} \text{ for } T_n$$
$$z = a + (p-1)d = AR^{p-1} \text{ for } T_n$$
$$\therefore \quad y - z = (n-p)d, \quad z - x = (p-m)d,$$
$$x - y = (m-n)d \qquad \ldots(1)$$
$$\therefore \quad x^{y-z} \cdot y^{z-x} \cdot z^{x-y}$$
$$= (AR^{m-1})^{(n-p)d} (AR^{n-1})^{(p-m)d} (AR^{p-1})^{(m-n)d}$$
$$= A^0 \cdot R^0 = 1$$
$$\therefore \quad (n - p + p - m + m - n)d = 0$$
and $d[(m-1)(n-p) + (n-1)(p-m)$
$$+ (p-1)(m-n)] = 0$$

(b) $a = AR^{p-1}, b = AR^{q-1}, c = AR^{r-1}$ for G.P.
$$a = \frac{1}{A_1 + (p-1)D}, \quad b = \frac{1}{A_1 + (q-1)D},$$
$$c = \frac{1}{A_1 + (r-1)D} \text{ for H.P.}$$
$$\frac{1}{b} - \frac{1}{c} = (q-r)D. \qquad \ldots(1)$$
$$\log a = \log A + (p-1)\log R$$
$$= (\log A - \log R) + (\log R)p. \qquad \ldots(2)$$
$$\sum \left(\frac{1}{b} - \frac{1}{c}\right)\log a = D(\log A - \log R)\sum(q-r)$$
$$+ D\log R \sum p(q-r) = 0$$
$$\sum \frac{(c-b)}{bc}\log a = 0 \qquad \text{by (1) and (2)}$$
Multiply by $-abc$
$$\sum a(b-c)\log a = 0.$$

42. (a) $2b = a + c \quad \because a, b, c$ are in A.P. $\qquad \ldots(1)$
$c^2 = bd \quad \because b, c, d$ are in G.P. $\qquad \ldots(2)$
$$d = \frac{2ce}{c+e} \quad \because c, d, e \text{ are in H.P.} \qquad \ldots(3)$$
From (2), $c^2 = bd = \frac{a+c}{2} \cdot \frac{2ce}{c+e}$, by (1) and (2)
$$c(c+e) = e(a+c) \quad \text{or} \quad c^2 + ec = ea + ec$$

or $\quad c^2 = ae \quad \therefore \quad a, c, e$ are in G.P. $\qquad \ldots(4)$

(b) We have proved that $c^2 = ae$
$$\therefore \quad e = \frac{c^2}{a} = \frac{(2b-a)^2}{a}, \text{ by (1)}.$$

(c) $a = 2$ and $e = 18$.
We have $c^2 = ae$ by (4)
or $\quad c^2 = 36 \quad \therefore \quad c = 6, -6$
$\quad 2b = a + c, \quad$ by (1)
or $\quad 2b = 2 + 6$ or $2 - 6$
$\therefore \quad b = 4, -2$

$\quad c^2 = bd, \quad$ by (2)
$\quad 36 = 4d \quad$ or $(-2)d$
$\therefore \quad d = 9, -18$.
Hence b, c, d are $4, 6, 9,$ or $-2, -6, -18$.
$\therefore \quad$ The five numbers a, b, c, d, e are
$\quad 2, 4, 6, 9, 18$ or $2, -2, -6, -18, 18$.

43. From the given relations, we have
$$b + c + d = 25, 2b = 2 + c; d^2 = 18c.$$
Eliminating b and c, we get
$\quad 2b + 2c + 2d = 50$
or $\quad (2+c) + 2c + 2d = 50$
or $\quad 3c = 48 - 2d \quad$ or $18c = 6(48 - 2d)$
or $\quad d^2 = 288 - 12d.$
$\quad d^2 + 12d - 288 = 0 \quad \therefore \quad d = 12.$ (only + ive)
$\therefore \quad c = 8$ and $b = 5$

44. $b = \frac{2ac}{a+c}, \quad \because a, b, c$ are in H.P. $\qquad \ldots(1)$
$c^2 = bd, \quad \because b, c, d$ are in G.P. $\qquad \ldots(2)$
$2d = c + e, \quad \because c, d, e$ are in A.P. $\qquad \ldots(3)$
We have to eliminate c and d and prove that
$$e = \frac{ab^2}{(2a-b)^2}.$$
Now $e = 2d - c$ by (3) $= \frac{2c^2}{b} - c$, by (2) $\qquad \ldots(4)$
and $b(a+c) = 2ac$ by (1) $\therefore ab = c(2a-b)$
or $\quad c = \frac{ab}{2a-b}.$ $\qquad \ldots(5)$
Eliminate c between (4) and (5).
From (4), $e = c\left(\frac{2c}{b} - 1\right)$
$$= \frac{ab}{2a-b}\left(\frac{2}{b} \cdot \frac{ab}{2a-b} - 1\right)$$
$$= \frac{ab}{2a-b} \cdot \frac{b}{2a-b} = \frac{ab^2}{(2a-b)^2}$$

45. $b^2 = ac \quad \because a, b, c$ are in G.P. $\qquad \ldots(1)$
$2x = a + b \quad \because x$ is A.M. of a and b $\qquad \ldots(2)$
$2y = b + c \quad \because y$ is A.M. of b and c $\qquad \ldots(3)$
$\therefore \quad \frac{a}{x} + \frac{c}{y} = a \cdot \frac{2}{a+b} + c \cdot \frac{2}{b+c},$ by (2) and (3)

$$= 2 \left[\frac{ab + ac + ac + bc}{ab + ac + b^2 + bc} \right] = 2$$

$\therefore \quad b^2 = ac, \text{ by (1)}$

Again $\quad \dfrac{1}{x} + \dfrac{1}{y} = \dfrac{2}{a+b} + \dfrac{2}{b+c} = \dfrac{2(a+c+2b)}{ab+ac+b^2+bc}$.

Put $b^2 = ac$

$$= \frac{2(a+c+2b)}{ab+2b^2+bc} = \frac{2(a+c+2b)}{b(a+c+2b)} = \frac{2}{b}.$$

46. (a) $\quad 2q = p + r \quad \because \quad p, q, r \text{ are in A.P.} \qquad ..(1)$

Let $\quad \dfrac{a-x}{px} = \dfrac{a-y}{qy} = \dfrac{a-z}{rz} = k \text{ say.} \qquad ...(2)$

$$p = \frac{a-x}{kx} = \frac{1}{k}\left(\frac{a}{x} - 1\right) \quad \text{etc.}$$

Since p, q, r are in A.P. $\quad \therefore \quad \dfrac{a}{x}, \dfrac{a}{y}, \dfrac{a}{z}$ are also in A.P. or x, y, z are in H.P.

(b) Ans. (b).

From 1st two, by cross-multiplication, we get
$2x(b^2 - ac) = 0 \Rightarrow b^2 - ac = 0 \text{ as } x \neq 0$

Similarly from 2nd and 3rd, we get $c^2 = bd$

$\therefore \quad \dfrac{a}{b} = \dfrac{b}{c} = \dfrac{c}{d} \quad \Rightarrow \quad a, b, c, d \text{ are in G.P.}$

47. (a) $\quad 2b = a + c \quad \because \quad a, b, c \text{ are in H.P} \qquad ...(1)$

$b^2 = \dfrac{2a^2c^2}{a^2 + c^2} \quad \because \quad a^2, b^2, c^2 \text{ are in A.P.} \qquad ...(2)$

$\therefore \quad b^2[(a+c)^2 - 2ac] = 2a^2c^2, \text{ by (2)}$

or $\quad b^2[(4b^2 - 2ac)] = 2a^2c^2, \text{ by (1)}$

or $\quad 2b^4 - b^2 ac - a^2c^2 = 0$. Factorize
$(b^2 - ac)(2b^2 + ac) = 0.$

Either $\quad b^2 - ac = 0 \quad \text{or} \quad 2b^2 + ac = 0.$

If $\quad b^2 = ac, \text{ then } \left(\dfrac{a+c}{2}\right)^2 = ac, \text{ by (1)}$

or $\quad (a+c)^2 - 4ac = 0 \text{ or } (a-c)^2 = 0 \therefore a = c$
and $2b = a + c = a + a = 2a \therefore b = a.$
Hence $\quad a = b = c.$

If $\quad 2b^2 + ac = 0 \text{ then } b^2 = -\dfrac{a}{2}c$

$\therefore \quad -\dfrac{a}{2}, b, c \text{ are in G.P.}$

(b) $\quad b^2 = ac \qquad ...(1)$

$$\frac{2}{c-a} = \frac{1}{b-c} + \frac{1}{a-b} = \frac{a-c}{(b-c)(a-b)}$$

or $\quad 2(ab - ca - b^2 + bc) = -(a-c)^2$

or $\quad 2(ab - 2b^2 + bc) = -(a-c)^2$

or $\quad 2b(a + c - 2\sqrt{ac}) = -[(\sqrt{a} - \sqrt{c})(\sqrt{a} + \sqrt{c})]^2$

or $\quad 2b(\sqrt{a} - \sqrt{c})^2 = -(\sqrt{a} - \sqrt{c})^2(\sqrt{a} + \sqrt{c})^2$

$\therefore \quad 2b = -(a + c + 2\sqrt{ac}) \quad \text{as} \quad a \neq c$

$\therefore \quad a + c = -4b, \text{ by (1)}$

or $\quad a + b + c = -3b = -3\sqrt{ac} \text{ by (1)}$

(c) See Q. 47 (a).

48. $\quad q^2 = pr \qquad ...(1)$

as $\quad p, q, r$ are in G.P.

T_p, T_q, T_r of an A.P. are in H.P.

$\therefore \quad \dfrac{1}{T_p}, \dfrac{1}{T_q}, \dfrac{1}{T_r}$ are in A.P.

$$\frac{1}{T_q} - \frac{1}{T_p} = \frac{1}{T_r} - \frac{1}{T_q}$$

or $\quad \dfrac{T_p - T_q}{T_p} = \dfrac{T_q - T_r}{T_r}, \quad \dfrac{(p-q)d}{a+(p-1)d} = \dfrac{(q-r)d}{a+(r-1)d}$

or $\quad a(p + r - 2q) = d[(p-1)(q-r) - (r-1)(p-q)]$

or $\quad \dfrac{a}{d} = \dfrac{pq - pr - q + r - (rp - rq - p + q)}{p + r - 2q}$

$\qquad = \dfrac{p(q+1) + r(q+1) - 2pr - 2q}{p + r - 2q}$

Put $pr = q^2$ in numerator

$\therefore \quad \dfrac{a}{d} = (q+1)\dfrac{(p+r-2q)}{p+r-2q} = q + 1$

49. $\quad d = b - a \text{ for A.P., } r = b/a \text{ for G.P.}$

$T_{n+2} = a + (n+1)d = a + (n+1)(b-a)$
$\qquad = -na + (n+1)b \text{ for A.P.} \qquad ...(2)$

$T_{n+2} = ar^{n+1} = a \cdot \dfrac{b^{n+1}}{a^{n+1}} = \dfrac{b^{n+1}}{a^n} \text{ for G.P.} \qquad ...(2)$

For getting T_{n+2} for H.P., replace a by $\dfrac{1}{a}$, b by $\dfrac{1}{b}$ in T_{n+2}
for A.P. *i.e.* in (1) and then take reciprocal.

$\therefore \quad T_{n+2}$ for H.P. = reciprocal of $-n\left(\dfrac{1}{a}\right) + (n+1)\dfrac{1}{b}$

or $\quad$ of $\quad \dfrac{(n+1)a - nb}{ab}$

$\therefore \quad T_{n+2} = \dfrac{ab}{(n+1)a - nb} \text{ for H.P.} \qquad ...(3)$

The above three terms are themselves in G.P.

$\therefore \quad \left(\dfrac{b^{n+1}}{a^n}\right)^2 = [-na + (n+1)b] \cdot \dfrac{ab}{(n+1)a - nb}.$

$\therefore \quad \dfrac{b^{2n+1}}{a^{2n+1}} = \dfrac{-na + (n+1)b}{(n+1)a - nb}. \quad$ Cancelled ab

Cross-multiply
$(n+1)[ab^{2n+1} - ba^{2n+1}] = n(b^{2n+2} - a^{2n+2})$

or $\quad \dfrac{n+1}{n} = \dfrac{b^{2n+2} - a^{2n+2}}{ab(b^{2n} - a^{2n})}.$

50. (a) $\quad T_r$ of A.P. $= a + (r-1)d$
where $b = a + (n-1)d$

$\therefore \quad T_r$ of A.P. $= a + (r-1)\dfrac{b-a}{n-1}$

$\qquad = \dfrac{a(n-r) + b(r-1)}{n-1} \qquad ...(1)$

T_r from end of H.P. $a, \ldots\ldots, b$ (n terms)

= Reciprocal of T_r from end of A.P. $\frac{1}{a} \ldots \frac{1}{b}$

Reciprocal of T_r from beginning of A.P.

$$\frac{1}{b} \ldots \frac{1}{a} \ (n \text{ terms})$$

Replace a by $\frac{1}{b}$ and b by $\frac{1}{a}$ in (1), then take reciprocal.

or   reciprocal of $\dfrac{\frac{1}{b}(n-r)+\frac{1}{a}(r-1)}{n-1}$

$$= \frac{ab\,(n-1)}{a\,(n-r)+b\,(r-1)} \qquad \ldots(2)$$

Multiplying (1) and (2), we get the product $= ab$, which is independent of r.

(b) Yes. $x = a + (n-1)(b-a)$

and $\frac{1}{y} = \frac{1}{a} + (n-1)\left[\frac{1}{b} - \frac{1}{a}\right]$

or $x - a = (n-1)(b-a)$ $\qquad \ldots(1)$

and $\frac{b}{y} = \frac{b + (n-1)(a-b)}{a}$ $\qquad \ldots(2)$

Also $y - a = \frac{(b-a)\,a\,(n-1)}{b+(n-1)(a-b)}$ by (2) $\quad \ldots(3)$

Hence $\frac{x-a}{y-a} = \frac{b+(n-1)(a-b)}{a} = \frac{b}{y}$ by (1), (3)

51. Let the numbers be x, y and z.

∴ $y = \frac{2xz}{x+z}$ or $y(x+z) = 2xz$ $\qquad \ldots(1)$

Again x^2, y^2, z^2 are in A.P.

$2y^2 = x^2 + z^2 = (x+z)^2 - 2xz$

or $2y^2 = (x+z)^2 - y(x+z)$, by (1)

or $(x+z)^2 - y(x+z) - 2y^2 = 0$

∴ $x+z = \frac{y \pm \sqrt{y^2 + 8y^2}}{2}$

or $x+z = 2y$ or $-y$

Case (I) $x + z = 2y$ $\qquad \ldots(2)$

Eliminate y between (1) and (2)

$(x+z)^2 = 4xz$

or $(x-z)^2 = 0$ ∴ $x = z$

Above is not true as the numbers are distinct.

Case (II) $x + z = -y$ $\qquad \ldots(3)$

Eliminate y between (1) and (3)

$-(x+z)^2 = 2xz$

∴ $x^2 + 4xz + z^2 = 0$ or $\left(\frac{x}{z}\right)^2 + 4\frac{x}{z} + 1 = 0$

∴ $\frac{x}{z} = -2 \pm \sqrt{3}$

Choose $\frac{x}{z} = -2 + \sqrt{3}$

∴ From (3), $\frac{-y}{z} = 1 + \frac{x}{z} = -1 + \sqrt{3}$

or $\frac{y}{z} = 1 - \sqrt{3}$

$$\frac{x}{\sqrt{3}-2} = \frac{y}{1-\sqrt{3}} = \frac{z}{1} \qquad \ldots(4)$$

Similarly if $\frac{x}{z} = -2 - \sqrt{3}$ then $\frac{y}{z} = 1 + \sqrt{3}$

∴ $\frac{x}{-(\sqrt{3}+2)} = \frac{y}{1+\sqrt{3}} = \frac{z}{1}$

The given ratios $1 - \sqrt{3} : -2 : 1 + \sqrt{3}$ is same

or $\frac{1-\sqrt{3}}{1+\sqrt{3}} : \frac{-2}{1+\sqrt{3}} : 1 = \frac{4-2\sqrt{3}}{1-3} : \frac{-2(1-\sqrt{3})}{1-3} : 1$

$= \sqrt{3} - 2 : 1 - \sqrt{3} : 1$ same as (4) etc.

Again taking $\frac{x}{z} = -2 - \sqrt{3}$, we will get the second answer.

52. By given condition,

$\alpha^2 = a^2 bc$, $\beta^2 = b^2 ca$, $\gamma^2 = c^2 ab$ and $2b = a + c$

$\alpha^2, \beta^2, \gamma^2$ will be in A.P. if $a^2 bc, b^2 ca, c^2 ab$ are in A.P. or a, b, c are in A.P. which is true.

Again $\beta + \gamma$, $\gamma + \alpha$, $\alpha + \beta$ will be in H.P. if

$\frac{1}{\beta+\gamma}, \frac{1}{\gamma+\alpha}, \frac{1}{\alpha+\beta}$ are in A.P.

or $\frac{1}{\gamma+\alpha} - \frac{1}{\beta+\gamma} = \frac{1}{\alpha+\beta} - \frac{1}{\gamma+\alpha}$

or $\frac{\beta-\alpha}{\beta+\gamma} = \frac{\gamma-\beta}{\alpha+\beta}$ or $\beta^2 - \alpha^2 = \gamma^2 - \beta^2$

or $\alpha^2, \beta^2, \gamma^2$ are in A.P. which we have already proved.

53. (a) $a + md$, $a + nd$, $a + rd$ are in G.P.

∴ $(a+nd)^2 = (a+md)(a+rd)$

or $a(2n-m-r) = d(mr - n^2)$

∴ $\frac{d}{a} = \frac{2n-(m+r)}{mr-n^2}$ $\qquad \ldots(1)$

But m, n, r are in H.P.

∴ $n = \frac{2mr}{m+r}$ $\qquad \ldots(2)$

∴ $\frac{d}{a} = \frac{2n-(m+r)}{(m+r)\,n/2 - n^2}$, by (1) and (2)

$= \frac{2}{n}\left[\frac{2n-(m+r)}{(m+r)-2n}\right] = -\frac{2}{n}$.

(b) $S_1 = \frac{n}{2}[2.1 + (n-1)d_1] = n + \frac{n(n-1)}{2}d_1$

∴ $d_1 = \frac{2(S_1 - n)}{n(n-1)}$ ∴ $\frac{1}{d_1} = \frac{n(n-1)}{2}\frac{1}{(S_1 - n)}$

d_1, d_2, d_3 are in H.P. $\Rightarrow \frac{1}{d_1}, \frac{1}{d_2}, \frac{1}{d_3}$ are in A.P.

or $\frac{1}{S_1 - n}, \frac{1}{S_2 - n}, \frac{1}{S_3 - n}$ are in A.P.

or $\dfrac{1}{S_2 - n} - \dfrac{1}{S_1 - n} = \dfrac{1}{S_3 - n} - \dfrac{1}{S_2 - n}$

or $(S_1 - S_2)(S_3 - n) = (S_2 - S_3) \cdot (S_1 - n)$

$\therefore \quad n = \text{etc.}$

54. $(y - x), \ 2(y - a), \ (y - z)$ are in H.P.

$\therefore \quad \dfrac{1}{y - x}, \ \dfrac{1}{2(y - a)}, \ \dfrac{1}{y - z}$ are in A.P.

or $\dfrac{1}{2(y - a)} - \dfrac{1}{y - x} = \dfrac{1}{y - z} - \dfrac{1}{2(y - a)}$

or $\dfrac{2a - y - x}{y - x} = \dfrac{y + z - 2a}{y - z}$

or $\dfrac{(x - a) + (y - a)}{(x - a) - (y - a)} = \dfrac{(y - a) + (z - a)}{(y - a) - (z - a)}$ **(Note)**

Apply componendo and dividendo.

$\dfrac{2(x - a)}{2(y - a)} = \dfrac{2(y - a)}{2(z - a)}$

or $(y - a)^2 = (x - a)(z - a)$

$\therefore \quad (x - a), \ (y - a), \ (z - a)$ are in G.P.

55. (a) $A = \dfrac{p + q + r}{3} = \dfrac{S_1}{3} \quad \therefore \quad S_1 = 3A$

$G = (pqr)^{1/3} \quad \therefore \quad G^3 = pqr = S_3$

$\dfrac{1}{H} = \dfrac{1}{3}\left(\dfrac{1}{p} + \dfrac{1}{q} + \dfrac{1}{r}\right) = \dfrac{\Sigma\, pq}{3pqr} = \dfrac{S_2}{3S_3}$

$\therefore \quad S_2 = \dfrac{3S_3}{H} = \dfrac{3G^3}{H}$

Now $(x - p)(x - q)(x - r) = x^3 - x^2 S_1 + x S_2 - S_3$

etc.

(b) (i) If the roots be in A.P., then their

$\text{sum} = (a - d) + a + (a - d) = 3a = \dfrac{-3a_1}{a_0}$

$\therefore \quad a = \dfrac{-a_1}{a_0}$

But a is a root of given equation

$\therefore \quad a_0\left(\dfrac{-a_1}{a_0}\right)^3 + 3a_1\left(\dfrac{-a_1}{a_0}\right)^2 + 3a_2\left(\dfrac{-a_1}{a_0}\right)$
$\hspace{9cm} + a_3 = 0$

or $2a_1^3 - 3a_0 a_1 a_2 + a_0^2 a_3 = 0 \qquad \dots(1)$

(ii) If the roots be in G.P., then their

$\text{product} = \dfrac{a}{r} \cdot a \cdot ar = a^3 = \dfrac{-a_3}{a_0} \qquad \dots(2)$

Since a is a root of given equation

$a_0 a^3 + 3a_1 a^2 + 3a_2 a + a_3 = 0$

or $3a_1 a^2 + 3a_2 a = 0$ as $a_0 a^3 + a_3 = 0 \qquad$ by (2)

or $a_1 a = -a_2$. Cube both sides

$a_1^3\left(\dfrac{-a_3}{a_0}\right) = -a_2^3 \qquad$ again by (2)

or $a_0 a_2^3 - a_3 a_1^3 = 0$

(iii) Replace x by $\dfrac{1}{x}$ and the equation becomes

$a_3 x^3 + 3a_2 x^2 + 3a_1 x + a_0 = 0$

Its roots will be in A.P. and proceeding as in (i), we get $\quad 2a_2^3 - 3a_3 a_1 a_2 + a_3^2 a_0 = 0.$

56. $S_1 = \dfrac{n}{2}[2.1 + (n - 1) d_1] \quad \therefore \quad \dfrac{2(S_1 - n)}{n(n - 1)} = d_1$

or $\dfrac{1}{d_1} = \dfrac{n(n - 1)}{2(S_1 - n)}$

Similarly for $\dfrac{1}{d_2}$ and $\dfrac{1}{d_3}$.

Since $d_1, \ d_2, \ d_3$ are given to be in H.P., therefore $\dfrac{1}{d_1}, \ \dfrac{1}{d_2}, \ \dfrac{1}{d_3}$ are in A.P. or on cancelling $\dfrac{n(n-1)}{2}$ we can say that

$\dfrac{1}{S_1 - n}, \ \dfrac{1}{S_2 - n}, \ \dfrac{1}{S_3 - n}$ are in A.P.

$\therefore \quad \dfrac{1}{S_2 - n} - \dfrac{1}{S_1 - n} = \dfrac{1}{S_3 - n} - \dfrac{1}{S_2 - n}$

or $\dfrac{S_1 - S_2}{S_1 - n} = \dfrac{S_2 - S_3}{S_3 - n}$. Cross-multiply

or $(S_1 - S_2) S_3 - (S_2 - S_3) S_1 = n(S_1 - 2S_2 + S_3)$

$\therefore \quad n = \text{as given.}$

57. (i) $a_1, \ a_2, \ a_3, \ a_4$ are in A.P.

$\therefore \quad a_2 = a_1 + d, \ a_3 = a_1 + 2d, \ a_4 = a_1 + 3d$

$\therefore \quad a_2 a_3 - a_1 a_4 = (a_1 + d)(a_1 + 2d) - a_1(a_1 + 3d)$
$\hspace{2.5cm} = (a_1^2 + 3a_1 d + 2d^2) - (a_1^2 + 3a_1 d)$
$\hspace{2.5cm} = 2d^2 = +\text{ive}$

(ii) $a_1, \ a_2, \ a_3, \ a_4$ are in G.P.

$\therefore \quad \dfrac{a_2}{a_1} = \dfrac{a_4}{a_3} \quad \therefore \quad a_2 a_3 - a_1 a_4 = 0$

(iii) $a_1, \ a_2, \ a_3, \ a_4$ are in H.P.

$\therefore \quad \dfrac{1}{a_1}, \ \dfrac{1}{a_2}, \ \dfrac{1}{a_3}, \ \dfrac{1}{a_4}$ are in A.P. of common

difference D, say

$\dfrac{1}{a_4} - \dfrac{1}{a_1} = 3D$ or $a_1 - a_4 = 3D a_1 a_4 \qquad \dots(1)$

$\dfrac{1}{a_2} = \dfrac{1}{a_1} + D = \dfrac{1 + a_1 D}{a_1} \quad \therefore \quad a_2 = \dfrac{a_1}{1 + a_1 D}$

$\dfrac{1}{a_3} = \dfrac{1}{a_4} - D = \dfrac{1 - a_4 D}{a_4} \quad \therefore \quad a_3 = \dfrac{a_4}{1 - a_4 D}$

(Note)

$\therefore \quad a_2 a_3 - a_1 a_4 = a_1 a_4\left[\dfrac{1}{(1 + a_1 D)(1 - a_4 D)} - 1\right]$

$= \dfrac{a_1 a_4 [1 - \{1 + (a_1 - a_4) D - a_1 a_4 D^2\}]}{1 + (a_1 - a_4) D - a_1 a_4 D^2}.$

Now use (1)

$= \dfrac{a_1 a_4 [-3D^2 a_1 a_4 + a_1 a_4 D^2]}{1 + 3D^2 a_1 a_4 - a_1 a_4 D^2}$

$$= -\frac{2(a_1 a_4 D)^2}{1 + 2D^2 a_1 a_4} = - \text{ive.}$$

58. (a) $2b = a + c$, $\beta = \dfrac{2\alpha\gamma}{\alpha + \gamma}$ and $b^2\beta^2 = ac\alpha\gamma$.

Eliminating b and β from these, we get

$$\frac{(a+c)^2}{4} \cdot \frac{4\alpha^2\gamma^2}{(\alpha+\gamma)^2} = ac\alpha\gamma$$

or $\dfrac{(a+c)^2}{ac} = \dfrac{(\alpha+\gamma)^2}{\alpha\gamma}$

This gives $\dfrac{a}{c} + \dfrac{c}{a} = \dfrac{\alpha}{\gamma} + \dfrac{\gamma}{\alpha}$. Multiply by $\dfrac{a}{c}$

or $\left(\dfrac{a}{c}\right)^2 - \dfrac{a}{c}\left(\dfrac{\alpha}{\gamma} + \dfrac{\gamma}{\alpha}\right) + 1 = 0$

or $\left(\dfrac{a}{c} - \dfrac{\alpha}{\gamma}\right)\left(\dfrac{a}{c} - \dfrac{\gamma}{\alpha}\right) = 0$

$\therefore \quad \dfrac{a}{c} = \dfrac{\alpha}{\gamma}$ i.e. $\dfrac{a}{1/\gamma} = \dfrac{c}{1/\alpha}$ ...(1)

or $\dfrac{a}{c} = \dfrac{\gamma}{\alpha}$ i.e., $a\alpha = c\gamma$. ...(2)

The condition (2) is ruled out since this with the help of $b^2\beta^2 = ac\alpha\gamma$ gives $b\beta = c\gamma$ so that $a\alpha = b\beta = c\gamma$ and so $a\alpha$, $b\beta$, $c\gamma$ are in G.P. with common ratio 1 which contradicts the hypothesis.

Now using (1) and $b^2\beta^2 = ac\alpha\gamma$, we get

$b^2\beta^2 = c^2\alpha^2$ or $b\beta = c\alpha$

Thus $\dfrac{b}{1/\beta} = \dfrac{c}{1/\alpha}$ ...(3)

Finally from (1) and (3), we get

$$\frac{a}{1/\gamma} = \frac{b}{1/\beta} = \frac{c}{1/\alpha}$$

(b) $a = a, b = ar, c = ar^2, a, b, c$ are in G.P.

$\log_c a = \dfrac{\log a}{\log c} = \dfrac{\log a}{\log ar^2} = \dfrac{\log a}{\log a + 2\log r}$

$= \dfrac{1}{1 + 2x}$, where $x = \dfrac{\log r}{\log a}$

Since $r \neq 1$ $\therefore \log r \neq 0$ or $x \neq 0$.

Thus $\dfrac{1}{1+2x}, \dfrac{1+2x}{1+x}, 1 + x$ are in A.P.

$\therefore 2\left(\dfrac{1+2x}{1+x}\right) = \dfrac{1}{1+2x} + (1+x)$

$2(1+2x)^2 = (1+x)[1 + (1+2x)(1+x)]$

or $2(4x^2 + 4x + 1) = [(x+1)(2x^2 + 3x + 2)]$

$\therefore 2x^3 - 3x^2 - 3x = 0$

or $2x^2 - 3x - 3 = 0$, as $x \neq 0$

$T_3 - T_1 = 2d = 1 + x - \dfrac{1}{1+2x} = \dfrac{2x^2 + 3x}{1+2x}$

$2d = \dfrac{3x+3+3x}{1+2x} = \dfrac{3(1+2x)}{1+2x} = 3$ $\therefore d = \dfrac{3}{2}$

Problem Set (5)

▶ Multiple Choice Questions

1. $\dfrac{1}{q+r}, \dfrac{1}{r+p}, \dfrac{1}{p+q}$ are in A.P., then

(a) p, q, r are in A.P.   (b) p^2, q^2, r^2 are in A.P.

(c) $\dfrac{1}{p}, \dfrac{1}{q}, \dfrac{1}{r}$ are in A.P.   (d) none of these.

2. 99th term of the series $2 + 7 + 14 + 23 + 34 + \ldots$ is

(a) 9998   (b) 9999

(c) 10000   (d) None of these.

3. The sum of 40 terms of an A.P. whose first term is 2 and common difference 4, will be

(a) 3200   (b) 1600   (c) 200   (d) 2800

4. α, β be the roots of $x^2 - 3x + a = 0$

and γ, δ the roots of $x^2 - 12x + b = 0$

and numbers $\alpha, \beta, \gamma, \delta$ (in order) form an increasing G.P., then

(a) $a = 3, b = 12$ (b) $a = 12, b = 3$

(c) $a = 2, b = 32$ (d) $a = 4, b = 16$.

5. If a, b, c are in A.P. as well as in G.P. then

(a) $a = b \neq c$ (b) $a \neq b = c$ (c) $a \neq b \neq c$ (d) $a = b = c$

6. If the harmonic mean between two positive numbers is to their Geometric mean as 12 : 13, the numbers are in the ratio

(a) 12 : 13   (b) 1 / 12 : 1 / 13

(c) 4 : 9   (d) 1 / 4 : 1 / 9.

7. The harmonic, geometric and arithmetic means between two positive quantities are in ascending order of magnitude.

(a) True   (b) False

8. In an A.P. the sum of terms equidistant from the beginning and end is equal to

(a) first term   (b) second term

(c) sum of first and last terms

(d) last term.

9. The nth term of the series $3, \sqrt{3}, 1, \ldots$ is $\dfrac{1}{243}$, then n is

(a) 12   (b) 13   (c) 14   (d) 15

10. If a, b, c are in G.P., then

(a) $a(b^2 + a^2) = c(b^2 + c^2)$ (b) $a(b^2 + c^2) = c(a^2 + b^2)$

(c) $a^2(b+c) = c^2(a+b)$ (d) none of these

11. The value of $9^{1/3} \times 9^{1/9} \times 9^{1/27} \times \ldots \infty$ is

(a) 9   (b) 1

(c) 3   (d) none of these.

12. If $\dfrac{1}{b-a} + \dfrac{1}{b-c} = \dfrac{1}{a} + \dfrac{1}{c}$, then a, b, c are in

(a) A.P.   (b) H.P.

(c) G.P.   (d) H.P. and G.P. both

13. (i) $2^{1/4} \cdot 4^{1/8} \cdot 8^{1/16} \cdot 16^{1/32} \ldots\ldots$ is equal to

    (a) 1   (b) 2

    (c) $\dfrac{3}{2}$ (d) $\dfrac{5}{2}$.

  (ii) Let $P = 3^{1/3} \cdot 3^{2/9} \cdot 3^{3/27} \ldots \infty$, then $P^{1/3}$ is equal to

    (a) $3^{2/3}$ (b) $\sqrt{3}$

    (c) $3^{1/3}$ (d) $3^{1/4}$

14. The sum of the series $\dfrac{1}{2} + \dfrac{1}{3} + \dfrac{1}{6} + \ldots\ldots$ to 9 terms is

  (a) $-\dfrac{5}{6}$ (b) $-\dfrac{1}{2}$ (c) 1   (d) $-\dfrac{3}{2}$

15. (i) If a, b, c are in A.P., then $\dfrac{a}{bc}, \dfrac{1}{c}, \dfrac{2}{b}$ are in

    (a) A.P.   (b) G.P.

    (c) H.P   (d) None.

  (ii) If a, b, c are in A.P. then prove $(a - c)^2 = 4(b^2 - ac)$.

16. If $\dfrac{3 + 5 + 7 + \ldots\ldots + n \text{ terms}}{5 + 8 + 11 + \ldots\ldots + 10 \text{ terms}} = 7$, the value of n is

  (a) 35   (b) 36   (c) 37   (d) 40

17. The first term of a G.P. whose second term is 2 and sum to infinity is 8 will be

  (a) 6   (b) 3   (c) 4   (d) 1

18. The sum of first n terms of the series

  $\dfrac{1}{2} + \dfrac{3}{4} + \dfrac{7}{8} + \dfrac{15}{16} + \ldots\ldots$ is equal to

  (a) $2^n - n - 1$ (b) $1 - 2^{-n}$

  (c) $n + 2^{-n} - 1$ (d) $2^n - 1$

19. If H is the harmonic mean between P and Q, then the value of $(H/P) + (H/Q)$ is

  (a) 2   (b) $PQ/(P+Q)$

  (c) $(P+Q)/PQ$ (d) none of these

                                 (M.N.R. 1990)

20. If the sum of the series $2, 5, 8, 11, \ldots\ldots$ is 60100, then n is

  (a) 100   (b) 200   (c) 150   (d) 250

                                 (M.N.R. 1991)

21. The following consecutive terms

  $\dfrac{1}{1 + \sqrt{x}}, \dfrac{1}{1 - x}, \dfrac{1}{1 - \sqrt{x}}$ of a series are in

  (a) H.P.   (b) G.P.   (c) A.P.   (d) None.

22. The sum of all two digit numbers which are odd is

  (a) 2475   (b) 2530   (c) 4905   (d) 5049

23. A G.P. consists of an even number of terms. If the sum of all the terms is five times the sum of the terms occupying odd places, the common ratio is

  (a) 2   (b) 3   (c) 4   (d) 5

24. If x, y, z are in G.P., $a^x = b^y = c^z$, then

  (a) $\log_c b = \log_a c$ (b) $\log_a c = \log_b a$

  (c) $\log_a b = \log_c b$ (d) $\log_b a = \log_c b$

25. $\log_3 2, \log_6 2, \log_{12} 2$ are in

  (a) A.P.   (b) G.P.   (c) H.P.   (d) None

26. If a, b, c are in G.P., then $\log_a 10, \log_b 10, \log_c 10$ are in

  (a) A.P.   (b) G.P.   (c) H.P.   (d) None

27. If the sum of first n natural numbers is one–fifth of the sum of their squares, then n is

  (a) 5   (b) 6   (c) 7   (d) 8

28. If a, b, c, d are in H.P., then the value of $\left(\dfrac{1}{a^2} - \dfrac{1}{d^2} \right) \left(\dfrac{1}{b^2} - \dfrac{1}{c^2} \right)$ is

  (a) 1   (b) 2   (c) 3   (d) 4

Solutions of Problem Set (5)

1. Ans. (b). See Q. 43 (i) **Page 130-139** of A.P.
2. Ans. (d.) Use method of difference.
3. Ans. (a).
4. $\alpha, \beta, \gamma, \delta$ being in G.P. they may be taken as k, kr, kr^2, kr^3.

    $S = k(1 + r) = 3, \quad kr^2 (1 + r) = 12$

    $\therefore \quad 3r^2 = 12$ or $r = 2$ $\therefore$ $k = 1$

    $P = k^2 r = a, \quad k^2 r^5 = b$.

  Putting for r and k, $a = 2$, $b = 32$.

5. Ans. (d). **See Q. 34 (b) P. 147.**
6. Arrange as a quadratic in $x = \sqrt{a/b}$ etc. (c) is correct.
7. Ans. (a). $A > G > H$ or $H < G < A$ $\therefore$ ascending
8. Ans. (c). 9. Ans. (b).
10. Ans. (b) $b^2 = ac$ satisfies (ii).
11. Ans. (c). $(9)^{S_\infty} = 9^{1/2} = 3$ $\because$ $S_\infty = \dfrac{1/3}{1 - (1/3)} = \dfrac{1}{2}$
12. Ans. (b). **See Q. 3 (a) 173-177.**
13. (i) Ans. (b). **See 1 (c) P. 171-173.**

  (ii) Ans. (d). Above in an infinite A.G.S. with $a = 1$, $d = 1$ for A.P., $b = \dfrac{1}{3}, r = \dfrac{1}{3}$ for G.P.

  $\therefore \quad S_\infty = \dfrac{ab}{1 - r} + \dfrac{dbr}{(1 - r)^2} = \dfrac{\frac{1}{3}}{1 - \frac{1}{3}} + \dfrac{1 \cdot \frac{1}{3} \cdot \frac{1}{3}}{\left(1 - \frac{1}{3}\right)^2} = \dfrac{1}{2} + \dfrac{1}{4} = \dfrac{3}{4}$

  $\therefore \quad P = 3^s = 3^{3/4}$ $\therefore$ $P^{1/3} = 3^{1/4}$

14. Ans. (d).

  This is an A.P. of common difference $-\dfrac{1}{6}$.

  $\therefore \quad$ Sum $= \dfrac{9}{2} \left[2 \times \dfrac{1}{2} + (9 - 1) \left(-\dfrac{1}{6} \right) \right] = -\dfrac{3}{2}$.

15. (i) a, b, c are in A.P. Dividing by bc, we get $\dfrac{a}{bc}, \dfrac{1}{c}, \dfrac{1}{b}$ are also in A.P. Hence either the last term should be $\dfrac{1}{b}$ in place of $\dfrac{2}{b}$ in the question and in that case (a) is correct answer, otherwise (d) is correct answer.

  (ii) R.H.S. $= 4b^2 - 4ac = (2b)^2 - 4ac$

            $= (a + c)^2 - 4ac = (a - c)^2 =$ L.H.S.

16. L.H.S. $= \dfrac{n(n+2)}{5.37} = 7$ $\therefore$ $n(n+2) = 35.37$

Above will hold when $n = 35$ $\therefore$ (a) is correct.

17. $ar = 2$, $\dfrac{a}{1-r} = \dfrac{1}{8}$. Eliminate r and we get

$a^2 - 8a + 16 = 0$ $\therefore$ $(a-4)^2 = 0$ or $a = 4$

$\therefore$ (c) is correct.

18. Ans. (c). **Hint :** $T_n = \dfrac{2^n - 1}{2^n} = 1 - (\dfrac{1}{2})^n$

$\therefore$ $S_n = n - \displaystyle\sum_{n=1}^{n} \left(\dfrac{1}{2}\right)^n = n - \dfrac{\dfrac{1}{2}.[1 - (1/2)^n]}{1 - 1/2}$

$\qquad\qquad = n + 2^{-n} - 1.$

19. Ans. (a). We have $\dfrac{2}{H} = \dfrac{1}{P} + \dfrac{1}{Q}$

$\quad$ [$\because$ H is the harmonic mean between P and Q]

or $H/P + H/Q = 2$.

20. Ans. (b). $S_n = 60100$ $\Rightarrow$ $3n^2 + n - 120200 = 0$

$\Rightarrow$ $(3n + 601)(n - 200) = 0$ $\therefore$ $n = 200$.

21. Ans. (c). $\because$ $2b = a + c$

22. Ans. (a). $11 + 13 + 15 + \dots + 99$

23. Ans. (c). $S_{2n} = 5(T_1 + T_3 + \dots + n \text{ terms})$

24. Ans. (d). $x \log a = y \log b = z \log c = k$ say

Also $y^2 = xz$ $\therefore$ $\dfrac{k^2}{(\log b)^2} = \dfrac{k^2}{\log a \log c}$.

or $\dfrac{\log a}{\log b} = \dfrac{\log b}{\log c}$ or $\log_b a = \log_c b$

25. Ans. (c). If the numbers be $\dfrac{1}{x}, \dfrac{1}{y}, \dfrac{1}{z}$, then

$x = \log_2 3$, $y = \log_2 2.3 = 1 + \log_2 3$,
$z = 2 + \log_2 3$. Clearly x, y, z are in A.P.

$\therefore$ $\dfrac{1}{x}, \dfrac{1}{y}, \dfrac{1}{z}$ are in H.P.

26. Ans. (c). $b^2 = ac$ $\therefore$ $2\log_{10} b = \log_{10} a + \log_{10} c$

$\therefore$ $\log_{10} a$; $\log_{10} b$; $\log_{10} c$ are in A.P.

$\therefore$ Their reciprocals are in H.P.

27. Ans. (c). $\Sigma n = \dfrac{1}{5} \Sigma n^2$

28. Ans. (c).

$\dfrac{1}{a}, \dfrac{1}{b}, \dfrac{1}{c}, \dfrac{1}{d}$ are in A.P. and let these four terms be

$\alpha - 3\beta, \alpha - \beta, \alpha + \beta, \alpha + 3\beta$

L.H.S. $= \dfrac{(\alpha - 3\beta)^2 - (\alpha + 3\beta)^2}{(\alpha - \beta)^2 - (\alpha + \beta)^2} = \dfrac{-12\alpha\beta}{-4\alpha\beta} = 3$

Problem Set (6)

▶ Multiple Choice Questions

1. Let t_n be the nth term of an A.P. If

$\displaystyle\sum_{r=1}^{10^{99}} a_{2r} = 10^{100}$ and $\displaystyle\sum_{r=1}^{10^{99}} a_{2r-1} = 10^{99}$,

then the common difference of A.P. is

(a) 1 $\qquad$ (b) 10 $\qquad$ (c) 9 $\qquad$ (d) 10^{99}

2. Let $f(x)$ be a polynomial function of second degree such that $f(1) = f(-1)$. If a, b, c are in A.P., then $f'(a), f'(b)$ and $f'(c)$ are in

(a) A.P. $\qquad$ (b) G.P. $\qquad$ (c) H.P. $\qquad$ (d) A.G.P.

(AIEEE 2003)

3. If x_1, x_2, x_3 and y_1, y_2, y_3 are both in G.P. with the same common ratio, then the points

$A(x_1, y_1), B(x_2, y_2), C(x_3, y_3)$

(a) lie on a st. line $\qquad$ (b) lie on a circle
(c) lie on an ellipse $\qquad$ (d) vertices of a Δ

(AIEEE 2003)

4. In an A.P., $\dfrac{S_p}{S_q} = \dfrac{p^2}{q^2}$, $p \neq q$, then $\dfrac{T_6}{T_{21}}$ is equal to

(a) $\dfrac{7}{2}$ $\qquad$ (b) $\dfrac{2}{7}$ $\qquad$ (c) $\dfrac{11}{41}$ $\qquad$ (d) $\dfrac{41}{11}$

(AIEEE 2006)

5. Let $a_1, a_2, a_3, \dots$ be in A.P. and $q_1, q_2, q_3, \dots$ be in G.P. such that $a_1 = q_1 = 2$ and $a_{10} = q_{10} = 3$ then :

(a) $a_7 q_{19}$ is not an integer (b) $a_{19} q_7$ is an integer
(c) $a_7 q_{19} = a_{19} q_{10}$ $\qquad$ (d) none

6. If a, b, c are respectively the T_p, T_{2q} and T_{3r} terms of an H.P., then

$\Delta = \begin{vmatrix} bc & ca & ab \\ p & 2q & 3r \\ 1 & 1 & 1 \end{vmatrix} =$

(a) 1 $\qquad$ (b) 0 $\qquad$ (c) $-p$ $\qquad$ (d) q

7. If $f : R \to R$ satisfies $f(x+y) = f(x) + f(y)$ and $f(1) = 7$ then $\displaystyle\sum_{r=1}^{n} f(r) =$

(a) $\dfrac{7n}{2}$ $\qquad\qquad$ (b) $\dfrac{7(n+1)}{2}$

(c) $7n(n+1)$ $\qquad$ (d) $\dfrac{7n(n+1)}{2}$

(AIEEE 2003)

8. In an H.P., $T_p = q(p+q)$, $T_q = p(p+q)$, then p and q are the roots of

(a) $x^2 - T_{p+q} \, x + T_{pq} = 0$

(b) $x^2 - T_{pq} \, x + T_{p+q} = 0$

(c) $x^2 - 2T_{p+q} \, x + T_{pq} = 0$

(d) $x^2 - T_{pq} \, x + 2T_{p+q} = 0$

9. If x, y, z are in G.P. $(x, y, z > 1)$, then

$\dfrac{1}{2x + \log x}, \dfrac{1}{4x + \log y}, \dfrac{1}{6x + \log z}$ are in :

(a) A.P. $\qquad$ (b) G.P. $\qquad$ (c) H.P. $\qquad$ (d) none

10. If $S_n = \displaystyle\sum_{r=1}^{n} \dfrac{2r+1}{r^4 + 2r^3 + r^2}$, then $S_{20} =$

(a) $\dfrac{220}{221}$ (b) $\dfrac{420}{441}$ (c) $\dfrac{439}{221}$ (d) $\dfrac{440}{441}$

11. The sum of infinite A.G.P. $3, 4, 4, \ldots$ is

(a) 16 (b) 18 (c) 24 (d) 27

12. $\displaystyle\sum_{r=1}^{10} \dfrac{r}{1 - 3r^2 + r^4} =$

(a) $-\dfrac{25}{109}$ (b) $-\dfrac{35}{109}$ (c) $-\dfrac{45}{109}$ (d) $-\dfrac{55}{109}$

13. $\displaystyle\sum_{r=1}^{50} \left[\dfrac{1}{49+r} - \dfrac{1}{2r(2r-1)} \right] =$

(a) $\dfrac{1}{50}$ (b) $\dfrac{1}{99}$ (c) $\dfrac{1}{100}$ (d) $\dfrac{1}{101}$

14. A player plays n matches ($n \geq 1$) and the total runs made by him in n matches is $\dfrac{(n+1)(2^{n+1} - n - 2)}{4}$. If he makes $(k \cdot 2^{n-k+1})$ runs in kth match, $1 \leq k \leq n$, find the value of n. **(I.I.T. 2005)**

15. If the sum of first n terms of an AP is Cn^2, then the sum of squares of these n terms is

(a) $\dfrac{n(4n^2 - 1)c^2}{6}$ (b) $\dfrac{n(4n^2 + 1)c^2}{3}$

(c) $\dfrac{n(4n^2 - 1)c^2}{3}$ (d) $\dfrac{n(4n^2 + 1)c^2}{6}$

(IIT JEE 2009)

16. A man saves Rs. 200 in each of the first three months of his service. In each of the subsequent months his saving increases by Rs. 40 more than the saving of immediately previous month. His total saving from the start of service will be Rs. 11040 after

(a) 18 months (b) 19 months

(c) 20 months (d) 21 months **(AIEEE 2011)**

17. A person is to count 4500 currency notes. Let a_n denote the number of notes he counts and $a_{10}, a_{11} \ldots$ are in an A.P. with common difference -2 then the time taken by him to count all notes is

(a) 24 minutes (b) 34 minutes

(c) 125 minutes (d) 135 minutes

(AIEEE 2010)

18. If 100 times the 100th term of an A.P. with non-zero common difference equals the 50 times its 50th term. Then 150th term of thus A.P. is

(a) -150

(b) 150 times the 50th term

(c) 150

(d) 0 **(AIEEE 2012)**

19. Let $a_1, a_2, \ldots$ be in H.P. with $a_1 = 5$ and $a_{20} = 25$. The least positive integer n for which $a_n < 0$ is

(a) 22 (b) 23 (c) 24 (d) 25

(IIT JEE 2012)

20. Let $a_1, a_2, \ldots a_{100}$ be an A.P. with $a_1 = 3$ and $s_p = \displaystyle\sum_{i=1}^{p} a_i$, $1 \leq p \leq 100$ for any integer n with $1 \leq n \leq 20$, let $m = \sqrt{n}$. If $\dfrac{s_m}{s_n}$ does not depend on n then a_2 is

(a) 9 (b) 0 (c) 1 (d) 18

(IIT JEE 2011)

21. Let $s_k : k = 1, 2 \ldots 100$ denote the sum of the infinite G.P. whose first term is $\dfrac{k-1}{k!}$ and the common ratio is $\dfrac{1}{k}$.

Then the value of $\dfrac{100^2}{100!} + \displaystyle\sum_{k=1}^{100} |(k^2 - 3k + 1) s_k|$ is

(a) 3 (b) 2 (c) 1 (d) 0

22. Let $a_1, a_2, \ldots a_{11}$ be real numbers satisfying $a_1 = 15$, $27 - 2a_2 > 0$ and $a_k = 2a_{k-1} - a_{k-2}$ for $k = 3, 4, \ldots 11$. If $\dfrac{a_1^2 + a_2^2 + \ldots + a_{11}^2}{11} = 90$, then the value of $\dfrac{a_1 + a_2 + \ldots + a_{11}}{11}$ is equal to

(a) 0 (b) 1 (c) 11 (d) 100

(IIT JEE 2010)

Solutions of Problem Set (5)

1. Ans. (c).

$\displaystyle\sum_{r=1}^{10^{99}} a_{2r} = \sum_{r=1}^{10^{99}} (a_{2r-1} + d) = \sum_{r=1}^{10^{99}} a_{2r-1} + (10^{99})d$

or $10^{100} = 10^{99} + 10^{99} \cdot d$

$\therefore \quad 10 - 1 = d$ or $d = 9 \Rightarrow$ (c)

2. Ans. (a)

Let $f(x) = px^2 + qx + r$

$f(1) = f(-1) = p + q + r = p - q + r$

$\therefore \quad 2q = 0$ or $q = 0$

$f(x) = px^2 + r \quad \therefore \quad f'(x) = 2px$

$f'(a) = 2pa, f'(b) = 2pb, f'(c) = 2pc$

They are in A.P. as a, b, c are in A.P.

3. Ans. (a). x_1, x_2, x_3 are a, ar, ar^2 resp.

y_1, y_2, y_3 are b, br, br^2 resp.

$\therefore \quad A, B, C$ are $(a, b), (ar, br), (ar^2, br^2)$ resp.

Slope of $AB = \dfrac{b}{a} =$ slope of BC.

Hence the points are collinear.

4. Ans. (c).

$\dfrac{S_p}{S_q} = \dfrac{p^2}{q^2} \Rightarrow \dfrac{2a + (p-1)d}{2a + (q-1)d} = \dfrac{p}{q}$ ...(1)

$\dfrac{T_6}{T_{21}} = \dfrac{a + 5d}{a + 20d} = \dfrac{2a + 10d}{2a + 40d}$

$\therefore \quad p - 1 = 10, q - 1 = 40$ by (1) $\quad \therefore \quad \dfrac{p}{q} = \dfrac{11}{41}$

5. Ans. (c).

$a_{10} = a_1 + 9d = 2 + 9d = 3 \quad \therefore \quad d = 1/9$ ...(1)

$q_{10} = q_1 r^9 = 2r^9 = 3$ ∴ $r^9 = 3/2$ ...(2)

Now $a_7 q_{19} = (2 + 6d) 2r^{18} = \left(2 + \dfrac{6}{9}\right) \cdot 2 \cdot \dfrac{9}{4}$

   $= 9 + 3 = 12$ by (1) and (2) ...(3)

Above is an integer. Hence (a) is ruled out

$a_{19} q_7 = (2 + 18d) 2r^6 = \left(2 + 18 \cdot \dfrac{1}{9}\right) 2r^6 = 8r^6$ is not an

integer by (2), therefore b is ruled out.

$a_{19} q_{10} = (2 + 18d) 2 \cdot r^9 = \left(2 + 18 \cdot \dfrac{1}{9}\right) \cdot 2 \cdot \dfrac{3}{2}$

   $= 4 \cdot 3 = 12$ by (1) and (2)

   $= a_7 q_{19}$ by (3)

Hence (c) holds good as each is 12.

6. **Ans. (b).**

$\dfrac{1}{a} = A + (p - 1) D,$

$\dfrac{1}{b} = A + (2q - 1) D,$

$\dfrac{1}{c} = A + (3r - 1) D$

Taking abc common from R_1,

$\Delta = abc \begin{vmatrix} \dfrac{1}{a} & \dfrac{1}{b} & \dfrac{1}{c} \\ p & 2q & 3r \\ 1 & 1 & 1 \end{vmatrix}$

$= abc \begin{vmatrix} (A-D)+pD & (A-D)+2qD & (A-D)+3rD \\ p & 2q & 3r \\ 1 & 1 & 1 \end{vmatrix}$

$= \Delta_1 + \Delta_2$ say

$= (A - D) \cdot 0 + D \cdot 0$ because of identical lines of 1, 1, 1 and $p, 2q, 3r$ respectively

7. **Ans. (d).**

Putting $x = 0, y = 1$, we have

   $f(0 + 1) = f(0) + f(1) \Rightarrow f(0) = 0$

Also $f(1) = 7$

∴ $f(2) = f(1 + 1) = f(1) + f(1) = 7.2$

   $f(3) = f(2 + 1) = f(2) + f(1) = 7.3$ etc.

∴ $\Sigma = 7(1 + 2 + 3 + ... + n) = \dfrac{7n(n + 1)}{2}.$

8. **Ans. (b).**

$\dfrac{1}{T_p} = \dfrac{1}{q(p + q)} = A + (p - 1) D$ ...(1)

$\dfrac{1}{T_q} = \dfrac{1}{p(p + q)} = A + (q - 1) D$ ...(2)

Solving the above, $A = \dfrac{1}{pq(p + q)} = D$ ...(3)

∴ $\dfrac{1}{T_{p+q}} = A + (p + q - 1) D = \dfrac{p + q}{pq(p + q)} = \dfrac{1}{pq}$ by (3)

$\dfrac{1}{T_{pq}} = A + (pq - 1) D = A(1 + pq - 1) = \dfrac{1}{p + q}$ by (3)

∴ $p + q = T_{pq}$ and $pq = T_{p+q}$

Hence p and q are the roots of $x^2 - xS + P = 0$

or $x^2 - x(T_{pq}) + T_{p+q} = 0 \Rightarrow$ (b).

9. **Ans. (c).** $2x + \log x = \log e^{2x} + \log x = \log xe^{2x}$

∴ $\dfrac{1}{\log xe^{2x}}, \dfrac{1}{\log ye^{4x}}, \dfrac{1}{\log ze^{6x}}$

Now, x, y, z are in G.P.

   e^{2x}, e^{4x}, e^{6x} are in G.P.

∴ $xe^{2x}, ye^{4x}, ze^{6x}$ are in G.P.

∴ $\log(xe^{2x}), \log(ye^{4x}), \log(ze^{6x})$ are in A.P.

   [See rule (3, 4), P. 143]

or $2x + \log x, 4x + \log y, 6x + \log z$ are in A.P. Hence their reciprocals are in H.P.

10. **Ans. (d).**

$\dfrac{2r + 1}{r^4 + 2r^3 + r^2} = \dfrac{2r + 1}{r^2(r + 1)^2} = \dfrac{(r + 1)^2 - r^2}{r^2(r + 1)^2}$

$= \dfrac{1}{r^2} - \dfrac{1}{(r + 1)^2}$ ∴ $\sum_{r=1}^{20} \left[\dfrac{1}{r^2} - \dfrac{1}{(r + 1)^2}\right]$

Put $r = 1, 2, 3, ..., 20$ and terms will cancel diagonally.

∴ $\Sigma = \dfrac{1}{1} - \dfrac{1}{(20 + 1)^2} = 1 - \dfrac{1}{441} = \dfrac{440}{441}.$

11. **Ans. (d).**

   $a + (a + d) r + (a + 2d) r^2 + ... \infty$

   $a = 3, (3 + d) r = 4, (3 + 2d) r^2 = 4$

Solving the last two, we have

$\dfrac{4}{r} - 3 = d = \left(\dfrac{4}{r^2} - 3\right) \cdot \dfrac{1}{2}$

or $(4 - 3r) \cdot 2r = 4 - 3r^2$

or $3r^2 - 8r + 4 = 0$ or $(r - 2)(3r - 2) = 0$

∴ $r = \dfrac{2}{3}$ as $r < 1$ ∴ $d = 3$

$S = 3 + 6 \cdot \dfrac{2}{3} + 9 \left(\dfrac{2}{3}\right)^2 + ... \infty$

$\dfrac{2}{3} S = \quad 3 \cdot \dfrac{2}{3} + 6 \left(\dfrac{2}{3}\right)^2 + ... \infty$

∴ $S \left(1 - \dfrac{2}{3}\right) = 3 + 3 \cdot \dfrac{2}{3} + 3 \cdot \left(\dfrac{2}{3}\right)^2 + ... \infty$

$\dfrac{S}{3} = \dfrac{3}{1 - (2/3)} = 9$ ∴ $S = 27$

12. **Ans. (d).**

$\dfrac{r}{1 - 3r^2 + r^4} = \dfrac{r}{(r^2 - 1)^2 - r^2}$

or $\dfrac{r}{(r^2 - 1 - r)(r^2 - 1 + r)}$

$= \dfrac{1}{2} \left[\dfrac{\{(r^2 - 1) + r\} - \{r^2 - 1 - r\}}{(r^2 - 1 - r)(r^2 - 1 + r)}\right]$

∴ $T_r = \dfrac{1}{2} \left[\dfrac{1}{r^2 - 1 - r} - \dfrac{1}{r^2 - 1 + r}\right]$

$$= \frac{1}{2}\left[\frac{1}{1-r(r+1)} - \frac{1}{1-r(r-1)}\right]$$

$$\sum_{r=1}^{10} T_r = \frac{1}{2}\left[\frac{1}{1-10.11} - \frac{1}{1-1.0}\right] = -\frac{55}{109}$$

The terms will cancel diagonally except the first and the last.

13. Ans. (c).

$$\sum_{r=1}^{50} \frac{1}{2r(2r-1)} = \sum_{r=1}^{50}\left(\frac{1}{2r-1} - \frac{1}{2r}\right)$$

$$= \left(1 - \frac{1}{2} + \frac{1}{3} - \frac{1}{4}\ldots + \frac{1}{99} - \frac{1}{100}\right)$$

$$= \left(1 + \frac{1}{2} + \frac{1}{3} + \frac{1}{4}\ldots + \frac{1}{100}\right) - 2\left(\frac{1}{2} + \frac{1}{4} + \ldots + \frac{1}{100}\right)$$

$$= \sum_{r=1}^{100}\frac{1}{r} - \left(1 + \frac{1}{2} + \ldots + \frac{1}{50}\right), i.e., \sum_{r=1}^{50}\frac{1}{r} = \sum_{r=51}^{100}\frac{1}{r}$$

$$\therefore E = \sum_{r=1}^{50}\frac{1}{49+r} - \sum_{r=51}^{100}\frac{1}{r}$$

$$= \left[\frac{1}{50} + \frac{1}{51} + \ldots + \frac{1}{99}\right] - \left[\frac{1}{51} + \frac{1}{52} + \ldots + \frac{1}{100}\right]$$

$$= \frac{1}{50} - \frac{1}{100} = \frac{2}{100} - \frac{1}{100} = \frac{1}{100} \Rightarrow (c).$$

14. $T_k = k \cdot 2^{n-k+1} = 2^{n+1} \cdot \frac{k}{2^k}$

Putting $k = 1, 2, 3, \ldots, n$ and adding, we get the total number of runs made in n matches as

$$2^{n+1}\left[1.\frac{1}{2} + 2.\left(\frac{1}{2}\right)^2 + 3.\left(\frac{1}{3}\right)^3 + \ldots n\text{ terms}\right]$$

$$= 2^{n+1} \cdot S_n \text{ of A. G. S.}$$

$$= 2^{n+1} \cdot 2\left[1 - \frac{1}{2^n} - \frac{n}{2^{n+1}}\right]$$

$$= 2[2^{n+1} - n - 2] = \frac{n+1}{4}[2^{n+1} - n - 2] \quad \text{as given.}$$

Above relation implies that

$$\frac{n+1}{4} = 2 \text{ or } n = 7.$$

15. Ans. (c). $s_n = cn^2$

$$s_{n-1} = c(n-1)^2 = cn^2 + c - 2cn$$

$$T_n = 2cn - c$$

$$T_n^2 = (2cn - c)^2 = 4c^2n^2 + c^2 - 4c^2n$$

Required sum

$$= \Sigma T_n^2 = 4c^2 \Sigma n^2 + nc^2 - 4c^2 \Sigma n$$

$$= \frac{4c^2 n(n+1)(2n+1)}{6} + nc^2 - 2c^2 n(n+1)$$

$$= \frac{2c^2 n(n+1)(2n+1) + 3nc^2 - 6c^2 n(n+1)}{3}$$

$$= \frac{nc^2[4n^2 + 6n + 2 + 3 - 6n - 6]}{3}$$

$$= \frac{nc^2(4n^2 - 1)}{3}$$

16. Ans. (d). $a = $ Rs. 200

$d = 40$

Saving in first two months = Rs. 400

Remained saving $= 200 + 240 + 280 + \ldots$ upto n terms

$$\Rightarrow \frac{n}{2}[400 + (n-1).40] = 11040 - 400$$

$$\Rightarrow 200n + 20n^2 - 20n = 10640$$

$$\Rightarrow 20n^2 + 180n - 10640 = 0$$

$$\Rightarrow n^2 + 9n - 532 = 0$$

$$\Rightarrow (n+28)(n-19) = 0 \Rightarrow n = 19$$

Hence, required number of months = 19 + 2 = 21

17. Ans. (b).

$4500 = 150 \times 10 + (148 + 146 + \ldots$ upto n terms)

$$= 1500 + \frac{n}{2}\{296 + (n-1) - 2\}$$

$$\Rightarrow n^2 - 149n + 3000 = 0$$

$$\Rightarrow (n-24)(n-125) = 0$$

$$\Rightarrow n = 24 \quad (\because n \neq 125)$$

Hence, total time taken = 10 + 24 = 34 minutes

18. Ans. (d).

$$100(a + 99d) = 50(a + 49d)$$

$$\Rightarrow 2a + 198d = a + 49d$$

$$a + 149d = 0$$

$$\therefore T_{150} = a + 149 = 0$$

19. Ans. (d).

Corresponding $AP = \frac{1}{5}, \ldots, \frac{1}{25}$ (20th term)

$$\Rightarrow \frac{1}{25} - \frac{1}{5} + 19d$$

$$\Rightarrow d = \frac{1}{19}\left(\frac{-4}{25}\right) = -\frac{4}{19 \times 25} \quad \text{Now, } a_n < 0$$

$$\Rightarrow \frac{1}{5} - \frac{4}{19 \times 25}(n-1) < 0$$

$$\Rightarrow \frac{19 \times 5}{4} < n - 1 \quad \Rightarrow n > 24.75$$

20. Ans. (a).

$$\frac{s_m}{s_n} = \frac{s_{5n}}{s_n} = \frac{\frac{5n}{2}[6 + (5n-1)d]}{\frac{n}{2}[6 + (n-1)d]} = \frac{5[(6-d) + 5nd]}{[(6-d) + nd]}$$

$d = 6$ or $d = 0$

If $d = 0$ then $a_2 = 3$ else $a_2 = 9$

For single choice, more appropriate choice is 9

$$\therefore a_2 = 3 + 6 = 9$$

21. Ans. (a). $\sum_{k=3}^{100}|(k^2 - 3k + 1)sk|$

for $k = 2, |(k^2 - 3k + 1) 5k| = 1$

$$\sum_{k=3}^{100} \left| \frac{k-1}{(k-2)!} + \frac{k-1+1}{(k-1)!} \right|$$

$$= \sum_{k=3}^{100} \frac{1}{(k-3)!} + \frac{1}{(k-2)!} \frac{1}{(k-2)!} - \frac{1}{(k-1)!}$$

$$\sum_{k=3}^{100} \left(\frac{1}{(k-3)!} - \frac{1}{(k-1)!} \right)$$

$$S = 1 + \left(1 - \frac{1}{2!}\right) + \left(\frac{1}{1!} - \frac{1}{3!}\right) + \left(\frac{1}{2!} - \frac{1}{4!}\right)$$
$$+ \left(\frac{1}{3!} - \frac{1}{5!}\right) + \left(\frac{1}{4!} - \frac{1}{6!}\right)$$
$$+ \ldots + \left(\frac{1}{94!} - \frac{1}{96!}\right) + \left(\frac{1}{95!} - \frac{1}{97!}\right) + \left(\frac{1}{96!} - \frac{1}{98!}\right)$$
$$+ \left(\frac{1}{97!} - \frac{1}{99!}\right)$$

$$= 2 - \frac{1}{98!} - \frac{1}{99!}$$

$$\therefore E = \frac{100^2}{100!} + 3 - \frac{1}{98!} - \frac{1}{99.98!} = \frac{100^2}{100!} + 3$$

$$- \frac{100}{99!} = \frac{100^2}{100.99!} + 3 - \frac{100}{99!} = 3$$

22. Ans. (a). $a_1 = 15$

$$\frac{a_k + a_{k-2}}{2} = a_{k-1} \text{ for } k = 3, 4, \ldots 11$$

$\Rightarrow a_1, a_2, \ldots a_{11}$ are in A.P.

$$\frac{a_1^2 + a_2^2 + \ldots a_{11}^2}{11} = 90$$

$$\Rightarrow \frac{(15)^2 + (15 + d)^2 + \ldots + (15 + 10.d)^2}{11} = 90$$

$$\Rightarrow 7d^2 + 30d + 27 = 0 \Rightarrow d = -3 \text{ or } -\frac{9}{7}$$

Since $27 - 2a_2 > 0 \Rightarrow a_2 < \frac{27}{2} \Rightarrow d = -3$

$$\frac{a_1 + a_2 + \ldots + a_{11}}{11} = \frac{11}{2} \frac{[(30 + 10 \, (-3)]}{11} = 0$$

MISCELLANEOUS EXERCISE

Matching Entries

♦ *Match the entries of List-A and List-B.*

1. If $\dfrac{a^{n+1} + b^{n+1}}{a^n + b^n}$ then

List-A		List-B	
(a)	A.M. of a and b	1.	-1
(b)	G.M. of a and b	2.	0
(c)	H.M. of a and b then $n =$	3.	$-1/2$

2.

List-A		List-B	
(a)	In an A.P., $S_p = a, S_q = b, S_r = c$, then $\frac{a}{p}(q - r) + \frac{b}{q}(r - p) + \frac{c}{r}(p - q) =$	1.	0
(b)	In a G.P., $T_r = R, T_s = S, T_t = T$, then $R^{s-t} \cdot S^{t-r} \cdot T^{r-s} =$	2.	0
(c)	In an H.P. $T_p = a, T_q = b, T_r = c$, then $bc(q - r) + ca(r - p) + ab(p - q) =$	3.	0
(d)	If both in A.P. and G.P., $T_m = x, T_n = y, T_p = z$ then $x^{y-z} \cdot y^{z-x} \cdot z^{x-y} =$	4.	0
(e)	If both in G.P. and H.P., $T_p = a, T_q = b, T_r = c$, then $a(b - c) \log a + b(c - a) \log b + c(a - b) \log c =$	5.	0

3.

List-A		List-B	
(a)	Sum of n A.M.'s between a and b is	1.	$(\sqrt{ab})^n$
(b)	Product of n G.M.'s between a and b is	2.	$2A pq$
(c)	If A, G, H are A.M., G.M., H.M. between the same two numbers, such that $A - G = 15$ and $A - H = 27$, then the numbers are	3.	$\dfrac{G_1 G_2}{H_1 H_2}$

(d) $A_1, A_2; G_1, G_2$ and H_1, H_2 are respective two A.M.'s, two G.M.'s and two H.M.'s between the same two numbers, then $\dfrac{A_1 + A_2}{H_1 + H_2} =$ 4. $\dfrac{n(a+b)}{2}$

(e) If one A.M. A and two G.M.'s p and q be inserted between any two numbers then the value of $p^3 + q^3$ is   5.   120, 30

4. $a, b, c \in \mathbf{R}$ and a, b, c are in $A.P.$ match the entries of column-I with those of column-II.

Column-I

(a) a^2, b^2, c^2 are in A.P.

(b) a^2, b^2, c^2 are in G.P.

(c) a^2, b^2, c^2 are in H.P.

(d) $a + b + c = 3/2$

Column-II

(p) $a = b = c$

(q) $-\dfrac{1}{2} a, b, c$ are in G.P.

(r) $a, b, -\dfrac{1}{2} c$ are in G.P.

(s) $b = 1/2$

5. For $0 < \theta < \dfrac{\pi}{4}$, let $x = \displaystyle\sum_{n=0}^{\infty} \sin^{2n} \theta, y = \sum_{n=0}^{\infty} \cos^{2n} \theta$, then match the entries of column-I with column-II

Column-I

(a) $\displaystyle\sum_{0}^{\infty} \sin^{2n} \theta \cos^{2n} \theta$

(b) $\displaystyle\sum_{0}^{\infty} \tan^{2n} \theta$

(c) $\displaystyle\sum_{0}^{\infty} \sin^{2n} \theta \cos^{4n} \theta$

(d) $\displaystyle\sum_{0}^{\infty} \cos^{2n} \theta \sin^{4n} \theta$

Column-II

(p) $\dfrac{xy^2}{xy^2 - 1}$

(q) $\dfrac{y}{y - x}$

(r) $\dfrac{xy}{xy - 1}$

(s) $\dfrac{x^2 y}{x^2 y - 1}$

Answers

1. (a) $\rightarrow$ 2. **Q. 40 P. 130**

(b) $\rightarrow$ 3. **Q. 40 (b) P. 147**

(c) $\rightarrow$ 1. **Q. 27 P. 175**

2. All (a), (b), (c), (d), (e) match to zero.

(a) **Q. 23 P. 129**

(b) **Q. 23 (a) P. 145**

(c) **Q. 28 (a) P. 175**

(d) **Q. 41 (a) P. 176**

(e) **Q. 41 (b) P. 176**

3. (a) $\rightarrow$ 4. **§ 1 c (ii) P. 126**

(b) $\rightarrow$ 1. **§ 2 P. 144**

(c) $\rightarrow$ 5. **Q. 18 (a) P. 174**

(d) $\rightarrow$ 3. **Q. 20 (a) P. 174**

(e) $\rightarrow$ 2. **Q. 39 (b) P. 147**

4. Ans. (a) $\rightarrow$ (p), (b) $\rightarrow$ (p), (c) $\rightarrow$ (p, q, r), (d) $\rightarrow$ (s)

(a) Given $2b = a + c$, $2b^2 = a^2 + c^2$

$2b^2 = (a+c)^2 - 2ac = 4b^2 - 2ac$

∴ $2ac = 4b^2 - 2b^2 = 2b^2$ ∴ $b^2 = ac$

$2b^2 = a^2 + c^2$ or $2ac = a^2 + c^2$ or $(a-c)^2 = 0$

∴ $a = c$ ∴ $2b = a + c = 2a$ ∴ $b = a$

Hence $a = b = c$ ∴ (a) $\rightarrow$ (p)

(b) a^2, b^2, c^2 are in G.P. $\Rightarrow (b^2)^2 = a^2 c^2$

∴ $b^2 = ac, b^2 = -ac$

$b^2 = ac \Rightarrow a, b, c$ are in G.P.

But a, b, c are in A.P. as well ∴ $a = b = c$

∴   (b) $\rightarrow$ (p)

(c) $b^2 = \dfrac{2a^2 c^2}{a^2 + c^2}$ or $b^2 [(a+c)^2 - 2ac] = 2a^2 c^2$

$\left(\dfrac{a+c}{2}\right)^2 [(a+c)^2 - 2ac] = 2a^2 c^2$

or $(a+c)^4 - 2ac(a+c)^2 - 8a^2 c^2 = 0$

or $[(a+c)^2 - 4ac][(a+c)^2 + 2ac] = 0$

or $(a-c)^2 = 0$ or $(a+c)^2 = -2ac$

or $a = c$ or $(2b)^2 = -2ac$

or $a = b = c$ ∵ $2b = a + c$ and $b^2 = -\dfrac{a}{2} c$

∴ a, b, c are in A.P.   or $-\dfrac{a}{2}, b, c$

or $a, b, -\dfrac{c}{2}$ are in G.P.   ∴   (c) $\rightarrow$ (p, q, r).

(d) $a + b + c = \dfrac{3}{2} \Rightarrow 2b + b = \dfrac{3}{2} \Rightarrow b = \dfrac{1}{2}$

∴   (d) $\rightarrow$ (s)

5. Ans. (a)→ (r), (b)→ (q), (c)→ (s), (d)→ (p)

x = sum of an infinite G.P. whose sum by

$$S_\infty = \frac{a}{1-r} \text{ is}$$

$$x = \frac{1}{1-\sin^2\theta} = \frac{1}{\cos^2\theta}, y = \frac{1}{1-\cos^2\theta} = \frac{1}{\sin^2\theta}$$

$$\therefore \quad \cos^2\theta = \frac{1}{x}, \sin^2\theta = \frac{1}{y} \qquad \qquad ...(1)$$

(a) $\dfrac{1}{1-\sin^2\theta\cos^2\theta} = \dfrac{1}{1-\dfrac{1}{xy}} = \dfrac{xy}{xy-1} \to$ (r)

(b) $\dfrac{1}{1-\tan^2\theta} = \dfrac{1}{1-\dfrac{x}{y}} = \dfrac{y}{y-x} \to$ (q)

(c) $\dfrac{1}{1-\sin^2\theta\cos^4\theta} = \dfrac{1}{1-\dfrac{1}{y}\cdot\dfrac{1}{x^2}} = \dfrac{x^2y}{x^2y-1} \to$ (s)

(d) $\dfrac{1}{1-\cos^2\theta\sin^4\theta} = \dfrac{1}{1-\dfrac{1}{x}\cdot\dfrac{1}{y^2}} = \dfrac{xy^2}{xy^2-1} \to$ (p)

Assertion / Reason

1. Suppose four distinct positive numbers a_1, a_2, a_3, a_4 are in G.P. Let $b_1 = a_1, b_2 = b_1 + a_2, b_3 = b_2 + a_3$ and $b_4 = b_3 + a_4$.

   Statement-1. The numbers b_1, b_2, b_3, b_4 are neither in A.P. nor in G.P. and

   Statement-2. The numbers b_1, b_2, b_3, b_4 are in H.P.

   (I.I.T. 2008)

Sol. (c). $b_1 = a_1, b_2 = b_1 + a_2 = a_1 + a_2$

$b_3 = b_2 + a_3 = a_1 + a_2 + a_3, b_4 = a_1 + a_2 + a_3 + a_4$

Clearly b_1, b_2, b_3, b_4 are neither in A.P. nor in G.P. Hence statement-1 is true.

Also b_1, b_2, b_3, b_4 are not in H.P. Hence statement-2 is false.

Comprehension

Paragraph for Question Nos. 1 to 3 : Let V_r denote the sum of the first r terms of an arithmetic progression (A.P.) whose first term is r and the common difference is $(2r-1)$. Let $T_r = V_{r+1} - V_r - 2$ and $Q_r = T_{r+1} - T_r$ for $r = 1, 2, ...$

1. The sum $V_1 + V_2 + ... + V_n$ is

   (a) $\dfrac{1}{12} n(n+1)(3n^2 - n + 1)$

   (b) $\dfrac{1}{12} n(n+1)(3n^2 + n + 2)$

   (c) $\dfrac{1}{2} n(2n^2 - n + 1)$

   (d) $\dfrac{1}{3}(2n^3 - 2n + 3)$

   (I.I.T. 2007)

Sol. Ans. (b).

$S = \dfrac{n}{2}[2a + (n-1)d]$ for an A.P.

$\therefore \quad V_r = \dfrac{r}{2}[2r + (r-1)(2r-1)]$

or $V_r = \dfrac{r}{2}[2r^2 - r + 1] = r^3 - \dfrac{1}{2}r^2 + \dfrac{1}{2}r \qquad ...(A)$

$\therefore \quad \sum_{r=1}^{n} V_r = \Sigma n^3 - \dfrac{1}{2}\Sigma n^2 + \dfrac{1}{2}\Sigma n$

$= \left[\dfrac{n(n+1)}{2}\right]^2 - \dfrac{1}{2}\cdot\dfrac{n(n+1)(2n+1)}{6} + \dfrac{1}{2}\dfrac{n(n+1)}{2}$

$= \dfrac{n(n+1)}{12}[3n(n+1) - (2n+1) + 3]$

$= \dfrac{n(n+1)}{12}(3n^2 + n + 2)$

2. T_r is always

   (a) an odd number   (b) an even number

   (c) a prime number   (d) a composite number

   (I.I.T. 2007)

Sol. Ans. (d).

$T_r = V_{r+1} - V_r - 2$ given

$= (r+1)^3 - \dfrac{1}{2}(r+1)^2 + \dfrac{1}{2}(r+1)$

$\qquad - \left(r^3 - \dfrac{1}{2}r^2 + \dfrac{1}{2}r\right) - 2$

by (A) of Q. 15

$= (3r^2 + 3r + 1) - \dfrac{1}{2}(2r+1) + \dfrac{1}{2} - 2$

$= 3r^2 + 2r - 1 = (r+1)(3r-1) \qquad ...(B)$

Above shows that T_r is a composite number.

3. Which one of the following is a correct statement?

   (a) $Q_1, Q_2, Q_3, ...$ are in A.P. with common difference 5

   (b) $Q_1, Q_2, Q_3, ...$ are in A.P. with common difference 6

   (c) $Q_1, Q_2, Q_3, ...$ are in A.P. with common difference 11

   (d) $Q_1 = Q_2 = Q_3 = ...$

   (I.I.T. 2007)

Sol. Ans. (b).

$Q_r = T_{r+1} - T_r \qquad \qquad$ given

$= 3(r+1)^2 + 2(r+1) - 1 - [3r^2 + 2r - 1]$

by (B) of Q. 16

$Q_r = (6r + 3) + 2 = 6r + 5$

Clearly $Q_1, Q_2, Q_3, \ldots$ will form an A.P. whose common difference is 6 **(See § I h P. 127)**.

Paragraph of Question Nos. 4 to 7 : Let A_1, G_1, H_1 denote the arithmetic, geometric and harmonic means, respectively, of two distinct positive numbers. For $n \geq 2$, let A_{n-1} and H_{n-1} has arithmetic, geometric and harmonic means as A_n, G_n, H_n respectively.

4. Which one of the following statements is correct ?

(a) $G_1 > G_2 > G_3 > \ldots$

(b) $G_1 < G_2 < G_3 < \ldots$

(c) $G_1 = G_2 = G_3 = \ldots$

(d) $G_1 < G_3 < G_5 < \ldots$ and $G_2 > G_4 > G_6 > \ldots$ **(I.I.T. 2007)**

Sol. If A, G, H be A.M., G.M. and H.M. then $G^2 = AH$ and $A > G > H$

Also we are given A_{n-1} and H_{n-1} have A.M., G.M. and H.M. as A_n, G_n and H_n.

∴ By definition we have the following relations

$$A_n = \frac{A_{n-1} + H_{n-1}}{2}, \quad G_n^2 = A_{n-1} \cdot H_{n-1}$$

and $\dfrac{2}{H_n} = \dfrac{1}{A_{n-1}} + \dfrac{1}{H_{n-1}}$

For $n = 2, \; G_2^2 = A_1 H_1 = G_1^2$

$G_3^2 = A_2 H_2 = G_2^2 = G_1^2$ so on

∴ $G_1^2 = G_2^2 = G_3^2 \ldots \Rightarrow G_1 = G_2 = G_3 \ldots$

5. Which of the following statements is correct ?

(a) $A_1 > A_2 > A_3 > \ldots$

(b) $A_1 < A_2 < A_3 < \ldots$

(c) $A_1 = A_2 = A_3 = \ldots$ and $A_2 < A_4 < A_6 < \ldots$

(d) $A_1 < A_3 < A_5 < \ldots$ and $A_2 > A_4 > A_6 > \ldots$

(I.I.T. 2007)

Sol. Ans. (a).

$$A_2 = \frac{A_1 + H_1}{2} \quad \text{and} \quad A_1 > H_1$$

∴ $A_1 > A_2$. Similarly $A_2 > A_3 \ldots$

∴ $A_1 > A_2 > A_3 \ldots$

6. Which of the following statements is correct ?

(a) $H_1 > H_2 > H_3 > \ldots$

(b) $H_1 < H_2 < H_3 < \ldots$

(c) $H_1 = H_2 = H_3 = \ldots$ and $H_2 < H_4 < H_6 < \ldots$

(d) $H_1 < H_3 < H_5 < \ldots$ and $H_2 > H_4 > H_6 > \ldots$

(i.I.T. 2007)

Sol. Ans. (b).

$$G_1^2 = A_1 H_1 \quad \therefore \quad H_1 = \frac{G_1^2}{A_1} \qquad \ldots(1)$$

$$H_2 = \frac{G_2^2}{A_2} = \frac{G_1^2}{A_2} \qquad \ldots(2)$$

But $A_1 > A_2$ ∴ $H_1 < H_2$ by (1) and (2) as their numerators same.

Hence continuing like this $H_1 < H_2 < H_3 \ldots$

7. Let $A_n = \dfrac{3}{4} - \left(\dfrac{3}{4}\right)^2 + \left(\dfrac{3}{4}\right)^3 - \ldots + (-1)^{n-1}\left(\dfrac{3}{4}\right)^n$

and $B_n = 1 - A_n$, then find the least value of $n_0, n_0 \in \mathbf{N}$ such that $B_n > A_n, \; \forall \, n \geq n_0$. **(I.I.T. 2006)**

Sol. Ans. 6

A_n = sum of a G.P. of n terms whose common radio is $-\dfrac{3}{4}$

$$\therefore \quad A_n = \frac{3}{4} \cdot \frac{\left[1 - \left(-\dfrac{3}{4}\right)^n\right]}{1 - \left(-\dfrac{3}{4}\right)} = \frac{3}{7}\left[1 - \left(-\dfrac{3}{4}\right)^n\right] \qquad \ldots(1)$$

$B_n = 1 - A_n$ and $B_n > A_n \Rightarrow 1 - A_n > A_n$

or $1 > 2A_n$ or $A_n < \dfrac{1}{2}$

$$\therefore \quad \frac{3}{7}\left[1 - \left(-\frac{3}{4}\right)^n\right] < \frac{1}{2} \text{ or } 1 - \left(-\frac{3}{4}\right)^n < \frac{7}{6}$$

or $1 - \dfrac{7}{6} < \left(-\dfrac{3}{4}\right)^n$ or $-\dfrac{1}{6} < \left(-\dfrac{3}{4}\right)^n$

or $\left(-\dfrac{3}{4}\right)^n > -\dfrac{1}{6}$

Above is true for all $n \geq 6$.

Paragraph for Question (8) and (9)

Let a_n denote the number of all digit positive integers formed by the digits 0, 1 or both such that no consecutive digits in them are 0. Let b_n = the number of such n-digit integers ending with digit 1 and C_n = the number of such n digit integers ending with digit 0.

8. Which of the following is correct

(a) $a_{17} = a_{16} + a_{15}$

(b) $c_{17} \neq c_{16} + c_{15}$

(c) $b_{17} \neq b_{16} + c_{16}$

(d) $a_{17} = c_{17} + b_{16}$

(IIT JEE 2012)

Sol. Ans. (a).

$\underline{1} \ldots \ldots \underline{1} \neq a_{n-1}$

$\ldots \ldots \underline{1}\underline{0} \neq a_{n-2}$

⇒ (a) is correct

Consider (b) choice

$c_{17} \neq c_{16} + c_{15}, \qquad c_{15} \neq c_{14} + c_{13}$ is not true

For choice (c) $b_{17} \neq b_{16} + c_{16}, a_{16} \neq a_{15} + a_{14}$ is not true

For choice (d) $a_{17} = c_{17} + b_{16}, a_{17} = a_{15} + a_{15}$, which is not true.

9. The value of b_6 is

(a) 7   (b) 8   (c) 9   (d) 11

(IIT JEE 2012)

Sol. Ans. (b). $b_6 = a_5$

$a_5 = \underline{1} \ldots \ldots \underline{1} \qquad\qquad \underline{1} \ldots \ldots \underline{0}$

$ ^3C_0 + {}^3C_1 + 1 + {}^2C_1 + 1$

$ 1 + 3 + 1 + 2 + 1$

$ = 4 + 4$

$ = 8$

Fascinating Facts

- If S_n is the sum of n terms of an A.P. whose first term is a and last term is l then $\delta_n = \dfrac{n}{2}(a + l)$

- If a is the first term and d be the common difference of an A.P. having m terms, then nth term from the end is $(m - n + 1)$th term from the begining. Therefore, nth term from the end $= a + (m - n)d$

- The sum of all possible products of the first n natural numbers taken two at a time is $\dfrac{1}{24} n(n^2 - 1)(3n + 2)$

- The Number a, b, c are in A.P., G.P., or H.P. according as $\dfrac{a - b}{b - c} = \dfrac{a}{a}, \dfrac{a}{b}$ or $\dfrac{a}{c}$

- If a, b, c are in A.P. as well as in G.P. then $a = b = c$

- The nth arithmetic mean is given by $A_n = a + \dfrac{m}{(n + 1)}(b - a)$ and nth genetic mean is given by $G_n = a \cdot \dfrac{m}{n + 1} \cdot \left(\dfrac{b}{a}\right)$

- If A and G are respectively arithmetic and geometric means between two positive numbers a and b then two positive numbers are $A \pm \sqrt{A^2 - G^2}$.

- If the pth term of an A.P. is q and qth term is p, then its $(p + q)$th term is zero and nth term is $(p + q - n)$

- If n G.M.'s inserted between a and b, then $r = \left(\dfrac{b}{a}\right)^{\frac{1}{n+1}}$

- The general form of an arithmetic-geometric sequence is $a, (a + d)r, (a + 2d)r^2, \ldots$ The nth term of this sequence is $[a + (n + 1) \cdot d]r^{n-1}$

- The sum of nth terms of an arithmetic-geometric sequence is given by

$$S_n = \dfrac{a}{(1 - r)} + \dfrac{dr}{(1 - r)^2} - \dfrac{dr^n}{(1 - r)^2} - \dfrac{|a + (n - 1)d|r^n}{(1 - r)}, \quad r \neq 1$$

- The sum of an infinite arithmetic-geometric segmence is given by

$$S_\infty = \dfrac{a}{(1 - r)} + \dfrac{dr}{(1 - r)^2}, \quad |r| < 1$$

- Between any two numbers, $\dfrac{\text{sum of } m \text{ A. M.'s}}{\text{sum of } n \text{ A. M.'s}} = \dfrac{m}{n}$

- If $a, b, c, d \ldots$ are in G.P. then they are also in continues poportion i.e., $\dfrac{a}{b} = \dfrac{b}{c} = \dfrac{c}{d} = \ldots = \dfrac{1}{r}$

- Product of n G.M.'s between a and b is equal to nth power of single geometric mean between a and b i.e., $G_1 G_2 \ldots G_n = (\sqrt{ab})^n$

- The product of n geometric means between a and $\dfrac{1}{a}$ is 1.

- If G_1 and G_2 are two G.M.'s between two numbers a and b is $G_1 = (a^2 b)^{1/3}, \ G_2 = (ab^2)^{1/3}$

- If H_1 and H_2 are two H.M.'s between a and b, then
$$H_1 = \dfrac{3ab}{a + 2b}, \qquad H_2 = \dfrac{3ab}{2a + b}$$

- If A, G, H respectively be the AM, G.M., H.M. between a and b, then

$$\dfrac{a^{n+1} + b^{n+1}}{a^n + b^n} = \begin{cases} A & \text{when} \quad n = 0 \\ G & \text{when} \quad n = \dfrac{1}{2} \\ H & \text{when} \quad n = -1 \end{cases}$$

- If A_1, A_2 be two A.M.'s, $G_1 G_2$ be two G.M.'s and H_1, H_2 be two H.M.'s between numbers a and b, then
$$\dfrac{G_1 G_2}{H_1 H_2} = \dfrac{A_1 + A_2}{H_1 + H_2}$$

Theory of Quadratic Equations

§ 1. Roots of the equation $ax^2 + bx + c = 0$.

Multiplying both sides by $4a$, we get
$$4a^2 x^2 + 4abx = -4ac$$

Add b^2 to both sides
$$4a^2 x^2 + 4abx + b^2 = b^2 - 4ac$$

or $\qquad (2ax + b)^2 = b^2 - 4ac$

Take square root
$$2ax + b = \pm\sqrt{b^2 - 4ac}.$$

$\therefore \quad x = \dfrac{-b \pm \sqrt{b^2 - 4ac}}{2a}$.

Sum and Product of the roots.

If α and β be the roots, then
$$\alpha = \frac{-b + \sqrt{b^2 - 4ac}}{2a}, \beta = \frac{-b - \sqrt{b^2 - 4ac}}{2a}$$

Sum of the roots $\quad = \alpha + \beta = -\dfrac{2b}{2a} = -\dfrac{b}{a}$

or $\quad \alpha + \beta = -\dfrac{b}{a} = -\dfrac{\text{coeff. of } x}{\text{coeff. of } x^2}$

Product of roots
$$= \alpha\beta = \frac{(-b)^2 - [\sqrt{b^2 - 4ac}]^2}{4a^2} = \frac{4ac}{4a^2} = \frac{c}{a}.$$

or $\quad \alpha\beta = \dfrac{\text{constant term}}{\text{coeff. of } x^2}$.

§ 2. To find the equation whose roots are α and β.

The required equation will be
$$(x - \alpha)(x - \beta) = 0$$

or $\quad x^2 - (\alpha + \beta) x + \alpha\beta = 0$

or $\quad x^2 - Sx + P = 0$

where S is sum and P is product of roots. If the roots be $3, -7$

then $S = \text{Sum} = 3 - 7 = -4$,

$\qquad P = \text{Product} = -21$

$\therefore \quad$ Equation is $x^2 - Sx + P = 0$

or $\quad x^2 - (-4) x + (-21) = 0$

or $\quad x^2 + 4x - 21 = 0$.

§ 3. Nature of the roots.

The roots of the equation $ax^2 + bx + c = 0$ are
$$\frac{-b \pm \sqrt{b^2 - 4ac}}{2a}.$$

The expression $b^2 - 4ac$ is called **discriminant**.

(a) If $b^2 - 4ac \geq 0$, roots are **real**.

(i) If $b^2 - 4ac > 0$, then the roots are **real and unequal**.

(ii) If $b^2 - 4ac = 0$, then the roots of the equation are **real and equal**.

In this case, each root $= \dfrac{-b \pm 0}{2a} = -\dfrac{b}{2a}$.

(iii) Also if $b^2 - 4ac$ be a **perfect square** then the roots are **rational** and in case it be not a perfect square then the roots are **irrational**.

(b) If $b^2 - 4ac < 0$ i.e. $-$ive, then $\sqrt{b^2 - 4ac}$ is imaginary.

Therefore the roots are **imaginary and unequal**. Imaginary or irrational roots of the equation $ax^2 + bx + c = 0$ where a, b, c are all real numbers, will occur in conjugate pairs i.e., if $2 + 3i$ is a root then $2 - 3i$ will also be a root. But **if however the coefficients a, b, c are not all real** or any of these is non-real or irrational, then it is not necessary that the roots will occur in conjugate pairs.

Particular Case. If $a + b + c = 0$, then $x = 1$ is a root of the equation $ax^2 + bx + c = 0$ and if $a - b + c = 0$, then $x = -1$ is a root of above.

Identity. In case any quadratic equation $ax^2 + bx + c = 0$ has more than two roots then it will be an identity which implies that all the coefficients a, b, c are zero. In this case, the equation is satisfied by all the values of x.

▶ Tabular form

D	Nature of roots	Value of the roots
$D = 0$	Real equal & rational	$\alpha = \beta = -\dfrac{b}{2a}$
$D > 0$ but not a perfect square	Real unequal and irrational	$\alpha = \dfrac{-b + \sqrt{D}}{2a}, \beta = \dfrac{-b - \sqrt{D}}{2a}$
$D > 0$ and perfect square	Real unequal and rational	$\alpha = \dfrac{-b + \sqrt{D}}{2a}, \beta = \dfrac{-b - \sqrt{D}}{2a}$ $\sqrt{D}$ = whole number
$D < 0$	Imaginary complex conjugates	$\alpha = \dfrac{-b + i\sqrt{D}}{2a}, \beta = \dfrac{-b - i\sqrt{D}}{2a}$
$D > 0$	Real	—

§ 4. Symmetric functions of the roots.

(a) Symmetric functions of the roots.

If α and β are the roots of $ax^2 + bx + c = 0$, then

$$\alpha + \beta = -\frac{b}{a} \qquad \qquad \dots(1)$$

$$\alpha\beta = \frac{c}{a}. \qquad \qquad \dots(2)$$

$*\therefore \quad \alpha^2 + \beta^2 = (\alpha + \beta)^2 - 2\alpha\beta = \dfrac{b^2 - 2ac}{a^2}$

$\alpha - \beta = \sqrt{(\alpha + \beta)^2 - 4\alpha\beta} = \dfrac{\sqrt{b^2 - 4ac}}{a}$

$* \quad \alpha^2 - \beta^2 = (\alpha + \beta)(\alpha - \beta) = -\dfrac{b}{a} \cdot \dfrac{\sqrt{b^2 - 4ac}}{a}$

$* \quad \alpha^3 + \beta^3 = (\alpha + \beta)^3 - 3\alpha\beta(\alpha + \beta)$

$\qquad = -\dfrac{b^3}{a^3} + \dfrac{3bc}{a^2} = -\dfrac{b(b^2 - 3ac)}{a^3}$

$* \quad \alpha^4 + \beta^4 = (\alpha^2 + \beta^2)^2 - 2\alpha^2\beta^2$

$\qquad = \left(\dfrac{b^2 - 2ac}{a^2}\right)^2 - \dfrac{2c^2}{a^2}$

(b) Transformation of Equations

Let α, β be the roots of the equation

$$ax^2 + bx + c = 0. \qquad \qquad \dots(1)$$

To find the equation whose roots are

(i) Negative of the roots of (1)

The required roots are $-\alpha, -\beta$.

This is effected by putting $y = -\alpha = -x$.

or $\quad x = -y$ in (1)

$\therefore \quad ay^2 - by + c = 0$

or $\quad ax^2 - bx + c = 0 \qquad \qquad \dots(2)$

(ii) Reciprocal of the roots of (1)

The required roots are $\dfrac{1}{\alpha}, \dfrac{1}{\beta}$.

This is effected by putting $y = \dfrac{1}{\alpha} = \dfrac{1}{x}$.

or $\quad x = \dfrac{1}{y}$ in (1)

$\dfrac{a}{y^2} + \dfrac{b}{y} + c = 0$

or $\quad cy^2 + by + a = 0 \qquad \qquad \dots(3)$

Illustration.

If α, β, γ are the roots of the equation $x^3 + qx + r = 0$, then form an equation whose roots are $\dfrac{\beta + \gamma}{\alpha^2}, \dfrac{\gamma + \alpha}{\beta^2}, \dfrac{\alpha + \beta}{\gamma^2}$.

$y = \dfrac{\beta + \gamma}{\alpha^2} = \dfrac{(\alpha + \beta + \gamma) - \alpha}{\alpha^2} = \dfrac{0 - \alpha}{\alpha^2} = -\dfrac{1}{\alpha} = -\dfrac{1}{x}$

Hence put $x = -\dfrac{1}{y}$ in the given equation

$\left(-\dfrac{1}{y}\right)^3 + 9\left(-\dfrac{1}{y}\right) + r = 0$ or $ry^3 - qy^2 - 1 = 0$

(iii) Square of the roots of (1)

The required roots are α^2, β^2.

This is effected by putting $y = \alpha^2 = x^2$

or $\quad x = \sqrt{y}$ in (1)

$ay + c = -b\sqrt{y}$. Square both sides

$a^2y^2 + c^2 + 2acy = b^2y$

or $\quad a^2y^2 + (2ac - b^2)y + c^2 = 0$

(iv) Cube of the roots of (1)

The required roots are α^3, β^3.

This is effected by putting $y = \alpha^3 = x^3$

or $\quad x = y^{1/3}$ in (1)

$\therefore \quad ay^{2/3} + by^{1/3} = -c$. Cube both sides

$a^3y^2 + b^3y + 3aby^{2/3}y^{1/3}(ay^{2/3} + by^{1/3}) = -c^3$

or $\quad a^3y^2 + b^3y + 3aby(-c) = -c^3$

or $\quad a^3y^2 + y(b^3 - 3abc) + c^3 = 0$

(v) Increased by h i.e., $\alpha + h, \beta + h$.

This is effected by putting $y = \alpha + h = x + h$

or by putting $x = y - h$ in the given equation (1)

$\therefore \quad a(y - h)^2 + b(y - h) + c = 0$

$ay^2 + y(b - 2ah) + (ah^2 - bh + c) = 0$

§ 5. The sign of the expression $(x - a)(x - b)$ $(a < b)$

Case I. $(x - a)(x - b) = +$ ive

Above is possible if either both factors are +ive or both − ive.

i.e. if $x - a > 0$, $x - b > 0$ i.e. $x > a$, $x > b$

Hence $\quad x > b \qquad (\because a < b) \qquad \dots(1)$

or $\quad x - a < 0$, $x - b < 0$ i.e. $x < a$, $x < b$

Hence $\quad x < a. \qquad \qquad \dots(2)$

From (1) and (2) we conclude that $(x - a)(x - b)$ is +ive if either $x < a$ or $x > b$ which in other words means that x **does not lie between a and b $(a < b)$. It lies outside.**

Case II. $(x - a)(x - b) = -$ **ive**

Above is possible if one factor is +ive and the other is – ive

Let $x - a = +$ive, $i.e. > 0$, $x - b = -$ive, $i.e. < 0$

∴ $x > a$, $x < b$ or $a < x < b$

$i.e.$ **x lies between a and b, $(a < b)$**

or $x - a = -$ive $i.e. < 0$, $x - b = +$ive $i.e. > 0$

$i.e.$ $x < a$ and $x > b$. This is not possible.

∴ $(x - a)(x - b) = +$ **ive if x does not lie between a and b and is – ive if x lies between a and b.**

$$(x + 3)(x - 5) = [x - (-3)](x - 5)$$
$$a = -3, b = 5 \quad ∴ \quad a < b$$

Above is +ive if x does not lie between – 3 and 5 and is – ive if x lies between – 3 and 5.

***Rule.** Put $(x - a)(x - b) = 0$

∴ Choose $x = a, b$; where $a < b$

In case we have more than two factors like

$$(x + 3)(x + 1) x (x - 2)(x - 3) \ldots$$

Put the given expression equal to zero and find the values of x and write them in ascending order of magnitude $i.e. - 3, - 1, 0, 2$ and 3. Now on the real line as shown below :

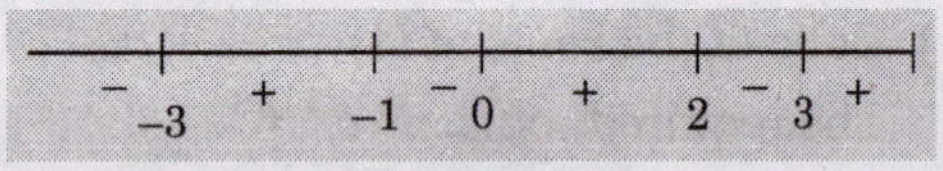

Fig. 1

Rule : Start with extetrme right with +ive sign and move towards left and write opposite signs alternately.

$x > 3$, +ive; $2 < x < 3$, – ive; $0 < x < 2$, +ive; $- 1 < x < 0$, – ive; $- 3 < x < - 1$, +ive; $x < - 3$, – ive

Modulus Function. $|x| = x$ if x is +ive and $|x| = -x$ if x is – ive

∴ $|x - a| = x - a$ if $x - a \geq 0$ or $x \geq a$
$$= -(x - a) \text{ if } x - a < 0 \text{ or } x < a$$

Greatest Integer function.

$[x] = n$ if $n \leq x < n + 1$

For more details **see** chapter on Functions.

§ 6. The sign of the expression $ax^2 + bx + c$.

We consider the following cases :

***Case I.** Let the roots be equal say α, α then

$$ax^2 + bx + c = a(x - \alpha)^2 \qquad \ldots(1)$$

Now for all real values of x, $(x - \alpha)^2$ is always +ive and hence the sign of $ax^2 + bx + c$ is same as that of a.

***Case II.** Let its roots be imaginary say $p + iq$ and $p - iq$ as we know that imaginary roots occur in conjugate pairs. Also in this case $b^2 - 4ac$ is – ive

∴ $ax^2 + bx + c = a[(x - p - iq)(x - p + iq)]$
$$= a[(x - p)^2 + q^2]$$

Now for all real values of x, $[(x - p)^2 + q^2]$ is always +ive and hence the sign of $ax^2 + bx + c$ is same as of a.

Case III. Let the roots be real say α, β ($\alpha < \beta$)

∴ $ax^2 + bx + c = a(x - \alpha)(x - \beta)$

Now for all values of x such that $x < \alpha$ or $x > \beta$ $i.e.$ for all those real values of x which do not lie between α and β ($\alpha < \beta$) the sign of $(x - \alpha)(x - \beta)$ is always +ive (§ 5). Hence the sign of $ax^2 + bx + c$ is same as of a.

If, however, x lies between the roots α and β then $(x - \alpha)(x - \beta)$ is – ive (§ 5). Hence the sign of $ax^2 + bx + c$ is opposite to the sign of a.

From cases I, II and III, we conclude :

For all real values of x, the expression $ax^2 + bx + c$ has the same sign as that of a except when the roots of the equation $ax^2 + bx + c = 0$ are real and unequal, and x has a value lying between them. **[Case III]**

Examples : (i) The sign of $x^2 + 4x + 8$ is positive for all real x since

$$b^2 - 4ac = 16 - 32 < 0 \text{ and } a = 1 > 0$$

(See case II of § 6)

(ii) The sign of $- 2x^2 + 7x - 11$ is – ive for all real x since

$$b^2 - 4ac = 49 - 4(-2)(-11) = - 39 < 0$$

and $a = - 2 < 0$ (See case II of § 6)

(iii) The sign of $x^2 + 5x + 6 = (x + 2)(x + 3)$ is

+ ive if either $x < - 3$ or $x > - 2$ and – ive if $- 3 < x < - 2$ (See case II of § 6)

(iv) The sign of $- 9x^2 + 12x - 4 = -(3x - 2)^2$

is – ive for all real x. (See case I of § 6)

Sign of coefficient determining the sign of both real roots of $ax^2 + bx + c = 0$

S.No.	Sign of coefficient	Sign of roots (real), $D > 0$
1	a, b, c are of same sign	Both roots are negative
2	a, c are of same sign	Both roots are positive.
3	a, c are of opposite sign	Both roots are of opposite sign.

§ 7. Common roots.

If α is a common root of the quadratics

$$f_1(x) = a_1 x^2 + b_1 x + c_1 = 0$$
$$f_2(x) = a_2 x^2 + b_2 x + c_2 = 0,$$

then α will satisfy both and by the method of cross multiplication,

$$\frac{\alpha^2}{b_1 c_2 - b_2 c_1} = \frac{\alpha}{c_1 a_2 - c_2 a_1} = \frac{1}{a_1 b_2 - a_2 b_1} = k \text{ (say)}$$

 I II III

The common root is given by

$$\alpha = \frac{\mathrm{I}}{\mathrm{II}} = \frac{\mathrm{II}}{\mathrm{III}}$$

The required condition is given by

$$(\mathrm{II})^2 = (\mathrm{I})\,(\mathrm{III})$$

or $(c_1 a_2 - c_2 a_1)^2 = (b_1 c_2 - b_2 c_1)(a_1 b_2 - a_2 b_1)$

Both the roots be common.

In this case both sum and product will be same

$$\therefore \quad -\frac{b_1}{a_1} = -\frac{b_2}{a_2} \quad \text{and} \quad \frac{c_1}{a_1} = \frac{c_2}{a_2} \quad \text{or} \quad \frac{a_1}{a_2} = \frac{b_1}{b_2} = \frac{c_1}{c_2}$$

Note. If the coefficient of x^2 in both the equations be unity or same then the value of common roots is obtained by subtracting their equations.

e.g., Let $x^2 + ax + b = 0$ and $x^2 + bx + a = 0$

have common root then, by subtracting

$$x(a - b) + (b - a) = 0$$

$\therefore \quad x = 1$ is common root which will satisfy both the equations and hence $1 + a + b = 0$

$\therefore \quad a + b = -1$

§ 8. Inequalities

(a) $x^2 > a^2$ or $(x^2 - a^2) = + \text{ive}$

or $[x - (-a)](x - a) + \text{ive}$

If $x < -a$ or $x > a$

(b) $x^2 < a^2$ if $-a < x < a$

(c) $a^2 < x^2 < b^2$ **Double inequality**

$\therefore \quad a < x < b$ or $-b < x < -a$ **(Note)**

§ 9. Certain important definitions.

1. **Identity :** A quardratic equation
$ax^2 + bx + c = 0$ is satisfied by only two values of x. However if it is satisfied by more than two values of x, then it is called an identity and in this case it is satisfied by every value of x in the domain of x. Also in this case $a = 0, b = 0, c = 0$. Consider the equation

$$(x - 2)^2 - (x^2 - 4x + 4) = 0.$$

It is satisfied by all values of x and it reduces to the form $0x^2 + 0x + 0 = 0$ i.e. $a = 0, b = 0, c = 0$.

2. If $f(a)$ and $f(b)$ are of opposite signs then at least one or in general odd number of roots of the equation $f(x) = 0$ lie between a and b.

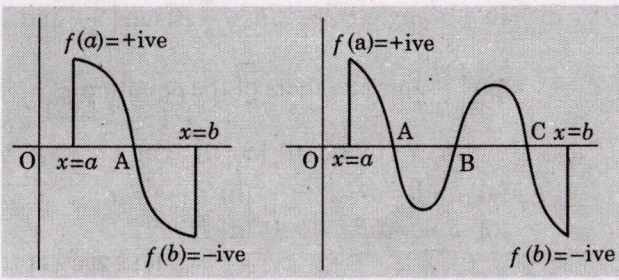

Fig. 2

3. If $f(a) = f(b)$ then there exists a point c between a and b such that $f'(c) = 0, a < c < b$.

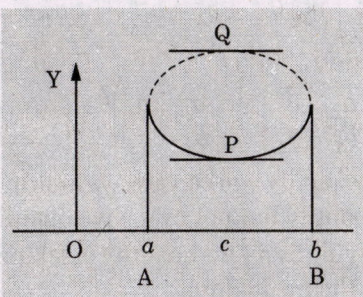

Fig. 3

As is clear from the figure, in either case there is a point P or Q at $x = c$ where tangent is parallel to x-axis i.e. $f'(x) = 0$ at $x = c$.

4. If $f(a)$ and $f(b)$ are of the same sign then either no root or an even number of roots will exist which either lie between a and b or lie outside a and b. Both at P and Q, $y = f(x) = 0$ and they lie between a and b. But at R and S, $y = f(x) = 0$ and they lie outside a and b as shown :

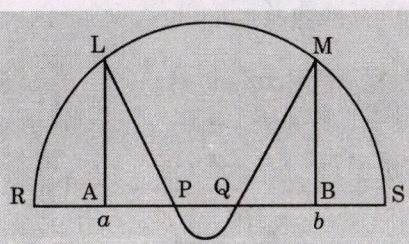

Fig. 4

5. Imaginary and irrational roots occur in conjugate pairs i.e. if $-3 + 2i$ is a root then $-3 - 2i$ will be the second. Similarly if $5 - 2\sqrt{7}$ is a root then $5 + 2\sqrt{7}$ will also be a root.

6. If $a_0 x^n + a_1 x^{n-1} + a_2 x^{n-2} + a_3 x^{n-3} + \ldots = 0$

$$= a_0 (x - \alpha_1)(x - \alpha_2)(x - \alpha_3)\ldots(x - \alpha_n)$$

$$= a_0 (x^n - S_1 x^{n-1} + S_2 x^{n-2} - S_3 x^{n-3} + \ldots)$$

then $\quad S_1 = -\dfrac{a_1}{a_0}, \quad S_2 = \dfrac{a_2}{a_0},$

$$S_3 = \frac{-a_3}{a_0}, \ldots S_r = (-1)^r \frac{a_r}{a_0},$$

where $S_1 = \Sigma \alpha, S_2 = \Sigma \alpha_1 \alpha_2, S_3 = \Sigma \alpha_1 \alpha_2 \alpha_3$ etc.

If the roots of the equation

$$ax^3 + bx^2 + cx + d = 0 \text{ be } \alpha, \beta, \gamma \text{ then}$$

$\Sigma \alpha = -\dfrac{b}{a}, \Sigma \alpha\beta = \dfrac{c}{a}$, $\alpha\beta\gamma = -\dfrac{d}{a}$ or if the roots of

$ax^4 + bx^3 + cx^2 + dx + e = 0$ be $\alpha, \beta, \gamma, \delta$ then

$$\Sigma \alpha = -\frac{b}{a}, \quad \Sigma \alpha\beta = \frac{c}{a},$$

$$\Sigma \alpha\beta\gamma = -\frac{d}{a}, \quad \alpha\beta\gamma\delta = \frac{e}{a}.$$

§10.* Lagrange's Identity.

$$(a_1^2 + a_2^2 + a_3^2)(b_1^2 + b_2^2 + b_3^2) - (a_1 b_1 + a_2 b_2 + a_3 b_3)^2$$

$$= (a_1 b_2 - a_2 b_1)^2 + (a_2 b_3 - a_3 b_2)^2 + (a_3 b_1 - a_1 b_3)^2$$

$$= \begin{vmatrix} a_1 & a_2 \\ b_1 & b_2 \end{vmatrix}^2 + \begin{vmatrix} a_2 & a_3 \\ b_2 & b_3 \end{vmatrix}^2 + \begin{vmatrix} a_3 & a_1 \\ b_3 & b_1 \end{vmatrix}^2$$

1. In an inequality you can always multiply or divide by a +ive quantity but not by a – ive quantity.

   Multiplying by a – ive quantity or taking reciprocal will reverse the inequality.

   e.g., $a > b \Rightarrow -a < -b$ or $\dfrac{1}{a} < \dfrac{1}{b}$

2.* $a^2 + b^2 + c^2 - ab - bc - ca$

   $= \dfrac{1}{2}[(a-b)^2 + (b-c)^2 + (c-a)^2] = +$ive always

   It will be zero only when $a - b = 0, b - c = 0, c - a = 0$ i.e. $a = b = c$.

§11.* Ratio Proportion.

We have already stated elsewhere in this book that if $\dfrac{a}{b} = \dfrac{c}{d}$ then each is equal to

$$\dfrac{a+c}{b+d} \quad \text{or} \quad \left(\dfrac{a^2 + c^2}{b^2 + d^2}\right)^{1/2} \quad \text{or} \quad \left(\dfrac{a^3 + c^3}{b^3 + d^3}\right)^{1/3}$$

$$\text{or} \quad \left(\dfrac{ac}{bd}\right)^{1/2} \quad \text{or} \quad \dfrac{pa^n + qc^n}{pb^n + qd^n} \quad \text{and so on.}$$

We can also have minus sign in place of plus and we can have as many ratios as we like instead of only two.

§12. Remainder Theorem :

If a polynomial is divided by $x - \alpha$ then the remainder is $f(\alpha)$

∴ $f(x) = (x - \alpha) \phi(x) + R$

∴ $f(\alpha) = 0 + R$

Factor Theorem

If $R = 0$ i.e., $f(\alpha) = 0$ then $f(x) = (x - \alpha)\Phi(x)$ i.e. $f(x)$ is divisible by $x - \alpha$.

In case α be a **double root of** $f(x) = 0$ then both $f(\alpha)$ and $f'(\alpha)$ are equal to 0.

§13. Cubic Equation $ax^3 + bx^2 + cx + d = 0$

If it roots be α, β, γ then

$$S_1 = \Sigma \alpha = -\dfrac{b}{a}, \ S_2 = \Sigma \alpha\beta = \dfrac{c}{a}, \ S_3 = \alpha\beta\gamma = -\dfrac{d}{a}$$

§14. Biquadratic Equation

$$ax^4 + bx^3 + cx^2 + dx + e = 0$$

$$S_1 = \Sigma\alpha = -\dfrac{b}{a}$$

$$S_2 = \Sigma\alpha\beta = (\alpha + \beta)(\gamma + \delta) + \alpha\beta + \gamma\delta = \dfrac{c}{a}$$

$$S_3 = \Sigma\alpha\beta\gamma = \alpha\beta(\gamma + \delta) + \gamma\delta(\alpha + \beta) = -\dfrac{d}{a}$$

$$S_4 = \alpha\beta\gamma\delta = \dfrac{e}{a}$$

Problem Set (1)

Symmetric functions of roots of a quadratic equation.
Formation of quadratic equations with given roots.

In Q. 1 and 2 if α and β are the roots of $ax^2 + bx + c = 0$, find the values of following :

1. (a) $\dfrac{1}{a\alpha + b} + \dfrac{1}{a\beta + b}$ (b)* $\dfrac{\beta}{a\alpha + b} + \dfrac{\alpha}{a\beta + b}$

2. (a) $(a\alpha + b)^{-3} + (a\beta + b)^{-3}$

   (b) $(a\alpha + b)^{-2} + (a\beta + b)^{-2}$

   In Q. 3 and 4 if α and β are the roots of the equation $ax^2 + bx + c = 0$ find the equation whose roots are as given below :

3. (a) $\dfrac{1}{\alpha + \beta}, \dfrac{1}{\alpha} + \dfrac{1}{\beta}$ (b) $\dfrac{\alpha}{\beta}, \dfrac{\beta}{\alpha}$

   (c) $\alpha + \dfrac{1}{\beta}, \beta + \dfrac{1}{\alpha}$

4. (a) $\alpha^2 + \beta^2, \dfrac{1}{\alpha^2} + \dfrac{1}{\beta^2}$ (b) $\dfrac{1}{a\alpha + b}, \dfrac{1}{a\beta + b}$.

5. (a) If $\alpha \neq \beta$, but $\alpha^2 = 5\alpha - 3, \beta^2 = 5\beta - 3$, find the equation whose roots are α/β and β/α.

(b) If α, β are the roots of $x^2 + ax + b = 0$, then prove that $\dfrac{\alpha}{\beta}$ is a root of the equation

$$bx^2 + (2b - a^2)x + b = 0.$$

6. (a) If α and β are the roots of $x^2 - p(x + 1) - c = 0$, show that $(\alpha + 1)(\beta + 1) = 1 - c$. Hence prove that

$$\dfrac{\alpha^2 + 2\alpha + 1}{\alpha^2 + 2\alpha + c} + \dfrac{\beta^2 + 2\beta + 1}{\beta^2 + 2\beta + c} = 1.$$

(b) In a triangle PQR, $\angle R = \dfrac{\pi}{2}$. If $\tan\left(\dfrac{P}{2}\right)$ and $\tan\left(\dfrac{Q}{2}\right)$ are the roots of the equation

$$ax^2 + bx + c = 0, (a \neq 0), \text{ then}$$

(a) $a + b = c$ (b) $b + c = a$

(c) $a + c = b$ (d) $b = c$

(AIEEE 2005; I.I.T. 1999)

(c) If the roots of the equation $x^2 + px - q = 0$ are $\tan 30°$ and $\tan 15°$, then the value of $2 + q - p$ is

(a) 0   (b) 1

(c) 2   (d) 3   **(AIEEE 2006)**

(d) If $\sin \theta$ and $\cos \theta$ are the roots of the equation $lx^2 + mx + n = 0$, then prove that $l^2 - m^2 + 2ln = 0$

(e) If α, β, γ are the roots of the equation $x^3 + ax + b = 0$, then $\dfrac{\alpha^3 + \beta^3 + \gamma^3}{\alpha^2 + \beta^2 + \gamma^2} =$

(a) $\dfrac{3b}{2a}$ (b) $\dfrac{-3b}{2a}$

(c) $3b$ (d) $2a$

7. (a) If one root of the equation $ix^2 - 2(i+1)x + (2-i) = 0$ is $2 - i$, then show that the other root is $-i$.

(b) Find the roots of the quadratic equation $8 \sec^2 x - 6 \sec x + 1 = 0$.

(c) Find the roots of the equation $a(b - 2c)x^2 + b(c - 2a)x + c(a - 2b) = 0$ if $ab + bc + ca = 0$

8. (a) If the roots of the equation $(x - a)(x - b) - k = 0$ be c and d, then prove that the roots of the equation $(x - c)(x - d) + k = 0$, are a and b.

                            (D.C.E. 1998; I.I.T. 1992)

(b) If α, β are the roots of the equation $(x - a)(x - b) + c = 0$ find the roots of the equation $(x - \alpha)(x - \beta) = c$.   **(Roorkee 2000)**

9. (a)* Ramesh and Mahesh solve an equation. In solving Ramesh commits a mistake in constant term and finds the root 8 and 2. Mahesh commits a mistake in the coefficient of x and finds the roots -9 and -1. Find the correct roots.

                              (Bihar C.E.E. 1999)

(b) Two candidates attempt to solve a quadratic of the form $x^2 + px + q = 0$. One starts with a wrong value of p and finds the roots to be 2 and 6. The other starts with a wrong value of q and finds the roots to be $2, -9$. Find the correct roots.

(c)* The coefficient of x in the quadratic equation $x^2 + px + q = 0$ was taken as 17 in place of 13, its roots were found to be -2 and -15. Find the roots of the original equation.

10. (a) Prove that A.M. of the roots of $x^2 - 2ax + b^2 = 0$ is equal to the geometric mean of the roots of the equation $x^2 - 2bx + a^2 = 0$, and vice-versa.

(b)* Let p and q be roots of the equation $x^2 - 2x + A = 0$ and let r and s be the roots of the equation $x^2 - 18x + B = 0$.

If $p < q < r < s$ are in arithmatic progression, then $A = \dots$ and $B = \dots$.   **(I.I.T. Re-ex. 1997)**

11. (a) Given that α, γ are roots of the equation $Ax^2 - 4x + 1 = 0$, and β, δ the roots of the equation $Bx^2 - 6x + 1 = 0$, find the values of A and B such that α, β, γ and δ are in H.P.   **(Roorkee 2000)**

(b)* The number of quadratic equations which are unchanged by squaring their roots is

(i) 2   (ii) 4

(iii) 6   (iv) None of these.

12. (a) If α and β are the roots of the equation $2x^2 - 3x - 6 = 0$, find the equation whose roots are $\alpha^2 + 2$, $\beta^2 + 2$.

(b) The roots of the quadratic equation $8x^2 - 10x + 3 = 0$ are α and β^2 where $\beta^2 > \dfrac{1}{2}$ then the equation whose roots are $(\alpha + i\beta)^{100}$ and $(\alpha - i\beta)^{100}$ is

(a) $x^2 - x + 1 = 0$ (b) $x^2 + x + 1 = 0$

(c) $x^2 - x - 1 = 0$ (d) $x^2 + x - 1 = 0$

13. If α and β are the roots of the equation $x^2 - 2x + 3 = 0$, find the equation whose roots are

(a) $\alpha + 2, \beta + 2$ (b) $\dfrac{\alpha - 1}{\alpha + 1}, \dfrac{\beta - 1}{\beta + 1}$.

14. (a) If α be a root of the equation $4x^2 + 2x - 1 = 0$, prove that $4\alpha^3 - 3\alpha$ is the other root.

(b)* Form a quadratic equation whose roots are $\dfrac{a}{\sqrt{(a)} \pm \sqrt{(a - b)}}$.

(c) α, β are the roots of the equation $x^2 - 2x + 3 = 0$. Determine the equation whose roots are $P = \alpha^3 - 3\alpha^2 + 5\alpha - 2$ and $Q = \beta^3 - \beta^2 + \beta + 5$.

15. Let a, b, c be real numbers with $a \neq 0$ and let α, β be the roots of the equation $ax^2 + bx + c = 0$.

Express the roots of $a^3x^2 + abcx + c^3 = 0$ in terms of α, β.   **(I.I.T. 2001)**

16. (a) If α, β be the roots of $ax^2 + bx + c = 0$ and γ, δ those of $lx^2 + mx + n = 0$, then find the equation whose roots are $\alpha\gamma + \beta\delta$ and $\alpha\delta + \beta\gamma$.

(b)* If $\alpha + \beta = 3$ and $\alpha^3 + \beta^3 = 7$, then α and β are the roots of $9x^2 - 27x + 20 = 0$.

(c) Find a quadratic equation whose roots α and β are connected by the relation

$$\alpha + \beta = 2 \text{ and } \frac{1 - \alpha}{1 + \beta} + \frac{1 - \beta}{1 + \alpha} = 2\left(\frac{4\lambda^2 + 15}{4\lambda^2 - 1}\right)$$

17. (a)* If α, β are the roots of the equation $x^2 - px + q = 0$, then find the equation the roots of which are $(\alpha^2 - \beta^2)(\alpha^3 - \beta^3)$ and $\alpha^3\beta^2 + \alpha^2\beta^3$.

                              (Roorkee 1994)

(b)* If α, β are the roots of the equation $x^2 - bx + c = 0$ then find the equation whose roots are $(\alpha^2 + \beta^2)(\alpha^3 + \beta^3)$ and $\alpha^5\beta^3 + \alpha^3\beta^5 - 2\alpha^4\beta^4$.

(Roorkee 1998)

(c) Find the equation whose roots are $(\alpha + \beta)^2$ and $(\alpha - \beta)^2$, where α and β are the roots of $2x^2 + 2(m+n)x + (m^2 + n^2) = 0$.

18. (a) If α, β be the roots of $x^2 - px + q = 0$ and α', β' be those of $x^2 - p'x + q' = 0$, find the value of $(\alpha - \alpha')^2 + (\beta - \alpha')^2 + (\alpha - \beta')^2 + (\beta - \beta')^2$.

(b) If α and β are the roots of the equation $6x^2 - 6x + 1 = 0$ then prove that

$$1/2(p + q\alpha + r\alpha^2 + s\alpha^3)$$
$$+ 1/2(p + q\beta + r\beta^2 + s\beta^3)$$

is $\dfrac{p}{1} + \dfrac{q}{2} + \dfrac{r}{3} + \dfrac{s}{4}$.

19. (a)* If α, β be the roots of $ax^2 + 2bx + c = 0$ and $\alpha + \delta$, $\beta + \delta$ be those of $Ax^2 + 2Bx + C = 0$, then prove that $\dfrac{b^2 - ac}{B^2 - AC} = \left(\dfrac{a}{A}\right)^2$.

(I.I.T. 2000)

Another form :

The two quadratics $ax^2 + bx + c = 0$ and $lx^2 + mx + n = 0$ have roots α, β and γ, δ respectively. If $\alpha, \beta, \gamma, \delta$ be in A.P. and Δ_1 and Δ_2 be the discriminants of these quadratics, then prove that $\dfrac{\Delta_1}{\Delta_2} = \dfrac{a^2}{l^2}$.

(b) The ratio of the roots of the equation $ax^2 + bx + c = 0$ is same as the ratio of the roots of the equation $Ax^2 + Bx + C = 0$. If D_1 and D_2 are the discriminants of $ax^2 + bx + c = 0$ and $Ax^2 + Bx + C = 0$ respectively, then show that $D_1 : D_2 = b^2 : B^2$

20. Let α, β be the roots of $x^2 - x + p = 0$ and γ, δ be the roots of $x^2 - 4x + q = 0$. If $\alpha, \beta, \gamma, \delta$ are in G.P., then the integral values of p and q respectively, are
(a) $-2, -32$
(b) $-2, 3$
(c) $-6, 3$
(d) $-6, -32$ **(I.I.T. Sc. 2001)**

21. (a) If α and β be the roots of $x^2 + px - q = 0$ and γ, δ the roots of $x^2 + px + r = 0$, prove that
$$(\alpha - \gamma)(\alpha - \delta) = (\beta - \gamma)(\beta - \delta) = q + r.$$

(b) If α and β are the roots of $x^2 + px + 1 = 0$ and γ, δ are the roots of $x^2 + qx + 1 = 0$, show that
$$q^2 - p^2 = (\alpha - \gamma)(\beta - \gamma)(\alpha + \delta)(\beta + \delta)$$

22. (a) If the roots of $px^2 + qx + 2 = 0$ are reciprocals of each other, then
(a) $p = 0$
(b) $p = -2$
(c) $p = \pm 2$
(d) $p = 2$.

(b) Let P, Q, R be defined as
$$P = a^2b + ab^2 - a^2c - ac^2,$$
$$Q = b^2c + bc^2 - a^2b - ab^2$$
$$R = a^2c + c^2a - c^2b - cb^2$$
where a, b, c are all +ive and the equation $Px^2 + Qx + R = 0$ has equal roots then a, b, c are in
(a) A.P.
(b) G.P.
(c) H.P.
(d) None of these

(c) Let α and β are the roots of equation $x^2 + x + 1 = 0$. The equation whose roots are α^{19}, β^7 is
(a) $x^2 - x - 1 = 0$
(b) $x^2 - x + 1 = 0$
(c) $x^2 + x - 1 = 0$
(d) $x^2 + x + 1 = 0$

(Screening 1994)

(d) If $x^2 + x + 1$ is a factor of $ax^3 + bx^2 + cx + d$, then the real root of $ax^3 + bx^2 + cx + d = 0$ is
(a) $-d/a$
(b) d/a
(c) a/d
(d) none of these

23. (a)* Find the condition that the roots of the equation $ax^2 + bx + c = 0$ be such that
(i) One root is n times the other.
(ii) One root is three times the other.
(iii) Both roots are equal.

(b) If one root of the equation $(a^2 - 5a + 3)x^2 + (3a - 1)x + 2 = 0$ be double the other, then the value of a is :
(a) $\dfrac{2}{3}$
(b) $-\dfrac{2}{3}$
(c) $\dfrac{1}{3}$
(d) $-\dfrac{1}{3}$ **(AIEEE 2003)**

24. If the roots of the equation $ax^2 + bx + c = 0$ are of the form $\dfrac{k+1}{k}$ and $\dfrac{k+2}{k+1}$, prove that $(a+b+c)^2 = b^2 - 4ac$.

25. Let a, b, c, d be real numbers in G.P. If u, v, w satisfy the system of equations
$$u + 2v + 3w = 6, 4u + 5v + 6w = 12, 6u + 9v = 4,$$
then show that the roots of the equation
$$\left(\dfrac{1}{u} + \dfrac{1}{v} + \dfrac{1}{w}\right)x^2 + [(b-c)^2 + (c-a)^2 + (d-b)^2]x$$
$$+ u + v + w = 0$$
and $20x^2 + 10(a - d)^2 x - 9 = 0$ are reciprocals of each other. **(I.I.T. 1999)**

26. (a)* If one root of the equation $ax^2 + bx + c = 0$ be the square of the other, then prove that $b^3 + ac^2 + a^2c = 3abc$.

(b) If one root of the equation $x^2 + px + q = 0$ is square of the other, then prove that $p^3 - q(3p - 1) + q^2 = 0$
(Screening 2004)

(c) For the equation $3x^2 + px + 3 = 0$, $p > 0$, if one of the roots is square of the other, then p is equal to

(a) 1/3   (b) 1
(c) 3   (d) 2/3   **(I.I.T. Sc. 2000)**

27. (a) If $x = 2 + 2^{2/3} + 2^{1/3}$, then the value of $x^3 - 6x^2 + 6x$ is ....

(b) If one root of the quadratic equation $ax^2 + bx + c = 0$ is equal to the nth power of the other root, then show that $(ac^n)^{1/(n+1)} + (a^n c)^{1/(n+1)} + b = 0$

28. (a) If the roots of the equation $\dfrac{1}{x+p} + \dfrac{1}{x+q} = \dfrac{1}{r}$ are equal in magnitude but opposite in sign show that $p + q = 2r$ and that the product of the roots is equal to $-\dfrac{1}{2}(p^2 + q^2)$.

(b) If the roots of the equation $3x^2 + 2(k^2 + 1)x + (k^2 - 3k + 2) = 0$ be of opposite signs, then prove that $1 < k < 2$.

29. (a) Solve the equation
$$\dfrac{(x-b)(x-c)}{(a-b)(a-c)} + \dfrac{(x-c)(x-a)}{(b-c)(b-a)} + \dfrac{(x-a)(x-b)}{(c-a)(c-b)} = 1.$$

(b) If the equation
$(k^2 - 5k + 6)x^2 + (k^2 - 3k + 2)x + (k^2 - 4) = 0$
is satisfied by more than two values of x, then determine the value of k.

30. (a) If the sum of the roots of $ax^2 + bx + c = 0$ be equal to sum of their squares prove that $2ac = ab + b^2$.

(b)* If the sum of the roots of the equation $ax^2 + bx + c = 0$ is equal to sum of the squares of their reciprocals, then show that bc^2, ca^2, ab^2 are in A.P. or $\dfrac{c}{b}, \dfrac{b}{a}, \dfrac{a}{c}$ are in H.P.
(Roorkee 2001)

31. (a) α, β are the roots of the equation $\lambda(x^2 - x) + x + 5 = 0$. If λ_1 and λ_2 are the two values of λ for which the roots α, β are connected by the relation $\dfrac{\alpha}{\beta} + \dfrac{\beta}{\alpha} = \dfrac{4}{5}$, find the value of $\dfrac{\lambda_1}{\lambda_2} + \dfrac{\lambda_2}{\lambda_1}$.

(b)* If α, β be the roots of the equation $\lambda^2(x^2 - x) + 2\lambda x + 3 = 0$ and λ_1, λ_2 be the two values of λ for which α and β are connected by the relation $\dfrac{\alpha}{\beta} + \dfrac{\beta}{\alpha} = \dfrac{4}{3}$ then find the equation whose roots are λ_1^2 / λ_2 and λ_2^2 / λ_1.

32. (a) If the ratio of the roots of the equation, $x^2 + px + q = 0$ be equal to ratio of the roots of $x^2 + lx + m = 0$, then prove that $p^2 m = l^2 q$.

(b) If the ratio of the roots of $a_1 x^2 + b_1 x + c_1 = 0$ be equal to the ratio of the roots of $a_2 x^2 + b_2 x + c_2 = 0$, then prove that $\dfrac{a_1}{a_2}, \dfrac{b_1}{b_2}, \dfrac{c_1}{c_2}$ are in G.P.

33. (a) If α, β are the roots of the equation $x + 1 = \lambda x(1 - \lambda x)$ and λ_1, λ_2 be the two values of λ determined from the equation $\dfrac{\alpha}{\beta} + \dfrac{\beta}{\alpha} = \pi - 2$, show that $\dfrac{\lambda_1^2}{\lambda_2^2} + \dfrac{\lambda_2^2}{\lambda_1^2} + 2 = 4\left(\dfrac{\pi + 1}{\pi - 1}\right)^2$.
(J.E.E., W.B. 1993)

(b) If the ratio of the roots of the equation $lx^2 + nx + n = 0$ be $p : q$, then prove that $\sqrt{\dfrac{p}{q}} + \sqrt{\dfrac{q}{p}} + \sqrt{\dfrac{n}{l}} = 0$.

34. (a) Find the value of p for which $x + 1$ is a factor of $x^4 + (p - 3)x^3 - (3p - 5)x^2 + (2p - 9)x + 6$. Find the remaining factors for this value of p.

(b) If $x^2 - 3x + 2$ is a factor of $x^4 - px^2 + q = 0$, prove $p = 5$, $q = 4$.

35. (a) The roots x_1 and x_2 of the equation $x^2 + px + 12 = 0$ possess the property $x_1 - x_2 = 1$. Find the value of p.

(b) Knowing that 2 and 3 are the roots of the equation $2x^3 + mx^2 - 13x + n = 0$, determine m and n and find the third root of the equation.

36. (a)* If $x^2 + \dfrac{x^2}{(x+1)^2} = 3$ and x be real, then prove that $x = \dfrac{1 \pm \sqrt{5}}{4}$.

(b) If $x^2 + x + 1$ is a factor of $ax^3 + bx^2 + cx + d$, then prove that the real root of $ax^3 + bx^2 + cx + d = 0$ is $-d/a$.

(c) If $\alpha + i\beta$ is one of the roots of the equation $x^3 + qx + r = 0$, then 2α is one of the roots of the equation :

(a) $x^3 - qx + r = 0$ (b) $x^3 - qx - r = 0$
(c) $x^3 + qx - r = 0$ (d) none

37. If $x = 2 + i\sqrt{3}$, then find the value of

(a) $4x^2 + 8x + 35$.

(b) If $2 + i\sqrt{3}$ is a root of $x^2 + px + q = 0$ where p, q are real, then $(p, q) = ($..........$)$ **(J.E.E., W.B. 1992)**

38. (a) If $x = 1 + 2i$ then prove that $x^3 + 7x^2 - 13x + 16 = -29$.

(b) Find the quadratic equation one of whose roots is $2 + \sqrt{3}$ and hence find the value of expression $x^3 - 7x^2 + 13x - 2$ for $x = 2 + \sqrt{3}$

(c) Find all the roots of the equation $4x^4 - 24x^3 + 57x^2 + 18x - 45 = 0$ if one of them is $3 + i\sqrt{6}$.

39. (a) Let $\alpha + i\beta; \alpha, \beta \in R$, be a root of the equation $x^3 + qx + r = 0; q, r \in R$. Find a real cubic equation, independent of α and β, whose one root is 2α.
    (Roorkee 1999)

    (b) Find a quadratic equation whose one root is square root of $-47 + 8\sqrt{-3}$. **(J.E.E.W.B. 1995)**

40. Solve the following equations :

    (a) $x^3 - 13x^2 + 15x + 189 = 0$ if one root exceeds other by 2.

    (b)* $x^4 - 2x^3 + 4x^2 + 6x - 21 = 0$ if two of its roots are equal in magnitude but opposite in sign.

    (c) If the sum of two roots of the equation $4x^4 - 8x^3 - 13x^2 + 2x + 3 = 0$ is zero, find all its roots.

41. Solve : $x^4 - 2x^2 + 8x - 3 = 0$

42.* If $1, a_1, a_2, \ldots\ldots a_{n-1}$ are the n, nth roots of unity, then show that $(1 - a_1)(1 - a_2)(1 - a_3)\ldots(1 - a_{n-1}) = n$.
    (M.N.R. 1992)

43. (a)* If α and β be the roots of the equation $x^2 - ax + b = 0$ and $V_n = \alpha^n + \beta^n$, then show that $V_{n+1} = aV_n - bV_{n-1}$. Hence obtain the value of $\alpha^5 + \beta^5$.

    (b)* If α, β are the roots of $x^2 + px + q = 0$ and also of $x^{2n} + p^n x^n + q^n = 0$ and if $\dfrac{\alpha}{\beta}, \dfrac{\beta}{\alpha}$ are the roots of $x^n + 1 + (x + 1)^n = 0$, then prove that n must be an even integer. **(J.E.E.W.B. 1992)**

44. Let $f(x) = Ax^2 + Bx + C$ where A, B, C are real numbers. Prove that if $f(x)$ is an integer whenever x is an integer, then the numbers $2A, A + B$ and C are all integers. Conversely, prove that if the numbers $2A, A + B$ and C are all intergers then $f(x)$ is an integer whenever x is an integer. **(I.I.T. 1998)**

45. (a)* Let a, b, c be real. If $ax^2 + bx + c = 0$ has two real roots α and β, where $\alpha < -1$ and $\beta > 1$, then show that $1 + \dfrac{c}{a} + \left|\dfrac{b}{a}\right| < 0$.
    (I.I.T. 1995)

    (b) If the roots of the equation $x^2 - 2ax + a^2 + a - 3 = 0$ are real and less than 3, then
    (a) $a < 2$ (b) $2 \le a \le 3$
    (c) $3 < a \le 4$ (d) $a > 4$ **(I.I.T. 1999)**

(c) Find the values of real parameter 'a' for which the equation $(\tan^2\theta + 1)^2 + 4a(\tan^2\theta + 1)\tan\theta + 16\tan^2\theta = 0$ has four distinct roots in $(0, \pi/2)$

46. (a)* If $a + b + c = 0$, then the quadratic equation $3ax^2 + 2bx + c = 0$ has at least one root in $(0, 1)$.
    (D.C.E. 1998; M.N.R. 1992)

    (b) If $2a + 3b + 6c = 0$ $(a, b, c \in R)$ then prove that the quadratic equation $ax^2 + bx + c = 0$ has at least one root in $[0, 1]$.

47. (a) If $b > a$, then the equation $(x - a)(x - b) - 1 = 0$, has
    (a) both roots in $[a, b]$
    (b) both roots in $(-\infty, a)$
    (c) both roots in $(b, +\infty)$
    (d) one root in $(-\infty, a)$ and other in $(b, +\infty)$
    (I.I.T. Sc. 2000)

    (b) If α and β $(\alpha < \beta)$, are the roots of the equation $x^2 + bx + c = 0$, where $c < 0 < b$, then
    (a) $0 < \alpha < \beta$ (b) $\alpha < 0 < \beta < |\alpha|$
    (c) $\alpha < \beta < 0$ (d) $\alpha < 0 < |\alpha| < \beta$
    (I.I.T. Sc. 2000)

48. (a) Prove that the value of λ for which $2x^2 - 2(2\lambda + 1)x + \lambda(\lambda + 1) = 0$ may have one root less than λ and other root greater than λ are given by $\lambda > 0$ or $\lambda < -1$.

    (b)* For the equation $x^2 - (k + 1)x + (k^2 + k - 8) = 0$ if one root is greater than 2 and other is less than 2, then prove that k lies between -2 and 3.

49. (a)* If a, b, c are real numbers, $a \neq 0$. If α is a root of $a^2x^2 + bx + c = 0$, β is a root of $a^2x^2 - bx - c = 0$ and $0 < \alpha < \beta$, then the equation $a^2x^2 + 2bx + 2c = 0$ has a root γ that always lies between α and β.

    (b) If 1 lies between the roots of the equation $3x^2 - 3\sin\alpha\, x - 2\cos^2\alpha = 0$ then α lies in the interval
    (a) $\left(0, \dfrac{\pi}{2}\right)$ (b) $\left(\dfrac{\pi}{12}, \dfrac{\pi}{2}\right)$
    (c) $\left(\dfrac{\pi}{6}, \dfrac{5\pi}{6}\right)$ (d) $\left(\dfrac{\pi}{6}, \dfrac{\pi}{2}\right) \cup \left(\dfrac{\pi}{2}, \dfrac{5\pi}{6}\right)$

50. Let $-1 \le p \le 1$. Show that the equation $4x^3 - 3x - p = 0$ has a unique root in the interval $[1/2, 1]$ and identify it.
    (I.I.T. 2001)

Solutions to Problem Set (1)

1. Since α and β are the roots of
$$ax^2 + bx + c = 0$$
$$a\alpha^2 + b\alpha + c = 0 \quad \text{or} \quad a\alpha + b = -\dfrac{c}{\alpha}.$$
$$a\beta^2 + b\beta + c = 0 \quad \text{or} \quad a\beta + b = -\dfrac{c}{\beta}.$$

Also $\alpha + \beta = -\dfrac{b}{a}$, $\alpha\beta = \dfrac{c}{a}$.

(a) $\dfrac{1}{a\alpha + b} + \dfrac{1}{a\beta + a} = -\dfrac{\alpha}{c} - \dfrac{\beta}{c}$

$$= -\dfrac{1}{c}(\alpha + \beta) = -\dfrac{1}{c}\left(-\dfrac{b}{a}\right) = \dfrac{b}{ac}.$$

(b) $\dfrac{\beta}{a\alpha + b} + \dfrac{\alpha}{a\beta + b} = -\dfrac{\alpha\beta}{c} - \dfrac{\alpha\beta}{c} = -\dfrac{2}{c}\cdot\dfrac{c}{a} = -\dfrac{2}{a}.$

2. (a) $(a\alpha + b)^{-3} + (a\beta + b)^{-3} = -\dfrac{\alpha^3 + \beta^3}{c^3}$

$$= -\dfrac{1}{c^3}[(\alpha + \beta)^3 - 3\alpha\beta(\alpha + \beta)] = \dfrac{b^3 - 3abc}{a^3 c^3}$$

(b) $(a\alpha + b)^{-2} + (a\beta + b)^{-2}$

$$= \dfrac{\alpha^2 + \beta^2}{c^2} = \dfrac{1}{c^2}[(\alpha + \beta)^2 - 2\alpha\beta] = \dfrac{b^2 - 2ac}{a^2 c^2}$$

3. $\alpha + \beta = -\dfrac{b}{a}$, $\alpha\beta = \dfrac{c}{a}$

(a) Sum $= \dfrac{1}{\alpha + \beta} + \dfrac{\alpha + \beta}{\alpha\beta} = -\dfrac{a}{b} - \dfrac{b}{c} = -\dfrac{(ac + b^2)}{bc}$

Product $= \dfrac{1}{\alpha + \beta}\cdot\dfrac{\alpha + \beta}{\alpha\beta} = \dfrac{1}{\alpha\beta} = \dfrac{a}{c}$

∴ Equation is $x^2 - Sx + P = 0$

or $x^2 + \dfrac{ac + b^2}{bc}x + \dfrac{a}{c} = 0$

or $bc\,x^2 + (b^2 + ac)x + ab = 0$

(b) Ans. $acx^2 - (b^2 - 2ac)x + ac = 0$.

(c) Ans. $acx^2 + b(a + c)x + (a + c)^2 = 0$.

4. (a) $S = \alpha^2 + \beta^2 + \dfrac{1}{\alpha^2} + \dfrac{1}{\beta^2} = (\alpha^2 + \beta^2)\left(1 + \dfrac{1}{\alpha^2\beta^2}\right)$

$$= \dfrac{b^2 - 2ac}{a^2}\cdot\dfrac{a^2 + c^2}{c^2}.$$ **(Page 201)**

$$P = (\alpha^2 + \beta^2)\cdot\dfrac{(\alpha^2 + \beta^2)}{\alpha^2\beta^2} = \dfrac{(b^2 - 2ac)^2}{a^2 c^2}$$

∴ Equation is :

$$a^2 c^2 x^2 - (b^2 - 2ac)(a^2 + c^2)x + (b^2 - 2ac)^2 = 0.$$

(b) By Q. 1, the roots are $-\dfrac{\alpha}{c}$, $-\dfrac{\beta}{c}$

∴ $ac\,x^2 - bx + 1 = 0$.

5. (a) By virtue of the given relations we can say that α and β satisfy $x^2 = 5x - 3$ or they are the roots of

$x^2 - 5x + 3 = 0$ ∴ $\alpha + \beta = 5$, $\alpha\beta = 3$

Now $S = 19/3$, $P = 1$ and the equation is $3x^2 - 19x + 3 = 0$.

(b) $\alpha + \beta = -a$, $\alpha\beta = b$ and we have to prove that

$$b\left(\dfrac{\alpha}{\beta}\right)^2 + (2b - a^2)\dfrac{\alpha}{\beta} + b = 0$$

or $b(\alpha^2 + \beta^2) + (2b - a^2)\alpha\beta = 0$

Now put the values of $\alpha\beta$ and $\alpha^2 + \beta^2$.

6. (a) The given equation is $x^2 - px - (p + c) = 0$

∴ $\alpha + \beta = p$, $\alpha\beta = -(p + c)$

$(\alpha + 1)(\beta + 1) = \alpha\beta + (\alpha + \beta) + 1$

$= -p - c + p + 1 = 1 - c.$ ...(1)

Again $\dfrac{\alpha^2 + 2\alpha + 1}{\alpha^2 + 2\alpha + c} + \dfrac{\beta^2 + 2\beta + 1}{\beta^2 + 2\beta + c}$

$$= \dfrac{(\alpha + 1)^2}{(\alpha + 1)^2 - (1 - c)} + \dfrac{(\beta + 1)^2}{(\beta + 1)^2 - (1 - c)}$$

$$= \dfrac{(\alpha + 1)^2}{(\alpha + 1)^2 - (\alpha + 1)(\beta + 1)}$$

$$+ \dfrac{(\beta + 1)^2}{(\beta + 1)^2 - (\alpha + 1)(\beta + 1)}, \text{ by (1)}$$

$$= \dfrac{\alpha + 1}{\alpha - \beta} + \dfrac{\beta + 1}{\beta - \alpha} = \dfrac{(\alpha + 1) - (\beta + 1)}{\alpha - \beta} = 1.$$

(b) Ans. (a). $t_1 + t_2 = -\dfrac{b}{a}$, $t_1 t_2 = \dfrac{c}{a}$

where $t_1 = \tan\dfrac{P}{2}$, $t_2 = \tan\dfrac{Q}{2}$

$P + Q = \pi - R = \dfrac{\pi}{2}$ as $R = \dfrac{\pi}{2}$

∴ $\dfrac{P}{2} + \dfrac{Q}{2} = \dfrac{\pi}{4}$

$\dfrac{t_1 + t_2}{1 - t_1 t_2} = \tan\dfrac{\pi}{4} = 1$

or $-\dfrac{b}{a} = 1 - \dfrac{c}{a} \Rightarrow a + b = c$

(c) Ans. (d).

$30° + 15° = 45°$

(d) $\sin\theta + \cos\theta = -m/l$, $\sin\theta\cos\theta = n/l$

Squaring, we have

$$1 + \dfrac{2n}{l} = \dfrac{m^2}{l^2}$$

∴ $l^2 - m^2 + 2ln = 0$

(e) Ans. (a).

$\alpha + \beta + \gamma = 0$, as coefficient of $x^2 = 0$

∴ $\alpha^3 + \beta^3 + \gamma^3 = 3\alpha\beta\gamma = -3b$

$\alpha^2 + \beta^2 + \gamma^2 = (\Sigma\alpha)^2 - 2\Sigma\alpha\beta = 0 - 2a = -2a$

∴ $\dfrac{\Sigma\alpha^3}{\Sigma\alpha^2} = \dfrac{-3b}{-2a} = \dfrac{3b}{2a} \Rightarrow$ (a).

7. (a) **One is tempted to say** that if one root is $2 - i$, the other root will be $2 + i$ as complex roots occur in conjugate pairs. This is so only when the coefficients are real. Here the coefficients are not real. Hence if other root is α, then

$\alpha (2 - i) = \text{Product} = \dfrac{2 - i}{i}$

$\therefore \quad \alpha = \dfrac{1}{i} = -i$ **See note on P. 203**

(b) No roots.

On solving, $\sec x = \dfrac{1}{2}$ or $\dfrac{1}{4}$

$\Rightarrow \quad \cos x = 2$ or   4

Both the values are not possible.

(c) If $f(x) = 0$ be the given equation, then

$f(1) = a(b - 2c) + b(c - 2a) + c(a - 2b)$

$\qquad = -\Sigma ab = 0 \quad \because \ \Sigma ab = 0$

Hence 1 is a root of $f(x) = 0$

If the other root be α, then

$1 . \alpha = \text{Product of roots} = \dfrac{c(a - 2b)}{a(b - 2c)}$

Hence 1 and $\dfrac{c}{a}\dfrac{a - 2b}{b - 2c}$ are the required roots.

8. (a) By given condition,

$\qquad (x - a)(x - b) - k = (x - c)(x - d)$

or $\qquad (x - c)(x - d) + k = (x - a)(x - b)$

Above shows that the roots of

$\qquad (x - c)(x - d) + k = 0$ are a and b.

(b) Proceed as in part (a). Roots are a, b.

9. (a) Take correct sum $= 8 + 2 = 10$ from Ramesh

Take correct product $= -9 \times -1 = 9$ from Mahesh

$\therefore \quad x^2 - Sx + P = 0$ or $x^2 - 10x + 9 = 0$

$\therefore \quad$ Correct roots are 9, 1.

(b) Proceed as above $p = 7, q = 12$, roots $-3, -4$.

(c) Here $q = -2 \times -15 = 30$, correct value of $p = 13$

$\therefore \quad x^2 + 13x + 30 = 0$ or $(x + 10)(x + 3) = 0$

$\therefore \quad$ Roots are $-10, -3$.

10. (a) $\alpha + \beta = 2a$ or $\dfrac{\alpha + \beta}{2} = a$,

$\gamma \delta = a^2 \qquad \therefore \quad \sqrt{\gamma \delta} = a$.

$\therefore \quad$ A.M. of roots of 1st = G.M. of roots of 2nd.

(b) Let the four numbers in A.P. be

$\begin{array}{cccc} a - 3d & a - d & a + d & a + 3d \\ p & q & r & s \end{array}$

$\qquad\qquad\qquad p < q < r < s$

$p + q = 2, \qquad r + s = 18$

$pq = A, \qquad rs = B$ given

$\therefore \quad p + q + r + s = 4a = 20 \ \therefore \ a = 5$

$\therefore \quad p + q = 2 \Rightarrow 10 - 4d = 2$

$r + s = 18 \Rightarrow 10 + 4d = 18 \ \therefore \ d = 2$

Hence the numbers are $-1, 3, 7, 11$ i.e., p, q, r, s.

$pq = A = -3, \quad rs = B = 77$.

11. (a) $\alpha, \beta, \gamma, \delta$ are in H.P. $\Rightarrow \dfrac{1}{\alpha}, \dfrac{1}{\beta}, \dfrac{1}{\gamma}, \dfrac{1}{\delta}$ are in A.P. and

they may be taken as $a - 3d, a - d, a + d, a + 3d$. Replacing x by $1/x$ we get the equation whose roots are $\dfrac{1}{\alpha}, \dfrac{1}{\beta}, \dfrac{1}{\gamma}, \dfrac{1}{\delta}$ etc.

$\therefore \quad x^2 - 4x + A = 0$ has roots $a - 3d, a + d$,

$\qquad x^2 - 6x + B = 0$ has roots $a - d, a + 3d$

Sum $= 2(a - d) = 4, \ 2(a + d) = 6$

$\therefore \quad a = 5/2, \ d = 1/2$.

Product $= (a - 3d)(a + d) = A = 3$.

$\qquad (a - d)(a + 3d) = B = 8$.

(b) $\alpha^2 + \beta^2 = \alpha + \beta$ ...(1)

$\qquad \alpha^2 \beta^2 = \alpha \beta$ ...(2)

$\therefore \quad \alpha \beta (\alpha \beta - 1) = 0$

$\therefore \quad \alpha = 0$ or $\beta = 0$, or $\alpha \beta = 1$

When $\alpha = 0$ then $\beta^2 - \beta = 0$ by (1) $\therefore \ \beta = 0, 1$

$\therefore \quad$ Roots are 0, 0 or 0, 1. Same roots will be obtained by taking $\beta = 0$

When $\alpha \beta = 1$ then from (1)

$\qquad (\alpha + \beta)^2 - 2\alpha \beta = \alpha + \beta$

Put $t = \alpha + \beta$ and $\alpha \beta = 1$

$\therefore \quad t^2 - t - 2 = 0$ or $(t - 2)(t + 1) = 0$

$\therefore \quad \alpha + \beta = 2$ or -1 and $\alpha \beta = 1$ for both

$\therefore \quad x^2 - 2x + 1 = 0$ or $x^2 + x + 1 = 0$

by using the formula $x^2 - Sx + P = 0$

$\therefore \quad x = 1, 1$ or ω, ω^2.   **See § 2 P. 200**

Thus there are 4 quadratics whose roots $(0, 0)$, $(0, 1), (1, 1), (\omega, \omega^2)$ satisfying the given property.

12. (a) $\alpha + \beta = 3/2, \ \alpha \beta = -6/2 = -3$

$S = \alpha^2 + \beta^2 + 4 = (\alpha + \beta)^2 - 2\alpha \beta + 4 = 49/4$

$P = \alpha^2 \beta^2 + 2(\alpha^2 + \beta^2) + 4$

$\quad = \alpha^2 \beta^2 + 4 + 2[(\alpha + \beta)^2 - 2\alpha \beta] = \dfrac{118}{4}$

$\therefore \quad$ The equation is $x^2 - (49/4)x + (118/4) = 0$

or $\quad 4x^2 - 49x + 118 = 0$.

(b) Ans. (b)

$\qquad f(x) = (2x - 1)(4x - 3) \quad \therefore \ x = \dfrac{1}{2}, \dfrac{3}{4}$

$\therefore \quad \alpha = \dfrac{1}{2}$ and $\beta^2 = \dfrac{3}{4} \left(\beta^2 > \dfrac{1}{2} = \dfrac{2}{4} \right)$

$\alpha + i\beta = \dfrac{1}{2} + \dfrac{i\sqrt{3}}{2} = re^{i\theta} = e^{i\pi/3}$

$\because \quad r = 1 \quad \theta = \dfrac{\pi}{3}$

$\therefore \quad \alpha - i\beta = e^{-i\pi/3}$ (Conjugate)

$(\alpha + i\beta)^{100} = e^{i100\pi/3} = e^{i.33\pi} \cdot e^{i\pi/3} = -e^{i\pi/3}$

as $e^{i33\pi} = e^{i.32\pi} \cdot e^{i\pi} = 1 . (-1) = -1$

$(\alpha - i\beta)^{100} = -e^{-i\pi/3}$ (Conjugate)

Sum $= -(e^{i\pi/3} + e^{-i\pi/3}) = -2\cos\dfrac{\pi}{3} = -1$

Product $= 1$

∴ Required equation is $x^2 + x + 1 = 0$

13. (a) $x^2 - 6x + 11 = 0$

(b) $3x^2 - 2x + 1 = 0$.

14. (a) $4x^2 + 2x - 1 = 0$.

∴ $\alpha + \beta = -\dfrac{1}{2}, \ \alpha\beta = -\dfrac{1}{4}$ ...(1)

Also $4\alpha^2 + 2\alpha - 1 = 0$ as α is a root and we have to prove that

$\beta = 4\alpha^3 - 3\alpha$.

Now $4\alpha^3 - 3\alpha = 4\alpha^2 \cdot \alpha - 3\alpha$

$= \alpha(1 - 2\alpha) - 3\alpha$

$= -2\alpha^2 - 2\alpha = -\dfrac{1}{2}[4\alpha^2 + 4\alpha]$

$= -\dfrac{1}{2}[1 - 2\alpha + 4\alpha]$

$= -\dfrac{1}{2}(1 + 2\alpha) = -\dfrac{1}{2} - \alpha = \beta$

∵ $\alpha + \beta = -\dfrac{1}{2}$, by (1).

Hence the other root β is $4\alpha^3 - 3\alpha$.

(b) On rationalizing, the roots are

$\dfrac{a}{b}[\sqrt{a} \pm \sqrt{a-b}]$ ∴ $S = \dfrac{2a\sqrt{a}}{b}, \ P = \dfrac{a^2}{b}$

Ans. $bx^2 - 2a\sqrt{a}\,x + a^2 = 0$.

(c) $\alpha^2 - 2\alpha + 3 = 0$ ...(1)

∴ $\alpha^2 = 2\alpha - 3, \ \alpha^3 = 2\alpha^2 - 3\alpha$

∴ $P = (2\alpha^2 - 3\alpha) - 3\alpha^2 + 5\alpha - 2$

$= -\alpha^2 + 2\alpha - 2 = 3 - 2 = 1$, by (1)

Similarly $Q = 2$ ∴ $S = 3, P = 2$

Reqd. eq. is $x^2 - 3x + 2 = 0$.

15. $\alpha + \beta = -\dfrac{b}{a}, \ \alpha\beta = \dfrac{c}{a}$ ...(1)

If α', β' be the roots of the second equation, then

$\alpha' + \beta' = -\dfrac{abc}{a^3} = -\dfrac{bc}{a^2}$

$= -\dfrac{b}{a} \cdot \dfrac{c}{a} = (\alpha + \beta)\alpha\beta$ by (1) ...(2)

$\alpha'\beta' = \dfrac{c^3}{a^3} = (\alpha\beta)^3$ by (1)

∴ $(\alpha' - \beta')^2 = (\alpha' + \beta')^2 - 4\alpha'\beta'$

$= (\alpha + \beta)^2 \alpha^2\beta^2 - 4\alpha^3\beta^3$

$= \alpha^2\beta^2[(\alpha + \beta)^2 - 4\alpha\beta] = \alpha^2\beta^2(\alpha - \beta)^2$

∴ $\alpha' - \beta' = (\alpha - \beta)\alpha\beta$ ...(3)

Adding and subtracting (2) and (3), the required roots are $2\alpha' = \alpha\beta \cdot 2\alpha, \ 2\beta' = \alpha\beta \cdot 2\beta$ or $\alpha' = \alpha^2\beta, \ \beta' = \alpha\beta^2$.

16. (a) $\alpha + \beta = -b/a, \ \alpha\beta = c/a, \ \gamma + \delta = -m/l, \ \gamma\delta = n/l$

$\alpha^2 + \beta^2 = (\alpha + \beta)^2 - 2\alpha\beta = \dfrac{b^2 - 2ac}{a^2}$,

$\gamma^2 + \delta^2 = \dfrac{m^2 - 2nl}{l^2}$

$S = (\alpha\gamma + \beta\delta) + (\alpha\delta + \beta\gamma) = \alpha(\gamma + \delta) + \beta(\gamma + \delta)$

$= (\alpha + \beta)(\gamma + \delta) = \dfrac{bm}{al}$

$P = (\alpha\gamma + \beta\delta)(\alpha\delta + \beta\gamma)$

$= \alpha^2\gamma\delta + \alpha\beta\delta^2 + \alpha\beta\gamma^2 + \beta^2\gamma\delta$

$= (\alpha^2 + \beta^2)\gamma\delta + \alpha\beta(\gamma^2 + \delta^2)$

$= \dfrac{n}{l}\left(\dfrac{b^2 - 2ac}{a^2}\right) + \dfrac{c}{a}\left(\dfrac{m^2 - 2nl}{l^2}\right)$

$= \dfrac{ln(b^2 - 2ac) + ac(m^2 - 2nl)}{a^2 l^2}$

$= \dfrac{b^2 nl + m^2 ac - 4acnl}{a^2 l^2}$

∴ Required equation is $x^2 - Sx + P = 0$

(b) Prove yourself. Find $\alpha\beta$ from $\alpha^3 + \beta^3 = 7$.

(c) $\alpha + \beta = 2$ and let $\alpha\beta = p$

∴ Equation is $x^2 - 2x + p = 0$ ...(1)

We have to find the value of p.

Now $\dfrac{1-\alpha}{1+\beta} + \dfrac{1-\beta}{1+\alpha} = \dfrac{(1-\alpha^2) + (1-\beta^2)}{1 + (\alpha + \beta) + p}$

or $\dfrac{2 - (\alpha^2 + \beta^2)}{1 + 2 + p} = \dfrac{2 - \{(\alpha + \beta)^2 - 2\alpha\beta\}}{3 + p}$

or $\dfrac{2 - 4 + 2p}{3 + p}$ or $\dfrac{2(p-1)}{p+3} = 2\left(\dfrac{4\lambda^2 + 15}{4\lambda^2 - 1}\right)$

or $\dfrac{p-1}{p+3} = \dfrac{4\lambda^2 + 15}{4\lambda^2 - 1}$

or $p[(4\lambda^2 - 1) - (4\lambda^2 + 15)]$

$= 3(4\lambda^2 + 15) + (4\lambda^2 - 1)$

or $-16p = 16\lambda^2 + 44 = 4(4\lambda^2 + 11)$

∴ $p = -\dfrac{(4\lambda^2 + 11)}{4}$

Putting for p in (1) we get the required equation as

$x^2 - 2x - \dfrac{(4\lambda^2 + 11)}{4} = 0$

17. (a) $\alpha + \beta = p, \ \alpha\beta = q$ ...(1)

If the given roots be A and B, then

$A = (\alpha - \beta)^2 (\alpha + \beta)(\alpha^2 + \beta^2 + \alpha\beta)$

$= (p^2 - 4q)p(p^2 - q) = p[p^4 - 5p^2 q + 4q^2]$.

$B = \alpha^2\beta^2(\alpha + \beta) = q^2 p$

∴ $S = A + B = p[p^4 - 5p^2 q + 5q^2]$

$P = p^2 q^2(p^4 - 5p^2 q + 4q^2)$

The required equation is $t^2 - St + P = 0$

(b) $\alpha + \beta = b$, $\alpha\beta = c \Rightarrow \alpha^2 + \beta^2 = b^2 - 2c$

$\qquad \alpha^3 + \beta^3 = (\alpha + \beta)^3 - 3\alpha\beta(\alpha + \beta) = b^3 - 3bc$

If p, q be the roots, then

$\qquad p = (\alpha^2 + \beta^2)(\alpha^3 + \beta^3) = (b^2 - 2c)(b^3 - 3bc)$

and $q = \alpha^3\beta^3(\alpha^2 + \beta^2) - 2\alpha^4\beta^4 = c^3[b^2 - 2c - 2c]$

$\qquad = c^3[b^2 - 4c]$

∴ Required equation is $x^2 - Sx + P = 0$, where

$\qquad S = p + q$ and $P = pq$.

(c) $\alpha + \beta = -(m + n)$, $\alpha\beta = \dfrac{m^2 + n^2}{2}$

$(\alpha - \beta)^2 = (\alpha + \beta)^2 - 4\alpha\beta = (m + n)^2 - 2(m^2 + n^2)$

$\qquad = -(m^2 + n^2 - 2mn) = -(m - n)^2$

and $(\alpha + \beta)^2 = (m + n)^2$.

∴ $S = (\alpha + \beta)^2 + (\alpha - \beta)^2$

$\qquad\qquad = (m + n)^2 - (m - n)^2 = 4mn$

$\qquad P = (\alpha + \beta)^2 (\alpha - \beta)^2$

$\qquad = -(m + n)^2 (m - n)^2 = -(m^2 - n^2)^2$

∴ Required equation is

$\qquad x^2 - 4mnx - (m^2 - n^2)^2 = 0$.

18. (a) On simplification, the given expression

$\qquad = 2(\alpha^2 + \beta^2 + \alpha'^2 + \beta'^2) - 2(\alpha + \beta)(\alpha' + \beta')$

$\qquad = 2[p^2 - 2q + p'^2 - 2q' - pp']$.

(b) $\alpha + \beta = 1$, $\alpha\beta = 1/6$.

Now calculate $\Sigma\alpha^2 = 2/3$, $\Sigma\alpha^3 = 1/2$ and put.

19. (a) Let the roots of the second equation be denoted by α' and β'

∴ $\alpha' = \alpha + \delta$, $\beta' = \beta + \delta$

∴ $\alpha' - \beta' = (\alpha + \delta) - (\beta + \delta) = \alpha - \beta$

∴ $(\alpha' - \beta')^2 = (\alpha - \beta)^2$

or $(\alpha' + \beta')^2 - 4\alpha'\beta' = (\alpha + \beta)^2 - 4\alpha\beta$

or $\dfrac{4B^2}{A^2} - 4\dfrac{C}{A} = 4\dfrac{b^2}{a^2} - 4\dfrac{c}{a}$

or $\dfrac{b^2 - ac}{a^2} = \dfrac{B^2 - AC}{A^2}$

or $\dfrac{b^2 - ac}{B^2 - AC} = \left(\dfrac{a}{A}\right)^2$.

Another form :

Hint : $\alpha - \beta = \gamma - \delta$ as $\alpha, \beta, \gamma, \delta$ are in A.P.

(b) $\dfrac{\alpha}{\beta} = \dfrac{\gamma}{\delta}$. Apply C and D

$\dfrac{\alpha + \beta}{\alpha - \beta} = \dfrac{\gamma + \delta}{\gamma - \delta}$ Square both sides

∴ $\dfrac{b^2}{b^2 - 4ac} = \dfrac{B^2}{B^2 - 4AC}$ ∴ $\dfrac{D_1}{D_2} = \dfrac{b^2}{B^2}$

20. Ans. (a).

Since $\alpha, \beta, \gamma, \delta$ are in G.P.

∴ $\dfrac{\alpha}{\beta} = \dfrac{\gamma}{\delta} = \dfrac{1}{r}$. Apply comp. and divid.

∴ $\dfrac{\alpha + \beta}{\alpha - \beta} = \dfrac{\gamma + \delta}{\gamma - \delta}$

or $(\alpha + \beta)^2[(\gamma + \delta)^2 - 4\gamma\delta] = (\gamma + \delta)^2[(\alpha + \beta)^2 - 4\alpha\beta]$

or $1 \cdot (16 - 4q) = 16(1 - 4p)$

or $q = 16p$ ...(1)

The values of p and q given in (a) satisfy the above relation (1).

21. (a) $\alpha + \beta = -p$, $\gamma + \delta = -p$, $\alpha\beta = -q$, $\gamma\delta = r$

∴ $\alpha + \beta = \gamma + \delta$

Hence $(\alpha - \gamma)(\alpha - \delta) = \alpha^2 - \alpha(\gamma + \delta) + \gamma\delta$

$\qquad = \alpha^2 - \alpha(\alpha + \beta) + \gamma\delta = -\alpha\beta + \gamma\delta = q + r$

Similarly, $(\beta - \gamma)(\beta - \delta) = q + r$.

(b) $\alpha + \beta = -p$, $\alpha\beta = 1$, $\gamma + \delta = -q$, $\gamma\delta = 1$.

R.H.S. $= [\alpha\beta - \gamma(\alpha + \beta) + \gamma^2] \cdot [\alpha\beta + \delta(\alpha + \beta) + \delta^2]$

$\qquad = (\gamma^2 + p\gamma + 1)(\delta^2 - p\delta + 1)$

But γ and δ are the roots of $x^2 + qx + 1 = 0$.

∴ $\gamma^2 + q\gamma + 1 = 0$ or $\gamma^2 + 1 = -q\gamma$

$\qquad \delta^2 + q\delta + 1 = 0$ or $\delta^2 + 1 = -q\delta$

∴ R.H.S. $= (p\gamma - q\gamma)(-q\delta - p\delta)$

$\qquad = -\gamma\delta(p - q)(p + q)$

$\qquad = -1 \cdot (p^2 - q^2) = q^2 - p^2$.

22. (a) $\alpha = \dfrac{1}{\beta}$ ∴ $\alpha\beta = 1$ or $\dfrac{2}{P} = 1$ ∴ $p = 2$

Hence (d) is the correct answer.

(b) Ans. (c).

$P = a^2(b - c) + a(b^2 - c^2) = a(b - c)[a + b + c]$

∴ $P + Q + R = (a + b + c)\Sigma a(b - c) = 0$

Hence 1 is a root of $Px^2 + Qx + R = 0$

Since it has equal roots therefore roots are 1, 1.

Product of roots $1 \cdot 1 = 1 = \dfrac{R}{P}$

or $P = R$ or $(a + b + c)a(b - c)$

$\qquad\qquad\qquad = (a + b + c)c(a - b)$

or $a(b - c) = c(a - b)$

or $b(a + c) = 2ac$ or $b = \dfrac{2ac}{a + c}$

or a, b, c are in H.P.

(c) Ans. (d).

Roots of $x^2 + x + 1 = 0$ are ω, ω^2

$\qquad \alpha = \omega, \beta = \omega^2$, ∴ $\alpha^{19} = \omega^{19} = \omega$

$\qquad \beta^7 = \omega^{14} = \omega^2$

(d) Ans. (a).

$$f(x) = (x^2 + x + 1)(ax + d)$$

The roots of 1st factor are ω, ω^2 which are imaginary. The third root is $-\dfrac{d}{a}$ which must be real as imaginary roots occur in conjugate pairs.

23. (a) (i) Let one root be α then the other root will be $n\alpha$ by given condition.

Sum $= \alpha + n\alpha = -\dfrac{b}{a}$ or $\alpha = -\dfrac{b}{a(1+n)}$ ...(1)

Product $= n\alpha^2 = \dfrac{c}{a}$ $\therefore$ $\alpha^2 = \dfrac{c}{an}$ ...(2)

Now $\alpha^2 = (\alpha)^2$ $\therefore$ $\dfrac{c}{an} = \dfrac{b^2}{a^2(1+n)^2}$,

by (1) and (2)

$\therefore$ $nb^2 = ac(n+1)^2$.

(ii) Putting $n = 3$, the condition is $3b^2 = 16ac$.

(iii) Putting $n = 1$, the condition is

$b^2 = 4ac$ i.e., $b^2 - 4ac = 0$

(b) Ans. (a).

$$S = \alpha + 2\alpha = 3\alpha, \quad P = \alpha \cdot 2\alpha = 2\alpha^2$$

$\therefore$ $P = 2\left(\dfrac{S}{3}\right)^2$ or $9P = 2S^2$

or $9 \cdot \dfrac{2}{a^2 - 5a + 3} = 2 \cdot \dfrac{(3a-1)^2}{(a^2 - 5a + 3)^2}$

or $9(a^2 - 5a + 3) = 9a^2 - 6a + 1$

$\therefore$ $39a = 26$ or $a = 2/3$

24. We have $S = \dfrac{k+1}{k} + \dfrac{k+2}{k+1} = \dfrac{-b}{a}$

and $P = \dfrac{k+1}{k} \cdot \dfrac{k+2}{k+1} = \dfrac{c}{a}$

or $\dfrac{k+2}{k} = \dfrac{c}{a}$ or $\dfrac{2}{k} = \dfrac{c}{a} - 1 = \dfrac{c-a}{a}$

$\therefore$ $k = \dfrac{2a}{c-a}$

Now eliminate k.

Putting the value of k in 1st relation, we get

$\dfrac{c+a}{2a} + \dfrac{2c}{(c+a)} = -\dfrac{b}{a}$

or $(a+c)^2 + 4ac = -2b(a+c)$

or $(a+c)^2 + 2b(a+c) = -4ac$.

Add b^2 to both sides.

$\therefore$ $(a+c+b)^2 = b^2 - 4ac$.

25. $b = ar, c = ar^2, d = ar^3$.

$\Sigma(b-c)^2 = a^2\{(r - r^2)^2 + (r^2 - 1)^2 + (r^3 - r)^2\}$

$= a^2(1-r)^2\{r^2 + (r+1)^2 + r^2(r+1)^2\}$

$= a^2(1-r)^2\{(r^2 + r)^2 + 2(r + r^2) + 1\}$

$= a^2(1-r)^2(1 + r + r^2)^2 = a^2(1 - r^3)^2 = (d-a)^2$

Again eliminating w between 1st two equations, we get

$2u + v = 0$ and solving with 3rd, we get $u = -\dfrac{1}{3}$, $v = \dfrac{2}{3}$

and hence from any $w = \dfrac{5}{3}$

$\therefore$ $\Sigma u = 2$ and $\Sigma \dfrac{1}{u} = -\dfrac{9}{10}$

Hence the equation becomes

$-9x^2 + 10(a-d)^2 x + 20 = 0$

Replacing x by $1/x$, we get

$20x^2 + 10(a-d)^2 x - 9 = 0$

which is 2nd equation whose roots will be reciprocal of the roots of the first equation.

26. (a) Here $S = \alpha + \alpha^2 = -\dfrac{b}{a}$

$P = \alpha \cdot \alpha^2 = \dfrac{c}{a}$ or $\alpha^3 = \dfrac{c}{a}$

We have to eliminate α to get the required condition. Cubing 1st relation, we get

$(\alpha + \alpha^2)^3 = -\dfrac{b^3}{a^3}$

or $\alpha^3 + \alpha^6 + 3\alpha \cdot \alpha^2(\alpha + \alpha^2) = -\dfrac{b^3}{a^3}$

or $\dfrac{c}{a} + \dfrac{c^2}{a^2} + \dfrac{3c}{a}\left(-\dfrac{b}{a}\right) = -\dfrac{b^3}{a^3}$ $\because$ $\alpha^3 = \dfrac{c}{a}$

or $b^3 + ac^2 + a^2c = 3abc$

is the required condition.

(b) Proceed as in part (a).

(c) Ans. (c). $\alpha + \alpha^2 = -p/3, \alpha \cdot \alpha^2 = \alpha^3 = 1$

Now we know that $\omega + \omega^2 = -1, \omega^3 = 1$

Comparing, $p = 3$.

Alt. Cubing the first relation, we get

$\alpha^3 + \alpha^6 + 3\alpha \cdot \alpha^2(\alpha + \alpha^2) = (-p/3)^3$

or $1 + 1 + 3 \cdot 1(-p/3) = -p^3/27$.

or $p^3 - 27p + 54 = 0$. Clearly $p = 3$ satisfies it.

$(p-3)(p^2 + 3p - 18) = 0$

or $(p-3)(p-3)(p+6) = 0$

or $(p-3)^2(p+6) = 0$

$\therefore$ $p = 3$. As $p > 0$ $\therefore$ $p = -6$ is rejected.

27. (a) Ans. 2. Given $x - 2 = 2^{2/3} + 2^{1/3}$.

Cube both sides

$(x-2)^3 = 2^2 + 2 + 3 \cdot 2^{2/3} \cdot 2^{1/3}(x-2)$

$= 6 + 6(x-2)$

or $x^3 - 6x^2 + 12x - 8 = -6 + 6x$.

$\therefore$ $x^3 - 6x^2 + 6x = 2$.

(b) $\alpha + \alpha^n = -b/a$, $\alpha \cdot \alpha^n = c/a$

$$\therefore \quad \alpha = \left(\frac{c}{a}\right)^{1/(n+1)}$$

Putting in 1st relation, we get

$$\left(\frac{c}{a}\right)^{1/(n+1)} + \left(\frac{c}{a}\right)^{n/(n+1)} = -\frac{b}{a}$$

or $\quad a\left(\frac{c}{a}\right)^{1/(n+1)} + a \cdot \left(\frac{c^n}{a^n}\right)^{1/(n+1)} + b = 0$

or $\quad (a^n c)^{1/(n+1)} + (ac^n)^{1/(n+1)} + b = 0$.

28. (a) On simplification, the given equation is
$$x^2 + x(p+q-2r) + (pq-pr-qr) = 0.$$
By given condition $\beta = -\alpha$ or $\alpha + \beta = 0$
$$\therefore \quad p+q-2r = 0 \quad \text{or} \quad p+q = 2r \qquad ...(1)$$
Product of roots $= pq - pr - qr = pq - r(p+q)$
$$= pq - \frac{p+q}{2}(p+q)$$
$$= \frac{1}{2}[2pq - (p+q)^2], \text{ by (1)}$$
$$= -\frac{1}{2}[p^2 + q^2].$$

(b) The roots will be of opposite signs if their product is – ive and also the roots are real.
$$\therefore \quad \Delta \ge 0 \text{ and } P = -\text{ive}.$$
$$4(k^2+1)^2 - 12(k^2 - 3k + 2) = +\text{ive} \qquad ...(1)$$
and $\dfrac{k^2 - 3k + 2}{3} = -\text{ive} < 0 \qquad ...(2)$

If (2) holds then (1) automatically holds. Hence we must have $(k-1)(k-2) = -\text{ive}$
$$\therefore \quad 1 < k < 2.$$

29. (a) The given equation is a quadratic but it is satisfied by $x = a, b$ or c i.e. three values. Hence it is an identity. As such it is satisfied by all values of x.

(b) The given equation is an identity hence all the coefficients should be zero. $k = 2, 3$; $k = 1, 2$; $k = 2, -2$

$k = 2$ is common value which will reduce the equation to the form $0x^2 + 0x + 0 = 0$ i.e. an identity.

30. (a) $\alpha + \beta = \alpha^2 + \beta^2 = (\alpha+\beta)^2 - 2\alpha\beta$ etc.

(b) $\alpha + \beta = \dfrac{1}{\alpha^2} + \dfrac{1}{\beta^2} = \dfrac{\alpha^2 + \beta^2}{\alpha^2\beta^2} = \dfrac{(\alpha+\beta)^2 - 2\alpha\beta}{\alpha^2\beta^2}$

or $\quad \left(-\dfrac{b}{a}\right)\left(\dfrac{c^2}{a^2}\right) = \dfrac{b^2}{a^2} - \dfrac{2c}{a}$

or $\quad -bc^2 = ab^2 - 2ca^2$ or $\quad 2ca^2 = ab^2 + bc^2$

$\therefore \quad bc^2, ca^2, ab^2$ are in A.P.

Dividing by abc, we get
$$\frac{c}{a}, \frac{a}{b}, \frac{b}{c} \text{ are in A.P.}$$
or $\quad \dfrac{a}{c}, \dfrac{b}{a}, \dfrac{c}{b}$ are in H.P. or $\dfrac{c}{b}, \dfrac{b}{a}, \dfrac{a}{c}$ are in H.P.

31. (a) The given equation is $\lambda x^2 - (\lambda - 1)x + 5 = 0$.

$$\therefore \quad \alpha + \beta = \frac{\lambda - 1}{\lambda}, \quad \alpha\beta = \frac{5}{\lambda}$$

Also $\quad \dfrac{\alpha}{\beta} + \dfrac{\beta}{\alpha} = \dfrac{4}{5}$ or $5(\alpha^2 + \beta^2) = 4\alpha\beta$

or $\quad 5[(\alpha+\beta)^2 - 2\alpha\beta] = 4\alpha\beta$

or $\quad 5\left(\dfrac{\lambda - 1}{\lambda}\right)^2 = 14 \cdot \dfrac{5}{\lambda}$

or $\quad \lambda^2 - 2\lambda + 1 = 14\lambda$ or $\lambda^2 - 16\lambda + 1 = 0$

Its roots are λ_1, λ_2
$$\therefore \quad \lambda_1 + \lambda_2 = 16, \quad \lambda_1 \lambda_2 = 1$$
Now $\quad \dfrac{\lambda_1}{\lambda_2} + \dfrac{\lambda_2}{\lambda_1} = \dfrac{\lambda_1^2 + \lambda_2^2}{\lambda_1 \lambda_2}$
$$= \frac{(\lambda_1 + \lambda_2)^2 - 2\lambda_1\lambda_2}{\lambda_1\lambda_2} = 256 - 2 = 254.$$

(b) $3x^2 + 68x - 18 = 0$, $\lambda^2 - 4\lambda - 6 = 0$, $(\lambda \ne 0)$

32. (a) We have $\dfrac{\alpha}{\beta} = \dfrac{\gamma}{\delta}$ or $\dfrac{\alpha}{\gamma} = \dfrac{\beta}{\delta}$

$\therefore \quad \dfrac{\alpha + \beta}{\gamma + \delta} = \sqrt{\left(\dfrac{\alpha\beta}{\gamma\delta}\right)}$ or $\left(\dfrac{\alpha+\beta}{\gamma+\delta}\right)^2 = \dfrac{\alpha\beta}{\gamma\delta}$

$\therefore \quad \dfrac{p^2}{l^2} = \dfrac{q}{m}$ or $p^2 m = q l^2$.

(b) Proceeding as in part (a), we have
$$\left(-\frac{b_1}{a_1} \div -\frac{b_2}{a_2}\right)^2 = \frac{c_1}{a_1} \div \frac{c_2}{a_2}$$
or $\quad \left(\dfrac{b_1}{b_2}\right)^2 = \dfrac{c_1}{c_2} \cdot \dfrac{a_2}{a_1} \cdot \dfrac{a_1^2}{a_2^2} = \dfrac{c_1}{c_2} \cdot \dfrac{a_1}{a_2}$.

33. (a) **Hint :** $(\pi - 1)\lambda^2 + 2\lambda + 1 = 0$ has roots λ_1, λ_2

$$\frac{\lambda_1^2}{\lambda_2^2} + \frac{\lambda_2^2}{\lambda_1^2} + 2 = \left[\frac{\lambda_1^2 + \lambda_2^2}{\lambda_1 \lambda_2}\right]^2$$

$$= \left[\frac{(\lambda_1 + \lambda_2)^2 - 2\lambda_1\lambda_2}{\lambda_1\lambda_2}\right]^2 \text{ etc.}$$

(b) $\alpha + \beta = -\dfrac{n}{l}, \quad \alpha\beta = \dfrac{n}{l} \qquad ...(1)$

Also $\quad \dfrac{\alpha}{\beta} = \dfrac{p}{q} \qquad ...(2)$

We have to prove that
$$\sqrt{\left(\frac{p}{q}\right)} + \sqrt{\left(\frac{q}{p}\right)} + \sqrt{\left(\frac{n}{l}\right)} = 0$$

Now $\sqrt{\left(\dfrac{p}{q}\right)} + \sqrt{\left(\dfrac{q}{p}\right)} = \sqrt{\left(\dfrac{\alpha}{\beta}\right)} + \sqrt{\left(\dfrac{\beta}{\alpha}\right)}$

$$= \frac{\alpha + \beta}{\sqrt{(\alpha\beta)}} = -\frac{n/l}{\sqrt{(n/l)}} = -\sqrt{\left(\frac{n}{l}\right)}$$

$\therefore \quad \sqrt{\left(\dfrac{p}{q}\right)} + \sqrt{\left(\dfrac{q}{p}\right)} + \sqrt{\left(\dfrac{n}{l}\right)} = 0.$

34. (a) Putting $x = -1$, we get $-6p + 24 = 0$

$\therefore \quad p = 4$

$x^4 + x^3 - 7x^2 - x + 6 = (x+1)(x^3 - 7x + 6)$

$= (x+1)(x-1)(x^2 + x - 6)$

$= (x+1)(x-1)(x+3)(x-2)$

The other factors are $x-1$, $x-2$, $x+3$.

(b) $x^2 - 3x + 2 = (x-2)(x-1)$

Put $x = 2$, $\qquad q - 4p + 16 = 0$

Put $x = 1$, $\qquad q - p + 1 = 0 \therefore \quad p = 5, q = 4$.

35. (a) Ans. $p = \pm 7$.

Hint : Use $(x_1 - x_2)^2 = (x_1 + x_2)^2 - 4x_1 x_2$.

(b) As 2 and 3 are the roots of the given equation we have $4m + n = 10$, and $9m + n = -15$. Solving, we get $m = -5$

$\therefore \quad n = 30$. Hence the given equation is

$2x^3 - 5x^2 - 13x + 30 = 0$

Now $\alpha + \beta + \gamma = 5/2$ or $2 + 3 + \gamma = 5/2$

$\therefore \quad \gamma = 5/2 - 5 = -5/2$

$(x^2 - 6x + 15)(4x^2 - 3) = 0$

36. (a) $P^2 + Q^2 = 3 \quad \Rightarrow \quad (P-Q)^2 + 2PQ = 3$

or $\left(x - \dfrac{x}{x+1}\right)^2 + 2 \cdot \dfrac{x^2}{(x+1)} = 3$

or $t^2 + 2t - 3 = 0 \qquad$ where $t = \dfrac{x^2}{(x+1)}$

$\therefore \quad t = 1, -3 \quad \therefore \quad x^2 - x - 1 = 0$

or $x^2 + 3x + 3 = 0$

$\therefore$ Roots are $\dfrac{1 \pm \sqrt{5}}{2}$, the other factor gives imaginary values of x.

(b) $f(x) = (x^2 + x + 1)(ax + d)$

The roots of 1st factor are ω, ω^2 which are imaginary. The third root is $-\dfrac{d}{a}$ which must be real as imaginary roots occur in conjugate pairs.

(c) Ans. (c).

We know that imaginary roots occur in conjugate pairs. Suppose the 3rd root is γ.

$\therefore \quad S_1 = (\alpha + i\beta) + (\alpha - i\beta) + \gamma = 0$

$\qquad\qquad\qquad (\because \text{Coeff. of } x^2 = 0)$

$\therefore \quad \gamma = -2\alpha$. But γ is a root of given equation

$\therefore \quad (-2\alpha)^3 + q(-2\alpha) + r = 0$

or $(2\alpha)^3 + q(2\alpha) - r = 0$

$\therefore \quad 2\alpha$ is a root of $x^3 + qx - r = 0$.

37. (a) $x = 2 + i\sqrt{3} \quad \therefore \quad (x-2)^2 = i^2 \cdot 3 = -3$

or $x^2 - 4x + 7 = 0$. $\qquad\qquad$ ...(1)

Now $4x^2 + 8x + 35 = 4(x^2 - 4x + 7)$

$\qquad\qquad\qquad\qquad + 16x - 28 + 8x + 35$

$= 0 + 24x + 7 = 24(2 + i\sqrt{3}) + 7$, by (1)

$= 55 + 24\sqrt{3}\, i$

(b) The equation whose root is $2 + i\sqrt{3}$ is by part (a)

$x^2 - 4x + 7 = 0$ and it is the same as $x^2 + px + q = 0$

$\therefore \quad p = -4, q = 7$.

Alt. If $2 + i\sqrt{3}$ is a root, then $2 - i\sqrt{3}$ will also be a root.

$\therefore \quad$ Sum $= 4 = -p$ and product $4 + 3 = q$

$\therefore \quad p = -4, q = 7$.

38. (a) $x = 1 + 2i \quad \therefore \quad (x-1)^2 = -4$.

$x^2 - 2x + 5 = 0$. $\qquad\qquad$ ...(1)

Dividing $x^3 + 7x^2 - 13x + 16$ by $x^2 - 2x + 5$ we get the quotient as $x + 9$ and remainder as -29.

$\therefore \quad x^3 + 7x^2 - 13x + 16 = (x^2 - 2x + 5)$

$\qquad\qquad\qquad\qquad\qquad\qquad (x+9) - 29$

$= 0 - 29 = -29$ by (1)

(b) $x = 2 + \sqrt{3}, \quad \therefore \quad (x-2)^2 = 3$

or $x^2 - 4x + 1 = 0$. $\qquad\qquad$ ...(1)

As above

$x^3 - 7x^2 + 13x - 2 = (x^2 - 4x + 1)(x-3) + 1$

$= 0 + 1 = 1 \qquad$ by (1)

(c) Ans. $\quad 3 \pm i\sqrt{6}, \quad \pm(\sqrt{3}/2)$.

39. (a) If $\alpha + i\beta$ is a root then $\alpha - i\beta$ will also be a root. If the third root be γ, then

$(\alpha + i\beta) + (\alpha - i\beta) + \gamma = 0 \quad \therefore \quad \gamma = -2\alpha$

But γ is a root of the given equation $x^3 + qx + r = 0$

$\therefore \quad (-2\alpha)^3 + q(-2\alpha) + r = 0$

or $(2\alpha)^3 + q(2\alpha) - r = 0$

$\therefore \quad 2\alpha$ is a root of $t^3 + qt - r = 0$, which is independent of α and β.

(b) Split $\dfrac{1}{2}(8\sqrt{3}) = 4\sqrt{3}$ into two factors a, b such that $a^2 - b^2 = -47$ i.e., $1, 4\sqrt{3}$.

Hence square root is $\pm(1 + 4\sqrt{3}\, i)$.

$\therefore \quad$ One root is $1 + 4\sqrt{3}\, i$ and other is its conjugate $1 - 4\sqrt{3}i$. Hence $S = 2, P = 49$

Similarly $-1 - 4\sqrt{3}\, i$ and $-1 + 4\sqrt{3}\, i$, are the roots.

$S = -2, P = 49$

$\therefore \quad$ Equations are $x^2 \pm 2x + 49 = 0$.

40. (a) Let the roots be $\alpha, \alpha + 2, \beta$

$S_1 = \Sigma \alpha = 2\alpha + \beta + 2 = 13$

$\therefore \quad \beta = 11 - 2\alpha$ $\qquad\qquad$ ...(1)

$S_2 = \Sigma \alpha\beta = \alpha(\alpha + 2) + (\alpha + 2)\beta + \beta\alpha = 15$

or $\alpha^2 + 2\alpha + 2(\alpha + 1)\beta = 15$ $\qquad$ ...(2)

$$S_3 = \alpha \beta \gamma$$

$$\therefore \quad \alpha \beta (\alpha + 2) = -189 \qquad \qquad ...(3)$$

Eliminating β between (1) and (2), we get

$$\alpha^2 + 2\alpha + 2(\alpha + 1)(11 - 2\alpha) = 15$$

or $\quad 3\alpha^2 - 20\alpha - 7 = 0$

$\therefore \quad (\alpha - 7)(3\alpha + 1) = 0$

$\therefore \quad \alpha = 7 \text{ or } -\dfrac{1}{3} \quad \therefore \quad \beta = -3, \dfrac{35}{3}$

Out of these values $\alpha = 7, \beta = -3$ satisfy the third relation $\alpha \beta (\alpha + 2) = -189$

i.e., $(-21)(9) = -189$

Hence the roots are $7, 7 + 2, -3$ or $7, 9, -3$.

(b) $\alpha + \beta = 0$ but $\alpha + \beta + \gamma + \delta = 2$

$\therefore \quad \gamma + \delta = 2$.

Let $\alpha \beta = p$ and $\gamma \delta = q$

$\therefore \quad$ Given equation is equivalent to

$$(x^2 + p)(x^2 - 2x + q) = 0.$$

Comparing the coefficients, we get

$$p + q = 4, -2p = 6, pq = -21$$

$\therefore \quad p = -3, q = 7$ and they satisfy $pq = -21$.

$$(x^2 - 3)(x^2 - 2x + 7) = 0$$

Roots are $\pm\sqrt{3}$, and $1 \pm i\sqrt{6}$.

(c) Proceed as in part (b).

Roots are $\pm\dfrac{1}{2}, 3, -1$.

41. Here we observe that coefficient of x^3 is zero.

$\therefore \quad S_1 = \alpha + \beta + \gamma + \delta = 0$

$\therefore \quad \alpha + \beta = -(\gamma + \delta) = p$, say.

Let $\alpha \beta = q$ and $\gamma \delta = r$

Hence the given equation is equivalent to

$$(x^2 - px + q)(x^2 + px + r) = 0$$

Compare the coefficients of x^2, x and constant

$$q + r - p^2 = -2, \ p(q - r) = 8, \ qr = -3$$

$$(q + r)^2 - (q - r)^2 = 4qr$$

$\therefore \quad (p^2 - 2)^2 - \dfrac{64}{p^2} = -12$

or $\quad (p^6 - 4p^4 + 4p^2) + 12p^2 - 64 = 0$

or $\quad t^3 - 4t^2 + 16t - 64 = 0$ where $t = p^2$

Clearly $t = p^2 = 4$ satisfies.

$\therefore \quad p = 2, q + r = 2, q - r = 4$

$\therefore \quad q = 3, r = -1$

Hence the given biquadratic is equivalent to

$$(x^2 - 2x + 3)(x^2 + 2x - 1) = 0$$

$\therefore \quad x = -1 \pm \sqrt{2}, -1 \pm \sqrt{2}\, i$

42. We have the identity, $x = 1^{1/n}$ or $x^n - 1 = 0$

$\therefore \quad x^n - 1 = (x - 1)(x - a_1)(x - a_2) \dots (x - a_{n-1})$

$$= (x - 1) P$$

Differentiate both sides w.r.t. x

$$nx^{n-1} = 1 \cdot P + (x - 1) P'$$

Putting $x = 1$, we get

$$n = (1 - a_1)(1 - a_2) \dots (1 - a_{n-1}) + 0$$

43. (a) We have $x^2 = ax - b$

Multiplying by x^{n-1}, we get

$$x^{n+1} = ax^n - bx^{n-1}.$$

In this putting $x = \alpha, \beta$ and adding, we get

$$\alpha^{n+1} + \beta^{n+1} = a(\alpha^n + \beta^n) - b(\alpha^{n-1} + \beta^{n-1})$$

$\therefore \quad V_{n+1} = aV_n - bV_{n-1}$

Also $\quad V_0 = \alpha^0 + \beta^0 = 2$ and $V_1 = \alpha + \beta = a$.

$\therefore \quad V_2 = aV_1 - bV_0 = a \cdot a - b \cdot 2 = a^2 - 2b$.

Similarly,

$$V_3 = aV_2 - bV_1 = a \cdot (a^2 - 2b) - b \cdot a = a^3 - 3ab$$

$$V_4 = aV_3 - bV_2$$

$$= a(a^3 - 3ab) - b(a^2 - 2b) = a^4 - 4a^2b + 2b^2$$

and $V_5 = aV_4 - bV_3$

$$= a(a^4 - 4a^2b + 2b^2) - b(a^3 - 3ab)$$

$$= a^5 - 5a^3b + 5ab^2.$$

(b) We have $\alpha + \beta = -p$ and $\alpha\beta = q$. $\qquad ...(1)$

Also since α, β are the roots of

$$x^{2n} + p^n x^n + q^n = 0$$

We have $\quad \alpha^{2n} + p^n \alpha^n + q^n = 0$

and $\qquad \beta^{2n} + p^n \beta^n + q^n = 0$.

Subtracting the above realtions, we get

$$(\alpha^{2n} - \beta^{2n}) + p^n(\alpha^n - \beta^n) = 0$$

$\therefore \quad \alpha^n + \beta^n = -p^n \qquad \qquad ...(2)$

If $\quad \alpha/\beta$ or β/α is a root of

$$x^n + 1 + (x + 1)^n = 0, \text{ then}$$

$$(\alpha/\beta)^n + 1 + [(\alpha/\beta) + 1]^n = 0$$

or $\quad (\alpha^n + \beta^n) + (\alpha + \beta)^n = 0$

or $\quad -p^n + (-p)^n = 0$, by (1) and (2).

Above is possible only when n is even.

44. Let us consider the integral values of x as $0, 1, -1$, then $f(0), f(1)$ and $f(-1)$ are all integers $\Rightarrow C, A + B + C$ and $A - B + C$ are all integers

$\therefore \quad C$ is integer and hence $A + B$ is an integer and also $A - B$ is an integer $2A = (A + B) + (A - B)$

$\therefore \quad 2A, A + B$ and C are all integers.

Conversely, let $n \in I$ then

$$f(n) = An^2 + Bn + C$$

$$= 2A\left[\dfrac{n(n-1)}{2}\right] + (A + B)n + C$$

Now, $A, A + B$ and C are all integers and $\dfrac{n(n-1)}{2} = \dfrac{\text{Even}}{2} = $ integer $\therefore$ $f(n)$ is also an integer.

45. (a) Taking $a > 0$, we have

$ax^2 + bx + c = f(x) = a(x - \alpha)(x - \beta), \alpha < \beta.$

$f(x)$ is +ive for all values of x which are such that either $x < \alpha$ or $x > \beta$,

and $f(x)$ is – ive for all values of x which are such that $\alpha < x < \beta$.

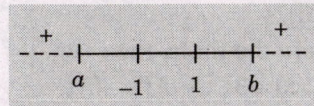

Fig. 5

Now under given condition both -1 and 1 lie between α and β.

$\therefore$ $f(1)$ and $f(-1)$ both are –ive.

or $a + b + c < 0$ and $a - b + c < 0$

Dividing by a which is +ive,

$$1 + \frac{c}{a} + \frac{b}{a} < 0 \quad \text{and} \quad 1 + \frac{c}{a} - \frac{b}{a} < 0$$

$\therefore$ $1 + \dfrac{c}{a} + \left|\dfrac{b}{a}\right| < 0.$

(b) Ans. (a). $\Delta > 0 \Rightarrow a < 3.$

Sum $< 6 \Rightarrow a < 3$

$f(x) = (x - \alpha)(x - \beta)$ where both α, β are less than 3.

$f(3) = (+)(+) = + \Rightarrow a^2 - 5a + 6 > 0$

or $(a - 2)(a - 3) > 0$ $\therefore$ $a < 2$ or $a > 3$

but $a < 3$ $\therefore$ $a < 2$ is the required answer.

(c) Dividing throughout by $\tan^2 \theta$, we have

$f(x) = x^2 + 4ax + 16 = 0$ where $x = \tan\theta + \cot\theta$

and x is + ive as $\theta \in (0, \pi/2)$

Also $x = \tan\theta + \cot\theta \geq 2\sqrt{(\tan\theta \cdot \cot\theta)} = 2$

Thus $f(x)$ has two real roots each of which is greater than 2

Hence we must have the following

$\Delta \geq 0, S > 4, f(2) = + \text{ive}$

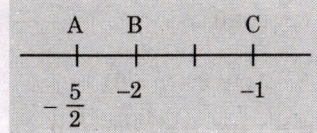

Fig. 6

$16a^2 - 64 > 0$ or $(a + 2)(a - 2) > 0$

$\therefore$ $a < -2$ or $a > 2$ ...(1)

$S = -4a > 4 \Rightarrow a < -1$ ...(2)

$f(2) = +\text{ive}$ $4 + 8a + 16 > 0$

or $a > -5/2$ ...(3)

$\therefore$ $a \in \left(-\dfrac{5}{2}, -2\right)$ by (1), (2) and (3)

46. (a) Let $F(x) = \int (3ax^2 + 2bx + c)\,dx = ax^3 + bx^2 + cx$

$\therefore$ $F(0) = 0, F(1) = a + b + c = 0$ by given condition.

Since both $F(0) = 0$ and $F(1) = 0$,

there will exist some value of x between 0 and 1 for which $F'(x) = 0$ by Rolle's theorem.

where $F'(x) = 3ax^2 + 2bx + c.$

(b) $f(x) = ax^2 + bx + c$

Let $F(x) = \int f(x)\,dx = \dfrac{ax^3}{3} + \dfrac{bx^2}{2} + cx$

Clearly $F(0) = 0,$

$F(1) = \dfrac{a}{3} + \dfrac{b}{2} + c = \dfrac{2a + 3b + 6c}{6} = 0$

by given relation.

Since $F(0) = F(1) = 0,$

there exists at least one point c in between 0 and 1 such that $F'(x) = 0$ or $ax^2 + bx + c = 0$ for some $x \in [0, 1].$

47. (a) Ans. (d). $y = x^2 - x(a + b) + ab - 1$

Add $\left(\dfrac{a+b}{2}\right)^2$ to both sides

$$y + \left(\frac{a+b}{2}\right)^2 - ab + 1 = \left(x - \frac{a+b}{2}\right)^2$$

or $\left(x - \dfrac{a+b}{2}\right)^2 = y + 1 + \left(\dfrac{a-b}{2}\right)^2$

Above equation represents a parabola with vertex at $\left[\dfrac{a+b}{2}, -1 - \left(\dfrac{a-b}{2}\right)^2\right]$

At $x = a$, $x = b$ both $y = -1$ where $a < b.$

If the roots of the equation $y = f(x)$ be α and β, then $f(\alpha) = 0, f(\beta) = 0$

From the figure $\alpha < a$ and $\beta > b$

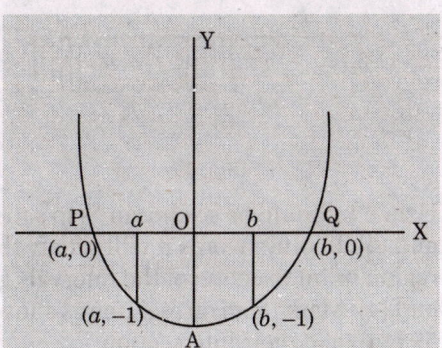

Fig. 7

Hence one root is in $(-\infty, a)$ and the other is in $(b, +\infty).$

(b) Ans. (b). Given $\alpha < \beta$, c is – ive and $b = +$ ive.

$\alpha + \beta = -b = -$ ive, $\alpha\beta = c = -$ ive

$\alpha < \beta \Rightarrow \alpha$ must be a $-$ive root and β a $+$ive root as $\alpha\beta$ is $-$ive.

Again $\alpha + \beta < 0 \Rightarrow \beta < -\alpha \Rightarrow \beta < |\alpha|$.

48. (a) If $f(x) = (x - \alpha)(x - \beta)$,

then $f(\lambda) = (\lambda - \alpha)(\lambda - \beta) = -$ive as the two factors are of opposite signs by given conditions. Also roots must be real

$\therefore \quad \Delta \geq 0 \Rightarrow 8\left(\lambda^2 + \lambda + \dfrac{1}{2}\right)$

$= 8\left[\left(\lambda + \dfrac{1}{2}\right)^2 + \dfrac{1}{4}\right]$ is $+$ive, which is true.

Now $f(\lambda) = -$ive

$\Rightarrow 2\lambda^2 - 2(2\lambda + 1)\lambda + \lambda(\lambda + 1) < 0$

or $-\lambda^2 - \lambda < 0$ or $\lambda(\lambda + 1) > 0$

or $\lambda < -1$ or $\lambda > 0$

(b) If α, β be the roots of the given equation $f(x) = 0$ then by the given condition

$\alpha < 2 < \beta$ ...(1)

Also $f(x) = 1 \cdot (x - \alpha)(x - \beta), \alpha < \beta$ ...(2)

We conclude from (1) that the roots of the given equation must be real as order relation does not exist in complex numbers. Secondly from (2) we conclude that $f(x) = -$ive for all values of x which lie between α and β. $\therefore f(2) = -$ive

$\therefore \Delta > 0$ (distinct) and $f(2) = -$ive

$\therefore (k+1)^2 - 4(k^2 + k - 8) = +$ive

or $3k^2 + 2k - 33 = -$ive

or $(3k + 11)(k - 3) = -$ive

$\therefore -\dfrac{11}{3} < k < 3$ ...(3)

Again $f(2) = -$ive

$\Rightarrow 4 - 2(k+1) + k^2 + k - 8$ is $-$ive

$k^2 - k - 6 = -$ive or $(k + 2)(k - 3) = -$ive

$\therefore -2 < k < 3$ ...(4)

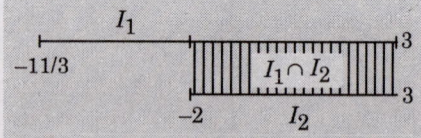

Fig. 8

Hence k should be so chosen as to satisfy both (3) and (4). In other words it will satisfy the common region or intersection of the intervals given by (3) and (4). Mark them on real line as shown above in 59 and take their intersection.

$\therefore$ Common region is $-2 < k < 3$.

49. (a) $a^2\alpha^2 + b\alpha + c = 0$ ...(1)

and $a^2\beta^2 - b\beta - c = 0$ ...(2)

Let $f(x) = a^2 x^2 + 2bx + 2c$

$f(\alpha) = a^2\alpha^2 + 2(b\alpha + c)$

$= a^2\alpha^2 - 2a^2\alpha^2 = -a^2\alpha^2 = -$ive, by (1)

$f(\beta) = a^2\beta^2 + 2(b\beta + c)$

$= a^2\beta^2 + 2a^2\beta^2 = 3a^2\beta^2 = +$ive, by (2)

Since $f(\alpha)$ and $f(\beta)$ are of opposite signs then we know from theory of equations that a root γ of the equation $f(x) = 0$ lies between α and β.

(b) Ans. (d).

If a, b are the roots, then

$f(x) = 3(x - a)(x - b)$

$f(1) = 3(1 - a)(1 - b) = -$ive as $a < 1 < b$

or $f(1) = 3 - 3\sin\alpha - 2(1 - \sin^2\alpha) < 0$

or $2\sin^2\alpha - 3\sin\alpha + 1 < 0$

$(2\sin\alpha - 1)(\sin\alpha - 1) < 0$

$2\left(\sin\alpha - \dfrac{1}{2}\right)(\sin\alpha - 1) < 0$

$\therefore \dfrac{1}{2} < \sin\alpha < 1$. Now $\sin 30° = \sin 150° = \dfrac{1}{2}$

$\therefore \alpha$ lies between $\dfrac{\pi}{6}$ to $\dfrac{5\pi}{6}$ excluding $\dfrac{\pi}{2}$ as $\sin\alpha$ is

not equal to 1 and hence (d) is correct.

50. $f(x) = 4x^3 - 3x - p = 0$

$f'(x) = 12x^2 - 3 = 12\left(x^2 - \dfrac{1}{4}\right)$

$= 12\left(x + \dfrac{1}{2}\right)\left(x - \dfrac{1}{2}\right) = +$ive for $x \geq \dfrac{1}{2}$

Thus $f(x)$ is an increasing function for $x \geq \dfrac{1}{2}$

Now $f\left(\dfrac{1}{2}\right) = \dfrac{1}{2} - \dfrac{3}{2} - p = -1 - p = -$ive

$f(1) = 4 - 3 - p = 1 - p = +$ive $\qquad \because -1 \leq p \leq 1$

Since $f(a)$ and $f(b)$ are of opposite signs there exists at least one or in general three roots of $f(x) = 0$ between a and b i.e. between $\dfrac{1}{2}$ and 1. But $f(x)$ is an increasing function for $x \geq \dfrac{1}{2}$. Hence there exists only one root in $\left[\dfrac{1}{2}, 1\right]$. Put $x = \cos\theta$

$\therefore 4\cos^3\theta - 3\cos\theta - p = 0$

or $\cos 3\theta = p$ or $\theta = \dfrac{1}{3}\cos^{-1} p$

or $\cos^{-1} x = \left(\dfrac{1}{3}\cos^{-1} p\right)$

or $x = \cos\left(\dfrac{1}{3}\cos^{-1} p\right)$ where $-1 \leq p \leq 1$.

Problem Set (2)

Nature of roots of a quadratic equation. Common roots of two quadratic equations. Sign of quadratic expression $ax^2 + bx + c$.

1.* Find the condition that in the equations
$$ax^2 + bx + c = 0 \quad \text{and} \quad a'x^2 + b'x + c' = 0$$
(a) One root be common.
(b) A root of first be reciprocal of a root of the second.
(c) Both have the same pair of roots.

2. (a) If the equations $x^2 + px + q = 0$ and $x^2 + p'x + q' = 0$ have a common root show that it must be equal to $\dfrac{pq' - p'q}{q - q'}$ or $\dfrac{q - q'}{p' - p}$.

(b) If the equations $f(x) \equiv ax^3 + 3bx^2 + 3cx + d = 0$
and $g(x) \equiv ax^2 + 2bx + c = 0$
have a common root, then show that
$$(bc - ad)^2 = 4(ac - b^2)(bd - c^2)$$

3. (a) Find k if the equations $4x^2 - 11x + 2k = 0$ and $x^2 - 3x - k = 0$ have a common root and obtain the common root for this value of k.

(b) Determine a such that $x^2 - 11x + a$ and $x^2 - 14x + 2a$ may have a common factor.

4. (a) Find the value of a so that the equations
$$(2a - 5)x^2 - 4x - 15 = 0$$
and $(3a - 8)x^2 - 5x - 21 = 0$
have a common root.

(b) If the equations $x^2 - x - p = 0$ and $x^2 + 2xp - 12 = 0$ have common root, find it.

(c) Find the condition on the complex constant α, β if $z^2 + \alpha z + \beta = 0$ has real roots.

5.* If a, b, c are in G.P., then the equations $ax^2 + 2bx + c = 0$ and $dx^2 + 2ex + f = 0$ have a common root if $\dfrac{d}{a}, \dfrac{e}{b}, \dfrac{f}{c}$ are in
(i) A.P.   (ii) G.P.
(iii) H.P.   (iv) None of these.

Another form :
If $ax^2 + 2bx + c = 0$ and $px^2 + 2qx + r = 0$ have a common root and $\dfrac{a}{p}, \dfrac{b}{q}, \dfrac{c}{r}$ in A.P. then prove that p, q, r are in G.P.

6. (a)* If α, β are the roots of $x^2 + px + q = 0$ and γ, δ are the roots of $x^2 + rx + s = 0$; evaluate $(\alpha - \gamma)(\alpha - \delta)(\beta - \gamma)(\beta - \delta)$ in terms of p, q, r and s. Deduce the condition that the equations have a common root.

(b) Eliminate x from the equations
$$a + c = (b/x) - dx, \quad a - c = (d/x) - bx$$

7.* α and β are the roots of $ax^2 + bx + c = 0$ and $f(x) = a_1 x^2 + b_1 x + c_1$, then prove that
$$f(\alpha) \cdot f(\beta) = \frac{1}{a^2}[(c_1 a - ca_1)^2 - (ab_1 - a_1 b)(bc_1 - b_1 c)]$$

8.* If α, β are the roots of $ax^2 + bx + c = 0$, $\alpha_1, -\beta$ are the roots of $a_1 x^2 + b_1 x + c_1 = 0$, show that α, α_1 are the roots of
$$\frac{x^2}{\dfrac{b}{a} + \dfrac{b_1}{a_1}} + x + \frac{1}{\dfrac{b}{c} + \dfrac{b_1}{c_1}} = 0.$$

9. (a) If the equations $x^2 + bx + ca = 0$ and $x^2 + cx + ab = 0$ have a common root, then their other roots are the roots of the equation, $x^2 + ax + bc = 0$.

(b)* If the equations $x^2 + abx + c = 0$ and $x^2 + acx + b = 0$ have a common root, then establish that their other roots are the roots of the equation $x^2 - a(b + c)x + a^2bc = 0$.

10. If one root of the equation $x^2 + ax + b = 0$ is a root of the equation $x^2 + cx + d = 0$, prove that the other roots satisfy the equation $x^2 + x(2a - c) + (a^2 - ac + d) = 0$.

11. (a)* If each pair of the three equations
$$x^2 + p_1 x + q_1 = 0, \; x^2 + p_2 x + q_2 = 0 \text{ and}$$
$$x^2 + p_3 x + q_3 = 0 \text{ has a common root, then prove}$$
that $p_1^2 + p_2^2 + p_3^2 + 4(q_1 + q_2 + q_3)$
$$= 2(p_1 p_2 + p_2 p_3 + p_3 p_1)$$

(b)* If every pair of equations $x^2 + ax + bc = 0$, $x^2 + bx + ca = 0$, $x^2 + cx + ab = 0$ has a common root, then find the sum and product of these common roots.

(c) If the three equations $x^2 + ax + 12 = 0$, $x^2 + bx + 15 = 0$ and $x^2 + (a + b)x + 36 = 0$ have a common possible root, then find a and b and the roots. **(J.E.E.W.B. 1993)**

12. If each pair of equations $a_1 x^2 + b_1 x + c_1 = 0$, $a_2 x^2 + b_2 x + c_2 = 0$ and $a_3 x^2 + b_3 x + c_3 = 0$ has a common root, then show that
(i) $\dfrac{c_1 a_2 + c_2 a_1}{c_1 a_2 - c_2 a_1} + \dfrac{a_1 a_2 b_3}{a_3(a_1 b_2 - a_2 b_1)} = 0$

(ii) $\left(\dfrac{a_1 b_2 - a_2 b_1}{a_1 c_2 - a_2 c_1}\right)^2 = \dfrac{a_1 a_2 c_3}{c_1 c_2 a_3}$

13.* If the equations $ax^2 + 2bx + c = 0$, $a' x^2 + 2b' x + c' = 0$ have a common root, prove that the equation $(b^2 - ac) x^2 + (2bb' - ac' - a'c) x + (b'^2 - a'c') = 0$ has equal roots.

14. (a)* If the equations $x^2 + ax + b = 0$ and $x^2 + bx + a = 0$ have a common root, then the numerical value of $a + b$ is ....

(b)* If the equations $x^2 + bx + c = 0$ and $bx^2 + cx + 1 = 0$ have a common root, then either $b + c + 1 = 0$ or $b^2 + c^2 + 1 = bc + b + c$

(c) Let α, β be the roots of the equation $x^2 - px + r = 0$ and $\dfrac{\alpha}{2}$, 2β be the roots of the equation $x^2 - qx + r = 0$. Then the value of r is

(a) $\dfrac{2}{9}(p - q)(2q - p)$ (b) $\dfrac{2}{9}(q - p)(2p - q)$

(c) $\dfrac{2}{9}(q - 2p)(2q - p)$ (d) $\dfrac{2}{9}(2p - q)(2q - p)$

(I.I.T. 2007)

15. If the equations $ax^2 + bx + c = 0$ and $x^3 + 3x^2 + 3x + 2 = 0$ have two common roots, then show that $a = b = c$.

Nature of the roots

16. (a) If the roots of the equation
$(c^2 - ab) x^2 - 2(a^2 - bc) x + (b^2 - ac) = 0$
be equal, prove that either $a = 0$
or $a^3 + b^3 + c^3 = 3abc$.

(b) For what values of m the roots of the equation $x^2 - 2x(1 + 3m) + 7(3 + 2m) = 0$ will be equal ?

17. (a) If the two roots of the equation $(\lambda - 1)(x^2 + x + 1)^2 - (\lambda + 1)(x^4 + x^2 + 1) = 0$ are real and distinct, then prove that λ lies in the interval $(-\infty, -2) \cup (2, \infty)$.

(b) Find the values of $t, t \in \left[-\dfrac{\pi}{2}, \dfrac{\pi}{2}\right]$ for all real solutions of the equation $2\sin t = \dfrac{5x^2 - 2x + 1}{3x^2 - 2x - 1}$.

(I.I.T. 2005)

(c) The equation $(6 - x)^4 + (8 - x)^4 = 16$ has

(a) Sum of roots 28

(b) Product of roots 2688

(c) Two real roots

(d) Two imaginary roots

(d) Determine the nature of the roots of the equation $(x - a)^3 + (x - b)^3 + (x - c)^3 = 0$.

(e) The number of real roots of the equation $(x + 3)^4 + (x + 5)^4 = 16$ is

(a) 0   (b) 2

(c) 4   (d) none

18. (a) Determine the values of m for which the equation $5x^2 - 4x + 2 + m(4x^2 - 2x - 1) = 0$ will have

(i) Equal roots

(ii) Product of roots as 2

(iii) Sum of the roots as 6.

(b) All the values of m for which both the roots of the equation $x^2 - 2mx + m^2 - 1 = 0$ are greater than -2 but less than 4, lie in the interval

(a) $m > 3$ (b) $-1 < m < 3$

(c) $1 < m < 4$ (d) $-2 < m < 4$ **(AIEEE 2006)**

(c)* The product of the roots of the equation $x^2 - 3\lambda x + 2 e^{2\log \lambda} - 1 = 0$ is 7. If the roots be real, then $\lambda = 2$.

(d) The expression $ax^2 + bx + c$ has the same sign as of a if

(a) $b^2 - 4ac > 0$

(b) $b^2 - 4ac = 0$

(c) $b^2 - 4ac \leq 0$

(d) b and c have the same sign as of a

(Kurukshetra 1995)

(e) If the graph of the function $y = 16x^2 + 8(a + 5) x - 7a - 5$ is strictly above the x-axis, then `a` must satisfy the inequality

(a) $-15 < a < -2$ (b) $-2 < a < -1$

(c) $5 < a < 7$ (d) none of these

19. (a) If the roots of the equation, $(b - c) x^2 + (c - a) x + (a - b) = 0$ be equal, then prove that a, b, c are in arithmetical progression.

(Bihar C.E.E. 1999)

(b) If $a(b - c) x^2 + b(c - a) x + c(a - b) = 0$ has equal roots, prove that a, b, c are in harmonical progression.

20. (a) Prove that the roots of $(x - a)(x - b) + (x - b)(x - c) + (x - c)(x - a) = 0$ are always real and they will be equal if and only if $a = b = c$.

(b) Examine the nature of the roots of the quadratic $(b - x)^2 - 4(a - x)(c - x) = 0$ where a, b, c are real.

(c) Discuss the nature of the roots of the equation $x^2 + 2(3\lambda + 5) x + 2(9\lambda^2 + 25) = 0$

21. (a) The equation $ax^2 + bx + c = 0$ where a, b, c are real numbers connected by the relation $4a + 2b + c = 0$ and $ab > 0$ has real roots.

(b) If a, b, c are positive and are in A. P., prove that the roots of the quadratic equation $ax^2 + bx + c = 0$ are real for $\left| \dfrac{c}{a} - 7 \right| \geq 4\sqrt{3}$.

(c) If a, b, c are +ive and $a = 2b + 3c$, then roots of the equation $ax^2 + bx + c = 0$ are real for

    (a) $\left| \dfrac{a}{c} - 11 \right| \geq 4\sqrt{7}$ (b) $\left| \dfrac{c}{a} - 11 \right| \geq 4\sqrt{7}$

    (c) $\left| \dfrac{b}{c} - 4 \right| \geq 2\sqrt{7}$ (d) $\left| \dfrac{c}{b} - 4 \right| \geq 2\sqrt{7}$

22. (a)* Show that the roots of
$$(a^2 + b^2) x^2 - 2b (a + c) x + (b^2 + c^2) = 0$$
will be real if a, b, c are in G.P. and in this case these roots will be equal as well.

    (b) If a, b, c be distinct real and + ive numbers which are in H.P., then the roots of the equation $ax^2 + 2bx + c = 0$ are real and distinct. Is this statement true or not ?

23. (a)* Discuss the nature of the roots of the equation $4ax^2 + 3bx + 2c = 0$ where $a, b, c \in R$ and are connected by the relation $a + b + c = 0$.

    (b)* If the roots of the equation
$$[a^2 + 2(1 - b)] x^2 + 2a(1 + b) x + 2b(b - 1) + a^2 = 0$$
be equal, then prove that $a^2 = 4b$.

24. (a) If the roots of the equation
$$(a^2 + b^2) x^2 - 2(bc + ad) x + (c^2 + d^2) = 0$$
be real, then prove that they will be equal as well and then $\dfrac{a}{b} = \dfrac{d}{c}$.

    (b) Prove that if the roots of the equation $(a^4 + b^4) x^2 + 4abcdx + (c^4 + d^4) = 0$ are real then they can't be unequal.

    (c) If a, b, c be real then prove that the roots of the equation $\dfrac{1}{x + a} + \dfrac{1}{x + b} + \dfrac{1}{x + c} = \dfrac{3}{x}, x \neq 0$ are all real.

25. Discuss the nature of the roots of the equations

    (a) $(a + c - b) x^2 + 2cx + (b + c - a) = 0$

    (b) $(b + c) x^2 - (a + b + c) x + a = 0$

    (c) $2(a^2 + b^2) x^2 + 2(a + b) x + 1 = 0$.

26. (a)* Show that the roots of the equation
$$(b + c - a) x^2 + (c + a - b) x + (a + b - c) = 0$$
are rational if a, b, c be all rationals such that $a + b + c = 0$

    (b)* Prove that the roots of the equation
$$(a + 2b - 3c) x^2 + (b + 2c - 3a) x + (c + 2a - 3b) = 0$$
are rational, if a, b, c are rationals. Hence determine the roots of the equation.

(c)* If $(ax^2 + bx + c) y + (d' x^2 + b' x + c') = 0$ and x is a rational function of y, then prove that $(ac' - d' c)^2 = (ab' - d' b) (bc' - b' c)$

(d) For what integral values of k, the roots of the equation $kx^2 + (2k - 1) x + (k - 2) = 0$ are rational ?

27. (a) If the roots of the equation $x^2 - 2cx + ab = 0$ be real and unequal, then prove that the roots of $x^2 - 2(a + b) x + (a^2 + b^2) + 2c^2 = 0$ will be imaginary.

    (b)* Consider the quadratic equations
$$ax^2 + 2bx + c = 0 \text{ and}$$
$$(a + c) (ax^2 + 2bx + c) - 2(ac - b^2) (x^2 + 1) = 0$$
If the roots of one are real (complex) then the roots of the other are complex (real).

28. (a)* If the roots of the equation $x^2 - ax + b = 0$ are real and differ by a quantity which is less than c ($c > 0$), then b lies between $\dfrac{a^2 - c^2}{4}$ and $\dfrac{a^2}{4}$.

    (b) If the roots of the equation
$$(a - 1) (x^2 + x + 1)^2 = (a + 1) (x^4 + x^2 + 1)$$
are real and distinct then, prove that $a^2 - 4 > 0$.

29. (a) Show that if p, q, r, s are real numbers and $pr = 2(q + s)$, then at least one of the equations $x^2 + px + q = 0$, $x^2 + rx + s = 0$ has real roots.

    (b)* If $P(x) = ax^2 + bx + c$ and
$$Q(x) = -ax^2 + dx + c \quad \text{where } ac \neq 0$$
then $P(x) Q(x) = 0$ has at least two real roots.

30.* If $a < b < c < d$, then the roots of the equation $(x - a) (x - c) + 2(x - b) (x - d) = 0$ are real and distinct.

    (i) True   (ii) False

31. (a) The equation $2(\log_3 x)^2 - |\log_3 x| + k = 0$ has four solutions; determine the interval in which k lies.

    (b)* If α and β are the roots of $x^2 + px + q = 0$ and α^4, β^4 are the roots of $x^2 - rx + s = 0$, then the equation $x^2 - 4qx + 2q^2 - r = 0$ has always two real roots.

32. (a) If the roots of the equation $x^2 + a^2 = 8x + 6a$ be real, then prove that a lies between -2 and 8.

                               (M.P.C.E.E. 1999)

    (b) Prove that if the roots of $9x^2 + 4ax + 4 = 0$ are imaginary, then a must lie between -3 and 3.

    (c) The equation $x^2 + 2(m - 1) x + m + 5 = 0$ has at least one + ive root. Determine the range for m.

33. (a) If $a \neq 1$ and $a \neq -2$, show that the roots of the equation

$(a^2 + a - 2) x^2 + (2a^2 + a + 3) x + a^2 - 1 = 0$ are rational. Hence solve the equation.

(b)* Let A, B, C be three angles such that $A = \dfrac{\pi}{4}$ and $\tan B \tan C = p$. Find all possible values of p such that A, B, C are the angles of a triangle.

(I.I.T. 1997)

(c) If $\tan A$ and $\tan B$ are the roots of the quadratic equation $x^2 - px + q = 0$, then the value of $\sin^2 (A + B)$ is

(a) $\dfrac{p^2}{p^2 + q^2}$ (b) $\dfrac{p^2}{(p + q)^2}$

(c) $1 - \dfrac{p}{(1 - q)^2}$ (d) $\dfrac{p^2}{(1 - q)^2 + p^2}$

34. (a) If p, q, r are real and $p \neq q$, then roots of the equation $(p - q) x^2 + 5 (p + q) x - 2 (p - q) = 0$ are

(i) Real and equal   (ii) Complex
(iii) Real and unequal (iv) None of these

(b) The roots of $px^2 + 2qx + r = 0$ and $qx^2 - 2\sqrt{pr}\, x + q = 0$ are simultaneously real then

(i) $p = q, \ r \neq 0$ (ii) $p/q = q/r$
(iii) $2q = \pm \sqrt{pr}$ (iv) none of these

(c) If $x^2 - 4x + \log_{1/2} a$ does not have two distinct roots, then the maximum value of a

(a) $-\dfrac{1}{4}$ (b) $\dfrac{1}{4}$

(c) $\dfrac{1}{16}$ (d) none

35. (a) If the roots α, β of $ax^2 + bx + c = 0$ be real, then establish the relation between the coefficients under the following conditions :

(i) Roots are equal and opposite.
(ii) Roots are of opposite signs.
(iii) Roots are both $-$ ive.
(iv) Roots are both $+$ ive.

(b) Let $a > 0, \ b > 0$, then both roots of the equation $ax^2 + bx + c = 0$

(i) are real and negative
(ii) have negative real parts
(iii) none of these.

(c) If the roots of the equation $bx^2 + cx + a = 0$ be imaginary, then for all real values of x, the expression $3b^2 x^2 + 6bcx + 2c^2$ is

(a) less than $-4ab$ (b) greater than $4ab$
(c) less than $4ab$ (d) greater than $-4ab$

(AIEEE 2009)

36. (a)* Prove that the roots of

$(a - b)^2 x^2 + 2 (a + b - 2c) x + 1 = 0$

are real or imaginary according as c does not or does lie between a and b, $a < b$.

(b) If the roots of the equation

$(m - 3) x^2 - 2 m x + 5m = 0$

are real and $+$ ive, then prove that $m \in \left] 3, \dfrac{15}{4} \right]$

(c) If the equation $x^2 + 2 (a + 1) x + 9a - 5 = 0$ has only negative roots, then show that $a \geq 6$.

(d) If both the roots of the equation $x^2 - 6ax + 2 - 2a + 9a^2 = 0$ exceed 3, then show that $a > \dfrac{11}{9}$.

▶ **Algebraic Expressions**

37. Find for what real values of x the expressions

(a) $x^2 - 2x - 3$

(b) $2x^2 + 5x - 3$ are positive or negative.

(c) If $x^2 + 2ax + 10 - 3a > 0$, for all $x \in R$, then

(a) $a < -5$ (b) $-5 < a < 2$
(c) $a > 5$ (d) $2 < a < 5$

(Screening 2004)

38. (a)* For real values of x, prove that the value of the expression $\dfrac{11x^2 + 12x + 6}{x^2 + 4x + 2}$ cannot lie between -5 and 3.

(b) $x^2 + (a - b) x + (1 - a - b) = 0, a, b \in R$. Find the condition on a, for which both roots of the equation are real and unequal. **(IIT 2003)**

(c) Determine the values of x which satisfy the inequalities $x^2 - 3x + 2 > 0$ and $x^2 - 3x - 4 \leq 0$

39. (a)* If x be real prove that the expression $\dfrac{x + 2}{2x^2 + 3x + 6}$ takes all values in the interval $\left[-\dfrac{1}{13}, \dfrac{1}{3} \right]$.

(b) Show that the value of

$\dfrac{\tan x}{\tan 3x}$ or $\dfrac{\sin x \cos 3x}{\cos x \sin 3x}$

whenever defined never lies between $1/3$ and 3.

(I.I.T. 1997, 92)

(c) If x is real, the maximum value of $\dfrac{3x^2 + 9x + 17}{3x^2 + 9x + 7}$ is :

(a) 41 (b) 1
(c) $\dfrac{17}{7}$ (d) $\dfrac{1}{4}$

(AIEEE 2006)

40. (a) Prove that for real values of x the expression $\dfrac{(x - 1) (x + 3)}{(x - 2) (x + 4)}$ cannot lie between $\dfrac{4}{9}$ and 1.

(b) If x is real, the expression $\dfrac{x^2 + 2x - 11}{x - 3}$ takes all values which do not lie between 4 and 12.

41. (a) If x is real, find the maximum and minimum values of $\dfrac{x^2 + 14x + 9}{x^2 + 2x + 3}$.

(b) Prove that for any real values of x the expression $\dfrac{x + a}{x^2 + bx + c^2}$ will have any value if $b^2 > 4c^2$ and $a^2 + c^2 < ab$.

42. (a) If x is real show that $\dfrac{x^2 - x + 1}{x^2 + x + 1}$ takes values from $\dfrac{1}{3}$ to 3.

(b) Show that $\dfrac{x^2 - 3x + 4}{x^2 + 3x + 4}$ can never be greater than 7 nor less than $1/7$ for real values of x.

(c) Find out the range in which the value of the function $\dfrac{x^2 + 34x - 71}{x^2 + 2x - 7}$ lies for all real values of x. Justify your answer. **(B.I.T.S. 1999)**

43. (a)* Find the values of x for which the following inequality holds $\dfrac{8x^2 + 16x - 51}{(2x - 3)(x + 4)} > 3$.

(b) Find the values of x, which satisfy the inequality $\dfrac{x - 2}{x + 2} > \dfrac{2x - 3}{4x - 1}$.

44.* Find the set of all x for which $\dfrac{2x}{(2x^2 + 5x + 2)} > \dfrac{1}{(x + 1)}$.

45. (a) Show that if x is real, the expression $\dfrac{x^2 - bc}{2x - b - c}$ has no real values between b and c.

(b)* For real x, the function $\dfrac{(x - a)(x - b)}{x - c}$ will assume all real values provided
(i) $a > b > c$ (ii) $a < b < c$
(iii) $a > c > b$ (iv) $a < c < b$

(c) If the roots of the equation $ax^2 + bx + c = 0$ are real and of opposite sign then the roots of the equation $\alpha(x - \beta)^2 + \beta(x - \alpha)^2 = 0$ are
(a) positive
(b) negative
(c) real and of opp. sign
(d) imaginary

46. (a) Show that the expression $\dfrac{px^2 + 3x - 4}{p + 3x - 4x^2}$ will be capable of all values when x is real, provided that p has any value between 1 and 7.

(b)* Suppose $f(x)$ is such a quadratic expession that it is positive for all real x. If $g(x) = f(x) + f'(x) + f''(x)$, then for any real x, prove that $g(x) > 0$. **(I.I.T. 1990)**

47. (a)* If x is real, prove that $\dfrac{x^2 - 2x\cos\alpha + 1}{x^2 - 2x\cos\beta + 1}$ lies between $\left(\sin^2\dfrac{\alpha}{2} \Big/ \sin^2\dfrac{\beta}{2}\right)$ and $\left(\cos^2\dfrac{\alpha}{2} \Big/ \cos^2\dfrac{\beta}{2}\right)$.

(b)* Prove that the expression $\dfrac{\tan(x + \theta)}{\tan(x - \theta)}$ does not lie between $\tan^2(\pi/4 - \theta)$ and $\tan^2(\pi/4 + \theta)$.

(c) Let x, y, z be real variables which satisfy the equation $xy + yz + zx = 7$ and $x + y + z = 6$. Find the range in which the variables lie.

48. (a) If x be real, then the expression $\dfrac{2a(x - 1)\sin^2\theta}{x^2 - \sin^2\theta}$ does not lie between $2a\sin^2(\theta/2)$ and $2a\cos^2(\theta/2)$.

(b)* A function $f : R \to R$, where R is the set of real numbers, is defined by $f(x) = \dfrac{\alpha x^2 + 6x - 8}{\alpha + 6x - 8x^2}$. Find the interval of values of α for which f is onto. Is the function one-to-one for $\alpha = 3$? Justify your answer. **(I.I.T. 1996)**

49. (a) Let $y = \sqrt{\left(\dfrac{(x + 1)(x - 3)}{x - 2}\right)}$. Find all the real values of x for which y takes real values.

(b) Determine all real values of x for which the expression $\left\{\dfrac{2}{x^2 - x + 1} - \dfrac{1}{x + 1} - \dfrac{2x + 1}{x^3 + 1}\right\}^{1/2}$ takes real values.

50. For real values of x, if the expression $\dfrac{(ax - b)(dx - c)}{(bx - a)(cx - d)}$ assumes all real values then $(a^2 - b^2)$ and $(c^2 - d^2)$ must have the same sign.

51. (a) Find all integral values of x for which
$$\underset{\text{I}}{(5x - 1)} < \underset{\text{II}}{(x + 1)^2} < \underset{\text{III}}{(7x - 3)}.$$

(b) Solve $\left|\dfrac{12x}{4x^2 + 9}\right| \leq 1$.

52. (a)* If x is real, find values of k for which $\left|\dfrac{x^2 + k \, x + 1}{x^2 + x + 1}\right| < 2$ is valid.

(b) For real values of x, it is given that
$$\left|\frac{x^2 - 3x - 1}{x^2 + x + 1}\right| < 3.$$
Find the limits for x.

53. For what values of m is the inequality

(a) $\left|\dfrac{x^2 + mx + 1}{x^2 + x + 1}\right| < 3$

(b) $-3 < \dfrac{x^2 + mx - 2}{x^2 - x + 1} < 2$

satisfied for all the values of x ? **(J.E.E.W.B. 2000)**

54.* The inequality $(x - 3m)(x - m - 3) < 0$ is satisfied for x in $[1, 3]$. Determine the values of m for this to hold good.

55.* The real numbers x_1, x_2, x_3 satisfying the equation $x^3 - x^2 + \beta x + \gamma = 0$ are in A.P. Find the intervals in which β and γ lie. **(I.I.T. 1996)**

56. (a) Examine whether for real values of a and b $a(x^2 - y^2) - bxy$ has real linear factors.

(b) If x and y (real) satisfy the relation $x^2 + y^2 = 6x - 8y$ then determine the intervals in which x and y will be. In other words find out their greatest and least values.

57. (a) If $\dfrac{1}{a} + \dfrac{1}{b} + \dfrac{1}{c} = \dfrac{1}{a+b+c}$ then prove that any two of a, b, c must be equal and opposite. All the quantities a, b, c being assumed to be real.

(b) Resolve into factors the expression
$$(a + b + c)^3 - a^3 - b^3 - c^3$$

58. (a) If $2x^2 - 3xy - 2y^2 = 7$, then prove that there will be only two integral pairs (x, y) satisfying the above relation.

(b) If $2x^2 y^2 + y^2 - 6x^2 - 12 = 0$, then prove that there will be only four integral pairs (x, y) satisfying the above relation.

59. If x and y are + ive integers, then find the solutions of the following equations separately :
(i) $7x + 12y = 220$ (ii) $14x - 11y = 29$.

60. (a) a, b, c are lengths of sides of an scalene triangle. If equation
$$x^2 + 2(a + b + c)x + 3\lambda(ab + bc + ac) = 0$$
has real and distinct roots, then the value of λ is given by :

(a) $\lambda < \dfrac{4}{3}$ (b) $\dfrac{11}{3} < \lambda < \dfrac{17}{3}$

(c) $\dfrac{11}{6} < \lambda < \dfrac{15}{4}$ (d) $\lambda \geq 1$
(I.I.T. 2006)

(b) If a, b are the roots of $x^2 - 10cx - 11d = 0$ and c, d are the roots of $x^2 - 10ax - 11b = 0$, then find the value of $a + b + c + d$. (a, b, c, d are distinct numbers). **(I.I.T. 2006)**

Solutions to Problem Set (2)

1. (a) Let α be a common root which will satisfy both the equations
$$\therefore \quad a\alpha^2 + b\alpha + c = 0$$
and $a'\alpha^2 + b'\alpha + c' = 0$.

Solving by the method of cross multiplication we get
$$\frac{\alpha^2}{bc' - b'c} = \frac{\alpha}{ca' - c'a} = \frac{1}{ab' - a'b}$$

or $\dfrac{\alpha^2}{P} = \dfrac{\alpha}{Q} = \dfrac{1}{R}$, say

$$\therefore \quad \alpha = \frac{\alpha^2}{\alpha} = \frac{bc' - b'c}{ca' - c'a} = \frac{P}{Q}$$

$$\alpha = \frac{\alpha}{1} = \frac{ca' - c'a}{ab' - a'b} = \frac{Q}{R} \qquad \ldots(1)$$

Since $\quad \alpha = \alpha$,
$$\therefore \quad \frac{bc' - b'c}{ca' - c'a} = \frac{ca' - c'a}{ab' - a'b}.$$

Required condition is
$$(bc' - b'c)(ab' - a'b) = (ca' - c'a)^2$$

or $\quad PR = Q^2$

The value of the common root is given by (1).

Note : The value of common root.

Make the coefficient of x^2 in the two equations same or unity and then subtract the two.
$$\alpha^2 + \frac{b}{a}\alpha + \frac{c}{a} = 0$$
$$\alpha^2 + \frac{b'}{a'}\alpha + \frac{c'}{a'} = 0$$

Now subtract
$$\therefore \quad \left(\frac{b}{a} - \frac{b'}{a'}\right)\alpha + \left(\frac{c}{a} - \frac{c'}{a'}\right) = 0$$

or $\quad \alpha = \dfrac{ca' - ac'}{ab' - a'b} = \dfrac{Q}{R} = \dfrac{P}{Q}$ as $PR = Q^2$

(b) If α be a root of first equation then $1/\alpha$ will be a root of the second.
$$\therefore \quad a\alpha^2 + b\alpha + c = 0$$
and $a' . (1/\alpha)^2 + b' . (1/\alpha) + c' = 0$
or $\quad c'\alpha^2 + b'\alpha + a' = 0$
$$\therefore \quad \frac{\alpha^2}{ba' - cb'} = \frac{\alpha}{cc' - aa'} = \frac{1}{ab' - bc'}$$
$$\therefore \quad (cc' - aa')^2 = (ba' - cb')(ab' - bc')$$
is the required condition.

(c) If both the roots are common then their sum and product will be same.
$$\therefore \quad S = -b/a = -b'/a' \quad \therefore \quad a/a' = b/b'$$
$$P = c/a = c'/a' \quad \text{or} \quad a/a' = c/c'.$$
Hence the condition is $a/a' = b/b' = c/c'$.

2. (a) Proceed as in Q. 1.

(b) $h(x) = f(x) - xg(x) = bx^2 + 2cx + d = 0$

will also have the same common root. Now determine the condition that $g(x) = 0$ and $h(x) = 0$ have a common root.

3. (a) As in Q. 1, $\dfrac{\alpha^2}{17k} = \dfrac{\alpha}{6k} = \dfrac{1}{-1}$ ...(1)

$\therefore (6k)^2 = 17k(-1)$ or $k(36k + 17) = 0$

$\therefore k = 0$ and $-17/36$.

Also from (1),

$\alpha = \dfrac{17k}{6k} = \dfrac{17}{6}$ or $\alpha = \dfrac{6k}{-1} = 0$ or $\dfrac{17}{6}$.

Hence the common root is either zero or $17/6$.

(b) Ans. $a = 0, 24$.

4. (a) $a = 4$ or 8. Just as in Q. 1 or Q. 3.

(b) Common root is 2.

(c) $\bar{z} = z$ as z is real.

Taking conjugate $z^2 + \bar{\alpha}z + \bar{\beta} = 0$

$\therefore \dfrac{z^2}{\alpha\bar{\beta} - \bar{\alpha}\beta} = \dfrac{z}{\beta - \bar{\beta}} = \dfrac{1}{\bar{\alpha} - \alpha}$

$\therefore (\beta - \bar{\beta})^2 = (\bar{\alpha} - \alpha)(\alpha\bar{\beta} - \bar{\alpha}\beta)$

5. Ans. (i).

a, b, c in G. P. $\Rightarrow b^2 - ac = 0$

$\Delta_1 = 4(b^2 - ac) = 0$ $\therefore$ It has equal roots

$\therefore \alpha + \alpha = -\dfrac{2b}{a}$ or $\alpha = -\dfrac{b}{a}$

Since the two equations have common roots therefore $\alpha = -b/a$ must also be a root of 2nd equation.

$\therefore d\left(-\dfrac{b}{a}\right)^2 + 2e\left(-\dfrac{b}{a}\right) + f = 0$

or $\dfrac{d}{a} \cdot \dfrac{b^2}{a} + \dfrac{2e}{b}\left(\dfrac{-b^2}{a}\right) + \dfrac{f}{c} \cdot c = 0$ **(Note)**

or $\dfrac{d}{a} \cdot \dfrac{b^2}{a} - \dfrac{2e}{b}\left(\dfrac{b^2}{a}\right) + \dfrac{f}{c}\left(\dfrac{b^2}{a}\right) = 0$

$\because b^2 = ac$

or $\dfrac{d}{a} - \dfrac{2e}{b} + \dfrac{f}{c} = 0$ or $\dfrac{d}{a}, \dfrac{e}{b}, \dfrac{f}{c}$ are in A.P.

Another form : Assume that p, q, r are in G.P., so that $q^2 = pr$ which implies that roots of 2nd equation are equal and rest as above.

6. (a) $\alpha + \beta = -p$, $\alpha\beta = q$, $\gamma + \delta = -r$, $\gamma\delta = s$

$(\alpha - \gamma)(\alpha - \delta)(\beta - \gamma)(\beta - \delta)$

$= [\alpha^2 - \alpha(\gamma + \delta) + \gamma\delta][\beta^2 - \beta(\gamma + \delta) + \gamma\delta]$

$= (\alpha^2 + r\alpha + s)(\beta^2 + r\beta + s)$ ...(1)

Since α is a root of $x^2 + px + q = 0$

$\therefore \alpha^2 + p\alpha + q = 0$

or $\alpha^2 = -p\alpha - q$ and similarly $\beta^2 = -p\beta - q$.

Hence from (1) we have to evaluate the value of

$(-p\alpha - q + r\alpha + s)(-p\beta - q + r\beta + s)$

$= [(r - p)\alpha - (q - s)][(r - p)\beta - (q - s)]$

$= (r - p)^2 \alpha\beta - (r - p)(q - s)(\alpha + \beta) + (q - s)^2$

$= (r - p)^2 q - (r - p)(q - s)(-p) + (q - s)^2$

$= (r - p)[(qr - pq) + (pq - ps)] + (q - s)^2$

$= (q - s)^2 - (p - r)(qr - ps)$ ...(2)

In case the equations have a common root then $\alpha = \gamma$ or $\alpha = \delta$ and in either case

$\alpha - \gamma = 0$ or $\alpha - \delta = 0$

and hence the given expression is zero

Therefore from (2) the required condition is

$(q - s)^2 = (p - r)(qr - ps)$.

This condition can be obtained directly also as in Q. 1.

(b) We have $dx^2 + (a + c)x - b = 0$

$bx^2 + (a - c)x - d = 0$

$\therefore \dfrac{x^2}{-d(a + c) + b(a - c)} = \dfrac{x}{-(b^2 - d^2)}$

$= \dfrac{1}{d(a - c) - b(a + c)}$

or $\dfrac{x^2}{a(b - d) - c(b + d)} = \dfrac{x}{-(b^2 - d^2)}$

$= \dfrac{1}{-a(b - d) - c(b + d)}$

or $\dfrac{x^2}{c(b + d) - a(b - d)} = \dfrac{x}{b^2 - d^2}$

$= \dfrac{1}{c(b + d) + a(b - d)}$

$\therefore M^2 = NL$

$(b^2 - d^2)^2 = c^2(b + d)^2 - a^2(b - d)^2$

7. $f(\alpha) = a_1\alpha^2 + b_1\alpha + c_1$

or $a_1\alpha^2 + b_1\alpha + [c_1 - f(\alpha)] = 0$ ...(1)

Again α is a root of $ax^2 + bx + c = 0$

$\therefore a\alpha^2 + b\alpha + c = 0$ ...(2)

Solving (1) and (2) by cross multiplication, we get

$\dfrac{\alpha^2}{b_1 c - bc_1 + bf(\alpha)} = \dfrac{\alpha}{ac_1 - ca_1 - af(\alpha)} = \dfrac{1}{a_1 b - ab_1}$

$\therefore [ac_1 - a_1 c - af(\alpha)]^2$

$= (a_1 b - ab_1)[b_1 c - bc_1 + bf(\alpha)]$

Writing above as a quadratic in $f(\alpha)$

$a^2[f(\alpha)]^2 + f(\alpha)[\ ] + (ac_1 - a_1 c)^2 - (a_1 b - ab_1)$

$(b_1 c - bc_1) = 0$

Above shows that $f(\alpha)$ is a root of

$a^2 t^2 + t[\ ] + (ac_1 - a_1 c)^2$

$-(a_1 b - ab_1)(b_1 c - bc_1) = 0$ ...(1)

Similarly we can assume that $f(\beta)$ will also be a root of (1). Hence the roots of t quadratic given by (1) are $f(\alpha)$ and $f(\beta)$.

$\therefore \quad f(\alpha) \cdot f(\beta) = $ Product of roots of (1).

or $\quad f(\alpha) \cdot f(\beta) = \dfrac{1}{a^2}[(ac_1 - a_1 c)^2$

$$- (a_1 b - a b_1)(b_1 c - b c_1)] \quad \dots(2)$$

It is same as given result if we change the signs of both the last brackets in the numerator.

In case α or β be a common root of

$ax^2 + bx + c = 0$ and $f(x) = a_1 x^2 + b_1 x + c = 0$

then $f(\alpha) = 0$.

Hence from (2), $f(\alpha) \cdot f(\beta) = 0$

$\therefore \quad (ac_1 - a_1 c)^2 - (a_1 b - a b_1)(b_1 c - b c_1) = 0$

or $\quad (ac_1 - a_1 c)^2 = (bc_1 - b_1 c)(ab_1 - a_1 b)$

is the required condition.

8. $\alpha + \beta = -b/a$ $\quad\dots(1)$

$\alpha\beta = c/a$ $\quad\dots(2)$

$\alpha_1 - \beta = -b_1/a_1$ $\quad\dots(3)$

$-\alpha_1\beta = c_1/a_1$ $\quad\dots(4)$

Adding (1) and (3),

$$\alpha + \alpha_1 = -\dfrac{b}{a} - \dfrac{b_1}{a_1} = S. \quad\dots(5)$$

Dividing (1) by (2) and (3) by (4), we get

$\dfrac{1}{\beta} + \dfrac{1}{\alpha} = -\dfrac{b}{c}$ and $-\dfrac{1}{\beta} + \dfrac{1}{\alpha_1} = -\dfrac{b_1}{c_1}$

Adding them, we get

$$\dfrac{1}{\alpha} + \dfrac{1}{\alpha_1} = -\dfrac{b}{c} - \dfrac{b_1}{c_1}$$

or $\quad \dfrac{\alpha + \alpha_1}{\alpha\alpha_1} = \dfrac{S}{P} = -\dfrac{b}{c} - \dfrac{b_1}{c_1}$ $\quad\dots(6)$

$\therefore$ The equation is $x^2 - xS + P = 0$

or $\quad \dfrac{x^2}{-S} + x - \dfrac{P}{S} = 0$. Now use (5) and (6)

9. **(a)** Let the roots of the equation be α, β and α, γ as one root is common.

$\alpha + \beta = -b, \quad \alpha\beta = ca$ $\quad\dots(1)$

$\alpha + \gamma = -c, \quad \alpha\gamma = ab$. $\quad\dots(2)$

We are to find the equation whose roots are β and γ for which we must know the values of $\beta + \gamma$ and $\beta\gamma$.

$\because x^2 + bx + ca = 0$ and $x^2 + cx + ab = 0$

have a common root

$\therefore \quad \dfrac{x^2}{a(b^2 - c^2)} = \dfrac{x}{a(c-b)} = \dfrac{1}{(c-b)}$

or $\quad \dfrac{x^2}{-a(b+c)} = \dfrac{x}{a} = \dfrac{1}{1}$ $\quad \therefore a^2 = 1 [-a(b+c)]$

or $\quad a = -(b+c)$ or $a + b + c = 0$

is the condition. $\quad\dots(3)$

Also the common root $x = a$. i.e. $\alpha = a$.

Putting $\alpha = a$ in (1) and (2), we get $\beta = c, \quad \gamma = b$

$\therefore \quad S = \beta + \gamma = b + c = -a,$ by (3)

$P = \beta\gamma = bc$. Hence the equation whose roots are β and γ is $x^2 - Sx + P = 0$ or $x^2 + ax + bc = 0$

(b) Refer part (b). Common root is $1/a$, and other roots are ac and ab.

$\therefore \quad S = a(b+c), P = a^2 bc$.

10. Both the equations have coefficient of x^2 unity and hence common root is obtained by subtracting the two equations.

$\therefore \quad x(a-c) + (b-d) = 0$

$\therefore \quad \alpha = -\dfrac{(b-d)}{(a-c)}$.

If the other other root of first equation be β, then

$\alpha + \beta = -a \quad \therefore \quad \beta = -a - \alpha$

or $\quad \beta = -a + \dfrac{b-d}{a-c} = \dfrac{-a^2 + ac + b - d}{a-c}$

$\therefore \quad \beta(a-c) + a^2 - ac - b + d = 0.$ $\quad\dots(1)$

Since β is a root of Ist.

$\therefore \quad \beta^2 + a\beta + b = 0.$ $\quad\dots(2)$

Add the above two, we get the results (1) and (2).

11. **(a)** Since each pair has a common root, the root of the three equations be taken as α, β; β, γ and γ, α respectively.

$\therefore \quad \alpha + \beta = -p_1, \quad \beta + \gamma = -p_2, \gamma + \alpha = -p_3$

$\alpha\beta = q_1, \beta\gamma = q_2, \gamma\alpha = q_3$.

The given result can be written as on adding $2\Sigma p_1 p_2$ in both sides.

$$(p_1 + p_2 + p_3)^2 = 4[\Sigma p_1 p_2 - \Sigma q_1]$$

L.H.S. $= [2(\alpha + \beta + \gamma)]^2 = 4(\alpha + \beta + \gamma)^2$

R.H.S. $= 4[(\alpha + \beta)(\beta + \gamma) + (\beta + \gamma)(\gamma + \alpha)$

$$+ (\gamma + \alpha)(\alpha + \beta) - (\alpha\beta + \beta\gamma + \gamma\alpha)]$$

$= 4[\alpha^2 + \beta^2 + \gamma^2 + 2\alpha\beta + 2\beta\gamma + 2\gamma\alpha]$

$= 4[\alpha + \beta + \gamma]^2 = $ L.H.S.

(b) Since each pair has common root, let the roots be α, β for I; β, γ for II; and γ, α for III.

$\therefore \quad \alpha + \beta = -a, \quad \alpha\beta = bc$

$\beta + \gamma = -b, \quad \beta\gamma = ca$

$\gamma + \alpha = -c, \quad \gamma\alpha = ab$

Adding and multiplying, we get

$2(\alpha + \beta + \gamma) = -(a + b + c)$

$\therefore \quad \Sigma\alpha = -\dfrac{1}{2}\Sigma a = $ sum

$\alpha^2\beta^2\gamma^2 = a^2 b^2 c^2$

$\therefore \quad \alpha\beta\gamma = abc = $ Product

(c) Let α be the common root of the three equations and their other roots be β, γ, δ respectively

$\therefore \quad \alpha + \beta = -a, \alpha\beta = 12$

$\qquad \alpha + \gamma = -b, \alpha\gamma = 15$

$\qquad \alpha + \delta = -(a+b), \alpha\delta = 36$

$\therefore \quad (\alpha+\beta) + (\alpha+\gamma) = -(a+b) = \alpha + \delta$

$\therefore \quad \alpha + \beta + \gamma = \delta$ ...(1)

Again $\alpha(\beta + \gamma + \delta) = 12 + 15 + 36 = 63$

or $\quad \alpha(2\delta - \alpha) = 63$ by (1)

or $\quad 2\alpha\delta - \alpha^2 - 63$ or $72 - \alpha^2 = 63$ $\because \alpha\delta = 36$

$\therefore \quad \alpha^2 = 9$ $\therefore$ $\alpha = 3, -3$

$\qquad \alpha = 3 \implies \beta = 4, \gamma = 5, \delta = 12$

$\qquad \alpha = -3 \implies \beta = -4, \gamma = -5, \delta = -12$

$\therefore \quad a = -(\alpha+\beta) = 7, -7; b = -(\alpha+\gamma) = 8, -8$

12. Since each pair has a common root, we choose them as α, β for I; β, γ for II and γ, α for III

$\therefore \quad \alpha + \beta = -\dfrac{b_1}{a_1}, \beta + \gamma = -\dfrac{b_2}{a_2}, \gamma + \alpha = -\dfrac{b_3}{a_3}$ ...(A)

$\qquad \alpha\beta = \dfrac{c_1}{a_1}, \beta\gamma = \dfrac{c_2}{a_2}, \gamma\alpha = \dfrac{c_3}{a_3}$ ...(B)

The first relation can be re-written as

(i) $\quad \dfrac{a_1 a_2 \left(\dfrac{c_1}{a_1} + \dfrac{c_2}{a_2}\right)}{a_1 a_2 \left(\dfrac{c_1}{a_1} - \dfrac{c_2}{a_2}\right)} + \dfrac{b_3}{a_3} \dfrac{1}{\left(\dfrac{b_2}{a_2} - \dfrac{b_1}{a_1}\right)}$

or $\quad \dfrac{(\alpha\beta + \beta\gamma)}{(\alpha\beta - \beta\gamma)} - (\gamma + \alpha) \dfrac{1}{-(\beta+\gamma) + (\alpha+\beta)}$

or $\quad \dfrac{\alpha + \gamma}{\alpha - \gamma} - \dfrac{\gamma + \alpha}{\alpha - \gamma} = 0$

Again L.H.S. of 2nd relation is

(1) $\quad \left[\dfrac{a_1 a_2 \left(\dfrac{b_2}{a_2} - \dfrac{b_1}{a_1}\right)}{a_1 a_2 \left(\dfrac{c_2}{a_2} - \dfrac{c_1}{a_1}\right)}\right]^2 = \left[\dfrac{-(\beta+\gamma) + (\alpha+\beta)}{(\beta\gamma - \alpha\beta)}\right]^2$

$\qquad = \dfrac{(\alpha - \gamma)^2}{[\beta(\gamma - \alpha)]^2} = \dfrac{1}{\beta^2}$

R.H.S. $= \dfrac{c_3}{a_3} \cdot \dfrac{1}{\dfrac{c_1}{a_1} \cdot \dfrac{c_2}{a_2}} = \gamma\alpha \cdot \dfrac{1}{\beta\gamma \cdot \alpha\beta} = \dfrac{1}{\beta^2}$

Hence L.H.S. = R.H.S. = $\dfrac{1}{\beta^2}$.

13. As in Q. 1, the condition for common roots is

$(cd' - c'a)^2 = 4(bc' - b'c)(ab' - d'b)$ ...(1)

For equality of roots of 2nd equation its discriminant $B^2 - 4AC = 0$

$\qquad (2bb' - ac' - d'c)^2 - 4(b^2 - ac)(b'^2 - d'c') = 0$

or $\quad 4b^2 b'^2 + (ac' + d'c)^2 - 4bb'(ac' + d'c)$

$= 4b^2 b'^2 - 4b^2 d'c' - 4b'^2 ac + 4ad'cc'$

or $\quad (ac' + d'c)^2 - 4ad'cc' = 4bb'(ac' + d'c)$

$\qquad\qquad\qquad\qquad - 4b^2 d'c' - 4b'^2 ac$

or $\quad (cd' - c'a)^2 = 4[bc'(ab' - d'b) - b'c(ab' - d'b)]$

$\qquad = 4[(ab' - d'b)(bc' - b'c)]$

which is true by (1).

14. (a) Ans. –1.

$\qquad \alpha^2 + a\alpha + b = 0,$

$\qquad \alpha^2 + b\alpha + a = 0$

Subtracting, $\alpha(a - b) - (a - b) = 0$ $\therefore$ $\alpha - 1 = 0$

Putting $\alpha = 1$ in any, $1 + a + b = 0$ $\therefore$ $a + b = -1$

(b) Proceeding as usual the condition of common root gives

$\qquad (bc - 1)^2 = (b - c^2)(-c - b^2)$

or $\quad b^3 + c^3 + 1 - 3bc \cdot 1 = 0$

or $\quad (b + c + 1)(b^2 + c^2 + 1 - bc - c - b) = 0$ etc.

$\because \quad x^3 + y^3 + z^3 - 3xyz$

$\qquad = (x + y + z)(x^2 + y^2 + z^2 - xy - yz - zx) = 0$

(c) Ans. (d).

We have the following relations

$\qquad \alpha + \beta = p$ ...(1)

$\qquad \alpha\beta = r$ ...(2)

and $\quad \dfrac{\alpha}{2} + 2\beta = q$ ...(3)

$\qquad \dfrac{\alpha}{2} \cdot 2\beta = \alpha\beta = r$ ...(4)

Solving (1) and (3) for α and β, we get

$\qquad \beta = \dfrac{2q - p}{3}$ and $\alpha = \dfrac{2(2p - q)}{3}$

$\therefore \quad r = \alpha\beta = \dfrac{2}{9}(2q - p)(2p - q) \implies$ (d)

15. $x^3 + 3x^2 + 3x + 2 = (ax^2 + bx + c)\left(\dfrac{x}{a} + \dfrac{2}{c}\right)$

The second factor is so chosen keeping in view the coefficients of x^3 and constant term.

Comparing coefficients of x^2 and x,

$\qquad \dfrac{b}{a} + \dfrac{2a}{c} = 3, \dfrac{c}{a} + \dfrac{2b}{c} = 3$

$\qquad bc + 2a^2 = 3ac, c^2 + 2ab = 3ac$

$\qquad 2a^2 = c(3a - b), c(c - 3a) + 2b = 0$

Eliminating c, we get

$\qquad 7a^3 - 12a^2 b + 6ab^2 - b^3 = 0$

or $\quad (a - b)(7a^2 - 5ab + b^2) = 0$

$\therefore \quad a = b$ (other factor gives imaginary as $\Delta < 0$)

Putting in $2a^2 = c(3a - b)$, we get $a = c$

$\therefore \quad a = b = c$

16. (a) $(c^2 - ab)x^2 - 2(a^2 - bc)x + (b^2 - ac) = 0$

If the roots be equal, then $B^2 - 4AC = 0$

$\therefore \quad 4(a^2 - bc)^2 - 4(c^2 - ab)(b^2 - ac) = 0$

or $\quad [a^4 - 2a^2bc + b^2c^2]$
$$\qquad - [b^2c^2 - ab^3 - ac^3 + a^2bc] = 0$$

or $\quad a(a^3 + b^3 + c^3 - 3abc) = 0$

$\therefore \quad$ Either $a = 0$ or $a^3 + b^3 + c^3 - 3abc = 0$.

(b) As above $m = 2$ or $-10/9$.

17. (a) $x^4 + x^2 + 1 = (x^2 + 1)^2 - x^2$
$$= (x^2 + x + 1)(x^2 - x + 1)$$

Hence the given equation is
$$(x^2 + x + 1)[(\lambda - 1)(x^2 + x + 1)$$
$$\qquad - (\lambda + 1)(x^2 - x + 1)] = 0$$

The first factor gives roots as ω, ω^2 which are imaginary.

The second factor is $-2x^2 + 2\lambda x - 2 = 0$

or $\quad x^2 - \lambda x + 1 = 0$

will have two real distinct roots.

$\therefore \quad \Delta = \lambda^2 - 4 > 0 \quad \therefore \quad (\lambda + 2)(\lambda - 2) > 0$

$\therefore \quad \lambda < -2 \quad$ or $\quad \lambda > 2$

$\therefore \quad \lambda \in (-\infty, -2) \cup (2, \infty)$

(b) Let $\dfrac{1 - 2x + 5x^2}{3x^2 - 2x - 1} = 2\sin t = y$, say.

$\therefore \quad x^2(3y - 5) + 2x(1 - y) - (y + 1) = 0$

Since x is real, $\quad \therefore \quad D \geq 0$

or $\quad 4(1 - y)^2 + 4(y + 1)(3y - 5) \geq 0$

or $\quad (1 - 2y + y^2) + (3y^2 - 2y - 5) \geq 0$

or $\quad y^2 - y - 1 \geq 0 \quad$ or $\quad y = \dfrac{1 \pm \sqrt{5}}{2}$

$\quad (x - a)(x - b) \geq 0$ if either $x < a$ or $x > b, a < b$

$\therefore \quad \sin t \leq \dfrac{1 - \sqrt{5}}{4} = -\sin 18° = \sin\left(-\dfrac{\pi}{10}\right)$

or $\quad > \dfrac{1 + \sqrt{5}}{4} = \cos 36° = \sin 54° = \sin\left(\dfrac{3\pi}{10}\right)$

$\therefore \quad t \in \left(-\dfrac{\pi}{2}, -\dfrac{\pi}{10}\right) \quad$ or $\quad t \in \left(\dfrac{3\pi}{10}, \dfrac{\pi}{2}\right)$

$\therefore \quad$ Range of t is $\left(-\dfrac{\pi}{2}, -\dfrac{\pi}{10}\right) \cup \left(\dfrac{3\pi}{10}, \dfrac{\pi}{2}\right)$.

(c) Ans. (a), (b), (c), (d).

The given equation can be written as
$$(7 - x - 1)^4 + (7 - x + 1)^4 = 16$$

or $\quad (t - 1)^4 + (t + 1)^4 = 16$ where $t = 7 - x$

or $\quad t^4 + 6t^2 - 7 = 0 \quad$ or $\quad (t^2 - 1)(t^2 + 7) = 0$

$\therefore \quad t^2 = (7 - x)^2 = 1, -7$

or $\quad 7 - x = 1, -1, \pm i\sqrt{7}$

$\therefore \quad x = 6, 8, 7 + i\sqrt{7}, 7 - i\sqrt{7}$

Two real and two imaginary roots $\Rightarrow$ (c), (d)
$$S = 28, P = 48 \times 56 = 2688 \quad \Rightarrow \quad (a), (b).$$

(d) If the given equation be $f(x) = 0$, then
$$f'(x) = 3[(x - a)^2 + (x - b)^2 + (x - c)^2]$$

Clearly $f'(x)$ is always $+$ ive for real values of x and hence $f'(x) = 0$ has no real roots. Therefore $f(x) = 0$ has one real root and consequently two imaginary roots.

Note : $f'(x) = 0$ when $x = a, b, c$ all together but this is not possible as a quadratic equation cannot have more than two roots.

(e) Ans.(b).

Let $y = x + 4$ so that given equation is $(y - 1)^4 + (y + 1)^4 = 16$

or $\quad 2(y^4 + 6y^2 + 1) = 16$ or $y^4 + 6y^2 - 7 = 0$

or $\quad (y^2 + 7)(y^2 - 1) = 0 \quad \therefore \quad y = \pm i\sqrt{7}, \pm 1$

or $\quad x + 4 = \pm 1$

or $\quad x = -3, -5$ are the only two real roots.

18. (a) The given equation can be put as
$$x^2(5 + 4m) - x(4 + 2m) + (2 - m) = 0.$$

(i) Roots Equal $\Rightarrow B^2 - 4AC = 0$

$\therefore \quad (4 + 2m)^2 - 4(5 + 4m)(2 - m) = 0$

or $\quad 5m^2 + m - 6 = 0$

or $\quad (m - 1)(5m + 6) = 0 \quad \therefore \quad m = 1, -6/5$.

(ii) Product $= 2 \quad \therefore \quad \dfrac{2 - m}{5 + 4m} = 2 \quad \therefore \quad m = -\dfrac{8}{9}$

(iii) Sum $= 6 \quad \therefore \quad \dfrac{4 + 2m}{5 + 4m} = 6 \quad \therefore \quad m = -\dfrac{13}{11}$.

(b) Ans. (d).

$\alpha + \beta > -2 - 2 = -4, \alpha + \beta < 4 + 4 = 8$

$\therefore \quad -4 < \alpha + \beta < 8 \quad$ or $\quad -4 < 2m < 8$

or $\quad -2 < m < 4$

(c) $P = 7 \Rightarrow 2e^{2\log\lambda} - 1 = 7 \quad \therefore \quad e^{\log\lambda^2} = 4$

$\therefore \quad \lambda^2 = 4 \quad$ or $\lambda = \pm 2$.

But by definition of $\log \lambda$,
$$\lambda \neq -2 \quad \therefore \quad \lambda = 2$$

Again $\Delta \geq 0 \quad \therefore \quad 9\lambda^2 - 4(7) \geq 0$

This inequality is also satisfied when $\lambda = 2$.

(d) Ans. (c).

$ax^2 + bx + c = a\left[x^2 + \dfrac{b}{a}x + \dfrac{c}{a}\right]$
$$= a\left[\left(x + \dfrac{b}{2a}\right)^2 + \dfrac{4ac - b^2}{4a^2}\right]$$

It will have the same sign as of a if the other factor is $+$ive. This means that $\dfrac{4ac - b^2}{4a^2} \geq 0$ or $b^2 - 4ac \leq 0$ *i.e.* the equation has either equal roots or imaginary roots.

(e) Ans. (a).

y has to be +ive

$\therefore \quad 16x^2 + 8(a+5)x - (7a+5) = +\text{ive}$

$\therefore$ Since sign of 1st term is +ive, therefore the expression will be +ive **§ 6 P. 202** if $\Delta < 0$

$64(a+5)^2 + 64(7a+5) < 0$

$\qquad a^2 + 17a + 30 < 0 \quad \text{or} \quad (a+15)(a+2) < 0$

or $\quad -15 < a < -2$

19. (a) $(c-a)^2 - 4(a-b)(b-c) = 0$

$\qquad c^2 + a^2 - 2ca - 4ab + 4ac + 4b^2 - 4bc = 0$

or $\quad c^2 + a^2 + 2ca + 4b^2 - 4b(c+a) = 0$

or $\quad (c+a)^2 + (2b)^2 - 2.2b(c+a) = 0.$

or $\quad [(c+a) - 2b]^2 = 0 \quad \therefore \quad c+a-2b = 0.$

or $\quad 2b = a+c \quad \therefore \quad a,b,c$ are in A.P.

Alternate : $\sum (b-c) = 0 \quad \therefore \quad x = 1$ is a root since roots are equal, therefore both the roots are 1, 1. Hence their product

$$P = 1 = \frac{a-b}{b-c} \quad \therefore \quad 2b = a+c$$

$\therefore \quad a,b,c$ are in A.P.

(b) $b^2(c-a)^2 - 4ac(b-c)(a-b) = 0$

or $\quad b^2(c^2 + a^2 - 2ac) - 4ac[ab - ac$

$$\qquad\qquad\qquad\qquad - b^2 + bc] = 0$$

or $\quad b^2(c^2 + a^2 - 2ac + 4ac) + 4a^2c^2$

$$\qquad\qquad\qquad\qquad - 4abc(c+a) = 0$$

or $\quad [b(c+a)]^2 + (2ac)^2 - 2.2ac.b(c+a) = 0$

or $\quad [b(c+a) - 2ac]^2 = 0, \quad \therefore \quad b(c+a) = 2ac$

or $\quad b = \dfrac{2ac}{a+c}$

$\therefore \quad b$ is H.M. of a and c i.e. a,b,c are in H.P.

Alternate : Here $\sum a(b-c) = 0$

$\therefore \quad x = 1$ is a root and since both roots are equal, they are 1, 1.

$\therefore \quad P = 1 = \dfrac{c(a-b)}{a(b-c)} \quad \text{or} \quad b = \dfrac{2ac}{a+c}$

$\therefore \quad a,b,c$ are in H.P.

20. (a) The given equation is

$$3x^2 - 2x(a+b+c) + (ab+bc+ca) = 0$$

Roots Equal. $\Rightarrow B^2 - 4AC = 0$

or $\quad 4(a+b+c)^2 - 12(ab+bc+ca) = 0$

or $\quad (a^2 + b^2 + c^2 + 2\sum ab - 3\sum ab) = 0$

or $\quad a^2 + b^2 + c^2 - ab - bc - ca = 0$

or $\quad \dfrac{1}{2}[2a^2 + 2b^2 + 2c^2 - 2ab - 2bc - 2ca] = 0$

or $\quad \Delta = \dfrac{1}{2}[(a-b)^2 + (b-c)^2 + (c-a)^2] = 0.$

Clearly $\Delta \geq 0 \quad \therefore \quad$ Roots are real

They will be equal if $\Delta = 0$. Hence

$a-b = 0, \ b-c = 0, \ c-a = 0 \quad \text{or} \quad a = b = c.$

Converse : If $a = b = c$ then the given equation reduces to $3(x-a)^2 = 0$ which clearly has equal roots.

(b) The given equation can be written as

$$3x^2 - [4(a+c) - 2b]x - (b^2 - 4ac) = 0$$

$\Delta = [4(a+c) - 2b]^2 + 12(b^2 - 4ac)$

$\quad = 4[2(a+c) - b]^2 + (3b^2 - 12ac)$

$\quad = 4[4(a^2 + c^2 + 2ac) + b^2 - 4b(a+c)$

$$\qquad\qquad\qquad\qquad\qquad + 3b^2 - 12ac]$$

$\quad = 16[a^2 + b^2 + c^2 - ab - bc - ca] \qquad \ldots(1)$

$\quad = 8[(a-b)^2 + (b-c)^2 + (c-a)^2] = +\text{ive}$

$\therefore \quad$ Roots are real.

Note : We can also use the inequality

$\quad a^2 + b^2 + c^2 > ab + bc + ca$ in (1)

as $a^2 + b^2 > 2ab, b^2 + c^2 > 2bc, c^2 + a^2 > 2ca.$

(c) $D = -4(3\lambda - 5)^2$. If $\lambda \neq \dfrac{5}{3}$ their D is always $-$ive and hence roots are complex. But if $\lambda = \dfrac{5}{3}$ their $D = 0$ and is that case the root will be equal.

21. (a) $\Delta = b^2 - 4ac = b^2 + 4a(4c + 2b)$, by given relation

$\quad = b^2 + 16a^2 + 8ab = +\text{ive as } ab \text{ is } +\text{ive}$

Hence both roots are real.

Alt. $x = 2$ is a real root as $4a + 2b + c = 0$ and since imaginary roots occur in pairs therefore the other root must also be real.

(b) $2b = a + c, b^2 - 4ac \geq 0$

$\Rightarrow \quad \left(\dfrac{a+c}{2}\right)^2 - 4ac \geq 0$

or $\quad a^2 - 14ac + c^2 \geq 0$

or $\quad t^2 - 14t + 1 = 0$ where $t = \dfrac{c}{a}$

$\quad (t-7)^2 \geq 48 \quad \therefore \quad |t-7| \geq 4\sqrt{3}$

or $\quad \left|\dfrac{c}{a} - 7\right| \geq 4\sqrt{3}$

(c) Ans. (a), (c).

$\quad \Delta \geq 0 \quad \Rightarrow \quad b^2 - 4ac \geq 0$

or $\quad \left(\dfrac{a-3c}{2}\right)^2 - 4ac \geq 0$ by given relations on eliminating b.

or $\quad a^2 - 22ac + 9c^2 \geq 0$

or $\left(\dfrac{a}{c}\right)^2 - 22\left(\dfrac{a}{c}\right) + 9 \geq 0$ or $t^2 - 22t + 9 \geq 0$

or $t^2 - 22t + 121 - 112 \geq 0$ where $t = \dfrac{a}{c}$

or $(t-11)^2 \geq (4\sqrt{7})^2$ or $\left|\dfrac{a}{c} - 11\right| \geq 4\sqrt{7}$

Similarly had we eliminated a we will get $t^2 - 8t - 12 \geq 0$ where $t = \dfrac{b}{c}$ and $\left|\dfrac{b}{c} - 4\right| \geq 2\sqrt{7}$.

22. (a) $B^2 - 4AC \geq 0$ for roots to be real.

Now $B^2 - 4AC = 4b^2(a+c)^2$
$$- 4(a^2+b^2)(b^2+c^2)$$
$$= 4[b^2 a^2 + b^2 c^2 + 2b^2 ac$$
$$- (a^2 b^2 + a^2 c^2 + b^4 + b^2 c^2)]$$
$$= 4[2b^2 ac - a^2 c^2 - b^4]$$
$$= -4[b^4 + a^2 c^2 - 2b^2 ac]$$
$$= -4[b^2 - ac]^2.$$

Now $4(b^2 - ac)^2$ is greater than or equal to zero, and hence the discriminant $B^2 - 4AC$ is always ≤ 0 so that the roots cannot be real unless $b^2 - ac = 0$ or $b^2 = ac$ i.e. a, b, c are in G.P. In this case the discriminant being zero the roots will be equal also.

(b) False. $b = \dfrac{2ac}{a+c}$

$$\Delta = 4b^2 - 4ac = 4\left[\dfrac{4a^2 c^2}{(a+c)^2} - ac\right]$$

$$= \dfrac{4ac}{(a+c)^2}[4ac - (a+c)^2] = -4ac\dfrac{(a-c)^2}{(a+c)^2}$$

Since a, b, c are distinct and +ive, $\Delta = -$ive. Hence the roots are imaginary.

23. (a) $\Delta = 9b^2 - 32ac = 9b^2 + 32a(a+b)$
$$= 9b^2 + 32ab + 32a^2 = b^2 + 8(b^2 + 4ab + 4a^2)$$
$$= b^2 + 8(b+2a)^2 = +\text{ive} \quad \therefore \quad \text{Real.}$$

(b) $\Delta = 0$
$$\Rightarrow \quad 4a^2(1+b)^2 - 4[a^2 + 2b(b-1)]$$
$$[a^2 - 2(b-1)] = 0$$

or $a^2\{(b-1)^2 + 4b\}$
$$- \{a^4 + 2a^2(b^2 - 2b+1) - 4b(b-1)^2\} = 0$$

or $a^4 + 2a^2(b-1)^2 - 4b(b-1)^2 - a^2(b-1)^2$
$$- 4ba^2 = 0$$

or $a^2(a^2 - 4b) + (b-1)^2\{a^2 - 4b\} = 0$

or $(a^2 - 4b)[a^2 + (b-1)^2] = 0$

$\therefore \quad a^2 - 4b = 0$ as the other factor cannot be zero.

24. (a) Proceeding as above,

$B^2 - 4AC = -(a^2 c^2 + b^2 d^2 - 2abcd) = -(ac - bd)^2$

Above is clearly ≤ 0 as $(ac - bd)^2$ is ≥ 0. Hence the roots will be real if $ac - bd = 0$ or $\dfrac{a}{b} = \dfrac{d}{c}$.

Also the roots will be equal as $B^2 - 4AC = 0$.

(b) $\Delta = (4abcd)^2 - 4(a^4 + b^4)(c^4 + d^4)$
$$= -4[(a^4 c^4 + b^4 c^4) + (b^4 c^4 + a^4 d^4)$$
$$- 4a^2 b^2 c^2 d^2]$$
$$= -4[(a^2 c^2 - b^2 d^2)^2 + (b^2 c^2 - a^2 d^2)^2]$$

Above is always $-$ive as the expression within bracket is always $+$ive. Hence if the roots are to be real then Δ must be zero and in that case roots will be equal as both $a^2 c^2 - b^2 d^2 = 0$ and $b^2 c^2 - a^2 d^2 = 0$ as $P^2 + Q^2 = 0 \Rightarrow P = 0, Q = 0$. Hence roots can't be unequal.

(c) We have
$$\left(\dfrac{1}{x+a} - \dfrac{1}{x}\right) + \left(\dfrac{1}{x+b} - \dfrac{1}{x}\right) + \left(\dfrac{1}{x+c} - \dfrac{1}{x}\right) = 0$$

or $-\left[\dfrac{a}{x+a} + \dfrac{b}{x+b} + \dfrac{c}{x+c}\right] = 0$

or $\Sigma a(x+b)(x+c) = 0$

or $\Sigma a[x^2 + x(b+c) + bc] = 0$

or $x^2(a+b+c) + 2x(ab+bc+ca) + 3abc = 0$

If the roots be real then $\Delta \geq 0$.

$\Delta = 4(ab+bc+ca)^2 - 12abc(a+b+c)$
$$= 4[\Sigma a^2 b^2 + 2\Sigma a^2 bc - 3\Sigma a^2 bc]$$
$$= 4[a^2 b^2 + b^2 c^2 + c^2 a^2 - a^2 bc - b^2 ca - c^2 ab]$$
$$= 4[l^2 + m^2 + n^2 - lm - mn - nl]$$

where $l = ab, m = bc, n = ca$.
$$= 4 \cdot \dfrac{1}{2}[(l-m)^2 + (m-n)^2 + (n-l)^2]$$

Above is clearly $+$ive.

Hence the roots are real.

25. (a) $B^2 - 4AC = 4(a-b)^2 = +$ive and perfect square.

$\therefore$ Roots are real, rational and unequal.

(b) $B^2 - 4AC = (b+c-a)^2 \geq 0$.

Roots are real, rational and unequal.

(c) $B^2 - 4AC = -4(a-b)^2 = -$ive.

Hence roots are imaginary.

26. (a) Making use of $a+b+c = 0$, the given equation can be written after cancelling -2,

$ax^2 + bx + c = 0 \quad \therefore \quad \Delta = b^2 - 4ac$
$$= (a+c)^2 - 4ac = (a-c)^2 = P. \text{ Square}$$

Hence rationals.

(b) The given equation can be written as
$$lx^2 + mx + n = 0 \text{ where}$$

$l + m + n = 0$ ...(1)

$\Delta = m^2 - 4nl = (l+n)^2 - 4(nl) = (l-n)^2$

= perfect square

Hence the roots are rational.

Clearly 1 is a root of the equation by virtue of relation $l + m + n = 0$. If the other root be α, then

$1 \cdot \alpha = \text{Product of roots} = \dfrac{n}{l}$

$\therefore \quad \alpha = \dfrac{c + 2a - 3b}{a + 2b - 3c}.$

(c) The given equation can be written as

$(ay + a') x^2 + (by + b') x + (cy + c') = 0$

Since roots are rational $\therefore \Delta$ is a perfect square.

$\therefore \quad (by + b')^2 - 4(ay + a')(cy + c')$ is P.S.

or $y^2 (b^2 - 4ac) + [2bb' - 4(ac' + a'c)] y$

$+ (b'^2 - 4a'c') = 0$

is a perfect square. In other words, the roots of the above are equal so that its $\Delta' = 0$

$\therefore \quad [2bb' - 4(ac' + a'c)]^2 - 4(b^2 - 4ac)$

$(b'^2 - 4a'c') = 0$

Cancel 4 and simplify as in the last part and you get the desired result.

(d) For roots to be rational Δ = perfect square

or $(2k-1)^2 - 4k(k-2)$ = perfect square

or $4k + 1$ is a perfect square.

Now k being an integer implies that $4k + 1$ is also an odd integer and it should be perfect square. Again square of an odd integer is always an integer.

$\therefore \quad 4k + 1 = (\text{odd integer})^2 = (2n+1)^2$

$\therefore \quad 4k + 1 = 4n^2 + 4n + 1$ or $k = n(n+1)$

where n is a rational number.

27. (a) $B^2 - 4AC > 0$ for 1st equation. $\therefore 4(c^2 - ab) > 0$

or $c^2 - ab$ is + ive.

$B^2 - 4AC$ for the 2nd equation is

$4(a+b)^2 - 4(a^2 + b^2 + 2c^2)$

$= 4[2ab - 2c^2] = -8(c^2 - ab) = -$ ive.

as $c^2 - ab$ is + ive.

Hence the roots of the second equation are imaginary.

(b) The 2nd equation can be written as

$[2b^2 + a(a-c)] x^2 + 2b(a+c) x$

$+ [2b^2 - c(a-c)] = 0$

$\Delta_1 = 4(b^2 - ac)$ ...(1)

$\Delta_2 = 4b^2 (a+c)^2 - 4[4b^4 + 2b^2 (a-c)^2$

$- ac(a-c)^2]$

We would like to express Δ_2 so as to contain Δ_1 i.e. $b^2 - ac$

$\Delta_2 = -4[4b^4 + b^2 (a-c)^2 + b^2 (a-c)^2$

$- ac(a-c)^2 - b^2 (a+c)^2]$ **(Note)**

$= -4[4b^4 + (a-c)^2 (b^2 - ac) - b^2 \cdot 4ac]$

$= -4[4b^2 (b^2 - ac) + (a-c)^2 (b^2 - ac)]$

$= -4\Delta_1 [4b^2 + (a-c)^2] = -4k^2 \Delta_1$

where k^2 is +ive.

Now if Δ_1 is + ive, then Δ_2 is – ive

and if Δ_1 is – ive, then Δ_2 is + ive.

28. (a) Given $a^2 - 4b > 0$ $\therefore$ $b < a^2/4$ ...(1)

Again α and β differ by a quantity less than c $(c > 0)$

$\therefore |\alpha - \beta| < c$ or $(\alpha - \beta)^2 < c^2$

$(\alpha + \beta)^2 - 4\alpha\beta < c^2$

or $a^2 - 4b < c^2$ or $\dfrac{a^2 - c^2}{4} < b$ ...(2)

$\therefore \quad \dfrac{a^2 - c^2}{4} < b < \dfrac{a^2}{4}$ by (1) and (2)

(b) $x^4 + x^2 + 1 = (x^2 + 1)^2 - x^2$

$= (x^2 + x + 1)(x^2 - x + 1)$

$x^2 + x + 1 = \left(x + \dfrac{1}{2}\right)^2 + \dfrac{3}{4} \neq 0$ $\forall$ real x

Therefore we can cancel this factor and we get

$(a-1)(x^2 - x + 1) = (a+1)(x^2 - x + 1)$

or $2x^2 - ax + 1 = 0$ has real and distinct roots

$\therefore \quad \Delta = a^2 - 4 > 0$

29. (a) Let us assume that neither of the equations has real roots i.e., they have imaginary roots

$\therefore \quad p^2 - 4q < 0$ and $r^2 - 4s < 0$.

Add the two relations

$\therefore \quad p^2 + r^2 - 4(q+s) < 0$. But $2(q+s) = pr$

$\therefore \quad p^2 + r^2 - 2pr < 0$ or $(p-r)^2 < 0$.

This is not possible as for real values of p and r, $(p-r)^2 \geq 0$. Hence our assumption that neither of the equations has real roots is wrong.

(b) Δ_1 of $P(x) = 0$ is $b^2 - 4ac$

Δ_2 of $Q(x) = 0$ is $d^2 + 4ac$

Since $ac \neq 0$ $\therefore$ $ac = +$ive or $-$ive

If ac is +ive then Δ_2 is +ive but Δ_1 may be +ive or – ive so that the roots of $Q(x) = 0$ are real.

If ac is – ive then Δ_1 is +ive but Δ_2 may be +ive or – ive so that the roots of $P(x) = 0$ are real.

Hence at least two roots are real.

30. Ans. (i).

The given equation can be written as

$$3x^2 - (a + c + 2b + 2d)\,x + ac + 2bd = 0$$

$$\Delta = (a + c + 2b + 2d)^2 - 12\,(ac + 2bd)$$

$$= [(a + 2d) - (c + 2b)]^2 + 4\,(a + 2d)\,(c + 2b)$$
$$- 12\,(ac + 2bd)$$

$$= [(a + 2d) - (c + 2b)]^2 + 8ab + 8cd - 8ac - 8bd$$

$$= [(a + 2d) - (c + 2b)]^2 + 8\,(c - b)\,(d - a) > 0$$

Since $a < b < c < d$ so that $(c - b)\,(d - a) > 0$.
Hence the roots are real and distinct.

31. (a) The following points must be noted :

(1) $\log_3 x$ is defined only for + ive values of x. Also

(2) $y^2 = |y|^2$ and $|y|$ is always + ive, and

(3) $|y| = a \Rightarrow y = \pm a$

The given equation is $2t^2 - t + k = 0$ ...(1)

where $t = |\log_3 x|$ where t is + ive *i.e.* > 0.

There will be two values of t and hence four of x.
Thus the roots of (1) are real and distinct and both
are + ive.

$$\therefore \quad \Delta > 0 \qquad \text{and} \qquad P = + \text{ive}$$

$$\text{or} \quad 1 - 8k > 0 \quad \text{and} \quad \frac{k}{2} > 0$$

$$\Rightarrow \quad k > 0 \text{ and } k < \frac{1}{8} \quad \therefore \quad k \in \left(0, \frac{1}{8}\right).$$

(b) From 1st we have

$\alpha^2 + \beta^2 = p^2 - 2q$, and from 2nd $\alpha^4 + \beta^4 = r$

or $(\alpha^2 + \beta^2)^2 - 2\alpha^2\beta^2 = r$

or $(p^2 - 2q)^2 - 2q^2 = r$ ...(1)

$$x^2 - 4qx + (2q^2 - r) = 0 \qquad \text{...(2)}$$

Again Δ for the above equation is

$$16q^2 - 4\,(2q^2 - r) = (8q^2 + 4r)$$

$$= 8q^2 + 4\{(p^2 - 2q)^2 - 2q^2\}, \text{ by (1)}$$

$$= 4\,(p^2 - 2q)^2 \text{ which is + ive.}$$

Hence the roots of (2) are real roots.

32. (a) $B^2 - 4AC = \Delta = + $ ive for real

$$\therefore \quad 4\,(16 + 6a - a^2) = -4\,(a + 2)\,(a - 8) = + \text{ive}$$

or $[a - (-2)]\,(a - 8) = -$ ive or $-2 < a < 8$.

Hence for roots to be real a should lie between
$- 2$ and 8.

(b) $B^2 - 4AC = 16a^2 - 36 \times 4$

$$= 16\,(a^2 - 9) = 16\,[a - (-3)]\,(a - 3) < 0$$

as the roots are imaginary. Hence a must lie
between $- 3$ and 3.

(c) **Atleast one + ive root means :**

(i) Both the roots are real (There cannot be one
complex root as they occur in conjugate pairs)

(ii) Both are not $-$ ive.

Condition (i) $\Rightarrow \Delta \geq 0$

or $4\,(m - 1)^2 - 4\,(m + 5) \geq 0$

or $m^2 - 2m + 1 - m - 5 \geq 0$

or $m^2 - 3m - 4 = +$ ive

or $(m + 1)\,(m - 4) = +$ ive

$$\therefore \quad m \leq -1, m \geq 4 \qquad \text{...(1)}$$

Both are not $-$ ive : Let us find the region when
both are $-$ ive.

$$\therefore \quad S = -\text{ive and } P = +\text{ive}$$

$$-2\,(m - 1) = -\text{ive and } m + 5 = +\text{ive}$$

$$m - 1 > 0 \quad \text{and} \quad m + 5 > 0$$

$$\therefore \quad m > 1 \quad \text{or} \quad m > -5$$

When $m > 1$, it is automatically greater than $- 5$.
Hence $m > 1$ is the condition for both the roots to
be $-$ ive. Hence when both the roots are not $-$ ive
i.e., at least one is $+$ ive, we must have

$$m \leq 1 \qquad \text{...(2)}$$

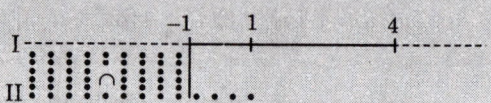

Fig. 9

Plotting both (1) and (2) on real line and then
taking their intersection *i.e.*, common region we
get the answer :

Condition (1) gives broken line region.

Condition (2) gives dotted line region.

Common region is given by $m \leq -1$.

$$\therefore \quad m \in (-\infty, -1].$$

33. (a) Here $\Delta = B^2 - 4AC$

$$= (2a^2 + a + 3)^2 - 4\,(a^2 + a - 2)\,(a^2 - 1)$$

$$= 25a^2 + 10a + 1 \text{ (after simplifications)}$$

$$= (5a + 1)^2$$

Since Δ is a perfect square, roots are rational.
The roots are given by

$$x = \frac{-(2a^2 + a + 3) \pm (5a + 1)}{2\,(a^2 + a - 2)} = -\frac{2\,(a - 1)^2}{2\,(a - 1)\,(a + 2)}$$

or $$\frac{-2\,(a + 2)\,(a + 1)}{2\,(a - 1)\,(a + 2)}$$

Since $a \neq 1$ and $a \neq -2$, the roots are

$$x_1 = -\frac{a - 1}{a + 2}, \quad x_2 = -\frac{a + 1}{a - 1}$$

(b) $A + B + C = \pi$,

$$\therefore \quad B + C = \pi - \frac{\pi}{4} = \frac{3\pi}{4} \qquad \text{...(1)}$$

$$\tan\,(B + C) = -1$$

or $\tan B + \tan C = -1\,(1 - \tan B \tan C)$

or $\tan B + \tan C = -1 + p$

or $\tan B + \tan\left\{\frac{3\pi}{4} - B\right\} = -1 + p$

or $t + \dfrac{-1 - t}{1 - t} = -1 + p.$

$\because \quad \tan\dfrac{3\pi}{4} = -1, t = \tan B$

or $\quad t^2 - t(p-1) + p = 0$

Since $t = \tan B$ is real $\quad \therefore \quad (p-1)^2 - 4p \geq 0$

$p^2 - 6p + 1 \geq 0 \quad p = a, b, \quad a < b;$

where $a = 3 - 2\sqrt{2}, \quad b = 3 + 2\sqrt{2}$

$\therefore \quad p \leq a$ or $p \geq b$

$\therefore \quad p \in\;]-\infty, 3 - 2\sqrt{2}\,] \cup [\,3 + 2\sqrt{2}, \infty\,[$

(c) Ans. (d).

$\tan A + \tan B = p, \quad \tan A \tan B = q$

$\therefore \quad \tan(A+B) = \dfrac{\tan A + \tan B}{1 - \tan A \tan B} = \dfrac{p}{1-q} = T \quad ...(1)$

Now $\quad \sin^2(A+B) = \dfrac{\tan^2(A+B)}{\sec^2(A+B)} = \dfrac{T^2}{1+T^2}$

$\qquad = \dfrac{p^2}{(1-q)^2 + p^2}$ by (1) $\Rightarrow$ (d)

34. (a) $B^2 - 4AC = 25(p+q)^2 + 2(p-q)^2 > 0$ for real p and q. Hence roots are real and unequal,

$\therefore \quad$ (iii) is correct answer.

(b) $4q^2 - 4pr \geq 0$ and $4pr - q^2 \geq 0$

or $\quad q^2 - pr \geq 0$ and $(q^2 - pr) \leq 0$

Above is possible only when $q^2 - pr = 0$ or $p/q = q/r$, $\therefore$ (ii) is correct.

(c) A quadratic equation **does not have** two distinct real root means either its roots are equal or imaginary $\therefore \Delta \leq 0$

or $16 - 4\log_{1/2} a \leq 0$ or $\log_{1/2} a \geq 4$

or $-\log_2 a \geq 4$ or $\log_2 a \leq -4$

or $a \leq 2^{-4}$ or $a \leq \dfrac{1}{16}$

Hence the maximum value of a is 1/16.

35. (a) We have $\Delta = b^2 - 4ac \geq 0, S = -\dfrac{b}{a}, P = \dfrac{c}{a}$

(i) $S = 0 \Rightarrow b = 0, \quad \Delta \geq 0 \Rightarrow ac = -$ ive

$\therefore \quad a$ and c are of opposite signs.

(ii) $P = -$ ive $\quad \therefore \quad \dfrac{c}{a} = -$ ive

i.e. a and c are of opposite signs so that ac is $-$ ive and $\Delta = b^2 - 4ac \geq 0$

(iii) $S = -$ ive, $P = +$ ive

$-\dfrac{b}{a} = -$ ive $\Rightarrow \dfrac{b}{a} = +$ ive

$\therefore \quad a, b$ are of same sign either $+$ive or $-$ive. In this case $P = \dfrac{c}{a} = +$ ive i.e. both c and a have the sign either $+$ ive or $-$ ive.

$\Rightarrow \quad a, b$ and a, c have the same sign.

or $\quad a, b, c$ have the same sign.

(iv) $S = +$ ive, $P = +$ive

$-\dfrac{b}{a} = +$ ive $\quad \therefore \quad \alpha, b$ of opposite sign $\quad ...(1)$

$\dfrac{c}{a} = +$ ive $\quad \therefore \quad c$ and a have same sign $\quad ...(2)$

If a, c are $+$ ive, then b is $-$ ive by (1)

If a, c are $-$ ive, then b is $+$ ive by (1)

$\therefore \quad a, c$ are of same sign and b is of opposite sign.

(b) Ans. (i), (ii).

Roots are given by $x = -\dfrac{b}{2a} \pm \dfrac{\sqrt{b^2 - 4ac}}{2a} \quad ...(1)$

since $a > 0, b > 0$, we have $-\dfrac{b}{2a} < 0$. If $b^2 - 4ac < 0$, then roots are imaginary of which the real part $-\dfrac{b}{2a}$ is negative. If $b^2 - 4ac > 0$ then the roots are real. If $ac = +$ ive i.e. c is $+$ive as a is given to be $+$ive then in this case $\sqrt{b^2 - 4ac} < b$. Hence both the roots will be real and $-$ive from (1).

If, however, $ac = -$ive i.e. c is $-$ive then $\sqrt{(b^2 - 4ac)} > b$ then one root will be $+$ive and other $-$ive.

(c) Ans. (d).

Given $c^2 - 4ab < 0, i.e., c^2 < 4ab \quad ...(1)$

Given expression is

$3(bx + c)^2 - c^2 \geq -c^2 > -4ab$ by (1)

36. (a) $B^2 - 4AC = 4(a + b - 2c)^2 - 4(a-b)^2$.

$\Delta = 4[(2a - 2c)(2b - 2c)]$

by factors of $p^2 - q^2$

$\Delta = 4 \times 2 \times 2(c - a)(c - b), \quad a < b.$

If c lies between a and b, i.e. $a < c < b$, then $\Delta = B^2 - 4AC$ is $-$ive.

Hence the roots will be imaginary.

If c does not lie between a and b i.e. either $c < a$ or $c > b$ then

$\Delta = B^2 - 4AC$ is $+$ive.

Hence the roots will be real.

(b) Roots are real and $+$ive if

(1) $\Delta \geq 0$, (2) S $+$ive, (3) P $+$ive

(1) $\Rightarrow m \in \left[0, \dfrac{15}{4}\right]$

(2) $\Rightarrow m(m-3) > 0$ or $m < 0$ or $m > 3$

(3) $\Rightarrow$ same as (2).

Hence combining, we can say

$m > 3$ and $\leq \dfrac{15}{4}$ or $m \in \left]3, \dfrac{15}{4}\right]$.

(c) Since both the roots are $-$ive, the roots are real so that

$\Delta \geq 0, S < 0, P > 0$

$\Delta \geq 0 \Rightarrow (a-1)(a-6) \geq 0$

or $a \le 1$ or $a \ge 6$ ...(1)

$S < 0 \Rightarrow -(a+1) < 0$

$\Rightarrow$ $a + 1 > 0 \Rightarrow a > -1$ ...(2)

$P > 0 \Rightarrow 9a - 5 > 0 \Rightarrow a > \dfrac{5}{9}$ ...(3)

The value $a \ge 6$ satisfies all the three criteria.

(d) $f(x) = (x - \alpha)(x - \beta) = 0$ must   satisfy   the following :

(a) $\Delta \ge 0$ (b) $S > 6$

and $f(3) = (3 - \alpha)(3 - \beta) = (-)(-) = + ive$

$\Delta \ge 0 \Rightarrow a \ge 1$ ...(1)

$S > 6 \Rightarrow a > 1$ ...(2)

$f(3) > 0 \Rightarrow 9a^2 - 20a + 11 > 0$

or $9(a - 1)(a - 11/9) > 0$

$\Rightarrow$ $a < 1$ or $a > 11/9$

Clearly $a > \dfrac{11}{9}$ satisfies both (1) and (2) also.

37. (a) $x^2 - 2x - 3 = (x - 3)(x + 1) = [x - (-1)](x - 3)$

$a = -1$ and $b = 3$, $a < b$.

By §5 the above expression is + ive if x does not lie between a and b i.e. if x does not lie between -1 and 3. Again it will be $-$ ive if x lies between a and b i.e., x lies between -1 and 3.

(b) + ive if x does not lie between -3 and $\dfrac{1}{2}$

$-$ ive if x lies between -3 and $\dfrac{1}{2}$.

(c) Ans. (b). $x^2 + 2ax + 10 - 3a = + ive \; \forall$ real values of x if disc $4a^2 - 4(10 - 3a) = -$ ive and sign of the first term i.e., 1 is + ive.

$\therefore$ $a^2 + 3a - 10 < 0$

or $(a + 5)(a - 2) < 0$ $\therefore$ $-5 < a < 2$

38. (a) Let $\dfrac{11x^2 + 12x + 6}{x^2 + 4x + 2} = y.$

$\therefore$ $x^2(11 - y) + 4x(3 - y) + 2(3 - y) = 0$ ...(1)

For real values of x, $B^2 - 4AC$ of (1) should be ≥ 0

or $16(3 - y)^2 - 8(11 - y)(3 - y) \ge 0$ i.e., + ive

$8(3 - y)[6 - 2y - 11 + y] \ge 0$

or $8(3 - y)(-5 - y) \ge 0$

or $8(y - 3)(y + 5) \ge 0$ i.e. + ive

or $8[y - (-5)](y - 3)$ is + ive.

Hence arguing as in part (a), y should not lie between -5 and 3.

(b) For roots to be real and unequal $D > 0$ i.e., + ive.

$\therefore$ $(a - b)^2 - 4(1 - a - b) > 0 \; \forall \, b \in R$

Arranging as a quadratic in b,

$b^2 - 2(a - 2)b + (a^2 + 4a - 4)$ is + ive $\forall \, b \in R.$

Its sign will be same as of its first term i.e., + ive provided its Δ is $-$ ive.

$\therefore$ $4(a^2 - 4a + 4) - 4(a^2 + 4a - 4) < 0$

or $-8a + 8 < 0$

or $a - 1 > 0$ $\therefore$ $a > 1.$

(c) $(x - 1)(x - 2) > 0 \Rightarrow x < 1, x > 2$

$(x + 1)(x - 4) \le 0 \Rightarrow -1 \le x \le 4.$

$\therefore$ $-1 \le x < 1$ and $2 < x \le 4$ for both

$\therefore$ $x \in [-1, 1) \cup (2, 4]$. Both are semi-open; 1 and 2 are not included.

39. (a) If the given expression be y, then

$2x^2 y + (3y - 1)x + (6y - 2) = 0$

If $y \ne 0$ then $\Delta \ge 0$ for real x i.e. $B^2 - 4AC \ge 0$

or $-39y^2 + 10y + 1 \ge 0$

or $(13y + 1)(3y - 1) \le 0$

$\therefore$ $-\dfrac{1}{13} \le y \le \dfrac{1}{3}$

If $y = 0$ then $x = -2$ which is real and this value of y is included in the above range.

(b) $y = \dfrac{\tan x}{\tan 3x} = \dfrac{t(1 - 3t^2)}{3t - t^3} = \dfrac{1 - 3t^2}{3 - t^2}$, as $t \ne 0$

$\because$ $t = 0$ will make y indeterminate

$\therefore$ $y(3 - t^2) = 1 - 3t^2$

or $t^2 = \dfrac{3y - 1}{y - 3} = + ive$

$= \dfrac{(3y - 1)(y - 3)}{(y - 3)^2} = \dfrac{3(y - 1/3)(y - 3)}{(y - 3)^2}.$

Above will be + ive if $y < 1/3$ or $y > 3$ as denominator is + ive

Hence we conclude that y cannot lie between $\dfrac{1}{3}$ and 3.

(c) Ans. (a).

Proceeding as in part (a), (b), $y \in [1, 41]$

$\therefore$ Max value of y is 41.

40. (a) Proceed as above.

(b) Do yourself.

41. (a) Let $\dfrac{x^2 + 14x + 9}{x^2 + 2x + 3} = y$

$\therefore$ $x^2(1 - y) + 2x(7 - y) + 3(3 - y) = 0$ ...(1)

For real values of x, $B^2 - 4AC$ of (1) should be ≥ 0

$\therefore$ $4(7 - y)^2 - 12(1 - y)(3 - y) \ge 0$

or $(49 - 14y + y^2) - 3(3 - 4y + y^2) \ge 0$

or $-2y^2 - 2y + 40 \ge 0$

or $-2(y^2 + y - 20) \ge 0$

or $(y + 5)(y - 4)$ is ≤ 0

or $[y - (-5)](y - 4)$ is $-$ ive.

By §5 y should lie between -5 and 4. Therefore the maximum value is 4 and minimum is -5.

(b) Let $y = \dfrac{x + a}{x^2 + bx + c^2}$

$\therefore \quad yx^2 + x(by - 1) + (c^2 y - a) = 0$

Since x is real $\quad \therefore \quad \Delta \geq 0$

$\therefore \quad (by - 1)^2 - 4y(c^2 y - a) \geq 0$

or $\quad y^2 (b^2 - 4c^2) + 2y(2a - b) + 1 = +\text{ive} \quad \dots(1)$

The sign of a quadratic expression is same as of its first terms *i.e.* of $b^2 - 4c^2$ provided its discriminant D is $-$ive

or $\quad 4(2a - b)^2 - 4(b^2 - 4c^2) = -\text{ive}$

or $\quad 16(a^2 + c^2 - ab) = -\text{ive}$ or $a^2 + c^2 < ab$

Hence the sign of expression (1) is same as of $b^2 - 4c^2$ *i.e.* $+$ive. Hence y will have any value.

42. (a) Proceeding as above for real values of x, we have

$-3y^2 + 10y - 3 \geq 0$

or $\quad 3y^2 - 10y + 3 \leq 0$ *i.e.* $-$ive

or $\quad (3y - 1)(y - 3) \leq 0$ *i.e.* $-$ive

or $\quad 3(y - 1/3)(y - 3)$ is $-$ive.

$\therefore \quad$ By §5, y lies between $\dfrac{1}{3}$ and 3.

(b) Do yourself.

(c) The value of the function can be ≤ 5 or ≥ 9.

43. (a) $\dfrac{8x^2 + 16x - 51}{(2x - 3)(x + 4)} > 3$

Here we cannot write

$8x^2 + 16x - 51 > 3(2x - 3)(x + 4)$

as in inequalities we can multiply both sides only by $+$ive quantity. But here we do not know whether $(2x - 3)(x + 4)$ is $+$ive or $-$ive. Hence we write the inquality as under :

$\dfrac{8x^2 + 16x - 51}{2x^2 + 5x - 12} - 3 > 0$

or $\quad \dfrac{2x^2 + x - 15}{2x^2 + 5x - 12} > 0$ or $\dfrac{(2x - 5)(x + 3)}{(2x - 3)(x + 4)} > 0$

Writing the above as under

or $\quad \dfrac{2[x - (-3)](x - 5/2)}{2[x - (-4)](x - 3/2)} > 0$

or $\quad \dfrac{(2x - 5)(x + 3)(2x - 3)(x + 4)}{(2x - 3)^2 (x + 4)^2} > 0$

$\therefore \quad N^r$ is > 0 as D^r is $+$ive.

The values of x obtained from $N^r = 0$ are

$\dfrac{5}{2}, -3, \dfrac{3}{2}, -4$

Mark them in ascending order on real line as shown below. Write $+$ in the extreme right and move towards left with opposite signs in successive intervals.

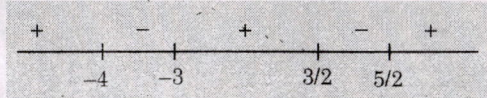

Fig. 61

From the above fig. it is clear that N^r is $+$ive for

$x > \dfrac{5}{2}, -3 < x < \dfrac{3}{2}, x < -4$

(b) $\dfrac{x - 2}{x + 2} - \dfrac{2x - 3}{4x - 1} > 0$

or $\quad \dfrac{2(x^2 - 5x + 4)}{(x + 2)(4x - 1)} > 0$

or $\quad \dfrac{2(x - 4)(x - 1)}{(x + 2)(4x - 1)} > 0$

or $\quad \dfrac{2(x - 1)(x - 4)}{4[x - (-2)]\left(x - \dfrac{1}{4}\right)} > 0$

Now proceed as in part (a). Then

$x < -2$ or $\dfrac{1}{4} < x < 1$ or $x > 4$.

44. The given inequality will hold if on transposing we have

$\dfrac{-(3x + 2)}{(x + 1)(x + 2)(2x + 1)} > 0$

or $\quad \dfrac{3x + 2}{(x + 1)(x + 2)(2x + 1)} < 0$

or $\quad \dfrac{(3x + 2)^2}{(x + 1)(x + 2)(2x + 1)(3x + 2)} < 0$

or $\quad \dfrac{(3x + 2)^2}{2.3[\{x - (-2)\}\{x - (-1)\}}{\{x - (-2/3)\}\{x - (-1/2)\}]} < 0 \quad \dots(1)$

Now consider the five cases given by values of x in ascending order $-2, -1, -\dfrac{2}{3}, -\dfrac{1}{2}$. The five cases are given by

(i) $x < -2$, $+$

(ii) $-2 < x < -1$, $-$

(iii) $-1 < x < -\dfrac{2}{3}$, $+$

(iv) $-\dfrac{2}{3} < x < -\dfrac{1}{2}$, $-$

(v) $x > -\dfrac{1}{2}$, $+$

Every ($+$) is followed by ($-$) and every ($-$) by ($+$)

The inequality (1) will hold good in case (ii) or (iv). Also the inequality (1) holds good for $x = -2$.

Hence $\quad -2 \leq x < -1$

and $\quad -2/3 < x < -\dfrac{1}{2}$.

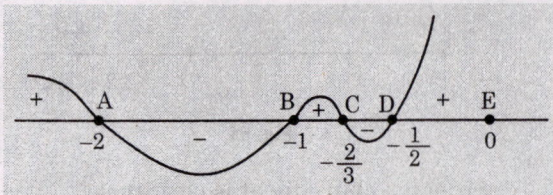

Fig. 10

Note : The above is exhibited by graph as shown in the figure. The same method can be applied for parts (a) and (b).

45. (a) Proceeding as ususal, $y^2 - y(b+c) + bc \geq 0$

or $(y-b)(y-c) \geq 0$ i.e., + ive.
Above is possible only when y does not lie between b and c.

(b) Ans. (iii) and (iv) are both correct.

Let $y = \dfrac{(x-a)(x-b)}{x-c}$

or $y(x-c) = x^2 - (a+b)x + ab$

or $x^2 - (a+b+y)x + ab + cy = 0$.

$\Delta = (a+b+y)^2 - 4(ab+cy)$

$= y^2 + 2y(a+b-2c) + (a-b)^2$

Since x is real and y assumes all real values, we must have $\Delta \geq 0$ for all real values of y. The sign of a quadratic in y is same as of first term provided its discriminant $B^2 - 4AC < 0$

This will be so if $4(a+b-2c)^2 - 4(a-b)^2 < 0$

or $4(a+b-2c+a-b)$
$\qquad (a+b-2c-a+b) < 0 \,[P^2 - Q^2]$

or $16(a-c)(b-c) < 0$

or $16(c-a)(c-b) = -$ ive

∴ c lies between a and b, i.e., $a < c < b$ ...(1)
where $a < b$, but if $b < a$ then the above condition will be

$\qquad b < c < a \quad$ or $\quad a > c > b \qquad$ ...(2)
Hence from (1) and (2) we observe that both (c) and (d) are correct answers.

(c) Ans. (c).

Given $b^2 = 4ac \geq 0$ and product $= \dfrac{c}{a} = -$ ive

The given equation is

$\qquad (\alpha + \beta)x^2 - 4\alpha\beta\, x + \alpha\beta\,(\alpha+\beta) = 0$

or $\quad x^2 - \dfrac{4\alpha\beta}{\alpha+\beta}x + \alpha\beta = 0$

or $\quad x^2 + 4\dfrac{c}{b}x + \dfrac{c}{a} = 0$

$\Delta = 16\dfrac{c^2}{b^2} - 4\dfrac{c}{a}$

Δ is clearly + ive as $\dfrac{c}{a}$ is − ive. Hence the roots are real and their product being $\dfrac{c}{a} = -$ ive so that they are of opposite sign. Hence (c) is correct.

46. (a) Let $\dfrac{px^2 + 3x - 4}{p + 3x - 4x^2} = y$.

Then $(4y + p)x^2 + 3x(1-y) - (4+yp) = 0$

Now $b^2 - 4ac = 9(1-y)^2 + 4(4y+p)(4+yp)$

$\qquad = (16p+9)y^2 + 2(2p^2+23)y + (16p+9) \geq 0$

for real values of x.

Arguing as in part (b), $B^2 - 4AC < 0$
and the sign is same as of $A = 16p + 9$ which is to be + ive

∴ $\quad 4(2p^2+23)^2 - 4(16p+9)^2 < 0$

and $16p + 9 > 0$

or $\quad 16(p+4)^2(p^2 - 8p + 7) < 0$

and $16p + 9 > 0$

or $(p+4)^2(p-1)(p-7) < 0$

and $16p + 9 > 0$
Both these inequalities are satisfied if $1 < p < 7$.

(b) Let $f(x) = ax^2 + bx + c$. Then

$g(x) = f(x) + f'(x) + f''(x)$

$\qquad = ax^2 + bx + c + 2ax + b + 2a$

$\qquad = ax^2 + (b+2a)x + c + b + 2a$.

Since $f(x)$ is positive for all real values of x.
We must have $b^2 - 4ac < 0$ and $a > 0$. ...(1)
Now discriminant of $g(x)$ is given by

$B^2 - 4AC = (b+2a)^2 - 4a(c+b+2a)$

$\qquad = b^2 + 4ab + 4a^2 - 4ac - 4ab - 8a^2$

$\qquad = b^2 - 4ac - 4a^2 < 0$

$\qquad [\because b^2 - 4ac < 0 \text{ by (1) and } -4a^2 < 0]$

Hence sign of $g(x)$ is the same as that of first term i.e. of a, which is positive **(§ 6 P. 1202)**

47. (a) If the given expression be y, then

$x^2(y-1) - 2x(y\cos\beta - \cos\alpha) + y - 1 = 0$

For real values of x, $b^2 - 4ac \geq 0$

i.e. $4(y\cos\beta - \cos\alpha)^2 - 4(y-1)^2 \geq 0$

or $[y(\cos\beta - 1) + (1 - \cos\alpha)]$
$\qquad [y(1+\cos\beta) - (1+\cos\alpha)] \geq 0$

$\because \quad a^2 - b^2 = (a-b)(a+b)$

or $\left[-2y\sin^2\dfrac{\beta}{2} + 2\sin^2\dfrac{\alpha}{2}\right]$

$\qquad\qquad \left[2y\cos^2\dfrac{\beta}{2} - 2\cos^2\dfrac{\alpha}{2}\right] \geq 0$

Multiplying by −ive sign and changing the sign of inequality, we get

$$\left(y - \frac{\sin^2{(\alpha/2)}}{\sin^2{(\beta/2)}}\right)\left(y - \frac{\cos^2{(\alpha/2)}}{\cos^2{(\beta/2)}}\right) \le 0$$

or $(y-a)(y-b) \le 0$ ∴ $a \le y \le b$.

(b) Let $\tan x = t, \tan \theta = a$

∴ $\tan\left(\frac{\pi}{4}+\theta\right) = \frac{1+t}{1-t}, \tan\left(\frac{\pi}{4}-\theta\right) = \frac{1-t}{1+t}$

where t is real.

Given expression is

$$y = \frac{\tan x + \tan \theta}{1 - \tan x \tan \theta} \cdot \frac{1 + \tan x \tan \theta}{\tan x - \tan \theta}$$

$$\frac{y}{1} = \frac{(t+a)(1+ta)}{(t-a)(1-ta)} = \frac{t(1+a^2) + a(1+t^2)}{t(1+a^2) - a(1+t^2)}$$

Apply componendo and dividendo

$$\frac{y+1}{y-1} = \frac{2t(1+a^2)}{2a(1+t^2)}$$

$$t^2\{a(y+1)\} - t(1+a^2)(y-1) + a(y+1) = 0$$

Since t is real ∴ $\Delta \ge 0$

$$(1+a^2)^2(y-1)^2 - 4a^2(y+1)^2 \ge 0$$

or $[(1+a^2)(y-1) + 2a(y+1)]$

$$[(1+a^2)(y-1) - 2a(y+1)] \ge 0$$

or $[y(1+a)^2 - (1-a)^2][y(1-a)^2 - (1+a)^2] \ge 0$

Divide the inequality by +ive quantity

$(1+a)^2 (1-a)^2$.

or $\left[y - \left(\frac{1-a}{1+a}\right)^2\right]\left[y - \left(\frac{1+a}{1-a}\right)^2\right] = +$ ive.

Hence y does not lie between

$\left(\frac{1-a}{1+a}\right)^2$ and $\left(\frac{1+a}{1-a}\right)^2$ where $a = \tan\theta$

or $\tan^2\left(\frac{\pi}{4}-\theta\right)$ and $\tan^2\left(\frac{\pi}{4}+\theta\right)$

∵ $\tan\left(\frac{\pi}{4}+\theta\right) = \frac{1+\tan\theta}{1-\tan\theta} = \frac{1+a}{1-a}$ etc.

(c) Eliminating z between the given relations

$xy + (x+y)z = 7$

or $xy + (x+y)\{6 - (x+y)\} = 7$

or $xy - (x+y)^2 + 6(x+y) = 7$

Arrange as a quadratic in y

$-x^2 - y^2 - xy + 6x + 6y - 7 = 0$

or $y^2 + y(x-6) + (x^2 - 6x + y) = 0$

y being real $\Rightarrow D \ge 0$

∴ $(x-6)^2 - 4(x^2 - 6x + 7) \ge 0$

or $3x^2 - 12x - 8 \le 0$ ...(1)

or $(x-\alpha)(x-\beta) \le 0$ where $\alpha \le \beta$

∴ x lies between α and β where α, β are the roots of (1), $\alpha < \beta$

$$\alpha, \beta = \frac{6 \pm 2\sqrt{15}}{3} \quad (\alpha < \beta)$$

∴ $\frac{6 - 2\sqrt{15}}{3} < x < \frac{6 + 2\sqrt{15}}{3}$ ∴ $x \in (\alpha, \beta)$

Again x, y, z are symmetrically placed and hence y, z also lie in the same interval.

48. (a) If the given expression be y, then

$y(x^2 - \sin^2\theta) = 2a(x-1)\sin^2\theta$

$x^2 y - 2ax\sin^2\theta - \sin^2\theta(y - 2a) = 0$

Since x is real ∴ $\Delta \ge 0$

$4a^2 \sin^4\theta + 4y\sin^2\theta(y - 2a) \ge 0$

Cancel $4\sin^2\theta$, a + ive quantity.

or $y^2 - 2ay + a^2\sin^2\theta = +$ ive

$(y-a)^2 - a^2\cos^2\theta = +$ ive

$(y - a + a\cos\theta)(y - a - a\cos\theta) = +$ ive

∴ y does not lie between p and q where $p < q$

or y does not lie between

$a(1-\cos\theta)$ and $a(1+\cos\theta)$

or $2a\sin^2\frac{\theta}{2}$ and $2a\cos^2\frac{\theta}{2}$.

(b) **Refer Q. 46 (a) P. 217-238.**

Let $y = \frac{\alpha x^2 + 6x - 8}{\alpha + 6x - 8x^2}$; then

$x^2(\alpha + 8y) + 6x(1-y) - (8 + \alpha y) = 0$

Since x is real $\Delta \ge 0$

∴ $36(1-y)^2 + 4(\alpha + 8y)(8 + \alpha y) \ge 0$

or $9(1 - 2y + y^2) + \{8\alpha y^2 + (64 + \alpha^2)y + 8\alpha\}$ ≥ 0

or $(9 + 8\alpha)y^2 + y(46 + \alpha^2) + (9 + 8\alpha) \ge 0$

i.e. +ive

The above quadratic expression has to be +ive for all real values of y as f is onto.

The condition as in last part is $\Delta \le 0$ and $9 + 8\alpha > 0$

or $(46 + \alpha^2)^2 - 4(9 + 8\alpha)^2 \le 0$

$(46 + \alpha^2 + 18 + 16\alpha)(46 + \alpha^2 - 18 - 16\alpha) \le 0$

or $(\alpha^2 + 16\alpha + 64)(\alpha^2 - 16\alpha + 28) \le 0$

$(\alpha + 8)^2(\alpha - 2)(\alpha - 14) \le 0$

or $2 \le \alpha \le 14$ and for this $9 + 8\alpha$ is +ive.

When $\alpha = 3$

$$y = \frac{3x^2 + 6x - 8}{3 + 6x - 8x^2}$$

when $y = 0$ we get

$3x^2 + 6x - 8 = 0$

∴ $x = \frac{1}{3}(-3 \pm \sqrt{33})$

Thus for $y = 0$ we get two values of x.

Hence the function is not one-one in this case.

49. (a) $y = \sqrt{\dfrac{(x+1)(x-3)}{x-2}}$

If y is real then y^2 is +ive or zero :

$\therefore \quad \dfrac{(x+1)(x-3)}{x-2} \geq 0$

or $\quad \dfrac{(x+1)(x-3)(x-2)}{(x-2)^2} \geq 0$

Now D^r is + ive $\therefore$ N^r is to be + ive

$N^r = 0$ if $x = -1, 3, 2$

Marking these values in ascending order on real line, write +ive in extreme right and move towards left with alternately changing the sign. From the fig. it is clear that N^r is +ive when $x \geq 3$, $-1 \leq x < 2$

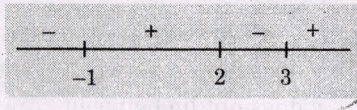

Fig. 11

($x = 2$ is excluded as it will make D^r infinite)

(b) $y = \sqrt{E}$ is real if $E \geq 0$

or $\quad \dfrac{-x^2 + x}{(x+1)(x^2 - x + 1)} \geq 0$

Now $x^2 - x + 1$ is a quadratic expression whose Discriminant $\Delta = -$ ive and hence its sign is same as that of Ist term $i.e. +$ ive.

Hence we must have $\dfrac{-x^2 + x}{x+1} \geq 0$

Multplying by '$-$' sign and changing the sign of inequality, we must have

$\dfrac{x(x-1)(x+1)}{(x+1)^2} \leq 0$

The change points are $-1, 0, 1$ in ascending order.

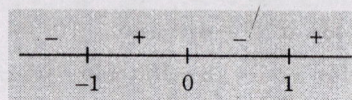

Fig. 11 (a)

As in part (a) the inequality is satisfied for

$\quad x \in [0, 1]$ and $]-\infty, -1[$,

$\quad x \in]-\infty, -1[\cup [0, 1]$

or $\quad 0 \leq x \leq 1$ and $x < -1$.

50. $y =$ given expression

$\Rightarrow (ad - bcy)x^2 + (ac + bd)(y-1)x$

$\qquad\qquad + (bc - ady) = 0$

Since x is real $\therefore \Delta \geq 0$

$(ac + bd)^2 (y-1)^2 - 4(ad - bcy)(bc - ady) \geq 0$

$\qquad\qquad\qquad \forall \ y \in R$

or $(ac - bd)^2 y^2 \neq 2\{2(a^2 d^2 + b^2 c^2)$

$\qquad - (ac + bd)^2\} y + (ac - bd)^2 \geq 0 \ \forall \ y \in R$

Above expression is to be + ive and its first term is + ive. Hence $\Delta < 0$.

$4\{2(a^2 d^2 + b^2 c^2) - (ac + bd)^2\}^2$

$\qquad\qquad\qquad - 4(ac - bd)^4 = -$ ive

Apply $L^2 - M^2 = (L + M)(L - M)$ and cancel 4.

or $[2a^2 d^2 + 2b^2 c^2 - (ac + bd)^2 - (ac - bd)^2]$

$\quad [2a^2 d^2 + 2b^2 c^2 - (ac + bd)^2 + (ac - bd)^2] < 0$

or $[2a^2 d^2 + 2b^2 c^2 - 2a^2 c^2 - 2b^2 d^2]$

$\quad [2a^2 d^2 + 2b^2 c^2 - 4abcd] < 0$

Again cancel 2, the second factor is $(ad - bc)^2$ which is + ive and first factor is

$a^2(d^2 - c^2) + b^2(c^2 - d^2)$

or $(c^2 - d^2)(b^2 - a^2) = -(a^2 - b^2)(c^2 - d^2)$

Hence the required condition is

$-(a^2 - b^2)(c^2 - d^2)(ad - bc)^2 < 0$

or $(a^2 - b^2)(c^2 - d^2) > 0$ $i.e.,$ + ive

Above will hold good if both $(a^2 - b^2)$ and $(c^2 - d^2)$ have the same sign $i.e.$, either both + ive or both $-$ive.

51. (a) Both the following inequalities have to hold good simultaneously.

$x^2 - 3x + 2 = (x-1)(x-2) > 0$ from I and II

$x^2 - 5x + 4 = (x-1)(x-4) < 0$ from II and III

$\therefore \quad x < 1$ or $x > 2$ and $1 < x < 4$

$\therefore$ From above we conclude that $2 < x < 4$ satisfy both. Since x is integral therefore $x = 3$.

(b) From the given relation we have

$-1 \leq \dfrac{12x}{4x^2 + 9} \leq 1$ by definition of mod.

Since $4x^2 + 9$ is +ive for all real x, we can multiply the inequality by $4x^2 + 9$.

$\therefore \quad -(4x^2 + 9) \leq 12x \leq (4x^2 + 9)$

$\quad (2x + 3)^2 \geq 0$ and $(2x - 3)^2 \geq 0$

Above is true for all real values of x being perfect squares.

52. (a) Proceed as above and note that

$x^2 + x + 1 = \left(x + \dfrac{1}{2}\right)^2 + \dfrac{3}{4}$ which is always +ive for all real values of x. Hence proceeding as in 51 (b), we have

$\quad 3x^2 + (k+2)x + 3 > 0$

and $x^2 + (2-k)x + 1 > 0$

Now the coefficients of x^2 in both are +ive $i.e.$ 3 and 1 therefore the signs of the quadratics will be +ive if $B^2 - 4AC < 0$ for both.

$\therefore \quad (k+2)^2 - 36 < 0$ or $(k+8)(k-4) < 0$

i.e. $-8 < k < 4$

and $(2-k)^2 - 4 < 0$ or $(k-0)(k-4) < 0$

i.e. $0 < k < 4$

The common region of the above two is $0 < k < 4$.

(b) The given inequality is equivalent to

$$-3 < \frac{x^2 - 3x - 1}{x^2 + x + 1} < 3.$$

Now $x^2 + x + 1$ is + ive for all real x as its Δ is –ive and sign of first term is + ive. Otherwise also

$$x^2 + x + 1 = \left(x + \frac{1}{2}\right)^2 + \frac{3}{4} = +ive$$

Hence we can multiply both sides by $x^2 + x + 1$

$\therefore \quad -3x^2 - 3x - 3 < x^2 - 3x - 1 < 3x^2 + 3x + 3$

The 1st part

$\Rightarrow \quad 4x^2 + 2 > 0$, which is true.

The 2nd part

$\Rightarrow \quad x^2 + 3x + 2 > 0$

or $(x+2)(x+1) = +$ ive or > 0 ...(1)

$\therefore \quad x < -2 \quad$ or $\quad x > -1$

$x \in (-\infty, 2) \quad$ or $\quad x \in (-1, \infty)$

$\therefore \quad x \in]-\infty, 2[\cup]-1, \infty[.$

53. (a) Ans. $-1 < m < 5$.

Hint : Since $x^2 + x + 1 > 0$ for all real x, the given inequality can be written as

$$-3(x^2 + x + 1) < x^2 + mx + 1 < 3(x^2 + x + 1)$$

$\therefore \quad 4x^2 + (m+3)x + 4 > 0$ ...(1)

and $\quad 2x^2 - (m-3)x + 2 > 0$ ...(2)

The inequality (1) will hold for all x if its

$\Delta = (m+3)^2 - 64 < 0 \qquad$ **See § 6. P. 202**

and the sign will be same as the coefficient of Ist term *i.e.,* +ive.

or $(m+11)(m-5) < 0$ which implies that

$-11 < m < 5$. ...(3)

Similarly, (2) will hold for all x if its $\Delta < 0$

$-1 < m < 7$ ...(4)

Finally from (3) and (4), $-1 < m < 5$.

(b) Ans. $-1 < m < 2$.

54. **Case I.** Choose $\alpha = 3m$ and $\beta = m + 3$ where

$\alpha < \beta \quad$ or $\quad 3m < m+3$ or $m < 3/2$ ...(1)

$(x - \alpha)(x - \beta) < 0 \quad \Rightarrow \quad \alpha < x < \beta$

But we are given that the inequality holds $\forall \; x \in [1, 3]$ and hence $[1, 3]$ should be a subset of $]\alpha, \beta[$

$\therefore \quad \alpha < 1$ and $\beta > 3$

$3m < 1$ and $m + 3 > 3$

$\therefore \quad m < \frac{1}{3}$ and $m > 0$, *i.e.* + ive

$\therefore \quad m \in \left(0, \frac{1}{3}\right).$

This also satisfies the condition I.

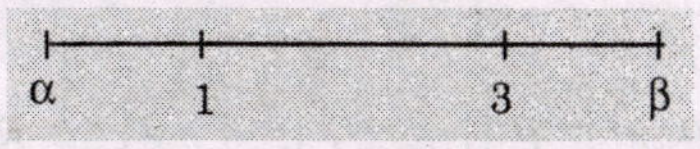

Fig. 12

Case II. If $\alpha > \beta$ *i.e.* $3m > m + 3$ or $m > 3/2$ ...(2)

then $\beta < x < \alpha$ and as above $\beta < 1$ and $\alpha > 3$

or $m + 3 < 1$ and $3m > 3$ $\therefore$ $m < -2$ and $m > 1$

There can't be any value of m satisfying both the above and also (2). Thus from case I, we get $m \in (0, 1/3)$.

55. Since x_1, x_2, x_3 are in A.P. $2x_2 = x_1 + x_3$

$\therefore \quad 3x_2 = \Sigma x_1 = 1 \quad \therefore \quad x_2 = \frac{1}{3}$

But x_2 is a root of given equation

$$\frac{1}{27} - \frac{1}{9} + \frac{1}{3}\beta + \gamma = 0$$

or $9\beta + 27\gamma = 2$ or $\beta + 3\gamma = 2/9$ ...(1)

Again $\Sigma x_1 x_2 = x_1 x_2 + x_2 x_3 + x_3 x_1 = \beta$

and $x_1 x_2 x_3 = -\gamma$

Putting $x_2 = \frac{1}{3}$, we get

$$\frac{1}{3}(x_1 + x_3) + x_1 x_3 = \beta \quad \text{and} \quad \frac{1}{3}x_1 x_3 = -\gamma$$

Eliminating x_3 from the above relation

$$\frac{1}{3}\left(x_1 - \frac{3\gamma}{x_1}\right) - 3\gamma = \beta$$

$$x_1^2 - 3(\beta + 3\gamma)x_1 - 3\gamma = 0$$

Since x_1 is real $\therefore$ $\Delta \geq 0$

$\therefore \quad 9(\beta + 3\gamma)^2 + 12\gamma \geq 0$ or $3(\beta + 3\gamma)^2 + 4\gamma \geq 0$ ...(2)

We have now to find the intervals for β and γ by the help of (1) and (2).

$\therefore \quad 3\left(\frac{2}{9}\right)^2 + 4\gamma \geq 0 \quad$ by (1)

or $\gamma + \frac{1}{27} \geq 0 \quad \therefore \quad \gamma \geq -\frac{1}{27}$ ...(3)

and from (1)

$9\beta + 27\gamma + 1 = 3$.

$3 - 9\beta = 27\gamma + 1 \geq 0$, by (3)

or $3\beta - 1 \leq 0 \quad \therefore \quad \beta \leq \frac{1}{3}.$

$\therefore \quad \beta \in \left]-\infty, \frac{1}{3}\right], \gamma \in \left]-\frac{1}{27}, \infty\right].$

56. (a) Dividing by y^2, we get

$$a\left(\frac{x}{y}\right)^2 - b\frac{x}{y} - a = 0$$

or $\quad az^2 - bz - a = 0$ where $z = \dfrac{x}{y}$.

It will have real roots if $b^2 + 4a^2 \geq 0$.

Above is clearly true for real values of b and a. Therefore it can be resolved into linear factors like
$$a(z - p)(z - q)$$
or $\quad a\left(\dfrac{x}{y} - p\right)\left(\dfrac{x}{y} - q\right)$ or $a(x - py)(x - qy)$.

(b) Write as a quadratic in y and its
$$\Delta_1 = 36 - 4(y^2 + 8y) \geq 0$$
or $\quad y^2 + 8y - 9 \leq 0$ or $(y + 9)(y - 1) \leq 0$
$$\therefore \quad -9 \leq y \leq 1$$
$\therefore$ Greatest value of y is 1 and least value is -9. Similarly writing as a quadratic in x, we will have greatest value of x is 8 and least value is -2.

57. (a) The given relation can be written as
$$(a + b + c)(ab + bc + ca) = abc$$
or $\quad a^2(b + c) + abc + b^2(c + a) + abc$
$$+ c^2(a + b) + abc = abc$$
or $\quad a^2(b + c) + b^2(c + a) + c^2(a + b) + 2abc = 0$

Above consists of 8 terms taking
$$2abc = abc + abc$$
L.H.S. is $(a + b)(b + c)(c + a) = 0$ **(Formula)**
It is satisfied if either $a + b = 0$ or $b + c = 0$ or $c + a = 0$ i.e. any two of the three quantities are equal and opposite.

(b) The given expression becomes 0 when either $a + b = 0$ or $b + c = 0$ or $c + a = 0$ and hence all these are its factors of 3rd degree.

Now assume
$$(a + b + c)^3 - a^3 - b^3 - c^3 = \lambda (a + b)(b + c)$$
$$(c + a)$$
Choose $a = 0, b = 1, c = 2$, we get $\lambda = 3$.

58. (a) We are given that $(2x + y)(x - 2y) = 7$
Since x and y are to be integers, hence L.H.S. is the product of two integers and R.H.S. is also the product of two integers 7 and 1, or 1 and 7, or -7 and -1, or -1 and -7.

Hence we can choose

$2x + y = 7$	and	$x - 2y = 1$	...(1)
$2x + y = 1$	and	$x - 2y = 7$	...(2)
$2x + y = -7$	and	$x - 2y = -1$	...(3)
$2x + y = -1$	and	$x - 2y = -7$	...(4)

Solve them as usual and only (1) and (3) give integral solutions as 3, 1 for (1) and $-3, -1$ for (3). Both (2) and (4) when solved do not give integral values of x and y.

(b) The given equation can be written as
$$2x^2(y^2 - 3) = 12 - y^2$$

$\therefore \quad 2x^2 = \dfrac{12 - y^2}{y^2 - 3}$ $\quad \therefore \quad 2x^2 + 1 = \dfrac{9}{y^2 - 3}$ $\quad$ ...(1)

Now L.H.S. for integral values of x is clearly an odd positive integer and hence $\dfrac{9}{y^2 - 3}$ must also

be an **odd positive integer for integral values of y** :
By inspection this is possible only
when $y^2 = 4$ $\quad \therefore \quad y = 2, -2$
$\therefore \quad 2x^2 + 1 = 9$ or $x^2 = 4$ $\quad \therefore \quad x = 2, -2$.
Hence $(2, 2), (2, -2), (-2, 2)$ and $(-2, -2)$ are the only four possible integral solutions.

59. (i) $x = \dfrac{1}{7}(220 - 12y)$ or $y = \dfrac{1}{12}(220 - 7x)$

Now give $+$ive integral values to y such that x also becomes $+$ive integral. The first $+$ive integral value of y is 2 (as $y = 1$ will not make x, $+$ive and integral) so that
$$x = \dfrac{1}{7}(220 - 12.2) = \dfrac{196}{7} = 28.$$
$\therefore \quad x = 28, y = 2$
Now the values of x form an A.P. whose common difference is -12.

$\because \quad T_n = pn + q$ forms an A.P. whose common difference is p and first term is $p + q$. Hence the other $+$ive integral values of x will be 16, 4, -8, $-20, \ldots$

We choose only $x = 16$ and 4, which are $+$ive
$\therefore \quad 12y = 220 - 112 = 108$ $\quad \therefore \quad y = 9$.
$\quad 12y = 220 - 28 = 192$ $\quad \therefore \quad y = 16$
Hence $(x, y) = (28, 2), (16, 9), (4, 16)$ only.
Note : You observe that the values of y, i.e. 16, 9, 2, ... form an A.P. of common difference -7.

(ii) **Ans.** $(x, y) = (6, 5), (17, 19), (28, 33), (39, 47), \ldots$

60. (a) Ans. (a).
A quadratic equation has real and distinct roots implies its $\Delta \geq 0$.
or $\quad 4(a + b + c)^2 - 12\lambda(ab + bc + ca) \geq 0$
or $\quad (\Sigma a^2 + 2\Sigma ab) - 3\lambda \Sigma ab \geq 0$
or $\quad \Sigma a^2 \geq (3\lambda - 2)\Sigma ab$ or $3\lambda - 2 < \dfrac{\Sigma a^2}{\Sigma ab}$ $\quad$ ...(1)

Now in any triangle sum of two sides is greater than the third.
$\therefore \quad a + b > c, \ b + c > a, \ c + a > b$
or $\quad a > c - b, \ b > a - c, \ c > b - a$
or $\quad a^2 + b^2 + c^2 > 2(a^2 + b^2 + c^2) - 2\Sigma ab$
or $\quad 2\Sigma ab > \Sigma a^2$ or $\dfrac{\Sigma a^2}{\Sigma ab} < 2$ $\quad$ ...(2)

Hence from (1) and (2),
$$3\lambda - 2 < 2 \text{ or } \lambda < 4/3.$$

(b) Ans. 1210

Given	$a + b = 10c, \ ab = -11d$	...(1)
	$c + d = 10a, \ cd = -11b$	...(2)

$\therefore \quad a + b + c + d = 10\,(a + c)$ ...(3)

So we have to find the value of $a + c$ so that by (3) we get the value of $a + b + c + d$.

From relations (1) and (2) on adding, we have

$\qquad b + d = 9\,(a + c)$ ...(4)

and multiplying relations in (1) and (2)

$\qquad (ac)\,bd = 121bd \quad \Rightarrow \quad ac = 121$ ...(5)

Multiplying (1) by a and (2) by c and adding,

$a^2 + c^2 + (ab + cd) = (10 + 10)\,ac$

or $\quad a^2 + c^2 - 11\,(b + d) = 20ac$ by (1), (2),

or $\quad (a + c)^2 - 11 \times 9\,(a + c) = 22ac$

or $\quad t^2 - 99t - 22\,(121) = 0$ $\qquad$ by (4) and (5)

or $\quad t^2 - (121 - 22)\,t - 22\,(121) = 0$

$\quad (t - 121)\,(t + 22) = 0 \quad \therefore \quad t = 121 = a + c$

Hence from (3),

$\qquad a + b + c + d = 10\,(a + c) = 10 \times 121 = 1210$

Problem Set (3)

▶ Objective Questions

1. A quadratic equation with rational coefficients can have
(a) both roots equal and irrational
(b) one roots rational and other irrational
(c) one root real and other imaginary
(d) none of these.

2. If the roots of $ax^2 + bx + c = 0$ are in the ratio $m : n$, then
(a) $mna^2 = (m + n)\,c^2$ $\qquad$ (b) $mnb^2 = (m + n)\,ac$
(c) $mnb^2 = (m + n)^2\,ac$ $\qquad$ (d) none of these.

3. For real x, the expression $[(x + m)^2 - 4mn]\,/\,[2\,(x - n)]$ can have any value except
(a) between m and $m + n$ $\quad$ (b) more than $m + 2n$
(c) between $2m$ and $2n$ $\qquad$ (d) all values are possible.

4. If the expression $y^2 + 2xy + 2x + my - 3$ can be resolved into two rational factors, then m must be
(a) any possible real number
(b) any negative real number
(c) -2 $\qquad\qquad$ (d) 3

5. If one root of $5x^2 + 13x + k = 0$ is reciprocal of the other, then
(a) $k = 0$ $\quad$ (b) $k = 5$ $\quad$ (c) $k = \dfrac{1}{6}$ $\quad$ (d) $k = 6$

6.* The equation $2x^2 + 3x + 1 = 0$ has an irrational root
(a) True $\qquad\qquad$ (b) False

7. If one root of the equation $x^2 + px + 12 = 0$ is 4, while the equation $x^2 + px + q = 0$ has equal roots, the value of q is
(a) $49\,/\,4$ $\qquad\qquad$ (b) $4\,/\,49$
(c) 4 $\qquad\qquad$ (d) none of these

8. If $x^2 + px + 1$ is a factor of $ax^3 + bx + c$, then
(a) $a^2 + c^2 = -ab$ $\qquad$ (b) $a^2 - c^2 = -ab$
(c) $a^2 - c^2 = ab$ $\qquad$ (d) none of these

9.* If $x = 2 + 2^{2/3} + 2^{1/3}$ then the value of $x^3 - 6x^2 + 6x$ is
(a) 3 $\qquad$ (b) 2 $\qquad$ (c) 1 $\qquad$ (d) none

10. If the equations $k\,(6x^2 + 3) + rx + 2x^2 - 1 = 0$ and $6k\,(2x^2 + 1) + px + 4x^2 - 2 = 0$ have both the roots common, find the value of $2r - p$

11. α and β are the roots of $4x^2 + 3x + 7 = 0$ then the value of $\dfrac{1}{\alpha} + \dfrac{1}{\beta}$ is
(a) $-3\,/\,4$ $\quad$ (b) $-3\,/\,7$ $\quad$ (c) $3\,/\,7$ $\quad$ (d) $7\,/\,4$

12. If one root of $x^2 - x - k = 0$ be square of the other, then $k =$
(a) $2 \pm \sqrt{3}$ $\quad$ (b) $3 \pm \sqrt{2}$ $\quad$ (c) $2 \pm \sqrt{5}$ $\quad$ (d) $5 \pm \sqrt{2}$

13. If 8, 2 are the roots of $x^2 + ax + \beta = 0$ and 3, 3 are the roots of $x^2 + \alpha x + b = 0$ then the roots of $x^2 + ax + b = 0$ are
(a) $8, -1$ $\quad$ (b) $-9, 2$ $\quad$ (c) $-8, -2$ $\quad$ (d) $9, 1$

14. If difference of roots of the equation $x^2 + px + 8 = 0$ is 2, then p is equal to
(a) ± 2 $\quad$ (b) ± 4 $\quad$ (c) ± 6 $\quad$ (d) ± 8

15. If 2, 3 be the roots of $2x^3 + mx^2 - 13x + n = 0$ then the values of m and n are respectively
(a) $-5, -30$ $\quad$ (b) $-5, 30$ $\quad$ (c) $5, 30$ $\quad$ (d) none

16.* The greatest negative integer satisfying $x^2 - 4x - 77 < 0$ and $x^2 > 4$ is ... $\qquad$ **(EAMCET 1991)**

17. Let $\alpha\,(a)$ and $\beta\,(b)$ be the roots of the equation of $(\sqrt[3]{1 + a} - 1)\,x^2 + (\sqrt{1 + a} - 1)\,x + (\sqrt[6]{1 + a} - 1) = 0$, $a > -1$
Then $\displaystyle\lim_{a \to 0^+} \alpha(a)$ and $\displaystyle\lim_{a \to 0^+} \beta(a)$ are
(a) $\dfrac{-5}{2}$ and 1 $\qquad$ (b) $-\dfrac{1}{2}$ and -1
(c) $-\dfrac{7}{2}$ and 2 $\qquad$ (d) $-\dfrac{9}{2}$ and 3 $\qquad$ **(IITJEE 2012)**

18. Let α, β are be real and z be a complex number. If $z^2 + 2z + \beta = 0$ has two distinct roots on the line $\mathrm{Re}(z) = 1$ then it is necessary that
(a) $\beta \in [0, 1[$ $\qquad$ (b) $\beta \in [-10[$
(c) $|\beta| = 1$ $\qquad$ (d) $\beta \in [1, \infty[$ $\quad$ **(AIEEE 2011)**

19. Let p and q be real number such that $p \neq 0$, $p^3 \neq q$ and $p^3 \neq -q$. If α and β are non-zero complex numbers satisfying $\alpha + \beta = -p$ and $\alpha^3 + \beta^3 = 7$, then a quadratic equation having $\dfrac{\alpha}{\beta}$ and $\dfrac{\beta}{\alpha}$ as its root is

(a) $(p^3 + q)x^2 - (p^3 + 2q)x + (p^3 + q) = 0$

(b) $(p^3 + q)x^2 - (p^3 - 2q)x + (p^3 + q) = 0$

(c) $(p^3 - q)x^2 - (5p^3 - 2q)x + (p^3 - q) = 0$

(d) $(p^3 - q)x^2 - (5p^3 + 2q)x + (p^3 - q) = 0$

(IIT-JEE 2010)

20. The value of b for which the equations $x^2 + bx - 1 = 0$ and $x^2 + x + b = 0$ have one root in common is

(a) $-\sqrt{2}$ (b) $-i\sqrt{3}$ (c) $i\sqrt{5}$ (d) $\sqrt{2}$

(IITJEE 2011)

21. The number of distinct real roots of $x^4 - 4x^3 + 12x^2 + x - 1 = 0$ is

(a) 2 (b) 3 (c) 0 (d) 4

(IIT JEE 2011)

Solutions to Problem Set (3)

1. Ans. (d).
Note that imaginary roots occur in conjugate pairs of the form $\alpha \pm \beta i$ and irrational roots occur in conjugate pairs of form $A \pm \sqrt{B}$ in surds.

2. Ans. (c). $\dfrac{\alpha}{\beta} = \dfrac{m}{n}$

or $\dfrac{\alpha}{m} = \dfrac{\beta}{n} = \dfrac{\alpha + \beta}{m + n} = \sqrt{\left(\dfrac{\alpha\beta}{mn}\right)}$ by Ratio Prop.

$\therefore$ $mn(\alpha + \beta)^2 = \alpha\beta(m + n)^2$

or $mn\left(-\dfrac{b}{a}\right)^2 = (m + n)^2 \dfrac{c}{a}$

or $mnb^2 = ac(m + n)^2$

3. $\Delta = (y - 2m)(y - 2n)$ is + ive.
$\therefore$ y shall not lie between $2m$ and $2n$
(c) is correct.

4. Treat as a quadratic in y
$$y^2 + y(2x + m) + (2x - 3) = 0$$
$\Delta = (2x + m)^2 - 4(2x - 3)$
$\quad = 4x^2 + 4xm - 8x + m^2 + 12$
$\quad = 4x^2 + 4x(m - 2) + (m^2 + 12)$
$\quad = [4x^2 + 4x(m - 2) + (m - 2)^2] + (m^2 + 12) - (m - 2)^2$
$\quad = [2x + (m - 2)]^2 + [12 + 4m - 4]$

For rational factors Δ should be a perfect square
$\therefore$ $8 + 4m = 0$ or $m = -2$.

5. Ans. (b). **6.** Ans. (b).

7. Ans. (a).
Since 4 is a root of $x^2 + px + 12 = 0$, we have
$\quad 16 + 4p + 12 = 0$ or $p = -7$.
Further, since the roots of $x^2 + px + q = 0$ are equal, we have

$p^2 - 4q = 0$ or $49 - 4q = 0$.
$\therefore$ $q = 49/4$.

8. Ans. (c).
$\quad x^2 + px + 1$ is a factor of given cubic
$\therefore$ $ax^3 + bx + c = (x^2 + px + 1)(ax + c)$
The other factor is of first degree whose coefficients are chosen keeping in view the coefficient of x^3 and constant term in cubic.
Comparing the coefficient of x^2 and x,
$\quad ap + c = 0$ $\therefore$ $p = -c/a$
and $a + cp = b$ or $a + c\left(\dfrac{-c}{a}\right) = b$
$\quad a^2 - c^2 = ab$.

9. Ans. (b). **See Q. 27 (a), P. 206.**

10. The two equations can be written as
$\quad x^2(6k + 2) + rx + (3k - 1) = 0$ ...(1)
and $\quad x^2(12k + 4) + px + (6k - 2) = 0$. ...(2)
Divide by 2
$\therefore$ $x^2(6k + 2) + \dfrac{p}{2}x + (3k - 1) = 0$ ...(3)
Comparing (1) and (3), we get
$\quad r = \dfrac{p}{2}$ $\therefore$ $2r - p = 0$.

11. Ans. (b) is correct.

12. Ans. (c).
Refer **Q. 26 (a), Page 206**, we have
$\quad k^2 - 4k - 1 = 0$.
k is as given in (c).

13. Ans. (d)
$\quad -a = 10, b = 9$ $\therefore$ $x^2 - 10x + 9 = 0$.

14. Ans. (c).

15. Ans. (b).
Solve $f(2) = 0$, $f(3) = 0$ for m and n.

16. Ans. -3.
$\quad (x + 7)(x - 11) < 0$, $(x + 2)(x - 2) > 0$
$\therefore$ $-7 < x < 11$ and $x < -2$ or $x > 2$
Mark these regions on real line and take their intersection.

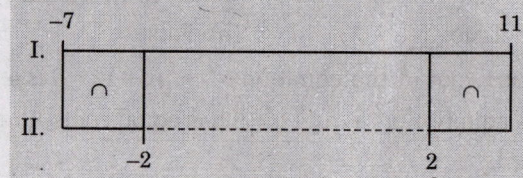

Fig. 13

The intersection of two regions is given by
$\quad -7 < x < -2$ or $2 < x < 11$
We are to find the greatest – ive integer.
Hence we choose $-7 < x < -2$.
Therefore all negative integers 6 to -3 will satisfy the above and the greatest amongst these is -3.

Therefore the greatest – ive integer is – 3.

17. And. (b).

$[(1+a)^{1/3} - 1]x^2 + [(a+1)^{1/2} - 1]x + [(a+1)^{1/6} - 1] = 0$

Let $1 + a = p^6$.

Then $(p^2 - 1)x^2 + (p^3 - 1)x + (p - 1) = 0$

$\Rightarrow \quad (p+1)x^2 + (p^2 + p + 1)x + 1 = 0$

As $a \to 0, p \to 1$

$\therefore \quad 2x^2 + 3x + 1 = 0 \quad \Rightarrow \quad x = -1 \text{ and } x = -\frac{1}{2}$

18. Ans. (d).

Let roots be $p + iq$ and $p - iq, p, q \in \mathbf{R}$

Some roots lie on the line $Re(z) = 1 \Rightarrow p = 1$

product of roots $= p^2 + q^2 = \beta = 1 + q^2$

$\Rightarrow \beta \in [1, \infty[\quad (q \neq 0 \because \text{roots are unequal})$

19. Ans. (b).

Product $= 1 \qquad$ sum $= \dfrac{\alpha^2 + \beta^2}{\alpha\beta} = \dfrac{(\alpha + \beta)^2 - 2\alpha\beta}{\alpha\beta}$

Since $\alpha^3 + \beta^3 = q \quad \Rightarrow \quad -p(\alpha^2 + \beta^2 - \alpha\beta) = q$

$\Rightarrow ((\alpha + \beta)^2 - 3\alpha\beta) = -\dfrac{q}{p} \Rightarrow p^2 + \dfrac{q}{p} = 3\alpha\beta$

$\therefore \quad$ sum $= \dfrac{\left\{p^2 - \frac{2}{3}\left(\dfrac{p^3 + q}{p}\right)\right\}3p}{(p^3 + q)} = \dfrac{p^3 - 2q}{p^3 + q}$

$\Rightarrow \quad$ Required equation to

$$x^2 + \left(\dfrac{p^3 - 2q}{p^3 + q}\right)x + 1 = 0$$

$\Rightarrow \quad (p^3 + q)x^2 - (p^3 - 2q)x + (p^3 + q) = 0$

20. Ans. (b).

$x^2 + x + b = 0, \qquad x^2 + bx - 1 = 0$

$\Rightarrow \quad \dfrac{x^2}{b^2 + 1} = \dfrac{x}{-1 - b} = \dfrac{1}{1 - b}$

$\Rightarrow \quad x = \dfrac{b^2 + 1}{-(b+1)} = \dfrac{-(b+1)}{1 - b}$

$\Rightarrow \quad (b^2 + 1)(1 - b) = (b + 1)^2$

$\Rightarrow \quad b^2 - b^3 + 1 - b = b^2 + 2b + 1$

$\Rightarrow \quad b^3 + 3b = 0 \qquad \Rightarrow \quad b = 0, b^2 = -3$

$\Rightarrow \quad b = 0, \pm\sqrt{3}\, i$

First let us suppose that all four roots are real and distined

Let $f(x) = x^4 - 4x^3 + 12x^2 + x - 1 = 0$

$\Rightarrow \quad f'(x) = 4x^3 - 12x^2 + 24x + 1$

Must have three distinct real roots

$f''(x) = 0 \quad \Rightarrow \quad 12x^2 - 24x + 24 = 0$

Most have two distinct real roots which is a contradiztion because $12x^2 - 24x + 24 = 0$

or $\quad x^2 - 2x + 2 = 0 \qquad \Rightarrow \quad D < 0$

Hence $f(x) = 0$ can not have all four equal roots.

As $f(0) = -1, f(1) = 9, f(-1) = 15$

$\Rightarrow \quad f(x) = 0$ must have two distinct real roots are in $[-1, 0[$ and other in $[0, 1[$.

MISCELLANEOUS EXERCISE

Matching Entries

♦ *Match the entries of List-A and List-B.*

1.

List-A

(a) If one root of the equation $ax^2 + bx + c = 0$ be square of the other, then

(b) If α, β be the roots of the equation $x^2 + x + 1 = 0$, then the equation whose roots are α^{19}, β^7 is

(c) A quadratic equation whose roots are $\dfrac{a}{\sqrt{a} \pm \sqrt{a - b}}$ is

(d) If α, β, γ are the roots of $x^3 + ax + b = 0$, then $\dfrac{\alpha^3 + \beta^3 + \gamma^3}{\alpha^2 + \beta^2 + \gamma^2} =$

(e) If $x^2 + x + 1$ is a factor of $E = ax^3 + bx^2 + cx + d$, then the real root of the equation $E = 0$ is

List-B

1. $bx^2 - 2a\sqrt{a}\, x + a^2 = 0$

2. $\dfrac{3b}{2a}$

3. $b^3 + ac(a + c) = 3abc$

4. $x^2 + x + 1 = 0$

5. $-\dfrac{d}{a}$

2. **List-A**   **List-B**

(a) If the roots of the equation $(b-c)x^2 + (c-a)x + (a-b) = 0$ be equal, then a, b, c are in which series ?

1. Imaginary

(b) If roots of the equation $a(b-c)x^2 + b(c-a)x + c(a-b) = 0$ be equal, then a, b, c are in which series ?

2. 0

(c) If the roots of $x^2 - 2cx + ab = 0$ be real and unequal then the roots of $x^2 - 2(a+b)x + (a^2 + b^2 + 2c^2) = 0$ are ......

3. H.P.

(d) The number of real roots of the equation $(\sin 2^x)(\cos 2^x) = \frac{1}{4}(2^x + 2^{-x})$ is ......

4. A.P.

3. **List-A**   **List-B**

(a) The expression $\alpha x^2 + bx + c$ has the same sign as of a if $b^2 - 4ac$ is

1. $y < \frac{1}{3}$ or $y > 3$

(b) If the graph of the function $y = 16x^2 + 8(a+5)x - 7a - 5$ is strictly above the x-axis then a lies in the interval

2. $b^2 - 4ac \leq 0$

(c) If x is real then $\dfrac{x^2 - 2x + 4}{x^2 + 2x + 4}$ takes values in the interval ......

3. $-15 < a < -2$

(d) If $y = \tan x \cot 3x, x \in R$, then y does not lie in the interval

4. $\left[\dfrac{1}{3}, 3\right]$

4. Let α, β, γ be three numbers such that $\dfrac{1}{\alpha} + \dfrac{1}{\beta} + \dfrac{1}{\gamma} = \dfrac{1}{2}, \dfrac{1}{\alpha^2} + \dfrac{1}{\beta^2} + \dfrac{1}{\gamma^2} = \dfrac{9}{4}$ and $\alpha + \beta + \gamma = 2$, then

Column-I   **Column-II**

(a) $\alpha\beta\gamma$ (p) 6

(b) $\sum \alpha\beta$ (q) -8

(c) $\sum \alpha^2$ (r) -2

(d) $\sum \alpha^3$ (s) -1

5. Let α, β be the roots of the equation $ax^2 + bx + c = 0$, then match the roots of the equation in left with roots given in right.

Column-I   **Column-II**

(a) $(x-b)^2 + b(x-b) + ac = 0$ (p) $2\alpha, 2\beta$

(b) $ax^2 + 2bx + 4c = 0$ (q) $-\dfrac{\alpha}{a}, -\dfrac{\beta}{b}$

(c) $4a^2x^2 - b^2 + 4ac = 0$ (r) $a\alpha + b, a\beta + b$

(d) $a^3x^2 - abx + c = 0$ (s) $\alpha + \dfrac{b}{2a}, \beta + \dfrac{b}{2a}$

Answers

1. (a) $\rightarrow$ 3. **Q. 26 (a) P. 206**
   (b) $\rightarrow$ 4. **Q. 22 (c) P. 206**
   (c) $\rightarrow$ 1. **Q. 14 (b) P. 205**
   (d) $\rightarrow$ 2. **Q. 6 (d) P. 204**
   (e) $\rightarrow$ 5. **Q. 22 (d) P. 206**
2. (a) $\rightarrow$ 4. **Q. 19 (a) P. 220**
   (b) $\rightarrow$ 3. **Q. 19 (b) P. 220**
   (c) $\rightarrow$ 1. **Q. 27 (a) P. 221**
   (d) $\rightarrow$ 2. L.H.S. < 1, R.H.S. > 1
3. (a) $\rightarrow$ 2. **§ 6 P. 206**
   (b) $\rightarrow$ 3. **Q. 18 (d) P. 220**

(c) $\rightarrow$ 4. Proceed as in **Q. 42 P. 222**
(d) $\rightarrow$ 1. **Q. 39 (b) P. 222**

4. Ans. (a)$\rightarrow$ (r), (b)$\rightarrow$ (s), (c)$\rightarrow$ (p), (d)$\rightarrow$ (q)

(a) $\left(\sum \dfrac{1}{\alpha}\right)^2 = \sum \dfrac{1}{\alpha^2} + 2\sum \dfrac{1}{\alpha\beta}$

or $\left(\dfrac{1}{2}\right)^2 = \dfrac{9}{4} + 2\dfrac{(\alpha + \beta + \gamma)}{\alpha\beta\gamma}$

or $\dfrac{1}{4} - \dfrac{9}{4} = \dfrac{2.2}{\alpha\beta\gamma} \Rightarrow \alpha\beta\gamma = -2$

$\therefore$ (a)$\rightarrow$ (r)

(b) $\dfrac{1}{\alpha} + \dfrac{1}{\beta} + \dfrac{1}{\gamma} = \dfrac{1}{2} \Rightarrow \dfrac{\sum \alpha\beta}{\alpha\beta\gamma} = \dfrac{1}{2}$

∴ $\dfrac{\sum \alpha\beta}{-2} = \dfrac{1}{2}$ by (a) $\Rightarrow \sum \alpha\beta = -1$

∴ (b) → (s)

(c) $\sum \alpha^2 = (\sum \alpha)^2 - 2\sum \alpha\beta$

$\qquad = (2)^2 - 2(-1) = 6$ by (b)

(d) $\alpha^3 + \beta^3 + \gamma^3 - 3\alpha\beta\gamma = (\alpha + \beta + \gamma)$

$\qquad\qquad\qquad (\alpha^2 + \beta^2 + \gamma^2 - \sum \alpha\beta)$

∴ $\sum \alpha^3 - 3(-2) = 2[-2 - (-1)] = -2$

∴ $\sum \alpha^3 = -6 - 2 = -8$

5. Ans. (a) → (r), (b) → (p), (c) → (s), (d) → (q)

Let $x - b = t$, then $t^2 + bt + ac = 0$

∴ $a\left(\dfrac{t}{a}\right)^2 + b\left(\dfrac{t}{a}\right) + c = 0$ ∴ $t = \alpha, \beta$

or $x - b = a\alpha, a\beta$ ∴ $x = a\alpha + b, a\beta + b$

∴ (a) → (r)

(b) $a\left(\dfrac{x}{2}\right)^2 + b\left(\dfrac{x}{2}\right) + c = 0$, on dividing by 4

∴ $\dfrac{x}{2} = \alpha, \beta.$ ∴ $x = 2\alpha, 2\beta$

∴ (b) → (p)

(c) $x = \pm \dfrac{\sqrt{b^2 - 4ac}}{2a}$

But α, β are $\dfrac{-b \pm \sqrt{b^2 - 4ac}}{2a}$

∴ $\alpha + \dfrac{b}{2a}$ and $\beta + \dfrac{b}{2a}$ are the roots of (c)

∴ (c) → (s)

(d) Let $ax = -t$ ∴ $at^2 + bt + c = 0$

∴ $t = d, \beta$ ∴ $-ax = \alpha, \beta$

∴ $x = -\dfrac{\alpha}{a}, -\dfrac{\beta}{b}$ ∴ (d) → (q)

Fascinating Facts

- A root which is obtained by solving an equation but does not satisfy it is called **extraneous root.** Such roots enter the equation in the process of squaring because this process is irreversible.
- If $a + b + c = 0$, then 1 is a root of the equation $ax^2 + bx + c = 0$
- If the roots are equal in magnitude but opposite in sign, then $b = 0, ac > 0$
- If $a = 1, b, c \in \mathbf{I}$ and the roots are rational numbers then these roots must be integers.
- If the roots are reciprocal to each other, then $a = c$
- Imeginary roots occur in conjugate pair and irrational roots occur in conjugate pair if the coefficient are rational.
- The condition that the roots of the equation $ax^2 + bx + c = 0$ may differ by one is $b^2 - a^2 = 4ac$
- The condition that the roots of the equation $ax^2 + bx + c = 0$ be in the ratio $p : q$ is $(p + q)^2 ac = b^2 pq$
- If the roots of $ax^2 + bx + c = 0$ are α, β then the roots of $ax^2 + bx + c = 0$ will be $\dfrac{1}{\alpha}, \dfrac{1}{\beta}$.
- If the equation $x^2 + bx + c = 0$ and $x^2 + cx + b = 0$ have a common root, then either $b = c$ or $b + c + 1 = 0$
- If the equations $ax^2 + bx + c = 0$ and $bx^2 + cx + a = 0$ have a common root then either $a + b + c = 0$ or $a = b = c$, $a, b, c \in \mathbf{R}$.
- The condition that one root of the equation $ax^2 + bx + c = 0$ may be square of the other is $ac(a + c) + b^3 = 3abc$
- The condition that the roots of the equation $ax^2 + bx + c = 0$ may differ by some constant k is $b^2 - a^2 k^2 = 4ac$
- The roots of the equation $ax^2 + bx + c = 0$ are reciprocal to $a' x^2 + b' x + c' = 0$
  if $(cc' - aa')^2 = (ba' - cb')(ab' - bc')$
- If sum of the roots is equal to sum of their squares, then $2ac = ab + b^2$
- If an equation has only one change of sign, it has only one positive root.
- If all the terms of an equation are positive and the equation involve no odd power of x, then its all roots are complex.
- If α is a repeated root of the quadratic equation $f(x) = ax^2 + bx + c$ then α is also a root of the equation $f'(x) = 0$.
- If two quadratic equations with real coefficients have an **imaginary roots** common then both roots will becomes and the two equations will be identical.
- If two quadratic equation have an irrational root common, then both roots will be common and the two equation will x identical.
- Value of coefficients determining the value of roots of $ax^2 + bx + c = 0$

a	b	c	Value of the roots
c	–	a	Reciprocal roots
0	–	–	One root is infinite
0	0	–	Both roots are infinite
-	0	–	Roots are equal but of opposite sign
-	–	0	One root is zero

Logarithms

§ 1. Introduction.

Let there be a number $a > 0$ and $a \neq 1$. A number x is called the logarithm of another number $y > 0$ to the base a if $a^x = y$.

We first observe that the logarithm of a number satisfying the conditions of the definition is **unique**. For if α and β are two distinct logarithms of the number y to base a, then by the above definition, we have

$$a^\alpha = y \text{ and } a^\beta = y$$

whence $a^\alpha = a^\beta$. ...(1)

But, by the properties of powers with positive base different from 1, we conclude from (1) that $\alpha = \beta$. Thus, if the number y has a logarithm to base a, then this logarithm is **unique**. **We denote it by the symbol $\log_a y$**. Thus by definition

$$x = \log_a y \text{ if } a^x = y.$$

Characteristic and mantissa. The integral part of a logarithm is called the **characteristic** and the decimal part is called **mantissa**. Logarithms to the base 10 are called **common logarithms**. The **characteristics** of common logarithms can be written down by inspection by the following rule. **(V. Imp.)**

Rule. The characteristic of the logarithm (base 10) of a number greater than 1 is less by one than the number of digits in the integral part, and is positive. The characteristic of the logarithm of a positive decimal fraction less than 1, is greater by unity than the number of consecutive zeros immediately after the decimal point, and is negative.

§ 2. Properties of Logarithms.

The students should commit to memory the following. We assume $a > 0$, $a \neq 1$, $m > 0$, $n > 0$.

1. $a^x = y$ then $x = \log_a y$

L.H.S. is called exponential form whereas R.H.S. is called corresponding logarithmic form.

2. $a^1 = a$, $b^1 = b$ etc. $\therefore \log_a a = \log_b b = 1$.

3. $a^0 = 1$, $b^0 = 1$ etc.

$\therefore \quad \log_a 1 = 0$, $\log_b 1 = 0$ etc.

4. $\log_b a \cdot \log_a b = 1$ or $\log_b a = \dfrac{1}{\log_a b}$

Let $\log_b a = x$ $\therefore$ $a = b^x$, $\log_a b = y$ $\therefore b = a^y$

Putting the value of b, we get $a = (a^y)^x = a^{xy}$

$\therefore \quad xy = 1$ or $x = \dfrac{1}{y}$.

5. **Base changing formula**

$\log_b a = \log_c a \log_b c$

$\log_b a = (\log_c a) / (\log_c b)$, by (4)

Let $\log_b a = x$ $\therefore$ $a = b^x$, ...(1)

$\log_c a = y$ $\therefore$ $a = c^y$ ...(2)

and $\log_b c = z$ $\therefore$ $c = b^z$ ...(3)

$\therefore \quad a = c^y = (b^z)^y = b^{yz}$ by (2) and (3) ...(4)

or $a = b^x = b^{yz}$ $\therefore$ $x = yz$ by (1), (4)

In general $\log_b a = \log_c a \log_d c \log_e d \ldots \log_b k$

6. $\log_a mn = \log_a m + \log_a n$,

$\log_a (m/n) = \log_a m - \log_a n$

Let $\log_a m = x$ $\therefore$ $m = a^x$,

$\log_a n = y$ $\therefore$ $n = a^y$

$\therefore \quad mn = a^x \cdot a^y = a^{x+y}$

$\therefore \quad \log_a mn = x + y = \log_a m + \log_a n$.

$\dfrac{m}{n} = \dfrac{a^x}{a^y} = a^{x-y}$

$\therefore \quad \log_a \dfrac{m}{n} = x - y = \log_a m - \log_a n$.

7. $\log_a m^n = n \log_a m$ or in particular $\log_a a^n = n$ **(Imp.)**

Let $\log_a m = x$ $\therefore$ $m = a^x$ and $m^n = (a^x)^n = a^{nx}$

$\therefore \quad \log_a m^n = nx = n \log_a m$ ...(A)

Particular case. Putting $m = a$ in (A), we get

$\log_a a^n = n \log_a a = n \cdot 1 = n$, by (2)

e.g. $\log_3 3^2 = 2$, $\log_4 64 = \log_4 4^3 = 3$,

$\log_2 \sqrt{8} = \log_2 2^{3/2} = 3/2$.

8.* $\log_{a^q} n^p = (p/q) \log_a n$. In particular,

$\log_{n^q} n^p = p/q$ **(Imp.)**

Let $z = \log_{a^q} n^p$ ∴ $(a^q)^z = n^p$

or $a^{qz} = n^p$ ...(B)

Let $y = \log_a n$ ∴ $a^y = n$ or $(a^y)^p = n^p$

∴ $a^{yp} = n^p$ ...(C)

∴ $a^{qz} = a^{yp}$ by (B) and (C)

∴ $qz = yp$ or $z = (p/q)\, y$.

or $\log_{a^q} n^p = (p/q) \log_a n$.

Particular case. Putting $a = n$, we get

$\log_{n^q} n^p = \dfrac{p}{q} \log_n n = \dfrac{p}{q} . 1 = \dfrac{p}{q}$, by (2)

9.* $a^{\log_a n} = n$ **(V. Imp.)**

Let $p = a^{\log_a n}$

Rewriting the above exponential form to logarithmic form, we get

$\log_a p = \log_a n$ ∴ $p = n$.

$e.g.\ 3^{\log_3 5} = 5, 10^{\log_{10} m} = m,$

$5^{-2\log_5 3} = 5^{\log_5 3^{-2}} = 3^{-2} = \dfrac{1}{9}.$

10. $\log_p a > \log_p b$ **(V. Imp.)**

⇒ $a \geq b$ if base p is +ive and > 1

or $a \leq b$ if base is +ive and less than 1

i.e. $0 < p < 1$

In other words if base is > 1 then inequality remains same and if base is +ive but less than 1 then the sign of inequality is reversed.

11. If $a > 1$, then $0 < \alpha < \beta \ \Leftrightarrow \ \log_a \alpha < \log_a \beta$

12. If $0 < a < 1$, then $0 < \alpha < \beta \ \Leftrightarrow \ \log_a \alpha > \log_a \beta$

13. If $a > 1, \alpha > 1$, then $\log_a \alpha > 0$

14. If $0 < a < 1, 0 < \alpha < 1$, then $\log_a \alpha > 0$

15. If $0 < a < 1, \alpha > 1$, then $\log_a \alpha < 0$

16. If $a > 1, 0 < \alpha < 1$, then $\log_a \alpha < 0$

17. If $a > 1, \alpha > 1$, and $\alpha > a$, then $\log_a \alpha > 1$

18. If $a > 1, \alpha > 1$ and $\alpha < a$, then $0 < \log_a \alpha < 1$

19. If $0 < a < 1, 0 < \alpha < 1$ and $\alpha > a$, then $0 < \log_a \alpha < 1$

20. If $0 < a < 1, 0 < \alpha < 1$ and $\alpha < a$, then $\log_a \alpha > 1$.

Problem Set (1)

Logarithms

1. Rewrite the following equations in the logarithm form :

   (a) $4^{3/2} = 8$
   (b) $5^0 = 1$

   (c) $(2\sqrt{2})^{-2/3} = \dfrac{1}{2}$.

2. Rewrite the following equalities in the exponential form.

   (a) $\log_2 32 = 5$,
   (b) $\log_3 \dfrac{1}{243} = -5$.

3. (a) $\log_{5\sqrt{5}} 5 = \dfrac{2}{3}$
   (b) $\log_{100} 0.1 = -\dfrac{1}{2}$

   In Q. 4 to 6 using the identity $a^{\log_a n} = n$, find :

4. (a) $3^{-\frac{1}{2}\log_3 9}$
   (b) $2^{2 - \log_2 5}$

   (c) $10^{\log_{10} m + \log_{10} n}$

5. (a) $2^{\log_{(2\sqrt{2})} 15}$
   (b)* $(5 \cdot 8)^{\log_{5 \cdot 8} 10 + 1}$

6. (a) $8^{\log_2 \sqrt[3]{121} + \frac{1}{3}}$
   (b) $\sqrt{\log_{0.5}^2 4}$

7. (a)* Prove that $(0 \cdot 16)^{\log_{2.5}\left(\frac{1}{3} + \frac{1}{3^2} + \frac{1}{3^3} + \dots \infty\right)} = 4.$

   (b)* The value of $(0 \cdot 2)^{\log_{\sqrt{5}}(1/4 + 1/8 + 1/16 + \dots \infty)}$ is 4.

   (c)* The sum of the series $\log_4 2 - \log_8 2 + \log_{16} 2 \dots$ is

   (a) e^2
   (b) $\log_e 2 + 1$
   (c) $\log_e 3 - 2$
   (d) $1 - \log_e 2$ **(M.N.R. 1994)**

   (d) If $y = (0 \cdot 64)^{\log_{0.25}\left(\frac{1}{3} + \frac{1}{3^2} + \frac{1}{3^3} + \dots \infty\right)}$ then $y =$

   (a) $0 \cdot 25$
   (b) $0 \cdot 6$
   (c) $0 \cdot 8$
   (d) $0 \cdot 9$

   In Q. 8 to 14 compute without using tables.

8. (a) $\log_\pi \tan(0 \cdot 25 \pi)$
   (b) $\log_2 (\log_3 81)$

9. (a)* $81^{(1/\log_5 3)} + 27^{\log_9 36} + 3^{4/\log_7 9}$

   (b) $2^{\log_3 5} - 5^{\log_3 2}$

   (c) If $p = \log_{245} 175$ and $q = \log_{1715} 875$, then $\dfrac{1 - pq}{p - q} =$

   (a) 1
   (b) 2
   (c) 3
   (d) 5

10. (a) $\log_3 5 \log_{25} 27$
    (b)* $\log_9 27 - \log_{27} 9$

11. (a) $\log_{10} \tan 40^\circ \log_{10} \tan 41^\circ \dots \log_{10} \tan 50^\circ$

    (b) $\log_{10} \tan 1^\circ + \log_{10} \tan 2^\circ + \dots \log_{10} \tan 89^\circ$

12. (a) $\log_3 4 \log_4 5 \log_5 6 \log_6 7 \log_7 8 \log_8 9$

    (b) $\log_3 2 \log_4 3 \log_5 4 \dots \log_{15} 14 \log_{16} 15$

13. (a) Evaluate $\log (216\sqrt{6})$ to the base 6.

    (b) $\dfrac{\log_2 \log_2 \log_4 256 + 2\log_{\sqrt{2}} 2}{}$

14.* $\sqrt{\left[\left(\dfrac{1}{\sqrt{(27)}}\right)^{2 - (\log_5 13)/(2\log_5 9)}\right]}$

15. Compute :

    (a) $\log_6 16$ if $\log_{12} 27 = a$.

    (b) $\log_{30} 8$ if $\log_{30} 3 = a$ and $\log_{30} 5 = b$.

16.* $\log_{25} 24$ if $\log_6 15 = \alpha$ and $\log_{12} 18 = \beta$.

17.* If $\log_{12} 18 = \alpha$ and $\log_{24} 54 = \beta$, prove that $\alpha\beta + 5(\alpha - \beta) = 1$.

18. Simplify : $7\log\dfrac{16}{15} + 5\log\dfrac{25}{24} + 3\log\dfrac{81}{80}$.

19.* (a) If $\log_{10} 2 = 0\cdot 30103$, determine how many zeros there are between the decimal point and the first significant digit in $(1/2)^{1000}$.

(b) Given $\log_{10} 2 = 0\cdot 30103$, $\log_{10} 3 = 0\cdot 47712$. Find the number of digits in $3^{12} \times 2^8$.

20.* Find the least integer n such that $7^n > 10^5$, given that $\log_{10} 343 = 2\cdot 5353$.

21.* Determine b satisfying

(a) $\log_{\sqrt 8} b = 3\dfrac{1}{3}$ (b) $\log_{\sqrt 8} b = 3^{1/3}$

(c) $\log_e 2 \log_b 625 = \log_{10} 16 \log_e 10$.

22. (a) Without using tables prove $\dfrac{1}{\log_3 \pi} + \dfrac{1}{\log_4 \pi} > 2$.

(b) Prove that $\log_2 17 \log_{1/5} 2 \log_3 \dfrac{1}{5} > 2$.

23.* If (i) $10^{\log_{10} a} = a$ (ii) $a^{\log_a 10} = 10$, determine the domain of a for the above two equations.

24. (a)* If $t = -2$ then $\log_4 \dfrac{t^2}{4} - 2\log_4 4t^4 =$

(a) 2   (b) -4
(c) -6 (d) 0

(b) $\dfrac{\log_a x}{\log_a y} = \dfrac{\log_b x}{\log_b y}$.

Is the above statement true or false ?

25. (a)* Prove that the equation $x^{\log_{\sqrt x} 2x} = 4$ has no solution.

(b) The solution set of the equation
$$\log_{1/5} (2x + 5) + \log_5 (16 - x^2) \le 1 \text{ is}$$

(a) $\left(-\dfrac{5}{2}, 1\right)$ (b) $[-1, 4[$

(c) $]-1, 4]$ (d) $\left[-\dfrac{5}{2}, 4\right]$

26. (a) Show that $x = 2$ is the only root of the equation
$$9^{\log_3 (\log_2 x)} = \log_2 x - (\log_2 x)^2 + 1.$$

(b) The number of solutions the equation
$$|x+1|^{\log_{x+1}(3+2x-x^2)} = (x-3)|x| \text{ has is}$$

(a) only one   (b) two
(c) no   (d) more than two

(c) The solution of the equation
$$4^{\log_2 (\log x)} = \log x - (\log x)^2 + 1 \text{ is given by } x =$$

(a) 1   (b) e
(c) 4   (d) e^2

(d) If $\log_a (ab) = x$, then evaluate $\log_b (ab)$ in terms of x.

27. (a) Prove that $|\log_b a + \log_a b| \ge 2$ where a and b are positive numbers not unity.

(b) Find the least value of the expression $2\log_{10} x - \log_x 0.01$ for $x > 1$.   **(D.C.E. 1998)**

28. Prove the following identities :

(a) $\dfrac{\log_a n}{\log_{ab} n} = 1 + \log_a b$,

(b)* $\log_{ab} x = \dfrac{\log_a x \log_b x}{\log_a x + \log_b x}$.

(c) If $a^2 + b^2 = 7ab$, prove that
$$\log\dfrac{1}{3}(a+b) = \dfrac{1}{2}[\log a + \log b].$$

29. (a)* Prove that $\log_{10} 2$ lies between $\dfrac{1}{4}$ and $\dfrac{1}{3}$.

(b) Prove that $\dfrac{2}{5} < \log_{10} 3 < \dfrac{1}{2}$.

30. (a)* Prove that $\log_2 3$ is an irrational number.

(b) The number $\log_2 7$ is an irrational number.   **(I.I.T. 1990)**

In Q. 31 to 32 (b) which is greater :

31. (a) $\log_2 3$ or $\log_{1/2} 5$.
(b) $\log_4 5$ or $\log_{1/16} (1/25)$.
(c) $\log_7 11$ or $\log_8 5$.

32. (a) $\log_2 3$ or $\log_3 11$.

(b) $\log_{1/3} \dfrac{1}{2}$ or $\log_{1/2} \dfrac{1}{3}$.

(c) If $x = \log_3 5$, $y = \log_{17} 25$, which one of the following is correct :

(a) $x < y$ (b) $x = y$
(c) $x > y$ **(J.E.E.,W.B. 1993)**

33. (a) If a, b, c are in G.P., prove that $\log_a n, \log_b n, \log_c n$ are in H.P.

(b)* If $\log_3 2$, $\log_3 (2^x - 5)$ and $\log_3 (2^x - 7/2)$ are in arithmetic progression, then find the value of x.   **(I.I.T. 1990)**

34. Solve the equations for x and y :
$$(3x)^{\log 3} = (4y)^{\log 4} \text{ and } 4^{\log x} = 3^{\log y}.$$
   (M.N.R. 1997)

35. (a)* Given that $\log_l x$, $\log_m x$ and $\log_n x$ are in arithmetic progression. Note that $x \ne 1$. Then prove that $n^2 = (ln)^{\log_l m}$

(b) Find the sum of
$$a\left(x^2 + \dfrac{1}{x^2}\right) - \dfrac{a^2}{2}\left(x^4 - \dfrac{1}{x^4}\right) + \dfrac{a^3}{3}\left(x^6 + \dfrac{1}{x^6}\right) \dots$$
and determine the values of a and x for which it is valid.   **(Roorkee 1993)**

36. Show that

(a) $\log_b a \log_c b \log_d c \log_a d = 1$.
(b) $\log_b a \log_c b \log_a c = 1$.
(c) Prove that if $x = \log_c b + \log_b c$, $y = \log_a c + \log_c a$, $z = \log_b a + \log_a b$ then $xyz = x^2 + y^2 + z^2 - 4$.

37. (a) Show that
$$\frac{1}{\log_2 n}+\frac{1}{\log_3 n}+\dots+\frac{1}{\log_{43} n}=\frac{1}{\log_{43!} n}.$$

(b)* If $n=1983!$, compute the sum
$$\frac{1}{\log_2 n}+\frac{1}{\log_3 n}+\frac{1}{\log_4 n}+\dots+\frac{1}{\log_{1983} n}.$$

(c) $\dfrac{1}{\log_{xy} xyz}+\dfrac{1}{\log_{xz} xyz}+\dfrac{1}{\log_{zx} xyz}=$

    (a) 0   (b) 1

    (c) 2   (d) $\log_x xyz$

38.* If $y=a^{1/(1-\log_a x)}$ and $z=a^{1/(1-\log_a y)}$, prove that $x=a^{1/(1-\log_a z)}$.

39. If $\dfrac{\log a}{b-c}=\dfrac{\log b}{c-a}=\dfrac{\log c}{a-b}$, prove that $a^a.b^b.c^c=1$.

(D.C.E. 1997)

40. If $\dfrac{\log x}{q-r}=\dfrac{\log y}{r-p}=\dfrac{\log z}{p-q}$, prove that
$$x^{q+r}.y^{r+p}.z^{p+q}=x^p.y^q.z^r.$$

41.* If $\dfrac{x(y+z-x)}{\log x}=\dfrac{y(z+x-y)}{\log y}=\dfrac{z(x+y-z)}{\log z}$, prove
that $x^y y^x=z^y y^z=x^z z^x$.   **(Bihar C.E.E. 1999)**

42.* Prove the identity
$$\log_a n\log_b n+\log_b n\log_c n+\log_c n\log_a n$$
$$=\frac{\log_a n\log_b n\log_c n}{\log_{abc} n}.$$

43.* If a,b,c are distinct positive numbers each different from 1 such that
$(\log_b a\log_c a-\log_a a)+(\log_a b\log_c b-\log_b b)$
$\qquad\qquad\qquad +(\log_a c\log_b c-\log_c c)=0,$
then prove that $abc=1$.

44.* If n is a natural number such that
$$n=p_1^{a_1}.p_2^{a_2}.p_3^{a_3},\dots\dots p_k^{a_k},$$
and $p_1,p_2,\dots\dots p_k$
are distinct primes, then show that $\log n\ge k\log 2$.

45. If $a>0,c>0,b=\sqrt{ac},a\ne 1,$
$c\ne 1,ac\ne 1$ and $n>0,$
prove that $\dfrac{\log_a n}{\log_c n}=\dfrac{\log_a n-\log_b n}{\log_b n-\log_c n}.$

46.* If a and b are the lengths of the sides and c the length of the hypotenuse of a right angled triangle, $c-b\ne 1$ and $c+b\ne 1$, prove that
$$\log_{c+b} a+\log_{c-b} a=2\log_{c+b} a\log_{c-b} a.$$

47. Given a geometric progression
$$a,a_1,a_2,a_3,\dots\dots\dots$$
and an arithmetic progression
$$b,b_1,b_2,b_3,\dots\dots\dots$$
with positive terms. The common difference of A.P. and common ratio of G.P. are both positive. Show that there always exists a system of logarithms for which
$$\log a_n-b_n=\log a-b \text{ (for any } n).$$
Find base β of the system.

1. (a) $\log_4 8=\dfrac{3}{2}$

(b) $\log_5 1=0$

(c) $\log_{2\sqrt2}\dfrac{1}{2}=-\dfrac{2}{3}$

2. (a) $32=2^5$

(b) $\dfrac{1}{243}=3^{-5}$

3. (a) $5=(5\sqrt5)^{2/3}$

(b) $0.1=100^{-1/2}$

4. (a) $3^{-\frac{1}{2}\log_3 9}=3^{\log_3 9^{-1/2}}=9^{-1/2}=\dfrac{1}{3}$

(b) $2^2.2^{-\log_2 5}=4.2^{\log_2 5^{-1}}=4.5^{-1}=\dfrac{4}{5}$

                       by (9) P. 247

(c) $10^{\log_{10} m+\log_{10} n}=10^{\log_{10} mn}=mn.$

5. (a) $(15)^{2/3}=\sqrt[3]{(225)}$

(b) $(5.8)^{\log_{5.8} 10}.(5.8)^1=10(5.8)=58$

                       by (9) P. 247

6. (a) $8^{\log_2 \sqrt[3]{121}+\frac{1}{3}}=2^{3\left[\log_2 121^{1/3}+\frac{1}{3}\right]}$
$$=2^{\log_2 121+1}=2^{\log_2 121}.2=121.2=242.$$

(b) **Hint :** Since $\log_{0.5} 4=\log_{2^{-1}} 2^2=-2\log_2 2=-2$

we have $\sqrt{\log_{0.5}^2 4}=\sqrt{(-2)^2}=\sqrt4=2.$

7. (a) Let the given expression be A^X, where
$$A=0\cdot16=\left(\frac{4}{10}\right)^2,\ S_\infty=\frac{1/3}{1-(1/3)}=\frac{1}{2}$$
$$X=\log_{5/2}(1/2)=\log_{10/4}(1/2)$$
$$=\log_{(4/10)^{-1}}(2^{-1})=\log_{4/10} 2$$
$$\therefore\quad A^X=\left(\frac{4}{10}\right)^{2\log_{4/10} 2}=\left(\frac{4}{10}\right)^{\log_{4/10} 4}=4.$$

(b) $S_\infty=2^{-1}$

L.H.S. $=(5^{-1})^{\log_{\sqrt5}(2^{-1})}$
$$=(5^{-1})^{-1/(1/2)\log_5 2}=5^{2\log_5 2}=5^{\log_5 2^2}=4$$

(c) Ans (d).
$$\log_{y^n} x^m=\frac{m}{n}\log_y x \text{ and } \log_x x=1$$
$$\therefore\quad S=\frac{1}{2}-\frac{1}{3}+\frac{1}{4}-\frac{1}{5}+\dots.$$
$$\log(1+x)=x-\frac{x^2}{2}+\frac{x^3}{3}-\frac{x^4}{4}+\dots.$$
$$\therefore\quad \text{Putting } x=1,\ S=1-\log_e 2$$

(d) Ans. (c).

$$S = \frac{1}{3} + \frac{1}{3^2} + \frac{1}{3^3} + \ldots \infty$$

$$= \frac{1/3}{1-(1/3)} = \frac{1}{2}$$

$$\therefore \quad \log_{025}\left(\frac{1}{2}\right) = \log_2^{-2}(2^{-1}) = \frac{-1}{-2}\log_2 2 = \frac{1}{2}$$

$$\therefore \quad y = (0 \cdot 64)^{1/2} = 0 \cdot 8 \Rightarrow (c)$$

8. (a) $\log_\pi \tan(0.25\pi) = \log_\pi \tan\left(\frac{1}{4}\pi\right) = \log_\pi 1 = 0$

(b) $\log_2(\log_3 81) = \log_2(\log_3 3^4) = \log_2 4$

$$= \log_2 2^2 = 2 \qquad \text{by (7) } \textbf{P. 246}$$

9. (a) 1st term $= 3^{4\log_3 5} = 3^{\log_3 5^4} = 5^4 = 625$

2nd term $= 27^{\frac{2}{2}\log_3 6} = 3^{3(\log_3 6)}$

$$= 3^{\log_3 6^3} = 6^3 = 216$$

3rd term $= 3^{4\log_9 7} = 3^{4 \cdot \frac{1}{2}\log_3 7} = 3^{\log_3 7^2} = 7^2 = 49$

$\therefore$ Sum $= 625 + 216 + 49 = 890.$

(b) We have

$$2^{\log_3 5} = 2^{\log_2 5 \log_3 2} = (2^{\log_2 5})^{\log_3 2} = 5^{\log_3 2} \quad \ldots(1)$$

$$\therefore \quad 2^{\log_3 5} - 5^{\log_3 2} = 5^{\log_3 2} - 5^{\log_3 2} = 0, \text{ by (1)}$$

(c) Ans. (d).

$$175 = 25 \times 7 = 5^2 \cdot 7, 245 = 49.5 = 5.7^2$$

$$875 = 125 \times 7 = 5^3 \cdot 7, 1715 = 5.343 = 5.7^3$$

Now we know that $\log_b a = \dfrac{\log a}{\log b}$

Put $\log 5 = \alpha, \log 7 = \beta$

$$p = \frac{\log 5^2 \cdot 7}{\log 5 \cdot 7^2} = \frac{2\log 5 + \log 7}{\log 5 + 2\log 7} = \frac{2\alpha + \beta}{\alpha + 2\beta}$$

$$q = \frac{3\alpha + \beta}{\alpha + 3\beta} \text{ as above}$$

$$\therefore \quad \frac{1-pq}{p-q} = \frac{(\alpha+2\beta)(\alpha+3\beta)-(2\alpha+\beta)(3\alpha+\beta)}{(2\alpha+\beta)(\alpha+3\beta)-(\alpha+2\beta)(3\alpha+\beta)}$$

$$= \frac{-5(\alpha^2 - \beta^2)}{-(\alpha^2 - \beta^2)} = 5 \Rightarrow (d)$$

10. (a) $\log_3 5 \log_{25} 27 = \log_3 5 \log_{5^2} 3^3$

$$= \log_3 5 \times \frac{3}{2}\log_5 3 \qquad \text{[See (8) P. 246-247]}$$

$$= \frac{3}{2}\log_3 5 \log_5 3 = \frac{3}{2} \qquad \text{[See (4) P. 246]}$$

(b) $\log_9 27 - \log_{27} 9 = \log_{3^2} 3^3 - \log_{3^3} 3^2$

$$= \frac{3}{2}\log_3 3 - \frac{2}{3}\log_3 3 \qquad \text{[See (8) P. 246-247]}$$

$$= \frac{3}{2} - \frac{2}{3} = \frac{5}{6}$$

11. (a) We have $\log_{10}\tan 45° = \log_{10} 1 = 0.$

Since $\log_{10}\tan 45°$ is one of the factors of the product, we get

$$\log_{10}\tan 40° \log_{10}\tan 41° \ldots\ldots.$$

$$\log_{10}\tan 50° = 0.$$

(b) $(\log_{10}\tan 1° + \log_{10}\tan 2° + \ldots\ldots$

$$+ \log_{10}\tan 89°)$$

$$= \log_{10}(\tan 1° \tan 2° \ldots.. \tan 44° \tan 45° \tan 46°$$

$$\ldots\ldots \tan 89°)$$

$$= \log_{10}[(\tan 1° \tan 89°)(\tan 2° \tan 88°)\ldots\ldots$$

$$(\tan 44° \tan 46°)\tan 45°]$$

$$= \log_{10}[(\tan 1° \cot 1°)(\tan 2° \cot 2°)\ldots\ldots$$

$$(\tan 44° \cot 44°)\tan 45°]$$

$$= \log_{10} 1 = 0$$

$[\because \tan 1° \cot 1° = \tan 2° \cot 2° = \ldots.$

$$\ldots.. = \tan 44° \cot 44° = 1 \text{ and } \tan 45° = 1]$$

12. (a) The given expression by (5) **P. 246** is

$$= \log_3 9 = \log_3 3^2 = 2, \text{ by (7) } \textbf{P. 246}$$

(b) The given expression by (5) of § 2 is

$$\log_{16} 2 = \log_{2^4} 2 = \frac{1}{4}\log_2 2 = \frac{1}{4}, \text{ by (8) } \textbf{P. 246-247}.$$

13. (a) $\log_6 216\sqrt{6} = \log_6 6^{7/2} = 7/2.$

(b) $\log_4 256 = \log_4 4^4 = 4 = 2^2 \quad \therefore \quad T_1 = 1$

and $2\log_{\sqrt{2}} 2 = 2.2\log_2 2 = 4 \quad \therefore \quad T_2 = 4$

$$\therefore \quad T_1 + T_2 = 1 + 4 = 5.$$

14. Given expression

$$= \sqrt{\left[\left(\frac{1}{\sqrt{(27)}}\right)^2 \times \left(\frac{1}{\sqrt{(27)}}\right)^{-(\log_5 13)/(2\log_5 9)}\right]}$$

$$= \frac{1}{\sqrt{(27)}} \times (\sqrt{27})^{\frac{1}{4}\log_9 13}$$

$$= 3^{-3/2} \times (3)^{\frac{3}{8}\log_9 13} = 3^{-3/2} \times 3^{\frac{3}{16}\log_3 13}$$

$$= 3^{-3/2} \times 3^{\log_3 (13)^{3/16}} = 3^{-3/2} \times 13^{3/16}$$

15. (a) $\log_6 16 = \log_6 2^4 = 4\log_6 2 = \dfrac{4}{\log_2 6}$

$$= \frac{4}{\log_2 2 + \log_2 3} = \frac{4}{1 + \log_2 3} \qquad \ldots(1)$$

and $a = \log_{12} 27 = \log_{12} 3^3$

$$= 3\log_{12} 3 = \frac{3}{\log_3 (3 \times 4)}$$

$$= \frac{3}{\log_3 3 + \log_3 4} = \frac{3}{1 + 2\log_3 2}$$

$$\therefore \quad a + 2a\log_3 2 = 3 \text{ or } \log_3 2 = \frac{3-a}{2a}.$$

Hence $\log_2 3 = \dfrac{2a}{3-a}$.

Substituting this value of $\log_2 3$ in (1), we get

$$\log_6 16 = \frac{4}{1 + 2a/(3-a)} = \frac{4(3-a)}{3+a}.$$

(b) **Hint :** $\log_{30} 8 = 3\log_{30} 2$

$= 3\log_{30}\dfrac{30}{15} = 3[1 - \log_{30} 3 - \log_{30} 5] = 3(1 - a - b).$

16. We change all the logarithms to base 5.

Thus $\log_{25} 24 = \log_{5^2}(2^3 \times 3)$

$= \log_{5^2}(2^3) + \log_{5^2}(3)$

$= \dfrac{3}{2}\log_5 2 + \dfrac{1}{2}\log_5 3$ ...(1)

Now $\alpha = \log_6 15 = \dfrac{\log_5 15}{\log_5 6} = \dfrac{\log_5 3 + 1}{\log_5 2 + \log_5 3}$

∵ $\log_5 5 = 1$ ...(2)

$\beta = \log_{12} 18 = \dfrac{\log_5 18}{\log_5 12} = \dfrac{\log_5(3^2 . 2)}{\log_5(2^2 . 3)}$

$= \dfrac{2\log_5 3 + \log_5 2}{2\log_5 2 + \log_5 3}$ ...(3)

Now putting $\log_5 2 = x$ and $\log_5 3 = y$, we get from (2) and (3)

$\alpha = \dfrac{y+1}{x+y}$

or $\alpha x + (\alpha - 1)y - 1 = 0$ ...(4)

$\beta = \dfrac{2y + x}{2x + y}$

$(2\beta - 1)x - (2 - \beta)y + 0 = 0$ ...(5)

Solving (4) and (5), we get

$\dfrac{x}{-(2-\beta)} = \dfrac{y}{-(2\beta-1)} = \dfrac{1}{-\{\alpha(2-\beta)+(\alpha-1)(2\beta-1)\}}$ by (4)

or $\dfrac{x}{2-\beta} = \dfrac{y}{2\beta-1} = \dfrac{1}{\alpha\beta + \alpha - 2\beta + 1}.$

$\log_5 2 = x = \dfrac{2-\beta}{\alpha\beta + \alpha - 2\beta + 1}$

and $\log_5 3 = y = \dfrac{2\beta-1}{\alpha\beta + \alpha - 2\beta + 1}$

Substituting these values of $\log_5 2$ and $\log_5 3$, we get

$$\log_{25} 24 = \frac{5-\beta}{2\alpha\beta + 2\alpha - 4\beta + 2}.$$

17. $\alpha = \log_{12} 18 = \dfrac{\log 18}{\log 12} = \dfrac{\log(3^2 . 2)}{\log(3 . 2^2)}$

$= \dfrac{2\log 3 + \log 2}{\log 3 + 2\log 2}$, by (5) of §2

$\beta = \log_{24} 54 = \dfrac{\log 54}{\log 24} = \dfrac{\log(3^3 . 2)}{\log(3 . 2^3)} = \dfrac{3\log 3 + \log 2}{\log 3 + 3\log 2}$

If $x = \log 2$ and $y = \log 3$, then

$\alpha = \dfrac{x+2y}{2x+y}$, $\beta = \dfrac{x+3y}{3x+y}$

∴ $\alpha\beta + 5(\alpha - \beta)$

$= \dfrac{(x+2y)(x+3y)}{(2x+y)(3x+y)}$

$\qquad + \dfrac{5[(x+2y)(3x+y) - (x+3y)(2x+y)]}{(2x+y)(3x+y)}$

$= \dfrac{(x^2 + 5xy + 6y^2) + 5(x^2 - y^2)}{6x^2 + 5xy + y^2}$

$= \dfrac{6x^2 + 5xy + y^2}{6x^2 + 5xy + y^2} = 1.$

18. Given expression

$= 7\log\left(\dfrac{2^4}{3\times 5}\right) + 5\log\left(\dfrac{5^2}{3\times 2^3}\right) + 3\log\left(\dfrac{3^4}{5\times 2^4}\right)$

$= 7[4\log 2 - \log 3 - \log 5]$

$\quad + 5[2\log 5 - \log 3 - 3\log 2]$

$\qquad + 3[4\log 3 - \log 5 - 4\log 2]$

$= \log 2.$

19. (a) Let $x = \left(\dfrac{1}{2}\right)^{1000}$.

Then $\log_{10} x = -1000\log 2 = -1000 \times .30103$

$= -301.03 = \overline{302}.97.$

Hence the number of zeros in $\left(\dfrac{1}{2}\right)^{1000}$ between the decimal point and the first significant digit is $(302-1) = 301.$ (See the rule in §1).

(b) Let $x = 3^{12} \times 2^8$. Then

$\log_{10} x = 12\log 3 + 8\log 2$

$= 12 \times .47712 + 8 \times .30103$

$= 5.72544 + 2.40824 = 8.13368.$

Hence the number of digits in $3^{12} \times 2^8$ is $8 + 1 = 9.$

20. $\log_{10} 343 = \log 7^3 = 3\log 7 = 2.5353.$

∴ $\log 7 = \dfrac{1}{3}(2.5353).$ Now $7^n > 10^5$ if

$n\log 7 > 5\log_{10} 10$

or $n.\dfrac{1}{3}(2.5353) > 5$ or $n(2.5353) > 15$ ...(1)

Clearly there can be infinite values of n satisfying the above inequality but there is only one least value of n which is clearly 6.

21. Writing in exponential form, we get

(a) $b = (\sqrt{8})^{10/3} = (2^{3/2})^{10/3} = 2^5 = 32.$

(b) $\log_{\sqrt{8}} b = 3^{1/3} \Rightarrow b = (\sqrt{8})^{3^{1/3}}$

$= (\sqrt{2})^{3\times 3^{1/3}} = (\sqrt{2})^{3^{4/3}}.$

(c) Clearly R.H.S. $= \log_e 16$, by (5) **P. 246**.

Hence the given relation can be written as

$\log_b 625 = \log_e 16 / \log_e 2 = \log_2 16 = \log_2 2^4 = 4,$

by (5) & (7) **P. 246**

$$\therefore \quad 625 = b^4 \quad \text{or} \quad 5^4 = b^4 \quad \therefore \quad b = 5.$$

22. (a) We have to prove that $\log_\pi 3 + \log_\pi 4 > 2$ ...(1)

L.H.S. $= \log_\pi 3.4 = \log_\pi 12 > \log_\pi \pi^2$ as $12 > \pi^2$

$$= 2 \log_\pi \pi = 2 \qquad \qquad ...(2)$$

Hence proved.

(b) Clearly L.H.S.$= \log_3 17 > \log_3 9 = \log_3 3^2 = 2.$

23. (i) $\log_{10} a$ is defined for $a + \text{ive}$, and $a \neq 0$

$$\therefore \quad a \in]0, \infty[\quad \text{or} \quad (0, \infty)$$

(ii) $\log_a 10$ is defined for $a + \text{ive}$, and $a \neq 1$.

$$\therefore \quad a \in (0, 1) \cup (1, \infty) \quad \text{or} \quad]0, 1[\cup]1, \infty[.$$

24. (a) Ans. (c).

$$[2 \log_4 |t| - \log_4 4] - 2 [\log_4 4 + 4 \log_4 |t|]$$

$$= [2 \log_4 2 - 1] - 2 [1 + 4 \log_4 2]$$

$$= 2 \cdot \frac{1}{2} - 1 - 2 - 8 \left(\frac{1}{2}\right) = -6.$$

(b) Ans. True. Each is equal to $\log_y x = \dfrac{\log x}{\log y}$

Base may be any + ive quantity not equal to 1.

25. (a) The given equation implies

$$(\sqrt{x})^{2 \log_{\sqrt{x}} 2x} = 4 \qquad [\sqrt{x} \neq 1, x > 0]$$

or $\quad \sqrt{x}^{\log_{\sqrt{x}} (2x)^2} = 4$

or $\quad 4x^2 = 4 \qquad \text{or} \quad x = 1, -1$

$x = 1$ is ruled out as $\sqrt{x} \neq 1$; $x = -1$ is also ruled out as $x > 0$. Hence no solution.

(b) Ans. (b).

Making the base 5, we have

$$\log_5 (16 - x^2) - \log_5 (2x + 5) \leq \log_5 5$$

$$\therefore \quad \frac{16 - x^2}{2x + 5} \leq 5 \quad \text{or} \quad (16 - x^2) \leq 10x + 25$$

or $\quad x^2 + 10x + 9 \geq 0$

or $\quad (x + 9)(x + 1) \geq 0 \quad \therefore \quad x \leq -9 \quad \text{or} \quad x \geq -1$

Now by definition of log, we must have $\qquad$ ...(1)

$$2x + 5 > 0, i.e., x > -5/2$$

and $16 - x^2 > 0 \quad \text{or} \quad x^2 - 16 < 0$

or $\quad (x + 4)(x - 4) < 0$

$$\therefore \quad -4 < x < 4 \quad \text{and} \quad x > -5/2 \qquad ...(2)$$

Hence from (1) and (2), $x \geq -1$ and $x < 4$.

$$\therefore \quad x \in [-1, 4[.$$

26. (a) $\log_3 (\log_2 x)$ is defined only when $\log_2 x = t$ is + ive, *i.e.*, $\log_2 x > 0 = \log_2 1$

$$\therefore \quad x > 1$$

Also $a^{\log_a n} = n \Rightarrow 3^{2 \log_3 (t)} = 3^{\log_3 (t^2)} = t^2$

$$\therefore \quad t^2 = t - t^2 + 1$$

or $\quad 2t^2 - t - 1 = 0 \quad \text{or} \quad (2t + 1)(t - 1) = 0$

$$\therefore \quad t = 1 \text{ only} \left(-\frac{1}{2} \text{ rejected as } t \text{ is } + \text{ive}\right)$$

$$\therefore \quad \log_2 x = 1 \quad \therefore \quad x = 2$$

Thus there is only one root 2.

(b) Ans. (c).

By definition of log we must have $x + 1 > 0$

$$\therefore \quad |x + 1| = x + 1 \qquad ...(1)$$

Also $3 + 2x - x^2 > 0 \Rightarrow x^2 - 2x - 3 < 0$

or $\quad (x - 3)(x + 1) < 0 \quad \therefore \quad -1 < x < 3$

or $\quad -1 < x < 0, x - \text{ive and } 0 < x < 3, x + \text{ive} \quad ...(2)$

Hence the given equation by (1) reduces to

$$3 + 2x - x^2 = (x - 3)|x| \quad \therefore \quad a^{\log_a (n)} = n$$

Now $|x| = -x$ if x is $-$ive, $|x| = x$ when x is $+$ive

When $-1 < x < 0$, then $\quad 3 + 2x - x^2 = (x - 3)(-x)$

or $\quad 3 + 2x - x^2 = -x^2 + 3x \quad \therefore \quad x = 3 \notin]-1, 0[$

When $0 < x < 3$, then by (2)

$$3 + 2x - x^2 = (x - 3)x = x^2 - 3x$$

or $\quad 2x^2 - 5x - 3 = 0 \quad \therefore \quad x = -\frac{1}{2}, 3$

These values do not lie in $0 < x < 3$.

Hence the equation has no solution.

(c) Ans. (b).

$$4^{\log_2 (\log x)} = 2^{2 \log_2 (\log x)} = 2^{\log_2 (\log x)^2} = (\log x)^2$$

Hence we have $(\log x)^2 = \log x - (\log x)^2 + 1$

or $\quad 2 (\log x)^2 - \log x - 1 = 0$

$$\therefore \quad (\log x - 1)(2 \log x + 1) = 0$$

$$\therefore \quad \log x = 1 = \log e \quad \therefore \quad x = e$$

(d) Ans. $\dfrac{x}{1 - x}$

If $y = \log_b (ab)$, then

$$\frac{1}{x} + \frac{1}{y} = \log_{ab} a + \log_{ab} b$$

or $\quad \dfrac{1}{x} + \dfrac{1}{y} = \log_{ab} (ab) = 1$

$$\therefore \quad \frac{1}{y} = 1 - \frac{1}{x} = \frac{x - 1}{x} \quad \therefore \quad y = \frac{x}{x - 1}$$

27. (a) Since $a \neq 1$, $b \neq 1$, $a > 0$, $b > 0$, it follows from properties (13) to (17) **P. 247** that $\log_b a$ and $\log_a b$ are both positive or both negative. Hence

$$|\log_b a + \log_a b| = |\log_b a| + |\log_a b| \quad ...(1)$$

Since A.M. of two positive quantities is greater than their G.M., we get

$$\frac{|\log_b a| + |\log_a b|}{2} > \sqrt{\log_b a \log_a b} = 1,$$

$$\text{by (4) of §2.} \quad ...(2)$$

Hence from (1) and (2), we obtain

$$|\log_b a + \log_a b| > 2.$$

(b) $2\log_{10} x - \log_x 0.01 = 2\log_{10} x - \dfrac{\log_{10} 0.01}{\log_{10} x}$

$$= 2\log_{10} x - \dfrac{\log_{10} 10^{-2}}{\log_{10} x} = 2\log_{10} x + \dfrac{2}{\log_{10} x}$$

$$= 2\left(\log_{10} x + \dfrac{1}{\log_{10} x}\right) \qquad \text{...(1)}$$

Since $x > 1$, $\log_{10} x > 0$.

But $\dfrac{1}{2}\left(\log_{10} x + \dfrac{1}{\log_{10} x}\right)$

$$\geq \sqrt{\left[\log_{10} x \times \dfrac{1}{\log_{10} x}\right]} = 1$$

$$[\because \ \text{A.M.} \geq \text{G.M.}]$$

$\therefore \quad \log_{10} x + \dfrac{1}{\log_{10} x} \geq 2. \qquad \text{...(2)}$

Thus $\quad 2\log_{10} x - \log_x 0.01 \geq 4.$ by (1), (2)
Hence the minimum value of
$2\log_{10} x - \log_x 0.01$ is 4.

28. (a) $\dfrac{\log_a n}{\log_{ab} n} = \dfrac{\log_n ab}{\log_n a} = \dfrac{\log_n a + \log_n b}{\log_n a}$

$$= 1 + \dfrac{\log_n b}{\log_n a} = 1 + \log_a b.$$

(b) $\log_{ab} x = \dfrac{1}{\log_x ab} = \dfrac{1}{\log_x a + \log_x b}$

$$= \dfrac{1}{\dfrac{1}{\log_a x} + \dfrac{1}{\log_b x}} = \dfrac{\log_a x \log_b x}{\log_a x + \log_b x}$$

(c) From $a^2 + b^2 = 7ab$, we have

$$(a+b)^2 = 9ab \text{ or } \left(\dfrac{a+b}{3}\right)^2 = ab$$

Taking logarithms of both sides, we get

$$2\log \dfrac{1}{3}(a+b) = \log a + \log b.$$

29. (a) $\log_{10} 2 > \dfrac{1}{4}$ if $2 > 10^{1/4}$.

or $\quad 2^4 > 10,$ which is true.

Again $\log_{10} 2 < \dfrac{1}{3}$ if $2 < 10^{1/3}$, i.e. if $2^3 < 10$,

which is again true.
Hence $\dfrac{1}{4} < \log_{10} 2 < \dfrac{1}{3}.$

(b) $2\log_{10} 3 = \log_{10} 9 < 1 \quad \therefore \quad \log_{10} 3 < \dfrac{1}{2}$

$\dfrac{2}{5} < \log_{10} 3$ if $2 < 5\log_{10} 3 = \log_{10} 3^5$

or $\quad \log_{10} 243 > 2.$ It is true because
$\log_{10} 243 > \log_{10} 10^2 = 2.$

30. (a) Suppose, if possible, that $\log_2 3$ is rational.

So we assume, $\log_2 3 = \dfrac{p}{q}$

where p and q are positive integers having no factor in common. Then

$$3 = 2^{p/q} \text{ or } 3^q = 2^p.$$

which is impossible since 3^q is odd and 2^p is even. Hence $\log_2 3$ cannot be rational, that is, it is irrational.

(b) Proceed as in part (a).
Suppose, if possible, $\log_2 7$ is rational, say p/q where p and q are integers prime to each other. Then $p/q = \log_2 7 \Rightarrow 7 = 2^{p/q} \Rightarrow 2^p = 7^q$, which is false since left hand side is even and right hand side is odd.
[Obviously $\log_2 7$ is not an integer and hence not a prime number.]

31. (a) Since $\log_2 3 = x \quad \therefore \quad 2^x = 3 \quad \therefore \quad x > 1$

and $\log_{1/2} 5 = y \quad \therefore \quad \left(\dfrac{1}{2}\right)^y = 5$

or $\quad 2^y = \dfrac{1}{5} \quad \therefore \quad y < 1$

we conclude that $x > y$ or $\log_2 3 > \log_{1/2} 5$

(b) $\log_{1/16} \dfrac{1}{25} = \log_{4^{-2}} 5^{-2} = \left(\dfrac{-2}{-2}\right)\log_4 5 = \log_4 5.$

Hence $\log_4 5$ and $\log_{1/16} \dfrac{1}{25}$ are equal.

(c) Since $\log_7 11 > 1.$ [See (16) **P. 247**]
and $0 < \log_8 5 < 1.$ [See (17) **P. 247**]
we conclude that $\log_7 11 > \log_8 5.$

32. (a) By (16) of §2, we have $\log_2 3 > 1$

and $\quad \log_2 3 < \log_2 4 = \log_2 2^2 = 2.$
Thus $\quad 1 < \log_2 3 < 2.$
Again $\quad \log_3 11 > \log_3 9 = \log_3 3^2 = 2.$
Since $\quad 1 < \log_2 3 < 2$ and $\log_3 11 > 2.$
we conclude that $\log_3 11 > \log_2 3.$

(b) Let $x = \log_{1/3} \dfrac{1}{2} = \dfrac{-1}{-1}\log_3 2 < \log_3 3 = 1$

$\therefore \quad x < 1$

$y = \log_{1/2} \dfrac{1}{3} = \dfrac{-1}{-1}\log_2 3 > \log_2 2 = 1$

$\therefore \quad y > 1$

Hence $y > x$ or $\log_{1/2} \dfrac{1}{3} > \log_{1/3} \dfrac{1}{2}.$

(c) Let $y = 2\log_{17} 5$ and $x = \log_3 5$

$\therefore \quad \dfrac{1}{y} = \dfrac{1}{2}\log_5 17$

$\dfrac{1}{x} = \log_5 3 = \dfrac{1}{2}\log_5 9$

Clearly $\dfrac{1}{y} > \dfrac{1}{x} \quad \therefore \quad y < x$ or $x > y$

33. (a) $\log_a n, \log_b n, \log_c n$ are in H.P.

Taking reciprocals

∴ $\log_n a, \log_n b, \log_n c$ are in A.P.

or $2\log_n b = \log_n a + \log_n c$

or $\log_n b^2 = \log_n ac$ ∴ $b^2 = ac$

Hence a, b, c are in G.P.

(b) We have, $2\log_3 (2^x - 5) = \log_3 2 + \log_3 (2^x - 7/2)$

$= \log_3 (2^{x+1} - 7)$

$\Rightarrow (2^x - 5)^2 = 2^{x+1} - 7$

$\Rightarrow 2^{2x} - 10 \cdot 2^x + 25 = 2 \cdot 2^x - 7$

or $2^{2x} - 12 \cdot 2^x + 32 = 0$

or $(2^x - 8)(2^x - 4) = 0$

∴ $2^x = 2^3$ or $2^x = 2^2$ $\Rightarrow x = 3$ or $x = 2$.

But $x = 2$ is ruled out since in that case

$2^x - 5 < 0$.

∴   Ans. $x = 3$.

34. Take log of both sides of given equations

$\log 3 (\log 3 + \log x) = \log 4 (\log 4 + \log y)$ ...(1)

and $\log x \log 4 = \log y \log 3$ ...(2)

From (1),

$(\log 4)^2 - (\log 3)^2 = \log 3 \log x - \log 4 \log y$ ...(3)

From (2), $\dfrac{\log x}{\log 3} = \dfrac{\log y}{\log 4} = \lambda$ say   ...(4)

From (4) and (3),

$(\log 4)^2 - (\log 3)^2 = \lambda \{(\log 3)^2 - (\log 4)^2\}$

∴ $\lambda = -1$

∴ $\log x = -\log 3 = \log (1/3)$

$\log y = -\log 4 = \log (1/4)$

∴ $x = 1/3, \ y = 1/4$

35. (a) Taking reciprocals, we get

$\log_x l, \log_x m, \log_x n$ are in H.P.

∴ $\log_x m = \dfrac{2\log_x l \log_x n}{\log_x l + \log_x n}$

or $\log_x m / \log_x l = \log_x n^2 / \log_x ln$

or $\log_l m = \log_{ln} n^2$,   by (5) **P. 246**

Writing the above in exponential form, we get

$n^2 = (ln)^{\log_l m}$

(b) $\log (1 + ax^2) + \log\left(1 + \dfrac{a}{x^2}\right)$, the expansions

are valid only when

$-1 < ax^2 \le 1$ and $-1 < \dfrac{a}{x^2} \le 1$

∴ $a^2 \le 1 \Rightarrow |a| \le 1$.

Again $ax^2 \le 1 \Rightarrow x^2 < \dfrac{1}{a}$ ∴ $|x| \le \dfrac{1}{\sqrt{a}}$.

Note : Actually this is a question on logarithmic series of Supplement for Roorkee and M.N.R.

36. (a) L.H.S. $= \log_a a = 1$.

(b) Prove yourself.

(c) Let $A = \log_c b, B = \log_a c, C = \log_b a$

∴ $ABC = 1$ clearly   ...(1)

$x = \log_c b + \log_b c = A + \dfrac{1}{A}$ ...(2)

∴ $xyz = \left(A + \dfrac{1}{A}\right)\left(B + \dfrac{1}{B}\right)\left(C + \dfrac{1}{C}\right)$

$= \left(A + \dfrac{1}{A}\right)\left[BC + \dfrac{1}{BC} + \dfrac{B}{C} + \dfrac{C}{B}\right]$

$= \left(A + \dfrac{1}{A}\right)\left[A + \dfrac{1}{A} + \dfrac{B}{C} + \dfrac{C}{B}\right]$ by (1)

$= \left(A + \dfrac{1}{A}\right)^2 + \left[\left(A + \dfrac{1}{A}\right)\left(\dfrac{B}{C} + \dfrac{C}{B}\right)\right]$

$= \left(A + \dfrac{1}{A}\right)^2 + \left[\left(BC + \dfrac{1}{BC}\right)\left(\dfrac{B}{C} + \dfrac{C}{B}\right)\right]$

$\because A = \dfrac{1}{BC}$

$= \left(A + \dfrac{1}{A}\right)^2 + \left[\left(B^2 + \dfrac{1}{B^2}\right) + \left(C^2 + \dfrac{1}{C^2}\right)\right]$

Add $2 + 2$ in 2nd bracket and subtract 4 and put $A + \dfrac{1}{A} = x$ by (2)

∴ $xyz = x^2 + y^2 + z^2 - 4$

37. (a) Do yourself.

(b) Since $\log_b a = \dfrac{1}{\log_a b}$, the expression

$= \log_n 2 + \log_n 3 + \log_n 4 + \ldots + \log_n 1983$

$= \log_n (2 \cdot 3 \cdot 4 \ldots \ldots 1983) = \log_n 1983!$

$= \log_n n = 1.$ [∵ $1983! = n$]

(c) Ans. (c). L.H.S. $= \log_{xyz} x^2 y^2 z^2 = 2 \cdot 1 = 2$

38. Writing the given relation in logarithmic form,

$\log_a y = \dfrac{1}{1 - \log_a x}$ and $\log_a z = \dfrac{1}{1 - \log_a y}$

We want a relation in z and x hence eliminate y by putting the value of $\log_a y$ from 1st in 2nd.

∴ $\log_a z = \dfrac{1}{1 - \dfrac{1}{1 - \log_a x}} = \dfrac{1 - \log_a x}{-\log_a x} = -\dfrac{1}{\log_a x} + 1$

∴ $\dfrac{1}{\log_a x} = 1 - \log_a z$

or $\log_a x = \dfrac{1}{1 - \log_a z}$ or $x = a^{\frac{1}{1 - \log_a z}}$

39. Let $\dfrac{\log a}{b - c} = \dfrac{\log b}{c - a} = \dfrac{\log c}{a - b} = k$.

Then $\log a = k(b - c), \log b = k(c - a)$

and $\log c = k(a - b)$.

Now $a \log a + b \log b + c \log c$

$= a \cdot k(b - c) + b \cdot k(c - a) + c \cdot k(a - b) = 0$

∴ $\log a^a b^b c^c = 0$ or $a^a b^b c^c = 1$.

Note that here it is understood that

$a > 0$, $b > 0$, $c > 0$,

$a \neq 1$, $b \neq 1$, $c \neq 1$.

40. Proceed as in problem 39.

41. Let $\dfrac{x(y + z - x)}{\log x} = \dfrac{y(z + x - y)}{\log y} = \dfrac{z(x + y - z)}{\log z} = \dfrac{1}{k}$

Then $\log x = kx(y + z - x)$, $\log y = ky(z + x - y)$

and $\log z = kz(x + y - z)$,

Hence $y \log x + x \log y = 2k\,xyz$

$\quad\quad y \log z + z \log y = 2k\,xyz$

and $z \log x + x \log z = 2k\,xyz$.

It follows that $y \log x + x \log y = y \log z + z \log y$

$\quad\quad\quad\quad\quad\quad\quad = z \log x + x \log z$

or $\log(x^y \cdot y^x) = \log(z^y \cdot y^z) = \log(x^z \cdot z^x)$.

∴ $x^y \cdot y^x = y^z \cdot z^y = z^x \cdot x^z$.

42. L.H.S. $= \dfrac{1}{\log_n a \log_n b} + \dfrac{1}{\log_n b \log_n c} + \dfrac{1}{\log_n c \log_n a}$

$= \dfrac{\log_n c + \log_n a + \log_n b}{\log_n a \log_n b \log_n c} = \dfrac{\log_n abc}{\log_n a \log_n b \log_n c}$

$= \dfrac{\log_a n \log_b n \log_c n}{\log_{abc} n} =$ R.H.S.

43. Changing all the logarithms to base α ($\alpha > 0$, $\alpha \neq 1$), the given equation yields

$\Sigma\left(\dfrac{x}{y} \cdot \dfrac{x}{z} - 1\right) = 0$ where $x = \log_\alpha a$ etc.

or $\dfrac{x^2}{yz} + \dfrac{y^2}{zx} + \dfrac{z^2}{xy} = 3$ or $x^3 + y^3 + z^3 - 3xyz = 0$

or $(x + y + z)(x^2 + y^2 + z^2 - xy - yz - zx) = 0$. ...(1)

Since $x \neq y \neq z$, we have

$x^2 + y^2 + z^2 - xy - yz - zx$

$\quad = \dfrac{1}{2}[(x - y)^2 + (y - z)^2 + (z - x)^2] \neq 0$.

Hence we conclude from (1) that $x + y + z = 0$

that is, $\log_\alpha a + \log_\alpha b + \log_\alpha c = 0$

or $\log_\alpha abc = 0$ or $abc = 1$.

44. Since n is a natural number and p_i's are primes, it follows that a_i's are also natural numbers.

Taking logarithms of both sides of given relation, we get

$\log n = \sum\limits_{i=1}^{k} a_i \log p_i \geq \sum\limits_{i=1}^{k} a_i \log 2$

[∵ Smallest prime number is 2]

$\geq k \log 2$, since each $a \geq 1$ and $p_i \geq 2$.

45. R.H.S. $= \dfrac{(1/\log_n a) - (1/\log_n b)}{(1/\log_n b) - (1/\log_n c)}$

$= \dfrac{\log_n b - \log_n a}{\log_n c - \log_n b} \cdot \dfrac{\log_n c}{\log_n a}$

$= \dfrac{\log_n (b/a)}{\log_n (c/b)} \cdot \dfrac{\log_n c}{\log_n a}$

$= 1 \cdot \dfrac{\log_n c}{\log_n a} = \dfrac{\log_a n}{\log_c n} =$ L.H.S.

$[\because b = \sqrt{ac} \Rightarrow b^2 = ac \Rightarrow b/a = c/b]$

46. From the property of right angled triangle, we get

$a^2 + b^2 = c^2$ or $a^2 = (c - b)(c + b)$ ...(1)

L.H.S. $= \log_{c+b} a + \log_{c-b} a$

$= \dfrac{1}{\log_a (c + b)} + \dfrac{1}{\log_a (c - b)}$

$= \dfrac{\log_a (c - b) + \log_a (c + b)}{\log_a (c + b) \log_a (c - b)}$

$= \dfrac{\log_a (c^2 - b^2)}{\log_a (c + b) \log_a (c - b)}$

$= \dfrac{\log_a a^2}{\log_a (c + b) \log_a (c - b)}$

$= \dfrac{2 \log_a a}{\log_a (c + b) \log_a (c - b)}$

$= 2 \log_{(c+b)} a \log_{(c-b)} a$

$\left(\because \log_a a = 1 \text{ and } \dfrac{1}{\log_y x} = \log_x y\right)$

47. Let r be the common ratio of G.P. and d the common difference of A.P.

Then $\quad a_n = ar^n$ ...(1)

and $\quad b_n = b + nd$. ...(2)

Taking logarithms of both sides of (1) to base β ($\beta \neq 1$, $\beta > 0$), we get

$\log_\beta a_n = \log_\beta a + n \log_\beta r$

∴ $\log_\beta a_n - b_n = \log_\beta a + n \log_\beta r - b - nd$. by (2) ...(3)

Now in order that the right hand side of (3) reduces to $\log_\beta a - b$, we must have

$n \log_\beta r - nd = 0$

or $\log_\beta r = d$ or $r = \beta^d$

that is, $\beta = r^{1/d}$.

Hence there exists a system of logarithms to base $r^{1/d}$ such that $\log a_n - b_n = \log_n a - b$.

Problem Set (2)

▶ Multiple Choice Questions

1. $16^{\log_4 5}$ equals
(a) 5   (b) 16
(c) 25   (d) none of these.

2. $\ln ab - \ln |b| =$
(a) $\ln a$ (b) $\ln |a|$
(c) $-\ln a$ (d) none of these.
[Note that $\ln x$ stands for $\log_e x$].

3.* $e^{\ln \ln 7} = 7$
(a) True   (b) False

4.* $3^{\sqrt{\log_3 7}} = 7^{\sqrt{\log_7 3}}$
(a) True   (b) False

5. $\log_5 5 \log_4 9 \log_3 2$ simplifies to
(a) 2   (b) 1
(c) 5   (d) none of these.

6. The value of $\dfrac{1}{\log_2 \pi} + \dfrac{1}{\log_6 \pi}$ is greater than 2.
(a) True   (b) False.

7. The value of $\log_b a \log_c b \log_a c$ is
(a) 0   (b) $\log abc$
(c) 1   (d) 10

8. If $a^x = b$, $b^y = c$, $c^z = a$, then the value of xyz is
(a) 0   (b) 1
(c) 2   (d) 3

9. If $\log_{0.3}(x-1) < \log_{0.09}(x-1)$, then x lies in the interval
(a) $(2, \infty)$ (b) $(-2, -1)$
(c) $(1, 2)$ (d) none of these

10. The equation $\log_e x + \log_e (1+x) = 0$ can be written as
(a) $x^2 + x - 1 = 0$ (b) $x^2 + x + 1 = 0$
(c) $x^2 + x - e = 0$ (d) $x^2 + x + e = 0$
(e) none of these.

11. Which is the correct order for a given number α in increasing order :
(a) $\log_2 \alpha, \log_3 \alpha, \log_e \alpha, \log_{10} \alpha$
(b) $\log_{10} \alpha, \log_3 \alpha, \log_e \alpha, \log_2 \alpha$
(c) $\log_{10} \alpha, \log_2 \alpha, \log_e \alpha, \log_3 \alpha$
(d) $\log_3 \alpha, \log_e \alpha, \log_2 \alpha, \log_{10} \alpha$

12. (a) If $a^2 + 4b^2 = 12ab$, then $\log(a + 2b) =$
(a) $\dfrac{1}{2}(\log a + \log b - \log 2)$
(b) $\log \dfrac{a}{2} + \log \dfrac{b}{2} + \log 2$
(c) $\dfrac{1}{2}(\log a + \log b + 4 \log 2)$
(d) $\dfrac{1}{2}(\log a - \log b + 4 \log 2)$

(b) If $\log_2 (a+b) + \log_2 (c+d) \geq 4$, then the minimum value of $a + b + c + d$ is
(a) 2   (b) 4
(c) 6   (d) 8

13.* If $7^{\log_7 (x^2 - 4x + 5)} = x - 1$ then x may have values ......

14. The value of
$$6 + \log_{3/2}\left(\frac{1}{3\sqrt{2}}\sqrt{4 - \frac{1}{3\sqrt{2}}\sqrt{4 - \frac{1}{3\sqrt{2}}\sqrt{4 - \frac{1}{3\sqrt{2}}\cdots}}}\right)$$
is
(a) 4   (b) 5
(c) 0   (d) 6   **(IT JEE 2012)**

Solutions to Problem Set (2)

1. Ans. (c).
2. Ans. (b).
3. Ans. (b).
Correct value is $\ln 7$.
4. Ans. (a).
Hint : Write $\sqrt{\log_3 7}$ as $\log_3 7 / \sqrt{\log_3 7}$.
∵ $\sqrt{x} = x / \sqrt{x}$ ∴ L.H.S. $= (3^{\log_3 7})^{1/\sqrt{\log_3 7}}$
$= 7^{1/\sqrt{\log_3 7}} = 7^{\sqrt{\log_7 3}} = $ R.H.S.
5. Ans. (b).
6. Ans. (a).
$\log_\pi 2 + \log_\pi 6 = \log_\pi 2 \cdot 6$
$= \log_\pi 12 > \log_\pi \pi^2 = 2$
∵ $\pi^2 = (3 \cdot 14)^2 < 12$.
Given expression is greater than 2.
7. Ans. (c).
8. Ans. (b).
9. Ans. (a).
$\log_{0.3}(x-1) < \log_{(0.3)^2}(x-1) = \frac{1}{2}\log_{0.3}(x-1)$
∴ $\frac{1}{2}\log_{0.3}(x-1) < 0$
or $\log_{0.3}(x-1) < 0 = \log 1$
∴ $(x-1) > 1$ or $x > 2$ as base is less than 1 the inequality is reversed. Now $x > 2 \Rightarrow x$ lies in $(2, \infty)$.
10. Ans. (a).
11. Ans. (b).
α is a number ∴ $\alpha > 1$
Now $10 > 3 > e > 2$
∴ $\log_\alpha 10 > \log_\alpha 3 > \log_\alpha e > \log_\alpha 2$
Taking reciprocal and changing the sign of inequality
$\log_{10} \alpha < \log_3 \alpha < \log_e \alpha < \log_2 \alpha$

(increasing order)

12. (a) Ans. (c).

$$a^2 + 4b^2 + 4ab = 16ab$$

$$\therefore \quad (a+2b)^2 = 16ab$$

$$\therefore \quad 2\log(a+2b) = 4\log 2 + \log a + \log b$$

(b) Ans. (d).

Given relation $\Rightarrow (a+b)(c+d) \geq 2^4 = 16$

Now $\dfrac{(a+b)+(c+d)}{2} \geq [(a+b)(c+d)]^{1/2}$

$$= 16^{1/2} = 4$$

$$\therefore \quad (a+b)+(c+d) \geq 2.4, \quad i.e., \quad 8$$

Hence minimum value is 8.

13. Ans. 2, 3.

$$a^{\log_a x} = x. \quad \therefore \quad x^2 - 5x + 6 = 0$$

or $x = 2, 3$

14. Ans. (a).

Let $\sqrt{4 - \dfrac{1}{3\sqrt{2}}\sqrt{4 - \dfrac{1}{3\sqrt{2}}\cdots}} = x$

$$\Rightarrow \sqrt{4 - \dfrac{1}{3\sqrt{2}}\cdot x} = x \quad \Rightarrow \quad 4 - \dfrac{1}{3\sqrt{2}}x = x^2$$

$$\Rightarrow x^2 + \dfrac{1}{3\sqrt{2}}x - 4 = 0$$

$$\Rightarrow 3\sqrt{2}\,x^2 + x - 12\sqrt{2} = 0$$

$$\therefore \quad x = \dfrac{-1 \pm \sqrt{1 + 4 \times 3\sqrt{2} \times 12\sqrt{2}}}{2 \times 3\sqrt{2}} = \dfrac{-1 \pm 17}{2 \times 3\sqrt{2}}$$

$$= \dfrac{16}{6\sqrt{2}}, \dfrac{-18}{6\sqrt{2}}$$

$$\Rightarrow x = \dfrac{8}{3\sqrt{2}}, \dfrac{-3}{\sqrt{2}} \text{ and } \dfrac{-3}{\sqrt{2}} \text{ is rejected.}$$

Therefore,

$$6 + \log_{3/2}\left(\dfrac{1}{3\sqrt{2}} \times \dfrac{8}{3\sqrt{2}}\right) = 6 + \log_{3/2}\left(\dfrac{4}{9}\right)$$

$$= 6 + \log_{3/2}\left(\dfrac{2}{3}\right)^2 = 6 - 2 = 4$$

MISCELLANEOUS EXERCISE

Matching Entries

▶ *Match the entries of List-A with List-B.*

1. **List-A** — **List-B**

(a) The number of solutions of the equation $\log_4(x-1) = \log_2(x-3)$ is — 1. only one

(b) If $4^{\log_9 3} + 9^{\log_2 4} = \log^{\log_x 83}$, then $x =$ — 2. $\pm 2, \pm\sqrt{2}$

(c) If $\log_{10}\left[\dfrac{1}{2^x + x - 1}\right] = x[\log_{10} 5 - 1]$, then $x =$ — 3. 1

(d) The sum of the roots of the equation $(x-4)^2 + 8|x-4| + 15 = 0$ is — 4. 10

(e) If $x \in R$, then the roots of the equation

$(5 + 2\sqrt{6})^{x^2 - 3} + (5 - 2\sqrt{6})^{x^2 - 3} = 10$ are ... — 5. 16

2. **List-A** — **List-B**

(a) $x^2 - 6x + 9 > 0 \Rightarrow x \in$ — 1. $(-1, 4)$

(b) $x^2 - 3x - 4 < 0 \Rightarrow x \in$ — 2. ϕ

(c) $2x^2 - 6x + 9 > 0 \Rightarrow x \in$ — 3. $R - \{3\}$

(d) $-3x^2 + 4x - 5 > 0 \Rightarrow x \in$ — 4. R

3. **List-A** — **List-B**

(a) $\log_2 \log_2 \log_4 256 + 2\log_{\sqrt{2}} 2$ — 1. 2

(b) $\dfrac{1}{\log_{xy} xyz} + \dfrac{1}{\log_{yz} xyz} + \dfrac{1}{\log_{zx} xyz}$ — 2. 890

(c) $\dfrac{1}{\log_3 \pi} + \dfrac{1}{\log_4 \pi} > x$ then $x =$ — 3. 5

(d) $81^{1/\log_5 3} + 27^{\log_9 36} + 3^{4/\log_7 9}$ — 4. 2

Hints / Solutions

1. (a) → 3. **Q. 28 (c) P. 253**
   (b) → 4. **Q. 10 (b) P. 250**
   (c) → 1. **Q. 13 (a) P. 250**
   (d) → 5. Proceed as in **Q. 37 (b) P. 254**
   (e) → 2. **Q. 26 (a), P. 252**
2. (a) → 3 (b) → 1 (c) → 4 (d) → 2
   (a) $(x-3)^2 > 0$ for all real values of x except $x = 3$
   (b) $(x+1)(x-4) < 0 \Rightarrow x$ lies between -1 and 4.

(c) $\Delta = -$ive and hence its sign is same as of the first term $\forall$ real values of x

(d) $-3x^2 + 4x - 5 > 0 \Rightarrow 3x^2 - 4x + 5 \leq 0$.

Arguing as in (c), $\Delta = -$ive and hence its sign is same as of 3 $i.e.$ + ive. Hence there will be no real values of x for which this will hold.

3. (a) → 3. **Q. 13 (b) P. 250**
   (b) → 1. **Q. 37 (c) P. 254**
   (c) → 4.
   (d) → 2. **Q. 9 (a) P. 250**

Fascinating Facts

- The logarithm of a number is always unique
- **Fundamental properties of logarithm**
  (i) $\log_a (xy) = \log_a x + \log_c y$
  (ii) $\log_a \left(\dfrac{x}{y}\right) = \log_a x - \log_a y$
  (iii) $\log_a (x^m) = m \log_a x$
  (iv) $\log_a x = \dfrac{1}{\log_x a}$
  (v) $\log_a x = \dfrac{\log x}{\log a}$
  (vi) $\log_a b . \log_b a = 1$
  (vii) $\log_b a = \log_c a . \log_b c$

- The logarithm of a number to a given positive real number ($\neq 1$) as base is the index or the power to which the base must be raised in order to make it equal to the even number.
- The integral part of a logarithm is called the characteristic and the decimal part is called the mantissa.
- If $a > 1$, then $0 < \alpha < \beta \Rightarrow \log_a \alpha > \log_a \beta$
- If $0 < a < 1$, then $0 < \alpha < \beta \Rightarrow \log_a \alpha < \log_a \beta$
- If $a > 1, \alpha > 1$, then $\log_a \alpha > 0$
- If $0 < a < 1, 0 < \alpha < 1$, then $\log_a \alpha > 0$
- If $0 < a < 1, \alpha > 1$, then $\log_a \alpha < 0$
- If $a > 1, 0 < \alpha < 1$, then $\log_a \alpha < 0$
- If $a > 1, \alpha > 0, \alpha < a$, then $0 < \log_a \alpha < 1$
- If $a > 1, \alpha > 1$ and $\alpha > a$, then $\log_a \alpha > 1$
- If $0 < a < 1; 0 < \alpha < 1, \alpha > 0$, then $0 < \log_a \alpha < 1$
- If $0 < a < 1, 0 < \alpha < 1, \alpha < 0$, then $\log_a \alpha > 1$

❑

Miscellaneous Equations

Problem Set (1)

Solutions of equations based on logarithms and modulus.

Solve the following equations for real roots :

Note : In $\log_a x$ both x and a are $+$ ive.

Also $a \neq 1$ and $x \neq 0$, $a^{\log_a n} = n$ **(V. Imp.)**

$|x| = x$ if $x = +$ ive, $|x| = -x$ if x is $-$ ive, $|x|^2 = x^2$

$|x| \geq a\,(a + \text{ive}) \Rightarrow x^2 \geq a^2$

or $(x+a)(x-a) \geq 0 \Rightarrow x \leq -a$ or $x \geq a$

$|x| \leq a\,(a + \text{ive}) \Rightarrow x^2 \leq a^2$

or $(x+a)(x-a) \leq 0 \Rightarrow -a \leq x \leq a$

1. (a) $2^{x^2} : 2^{2x} = 8 : 1$.

   (b) $3^{2x} - 3^{x+1} - 3^{x-1} + 1 = 0$.

2. Solve for x :

   $$(0 \cdot 125) \cdot 4^{2x-8} = \left(\frac{0 \cdot 25}{\sqrt{2}}\right)^{-x}.$$

3. $a^{2x}(a^2 + 1) = (a^{3x} + a^x)\,a$.

4. (a) $3^x\,8^{x/(x+2)} = 6$. (b) $4^x + 6^x = 9^x$.

5. $3^x + 4^x = 5^x$.

6. (a) $2^{2x+2} - 6^x - 2 \times 3^{2x+2} = 0$.

   (b) $2 \times 81^x = 36^x + 3 \times 16^x$.

7. (a) $16^{\sin^2 x} + 16^{\cos^2 x} = 10$.

   (b)* $5\,(1/25)^{\sin^2 x} + 4 \times 5^{\cos 2x} = 25^{(\sin 2x)/2}$.

8. (a) $\log_{10} \log_{10} \log_{10} x = 0$. (b) $\log_x (3x^2 + 10x) = 3$.

9. (a) $\log_{10}\left[98 + \sqrt{x^3 - x^2 - 12x + 36}\right] = 2$.

   (b) $x^2 + \dfrac{x^2}{(x+1)^2} = 3$

10. (a)* For $a > 0$, solve for x the equations

    $$2\log_x a + \log_{ax} a + 3\log_{(a^2 x)} a = 0$$

    (b)* $4^{\log_9 3} + 9^{\log_2 4} = 10^{\log_x 83}$.

11. Find all real numbers x which satisfy the equation

    $$2\log_2 \log_2 x + \log_{(1/2)} \log_2 (2\sqrt{2}\,x) = 1.$$

    (Roorkee 1999)

12. Solve for x the following equations :

    (a) $\dfrac{\log_2 x}{\log_4 2x} = \dfrac{\log_8 4x}{\log_8 8x}$. (b) $\log_{3x} x = \log_{9x} x$.

13. (a)* $\log_{10}\left(\dfrac{1}{2^x + x - 1}\right) = x\,[\log_{10} 5 - 1]$

    (b) $\log_{10}(x^2 - x - 6) - x = \log_{10}(x + 2) - 4$.

14. (a) $x^x = x$ (b) $x^{\sqrt{x}} = (\sqrt{x})^x$.

15. (a)* $5^{1 + \log_4 x} + 5^{\log \cdot 25\, x - 1} = \dfrac{26}{5}$.

    (b) $\log_9 x + \log_{x^2} 3 = 1$.

16. (a) $5^{\log_{10} x} = 50 - x^{\log_{10} 5}$

    (b) $\log_5 x + \log_x 5 = \dfrac{5}{2}$.

17. (a)* $\log_{10} x + \log_{10} x^{1/2} + \log_{10} x^{1/4} + \ldots\ldots = y$.

    and $\dfrac{1 + 3 + 5 + \ldots\ldots + (2y - 1)}{4 + 7 + 10 + \ldots\ldots + (3y + 1)} = \dfrac{20}{7\log_{10} x}$

    (b) Solve the following equations for x and y :

    $\log_2 x + \log_4 x + \log_{16} x + \ldots = y$,

    $\dfrac{5 + 9 + 13 + \ldots + (4y + 1)}{1 + 3 + 5 + \ldots + (2y + 1)} = 4\log_4 x$.

    (Roorkee 2001)

18. (a) $\log_{16} x + \log_4 x + \log_2 x = 7$.

    (b)* $\log_{(2x+3)}(6x^2 + 23x + 21)$

    $= 4 - \log_{(3x+7)}(4x^2 + 12x + 9)$

19. (a) $4^x - 3^{x - \frac{1}{2}} = 3^{x + \frac{1}{2}} - 2^{2x-1}$.

    (b) If $\log 2 = 0 \cdot 30103$, $\log 3 = 0 \cdot 4771213$,
    $\log 7 = 0 \cdot 8450980$, then solve :

    (i) $21^x = 2^{2x+1} \cdot 5^x$ (ii) $3^{1+x} = 7^{x/2}$.

20. (a)* $x + \log_{10}(1 + 2^x) = x\log_{10} 5 + \log_{10} 6$.

(b) $x \log_{10}(10/3) + \log_{10} 3 = \log_{10}(2 + 3^x) + x$

21.* $\log_a (ax) \log_x (ax) = \log_{a^2}(1/a)$ $\qquad (a > 0, \ a \neq 1)$.

22. (a) $6^x (2/3)^y - 3 \cdot 2^{x+y} - 8 \cdot 3^{x-y} + 24 = 0, \ xy = 2$.

(b) $3 \cdot x^{2y-1} = 4$ and $x^{y+1} = 6$

23. (a) If $x, y \in R$, then solve the equations :

$$(3y^2 + 1) \log_3 x = 1 \text{ and } x^{2y^2 + 10} = 27$$

(b)* Solve for x and y the equations

$$(x+y)^{1/(x-y)} = \frac{\sqrt{52 - 2x}}{\sqrt[4]{(x-y)}}$$

and $\dfrac{3}{2} \log_8 (x - y) - \log_{1/\sqrt{2}} (x - y) = 5$

24.* $3^x 5^y = 75, \ 3^y 5^x = 45$.

25. Solve the equations :

(b) $\log_3 x + \log_3 y = 2 + \log_3 2, \ \log_{27}(x + y) = \dfrac{2}{3}$

(b) $\log_y x + \log_x y = 2, \ x^2 + y = 12$.

26.* $\log^2 \left(1 + \dfrac{4}{x}\right) + \log^2 \left(1 - \dfrac{4}{x+4}\right) = 2 \log^2 \left(\dfrac{2}{x-1} - 1\right)$

where $\log^2 t = [\log t]^2 = \left[\log \dfrac{1}{t}\right]^2$

27. (a) Solve : $\log_2 xy = 5, \ \log_{1/2}(x/y) = 1$.

(b) If $\log_2 x + \log_x 2 = \dfrac{10}{3} = \log_2 y + \log_y 2$ and $x \neq y$

then prove that $x + y = 8 + 2^{1/3}$.

28. (a) Solve : $5 (\log_y x + \log_x y) = 26, \ xy = 64$.

(b) Solve : $2^{x+y} = 6^y, \ 3^x = 3 \cdot 2^{y+1}$.

(c) The number of solutions of

$$\log_4 (x - 1) = \log_2 (x - 3) \text{ is}$$

(a) 3 $\qquad\qquad$ (b) 1

(c) 2 $\qquad\qquad$ (d) 0 $\qquad$ **(I.I.T. Sc. 2001)**

29.* Solve for x, y and z :

$\log_2 x + \log_4 y + \log_4 z = 2$.

$\log_3 y + \log_9 z + \log_9 x = 2$.

$\log_4 z + \log_{16} x + \log_{16} y = 2$.

30. The equation $e^{\sin x} - e^{-\sin x} - 4 = 0$ has no real solution.

31. (a) The equation $x - [2/(x-1)] = 1 - [2/(x-1)]$ has no roots. T or F ?

(b)* The number of real roots of the equation $\sin(e^x) = 5^x + 5^{-x}$ is 0. T or F ?

$\qquad\qquad\qquad\qquad$ **(D.C.E. 1997; I.I.T. 1990)**

(c) Solve for x if $x = 1 + \dfrac{1}{3 + } \dfrac{1}{2 + } \dfrac{1}{3 + } \dfrac{1}{2 + } \ldots \infty$

(d) Solve for x :

$(x-1)^3 + (x-2)^3 + (x-3)^3 + (x-4)^3 + (x-5)^3 = 0$

32. (a) The set of all real numbers x for which $x^2 - |x + 2| + x > 0$, is

(a) $(-\infty, -2) \cup (2, \infty)$ (b) $(-\infty, -\sqrt{2}) \cup (\sqrt{2}, \infty)$

(c) $(-\infty, -1) \cup (1, \infty)$ (d) $(\sqrt{2}, \infty)$ **(I.I.T. Sc. 2002)**

(b)* Find all solutions of $|x^2 - x - 6| = x + 2$.

Note that x is a real variable.

33. (a)* $|x^2 + 4x + 3| + 2x + 5 = 0$

(b) $|x^2 + 2x - 8| + x - 2 = 0$

34. (a) If $|x - 6| > |x^2 - 5x + 9|$, then $1 < x < 3$.

(b) If $|6x^2 - 5x - 1| = 5x - 6x^2 - 1$, then determine x.

35. (a) Solve the equation $(x + 1)(|x| - 1) = -\dfrac{1}{2}$.

(b) Solve : $x^2 - 2|x| - 3 = 0$.

36. (a) The number of solutions of the equation $|x|^2 - 3|x| + 2 = 0$ is 4.

(b) The real roots of the equation $x^2 + 5|x| + 4 = 0$ are none. $\qquad$ **(M.N.R. 1993)**

37. (a)* The number of real roots of the equation $|x|^2 - 7|x| + 12 = 0$ is 4. $\qquad$ **(M.N.R. 1995)**

(b)* The sum of all the real roots of the equation $|x - 2|^2 + |x - 2| - 2 = 0$ is .... **(I.I.T. Re-ex. 1997)**

38.* Solve : $\left| \dfrac{x^2 - 5x + 4}{x^2 - 4} \right| = 1$.

39.* If the expression $\sqrt{\log_{1/2} \dfrac{x}{x^2 - 1}}$ is real, then

determine the values of x for which this will hold.

40. If $\log_{(x+5/2)} \left(\dfrac{x-5}{2x-3} \right)^2 < 0$, then determine the range

of x.

41. For points $P = (x_1, y_1)$ and $Q = (x_2, y_2)$ of the co-ordinate plane, a new distance $d(P, Q)$ is defined by $d(P, Q) = |x_1 - x_2| + |y_1 - y_2|$. Let $O = (0, 0)$ and $A = (3, 2)$. Prove that the set of points in the first quadrant which are equidistant (with respect to the new distance) from O and A consists of the union of a line segment of finite length and an infinite ray. Sketch this set in a labelled diagram. $\qquad$ **(I.I.T. 2000)**

42. (a) Find all numbers x such that

$$|x+1| - |x| + 3|x-1| - 2|x-2| = x + 2$$

(b) If x satisfies $|x-1| + |x-2| + |x-3| \geq 6$, then prove that all numbers x which satisfy the above relation are given by $x \leq 0$ or $x \geq 4$.

43.* Solve the equation $|x^2 - 9| + |x^2 - 4| = 5$.

44. (a)* Find the solution to the equation

$$2^{|x+2|} - |2^{x+1} - 1| = 2^{x+1} + 1$$

(b)* Solve $2^{|x+1|} - 2^x = |2^x - 1| + 1$.

45. If x be real, then solve the following equations :

(a) $4^{-|x-2|} - 4 \cdot 2^{-|x-2|} + 2 = 0$

(b) $(144)^{|x|} - 2(12)^{|x|} + a = 0$

46.* Find the set of all solutions of the equation
$2^{|y|} - |2^{y-1} - 1| = 2^{y-1} + 1$ (I.I.T. 1997)

47. Solve the equation
$\frac{3}{2}\log_{1/4}(x+2)^2 - 3 = \log_{1/4}(4-x)^3 + \log_{1/4}(x+6)^3$.

48. Solve the equation $x|x+1| + a = 0$ for every real number a.

49. Solve the system of equations
$|x^2 - 2x| + y = 1, \quad x^2 + |y| = 1$.

50. (a) The equation $2\cos^2\left(\frac{1}{2}x\right)\sin^2 x = x^2 + x^{-2}$,
$0 < x \le \pi/2$ has
(a) no real solution
(b) one real solution
(c) more than one real solution.

(b) The number of real roots of the equation
$(\sin 2^x)\cos(2^x) = \frac{1}{4}(2^x + 2^{-x})$ is equal to
(a) 1   (b) 2
(c) 3   (d) 0

51. (a) Prove that there does not exist any solution of the equation $\frac{\log 5 + \log(x^2+1)}{\log(x-2)} = 2$

(b) The number of solutions of the equation
$2^x + 2^{x-1} + 2^{x-2} = 5^x + 5^{x-1} + 5^{x-2}$ is equal to
(a) 1   (b) 2
(c) 3   (d) none of these

(c) The number of solutions of the equation
$2x^{\log_{10} x} + 3x^{\log_{10}(1/x)} = 5$ is
(a) 1   (b) 2
(c) 3   (d) none of these

52.* Solve the equations
(a) $\sin x = x^2 + x + 1$ (b) $7^{6-x} = x + 2$.

53. (a) Solve the equation $2\cos^2\frac{x^2+x}{2} = 2^x + 2^{-x}$

(b) Find all the real values of $x \in (-2, 3)$ which satisfy the equation
$(x^2+x+1)^2 + 1 = (x^2+x+1)(x^2-x-5)$.

54. Solve for x :
(a)* $(5+2\sqrt{6})^{x^2-3} + (5-2\sqrt{6})^{x^2-3} = 10$.
(J.E.E.W.B. 1998; EAMCET 1992)

(b)* Solve the following equations for x
$(15+4\sqrt{14})^t + (15-4\sqrt{14})^t = 30$
where $t = x^2 - 2|x|$. (Roorkee 1991)

55. (a) $(7-4\sqrt{3})^{x^2-4x+3} + (7+4\sqrt{3})^{x^2-4x+3} = 14$.
(b) $[\sqrt{5}+2\sqrt{(6)}]^x + [\sqrt{5}-2\sqrt{(6)}]^x = 10$.
(c) $(\sqrt{3}+\sqrt{2})^x + (\sqrt{3}-\sqrt{2})^x = 10$

56. For $a \le 0$ determine all real roots of the equation,
$x^2 - 2a|x-a| - 3a^2 = 0$.

57.* $\frac{6}{5} \cdot a^{\log_a x \log_{10} a \log_a 5} - 3^{\log_{10}(x/10)} = 9^{\log_{100} x + \log_4 2}$

58.* Find the values of x satisfying the equation,
$|x-1|^{\log_3 x^2 - 2\log_x 9} = (x-1)^7$.

59.* Solve the following equation for x
$x^{\frac{2}{3}[(\log_2 x)^2 + \log_2 x - 5/4]} = \sqrt{2}$

60.* Solve the following equation for x.
$x^{\left[\frac{3}{4}(\log_2 x)^2 + \log_2 x - 5/4\right]} = \sqrt{2}$. (M.N.R. 1992)

61. (a) Solve for x :
$\log_{3/4}\log_8(x^2+7) + \log_{1/2}\log_{1/4}(x^2+7)^{-1} = -2$
(Roorkee 2000)

(b) $\sqrt{x}(9^{\sqrt{x^2-3}} - 3^{\sqrt{x^2-3}}) = 3^{2\sqrt{x^2-3}+1}$
$- 3^{\sqrt{x^2-3}+1} + 6\sqrt{x} - 18$

62.* Let $\{x\}$ and $[x]$ denote the fractional and integral part of a real number x respectively. Solve $4\{x\} = x + [x]$. (I.I.T. 1994)

63. If $\sqrt[3]{(1-x^3)}(y-z) + \sqrt[3]{(1-y^3)}(z-x)$
$+ \sqrt[3]{(1-z^3)}(x-y) = 0$
then prove that $(1-x^3)(1-y^3)(1-z^3) = (1-xyz)^3$

Solutions to Problem Set (1)

1. (a) The given equation can be written as
$\frac{2^{x^2}}{2^{2x}} = 8$ or $2^{x^2-2x} = 2^3$
Hence $x^2 - 2x = 3$ or $x^2 - 2x - 3 = 0$
or $(x-3)(x+1) = 0$; $\therefore x = 3, -1$.

(b) Ans. $x = \pm 1$.

2. $\frac{1}{8} \cdot 2^{2(2x-8)} = \left(\frac{1}{4\sqrt{2}}\right)^{-x} = (2^{-5/2})^{-x}$
or $2^{4x-16-3} = 2^{(5/2)x}$
$\therefore 2(4x-19) = 5x$ or $x = 38/3$.

3. Ans. $x = \pm 1$.
Hint : $a^x = t$ then $t(t-a)(at-1) = 0$
$\therefore a^x = a^1, a^{-1}$
$t = a^x \ne 0$ as exponential function is always + ive.

4. (a) By trial, we see that $x_1 = 1$ is a solution of the given equation. Now taking logarithms to base 10, we get
$x\log_{10} 3 + \frac{3x}{x+2}\log_{10} 2 = \log_{10} 6$
or $x^2\log_{10} 3 + (3\log_{10} 2 + 2\log_{10} 3$
$- \log_{10} 6)x - 2\log_{10} 6 = 0$
Let x_1, x_2 be its roots. Then

$x_1 x_2 = -2 \log_{10} 6 / \log_{10} 3$.

or $1 . x_2 = -2 \log_3 6$.

Hence the original equation has two roots $x_1 = 1$, $x_2 = -2 \log_3 6$.

Remark. Students must not think that the solution found by trial $x_1 = 1$ is the only solution. So it is useful to be able to guess a root, but never consider the guessing as the whole solution.

(b) $4^x + 6^x = 9^x$

or $\dfrac{4^x}{3^{2x}} + \dfrac{6^x}{3^{2x}} = 1$ or $\left(\dfrac{2}{3}\right)^{2x} + \left(\dfrac{2}{3}\right)^x - 1 = 0$

∴ $\left(\dfrac{2}{3}\right)^x = \dfrac{-1 \pm \sqrt{1+4}}{2} = \dfrac{-1 \pm \sqrt{5}}{2}$.

Since exponential function is always positive, we have

$\left(\dfrac{2}{3}\right)^x = \dfrac{\sqrt{5}-1}{2}$

∴ $x [\log_{10} 2 - \log_{10} 3] = \log_{10}(\sqrt{5}-1) - \log_{10} 2$

or $x = \dfrac{\log_{10}(\sqrt{5}-1) - \log_{10} 2}{\log_{10} 2 - \log_{10} 3}$.

5. By trial, $x = 2$ is a root of the equation. Dividing the equation by 5^x, we get

$$\left(\dfrac{3}{5}\right)^x + \left(\dfrac{4}{5}\right)^x = 1 \qquad \dots(1)$$

If $x < 2$, then $(3/5)^x > (3/5)^2$

and $(4/5)^x > (4/5)^2$ and so on

$(3/5)^x + (4/5)^x > (3/5)^2 + (4/5)^2 = 1$.

Hence (1) is not satisfied for any value of $x < 2$. Similarly, for $x > 2$, we will always have the inequality $(3/5)^x + (4/5)^x < 1$.

Thus $x = 2$ is the only root of the given equation. Note that it is immaterial how we found a root, but it is necessary to show that there are no other roots.

6. (a) The equation can be written as

$$4 . 2^{2x} - 2^x . 3^x - 18 . 3^{2x} = 0$$

Dividing by $2^x . 3^x$, we get

$$4 \left(\dfrac{2}{3}\right)^x - 1 - 18 \left(\dfrac{3}{2}\right)^x = 0.$$

Put $\left(\dfrac{3}{2}\right)^x = t$. Then $\dfrac{4}{t} - 1 - 18t = 0$

or $18t^2 + t - 4 = 0$ or $(2t + 1)(9t - 4) = 0$

∴ $t = 4/9$ or $-1/2$

∴ $t = \left(\dfrac{3}{2}\right)^x = \left(\dfrac{4}{9}\right) = \left(\dfrac{2}{3}\right)^2 = \left(\dfrac{3}{2}\right)^{-2}$,

giving $x = -2$.

Note that here we reject $t = \left(\dfrac{3}{2}\right)^x = -\dfrac{1}{2}$, since exponential function can never be negative. Hence the only solution is $x = -2$.

(b) Do yourself. Ans. $x = \dfrac{1}{2}$.

7. (a) $16^{\sin^2 x} + 16^{\cos^2 x} = 10$.

or $16^{\sin^2 x} + 16^{1 - \sin^2 x} = 10$

or $16^{\sin^2 x} + 16 . 16^{-\sin^2 x} = 10$

Put $16^{\sin^2 x} = t$.

Then $t + 16/t = 10$ or $t^2 - 10t + 16 = 0$

or $(t - 2)(t - 8) = 0$, giving $t = 2$ or 8.

Hence $16^{\sin^2 x} = 2$ or $2^{4 \sin^2 x} = 2$, which gives

$4 \sin^2 x = 1$

or $\sin^2 x = \dfrac{1}{4} = \sin^2 (\pi/6)$ ...(1)

∴ Solution of (1) is, $x = n\pi \pm \dfrac{\pi}{6}$

where $n = 0, \pm 1, \pm 2, \pm 3, \dots\dots$

Again $t = 8$ gives $2^{4 \sin^2 x} = 8 = 2^3$

or $4 \sin^2 x = 3$ i.e. $\sin^2 x = \dfrac{3}{4} = \sin^2 \dfrac{\pi}{3}$ ...(2)

∴ The solution of (2) is, $x = n\pi \pm \dfrac{\pi}{3}$.

where $n = 0, \pm 1, \pm 2, \pm 3, \dots\dots$

(b) **Hint :** The equation will reduce to $5^{1 + \cos 2x} = 5^{\sin 2x}$

Ans. $x = n\pi + \pi/4$, $x = n\pi + \pi/2$, $n \in I$.

8. (a) $\log_{10} \log_{10} \log_{10} x = 0$.

Taking anti-logarithm, $\log_{10} \log_{10} x = 10^0 = 1$.

Again anti-logarithm, $\log_{10} x = 10^1 = 10$.

Hence $x = 10^{10}$.

(b) The domain of x is $x > 0$, $x \neq 1$. The given equation is equivalent to

or $3x^2 + 10x = x^3$ or $x^3 - 3x^2 - 10x = 0$

or $x(x - 5)(x + 2) = 0$

Since $x = 0$ and $x = -2$ do not lie in the domain of x, the only solution of the given equation is $x = 5$.

9. (a) The equation can be written as

$$98 + \sqrt{x^3 - x^2 - 12x + 36} = 10^2 = 100$$

or $\sqrt{x^3 - x^2 - 12x + 36} = 2$

or $x^3 - x^2 - 12x + 36 = 4$

or $x^3 - x^2 - 12x + 32 = 0$

Now $(-64 - 16) + (48 + 32) = 0$

∴ $x = -4$ satisfies above.

or $(x+4)(x^2-5x+8)=0$

$\therefore \quad x=-4.$

or $x=\dfrac{5\pm\sqrt{25-32}}{2}=\dfrac{5\pm\sqrt{-7}}{2}$

Note. If we consider only real roots, then the only solution is $x=-4$.

(b) We know that $p^2+q^2=(p-q)^2+2pq$ ...(1)

where $p=x$, $q=\dfrac{x}{x+1}$

$\therefore \quad p-q=\dfrac{x^2}{x+1}=t, pq=\dfrac{x^2}{x+1}=t$ ...(2)

Hence the given equation by (1) and (2) is

$t^2+2t-3=0 \quad \therefore (t+3)(t-1)=0$

$\therefore \quad t=-3$ or 1

$\dfrac{x^2}{x+1}=-3$ or $1 \Rightarrow x^2+3x+3=0, D<0$

or $x^2-x-1=0 \quad \therefore x=\dfrac{1\pm\sqrt{5}}{2}$.

10. (a) The given equation can be written as

$\dfrac{2}{\log_a x}+\dfrac{1}{\log_a a+\log_a x}+\dfrac{3}{2\log_a a+\log_a x}=0$

Now put $\log_a x=y$. Then

$\dfrac{2}{y}+\dfrac{1}{1+y}+\dfrac{3}{2+y}=0$

or $2(1+y)(2+y)+y(2+y)+3y(1+y)=0$

or $6y^2+11y+4=0$

or $6y^2+8y+3y+4=0$

or $(3y+4)(2y+1)=0, \quad \therefore y=-\dfrac{4}{3}, -\dfrac{1}{2}$.

Hence $\log_a x=-\dfrac{4}{3}$ or $-\dfrac{1}{2}$,

or $x=a^{-4/3}$ or $a^{-1/2}$

(b) Since $\log_9 3=\log_{3^2} 3=\dfrac{1}{2}, \log_2 4=\log_2 2^2=2$

The given equation can be written as

$4^{1/2}+9^2=10^{\log_x 83}$

or $83=(10^{\log_x 83})$ or $\log_{10} 83=\log_x 83$

Hence $x=10$.

11. Put $\log_2 x=y$, then

$\log_{1/2} x=\log_{2^{-1}} x=-\log_2 x=-y$

Also $\log_2 2\sqrt{2}=\log_2 2^{3/2}=\dfrac{3}{2}\log_2 2=\dfrac{3}{2}$

The given equation is

$2\log_2 y-\log_2 [\log_2 (2\sqrt{2})+\log_2 x]=1$

or $2\log_2 y-\log_2 \left[\dfrac{3}{2}+y\right]=1$

$\log_2 \dfrac{y^2}{\left(\dfrac{3}{2}+y\right)}=1$

$\therefore \quad \dfrac{2y^2}{3+2y}=2$ or $y^2-2y-3=0$

or $(y-3)(y+1)=0 \quad \therefore \log_2 x=3,-1$

or $x=2^3, 2^{-1}$ i.e. $8, 1/2$.

12. (a) Put $\log_2 x=t$

$\therefore \quad \log_4 2x=\dfrac{1}{2}(\log_2 2+\log_2 x)=\dfrac{1}{2}(1+t)$

Hence the given equation is

$\dfrac{t}{1+t}=\dfrac{2(2+t)}{3(3+t)}$

or $t^2+3t-4=0$ or $t=1,-4=\log_2 x$

$\therefore \quad x=2$ or 2^{-4}.

(b) $\log_{3x} x=\log_{9x} x=k$, say.

$\therefore \quad (3x)^k=(9x)^k=x$ ...(1)

Above is possible only when $k=0$, and in that case $x=1$, from (1).

13. (a) L.H.S. $=x[\log_{10} 5-\log_{10} 10]$

$=x\log_{10}\left(\dfrac{5}{10}\right)=x\log_{10}\left(\dfrac{1}{2}\right)=\log_{10}\dfrac{1}{2^x}$

The given equation can be written as

$\log_{10}\left(\dfrac{1}{2^x+x-1}\right)=\log_{10}\dfrac{1}{2^x}$

$\therefore \quad \dfrac{1}{2^x+x-1}=\dfrac{1}{2^x}$

or $2^x+x-1=2^x. \quad \therefore x-1=0$ or $x=1$

Hence $x=1$ is the solution of the given equation.

(b) The equation can be written as

$\log_{10}\left(\dfrac{x^2-x-6}{x+2}\right)=x-4$

or $\log_{10}\dfrac{(x-3)(x+2)}{(x+2)}=x-4$

or $\log_{10}(x-3)=x-4$

or $x-3=10^{x-4}$. ...(1)

By trial, $x=4$ is the solution of (1) which is, therefore, the solution of the given equation. Observe that $x>4$ or $x<4$ does not satisfy (1). Hence $x=4$ is the only solution of the original equation.

14. (a) $x^x=x$.

Taking logarithm to the base 10, we get

$x\log_{10}|x|=\log_{10}|x|$

or $(x-1)\log_{10}|x|=0$

Hence $x=1$

or $\log_{10}|x|=0$ which gives

$|x|=1$ or $x=\pm 1$.

Hence the solution of the given equation is $x = \pm 1$.

(b) The equation can be re-written as $x^{\sqrt{x}} = x^{x/2}$

By trial, $x = 1$ is a solution.

Now equating the exponents, we have

$$\sqrt{x} = \frac{1}{2}x \quad \text{or} \quad x = \frac{1}{4}x^2 \quad \text{or} \quad x(x-4) = 0.$$

Since $x = 0$ does not satisfy the given equation, we get $x = 4$.

Hence the roots of the given equation are $x = 1, \ 4$.

15. (a) If $\log_4 x = t$, then

$$\log_{.25} x = \log_{4^{-1}} x = -\log_4 x = -t$$

$$\therefore \quad 5^{1+t} + 5^{-(1+t)} = \frac{26}{5}.$$

Put $5^{(1+t)} = z \qquad \therefore \quad z + \frac{1}{z} = \frac{26}{5}$

or $\quad 5z^2 - 26z + 1 = 0 \quad \therefore \quad z = 5, 1/5 \ \text{or} \ = 5^{-1}$

$$\therefore \quad 5^{1+t} = 5^1 \ \text{or} \ 5^{-1} \quad \therefore \quad 1 + t = 1 \ \text{or} \ -1$$

Hence, $\quad t = 0 \ \text{or} \ -2$

$$\therefore \quad \log_4 x = 0 \ \text{or} \ -2 \quad \therefore \quad x = 4^0 \ \text{or} \ 4^{-2}$$

or $\quad x = 1, 1/16$.

(b) Ans. $x = 3$.

16. (a) Ans. $x = 100$.

$$x^{\log_{10} 5} = x^{\log_x 5 \log_{10} x} = 5^{\log_{10} x}$$

$\therefore$ We have $\quad 2 \cdot 5^{\log_{10} x} = 50 \ \text{or} \ 5^{\log_{10} x} = 5^2$

$$\therefore \quad \log_{10} x = 2 \ \text{or} \ x = 10^2 = 100$$

(b) Ans. $x = 25, \sqrt{5}$.

17. (a) Sum of G.P. $1 + \frac{1}{2} + \frac{1}{4} + \frac{1}{8} + \dots \infty = \dfrac{1}{1 - \frac{1}{2}} = 2$

Sum of A.P. $= \dfrac{n}{2}[a + l] = y^2$ for N^r

and $\dfrac{y}{2}(3y + 5)$ for D^r

The given equations can be re-written as

$$\log_{10} x^2 = y \quad \text{or} \quad 2\log_{10} x = y \qquad \dots(1)$$

and $\dfrac{2y^2}{y(3y+5)} = \dfrac{20}{7\log_{10} x}$

or $\dfrac{2y}{3y+5} = \dfrac{40}{7 \cdot 2\log_{10} x} = \dfrac{40}{7y} \qquad \text{by (1)}$

$\therefore \quad 7y^2 = 60y + 100$

or $\quad 7y^2 - 70y + 10y - 100 = 0$

or $\quad (y - 10)(7y + 10) = 0 \quad \therefore \quad y = 10, \dfrac{-10}{7}$.

Since y is a + ive integer as it represents the number of terms of A.P. $\therefore \ y = 10$

$\therefore \quad 2\log_{10} x = 10$ by (1)

or $\quad \log_{10} x = 5 \quad \therefore \quad x = (10)^5$.

(b) Proceed as in part (a).

18. (a) The given equation can be re-written as

$$\log_{2^4} x + \log_{2^2} x + \log_2 x = 7$$

or $\quad \dfrac{1}{4}\log_2 x + \dfrac{1}{2}\log_2 x + \log_2 x = 7$

or $\quad \dfrac{7}{4}\log_2 x = 7 \ \text{or} \ \log_2 x = 4.$

Hence $x = 2^4 = 16$.

(b) The given equation can be re-written as

$$\log_{(2x+3)}(2x+3)(3x+7) + \log_{(3x+7)}(2x+3)^2 = 4$$

or $\quad \log_{(2x+3)}(2x+3) + \log_{(2x+3)}(3x+7)$
$$\qquad\qquad + 2\log_{(3x+7)}(2x+3) = 4$$

or $\quad y + 2 \cdot \dfrac{1}{y} = 3 \quad \therefore \quad \log_b a = \dfrac{1}{\log_a b}$

where $\quad y = \log_{(2x+3)}(3x+7)$

or $\quad y^2 - 3y + 2 = 0 \quad \therefore \quad y = 1, 2$

$\therefore \quad \log_{(2x+3)}(3x+7) = 1 \ \text{or} \ 2$

$\therefore \quad 3x+7 = 2x+3 \quad \text{or} \quad 3x+7 = (2x+3)^2$

$\therefore \quad x = -4, \ \text{and} \ \ 4x^2 + 9x + 2 = 0$

or $\quad x = -2, \ -\dfrac{1}{4}$

Thus we have three values of x namely

$$-4, -2, -\frac{1}{4} \qquad\qquad \dots(1)$$

Now by definitions of logarithms as on **P. 246**

$$2x + 3 > 0, \ \ 2x + 3 \neq 1 \ \ \text{or} \ \ 2x \neq -2$$

$$\therefore \quad x > -\frac{3}{2}, \ x \neq -1, \qquad\qquad \dots(2)$$

and $3x + 7 > 0$ and $3x + 7 \neq 1$ or $3x \neq -6$

$$\therefore \quad x > -\frac{7}{3}, \ x \neq -2 \qquad\qquad \dots(3)$$

Clearly from (1), (2) and (3), $x = -4$, $x = -2$ are rejected and the only solution left is $x = -1/4$.

19. (a) The given equation can be re-written as

$$2^{2x} + 2^{2x-1} = 3^{x-1/2} + 3^{x+1/2}$$

$$2^{2x}\left(1 + \frac{1}{2}\right) = 3^x\left(\frac{1}{\sqrt{(3)}} + \sqrt{3}\right)$$

or $\quad 3 \cdot 2^{2x-1} = 4 \cdot 3^{x-1/2}$

or $\quad 2^{2x-3} = 3^{x-3/2}$

Now by trial, $x = \dfrac{3}{2}$ is one solution.

Now taking logarithm to the base 10, we get

$$(2x - 3)\log_{10} 2 = \left(x - \frac{3}{2}\right)\log_{10} 3$$

or $\quad (2\log 2 - \log 3)x = \dfrac{3}{2}(2\log 2 - \log 3)$

This also gives $x = \dfrac{3}{2}$.

Hence $x = \dfrac{3}{2}$ is the only solution.

(b) We write the given equation as

$$(7 \times 3)^x = 2^{2x+1} \cdot (10/2)^x$$

Taking logarithm of both sides, we have

$$x(\log 7 + \log 3) = (2x+1)\log 2 + x(\log 10 - \log 2)$$

or $\quad x[\log 7 + \log 3 - 2\log 2 - \log 10$
$$+ \log 2] = \log 2$$

or $\quad x[\log 7 + \log 3 - \log 2 - 1] = \log 2$

or $\quad x[0 \cdot 8450980 + 0 \cdot 4771213 - 0 \cdot 3010300 - 1]$
$$= 0 \cdot 30103$$

or $\quad x(0 \cdot 0211893) = 0 \cdot 30103$

$\therefore \quad x = 14 \cdot 207$ (approx.)

20. (a) The given equation can be written as

$$x + \log_{10}(1 + 2^x) - x\log_{10} 5 = \log_{10} 6$$

or $\quad x\log_{10} 10 + \log_{10}(1 + 2^x)$
$$- x\log_{10} 5 = \log_{10} 6$$

or $\quad x\log_{10}(10/5) + \log_{10}(1 + 2^x) = \log_{10} 6$

or $\quad \log_{10} 2^x + \log_{10}(1 + 2^x) = \log_{10} 6$

or $\quad \log_{10} 2^x(1 + 2^x) = \log_{10} 6$

Hence $2^x(1 + 2^x) = 6$ or $2^{2x} + 2^x - 6 = 0$

or $\quad (2^x + 3)(2^x - 2) = 0$

Since $2^x > 0$, $2^x = -3$ is rejected. So we have

$$2^x = 2 \quad \text{or} \quad x = 1.$$

Hence $x = 1$ is the only root of the given equation.

(b) $x[\log_{10} 10 - \log_{10} 3] + \log_{10} 3 = \log_{10}(2 + 3^x) + x$

or $\quad (1 - x)\log_{10} 3 = \log_{10}(2 + 3^x)$

or $\quad 3^{1-x} = 2 + 3^x$

or $\quad \dfrac{3}{t} = 2 + t$ or $t^2 + 2t - 3 = 0$ where $t = 3^x$

or $\quad (t + 3)(t - 1) = 0$ $\quad \therefore \quad t = 3^x = -3$ or 1

$\therefore \quad 3^x = 1 = 3^0$ or $x = 0$. $(3^x = -3$ rejected$)$

21. The roots must satisfy the condition $x > 0$, $x \neq 1$. (why?)

The equation can be written as

$$[\log_a a + \log_a x][\log_x a + \log_x x] = \log_{a^2} a^{-1}$$

or $\quad (1 + \log_a x)\left(\dfrac{1}{\log_a x} + 1\right) = -\dfrac{1}{2}$

Now put $\log_a x = y$. Then

$$\dfrac{(1 + y)^2}{y} = -\dfrac{1}{2} \quad \text{or} \quad 2y^2 + 5y + 2 = 0$$

or $\quad (y + 2)(2y + 1) = 0$.

This gives $y = -2$ or $-\dfrac{1}{2}$, that is,

$$\log_a x = -2 \quad \text{or} \quad -\dfrac{1}{2}.$$

Hence $x = a^{-2}$ or $a^{-1/2}$.

22. (a) **Hint :**

$$2^x \cdot 3^x \cdot \left(\dfrac{2}{3}\right)^y - 3 \cdot 2^{x+y} - 8 \cdot 3^{x-y} + 24 = 0$$

or $\quad 2^{x+y} \cdot 3^{x-y} - 3 \cdot 2^{x+y} - 8 \cdot 3^{x-y} + 24 = 0$

or $\quad (2^{x+y} - 8)(3^{x-y} - 3) = 0$

Hence $\quad 2^{x+y} = 2^3$ or $3^{x-y} = 3^1$

$\therefore \quad x + y = 3$ $\hspace{3cm}$ ...(1)

or $\quad x - y = 1$ $\hspace{3cm}$ ...(2)

Also second given equation is $\quad xy = 2$ $\quad$ ...(3)

Now solve (1) and (3); and (2) and (3).

Ans. $x = 2$, $y = 1$ or $x = 1$, $y = 2$

or $\quad x = -1$, $y = -2$.

(b) $3 \cdot x^{2y-1} = 4 \Rightarrow 3 \cdot x^{2(y+1)-3} = 4$.

or $\quad 3 \cdot (x^{y+1})^2 \cdot x^{-3} = 4$

or $\quad 3 \cdot 36 \cdot \dfrac{1}{x^3} = 4$ $\quad \therefore \quad x^3 = 27$ $\quad$ or $\quad x = 3$.

$$x^{y+1} = 6 \Rightarrow y + 1 = \log_x 6 = \log_3(3 \cdot 2)$$

or $\quad y + 1 = 1 + \log_3 2$ $\quad \therefore \quad y = \log_3 2$.

Hence $x = 3$, $y = \log_3 2$.

23. (a) By definition $x > 0$ and $x \neq 0$

$$(3y^2 + 1)\log_3 x = 1 \hspace{2cm} \text{...(1)}$$

and $(2y^2 + 10) = \log_x 27 = 3\log_x 3 = \dfrac{3}{\log_3 x}$

or $\quad (2y^2 + 10)\log_3 x = 3$ $\hspace{2cm}$ ...(2)

Dividing (1) and (2), we get

$$\dfrac{2y^2 + 10}{3y^2 + 1} = \dfrac{3}{1}$$

or $\quad 2y^2 + 10 = 9y^2 + 3$

$\therefore \quad y^2 = 1$ and from (1), $\quad 4\log_3 x = 1$

or $\quad \log_3 x = \dfrac{1}{4}$ $\quad$ or $\quad x = 3^{1/4}$

$\therefore \quad x = 3^{1/4}$, $y = \pm 1$.

(b) The second equation on making the base 2 can be written as

$$\dfrac{3}{2} \cdot \dfrac{1}{3}\log_2(x - y) - 1(-2)\log_2(x + y) = 5$$

$$\left(\dfrac{1}{2} + 2\right)\log_2(x - y) = 5$$

$\therefore \quad \log_2(x - y) = 2$ $\quad \therefore \quad x - y = 2^2 = 4$.

The first equation can be written as

$$(x + y)^{\frac{1}{x-y}} \cdot (x - y)^{1/4} = (52 - 2x)^{1/2}$$

Put $x - y = 4$ $\quad$ or $\quad x - 4 = y$

$\therefore \quad (2x - 4)^{1/4} \, 4^{1/4} = (52 - 2x)^{1/2}$

or $\quad (2x - 4) \cdot 4 = [2(26 - x)]^2$

or $\quad 2x - 4 = 676 - 52x + x^2$

or $\quad x^2 - 54x + 680 = 0$

$(x - 34)(x - 20) = 0 \quad \therefore \quad 680 = 34 \times 20$

$\therefore \quad x = 20, 34$

But when $x = 34, 26 - x = -$ ive and

hence $\sqrt{(26 - x)}$ becomes imaginary. Therefore we

choose $x = 20$ and hence $y = x - 4 = 16$.

24. Dividing the given equations, we get

$3^{x-y} \cdot 5^{y-x} = \dfrac{75}{45}$ or $\left(\dfrac{3}{5}\right)^{x-y} = \left(\dfrac{3}{5}\right)^{-1}$

Hence $\quad x - y = -1 \qquad \qquad \ldots(1)$

Again multiplying the equations, we get

$(3^x \times 5^x)(3^y \times 5^y) = 75 \times 45$

$15^{x+y} = 15^3$

Hence $x + y = 3 \qquad \qquad \ldots(2)$

Solving (1) and (2), we get

$\qquad x = 1, \ y = 2$

Alt. $3^x 5^y = 75 = 5^2 \cdot 3$

$\therefore \quad 3^{x-1} = 5^{2-y} \qquad \qquad \ldots(1)$

$3^y 5^x = 45 = 3^2 \cdot 5$

$\therefore \quad 3^{y-2} = 5^{1-x} \qquad \qquad \ldots(2)$

Since bases both in (1) and (2) are different, the equality is possible only when each power is zero.

$\therefore \quad x - 1 = 0, \ 2 - y = 0 \ \therefore \ x = 1, y = 2.$

25. (a) $\log_3 \left(\dfrac{xy}{2}\right) = 2$ from 1st

$\therefore \quad \dfrac{xy}{2} = 3^2 \quad$ or $\quad xy = 18$

$x + y = (3^3)^{2/3} = 9$ from 2nd

$\therefore \quad x, y$ are roots of $t^2 - 9t + 18 = 0$

$\therefore \quad (t - 6)(t - 3) = 0$

$\therefore \quad (x, y) = (3, 6) \quad$ or $\quad (6, 3).$

(b) The first equation can be written as

$\log_y x + \dfrac{1}{\log_y x} = 2$

or $\quad (\log_y x)^2 - 2 \log_y x + 1 = 0$

or $\quad (\log_y x - 1)^2 = 0 \ i.e. \ \log_y x = 1$

This gives $x = y \ (x > 0, \ y > 0, \ x \neq 1, y \neq 1).$

Then the second given equation gives

$\qquad x^2 + x - 12 = 0 \quad$ or $\quad (x + 4)(x - 3) = 0$

Since $x = -4$ is not in the domain of x, the only solution is $x = y = 3.$

26. $\log^2 p = \log^2 q \ \Rightarrow \ (\log p + \log q)(\log p - \log q) = 0$

$= \log(pq) \log\left(\dfrac{p}{q}\right) = 0$

$\therefore \quad pq = 1 \quad$ or $\quad \dfrac{p}{q} = 1 \quad$ or $\quad p = q \quad$ or $\quad p = \dfrac{1}{q} \quad \ldots(A)$

L.H.S. $= \log^2 \dfrac{x+4}{x} + \log^2 \dfrac{x}{x+4}$

$\qquad = \log^2 \dfrac{x+4}{x} + \log^2 \dfrac{x+4}{x} \qquad$ by (A)

$\qquad = 2 \log^2 \dfrac{x+4}{x} \qquad \qquad \ldots(1)$

R.H.S. $= 2 \log^2 \dfrac{3-x}{x-1} \qquad \qquad \ldots(2)$

From (1) and (2), we get

$\dfrac{x+4}{x} = \dfrac{3-x}{x-1} \quad$ or $\quad \dfrac{x-1}{3-x} \qquad$ by (A)

These two equations imply $x^2 = 2$ or $x^2 = 6$

$\therefore \quad x = \pm\sqrt{2}, \pm\sqrt{6}$

But by definition of $\log t$, $x \neq -\sqrt{2} \neq -\sqrt{6}$

$\therefore \quad x = \sqrt{2}, \sqrt{6}.$

27. (a) By definition, xy and $\dfrac{x}{y}$ are both + ive and

hence they can be written as $|xy|$ and $\left|\dfrac{x}{y}\right|$.

Thus we have the following equations.

$|xy| = |x||y| = 2^5, \qquad \qquad \ldots(1)$

$\left|\dfrac{x}{y}\right| = \dfrac{|x|}{|y|} = \dfrac{1}{2} \qquad \qquad \ldots(2)$

Multiplying, $|x|^2 = 2^4 = 16$

$\therefore \quad |x| = 4$ only, as mod is +ive.

$\therefore \quad x = \pm 4, y = \pm 8.$

$\therefore \quad x = 4, y = 8$ or $x = -4, y = -8$ only.

as both xy and (x/y) have to be +ive.

(b) $\dfrac{10}{3} = 3 + \dfrac{1}{3}$

The given equation is of the from

$p + \dfrac{1}{p} = 3 + \dfrac{1}{3} = q + \dfrac{1}{q}$

where $p \neq q$ as $x \neq y$

$\therefore \quad \log_2 x = 3, \qquad \log_2 y = 1/3$

$\therefore \quad x = 2^3, y = 2^{1/3}. \quad \therefore \quad x + y = 8 + 2^{1/3}$

28. (a) We first observe that $x > 0, y > 0, x \neq 1$ and $y \neq 1$. The first equation can be written as

$5\left[\log_y x + \dfrac{1}{\log_y x}\right] = 26.$

Putting $\log_y x = u$, this becomes

$5u^2 - 26u + 5 = 0 \quad$ or $\quad (u - 5)(5u - 1) = 0.$

Hence $u = 5, \ 5^{-1} \quad$ or $\quad \log_y x = 5, \ 5^{-1}.$

Hence the solution of the given equation to be found among the system of equations

$\log_y x = 5, \ xy = 64 \quad \therefore \quad x = y^5, \ xy = 64$

$\therefore \quad y^6 = 64, \ y = 2 \ \therefore \ x = 32$

and of the system

$$\log_y x = \frac{1}{5}, \quad xy = 64 \quad \therefore \quad x = y^{1/5}$$

or $\quad y = x^5, \quad xy = 64 \quad \therefore \quad x^6 = 64$

$\therefore \quad x = 2, y = 32.$

(b) Taking log, we have

$(x + y) \log 2 = y (\log 2 + \log 3),$ by 1st

$\therefore \quad x \log 2 = y \log 3$

or $\quad \dfrac{x}{\log 3} = \dfrac{y}{\log 2} = k$ ...(1)

$x \log 3 = \log 3 + (y + 1) \log 2$ by 2nd   ...(2)

Now put for x and y from (1) in (2)

$\therefore \quad k = \dfrac{1}{\log 3 - \log 2}$

Ans. $x = \dfrac{\log 3}{\log 3 - \log 2},$

$\quad y = \dfrac{\log 2}{\log 3 - \log 2}.$

(c) Ans. (b).

$x > 3$ for the given equation to hold good. The given equation can be written as

$\dfrac{\log (x - 1)}{\log 4} = \dfrac{\log (x - 3)}{\log 2}$. Put $\log 4 = 2 \log 2$

or $\quad \log (x - 1) = 2 \log (x - 3) = \log (x - 3)^2$

$\therefore \quad (x - 3)^2 - (x - 1) = 0$

or $\quad x^2 - 7x + 10 = 0$

$\therefore \quad (x - 2)(x - 5) = 0 \quad \therefore \quad x = 2, 5$

We reject $x = 2$ as $x > 3$. Hence $x = 5$ is the only solution.

29. Hint : First equation can be written as

$\log_2 x + \log_{2^2} y + \log_{2^2} z = 2$

or $\quad \log_2 x + \dfrac{1}{2} \log_2 y + \dfrac{1}{2} \log_2 z = 2$

or $\quad \log_2 x\sqrt{yz} = 2$ or $\quad x\sqrt{yz} = 2^2 = 4$

or $\quad x^2 yz = 16.$ ...(1)

Similarly $y^2 zx = 81$ ...(2)

and $\quad z^2 xy = 256$ ...(3)

The equations (1), (2) and (3) can now be easily solved. This is left for the students.

Ans. $x = 2/3, \ y = 27/8, \ z = 32/3.$

30. Put $e^{\sin x} = y$. Then the given equation reduces to

$\quad y - \dfrac{1}{y} - 4 = 0$ or $\quad y^2 - 4y - 1 = 0$

$\therefore \quad y = \dfrac{4 \pm \sqrt{16 + 4}}{2} = 2 \pm \sqrt{5}.$

or $\quad e^{\sin x} = 2 \pm \sqrt{5}.$

Since exponential function is always positive, we cannot have

$e^{\sin x} = 2 - \sqrt{5}$

And for $e^{\sin x} = 2 + \sqrt{5}$, we have

$\sin x = \log_e (2 + \sqrt{5}) > 1, \quad [\because \ e > 1 \text{ and } 2 + \sqrt{5} > e]$

which is impossible.

Hence the equation can have no real solution.

31. (a) Ans. False. First note that for $x = 1$, the equation becomes meaningless and so the solution $x = 1$ is ruled out. Now when $x \neq 1$, cancelling $2 / (x - 1)$ from both sides, we get $x = 1$, which is false since $x \neq 1$.

Hence the given equation has no solution.

(b) Ans. True. L.H.S. $= \sin (e^x) \leq 1$

and R.H.S. $= 5^x + 5^{-x} \geq 2$ [Use A.M. $\geq$ G.M.]

Hence the equation has no real roots.

(c) Here x is expressed as a continued fraction.

Here $x - 1 = \dfrac{1}{3+} \dfrac{1}{2+} \dfrac{1}{3+} \dfrac{1}{2+} \cdots$

or $\quad x - 1 = \dfrac{1}{3 + \dfrac{1}{2 + x - 1}} = \dfrac{1}{3 + \dfrac{1}{1 + x}} = \dfrac{1 + x}{4 + 3x}$

$\therefore \quad (x - 1)(3x + 4) = 1 + x$

or $\quad 3x^2 + x - 4 = 1 + x$

or $\quad 3x^2 = 5 \quad \therefore \quad x = \pm \sqrt{5/3}$

Clearly x is + ive and hence we reject $x = -\sqrt{5/3}$.

(d) Observe that A.M. of pair $(x - 1), (x - 5)$ and $(x - 2), (x - 4)$ is $(x - 3)$.

Hence we put $x - 3 = y$ and change the equation in y.

$\therefore \quad x = y + 3$. Putting for x, the given equation becomes

$(y + 2)^3 + (y + 1)^3 + y^3 + (y - 1)^3 + (y - 2)^3 = 0$

$2 [y^3 + 3y (4)] + 2 [y^3 + 3y (1)^2] + y^3 = 0$

or $\quad 5y^3 + 30y = 0$ or $\quad y (y^2 + 6) = 0$

$\therefore \quad y = 0, \pm i\sqrt{6} \quad \therefore \quad x = y + 3 = 3, 3 \pm i\sqrt{6}.$

32. (a) Ans. (b).

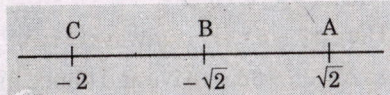

Fig. 1

$x + 2 > 0, \ i.e. \ x > -2$ then $x^2 - (x + 2) + x > 0$

or $\quad (x + \sqrt{2})(x - \sqrt{2}) > 0$

$\therefore \quad x < -\sqrt{2}$ or $x > \sqrt{2}$ ...(1)

$x + 2 < 0, \ i.e. \ x < -2$ then $x^2 + (x + 2) + x > 0$

or $\quad x^2 + 2x + 2 > 0$ or $(x + 1)^2 + 1 > 0$, from (1)

Above is true for all values of x. Hence x lies in $(-\infty, -\sqrt{2}) \cup (\sqrt{2}, \infty)$, by (1).

(b) We consider two cases :

(i) $x^2 - x - 6 < 0$ or $(x-3)(x+2) < 0$

or $[x-(-2)][x-3] < 0$, i.e. $-2 < x < 3$ ...(1)

In this case, the given equation reduces to

$$-(x^2 - x - 6) = x + 2 \quad \text{or} \quad x^2 = 4$$

which gives $x = \pm 2$. So in this case $x = 2$ is the only root of the given equation which satisfies (1).

(ii) $x^2 - x - 6 \geq 0$.

i.e. $x \leq -2$ or $x \geq 3$ ...(2)

In this case, we obtain the equation

$$x^2 - x - 6 = x + 2 \quad \text{or} \quad x^2 - 2x - 8 = 0.$$

The roots of this equation are $x = 4$, $x = -2$. Since both these values satisfy condition (2), both 4 and -2 are the roots of the original equation. Hence the original equation has three roots : $-2, 2$ and 4.

33. (a) $x^2 + 4x + 3 = (x+3)(x+1) = \{x-(-3)\}\{x-(-1)\}$

The above expression is + ive when x does not lie between -3 and -1 and is $-$ive when x lies between -3 and -1.

Case I. x does not lie between -3 and -1

$$x^2 + 4x + 3 + 2x + 5 = 0$$

or $x^2 + 6x + 8 = 0$

or $(x+2)(x+4) = 0$ or $x = -2$ and -4

∴ $x = -4$

Case II. x lies between -3 and -1

$$-(x^2 + 4x + 3) + 2x + 5 = 0$$

or $x^2 + 2x - 2 = 0$.

∴ $x = -1 + \sqrt{3}$ and $-1 - \sqrt{3}$.

But $-1 + \sqrt{3}$ does not lie between -3 and -1 and hence $-1 - \sqrt{3}$ is the required root lying between -3 and -1.

Ans. $-4, (-1 - \sqrt{3})$.

(b) Proceed as in part (a).

Ans. $x = -5, -3, 2$.

34. (a) Here $x^2 - 5x + 9$ is always +ive,

as $\Delta = 25 - 36 = -$ive and hence its sign is same as that of 1st term. Hence the equation reduces to

$$x^2 - 5x + 9 < |x - 6|$$

Now consider two cases $x > 6$ and $x < 6$.

1st Case : $x^2 - 5x + 9 < x - 6$, $x > 6$

$$x^2 - 6x + 15 < 0$$

L.H.S. is always +ive as its Δ is $-$ive and its sign is same as that of 1st term. Hence this is ruled out as +ive cannot be < 0

2nd Case : $x^2 - 5x + 9 < -(x-6)$, $x < 6$.

or $x^2 - 4x + 3 < 0$ or $(x-1)(x-3) < 0$

∴ $1 < x < 3$.

(b) $6x^2 - 5x - 1 = (x - 1)(6x + 1)$

∴ $x = -1/6, 1$

Consider two cases :

(I) $x < -\dfrac{1}{6}$, or $x > 1$, L.H.S. = +ive

or   (II) $-\dfrac{1}{6} \leq x \leq 1$, L.H.S. = $-$ive

Ans. $\dfrac{1}{2}(-1 \pm \sqrt{5})$.

35. (a) Ans. $\dfrac{1}{\sqrt{(2)}}, -1 \pm \left(\dfrac{1}{\sqrt{(2)}}\right)$.

(b) We can solve this problem as in problem 33, 34 or 42 by considering two cases (a) $x < 0$ (b) $x \geq 0$. Another method to solve this equation is as given below :

Put $|x| = y$. Then $x^2 = |x|^2 = y^2$.

Hence the given equation can be written as

$$y^2 - 2y - 3 = 0 \quad \text{or} \quad (y-3)(y+1) = 0$$

This gives $|x| = y = 3$ or -1 of which $|x| = -1$ is meaningless.

and $|x| = 3$ gives $x = \pm 3$,

which is the required solution of the original equation.

36. (a) (i) $|x| = 2, 1$ ∴ $x = \pm 2, \pm 1$

(b) Put $x^2 = |x|^2$ ∴ $|x| = -1, -4$ not possible as mod is always positive.

37. (a) $|x| = 3, 4$ ∴ $x = \pm 3, \pm 4$

(b) Ans. 4. Put $|x-2| = t$ ∴ $t^2 + t - 2 = 0$

∴ $t = 1, -2$

∴ $|x-2| = 1$ or $x - 2 = \pm 1$

∴ $x = 3, 1$.

$|x-2| \neq -2$

Hence only two real roots whose sum is 4.

38. We have $|x^2 - 5x + 4| = |x^2 - 4|$, $x \neq \pm 2$

$$|(x-4)||(x-1)| = |(x+2)||(x-2)| \quad \text{...(1)}$$

The values of x are $-2, 1, 2, 4$ in ascending order

1st case : $x < -2$. L.H.S. is + ive, R.H.S. is + ive

$x^2 - 5x + 4 = x^2 - 4$. ∴ $x = 8/5$ rejected as $x < -2$

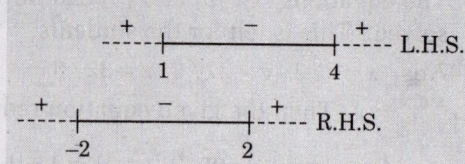

Fig. 2

2nd Case : $-2 < x < 1$. L.H.S. is + ive, R.H.S. is $-$ive

∴ $x^2 - 5x + 4 = -(x^2 - 4)$

∴ $2x^2 - 5x = 0$ or $x = 0, 5/2$

∴ $x = 0$ is the only solution in this case.

3rd Case : $1 \leq x < 2$. L.H.S. is $-$ ive, R.H.S. is $-$ ive

$$\therefore \quad -(x^2 - 5x + 4) = -(x^2 - 4)$$

$$\therefore \quad 5x = 8 \quad \text{or} \quad x = 8/5$$

It is in the domain.

4th Case : $2 < x < 4$. L.H.S. is $-$ ive, R.H.S. $+$ ive

$$\therefore \quad (x^2 - 5x + 4) = x^2 - 4 \quad \therefore \quad 2x^2 - 5x = 0$$

$$\therefore \quad x = 0, 5/2$$

$\therefore \quad 5/2$ is the only solution in the domain.

5th Case : $x \geq 4$. Both L.H.S. and R.H.S. are $+$ ive

$$\therefore \quad x^2 - 5x + 4 = x^2 - 4 \quad \therefore \quad x = 8/5$$

but i does not lie in the domain.

Hence the required values of x are $0, 8/5$ and $5/2$.

39. For reality, we must have

$$\log_{1/2}\left(\frac{x}{x^2 - 1}\right) \geq 0 = \log_{1/2} 1$$

$$\therefore \quad \frac{x}{x^2 - 1} \leq 1 \qquad \qquad \dots(1)$$

$$(\because \text{ Base } 1/2 \text{ is less than 1})$$

Also by definition of $\log_a x$, x must be $+$ ive, $\neq 0$.

$$\therefore \quad \frac{x}{x^2 - 1} > 0 \qquad \qquad \dots(2)$$

The required region will consist of those x which satisfy both the inequalities (1) and (2).

Now (2) $\Rightarrow \dfrac{x^2}{(x+1) \, x \, (x-1)} > 0$

$$\Rightarrow \quad (x+1)(x-0)(x-1) > 0$$

Again (1) $\Rightarrow \dfrac{x}{x^2 - 1} - 1 \leq 0$

or $\dfrac{x - x^2 + 1}{(x^2 - 1)} \leq 0 \qquad$ or $\dfrac{x^2 - x - 1}{(x+1)(x-1)} \geq 0$

$$\frac{(x^2 - x - 1)(x+1)(x-1)}{(x+1)^2 (x-1)^2} \geq 0$$

or $(x^2 - x - 1)(x+1)(x-1) \geq 0$

The values of x are given by

$$-1, -\frac{1}{2}(\sqrt{5} - 1), 1, \frac{1}{2}(\sqrt{5} + 1)$$

Mark them on real line in ascending order as shown below :

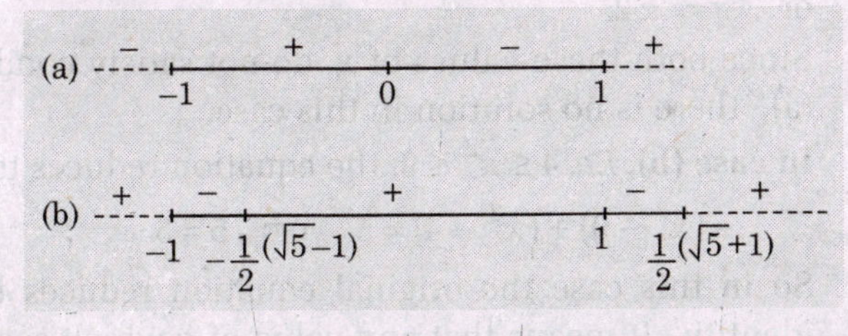

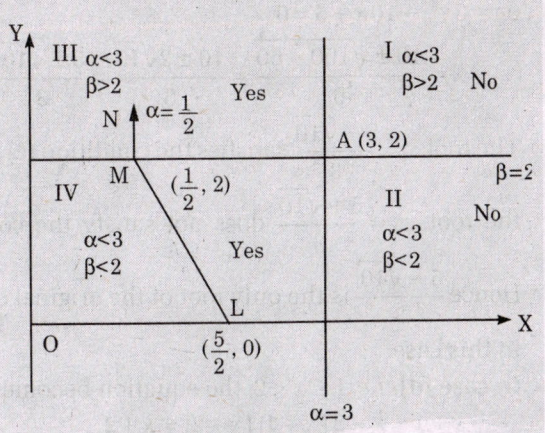

Fig. 3

We have to take the intersection *i.e.*, common region marked in figures (a) and (b), *i.e.*, $+$ ive.

$$x \geq \frac{1}{2}(\sqrt{5} + 1), -\frac{1}{2}(\sqrt{5} - 1) \leq x < 0.$$

40. Refer **Rule 14, 15 P. 247.**

$\log_a \alpha$ is defined if both α and a are $+$ ive and $\alpha \neq 0$, $a \neq 1$ or $x \neq 5$ and $x \neq -3/2$

Also $\log_a \alpha < 0$ if base a satisfies

$$\log_a \alpha < 0 = \log_a 1$$

$\Rightarrow \quad \alpha < 1$ if $a > 1$ $\qquad \qquad \dots(\text{I})$

$\Rightarrow \quad \alpha > 1$ if $0 < a < 1$ $\qquad \qquad \dots(\text{II})$

The inequalities in (I) $\Rightarrow x + \dfrac{5}{2} > 1$ or $x > -\dfrac{3}{2}$, and

$$0 < \left(\frac{x-5}{2x-3}\right)^2 < 1 \quad \text{or} \quad (2x-3)^2 - (x-5)^2 > 0$$

or $(3x - 8)(x + 2) > 0$

or $x < -2$ or $x > 8/3$ but $x \neq 5$

But $x > -3/2$

Hence $x > 8/3$ satisfies all except $x = 5$.

$$\therefore \quad x \in (8/3, \infty) - \{5\} \qquad \qquad \dots(1)$$

The inequality in (II)

$\Rightarrow \quad 0 < x + \dfrac{5}{2} < 1 \qquad$ or $\quad -\dfrac{5}{2} < x < -\dfrac{3}{2}$

and $(x + 2)(3x - 8) < 0$

$$\therefore \quad x \in \left(-2, \frac{8}{3}\right) - \left\{\frac{3}{2}\right\}$$

Clearly $x \in (-2, -3/2) \qquad \qquad \dots(2)$

From (1) and (2), we finally have

$$x \in (-2, -3/2) \cup (8/3, \infty) - \{5\}$$

41. Let P be (α, β) where both α and β are $+$ ive being in the first quadrant be points equidistant from O and A i.e. $OP = AP$.

$$|\alpha - 0| + |\beta - 0| = |\alpha - 3| + |\beta - 2| \qquad \dots(1)$$

or $\alpha + \beta = |\alpha - 3| + |\beta - 2|$,

as α, β are both positive.

Because of $|\alpha - 3|$ and $|\beta - 2|$ we will consider $\alpha > 3, \alpha < 3$; $\beta > 2, \beta < 2$.

1st $\alpha > 3, \beta > 2$

$$\alpha + \beta = \alpha - 3 + \beta - 2 \Rightarrow -5 = 0 \text{ No solution.}$$

2nd $\alpha > 3, \beta < 2$

Fig. 4

$\alpha + \beta = \alpha - 3 - (\beta - 2) \Rightarrow \beta = -\dfrac{1}{2}$ rejected as $\beta > 0$

3rd $\alpha < 3, \beta > 2$

$\alpha + \beta = -(\alpha - 3) + \beta - 2$ or $2\alpha = 1$, $\therefore \quad \alpha = \dfrac{1}{2}$

4th $\alpha < 3, \beta < 2$

$\alpha + \beta = -(\alpha - 3) - (\beta - 2) \quad \therefore \quad \alpha + \beta = \dfrac{5}{2}$

Above are shown in the figure by *MN* and *LM*.

42. The given equation can be re-written as
$$|x+1| - |x| + 3|(x-1)(x-2)| = x + 2$$
The change points as marked on real line are $-1, 0, 1, 2$.

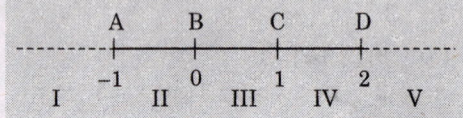

Fig. 5

Consider five cases :

(a) $x < -1$ (b) $-1 \le x < 0$

(c) $0 \le x < 1$ (d) $1 \le x < 2$.

(e) $x \ge 2$.

In case (a), *i.e.* $x < -1$, the equation reduces to
$$-(x+1) - (-x) + 3(x-1)(x-2) = x + 2$$
or $3x^2 - 10x + 3 = 0$ or $(x-3)(3x-1) = 0$

$\therefore \quad x = 3$ or $\dfrac{1}{3}$.

Since these values of x do not satisfy condition (a), the original equation has no solution in this case.

In case (b), *i.e.* $-1 \le x < 0$, the equation reduces to
$$x + 1 - (-x) + 3(x-1)(x-2) = x + 2$$
or $3x^2 - 8x + 5 = 0$ or $(x-1)(3x-5) = 0$

$\therefore \quad x = 1, \dfrac{5}{3}$.

Since these values of x do not satisfy the condition (b), the original equation has no solution in this case also.

In case (c), *i.e.* $0 \le x < 1$, the equation is :
$$x + 1 - x + 3(x-1)(x-2) = x + 2$$
or $3x^2 - 10x + 5 = 0$

$\therefore \quad x = \dfrac{10 \pm \sqrt{100-60}}{6} = \dfrac{10 \pm 2\sqrt{10}}{6} = \dfrac{5 \pm \sqrt{10}}{3}$.

The root $x = \dfrac{5 - \sqrt{10}}{3}$ satisfies the condition (c) whereas the root $x = \dfrac{5 + \sqrt{10}}{3}$ does not satisfy the condition.

Hence $\dfrac{5 - \sqrt{10}}{3}$ is the only root of the original equation in this case.

In case (d), *i.e.* $1 \le x < 2$, the equation becomes
$$x + 1 - x - 3(x-1)(x-2) = x + 2$$
or $3x^2 - 8x + 7 = 0$

which gives imaginary values of x.
Hence there is no solution in this case.

In case (e), *i.e.* $x \ge 2$, the equation reduces to
$$x + 1 - x + 3(x-1)(x-2) = x + 2$$
$$3x^2 - 10x + 5 = 0.$$

As in case (c), the roots are $x = \dfrac{5 \pm \sqrt{10}}{3}$.

Since the root $(5 - \sqrt{10})/3$ does not satisfy the condition (e) whereas the root $(5 + \sqrt{10})/3$ satisfies it, the only root of the original equation is at $x = (5 + \sqrt{10})/3$.

Thus from the above discussion, we see that the roots of the given equation are at $x = \dfrac{5 \pm \sqrt{10}}{3}$.

(b)   Here the change points are $x = 1, 2, 3$.

Hence we consider the following cases :

(I) $x < 1$ (II) $1 \le x < 2$ (III) $2 \le x < 3$ (IV) $x \ge 3$

Case I. $x < 1$
$$-(x-1) - (x-2) - (x-3) \ge 6$$
$$-3x + 6 \ge 6 \quad \text{or} \quad -3x \ge 0 \quad \therefore \quad x \le 0$$
which is < 1 and hence a solution.

Case II. $1 \le x < 2$
$$(x-1) - (x-2) - (x-3) \ge 6$$
or $-x + 4 \ge 6$ or $-x \ge 2$ or $x \le -2$

This does not satisfy given condition of case II. Hence no solution.

Case III. $2 \le x < 3$
$$(x-1) + (x-2) - (x-3) \ge 6 \quad \text{or} \quad x \ge 6$$

This also does not satisfy given relation of case III. Hence no solution.

Case IV. $x \ge 3$
$$x - 1 + x - 2 + x - 3 \ge 6 \quad \text{or} \quad 3x \ge 12 \text{ or } x \ge 4$$

This satisfies the given relation and hence is a solution. Thus the required solution by case I and IV are $x \le 0$ or $x \ge 4$.

43. We consider three cases :

(a) $x^2 < 4$ (b) $4 \le x^2 \le 9$

(c) $x^2 > 9$

In case (a), *i.e.* $x^2 < 4$, the equation reduces to
$$-(x^2 - 9) - (x^2 - 4) = 5 \quad \text{or} \quad x^2 = 4$$
or $x = \pm 2$.

Since both these values of x do not satisfy condition (a), there is no solution in this case.

In case (b), *i.e.* $4 \le x^2 \le 9$, the equation reduces to
$$-(x^2 - 9) + (x^2 - 4) = 5 \quad \text{or} \quad 5 = 5.$$

So in this case the original equation reduces to an identity. It means that any value of x which satisfies the condition $4 \le x^2 \le 9$ is solution of the given equation. Now the double inequality $4 \le x^2 \le 9$ is

equivalent to two inequalities
$2 \leq x \leq 3$ and $-3 \leq x \leq -2$

In case (c), i.e. $x^2 > 9$, the equation becomes

$$x^2 - 9 + x^2 - 4 = 5 \quad \text{or} \quad x^2 = 9$$

or $x = \pm 3$.

Since these values of x do not satisfy the condition (c), there is no solution in this case.

From the above discussion, we conclude that the solution sets of the given equation are :

$2 \leq x \leq 3$ and $-3 \leq x \leq -2$

44. (a) The various mods depend on the signs of $x + 2$ and $x + 1$ which give $x = -2, -1$.

We consider three cases :

$$\underset{\text{I}}{x \leq -2}, \quad \underset{\text{II}}{-2 < x < -1}, \quad \underset{\text{III}}{x \geq -1}$$

The equation can be re-written as below under different cases :

I. $2^{-(x+2)} - \{-(2^{x+1} - 1)\} = 2^{x+1} + 1$

or $2^{-x-2} = 2^1$ ∴ $-x - 2 = 1$ or $x = -3$

This value satisfies I also.

II. $2^{x+2} - \{-(2^{x+1} - 1)\} = 2^{x+1} + 1$

∴ $2^{x+2} = 2^1$ or $x + 2 = 1$ ∴ $x = -1$

It does not satisfy II.

III. $2^{x+2} - \{2^{x+1} - 1\} = 2^{x+1} + 1$

or $2^{x+2} = 2 . 2^{x+1} = 2^{x+2}$

Above is true $\forall$ x which satisfy III.

∴ $x \geq -1$ also are solutions.

Ans. $x = -3, x \geq -1$.

(b) The various mods depend on the sign of $x + 1$ and x which give change points as -1 and 0.

We consider three cases

(i) $x \leq -1$ (ii) $-1 < x < 0$

(iii) $x \geq 0$.

In case (i), i.e. $x \leq -1$, the equation takes the form

$$2^{-(x+1)} - 2^x = -(2^x - 1) + 1$$

or $2^{-(x+1)} = 2^1$, ∴ $-(x+1) = 1$

Hence $x = -2$.

Since $x = -2$ satisfies (i), it is a solution of the given equation.

In case (ii), i.e. $-1 < x < 0$, the equation reduces to

$$2^{x+1} - 2^x = 1 - 2^x + 1$$

or $2^{x+1} = 2^1$ or $x + 1 = 1$ or $x = 0$

Since $x = 0$ does not satisfy (ii), it is not a solution of the given equation.

In case (iii) i.e. $x \geq 0$, the equation becomes

$$2^{x+1} - 2^x = 2^x - 1 + 1 \quad \text{or} \quad 2^{x+1} = 2 . 2^x$$

or $2^{x+1} = 2^{x+1}$, which is an identity.

Hence (iii) implies that all real values of $x \geq 0$ constitute the solution in this case. From the above discussion, the required solution is
$x = -2$ and $x \geq 0$.

45. (a) Let us put $2^{-|x-2|} = t$

Since base 2 is +ive and exponential function is +ive. Also $t = \dfrac{1}{2^{|x-2|}} \leq 1$

∴ $0 < t \leq 1$ ...(1)

The given equation can be written as

$$t^2 - 4t + 2 = 0 \quad \therefore \quad t = 2 \pm \sqrt{2},$$

But $t = 2 + \sqrt{2}$ being > 1 is rejected by (1)

∴ $t = 2^{-|x-2|} = 2 - \sqrt{2}$

∴ $2^{|x-2|} = \dfrac{1}{2 - \sqrt{2}} = \dfrac{2 + \sqrt{2}}{2}$

∴ $|x - 2| = \log_2 \left(\dfrac{2 + \sqrt{2}}{2} \right)$

∴ $x = 2 \pm \log \left(\dfrac{2 + \sqrt{2}}{2} \right)$.

(b) $x = \pm \log_{12} [1 + \sqrt{1 - a}]$ if $a \leq 1$

If $a > 1$, then there is no solution.

46. $2^{|y|} - |2^{y-1} - 1| = 2^{y-1} + 1$

We shall consider the following cases keeping in view mod.

I. $y < 0$, $2^{-y} - \{-(2^{y-1} - 1)\} = 2^{y-1} + 1$

or $2^{-y} + 2^{y-1} - 1 = 2^{y-1} + 1$

∴ $2^{-y} = 2$ or $y = -1$ which is true.

II. $0 \leq y < 1, 2^y - \{-(2^{y-1} - 1)\} = 2^{y-1} + 1$

$2^y = 2$ ∴ $y = 1$ which is not true as $0 \leq y < 1$

III. $y \leq 1, 2^y - (2^{y-1} - 1) = 2^{y-1} + 1$

∴ $2^y = 2 . 2^{y-1} = 2^y$.

This is true for all y such that $y \geq 1$.

Hence from (1) and (3), $y \in \{-1\} \cup [1, \infty [$

47. Since $\log_{1/4} (x + 2)^2 = 2 \log_{1/4} |x + 2|$,

$$\log_{1/4} (4 - x)^3 = 3 \log_{1/4} (4 - x)$$

and $\log_{1/4} (x + 6)^3 = 3 \log_{1/4} (x + 6)$;

the given equation can be written as

$3 \log_{1/4} |x + 2| - 3 = 3 \log_{1/4} (4 - x) + 3 \log_{1/4} (x + 6)$

or $\log_{1/4} |x + 2| + \log_{1/4} 4$

     $= \log_{1/4} (4 - x)(x + 6)$ $[\because \log_{1/4} 4 = -1]$

or $\log_{1/4} 4|x + 2| = \log_{1/4} (4 - x)(x + 6)$

Hence $4|x + 2| = (4 - x)(x + 6)$.   ...(1)

We now consider two cases :

(a) $x + 2 < 0$ (b) $x + 2 \geq 0$.

In case (a), the equation (1) becomes

$-4(x + 2) = (4 - x)(x + 6)$

or $\quad x^2 - 2x - 32 = 0$

$\therefore \quad x = \dfrac{2 \pm \sqrt{4 + 128}}{2} = 1 \pm \sqrt{33}$

The root $1 + \sqrt{33}$ does not satisfy condition (a) and so it is not a root of (1).

But $1 - \sqrt{33}$ is a root of (1) since it satisfies condition (a).

In case (b), the equation (1) becomes

$\qquad 4(x + 2) = (4 - x)(x + 6)$

or $\quad x^2 + 6x - 16 = 0$

or $\quad (x + 8)(x - 2) = 0$.

This gives $\quad x = -8, 2$.

The root $x = -8$ does not satisfy condition (b), so it is not a root of (1). Hence $x = 2$ is the only root of (1) in this case. Combining cases (a) and (b), we see that the roots of equation (a) are

$\qquad x_1 = 2 \quad \text{and} \quad x_2 = 1 - \sqrt{33}$

We must now check whether these roots satisfy the original equation or not. It is easily seen that all the expressions under the sign of logarithm in the given equation for $x = x_1$ and $x = x_2$ are positive and so both these numbers lie in the domain of x and are therefore roots of the given equation.

Thus we get the answer

$\qquad x_1 = 2, \ x_2 = 1 - \sqrt{33}.$

48. We consider two cases :

(a) $x < -1$, \qquad (b) $x \geq -1$.

In case (a), the equation reduces to the form

$\qquad x(-x - 1) + a = 0$

or $\quad x^2 + x - a = 0$ \hfill ...(1)

We are interested in finding real roots of (1) which satisfy the condition (a).

Now the condition for (1) to have real roots is

$\qquad 1 + 4a \geq 0 \quad \text{or} \quad a \geq -\dfrac{1}{4}.$

[Note that for real roots, the discriminant of (1) must be non-negative].

The roots of (1) are

$\qquad x_1 = \dfrac{-1 + \sqrt{1 + 4a}}{2}, \quad x_2 = \dfrac{-1 - \sqrt{1 + 4a}}{2}$

Out of these roots, we have to take those which satisfy the condition $x < -1$.

To do this, we have to solve the inequalities

$\qquad \dfrac{-1 + \sqrt{1 + 4a}}{2} < -1$

and $\quad \dfrac{-1 - \sqrt{1 + 4a}}{2} < -1$.

The first inequality reduces to $1 + \sqrt{1 + 4a} < 0$,

which does not hold for values of $a \geq -\dfrac{1}{4}$.

The second inequality reduces to $\sqrt{1 + 4a} > 1$

and is valid for $a > 0$ as can be easily seen.

Hence, for $a > 0$, the original equation has one real root

at $\quad x = \dfrac{-1 - \sqrt{1 + 4a}}{2}$

that satisfies the condition $x < -1$ and for $a \leq 0$, it has no such root.

In case (b), the given equation takes the form

$\qquad x^2 + x + a = 0$.

Discussing as in case (a), we will see that the given equation has two real roots for $0 \leq a \leq \dfrac{1}{4}$.

$\qquad \dfrac{-1 + \sqrt{1 - 4a}}{2} \quad \text{and} \quad \dfrac{-1 - \sqrt{1 - 4a}}{2}.$

For $a < 0$, the equation has the root at

$\qquad x = \dfrac{-1 + \sqrt{1 - 4a}}{2}.$

For $a > \dfrac{1}{4}$, the equation has no roots in the domain $x > -1$.

Combining the cases (a) and (b), we get the final answer.

For $a < 0$, $x = \dfrac{-1 + \sqrt{1 - 4a}}{2}.$

For $0 \leq a \leq \dfrac{1}{4}$, $x = \dfrac{-1 - \sqrt{1 - 4a}}{2}, \ \dfrac{-1 + \sqrt{1 - 4a}}{2}$

and for $a > \dfrac{1}{4}$, the equation has no root.

49. We consider four cases :

(a) $x^2 - 2x \geq 0, \ y \geq 0$ \qquad (b) $x^2 - 2x \geq 0, \ y < 0$

(c) $x^2 - 2x < 0, \ y \geq 0$ \qquad (d) $x^2 - 2x < 0, \ y < 0$

In case (a), the equations are

$\qquad x^2 - 2x + y = 1, \quad x^2 + y = 1.$

Solving these equations, we get $x = 0, \ y = 1$.

This pair satisfies condition (a) and so is a solution of the given equations.

In case (b), the given equations reduce to the form

$\qquad x^2 - 2x + y = 1$ \hfill ...(1)

$\qquad x^2 - y = 1$ \hfill ...(2)

Substracting $2x = 2y$ or $x = y$ \hfill ...(3)

Adding, $2x^2 - 2x = 2$

or $\quad x^2 - x - 1 = 0$ \hfill ...(4)

$\therefore \quad$ From (3), $x = \dfrac{1 \pm \sqrt{1 + 4}}{2} = \dfrac{1 \pm \sqrt{5}}{2}.$

Now from (3) and (4), we get

$\qquad y = x = (1 \pm \sqrt{5})/2$

Hence the solutions in this case are

$\qquad x_1 = \dfrac{1 + \sqrt{5}}{2}, \quad y_1 = \dfrac{1 + \sqrt{5}}{2}$

or $x_2 = \dfrac{1-\sqrt{5}}{2}$, $y_2 = \dfrac{1-\sqrt{5}}{2}$.

Since $y_1 > 0$, the pair (x_1, y_1) does not satisfy the condition (b) and it must be rejected. Now since $y_2 < 0$ and $x_2^2 - 2x_2 > 0$, the pair (x_2, y_2) satisfies (b). Hence in this case, the solution is

$x = y = (1-\sqrt{5})/2$.

In case (c), the given equations take the form

$-x^2 + 2x + y = 1$, $x^2 + y = 1$.

Solutions of these equations are easily found to be

$x_1 = 0, y_1 = 1$ or $x_2 = 1, y_2 = 0$.

The pair (x_1, y_1) does not satisfy condition (c) and (x_2, y_2) satisfies it.

Hence the solution in this case is:

$x = 1, y = 0$.

In case (d), Here the equations are

$-x^2 + 2x + y = 1$, $x^2 - y = 1$.

Adding, $2x = 2$ or $x = 1$ and $y = 0$.

Since this pair does not satisfy (d), there is no solution in this case.

Combining the cases (a) to (d), the given system of equations has the following three solutions

$x_1 = 0, y_1 = 1; x_2 = y_2 = \dfrac{1-\sqrt{5}}{2}$;

$x_3 = 1, y_3 = 0$.

50. (a) It is evident that the function

$f(x) = 2\cos^2\left(\dfrac{1}{2}x\right)\sin^2 x < 2$

in the interval $\left[0, \dfrac{\pi}{2}\right]$. At $x = \dfrac{\pi}{2}$, $f(x) = 1$,

At $x = \pi/3, f(x) = 9/8$

Thus we have $2\cos^2\dfrac{1}{2}x\sin^2 x < 2$.

Again since arithmetic mean of two positive numbers is greater than their geometric mean, we have

$\dfrac{x^2 + x^{-2}}{2} > \sqrt{x^2 \cdot x^{-2}}$, i.e. $x^2 + x^{-2} > 2$.

Thus the left hand member of the given equation is < 2 whereas the right hand member is > 2. It follows that the equation has no real solution. Hence alternative (a) is correct.

(b) Ans. (d). $2.2\sin\theta\cdot\cos\theta = 2^x + 2^{-x}$

$2(\sin 2.2^x) = 2^x + 2^{-x}$

L.H.S. ≤ 2 whereas R.H.S. > 2

Hence the equation has no solution.

51. (a) By definition of log, we must have $x > 2$

From the given relation, we have

$\log\{5(x^2+1)\} = \log(x-2)^2$

or $5x^2 + 5 = x^2 - 4x + 4$

or $4x^2 + 4x + 1 = 0$

or $(2x+1)^2 = 0$ $\therefore x = -\dfrac{1}{2}$

But we must have $x > 2$, hence no solution.

(b) Ans. (a).

$2^x\left(1 + \dfrac{1}{2} + \dfrac{1}{4}\right) = 5^x\left(1 + \dfrac{1}{5} + \dfrac{1}{25}\right)$

or $2^x\cdot\dfrac{7}{4} = 5^x\cdot\dfrac{31}{25}$ or $\left(\dfrac{5}{2}\right)^x = \dfrac{7.5^2}{31.2^2}$

Take log on both sides, we have

$x(\log 5 - \log 2) = \log 7 + 2\log 5 - \log 31 - 2\log 2$

$\therefore x$ is etc. $\therefore$ only one solution.

(c) Ans. (c).

Put $\log_{10} x = t$ $\therefore 2x^t + 3x^{-t} = 5$

$2(x^t)^2 - 5x^t + 3 = 0$

$\therefore (x^t - 1)(2x^t - 3) = 0$

$\therefore x^t = 1$ or $\dfrac{3}{2}$

$x^t = 1 = x^0 \Rightarrow t = 0$

or $\log_{10} x = 0$ $\therefore x = 1$ ...(1)

$x^t = \dfrac{3}{2} \Rightarrow t = \log_x \dfrac{3}{2}$

or $\log_{10} x = \log_x \dfrac{3}{2} = \log_{10}\dfrac{3}{2}\cdot\log_x 10$

$(\because \log_b a = \log_c a\cdot\log_b c)$

or $(\log_{10} x)^2 = \log_{10}\dfrac{3}{2}$

$\therefore \log_{10} x = \pm\sqrt{\log_{10}\dfrac{3}{2}}$

$\therefore x = 10^{\pm\sqrt{\log_{10} 3/2}}$ ...(2)

Hence only 3 solutions by (1) and (2).

52. (a) $x^2 + x = x(x+1) = +$ive for $x < -1$ and $x > 0$

$\therefore x^2 + x + 1 = \sin x > 1$.

This is not possible. Hence the given equation has no solution for $x < -1$ and $x > 0$. However, when $-1 \leq x \leq 0$ then $x^2 + x$ is $-$ive lying between -1 and 0 and x is also $-$ive.

$\therefore x^2 + x + 1 = +$ive and $\sin x = -$ive as x is $-$ive.

$\therefore x^2 + x + 1 = \sin x$ has no solution in this case also as L.H.S. $= +$ive and R.H.S. $= -$ive.

(b) By trial, we see that $x = 5$ is a solution. There can be no other solution since the function 7^{6-x} decreases monotonically whereas the function $x+2$ increases monotonically so that the graphs of these functions cannot intersect more than once.

53. (a) Since the value of $\cos^2\dfrac{x^2+x}{2}$ cannot exceed 1. For any real x, we have

$$2\cos^2\frac{x^2+x}{2}\le 2. \qquad \ldots(1)$$

On the other hand, we have

$$\frac{2^x+2^{-x}}{2}\ge\sqrt{2^x.2^{-x}}=1 \qquad [\because \text{ A.M.}\ge\text{G.M.}]$$

or $2^x+2^{-x}\ge 2.$ ...(2)

From (1) and (2), we see that the left and right members of the given equation are equal if and only if they are both equal to 2. In other words, the following system of two equations in one unknown must hold

$$2\cos^2\left(\frac{x^2+x}{2}\right)=2, 2^x+2^{-x}=2.$$

The equation $2^x+2^{-x}=2$ has the unique solution $x=0$.

This value of x also satisfies

$$2\cos^2\left(\frac{x^2+x}{2}\right)=2.$$

Hence the only solution of the given equation is at $x=0$.

(b) On dividing by x^2+x+1 we have

$$y+\frac{1}{y}=x^2-x-5 \qquad \ldots(1)$$

where $y=x^2+x+1=\left(x+\frac{1}{2}\right)^2+\frac{3}{4}=+\text{ive}$

Also $x\in(-2,3)\Rightarrow(x+2)(x-3)<0$

or $x^2-x-6<0$

or $x^2-x-5<1$ or $y+\frac{1}{y}<1$ ...(2)

Now $y+\frac{1}{y}\ge 2$ A.M. $\ge$ G.M. ...(3)

$\therefore$ L.H.S. ≥ 2. But L.H.S. <1 by (1) and (2)

Thus the equality can never arise. Hence no value of $x\in(-2,3)$ exists which satisfies the given equation.

54. (a) We have

$$5-2\sqrt{6}=\frac{(5+2\sqrt{6})(5-2\sqrt{6})}{5+2\sqrt{(6)}}$$

$$=\frac{25-24}{5+2\sqrt{(6)}}=\frac{1}{5+2\sqrt{(6)}}.$$

Now put $(5+2\sqrt{6})^{x^2-3}=y.$

Then $(5-2\sqrt{6})^{x^2-3}=1/y$ so that the equation transforms into

$$y+\frac{1}{y}=10 \quad\text{or}\quad y^2-10y+1=0$$

or $y=\dfrac{10\pm\sqrt{96}}{2}=\dfrac{10\pm 4\sqrt{6}}{2}=5\pm 2\sqrt{6}.$

or $(5+2\sqrt{6})^{(x^2-3)}=5\pm 2\sqrt{6}.$

Taking $+$ive sign, we get $x^2-3=1$ which gives $x=\pm 2$. Taking $-$ sign, we get $x^2-3=-1.$

$\therefore x=\pm\sqrt{2}.$

$$\left[\text{Note that } 5-2\sqrt{6}=\frac{1}{5+2\sqrt{(6)}}=(5+2\sqrt{6})^{-1}\right]$$

Hence the solution set is given by $x=\pm 2,\ \pm\sqrt{2}.$

(b) Refer part (a); we have

$$y+\frac{1}{y}=30 \quad\text{where}\quad y=(15+4\sqrt{14})^t$$

or $y^2-30y+1=0$

$\therefore y=15\pm 4\sqrt{14}=15+4\sqrt{14}$

or $(15+4\sqrt{14})^{-1}$

$\therefore t=1,-1$ where $t=x^2-2|x|$

$\therefore x^2-2|x|-1=0$ or $x^2-2|x|+1=0$

or $|x|^2-2|x|-1=0$ or $|x|^2-2|x|+1=0$

See Q. 35, 36 P. 260-268

$\therefore |x|=1\pm\sqrt{2}$ or $[|x|-1]^2=0$

or $|x|=1$ $\therefore$ $x=\pm 1.$

$\therefore |x|=1+\sqrt{2}$ only as $|x|$ cannot be $1-\sqrt{2}$ which is $-$ive.

$\therefore x=\pm(1+\sqrt{2})$ $\therefore$ $x=\pm(1+\sqrt{2})$ or $x=\pm 1$

55. (a) $(7-4\sqrt{3})(7+4\sqrt{3})=49-48=1$

$\therefore y+\frac{1}{y}=14 \Rightarrow y^2-14y+1=0$

$\therefore y=7\pm 4\sqrt{3}$

$(7-4\sqrt{3})^{x^2-4x+3}=7-4\sqrt{3}$ or $7+4\sqrt{3}$

i.e., $\dfrac{1}{7-4\sqrt{3}}$

$\therefore x^2-4x+3=1$ or -1

or $x^2-4x+2=0$ or $x^2-4x+4=0$

$\therefore x=2\pm\sqrt{2}$ or $x=2,2$

(b) and (c) Ans. $x=-2,2.$

56. Case I. Let $x>a$, *i.e.* $x-a=+$ive; then

$x^2-2a(x-a)-3a^2=0$

or $x^2-2ax-a^2=0$

$\therefore x=a(1\pm\sqrt{2})$ $\therefore$ $x-a=\pm a\sqrt{2}.$

But as $a\le 0$, therefore we must choose

$x-a=-a\sqrt{2}=+$ive.

Hence out of two roots $x=a(1-\sqrt{2})$ satisfies the given condition. ...(1)

Case II. Let $x<a$ so that $x-a$ is $-$ive; then the given equation is

$x^2+2a(x-a)-3a^2=0$

or $\quad x^2 + 2ax - 5a^2 = 0$

$\therefore \quad x = a(-1 \pm \sqrt{6})$ ...(2)

$\therefore \quad x - a = a(-2 \pm \sqrt{6}) = -\text{ive}$

Since a is ≤ 0, above will hold good if $-2 \pm \sqrt{6}$ is +ive and hence we choose $-2 + \sqrt{6}$ which is +ive.

$\therefore \quad$ Roots are $a(1 - \sqrt{2})$, $\quad a(-1 + \sqrt{6})$

57. Since $\log_a x \log_{10} a = \log_{10} x$,

$$\log_{10}\left(\frac{x}{10}\right) = \log_{10} x - 1$$

$$\log_{100} x = \frac{1}{2} \log_{10} x$$

and $\log_4 2 = \frac{1}{2} \log_2 2 = \frac{1}{2}$

The given equation can be written as

$$\frac{6}{5} a^{\log_{10} x \log_a 5} - 3^{(\log_{10} x - 1)} = 9^{\frac{1}{2}\log_{10} x + \frac{1}{2}}$$

or $\quad \dfrac{6}{5}(a^{\log_a 5})^{\log_{10} x} = 3^{\log_{10} x} \cdot 3^{-1} + 3^{\log_{10} x} \cdot 3$

or $\quad \dfrac{6}{5} \cdot 5^{\log_{10} x} = 3^{\log_{10} x}\left(\dfrac{1}{3} + 3\right) = \dfrac{10}{3} \cdot 3^{\log_{10} x}$

or $\quad \dfrac{1}{5^2} 5^{\log_{10} x} = \dfrac{1}{3^2} 3^{\log_{10} x}$

or $\quad 5^{(\log_{10} x - 2)} = 3^{(\log_{10} x - 2)}$

Since the basis are different, above will hold only when

$$\log_{10} x - 2 = 0 \quad \therefore \quad x = 10^2 = 100.$$

58. By definition of logarithm, L.H.S. which contains $2\log_x 9$ is meaningful if $x > 0$ and $x \ne 1$ and then because exponential function is always positive, L.H.S. is +ive. Hence R.H.S. must also be positive which will happen if $x > 1$ i.e. $x - 1 = +$ive so that $|x - 1| = x - 1$.

Hence we can write the given equation as,

$$(x-1)^{\log_3 x^2 - 2\log_x 9} = (x-1)^7$$

This gives $\log_3 x^2 - 2\log_x 9 = 7$

or $\quad 2\log_3 x - 2\log_x 3^2 = 7$

or $\quad 2\log_3 x - 4\log_x 3 = 7.$

Now if $\log_3 x = y$, then equation reduces to

$2y - 4/y = 7 \quad$ or $\quad 2y^2 - 7y - 4 = 0$

or $\quad (y - 4)(2y + 1) = 0$

$\therefore \quad y = 4$ or $-\dfrac{1}{2}$ or $\log_3 x = 4$ or $-\dfrac{1}{2}$.

Hence $x = 3^4 = 81$ or $x = 3^{-1/2} = \dfrac{1}{\sqrt{(3)}}$.

Since $x > 1$, the value $x = 1/\sqrt{3}$ is rejected.

$\therefore \quad x = 81$

59. $x^{(2/3)[(\log_2 x)^2 + \log_2 x - 5/4]} = \sqrt{2}$

Put $\log_2 x = t \quad \therefore \quad x = 2^t$ ...(1)

$$\frac{2}{3}\left[t^2 + t - \frac{5}{4}\right] = \log_x \sqrt{2} = \frac{1}{2}\log_x 2 = \frac{1}{2t}.$$

$4t\left(t^2 + t - 5/4\right) = 3$

or $\quad 4t^3 + 4t^2 - 5t - 3 = 0$

or $\quad (t - 1)(4t^2 + 8t + 3) = 0$

or $\quad (t - 1)(2t + 3)(2t + 1) = 0$

$\therefore \quad t = -3/2, \ -1/2, \ 1 = \log_2 x$

$\therefore \quad x = 2^{-3/2}, \ 2^{-1/2}, \ 2^1 = \dfrac{1}{2\sqrt{(2)}}, \ \dfrac{1}{\sqrt{(2)}}, \ 2.$

60. Proceeding as above, we get

$3t^3 + 4t^2 - 5t - 2 = 0$

or $\quad (t - 1)(3t^2 + 7t + 2) = 0$

or $\quad (t - 1)(t + 2)(3t + 1) = 0$

or $\quad t = \log_2 x = 1, -2, -1/3$

$\therefore \quad x = 2, 2^{-2}, 2^{-1/3}$ or $x = 2, 1/4, 1/2^{1/3}$

61. (a) $\log_{3/4}\left[\dfrac{1}{3}\log_2 (x^2 + 7)\right]$

$\qquad\qquad\qquad + \log_{1/2}\left[\dfrac{1}{2}\log_2 (x^2 + 7)\right] = -2$

By $\log_{b^p} a^n = \dfrac{n}{p}\log_b a$

$$\log_{2^{-2}}(x^2 + 7)^{-1} = \frac{-1}{-2}\log_2 (x^2 + 7)$$

Let $\log_2 (x^2 + 7) = t \quad \therefore \quad x^2 + 7 = 2^t$

$$\log_{3/4}\left(\frac{1}{3}t\right) + \log_{1/2}\left(\frac{1}{2}t\right) = -2$$

$$\frac{\log(t/3)}{\log(3/4)} + \log_{1/2}\frac{1}{2} + \log_{1/2} t = -2$$

$$\frac{\log t - \log 3}{\log 3 - \log 4} + \log_{1/2}\frac{1}{2} + \log_{1/2} t = -2$$

$$\frac{\log t}{\log 3 - 2\log 2} - \frac{\log 3}{\log 3 - 2\log 2} + 1 - \frac{\log t}{\log 2} = -2$$

$\therefore \quad \log t \dfrac{[\log 2 - \log 3 + 2\log 2]}{(\log 3 - 2\log 2)\log 2}$

$$= -3 + \frac{\log 3}{\log 3 - 2\log 2}$$

$\log t \dfrac{[3\log 2 - \log 3]}{(\log 3 - 2\log 2)\log 2} = \dfrac{6\log 2 - 2\log 3}{\log 3 - 2\log 2}$

$\therefore \quad \log t = 2\log 2 = \log 2^2 = \log 4$

$\therefore \quad t = 4 \quad \therefore \quad x^2 + 7 = 2^t = 2^4 = 16$

or $\quad x^2 = 9 \quad \therefore \quad x = \pm 3.$

(b) Put $3^{\sqrt{x^2 - 3}} = t$

$\therefore \quad \sqrt{x}(t^2 - t) = 3 \cdot t^2 - 3 \cdot t + 6(\sqrt{x} - 3)$

or $\quad t^2(\sqrt{x} - 3) - t(\sqrt{x} - 3) - 6(\sqrt{x} - 3) = 0$

or $\quad (\sqrt{x} - 3)(t^2 - t - 6) = 0$

$\therefore \quad \sqrt{x} = 3 \quad \Rightarrow \quad x = 9$

or $(t-3)(t+2)=0$ ∴ $t=3,-2$ (rejected)
as t is an exponential function is always +ive.
Again $t=3 \Rightarrow \sqrt{x^2-3}=1$ or $x^2=4$ ∴ $x=\pm 2$.

62. $x=I+f$ where $0<f<1$. ...(1)
Putting in the given relation, we get
$4f=I+f+I$
∴ $3f=2I$ or $f=\dfrac{2}{3}I$ ...(2)

Since f lies between 0 and 1, therefore from (2) we get
$I=0$ or 1
and hence $f=0$ when $I=0$ or $2/3$ when $I=1$
∴ $x=I+f=0+0=0$ or $1+2/3$ i.e. $5/3$.

63. It is a question based on the formula that if
$A+B+C=0$ then $A^3+B^3+C^3=3ABC$
Let $(1-x^3)^{1/3}=a$ etc. $y-z=l$ etc.

We are given that
$al+bm+cn=0$ ...(1)
$l+m+n=\Sigma(y-z)=0$ ...(2)
$lx+my+nz=\Sigma x(y-z)=0$ ...(3)
∴ $a^3l^3+b^3m^3+c^2n^3=3abclmn$, by (1) ...(4)
$x^3l^3+y^3m^3+z^3n^3=3xyzlmn$, by (3) ...(5)
$l^3+m^3+n^3=3lmn$, by (2) ...(6)
Subtracting the last two, we get
$\Sigma l^3(1-x^3)=3lmn(1-xyz)$
$a^3l^3+b^3m^3+c^3n^3=3lmn(1-xyz)$ ∵ $1-x^3=a^3$
or $3abclmn=3lmn(1-xyz)$ by (4)
Cancel $3lmn$ and cube both sides
∴ $a^3b^3c^3=(1-xyz)^3$
or $(1-x^3)(1-y^3)(1-z^3)=(1-xyz)^3$

Problem Set (2)

Miscellaneous Equations.

Solve the following equations :

1. $\dfrac{x-2}{x+2}+\dfrac{x+2}{x-2}=\dfrac{2(x+3)}{x-3}$.

2. $\sqrt{\left(\dfrac{x}{1-x}\right)}+\sqrt{\left(\dfrac{1-x}{x}\right)}=2\dfrac{1}{6}$.

3.* $(2x-7)(x^2-9)(2x+5)=91$.

4. $\dfrac{3x-2}{2}+\sqrt{2x^2-5x+3}=\dfrac{(x+1)^2}{3}$.

5. (i) $3x^2-4\sqrt{3x^2-4x+1}=4x-4$.

(ii) $x^2-\sqrt{2x^2-8x+12}=4x+6$.

6. (i) $\sqrt{x+1}+\sqrt{x-1}=1$.

(ii) $\sqrt{x+1}-\sqrt{x-1}=1$.

(iii)* The equation $\sqrt{x+1}-\sqrt{x-1}=\sqrt{4x-1}$ has
(a) no solution
(b) one solution
(c) two solutions
(d) more than two solutions **(I.I.T. 1997)**

(iv) $\dfrac{x-8}{\sqrt{(x+1)}+3}+\dfrac{x-26}{\sqrt{(x-1)}-25}=\dfrac{4x-5}{\sqrt{(4x-1)}-2}$

(v) $x^2-6x-\sqrt{x^2-6x-3}=5$.

7. (i) $\sqrt{2x-2}+\sqrt{x-3}=2$.

(ii) $\sqrt{2x-6}+\sqrt{x+4}=5$.

8. $\sqrt{5x+7}-\sqrt{3x+1}=\sqrt{x+3}$.

9. (a) $\sqrt{2x^2-9x+4}+3\sqrt{2x-1}=\sqrt{2x^2+21x-11}$.

(b)* $\sqrt{5x^2-6x+8}-\sqrt{5x^2-6x-7}=1$.

(c)* Solve for x :
$\sqrt{(3x^2+6x+7)}+\sqrt{(5x^2+10x+14)}=4-2x-x^2$

10.* $\dfrac{x-ab}{a+b}+\dfrac{x-ac}{a+c}+\dfrac{x-bc}{b+c}=a+b+c$.

11. (a)* $\dfrac{x-a}{bc}+\dfrac{x-b}{ca}+\dfrac{x-c}{ab}=2\left(\dfrac{1}{a}+\dfrac{1}{b}+\dfrac{1}{c}\right)$.

(b) $\dfrac{(x-a)(x-b)}{x-a-b}=\dfrac{(x-c)(x-d)}{x-c-d}$

12. $x-1=\sqrt{a-x^2}$.

13. $\dfrac{p+q-x}{r}+\dfrac{q+r-x}{p}+\dfrac{r+p-x}{q}+\dfrac{4x}{p+q+r}=1$.

14. (a) $x^4+\dfrac{8}{9}x^2+1=3x^3+3x$.

(b) $(x^4+1)-4x(x^2+1)-3x^2=0$.

15. $x(x^2-1)(x+2)+1=0$

16. $6x^3-11x^2+6x-1=0$, if its roots are in harmonic progression.

17. $\dfrac{a+2x+\sqrt{a^2-4x^2}}{a+2x-\sqrt{(a^2-4x^2)}}=\dfrac{5x}{a}$.

18. $\sqrt{x^2+x}+\dfrac{\sqrt{x-1}}{\sqrt{(x^3-x)}}=\dfrac{5}{2}$.

19. $x^4-2x^3+x-380=0$.

20. $\dfrac{(x-a)(x-b)}{x-a-b}=\dfrac{(x-c)(x-d)}{x-c-d}$.

21. (a)* $x^4-5x^2-6x-5=0$.

(b)* $(x^2+2)^2+8x^2=6x(x^2+2)$.

22. $x^4+3x^2=16x+60$.

23. $\sqrt[3]{6(5x+6)}-\sqrt[3]{5(6x-11)}=1$.

24.* $(a+x)^{2/3}+4(a-x)^{2/3}=5(a^2-x^2)^{1/3}$.

25. $(a+\sqrt{x})^{1/3}+(a-\sqrt{x})^{1/3}=b^{1/3}$.

26. $\sqrt{x} + \sqrt{x - \sqrt{(1-x)}} = 1$.

27.* $x^3 - 5x^2 - 2x + 24 = 0$, given that the product of two roots is 12.

28.* $\sqrt{4a + b - 5x} + \sqrt{4b + a - 5x} = 3\sqrt{a + b - 2x}$.

29. $\dfrac{(a-x)\sqrt{a-x} - (b-x)\sqrt{x-b}}{\sqrt{(a-x)} + \sqrt{(x-b)}} = a - b$.

30. Evaluate $\sqrt{6 + \sqrt{6 + \sqrt{6 + \cdots}}}$.

31.* $3x^3 = [x^2 + \sqrt{18}x + \sqrt{32}] \cdot [x^2 - \sqrt{18}x - \sqrt{32}] - 4x^2$.

Solutions to Problem Set (2)

1. The given equations can be written as
$$\left(\frac{x-2}{x+2} - 1\right) + \left(\frac{x+2}{x-2} - 1\right) = \frac{2(x+3)}{x-3} - 2$$
or $-\dfrac{4}{x+2} + \dfrac{4}{x-2} = \dfrac{12}{x-3}$

or $\dfrac{-x + 2 + x + 2}{(x+2)(x-2)} = \dfrac{3}{x-3}$

or $3(x^2 - 4) = 4x - 12$ or $3x^2 - 4x = 0$

∴ $x = 0, \dfrac{4}{3}$.

2. $t + \dfrac{1}{t} = 2\dfrac{1}{6}$ ∴ $6t^2 - 13t + 6 = 0$,

where t is $\sqrt{\left(\dfrac{x}{1-x}\right)}$

∴ $t = \dfrac{3}{2}, \dfrac{2}{3}$ or $t^2 = \dfrac{x}{1-x} = \dfrac{9}{4}$ or $\dfrac{4}{9}$

∴ $x = \dfrac{9}{13}, \dfrac{4}{13}$

3. Do yourself. Combine
$$[(2x - 7)(x + 3) \text{ and } (x - 3)(2x + 5)].$$

4. Put $(2x^2 - 5x + 3)^{1/2} = y$ and combine the other two terms.

Ans. $\dfrac{1}{2}, 2, \dfrac{1}{4}[5 \pm \sqrt{41}]$.

5. (i) Put $3x^2 - 4x + 1 = y^2$ and combine the other two terms.

Ans. $0, \dfrac{4}{3}, \dfrac{1}{3}[2 \pm \sqrt{10}]$.

(ii) Ans. $x = -2, 6$.

(iii) Ans. $x = 7, -1$.

Hint : Put $x^2 - 6x - 3 = y^2$.

6. (i) Squaring both members of the given equation, we get
$$x + 1 + x - 1 + 2\sqrt{x^2 - 1} = 1$$
or $2\sqrt{x^2 - 1} = 1 - 2x$

or $4(x^2 - 1) = 1 - 4x + 4x^2$ ∴ $x = 5/4$.

Since $x = 5/4$ does not satisfy the given equation, the equation has no roots.

Important Note : Squaring an equation generally leads to an equation not equivalent to the given equation and this new equation in addition to the roots of the given equation may have other roots different from them (the so-called extraneous roots). Hence it is necessary to check, by substitution, whether $5/4$ is really the root of the original equation. The check shows that $5/4$ does not satisfy the original equation. Another important point to be noted is that only principal values of the roots are to be considered.

Thus if n is odd, the symbol $\sqrt[n]{a}$ is understood as the only real number whose nth power is equal to a. In this case a may be positive or negative. For example, principal value of $\sqrt[3]{8}$ is 2 and the principal value of $\sqrt[3]{-27}$ is -3. If n is even, the symbol $\sqrt[n]{a}$ is understood as the only positive number nth power of which is equal to a. Here, necessarily $a \geq 0$. Under these conditions, for example, we have

$$\sqrt{a^2} = a \text{ if } a > 0 \text{ and } \sqrt{a^2} = -a \text{ if } a < 0.$$

Thus the principal value of $\sqrt{4}$ is 2, the principal value of $\sqrt[4]{81}$ is 3 and the principal value of $\sqrt{(-3)^2}$ is $-(-3) = 3$ etc.

Alternative. $l + m = 1$. But $l^2 - m^2 = 2$

∴ $l - m = 2$ ∴ $2l = 3$

or $l^2 = x + 1 = 9/4$ ∴ $x = 5/4$

But this value does not satisfy as it will make $2 = 1$

(ii) Proceeding as in part (i), we find that $x = 5/4$ is the root of the equation. Here check shows that $x = 5/4$ is really a root of the equation.

(iii) Ans. (a).

Squaring twice, we get $4x = 5$ but this does not satisfy the given equation as it leads to $1 = 2$.

(iv) On rationalizing, the equation reduces to
$$\frac{(x-8)[\sqrt{x+1} - 3]}{x - 8} + \frac{(x-26)[\sqrt{x-1} + 5]}{x - 26}$$
$$= \frac{(4x - 5)[\sqrt{4x - 1} + 2]}{4x - 5}$$

where $x \neq 8$, $x \neq 26$, $x \neq 5/4$

It further reduces to $\sqrt{x+1} + \sqrt{x-1} = \sqrt{4x-1}$ etc.

Above gives $x = 5/4$ but $x \neq 5/4$. Hence there is no solution.

7. (i) $\sqrt{2x - 2} = 2 - \sqrt{x - 3}$

Squaring, $2x - 2 = 4 + x - 3 - 4\sqrt{x - 3}$

or $x - 3 = -4\sqrt{x - 3}$

Squaring again, $x^2 - 6x + 9 = 16x - 48$

or $x^2 - 22x + 57 = 0$

or $(x - 3)(x - 19) = 0$; ∴ $x = 3, 19$.

Check shows that $x = 3$ satisfies the equation whereas $x = 19$ does not satisfy the equation. Hence $x = 3$ is the only root.

(ii) Ans. $x = 5$.

8. **L–M Method.**

$$\sqrt{(5x+7)} - \sqrt{(3x+1)} = \sqrt{(x+3)}$$

We see $(5x+7) - (3x+1) = 2(x+3)$

Divide $\sqrt{(5x+7)} + \sqrt{(3x+1)} = 2\sqrt{(x+3)}$

Add $2\sqrt{(5x+7)} = 3\sqrt{(x+3)}$

Square $4(5x+7) = 9(x+3)$

$11x = -1$ ∴ $x = -1/11$.

9. (a) The equation can be written as

$$\sqrt{(2x-1)(x-4)} + 3\sqrt{2x-1} = \sqrt{(2x-1)(x+11)}$$

Clearly one root is given by $2x - 1 = 0$, that is, $x = \dfrac{1}{2}$

is a root.

Now cancelling the factor $\sqrt{2x-1}$, we have

$$\sqrt{x-4} + 3 = \sqrt{x+11}$$

Squaring, $x - 4 + 9 + 6\sqrt{x-4} = x + 11$

or $\sqrt{x-4} = 1$ or $x - 4 = 1$, that is, $x = 5$.

Since $x = 5$ satisfies the original equation, $x = 5$ is also a root.

Ans. $x = \dfrac{1}{2}$, 5.

(b) $L - M = 1$, $L^2 - M^2 = 15$ ∴ $L + M = 15$.

Adding, $2L = 16$ ∴ $L^2 = 64$

or $5x^2 - 6x + 8 = 64$

or $5x^2 - 6x - 56 = 0$

or $(x - 4)(5x + 14) = 0$ ∴ $x = 4, -14/5$.

(c) The given equation can be written as

$$\sqrt{3(x+1)^2 + 4} + \sqrt{5(x+1)^2 + 9} = -\{(x+1)^2 - 5\}$$

Now $\sqrt{4} + \sqrt{9} = 2 + 3 = 5$

Hence we must have $(x+1)^2 = 0$ or $x = -1$.

10. The equation can be written as

$$\left(\frac{x-ab}{a+b} - c\right) + \left(\frac{x-ac}{a+c} - b\right) + \left(\frac{x-bc}{b+c} - a\right) = 0.$$

or $\dfrac{x - ab - bc - ca}{a+b} + \dfrac{x - ab - bc - ca}{a+c}$

$$+ \frac{x - ab - bc - ca}{b+c} = 0$$

$$(x - ab - bc - ca)\left(\frac{1}{a+b} + \frac{1}{b+c} + \frac{1}{c+a}\right) = 0.$$

Assuming $\dfrac{1}{a+b} + \dfrac{1}{b+c} + \dfrac{1}{c+a} \neq 0$, we obtain

$x = ab + bc + ca$ as the root of the equation. If, however,

$\dfrac{1}{a+b} + \dfrac{1}{b+c} + \dfrac{1}{c+a} = 0$, the given equation turns into

an identity which holds for every value of x.

11. (a) The given equation can be re-written as

$$\Sigma ax - \Sigma a^2 = 2\Sigma bc$$

or $x\Sigma a = \Sigma a^2 + 2\Sigma bc$

or $x\Sigma a = (\Sigma a)^2$ or $\Sigma a(x - \Sigma a) = 0$

∴ $x = \Sigma a = a + b + c$,

provided $a + b + c \neq 0$

(b) L.H.S. $= \dfrac{x^2 - ax - bx + ab}{x - a - b}$

$$= \frac{x(x-a-b)}{x-a-b} + \frac{ab}{x-a-b} = x + \frac{ab}{x-a-b}$$

∴ $\dfrac{ab}{x-a-b} = \dfrac{cd}{x-c-d}$

or $ab(x - c - d) = cd(x - a - b)$

or $x = \dfrac{ac(b-d) + bd(a-c)}{ab - cd}$

12. Right hand side is non-negative for all (permissible) x, that is, for all x for which $a - x^2 \geq 0$, and left hand side is non-negative for $x \geq 1$. Squaring, we get

$$(x-1)^2 = a - x^2$$

or $2x^2 - 2x + 1 - a = 0$

or $x = \dfrac{2 \pm \sqrt{4 - 8(1-a)}}{4} = \dfrac{1 \pm \sqrt{2a-1}}{2}$.

These values of x are real if $2a - 1 > 0$ i.e. $a > \dfrac{1}{2}$.

The root $x = \dfrac{1 - \sqrt{2a-1}}{2}$ does not satisfy the condition

$x > 1$ and so is not a root of the given equation.

And the root $x = [1 + \sqrt{2a-1}]/2$ satisfies the equation for $a \geq 1$. Hence for $a < 1$, the equation has no root and for $a \geq 1$, it has the root $x = [1 + \sqrt{2a-1}]/2$.

13. The given equation can be re-written as

$$\left(\frac{p+q-x}{r} + 1\right) + \left(\frac{p+r-x}{q} + 1\right) + \left(\frac{q+r-x}{p} + 1\right)$$

$$= 4 - \frac{4x}{p+q+r}$$

or $(p+q+r-x)\left(\dfrac{1}{p} + \dfrac{1}{q} + \dfrac{1}{r}\right) = \dfrac{4(p+q+r-x)}{p+q+r}$

or $(p+q+r-x)\left(\dfrac{1}{p} + \dfrac{1}{q} + \dfrac{1}{r} - \dfrac{4}{p+q+r}\right) = 0$.

Hence $p + q + r - x = 0$ or $x = p + q + r$.

14. (a) We rewrite the equation as

$$(x^4 + 1) - 3x(x^2 + 1) + \frac{8}{9}x^2 = 0.$$

Dividing by x^2, we get

$$\left(x^2 + \frac{1}{x^2}\right) - 3\left(x + \frac{1}{x}\right) + \frac{8}{9} = 0$$

Now put $x + \dfrac{1}{x} = y$ so that $x^2 + \dfrac{1}{x^2} + 2 = y^2$

Hence $y^2 - 2 - 3y + \dfrac{8}{9} = 0$

or $9y^2 - 27y - 10 = 0$ or $(3y - 10)(3y + 1) = 0$.

∴ $y = \dfrac{10}{3}$ or $-\dfrac{1}{3}$.

Taking $y = \dfrac{10}{3}$, we get $x + \dfrac{1}{x} = \dfrac{10}{3}$

or $3x^2 - 10x + 3 = 0$, this gives $x = \dfrac{1}{3}, 3$.

Again taking $y = -\dfrac{1}{3}$, we get

$x + \dfrac{1}{x} = -\dfrac{1}{3}$ or $3x^2 + x + 3 = 0$

∴ $x = \dfrac{-1 \pm \sqrt{1 - 36}}{6} = \dfrac{-1 \pm \sqrt{-35}}{6}$

Ans. $x = \dfrac{1}{3}, 3, \dfrac{-1 \pm \sqrt{-35}}{6}$.

(b) Proceed as in part (a).

Ans. $x = \dfrac{5 \pm \sqrt{21}}{6}, \dfrac{-1 \pm \sqrt{-3}}{2}$.

15. $x(x + 1)(x - 1)(x + 2) + 1 = 0$

$(x^2 + x)(x^2 + x - 2) + 1 = 0$

Put $x^2 + x = y$ etc. ∴ $(y - 1)^2 = 0$

Ans. $y = 1$ ∴ $x = \dfrac{-1 \pm \sqrt{5}}{2}$

16. Put $x = 1/y$. Then new equation is

$\dfrac{6}{y^3} - \dfrac{11}{y^2} + \dfrac{6}{y} - 1 = 0$

or $y^3 - 6y^2 + 11y - 6 = 0$. ...(1)

Since the roots of the original equation are in H.P., roots of (1) must be in A.P. Let the roots of (1) be $\alpha - \delta, \alpha, \alpha + \delta$.

Then $(\alpha - \delta) + \alpha + (\alpha + \delta) = 6$

or $3\alpha = 6$ or $\alpha = 2$

and $(\alpha - \delta)\alpha(\alpha + \delta) = 6$

or $(2 - \delta) \cdot 2(2 + \delta) = 6$

or $4 - \delta^2 = 3$, that is, $\delta = \pm 1$.

Hence roots of (1) are $1, 2$ and 3.

∴ The roots of the original equation are $1, \dfrac{1}{2}$ and $\dfrac{1}{3}$.

17. Ans. $x = \pm \dfrac{2a}{5}$.

Cancel $\sqrt{(a + 2x)}$ and then apply componendo and dividendo.

18. Ans. $x = \dfrac{-1 \pm \sqrt{17}}{2}, \dfrac{-1 \pm \sqrt{2}}{2}$.

19. The equation can be re-written as

$(x^2 - x)^2 - (x^2 - x) - 380 = 0$.

Now put $x^2 - x = y$. Then equation becomes

$y^2 - y - 380 = 0$

or $(y - 20)(y + 19) = 0$

∴ $y = 20, -19$.

∴ Taking $y = 20$, we have $x^2 - x = 20$

or $x^2 - x - 20 = 0$ or $(x - 5)(x + 4) = 0$

∴ $x = 5, -4$.

Again taking $y = -19$, we get $x^2 - x + 19 = 0$

∴ $x = \dfrac{1 \pm \sqrt{1 - 76}}{2} = \dfrac{1 \pm \sqrt{-75}}{2}$.

20. Subtracting x from both the members of the given equation, we get

$\dfrac{(x - a)(x - b)}{x - a - b} - x = \dfrac{(x - c)(x - d)}{x - c - d} - x$

or $\dfrac{ab}{x - a - b} = \dfrac{cd}{x - c - d}$

or $x(ab - cd) = ab(c + d) - cd(a + b)$

∴ $x = \dfrac{ab(c + d) - cd(a + b)}{ab - cd}$.

21. (a) The equation can be written as

$x^4 - 4x^2 - x^2 - 6x - 5 = 0$

or $x^4 - 4x^2 + 4 - (x^2 + 6x + 9) = 0$

or $(x^2 - 2)^2 - (x + 3)^2 = 0$

or $(x^2 + x + 1)(x^2 - x - 5) = 0$

by factors of $L^2 - M^2$ etc.

Alt. We may write it as

$(x^4 - x) - 5(x^2 + x + 1) = 0$

or $x(x - 1)(x^2 + x + 1) - 5(x^2 + x + 1) = 0$ etc.

$(x^2 + x + 1)(x^2 - x - 5) = 0$

∴ $x = \dfrac{-1 \pm \sqrt{1 - 4}}{2}, \dfrac{1 \pm \sqrt{1 + 20}}{2}$

or $x = \dfrac{-1 \pm \sqrt{-3}}{2}, \dfrac{1 \pm \sqrt{21}}{2}$.

(b) Put $x^2 + 2 = y$. The given equation reduces to

$y^2 - 6xy + 8x^2 = 0$

or $(y - 4x)(y - 2x) = 0$

or $(x^2 - 4x + 2) = 0$ and $x^2 - 2x + 2 = 0$

Ans. $x = 1 \pm i, 2 \pm \sqrt{2}$

22. Adding $x^2 + 4$ to both sides of the given equation, we get

$x^4 + 4x^2 + 4 = x^2 + 16x + 64$

or $(x^2 + 2)^2 - (x + 8)^2 = 0$

Apply $a^2 - b^2 = (a + b)(a - b)$

∴ $(x^2 + x + 10)(x^2 - x - 6) = 0$

∴ $x = 3, -2$ and $\dfrac{-1 \pm \sqrt{-39}}{2}$.

23. Ans. $x = 6, -\dfrac{161}{30}$.

24. Dividing both members of the equation by $(a+x)^{1/3}(a-x)^{1/3}$, we get

$$\left(\frac{a+x}{a-x}\right)^{1/3} + 4\left(\frac{a-x}{a+x}\right)^{1/3} = 5.$$

Now, put $\left(\dfrac{a+x}{a-x}\right)^{1/3} = y$.

Then $y + \dfrac{4}{y} = 5$ or $y^2 - 5y + 4 = 0$

or $(y-4)(y-1) = 0$, $\therefore y = 1, 4$.

Hence, $\left(\dfrac{a+x}{a-x}\right)^{1/3} = 1, 4$ or $\dfrac{a+x}{a-x} = 1, 64$

whence $x = 0, \dfrac{63a}{65}$.

25. Ans. $x = a^2 - \dfrac{(b-2a)^3}{27b}$.

[**Hint :** Cube both sides of the given equation]

26. $\sqrt{x - \sqrt{(1-x)}} = 1 - \sqrt{x}$.

Squaring, $x - \sqrt{1-x} = 1 + x - 2\sqrt{x}$

or $\sqrt{1-x} = 2\sqrt{x} - 1$.

Squaring again, $1 - x = 4x + 1 - 4\sqrt{x}$

or $4\sqrt{x} = 5x$ or $\sqrt{x}(4 - 5\sqrt{x}) = 0$

$\therefore x = 0$ or $\dfrac{16}{25}$.

$x = 0$ does not satisfy the given equation.

Hence $x = \dfrac{16}{25}$ is the only root of the equation.

27. Let the roots be α, β, γ.

$\alpha\beta\gamma = -24, \alpha\beta = 12$

$\therefore \gamma = -2$ is a root.

Dividing the equation by $x + 2$, we get

$x^2 - 7x + 12 = 0$ giving $x = 4, 3$.

Thus the roots are $4, 3, -2$.

28. Ans. $x = a, b$.

Put $a - x = p$ and $b - x = q$

On squaring twice, we get $15\, pq = 0$

$\therefore p = 0, q = 0$ i.e., $x = a, b$

[Note that if the operations with complex numbers are regarded as unknown, there will be only one root either a or b].

29. The equation can be written as

$$\frac{(a-x)^{3/2} + (x-b)^{3/2}}{(a-x)^{1/2} + (x-b)^{1/2}} = a - b.$$

Form $\dfrac{p^3 + q^3}{p + q}$ or $p^2 = pq + q^2$

Whence we have

$(a-x) - (a-x)^{1/2}(x-b)^{1/2} + (x-b) = a - b$

or $\sqrt{(a-x)(x-b)} = 0$.

Hence $x = a$ or $x = b$.

30. Let $x = \sqrt{[6 + \sqrt{6 + \sqrt{(6 + \ldots)}}]}$. Then $x = \sqrt{6 + x}$

or $x^2 - x - 6 = 0$ $\therefore x = 3, -2$.

Since x is clearly positive, we have $x = 3$, rejecting $x = -2$.

31. We have

$3x^3 = x^4 - \{\sqrt{18}x + \sqrt{32}\}^2 - 4x^2$

$\quad = x^4 - \{18x^2 + 32 + 2 \cdot 3\sqrt{2} \cdot 4\sqrt{2}x\} - 4x^2$

or $x^4 - 2(9x^2 + 16 + 24x) - 3x^3 - 4x^2 = 0$

or $x^4 - 2(3x + 4)^2 - x^2(3x + 4) = 0$

or $x^4 - x^2(3x + 4) - 2(3x + 4)^2 = 0$

$p^2 - pq - 2q^2 = 0$, where $p = x^2, q = 3x + 4$

$(p - 2q)(p + q) = 0$

or $(x^2 + 3x + 4)(x^2 - 6x - 8) = 0$

$\therefore x = 3 \pm \sqrt{17}, \dfrac{1}{2}[-3 \pm i\sqrt{7}]$.

Problem Set (3)

Miscellaneous Equations.

Solve the following equations :

1. $\sqrt{x/y} + \sqrt{y/x} = 5/2$, $x + y = 6$.

2. $(x^2/y) + (y^2/x) = 9/2$, $x + y = 3$.

3. (i) $2^x + 2^y = 20$, $x + y = 6$.

(ii)* $6^x + 6^y = 42$, $x + y = 3$.

4. Solve the equations :

(i)* $x^2 - xy + y^2 = 7$, $x^4 + x^2y^2 + y^4 = 133$.

(ii) $x + y - \sqrt{xy} = 6$, $x^2 + y^2 + xy = 84$.

5. $x - y = 13 - 3xy$, $x^2y - y^2x = 12$.

6. $x + y + xy = 11$, $x^2y + xy^2 = 30$.

7. $3x^2 - 4xy - 4 = 0$, $x^2 - 2y^2 - 2 = 0$.

8.* $x^3 - y^3 = 127$, $x^2y - xy^2 = 42$.

9. $x^2 + y(x+1) = 17$, $y^2 + x(y+1) = 13$.

10. $\dfrac{bx}{y+b} + \dfrac{ay}{x+a} = \dfrac{a+b}{2}$, $\dfrac{x}{a} + \dfrac{y}{b} = 2$.

11. (i) $x^4 - y^4 = 15$, $x - y = 1$

(ii) $\sqrt[4]{1+5x} + \sqrt[4]{5-y} = 3$, $5x - y = 11$.

12. $(x+y)^{2/3} + 2(x-y)^{2/3} = 3(x^2 - y^2)^{1/3}$, $3x - 2y = 13$.

13. $4x^2 + 5y = 6 + 20xy - 25y^2 + 2x, 7x - 11y = 17$.

14. $\dfrac{x-a}{a^2} + \dfrac{y-b}{b^2} = \dfrac{1}{x-b} - \dfrac{1}{y-a} - \dfrac{1}{a-b} = 0$.

15. $*\left(3 - \dfrac{6y}{x+y}\right)^2 + \left(3 + \dfrac{6y}{x-y}\right)^2 = 82, \ 3x + 7y = 26.$

16. $x^2 y^2 - 2x + y^2 = 0, \qquad 2x^2 - 4x + 3 + y^3 = 0.$

17. (a)* If the equations $ax + by = 1, \ cx^2 + dy^2 = 1$ have only one solution, prove that $\dfrac{a^2}{c} + \dfrac{b^2}{d} = 1$ and $x = \dfrac{a}{c}, \ y = \dfrac{b}{d}.$

    (b) If $x < 0, \ y < 0, \ x + y + x/y = 1/2$ and $(x + y)(x/y) = -1/2$, then $x = \dots\dots$ and $y = \dots\dots$

                          (I.I.T. 1990)

18. * Find the positive solutions of the system of equations $x^{x+y} = y^n$ and $y^{x+y} = x^{2n} y^n$ where $n > 0$.

                          (Roorkee 1992)

19. * Obtain real solutions of simultaneous equations
$$xy + 3y^2 - x + 4y - 7 = 0$$
$$2xy + y^2 - 2x - 2y + 1 = 0$$

                          (Roorkee 1993)

Solutions to Problem Set (3)

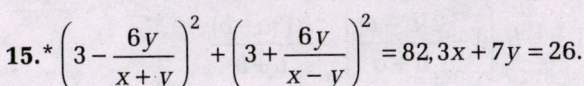

1. The equations can be written as
$$2(x + y) = 5\sqrt{xy} \qquad \dots(1)$$
$$x + y = 6. \qquad \dots(2)$$
These equations give $xy = 144/25.$
Since $x + y = 6, \ xy = 144/25$, we can say that x and y are the roots of
$$t^2 - 6t + 144/25 = 0 \ \text{ or } \ 25t^2 - 150t + 144 = 0$$
$$(5t - 24)(5t - 6) = 0 \quad \therefore \quad t = \frac{24}{5} \ \text{ or } \ \frac{6}{5}.$$
Hence $x = \dfrac{24}{5}, \ y = \dfrac{6}{5} \ \text{ or } \ x = \dfrac{6}{5}, \ y = \dfrac{24}{5}.$

2. Ans. $x = 2, \ y = 1 \ \text{ or } \ x = 1, \ y = 2.$

3. (i) Ans. $x = 2, \ y = 4 \ \text{ or } \ x = 4, \ y = 2.$
    (ii) Ans. $x = 1, \ y = 2 \ \text{ or } \ x = 2, \ y = 1.$

4. (i) From 2nd equation, we have
$$(x^2 + y^2)^2 - x^2 y^2 = 133$$
or $(x^2 + y^2 - xy)(x^2 + y^2 + xy) = 133$
$$\therefore \quad x^2 + y^2 + xy = 133/7 = 19.$$
$$x^2 + y^2 - xy = 7 \ \text{(given)}$$
Adding and subtracting, we get
$$x^2 + y^2 = 13, \quad xy = 6$$
$$\therefore \quad x^2 y^2 = 36$$
$$\therefore \quad x^2, y^2 \text{ are the roots of } t^2 - 13t + 36 = 0$$
$$\therefore \quad (t - 4)(t - 9) = 0 \ \therefore \ t = 4, 9$$
$$x^2 = 4, y^2 = 9 \ \text{ or } \ x^2 = 9, y^2 = 4$$
$$\therefore \quad x = 3, \ y = 2 \quad \text{or} \quad x = -3, \ y = -2.$$
Similarly $x = 2, y = 3 \ \text{ or } \ x = -2, y = -3.$
Note : We have taken the roots keeping in view that $xy = 6$.

    (ii) Proceed as above.
        Ans. $x = 8, \ y = 2 \ \text{ or } \ x = 2, \ y = 8.$

5. Ans. $x = 2 + \sqrt{7}, \ y = -2 + \sqrt{7}$
    or $x = 2 - \sqrt{7}, \ y = -2 - \sqrt{7}.$

6. Put $x + y = u$ and $xy = v$. Then the given equations can be written as
$$u + v = 11, \quad uv = 30$$
$\therefore \quad u$ and v are the roots of $t^2 - 11t + 30 = 0$
Hence $u = 6, \ v = 5 \ \text{ or } \ u = 5, \ v = 6.$
Thus $x + y = 6, \ xy = 5 \ \text{ or } \ x + y = 5, \ xy = 6.$
First we take $x + y = 6 \qquad \dots(1)$
and $xy = 5$
$\therefore \quad x$ and y are the roots of $t^2 - 6t + 5 = 0$
or $(t - 5)(t - 1) = 0, \ \therefore \ t = 5, 1.$
Hence $x = 5, \ y = 1 \ \text{ or } \ x = 1, \ y = 5.$
We now take $x + y = 5, \ xy = 6.$
Solving these, we shall get $t^2 - 5t + 6 = 0$
$$x = 3, \ y = 2 \ \text{ or } \ x = 2, \ y = 3.$$
Hence the solution set is
$$(5, 1), \ (1, 5), \ (3, 2), \ (2, 3).$$

7. Ans. $x = 2, \ y = 1 \ \text{ or } \ x = -2, \ y = -1.$
Eliminating the constant term by multiplying 2nd equation by 2 and subtracting from 1st
$$\therefore \quad x^2 - 4xy + 4y^2 = 0 \ \text{ or } \ (x - 2y)^2 = 0$$
$$\therefore \quad x = 2y$$
Putting in 2nd, we get
$$4y^2 - 2y^2 = 2 \ \therefore \ y^2 = 1 \ \therefore \ y = 1, -1$$
$$\therefore \quad x = 2, -2.$$
You may also follow homogeneous method.

8. Putting $y = mx$, the given equations can be written as
$$x^3 (1 - m^3) = 127 \qquad \dots(1)$$
and $x^3 (m - m^2) = 42 \qquad \dots(2)$
Dividing, we get
$$\frac{1 - m^3}{m - m^2} = \frac{127}{42} \ \text{ or } \ \frac{1 + m + m^2}{m} = \frac{127}{42}$$
or $42m^2 - 85m + 42 = 0$
or $42m^2 - 49m - 36m + 42 = 0$
or $(6m - 7)(7m - 6) = 0.$
$$\therefore \quad m = 7/6 \ \text{ or } \ 6/7.$$
We first take $m = 7/6$ and we get from (1)
$$x^3 (1 - 343/216) = 127 \ \text{ or } \ x = -6$$
and $y = mx = \dfrac{7}{6}(-6) = -7.$
Similarly taking $m = 6/7$, we shall get $x = 7, y = 6.$
Hence solutions are
$$x = 7, \ y = 6 \ \text{ or } \ x = -6, \ y = -7.$$
Alternative method :
Multiply the second equation by (3) and subtract it from first and we get
$$(x - y)^3 = 1, \ \therefore \ x - y = 1 \ \text{ or } \ x = y + 1$$

Putting in 2nd equation, *i.e.* $xy(x - y) = 42$, we get

$$y(y + 1) \cdot 1 = 42 \quad \text{or} \quad y^2 + y - 42 = 0$$

$\therefore \quad y = -7, 6$ and hence $x = -6, 7$

$\therefore \quad 7, 6 \; ; \; -6, -7.$

9. The given equations are

$$x^2 + xy + y = 17 \qquad \qquad \text{...(1)}$$

$$y^2 + xy + x = 13. \qquad \qquad \text{...(2)}$$

Adding (1) and (2), we get

$$x^2 + 2xy + y^2 + (x + y) = 30$$

or $\quad (x + y)^2 + (x + y) - 30 = 0$

or $\quad (x + y + 6)(x + y - 5) = 0$

$\therefore \quad x + y = -6 \qquad \qquad \text{...(3)}$

or $\quad x + y = 5. \qquad \qquad \text{...(4)}$

We have now to solve equations (1) and (3), and (1) and (4).

Or we may solve (2) and (3) ; and (2) and (4)

Eliminating y from (1) and (3), we get

$$-6x - x - 6 = 17 \quad \text{or} \quad x = -23 / 7.$$

Then $y = -x - 6 = 23 / 7 - 6 = -19 / 7.$

$\therefore \quad$ One solution is :

$$x = -23 / 7, \; y = -19 / 7.$$

Similarly solving (1) and (4), we shall get

$$x = 3 \text{ and } y = 2.$$

Hence the solutions are

$$x = -\frac{23}{7}, \; y = -\frac{19}{7} \quad \text{or} \quad x = 3, \; y = 2.$$

10. From the second equation, we get

$$\frac{x}{a} - 1 = 1 - \frac{y}{b} \quad \text{or} \quad \frac{x - a}{a} = \frac{b - y}{b} = k, \text{say.}$$

Then $x = a(1 + k)$ and $y = b(1 - k).$ ...(1)

Substituting these values of x and y in first equation, we have

$$\frac{ab(1 + k)}{b(2 - k)} + \frac{ab(1 - k)}{a(2 + k)} = \frac{a + b}{2}$$

or $\quad \dfrac{a(1 + k)}{2 - k} + \dfrac{b(1 - k)}{2 + k} = \dfrac{a + b}{2}$

or $\quad \left[\dfrac{a(1 + k)}{2 - k} - \dfrac{a}{2} \right] + \left[\dfrac{b(1 - k)}{2 + k} - \dfrac{b}{2} \right] = 0$

or $\quad \dfrac{3ak}{2 - k} - \dfrac{3bk}{2 + k} = 0$

or $\quad k \left[\dfrac{a(2 + k) - b(2 - k)}{(2 - k)(2 + k)} \right] = 0$

or $\quad k[(a + b)k - 2(b - a)] = 0$

$\therefore \quad k = 0 \quad \text{or} \quad k = \dfrac{2(b - a)}{b + a}$

Substituting these values of k in (1), we get

$$x = a(1 + 0) = a \text{ and } y = b(1 - 0) = b$$

or $\quad x = a \left\{ 1 + \dfrac{2(b - a)}{b + a} \right\} = \dfrac{a(3b - a)}{a + b},$

and $\quad y = b \left\{ 1 - \dfrac{2(b - a)}{b + a} \right\} = \dfrac{b(3a - b)}{a + b}.$

Hence the solutions are

$$x = a, \; y = b \quad \text{or} \quad x = \frac{a(3b - a)}{a + b}, \; y = \frac{b(3a - b)}{a + b}.$$

11. (i) **Hint :** Put $x = u + v, \; y = u - v$

Ans. $\quad x = 2, \; \dfrac{-1 \pm \sqrt{-31}}{4}, \; y = 1, \; \dfrac{-5 \pm \sqrt{-31}}{4}.$

There is only one real solution $x = 2, \; y = 1.$

(ii) **Ans.** $x = 0, \; y = -11 \quad \text{or} \quad x = 3, \; y = 4.$

Hint : Put $\sqrt[4]{1 + 5x} = u$ and $\sqrt[4]{5 - y} = v.$ Then

$$u + v = 3, \; u^4 + v^4 = 17.$$

Solving these symmetric equations, we shall get

$$u = 1, \; v = 2 \quad \text{or} \quad u = 2, \; v = 1 \text{ etc.}$$

12. Dividing the first equation by $(x^2 - y^2)^{1/3}$, we get

$$\left(\frac{x + y}{x - y} \right)^{1/3} + 2 \left(\frac{x - y}{x + y} \right)^{1/3} = 3$$

Put $\left(\dfrac{x + y}{x - y} \right)^{1/3} = u.$ Then $u + \dfrac{2}{u} = 3 \quad \text{or} \quad u^2 - 3u + 2 = 0$

or $\quad (u - 1)(u - 2) = 0 \quad \text{or} \quad u = 1 \quad \text{or} \quad 2.$

Hence $\quad \left(\dfrac{x + y}{x - y} \right)^{1/3} = 1 \quad \text{or} \quad 2$

First take $\quad x + y = x - y,$ that is, $y = 0.$

Then from the second equation

$$3x - 2y = 13$$

we get $x = 13 / 3.$ ...(1)

Again $\left(\dfrac{x + y}{x - y} \right)^{1/3} = 2 \quad \text{or} \quad x + y = 8x - 8y$

or $\quad 7x - 9y = 0.$ ...(2)

Solving (1) and (2), we get $x = 9, \; y = 7.$

Hence the solutions are :

$$x = 13 / 3, \; y = 0 \quad \text{or} \quad x = 9, \; y = 7.$$

13. First equation can be written as

$$4x^2 - 20xy + 25y^2 + (5y - 2x) - 6 = 0$$

or $\quad (5y - 2x)^2 + (5y - 2x) - 6 = 0.$

or $\quad (5y - 2x + 3)(5y - 2x - 2) = 0$

Hence $5y - 2x + 3 = 0$ ...(1)

or $\quad 5y - 2x - 2 = 0$ ...(2)

And the second given equation is

$$7x - 11y = 17$$ ...(3)

Solving (1) and (3), we get $x = 4, \; y = 1$

Again solving (2) and (3), we get

$$x = \frac{107}{13}, \; y = \frac{48}{13}.$$

Hence solutions are : $x = 4, \; y = 1$

or $\quad x = \dfrac{107}{13}, \; y = \dfrac{48}{13}$

14. Ans. $x = \dfrac{a^2}{b}, \dfrac{a(2b-a)}{b}; y = \dfrac{b^2}{a}, \dfrac{b(2a-b)}{a}$.

Hint : From second equation, we get

$$\frac{1}{x-b} - \frac{1}{a-b} = \frac{1}{y-a}$$

or $\dfrac{a-x}{(x-b)(a-b)} = \dfrac{1}{y-a}$ or $\dfrac{(x-b)(a-b)}{a-x} = y-a$

or $y = a + \dfrac{(x-b)(a-b)}{a-x} = \dfrac{a^2 - ab + b^2 - bx}{a-x}$.

Now substitute this value of y in first equation etc.

15. From first equation, we get

$$\left\{\frac{3(x-y)}{x+y}\right\}^2 + \left\{\frac{3(x+y)}{x-y}\right\}^2 = 82.$$

Put $\dfrac{x+y}{x-y} = z$, we then have

$$9\left(\frac{1}{z^2} + z^2\right) = 82.$$

or $9z^4 - 82z^2 + 9 = 0$

or $(z^2 - 9)(9z^2 - 1) = 0$

$\therefore \quad z = \pm 3$ or $z = \pm \dfrac{1}{3}$

Taking $z = 3$, we get $\dfrac{x+y}{x-y} = 3$

or $x = 2y$ ...(1)

Also second given equation is

$3x + 7y = 26$. ...(2)

Solving (1) and (2), we get $x = 4, y = 2$.

Similarly solving $z = -3$, that is $\dfrac{x+y}{x-y} = -3$ with (2),

we shall get

$$x = \frac{26}{17}, \quad y = \frac{52}{17}.$$

Again solving $z = \dfrac{x+y}{x-y} = \dfrac{1}{3}$ with (2), we shall obtain

$$x = -52, \quad y = 26.$$

And finally solving $z = \dfrac{x+y}{x-y} = -\dfrac{1}{3}$, we shall get

$$x = -\frac{26}{11}, \quad y = \frac{52}{11}.$$

16. The given system of equations is equivalent to

$$y^2 = 2x/(1+x^2), \quad 2(x-1)^2 + 1 + y^3 = 0.$$

Since $2x/(1+x^2) \le 1$ for all real x, it follows from the first of these equations that $y^2 \le 1$ or $-1 \le y \le 1$. Again from the second equation of the system, we get

$$y^3 = -1 - 2(x-1)^2 \le -1.$$

Now since $y \le -1$ and $y \ge -1$, we must have $y = -1$. Then $x = 1$. Thus the solution is $x = 1, \ y = -1$.

17. (a) The given equations are

$ax + by = 1$ ...(1)

$cx^2 + dy^2 = 1$ ...(2)

Eliminating y from (1) and (2), we obtain

$$cx^2 + d\left(\frac{1-ax}{b}\right)^2 = 1$$

or $b^2 c\, x^2 + d - 2adx + a^2 dx^2 = b^2$

or $(b^2 c + a^2 d)x^2 - 2adx + d - b^2 = 0$ ...(3)

Since the given equations have only one solution, the roots of (3) must be equal, the condition for which is

$$4a^2 d^2 - 4(b^2 c + a^2 d)(d - b^2) = 0$$

or $a^2 d^2 - b^2 cd + b^4 c - a^2 d^2 + a^2 b^2 d = 0$

or $b^4 c + a^2 b^2 d - b^2 cd = 0$

or $b^2 c + a^2 d - cd = 0$

or $\dfrac{a^2}{c} + \dfrac{b^2}{d} = 1$. ...(4)

Under the condition (4), the root of (3) is given by $x + x = \text{sum}$

$$x = \frac{2ad}{2(b^2 c + a^2 d)} = \frac{2ad}{2cd\left(\dfrac{b^2}{d} + \dfrac{a^2}{c}\right)} = \frac{a}{c}, \quad \text{by (4)}$$

Then $y = \dfrac{1-ax}{b} = \dfrac{1 - \dfrac{a^2}{c}}{b} = \dfrac{\dfrac{b^2}{d}}{b}$ by (4) $= \dfrac{b}{d}$.

Hence the only one solution of the given equations is $x = \dfrac{a}{c}, \ y = \dfrac{b}{d}$.

(b) Put $x + y = u$, $x/y = v$, $u + v = 1/2$, $uv = -1/2$ then u and v are roots of $t^2 - \dfrac{1}{2}t - \dfrac{1}{2} = 0$

or $2t^2 - t - 1 = 0$

Hence $u = 1, v = -1/2$ or $u = -1/2, v = 1$.

$\therefore \quad x + y = 1, \ x/y = -1/2$

or $x + y = -1/2, \ x/y = 1$.

Solving these, we shall get

$x = -1, \ y = 2$ or $x = y = -1/4$.

Since $x < 0, \ y < 0$, we get the answer

$x = y = -1/4$.

18. $x^{x+y} = y^n$ ...(1)

$y^{x+y} = x^{2n} y^n$ ...(2)

Multiplying the above, we get

$(xy)^{x+y} = (xy)^{2n}$ $\therefore \quad x + y = 2n$ ...(3)

Hence from (1), $x^{2n} = y^n$ or $(x^2)^n = y^n$ $\therefore x^2 = y$

Putting for y in (3), we get

$$x^2 + x - 2n = 0 \quad \therefore \quad x = \frac{-1 \pm \sqrt{1 + 8n}}{2}$$

Since we have to find positive solution, x must be +ive.

$$\therefore \quad x = \frac{-1 + \sqrt{1 + 8n}}{2}$$

$$\therefore \quad y = 2n - x = 2n - \frac{-1 + \sqrt{1 + 8n}}{2}$$

$$= \frac{4n + 1 - \sqrt{1 + 8n}}{2}.$$

19. $x = 2, y = -3$.

Multiplying (1) by 2 and subtracting from (2),

we get $\quad 5y^2 + 10y - 15 = 0$

or $\qquad y^2 + 2y - 3 = 0$

or $\qquad (y + 3)(y - 1) = 0 \quad \therefore \quad y = -3$

and hence $x = 2$. Note $y \neq 1$ as $y = 1$ will make x infinite or reduce the equation to an identity.

Problem Set (4)

Solution of equations in three variables x, y, z.

Solve the following equations :

1. $3x + y - 2z = 0$, $4x - y - 3z = 0$,
$x^3 + y^3 + z^3 = 467$.

2. $xz + y = 7z$, $yz + x = 8z$, $x + y + z = 12$.

3.* $\dfrac{xy}{ay + bx} = c$, $\dfrac{xz}{az + cx} = b$, $\dfrac{yz}{bz + cy} = a$.

4. $x + y - 4xy = 0$, $y + z - 6yz = 0$, $z + x - 8zx = 0$.

5. $xy = a(x + y)$, $yz = c(y + z)$, $zx = b(z + x)$.

6. $xyz = a^2(y + z) = b^2(z + x) = c^2(x + y)$.

7. $y + z - x = \dfrac{xyz}{a^2}$, $z + x - y = \dfrac{xyz}{b^2}$, $x + y - z = \dfrac{xyz}{c^2}$.

8.* $x^2 + xy + xz = 18$, $y^2 + yz + yx + 12 = 0$,
$z^2 + zx + zy = 30$.

9. $x(x + y + z) = a^2$, $y(x + y + z) = b^2$, $z(x + y + z) = c^2$.

10. (a)* Solve $x^2 - yz = a^2$, $y^2 - zx = b^2$, $z^2 - xy = c^2$,

(b)* If $\dfrac{x^2 - yz}{a} = \dfrac{y^2 - zx}{b} = \dfrac{z^2 - xy}{c}$, show that
$(x + y + z)(a + b + c) = ax + by + cz$.

11. $y^2 + z^2 - (y + z)x = 12$, $x^2 + z^2 - (x + z)y = 8$,
$x^2 + y^2 - (x + y)z = 2$.

12. $(b + c)(y + z) - ax = b - c$,
$(c + a)(z + x) - by = c - a$,
$(a + b)(x + y) - cz = a - b$,
where $\quad a + b + c \neq 0$.

13. $x(y + z) = a^2$, $y(z + x) = b^2$, $z(x + y) = c^2$.

14. $x^2 + y^2 - z^2 = 21$, $3xz + 3yz - 2xy = 18$,
$x + y - z = 5$.

15. $2xy - 4x + y = 17$, $3yz + y - 6z = 52$,
$6xz + 3z + 2x = 29$.

16. (a)* $y + z + yz = a$, $z + x + zx = b$, $x + y + xy = c$.
(b)* $xy + x + y = 23$, $xz + z + x = 41$, $yz + y + z = 27$.

17. $(y - z)(z + x) = 22$, $(z + x)(x - y) = 33$,
$(x - y)(y - z) = 6$.

18. (a)* $x^2 = a + (y - z)^2$, $y^2 = b + (z - x)^2$,
$z^2 = c + (x - y)^2$.

(b) $(x + y)^2 - z^2 = -9$, $(y + z)^2 - x^2 = 15$,
$(z + x)^2 - y^2 = 3$.

19. (a)* Solve the equations
$x^2 + xy + y^2 = 37$, $y^2 + yz + z^2 = 61$,
$z^2 + zx + x^2 = 49$.

(b) $x^2 + y^2 + xy = 9$, $z^2 + x^2 + xz = 4$
$y^2 + z^2 + yz = 1$.

20. $x^2 + xy + y^2 = 37$, $y^2 + yz + z^2 = 19$,
$z^2 + zx + x^2 = 28$.

21. $x + y + z + u = 2a$, $x + y - z - u = 2b$,
$x - y + z - u = 2c$, $x - y - z + u = 2d$.

22. (i)* $z + ay + a^2x + a^3 = 0$, $z + by + b^2x + b^3 = 0$,
$z + cy + c^2x + c^3 = 0$.

(ii) $\dfrac{x}{a + \lambda} + \dfrac{y}{b + \lambda} + \dfrac{z}{c + \lambda} = 1$, $\dfrac{x}{a + \mu} + \dfrac{y}{b + \mu} + \dfrac{z}{c + \mu} = 1$,

$\dfrac{x}{a + \nu} + \dfrac{y}{b + \nu} + \dfrac{z}{c + \nu} = 1$.

23.* $x + y + z = \dfrac{1}{x} + \dfrac{1}{y} + \dfrac{1}{z} = \dfrac{7}{2}$, $xyz = 1$.

24. (i)* $x + y + z = 12$, $x^2 + y^2 + z^2 = 50$,
$x^3 + y^3 + z^3 = 216$.

(ii) $x + y + z = 1$, $x^2 + y^2 + z^2 = 1$, $x^3 + y^3 + z^3 = 1$.

25. $yz = a(y + z) + \alpha$, $zx = a(z + x) + \beta$, $xy = a(x + y) + \gamma$

26. $x^2 + (y - z)^2 = a^2$, $y^2 + (z - x)^2 = b^2$,
$z^2 + (x - y)^2 = c^2$.

27. $x + y + z = a + b + c$, $\dfrac{x}{a} + \dfrac{y}{b} + \dfrac{z}{c} = 3$,

$ax + by + cz = bc + ca + ab$.

28. Find real values of x, y, z satisfying the equations
$x + y = 2$, $xy - z^2 = 1$.

29. (a)* Given $y^2 + z^2 = ayz$, $z^2 + x^2 = bxz$, $x^2 + y^2 = cxy$

express $\dfrac{y^2}{xz} + \dfrac{xz}{y^2}$ in terms of a, b, c.

(b)* If $\dfrac{x}{a} + \dfrac{y}{b} = 1$ and $\dfrac{x^2}{a^2} + \dfrac{y^2}{b^2} = -\dfrac{ab}{a + b}$, then prove that $\dfrac{x^{n+1}}{a} + \dfrac{y^{n+1}}{b} = \left(\dfrac{ab}{a+b}\right)^n$.

30. $y^3 - 9x^2 + 27x - 27 = 0$

$z^3 - 9y^2 + 27y - 27 = 0$

$x^3 - 9z^2 + 27z - 27 = 0$

Solutions to Problem Set (4)

1. $3x + y - 2z = 0$ ...(1)

$4x - y - 3z = 0$ ...(2)

$x^3 + y^3 + z^3 = 467$ ...(3)

Solving (1) and (2) by the method of cross-multiplication, we obtain

$$\frac{x}{-3-2} = \frac{y}{-8+9} = \frac{z}{-3-4}$$

or $\dfrac{x}{5} = \dfrac{y}{-1} = \dfrac{z}{7} = k$, say

∴ $x = 5k$, $y = -k$, $z = 7k$.

Substituting in (3), we get

$125k^3 - k^3 + 343k^3 = 467$

or $467k^3 = 467$ or $k = 1$.

∴ The solution is $x = 5$, $y = -1$, $z = 7$.

2. Ans. $x = 4, \dfrac{60}{7}$, $y = 6, \dfrac{66}{7}$; $z = 2, -6$.

Add the first two and eliminate $x + y$ and you get

$z = 2, -6$

3. Rewriting the given equations, we get

$$\frac{ay + bx}{xy} = \frac{1}{c}, \quad \frac{az + cx}{xz} = \frac{1}{b}, \quad \frac{bz + cy}{yz} = \frac{1}{a}$$

or $\dfrac{a}{x} + \dfrac{b}{y} = \dfrac{1}{c}, \dfrac{a}{x} + \dfrac{c}{z} = \dfrac{1}{b}, \dfrac{b}{y} + \dfrac{c}{z} = \dfrac{1}{a}$.

Adding, $2\left(\dfrac{a}{x} + \dfrac{b}{y} + \dfrac{c}{z}\right) = \dfrac{1}{a} + \dfrac{1}{b} + \dfrac{1}{c}$

Hence $2\left[\dfrac{a}{x} + \dfrac{1}{a}\right] = \dfrac{1}{a} + \dfrac{1}{b} + \dfrac{1}{c}$

or $\dfrac{2a}{x} = \dfrac{1}{a} + \dfrac{1}{b} + \dfrac{1}{c} - \dfrac{2}{a} = \dfrac{1}{b} + \dfrac{1}{c} - \dfrac{1}{a}$,

∴ $x = \dfrac{2a^2bc}{ac + ab - bc}$.

Similarly, $y = \dfrac{2ab^2c}{bc + ab - ac}$

and $z = \dfrac{2abc^2}{bc + ac - ab}$.

4. Do as in Problem 3.

Ans. $x = \dfrac{1}{3}$, $y = 1$, $z = \dfrac{1}{5}$.

5. Do as in Problem 3.

Ans. $x = \dfrac{2abc}{ca + ab - bc}$, $y = \dfrac{2abc}{ab + bc - ca}$,

$z = \dfrac{2abc}{bc + ca - ab}$.

6. Ans. $x = \pm \dfrac{\sqrt{2(1/b^2 + 1/c^2 - 1/a^2)}}{\sqrt{[(1/a^2 + 1/c^2 - 1/b^2) \cdot (1/a^2 + 1/b^2 - 1/c^2)]}}$ etc.

7. One obvious solution is $x = 0$, $y = 0$, $z = 0$.

Adding the given equations pairwise, we get

$2z = xyz\left(\dfrac{1}{a^2} + \dfrac{1}{b^2}\right)$ etc.

Hence $\dfrac{2}{xy} = \dfrac{1}{a^2} + \dfrac{1}{b^2}$.

Similarly, $\dfrac{2}{yz} = \dfrac{1}{b^2} + \dfrac{1}{c^2}, \dfrac{2}{zx} = \dfrac{1}{a^2} + \dfrac{1}{c^2}$.

Multiplying these, we obtain

$$x^2y^2z^2 = \frac{8a^4b^4c^4}{(a^2 + b^2)(b^2 + c^2)(c^2 + a^2)}$$

Hence $xyz = \pm \dfrac{2\sqrt{2} \cdot a^2b^2c^2}{\sqrt{[(a^2 + b^2)(b^2 + c^2)(c^2 + a^2)]}}$

Now using the equality $xy = \dfrac{2a^2b^2}{a^2 + b^2}$, we find

$$z = \pm \frac{\sqrt{2} \cdot c^2 \sqrt{(a^2 + b^2)}}{\sqrt{[(b^2 + c^2)(c^2 + a^2)]}}$$

Similar expressions for values of x and y can be found.

8. Given equations can be rewritten as

$x(x + y + z) = 18$ ...(1)

$y(x + y + z) = -12$ ...(2)

$z(x + y + z) = 30$ ...(3)

Adding (1), (2) and (3), we get

$(x + y + z)^2 = 36$ or $x + y + z = \pm 6$ ...(4)

Then from (1) and (4), we get $x = \pm 3$

Similarly from (2) and (4), $y = \mp 2$,

and from (3) and (4), $z = \pm 5$.

Hence the solutions are

$x = 3$, $y = -2$, $z = 5$

or $x = -3$, $y = 2$, $z = -5$,

9. Do as in Problem 8.

Ans. $x = \pm \dfrac{a^2}{\sqrt{[a^2 + b^2 + c^2]}}$,

$y = \pm \dfrac{b^2}{\sqrt{[a^2 + b^2 + c^2]}}$

$z = \pm \dfrac{c^2}{\sqrt{[a^2 + b^2 + c^2]}}$.

10. (a) Multiplying the given equations by y, z, x respectively and adding, we get

$$c^2 x + a^2 y + b^2 z = 0. \qquad \ldots(1)$$

Again multiplying the given equations by z, x, y respectively and adding, we get

$$b^2 x + c^2 y + a^2 z = 0. \qquad \ldots(2)$$

Solving (1) and (2) by cross-multiplication,

$$\frac{x}{a^4 - b^2 c^2} = \frac{y}{b^4 - c^2 a^2} = \frac{z}{c^4 - a^2 b^2} = k, \text{ say } \ldots(3)$$

Substituting in any one of the given equations, for x, y, z in terms of k from (3), we get

$$k^2 (a^6 + b^6 + c^6 - 3a^2 b^2 c^2) = 1$$

$$\therefore \quad \frac{x}{a^4 - b^2 c^2} = \frac{y}{b^4 - c^2 a^2} = \frac{z}{c^4 - a^2 b^2}$$

$$= \pm \frac{1}{\sqrt{[a^6 + b^6 + c^6 - 3a^2 b^2 c^2]}}$$

(b) $\quad \dfrac{x^2 - yz}{a} = \dfrac{y^2 - zx}{b} = \dfrac{z^2 - xy}{c} \qquad \ldots(1)$

$$= \frac{x^2 - yz + y^2 - zx + z^2 - xy}{a + b + c} \qquad \ldots(2)$$

$$= \frac{x(x^2 - yz) + y(y^2 - zx) + z(z^2 - xy)}{ax + by + cz}$$

$$= \frac{x^3 + y^3 + z^3 - 3xyz}{ax + by + cz}$$

$$= \frac{(x + y + z)(x^2 + y^2 + z^2 - xy - yz - zx)}{ax + by + cz} \qquad \ldots(3)$$

$\therefore \ (x + y + z)(a + b + c) = ax + by + cz$, by (2) and (3)

11. We rewrite the equations as

$$(y^2 - zx) + (z^2 - xy) = 12 \qquad \ldots(1)$$
$$(x^2 - yz) + (z^2 - xy) = 8 \qquad \ldots(2)$$
$$(x^2 - yz) + (y^2 - zx) = 2 \qquad \ldots(3)$$

Adding (1), (2) and (3), we get

$$2(y^2 - zx) + 2(z^2 - xy) + 2(x^2 - yz) = 22$$

or $\quad (y^2 - zx) + (z^2 - xy) + (x^2 - yz) = 11 \qquad \ldots(4)$

From (1) and (4),

$$x^2 - yz = -1 \qquad \ldots(5)$$

Similarly from (2) and (4),

$$y^2 - zx = 3 \qquad \ldots(6)$$

and from (3) and (4),

$$z^2 - xy = 9 \qquad \ldots(7)$$

Multiplying (5), (6), (7) by y, z, x respectively and adding, we get

$$-y + 3z + 9x = 0 \quad \text{or} \quad 9x - y + 3z = 0 \qquad \ldots(8)$$

Again multiplying these equations by z, x and y and adding, we get

$$-z + 3x + 9y = 0$$

or $\quad 3x + 9y - z = 0 \qquad \ldots(9)$

Solving (8) and (9) by cross-multiplication, we get

$$\frac{x}{1 - 27} = \frac{y}{9 + 9} = \frac{z}{81 + 3}$$

or $\quad \dfrac{x}{-26} = \dfrac{y}{18} = \dfrac{z}{84} \quad$ or $\quad \dfrac{x}{-13} = \dfrac{y}{9} = \dfrac{z}{42} = k$, say

Substituting these values in (5), we get

$$169 k^2 - 378 k^2 = -1$$

or $\quad 209 k^2 = 1 \quad$ or $\quad k = \pm \dfrac{1}{\sqrt{(209)}}.$

Hence $x = \mp \dfrac{13}{\sqrt{(209)}}, \ y = \pm \dfrac{9}{\sqrt{(209)}},$

$$z = \pm \frac{42}{\sqrt{(209)}}.$$

12. Adding all the three equations, we get

$$(x + y + z)(a + b + c) = 0,$$

Hence $\quad x + y + z = 0.$

Then from first of the given equations and this equation, we get

$$(b + c)(-x) - ax = b - c$$

or $\quad x = \dfrac{c - b}{a + b + c}.$

Similarly $y = \dfrac{a - c}{a + b + c}, \ z = \dfrac{b - a}{a + b + c}.$

13. The given system of equations can be written as

$$xy + xz = a^2 \qquad \ldots(1)$$
$$yz + yx = b^2 \qquad \ldots(2)$$
$$zx + zy = c^2 \qquad \ldots(3)$$

Adding, $\quad xy + yz + zx = \dfrac{1}{2}(a^2 + b^2 + c^2)$

Then from (1) and (4), $\quad yz = \dfrac{1}{2}(b^2 + c^2 - a^2)$

Similarly, $zx = \dfrac{c^2 + a^2 - b^2}{2} \quad$ and $\quad xy = \dfrac{a^2 + b^2 - c^2}{2}$

Multiplying these,

$$(xyz)^2 = \frac{(b^2 + c^2 - a^2)(c^2 + a^2 - b^2)(a^2 + b^2 - c^2)}{8}$$

$$\therefore \quad xyz = \pm \sqrt{\frac{1}{8}(b^2 + c^2 - a^2)(c^2 + a^2 - b^2)}$$
$$(a^2 + b^2 - c^2)$$

Now we easily get

$$x = \pm \sqrt{\left\{ \frac{(c^2 + a^2 - b^2)(a^2 + b^2 - c^2)}{2(b^2 + c^2 - a^2)} \right\}}$$

$$y = \pm \sqrt{\left\{ \frac{(a^2 + b^2 - c^2)(b^2 + c^2 - a^2)}{2(c^2 + a^2 - b^2)} \right\}}$$

$$z = \pm \sqrt{\left\{ \frac{(c^2 + a^2 - b^2)(b^2 + c^2 - a^2)}{2(a^2 + b^2 - c^2)} \right\}}.$$

14. Do yourself. First eliminate x and y and you get
$$3z^2 + 5z - 22 = 0$$
$$\therefore \quad z = 2, -\frac{11}{3}$$
Ans. $\quad x = 4, 3, \dfrac{2 \pm \sqrt{151}}{3}; \; y = 3, 4, \dfrac{2 \mp \sqrt{151}}{3}$

and $z = 2, -\dfrac{11}{3}$

15. The equations can be rewritten as
$$2x(y - 2) + (y - 2) = 17 - 2$$
or $\quad (2x + 1)(y - 2) = 15 \qquad \qquad \ldots(1)$
Similarly $(y - 2)(3z + 1) = 50 \qquad \ldots(2)$
and $(3z + 1)(2x + 1) = 30 \qquad \ldots(3)$
Multiplying (1), (2) and (3), we get
$$[(2x + 1)(y - 2)(3z + 1)]^2 = 15 \times 50 \times 30$$
$$\therefore \quad (2x + 1)(y - 2)(3z + 1) = \pm 150 \qquad \ldots(4)$$
Now from (1) and (4),
$$3z + 1 = \pm\frac{150}{15} = \pm 10 \text{ so that } z = 3, -\frac{11}{3}.$$
From (2) and (4),
$$2x + 1 = \pm\frac{150}{50} = \pm 3 \text{ or } x = 1, -2.$$
From (3) and (4),
$$y - 2 = \pm\frac{150}{30} = \pm 5 \text{ or } y = 7, -3.$$
Hence the solution sets are
$$x = 1, y = 7, z = 3 \quad \text{or} \quad x = -2, y = -3, z = -\frac{11}{3}.$$

16. (a) **Hint :** The equations can be rewritten as
$(y + 1)(z + 1) = a + 1, \quad (z + 1)(x + 1) = b + 1,$
$(x + 1)(y + 1) = c + 1.$
Now proceeding as in Problem 15, we shall get
$$x = \pm\sqrt{\left\{\frac{(1 + b)(1 + c)}{1 + a}\right\}} - 1,$$
$$y = \pm\sqrt{\left\{\frac{(1 + c)(1 + a)}{1 + b}\right\}} - 1$$
$$\text{and } z = \pm\sqrt{\left\{\frac{(1 + a)(1 + b)}{1 + c}\right\}} - 1.$$

(b) Ans. $\quad x = 5, \; y = 3, \; z = 6.$
or $\quad x = -7, \; y = -5, \; z = -8.$

17. Ans. $x = 8, y = 5, z = 3$
or $\quad x = -8, y = -5, z = -3.$

18. (a) The equations can be rewritten as
$$x^2 - (y - z)^2 = a$$
or $\qquad (x + y - z)(x + z - y) = a.$
Similarly $(y + z - x)(y + x - z) = b$
and $\qquad (z + x - y)(z + y - x) = c.$
Multiplying and taking square root, we get
$$(x + y - z)(z + x - y)(y + z - x) = \pm\sqrt{abc}$$

Hence $y + z - x = \pm\sqrt{\left(\dfrac{bc}{a}\right)},$

$z + x - y = \pm\sqrt{\left(\dfrac{ca}{b}\right)}$

and $\quad x + y - z = \pm\sqrt{\left(\dfrac{ab}{c}\right)}.$

Adding last two equations, we get
$$x = \pm\frac{1}{2}\left\{\sqrt{\frac{ca}{b}} + \sqrt{\frac{ab}{c}}\right\}.$$
Similarly, $y = \pm\dfrac{1}{2}\left\{\sqrt{\dfrac{bc}{a}} + \sqrt{\dfrac{ab}{c}}\right\}$

and $z = \pm\dfrac{1}{2}\left\{\sqrt{\dfrac{bc}{a}} + \sqrt{\dfrac{ca}{b}}\right\}.$

(b) Ans. $x = 1, \; y = -1, \; z = -3$
$x = -1, \; y = 1, \; z = 3;$
$\Sigma x \cdot (x + y - z) = -9 \text{ etc.}$
Add all $(\Sigma x)^2 = 9$
$\therefore \quad \Sigma x = \pm 3 \therefore x + y - z = -3, y + z - x = 5,$
$z + x - y = 1$ etc.

19. (a) Multiplying the given equations by $x - y, y - z$ and $z - x$ respectively and adding,
$$\Sigma(x^3 - y^3) = 37(x - y) + 61(y - z) + 49(z - x) = 0$$
$$0 = -12x + 24y - 12z$$
or $\quad 2y = x + z.$ Hence x, y, z are in A.P.
Hence the numbers can be taken as $y - d, y, y + d.$
Putting in the given equations, we get
$$3y^2 - 3yd + d^2 = 37$$
$$3y^2 + 3yd + d^2 = 61$$
$$3y^2 + d^2 = 49$$
Putting the value of $3y^2 + d^2$ in any, we get $yd = 4$
and now solve this with $3y^2 + d^2 = 49.$
or $\quad 3y^2 + \dfrac{16}{y^2} = 49$
or $\quad 3y^4 - 49y^2 + 16 = 0$
$$(y^2 - 16)(3y^2 - 1) = 0$$
$\therefore \quad y^2 = 16 \quad \text{or} \quad y = 4, -4$
$\therefore \quad d = 1, -1 \quad \because \quad yd = 4$
$x = y - d = 3, -3; \quad z = y + d = 5, -5.$
Hence the numbers are $(3, 4, 5)$ or $(-3, -4, -5)$
Note : $3y^2 - 1 = 0 \Rightarrow y^2 = 1/3$ and these values do not satisfy the given relations.

(b) $x^2 + y^2 + xy = 9 \qquad \ldots(1)$
$z^2 + x^2 + xz = 4 \qquad \ldots(2)$
$y^2 + z^2 + yz = 1 \qquad \ldots(3)$
Subtracting (2) from (1) and factorizing, we get
$$(y - z)(x + y + z) = 5 \qquad \ldots(4)$$

Similarly, $(x - y)(x + y + z) = 3$ ...(5)

$(z - x)(x + y + z) = -8$ ...(6)

Again subtracting (5) from (4), we get

$(2y - x - z)(x + y + z) = 2$ ...(7)

Similarly, $(2x - y - z)(x + y + z) = 11$. ...(8)

Now putting $x + y + z = t$, we get from (7) and (8),

$$(3y - t)t = 2 \quad \text{or} \quad y = \frac{t^2 + 2}{3t},$$

and $(3x - t)t = 11$ or $x = \frac{t^2 + 11}{3t}$.

Substituting these values of x and y in (1),

$$\frac{(t^2 + 11)^2}{9t^2} + \frac{(t^2 + 2)^2}{9t^2} + \frac{(t^2 + 11)(t^2 + 2)}{9t^2} = 9$$

or $3t^4 - 42t^2 + 147 = 0$ or $t^4 - 14t^2 + 49 = 0$

or $(t^2 - 7)^2 = 0$.

$\therefore \quad (x + y + z)^2 = t^2 = 7$ or $x + y + z = t = \pm\sqrt{7}$.

Hence $x = \pm\dfrac{7 + 11}{3\sqrt{(7)}} = \pm\dfrac{6}{\sqrt{(7)}}$,

and $y = \pm\dfrac{7 + 2}{3\sqrt{(7)}} = \pm\dfrac{3}{\sqrt{(7)}}$.

Then from (4), we get

$$\left(\frac{3}{\sqrt{(7)}} - z\right)\sqrt{7} = 5 \quad \text{or} \quad \left(-\frac{3}{\sqrt{(7)}} - z\right)(-\sqrt{7}) = 5.$$

$\therefore \quad z = -\dfrac{2}{\sqrt{(7)}} \quad \text{or} \quad z = \dfrac{2}{\sqrt{(7)}}$.

Hence the solution sets are :

$$x = \frac{6}{\sqrt{(7)}}, \ y = \frac{3}{\sqrt{(7)}}, \ z = \frac{2}{\sqrt{(7)}}$$

or $\quad x = -\dfrac{6}{\sqrt{(7)}}, \ y = -\dfrac{3}{\sqrt{(7)}}, \ z = -\dfrac{2}{\sqrt{(7)}}$.

20. Do as in Problem 19.

Ans. $x = 4, \ -4, \ \dfrac{10\sqrt{3}}{3}, \ -\dfrac{10\sqrt{3}}{3}$.

$y = 3, \ -3, \ \dfrac{1}{3}\sqrt{3}, \ -\dfrac{1}{3}\sqrt{3}$,

$z = 2, \ -2, \ -\dfrac{8}{3}\sqrt{3}, \ \dfrac{8}{3}\sqrt{3}$.

21. Adding first two and adding last two,

$x + y = a + b, \ x - y = c + d$

$\therefore \quad x = \dfrac{1}{2}(a + b + c + d), \ y = \dfrac{1}{2}(a + b - c - d)$

Subtracting first two and subtracting last two,

$z + u = a - b$ and $z - u = c - d$.

$\therefore \quad z = \dfrac{1}{2}(a - b + c - d), \ u = \dfrac{1}{2}(a - b - c + d)$.

22. (i) The given equations show that the polynomial

$f(t) = t^3 + xt^2 + yt + z$

vanishes at three different values of t, namely at $t = a$, $t = b$, and $t = c$.

Set up a difference

$t^3 + xt^2 + yt + z - (t - a)(t - b)(t - c)$.

This difference also becomes zero at $t = a, b, c$. Expanding this expression in powers of t, we get

$$(x + a + b + c)t^2 + (y - ab - bc - ca)t + (z + abc) = 0.$$

This *second degree* equation in t vanishes at *three different* values of t and is therefore identically zero, and so each of its coefficient must vanish separately. Hence

$x + a + b + c = 0, \ y - ab - bc - ca = 0$

and $z + abc = 0$

$\therefore \quad x = -(a + b + c), \ y = ab + bc + ca,$

and $z = -abc$.

(ii) Consider the following equation in t,

$$\frac{x}{a + t} + \frac{y}{b + t} + \frac{z}{c + t} = 1 - \frac{(t - \lambda)(t - \mu)(t - \gamma)}{(t + a)(t + b)(t + c)} \quad ...(1)$$

x, y, z being for the present regarded as known quantities.

This equation when cleared of fractions is of second degree in t, and is satisfied for three values $t = \lambda$, $t = \mu$ and $t = \nu$ by virtue of the given equations; hence it must be an identity.

To find the value of x, we multiply (1) by $a + t$, and then put $t = -a$. Thus

$$x = -\frac{(-a - \lambda)(-a - \mu)(-a - \nu)}{(-a + b)(-a + c)}$$

or $\quad x = \dfrac{(a + \lambda)(a + \mu)(a + \nu)}{(a - b)(a - c)}$.

By reason of symmetry, we have

$$y = \frac{(b + \lambda)(b + \mu)(b + \nu)}{(b - c)(b - a)}$$

and $z = \dfrac{(c + \lambda)(c + \mu)(c + \nu)}{(c - a)(c - b)}$

Note : We know that if α, β are the roots of an equation, then this equation is

$x^2 - (\alpha + \beta)x + \alpha\beta = 0$

or $\quad x^2 - S_1 x + S_2 = 0$

where S_1 is sum of roots taken one at a time and S_2 is sum of products of roots taken two at a time. Similarly if there is an equation whose roots are α, β, γ then $\quad S_1 = \alpha + \beta + \gamma, \ S_2 = \alpha\beta + \beta\gamma + \gamma\alpha$, $S_3 = \alpha\beta\gamma$ and the corresponding equation will be $t^3 - S_1 t^2 + S_2 t - S_3 = 0$

Again we know that if a is a root of the equation $f(x) = 0$ then a will satisfy the equation, *i.e.* $f(a) = 0$.

Alternative Solution of Q. 22 (i).

Consider the equation $z + ty + t^2 x + t^3 = 0$

It is clear that the above equation is satisfied by $t = a, b, c$ by virtue of the above three given equations.

$\because\ z + a y + a^2 x + a^3 = 0,$

which is true by 1st equation and so on. Thus a, b, c are the roots of the equation

$$t^3 + t^2 x + t y + z = 0$$

$\therefore\ S_1 = a + b + c = -x,$

$S_2 = ab + bc + ca = y,\ S_3 = abc = -z$

$\therefore\ x = -(a + b + c),\ y = \Sigma\ ab,\ z = -abc.$

23. The given equation can be re-written as

$x + y + z = 7/2$ ...(1)

$yz + zx + xy = 7/2$ ...(2)

$xyz = 1$ ...(3)

From (2), $yz + x(y + z) = 7/2$

Hence from (3) and (1),

$\dfrac{1}{x} + x(7/2 - x) = 7/2$

or $2x^3 - 7x^2 + 7x - 2 = 0$

or $2(x^3 - 1) - 7x(x - 1) = 0$

or $(x - 1)(2x^2 - 5x + 2) = 0$

or $(x - 1)(x - 2)(2x - 1) = 0$

$\therefore\ x = 1, 2$ or $\dfrac{1}{2}.$

Taking $x = 1$, we have from (1),

$y + z = \dfrac{5}{2}$, and from (3), $yz = 1$

whence $\begin{cases} y = 2 \\ z = \frac{1}{2} \end{cases}$ or $\begin{cases} y = \frac{1}{2} \\ z = 2 \end{cases}$

Hence solutions are

$x = 1,\ y = 2,\ z = \dfrac{1}{2}$ and $x = 1,\ y = \dfrac{1}{2},\ z = 2.$

Similarly taking $x = 2$ and $\dfrac{1}{2}$, the other sets of solutions are

$x = 2,\ y = \dfrac{1}{2},\ z = 1;\ \ x = 2,\ y = 1,\ z = \dfrac{1}{2};$

$x = \dfrac{1}{2},\ y = 2,\ z = 1$ and $x = \dfrac{1}{2},\ y = 1,\ z = 2.$

Thus in all there are six sets of solutions.

Alt. Let $S_1 = x + y + z = 7/2,$

$S_2 = xy + yz + zx = 7/2,\ S_3 = xyz = 1.$

$\therefore\ x, y, z$ are the roots of

$t^3 - S_1 t^2 + S_2 t - S_3 = 0$

or $t^3 - \dfrac{7}{2} t^2 + \dfrac{7}{2} t - 1 = 0$

or $2t^3 - 7t^2 + 7t - 2 = 0$

$\therefore$ clearly $t = 1$ satisfies it.

$\therefore\ (t - 1)(2t^2 - 5t + 2) = 0$

or $(t - 1)(t - 2)(2t - 1) = 0$

$\therefore\ t = 1, 2, 1/2$ are the values of x, y, z.

x	y	z
or 1	2	1/2
1	1/2	2

Similarly choosing $x = 2$ and then $x = \dfrac{1}{2}$ we can have the following four other solution sets :

x	y	z	x	y	z
2	1	1/2	1/2	1	2
2	1/2	1	1/2	2	1

Thus there are six solution sets of the given equations.

24. (i) From first two equations, we get

$xy + yz + zx = \dfrac{1}{2}[(x + y + z)^2 - (x^2 + y^2 + z^2)]$

$= \dfrac{1}{2}[144 - 50] = 47$

Also $x^3 + y^3 + z^3 - 3xyz = (x + y + z)$

$\cdot (x^2 + y^2 + z^2 - yz - zx - xy)$

or $216 - 3xyz = 12(50 - 47)$

or $xyz = 60.$

Hence the given equations reduce to

$x + y + z = 12,\ yz + zx + xy = 47,\ xyz = 60.$

Now proceed as in Problem 23.

Solution sets in this case are :

$(3, 4, 5), (3, 5, 4), (4, 3, 5), (4, 5, 3), (5, 3, 4)$ and $(5, 4, 3).$

Alt. Here $S_1 = 12.$ Also $x^2 + y^2 + z^2 = 50$ gives

$(x + y + z)^2 - 2(xy + yz + zx) = 50$

or $144 - 2S_2 = 50\ \therefore\ 2S_2 = 94$ or $S_2 = 47$

Again $x^3 + y^3 + z^3 = 216.$

But $x^3 + y^3 + z^3 - 3xyz = (x + y + z)$

$\cdot (x^2 + y^2 + z^2 - \Sigma\ xy)$

or $216 - 3S_3 = 12(50 - 47) = 36$

or $216 - 36 = 3S_3\ \therefore\ S_3 = 60$

$\therefore\ S_1 = 12,\ S_2 = 47,\ S_3 = 60$

$\therefore\ x, y, z$ are the roots of cubic in t :

$t^3 - S_1 t^2 + S_2 t - S_3 = 0$

or $t^3 - 12t^2 + 47t - 60 = 0$

By trial $t = 3$ satisfies it

$\therefore\ (t - 3)(t^2 - 9t + 20) = 4$

or $(t - 3)(t - 4)(t - 5) = 0$

$\therefore\ t = 3, 4, 5.$

Hence the solution sets as above are

$\begin{matrix}(3, 4, 5) \\ (3, 5, 4)\end{matrix}$ or $\begin{matrix}(4, 3, 5) \\ (4, 5, 3)\end{matrix}$ or $\begin{matrix}(5, 3, 4) \\ (5, 4, 3)\end{matrix}$

(ii) Ans. $(1, 0, 0), (0, 1, 0), (0, 0, 1).$

25. Hint. The equation can be re-written as

$y(z - a) - a(z - a) = \alpha + a^2$

or $(y - a)(z - a) = \alpha + a^2$

Similarly $(z-a)(x-a)=\beta+a^2$.

and $(x-a)(y-a)=\gamma+a^2$ etc.

Ans. $x=a\pm\sqrt{\left\{\dfrac{(a^2+\beta)(a^2+\gamma)}{a^2+\alpha}\right\}}$, etc.

26. Subtracting the given equations in pairs,
$$x^2-y^2+(y-z)^2-(z-x)^2=a^2-b^2$$

i.e. $(x-y)(x+y)+(y-z+z-x)$
$$.(y-z-z+x)=a^2-b^2$$

or $(x-y)2z=a^2-b^2$ ...(1)

Similarly, $(y-z)2x=b^2-c^2$ ...(2)

and $(z-x)2y=c^2-a^2$. ...(3)

Now adding first of the given equations and (2), we get
$$x^2+2x(y-z)+(y-z)^2=a^2+b^2-c^2$$

or $(x+y-z)^2=a^2+b^2-c^2$

Similarly, $(y+z-x)^2=b^2+c^2-a^2$

and $(z+x-y)^2=c^2+a^2-b^2$

Taking square roots and then adding first two, we get
$$2y=\pm\sqrt{a^2+b^2-c^2}\pm\sqrt{b^2+c^2-a^2}\ \text{etc.}$$

27. We write the equations as
$$(x-a)+(y-b)+(z-c)=0$$
$$\left(\dfrac{x}{a}-1\right)+\left(\dfrac{y}{b}-1\right)+\left(\dfrac{z}{c}-1\right)=0 \quad\ldots(1)$$

or $bc(x-a)+ca(y-b)+ab(z-c)=0$ ...(2)

and $ax+by+cz=bc+ca+ab,$ ...(3)

From (1) and (2), by cross-multiplication, we have
$$\dfrac{x-a}{ab-ca}=\dfrac{y-b}{bc-ab}=\dfrac{z-c}{ca-bc}=k,\ \text{say}$$

Then $x=a+a(b-c)k,\ y=b+b(c-a)k,$
$$z=c+c(a-b)k. \quad\ldots(4)$$

Substituting in (3), we get
$$a^2+b^2+c^2+[a^2(b-c)+b^2(c-a)$$
$$+c^2(a-b)]k=bc+ca+ab$$

or $a^2+b^2+c^2-(b-c)(c-a)(a-b)k$
$$=bc+ca+ab$$

(Factorizing the coefficient of k)

or $k=\dfrac{a^2+b^2+c^2-bc-ca-ab}{(b-c)(c-a)(a-b)}$ ...(5)

Hence solution is given by (4) where k is given by (5).

28. We have $x+y=2,\ xy=1+z^2$

Eliminating y, we get
$$x(2-x)=1+z^2$$

∴ $x^2-2x+(1+z^2)=0.$ For real x
$$\Delta=4-4(1+z^2)\geq0\ \text{ or }\ -4z^2\geq0$$

∴ $z=0$

Hence $x+y=2,\ xy=1$

∴ x,y are roots of $t^2-2t+1=0$

∴ $x=1,y=1,z=0$

29. (a) Multiplying 1st and 3rd relations, we get
$$y^2x^2+y^4+z^2x^2+z^2y^2=acy^2xz$$

or $(y^2x^2+y^2z^2)+(y^4+z^2x^2)=acy^2xz$

Dividing by y^2xz, we get
$$\dfrac{x^2+z^2}{xz}+\dfrac{y^2}{xz}+\dfrac{xz}{y^2}=ac \quad\ldots(1)$$

Substituting $\dfrac{x^2+z^2}{xz}=b$ from 2nd relation in (1),
we get
$$\dfrac{y^2}{zx}+\dfrac{zx}{y^2}=ac-b$$

(b) Solving the first two equations for x and y we have
by eliminating y,
$$[(a+b)x-ab]^2=0$$

∴ $x=\dfrac{ab}{a+b}=y.$

$$\dfrac{x^{n+1}}{a}+\dfrac{y^{n+1}}{b}=\left(\dfrac{ab}{a+b}\right)^{n+1}\left[\dfrac{1}{a}+\dfrac{1}{b}\right]$$

$$=\left(\dfrac{ab}{a+b}\right)^{n+1}\left[\dfrac{a+b}{ab}\right]=\left(\dfrac{ab}{a+b}\right)^{n}$$

30. Adding the equation, we get
$$(x-3)^3+(y-3)^3+(z-3)^3=0 \quad\ldots(1)$$

The triplet $(3,3,3)$ is a solution of (1).

It can be verified that it is also a solution of the given system of equations. (Note that verification of this statement is obligatory)

Let us now show that the system has no other solutions. From the first equation of the system, we have $y^3=9x^2-27x+27.$

The discriminant of the quadratic $9x^2-27x+27$ is negative.

Hence if (x_0,y_0,z_0) is a solution of the system, then $y_0^3>0$. Consequently $y_0>0$. Similarly $z_0>0$ and $x_0>0$.

Now from the first equation of the system, we have
$$(y_0-3)(y_0^2+3y_0+9)=9x_0(x_0-3). \quad\ldots(2)$$

Since $x_0>0$ and $y^2+3y_0+9>0$.

It follows from (2) that the numbers y_0-3 and x_0-3 cannot differ in sign. Similarly it follows from the second equation that z_0-3 and y_0-3 cannot have different signs either.

Thus if $x_0>3$, then $y_0>3$ and $z_0>3$; and if $x_0<3$, then $y_0<3$, and $z_0<3$. Thus neither $x_0>3,y_0>3,z_0>3$ nor $x_0<3,\ y_0<3,z_0<3$ are suitable. Hence $x_0=3,\ y_0=3$ and $z_0=3$ is the only solution.

Problem Set (5)

1. The solution of the equation $2^{3/\log_3 x} = \dfrac{1}{64}$ is

   (a) 3

   (b) $\dfrac{1}{3}$

   (c) $\dfrac{1}{\sqrt{(3)}}$

   (d) None of these.

2. The solution set of $|3 - x| = a$ is
   (a) $\{3 - a, 3 + a\}$ for $a \geq 0$ and ϕ for $a < 0$
   (b) $[3 - a, 3 + a]$
   (c) ϕ
   (d) none of these.

3. The solution set of the equation
   $\log_2 (3 - x) + \log_2 (1 - x) = 3$ is
   (a) $\{-1, 5\}$
   (b) $\{-1\}$
   (c) $\{5\}$,
   (d) ϕ

4. The solution set of the equation $x^{\log_x (1-x)^2} = 9$ is
   (a) $\{-2, 4\}$
   (b) $\{4\}$
   (c) $\{0, -2, 4\}$
   (d) None of these

5. The equation $3^{|3x-4|} = 9^{2x-2}$ has the solution
   ....

6. The equation $|x + 2| = -2$ has
   (a) only one solution
   (b) infinite number of solutions
   (c) no solution
   (d) none of these.

7. The solution set of the equation $|x - 3| = x - 3$ is
   (a) $]3, \infty[$
   (b) $[3, \infty]$
   (c) ϕ
   (d) the set **R** of all real numbers.

8. The equation $|2x - x^2 - 3| = 1$ has
   (a) only one solution
   (b) no solution
   (c) 4 solutions
   (d) infinite no. of solutions.

9. The solution of the equation
   $|x| - 2|x + 1| + 3|x + 2| = 0$ is ....

10. The solution set of the equation
    $||x - 1| + 2| = 1$ is ....

11. The equation $x^{(3/4)(\log_2 x)^2 + \log_2 x - 5/4} = \sqrt{2}$ has
    (a) at least one real solution
    (b) exactly three real solutions
    (c) exactly one irrational solution
    (d) complex roots.

12. The solution of $\log_7 \log_5 (\sqrt{x + 5} + \sqrt{x}) = 0$ is ....

13. The equations $x + y = 2$, $2x + 2y = 3$ have
    (a) a unique solution

(b) no solution
(c) infinitely many solutions
(d) none of these.

14. The value of x which satisfy
    $$yz = a^2, \quad zx = b^2, \quad xy = c^2 \quad \text{are}$$
    (a) $\pm ca / b$
    (b) $\pm a / bc$
    (c) $\pm bc / a$
    (d) $\pm b / ca$

15. For the equation $|x|^2 + |x| - 6 = 0$ the roots are
    (a) one and only one real number
    (b) real with sum one
    (c) real with sum zero
    (d) real with product zero

Solution to Problem Set (5)

1. Ans. (c). **Hint** : $\dfrac{3}{\log_3 x} = -6$ ∵ $64 = 2^6$

   ∴ $\log_3 x = -\dfrac{1}{2}$ or $x = 3^{-1/2} = \dfrac{1}{\sqrt{3}}$

2. Ans. (a).

3. Ans. (b).
   Hint. The equation will be meaningful if $x < 1$. The equation reduces to $\log_2 (3 - x)(1 - x) = 3$ from which we obtain $(3 - x)(1 - x) = 2^3 = 8$ or $x^2 - 4x - 5 = 0$. Its roots are -1 and 5. The root 5 is rejected since it does not satisfy the condition $x < 1$.

4. Ans. (b).   5. Ans. $8/7$
6. Ans. (c).   7. Ans. (b).
8. Ans. (b).   9. Ans. $[-2]$
10. Ans. ϕ.
11. Ans. (a) and (b).
    First note that $x > 0$. **Refer Q. 59, 60 P. 261-275.**
    ∴ $x = 2, \ 2^{-2}, \ 2^{-1/3} = 2, \ \dfrac{1}{4}, \ \dfrac{1}{2^{1/3}}$.

    Thus we have exactly three real solutions. Again we know that a cubic equation has at least one real solution.
    ∴ (a) and (b) are correct.

12. Ans. $x = 4$. We have
    $$\log_7 \log_5 [\sqrt{x + 5} + \sqrt{x}] = 0$$
    $\Rightarrow \log_5 [\sqrt{x + 5} + \sqrt{x}] = 7^0 = 1$
    $\Rightarrow \sqrt{x + 5} + \sqrt{x} = 5 \quad \Rightarrow \sqrt{x + 5} = 5 - \sqrt{x}$
    $\Rightarrow x + 5 = 25 + x - 10\sqrt{x}$
    $\Rightarrow 2 = \sqrt{x} \quad \Rightarrow x = 4$.

13. Ans. (b).

14. Ans. (c).

15. Ans. (c).
    $|x| = 2$ as $|x| \neq -3$ ∴ $x = \pm 2$.

CHAPTER

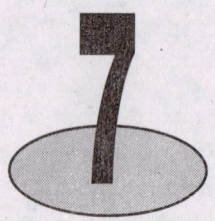

Algebra

Permutations and Combinations

§1. Introduction.

Permutation. Each of the different arrangements which can be made by taking some or all of a number of things is called a **permutation.**

Combination. Each of the different groups or selections which can be made by taking some or all of a number of things (irrespective of order) is called a **combination.**

Illustration. Suppose there are 4 questions marked 1, 2, 3, 4 and out of these you are to select any three. You can choose them as 123, 124, 341, 342, *i.e.* 4 ways of selection. But on the other hand if you consider the order also in which you attempt the questions of each selection then it would be permutation.

Consider the selection 123. These three questions can be arranged as 123, 132, 231, 213, 312, 321, *i.e.*, 6 arrangements for one selection. Since there are 4 selections, hence the total number of arrangements of the three questions will be $4 \times 6 = 24$ permutations which is therefore the number of arrangements of 3 things taken out of four.

Fundamental Theorem

If there are m ways of doing a thing and for each of the m ways there are associated n ways of doing a second thing then the total number of ways of doing the two things will be mn.

As an example suppose six subjects are to be taught in four periods. For the first period we can put any of the six subjects, *i.e.* there are 6 ways of filling the first period. For the second period we are left with remaining subjects and hence there are 5 ways of filling the second period. Hence the number of ways in which first two periods can be filled up is $6 \times 5 = 30$ ways.

Important results.

(a) **Number of permutations of n dissimilar things taken r at a time.**

$$^{n}P_{r} = \frac{n!}{(n-r)!} = n(n-1)(n-2)....(n-r+1).$$

The last factor is $[n-(r-1)] = n-r+1$.

where $n! = 1.2.3.......n$.

Note that $n! = n.(n-1)!$

$= n(n-1).(n-2)!$ etc.

Note : In the above **repetition was not allowed** so that if we could fill the first place in n ways then second could be filled in $(n-1)$, third in $(n-2),...$ and rth in $(n-r+1)$ ways. Hence the total by fundamental theorem was

$n(n-1)(n-2)...(n-r+1)$ ways.

Now if **repetition is allowed.**

In this case each of the r places can be filled in n ways. Hence by fundamental theorem all the r places can be filled in $n.n.n.n...r$ times $= n^{r}$ ways.

(b) **Number of permutations of n dissimilar things taken all at a time.**

$$^{n}P_{n} = n(n-1)(n-2)............[n-(n-1)]$$

$$= n(n-1)(n-2)...........3.2.1 = n!$$

(c)* **Number of combinations of n dissimilar things taken r at a time.**

$$^{n}C_{r} = \frac{n!}{(n-r)!\,r!} = \frac{^{n}P_{r}}{r!} \quad \text{or} \quad r!\,^{n}C_{r} = {}^{n}P_{r}.$$

(d) **Number of combinations of n dissimilar things taken all at a time.**

$$^{n}C_{n} = \frac{n!}{n!(n-n)!} = \frac{1}{0!} = 1 \qquad \because \ 0! = 1$$

(e) **If out of n things p are exactly alike of one kind, q exactly alike of second kind and r exactly alike of third kind** and the rest all different, then the number of permutations of n things taken all at a time

$$= \frac{n!}{p!.q!.r!}.$$

(f)* **Number of circular permutations of n different things taken all at a time.**

Here having fixed one thing, the remaining $(n-1)$ things can be arranged round the table in $(n-1)!$ ways.

Note : If, however, n persons are to be arranged in a row, then as shown in (b) the number of arrangements was $n!$, whereas for a circular table as shown above the number of arrangements is $(n-1)!$

Particular Case : Necklace : Number of arrangements of n beads all different to form a necklace or on a circular wire will be $\frac{1}{2}(n-1)!$ as explained in the figure below :

R = Ram, G = Ganesh, B = Brahma
R = Red, G = Green, B = Blue

The above seating arrangement of three persons on the round table are different as shown in upper figure and that is why we say $(n-1)!$ clockwise and anticlockwise make different arrangements.

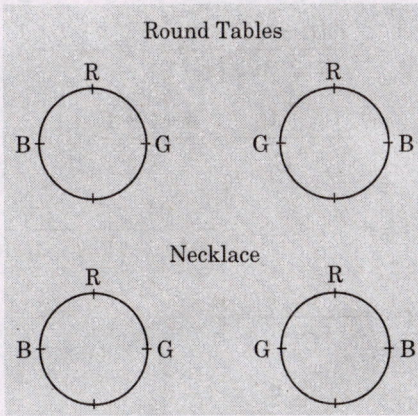

Round Tables

Necklace

Fig. 1

In the lower figure, the above two arrangements of three flowers to form a necklace is the same because on the necklace we get the same arrangement and that is why we say the total number of arrangements of n beads for forming a necklace is $\frac{1}{2}(n-1)!$. Here clockwise or anticlockwise does not change the character of the necklace. It remains the same.

Ex. In how many ways a wedding garland can be formed out of 15 flowers of different colours ?

Sol. Refer particular case above.

Ans. $\frac{1}{2}(15-1)! = \frac{1}{2}(14!)$

(g) **If some or all of n things be taken at a time then the number of combinations will be**

$$2^n - 1. \quad \because \quad {}^nC_1 + {}^nC_2 + \dots + {}^nC_n = 2^n - 1$$

(h)* ${}^nC_r = {}^nC_{n-r}$.

(i) ${}^nC_{r_1} = {}^nC_{r_2} \Rightarrow r_1 = r_2$ or $r_1 + r_2 = n$.

(j) ${}^nC_r + {}^nC_{r-1} = {}^{n+1}C_r$ **(Important)**

(k) Number of combinations of n dissimilar things taken r at a time when p particular things always occur
$$= {}^{n-p}C_{r-p}.$$

(l) Number of combinations of n dissimilar things taken r at a time when p particular things never occur
$$= {}^{n-p}C_r.$$

(m) Number of permutations of n dissimilar things taken r at a time when p particular things always occur
$$= {}^{n-p}C_{r-p} \cdot r!$$

(n) Number of permutations of n dissimilar things taken r at a time when p particular things never occur
$$= {}^{n-p}C_r \, r!.$$

(o)* **Division into groups.**

(i) The number of ways in which $m+n$ things can be divided into two groups containing m and n things respectively $= \dfrac{(m+n)!}{m! \, n!}$.

(ii) If $n=m$, the groups are equal, and in this case the number of **different** ways of subdivision
$$= \frac{2m!}{m!\,m!\,2!},$$

for in any one way it is possible to interchange the two groups without obtaining new division.

(iii) But if $2m$ things are to be divided equally between two persons, then the number of divisions
$$= \frac{2m!}{m!\,m!}.$$

(iv) Similarly the number of divisions of $m+n+p$ things into groups of m, n and p things respectively $= \dfrac{(m+n+p)!}{m!\,n!\,p!}$.

(v) If $3m$ things are divided into three equal groups, then the number of divisions $= \dfrac{(3m)!}{m!\,m!\,m!\,3!}$.

(vi) But if $3m$ things are to be divided among three persons, then the number of divisions
$$= \frac{(3m)!}{m!\,m!\,m!}.$$

(p) Number of permutations of n dissimilar things taken r at a time when each thing can be repeated once, twice, ...upto r times $= n^r$.

Note : From above we conclude the following : While distributing certain m things equally amongst four persons, the thing which has gone to one person shall not go to the other and hence in this case we shall not divide by 4!. But if however we form four equal groups then we shall divide by 4!.

For example : If 20 different things are to be equally distributed amongst 4 persons the answer will be $\dfrac{(20!)}{(5!)^4}$

but if 20 things are to form 4 equal groups then the answer will be $\dfrac{(20!)}{(5!)^4\,4!}$. This 4 ! corresponds to the number of these four groups.

(q) **Selection out of identical things.**

(i)* If there be n **identical** things out of which we have to draw r things then the number of combinations or selection will be 1.

But if there be n **different** things then the number of selections of r things will be ^nC_r.

(ii) If there be n **identical** things and we have to make a selection of **any number**, it would mean that we may **select none, one, two,** or **three, ...,** or n things. Thus the number of selections will be $n + 1$.

But for **non-empty selection** it will be n only, as the case of 'none' will be excluded.

But if there be n **different** things then the number of selections of any number r (r may be 0, 1, 2, ..., n) will be

$$^nC_0 + {}^nC_1 + {}^nC_2 + ... + {}^nC_n = 2^n.$$

But for **non-empty selection** it will be

$2^n - 1$ (1 corresponds to $^nC_0$)

(iii) Total number of ways in which it is possible to make selection by taking some or all out of $p + q + r$ things, where p are alike of one kind, q alike of a second kind, r alike of a third kind and so on.

$$= (p + 1)(q + 1)(r + 1) ...... - 1$$

(iv) If there be p things alike of one kind, q alike of another kind while r are all different, then the total number of **non-empty** selection is $(p + 1)(q + 1).2^r - 1$.

There is no restriction about the number of things to be selected except that non-empty. Hence $(p + 1)$ and $(q + 1)$ correspond to p alike and q alike, 2^r corresponds to r different things as each can be dealt in two ways (either taken or not taken). $- 1$ in the above corresponds when neither of three types of things is taken. For illustration **see Q. 25 Misc. set P. 328-334.**

(r) Number of combinations of n things taken r at a time when each may occur once, twice, thrice etc. upto r times in any combination $= {}^{n+r-1}C_r$

$$\therefore \quad {}^nC_1 + {}^nC_2 + {}^nC_3 + ... + {}^nC_r$$
$$= {}^{n+1}C_2 + {}^{n+1}C_3 + ... + {}^nC_r, \qquad \text{by (j)}$$
$$= {}^{n+2}C_3 + ... + {}^nC_r = {}^{n+r-1}C_r.$$

(s) **The greatest value of ^nC_r.**

(i)* When n **is even,** ^nC_r is greatest when

$$r = n/2.$$

(ii)* When n **is odd** ^nC_r is greatest when

$$r = (n-1)/2 \quad \text{or} \quad (n+1)/2.$$

(iii)* $^nC_r = \dfrac{r \text{ decreasing numbers starting with } n}{r \text{ increasing numbers starting with } 1}$

$$^nC_3 = \frac{n(n-1)(n-2)}{1.2.3}$$

$$^nC_r = \frac{n(n-1)(n-2)........(n-r+1)}{1.2.3........r}$$

(iv)* $^nC_r \div {}^nC_{r-1} = \dfrac{n(n-1)...(n-r+1)}{1.2.3....r}$

$$\div \frac{n(n-1).....(n-r)}{1.2.3....(r-1)} = \frac{n-r+1}{r}$$

$$\therefore \quad \frac{^nC_r}{^nC_{r-1}} = \frac{n-r+1}{r}$$

$$^nC_r \div {}^{n-1}C_{r-1} = \frac{n!}{r!(n-r)!} \frac{(n-1)!}{(r-1)!(n-r)!} = \frac{n}{r}$$

or $\dfrac{^nC_r}{^{n-1}C_{r-1}} = \dfrac{n}{r}$

or $^nC_r = \dfrac{n}{r} {}^{n-1}C_{r-1}$

$^nP_r = r$ **decreasing numbers starting with** n

$\ast \quad ^nP_3 = n(n-1)(n-2)$

$^nP_r = n(n-1)(n-2)........(n-r+1)$

$$\therefore \quad \frac{^nP_r}{^nP_{r-1}} = n-r+1$$

(t)* **Gap Method.** Suppose 5 males A, B, C, D, E are arranged in a row as

$$\times A \times B \times C \times D \times E \times$$

There will be six gaps between these five. Four in between and two at either end. Now if three females P, Q, R are to be arranged so that they are never together we shall use gap method *i.e.* arrange them in between these 6 gaps. Hence the answer will be $^6P_3$.

(u)* **String Method.**

Together. Suppose we have to arrange 6 persons in a row which can be done in $6! = 720$ ways. But if two particular persons are to be together always, then, we tie these two particular persons with a string. Thus we have $6 - 2 + 1$ (1 corresponding to these two together) $= 4 + 1 = 5$ units, which can be arranged in $5!$ ways. Now we loosen the string and these two particular persons can be arranged amongst themselves in $2!$ ways. Thus the total arrangements will be $5!.2! = 120 \times 2 = 240$.

Never together. $=$ Total $-$ together
$$= 720 - 240 = 480.$$

(v) Selection of **at least one lady** for the committee out of gents and ladies = **Total – No lady** = selection of committees with at least one. Similarly **at least two ladies = Total – {No lady + one lady}**

(w)* **Zero in the L.H.S. or zero in the R.H.S. of a given number**

      053247   532470

Both have six digits but actually number on the L.H.S. is of five digits whereas number in the R.H.S. is of six digits.

(x) **Numbers divisible by (i) 2 (ii) 3 (iii) 4 (iv) 5 (v) 25 (vi) 9**
    (i) All the numbers whose last digit is an even number 0, 2, 4, 6 or 8 are divisible by 2.
    (ii) All the numbers sum of whose digit is divisible by 3 will be divisible by 3 e.g.534. Sum of the digits is 12 which is divisible by 3 and hence 534 is also divisible by 3.
    (iii) All those numbers whose last two digits number is divisible by 4 are all divisible by 4. e.g. 7312, 8936, 2752 are such that 12, 36, 52 are all divisible by 4 and hence the given numbers are also divisible by 4.
    (iv) All those numbers which have either 0 or 5 as the last digit are divisible by 5.

(v) As in (iii) all those numbers whose last two digits are divisible by 25 are all divisible by 25 e.g. 73125, 2400, 3150 etc.

(vi) All those numbers sum of whose digits is divisible by 9 i.e., the sum should be 9, 18, 27, etc.

(y) **Where to add and where to multiply.**

When the occurrence of event B is dependent on the occurrence of event A then we multiply their corresponding no. of ways by fundamental theorem to get the total number of ways. But when they are independent we just add them.

(z)* **Where to use permutation and where to use combination :**
    (i) The word arrangement is associated with permutation and selection is associated with combination.
    (ii) **Permutation via combination**
$$^nP_r = {}^nC_r \, (r!) \qquad \text{[See (c)]}$$
    (iii)* Questions on Letters of alphabet forming words will be of permutation. Similarly questions on numbers involving digits will be of permutation and also seating arrangements in a line or around a table.
    (iv)* Questions on formation of committees and distribution into groups will be of combination.

Problem Set (1)

Questions based upon definition of ^nC_r and ^nP_r and allied formulae.

1. (a) Prove that $^nC_r = {}^nC_{n-r}$.

    (b) If $0 < r < s \le n$ and $^nP_r = {}^nP_s$, then the value of $r + s$ is
    (a) 1   (b) 2
    (c) $2n-1$ (d) $2n-2$

2. If $^nC_{10} = {}^nC_{15}$, find $^{27}C_n$.

3. (a) If $^nC_7 = {}^nC_4$, find n.

    (b) If the number of radical axes formed out of a given number of circles be same as the number of radical centres, then find the number of given circles.

4. (a) If $^{15}C_{3r} = {}^{15}C_{r+3}$, find r.

    (b) If $p = {}^{n+2}P_{n+2}; q = {}^nP_{11}, r = {}^{(n-11)}P_{n-11}$ and if $p = 182\,qr$, then show that the value of r is 12.

5. (a)* If $^nC_{12} = {}^nC_8$, find $^nC_{17}$ and $^{22}C_n$.

    (b) If $^{k^2-k}C_2 = {}^{k^2-k}C_4$, then $k =$
    (a) 2   (b) 3
    (c) 4   (d) none of these

6.* Prove that $^nC_{r-1} + {}^nC_r = {}^{n+1}C_r$.   **(D.C.E. 1997)**

7. Prove with or without the use of the formula
$$^nP_r = {}^{n-1}P_r + r \cdot {}^{n-1}P_{r-1}.$$

8. If $^9P_5 + 5 \cdot {}^9P_4 = {}^{10}P_r$, find r.

9. (a) Prove that $^nP_n = {}^nP_{n-1}$ and $^nP_n = 2\,{}^nP_{n-2}$

    (b) Prove with or without the use of the formula
$$^nP_r = n \cdot {}^{n-1}P_{r-1}.$$

    (c) The value of $\sum\limits_{r=1}^{n} \dfrac{{}^nP_r}{r!}$ is
    (a) 2^n (b) $2^n - 1$
    (c) 2^{n-1} (d) $2^n + 1$

10. (a) If $^8C_r - {}^7C_3 = {}^7C_2$, find r.

    (b) Let T_n denote the number of triangles which can be formed using the vertices of a regular polygon of n sides. If $T_{n+1} - T_n = 21$, then n equals
    (a) 5   (b) 7
    (c) 6   (d) 4   **(I.I.T. Sc. 2001)**

11. (a) Evaluate $^{15}C_8 + {}^{15}C_9 - {}^{15}C_6 - {}^{15}C_7$.

    (b) The value of
$$({}^7C_0 + {}^7C_1) + ({}^7C_1 + {}^7C_2) + \ldots + ({}^7C_6 + {}^7C_7) \text{ is}$$

(a) $2^8 - 2$ (b) $2^8 - 1$

(c) $2^8 + 1$ (d) 2^8 **(C.E.T. Haryana 1996)**

12. (a)* Prove that $^nC_r + 2 \cdot {}^nC_{r-1} + {}^nC_{r-2} = {}^{n+2}C_r$.

   (b)* If $^nC_{n-r} + 3\,{}^nC_{n-r+1} + 3\,{}^nC_{n-r+2}$
$$+\ {}^nC_{n-r+3} = {}^pC_r$$

     then prove that $p = n + 3$.

   (c) If
$$\frac{{}^nC_r + 4\,{}^nC_{r+1} + 6\,{}^nC_{r+2} + 4\,{}^nC_{r+3} + {}^nC_{r+4}}{{}^nC_r + 3\,{}^nC_{r+1} + 3\,{}^nC_{r+2} + {}^nC_{r+3}}$$
$$= \frac{n+k}{r+k}, \text{ then the value of } k \text{ is}$$

     (a) 1   (b) 2

     (c) 4   (d) 5

   (d)* Prove that $\displaystyle\sum_{k=m}^{n} {}^kC_r = {}^{n+1}C_{r+1} - {}^mC_{r+1}$

                             (M.N.R. 1997)

13. (a)* Prove that $^{n-1}C_3 + {}^{n-1}C_4 > {}^nC_3$ if $n > 7$.

   (b) $^{n+1}C_6 + {}^nC_4 > {}^{n+2}C_5 - {}^nC_5$ will hold good

     for all n greater than

     (a) 1   (b) 10

     (c) 9   (d) 8

14.* Find the value of $^{47}C_4 + \displaystyle\sum_{r=1}^{5} {}^{(52-r)}C_3$

15. (a)* If $^nC_6 : {}^{n-3}C_3 = 33 : 4$, find n.

   (b) If $^{56}P_{r+6} : {}^{54}P_{r+3} = 30800 : 1$, find r

   (c) If $^{n+2}C_8 : {}^{n-2}P_4 = 57 : 16$, find n.

16. If $^{10}P_r = 604800$ and $^{10}C_r = 120$, find r.

17. If $^{2n+1}P_{n-1} : {}^{2n-1}P_n = 3 : 5$, find n.

18. (a)* If $^nP_r = {}^nP_{r+1}$ and $^nC_r = {}^nC_{r-1}$, find n and r.

   (b) If $^{m+n}P_2 = 90$ and $^{m-n}P_2 = 30$, then $(m, n) =$

     (a) $(16, 8)$ (b) $(9, 2)$

     (c) $(8, 2)$ (d) $(7, 3)$

19. Prove $^{4n}C_{2n} : {}^{2n}C_n = [1.3.5 \dots (4n-1)]$
$$: [1.3.5 \dots (2n-1)]^2.$$

20. (a) If $^{15}C_r : {}^{15}C_{r-1} = 11 : 5$, find r.

   (b) The smallest value of r satisfying the inequality $^{10}C_{r-1} > 2 \cdot {}^{10}C_r$ is

     (a) 7   (b) 10

     (c) 9   (d) 8

   (c) If $^6C_n + 2\,{}^6C_{n+1} + {}^6C_{n+2} > {}^8C_3$, then the quadratic equations whose roots are α, β and $\alpha^{n-1}, \beta^{n-1}$ have

     (a) no common root   (b) 1 common root

21. (a)* If $^nC_{r-1} = 36$, $^nC_r = 84$ and $^nC_{r+1} = 126$, find the values of n and r.

   (b) If $^nC_r : {}^nC_{r+1} : {}^nC_{r+2} = 3 : 4 : 5$, then the value of $2n + 3r$ is

     (a) 201   (b) 202

     (c) 203   (d) 204

22. If $^{28}C_{2r} : {}^{24}C_{2r-4} = 225 : 11$, then

     (a) $r = 24$,   (b) $r = 14$,

     (c) $r = 7$,   (d) none of these.

23.* Evaluate $\dfrac{{}^{20}C_r}{{}^{25}C_R}$ when both numerator and denominator have their greatest values.

24.* If $a_n = \displaystyle\sum_{r=0}^{n} \frac{1}{{}^nC_r}$, then $\displaystyle\sum_{r=0}^{n} \frac{r}{{}^nC_r}$ equals

     (A) $(n-1)\,a_n$ (B) na_n

     (C) $\dfrac{1}{2} na_n$ (D) None of the above.

                                (I.I.T. 1998)

25. If C_k stands for ^nC_k then $\displaystyle\sum_{k=1}^{n} \left(\frac{kC_k}{C_k + C_{n-k}}\right)^2$ is equal to $\dfrac{n(n+1)\,2n+1)}{24}$.

26. Prove that the product of r consecutive integers is divisible by r!

27. If $^{n-1}C_4 - {}^{n-1}C_3 - \dfrac{5}{4}\,{}^{n-2}P_2 < 0$ then the number of values $n \in N$ has is

     (a) 5   (b) 6   (c) 7   (d) 8

28. If $^{n-1}C_r = (k^2 - 3)\,{}^nC_{r+1}$, then $k \in$

     (a) $(-\sqrt{3}, \sqrt{3})$ (b) $(\sqrt{3}, 2]$

     (c) $[0, \sqrt{3}]$ (d) $(\sqrt{3}, 2)$ **(Screening 2004)**

29. Using permutation or otherwise prove that $\dfrac{n^2!}{(n!)^n}$ is an integer, where n is a positive integer.   **(I.I.T. 2004)**

30. Sum of the series $\displaystyle\sum_{r=1}^{n} (r^2 + 1)\,(r!)$ is

     (a) $(n+1)!$ (b) $(n+2)! - 1$

     (c) $n(n+1)!$ (d) none of these

31. The number of integral points that lie exactly in the interior of the triangle with vertices $O(0, 0)$, $A(21, 0)$, $B(0, 21)$ is

     (a) 105   (b) 133

     (c) 190   (d) 233

Solutions to Problem Set (1)

1. (a) $^nC_r = {}^nC_{n-r}$

   The number of combinations of n dissimilar things taken r at a time will be ^nC_r. Now if we take out a group of r things, we are left with a group of $(n-r)$ things. Hence the number of combinations of n things taken r at a time is equal to the number of combinations of n things taken $(n-r)$ at a time.

   $\therefore \quad ^nC_r = {}^nC_{n-r}$

   Alternative Method. We know that

   $$^nC_r = \frac{n!}{r!(n-r)!}$$

   $$^nC_{n-r} = \frac{n!}{(n-r)!(n-n+r)!} = \frac{n!}{r!(n-r)!}$$

   $\therefore \quad ^nC_r = {}^nC_{n-r}$

   (b) Ans. (c).

   $$\frac{n!}{(n-r)!} = \frac{n!}{(n-s)!}$$

   $\therefore \quad (n-r)! = (n-s)!$

   Given $r < s \Rightarrow -r > -s \quad \therefore \quad (n-r) > (n-s)$

   We know that two different factorials are zero and one

   $\therefore \quad n - r = 1$ and $n - s = 0$

   $\therefore \quad r = n-1, s = n \quad \therefore \quad r + s = 2n - 1$

2. $^nC_{10} = {}^nC_{15}$. ...(1)

   We know that $^nC_r = {}^nC_{n-r}$

   $\therefore \quad ^nC_{10} = {}^nC_{n-10} = {}^nC_{15}$, by (1)

   $\therefore \quad n - 10 = 15$ or $n = 25$

   or If $^nC_x = {}^nC_y$ then $x + y = n$.

   Hence from (1), we get $10 + 15 = 25 = n$

   $\therefore \quad ^{27}C_n = {}^{27}C_{25} = {}^{27}C_{27-25} = {}^{27}C_2$

   $$= \frac{27 \times 26}{1 \times 2} = 27 \times 13 = 351 \qquad \text{by (s) (iii) P. 294.}$$

3. (a) Ans. 11.

   (b) Let there be n circles. Radical axis is obtained by taking 2 circles at a time and radical centre is obtained by taking 3 circles at a time.

   $\therefore \quad ^nC_2 = {}^nC_3 \quad \therefore \quad n = 2 + 3 = 5$

4. (a) $\because \quad ^{15}C_{3r} = {}^{15}C_{r+3} \quad \therefore \quad 3r + r + 3 = 15$

   $\therefore \quad 4r = 12$ or $r = 3$.

   (b) $p = (n+2)!, q = \dfrac{n!}{(n-11)!}; r = (n-11)!$

   From the given relation we have

   $$(n+2)! = 182 \frac{n!}{(n-11)!}(n-11)! = 182 \cdot n!$$

$(n+2)(n+1) = 182$ or $n^2 + 3n - 180 = 0$

or $(n+15)(n-12) = 0$

$\therefore \quad n = 12$ [+ive value]

5. (a) $^nC_{12} = {}^nC_8 \quad \therefore \quad 12 + 8 = n$ or $n = 20$

   $\therefore \quad ^nC_{17} = {}^{20}C_{17} = {}^{20}C_{20-17} = {}^{20}C_3$

   $$= \frac{20 \times 19 \times 18}{1 \times 2 \times 3} = 20 \times 19 \times 3 = 1140.$$

   $$^{22}C_n = {}^{22}C_{20} = {}^{22}C_{22-20}$$

   $$= {}^{22}C_2 = \frac{22 \times 21}{1 \times 2} = 11 \times 21 = 231$$

   (b) Ans. (b).

   We know that if $^nC_p = {}^nC_q$ then $p + q = n$

   $\therefore \quad 2 + 4 = k^2 - k$ or $k^2 - k - 6 = 0$

   or $(k-3)(k+2) = 0$

   $\therefore \quad k = 3, -2$ but -2 is $-$ive so rejected.

   $\therefore \quad k = 3 \Rightarrow$ (b)

6. $^nC_{r-1} + {}^nC_r = {}^{n+1}C_r$.

   Without the use of formula :

   Suppose we have to take r things out of $(n+1)$ things. Then there are $^{n+1}C_r$ combinations.

   Now to find the combinations in which a **particular thing always occurs** we shall set aside that particular thing and form the combinations from the remaining n things taking $r-1$ at a time which will be

   $^nC_{r-1}$. ...(1)

   Again we shall find the combinations in which a particular thing never occurs. Excluding this particular thing we have only n things from which we have to form combinations of taken r at a time which will be ^nC_r. ...(2)

   Clearly the sum of the combinations formed in the above two ways will be $^{n+1}C_r$

   $\therefore \quad ^nC_{r-1} + {}^nC_r = {}^{n+1}C_r$.

   Alternative Method : With the use of formula

   $$^{n+1}C_r = \frac{(n+1)!}{r!(n-r+1)!} \qquad ...(1)$$

   $$^nC_{r-1} + {}^nC_r = \frac{n!}{(r-1)!(n-r+1)!} + \frac{n!}{r!(n-r)!}$$

   Now $(n-r+1)! = (n-r+1) \cdot (n-r)!$

   and $r! = r \cdot (r-1)!$

   $\therefore \quad$ R.H.S. $= \dfrac{n!}{(r-1)!(n-r)!}\left[\dfrac{1}{n-r+1} + \dfrac{1}{r}\right]$

   $$= \frac{n!(r+n-r+1)}{(r-1)!(n-r)!(n-r+1)r}$$

   $$= \frac{n!(n+1)}{r \cdot (r-1)!(n-r+1) \cdot (n-r)!}$$

$= \dfrac{(n+1)!}{r!\,(n-r+1)!}$ ...(2)

Hence from (1) and (2), we get

$^nC_{r-1} + {}^nC_r = {}^{n+1}C_r$.

7. **With the use of formula :**

L.H.S. $= {}^nP_r = \dfrac{n!}{(n-r)!}$ ...(1)

R.H.S. $= {}^{n-1}P_r + r \cdot {}^{n-1}P_{r-1} = \dfrac{(n-1)!}{(n-r-1)!} + r \cdot \dfrac{(n-1)!}{(n-r)!}$

$= \dfrac{(n-1)!}{(n-r-1)!}\left[1 + \dfrac{r}{n-r}\right]$

$[\because\ (n-r)! = (n-r)\cdot(n-r-1)!]$

$= \dfrac{n\cdot(n-1)!}{(n-r)\cdot(n-r-1)!} = \dfrac{n!}{(n-r)!}$ ...(2)

Hence from (1) and (2),

$^nP_r = {}^{n-1}P_r + r\cdot{}^{n-1}P_{r-1}$.

Without the use of formula :

As in Q. 6 we shall divide the number of permutations of n dissimilar things taken r at a time, *i.e.* ^nP_r into two parts. Suppose **a particular thing is not to be included**, then the number of permutations of the remaining $(n-1)$ things taken r at a time will be $^{n-1}P_r$.

Now suppose that a particular thing x is **always to be included** then the number of permutations of $(r-1)$ things out of the remaining $(n-1)$ things will be $^{n-1}P_{r-1}$. But in permutations we have to note order of things. This particular thing x which is always to be included **in each of the** $^{n-1}P_{r-1}$ ways can be placed in any of the r places [**see (t) P. 294**]. Thus there will be $r\cdot{}^{n-1}P_{r-1}$ permutations in this case. Clearly the sum of the permutations formed in the above two ways is equal to ^nP_r.

$\therefore\quad {}^nP_r = {}^{n-1}P_r + r\cdot{}^{n-1}P_{r-1}$.

8. $^9P_5 + 5\cdot{}^9P_4 = {}^{10}P_r$

L.H.S. $= \dfrac{9!}{4!} + 5\cdot\dfrac{9!}{5!}$, but $\dfrac{5}{5!} = \dfrac{1}{4!}$

$= \dfrac{2\cdot9!}{4!} = \dfrac{2\times5\cdot9!}{5\times4!} = \dfrac{10\cdot9!}{5!} = \dfrac{10!}{5!}$

R.H.S. $= \dfrac{10!}{(10-r)!} = \dfrac{10!}{5!} = $ L.H.S.

$\therefore\quad 10 - r = 5$ or $r = 5$.

9. (a) $^nP_n = n!$ and $^nP_{n-1} = \dfrac{n!}{[n-(n-1)]!} = \dfrac{n!}{1}$

$2\,{}^nP_{n-2} = 2\dfrac{n!}{[n-(n-2)]!} = \dfrac{2\,(n!)}{2!} = n!$

(b) $^nP_r = n\cdot{}^{n-1}P_{r-1}$.

R.H.S. $= n\dfrac{(n-1)!}{(n-r)!} = \dfrac{n!}{(n-r)!} = {}^nP_r = $ L.H.S.

Without the use of formula :

Let there be n things $a_1, a_2, \ldots, a_n$. If we put a_1 in the first place then from the remaining $(n-1)$ things we have to choose $(r-1)$ and the number of permutations will be $^{n-1}P_{r-1}$. Similarly we put a_2 in the first place then again the number of permutations will be $^{n-1}P_{r-1}$. Since each of the n things can occupy the first place therefore the total number of permutations will be $n\cdot{}^{n-1}P_{r-1}$.

This will be equal to the number of permutations of n things taken r at a time.

(c) Ans. (b).

$\dfrac{^nP_r}{r!} = {}^nC_r$

$\therefore\quad \sum\limits_{r=1}^{n} {}^nC_r = 2^n - 1$ (1 corresponds to $^nC_0$)

10. (a) $^8C_r - {}^7C_3 = {}^7C_2$

or $^8C_r = {}^7C_2 + {}^7C_3 = {}^8C_3 = {}^8C_5$

$\therefore\quad r = 3$ or 5.

(b) Ans. (b).

$^{n+1}C_3 - {}^nC_3 = 21$ ...(1)

But $^nC_2 + {}^nC_3 = {}^{n+1}C_3 = 21 + {}^nC_3$ by (i)

$\therefore\quad {}^nC_2 = 21$ or $\dfrac{n\,(n-1)}{1.2} = 21$

or $n^2 - n - 42 = 0$ or $(n-7)\,(n+6) = 0$

$\therefore\quad n = 7$.

11. (a) $({}^{15}C_8 + {}^{15}C_9) - ({}^{15}C_6 + {}^{15}C_7)$

$= {}^{16}C_9 - {}^{16}C_7$

$= {}^{16}C_9 - {}^{16}C_{16-7} = {}^{16}C_9 - {}^{16}C_9 = 0$,

$\because\quad {}^nC_r = {}^nC_{n-r}$

(b) Ans. (a).

$E = {}^8C_1 + {}^8C_2 + \ldots + {}^8C_7$

$= ({}^8C_0 + {}^8C_1 + \ldots + {}^8C_7 + {}^8C_8) - {}^8C_0 - {}^8C_8$

$= 2^8 - 1 - 1 = 2^8 - 2$.

12. (a) L.H.S. $= {}^nC_r + {}^nC_{r-1} + {}^nC_{r-1} + {}^nC_{r-2}$.

$= {}^{n+1}C_r + {}^{n+1}C_{r-1} = {}^{n+2}C_r$, by Q. 6

(b) $({}^nC_{n-r} + {}^nC_{n-r+1})$

$+ 2\,({}^nC_{n-r+1} + {}^nC_{n-r+2})$

$+ ({}^nC_{n-r+2} + {}^nC_{n-r+3})$

$= {}^{n+1}C_{n-r+1} + 2\cdot{}^{n+1}C_{n-r+2} + {}^{n+1}C_{n-r+3}$

$$=(^{n+1}C_{n-r+1} + {}^{n+1}C_{n-r+2})$$
$$+ (^{n+1}C_{n-r+2} + {}^{n+1}C_{n-r+3})$$
$$= {}^{n+2}C_{n-r+2} + {}^{n+2}C_{n-r+3}$$
$$= {}^{n+3}C_{n-r+3} = {}^{n+3}C_r \qquad [\because {}^nC_r = {}^nC_{n-r}]$$
$$\therefore \quad p = n+3.$$

(c) Ans. (c).
Use $^nC_r + {}^nC_{r-1} = {}^{n+1}C_r$ repeatedly.
$$D^r = {}^{n+1}C_{r+1} + 2\,{}^{n+1}C_{r+2} + {}^{n+1}C_{r+3}$$
$$= {}^{n+2}C_{r+2} + {}^{n+2}C_{r+3} = {}^{n+3}C_{r+3}$$
$$N^r = {}^{n+1}C_{r+1} + 3({}^{n+1}C_{r+2} + {}^{n+1}C_{r+3})$$
$$+ {}^{n+1}C_{r+4}$$

Middle term $= (1+2)\,{}^{n+2}C_{r+3}$
$$= {}^{n+2}C_{r+2} + 2\,{}^{n+2}C_{r+3} + {}^{n+2}C_{r+4}$$
$$= {}^{n+3}C_{r+3} + {}^{n+3}C_{r+4} = {}^{n+4}C_{r+4}$$
$$\therefore \quad E = \frac{N^r}{D^r} = \frac{(n+4)!}{(n-r)!(r+4)!} \frac{(r+3)!(n-r)!}{(n+3)!}$$
$$= \frac{n+4}{r+4} = \frac{n+k}{r+k} \qquad \therefore \quad k=4.$$

(d) We know that $^nC_r + {}^nC_{r+1} = {}^{n+1}C_{r+1}$
$$\therefore \quad {}^nC_r = {}^{n+1}C_{r+1} - {}^nC_{r+1} \qquad \dots(1)$$
Now put $n = m, m+1, m+2, \dots n$ and add and cancelling diagonally we shall be left only with two terms in R.H.S.
$$\sum_{k=m}^{n} {}^kC_r = {}^{n+1}C_{r+1} - {}^mC_{r+1}$$

13. (a) $^{n-1}C_3 + {}^{n-1}C_4 > {}^nC_3$
$$\Rightarrow {}^nC_4 > {}^nC_3$$
or $^nC_4 / {}^nC_3 > 1$
$$\therefore \quad \frac{n-4+1}{4} > 1 \quad \text{or} \quad n-3 > 4$$
$$\therefore \quad n > 7, \text{ by (s) (iv) P. 294.}$$

(b) Ans. (c). Consider
$$^nC_4 + {}^nC_5 + {}^{n+1}C_6 = {}^{n+1}C_5 + {}^{n+1}C_6$$
$$= {}^{n+2}C_6 > {}^{n+2}C_5 \text{ by given relation}$$
Since $6+5 = 11$, above will hold if $n+2 > 11$ or $n > 9$.

14. The given expression on putting $r = 1, 2, 3, 4, 5$ is
$$^{47}C_4 + {}^{51}C_3 + {}^{50}C_3 + {}^{49}C_3 + {}^{48}C_3 + {}^{47}C_3 = A, \text{ say}$$
Combining 1st and last,
$$^{47}C_3 + {}^{47}C_4 = {}^{48}C_4, \text{ by Q. 2.}$$
$$\therefore \quad A = {}^{48}C_4 + {}^{51}C_3 + {}^{50}C_3 + {}^{49}C_3 + {}^{48}C_3.$$

Again combining 1st and last,
$$A = {}^{49}C_4 + {}^{51}C_3 + {}^{50}C_3 + {}^{49}C_3$$
$$= {}^{50}C_4 + {}^{51}C_3 + {}^{50}C_3$$
$$= {}^{51}C_4 + {}^{51}C_3 = {}^{52}C_4.$$

15. (a) $\dfrac{{}^nC_6}{{}^{n-3}C_3} = \dfrac{33}{4}.$
or $\dfrac{n!}{6!(n-6)!} \cdot \dfrac{3!(n-6)!}{(n-3)!} = \dfrac{33}{4}$
or $\dfrac{n(n-1)(n-2)}{6.5.4} = \dfrac{33}{4}$
or $n(n-1)(n-2) = 30 \times 33 = 11 \times 3 \times 3 \times 10$
$$= 11 \times 10 \times 9 = 11(11-1)(11-2)$$
Hence clearly $n = 11$.

(b) Ans. $r = 41$.
$$56.55.(51-r) = 11 \times 14 \times 10 \times 20$$
or $51 - r = 10 \quad \therefore \quad r = 41$.

(c) Ans. $n = 19$.
$$(n+2)(n+1)n(n-1) = 21.20.19.18$$

16. We know that
$$^nP_r = r! \cdot {}^nC_r$$
Put the values of ^nP_r and ^nC_r
$$\therefore \quad 604800 = r! \, 120$$
$$r! = 5040 = 24 \times 210 = 4! \times 5 \times 42$$
$$= 5! \, 6 \times 7 = 6! \times 7 = 7!$$
$$\therefore \quad r = 7.$$

17. $5 \cdot {}^{2n+1}P_{n-1} = 3 \cdot {}^{2n-1}P_n$ by given condition
$$\therefore \quad 5 \cdot \frac{(2n+1)!}{(n+2)!} = 3 \cdot \frac{(2n-1)!}{(n-1)!}$$
$$5 \cdot \frac{(2n+1)2n.(2n-1)!}{(n+2)(n+1)n.(n-1)!} = 3 \cdot \frac{(2n-1)!}{(n-1)!}$$
or $10(2n+1) = 3(n+2)(n+1)$
or $20n + 10 = 3n^2 + 9n + 6.$
or $3n^2 - 11n - 4 = 0$
$$\therefore \quad (n-4)(3n+1) = 0 \quad \therefore \quad n = 4.$$

18. (a) $^nP_r = {}^nP_{r+1}$
$$\therefore \quad \frac{n!}{(n-r)!} = \frac{n!}{(n-r-1)!}$$
or $\dfrac{1}{(n-r)} = 1$ or $n - r = 1 \qquad \dots(1)$
$$^nC_r = {}^nC_{r-1} \quad \therefore \quad r + r - 1 = n$$
or $2r - n = 1 \qquad \dots(2)$
Solving (1) and (2), we get $r = 2$ and $n = 3$.

(b) Ans. (c). $(m+n)(m+n-1) = 90$
$$\Rightarrow (m+n)^2 - (m+n) - 90 = 0$$
$$(m+n-10)(m+n+9) = 0 \quad \therefore \quad m+n = 10$$
Similarly from 2nd relation, $m - n = 6$
$$\therefore \quad m = 8, n = 2.$$

19. R.H.S. $= {}^{4n}C_{2n} \div {}^{2n}C_n$

$$= \frac{4n!}{2n!\,2n!} \cdot \frac{n!\,n!}{2n!} = \frac{4n!}{2n!}\left[\frac{n!}{2n!}\right]^2 \qquad \dots(1)$$

Now $4n! = 1.2.3.4.5\dots\dots(4n-1)(4n)$

$$= (2.4.6\dots 4n)\,[1.3.5\dots(4n-1)]$$
$$= 2^{2n}\,(1.2.3\dots 2n)\,[1.3.5\dots(4n-1)]$$
$$= 2^{2n}.2n!\,[1.3.5\dots\dots(4n-1)]$$

$$\therefore \quad \frac{4n!}{2n!} = 2^{2n}\,[1.3.5\dots\dots(4n-1)] \qquad \dots(2)$$

Replacing $2n$ by n in (2) and taking reciprocal, we get

$$\frac{n!}{(2n)!} = \frac{1}{2^n\,[1.3.5\dots\dots(2n-1)]} \qquad \dots(3)$$

Putting the values from (2) and (3) in (1), we get the result.

20. (a) $\dfrac{{}^{15}C_r}{{}^{15}C_{r-1}} = \dfrac{11}{5} \quad \therefore \quad \dfrac{n-r+1}{r} = \dfrac{11}{5}$,

by (s) (iv), P. 294.

$$\therefore \quad 5(15-r+1) = 11\,.\,r \quad \text{as } n = 15$$
or $\quad 80 = 16r, \quad \therefore \quad r = 5$

(b) Ans. (d).

$$\frac{1}{2} > \frac{{}^{10}C_r}{{}^{10}C_{r-1}} = \frac{n-r+1}{r} = \frac{11-r}{r} \qquad \because\ n = 10$$

$$r > 22 - 2r \quad \text{or} \quad 3r > 22 \quad \text{or} \quad r > \frac{22}{3}$$

Since r is an integer, hence the smallest value of r satisfying the above is 8.

(c) Ans. (c).

Write $2 = 1 + 1$

L.H.S. $= {}^7C_{n+1} + {}^7C_{n+2} = {}^8C_{n+2} > {}^8C_3$ given

$\therefore \quad n+2 = 4$ as ${}^8C_4 > {}^8C_3$ **(as shown below)**

$n + 2 = 4 \quad \text{or} \quad n = 2 \quad \text{or} \quad n - 1 = 1.$

Hence the roots of both the equations are α, β, *i.e.,* both common

$$\frac{{}^nC_r}{{}^nC_{r-1}} = \frac{n-r+1}{r} \quad \therefore \quad \frac{{}^8C_4}{{}^8C_3} = \frac{8-4+1}{4} = \frac{5}{4} > 1$$

by s (iv) P. 294.

21. (a) We have as in Q. 20, $\dfrac{n-r+1}{r} = \dfrac{84}{36} = \dfrac{7}{3}$

and $\dfrac{n-r}{r+1} = \dfrac{126}{84} = \dfrac{3}{2}$

$$\therefore \quad \frac{7}{3}r - 1 = n - r = \frac{3}{2}(r+1)$$

or $\quad 14r - 6 = 9r + 9 \quad \text{or} \quad r = 3$

Now, $n = \dfrac{10}{3}r - 1 = \dfrac{10}{3} \times 3 - 1 = 9$

(b) Ans. (b). Proceed as in part (a). $n = 62, r = 26$ etc.

22. ${}^{28}C_{2r} \div {}^{24}C_{2r-4} = \dfrac{225}{11}$,

$$\therefore \quad \frac{28!}{(28-2r)!\,2r!} \times \frac{(28-2r)!\,(2r-4)!}{24!} = \frac{225}{11}$$

$$\therefore \quad \frac{28 \times 27 \times 26 \times 25}{2r(2r-1)(2r-2)(2r-3)} = \frac{225}{11}$$

$$\therefore \quad 2r(2r-1)(2r-2)(2r-3)$$
$$= \frac{11 \times 28 \times 27 \times 26 \times 25}{225}$$
$$= 11 \times 28 \times 3 \times 26 \qquad \because\ 25 \times 9 = 225$$
$$= 11 \times 14 \times 2 \times 3 \times 13 \times 2$$
$$= 11 \times 12 \times 13 \times 14$$
$$= 14(14-1)(14-2)(14-3)$$

$\therefore \quad 2r = 14 \quad \text{or} \quad r = 7.$

Hence (c) is the correct answer.

23. ${}^nC_r$ is greatest when $r = \dfrac{n}{2}$ (n even)

or when $r = \dfrac{n-1}{2}, \dfrac{n+1}{2}$ (n odd) **by (s) (i, ii) P. 294.**

$$\therefore \quad {}^{20}C_{10} \div {}^{25}C_{12} = \frac{20!}{10!\,10!} \cdot \frac{12!\,13!}{25!} = \frac{143}{4025}$$

24. Ans. (C).

The given sigma will contain $(n+1)$ terms out of which one will be zero corresponding to $r = 0$

$$\therefore \quad \Sigma = \left[\frac{1}{{}^nC_1} + \frac{2}{{}^nC_2} + \dots + \frac{n-2}{{}^nC_{n-2}} + \frac{n-1}{{}^nC_{n-1}} + \frac{n}{{}^nC_n}\right]$$

Now apply ${}^nC_r = {}^nC_{n-r}$ and ${}^nC_n = 1 = {}^nC_0$

$$1 + (n-1) = 2 + (n-2) = \dots = n$$

The last term is n and combine

$$n\left[\frac{1}{{}^nC_1} + \frac{1}{{}^nC_2} + \dots + \frac{1}{{}^nC_n}\right]$$

$$= n\left[\frac{1}{{}^nC_0} + \frac{1}{{}^nC_1} + \frac{1}{{}^nC_2} + \dots\right] \qquad (\because\ {}^nC_n = {}^nC_0)$$

$$= \frac{n}{2}\left[\frac{2}{{}^nC_0} + \frac{2}{{}^nC_1} + \dots\right]$$

$$= \frac{n}{2}\left[\left(\frac{1}{{}^nC_0} + \frac{1}{{}^nC_n}\right) + \left(\frac{1}{{}^nC_1} + \frac{1}{{}^nC_{n-1}}\right) + \dots\right]$$

$$= \frac{n}{2}\sum_{r=0}^{n}\frac{1}{{}^nC_r} = \frac{1}{2}\,n a_n$$

25. We know that ${}^nC_r = {}^nC_{n-r} \quad \therefore\ D^r = 2C_k$

$$\therefore \quad \sum_{k=1}^{n}\left(\frac{kC_k}{C_k + C_{n-k}}\right)^2 = \sum_{k=1}^{n}\left(\frac{k}{2}\right)^2$$

$$= \frac{1}{4} \cdot \frac{n(n+1)(2n+1)}{6} = \frac{n(n+1)(2n+1)}{24}$$

26. Let $P = (n+1)(n+2)...(n+r)$ be the product of r consecutive integers.

Mutliply above and below by $1.2.3....n$ i.e., $n!$

$\therefore \quad P = \dfrac{(n+r)!}{n!} = \dfrac{(n+r)!}{r![n+r-r]!} r!$ **(Note)**

$= {}^{n+r}C_r (r!) = \lambda (r!)$ where λ is some integer. Hence P is divisible by $r!$.

27. Ans. (b).

${}^nC_r$ is meaningful if $n \ge r$. Hence we must have

$\quad n - 1 \ge 4 \quad$ or $\quad n \ge 5$.   ...(1)

Dividing by ${}^{n-2}P_2$ and putting the values,

$\dfrac{{}^{n-1}C_4}{{}^{n-2}P_2} - \dfrac{{}^{n-1}C_3}{{}^{n-2}P_2} - \dfrac{5}{4} < 0$

$\dfrac{(n-1)!}{(n-5)!\,4!} \dfrac{(n-4)!}{(n-2)!} - \dfrac{(n-1)!}{(n-4)!\,3!} \cdot \dfrac{(n-4)!}{(n-2)!} - \dfrac{5}{4} < 0$

or $\dfrac{(n-1).(n-4)}{24} - \dfrac{n-1}{6} - \dfrac{5}{4} < 0$

or $(n^2 - 5n + 4) - (4n - 4) - 30 < 0$

or $n^2 - 9n - 22 < 0$ or $(n+2)(n-11) < 0$

$\therefore \quad -2 < n < 11$ ...(2)

or $5 \le n < 11$ by (1)

$\therefore \quad n = 5, 6, 7, 8, 9, 10$

i.e., six values as $n \in N$.

28. Ans. (b).

$\dfrac{{}^{n-1}C_r}{{}^nC_{r+1}} = k^2 - 3$

where by definition $n \ge r + 1$ or $n - 1 \ge r$

$\dfrac{(n-1)!}{r!} \dfrac{(r+1)!}{n!} = k^2 - 3$ or $\dfrac{r+1}{n} = k^2 - 3$

Now $n \ge r + 1$ $\therefore \dfrac{r+1}{n} \le 1$ and $+ve$ i.e., > 0

$\therefore \quad 0 < k^2 - 3 \le 1$ or $3 < k^2 \le 4$

Above is equivalent to

$\sqrt{3} < \bar{k} \le 2$ or $-2 \le k < -\sqrt{3}$

$\therefore \quad k \in (\sqrt{3}, 2]$

29. **Refer o (vi) P. 293.** If $3m$ things are to be divided among three persons, then the number of divisions $= \dfrac{(3m)!}{m!\,m!\,m!}$. Similarly if $n \cdot n$ things are to be divided amongst n persons then the number of divisions is $\dfrac{(n \cdot n)!}{n!\cdot n!\cdot n!...n\,\text{times}} = \dfrac{(n^2\,!)}{(n!)^n}$ which certainly is an integer.

30. Ans. (c).

$r^2 + 1 = (r+2)(r+1) - 3r - 1$

$= (r+2)(r+1) - 3(r+1) + (3-1)$

$\displaystyle\sum_{r=1}^{n} = \sum_{r=1}^{n} [(r+2)(r+1) - 3(r+1) + 2]\, r!$

$= \displaystyle\sum_{r=1}^{n} [(r+2)! - 3(r+1)! + 2(r)!]$

$= \displaystyle\sum_{r=1}^{n} [(r+2)! - (r+1)! - 2\{(r+1)! - r!\}]$

Putting $r = 1, 2, 3, ..., n$ and cancelling the terms diagonally,

$\therefore \quad \Sigma = [(n+2)! - 2!] - 2[(n+1)! - 1]$

$= [(n+2)! - 2(n+1)! = (n+2)(n+1)! - 2(n+1)!$

$= (n+1)![n+2-2] = n.(n+1)! \Rightarrow \text{(c)}$

31. Ans. (c).

By integral co-ordinates of the vertex, we mean that both the x, y co-ordinates be integral and the point must lie in the interior of the triangle OAB. Equation of line AB is $\dfrac{x}{21} + \dfrac{y}{21} = 1$ or $x + y = 21$.

$P(x, y) = \{x, y$ both integrals and lie inside $\Delta OAB\}$. On the ordinate $x = 1$ there will be 19 points inside the triangle , i.e., $(1,1), (1,2), ...(1,19)$, i.e., 19 points. The point $(1, 20)$ will lie on the line AB but not inside the triangle.

Similarly, on the ordinate $x = 2$, there will be 18 points like $(2,1), (2,2), (2,3), ..., (2,18)$.

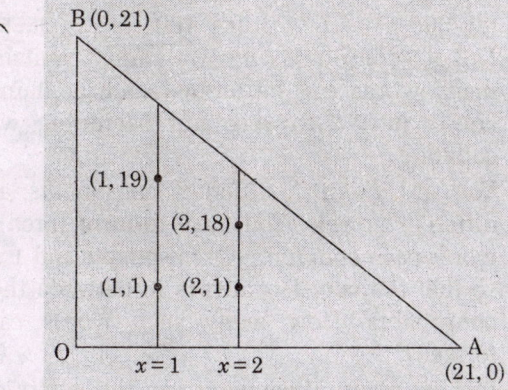

Fig. 2)

But $(2, 19)$ will be on the line AB but not inside the triangle.

Hence number of points with integral co-ordinates and lying inside the triangle

$\quad 19 + 18 + 17 + ... + 1$

the last being $x = 18, y = 1$. But $x = 20, y = 1$ will lie on the line and not in the interior. Thus, the total number of points satisfying the given condition will be

$19 + 18 + 17 ... + 1 = \Sigma n = \dfrac{n(n+1)}{2} = \dfrac{19.20}{2} = 190 \Rightarrow \text{(c)}$

Problem Set (2)

Arrangements of letters of words, consonants and vowels, alike together or not together.

1. **Very Important question from the point of view of practice.**
   How many different words can be formed from the letters of the word GANESHPURI when :
   (a) All the letters are taken
   (b) The letter G always occupies the first place
   (c) The letters P and I respectively occupy the first and last places
   (d) The vowels are always together
   (e)* The letters E, H, P are never together
   (f) The vowels always occupy even places (*i.e.* 2nd, 4th etc.)
   (g) How many words of 5 letters each can be formed each containing 3 consonants and 2 vowels ?

2. (a) Show that the number of permutations of n different things taken all at a time in which p particular things are never together is
   $$n! - (n - p + 1)!\, p!.$$
   (b) How many words can be formed out of the letters of the word ARTICLE so that vowels occupy the even places ?
   (c) How many ways are there to arrange the letters of the word GARDEN with the vowels in alphabet order ?
   (a) 120   (b) 240
   (c) 360   (d) 480   **(AIEEE 2004)**

3. (a)* Out of 5 consonants, 4 vowels and 3 capitals how many words can be formed each containing 3 consonants, 2 vowels and beginning with a capital ?
   (b) You are given 7 different consonants and 3 different vowels. You have to form three letter words each containing 2 consonants and 1 vowel so that the vowel is always in between the two consonants. How many such words can be formed?

4. (a) In how many **other ways** can the letters of the word SIMPLETON be rearranged ?
   (b)* Ten different letters of an alphabet are given. Words with five letters are formed from these given letters. Then the number of words which have at least one letter repeated is 69760.

5. (a) Show that the number of six letter words that can be formed using the letters of the word "assist" in which s's alternate with other letters is 12.
   (b) We are required to form different words with the help of letters of the word INTEGER. Let m_1 be the number of words in which I and N are never together and m_2 be the number of words which begin with I and mend with R, then prove that $m_1 / m_2 = 30$.

6. (a) How many different words ending and beginning with a consonant can be made out of the letters of the word EQUATION ?
   (b)* Five letter words are formed each containing 2 consonants and 3 vowels out of the letters of the word EQUATION. In how many of these the two consonants are always together ?

7. In how many ways can the letters of the word COMBINE be arranged so as to begin and end with a vowel ? Also find the number of words that can be formed without changing the relative order of the vowels and consonants.

8. (a) How many different words can be formed with the letters of the word ORDINATE so that
   (i) The vowels occupy odd places
   (ii) Beginning with O
   (iii) Beginning with O and ending with E.
   (b) The letters of word '**postage**' are to be arranged in the following manner :
   (i) Vowels occupy even places
   (ii) Consonants are always together. What will be number of words formed in (i) and (ii) ?

9. (a)* How many different words can be formed from the letters of the word INTERMEDIATE ? In how many of them, two vowels never come together ?
   (J.E.E.W.B. 1998)
   (b) How many words can be formed with the letters of the word PATALIPUTRA without changing the relative order of vowels and consonants ?

10. (a) Prove that the total number of arrangements which can be made out of the letters of the word ALGEBRA without altering the relative position of vowels and consonants is $\dfrac{4!\,3!}{2}$.
   (b) The letters in the word VICE CHANCELLOR are to be so arranged so that the vowels are not together.

11.* Find the number of ways of arranging the letters
   AAAAA   BBB   CCC   D   EE   F
   in a row if the letters C are separated from one another.

12. (a) The number of arrangements of the letters of the word BANANA in which the two N's do not appear adjacently is
   (a) 40   (b) 60
   (c) 80   (d) 100   **(I.I.T. Sc. 2002)**
   (b) Find the number of different permutations of the letters of the word BANANA.
   (c)* There are 21 balls which are either white or black and the balls of the same colour are alike. Find the number of white balls so that the number of arrangements of these balls in a row be maximum.

13. How many different words can be formed out of the letters of the word ALLAHABAD ? In how many of them the vowels occupy the even positions ?

14.* The letters of the word '**Constantinople**' are to be arranged in the following manner :
    (i)   There is no restriction
    (ii) Begin with *tt*.
    (iii) End with *a*.
    (iv) Have *s* in the 3rd place with *e* at the end.

15. (a) How many different words can be made out of the letters of the word '**Mississippi**' ?
    (b) Show that the total number of different combinations of letters which can be made from the letters of the word MISSISSIPPI is 149.

16. How many different words can be formed with the letters of the word HARYANA ? In how many of these *H* and *N* are together and how many of these begin with *H* and end with *N* ?

17. Prove that the number of words which can be formed out of the letters *a,b,c,d,e,f* taken 3 together, each word containing one vowel at least is 96.

18. A person wishes to make up as many different parties as he can out of 20 friends, each party consisting of the same number. How many should he invite at a time ? In how many of these would the same man be found ?

19.* Eleven animals of a circus have to be placed in eleven cages one in each cage. If 4 of the cages are too small for 6 of the animals, find the number of ways of caging the animals. **(Bihar C.E.E. 1999)**

20.* In how many ways can the letters of the word ARRANGE be arranged so that
    (i)   The two *R*'s are never together
    (ii) The two *A*'s are together but not two *R*'s
    (iii) Neither two *A*'s nor the two *R*'s are together.

21. In how many ways can the letters of the word SUCCESS be arranged so that
    (i)   The two *C*'s are together but no two *S*'s are together.
    (ii) No two *C*'s and no two *S*'s are together.

22. (a)* How many different arrangements can be made by using all the letters in the word MATHEMATICS ? How many of them begin with *C* ? How many of them begin with *T* ?
    (b)* A five letter word is to be formed such that the letters appearing in the odd positions are taken from the unrepeated letters of the word MATHEMATICS whereas the letters which occupy even places are taken from amongst the repeated letters. **(Dhanbad 1993)**

23. (a)* How many words can be formed by taking 4 letters at a time out of the letters of the word MATHEMATICS ?
    (b) How many different permutations can be formed from the letters of the word EXAMINATION taken four at a time ?

24. Find the number of ways in which (a) selection (b) an arrangement of 4 letters can be made from the letters of the word PROPORTION.

25. Show that only 286, 4-letter words can be formed out of the letters of word '**infinite**'.

26. (a)* Find the total number of ways of selecting five letters from the letters of the word INDEPENDENT. **(Roorkee 1997)**
    (b) Show that the total number of natural numbers of six digits that can be made with digits 1, 2, 3, 4, if all numbers are to appear in the same number at least once is 1560.
    (c) Prove that there are only seven number of ways in which any four letters can be selected out of the letters of the word GORCOO.
    (d) Prove that the total number of arrangements of the letters in the expression $x^3 y^2 z^4$ when written at full length is 1260.
    (e) *r,s,t* are prime numbers, '*p*' and '*q*' are two numbers whose LCM is $r^2 s^4 t^2$, then number of possible pairs of (p,q) are :
        (a) 225   (b) 254
        (c) 256   (d) 248   **(I.I.T. 2006)**

27. If combinations of letters be formed by taking only 5 letters at a time out of the letters of the word "METAPHYSICS". In how many of them will letter *T* occur ?

28. The number of ways in which we can select 5 letters of the word INTERNATIONAL is equal to
    (a) 200   (b) 220
    (c) 242   (d) 256

29. How many different words can be formed by taking 4 letters at a time out of the letters of the word EXPRESSION ?

30. (a) How many different words can be formed out of the letters of the word MORADABAD taken four at a time ?
    (b) Prove that only 1422 different four letter words can be formed out of the letters of the word INEFFECTIVE.

31. (a)* Five-letter words are to be formed out of the letters of the word INFINITESIMAL. What is their number ?
    (b) Prove that out of the letters of the word **I N E F F E C T I V E** only 1222 four letter words can be formed.

Solutions to Problem Set (2)

1. GANESHPURI : No. of letters = 10; vowels are AEUI *i.e.* 4 and consonants 6.
   (a) When all the letters are taken, then they can be arranged in $^{10}P_{10}$, *i.e.* 10 ! ways.

(b) Having fixed up G at first place we are left with the permutations of remaining 9 letters which can be arranged in 9! ways.

(c) P occupies 1st and I occupies the last place and so we have to arrange the remaining 8 letters which can be done in 8! ways.

(d) The four vowels $AEUI$ are to be together. Take these four letters as one letter and so we have in all $10 - 4 + 1 = 7$ letters which can be arranged in 7! ways. In each of these 7! arrangements the four vowels are together and these can be arranged amongst themselves in 4! ways. Hence by fundamental theorem the number of words will be $7! . 4!$ in which the vowels will be together.

(e) Take E, H, P as one letter and so the number of letters will be $10 - 3 + 1 = 8$. As in part (d), the number of words in which E, H, P are together will be $8! . 3!$ The total number of arrangements by (a) is 10!. Hence the number of words when E, H, P are never together is

$10! - 8! . 3! = 8! [10 \times 9 - 6] = 84 . 8!$.

Note : Some students may try the question with gap method. Arrange the seven letters (E, H, P excluded) in 7! ways. We will have 8 gaps in which these three can be arranged in

$$^8P_3 = \frac{8!}{5!} = 8.7.6 \text{ ways.}$$

Hence the required number is

$$7! (8.7.6) = 8! (7.6) = 42.8!.$$

This is half the number of ways we have calculated above.

Reason : Our condition is that the three letters E, H, P **all** are never together. Any two of them could be together, or all of them could be separate.

(f) We have ten places out of which 5 places are odd i.e. 1st, 3rd, 5th, 7th, 9th and five are even i.e. 2nd, fourth, sixth, eighth and tenth. In the five even places we have to fix up 4 vowels which can be done in $^5P_4$ ways. Having fixed up the vowels in even places, we will be left with six places namely 5 odd and one even left after fixing the four vowels. In these six places we have to fix six consonants which can be done in $^6P_6$ i.e. 6! ways.

Thus the total number of ways is $^5P_4 \times {}^6P_6$.

or $5! \times 6! = 120 \times 720 = 6 (120)^2$.

(g) Each word is to contain 3 consonants out of 6 and 2 vowels out of 4.

We can **select** them in $^6C_3$ and $^4C_2$ ways. Thus the total number of combinations (groups) of 5 letters will be $^6C_3 \times {}^4C_2$ by fundamental theorem.

But $\quad ^6C_3 \times {}^4C_2 = \dfrac{6!}{3! \, 3!} \times \dfrac{4!}{2! \, 2!}$

$$= \frac{6 \times 5 \times 4}{3 . 2 . 1} . \frac{4.3}{1.2} = 120 \text{ ways}$$

Thus we have 120 groups each containing 5 letters, i.e. 3 consonants and 2 vowels. Now the 5 letters in each group can be arranged amongst themselves in 5! ways i.e. 120 ways. Hence the total number of different words will be $120 \times 120 = 14400$, by fundamental theorem.

2. (a) Refer Q. 1 (a) and (e). Total is $n!$ and when they are together is $(n - p + 1)! \, p!$

∴ when p things are never together is

$n! - (n - p + 1)! . p!$

(b) See Q. 1 (f) seven places : 3 even and 4 odd; 3 vow. and 4 cons.

∴ $\quad ^3P_3 \times {}^4P_4 = 3! \times 4! = 6 \times 24 = 144.$

(c) Ans. (c).

$$\frac{1}{2}(6!) = \frac{1}{2}(720) = 360$$

6! corresponds to total number of arrangements of 6 letters. In half of all the 6! arrangements, A will precede E and in half A will follow E. We have to take only such arrangements where A precedes E, as in alphabetical order.

3. (a) Cap. (3). Con. (5). Vow (4)

$^3C_1 . \quad ^5C_3 . \quad ^4C_2 \times 5!$

$= 3 \times 10 \times 6 \times 120 = 216000.$

Note : 5! and not 6! as capital letter is fixed in the beginning.

(b) Con. Vow

$^7C_2 \times {}^3C_1 = 21 \times 3 = 63$ selections of 3 letter words consisting of 2 consonants and one vowel. Now vowel is to be between the consonants. Hence the arrangement will be only of the consonants i.e., 2!

Hence $63 \times 2! = 126.$

4. (a) Nine letters. Total no. of words 9!

Hence no. of other words is $9! - 1.$

We have excluded one arrangement i.e. Simpleton as we want other ways.

(b) Number of words in which all the 5 letters are repeated $= 10^5 = 100000.$

and the number of words in which no letter is repeated

$= {}^{10}P_5 = 10.9.8.7.6 = 30240.$

Hence the number of words which have at least one letter repeated $= 100000 - 30240 = 69760.$

5. (a) The three letters $a \times i \times t \times$ can be arranged in $3! = 6$ ways. If the word is to start with any of three letters a, i or t then we have three places marked by $\times$ in which three alike s can be arranged in

$\frac{3!}{3!} = 1$ way. Thus $6 \times 1 = 6$ ways

If they are to begin with s then $\times a \times i \times t$ and as above we have again $6 \times 1 = 6$ ways

$\therefore$ Total $= 6 + 6 = 12$.

(b) m_1 = never together

$\quad = $ Total – together

$\quad = 7! - 6!\,2! = 6!.5$

m_2 = Begin with I and end with $R = 5!$

$\therefore \quad \dfrac{m_1}{m_2} = \dfrac{6!.5}{5!} = 6.5 = 30$

6. (a) 8 letters i.e. 3 consonants and 5 vowels. The consonants are to occupy 1st and last place and it can be done in $^3P_2$ ways. We will now be left with 5 vowels and 1 consonant i.e. 6 letters which can be arranged in $6!$ ways. Hence the number of words under given condition is

$\quad ^3P_2 \times 6! = 6 \times 720 = 4320.$

(b) Total 3 C and 5 V

Choose 2 C and 3 V

Total $\quad ^3C_2 \cdot {}^5C_3 \cdot 5! = 3 . 10 \times 120 = 3600$

Two consonants together. Tie them after selecting 2 consonants and then untie.

There will be 3 vowels and one unit of third consonant. In all four units which can be arranged in $4!$ ways. Now untie the two consonants which can be arranged in $2!$ ways. Hence the total number of words will be

$^3C_2 \cdot {}^5C_3 \cdot \{4! \times 2!\} = 3 \times 10 \times 24 \times 2 = 1440$

Alternative method :

Total – Never together

3 vowels can be arranged in $^5P_3 = 60$ ways.

2 consonants can be selected in $^3C_2 = 3$ ways

There will be 4 gaps in between the vowels in which two can be arranged in $^4P_2 = 4.3 = 12$.

Hence the total when consonants are separated

$\quad = 60 \times 3 \times 12 = 2160.$

Required number when the consonants are together

$\quad = 3600 - 2160 = 1440$

7. Total $= 7$ out of which 3 vowels, 4 consonants

(i) $^3P_2 \times 5! = 6 \times 120 = 720$

(ii) The three vowels shall continue to occupy the 2nd, 5th and 7th positions only. In other words, these three vowels can be arranged in these three places in $3! = 6$ ways. Similarly the four consonants can be arranged in $4! = 24$ ways. Thus the total number of letters is $6 \times 24 = 144$ in which the relative order is maintained.

8. (a) 4 vowels and 4 consonants. Total 8 letters.

(i) No. of words $= 4! \times 4! = 24 \times 24 = 576$.

Because 4 vowels are to be adjusted in 4 odd places and the 4 consonants in the remaining 4 even places.

(ii) $7!$ ways, O being fixed.

(iii) $6!$ ways, O fixed in Ist and E fixed in last.

(b) Letters 7, V 3 (a, e, o), C 4 (p, s, t, g)

Total $= 7!$

(i) Three even places 2nd, 4th and 6th in which 3 vowels can be fixed up in $3!$ ways and the remaining 4 consonants can be fixed up in $4!$ ways. Thus total is

$\quad 3! . 4! = 6 \times 24 = 144.$

(ii) Consonants together. Follow string method.

Total number $= 4! . 4! = 576.$

9. (a) No. of letters $= 12$; 6 vowels $(2I, 3E, 1A)$ and 6 consonants $(2T, 1R, 1M, 1N, 1D)$.

Total words $= \dfrac{12!}{2!\,3!\,2!}$

Gap Method :

No. of ways of arranging 6 consonants (2 alike) is

$\quad \dfrac{6!}{2} = 360$ ...(1)

There will be 7 gaps in which 6 vowels if all different can be arranged in $^7P_6$ ways but as 2 are alike of one kind and 3 of other kind

$\therefore \quad$ Number of arranging the vowels is

$\quad ^7P_6 \cdot \dfrac{1}{3!\,2!} = \dfrac{7!}{12} = \dfrac{5040}{12} = 420$ ...(2)

Hence the total number of ways when the two vowels never come together by fundamental theorem is $360 \times 420 = 151200$ by (1), (2).

(b) 11 Letters, $5V$ $(3A, 1I, 1U)$, $6C$ $(2P, 2T, 1L, 1R)$

$\therefore \quad$ Total number $= \dfrac{5!}{3!} \times \dfrac{6!}{2!\,2!} = 20 \times 180 = 3600.$

10. (a) The four consonants all different can be arranged in the four places in $4! = 24$ ways and three vowels A, E, A out of which two are alike can be arranged in $\dfrac{3!}{2!} = 3$ ways.

Hence total number of ways is $24 \times 3 = 72.$

(c) **Refer Q. 9. above.**

14 letters : $\qquad 5V$ $(2E)$, $9C$ $(3C, 2L)$

Not together = Total – together

Total $= \dfrac{14!}{2!\,3!\,2!}$ ...(1)

Totgether = 9 consonants and 1 unit of vowels

$\quad = \dfrac{10!}{3!\,(C).2!(L)} \times \dfrac{5!}{2}\ (E)$ ...(2)

Not together = (1) – (2)

11. As in Q. 6 there are 15 letters. Let us ignore $3C^s$ and thus we have 12 letters $(5A^s, 3B^s, 2E^s, 1D, 1F)$ and these can be arranged in

$$\frac{12!}{5!\,3!\,2!} \text{ ways.} \qquad \ldots(1)$$

Now after arranging these 12 letters (No C^s) there will be 13 gaps as in Q. 6 in which 3 different letters can be arranged in $^{13}P_3$ ways. But since the 3 letters are alike, the number of distinct ways will be

$$\frac{1}{3!}(^{13}P_3) = \frac{1}{6} \cdot \frac{13!}{10!} \qquad \ldots(2)$$

∴ The total number of words in which C^s are separated from one another is

$$\frac{12!}{5! \times 3! \times 2!} \times \frac{1}{6} \cdot \frac{13!}{10!}$$

$$= \frac{12 \times 11 \times 10 \times 9 \times 8 \times 7 \times 6}{6 \times 2} \times \frac{1}{6}(13 \times 12 \times 11)$$

$$= 95135040$$

12. (a) Total – Together (string method)
$$3A^s, 2N^s, 1B$$
$$= \frac{6!}{3!\,2!} - \frac{5!\,2!}{3!\,2!} = 60 - 20 = 40$$

(b) **BANANA.**
$3A^s, 2N^s, B$ i.e. 6 letters, 3 alike of one type and 2 of another type. Number of words taken all at a time is

$$\frac{6!}{3!\,2!} = \frac{6 \times 5 \times 4}{2} = 60.$$

(c) Let there be r white (alike) balls so that the number of black balls is $(21 - r)$. (These are also alike.) Number of arrangements of these balls total 21 is

$$A = \frac{21!}{r!\,(21-r)!} = {}^{21}C_r$$

If all were different then 21!.
Since r are alike of one kind and $(21 - r)$ are alike of other kind we have divided by $r!$ and $(21 - r)!$

Again $A = {}^{21}C_r$ will be maximum when

$$r = \frac{21+1}{2} \quad \text{or} \quad \frac{21-1}{2} \quad \text{i.e., 10 or 11.}$$

13. ALLAHABAD.
$4A^s, 2L^s, H, B, D,$ i.e. 9 letters.
Number of words $= \dfrac{9!}{4!\,2!} = \dfrac{9 \times 8 \times 7 \times 6 \times 5}{2}$
$$= 72 \times 105 = 7560.$$

There are 4 vowels, and all are alike, i.e. $4A^s$.

There are 4 even places, i.e. 2nd, 4th, 6th, and 8th.

These 4 even positions can be filled by 4 vowels in $\dfrac{4!}{4!} = 1$ way.

Now we are left with 5 places in which 5 letters out of which $2L^s$ are alike and rest different can be filled in

$$\frac{5!}{2!} = 5 \times 4 \times 3 = 60 \text{ ways}.$$

Hence the total number of words is $60 \times 1 = 60$.

14. 14, $(3n, 2o, 2t$ and 7 different)

(i) Total $= \dfrac{14!}{3!\,2!\,2!} = \dfrac{1}{24}(14)!$

(ii) Begin with $tt = \dfrac{(12)!}{3!\,2!}$

(iii) Begin with $a = \dfrac{(13)!}{3!\,2!\,2!} = \dfrac{1}{24}(13)!$

(iv) Fix up s and e in 3rd and last place respectively; we are left with 12 places to be filled up by 12 letters some of which are alike.

∴ Number of words

$$= \frac{(12)!}{3!\,2!\,2!} = \frac{(12)(11)!}{24} = \frac{1}{2}(11)!$$

15. (a) Letters 11, $(4s, 4i, 2p, 1M)$

Ans. $\dfrac{(11)!}{4!\,.4!\,.2!}$

(b) There are $4I, 4S, 2P, 1M$.
It is not given how many alphabets are to be taken. Hence we are at liberty to choose any number of alphabets and hence by **(q) P. 294**, the number of selections is $(4+1)(4+1)(2+1)(1+1) - 1$ (This -1 is corresponding to the situation when all are left out.

∴ $5 . 5 . 3 . 2 - 1 = 150 - 1 = 149.$

16. HARYANA. 7 letters
$3A^s, H, R, Y, N$.

(i) The number of words $= \dfrac{7!}{3!} = 7 \times 6 \times 5 \times 4 = 840$.

(ii) Treating H and N together we have $7 - 2 + 1 = 6$ letters out of, which three are alike i.e., A^s and hence they can be arranged in

$$\frac{6!}{3!} = 120 \text{ ways}.$$

But H and N can be arranged amongst themselves in $2! = 2$ ways.
Hence the number of ways is $120 \times 2 = 240$.

(iii) Fix up H in first and N in last; we have 5 letters out of these three are alike i.e. A^s and hence the number of words is $\dfrac{5!}{3!} = 5 \times 4 = 20$.

17. Hint : Reqd. no. of words
$$= ({}^2C_1 \times {}^4C_2 + {}^2C_2 \times {}^4C_1)\,3!$$
$$= (12 + 4) \times 6 = 96.$$
Alt. 6 letters, 2 vowels, 4 consonants
Total – No vowel $= {}^6P_3 - {}^4P_3$
$$= 120 - 24 = 96$$

18. Since $n = 20$ is even, $^{20}C_r$ is greatest when $r = \dfrac{20}{2} = 10$.

Hence the maximum number of parties = $^{20}C_{10}$. Thus he should invite 10 friends at a time in order to form the max. number of parties. Also the same man will be found in $^{19}C_9$ parties.

19. Large animals 6   Small animals 5
Large cages 7   Small cages 4

6 large animals can be caged in 7 large cages in $^7P_6 = 7!$ ways. 5 small animals can be caged in remaining 5 cages (4 small + 1 large) in 5! ways. Hence the number of ways is

$7! \times 5! = 5040 \times 120 = 604800$

20. There are 7 letters $2A^s, 2R^s$ and 3 different.

(i) **Two R^s never together.**

Ignore the $2R^s$ and thus we have to arrange remaining 5 letters in which $2A^s$ are alike and we can have

$\dfrac{5!}{2!} = 5 \times 4 \times 3 = 60$ ways.   ...(1)

After arranging these five letters in a line we have 6 gaps in which 2 **different** words can be placed in $^6P_2$ ways. But these two R^s are alike and hence the number of ways will be

$\dfrac{1}{2!} \cdot {}^6P_2 = \dfrac{1}{2!} \cdot \dfrac{6!}{4!} = 15.$

Hence the number of ways when R^s are never together is

$60 \times 15 = 900$,   by Fundamental Th.

(ii) **The two A^s are together but not two R^s.**

Let us ignore the two R^s and thus we have $7 - 2 = 5$ letters.

Treat the $2A^s$ as one letter (AA) NGE thus we have 4 letters which can be arranged in

$4! \dfrac{2!}{2!} = 24$ ways.   ...(1)

$\times AA \times N \times G \times E \times$

Between these 4 letters (A^s together) we have 5 gaps in which 2 different letters can be arranged in $^5P_2$ ways.

But here $2R^s$ are alike and hence the number of ways will be

$\dfrac{1}{2!} {}^5P_2 = \dfrac{1}{2} \cdot \dfrac{5!}{3!} = 10$ ways.   ...(2)

Hence the number of words when A^s are together and R^s are not together is $24 \times 10 = 240$ by fundamental theorem .

(iii) **Neither $2A^s$ nor $2R^s$ are together.**

From Part (i), $2R^s$ are never together in 900 ways. This includes the ways when $2A^s$ may be together and may not be together.

From Part (ii), no. of ways that $2A^s$ are together but not $2R^s = 240$.

Hence the number of ways when neither $2A^s$ nor $2R^s$ are together is $900 - 240 = 660$.

21. (i) Take out three S's and tie up two C's so that we are left with U, E and one bundle of C's. Thus we have 3 letters which can be arranged in $3! \left(\dfrac{2!}{2!} \right) = 6$ ways. We have 4 places (two in between and two in the corners). In these 4 places 3 different objects can be arranged in $^4P_3$ ways but three alike can be arranged in $\dfrac{1}{3!} \cdot {}^4P_3$ ways i.e. 4 ways.

Hence by fundamental theorem, the number of desired arrangements is $4 \times 6 = 24.$

(ii) Now take out SSS and arrange remaining 4 letters out of which two are alike $\therefore \dfrac{4!}{2!} = 12$. There will be 5 gaps in between these 4 (3 in between and 2 at corners) in which three alike SSS can be placed in $\dfrac{^5P_3}{3!}$ ways, i.e. $\dfrac{5 \cdot 4 \cdot 3}{6} = 10$ ways.

Hence by fundamental theorem there will be $12 \times 10 = 120$ ways in which all the S's are separated. In the above 120 ways no two S's are together but two C's may be together or may not be together. Also by part (i) no two S's are together but two C's are together in 24 ways.

$\therefore$ In $120 - 24 = 96$ ways no two S's and no two C's are together.

22. (a) There are 11 words $2M^s, 2A^s, 2T^s, H, E, I, C, S.$

(i) **Hence the number of words by taking all at a time.**

$= \dfrac{11!}{2! \, 2! \, 2!} = \dfrac{11 \times 10 \times 9 \times 8 \times 7 \times 6!}{2 \times 2 \times 2}$

$= 990 \times 7 \times 720 = 990 \times 5040 = 4989600.$

(ii) **To begin with C.**

Having fixed C at first place we have 10 letters in which 2 are $M^s, 2$ are A^s and 2 are T^s and rest 4 different.

Hence the number of words will be

$\dfrac{10!}{2! \, 2! \, 2!} = \dfrac{10 \times 9 \times 8 \times 7 \times 6!}{2 \times 2 \times 2}$

$= 90 \times 7 \times 720 = 630 \times 720 = 453600.$

(iii) **To begin with T.**

Having fixed T in the first place we will have only 10 letters out of which 2 are M^s and 2 are A^s and rest six are H, E, I, C, S and $T.$

Hence the number of words is

$$\frac{10!}{2!.2!} = 907200 \quad (i.e. \text{ double of part (ii)})$$

(b) There are 3 odd places namely 1st, 3rd and 5th which are to be filled by unrepeated 5 letters H, E, I, C, S. This can be done in $^5P_3 = 5.4.3 = 60$ ways. We have two even places namely 2nd and 4th which is to be filled by repeated letters $(2M, 2A, 2T)$ i.e. 6 letters. These two even places can be filled by 3 different types of letters as under.

(i) All different ∴ $^3P_2 = 3.2 = 6$

(ii) Both alike $^3C_1 \cdot \frac{2!}{2!} = 3$

Thus even places can be filled in $6 + 3 = 9$ ways. Hence by fundamental theorem, the required number of words is $60 \times 9 = 540$.

23. (a) We can choose 4 letters from the 11 listed in part (a) as under.

(i) **All the four different :**
We have 8 different types of letters and out of these 4 can be arranged in

$$^8P_4 = \frac{8!}{4!} = 8 \times 7 \times 6 \times 5 = 1680$$

or 4 can be selected in

$^8C_4$ ways and arranged in

$$^8C_4 \times 4! = \frac{8!}{4!\,4!} \cdot 4! = \frac{8!}{4!} = 1680 \qquad ...(1)$$

(ii) **Two different and two alike.**
We have 3 pairs of like letters out of which one pair can be chosen in $^3C_1 = 3$ ways. Now we have to choose two out of the remaining 7 different types of letters which can be done in

$$= {}^7C_2 = \frac{7!}{5!\,2!} = \frac{7 \times 6}{2} = 21 \text{ ways.}$$

Hence the total number of groups of 4 letters in which 2 are different and 2 are alike is $3 \times 21 = 63$ groups.

Let one such group be M, H, M, I.

Each such group has 4 letters out of which 2 are alike and they can be arranged amongst themselves in $\frac{4!}{2!} = 12$ ways. Hence the total number of words is

$$63 \times 12 = 756. \qquad ...(2)$$

(iii) **Two alike of one kind and two alike of other kind.**
Out of 3 pairs of like letters we can choose 2 pairs in

$$^3C_2 \text{ ways} = 3 \text{ ways.}$$

One such group is $MM\,AA$.

These four letters out of which 2 are alike of one kind and 2 alike of other kind, can be arranged in

$$\frac{4!}{2!2!} = 6 \text{ ways.}$$

Hence the total number of words of this type is

$$3 \times 6 = 18 \qquad ...(3)$$

Therefore from (i), (ii) and (iii) the number of 4 letter words is

$$1680 + 756 + 18 = 2454.$$

by (1), (2) and (3)

(b) Exactly as part (a). Ans. 2454.

24. We have got $2P^s, 2R^s, 3O^s, 1I, 1T, 1N$, i.e. 6 types of letters. We have to form words of 4 letters. We consider four cases :

(i) **All 4 different.**
Selections $^6C_4 = 15$, Arrangements

$$15.4! = 15 \times 24 = 360$$

Alt. $^6P_4 = \frac{6!}{2!} = 6 \times 5 \times 4 \times 3 = 360.$

(ii) **Two different and two alike.**
P^s, R^s and O^s in $^3C_1 = 3$ ways. Having chosen one pair we have to choose 2 different letters out of the remaining 5 different letters in $^5C_2 = 10$ ways. Hence the number of selections is $10 \times 3 = 30$. Each of the above 30 selections has 4 letters out of which 2 are alike and they can be arranged in $\frac{4!}{2!} = 12$ ways.

Hence the number of arrangements will be $12 \times 30 = 360.$

(iii) **2 alike of one kind and 2 of other.**
Out of three sets of two like letters we can choose 2 sets in $^3C_2 = 3$ ways. Each such selection will consist of 4 letters out of which 2 are alike of one kind, 2 of the other. They can be arranged in

$$\frac{4!}{2!.2!} = 6 \text{ ways.}$$

Hence the number of arrangements is

$$3 \times 6 = 18.$$

(iv) **3 alike and 1 different.**
There is only one set consisting of 3 like letters and it can be chosen in 1 way. The remaining one letter can be chosen out of the remaining 5 types of letters in 5 ways.

Hence the number of selections $= 5 \times 1$. Each consists of 4 letters out of which 3 are alike and each of them can be arranged in $\frac{4!}{3!} = 4$ ways.

Hence the number of arrangements is $5 \times 4 = 20$

From (i), (ii) and (iv), we get

Number of Selections $= 15 + 30 + 3 + 5 = 53$.

Number of Arrangements

$$= 360 + 360 + 18 + 20 = 758.$$

25. $8, (3i, 2n, 3 \text{ different})$ 5 types

We have to from 4 letter words.

I **All different** $= {}^5C_4 . 4!$ or ${}^5P_4 = 120$

II **2 alike, 2 diff.** $= {}^2C_1 . {}^4C_2 . \dfrac{4!}{2!} = 144$

III **2 alike, 2 alike** $= {}^2C_2 . \dfrac{4!}{2!2!} = 6$

IV **3 alike, 1 diff.** $= {}^1C_1 . {}^4C_1 . \dfrac{4!}{3!} = 16$

Total $= 120 + 144 + 6 + 16 = 286.$

26. (a) **INDEPENDENT**

11 letters $(3N, 3E, 2D), I, P, T = 6$ types.

We have to form 5 letter-words

I. **All different** $= {}^6C_5 . 5! = (6) . 5! = 720.$

II. **2 alike, 3 diff.** $= {}^3C_1 . {}^5C_3 . \dfrac{5!}{2!}$

$$= (3 . 10) . 60 = 1800.$$

III. **3 alike, 2 diff.** $= {}^2C_1 . {}^5C_2 . \dfrac{5!}{3!}$

$$= (2 . 10) . 20 = 400.$$

IV. **2 alike, 2 alike, 1 diff.** $= {}^3C_2 . {}^4C_1 . \dfrac{5!}{2!2!}$

$$= (3 . 4) . 30 = 360.$$

V. **3 alike, 2 alike** $= {}^2C_1 . {}^1C_1 . \dfrac{5!}{3!2!}$

$$= (2 . 1) . 10 = 20$$

Total selections $= 6 + 30 + 20 + 12 + 2 = 70$.

Total words $= 3300$.

(b) We have to choose numbers of 6 digits out of given 4 digits using all the four. This is possible if some of the digits repeat to make 6 digits.

I. **3 different, 3 alike** $(1, 1, 1, 2, 3, 4)$

Only one number out of four will appear three times. This can be done in ${}^4C_1 = 4$ ways.

Now we have a set of 6 digits out of which three are alike and they can be arranged in

$$\dfrac{6!}{3! \, (\text{alike})} = 6 . 5 . 4 = 120$$

Hence by fundamental theorem the number of such numbers $= 4 \times 120 = 480$.

II. **2 alike, 2 alike, 2 different** $(1, 1, 2, 2, 3, 4)$ out of 4 digits we can select 2 sets of alike in

$${}^4C_2 = \dfrac{4 . 3}{1 . 2} = 6 \text{ ways}$$

Now we have a set of 6 digits out of which 2 are alike of one kind and 2 of other kind. They can be arranged in $\dfrac{6!}{2!2! \, (\text{alike})} = \dfrac{720}{4} = 180$ ways.

Hence by fundamental theorem the number of such numbers $= 6 \times 180 = 1080$ ways

Total $= 480 + 1080 = 1560$

(c) We have 6 letters out of which 3 are alike of one type and 3 different but in all 4 types : we can select them in the following manner :

(i) All different $= {}^4C_4 = 1$

(ii) 2 alike 2 different $= {}^1C_1 \, {}^3C_2 = 1 . 3 = 3$

(iii) 3 alike and 1 different $= {}^1C_1 . {}^3C_1 = 1 . 3 = 3$

Hence the total number of ways is $1 + 3 + 3 = 7$.

Note : Out of three alike $O \, O \, O$ you may select one O or two O or three O, this can be done only in one way.

(d) There will be $3 + 2 + 4 = 9$ letters when the expression is written at full length. Out of these 9 we have 3 alike of one kind, 2 alike of another and 4 alike of third kind.

Hence the required number of arrangements is

$$\dfrac{9! \, (\text{different})}{(3!) \, (2!) \, (4!) \, (\text{alike})} = \dfrac{9 . 8 . 7 . 6 . 5}{6 . 2}$$

$$= \dfrac{(72) \, (7) \, (30)}{12} = 42 \times 30 = 1260$$

(e) Ans. (a).

Required number of ordered pairs in (p, q) is

$$(2 \times 3 - 1)(2 \times 5 - 1)(2 \times 3 - 1) = 5 . 9 . 5 = 225$$

27. There are 11 letters T, S, S and 8 all different since T is a must we have to select only 4 out of remaining S, S and 8 all different. Mind we have to find only combination and not words (arrangement not to be considered)

(a) 2 alike (S, S), 2 different $= {}^2C_1 . {}^8C_2 = 28$

(b) $1S, 3$ different $= {}^8C_3 = 56$

(c) No $S, 4$ different $= {}^8C_4 = 70$

Alt. for (b), (c).

Now (b) and (c) would mean that we have to select 4 out of 9 different letters $= {}^9C_4 = \dfrac{9 . 8 . 7 . 6}{1 . 2 . 3 . 4} = 126$

otherwise also ${}^8C_3 + {}^8C_4 = {}^9C_4.$

Hence total $= 28 + 56 + 70 = 28 + 126 = 154$ ways.

28. Ans. (d).

We have thirteen letters.

$2I, 3N, 2T, 2A$ and (E, O, L, R) 8 (types)

We can select 5 (five) letters in the following manner :

1. All different ${}^8C_5 = \dfrac{8 . 7 . 6}{1 . 2 . 3} = 56$ ways

2. 2 alike, 3 different ${}^4C_1 . {}^7C_3 = 4 . 35 = 140$ ways

   (we have 4 sets of alike letters)

3. 3 alike, 2 different ${}^1C_1 . {}^7C_2 = 1 . 21 = 21$ ways

   (we have only one set of 3 alike)

4. 3 alike and 2 alike ${}^1C_1 . {}^3C_1 = 1 . 3 = 3$ ways

5. Two sets of alike and one different
    $= {}^4C_2 \cdot {}^6C_1 = 6 \cdot 6 = 36$ ways

∴   Total number of selections is
    $56 + 140 + 21 + 3 + 36 = 256$ ways $\Rightarrow$ (d)

29. EXPRESSION

10, $(2E, 2S,$ rest all six different), in all 8 types.

1. **All different** ${}^8C_4$ selections

    Arrangements ${}^8C_4 \cdot 4!$

2. **2 alike, 2 different** ${}^2C_1 \cdot {}^7C_2$ selections

    Arrangements ${}^2C_1 \cdot {}^7C_2 \cdot \dfrac{4!}{2!}$

3. **2 alike, 2 alike** ${}^2C_2 = 1$ selection

    Arrangements $= \dfrac{4!}{2!\,2!}$

∴   Total no. of selections is $70 + 42 + 1 = 113$.
Total arrangements $= 1680 + 504 + 6 = 2190$.

30. (a) In **MORADABAD**, we have 6 different types of letters $3A^s, 2D^s$ and rest four different.

We have to form words of 4 letters.

(i) All different. ${}^6P_4 = 6 \times 5 \times 4 \times 3 = 360$.

(ii) Two different, two alike.

$${}^2C_1 \times {}^5C_2 \times \dfrac{4!}{2!} = 240$$

(iii) 3 alike, 1 different.

$${}^1C_1 \times {}^5C_1 \times \dfrac{4!}{3!} = 20$$

(iv) 2 alike of one type and 2 alike of other type.

$${}^2C_2 \times \dfrac{4!}{2!\,2!} = 6.$$

∴   Total number of words $= 360 + 240 + 20 + 6 = 626$.

(b) Total $(3e, 2f, 2i,$ rest 4 all different) i.e. 7 types. Proceed as in part (a).

31. (a) INFINITESIMAL

13 letters $(4I, 2N, 7$ diff.) 9 types

All diff.	${}^9C_5 \cdot 5! = 15120$
2 alike, 3 diff.	${}^2C_1 \cdot {}^8C_3 \cdot \dfrac{5!}{2!} = 6720$
2 alike, 2 alike, 1 diff.	${}^2C_2 \cdot {}^7C_1 \cdot \dfrac{5!}{2!\,2!} = 210$
3 alike, 2 diff.	${}^1C_1 \cdot {}^8C_2 \cdot \dfrac{5!}{3!} = 560$
3 alike, 2 alike	${}^1C_1 \cdot {}^1C_1 \cdot \dfrac{5!}{3!\,2!} = 10$
4 alike, 1 diff.	${}^1C_1 \cdot {}^8C_1 \cdot \dfrac{5!}{4!} = 40$

Total $= 22660$.

(b) 11 letters $(3 E, 2 F, 2 I, 4$ diff) 7 types etc.

*§ 2. Arrangement of Numbers

Notation. 4 digit numbers 7038, 7308, 7380 or 8307, ... are all four digit numbers but 0738, 0837, 0378, ... are **not four digit numbers** as they begin with zero. However 0 can come anywhere in between or in the end.

Notation 0 | i.e. numbers beginning with zero or 0 in the left, i.e. 0532.

| 0 i.e. numbers ending with zero or 0 in the right i.e. 5970.

Similarly **3 |** i.e. numbers beginning with 3 or 3 in the left i.e. 3789

| 4 i.e. numbers ending with 4 or 4 in the right i.e. 3284

Repetition is not allowed unless stated otherwise.

1st Case : Number of **5 digit** numbers formed out of digits 1, 2, 3, 4, 5, 6, 7, 8, 9 (9 digits, **No zero**)

Places	I	II	III	IV	V	Ans.
No repetition	9	8	7	6	5	or ${}^9P_5$
Repetition	9	9	9	9	9	or 9^5

*2nd Case : Number of **5 digit** numbers formed out of digits 0, 1, 2, 3, 4, 5, 6, 7, 8, 9 (10 digits **including zero**)

*No repeat

I	II	III	IV	V
9	9	8	7	6	...(A)

(Not 10) $\neq 0$ (0 can be here)

Alternative = Total $- 0 |$

$${}^{10}P_5 - {}^9P_4$$

Total $- 0|$ (beginning with zero)

$= (10 \cdot 9 \cdot 8 \cdot 7 \cdot 6) - (9 \cdot 8 \cdot 7 \cdot 6)$

$= (10 - 1)(9 \cdot 8 \cdot 7 \cdot 6)$

$= 9 \cdot 9 \cdot 8 \cdot 7 \cdot 6$ ...(B)

Both A and B are same.

*Repetition allowed.

I	II	III	IV	V	
9	10	10	10	10	$= 9 \cdot 10^4$

(Not 10)   (Repetition allowed and zero can be
$\neq 0$ anywhere)

At least one digit repeated

Repetition allowed $-$ (No repetition)

*Example. 4 digit numbers formed out of 0, 1, 2, 3, 4, 5, 6 (seven digits)

	I	II	III	IV
No repetition	6	6	5	4

or ${}^7P_4 - {}^6P_3$

Total $- 0|$ (beginning with zero)

$= (7 \cdot 6 \cdot 5 \cdot 4) - (6 \cdot 5 \cdot 4)$

$= (7 - 1)(6 \cdot 5 \cdot 4) = 6 \cdot 6 \cdot 5 \cdot 4$

	I	II	III	IV	
Repetition	6	7	7	7	$= 6 \cdot 7^3$

(Not 7) $\neq 0$ (Rep. allowed, zero can come)

Problem Set (3)

Formation of numbers of different digits with or without repetition, even or odd or greater or less than a particular number.

1. How many numbers divisible by 5 and lying between 3000 and 4000 can be formed from the digits 3, 4, 5, 6, 7 and 8, no digit being repeated in any number?

2. How many different numbers of six digits each (without repetition of digits) can be formed from the digits 4, 5, 6, 7, 8, 9?
How many of these **are not divisible by 5**?

3.* How many different numbers of six digits (without repetition of digits) can be formed from the digits 3, 1, 7, 0, 9, 5?
   (i)   How many of them will have 0 in the unit place?
   (ii) How many of them are divisible by 5?
   (iii) How many of them are not divisible by 5?

4. How many different numbers of 4 digits can be formed from the ten digits 0, 1, 2,...9, no digit being repeated in any number?

5. Find the total number of 9 digit numbers which have all different digits.

6.* How many different numbers (without repetition of digits) can be formed from the digits 1, 3, 5, 7, 9 when taken all at a time and what is their sum?

7. How many numbers greater than 23000 can be formed from the digits 1, 2, 3, 4, 5?

8. Prove that only 18 numbers with different digits greater than 1000 can be formed from the digits 1, 0, 2, 3.

9. Prove that only 18 numbers can be formed by using all the digits 1, 2, 3, 4, 3, 2, 1 so that the odd digits always occupy the odd places.

10. How many numbers lying between 99 and 1000 can be formed from the digits 2, 3, 7, 0, 8, 6?

11. How many numbers which are
    (i)   Even
    (ii) Less than 40,000
          can be formed by taking all the digits 1, 2, 3, 4, 5?
    (iii) The number of odd numbers between 1000 and 10,000 can be formed with the digits 1, 2, 3, 4, 5, 6, 7, 8, 9 is
          (a) 1280   (b) 1836
          (c) 2572   (d) 1680

12. (i)* A number of 4 different digits is formed by using the digits 1, 2, 3, 4, 5, 6, 7 in all possible ways. Find
    (a) How many such numbers can be formed?
    (b) How many of them are greater than 3400?
    (c) How many of them are exactly divisible by 2?
    (d) How many of these are exactly divisible by 25?

(e) How many of these are exactly divisible by 4?

(ii) A number of 6 different digits is formed by using the digits 0, 1, 2, 3, 4, 5. Find
    (a) How many such numbers can be formed?
    (b) How many of these are even?
    (c) How many of these are divisible by 4?
    (d) How many of these are divisible by 25?

(iii) A seven digit number made up of all distinct digits 8, 7, 6, 4, 2, x, y is divisible by 3. The possible number of ordered pairs (x, y) is:
    (a) 4   (b) 8
    (c) 2   (d) None

13. Find the number of + ive integers which can be formed by using any number of digits from 0, 1, 2, 3, 4, 5 but using each digit not more than once in each number. How many of these integers are greater than 3000?

14. (a) How many numbers greater than 1000, but not greater than 4000 can be formed with the digits 0, 1, 2, 3, 4, **repetition of digits being allowed**?

(b)* How many numbers greater than 6×10^5 can be formed from the digits 5, 6, 7, 8 and 9 when (a) **repetition not allowed** (b) **repetition allowed**.

15. (i) How many different numbers, greater than 50000 can be formed with the digits 1, 1, 5, 9, 0?

(ii) How many different nine digit numbers can be formed from the number 223355888 by rearranging its digits so that the odd digits occupy even positions?
    (a) 16   (b) 36
    (c) 60   (d) 180   **(I.I.T. Sc. 2000)**

16. (i) How many odd numbers, greater than 600000 can be formed from the digits 5, 6, 7, 8, 9, 0 if
    (a) Repetitions are allowed,
    (b) Repetitions are not allowed.

(ii) How many numbers greater than 10 lakhs be formed from 2, 3, 0, 3, 4, 2, 3.
    (a) 420   (b) 360
    (c) 400   (d) 300

(iii) Five digit numbers divisible by 9 are to be formed by using the digits 0, 1, 2, 3, 4, 7, 8 (without repetition). The total number of such numbers is equal to
    (a) 216   (b) 214
    (c) 212   (d) 200

(iv) Even numbers are formed with three digits such that if 5 is one of the digits then 7 is the next digit. The number of such numbers is (Repetition allowed.)

(a) 360   (b) 365
(c) 325   (d) 300

(v) The number of seven digit integers, with sum of the digits equal to 10 and formed by using the digits 1, 2 and 3 only, is

(a) 55   (b) 66
(c) 77   (d) 88   **(I.I.T. 2009)**

17. (a)* Number plates of cars must contain 3 letters of the alphabet denoting the place and area to which its owner belongs. This is to be followed by a three-digit number. How many different number plates can be formed if :

(i) repetition of letters and digits is not allowed.

(ii) repetition of letters and digits is allowed.

(b) Number plate of cars is to be made having 2 letters of alphabet followed by three-digit number but not beginning with zero. How many different number plates can be made (i) when repetition is allowed, and

(ii) when repetition is not allowed ?

18. How many numbers less than 10,000 be formed by using different digits from 0 to 9 **repetition not allowed** which are such that they are :

(a) divisible by 5

(b) divisible by 25,

What will be the corresponding answers for (a) and (b) if **repetition is allowed** ?

19. What is the number of 6 digit telephone numbers which **have at least one of their digits repeated ?**

20.* Four digit numbers are to be formed by using the digits 0, 1, 2, 3, 4, 5. What is the number of such numbers if :

(a) Repetition is not allowed,

(b) Repetition is allowed,

(c) At least one digit is repeated ?

21. (a)* The number of divisors of 9600 including 1 and 9600 is

(i) 60   (ii) 58
(iii) 48   (iv) 46   **(D.C.E. 1997)**

(b) Number of divisors of the form $4n + 2$ $(n \geq 0)$ of the integer 240 is

(A) 4   (B) 8
(C) 10   (D) 3   **(I.I.T. 1998)**

(c) Prove that the number of divisors of 8400 is 58 only (excluding the number itself and one). Also find the sum of the divisors.

(d) Find the number of proper divisors of the number $N = 2^p . 3^q . 5^r$. Also find the sum of

(i) all the divisors of N

(ii) all the proper divisors of N

(iii) all the proper divisors of N which are multiple of 3.

(e) The number of divisors of $2^6 . 3^5 . 5^3 . 7^4 , 11$ is equal to

(a) $11^2 - 1$ (b) $21^2 - 1$
(c) $31^2 - 1$ (d) $41^2 - 1$

(f) The number of divisors of 441, 1125 and 384 are in

(a) A.P.   (b) G.P.
(c) H.P.   (d) none

22. If $n_1 , n_2 , ..., n_p$ are p positive integers, whose sum is an even number, then the number of odd integers among them is odd.

(a) True   (b) False

Solutions to Problem Set (3)

1. 3, 4, 5, 6, 7, 8. $3 \begin{vmatrix} \text{out of 4} \\ \hline \text{any two} \end{vmatrix} 5$

Since the number is to be divisible by 5, it must have 5 in the last place. Again as it is to lie between 3000 and 4000 it must have 3 in first place. The number must contain only 4 digits. The first and last digits have been fixed by 3 and 5 respectively so we have now to choose 2 digits out of the remaining 4.

Hence the number of arrangements is

$$^4P_2 = \frac{4!}{2!} = 12.$$

2. Here we have to use all six digits 4, 5, 6, 7, 8, 9.
∴ Number of six digit numbers $= 6! = 720$.
Now 5 ! numbers are divisible by 5 as 5 is fixed in the last place.
Hence total no. of numbers which are not divisible by 5 is

$$6! - 5! = 720 - 120 = 600.$$

3. 3, 1, 7, 0, 9, 5, *i.e.* 6 digits.
The total numbers of 6 digit numbers

$$6! - 5! = 720 - 120 = 600.$$

Alt. 5.   5. 4. 3. 2. 1 = 600.
   (No zero)   (0 can be)

(i) $5! = 120$ having 0 at the end.

(ii) **Divisible by 5.**
They will have zero in the last place and hence the remaining 5 can be arranged in $5! = 120$ ways.
They may have 5 in the last place and as above we will have $5! = 120$ ways. These will also include numbers which will have zero in the first place. Therefore the numbers having zero in 1st and 5 in last place will be 4 !
∴ Therefore 6 digit numbers having 5 in the end will be

$$5! - 4! = 120 - 24 = 96.$$

Alt. I   II   III   IV   V
     4.   4.   3.   2.   1 = 96
  (No zero)   (0 can be)

Therefore the total number of 6 digit numbers divisible by 5 is

$$120 + 96 = 216.$$

(iii) Not divisible by 5.

$$= \text{Total} - (\text{divisible by 5})$$
$$= 600 - 216 = 384.$$

4. 0, 1, 2, ... 9. Ten digits.

Then required number of 4 digit numbers

$$= {}^{10}P_4 - {}^9P_3.$$

where ${}^9P_3$ corresponds to those numbers which will have zero in the first place.

$$= \frac{10 \times 9 \times 8 \times 7 \times 6!}{6!} - \frac{9 \times 8 \times 7 \times 6!}{6!}$$
$$= 9 \times 8 \times 7 (10 - 1) = 81 \times 56 = 4536.$$

5. ${}^{10}P_9 - {}^9P_8 = \frac{10!}{1!} - \frac{9!}{1} = 9!(10-1) = 9(9!)$

$$= 9 \times (9 \times 8 \times 7 \times 6!)$$
$$= 81 \times 56 \times 720 = 3265920.$$

Alternative : The number is to be of 9 digits. The first place can be filled in 9 ways only (as zero can not be in the first place). Having filled up the first place the remaining 8 places can be filled up by the remaining 9 digits in ${}^9P_8 = 9!$ ways.

Hence the total is $9 \times 9!$

6. 1, 3, 5, 7, 9. five digits.

∴ No. of numbers $= 5! = 120.$

We have to find the sum of these 120 numbers. Suppose 9 is in the unit place then the remaining 4 can be arranged in $4! = 24$ ways. Similarly other digits can occupy the first place in 24 ways.

Hence sum due to the unit place of all the 120 numbers.

$$= 24 (9 + 7 + 5 + 3 + 1) \text{ units.}$$
$$= 24 \times 25 \text{ units} = 600 \text{ units}$$

Again suppose 9 is in the 2nd place i.e. ten's place and it will be so in 24 numbers. Similarly each digit will be in ten's place 24 times. Hence the sum of digits due to ten's place of all the 120 numbers is

$$24 (9 + 7 + 5 + 3 + 1) \text{ tens}$$
$$= 24 \times 25 \text{ tens} = 600 \text{ tens} = 6000.$$

Proceeding exactly for hundreds, thousands and ten thousands, we have the sum of the numbers

$$= 600 (1 + 10 + 100 + 1000 + 10000)$$
$$= 600 (11111) = 6666600.$$

7. The digits are 1, 2, 3, 4, 5. We have to form numbers greater than 23000.

Required number will be

$$= \text{Total} - (\text{those beginning with 1})$$
$$- (\text{those beginning with 21})$$
$$= 5! - 4! - 3! = 120 - 24 - 6 = 90.$$

8. The digits are 1, 0, 2, 3. We have to form numbers greater than 1000.

∴ Required number $= 4! - 3!$

(3 ! for those having 0 in the 1st place)

$$= 24 - 6 = 18.$$

9. There are 4 odd places and there are 4 odd numbers (2 are alike i.e. 1, 1; and 2 are alike i.e. 3, 3). These can be arranged in four places in

$$\frac{4!}{2! \, 2!} = \frac{4 \times 3}{2} = 6 \text{ ways.}$$

There will be 3 even places namely 2nd, 4th and 6th in which 3 even numbers (2 are alike i.e. 2, 2). These can be arranged in

$$\frac{3!}{2!} = \frac{3 \times 2}{2} = 3 \text{ ways.}$$

Hence the total number of the numbers thus formed is

$$6 \times 3 = 18.$$

10. Digits are 2, 3, 7, 0, 8, 6 i.e. six in all.

We have to form numbers between 99 and 1000. Clearly they will be of three digits and their number will be

$${}^6P_3 = \frac{6!}{3!} = 6 \times 5 \times 4 = 120.$$

Out of these we have to exclude those numbers of 3 digits which have zero in the first place.

Their number is ${}^5P_2 = \frac{5!}{3!} = 5 \times 4 = 20.$

∴ The required number $= 120 - 20 = 100.$

11. 1, 2, 3, 4, 5 : 5 digits

(i) Even numbers which will have 2 in the last place $= 4! = 24.$

Similarly those which will have 4 in the last place $= 4! = 24.$

∴ Total is $24 + 24 = 48.$

(ii) Numbers less than 40,000 will have either 1 or 2 or 3 in the first place and hence as above total of such numbers will be $24 + 24 + 24 = 72.$

(iii) Ans. (d).

It will be 4 digit number and as it is to be odd the unit place can be filled in 5 ways by any of the 5 odd numbers. Out of remaining 8 we have to arrange 3 in ${}^8P_3$ ways.

∴ $(8 \times 7 \times 6) \times 5 = 1680$ by fundamental theorem.

12. 1, 2, 3, 4, 5, 6, 7 : 7 digits in all and we have to use 4 digits

(a) ${}^7P_4 = \frac{7!}{3!} = 7 \times 6 \times 5 \times 4 = 840.$

(b) Numbers greater than 3400 will have, 4 or 5 or 6 or 7 in the first place i.e. there are 4 ways of filling the first place. (i.e. 4 ways) Having filled the first place say by 4 we have to choose 3 digits out of the remaining 6 and the number will be

$${}^6P_3 = \frac{6!}{3!} = 6 \times 5 \times 4 = 120.$$

Therefore total of such numbers by fundamental theorem will be

$$4 \times 120 = 480. \qquad \text{...(1)}$$

Numbers greater than 3400 can be those which have 34, 35, 36, 37 in the first two places (*i.e.* 4 ways).

Having filled up 34 in the first two places we will have to choose 2 more out of remaining 5 and the number will be

$$^5P_2 = \frac{5!}{3!} = 5 \times 4 = 20.$$

Therefore total as above will be

$$20 \times 4 = 80. \qquad \text{...(2)}$$

Hence all the numbers greater than 3400 will be
480 + 80 = 560, by (1) and (2).

Alternative Easier Method :

Numbers less than 3400 will have 1 or 2 in 1st place or 31, 32 in the first two positions.

$$^6P_3 + {}^6P_3 = 120 + 120 = 240$$

$$^5P_2 + {}^5P_2 = 20 + 20 = 40.$$

Total numbers which are less than

$$3400 = 240 + 40 = 280.$$

Also from part (a) total number of numbers formed is $^7P_4 = 840$

Hence numbers greater than 3400 is 840 − 280 = 560.

(c) The numbers will be divisible by 2 if the last digit is divisible by 2 which can be done in 3 ways by fixing 2 or 4 or 6, and the remaining 3 places can be filled up out of remaining 6 digits in $^6P_3$ ways.

Hence the required no.

$$= 3 \times {}^6P_3 = 3 \times 120 = 360.$$

(d) A number will be divisible by 25 if the last two digits are divisible by 25 and this can be done in two ways for either 25 or 75 can be there and remaining two places out of 5 digits can be filled in $^5P_2$ ways.

Hence the required number

$$= 2 \times {}^5P_2 = 2 \times 20 = 40.$$

(e) A number is divisible by 4 if the last two digits are divisible by 4 which can be done in 10 ways (12, 16, 24, 32, 36, 52, 56, 64, 72, 76).

Hence number = $10 \times {}^5P_2 = 10 \times 20 = 200$.

(ii) It is same type of question as part (i) but care has to be taken because of 0 as 032451 is not of six digit but of five digit. See Q. 3 which has 0 as one of the digit

(a) 6! − 5! = 720 − 120 = 600

5! coresponds to the number which start with zero.

(b) **Even numbers.** These numbers will have 0, 2, 4, in the end.

Having 0 in the end we have to arrange the remaining 5 in 5! = 120 ways.

Having 2 in the end. $5! - 4! \left(\begin{array}{ccc} \text{Ist} & \text{......} & \text{last} \\ 0 & & 2 \end{array} \right)$

$$= 120 - 24 = 96$$

Having 4 in the end = 96 as above $\left(\begin{array}{ccc} \text{Ist} & \text{......} & \text{last} \\ 0 & & 2 \end{array} \right)$

$$\therefore \quad \text{Total} = 120 + 96 + 96 = 312$$

(c) **Divisible by 4**

The last two digits will be divisible by 4. They will be of the type (12, 24, 52) or (04, 20, 40) we have to arrange remaining 4 digits.

For Ist bracket the remaining 4 digits will include 0 which cannot occupy the first place.

Hence $4! - 3! (0 \cdots) = 18$

Thus total = 18 + 18 + 18 = 54

For each of 2nd bracket we will have to arrange remaining 4 non-zero digit which can be done in 4! = 24 ways.

$$\therefore \quad \text{Total for 2nd brackets} = 24 + 24 + 24 = 72$$

Hence their will be = 54 + 72 = 126 numbers divisible by 4.

(d) **Divisible by 25**

The last two digit be will be 25 or 50. Arranging as above for 50 it will be 4! = 24 and for 50 it will be $4! - 3! (0 \cdots) = 18$

$$\therefore \quad \text{Total divisible by 25 is } 24 + 18 = 42$$

(iii) Ans. (b).

We know that a number is divisible by 3 if sum of its digits is divisible by 3.

Hence we must have

$$(8 + 7 + 6 + 4 + 2) + (x + y) = 3k$$

or $27 + (x + y) = 3k$ \qquad ...(1)

$$\therefore \quad x + y \text{ is also multiple of 3} \qquad \text{...(2)}$$

Again since all the seven digit numbers is to have distinct digits therefore x and y must be chosen from 0, 1, 3, 5, 9 (excluding 8, 7, 6, 42) such that **x + y is a multiple of 3 by (2).**

If $x = 0$, then $y = 3, 9$ \quad $\therefore$ \quad (0, 3), (0, 9)

If $x = 1$, then $y = 5$ \quad $\therefore$ \quad (1, 5)

If $x = 3$, then $y = 0, 9$ \quad $\therefore$ \quad (3, 0), (3, 9)

If $x = 5$, then $y = 1$ \quad $\therefore$ \quad (5, 1)

If $x = 9$, then $y = 0, 3$ \quad $\therefore$ \quad (9, 0), (9, 3)

Hence in all 8 pairs (x, y) as listed above.

13. 0, 1, 2, 3, 4, 5. Six digits : 5 are + ive and one zero. We are at liberty to use any number of digits out of the six. Single digit numbers are clearly 5 which are + ive.
\qquad ...(1)

Two digit numbers

$$^6P_2 - {}^5P_1 = \frac{6!}{4!} - 5 = 30 - 5 = 25 \qquad \text{...(2)}$$

$^5P_1$ corresponds to the two digit numbers having 0 in the first place.

Three digit numbers

$$^6P_3 - {}^5P_2 = \frac{6!}{3!} - \frac{5!}{3!} = \frac{720 - 120}{6} = 100. \qquad ...(3)$$

Four digit numbers

$$^6P_4 - {}^5P_3 = \frac{6!}{2!} - \frac{5!}{2!} = \frac{720 - 120}{2} = 300. \qquad ...(4)$$

Five digit numbers $^6P_5 - {}^5P_4 = 6! - 5!$

$$= 720 - 120 = 600. \qquad ...(5)$$

Six digit numbers $^6P_6 - {}^5P_5 = 6! - 5!$

$$= 720 - 120 = 600. \qquad ...(6)$$

Total $= 600 + 600 + 300 + 100 + 25 + 5 = 1630$.

2nd part. Numbers greater than 3000.

All the five digit numbers 600 and six digit numbers 600 will be greater than 3000 by (5) and (6).

All the four digit numbers with either 3 or 4 or 5 in the first place will be greater than 3000.

Numbers of 4 digit having 3 in the first place will be

$$^5P_3 = \frac{5!}{2!} = \frac{120}{2} = 60.$$

Similarly those having 4 and 5 in the first place.

Therefore 4 digit numbers greater than 3000 is

$$60 + 60 + 60 = 180.$$

Hence total numbers greater than 3000 will be

$$600 + 600 + 180 = 1380.$$

Alternative for 4 digit numbers 180 found above.

Total number of 4 digit numbers is 300 as found before. Out of these we have to exclude those which have either 1 or 2 in the first place. If 1 is in the first place we have to choose 3 out of remaining five and hence it will be

$$^5P_3 = \frac{5!}{2!} = \frac{120}{2} = 60.$$

Similarly those which have 2 in the first place will be 60.

Hence four digit numbers which do not have either 1 or 2 in the first place i.e. which are greater than 3000 will be

$$300 - 60 - 60 = 180.$$

∴ Total is $600 + 600 + 180 = 1380$.

14. (a) 0, 1, 2, 3, 4. Five digits.

Numbers **greater than** 1000 and **less than** or **equal** to 4000 will be of four digits and will have either 1 (except 1000) or 2 or 3 in the first place or 4 in the first place with 0 in each of the remaining places.

Numbers having 1 in first place. After fixing 1st place, the second place can be filled by any of the 5 digits (not 4 digits because repetition is allowed i.e. 1 can appear again). Similarly 3rd place can be filled up in 5 ways and 4th place can be filled in 5 ways. Thus there will be $5 \times 5 \times 5 = 125$ ways in

which 1 will be in the first place. But this includes 1000 also which does not satisfy the given condition of being greater than 1000. Hence there will be 124 numbers having 1 in the first place. Similarly 125 each when 2 or 3 are in the first place. Only one number with 4 in the first place is formed, namely 4000 because of the condition of being less than or equal to 4000. Therefore total number of such numbers is

$$124 + 125 + 125 + 1 = 375.$$

(b) No repetition $4.5!$ (beginning with 6, 7, 8 or 9)

Repetition $4.6^5 - 1$

This 1 corresponds to the number $6 \times 10^5 = 600000$ as it is not greater than 6×10^5.

15. (i) 1, 1, 5, 9, 0. Five digits are, 2 alike and 3 different. Numbers greater than 50000 will have either 5 or 9 in the first place and will consist of 5 digits.

Let 5 be in the first place then we have to fill the remaining 4 places by remaining 4 digits 1, 1, 9, 0 out of which 2 are alike and hence it will be

$$\frac{4!}{2!} = \frac{24}{2} = 12.$$

Similarly 12 is the number when 9 is in the first place.

Therefore total numbers are $12 + 12 = 24$ which are greater than 50000.

(ii) Ans. (c).

4 odd digits in 4 even places can be arranged in 4! ways. But because 2 alike (3, 3), 2 alike (5, 5)

Number of ways is $\dfrac{4!}{2!\,2!} = \dfrac{24}{4} = 6$ \qquad ...(1)

Remaining 5 even digits (2 alike, 3 alike) in 5 places can be arranged as above in

$$\frac{5!}{2!\,3!} = \frac{120}{2.6} = 10 \text{ ways} \qquad ...(2)$$

By fundamental theorem total number is $10 \times 6 = 60$.

16. (i) **Repetition allowed.** 5, 6, 7, 8, 9, 0 : Six digits.

The first place can be filled by 6, 7, 8, 9 i.e. in 4 ways as the number is to be greater than 600000. The last place can be filled in by 5, 7, 9 i.e. 3 ways as the number is to be odd and because of repetition. Hence the number of ways of filling the 1st and the last place is

$$4 \times 3 = 12 \text{ ways}$$

We have to fill in the remaining 4 places of the six digit number i.e. 2nd, 3rd, 4th and 5th place. Since repetition is allowed each place can be filled in 6 ways. Hence the 4 places can be filled in $6 \times 6 \times 6 \times 6 = 1296$ ways.

Hence by fundamental theorem the total numbers will be

$$1296 \times 12 = 15552.$$

Repetition not allowed.

1st Place	Last (Number to be odd)	
6	5, 7, 9 = 3 ways	
8	5, 7, 9 = 3 ways	
7	5, 9 = 2 ways	(not 7)
9	5, 7 = 2 ways	(not 9)

Total number of ways of filling the first and the last place under given condition is

$$3 + 3 + 2 + 2 = 10 \text{ ways}.$$

(It was 12 when repetition was allowed).

Having filled in the first and the last places in 10 ways, we can fill in the remaining 4 places out of 4 digits (repetition not allowed) in $4! = 24$ ways.

∴ Total number of ways is $10 \times 24 = 240$.

(ii) Ans. (b).

Since the number is to be greater than 10 lakhs *i.e.* 10,00,000 it must be of seven digits and should begin with either 2 or 3 or 4.

Beginning with 2. Remaining 6 (Three 3's are alike)

∴ $\dfrac{6!}{3!} = 120$

Beginning with 3. Remaining 6 (Two 2's and two 3's are alike)

∴ $\dfrac{6!}{2!\,2!} = 180$

Beginning with 4. Remaining 6 (Two 2's and three 3's)

$\dfrac{6!}{3!\,.2!} = 60$

∴ Required number is $120 + 180 + 60 = 360$
⇒ (b).

(iii) Ans. (a).

We know that if a number is divisible by 9, then sum of the digits must be divisible by 9. If we follow the method as in last question we will have $^7C_5 = \dfrac{7.6}{1.2} = 21$. Out of these 21 selections we will choose those whose sum is divisible by 9. It will be very lengthy, so we choose the alternative method.

Sum of given digits $= 0 + 1 + 2 + 3 + 4 + 7 + 8 = 25$

Hence we will select only those five numbers whose sum is 18 or 9. But no five numbers will make the sum 9. So we choose the five numbers which make their sum 18. Since the sum of all the seven digits is 25 so we exclude those two digits out of given seven digits whose sum is 7.

Thus we exclude either 0, 7 or 3, 4 as both these have sum 7. Hence we have the following two sets.

(a) 1, 2, 3, 4, 8, (0, 7 excluded) ∴ Sum = 18
They can be arranged in $5! = 120$ ways

(b) 0, 1, 2, 7, 8, (3, 4 excluded) ∴ Sum = 18
∴ They can be arranged in
$5! - 4! \, (0, \text{in beginning}) = 120 - 24 = 96$ ways
Thus the total number of numbers divisible by 9 is $120 + 96 = 216 \Rightarrow$ (a).

(iv) Ans. (b).

Note that of the three digit numbers 5 is to be followed by 7 *i.e.* 57 should appear together. Since the number is to be even, the unit place must be occupied by 0, 2, 4, 6, 8.

Case I. Beginning with 5

H	T	U	Any of 0, 2, 4, 6, 8
1	1	5	(5 numbers)
(5)	(7)	(0, 2, 4, 6, 8)	

Note 5 can't come in middle place because then the last place has to be seven and it will not be even.

Case II. Not beginning with 5

H	T	U	(repetition allowed)
8	9	5	Any of 5 even
(≠0,	≠5)	(≠5)	

∴ Number of ways $= 8 \times 9 \times 5 = 360$
∴ Total ways $= 360 + 5 = 365 \Rightarrow$ (b)

(v) Ans. (c).

Out of digits 1, 2, 3 we have to choose seven digits whose sum is 10. It can be done in the following ways :

I. 3, 2, 1, 1, 1, 1, 1. Sum is 10.

No. of different integers formed is $\dfrac{7!}{5! \, (\text{alike})}$

$$= 7.6 = 42$$

II. 2, 2, 2, 1, 1, 1, 1. Sum is 10.

No. of different integers formed is $\dfrac{7!}{3!\,4! \, (\text{alike})}$

$$= \dfrac{7 \cdot 6 \cdot 5}{1 \cdot 2 \cdot 3} = 35$$

∴ Total $= 42 + 35 = 77$

17. (a) There are 26 letters of alphabet and 10 digits from 0 to 9.

Repetition not allowed :

3 letters $26 \times 25 \times 24$

3 digit numbers $= {}^{10}P_3 - {}^9P_2$ (beginning with zero)

$$= 10.9.8 - 9.8 = 9.8(10 - 1) = 9.9.8$$

∴ Number of plates $= 26 \times 25 \times 24 \times 9 \times 9 \times 8$
$$= 10108800.$$

Repetition allowed :

3 letters $26 \times 26 \times 26$

3 digit numbers $= 9 \times 10 \times 10 = 900$

1st place can't be filled by 0, 2nd can be filled by 10 and so is 3rd as repetition is allowed.

∴ Number of plates $= 26 \times 26 \times 26 \times 900$
$= 15818400.$

(b) **With repetition** $= 26 \times 26 \times 900$

Without repetition $= 26 \times 25 \times 9 \times 9 \times 8$

18. (a) **Repetition not allowed and ÷ 5**

Numbers less than 10,000 will at the most contain 4 digits (how many digits not given) Hence any number of digits but ≤ 4 digits from 0 to 9 may be used. Hence the number may be of one digit or two digits or three digits and at the most of 4 digits. Other condition is divisible by 5 for (a) and divisible by 25 for (b).

First Method :

(a) (i) One digit number $(5) = 1$

(ii) Two digit numbers $= \|5 + \|0$

i.e. those having 5 in the unit place or 0 in the unit place $= ({}^9P_1 - {}^8P_0) + {}^9P_1 = (9 - 1) + 9 = 17$

(iii) Three digit numbers $= \|5 + \|0$ as above
$= ({}^9P_2 - {}^8P_1) + {}^9P_2 = 2(9 \cdot 8) - 8 = 136$

(iv) Four digit numbers $= \|5 + \|0$ as above
$= ({}^9P_3 - {}^8P_2) + {}^9P_3 = 2(9 \cdot 8 \cdot 7) - 8 \cdot 7$
$= (8 \cdot 7) \cdot 17 = 56 \times 17 = 952.$

Hence total is $1 + 17 + 136 + 952 = 1106.$

Second Method :

All the numbers 5 will have either 5 or 0 in the end.

(i) 1 digit 5 only 5 ∴ 1 number

(ii) 2 digit number $\neq 0 \mid 5 = 8 \times 1 = 8$
or $9 \mid 0 = 9$ } 17

$\neq 0 \mid 5$ means that 5 will be in the end and 0 will not be in the beginning. Hence we are left with the option of only 8 digits in 1st place in L.H.S. Similarly $9 \mid 0$ means that 0 has been placed in the end and hence the first place can be filled in by any of the remaining 9 digits. Thus there are in all $9 + 8 = 17$ two digit numbers divisible by 5.

(iii) 3 digit numbers $\neq 0 \mid 8 \times 8 \mid 5 = 64$
$9 \times 8 \mid 0 = 72$ } 136

Having fixed 5 in R.H.S. and excluded 0 for L.H.S. we have only 8 choices for 1st place. Since 0 can come in 2nd place we have again 8 choices. In the 2nd case 0 comes in R.H.S. and hence 1st place in L.H.S. can be filled in 9 ways and 2nd in 8 ways

(iv) 4 digit numbers $\neq 0 \mid 8 \times 8 \times 7 \mid 5 = 448$
$9 \times 8 \times 7 \mid 0 = 504$ } 952

∴ Total $= 1 + 17 + 136 + 952 = 1106.$

Repetition allowed and ÷ 5

(i) 1 digit 5 1 only

(ii) 2 digit $\neq 0 \mid 9 \mid 5 = 9$
$9 \mid 0 = 9$ } 18

After fixing 5 in the unit place the first place can be filled again by 9 ways (excluding zero) as 5 can again come because repetition is allowed.

(iii) 3 digit $\neq 0 \mid 9 \times 10 \mid 5 = 90$
$9 \times 10 \mid 0 = 90$ } 180

(iv) 4 digit $\neq 0 \mid 9 \times 10 \times 10 \mid 5 = 900$
$9 \times 10 \times 10 \mid 0 = 900$ } 1800

Total $= 1 + 18 + 180 + 1800 = 1999.$

(b) **Numbers divisible by 25.**

Repetition not allowed and ÷ 25

1 digit No — 0

2 digit 25 or 50,75 — 3

3 digit $\neq 0 \mid 7 \mid 25$
$\mid 7 \mid 75$ } $7 + 7 + 8 = 22.$
$\mid 8 \mid 50$

4 digit $\neq 0 \mid 7 \times 7^* \mid 25$
$\neq 0 \mid 7 \times 7 \mid 75$ } $49 + 49 + 56 = 154$
$\mid 8 \times 7 \mid 50$

Two digits have been fixed in R.H.S., 0 cannot come in L.H.S. and hence we are left with only 7 choices for first number in L.H.S. For 2nd number from L.H.S. since 0 can come in between we have again 7 choices.

Total $= 3 + 22 + 154 = 179$

Repetition allowed and ÷ 25

1 digit — 0

2 digit 25, 50, 75 — 3

3 digit $\neq 0 \mid 9 \mid 25$
$\mid 9 \mid 75$
$\mid 9 \mid 50$ } $9 \times 4 = 36$
$\mid 9 \mid 00$

4 digit $\neq 0 \mid 9 \times 10 \mid 25$
$\mid 9 \times 10 \mid 75$
$\mid 9 \times 10 \mid 50$ } $4 \times 90 = 360$
$\mid 9 \times 10 \mid 00$

Total $= 3 + 36 + 360 = 399.$

19. Number will be formed by using 10 digits from 0 to 9.

At least one digit repeated = Total − (number when no digit is repeated)

Total = Each of the six places can be filled in 10 ways. Hence total is 10^6.

When no repetition is allowed then it will be ${}^{10}P_6$

[Mind not $({}^{10}P_6 - {}^9P_5)$ where ${}^9P_5$ corresponds to numbers beginning with zero in L.H.S.]. In telephone numbers this is permissible

∴ Required answer is $10^6 - {}^{10}P_6$

20. (a) ${}^6P_4 - {}^5P_3 = (6 \cdot 5 \cdot 4 \cdot 3) - (5 \cdot 4 \cdot 3)$
$= 60 \cdot (6 - 1) = 300.$

(b) **Repetition allowed :**

Ist place in 5 ways (no zero), 2nd in 6, 3rd in 6 and 4th also in 6. ∴ $5 \times 6^3.$

(c) At least one repeated = Total with repetition
$$- \text{No repetition}$$
$$= 5 \times 6^3 - 300$$
$$= 1080 - 300 = 780$$

21. (a) Ans. (iii). $9600 = 96 \times 100$
$$= 3 \times 2^5 \times 2^2 \times 5^2 = 2^7 . 3^1 . 5^2$$
$$\therefore \quad 9600 = 2^a \, 3^b \, 5^c$$

where a varies from 0 to 7.
i.e. $2^0, 2^1, 2^2, \ldots 2^7$ i.e. 8 divisors.

Similarly b varies from 0 to 1 i.e. 2 divisors, and c varies from 0 to 2 i.e. 3 divisors.

$a = b = c = 0$ corresponds to 1 and $a = 7, b = 1, c = 2$ i.e. highest values correspond to given number 9600. Hence the total number of divisors is $8 \times 2 \times 3 = 48$.

Note : If the number 9600 and 1 were to be excluded, then the corresponding divisors will be $48 - 2 = 46$.

(b) Ans. (A).
$$240 = 2^4 . 3^1 . 5^1$$

$\therefore$ Number of divisors of 240 are $5 \times 2 \times 2 = 20$
$$1, 2, 4, 8, 16$$
$$3, 6, 12, 24, 48$$
$$5, 10, 20, 40, 80$$
$$15, 30, 60, 120, 240$$

But only 2, 6, 10, 30 of column (2) correspond to the form $4n + 2$ for $n = 0, 1, 2, 7$.

(c) $8400 = 4 \times 100 \times 21 = 16 \times 25 \times 3 \times 7$
$$= 3^1 . 2^4 . 5^2 . 7^1 = 3^a \, 2^b \, 5^c \, 7^d$$

a varies from 0 to 1, b from 0 to 4, c from 0 to 2 and d again from 0 to 1.
Thus the total number of divisors is
$$= 2 \times 5 \times 3 \times 2 = 60$$

We have to exclude the divisor 1 and the divisor 8400, i.e. the number itself. Hence required number is $60 - 2 = 58$.

Sum of the divisors

Any divisor is of the form $3^a \, 2^b \, 5^c \, 7^d$

$\therefore$ Sum $= \sum\limits_{0}^{1} 3^a \sum\limits_{0}^{4} 2^b \sum\limits_{0}^{2} 5^c \sum\limits_{0}^{1} 7^d$

$$= (1 + 3)(1 + 2 + 2^2 + 2^3 + 2^4)(1 + 5 + 5^2)$$
$$(1 + 7)$$
$$= 4 \times 31 \times 31 \times 8$$

or $\dfrac{3^2 - 1}{3 - 1} . \dfrac{2^5 - 1}{2 - 1} . \dfrac{5^3 - 1}{5 - 1} . \dfrac{7^2 - 1}{7 - 1}$ (G.P.)

(d) Number of divisors is $(p + 1)(q + 1)(r + 1)$.

Number of proper divisors is
$$(p + 1)(q + 1)(r + 1) - 2$$
where -2 corresponds to 1 and N itself which are not proper divisors of N

Sum of all the divisors of N

$$\sum\limits_{a = 0}^{p} 2^a \sum\limits_{b = 0}^{q} 3^b \sum\limits_{c = 0}^{r} 5^c$$

$$= \left(\dfrac{2^{p+1} - 1}{2 - 1} \dfrac{3^{q+1} - 1}{3 - 1} \dfrac{5^{r+1} - 1}{5 - 1} \right) \text{ by sum of a G.P.}$$
$$\ldots (1)$$

Sum of all the proper divisors of N

Exclude 1 and $N = 2^p . 3^q . 5^r$ from (1)
$$\dfrac{1}{8} (2^{p+1} - 1)(3^{q+1} - 1)(5^{r+1} - 1)$$
$$- 1 - 2^p \, 3^q \, 5^r \quad \ldots (2)$$

If the divisor is to be a multiple of 3, then
$$N = 3 [2^p . 3^{q-1} . 5^r] = 3N'$$

Hence in this case the sum of all the divisors as in (1) will be
$$3 \cdot \dfrac{1}{8} [(2^{p+1} - 1)(3^q - 1)(5^{r+1} - 1)] \quad \ldots (3)$$

Sum of all the proper divisors which are multiple of 3 will be obtained from (3) by excluding the number $2^p . 3^q . 5^r$ as it will not be proper.

(e) Ans. (d).
Consider the factor 2^6,
$2^0, 2^1, 2^2, 2^3, 2^4, 2^5, 2^6$. Any of the seven could be divisors. Arguing as above for the other factors we can say that the number of divisors are
$$7 \times 6 \times 4 \times 5 \times 2 = 42 \times 40 = 1680 = 1600 + 80$$
$$= 40^2 + 2.40 + 1 - 1 = (40 + 1)^2 - 1 = 41^2 - 1 \Rightarrow (d)$$

(f) Ans. (b).
The given numbers can be written as
$$9 \times 49, \quad 9 \times 125, \quad 3 \times 128 \text{ or } 3^2 . 7^2, 3^2 . 5^3$$
and $3^1 . 2^7$.
Hence the number of divisors are
$$3.3, \quad 3.4, \quad 2.8 \text{ or } 9, 12, 16$$
which are in G.P. of $r = \dfrac{4}{3}$.

22. Ans. (b).
For, if the number of odd integers is odd, the sum of these odd integers will be odd whereas the sum of remaining even integers will be even so that the sum of all integers will be odd which is false since the sum is given to be even.

Problem Set (4)

Formation of committees, seating arrangements on a round table, diagonals of geometrical figures, selection of teams, giving away of prizes.

1. How many committees of 5 members each can be formed from 8 official and 4 non-official members in the following cases :
(a) Each consisting of 3 official and 2 non-official members.
(b) Each contains at least two non-official members.
(c) A particular official member is never included.
(d) A particular non-official member is always included.

2. (a)* A committee of 12 is to be formed from 9 women and 8 men. In how many ways this can be done if at least five women have to be included in a committee ? In how many of these committees (i) the women are in majority (ii) the men are in majority ? **(I.I.T. 1994)**
(b) Out of 10 persons (6 males, 4 females) a committee of 5 is formed.
p = number of such committees which include at least one lady.
q = number of such committees which include at least two men.
Find the ratio $p : q$.

3.* Out of 8 men and 10 women a committee consisting of 6 men and 5 women is to be formed. How many such committees can be formed when one particular man A refuses to be a member of the committee in which his boss B's wife is there?

4. There are 10 professors and 20 students out of whom a committee of 2 professors and 3 students is to be formed. Find the number of ways in which this can be done. Further find in how many of these committees
(i) A particular professor is included
(ii) A particular student is included
(iii) A particular student is excluded.

5. From 6 gentlemen and 4 ladies a committee of 5 is to be formed. In how many ways can this be done if
(i) The committee is to include at least one lady
(ii) There is no restriction about its formation.

6. (a) From 4 officers and 8 jawans in how many ways can 6 be chosen (i) to include exactly one officer (ii) to include at least one officer ?
(b) The number of ways in which a committee of 5 can be chosen from 10 candidates so as to exclude the youngest if it includes the oldest
(a) 178 (b) 196
(c) 202 (d) none

7. (a) A candidate is required to answer 6 out of 10 questions which are divided into two groups each containing 5 questions and he is not permitted to attempt more than 4 from each group. In how many ways can he make up his choice ?
(b)* A candidate is required to answer 7 out of 15 questions which are divided into three groups A, B, C each containing 4, 5, 6 questions respectively. He is required to select at least 2 questions from each group. In how many ways can he make up his choice ?
(c) A candidate is required to answer 7 questions out of 12 questions which are divided into two groups, each containing 6 questions. He is not permitted to attempt more than 5 questions from either group. In how many different ways can he choose the 7 questions ?

8. (a)* A question paper consists of two sections having respectively 3 and 4 questions. The following note is given on the paper "It is not necessary to attempt all the questions. One question from each section is compulsory". In how many ways can a candidate select the questions ?
(b) A question paper consists of three sections A, B, C having 6, 4, 3 questions respectively. A student has the freedom to answer any number of questions but atleast one question from each section is compulsory. In how may ways can the paper be attempted by the student ?

9. (a) If some or all of n things be taken at a time, prove that the number of combinations is $2^n - 1$.
(b) The total number of combinations of $2n$ different things taken any one or more at a time and total number of combinations of n different things taken one or more at a time is in the ratio 65 : 1, then the value of n is equal to
(a) 4 (b) 5
(c) 6 (d) none of these

10. (a)* Given 5 different green dyes, four different blue dyes and three different red dyes, how many combinations of dyes can be chosen taking at least one green and one blue dye ?
(b)* There are 3 books on Maths, 4 on Physics and 5 on English. How many different collections can be made such that each collection consists of :
(i) One book of each subject
(ii) At least one book of each subject
(iii) At least one book of English.
(c) From 6 different novels and 3 different dictionaries, 4 novels and 1 dictionary are to be selected and arranged in a row on a shelf so that

the dictionary is always in the middle. Then the number of such arrangements is
(a) at least 1000
(b) less than 500
(c) at least 500 but less than 750
(d) at least 750 but less than 1000   **(AIEEE 2009)**

11. (a) There are 10 lamps in a hall. Each one of them can be switched on independently. The number of ways in which the hall can be illuminated is $2^{10} - 1$.

    (b) How many ten digit numbers can be formed by using the digits 3 and 7 only ?

12. At an election, three wards of a town are canvassed by 4, 5 and 8 men respectively. If 20 men volunteer in, how many ways can they be allotted to the different wards ?

13. A guard of 12 men is formed from a group of n soldiers in all possible ways. Find :
    (i) The number of times two particular soldiers A and B are together on guard.
    (ii) The number of times three particular soldiers C, D, E are together on guard.
    (iii) Also find n if it is found that A and B are three times as often together on guard as C, D, E are.

14. (a) There are 16 vacancies for clerks in a certain office. 20 applications are received. In how many ways can the clerks be appointed ? How many times may a particular candidate be selected ?

    (b)* To fill 12 vacancies there are 25 candidates of which 5 are from scheduled castes. If 3 of the vacancies are reserved for scheduled caste candidates while the rest are open to all, find the number of ways in which the selection can be made.

    (c) Find the number of ways of selecting 10 clerks from 27 male 17 female applicants if the selection is to consist of either all males or all females.

15.* A box contains two white balls, three black balls and 4 red balls. In how many ways can three balls be drawn from the box if at least one black ball is to be included in the draw ?

16. In how many ways can a lawn tennis mixed double be made up from seven married couples if no husband and wife play in the same set ?

17. (a) Two men enter a railway compartment having 6 seats unoccupied. In how many ways can they be seated ?

    (b) Six boys and four girls enter a railway compartment having 5 seats on each side. In how many ways can they occupy the seats if the girls are to occupy only the corner seats ?

18. In how many ways can n men be seated around a round table when in no two ways a man has the same neighbours ?

19. (a) In how many ways may 6 Hindus and 6 Muslims sit around a round table so that two Hindus may never sit together ?

    (b) m men and n women are to be seated in a row so that no two women sit together. If $m > n$, then show that the number of ways in which they can be seated is $\dfrac{m! \, (m+1)!}{(m-n+1)!}$.

20. A business man hosts a dinner to 21 guests. He is having 2 round tables which can accommodate 15 and 6 persons each. In how many ways can he arrange the guests ?

21. A tea party is arranged for 16 people along two sides of a long table with 8 chairs on each side. Four men wish to sit on one particular side and two on the other side. In how many ways can they be seated ?

22. (a)* Out of 8 sailors on a boat, 3 can work only on one side and 2 only on the other side. In how many ways can the sailors be **arranged** on the boat ?

    (b)* Out of a crew of 43 persons on a ship, only 3 can do the steering and one is needed. Of the remaining 40, 8 persons wish to go **only** on one side and 3 persons wish to go on the other side. In how many ways can they be arranged so that there are 20 rowers on each side of the ship ?

23. (a) Eighteen guests have to be seated, half on each side of a long table. Four particular guests desire to sit on one particular side and three others on other side. Determine the number of ways in which the seating arrangements can be made.   **(I.I.T 1991)**

    (b) Eight chairs are numbered 1 to 8. Two women and three men wish to occupy one chair each. First the women choose the chairs from amongst the chairs marked 1 to 4; and then the men select the chairs from amongst the remaining. The number of possible arrangements is
    (i) $^4C_3 \times \,^4C_2$ (ii) $^4C_2 \times \,^4P_3$
    (iii) $^4P_2 \times \,^4P_3$ (iv) None of these.

24. (a)* There are 6 teachers of whom two are from Science, 2 from Arts and the remaining two from Commerce. They have to stand in a line so that the two Science teachers, two arts teachers and also the two Commerce teachers are together. Find the number of ways in which they can do so.

    (b) Eleven books consisting of 5 Mathematics, 4 Physics and 2 on Chemistry are placed on a shelf at random. Find the number of possible ways of arranging them on the assumption that the books on the same subject are all together.

25. A family consists of a grandfather, 6 sons and daughters and 4 grand children. They are to be seated in a row for dinner. The grand children wish to occupy the two seats at each end and the grandfather refuses to

have a grand child on either side of him. In how many ways can the seating arrangements be made for the dinner ?

Miscellaneous Types.

26. (a) 930 Deepawali greeting cards are exchanged amongst the students of a class. If every student sends a card to every other student then what is the number of students in the class?

(b)* In a class tournament where the participants were to play one game with another, two class players fell ill, having played 3 games each. If the total number of games played is 84, the number of participants at the beginning was ....

27. (a) In a football championship, there were played 153 matches. Every two teams played one match with each other. The number of teams, participating in the championship is .... **(J.E.E.,W.B. 1992)**

(b)* Everybody in a room shakes hands with everybody else. The total number of hand shakes is 66. The total number of persons in the room is 12. True or False ? **(M.N.R. 1991)**

28. (a) Show that the number of diagonals of a polygon of n sides is $\dfrac{n(n-3)}{2}$.

(b) Find the number of
   (i) diagonals
   (ii) triangles formed in a decagon.

29. (a)* The sides AB, BC, CA of a triangle ABC have 3, 4 and 5 interior points respectively on them. Find the number of triangles that can be constructed using these points as vertices.

(b) Show that the greatest possible number of points of intersection of 8 straight lines and 4 circles is 104.

30. Out of 18 points in a plane, no three are in the same straight line except five points which are collinear. How many
   (i) straight lines
   (ii) triangles can be formed by joining them ? **(J.E.E., W.B. 1992)**

31.* There are n points in a plane, no three of which are in the same straight line with the exception of p, which are all in the same straight line ; find the number (i) of straight lines, (ii) of triangles which result from joining them.

32. (a) There are n points in space, no four of which are in the same plane with the exception of p which are all in the same plane. Find how many planes there are each containing three of the points.

(b) There are p, q, r points on three parallel lines L_1, L_2 and L_3 all of which lie in one plane. Prove that the number of triangles which can be formed with vertices at their points is

$$^{p+q+r}C_3 - {}^pC_3 - {}^qC_3 - {}^rC_3$$

33. There are 12 points in a plane of which 5 are collinear. Find (i) the number of straight lines obtained by joining these points in pairs (ii) the number of triangles that can be formed with vertices at these points.

34. (a) Determine the number of rectangles that can be formed on a chess-board.

(b) There are two sets of parallel lines-one contains m lines and the other n lines. How many parallelograms are formed by these two sets ?

(c) The number of parallelograms that can be formed from a set of four parallel lines intersecting another set of three parallel lines is .... **(J.E.E., W.B. 1993)**

(d) A parallelogram is cut by two sets of m lines parallel to its sides. Find the number of parallelograms then formed.

35. (a) How many different signals can be given by using any number of flags from six flags of different colours ?

(b) Three men have 4 coats, 5 waist coats and 6 caps. In how many ways can they wear them ?

36. (a) In how many ways can three letters be posted in four letter boxes in a village ? If all the three letters are not posted in the same letter box, find the corresponding number of ways of posting.

(b) In how many ways can 5 rings of different type can be put in 4 fingers ?

37. (a)* If there are n students and r prizes $(r < n)$, prove that they can be given away (i) in n^r ways when a student can receive any number of prizes (ii) in $n^r - n$ ways when a student cannot receive all the prizes.

(b) There are 3 copies each of 4 different books. In how many ways can they be arranged in a shelf ?

38. (a) Find the number of ways of dividing 15 things into groups of 8, 4 and 3 respectively.

(b) Fruits are to be distributed amongst 11 children from a basket of fruits containing 5 mangoes, 4 apples and 2 bananas. Each child is to get one fruit. In how many ways the fruits can be distributed ?

39. In how many ways can a pack of 52 cards be
   (a)* divided equally among four players in order
   (b)* formed into 4 groups of 13 cards each
   (c)* divided into 4 sets, three of them having 17 cards each and the fourth just 1 card.

40. In how many ways can 10 balls be divided between two boys, one receiving two and the other eight balls ?

41. (a) In how many ways can the following prizes be given to a class of 20 boys. First and second Mathematics, first and second Physics, first Chemistry, and first English ?

(b)* Sixteen men compete with one another in running, swimming and riding. How many prize lists could be made if there were altogether 6 prizes of different values, one for running, 2 for swimming and 3 for riding ?

42. (a)* In a steamer there are stalls for 12 animals, and there are horses, cows and calves (not less than 12 each) ready to be shipped, in how many ways can the shipload be made ?

(b) A letter lock consists of three rings each worked with 12 different letters: find in how many ways it is possible to make an unsuccessful attempt to open the lock.

Solutions to Problem Set (4)

1. In this question we must bear in mind that we have only to form committees. We are not concerned with the arrangement of officials or non-officials.

   8 officials, 4 non-officials.

(a) **3 officials and 2 non-officials.**

   3 officials out of 8 can be selected **by (s) (iii), P. 294** in

   $$^8C_3 = \frac{8!}{5!\,3!} = \frac{8 \times 7 \times 6}{1 \times 2 \times 3} = 56 \text{ ways}$$

   2 non-officials out of 4 can be selected in

   $$^4C_2 = \frac{4 \cdot 3}{1 \cdot 2} = 6 \text{ ways.}$$

   ∴ By fundamental theorem the number of ways in which the committee can be formed is

   $$56 \times 6 = 336.$$

(b) **At least two non-official members.**

   ∴ Two non-officials and 3 officials $i.e.$

   $$^4C_2 \times {}^8C_3 = 6 \times 56 = 336.$$

   Three non-officials and 2 officials

   $$^4C_3 \times {}^8C_2 = 4 \times 28 = 112.$$

   Four non-officials and 1 official

   $$^4C_4 \times {}^8C_1 = 1 \times 8 = 8$$

   Total $= 336 + 112 + 8 = 456.$

   Alternative : At least two non-officials = Total – One non-official – No non-off. **See (v) Page 295.**

   $$= {}^{12}C_5 - ({}^8C_4 \cdot {}^4C_1) - {}^8C_5$$

   $$= 792 - 280 - 56 = 456.$$

(c) **A particular official never included.**
   Required no. of ways

   $$= {}^{12-1}C_5 = {}^{11}C_5 = \frac{11 \cdot 10 \cdot 9 \cdot 8 \cdot 7}{1 \cdot 2 \cdot 3 \cdot 4 \cdot 5} = 462$$

   [See (l) Page 293]

   [Here $p = 1$, $r = 5$ and $n = 12$]

(d) **A particular non-official is to be always included**
   The required number of ways

   $$= {}^{11}C_4 = \frac{11 \cdot 10 \cdot 9 \cdot 8}{1 \cdot 2 \cdot 3 \cdot 4} = 330.$$

   [See (k) Page 293 $p = 1$, $r = 5$ and $n = 12$]

2. (a) $(9W, 8M)$ committee of 12 with at least 5 women
   $(5W, 7M) + (6W, 6M) + (7W, 5M)$
   $\qquad\qquad + (8W, 4M) + (9W, 3M)$

   $({}^9C_5 \times {}^8C_7) + ({}^9C_6 \times {}^8C_6) + ({}^9C_7 \times {}^8C_5)$
   $\qquad\qquad + ({}^9C_8 \times {}^8C_4) + ({}^9C_9 \times {}^8C_3)$

   $(126 \times 8) + (84 \times 28) + (36 \times 56) + (9 \times 70) + (1 \times 56)$
   $\quad$ I $\qquad$ II $\qquad$ III $\qquad$ IV $\qquad$ V

   Add III, IV, V for women to be in majority and in I men are in majority.

(b) $6M, 4F$: Committee of 5.

   $p = $ At least one lady = Total – No lady

   $$= {}^{10}C_5 - {}^6C_5$$

   $$= \frac{10 \cdot 9 \cdot 8 \cdot 7 \cdot 6}{120} - 6$$

   $$= 252 - 6 = 246.$$

   $q = $ At least two men

   $= $ Total $- \{$(No man) + (One man)$\}$

   $= {}^{10}C_5 - 0 + \{{}^6C_1 \cdot {}^4C_4\} = 252 - 6 = 246.$

   ∴ $p = q$ or $\dfrac{p}{q} = 1.$

3. $8M, 10W$
   Committee of $6M$, $5W$
   Condition is that : A and Mrs. B refuse to serve in the same committee.

(i) **A is there and Mrs. B is excluded :**
   Total $\quad 7M\,9W$, $\qquad A$ included, B excluded
   Chosen $\quad 5M\,5W$,
   Number $= {}^7C_5 \times {}^9C_5 = {}^7C_2 \times {}^9C_4 = 21 \times 126$

(ii) **A is not there and Mrs. B is included :**
   Total $\quad 7M\,9W$, $\qquad A$ excluded, B included
   Chosen $6M\,4W$,
   Number $= {}^7C_6 \times {}^9C_4 = {}^7C_1 \times {}^9C_4 = 7 \times 126$

(iii) Neither A is there nor B's wife there.
   Total $7M \quad 9W$ Both A and B's wife excluded
   Chosen $\quad 6 \qquad 5$
   $\qquad {}^7C_6 \cdot {}^9C_5 = 7.126$

   Hence the total from (i), (ii) and (iii) is
   $$126\,(21 + 7 + 7) = 126 \times 35 = 4410$$

   Alternative easier method :
   Total $-$ (A and B's wife are together)

   $$= \begin{Bmatrix} 8M & 10W \\ 6 & 5 \end{Bmatrix} - \begin{Bmatrix} 7M & 9W \\ 5 & 4 \end{Bmatrix}$$

   A and B's wife are there

$$= ({}^8C_6 \cdot {}^{10}C_5) - ({}^7C_5 \cdot {}^9C_4)$$

$$= \frac{8.7}{1.2} \cdot \frac{10.9.8.7.6}{1.2.3.4.5} - \frac{7.6}{1.2} \cdot \frac{9.8.7.6}{1.2.3.4}$$

$$= 7056 - 2646 = 4410.$$

4. 10 Professors and 20 Students

(a) **2P and 3S**

$${}^{10}C_2 \times {}^{20}C_3 = 45 \times (20 \times 19 \times 3) = 51300.$$

(b) **Particular professor is included.**

$${}^9C_1 \times {}^{20}C_3 = 9 \times (20 \times 19 \times 3) = 180 \times 57 = 10260.$$

(c) **Particular student included.**

$${}^{10}C_2 \times {}^{19}C_2 = 45 \times (19 \times 9) = 7695.$$

(d) **Particular Student excluded.**

$${}^{10}C_2 \times {}^{19}C_3 = 45 \times (57 \times 17) = 43605.$$

5. (a) **6 Gentlemen, 4 Ladies**; Committee of 5.

At least one lady to be included

$(1L, 4G),$ or $(2L, 3G),$ or $(3L, 2G),$ or $(4L, 1G)$

$${}^4C_1 \times {}^6C_4 + {}^4C_2 \times {}^6C_3 + {}^4C_3 \times {}^6C_2 + {}^4C_4 \times {}^6C_1$$

$$= 60 + 120 + 60 + 6 = 246.$$

Alternative : At least one lady = Total – No lady

$$= {}^{10}C_5 - {}^6C_5 \text{ (all gents)} = 252 - 6 = 246.$$

(ii) No restriction on the formation, then out of 10 persons we have to choose 5.

$$\therefore \quad {}^{10}C_5 = \frac{10 \times 9 \times 8 \times 7 \times 6}{1 \times 2 \times 3 \times 4 \times 5} = 63 \times 4 = 252.$$

6. (a) (i) Ans. ${}^4C_1 \times {}^8C_5 = 224.$

(ii) At least one officer = Total – No officer

$$= {}^{12}C_6 - {}^8C_6 = \frac{(12)!}{6!6!} - \frac{8!}{6!2!}$$

$$= \frac{8!}{6!}\left[\frac{12 \times 11 \times 10 \times 9}{720} - \frac{1}{2}\right] = 56 \times 16 = 896$$

(b) Ans. (b).

It should be clearly understood that youngest is excluded only when oldest is included. There are two ways of forming the committee :

(i) **Oldest included** and youngest excluded, then out of remaining 8 candidates only 4 are to be selected.

i.e., $ {}^8C_4 = \frac{8.7.6.5}{1.2.3.4} = 70.$

(ii) **Oldest not included** then youngest need not be excluded. In this case out of remaining 9 we have to choose 5 members in

$${}^9C_5 = {}^9C_4 = \frac{9.8.7.6}{1.2.3.4} = 126 \text{ ways}$$

7. (a) Group A 5, Group B 5. Questions to be attempted 6 but not more than 4 from any group

$(4A, 2B), (3A, 3B), (2A, 4B)$

$${}^5C_4 \times {}^5C_2 + {}^5C_3 \times {}^5C_3 + {}^5C_2 \times {}^5C_4$$

$$= 50 + 100 + 50 = 200.$$

(b) $A(4) B(5) C(6).$ Only 7 but at least 2 from each group. Hence he has the following choice

$(2A, 2B, 3C) + (2A, 3B, 2C) + (3A, 2B, 2C)$

i.e. $ ({}^4C_2 \cdot {}^5C_2 \cdot {}^6C_3) + ({}^4C_2 \cdot {}^5C_3 \cdot {}^6C_2)$
$$+ ({}^4C_3 \cdot {}^5C_2 \cdot {}^6C_2)$$

$$= 1200 + 900 + 600 = 2700.$$

(c) Exactly as above

$${}^6C_5 \times {}^6C_2 + {}^6C_4 \times {}^6C_3 + {}^6C_3 \times {}^6C_4 + {}^6C_2 \times {}^6C_5$$

$$= (6 \times 15) + (15 \times 20) + (20 \times 15) + (15 \times 6)$$

$$= 90 + 300 + 300 + 90 = 780.$$

8. (a) Now if some or all of n things be taken at a time, then the number of combinations will be $2^n - 1$, as explained below. Each of the things can be taken or left, i.e. each gives 2 combinations. So the combinations of n things will be 2^n. But this includes the case when all have been left. Hence the number of combinations will be $2^n - 1$.

Section A : 3 questions, Section B : 4 questions and one question from each section is compulsory i.e. all of a particular section cannot be left.

$$\therefore \quad 2^3 - 1 = 7, \ 2^4 - 1 = 15.$$

$\therefore$ Total is $7 \times 15 = 105$ by fundamental theorem.

(b) Proceed exactly as in part (b).

$$(2^6 - 1)(2^4 - 1)(2^3 - 1) = 63 \times 15 \times 7 = 6615$$

9. (a) Each of the things can be taken or left out i.e. each gives two ways. So the combinations of n things will be

$2 \times 2 \times 2 \times \ldots \ldots n$ factors $= 2^n$. But this includes the case when all have been left out. So the number of combinations is $2^n - 1$.

(b) Ans. (c).

Refer **(g) P. 293 or part (a)** for non-empty selection (any one or more) we are given that

$$\frac{2^{2n} - 1}{2^n - 1} = \frac{65}{1} \quad \text{Put } 2^n = t$$

$$t^2 - 1 = 65t - 65$$

or $t^2 - 65t + 64 = 0$ or $(t - 64)(t - 1) = 0$

$$\therefore \quad 2^n = 2^6 \text{ or } 2^0 \ \therefore n = 6 \ \Rightarrow \text{(c)}$$

10. (a) At least one green dye can be selected out of 5 green dyes in $2^5 - 1$, i.e. in 31 ways. Similarly at least one blue dye can be selected out of 4 in $2^4 - 1$ in 15 ways. For red dyes there is no restriction; you may include it or not include it. Thus there are two ways of disposing of each of red dye. Thus the total number of selection of red dye is $2^3 = 8$

Hence the required number of ways $31 \times 15 \times 8 = 3720.$

(b) (i) $^3C_1 \times {}^4C_1 \times {}^5C_1 = 3 . 4 . 5 = 60$

(ii) $(2^3 - 1)(2^4 - 1)(2^5 - 1) = 7 \times 15 \times 31 = 3255$

(iii) $2^3 . 2^4 . (2^5 - 1) = 8 \times 16 \times 31 = 3968.$

(c) Ans. (a).

Selection of 4 novels out of 6 is $^6C_4 = 15$

Selection of 1 dictionary out of 3 is $^3C_1 = 3$

Now 4 novels are to be divided into groups of 2 each so that the dictionary is in the middle $^4C_2 . (2!)^2 = 6 \times 4$

Hence the required number of ways is

$15 \times 3 \times 6 \times 4 = 1080$

11. (a) Ans. $2^{10} - 1 = 1023$; -1 corresponds to none of lamps is being switched on.

(d) Ans. 2^{10}. Each of the 10 places can be filled in 2 ways.

12. (a)

Ward A	Ward B	Ward C
4	5	8

For ward A we have to choose 4 out of 20 and then for ward B, 5 out of remaining 16 and then for ward C, 8 out of remaining 11.

$$^{20}C_4 \quad \times \quad {}^{16}C_5 \quad \times \quad {}^{11}C_8$$

$$= \frac{20!}{16! \, 4!} \times \frac{16!}{11! \times 5!} \times \frac{11!}{8! \times 3!} = \frac{20!}{4! \, 5! \, 3! \, 8!}$$

$$= \frac{20 \times 19 \times 18 \times 17}{24} \times \frac{16 \times 15 \times 14 \times 13 \times 12}{120} \times \frac{11 \times 10 \times 9}{6}$$

$$= 4845 \times 4368 \times 165 = 349188400 .$$

13. (i) A and B are together and so out of remaining $n - 2$ we have to choose 10.

$$\therefore {}^{n-2}C_{10} = \frac{(n-2)!}{(10)! \, (n-12)!} .$$

(ii) C, D, E are together and so out of remaining $n - 3$ we have to choose 9

$$\therefore {}^{n-3}C_9 = \frac{(n-3)!}{9! \, (n-12)!}$$

(iii) By given condition $\dfrac{(n-2)!}{(10)! \, (n-12)!} = 3 . \dfrac{(n-3)!}{9! \, (n-12)!}$

or $\dfrac{(n-2) . (n-3)!}{10 \times 9!} = 3 . \dfrac{(n-3)!}{9!}$

or $n - 2 = 30$ or $n = 32.$

14. (a) Ans. $^{20}C_{16} = 4845$, $^{19}C_{15} = 3876.$

(b) Ans. $^5C_3 \times {}^{22}C_9 = 4974200.$

(c) Males   Females

$^{27}C_{10} + {}^{17}C_{10}.$

15. Total selection – Selection with no Black

$= {}^9C_3$ (Total) $- {}^6C_3$ (No Black)

$= \dfrac{9.8.7}{1.2.3} - \dfrac{6.5.4}{1.2.3} = 84 - 20 = 64.$

16. Let the two husbands A, B be selected out of seven males in $^7C_2 = 21$ ways. Excluding their wives we have to select two ladies C, D out of remaining 5 wives in $^5C_2 = 10$ ways.

Thus the number of ways of selecting the players for mixed double is $21 \times 10 = 210.$

Now suppose A chooses C as partner (B will automatically go to D) or A chooses D as partner, (B will automatically go to C). Thus we have 2 choices for the teams. Required number of ways is $210 \times 2 = 420.$

17. (a) The first man can occupy the seat in 6 ways and now the second man has only 5 ways left for choosing a seat. Hence the number of ways for the two to occupy two seats is $6 \times 5 = 30.$

(b) Here 4 girls can occupy the 4 corner seats (2 on either side) in 4! ways and the remaining 6 seats can be occupied by 6 boys in 6! ways. Hence total number of ways

$= 6! . 4! = 720 \times 24 = 17280.$

18. For seating on a round table we have to fix up, one man at a place then there are $n - 1$ persons left which can be arranged in $(n - 1)!$ ways. Now suppose Mr. Khanna is seated first and in any arrangement he has Mr. Lal and Mr. Sehgal on right and left or on left and right. In the two ways Mr. Khanna has the same neighbours.

Hence the required number of arrangements is $\dfrac{1}{2}(n - 1)!$ because in no two ways a person has the same neighbours.

19. (a) Fix up a Muslim and the remaining 5 Muslims can be seated in 5! ways. Now no two Hindus are to sit together and as such the 6 Hindus are to be arranged in six empty seats between two consecutive Muslims and number of arrangements will be 6!.

Hence by fundamental theorem the total number of ways is $5! \times 6! = 120 \times 720 = 86400.$

(b) m men can be arranged in $m!$ ways in a row and we have now $(m + 1)$ places in which n women can be arranged in

$$^{m+1}P_n = \frac{(m+1)!}{(m+1-n)!} \text{ ways.}$$

Hence by fundamental theorem the number of ways is as given.

20. Out of 21 we can choose 15 for one table in $^{21}C_{15}$ ways and for each selection we are left with 6 guests for the second table having 6 seats. This can be chosen in $^6C_6$ ways. Now 15 for round table A can be arranged in $(14)!$ ways and 6 for round table B can be arranged in 5! ways. Hence the total number is

$^{21}C_{15} \times {}^6C_6 \times 14! \times 5!.$

21. Having seated 4 on side A and 2 on side B we are left with 10 persons. Out of which we choose 4 for side A in $^{10}C_4$ ways and now for side B we are left with 6 persons and 6 have to be seated so that they can be seated in $^6C_6 = 1$ way.

Hence the number of selections for the two sides is

$$^{10}C_4 \times 1 = \frac{(10)!}{6!\,4!}.$$

Again 8 persons on each side can be arranged amongst themselves in 8! ways.

∴ The total number of seating arrangements is

$$\frac{(10)!}{6!\,4!} \times 8! \times 8!$$

$$= \frac{(10)!}{6!\,4!} \times 8 \times 7.6! \times 8 \times 7 \times 6 \times 5.4!$$

$$= 30 \times 8^2 \times 7^2 \times 10! = 341397504000.$$

Alternative Method :

The four persons who wish to occupy side A can be accommodated on eight chairs in

$$^8P_4 = \frac{8!}{4!} = 8 \times 7 \times 6 \times 5 \text{ ways.}$$

(direct arrangement)

The two persons who wish to occupy side B can be accommodated on eight chairs in

$$^8P_2 = \frac{8!}{6!} = 8 \times 7 \text{ ways.}$$

Having seated 6 persons on 6 chairs we are left with 10 persons on 10 chairs on both sides and they can be seated in 10! ways.

∴ The number of arrangements is

$$(10)!\,(8 \times 7 \times 6 \times 5) \times (8 \times 7)$$

$$= (10)! \times 30 \times 8^2 \times 7^2 \text{ etc.}$$

22. (a) Note here that we have to first make a selection and then **arrange** the sailors, 4 on each side. Let us call the two sides as A and B. Three are to be fixed on side A and two on side B. Having fixed these five we are left with 3 sailors out of 8. From these 3 we choose 1 for side A to make four in A, and this can be done in $^3C_1 = 3$ ways. Now we are left with 2 sailors and only two are needed for side B and this can be done in $^2C_2 = 1$ way.

Hence the number of selections is $3 \times 1 = 3$.

Now the sailors on side A can be arranged amongst themselves in 4! ways i.e. 24 ways and so also the sailors on side B can be arranged in 24 ways. Hence the total number of arrangements is

$$3 \times 24 \times 24 = 3 \times 576 = 1728.$$

(b) $^3C_1 = 3$ for steering.

Out of 40 rowers 8A 3B (by choice)
Remaining 29   12A 17B (by selection)

This selection can be done in $^{29}C_{12} \cdot {}^{17}C_{17}$

Thus total selections are $^3C_1 \cdot {}^{29}C_{12} \cdot {}^{17}C_{17}$

Now 20 rowers on side A can be arranged amongst themselves in 20 ! ways and similarly on side B. Hence total number is

$$^3C_1 \cdot {}^{29}C_{12} \cdot {}^{17}C_{17} \cdot 20!\,20!$$

23. (a) Ans. $\dfrac{11!}{5!\,6!}.9!\,9!.$ [Proceed as in Q. 21]

(b) Ans. (iv). The required no. of arrangements $= {}^4P_2 \times {}^6P_3$.

24. (a) Treat them as 3 units which can be arranged in $3! = 6$ ways. The two persons corresponding to each of these can be arranged in $2! = 2$ ways each. Hence the total number is $6 \times 2 \times 2 \times 2 = 48$.

(b) 3 units of different books can be arranged in 3 ! ways. Now arrange the books on the same subject.

∴ $3!\,.5!\,4!\,2! = 34560$

25. There are 6 adults, 4 children and 1 grand father.
Let us the seats for 11 persons from 1 to 11

C C C C
1 2 3 4 5 6 7 8 9 10 11

Seats no. 1, 2 and 10, 11 at the ends are to be occupied by 4 grand children and it can be done in $^4P_4 = 4! = 24$ ways.

Now we will seat the grandfather who cannot occupy seat no. 3 or seat no. 9 because he does not want to have a child by his side. Hence he has to choose any of five seats 4, 5, 6, 7, 8 i.e. he can seat himself in 5 ways.

Now there are six seats left on which six adults can be arranged in $^6P_6 = 6! = 720$ ways.

Hence by fundamental theorem, total number of seating arrangements for the family is

$$24 \times 5 \times 720 = 86400.$$

26. (a) $^nC_2$ groups. A gives card to B and B to A. Hence

$2.\,{}^nC_2 = 930$ or $n(n-1) - 930 = 0$

or $n^2 - n - 30 \times 31 = 0$

or $(n - 31)(n + 30) = 0$ ∴ $n = 31$.

(b) Ans. 15.

Suppose the two players did not play at all so that the remaining $(n-2)$ players played $^{n-2}C_2$ matches. Since these two players played 3 matches each, hence the total number of matches is $^{n-2}C_2 + 3 + 3 = 84$ (given)

$$\frac{(n-2)(n-3)}{1.2} = 78$$

or $n^2 - 5n + 6 = 156$ or $n^2 - 5n - 150 = 0$

or $(n - 15)(n + 10) = 0$ ∴ $n = 15\,(n \neq -10)$

27. (a) Ans. 18.

If n is the number of teams, then
$$^nC_2 = 153 \text{ to } n^2 - n - 306 = 0$$
or $(n - 18)(n + 17) = 0$
$\therefore \quad n = 18 \quad [\because \ n \ne -17].$

(b) True. Refer Part (i) above. $^nC_2 = 66$ will give $n = 12$.

28. (a) The number of lines each joining 2 out of the n points is
$$^nC_2 = \frac{n!}{2!(n-2)!} = \frac{n(n-1)}{2}.$$

But these will include the n sides of the polygon. Hence the number of diagonals is
$$\frac{n(n-1)}{2} - n = \frac{n(n-3)}{2}.$$

(b) (i) $^{10}C_2 - 10 = 45 - 10 = 35$ as in Q. 25.

(ii) $^{10}C_3 = \frac{10!}{3! \, 7!} = \frac{10 \times 9 \times 8}{6} = 120.$

29. (a) First note in all $3 + 4 + 5$, that is, 12 points are used for forming the triangles. Since 3 points are needed to form a triangle, the total number of triangles (including the triangle formed by collinear points and as these collinear points will not form triangles their number has to be subtracted from total) is $^{12}C_3 = 220$. But this includes the number of triangles formed by 3 points on $AB = {}^3C_3 = 1$, the number of triangles formed by 4 points on $BC = {}^4C_3 = 4$, and the number of triangles formed by 5 points on $CA = {}^5C_3 = 10$.

Hence the required number of triangles
$$= 220 - (1 + 4 + 10) = 205.$$

(b) Two lines meet in a point
$$\therefore \quad {}^8C_2 \times 1 = \frac{8.7}{1.2} = 28$$

Line and Circle meet in two points
$$\therefore \quad ({}^8C_1 \times {}^4C_1) \times 2 = 8.4.2 = 64$$

Two circles meet in two points
$$({}^4C_2) \times 2 = \frac{4.3}{1.2}.2 = 12$$

Total $= 28 + 64 + 12 = 104.$

30. 18 points, 5 collinear :

(a) No. of lines $= {}^{18}C_2 - {}^5C_2 + 1 = 153 - 10 + 1 = 144$

(b) No. of $\Delta^s = {}^{18}C_3 - {}^5C_3 = 816 - 10 = 806.$

31. Ans. (i) $^nC_2 - {}^pC_2 + 1$, (ii) $^nC_3 - {}^pC_3$

32. (a) Ans. $^nC_3 - {}^pC_3 + 1.$

(b) Total number of points are $p + q + r$. Number of triangles is $^{p+q+r}C_3$.

The points on L_1 will not form a triangle. Hence exclude $^pC_3$ and similarly exclude $^qC_3$ and $^rC_3$ for q points on L_2 and r points on L_3.

33. (i) No. of lines $= {}^{12}C_2 - {}^5C_2 + 1 = 66 - 10 + 1 = 57.$

(ii) No. of $\Delta^s = {}^{12}C_3 - {}^5C_3 = 220 - 10 = 210.$

34. (a) There are 64 squares in a chess board and there are nine horizontal lines and nine vertical lines. To form rectangles we shall need 2 horizontal lines and two vertical lines from each set. This can be done in
$$^9C_2 \times {}^9C_2 \text{ ways } = \left(\frac{9.8}{1.2}\right)^2 = 36 \times 36 = 1296.$$

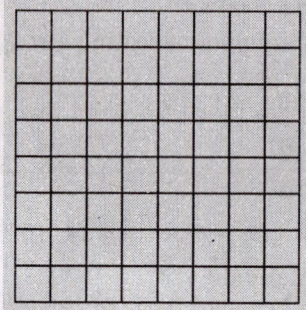

Fig. 3

(b) Ans. $^mC_2 . {}^nC_2$

(c) $^4C_2 \times {}^3C_2 = 6 \times 3 = 18.$

(d) The two sets of m parallel lines along with two sets of 2 parallel lines of the given parallelogram will form two sets of $m + 2$ parallel lines. To form a parallelogram we have to choose sets of 2 parallel lines from each of the above.
Hence $^{m+2}C_2 . {}^{m+2}C_2 = ({}^{m+2}C_2)^2$ is the required number of parallelograms.

35. (a) By alteration in the arrangement of flags the signals will change. So we have to find permutations $i.e.$ arrangements of flags. We are at liberty to use any number of flags at a time. Therefore the required number of signals is
$$^6P_1 + {}^6P_2 + {}^6P_3 + {}^6P_4 + {}^6P_5 + {}^6P_6$$
$$= 6 + 30 + 120 + 360 + 720 + 720 = 1956.$$

(b) $^4P_3 \times {}^5P_3 \times {}^6P_3 = 172800.$

36. (a) We can post the first letter in 4 ways and 2nd too in 4 ways, as well as the third. Therefore the total number of ways is $4 \times 4 \times 4 = 64.$

All the three letters can be posted in any of the four letter boxes in 4 ways.

Hence the corresponding number when all are not posted in the same letter box is $64 - 4 = 60.$

(b) Ans. 4^5. Each ring can be put in four ways.

37. (a) The answers are self-explanatory.

(b) $\dfrac{12!}{(3!)^4}$ since there are 4 sets of 3 alike books.

38. (a) Ans. $\dfrac{15!}{8! \, 4! \, 3!}.$

(b) $11 = 5 + 4 + 2$. Hence $\dfrac{(11)!}{5!\,4!\,2!}$

$= \dfrac{11.10.9.8.7.6}{24 \times 2} = 11 \times 10 \times 63 = 6930$

or $^{11}C_5 \cdot {}^6C_2 \cdot {}^4C_4$

39. (a) $\dfrac{52!}{(13!)^4}$. (b) $\dfrac{52!}{(13!)^4\,4!}$

(c) $\dfrac{52!}{(17!)^3\,.1!\,3!}$ **[See (o) P. 293]**

40. When A receives 2 and B gets 8, then $\dfrac{(10!)}{2!\,.8!} = 45$

When A receives 8 and B gets 2, then also $\dfrac{(10!)}{2!\,.8!} = 45$.

∴ Total is $45 + 45 = 90$.

41. (a) Four first prizes can be given in 20^4 ways since first prize of Mathematics can be given in 20 ways,

first prize of Physics also in 20 ways, similarly first prizes of Chemistry and English can be given in 20 ways each. (Note that a boy can stand first in all the four subjects). Then two second prizes can be given in 19^2 ways since a boy cannot get both the first and second prizes.

Hence the required number of ways

$= 20^4 \times 19^2 = 57760000$.

(b) Ans. $16^3 \times 15^2 \times 14 = 12902400$.

42. (a) Ans. $3^{12} = 531441$

The number of each type of different animals is not less than 12. Therefore the first stall on the ship can be filled in 3 ways by any of three animals. Similarly the second stall can also be filled in 12 ways etc. Hence all the 12 stalls can be filled in 3^{12} ways.

(b) Ans. $12^3 - 1 = 1727$.

1 corresponds to succesful attempt.

Miscellaneous Problem Set (5)

1. (a)* A student is allowed to select at most n books from a collection of $(2n + 1)$ books. If the total number of ways in which he can select a book is 63, find the value of n.

(b) A set contains $(2n + 1)$ elements. What is the number of subsets of this set which contain at the most n elements ?

2. (a)* In an election a man can vote in 56 ways. If the number of candidates exceeds the number to be elected by 2, then find the number of candidates.

(b) In an election a man can vote in 30 ways. If the number of candidates exceeds the number of candidates to be elected by 1, find the number of candidates if a voter has to vote for at least one candidate.

3. (a)* Between two junction stations there are 12 intermediate stations. In how many ways can a train be made to stop at 4 of these if no two of these halting stations are consecutive?

(b) There are p intermediate stations on a railway line from Delhi to Amritsar. In how many way can a super-fast train stop at three of these intermediate stations if no two of them are to be consecutive?

4. A committee of 6 is chosen from 10 men and 7 women so as to contain at least 3 men and 2 women. In how many different ways can this be done if two particular women refuse to serve on the same committee ?

5.* Five boys and five girls form a line with the boys and girls **alternating**. Find the number of ways of making the line. In how many different ways could they form a circle such that the boys and girls alternate ?

6. Six boys and six girls sit along a line alternatively in x ways and along a circle (again alternatively) in y ways, then

(a) $x = y$ (b) $y = 12x$

(c) $x = 10y$ (d) $x = 12y$

7.* Find the number of ways in which 5 boys and 5 girls be seated in a row so that

(a) No two girls may sit together.

(b) All the girls sit together and all the boys sit together.

(c) All the girls are never together.

8. In how many ways can 7 boys be seated at a round table so that two particular boys are

(a) next to each other   (b) separated ?

9. There are six students A, B, C, D, E, F.

(i) In how many ways can they be seated in a line so that C and D do not sit together ?

(ii) In how many ways can a committee of four be formed so as always to include C ?

(iii) In how many ways can a committee of four be formed so as to always include C but exclude D ?

10.* In how many ways three girls and nine boys can be seated in two vans, each having numbered seats, 3 in the front and 4 at the back ? How many seating arrangements are possible if 3 girls should sit together in a back row on adjacent seats ? Now, if all the seating arrangements are equally likely, what is the probability of 3 girls sitting together in a back row on adjacent seats ?   **(I.I.T. 1996)**

11. Prove that the number of ways in which 8 different flowers can be strung to form a garland so that 4 particular flowers are never separated is $\dfrac{1}{2}\,4!\,4!$.

12. A round table conference is to be held between 20 delegates of 2 countries. In how many ways can they be seated if two particular delegates are
    (a) always to sit together
    (b) or never to sit together ?

13.* There are 20 persons including two brothers. In how many ways can they be arranged on a round table if :
    (a) There is exactly one person between the two brothers.
    (b) The two brothers are always separated.
    (c) What will be the corresponding answers if the two brothers were twins (alike in all respects) ?

14. 20 persons were invited for a party. In how many ways can they and the host be seated at a circular table ? In how many of these ways will two particular persons be seated on either side of the host ?

15.* Find the number of ways in which ten candidates $A_1, A_2, A_3, ..., A_{10}$ can be ranked
    (a) if A_1 and A_2 are next to each other, and
    (b) A_1 is just above A_2
    (c) if A_1 is always above A_2.

16. (i)* At an election meeting six speakers have to address the meeting. The President of the party is to speak before the M.L.A. of the constituency. In how many ways can this be done ? In how many of these arrangements will the M.L.A. speak just after the speech of the President ?
    (ii)* At an election meeting 10 speakers are to address the meeting. The only protocol to be observed is that whenever they speak P.M. will speak before M.P. and M.P. will speak before M.L.A. In how many ways can the meeting be addressed ?

17. In how many ways can the letters of the word *multiple* be arranged in the following cases :
    (i) Without changing the order of the vowels :
    (ii) Keeping the position of the vowels fixed ;
    (iii) Without changing the relative order of vowels and consonants ?

18. (a) In a class of 10 students there are 3 girls, A, B, C. In how many different ways can they be arranged in a row such that no two of the three girls are consecutive ?
    (b)* The total number of ways in which six '+' and four '−' signs can be arranged in a line such that no two '−' signs occur together is ....

19. (a) The faces of a cube are to be painted by 6 different colours. In how many ways can this be done ?
    (b) In how many ways can 21 identical white balls and 19 identical black balls be arranged in a row so that no two black balls be together ? What will be the result if all the balls are considered to be different ?

20.* A man has 7 relatives, 4 of them are ladies and 3 gentlemen; his wife has 7 relatives, and 3 of them are ladies and 4 gentlemen. In how many ways can they invite a dinner party of 3 ladies and 3 gentlemen so that there are 3 of man's relatives and 3 of wife's relatives.

21. Husband has 12 relatives $(7M, 5F)$ and his wife too has 12 relatives $(5M, 7F)$. In how many ways can they invite $(6M, 6F)$ for a dinner party so that each invites 6 of his/her relations ?

22. (a) Show that the number of triangles whose vertices are at the vertices of an octagon but none of whose sides happen to come from the sides of the octagon is 16.
    (b) Find the number of triangles that can be formed with the angular points of a polygon of n sides. What will be the corresponding number of triangles if none of the sides are to be the sides of the polygon ?

23. (a)* Six X^s have to be placed in the squares of the figure such that each row contains at least one X. In how many different ways can this be done ?

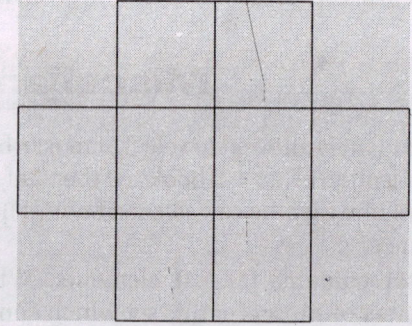

Fig. 4

(b)* In how many ways the letters of the word '**person**' can be placed in the squares of the adjoining figure (75) so that no row remains empty ?

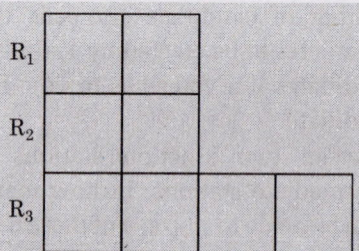

Fig. 5

24.* Out of 16 players of a cricket team, 4 are bowlers and 2 are wicket-keepers. A team of 11 players is to be chosen so as to contain at least 3 bowlers and at least 1 wicket-keeper. In how many ways can the team be selected ?

25. (a)* Prove that there will be only 24 selections containing at least one red ball out of a bag containing 4 red and 5 black balls. It being given that the balls of the same colour are identical.
    (b)* There are p copies each of n different books, find the number of different ways in which a non-empty selection can be made from them.

26.* A fruit basket contains 4 oranges, 5 apples and 6 mangoes. In how many ways can a person make a selection of fruits from among the fruits in the basket ?

27.* A picnic party of 10 persons is to go by two Vechicles one matador with a seating capacity of 8 and a Maruti car with a seating capacity of 4. In how many ways can the travel arrangements be made ?

28. Find the number of ways in which 5 identical balls can be distributed among 10 identical boxes, if not more than one ball can go into a box.

29. (a) There are 12 balls of which 4 are red, 3 black and 5 white. In how many ways can you arrange the balls so that no two white balls may occupy consecutive positions if
   (a) Balls of the same colour are identical,
   (b) All balls are considered to be different.

30. Show that the total number of permutations of n different things taken **not more** than r at a time, when each thing may be repeated any number of times is $\dfrac{n(n^r - 1)}{n - 1}$.

31.* Five balls of different colours are to be placed in three boxes of different sizes. Each box can hold all five balls. In how many different ways can we place the balls so that no box remains empty ?

32.* There are four balls of different colours and four boxes of colours, same as those of the balls. The number of ways in which the balls, one each in a box, could be placed such that a ball does not go to a box of its own colour is ..... **(IIT 1992)**

33. In how many ways can 10 different prizes be given to five students if the head boy must get 4 prizes and rest of the students can get any number of prizes ?

34. (a) The letters of the word NUMBER are written in all possible manners and these words are written as in a dictionary. What will be the rank of the word?
   (b) The letters of the word **COCHIN** are permuted and all the permutations are arranged in an alphabetical order as in an English dictionary. The number of words that appear before the word **COCHIN** is
   (a) 360   (b) 192
   (c) 96   (d) 48   **(I.I.T. 2007)**

35. What will be the corresponding ranks of words (i) MOTHER (ii) RACHIT (iii) ZENITH ?

36. There are m points in a plane such that no two of the lines joining them are parallel and no three are concurrent **except at the given points**. What is the number of points of intersection of the lines thus obtained ?

37. A person goes in for an examination in which there are four papers with a maximum of m marks for each paper; find the number of ways of getting $2m$ marks on the whole.

38. In an examination, the maximum marks for each of the three papers are 50 each. Maximum marks for the fourth paper are 100. Find the number of ways in which the candidate can score 60% in the aggregate.

Solutions to Miscellaneous Problem Set (15)

1. (a) Since the student is allowed to select at the most n books out of $(2n + 1)$ books, therefore he can select, one book, two books or at the most n books. Hence the number of selecting at least one book is

$$^{2n+1}C_1 + {}^{2n+1}C_2 + ... + {}^{2n+1}C_n = S = 63$$

Again we know that
$$^{2n+1}C_0 + {}^{2n+1}C_1 + {}^{2n+1}C_2 + ... + {}^{2n+1}C_{2n} + {}^{2n+1}C_{2n+1} = 2^{2n+1}$$

Now $^{2n+1}C_0 = {}^{2n+1}C_{2n+1} = 1$,
$^{2n+1}C_1 = {}^{2n+1}C_{2n}$ etc.

Hence we have
$$1 + 1 + 2S = 2^{2n+1} \quad \text{or} \quad 2 + 2.63 = 2^{2n+1}$$
$$\text{or} \quad 128 = 2^{2n+1} \quad \text{or} \quad 2^7 = 2^{2n+1}$$
$$\therefore \quad 2n + 1 = 7$$
$$\text{or} \quad 2n = 6 \quad \therefore \quad n = 3.$$

(b) $^{2n+1}C_0 + {}^{2n+1}C_1 + ... + {}^{2n+1}C_n = k$

Now $^{2n+1}C_0 + {}^{2n+1}C_1 + ... + {}^{2n+1}C_{2n} + {}^{2n+1}C_{2n+1} = 2^{2n+1}$

But $^{2n+1}C_{2n+1} = {}^{2n+1}C_0$, $^{2n+1}C_{2n} = {}^{2n+1}C_1$

$\therefore \quad 2k = 2^{2n+1} = 2^{2n}.2 \quad \therefore \quad k = 2^{2n}$

2. (a) Let the number of candidates be n so that the number of candidates to be elected is $(n - 2)$.
Now a man can vote for 1, 2, 3, ... or $(n - 2)$ candidates.
Hence number of ways he can vote is

$$^nC_1 + {}^nC_2 + ... + {}^nC_{n-2} = 56, \text{ given.}$$

Add and subtract $^nC_0 + {}^nC_{n-1} + {}^nC_n$

$$2^n - \{1 + {}^nC_1 + {}^nC_0\} = 56$$
$$\because \quad {}^nC_{n-1} = {}^nC_1 = n, \ {}^nC_n = {}^nC_0 = 1$$
$$\text{or} \quad 2^n - \{1 + n + 1\} = 56$$
$$\text{or} \quad 2^n - n = 58 \quad \text{or} \quad 2^n = 58 + n$$

By inspection it is satisfied by $n = 6$
$$\because \quad 2^6 = 64, 58 + 6 = 64$$

(b) $\displaystyle\sum_{k=1}^{n-1} {}^nC_k = 30$ or $\displaystyle\sum_{k=0}^{n} {}^nC_k - ({}^nC_0 + {}^nC_n)$
$$\text{or} \quad 2^n = 30 + 2 = 32. \quad \therefore \quad n = 5.$$

3. (a) Out of 12 stations, 4 are halting stations and 8 are non-halting stations. Since the halting stations are not to be consecutive therefore

$$* | * | * | * | * | * | * | * \text{ Halting}$$
$$\overline{\quad 1 \quad 2 \quad 3 \quad 4 \quad 5 \quad 6 \quad 7 \quad 8 \quad} \text{Non-stopping}$$

these four stations must be on places marked by * which are 7 in between non-stopping stations two on either side just as in gap method. We have to choose 4 stations out of these 9. (*i.e.*, 7 + 2 or 8 + 1)

$$\therefore \quad {}^9C_4 = \frac{9 \cdot 8 \cdot 7 \cdot 6}{1 \cdot 2 \cdot 3 \cdot 4} = 126$$

(b) $(p-3)$ non-stopping. There will be $(p-3)+1 = p-2$ gaps where three stopping stations could be located.

$$\therefore \quad {}^{p-2}C_3 \text{ ways.}$$

4. $10\,M, 7\,W$. Committee of 6.
At least 3 Men and 2 Women. ⎫
Either $(3M, 3W)$ or $(4M, 2W)$ ⎬ ...(A)

$$= {}^{10}C_3 \cdot {}^7C_3 + {}^{10}C_4 \cdot {}^7C_2 = 8610.$$

Above gives the total number.

Now let us consider the case when **2 particular women are always there** in the same committee. Subtract $2W$ from the data (A) above.

$10\,M, 5\,W$

At least $3M, 0W$

Either $(4M, 0W)$ or $(3M, 1W)$

In this case we have to make a selection of 4 persons out of above data.

$(4M, \text{No } W)\,(3M, 1W)$

$$\therefore \quad {}^{10}C_4 + {}^{10}C_3 \times {}^5C_1$$

$$= \frac{10!}{6!\,4!} + \frac{10!}{7!\,3!} \times \frac{5!}{4!\,1!}$$

$$= \frac{10 \times 9 \times 8 \times 7}{24} + \frac{10 \times 9 \times 8}{6} \times 5$$

$$= 210 + 600 = 810.$$

Hence the number of committees **when two particular women are never together is**

$$= \text{Total} - \text{together}$$
$$= 8610 - 810 = 7800.$$

5. 5 boys can be arranged in a line in 5! ways. Now here the boys and girls are **alternating.** Let the boys be

$$B_1 \times B_2 \times B_3 \times B_4 \times B_5 \times \qquad \text{...(1)}$$

We are left with 5 places marked by cross where five girls can be arranged in 5! ways. Thus by fundamental theorem it will be $5! \times 5! = (5!)^2$

Now the position (1) could be

$$\times B_1 \times B_2 \times B_3 \times B_4 \times B_5 \qquad \text{...(2)}$$

We are left with 5 places marked by cross where five girls can be arranged in 5! ways. Thus by fundamental theorem it will be $5! \times 5! = (5!)^2$ Hence the total number of ways will be $(5!)^2 + (5!)^2 = 2(5!)^2$.

In other words we can say if we start the line with the boy in the 1st position as in (1) there are $(5!)^2$ ways & if we start with girl in 1st position as in (2) then also there are $(5!)^2$ ways. Thus the total number of ways will be

$$(5!)^2 + (5!)^2 = 2(5!)^2$$

Had the condition been that **no two girls are together** instead of boys and girls alternating then we would have followed gap method as in **Q. 18 (a), P. 328-332** After fixing the boys

$$\times B_1 \times B_2 \times B_3 \times B_4 \times B_5 \times \qquad \text{...(3)}$$

We have six places marked by cross where 5 girls can be arranged in ${}^6P_5 = \frac{6!}{1!} = 6!$ ways and hence the answer in this case would be $5!.6!$. In this case two boys can sit together because you have to ignore one cross say between B_3 and B_4 and these two boys will be together.

2nd part. After fixing up one boy on the table the remaining 4 can be arranged in 4! ways. Since the boys and girls are to alternate, there will be 5 crosses between these boys sitting on the round table in which five girls can be arranged in 5! ways. Hence by fundamental theorem answer is $4!.5! = 2880$.

6. Ans. (d).

Sitting in a line starting with a boy

Starting with boys we will have six places where six girls can sit (Boys and girls alternating).

Hence number of ways is $6! \cdot 6!$
$\qquad\qquad\qquad\qquad\qquad B \quad G$

G_1	G_2	G_3	G_4	G_5	G_6
B_1	B_2	B_3	B_4	B_5	B_6

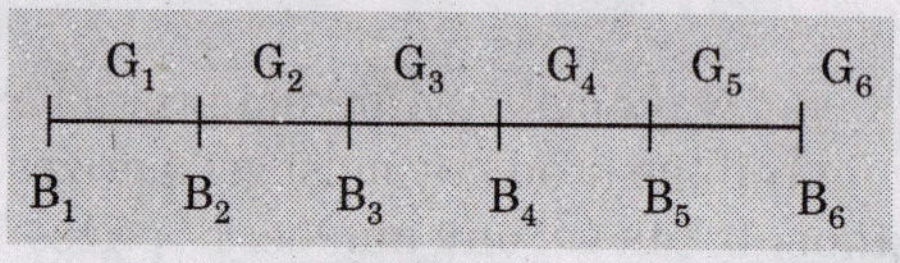

Fig. 6

Similarly, starting with girls we will again have $6! \cdot 6!$
$\qquad\qquad\qquad\qquad\qquad\qquad\qquad\qquad\qquad G \quad B$

Hence total number is $x = 6!.6! + 6!.6! = 2(6!6!)$

Sitting alternatively on a circular table

5! for any $(B$ or $G)$ and 6! for remaining.

$$\therefore \quad y = (5!)(6!)$$

$$\therefore \quad \frac{x}{y} = \frac{2.6!.6!}{5!6!} = 2.6 = 12$$

$$\therefore \quad x = 12y \Rightarrow \text{(d)}$$

7. (a) $5! \cdot {}^6P_5 = 5!\,6!$

We have first arranged the boys in a row in 5! ways and in the 6 gaps we have arranged 5 girls.

(b) The two groups of boys and girls can be arranged in 2! ways and the group of 5 girls can be arranged amongst themselves in 5! ways and so the group of boys. Hence by fundamental theorem the number of ways is $2.5! .5! = 2(5!)^2$

(c) **Total − together** *i.e.* $10! - 5!.6!$, by string method.

(See (u) P. 294).

8. The boys can be seated on a round table in $6! = 720$ ways as we have to fix one boy first.

(a) **Two particular boys are together**

Now treat the two boys together and treat them as one unit. So we have six boys and having fixed one we will have $5! = 120$ ways.

But the two particular boys can be arranged amongst themselves in $2! = 2$ ways. Therefore the total number of arrangements when the two particular boys are next to each other is $120 \times 2 = 240$.

(b) **Two particular boys are separated.**

Hence when the two particular boys are never together is $720 - 240 = 480$.

9. (i) It is exactly last Q. 8.

Total no. of ways $= 6! = 720$. Treat C and D as one and we have $6 - 2 + 1 = 5$ units which can be arranged in $5! = 120$ ways. But C and D can be arranged in $2! = 2$ ways. Hence the no. of ways when they are together is $120 \times 2 = 240$.

Hence the arrangements when C and D will not be together is $720 - 240 = 480$.

Alternative Method :

Ignore C and D. The rest four can be arranged in $4! = 24$ ways. There will be 5 gaps in between each arrangement of these 4 students. In these 5 gaps two C and D can be arranged in $^5P_2 = 5 \times 4 = 20$ ways. Hence the total number of ways when C and D are together is $24 \times 20 = 480$.

(ii) Ans. $^5C_3 = \dfrac{5!}{3! \cdot 2!} = \dfrac{5 \times 4}{2} = 10$.

(iii) Exclude D so that out of remaining 5 we have to select 4.

Since C is to be included always, we are left with only 4 students out of which we have to choose 3 (the committee to consist of only 4 students out of which C is a must).

Hence the required number of committees is $^4C_3 = 4$ in which D is excluded but C is included.

10. $3G, 9B = 12$ persons

3, 3 Front, 4, 4 Back $= 14$ seats (numbered)

Number of arrangements (No condition) $^{14}P_{12}$ ...(1)

Take out $3G$ and tie them together.

Number of seating of $3G$ together on adjacent seats. There are 4 ways of selecting three seats 1, 2, 3 or 2, 3, 4 of one Van

and 1, 2, 3 or 2, 3, 4 of 2nd Van

In each set the three girls can be arranged in $3!$ ways each. Hence the total number of ways of seating the girls is $4.3! = 24$

After seating the three girls as desired we are left with 9 boys to be seated on remaining 11 seats which can be done in $^{11}P_9$ ways.

Hence by fundamental theorem total number of seating arrangements is $^{11}P_9 . 24$.

∴ Required probability is

$(^{11}P_9 . 24) \div {}^{14}P_{12} = \dfrac{11!}{2!} \times (24) \dfrac{2!}{14!}$

$= \dfrac{24}{14.13.12} = \dfrac{1}{91}$

11. Tie 4 flowers so that we have now in all five (4 different and one bunch). These five can be arranged in a garland in $\dfrac{1}{2}(n-1)!$ i.e. $\dfrac{1}{2}(4!)$ ways. The bunch can be arranged in $4!$ ways. Hence by fundamental theorem total is $\dfrac{1}{2}(4! . 4!)$.

12. Exactly as in Q. 8 above.

(a) $(18)! \times 2! = 2(18)!$

(b) $(19)! - 2(18)!$.

13. (a) Let the two brothers be taken out and the remaining 18 persons can be arranged on a circular table in $(17!)$ ways. Now there are 18 persons on the table. Two brothers can be arranged about each of them on either side in $2! = 2$ ways because there is to be exactly one person between the two brothers. Hence the required number by fundamental theorem is $(17)! . (18 . 2) = 2(18)!$

(b) In the 2nd case in between 18 gaps on the round table between 18 persons we have to arrange these two brothers and it can be done in $^{18}P_2$ ways. Hence the required number in this case will be $^{18}P_2 (17)! = 18 . 17 . (17)! = 17(18)!$

(c) Divide each of the answers of (i) and (ii) by $2!$ because of being alike.

14. 20 guests $+ 1$ host $= 21$ persons. They can be seated on a round table in $(20)!$ ways. Treat the host and two particular persons as one unit. So we have now $21 - 3 + 1 = 19$ and the number of arrangements will be $(18)!$. But these two persons can be arranged on either side of the host in 2 ways. Hence there will be $2(18)!$ ways.

15. (i) Regard A_1, A_2 as one group so that there are now $10 - 2 + 1 = 9$ candidates which can be arranged amongst themselves in $9!$ ways.

But these two A_1 and A_2 can be arranged amongst themselves in $2! = 2$ ways.

Hence the number of ways when A_1 and A_2 are together is $2.9! = 725760$.

(ii) $9!$ (A_1 is always just above A_2, they are not to be arranged as in (i).)

(iii) Total number of arrangements for 10 persons is $10!$.

In any arrangement A_1 can be above A_2 or A_2 can be above A_1. **(Note : not just above)**

Hence in half of these A_1 is above A_2.

$$= \frac{1}{2}(10)! = 1814400.$$

16. (i) This question is another version of above question.

Let P = President, Q = M.L.A.

6 speakers can be arranged in 6! ways. In these arrangements P may speak either before Q or after Q. Since we want P to address before Q

∴ Required number is $\frac{1}{2}.(6!) = 360$.

In case P and Q are to be consecutive speakers then follow string method, *i.e.*, tie them and we are left with 5 units (P and Q being counted as one). They can address in $5!.2! = 240$ ways.

2! corresponds to 2 arrangements of P and Q. But we want only PQ and not QP, as Q is to address just after P. Hence the required number is $\frac{1}{2}(240) = 120$.

(ii) Here we select three places for P = P.M.,
Q = M.P., R = M.L.A.

Ten speakers can address in 10! ways including the P, Q, R. Now P, Q, R can be arranged amongst themselves in $3! = 6$ ways like $PQR, PRQ, QRP,$ QPR, RPQ, RQP. Since we want only PQR order, hence we will take $\frac{1}{6}$th of the total.

Hence the required number is $\frac{1}{6}(10!)$.

17. (i) There are 3 vowels u, i, e which can be arranged in 3! ways. Since we are not to change their order, therefore out of 3! arrangements $uie, uei, iue, ieu,$ eiu, eui, we have to choose only one i.e. uie. Hence we will divide the total arrangements by 3!. Also l occurs twice. This has been explained in part (b) (ii) **above** also.

Hence, the total no. of arrangements of the letters in this case. $= \frac{8!}{3!2!} = 8.7.6.5.2 = 3360.$

(ii) Since vowels remain fixed in their positions, it is clear that the total no. of arrangements of the letters is, the same as the no. of arrangements of the other 5 letters in the remaining 5 positions and therefore $= \frac{5!}{2!} = 60.$(l being twice)

(iii) Since the relative order of vowels and consonants remains the same, they are to be arranged in their respective positions. Hence, number of arrangements in this case

$$= \frac{5!}{2!} \times 3! = 360.$$

18. (a) After arranging boys in 7! ways we will have 8 places in which we can arrange the girls in $^8P_3$ ways.

Hence by fundamental theorem the number of arrangements is

$$7! \times {}^8P_3 = 7! \times \frac{8!}{5!} = 7! \times 8 \times 7 \times 6 = 336 \times 7!$$

(b) **By Combination.** There will be seven gaps in between six + ive signs in which we have to arrange 4 − ive signs. Thus we have to make a selection of 4 out of seven ∴ $^7C_4 = \frac{7 \cdot 6 \cdot 5 \cdot 4}{1 \cdot 2 \cdot 3 \cdot 4} = 35.$

By permutation. Six different things could be arranged in 6! ways but as all the six are identical therefore the number of ways of arranging the six identical signs of + is $\frac{6!}{6!} = 1.$

Now we are left with seven places in which 4 different things can be arranged is $^7P_4$ ways but as all the four − ive signs are identical therefore the number of ways is

$$\frac{^7P_4}{4!} = \frac{7!}{4!3!} = 35$$

Hence by fundamental theorem the number of ways is $1 \times 35 = 35.$

19. (a) **A very ticklish question.** Obvious answer is 6!. Now consider 6 boys to be arranged in 6 places. 1st place can be occupied in 6 ways, 2nd in 5 ways and so on... and hence $6.5.4.3.2.1 = 6!$ but if all the persons to occupy were **alike** then $6! \div 6! = 1$ Here all the faces are alike.

You have done the number of arrangements of six + + + + + in $\frac{6!}{6!} = 1.$ Here also the faces are identical and hence the correct answer is $\frac{6!}{6!} = 1.$

(b) There will be only one way of arranging all the 21 white identical balls and there will be 22 gaps in which we have to place 19 identical black balls. Hence we have only to select 19 places out of these 22. Therefore the required number is

$$^{22}C_{19} = {}^{22}C_3 = \frac{22 \times 21 \times 20}{1.2.3} = 1540.$$

2nd Case : If the balls were all different then these can be arranged in 21 ! ways and there will be 22 gaps in which 19 different balls can be arranged in $^{22}P_{19}$ ways i.e. $\frac{22!}{3!}$ ways. Hence by fundamental theorem, the required number of ways is $\frac{1}{6}(21)!(22)!.$

20. There are four possibilities.

(i) 3 ladies from husband's side and 3 gentlemen from wife's side.

No. of ways in this case $= {}^4C_3 \times {}^4C_3 = 16$

(ii) 3 gentlemen from husband's side and 3 ladies from wife's side.

No. of ways in this case $= {}^3C_3 \times {}^3C_3 = 1$

(iii) 2 ladies and one gentlemen from husband's side and one lady and 2 gentlemen from wife's side.

No. of ways in this case
$$= ({}^4C_2 \times {}^3C_1) \times ({}^3C_1 \times {}^4C_2) = 324$$

(iv) One lady and 2 gentlemen from husband's side and 2 ladies and one gentlemen from wife's side.

No. of ways in this case
$$= ({}^4C_1 \times {}^3C_2) \times ({}^3C_2 \times {}^4C_1) = 144.$$

Hence the total no. of ways
$$= 16 + 1 + 324 + 144 = 485.$$

21. $7M, 5F \qquad\qquad 5M, 7F$

Husband	**Wife**
$6M, 0F$	$0M, 6F$
$5M, 1F$	$1M, 5F$
$4M, 2F$	$2M, 4F$
$3M, 3F$	$3M, 3F$
$2M, 4F$	$4M, 2F$
$1M, 5F$	$5M, 1F$

Total number of ways
$$= ({}^7C_6 \cdot {}^5C_0) \times ({}^5C_0 \cdot {}^7C_6) + ({}^7C_5 \cdot {}^5C_1)$$
$$\qquad\quad {}_H \qquad\qquad {}_W \qquad\qquad {}_H$$
$$\times ({}^5C_1 \cdot {}^7C_5) + ({}^7C_4 \cdot {}^5C_2) \times ({}^5C_2 \cdot {}^7C_4)$$
$$\quad {}_W \qquad\qquad {}_H \qquad\qquad\quad {}_W$$
$$+ ({}^7C_3 \cdot {}^5C_3) \times ({}^5C_3 \cdot {}^7C_3) + ({}^7C_2 \cdot {}^5C_4)$$
$$\quad {}_H \qquad\qquad {}_W \qquad\qquad {}_H$$
$$\times ({}^5C_4 \cdot {}^7C_2) + ({}^7C_1 \cdot {}^5C_5) \times ({}^5C_5 \cdot {}^7C_1)$$
$$\quad {}_W \qquad\qquad {}_H \qquad\qquad\quad {}_W$$

22. (a) Let the eight vertices be denoted by $ABCDEFGH$.

Total number of triangles is ${}^8C_3 = \dfrac{8.7.6}{1.2.3} = 56$

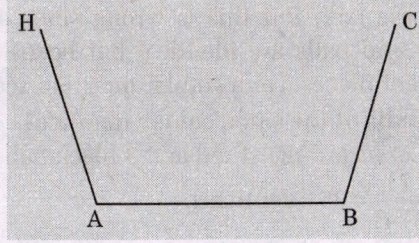

Fig. 7

Out of this total number we will exclude the number of triangles which have (a) one side of octagon (b) two sides of octagon. **For one side common** say AB, we will have to exclude the two vertices C and H which are next to B on the right and next to A on the left. Thus AB will be joined to

remaining four vertices D, E, F, G. Thus there will be 4 such triangles. Since there are eight sides like AB, therefore we will have $4 \times 8 = 32$ triangles which have only one side of octagon.

Two sides common.

$ABC, BCD, CDE, DEF, EFG, FGH, GHA$ and HAB. These 8 triangles will have two sides of the octagon. Hence the number of triangles which do not have any side of the octagon is $56 - 32 - 8 = 16$.

(b) Number of triangles $= {}^nC_3$. ...(1)

This will include the triangles whose sides are also the sides of the polygon. We have to subtract the number of such triangles.

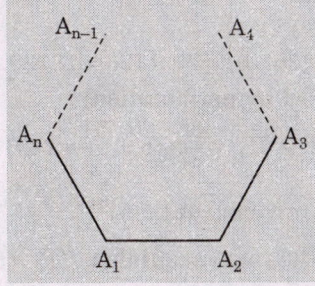

Fig. 8

Δ^s **having one side of the polygon.** Now consider one side say $A_1 A_2$. We ignore the vertices A_3 and A_n because $\Delta^s, A_1 A_2 A_3$ and $A_2 A_1 A_n$ will have two sides which will also be the sides of the polygon. But when $A_1 A_2$ are joined with the rest of vertices $(n-4)$ in number $(A_1, A_2, A_3, A_n$ excluded) we will have $(n-4)$ triangles with only one side $A_1 A_2$ as the side of the polygon. Since there are n sides like $A_1 A_2$ hence the number of such triangles will be $n(n-4)$. ...(2)

Δ^s **having two sides of the polygon common.**
$A_1 A_2 A_3$,
$A_2 A_3 A_4, A_3 A_4 A_5, ... A_{n-1} A_n A_1, A_n A_1 A_2$ Clearly number of such triangles is n.

∴ Required number is ${}^nC_3 - \{n(n-4) + n\}$
$$= \frac{n(n-1)(n-2)}{1.2.3} - n(n-3)$$
$$= \frac{n}{6}(n^2 - 3n + 2 - 6n + 18) = \frac{n}{6}(n^2 - 9n + 20)$$
$$\text{by (1), (2) and (3)}$$
$$= \frac{n}{6}(n-4)(n-5).$$

23. (a) In all we have 8 squares in which $6\ X^s$ have to be placed and it can be done in
$${}^8C_6 = \frac{8!}{6! \cdot 2!} = \frac{8 \times 7}{2} = 28 \text{ ways.}$$

But this includes the possibility that either the top horizontal row does not have any X (when $2\ X$ are placed in bottom row and 4 in the middle) and similarly the bottom horizontal row has no X. Since we want that each row must have at least one X, these two possibilities are to be excluded. Therefore the required number is $28 - 2 = 26$.

Since all X^s are identical, it is a question of selection and not arrangement. You may also say

$$26 \cdot \frac{6!}{6!} = 26$$

(b) As in part (a) we make a selection of 6 squares out of 8 in $^8C_2 - 2 = 28 - 2 = 26$ ways

-2 corresponds to the position when either top row or middle row is vacant. Six different letters can be arranged in $6!$ ways.

Hence by fundamental theorem the total number of ways is

$$(26) \cdot 6! = 26 \times 720 = 18720.$$

Alt. (Direct by permutation) :

$$\text{Total} = {}^8P_6 = \frac{8!}{2!} = 8 \cdot 7 \cdot \frac{6!}{2} = 28 \cdot 6!$$

Top row **vacant** then $^6P_6 = 6!$

Middle row **vacant** then $^6P_6 = 6!$

Bottom row cannot be vacant as the upper two rows can have only four letters.

Hence when no row is vacant is

$$28 \cdot 6! - (6! + 6!) = 6! \cdot 26 = 18720.$$

24. Let B stand for bowler, W for wicket-keeper and O for others. Thus we have $B(4), W(2), O(10)$. Now we have to keep in mind the restrictions of at least 3 bowlers so that there could be either 3 or 4 bowlers, at least one wicket-keeper, so that there could be either 1 or 2 wicket-keepers.

$B(4)$	$W(2)$	$O(10)$	
3	1	7	$^4C_3 \cdot {}^2C_1 \cdot {}^{10}C_7 = 960$
3	2	6	$^4C_3 \cdot {}^2C_2 \cdot {}^{10}C_6 = 840$
4	1	6	$^4C_4 \cdot {}^2C_1 \cdot {}^{10}C_6 = 420$
4	2	5	$^4C_4 \cdot {}^2C_2 \cdot {}^{10}C_5 = 252$

∴ Total selection on adding $= 2472$

25. (a) There is no restriction about the number of balls (identical) to be drawn except that there will be **at least one red ball**. Hence we can have 1 or 2 or 3 or 4 red balls in the selection *i.e.* there are 4 ways of selection of red balls. For black balls **there is no restriction**. We may select 1 or 2 or 3 or 4 or 5 **or no black ball** *i.e.* there are 6 ways of selection of black balls. Hence the total number of selection is $4 \times 6 = 24$.

(b) Let the n subjects be Maths, Chemistry, Physics, ... with p copies of each subject. Here again there is no restriction about the number of books to be selected. We can have for each subject 1 or 2 or 3 or .... p or **no book** *i.e.* $p + 1$ ways. This holds good

for each of the n subjects. Hence by fundamental theorem the number of selections is $(p + 1)(p + 1)(p + 1) \dots n$ times $= (p + 1)^n$.

But this includes one particular case **when no book of any of the subjects is chosen**. This has to be excluded because we have to make a **non-empty selection**. Therefore required number of selection is $(p + 1)^n - 1$.

26. Fruits of the same type to be treated as identical.

Oranges 1, 2, 3, 4, 0, $= 5$

Apples 1, 2, 3, 4, 5, 0 $= 6$

Mangoes 1, 2, 3, 4, 5, 6, 0 $= 7$

Total $= 5 \times 6 \times 7 - 1 = 209$

1 corresponds to the number when no fruit is drawn.

27.

$A(8)$	10	$B(4)$
8		2
7		3
6		4

Total no. of ways

$$= (\underset{A}{{}^{10}C_8} \times \underset{B}{{}^2C_2}) + (\underset{A}{{}^{10}C_7} \times \underset{B}{{}^3C_3}) + (\underset{A}{{}^{10}C_6} \times \underset{B}{{}^4C_4})$$

$$= {}^{10}C_2 + {}^{10}C_3 + {}^{10}C_4 \qquad (\because {}^{10}C_6 = {}^{10}C_4)$$

$$= \frac{10 \cdot 9}{1 \cdot 2} + \frac{10 \cdot 9 \cdot 8}{1 \cdot 2 \cdot 3} + \frac{10 \cdot 9 \cdot 8 \cdot 7}{1 \cdot 2 \cdot 3 \cdot 4}$$

$$= 45 + 120 + 210 = 375$$

Note : We could write the answer straight away by following **Rule (o), P. 293** of division into groups.

$$\frac{10!}{8! \, 2!} + \frac{10!}{7! \, 3!} + \frac{10!}{6! \, 4!}$$

28. Out of 10 boxes we have to choose only 5 boxes. (select).

Because the balls are identical and the boxes are also identical (but they can occupy different places like **Q. 23**), the required number of ways

$$= {}^{10}C_5 = \frac{(10!)}{5! \, 5!} = 252.$$

Remark : Some students may think that the answer in this case is 1. But this is wrong since although the boxes and balls are identical but boxes will occupy different places. For a similar question see **Q. 23**.

29. (a) **Balls of the same colour identical.**

Let us arrange 4 red and 3 black balls in a row in $\frac{7!}{3! \, 4!} = 35$ **(identical)**.

Now there will be 8 gaps in which 5 **identical** white balls can be arranged in $\frac{1}{5!} \, {}^8P_5$ or in

$$^8C_5 \cdot \frac{5!}{5!} = \frac{8!}{3! \, 5!} = 42$$

Hence by fundamental theorem $35 \times 42 = 1960$ ways.

(b) All balls are considered to be **different**. As above arrange 7 non-white balls in 7 ! ways and in the 8 gaps arrange 5 different white balls in

$$^8P_5 = \frac{8!}{3!} \text{ ways. Hence by fundamental theorem}$$

$\dfrac{7!\,8!}{3!}$ is the required number of ways.

30. Here the restriction is : **taken not more than r at a time and repetition is allowed.**

Arranging 1 at a time will be n.

Now suppose we take 2 at a time. The first place can be filled in n ways and then the second place can again be filled in n ways as repetition is allowed. Hence the number of ways when taken 2 at a time will be $n \times n = n^2$.

Similarly when taken 3 at a time will be

$$n \times n \times n = n^3,$$

and when taken r at a time will be

$$n \times n \times n \times \ldots\ldots r \text{ times} = n^r.$$

Hence the total number of ways

$$= n + n^2 + \ldots + n^r.$$

$$= \frac{n(n^r - 1)}{n - 1}.$$

Sum of G.P. whose $a = n$ and $r = n$.

31. Let the boxes be marked as A, B, C. We have to ensure that no box remains empty and in all five balls have to put in. There will be two possiblities.

(i) **Any two containing one and 3rd containing 3.**

$A\,(1)\,B\,(1)\,C\,(3)$

$$^5C_1 \cdot {}^4C_1 \cdot {}^3C_3 = 5.4.1 = 20.$$

or $\dfrac{5!}{3!.1!.1!} = \dfrac{120}{6} = 20$ **[Refer (o) P. 293]**

Similarly for $A\,(1)\,B\,(3)\,C\,(1)$

$$= {}^5C_1 \cdot {}^4C_3 \cdot {}^1C_1 = 5.\,4.\,1 = 20$$

and $A\,(3)\,B\,(1)\,C\,(1)$

$$= {}^5C_3 \cdot {}^2C_1 \cdot {}^1C_1 = 10.2.1 = 20$$

Hence the required number is $20 + 20 + 20 = 60$

(ii) **Any two containing 2 each and 3rd containing 1**

$A\,(2)\,B\,(2)\,C\,(1)$

$$^5C_2 \cdot {}^3C_2 \cdot {}^1C_1 = 10 \times 3 \times 1 = 30$$

or $\dfrac{5!}{2!.2!.1!} = \dfrac{120}{4} = 30$

Similarly as above for

$A\,(2)\,B\,(1)\,C\,(2)$ and $A\,(1)\,B\,(2)\,C\,(2)$

we will have 30 ways each.

Hence the required number is $30 + 30 + 30 = 90$.

∴ Total number is $60 + 90 = 150$.

32. Let the four balls be B_1, B_2, B_3 and B_4 and the four boxes of the corresponding colours be denoted by C_1, C_2, C_3 and C_4 respectively. Now B_1 is not to be placed in C_1 and as such it can be placed in either of C_2, C_3 or C_4. Thus B_1 can be placed in 3 ways under given condition.

After this has been done in any one way say B_1 has been placed in C_2 then B_2, B_3, B_4 with the given condition, (not to be placed in the box of the same colour) can be placed as under :

C_2	C_1	C_3	C_4
B_1	B_4	B_2	B_3
B_1	B_3	B_4	B_2
B_1	B_2	B_4	B_3

Under the above setting only, no ball will go to the box of the same colour. Above gives us 3 ways corresponding to B_1 being placed in C_2. Hence by fundamental theorem the total number of ways of placing the balls is $3 \times 3 = 9$.

33. Out of 10 prizes we have to select four for the head boy which can be done in $^{10}C_4$ ways. Now we are left with 6 prizes and 4 other boys. Each prize can be given in 4 ways. Hence the remaining 6 prizes can be given in 4^6 ways. By fundamental theorem total ways

$$= {}^{10}C_4 \times 4^6 = 210 \times 4096 = 860160.$$

34. (a) Write the letters of word NUMBER in alphabetical order *i.e.* as BEMNRU. We have to find its placing as in dictionary.

There are 6 places to be filled up with the letters of NUMBER so that all the words so formed come before the word NUMBER as in a dictionary.

All the words beginning with the letter which come.

1. Before N $BEM\ N^0 RU$

   i.e., beginning with B, E, M

   i.e., $5! + 5! + 5! = 3\,(5!) = 3 \times 120 = 360$

2. Before NU $BEM\ N^0\ R\,U^0$

   i.e., beginning with NB, NE, NM, NR

   i.e., $4! + 4! + 4! + 4! = 4\,(4!) = 96$

3. Before NUM $BEM^0\ N^0\ R\,U^0$

   i.e., beginning with $NUB, NUE\ (\neq NUR)$

   as R comes after last letter M of NUM

   i.e., $3! + 3! = 2\,(3!) = 12$

4. Before $NUMB$ $B^0\ E\,M^0\ N^0\ R\,U^0$

   None as both E and R come after, last letter B

5. Before $NUMBE$ $B^0\ E^0\ M^0\ N^0\ R\,U^0$

   None as R comes after last letter E

6. $NUMBER$ $= 1$

   ∴ Rank is $360 + 96 + 12 + 1 = 469$

(b) Ans. (c).

Let us rewrite the letters of the word Cochin according to alphabetical order

C C H I N O

The words beginning with CC, CH, CI, CN,

C C	Arrange	H I N O in 4! ways
C H	Arrange	C I N O in 4! ways
C I	Arrange	C H N O in 4! ways
C N	Arrange	C H I O in 4! ways

C O   C H I N is the word Cochin

Hence there will 4! + 4! + 4! + 4! = 96 words which will appear before the word Cochin in dictionary.

35. (i) Write in alphabetical order the letters of the word mother as $E\ H\ M\ O\ R\ T$

Now proceeding as in part (a)

1. Before $M E H\ M^o\ O R T$

   i.e., beginning with E or $H = 2\,(5!) = 240$

2. Before MO \qquad $E H M^o\ O^o\ R T$

   i.e., beginning with $ME, MH = 2\,(4!) = 48$

3. Before MOT \qquad $E H M^o\ O^o\ R T^o$

   i.e., beginning with MOE, MOH, MOR

   $\qquad = 3\,(3!) = 18$

4. Before \quad $MOTH$ \quad $E H^o\ M^o\ O^o\ R T^{\,o}$

   beginning $MOTE\,(\ne MOTR) = 2! = 2$

5. Before $MOTHE$ \quad $E^o\ H^o\ M^o\ O^o\ R T^o$

   None as R comes after E

6. $M O T H E R = 1$

   Rank is $240 + 48 + 18 + 2 + 1 = 309$

(ii) Rank of RACHIT.

ACHIRT (alphabetical order)

1. Before R \qquad $ACHIR^o T$

   i.e. beginning with A, C, H, I

   i.e., $4\,(5!) = 480$

2. Before RA \qquad $A^o\ C H I R^o\ T$

   None \qquad All come after last letter A

3. Before RAC \qquad None

4. Before $RACH$ \qquad None

5. Before $RACHI$ \qquad None

6. $R A C H I T = 1$

   $\therefore$ \quad Rank is $480 + 1 = 481$

(iii) Rank of ZENITH is 616.

36. Since there are m points, the number of lines will be $^m C_2 = \dfrac{m\,(m-1)}{2}$ and none of them is parallel to each other. Hence their points of intersection are

$$^{\frac{m(m-1)}{2}}C_2 = \text{Total} \qquad \qquad ...(1)$$

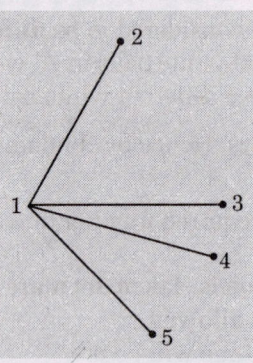

Fig. 9

Now if there were 5 points then 4 lines will pass through a particular point. say at 1. If these four lines were not concurrent at 1, then their points of intersection would be $^4C_2$.

Similarly if they occur at 2, then also $^4C_2$. Hence the number of points of intersection will be $5 \cdot {}^4C_2$ for these 5 points. Since we have m points therefore we have to exclude from total the number of distinct points of intersection at the given m points whose number as explained above will be $m \cdot {}^{m-1}C_2$.

Hence the required number of points of intersection is

$$= {}^{\frac{m(m-1)}{2}}C_2 - m \cdot {}^{m-1}C_2$$

$$= \frac{1}{2}\frac{m(m-1)}{2}\left[\frac{m(m-1)}{2} - 1\right] - m \cdot \frac{1}{2}(m-1)(m-2)$$

$$= \frac{m(m-1)}{2}\left[\frac{m(m-1)-2}{2} - (m-2)\right].$$

37. Number of ways of getting $2m$ marks

$= \text{coeff. of } x^{2m} \text{ in } (x^0 + x^1 + x^2 + x^3 + ... + x^m)^4$

$= \text{coeff. of } x^{2m} \text{ in } (1 + x + x^2 + ... + x^m)^4$

$= \text{coeff. of } x^{2m} \text{ in } \left(\dfrac{1 - x^{m+1}}{1 - x}\right)^4$

$= \text{coeff. of } x^{2m} \text{ in } (1 - x^{m+1})^4\,(1-x)^{-4}$

$= \text{coeff. of } x^{2m} \text{ in } (1 - 4x^{m+1} + 6x^{2m+2}$

$$- 4x^{3m+3} + x^{4m+4})$$

$$\times \left[1 + 4x + ... + \frac{(r+1)(r+2)(r+3)}{3!}x^r + ...\right]$$

$$= 1 \times \frac{(2m+1)(2m+2)(2m+3)}{6} - 4 \times \frac{m(m+1)(m+2)}{6}$$

$$= \frac{(m+1)}{3}[(2m+1)(2m+3) - 2m(m+2)]$$

$$= \frac{1}{3}(m+1)(2m^2 + 4m + 3).$$

38. Aggregate of marks $= 50 \times 3 + 100 = 250.$

$\therefore$ \quad 60% of the aggregate $= \dfrac{3}{5} \times 250 = 150.$

Now the number of ways of getting 150 marks in the aggregate

$= $ coeff. of x^{150} in $(x^0 + x^1 + x^2 + x^3 + ... + x^{50})^3$

$\qquad . (x^0 + x^1 + x^2 + x^3 + ... + x^{100})$

$= $ coeff. of $x^{150} \left(\dfrac{1-x^{51}}{1-x}\right)^3 \left(\dfrac{1-x^{101}}{1-x}\right)$

$= $ coeff of $x^{150} (1-x^{51})^3 (1-x^{101})(1-x)^{-4}$

$= $ coeff. of $x^{150} (1 - 3 x^{51} + 3 . x^{102} - x^{153})$

$\qquad . (1 - x^{101})(1-x)^{-4}$

$= $ coeff. of $x^{150} [1 - 3 . x^{51} - x^{101} + 3 . x^{102}$

$\qquad\qquad\qquad\qquad + 3 . x^{152} ....]$

$\qquad \cdot \left[1 + 4x + ... + \dfrac{(r+1)(r+2)(r+3)}{6} x^r .... \right]$

$= 1 . \dfrac{151 . 152 . 153}{6} - 3 \dfrac{100 . 101 . 102}{6}$

$\qquad\qquad - 1 . \dfrac{50 . 51 . 52}{6} + 3 . \dfrac{49 . 50 . 51}{6}$

$= 151 . 76 . 51 - 100 . 101 . 51 - 50 . 17 . 26 + 49 . 25 . 51$

$= 51 (151 . 76 - 100 . 101) + 17 (49 . 25 . 3 - 50 . 26)$

$= 51 (11476 - 10100) + 17 (3675 - 1300)$

$= 51 . 1376 + 17 . 2375 = 70176 + 40375 = 110551.$

Problem Set (6)

▶ **Objective Questions**

1. $\sum\limits_{r=0}^{m} {}^{n+r}C_n$ is equal to

   (a) ${}^{n+m+1}C_{n+1}$ (b) ${}^{n+m+2}C_n$

   (c) ${}^{n+m+3}C_{n-1}$ (d) None of these.

2. A polygon has 44 diagonals, then the number of its sides are

   (a) 11   (b) 7

   (c) 8   (d) None of these.

3. If 7 points out of 12 are in the same straight line, then the number of triangles formed is

   (a) 19   (b) 185

   (c) 201   (d) None of these

4. All the letters of the word EAMCET are arranged in all possible ways. The number of such arrangements in which no two vowels are adjacent to each other is

   (a) 360   (b) 144   (c) 72   (d) 54

5. Out of 10 red and 8 white balls, 5 red and 4 white balls can be drawn in number of ways

   (a) ${}^{8}C_5 \times {}^{10}C_4$ (b) ${}^{10}C_5 \times {}^{8}C_4$

   (c) ${}^{18}C_9$ (d) None   **(EAMCET 1991)**

6. 7 men and 7 women are to sit round a table so that there is a man on either side of a woman. The number of seating arrangement is

   (a) $(7!)^2$ (b) $(6!)^2$ (c) $6! . 7!$ (d) $7!$

   (EAMCET 1990)

7. The number of seven digit integers with sum of the digits equals to 10 and formed by using the digits 1, 2 and 3 only is

   (a) 55   (b) 66   (c) 77   (d) 88

   (ITT JEE 2009)

8. The total number of ways in which 5 balls of different colours can be distributed among 3 persons so that each person gets at least one ball is

   (a) 75   (b) 150   (c) 210   (d) 243

   (IIT JEE 2012)

9. Assuming the balls to be identical except for difference in colours, the number of ways in which one or more balls can be selected from 10 white, 9 green and 7 black balls is

   (a) 880   (b) 629   (c) 630   (d) 879

   (AIEEE 2012)

10. How may different words can be formed by jumbling the letters in the word MISSISSIPPI in which no two S are adjacent ?

    (a) $6 . 7 . {}^{8}C_4$ (b) $6 . 8 . {}^{7}C_4$

    (c) $7 . {}^{6}C_4 . {}^{8}C_4$ (d) $8 . {}^{6}C_4 . {}^{7}C_4$

    (AIEEE 2008)

Solutions to Problem Set (6)

1. Ans. (a). Since ${}^nC_r = {}^nC_{n-r}$

   and ${}^nC_{r-1} + {}^nC_r = {}^{n+1}C_r$, we have

   $\sum\limits_{r=0}^{m} {}^{n+r}C_n = \sum\limits_{r=0}^{m} {}^{n+r}C_r = {}^nC_0 + {}^{n+1}C_1 + {}^{n+2}C_2$

   $\qquad\qquad\qquad\qquad\qquad + ... + {}^{n+m}C_m$

   $= [1 + (n+1)] + {}^{n+2}C_2 + {}^{n+3}C_3 + ... + {}^{n+m}C_m$

   $= ({}^{n+2}C_1 + {}^{n+2}C_2) + {}^{n+3}C_3 ...... + {}^{n+m}C_m$

   $\qquad\qquad\qquad \therefore n + 2 = {}^{n+2}C_1 \text{ or } {}^nC_1 = n$

   $= ({}^{n+3}C_2 + {}^{n+3}C_3) + ... + {}^{n+m}C_m$

   $= ({}^{n+4}C_3 + {}^{n+4}C_4) + ... + {}^{n+m}C_m$

   $\cdots\cdots\cdots\cdots\cdots\cdots\cdots\cdots\cdots\cdots\cdots\cdots\cdots$

   $\cdots\cdots\cdots\cdots\cdots\cdots\cdots\cdots\cdots\cdots\cdots\cdots\cdots$

   $= {}^{n+m}C_{m-1} + {}^{n+m}C_m$

   $= {}^{n+m+1}C_m = {}^{n+m+1}C_{n+1}$ $[\because {}^nC_r = {}^nC_{n-r}]$

2. Ans. (a). We have

   $\qquad 44 = {}^nC_2 - n = \dfrac{1}{2} n(n-1) - n$

or $n^2 - 3n - 88 = 0$ or $(n - 11)(n + 8) = 0$

∴ $n = 11$, since $n \neq -8$.

3. **Ans. 185.**

Numbers of $\Delta^s = {}^{12}C_3 - {}^7C_3$

$= \dfrac{12.11.10}{1.2.3} - \dfrac{7.6.5}{1.2.3} = 220 - 35 = 185$.

4. **Ans. (c).** Gap Method. Consonants M, C, T in $3! = 6$ ways

and 4 gaps and 3 vowels (2 alike) in ${}^4P_3 \cdot \dfrac{1}{2!} = 12$ ways.

Ans. $12 \times 6 = 72$

5. **Ans. (b).** ${}^{10}C_5 \times {}^8C_4$.

6. **Ans. (c). Refer Q. 5 P 1341-44.**

7. **Ans. (c).** Three are following two cases which are possible

(i) five 1's, one 2's, one 3's

∴ number of numbers $= \dfrac{7!}{5!} = 42$

(ii) four 1's, three 2's

∴ number of numbers $= \dfrac{7!}{4!.3!} = 35$

Hence, total number of numbers $= 42 + 35 = 77$

8. **Ans. (b).**

	B_1	B_2	B_3
Case I	1	1	3
Case II	2	2	1

Total ways of distribution

$= \dfrac{5!}{1!.1!.3!.2!} \cdot 3! + \dfrac{5!}{2!.2!.1!.2!} \cdot 3!$

$= 150$.

9. **Ans. (d).** Required number of ways are given by

$(10 + 1)(9 + 1)(7 + 1) - 1 = 11 \times 10 \times 8 - 1 = 879$

10. **Ans. (c).** $\times \bullet \times \bullet \times \bullet \times \bullet \times \bullet \times \bullet \times$

Total letters $= 11$,   No. of S's $= 4$

First place 7 letters at dot place other than $S = \dfrac{7!}{4!2!}$

Now place S at $\times$ places such that no two S are adjacent

$= \dfrac{{}^8P_4}{4!} = {}^8C_4$

Hence, total number of arrangements

$= \dfrac{7!}{4!.2!} \times {}^8C_4 = 7 \cdot {}^6C_4 \times {}^8C_4$

MISCELLANEOUS EXERCISE

Matching Entries

▸ *Match the entries of List-A and List-B.*

1.   **List-A**

(a) If ${}^nC_{r-1} = 36$, ${}^nC_r = 84$, ${}^nC_{r+1} = 126$, then $(n, r) =$

(b) ${}^nC_r + 2 \, {}^nC_{r-1} + {}^nC_{r-2} =$

(c) $\displaystyle\sum_{k=1}^n \left[\dfrac{k \, {}^nC_k}{{}^nC_k + {}^nC_{n-k}} \right]^2 =$

(d) If ${}^{n-1}C_6 + {}^{n-1}C_7 > {}^nC_6$, then n is greater than ...

List-B

1. 13

2. $(9, 3)$

3. ${}^{n+2}C_r$

4. $\dfrac{n(n+1)(2n+1)}{24}$

2.   **List-A**

(a) The number of arrangements of the letters of the word EAMCET in which no two vowels are together is ...

(b) Total number of words formed by 2 vowels and 3 consonants taken from 4 vowels and 5 consonants is ...

(c) The number of odd numbers between 1000 and 10,000 that can be formed with the digits 1, 2, 3, 4, 5, 6, 7, 8, 9 is ...

(d) Number of all four-digit numbers having different digits formed of the digits 1, 2, 3, 4 and 5 and divisible by 4 is ...

List-B

1. 24

2. 1680

3. 7200

4. 72

3.   **List-A**

(a) The greatest possible number of points intersection of 8 straight lines and 4 circles is ...

List-B

1. $20^4 \times 19^2$

(b) six + and four – signs are to be arranged in a line such that no two
– signs occur together. The number of such arrangements is ...   2.   196

(c) The numbers of ways in which a committee of 5 can be chosen from
10 candidates so as to exclude the youngest if it includes the oldest   3.   104

(d) The following prizes are to be distributed in a class of 20 boys.
1st and 2nd in Maths, 1st and 2nd in Physics, 1st in Chemistry and
1st in English. Total number of ways is ...   4.   35

4.   **List-A**   **List-B**

(a) $\displaystyle\sum_{r=1}^{n} \frac{{}^nP_r}{r!}$ 1. $41^2 - 1 = 1680$

(b) The number of proper divisors of $2^6 . 3^5 . 5^3 . 7^4 . 11$ is   2.   144

(c) There are 18 points in a plane out of which 5 are collinear. Number
of straight lines that can be formed is   3.   806

(d) Number of triangles that can be formed by points in (c) is   4. $2^n - 1$

5. Consider all possible permutations of the letters of the word **ENDEANOEL**.

   Column-I   **Column-II**

(a) The number of permutations containing the word ENDEA is   (p) $5!$

(b) The number of permutations in which the letter E occurs in
the first and the last positions is   (q) $2 \times 5!$

(c) The number of permutations in which none of the
letters D, L, N occurs in the last five positions is   (r) $7 \times 5!$

(d) The number of permutations in which the letters
A, E, O occur only in odd positions is   (s) $21 \times 5!$ **(I.I.T. 2008)**

Hints / Solutions

1. (a) $\rightarrow$ 2. **Q. 21 (a) P. 296**
     (b) $\rightarrow$ 3. **Q. 12 (a) P. 296**
     (c) $\rightarrow$ 4. **Q. 25 P. 296**
     (d) $\rightarrow$ 1. As in **Q. 13 (a) P. 296**

2. (a) $\rightarrow$ 4. **Q. 4 P. 9 (a), P. 302**
     (b) $\rightarrow$ 3.
$$\underset{V}{{}^4C_2} \times \underset{C}{{}^5C_3} \times 5! = 6 \times 10 \times 120 = 7200$$

     (c) $\rightarrow$ 2.
It will be 4 digit number and as it is to be odd the unit
place can be filled in 5 ways by any of the 5 odd
numbers. Out of remaining 8 we have to arrange 3 in
${}^8P_3$ ways.

$\therefore$ $(8 \times 7 \times 6) \times 5 = 1680$ by fundamental theorem.

     (d) $\rightarrow$ 1.
The number under given condition will have the last
two digits 12, 24, 32, 52 having fixed 12 in the end we
have to arrange 2 more out of remaining 3 which can be
done in ${}^3P_2 = 3! = 6$ ways.

Total number of such numbers by fundemental
theorem is $4 \times 6 = 24$.

3. (a) $\rightarrow$ 3. **Q. 29 (b) P. 321**
     (b) $\rightarrow$ 4. **Q. 18 (b) P. 328**
     (c) $\rightarrow$ 2. **Q. 6 (b) P. 319**
     (d) $\rightarrow$ 1. **Q. 41 (a) P. 319**

4. (a) $\rightarrow$ 4. **Q. 9 (c) P. 295**

(b) $\rightarrow$ 1. **Q. 21 (e) P. 312**
(c) $\rightarrow$ 2. **Q. 30 P. 329**
(d) $\rightarrow$ 3. **Q. 30 P. 329**

5.   **ENDEANOEL**
Nine letters : $3E^s, 2N^s$, 4 different D, A, O, L.

(a) $\rightarrow$ (p), (b) $\rightarrow$ (s), (c) $\rightarrow$ (q), (d) $\rightarrow$ (q)

$\boxed{\text{ENDEA}}$, N, O, E, L   Five different

(a) $\rightarrow$ (p) String Method. We have five different units whose
permutation is $5!$.

(b) $\rightarrow$ (s) E   ENNDAOL   E

1st and last places are filled with E^s. We have to
arrange remaining 7 letters out of which $2N^s$ are alike.

$\therefore$ $\dfrac{7!}{2!} = \dfrac{7.6.5!}{2} = 21(5!)$

(c) $\rightarrow$ (q) D, L, N, N will not occur in last five and hence they
have to be arranged in first 4 positions. $\therefore$ $\dfrac{4!}{2!}$

For the last five letters out of which $3E^s$ are alike $\dfrac{5!}{3!}$.

Hence total $= \dfrac{4!}{2!} \cdot \dfrac{5!}{3!} = \dfrac{4.(3!)}{2} \cdot \dfrac{5!}{3!} = 2(5!)$

(d) $\rightarrow$ (q) $A E O$ to occur in odd positions. *i.e.*, 1st, 3rd, 5th,
7th and 9th.

$$\frac{5!}{3! \,(\text{alike } E)} \cdot \frac{4!}{2! \,(\text{alike } N)} = 5! \frac{4}{2} = 2(5!)$$

Assertion/Reason

1. **Statement 1 :** The number of ways of distributing 10 identical balls in 4 distinct boxes such that no two box is empty is $^9C_3$.

   Statement 2 : The number of ways of choosing any 3 places from 9 different places is $^9C_3$. **(AIEEE 2011)**

Sol. (b) **Statement 1.**

$B_1 + B_2 + B_3 + B_4 = 10$

= coefficient of x^{10} in $(x^1 + x^2 + ... + x^7)^4$

= coefficient of x^6 in $(1 - x^7)^4 (1 - x)^{-4}$

= $^{4+6-1}C_3 = {}^9C_3$

Statement 2 : Obviously $^9C_3$.

Fascinating Facts

- Selecting things without any order is called combination and arrangement of things in some order is called permutation.
- In a combination while forming a group or selection we are only concerned with the number of things each group or selection contains while in a permutation we are also concerned with the order of things which forms the arrangement. Therefore, if order is important, then problem of permutation and number of possible samples are the required number of arrangements. On the other hand, if order is not important, then the problem is of combinations and the number of possible samples are the required number of combinations.
- The number of ways in which a selection of one or more (*i.e.*, at least one) object can be made n distinct objects is

$$^nC_1 + {}^nC_2 + {}^nC_3 + ... + {}^nC_n = 2^n - 1$$

- The number of ways in which a selection of none, one or more objects can be made from n distinct objects is

$$^nC_0 + {}^nC_1 + {}^nC_2 + ... + {}^nC_n = 2^n$$

- The number of combinations of n different things taken r at a time

  (i) when p particular things are never included is $^{n-p}C_r$

  (ii) when p particular things are always included is $^{n-p}C_{r-p}$

  (iii) when p particular things are not together in any selection is $^nC_r - {}^{n-p}C_{r-p}$

- If n distinct points are given on the circumference of a circle, then

  (i) number of straight lines = $^nC_2$

  (ii) number of triangles = $^nC_3$

  (iii) number of quadrilaterals = $^nC_4$,... and so on.

❑

CHAPTER

Algebra

Mathematical Induction

§ 1. Principle of Mathematical Induction.

Let $n \in \mathbf{N}$ and $P(n)$ denote a certain statement or formula or theorem. Then $P(n)$ holds for every natural number n if

(1) it holds for $n = 1$, and

(2) it holds for $n = m + 1$ whenever it holds for $n = m$.

Remark. We emphasize that proof by mathematical induction requires the fulfilment of both the conditions (1) and (2) as stated above. Even if we prove a certain statement for larger number of values of n say $n = 1, 2, 3, 100$, we cannot say that the statement is true for all n unless we establish condition (2). For example consider trinomial $f(n) = n^2 + n + 41$. Substituting 1, 2, 3, 4, 5, 6, 7, 8, 9, 10 in turn we obtain 43, 47, 53, 61, 71, 83, 97, 113, 131, 151 which are all prime numbers. On the basis of these results, we assert that the substitution of any positive integer for n in $f(n)$ will **always** yield a prime number. But this reasoning is **fallacious**. In fact $f(n)$ yields a prime number for $n = 1, 2, \ldots, 39$, but for $n = 40$ we have

$$f(40) = 40^2 + 40 + 41$$
$$= 40^2 + 2.40 + 1 = (40 + 1)^2$$
$$= 41 \times 41$$

which is a composite number.

This example shows that we cannot make **general assertion** with respect to any n unless we prove condition (2).

We now show that the condition (1) cannot be omitted either.

For example, we make the following assertion.

Every natural number is equal to the next natural number.

To prove this, we assume.

$$m = m + 1 \qquad \ldots(1)$$

where m is a natural number. On the basis of this, we prove

$$m + 1 = m + 2 \qquad \ldots(2)$$

In fact adding 1 to each side of (1), we obtain the equation (2).

This shows that if our assertion is valid for $n = m$, then it is also valid for $n = m + 1$. Hence we conclude that the assertion holds for all natural number n. But this arrangement is again fallacious since we have drawn the conclusion proving the condition (2) only and omitted condition (1). But for $n = 1$, the statement is clearly false since $1 \neq 2$.

The above remarks show that in order to prove a certain statement for all natural numbers n, it is essential to establish both the conditions (1) and (2).

As a matter of fact, condition (1) creates the basis for carrying out induction and condition (2) gives us the right of an unlimited automatic **extension** of this bais.

$$P(n) \text{ for } n = 1$$

Consider the statement

(a) $2 + 4 + 6 + \ldots + (2n + 2) = (n + 1)(n + 2) \quad \forall n \in \mathbf{N}$

Here we have $n + 1$ terms in L.H.S.

and R.H.S. $= (n + 1)(n + 2)$.

$P(1)$ means $1 + 1 = 2$ terms in

L.H.S. $= 2 + 4 = 6$.

$P(1)$ in R.H.S. $= (1 + 1)(1 + 2) = 2 \times 3 = 6$

Hence $P(1)$ holds good.

(b) Consider $1.3 + 2.4 + 3.5 + \ldots (n - 1)(n + 1)$

$$= \frac{1}{6} n(n - 1)(2n + 5) \, \forall \, n \geq 2$$

Here there are $(n - 1)$ terms in L.H.S.

where $n \geq 2$ and as such we have to choose $n = 2$ so that in the L.H.S. we have $2 - 1 = 1$ term, which gives $1.3 = 3$.

R.H.S. on putting $n = 2$ gives $\frac{1}{6} 2.1.9 = 3$

Problem Set (1)

Prove by the method of induction that :

1. $2 + 5 + 8 + 11 + .. (3n - 1) = \frac{1}{2} n (3n + 1)$ $n \in N$

2. $1.3 + 2.4 + 3.5 + ... + n.(n + 2)$
$$= \frac{1}{6} n (n + 1) (2n + 7), n \in N.$$

3. (a) $1.2.3. + 2.3.4 + 3.4.5 + ... + n (n + 1) (n + 2)$
$$= \frac{1}{4} n (n + 1) (n + 2) (n + 3)$$

   *(b) Prove by induction that
$$1^2 + 3^2 + 5^2 + .. + (2n - 1)^2 = \frac{1}{3} n (4n^2 - 1).$$

   (c) $1^6 - 2^6 + 3^6 - ... + (-1)^{n-1} n^6$
$$= \frac{(-1)^{n-1}}{2} (n^6 + 3n^5 - 5n^3 + 3n)$$

4. (i) $1.6 + 2.9 + 3.12 + ... + n (3n + 3)$
$$= n (n + 1) (n + 2)$$

   *(ii) $7 + 77 + 777 + ... + 777...7 n$ digits
$$= \frac{7}{81} (10^{n+1} - 9n - 10).$$

   (iii) $1 + \frac{x}{a_1} + \frac{x(x + a_1)}{a_1 a_2} + ...$
$$+ \frac{x(x + a_1)(x + a_2)...(x + a_{n-1})}{a_1 a_2 a_3 ... a_n}$$
$$= \frac{(x + a_1)(x + a_2)...(x + a_n)}{a_1 a_2 a_3 ... a_n}$$

5. (a) $\frac{1}{2.5} + \frac{1}{5.8} + \frac{1}{8.11} + ... + \frac{1}{(3n - 1)(3n + 2)} = \frac{n}{6n + 4}$

   (b) $\frac{1}{3.7} + \frac{1}{7.11} + \frac{1}{11.15} + ... + \frac{1}{(4n - 1)(4n + 3)} = \frac{n}{3(4n + 3)}$

*6. (a) $\frac{1}{1.2.3} + \frac{1}{2.3.4} + ... + \frac{1}{n(n + 1)(n + 2)}$
$$= \frac{n(n + 3)}{4(n + 1)(n + 2)}$$

   *(b) $\sqrt{[2 + \sqrt{\{(2 + \sqrt{(2 + ... n \text{ terms})\}}]}}$
$$= 2 \cos \frac{\pi}{2^{n+1}}, n \in N$$

7. (a) Assuming that $\log (mn) = \log m + \log n$ prove that $\log x^n = n \log x.$

   (b) Prove by mathematical induction that
$$\frac{1}{\log_x 2 . \log_x 4} + \frac{1}{\log_x 4 . \log_x 8} + ...$$
$$+ \frac{1}{\log_x 2^{n-1} . \log_x 2^n}$$
$$= \left(1 - \frac{1}{n}\right) \frac{1}{(\log_x 2)^2}, x > 0, \neq -1, n \in N$$

8. (a) $(1 + x)^n > 1 + nx$ for $n \geq 2, n \in N,$ $x > -1, x \neq 0.$

   (b) $(1 + x)^l (1 + y)^m (1 + z)^n > 1 + lx + my + nz$
   for $l, m, n \geq 0$ and $\in N . x, y, z > 0.$

9. $(\cos \theta + i \sin \theta)^n = \cos n\theta + i \sin n\theta.$

10. Prove that $2^n > n$ for all natural numbers $n.$

*11. For what natural numbers n the inequality $2^n > 2n + 1$ is valid ?

*12. For what natural numbers n is the inequality $2^n > n^2$ valid ?

13. $5^{2n} - 1$ is divisible by 24 where n is a +ive integer.

14. $3^{2n} + 7$ is divisible by 8 where n is a +ive integer.

*15. Prove that $7^{2n} + (2^{3n-3}) 3^{n-1}$ is divisible by 25, $n \in N.$
(I.I.T. 1982)

16. Prove that $4^n + 15n - 1$ is divisible by 9 for all natural numbers $n.$ **(Roorkee 1994)**

*17. Explain the method of mathematical induction and use it to show that $11^{n+2} + 12^{2n+1}$ where n is natural number is divisible by 133   **(Roorkee 1982)**

18. (a) Prove that $5^{2n+2} - 24n - 25$ is divisible by 576.

   *(b) Use mathematical induction to prove that $2.7^n + 3.5^n - 5$ is divisible by 24 for all $n > 0.$
(I.I.T. 1985)

19. $a^n - b^n$ is divisible by $a - b$ where n is a +ive integer.

20. Prove that $x^n - y^n$ is divisible by $x + y$ when n is even.

*21. If p be a natural number, then prove that $p^{n+1} + (p + 1)^{2n-1}$ is divisible by $p^2 + p + 1$ for every positive integer $n.$ **(I.I.T. 1984)**

22. Prove that $x(x^{n-1} - na^{n-1}) + a^n (n - 1)$ is divisible by $(x - a)^2$ for all positive integers n greater than 1.

*23. Prove by the method of induction that every even power of every odd number greater than 1 when divided by 8 leaves 1 for a remainder.   **(M.N.R. 1996)**

*24. (a) Prove that the sum of the cubes of three successive natural numbers is divisible by 9.

   (b)* Let p be a prime and m a positive integer. By mathematical induction on $m,$ or otherwise, prove that whenever r is an integer such that p does not divide r, p divides $^{mp}C_r.$

   [Hints : You may use the fact that
$$(1 + x)^{(m+1)P} = (1 + x)^p (1 + x)^{mp}]$$ **(I.I.T. 1998)**

25. Use mathematical induction to prove :
   If n is any odd positive integer then $n(n^2 - 1)$ is divisible by 24.   **(I.I.T. 1983)**

26. (a) For any natural numbers $n > 1$, prove

$$\frac{1}{n+1} + \frac{1}{n+2} + \ldots + \frac{1}{2n} > \frac{13}{24}.$$

(b) Prove by mathematical induction that

$$n.1 + (n-1).2 + (n-2).3 + \ldots + 2(n-1) + 1.n$$

$$= \frac{n}{6}(n+1)(n+2)$$

27. Prove the identities

(i) $\cos\alpha\cos 2\alpha\cos 4\alpha\ldots\cos 2^{n-1}\alpha = \dfrac{\sin 2^n\alpha}{2^n\sin\alpha}.$

*(ii) $\sin(\pi/3) + \sin(2\pi/3) + \sin(3\pi/3) + \ldots + \sin(n\pi/3)$

$$= 2\sin\frac{n\pi}{6}\sin\frac{n+1}{6}\pi.$$

*(iii) Let $0 < A_i < \pi$ for $i = 1, 2, \ldots n$. Use mathematical induction to prove that

$$\sin A_1 + \sin A_2 + \ldots + \sin A_n$$

$$\leq n\sin\left(\frac{A_1 + A_2 + \ldots + A_n}{n}\right),$$

where $n \geq 1$ is a material number.

{You may use the fact that}

$p\sin x + (1-p)\sin y \leq \sin\{px + (1-p)y\}.$

where $0 \leq p \leq 1$ and $0 \leq x, y \leq \pi\}$ (I.I.T. Re-ex. 1997)

*(iv) Using mathematical induction, prove that

$$\tan^{-1}(1/3) + \tan^{-1}(1/7) + \ldots$$

$$+ \tan^{-1}[1/(n^2 + n + 1)]$$

$$= \tan^{-1}[n/(n+2)]$$

(I.I.T. 1993)

Another Form :

$$\tan^{-1}\frac{1}{1+1+1^2} + \tan^{-1}\frac{1}{1+2+2^2} + \ldots$$

$$+ \tan^{-1}\frac{1}{1+n+n^2}$$

$$= \tan^{-1}(n+1) - \frac{\pi}{4} \; \forall \; n \in N$$

(v) $\tan^{-1}\dfrac{x}{1.2 + x^2} + \tan^{-1}\dfrac{x}{2.3 + x^2} + \ldots$

$$+ \tan^{-1}\frac{x}{n(n+1) + x^2}$$

$$= \tan^{-1}x - \tan^{-1}\frac{x}{n+1}, \; \forall \; n \in N \text{ and } x \in R$$

*(vi) If x is not a multiple of 2π, use mathematical induction to prove that

$$\cos x + \cos 2x + \ldots + \cos nx$$

$$= \frac{\cos\left(\dfrac{n+1}{2}\right)x\sin\dfrac{nx}{2}}{\sin\dfrac{x}{2}}$$

(I.I.T. 1994)

(vii) Prove by induction that

$$\sin x + \sin 3x + \ldots + \sin(2n-1)x = \frac{\sin^2 nx}{\sin x}$$

(viii) $\tan\alpha + 2\tan 2\alpha + 2^2\tan 2^2\alpha + \ldots n$ terms

$$= \cot\alpha - 2^n\cos 2^n\alpha$$

(ix) $\dfrac{1}{2}\tan\dfrac{x}{2} + \dfrac{1}{2^2}\tan\dfrac{x}{2^2} + \ldots + \dfrac{1}{2^n}\tan\left(\dfrac{x}{2^n}\right)$

$$= \frac{1}{2^n}\cot\left(\frac{x}{2^n}\right) - \cot x$$

(x) By applying the principle of Mathematical induction prove that

$$\frac{2\sin\theta}{\cos\theta + \cos 3\theta} + \frac{2\sin\theta}{\cos\theta + \cos 5\theta} + \ldots$$

$$+ \frac{2\sin\theta}{\cos\theta + \cos(2n+1)\theta}$$

$$= \tan(n+1)\theta - \tan\theta$$

(xi) Show by mathematical induction that

$$\frac{1}{\sin 2x} + \frac{1}{\sin 4x} + \ldots + \frac{1}{\sin 2^n x} = \cot x - \cot 2^n x$$

28. Prove that $(1+i)^n = 2^{n/2}\left(\cos\dfrac{n\pi}{4} + i\sin\dfrac{n\pi}{4}\right)$

29. If $n > 1$, prove that

*(i) $n! < \left(\dfrac{n+1}{2}\right)^n$

(I.I.T. 1981)

(ii) $\dfrac{2n!}{(n!)^2} > \dfrac{4n}{2n+1}$

*(iii) $^{2n}C_n > \dfrac{4^n}{n+1}$

(iv) Prove by mathematical induction that

$$1 + \frac{1}{2} + \frac{1}{3} + \frac{1}{4} + \ldots + \frac{1}{2^n} \geq 1 + \frac{n}{2}$$

for each no-negative integer n.

*(v) Prove by mathematical induction that

$$\frac{(2n)!}{2^{2n}(n!)^2} \leq \frac{1}{(3n+1)^{1/2}}, n \in N$$

(I.I.T. 1987)

*30. (a) For any natural number n, prove the inequality
$$|\sin nx| \leq n|\sin x|.$$

(b) If $0 < \alpha < \dfrac{\pi}{4(n-1)}$, where $n > 1$, then prove that

$\tan n\alpha > n\tan\alpha.$

*(c) If a, b are +ive, then for any integer n prove that
$$(a+b)^n < 2^n(a^n + b^n).$$

(d) If $x + y = a + b$, $x^2 + y^2 = a^2 + b^2$, then prove by mathematical induction that $x^n + y^n = a^n + b^n$ for all natural numbers n.

31. Prove that $A_n = \cos n\theta$ if it is known that
$$A_1 = \cos\theta, A_2 = \cos 2\theta$$

and for every natural number $m > 2$, the relations
$$A_m = 2A_{m-1} \cos\theta - A_{m-2} \text{ hold.}$$

32. Given $u_{n+1} = 3u_n - 2u_{n-1}$ and $u_0 = 2, u_1 = 3$.
Prove that $u_n = 2^n + 1$ for all positive integers n.

33. Let $v_{n+1} = 3v_n - 2v_{n-1}$ and $v_0 = 0, v_1 = 1$.
Prove that $v_n = 2^n - 1$.

*34. Let $u_1 = 1, u_2 = 1$ and $u_{n+2} = u_{n+1} + u_n$ for $n \geq 1$.
Use mathematical induction to show that
$$u_n = \frac{1}{\sqrt{(5)}} \left[\left(\frac{1+\sqrt{5}}{2} \right)^n - \left(\frac{1-\sqrt{5}}{2} \right)^n \right] \text{ for all } n \geq 1.$$

(I.I.T. 1981)

*35. Given $a_1 = \frac{1}{2} \left(a_0 + \frac{A}{a_0} \right)$, $a_2 = \frac{1}{2} \left(a_1 + \frac{A}{a_1} \right)$

and $a_{n+1} = \frac{1}{2} \left(a_n + \frac{A}{a_n} \right)$

for $n \geq 2$ where $a > 0, A > 0$, prove that
$$\frac{a_n - \sqrt{A}}{a_n + \sqrt{(A)}} = \left(\frac{a_1 - \sqrt{A}}{a_1 + \sqrt{(A)}} \right)^{2^{n-1}}$$

using mathematical induction.

36. Prove the binomial theorem
$$(x+a)^n = x^n + {}^nC_1 x^{n-1} a + {}^nC_2 x^{n-2} a^2 + \dots$$
$${}^nC_r x^{n-r} a^r + \dots + a^n$$

*37. (a) $\sum_{k=0}^{n} k \cdot {}^nC_k = n \cdot 2^{n-1}, \quad n \in N.$

(b) Use mathematical induction to prove that
$$\sum_{k=0}^{n} k^2 \cdot {}^nC_k = n(n+1) 2^{n-2} \text{ for } n \geq 1.$$

(I.I.T. 1986)

(c) ${}^nC_0 + {}^{n+1}C_1 + {}^{n+2}C_2 + \dots {}^{n+m}C_m = {}^{n+m+1}C_m$

for each pair of +ive integers n and m.

*38. Using mathematical induction, prove that
$${}^mC_0 \, {}^nC_k + {}^mC_1 \, {}^nC_{k-1} + \dots + {}^mC_k \, {}^nC_0 = {}^{m+n}C_k,$$

where m, n, k are positive integers,
and ${}^PC_q = 0$ for $p < q$.

(I.I.T. 1989)

*39. (a) For all positive integers n, prove that
$$n^7/7 + n^5/5 + 2n^3/3 - n/105 \text{ is an integer.}$$

(I.I.T. 1990)

(b) By mathematical induction, prove that
$$\frac{n^5}{5} + \frac{n^3}{3} + \frac{7n}{15} \text{ is a +ive integer } \forall n \in N.$$

(c) Prove by mathematical induction that
$$\frac{1}{1+x} + \frac{2}{1+x^2} + \frac{4}{1+x^4} + \dots + \frac{2^n}{1+x^{2^n}}$$

$$= \frac{1}{x-1} + \frac{2^{n+1}}{1-x^{2^{n+1}}}$$

(d) Observing that $1^3 = 1, 2^3 = 3+5$,
$$3^3 = 7+9+11, 4^3 = 13+15+17+19$$

find a general formula for the cube of natural number n and prove it by the principle of mathematical induction.

(Roorkee 1997)

40. Using induction of otherwise, prove that for any non-negative integers m, n, r and k,
$$\sum_{m=0}^{k} (n-m) \frac{(r+m)!}{m!} = \frac{(r+k+1)!}{k!} \left[\frac{n}{r+1} - \frac{k}{r+2} \right]$$

(I.I.T. 1991)

*41. (a) Using the principle of mathematical induction, prove that $\forall n \in N$ if
$$y = \cot^{-1} x \text{ then}$$
$$y_n = (-1)^n (n-1)! \sin^n y \sin ny.$$

(b) Prove by induction $\forall n \in N$ if $y = \dfrac{x}{x^2 + a^2}$

then $y_n = \dfrac{(-1)^n n!}{a^{n+1}} \sin^{n+1}\theta \cos(n+1)\theta$

where $\theta = \cot^{-1} \dfrac{x}{a}$

(c) If $y = \dfrac{\log x}{x}$, then prove by mathematical induction
$$y_n = \frac{(-1)^n (n!)}{x^{n+1}} \left[\log x - 1 - \frac{1}{2} - \dots - \frac{1}{n} \right]$$

(d) If $y = x^n \log x$ then
$$y_n = n! \left[\log x + 1 + \frac{1}{2} + \frac{1}{3} + \dots + \frac{1}{n} \right]$$
$$\forall n \in N \text{ and } x > 0$$

*42. (a) Using the principle of mathematical induction, prove that $\forall n \in N$
$$I_n = \int_0^{\pi/2} \cos^n x \sin nx \, dx$$
$$= \frac{1}{2^{n+1}} \left[2 + \frac{2^2}{2} + \frac{2^3}{3} + \dots + \frac{2^n}{n} \right]$$

(b) Let $I_m = \int_0^{\pi} \dfrac{1 - \cos mx}{1 - \cos x} dx$

Use mathematical induction to prove that
$$I_m = m\pi, m \, 0, 1, 2, \dots$$

(I.I.T. 1995)

(c) $\int_0^{\pi} \dfrac{\sin(2nx)}{\sin x} dx = 0, \forall n \in N.$

(d) $\int_0^{\pi/2} \dfrac{\sin^2 nx}{\sin x} dx = 1 + \frac{1}{3} + \frac{1}{5} + \dots + \frac{1}{2n-1} \forall n \in N$

(e) $\int_0^{\pi/2} \cos^n x \cos nx \, dx = \dfrac{\pi}{2^{n+1}}, \forall n \in N$

(f) Prove by induction method that for all $n \geq 1$

$$\int x^n e^x \, dx = n! \, e^x \left[\frac{x^n}{n!} - \frac{x^{n-1}}{(n-1)!} + \frac{n^{n-2}!}{(n-2)!} \right.$$
$$\left. + \ldots + (-1)^n \right]$$

43. Let $p \geq 3$ be an integer and α, β be the roots of $x^2 - (p+1)x + 1 = 0$. Using mathematical induction show that $\alpha^n + \beta^n$ (i) is an integer (ii) is not divisible by p. **(I.I.T. 1992)**

44. Prove that at any time, the total number of persons on the earth who shake hands an odd number of times is even.

45. If p is a prime number, prove that $n^p - n$ is divisible by p when n is a natural number greater than 1.

46. Prove that n distinct straight line drawn in a plane through a point divide the plane into $2n$ parts.

47. If $x^3 = x + 1$, then show that
$$x^{3n} = a_n x + b_n - c_n x^{-1}$$
where $a_{n+1} = a_n b_n$; $b_{n+1} = a_n + b_n + c_n$, and $c_{n+1} = a_n + c_n$.

48. If $x_1 x_2 x_3 \ldots x_n = 1 \, (x_1 > 0, i = 1, 2, \ldots n)$, prove that $x_1 + x_2 + \ldots x_n \geq n \, (n \geq 2)$

49. Prove that $(x + a_1)(x + a_2)(x + a_3)\ldots(x + a_n)$
$$= x^n + P_1 x^{n-1} + P_2 x^{n-2} + \ldots P_{n-1} x + P_n,$$
where $P_1 = \Sigma a_i$, $P_2 = \Sigma a_i a_j$, $P_3 = \Sigma a_i a_j a_k$,
$$1 \leq i \leq n \quad 1 \leq i < j \leq n \quad 1 \leq i < j < k \leq n$$
$$P_n = a_1 a_2 a_3 \ldots a_n.$$

50. Using mathematical induction prove that for every integer $n \geq 1$, $(3^{2^n} - 1)$ is divisible by 2^{n+2} but not by 2^{n+3}. **(I.I.T. 1996)**

Solution to Problem Set (1)

1. Let $P(n)$ be true for $n = m$, that is, we suppose that
$$P(m) = 2 + 5 + 8 + 11 + \ldots + (3m - 1)$$
$$= \frac{1}{2} m(3m + 1)$$
Now $P(m+1) = P(m) + T_{m+1}$
$$= \frac{1}{2} m(3m + 1) + [3(m+1) - 1]$$
$$= \frac{1}{2} [3m^2 + m + 6m + 6 - 2]$$
$$= \frac{1}{2} [3m^2 + 7m + 4]$$
$$= \frac{1}{2} (m+1)(3m + 4)$$
$$= \frac{1}{2} (m+1)[3(m+1) + 1].$$
Above relation shows that $P(n)$ is true for $n = m + 1$.

Also when $n = 1$, $P(n) = 2 = \frac{1}{2}(3.1 + 1)$
$$n = 2, (P(n) = 2 + 5 = 7 = \frac{1}{2} . 2(3.2 + 1).$$
Above relation shows that $P(n)$ is true for $n = 1, 2$ etc. Hence $P(n)$ is universally true by mathematical induction.

2. Let $P(n)$ be true for $n = m$
$$1.3 + 2.4 + 3.5 + \ldots + m(m+2)$$
$$\frac{1}{6} m(m+1)(2m+7).$$
$$P(m+1) = P(m) + T_{m+1}.$$
$$= \frac{1}{6} m(m+1)(2m+7) + (m+1)(m+1+2).$$
$$= \frac{1}{6}(m+1)[m(2m+7) + 6(m+3)]$$
$$= \frac{1}{6}(m+1)[2m^2 + 13m + 18]$$
$$= \frac{1}{6}(m+1)(m+2)(2m+9)$$
$$= \frac{1}{6}(m+1)[(m+1)+][2(m+1)+7].$$
Above relation shows that $P(n)$ is true for $n = m + 1$. Now consider $n = 1$,
$$P(1) = 1.3 = \frac{1}{6} . 1 . (1+1)(2.1+7).$$
When $n = 2$, $P(n) = 1.3 + 2.4 = 3 + 8 = 11$
$$= \frac{1}{6} . 2(2+1)(2.2+7).$$
Above relation shows that $P(n)$ is true for $n = 1, 2$. Hence $P(n)$ is universally true.

3. (a) Proceed as above.
(b) $P(1)$ holds good; assume $P(m)$, then
$$P(m+1) = P(m) + (2m+1)^2$$
$$= \frac{1}{3} m(4m^2 - 1) + (2m+1)^2$$
$$= \frac{1}{3}[4m^3 - m + 3(4m^2 + 4m + 1)]$$
$$= \frac{1}{3}[4m^3 + 12m^2 + 11m + 3]$$
$$= \frac{1}{3}(m+1)(4m^2 + 8m + 3)$$
$$= \frac{1}{3}(m+1)[4(m+1)^2 - 1].$$
Hence $P(m+1)$ also holds good.

(c) R.H.S. $= \dfrac{(-1)^{n-1}}{2} n(n^5 + 3n^4 - 5n^2 + 3)$
$$= \frac{(-1)^{n-1}}{2} n(n+1)(n^4 + 2n^3 - 2n^2 - 3n + 3) \ldots(1)$$
by actual division.
$\quad P(1)$ is obviously true. Assume $P(n)$.
$$\therefore \quad P(n+1) = P(n) + (-1)^n (n+1)^6$$

$$= \frac{(-1)^{n-1}}{2} n(n+1)(n^4 + 2n^3 - 2n^2 - 3n + 3)$$
$$+ (-1)^n (n+1)^6, \text{ by (1)}$$

$$= \frac{(-1)^n}{2}(n+1)$$
$$[-(n^5 + 2n^4 - 2n^3 - 3n^2 + 3n) + 2(n+1)^5]$$

$$= \frac{(-1)^n}{2}(n+1)$$
$$[2(n^5 + 5n^4 + 10n^3 + 10n^2 + 5n + 1)$$
$$- n^5 - 2n^4 + 2n^3 + 3n^2 - 3n]$$

$$= \frac{(-1)^n}{2}(n+1)$$
$$[n^5 + 8n^4 + 22n^3 + 23n^2 + 7n + 2]$$

$$= \frac{(-1)^n}{2}(n+1)(n+2)$$
$$[n^4 + 6n^3 + 10n^2 + 3n + 1] \qquad \ldots(2)$$

Now keeping in view the form (1) the expression within the bracket can be re-written as
$$\{(n+1)^4 + 2(n+1)^3 - 2(n+1)^2 - 3(n+1) + 3\}$$

Hence (2) takes the form of (1) with

$$n \to (n+1) \quad \therefore \quad P(n) \implies P(n+1)$$

4. **(i)** Proceed as above.

(ii) $P(1) = 7 = \frac{7}{81}(10^2 - 9.1 - 10) = 7$

$$P(2) = 7 + 77 = \frac{7}{81}(10^3 - 9.2 - 10)$$

$$= \frac{7}{81}.972 = 7.12 = 84$$

Assume $P(n) = \frac{7}{81}(10^{n+1} - 9n - 10)$

$\therefore \quad P(n+1) = P(n) + \underset{(n+1)\text{ digits}}{7777\ldots7}$

Now $\underset{(n+1)\text{ digits}}{7777\ldots7} = 7 + 7.10^1 + 7.10^2 + \ldots (n+1)$

$$= \frac{7(10^{n+1} - 1)}{10 - 1} = \frac{7}{9}(10^{n+1} - 1).$$

$\therefore \quad p(n+1)$

$$= \frac{7}{81}(10^{n+1} - 9n - 10) + \frac{7}{9}[10^{n+1} - 1]$$

$$= \frac{7}{81}[10^{n+1} - 9n - 10 + 9.10^{n+1} - 9]$$

$$= \frac{7}{81}[(1+9)10^{n+1} - 9(n+1) - 10]$$

$$= \frac{7}{81}[10^{n+2} - 9(n+1) - 10]$$

$$= \frac{7}{81}[10^{n+1+1} - 9(n+1) - 10]$$

$\therefore \quad P(n+1)$ also holds good.

(iii) $P(1) = 1 + \frac{x}{a_1} = \frac{x + a_1}{a_1}$

$\therefore \quad P(1)$ holds good.

Assume $P(n)$ also holds good.

$$P(n+1) = P(n)$$
$$+ \frac{x(x+a_1)\ldots(x+a_{n-1})(x+a_n)}{a_1 a_2 \ldots a_{n+1}}$$

$$= \frac{(x+a_1)(x+a_2)\ldots(x+a_n)}{a_1 a_2 \ldots a_n}$$

$$+ \frac{x(x+a_1)\ldots(x+a_n)}{a_1 a_2 \ldots a_{n+1}}$$

$$= \frac{(x+a_1)(x+a_2)\ldots(x+a_n)}{a_1 a_2 \ldots a_n}\left[1 + \frac{x}{a_{n+1}}\right]$$

$$= \frac{(x+a_1)(x+a_2)\ldots(x+a_{n+1})}{a_1 a_2 \ldots a_n \, a_{n+1}}$$

Thus $P(n+1)$ also holds good.

5. **(a)** Let $P(n)$ be true for $n = m$

$\therefore \quad \frac{1}{2.5} + \frac{1}{5.8} + \frac{1}{8.11} + \ldots$

$$+ \frac{1}{(3m-1)(3m+2)} = \frac{m}{6m+4}$$

$\therefore \quad P(m+1) = P(m) + T_{m-3}$

$$= \frac{m}{6m+4} + \frac{1}{[3(m+1)-1][3(m+1)+2]}$$

$$= \frac{m}{2(3m+2)} + \frac{1}{(3m+2)(3m+5)}$$

$$= \frac{m(3m+5) + 2}{2(3m+2)(3m+5)} = \frac{3m^2 + 5m + 2}{2(3m+2)(3m+5)}$$

$$= \frac{(3m+2)(m+1)}{2(3m+2)(3m+5)} = \frac{m+1}{6m+10}$$

$$= \frac{m+1}{6(m+1)+4}.$$

Above relation shows that $P(n)$ is true for $n = m+1$.

Also when $n = 1$, $P(n) = \frac{1}{2.5} = \frac{1}{10} = \frac{1}{6.1+4}$

when $n = 2$; $P(n) = \frac{1}{2.5} + \frac{1}{5.8} = \frac{5}{40} = \frac{1}{8}$

$$= \frac{2}{16} = \frac{2}{6.2+4}$$

Above relation shows that $P(n)$ is true for $n = 1, 2$. Hence $P(n)$ is universally true.

(b) Proceed as above.

6. **(a)** $P(1) = \frac{1}{6} = \frac{1.4}{4(2.3)} = \frac{1}{6}$

Similarly $P(2)$ also holds.

Assume $P(n)$.

$$\therefore \quad P(n+1) = P(n) + \frac{1}{(n+1)(n+2)(n+3)}$$

$$= \frac{n(n+3)}{4(n+1)(n+2)} + \frac{1}{(n+1)(n+2)(n+3)}$$

$$= \frac{1}{4(n+1)(n+2)(n+3)}[n(n+3)^2 + 4]$$

$$= \frac{n^3 + 6n^2 + 9n + 4}{4(n+1)(n+2)(n+3)}$$

$$= \frac{(n+1)^2(n+4)}{4(n+1)(n+2)(n+3)}$$

$$= \frac{(n+1)(n+4)}{4(n+2)(n+3)} = \frac{N(N+3)}{4(N+1)(N-2)}$$

where $N = n+1$

(b) $P(1) = \sqrt{2} = 2\cos\frac{\pi}{2^2} = 2.\frac{1}{\sqrt{2}} = \sqrt{2}$

$P(1)$ holds good. Assume $P(n)$.

$$P(n+1) = \sqrt{2 + P(n)} = \sqrt{2 + 2\cos\frac{\pi}{2^{n+1}}}$$

$$= \sqrt{2\left(1 + \cos\frac{\pi}{2^{n-1}}\right)} = \sqrt{2.2\cos^2\frac{\pi}{2^{n-2}}}$$

$$= 2\cos\frac{\pi}{2^{n+2}}$$

Thus $P(n+1)$ holds good.

7. (a) Let $P(n)$ be true for $n = m$

$\therefore \quad \log x^m = m\log x$

$\therefore \quad P(m+1) = \log x^{m+1}$

$$= \log x^m . x = \log x^m + \log x$$

$$= m\log x + \log x = (m+1)\log x$$

Above relation shows that $P(n)$ is true for $n = m+1$.

Now when $n = 1, \log x^1 = 1\log x$

$n = 2, \log x^2 = \log x . x = \log x + \log x = 2\log x$

Above relations show that $P(n)$ is true for $n = 1.2$.

Hence $P(n)$ is universally true.

(b) $P(1)$ holds good as R.H.S. $= 0$ and L.H.S. $= 0$

$$P(2) = \frac{1}{\log_x 2 . \log_x 2^2} = \frac{1}{2(\log_x 2)^2}$$

$$= \left(1 - \frac{1}{2}\right)\frac{1}{(\log_x 2)^2}$$

Assume $P(n) = \left(1 - \frac{1}{n}\right)\frac{1}{(\log_x 2)^2}$ ...(1)

$$P(n+1) = P(n) + \frac{1}{\log_x 2^n . \log_x 2^{n+1}}$$

Apply $\log p^q = q\log p$ on 2nd term

$$= \left(1 - \frac{1}{n}\right)\frac{1}{(\log_x 2)^2} + \frac{1}{n(n+1)} . \frac{1}{(\log_x 2)^2} \text{ by (1)}$$

$$= \left[1 - \frac{1}{n} + \left(\frac{1}{n} - \frac{1}{n+1}\right)\right]\frac{1}{(\log_x 2)^2}$$

$$= \left(1 - \frac{1}{n+1}\right)\frac{1}{(\log_x 2)^2}$$

$\therefore \quad P(n+1)$ holds good.

Hence the result is true universally.

8. (a) Let $P(n)$ be true for $n = m$

Also when $n = 1, (1+x)^1 = 1 + 1.x$. So in this case, inequality does not hold.

But when $n = 2$.

$\therefore \quad (1+x)^2 = 1 + 2x + x^2 > 1 + 2x$.

Thus $P(n)$ is true for $n = 2$.

$$(1+x)^m > 1 + mx \qquad \text{...(1)}$$

Since $x > -1$, multiplying by $x+1$,

$$P(m+1) = (1+x)^{m+1} = (1+x)^m (1+x)$$

$$> (1+mx)(1+x), \qquad \text{by (1)}$$

$$= 1 + (m+1)x + mx^2$$

$$> 1 + (m+1)x \quad \because \quad mx^2 > 0$$

Above relation shows that $P(n)$ is true for $n = m+1$.

Hence $P(n)$ is true universally if $n \geq 2$.

(b) From part (a) $(1+x)^1 > 1 + lx$

$\therefore \quad$ L.H.S. $> (1+lx)(1+my)(1+nz)$

$$= 1 + (lx + my + nz) + (lmxy + mnyz + nlzx) + lmnxyz.$$

$$> 1 + lx + my + nz.$$

9. Let $P(n)$ be true for $n = m$

$\therefore \quad (\cos\theta + i\sin\theta)^m = \cos m\theta + i\sin m\theta$

$\therefore \quad P(m+1) = (\cos\theta + i\sin\theta)^{m+1}$

$$= (\cos\theta + i\sin\theta)^m (\cos\theta + i\sin\theta)$$

$$= (\cos m\theta + i\sin m\theta)(\cos\theta + i\sin\theta)$$

$$= (\cos m\theta\cos\theta - \sin m\theta\sin\theta)$$

$$\qquad + i(\sin m\theta\cos\theta + \cos m\theta\sin\theta)$$

$$= \cos(m+1)\theta + i\sin(m+1)\theta.$$

Above relation shows that $P(n)$ is true for $n = m+1$.

Again when $n = 1$.

$$(\cos\theta + i\sin\theta)^1 = \cos 1.\theta + i\sin 1.\theta.$$

when $n = 2, (\cos\theta + i\sin\theta)^2$

$$= \cos^2\theta + i^2\sin^2\theta + 2i\sin\theta\cos\theta$$

$$= (\cos^2\theta - \sin^2\theta) + i(2\sin\theta\cos\theta)$$

$$= \cos 2\theta + i\sin 2\theta$$

Above relation shows that $P(n)$ is true for $n = 1, 2$.

Hence $P(n)$ is universally true.

10. The inequality clearly holds for $n = 1$ since $2 > 1$. Now assume

$$2^m > m \qquad \ldots(1)$$

But $2^m > 1$ for all positive integers m. $\qquad \ldots(2)$

Adding (1) and (2). we get

$$2^m + 2^m > m + 1 \ i.e., 2 \cdot 2^m > m + 1$$

or $\qquad 2^{m+1} > m + 1$.

Hence the inequality holds for $n = m + 1$.

Therefore the inequality $2^n > n$ holds for all natural numbers n by mathematical induction.

11. The inequality obviously does not hold for $n = 1$ and 2. But the inequality holds for $n = 3$, for we have

$$2^3 > 2 \cdot 3 + 1$$

Now assume

$$2^m > 2m + 1$$

where m is a natural number > 3.

But $2^m > 2$ for all $m > 1$.

Adding the two inequalities we obtain for $m > 3$.

$$2^m + 2^m > 2m + 1 + 2$$

that is, $2^{m+1} > 2 (m + 1) + 1$.

Hence the inequality holds for $n = m + 1$.

It follows by mathematical induction that the inequality

$$2^n > 2n + 1 \text{ holds for all natural numbers } n \geq 3.$$

12. The inequality holds for $n = 1$, since $2^1 > 1^2$.

The inequality does not holds for $n = 2$, since $2^2 = 2^2$.

The inequality does not holds for $n = 3$, since $2^3 < 3^2$.

The inequality does not holds for $n = 4$, since $2^4 = 4^2$.

The inequality holds for $n = 5$, since $2^5 > 5^2$.

The inequality holds for $n = 6$, since $2^6 > 6^2$.

Now assume

$$2^m > m^2$$

where m is a natural number ≥ 5. $\qquad \ldots(1)$

But problem 11, we have that

$$2^m > 2m + 1 \text{ for } m \geq 3. \qquad \ldots(2)$$

Adding the inequalities (1) and (2), we obtain

$$2^m + 2^m > m^2 + 2m + 1$$

that is, $2^{m+1} > (m + 1)^2$

Hence the inequality holds for $n = m + 1$.

It follows by mathematical induction that the inequality $2^n > n^2$ holds for $n = 1$ and for all natural numbers $n \geq 5$.

13. Let $P(n)$ be true for $n = m$, that is , we assume that $5^{2m} - 1$ is divisible by 24 so that

$$\frac{5^{2m} - 1}{24} = k, \text{ say, where } k \in N.$$

$\therefore \quad 5^{2m} = 24k + 1 \qquad \ldots(1)$

Now $P(m + 1) = 5^{2(m+1)} - 1 = 5^{2m} \cdot 5^2 - 1$

$$= (24k + 1) \cdot 25 - 1, \qquad \text{by (1)}$$
$$= (24)(25) k + (25 - 1) = 24 [25k + 1]$$

$\therefore \quad \dfrac{P(m+1)}{24} = 25k + 1 \in N,$

$\therefore \quad P(n)$ is true for $n = m + 1$.

Also when $n = 1, 5^{2 \cdot 1} - 1 = 25 - 1 = 24 \cdot 1$

when $n = 2, 5^{2 \cdot 2} - 1 = 625 - 1.$

$$= 624 = 24 (26)$$

Above relation shows that $P(n)$ is divisible by 24 for $n = 1; 2$.

Hence $P(n)$ is universally true.

14. Proceed as in Q. 13.

15. Let $P(n) = 7^{2n} + 2^{3n-3} 3^{n-1}$

For $n = 1, P(1) = 7^2 + 2^0 \cdot 3^0$.

$$= 49 + 1 = 50 = 25 \times 2$$

Thus $P(1)$ is divisible by 25.

Now assume $P(m)$ is divisible by 25 so that we may write

$$7^{2m} + 2^{3m-3} \cdot 3^{m-1} = 25k \qquad \ldots(1)$$

when k is a positive integer.

Then $P(m + 1) = 7^{2(m+1)} + 2^{3(m+1)-3} \cdot 3^{(m+1)-1}$

$$= 7^{2m} \cdot 7^2 + 2^{3m-3} \cdot 2^3 \cdot 3^{m-1} \cdot 3$$
$$= 49 [25k - 2^{3m-3} \cdot 3^{m-1}] + 24 \cdot 2^{3m-3} \cdot 3^{m-1} \text{ by (1)}$$
$$= 49 \cdot 25k - (49 - 24) \cdot 2^{3m-3} \cdot 3^{m-1}$$
$$= 25 [49k - 2^{3m-3} \cdot 3^{m-1}]$$

Hence $P(m + 1)$ is divisible by 25.

It follows by mathematical induction that $P(n)$ is divisible by 25 for all positive integers n.

16. $P(1) = 18, P(2) = 45$ etc.

Divisible by 9. Now assume that $P(n)$ holds.

$$4^n + 15n - 1 = 9k \qquad \ldots(1)$$
$$P(n + 1) = 4^{n+1} + 15(n + 1) - 1$$
$$= 4 \cdot 4^n + 15n + 14$$
$$= 4(9k - 15n + 1) + 15n + 14, \qquad \text{by (1)}$$
$$= 36k - 45n + 18 = 9(4k - 5n + 2)$$

$\therefore \quad P(n + 1)$ holds good.

17. Let $A_n = 11^{n+2} + 12^{2n+1}$

The assertion is valid for $n = 1$, since

$$A_1 = (11)^{1+2} + (12)^{2+1} = 3059 = 133 \times 23.$$

Assume that the assertion holds for $n = m$, that is, let

$$A_m = 11^{m+2} + 12^{2m+1} = 133k \qquad \ldots(1)$$

where k is a positive integer.

Then $A_{m+1} = 11^{m+3} + 12^{2(m+1)+1}$

$= 11^{m+3} + 12^{2m+3}$

$= 11.11^{m+2} + 144.12^{2m+1}$

$= 11(133k - 12^{2m+1}) + 144.12^{2m+1}$ by (1)

$= 11.(133k) + (144 - 11) 12^{2m+1}$

$= 11.133k + 133.12^{2m+1}$

$= 133(11k + 12^{2m+1})$.

This shows that A_{m+1} is divisible by 133. Hence by induction, A_n is divisible by 133 for all natural numbers n.

18. (a) Let $A_n = 5^{2n+2} - 24n - 25$

   Then $A_1 = 5^4 - 24 - 25 = 576$.

   Thus A_1 is divisible by 576.

   Now assume that A_m is divisible by 576, that is, assume

   $$A_m = 5^{2m+2} - 24m - 25 = 576k \qquad ...(1)$$

   where k is a positive integer.

   Then $A_{m+1} = 5^{2(m+1)+2} - 24(m+1) - 25$

   $= 5^2 . 5^{2m+2} - 24m - 49$

   $= 25[5^{2m+2} - 24m - 25] + 25.24m$
   $\qquad\qquad + 25.25 - 24m - 49$

   $= 25 A_m + 576m + 576$

   $= 25.576k + 576(m+1)$, by (1)

   $= 576(25k + m + 1)$.

   Hence A_{m+1} is divisible by 576.

   It follows by mathematical induction that A_n is divisible by 576 for all positive integers.

   (b) Let $A_n = 2.7^n + 3.5^n - 5$.

   Then $A_1 = 2.7 + 3.5 - 5 = 14 + 15 - 5 = 24$.

   Hence A_1 is divisible by 24.

   Now assume that A_m is divisible by 24 so that we may write

   $$A_m = 2.7^m + 3.5^m - 5 = 24k, \quad k \in N \quad ...(1)$$

   Then $A_{m+1} - A_m = 2(7^{m+1} - 7^m)$
   $$\qquad\qquad + 3.(5^{m+1} - 5^m) - 5 + 5$$

   $= 2.7^m (7-1) + 3.5^m (5-1) = 12(7^m + 5^m)$

   Since 7^m and 5^m are odd integers for all $m \in N$, their sum must be an even integer, say

   $$7^m + 5^m = 2p, p \in N.$$

   Hence $A_{m+1} - A_m = 12.2p = 24p$

   or $A_{m+1} = A_m + 24p = 24k + 24p$, by (1).

   Hence A_{m+1} is divisible by 24.

   If follows by mathematical induction that A_n is divisible by 24 for all $n \in N$.

19. Let $P(n)$ be true for $n = m$, that is, we assume that $\dfrac{a^m - b^m}{a - b}$ is divisible by $a - b$.

$\therefore \quad \dfrac{a^m - b^m}{a - b} = f(a,b)$, say.

or $a^m - b^m = f(a,b)(a-b)$

or $a^m = b^m + f(a,b)(a-b)$ \qquad\qquad ...(1)

Now $P(m+1) = a^{m+1} - b^{m+1} = a^m.a - b^m.b$

$= a[b^m + f(a,b)(a-b)] - b^m.b$,   by (1)

$= b^m(a-b) + a f(a,b)(a-b)$

$= (a-b)(b^m + a f(a,b))$.

$\therefore \quad a^{m+1} - b^{m+1}$ is also divisible by $a - b$.

Hence $P(n)$ is true for $n = m + 1$.

Also when $n = 1$, we get $a - b$ which is divisible by $a - b$.

when $n = 2$, we get $a^2 - b^2$ which is also divisible by $a - b$.

Hence $P(n)$ is universally true.

20. $x^2 - y^2 = (x+y)(x-y)$

Hence $x^2 - y^2$ is a divisible by $x + y$.

Thus the given statement holds for $n = 2$.

Now assume $x^m - y^m = (x+y) f(x,y)$ \qquad ...(1)

where $f(x,y)$ is a polynomial of degree $m - 1$ in x and y and m is an even integer.

Then $x^{m+2} - y^{m+2} = x^{m+2} - x^m y^2 + x^m y^2 - y^{m+2}$

$= x^m(x^2 - y^2) + y^2(x^m - y^m)$

$= (x+y)(x-y) x^m + y^2(x+y) f(x,y)$,   by (1)

$= (x+y)[(x-y) x^m + y^2 f(x,y)]$

Hence $x^{m+2} - y^{m+2}$ is divisible by $x + y$.

thus we have shown that $x^n - y^n$ is divisible by $x + y$ for $n = 2$ and whenever it is divisible by $x + y$ for any even integer, it is divisible by $x + y$ for the next even integer. Hence by mathematical induction $x^n - y^n$ is divisible by $x + y$ when n is any even integer.

21. Let $f(n) = p^{n+1} + (p+1)^{2n-1}$

We have $f(1) = p^2 + p + 1$ so that $f(1)$ is divisible by $p^2 + p + 1$.

Now assume that $f(m)$ is divisible by $p^2 + p + 1$ i.e., we assume that

$$p^{m+1} + (p+1)^{2m-1} = k(p^2 + p + 1) \qquad ...(1)$$

Now $f(m+1) = p^{m+2} + (p+1)^{2m+2-1}$

$= p^{m+2} + (p+1)^{2m-1} (p+1)^2$

$= p^{m+2} + [k(p^2 + p + 1) - p^{m+1}](p+1)^2$ by (1)

$= p^{m+2} - (p+1)^2 p^{m+1} + k(p+1)^2 (p^2 + p + 1)$

$$= p^{m+1} (p - p^2 - 2p - 1) + k (p+1)^2 (p^2 + p + 1)$$
$$= (p^2 + p + 1) [k (p+1)^2 - p^{m+1}]$$

Hence $f(m+1)$ is divisible by $p^2 + p + 1$.

∴ By induction, $f(x)$ is divisible by $p^2 + p + 1$ for all $n \in N$.

22. Let $A_n = x(x^{n-1} - na^{n-1}) + a^n (n-1)$ ...(1)

For $n = 2$, $A_2 = x(x - 2a) + a^2$
$$= x^2 - 2ax + a^2 = (x - a)^2.$$

Thus A_2 is divisible by $(x - a)^2$.

Now assume that A_m is divisible by $(x - a)^2$ for $m \geq 2$, that is, assume

$$A_m = x(x^{m-1} - ma^{m-1}) + a^m (m-1)$$
$$= (x - a)^2 f(x)$$

so that $x^m = mxa^{m-1} - a^m (m-1) + (x-a)^2 f(x)$
   ...(2)

We then have
$$A_{m+1} = x[x^m - (m+1) a^m] + a^{m+1} m$$
$$= x \cdot x^m - (m+1) xa^m + ma^{m+1}$$
$$= x[mxa^{m-1} - a^m (m-1) + (x-a)^2 f(x)]$$
$$\qquad - (m+1) xa^m + ma^{m+1}, \quad \text{by (2)}$$
$$= ma^{m-1} [(x^2 - 2xa + a^2) + x(x-a)^2 f(x)]$$
$$= ma^{m-1} (x-a)^2 + x(x-a)^2 f(x)$$
$$= (x-a)^2 [ma^{m-1} + xf(x)],$$

After simplification.

This shows that A_{m+1} is divisible by $(x - a)^2$.

Hence by induction, A_n is divisible by $(x - a)^2$ for all positive integers $n > 1$.

23. We first prove that the square of every odd number greater than 1 when divided by 8 leaves 1 as a remainder.

First odd integer greater than 1 is 3 and
$$3^2 = 9 = 8.1 + 1$$

Thus the square of 3 when divided by 8 leaves 1 as remainder.

Now assume $(2m+1)^2 = 8k + 1$ ...(1)

where k is a positive integer.

We then have
$$(2m+3)^2 = (2m+1+2)^2$$
$$(2m+1)^2 + 4(2m+1) + 4$$

so that $(2m+3)^2 = (2m+1)^2 + 8(m+1)$
$$= 8k + 1 + 8(m+1), \qquad \text{by (1)}$$
$$= 8(k + m + 1) + 1.$$

Hence $(2m+3)^2$ when divided by 8 leaves 1 as remainder. It follows by mathematical induction that for all $n, (2n+1)^2$ when divided by 8 leaves 1 as a remainder, that is, we have proved that
$$(2n+1)^2 = 8k + 1 \qquad ...(2)$$

Let us now assume that $(2n+1)^{2m}$, when m is any positive integer, when divided by 8 leaves 1 as remainder, that is, assume
$$(2n+1)^{2m} = 8p + 1. \qquad ...(3)$$

where p is positive integer.

Then $(2n+1)^{2m+2} = (2n+1)^{2m} (2n+1)^2$
$$= (8p + 1)(8k + 1) \qquad \text{by (2) and (3)}$$
$$= 8(8pk + p + k) + 1.$$

This shows that $(2n+1)^{2m+2}$ when divided by 8 leaves 1 as remainder. Hence by mathematical induction the required assertion is proved.

Alternative : Let any odd number be chosen as $(2m+1)$, then we have to prove that
$$P(n) = [(2m+1)^2]^n = 8p + 1$$

$P(n) = (2m+1)^{2n} - 1$ is divisible by 8.

$P(1) = (2m+1)^2 - 1$
$$= (2m+1+1)(2m+1-1)$$
$$= 2m.2(m+1) = 4m(m+1) = 8p \qquad ...(1)$$

Since $m(m+1)$ being the product of two consecutive natural numbers, is always even say $2p$.

Now let us assume that
$$P(k) = (2m+1)^{2k} - 1 = 8q \qquad ...(2)$$

∴ $P(k+1) = (2m+1)^{2(k+1)} - 1$
$$= (2m+1)^{2k} (2m+1)^1 - 1 \cdot$$
$$= (8q + 1)(8p + 1) - 1, \qquad \text{by (1) and (2)}$$
$$= 64pq + 8p + 8q$$
$$= 8(8pq + p + q)$$
$$= 8r, \qquad \text{say}.$$

Hence the formula is universally true.

24. (a) The sum $1^3 + 2^3 + 3^3$ i.e., 36 is divisible by 9. Hence the assertion is valid when the first of three successive numbers is 1.

Now let the sum
$$P(m) = m^3 + (m+1)^3 + (m+2)^3$$

where m is some natural number, be divisible by 9, that is, assume
$$m^3 + (m+1)^3 + (m+2)^3 = 9k.$$

where k is a positive integer.

We now have
$$P(m+1) = (m+1)^3 + (m+2)^3 + (m+3)^3$$
$$= (m+1)^3 + (m+2)^3 + m^3 + 9m^2 + 27m + 27$$

$$= m^3 + (m+1)^3 + (m+2)^3 + 9(m^2 + 3m + 3)$$
$$= 9k + 9(m^2 + 3m + 3), \qquad \text{by (1)}$$
$$= 9(k + m^2 + 3m + 3).$$

Hence by induction, the required assertion is proved.

(b) $\quad {}^nC_r = \dfrac{n}{r} \, {}^{n-1}C_{r-1}$

$$\therefore \quad {}^{mp}C_r = \frac{mp}{r} \, {}^{mp-1}C_{r-1} = \left[\frac{m \cdot {}^{mp-1}C_{r-1}}{r} \right] p$$

L.H.S. is an integer $\Rightarrow$ R.H.S. is an integer and p is prime such that p does not divide r.

$$\therefore \quad \frac{{}^{mp}C_r}{p} = \text{integer which is turn means that } p$$

divides ${}^{mp}C_r$.

Proof by Induction :

For $m = 1$, ${}^{mp}C_r = {}^p C_r$

$$= \frac{p(p-1)(p-2)\dots r \text{ factors}}{r(r-1)(r-2)\dots r \text{ factors}}$$

Above is clearly divisible by $p \, . \, (r < p)$ ...(1)

Assume ${}^{mp}C_r$ is divisible by p. ...(2)

We shall prove that ${}^{(m+1)p}C_r$ is also divisible by p to complete the proof.

Now $(1+x)^{(m+1)p} = (1+x)^{mp}(1+x)^p$

Expanding both sides and equating the coefficient of x^r on both sides, we get

$${}^{(m+1)p}C_r = 1 \cdot {}^p C_r + {}^{mp}C_1 \, {}^p C_{r-1} + {}^{mp}C_2 \, {}^p C_{r-2} + \dots$$

R.H.S. is clearly divisible by p by (1) and (2) and hence L.H.S. i.e., ${}^{(m+1)p}C_r$ is also divisible by p.

25. Let $f(n) = n(n^2 - 1)$.

Then $f(1) = 0$, $f(3) = 24$.

Hence $f(1)$ and $f(3)$ are divisible by 24. Now assume that $f(n)$ is divisible by 24, that is, we assume that

$$f(n) = n(n^2 - 1) = 24k \qquad \text{...(1)}$$

When n is odd next odd number will be $n + 2$.

$$f(n+2) = (n+2)[(n+2)^2 - 1]$$
$$= (n+2)(n+3)(n+1)$$
$$= n^3 + 6n^2 + 11n + 6$$
$$= (24k + n) + 6n^2 + 11n + 6, \qquad \text{by (1)}$$
$$= 24k + 6n^2 + 12n + 6$$
$$= 24k + 6(n+1)^2 \quad \because \; n = \text{odd}$$
$$= 24k + 6(\text{even})^2 \quad \therefore \; n+1 = \text{even} = 2d$$
$$= 24k + 6(2d)^2 = 24(k + d^2). \quad \textbf{Hence proved.}$$

26. (a) Let $S_n = \dfrac{1}{n+1} + \dfrac{1}{n+2} + \dots + \dfrac{1}{2n}$.

For $n = 2$, we have

$$\frac{1}{3} + \frac{1}{4} = \frac{7}{12} = \frac{14}{24} > \frac{13}{24}.$$

Hence the inequality holds for $n = 2$.

Now assume $S_m > \dfrac{13}{24}$ for some positive integer $m > 1$.

We have $S_m = \dfrac{1}{m+1} + \dfrac{1}{m+2} + \dots + \dfrac{1}{2m}$

and $\qquad S_{m+1} = \dfrac{1}{m+2} + \dfrac{1}{m+3} + \dots$

$$+ \frac{1}{2m} + \frac{1}{2m+1} + \frac{1}{2m+2}$$

$$\therefore \quad S_{m+1} - S_m = \frac{1}{2m+1} + \frac{1}{2m+2} - \frac{1}{m+1}$$

that is, $S_{m+1} - S_m = \dfrac{1}{2(m+1)(2m+1)}$

But $\dfrac{1}{2(m+1)(2m+1)} > 0$ for any natural number

m. It follows that

$$S_{m+1} - S_m > 0, \text{ that is, } S_{m+1} > S_m.$$

But $S_m > \dfrac{13}{24}$ by our assumption.

$$\therefore \quad S_{m+1} > \frac{13}{24}.$$

Hence by mathematical induction. The given inequality holds for all natural numbers $n > 1$.

(b) Result is obviously true for $n = 1$. Assume $P(n)$ i.e.,

$$P(n) = n \cdot 1 + (n-1) \cdot 2 + \dots + 2(n-1) + 1 \cdot n$$
$$= \frac{n}{6}(n+1)(n+2)$$

$$P(n+1) = (n+1) \cdot 1 + n \cdot 2 + \dots + 3(n-1)$$
$$+ 2 \cdot n + 1 \cdot (n+1)$$

$$\therefore \quad P(n+1) - P(n) = 1 \cdot 1 + 1 \cdot 2 + 1 \cdot 3 + \dots$$
$$+ 1 \cdot (n-1) + 1 \cdot n + 1 \cdot (n+1)$$
$$= 1 + 2 + 3 + \dots + n + 1 \cdot (n+1)$$
$$= \frac{n(n+1)}{2} + (n+1) = \frac{(n+1)(n+2)}{2}$$

$$\therefore \quad P(n+1) = \frac{(n+1)(n+2)}{2} + P(n)$$
$$= \frac{(n+1)(n+2)}{2} + \frac{n(n+1)(n+2)}{6}$$
$$= \frac{(n+1)(n+2)}{2}\left[1 + \frac{n}{3}\right]$$
$$= \frac{(n+1)(n+2)(n+3)}{6} = \frac{N}{6}(N+1)(N+2)$$

Thus $P(n+1)$ also holds good.

27. (i) The identity is valid for $n = 1$, for we have

$$\cos \alpha \, \frac{\sin 2\alpha}{2 \sin \alpha} = \frac{2 \sin \alpha \cos \alpha}{2 \sin \alpha} = \cos \alpha.$$

Now let the identity hold for $n = m$, that is, let

$$\cos \alpha \cos 2\alpha \ldots \cos 2^{m-1}\alpha = \frac{\sin 2^m \alpha}{2^m \sin \alpha}$$

Multiplying both sides of this identity by $\cos 2^m \alpha$, we obtain

$$\cos \alpha \cos 2\alpha \ldots \cos 2^{m-1}\alpha \cos 2^m \alpha$$

$$= \frac{\sin 2^m \alpha}{2^m \sin \alpha} \cos 2^m \alpha$$

$$= \frac{2 \sin 2^m \alpha \cos 2^m \alpha}{2^{m+1} \sin \alpha} = \frac{\sin 2^{m+1}\alpha}{2^{m+1}\sin \alpha}$$

Thus the identity holds for $n = m+1$.

Hence the identity is proved for all positive integers n by mathematical induction.

(ii) $P_1 = \dfrac{\sqrt{3}}{2}$, $P_2 = \sqrt{3}$ etc.

Also for $n = 1$, R.H.S. $= 2 . \dfrac{1}{2} . \dfrac{\sqrt{3}}{2} = \dfrac{\sqrt{3}}{2}$

and for $n = 2$, R.H.S. $= 2 \dfrac{\sqrt{3}}{2} .1 = \sqrt{3}$.

∴ Equality holds for $n = 1$ and $n = 2$.

Now let the equality hold for any $n > 2$.

Then $P_{n+1} = P_n + \sin (n+1) \dfrac{\pi}{3}$

$$= 2 \sin \frac{n\pi}{6} \sin (n+1) \frac{\pi}{6} + 2 \sin (n+1) \frac{\pi}{6} \cos (n+1) \frac{\pi}{6}$$

$$= 2 \sin (n+1) \frac{\pi}{6} \left[\cos (n+1) \frac{\pi}{6} - \cos \left(\frac{\pi}{2} + \frac{n\pi}{6} \right) \right]$$

∵ $\sin \theta = -\cos \left(\dfrac{\pi}{2} + \theta \right)$ **(Note)**

$$= 2 \sin (n+1) \frac{\pi}{6} \left[\cos (n+1) \frac{\pi}{6} - \cos (n+3) \frac{\pi}{6} \right]$$

$$= 2 \sin (n+1) \frac{\pi}{6} \left[2 \sin (2n+4 \frac{\pi}{12} \sin \frac{\pi}{6} \right]$$

Put $\sin \dfrac{\pi}{6} = \dfrac{1}{2}$

$$= 2 \sin (n+1) \frac{\pi}{6} \sin (n+2) \frac{\pi}{6}.$$

(iii) $P(1) = \sin A \le 1 \sin \dfrac{A_1}{1}$

$P(2) = \sin A_1 + \sin A_2$

$$= 2 \sin \frac{A_1 + A_2}{2} \cos \frac{A_1 - A_2}{2} \le 2 \sin \frac{A_1 + A_2}{2}$$

Assume $P(n)$ i.e.

$$\sin A_1 + \sin A_2 + \ldots + \sin A_n$$

$$\le \sin \left(\frac{A_1 + A_2 \ldots A_n}{n} \right) \qquad \ldots (1)$$

To prove that $P(n+1)$ also holds good.

i.e. $\sin A_1 + \sin A_2 + \sin A_n + \ldots \sin A_{n+1}$

$$\le \left(\frac{A_1 + A_2 + \ldots A_{n+1}}{n+1} \right)$$

$P(n+1) = P(n) + \sin A_{n+1}$

$$\le n \sin \left(\frac{A_1 + A_2 + \ldots A_n}{n} \right) + \sin A_{n+1}$$

$$= (n+1) \left[\frac{n}{n+1} \sin \left(\frac{A_1 + A_2 + \ldots A_n}{n} \right) \right.$$

$$\left. + \frac{1}{n+1} \sin A_{n+1} \right]$$

$$= (n+1) \left[\frac{n}{n+1} \sin \left(\frac{A_1 + A_2 + \ldots + A_n}{n} \right) \right.$$

$$\left. + \left(1 - \frac{n}{n+1} \right) \sin A_{n+1} \right]$$

$$= (n+1) [p \sin x + (1-p) \sin y]$$

where $p = \dfrac{n}{n+1}$ and $1 - p = \dfrac{1}{n+1}$

$$\le (n+1) \sin [px + (1-p) y] \text{ by given rule}$$

$$= (n+1) \sin \left[\frac{n}{n+1} . \frac{A_1 + A_2 + \ldots A_n}{n} \right.$$

$$\left. + \frac{1}{n+1} A_{n+1} \right]$$

$$= (n+1) \sin \left[\frac{A_1 + A_2 + \ldots + A_{n+1}}{n+1} \right]$$

(iv) $P(1)$ and $P(2)$ can easily be shown to hold good. Assume

$$P(m) = \tan^{-1} \frac{m}{m+2}$$

∴ $P(m+1) = P(m) + T_{m+1}$

$$= \tan^{-1} \frac{m}{m+2} + \tan^{-1} \frac{1}{(m+1)^2 + (m+1) + 1}$$

$$= \tan^{-1} \frac{m}{m+2} + \tan^{-1} \frac{1}{m^2 + 3m + 3}$$

$$= \tan^{-1} \left(\frac{\dfrac{m}{m+2} + \dfrac{1}{m^2 + 3m + 3}}{1 - \dfrac{m}{(m+2)(m^2+3m+3)}} \right)$$

$$= \tan^{-1} \left(\frac{m^3 + 3m^2 + 4m + 2}{m^3 + 5m^2 + 8m + 6} \right)$$

$$= \tan^{-1} \frac{(m+1)(m^2 + 2m + 2)}{(m+3)(m^2 + 2m + 2)}$$

$$= \tan^{-1} \frac{m+1}{(m+1) + 2}$$

Thus $P(m+1)$ holds good. Hence the formula is universelly true.

It is same question as proved above.

$\because \quad \dfrac{\pi}{4} = \tan^{-1} 1$

$\therefore \quad \text{R.H.S.} = \tan^{-1} \dfrac{(n+1)-1}{1+(n+1)\cdot 1} = \tan^{-1} \dfrac{n}{n+2}$

(v) $P(1) = \tan^{-1} \dfrac{x}{1.2+x^2} = \tan^{-1} \dfrac{x/2}{1+(x^2/2)}$

$= \tan^{-1} \dfrac{x-(x/2)}{1+x\cdot(x/2)} = \tan^{-1} x - \tan^{-1} \dfrac{x}{1+1}$

Thus $P(1)$ holds.

Assume $P(n) = \tan^{-1} x - \tan^{-1} \dfrac{x}{n+1}$ $\qquad$ ...(1)

$P(n+1) = P(n) + \tan^{-1} \dfrac{x}{(n+1)(n+2)+x^2}$

$= P(n) + \tan^{-1} \dfrac{\dfrac{x}{(n+1)(n+2)}}{1+\dfrac{x}{n+1}\cdot\dfrac{x}{n+2}}$

$= P_n + \tan^{-1} \dfrac{\left[\dfrac{x}{n+1}-\dfrac{x}{n+2}\right]}{1+\dfrac{x}{n+1}\cdot\dfrac{x}{n+2}}$ $\qquad$ ...(2)

$= \left(\tan^{-1} x - \tan^{-1} \dfrac{x}{n+1}\right)$

$\qquad\qquad + \left(\tan^{-1} \dfrac{x}{n+1} - \tan^{-1} \dfrac{x}{n+2}\right)$

$\qquad\qquad\qquad\qquad$ by (1) and (2)

$= \tan^{-1} x - \tan^{-1} \dfrac{x}{n+2}$

(vi) $P(1), P(2)$ can be easily verified and $P(n)$ is assumed.

Now $P(n+1) = P(n) + \cos(n+1)x$

$= \dfrac{\cos(n+1)\dfrac{x}{2}\sin n\dfrac{x}{2}}{\sin\dfrac{x}{2}} + \cos(n+1)x$

$= \dfrac{1}{2\sin\dfrac{x}{2}}\left[2\sin\dfrac{nx}{2}\cos(n+1)\dfrac{x}{2}\right.$

$\qquad\qquad\qquad\left. + 2\sin\dfrac{x}{2}\cos(2n+2)\dfrac{x}{2}\right]$

Note : $(2n+2)\dfrac{x}{2}$.

Now $2\sin A\cos B = \sin(A+B)+\sin(A-B)$

$= \dfrac{1}{2\sin\dfrac{x}{2}}\left[\sin(2n+1)\dfrac{x}{2}+\sin\left(-\dfrac{x}{2}\right)+\sin(2n+3)\dfrac{x}{2}\right.$

$\qquad\qquad\qquad\qquad\left. + \sin\left\{-(2n+1)\dfrac{x}{2}\right\}\right]$

$= \dfrac{1}{2\sin\dfrac{x}{2}}\left[\sin(2n+3)\dfrac{x}{2}-\sin\dfrac{x}{2}\right]$

$= \dfrac{1}{2\sin\dfrac{x}{2}}\cdot 2\sin(n+1)\dfrac{x}{2}\cos(n+2)\dfrac{x}{2}$

$= \dfrac{\cos(N+1)\dfrac{x}{2}\sin N\dfrac{x}{2}}{\sin\dfrac{x}{2}}, \text{ where } N = n+1$

(vii) $\sin x = \dfrac{\sin^2 x}{\sin x} = \sin x \quad \therefore \quad P(1)$ is true.

Assume $P(m)$ holds good.

$P(m+1) = P(m) + \sin(2m+1)x$

$= \dfrac{\sin^2 mx}{\sin x} + \sin(2m+1)x$

$= \dfrac{1}{2\sin x}[2\sin^2 mx + 2\sin x\sin(2m+1)x]$

$= \dfrac{1}{2\sin x}[(1-\cos 2mx)+\cos 2mx-\cos(2m+2)x]$

$= \dfrac{1}{2\sin x}[1-\cos(2m+2)x]$

$= \dfrac{1}{2\sin x}[2\sin^2(m+)x] = \dfrac{\sin^2(m+1)x}{\sin x}$

Thus $P(m+1)$ also holds good.

(viii) For $n=1$ R.H.S. $= \cot\alpha - 2\cot 2\alpha$

$= \dfrac{1}{\tan\alpha} - 2\cdot\dfrac{1-\tan^2\alpha}{2\tan\alpha}$

$= \dfrac{1-(1-\tan^2\alpha)}{\tan\alpha} = \tan\alpha = \text{L.H.S.}$

Hence $P(1)$ is true.

Assume $P(n)$.

$\therefore \quad P(n+1) = P(n) + T_{n+1}$

$= (\cot\alpha - 2^n\cot 2^n\alpha) + 2^n\tan 2^n\alpha.$

$= \cot\alpha - 2^n\left[\dfrac{1}{T}-T\right], T = \tan\theta, \theta = 2^n\alpha$

$= \cot\alpha - 2^{n+1}\cdot\dfrac{1+T^2}{2T}$

$= \cot\alpha - 2^{n+1}\dfrac{1}{\tan 2\theta}$

$= \cot\alpha - 2^{n+1}\cot 2^{n+1}\alpha$

$\because \quad$ If $T = \tan A$, then $\dfrac{2T}{1-T^2} = \tan 2A$ etc.

(ix) Proceed as in last part.

(x) $\tan A - \tan B = \dfrac{\sin(A-B)}{\cos A\cos B}$

For $P(1)$,

$\text{L.H.S.} = \dfrac{2\sin\theta}{\cos\theta+\cos 3\theta} = \dfrac{2\sin\theta}{2\cos\theta\cdot\cos 2\theta}$

$= \dfrac{\sin(2\theta-\theta)}{\cos\theta\cos 2\theta} = \tan 2\theta - \tan\theta$

R.H.S. $= \tan 2\theta - \tan \theta$ for $n = 1$.

thus $P(1)$ holds good. Assume $P(n)$.

$$P(n+1) = P(n) + \frac{2\sin\theta}{\cos\theta + \cos(2n+3)\theta}$$

$$= P(n) + \frac{2\sin\{(n+2)\theta - (n+1)\theta\}}{2\cos(n+2)\theta\cos(n+1)\theta}$$

$$= \{\tan(n+1)\theta - \tan\theta\} + \{\tan(n+2)\theta$$
$$- \tan(n+1)\theta\}$$

$$= \tan(n+2)\theta - \tan\theta$$

Hence $P(n+1)$ also holds good.

(xi) $\cot A - \cot B = \dfrac{\sin(B-A)}{\sin A \sin B}$

For $P(1)$, L.H.S. $= \dfrac{1}{\sin 2x}$

R.H.S. $= \cot x - \cot 2x = \dfrac{\sin(2x - x)}{\sin x \sin 2x} = \dfrac{1}{\sin 2x}$

Thus $P(1)$ holds good. Assume $P(n)$.

$$P(n+1) = P(n) + \frac{1}{\sin 2^{n+1} x}$$

$$= P(n) + \frac{\sin 2^n x}{\sin 2^n x \sin 2^{n+1} x}$$

$$= P(n) + \frac{\sin(2^{n+1} - 2^n)x}{\sin 2^n x \sin 2^{n+1} x}$$

$$= (\cot x - \cot 2^n x) + (\cot 2^n x - \cot 2^{n+1} x)$$

$$= \cot x - \cot 2^{n+1} x$$

Thus $P(n+1)$ also holds good.

28. Do your self.

29. (i) For $n = 2$, the inequality is valid since

$$2! < \left(\frac{2+1}{2}\right)^2 \ i.e., 2 < \frac{9}{4}.$$

Now suppose $m! < \left(\dfrac{m+1}{2}\right)^m$ ...(1)

We shall prove that $(m+1)! < \left(\dfrac{m+2}{2}\right)^{m+1}$

We have,

$$(m+1)! = (m+1)\, m! < (m+1)\left(\frac{m+1}{2}\right)^m \quad ...(2)$$

by (1)

We now prove that

$$(m+1)\left(\frac{m+1}{2}\right)^m < \left(\frac{m+2}{2}\right)^{m+1} \quad ...(3)$$

Inequality (3) can clearly be rewritten as

$$\frac{2^{m+1}}{2^m} < \left(\frac{m+2}{m+1}\right)^{m+1}$$

or $\quad 2 < \left(1 + \dfrac{1}{m+1}\right)^{m+1}$

But by the binomial theorem

$$\left(1 + \frac{1}{m+1}\right)^{m+1} = 1 + (m+1)\frac{1}{m+1} + ... > 2.$$

So the inequality (3) holds. It now follows from (2) and (3) that

$$(m+1)! < \left(\frac{m+2}{2}\right)^{m+1}$$

The inequality thus holds for $n = m+1$.

Hence the inequality $n! < \left(\dfrac{n+1}{2}\right)^n$ holds for all

natural numbers $n > 1$.

(ii) We can verify for $n = 2$ as in part (i).

Assume $P(n)$ i.e.

$$\frac{(2n)!}{(n!)^2} > \frac{4n}{2n+1} \quad ...(1)$$

$$P(n+1) = \frac{(2n+2)!}{[(n+1)!]^2}$$

$$= \frac{(2n+2)(2n+1)}{(n+1)^2}\frac{(2n)!}{(n!)^2}$$

$$= \frac{2(2n+1)}{n+1}P(n) > \frac{2(2n+1)}{n+1}\cdot\frac{4n}{2n+1} \quad \text{by (1)}$$

$$= \frac{8n}{n+1}$$

We have to prove $P(n+1) > \dfrac{4(n+1)}{2n+3}$

or $\quad \dfrac{8n}{n+1} > \dfrac{4(n+1)}{2n+3}$

or $\quad 2n(2n+3) - (n^2 + 2n + 1) > 0$

or $\quad 3n^2 + 3n + n - 1 > 0$

or $\quad 3n(n+1) + (n-1) > 0$

Above is true for $n > 1$.

(iii) $P(2)$ holds good as ${}^4C_2 = 6 > \dfrac{16}{3}$

Assume $P(n)$.

$$P(n+1) = {}^{2n+2}C_{n+1} = \frac{(2n+2)!}{(n+1)!(n+1)!}$$

$$= \frac{(2n+2)(2n+1)}{(n+1)\cdot(n+1)}\cdot\frac{(2n)!}{n!\,n!}$$

or $\quad \dfrac{2(2n+1)}{(n+1)}{}^{2n}C_n > \dfrac{2(2n+1)}{(n+1)}\dfrac{4^n}{n+1}$

Now $P(n+1)$ will hold good if we show that

$$\frac{2(2n+1)}{(n+1)(n+1)}\cdot 4^n > \frac{4^{n+1}}{(n+2)}$$

or $\quad (2n+1)(n+2) > 2(n+1)^2$

or $\quad 2n^2 + 5n + 2 > 2n^2 + 4n + 2$

or $\quad 5 > 4$ which is true.

Hence $P(n+1)$ holds good.

(iv) $P(0), P(1)$ clearly hold good.

$$P(2) = 1 + \frac{1}{2} + \frac{1}{3} + \frac{1}{4} = \frac{25}{12} > \frac{24}{12} = 2 = 1 + \frac{2}{2}$$

Thus $P(2)$ also holds good.

Assume $P(n)$.

$$P(n+1) = \left(1 + \frac{1}{2} + \frac{1}{3} + \frac{1}{4} + \ldots + \frac{1}{2^n}\right) + \ldots + \frac{1}{2^{n+1}}$$

$$= P(n) + \left(\frac{1}{1+2^n} + \frac{1}{2+2^n} + \ldots + \frac{1}{2^n + 2^n}\right)$$

The 2nd bracket contains $1 . 2 . 3 \ldots 2^n$ i.e., 2 terms.

Each term of this bracket

$$> \frac{1}{2^n + 2^n} = \frac{1}{2 . 2^n} = \frac{1}{2^{n+1}}$$

$$\therefore \quad P(n+1) \geq \left(1 + \frac{n}{2}\right) + 2^n . \frac{1}{2^{n+1}}$$

$$= 1 + \frac{n}{2} + \frac{1}{2} = 1 + \frac{n+1}{2}$$

$$\therefore \quad P(n+1) \geq 1 + \frac{n+1}{2}$$

Thus $P(n)$ is universally true.

(v) For $n = 1$ both L.H.S. and R.H.S. are each $1/2$.

For $n = 2$, L.H.S. $= \frac{3}{8} = \frac{3}{\sqrt{(64)}}$ and

R.H.S. $= \frac{1}{\sqrt{7}} = \frac{3}{3\sqrt{7}} = \frac{3}{\sqrt{(63)}}$

$\therefore$ L.H.S. $\leq$ R.H.S.

Let us assume the inequality holds for $n = m$ that is, let

$$\frac{(2m)!}{2^{2m}(m!)^2} \leq \frac{1}{(3m+1)^{1/2}} \quad (m \geq 1) \qquad \ldots(1)$$

Now we shall prove that it holds for $n = m+1$ for which we will have to establish that

$$\frac{(2m+2)!}{2^{2m+2}[(m+1)!]^2} \leq \frac{1}{(3m+4)^{1/2}} \qquad \ldots(2)$$

L.H.S. $= \frac{(2m+2)(2m+1)(2m)!}{4(m+1)^2 . 2^{2m}(m!)^2}$

$$\leq \frac{(2m+2)(2m+1)}{4(m+1)^2} \times \frac{1}{(3m+1)^{1/2}} \quad \text{by (1)}$$

$$= \frac{2m+1}{2(m+1)} . \frac{1}{(3m+1)^{1/2}} \leq \frac{1}{(3m+4)^{1/2}}$$

[To be proved by (2) as shown below.]

Above will be proved if on squaring we establish that

$$(3m+4)(2m+1)^2 \leq 4(m+1)^2(3m+1) \quad \ldots(3)$$

(It should be noted that all, the factors are +ive)

or $3m[(2m+1)^2 - 4(m+1)^2] + 4[(2m+1)$

$$- (m+1)^2] \leq 0$$

or $3m[-4m-3] + 4[3m^2 + 2m] \leq 0$

or $-m \leq 0$ or $m > 0$ i.e., + ive

Above is true since $m \geq 1$. Hence (2) is proved.

30. (a) The inequality clearly holds for $n = 1$

We now assume

$$|\sin mx| \leq m |\sin x| \qquad \ldots(1)$$

Now, $|\sin(m+1)x| = |\sin mx \cos x$

$$+ \cos mx \sin x|$$

$$\leq |\sin mx||\cos x| + |\cos mx||\sin x|$$

$$\leq |\sin mx| + |\sin x|$$

$$[\because |\cos x| \leq 1 \text{ and } |\cos mx| \leq 1]$$

$$\leq m|\sin x| + |\sin x|, \qquad \text{by (1)}$$

Thus $|\sin(m+1)x| \leq (m+1)|\sin x|$.

Hence by induction, the required inequality holds for every positive integer n.

(b) Since $n > 1$, $P(2)$ holds as

$$\tan 2\alpha > 2 \tan \alpha$$

when $0 < \alpha < \pi/4$ $(n = 2)$

$\therefore \quad \frac{2\tan\alpha}{1-\tan^2\alpha} > 2\tan\alpha$ as $\tan\alpha$ is +ive and < 1

Now assume $P(m)$ i.e., $\tan m\alpha > m\tan\alpha$

Now $\tan(m+1)\alpha = \frac{\tan m\alpha + \tan\alpha}{1 - \tan m\alpha \tan\alpha} \qquad \ldots(1)$

where $\quad 0 < \alpha < \frac{\pi}{4(m+1-1)}$

or $\quad 0 < \alpha < \frac{\pi}{4m}$ or $0 < m\alpha < \frac{\pi}{4}$

$\therefore \quad \tan m\alpha < 1$ and is +ive. Also $\tan\alpha$ is < 1 and +ive. Hence from (1),

$\tan(m+1)\alpha > m\tan\alpha + \tan\alpha = (m+1)\tan\alpha$

$\therefore \quad P(m+1)$ also holds good.

Hence universally true.

(c) $(a+b) < 2(a+b)$ $\quad \therefore$ $P(1)$ holds good.

Assume $P(m)$ i.e. $(a+b)^m < 2^m(a^m + b^m)$ $\ldots(1)$

We have to prove $P(m+1)$

i.e. $(a+b)^{m+1} < 2^{m+1}(a^{m+1} + b^{m+1})$ $\qquad \ldots(A)$

Now $(a+b)^{m+1} = (a+b)^m(a+b)$

$$< 2^m(a^m + b^m)(a+b)$$

$$= 2^m[a^{m+1} + b^{m+1} + a^m b + b^m a] \qquad \ldots(2)$$

$$< 2^m[a^{m+1} + b^{m+1} + a^{m+1} + b^{m+1}],$$

as shown below in *.

$$= 2^{m+1}[a^{m+1} + b^{m+1}]$$

*Now, $a^m b + b^m a < a^{m+1} + b^{m+1}$ **(To be shown)**

or $a^m(b-a) + b^m(a-b) < 0$

or $(a^m - b^m)(b-a) < 0$

or $(a^m - b^m)(a-b) > 0$ $\qquad \ldots(B)$

above is true because when a and b are both +ive then either $a < b$ or $a > b$

When $a < b$ i.e., $a^m - b^m < 0$, $a - b < 0$

$\therefore \quad$ (B) holds

When $a > b$ i.e. $a^m - b^m > 0$ and $a - b > 0$

∴　(B) holds

∴　$P(m+1)$ holds good. Hence universally true.

(d)　Clearly $P(1)$ and $P(2)$ hold. Assume $P(n)$.

$$P(n+1) = x^{n+1} + y^{n+1} = x \cdot x^n + y \cdot y^n$$

$$= x(a^n + b^n - y^n) + y \cdot (a^n + b^n - x^n)$$

$$= (a^n + b^n)(x + y) - xy(x^{n-y} + y^{n-1}) \quad ...(1)$$

Now from given relations

$$(x+y)^2 - (x^2 + y^2) = (a+b)^2 - (a^2 + b^2)$$

∴　$2xy = 2ab$ or $xy = ab$

Hence from (1)

$$P(n+1) = (a^n + b^n)(a+b) - ab(a^{n-1} + b^{n-1})$$

$$\text{by } p(n-1)$$

$$= a^{n+1} + b^{n+1}$$

Above shows that $P(n+1)$ also holds good.

31. The statement is valid for $n = 1$ and $n = 2$

Now let $A_{m-2} = \cos(m-2)\theta$,

$\quad A_{m-1} = \cos(m-1)\theta$

Then $A_m = 2\cos\theta A_{m-1} - A_{m-2}$

$\quad = 2\cos\theta\cos(m-1)\theta - \cos(m-2)\theta$

$\quad = \cos m\theta + \cos(m-2)\theta - \cos(m-2)\theta$

$\quad = \cos m\theta.$

It follows by mathematical induction that

$\quad A_n = \cos n\theta$ for all positive integers n.

32. Putting $n = 1$ in the basic formula, we get

$$u_2 = 3u_1 - 2u_0 = 3.3 - 2.2 = 5 = 2^2 + 1$$

Now assume $u_k = 2^k + 1 \quad (k = 1, 2, 3, ..., m)$

and let us prove

$$u_{m+1} = 2^{m+1} + 1.$$

Indeed, we have

$$u_{m+1} = 3u_m - 2u_{m-1}$$

$$= 3(2^m + 1) - 2(2^{m-1} + 1)$$

$$= 2^m(3-1) + 1 = 2^{m+1} + 1.$$

Hence by induction, $u_n = 2^n + 1$ holds for all positive integers n.

33. Do yourself

34. We have to prove

$$u_n = \frac{1}{\sqrt{(5)}}\left[\left(\frac{1+\sqrt{5}}{2}\right)^n - \left(\frac{1-\sqrt{(5)}}{2}\right)^n\right]$$

for all $n \geq 1$.

We obviously have

$$u_1 = 1 = \frac{1}{\sqrt{(5)}}\left[\frac{1+\sqrt{5}}{2} - \frac{1-\sqrt{5}}{2}\right]$$

and $u_2 = 1 = \dfrac{1}{\sqrt{(5)}}\left[\left(\dfrac{1+\sqrt{5}}{2}\right)^2 - \left(\dfrac{1-\sqrt{5}}{2}\right)^2\right]$

Hence (1) holds for $n = 1$ and $n = 2$.

Now assume

$$u_k = \frac{1}{\sqrt{(5)}}\left[\left(\frac{1+\sqrt{5}}{2}\right)^k - \left(\frac{1-\sqrt{5}}{2}\right)^k\right]$$

$(k = 1, 2, 3, ...\, m)$

Now $u_{m+2} = u_{m+1} + u_m \qquad$ for $m \geq 1$

$\Rightarrow \quad u_{m+1} = u_m + u_{m-1} \qquad$ for $m \geq 2$.

Hence by induction hypothesis on u_k, we have

$$u_{m+1} = u_m + u_{m-1}$$

$$= \frac{1}{\sqrt{(5)}}\left[\left(1+\frac{\sqrt{5}}{2}\right)^m - \left(\frac{1-\sqrt{5}}{2}\right)^m\right]$$

$$+ \frac{1}{\sqrt{(5)}}\left[\left(\frac{1+\sqrt{5}}{2}\right)^{m-1} - \left(\frac{1-\sqrt{5}}{2}\right)^{m-1}\right]$$

$$= \frac{1}{\sqrt{(5)}}\left[\left(\frac{1+\sqrt{5}}{2}\right)^{m-1}\left\{\frac{1+\sqrt{5}}{2} + 1\right\}\right.$$

$$\left. - \left(\frac{1-\sqrt{5}}{2}\right)^{m-1}\left\{\frac{1-\sqrt{5}}{2} + 1\right\}\right]$$

$$= \frac{1}{\sqrt{(5)}}\left[\left(\frac{1+\sqrt{5}}{2}\right)^{m-1}\left(\frac{6+2\sqrt{5}}{4}\right)\right.$$

$$\left. - \left(\frac{1-\sqrt{5}}{2}\right)^{m-1}\left(\frac{6-2\sqrt{5}}{4}\right)\right]$$

$$= \frac{1}{\sqrt{(5)}}\left[\left(\frac{1+\sqrt{5}}{2}\right)^{m-1}\left(\frac{1+\sqrt{5}}{2}\right)^2\right.$$

$$\left. - \left[\left(\frac{1-\sqrt{5}}{2}\right)^{m-1}\left(\frac{1-\sqrt{5}}{2}\right)^2\right]\right]$$

$$= \frac{1}{\sqrt{(5)}}\left[\left(\frac{1+\sqrt{5}}{2}\right)^{m+1} - \left(\frac{1-\sqrt{5}}{2}\right)^{m+1}\right].$$

Thus the formula (1) holds for $k = m + 1$

Hence (1) holds for all positive integers n by induction.

35. We have to prove

$$\frac{a_n - \sqrt{A}}{a_n + \sqrt{(A)}} = \left(\frac{a_1 - \sqrt{A}}{a_1 + \sqrt{(A)}}\right)^{2^{n-1}} \quad \text{for all } n \in N \quad ...(1)$$

Clearly for $n = 1$, equality (1) holds.

Now from the given relation $a_2 = \dfrac{1}{2}\left(a_1 + \dfrac{A}{a_1}\right)$

We have

$$\frac{a_2}{\sqrt{(A)}} = \frac{1}{2\sqrt{(A)}}\left(a_1 + \frac{A}{a_1}\right) = \frac{a_1^2 + A}{2a_1\sqrt{(A)}}$$

Using componendo and dividendo, this gives

$$\frac{a_2 - \sqrt{A}}{a_2 + \sqrt{(A)}} = \frac{a_1^2 + A - 2a_1\sqrt{A}}{a_1^2 + A + 2a_1\sqrt{A}} = \left(\frac{a_1 - \sqrt{A}}{a_1 + \sqrt{(A)}}\right)^2$$

Hence the equality (1) holds for $n = 2$.

Now assume that (1) holds for $n = m \, (m \geq 2)$, that is, we assume

$$\frac{a_m - \sqrt{A}}{a_m + \sqrt{(A)}} = \left(\frac{a_1 - \sqrt{A}}{a_1 + \sqrt{(A)}}\right)^{2^{m-1}} \qquad \ldots(2)$$

Then by the given relation

$$a_{n+1} = \frac{1}{2}\left(a_n + \frac{A}{a_n}\right), \text{ we have}$$

$$\frac{a_{m+1}}{\sqrt{(A)}} = \frac{1}{2\sqrt{(A)}}\left(a_m + \frac{A}{a_m}\right)(m \geq 2) \text{ so that}$$

$$\frac{a_{m+1} - \sqrt{A}}{a_{m+1} + \sqrt{(A)}} = \frac{\frac{1}{2}\left(a_m + \frac{A}{a_m}\right) - \sqrt{A}}{\frac{1}{2}\left(a_m + \frac{A}{a_m}\right) + \sqrt{(A)}}$$

$$= \frac{am^2 - 2a_m\sqrt{A} + A}{a_m^2 + 2a_m\sqrt{A} + A}$$

$$= \left(\frac{a_m - \sqrt{A}}{a_m + \sqrt{(A)}}\right)^2 = \left(\frac{a_1 - \sqrt{A}}{a_1 + \sqrt{(A)}}\right)^{2^m}, \text{ by} \quad (2)$$

Hence the equality (1) holds for $n = m + 1$.

Hence it holds for all $n \in N$.

36. Prove yourself.

37. (a) $P(1) = \sum\limits_{k=0}^{1} k \, {}^1C_k = 0 + 1. \, {}^1C_1 = 1 2^0 = 1$

Hence the given statement holds for $n = 1$

Now assume that it holds for $n = m$

$$\therefore \quad P(m) = \sum\limits_{k=0}^{m} k. \, {}^mC_k = m.2^{m-1} \qquad \ldots(1)$$

Now $P(m+1) = \sum\limits_{k=0}^{m+1} k. \, {}^{m+1}C_k$

$$= \sum\limits_{k=0}^{m+1} k \, [{}^mC_{k-1} + {}^mC_k]$$

$$= \sum\limits_{k=0}^{m+1} k \, {}^mC_{k-1} + \sum\limits_{k=0}^{m+1} k. \, {}^mC_k$$

The first summation is meaningless for $k = 0$ as ${}^mC_{-1}$ has no meaning and the second is meaningless for $k = m+1$ as ${}^mC_{m+1}$ is also meaningless.

$$\therefore \quad P(m+1) = \sum\limits_{k=1}^{m+1} k \, {}^mC_{k-1} + \sum\limits_{k=0}^{m} k \, {}^mC_k$$

Put $k = p + 1$ in 1st sigma and adjust the limits

$$\therefore \quad P(m+1) = \sum\limits_{p=0}^{m} (p+1) \, {}^mC_p + \sum\limits_{k=0}^{m} k \, {}^mC_k$$

$$= \sum\limits_{k=0}^{m} (k+1) \, {}^mC_k + \sum\limits_{k=0}^{m} k. \, {}^mC_k$$

$$= \sum\limits_{k=0}^{m} (2k+1) \, {}^mC_k$$

$$= 2\sum\limits_{k=0}^{m} k \, {}^mC_k + \sum\limits_{k=0}^{m} {}^mC_k$$

$$= 2(m.2^{m-1}) + 2^m = m.2^m + 2^m$$

$$= (m+1) 2^m$$

$\therefore$ The statement holds good for $n = m + 1$.

Note : $C_0 + C_1 + C_2 + \ldots + C_m = 2^n$, being the sum of binomial coefficients.

(b) Let $P(n) = \sum\limits_{k=0}^{n} k^2 \, {}^nC_k$

Then $P(1) = \sum\limits_{k=0}^{1} k^2 \, {}^1C_k$

$$= 0 + 1^2. \, {}^1C_1 = 1 = \text{L.H.S.}$$

and for $n = 1$, $n(n+1) 2^{n-2}$

$$= 1.2.2^{-1} = 1 = \text{R.H.S.}$$

Hence the given statement holds for $n = 1$.

Now assume that the statement holds for $n = m$, that is, assume that

$$P(m) = \sum\limits_{k=0}^{m} k^2 \, {}^mC_k$$

$$= m(m+1) 2^{m-2}, m \geq 1 \qquad \ldots(1)$$

Now $P(m+1) = \sum\limits_{k=0}^{m+1} k^2 \, {}^{m+1}C_k$

$$= \sum\limits_{k=0}^{m+1} k^2 \, ({}^mC_{k-1} + {}^mC_k)$$

$$= \sum\limits_{k=0}^{m+1} k^2. \, {}^mC_{k-1} + \sum\limits_{k=0}^{m+1} k^2. \, {}^mC_k$$

$$= \sum\limits_{k=0}^{m+1} k^2 \, {}^mC_{k-1} + \sum\limits_{k=0}^{m} k^2. \, {}^mC_k$$

[$\because$ First summation becomes meaningless for $k = 0$ and second for $k = m+1$].

Now we can write

$$\sum\limits_{k=1}^{m+1} k^2. \, {}^mC_{k-1} \text{ as } \sum\limits_{k=0}^{m} (k+1)^2 \, {}^mC_k \quad \text{as in (a)}$$

$$\therefore \quad P(m+1) = \sum\limits_{k=0}^{m} (k+1)^2 \, {}^mC_k + \sum\limits_{k=0}^{m} k^2 \, {}^mC_k$$

$$= \sum\limits_{k=0}^{m} (k^2 + 2k + 1) \, {}^mC_k + \sum\limits_{k=0}^{m} k^2 \, {}^mC_k$$

$$= 2\sum\limits_{k=0}^{m} (k^2) \, {}^mC_k + 2\sum\limits_{k=0}^{m} k. \, {}^mC_k + \sum\limits_{k=0}^{m} {}^mC_k \ldots(A)$$

$$(1+x)^n = C_0 + C_1 x + C_2 x^2 + \ldots + C_n x^n$$

or $(1+x)^n = \sum_{r=0}^{n} C_r x^r$ ...(1)

Putting $x = 1$ $\therefore$ $2^n \sum_{r=0}^{n} C_r$

Again differentiating (1), we get

$$n(1+x)^{n-1} = \sum_{r=0}^{n} r C_r x^{r-1}. \text{ Put } x = 1$$

$\therefore$ $n \cdot 2^{n-1} = \sum_{r=0}^{n} r \cdot C_r$ ...(2)

$\therefore$ $P(m+1) = 2m(m+1)2^{m-2}$

$$+ 2m \cdot 2^{m-1} + 2^m.$$

by (1) and (2)

$$= 2^{m-1}(m^2 + m + 2m + 2)$$

$$= (m+1)(m+2) \cdot 2^{m-1}$$

$\therefore$ The statement holds for $n = m+1$.

Hence by mathematical induction, the result holds for all $n \geq 1$.

(c) Let us fix n and prove induction for m

$$P(1) = {}^nC_0 + {}^{n+1}C_1 = 1 + (n+1) = n+2 = {}^{n+2}C_1$$

$$= {}^{n+1+1}C_1$$

Now assume $P(m) = {}^{n+m+1}C_m$ ...(1)

$$P(m+1) = P(m) + {}^{n+m+1}C_{m+1}$$

$$= {}^{n+m+1}C_m + {}^{n+m+1}C_{m+1}$$

$$= {}^{n+m+2}C_{m+1} = {}^{n+m+1+1}C_{m+1}$$

Thus $P(m+1)$ holds good. Hence the formula is true universally.

38. First let $m = n = 1$, since k is a positive integer less than or equal to the smaller of m and n, we have $k = 1$ when $m = n = 1$.

So in this case,

L.H.S. $= {}^1C_0 \, {}^1C_1 + {}^1C_1 \, {}^1C_0 = 1 + 1 = 2$

and R.H.S. $= {}^{1+1}C_1 = {}^2C_1 = 2$

Hence the theorem holds for $m = n = 1$.

Now assume that the theorem holds for any fixed positive integers m and n, that is, we assume

$${}^mC_0 \, {}^nC_k + {}^mC_1 \, {}^nC_{k-1} + {}^mC_2 \, {}^nC_{k-2} + \ldots$$

$$+ {}^mC_{k-1} \, {}^nC_1 + {}^mC_k \, {}^nC_0$$

$$= {}^{m+n}C_k \qquad \ldots(1)$$

Now ${}^{m+1}C_0 \, {}^{n+1}C_k + {}^{m+1}C_1 \, {}^{n+1}C_{k-1}$

$$+ {}^{m+1}C_2 \, {}^{n+1}C_{k-2} +$$

$$\ldots + {}^{m+1}C_{k-1} \, {}^{n+1}C_1 + {}^{m+1}C_k \, {}^{n+1}C_0$$

$$= 1 \cdot ({}^nC_{k-1} + {}^nC_k) + ({}^mC_0 + {}^mC_1)$$

$$({}^nC_{k-2} + {}^nC_{k-1}) + ({}^mC_1 + {}^mC_2)({}^nC_{k-3} + {}^nC_{k-2})$$

$$+ \ldots ({}^mC_{k-2} + {}^mC_{k-1})({}^nC_0 + {}^nC_1)$$

$$+ ({}^mC_{k-1} + {}^mC_k) \cdot 1$$

$$= ({}^nC_{k-1} + {}^mC_1 \, {}^nC_{k-2} + {}^mC_2 \, {}^nC_{k-3} + \ldots$$

$$+ {}^mC_{k-1} \, {}^nC_0)$$

$$+ ({}^nC_k + {}^mC_1 \, {}^nC_{k-1} + {}^mC_2 \, {}^nC_{k-2} + \ldots$$

$$+ {}^mC_{k-1} \, {}^nC_1 + {}^mC_k) + ({}^mC_0 \, {}^nC_{k-2}$$

$$+ {}^mC_1 \, {}^nC_{k-3} + \ldots {}^mC_{k-2} \, {}^nC_0)$$

$$+ ({}^mC_0 \, {}^nC_{k-1} + {}^mC_1 \, {}^nC_{k-2} + \ldots$$

$$+ {}^mC_{k-2} \, {}^nC_1 + {}^mC_{k-1})$$

$$= {}^{m+n}C_{k-1} + {}^{m+n}C_k + {}^{m+n}C_{k-2} + {}^{m+n}C_{k-1},$$

by (1)

$$= {}^{m+n+1}C_k + {}^{m+n+1}C_{k-1} = {}^{m+n+2}C_k.$$

Hence the theorem holds for the next integers $m+1$ and $n+1$. Then by mathematical induction the theorem holds for all positive integral values of m and n. This completes the proof.

39. (a) Let $P(n) = n^7/7 + n^5/5 + 2n^3/3 - n/105$

For $n = 1$, $P(1) = 1/7 + 1/5 + 2/3 - 1/105 = 1$.

So $P(1)$ is an integer.

Now suppose $P(m)$ is an integer where $m \in \mathbf{N}$, that is, let $P(m) = k, k \in \mathbf{I}.$ ...(1)

We have,

$$P(m+1) = (m+1)^7/7 + (m+1)^5/5$$

$$+ 2(m+1)^3/3 - (m+1)/105.$$

$$= m^7/7 + m^5/5 + 2m^3/3 - m/105$$

$$+ (1/7)[{}^7C_1 m^6 + {}^7C_2 m^5 + {}^7C_3 m^4$$

$$+ {}^7C_4 m^3 + {}^7C_5 m^2 + {}^7C_6 m + {}^7C_7]$$

$$+ (1/5)[{}^5C_1 m^4 + {}^5C_2 m^3 + {}^5C_3 m^2$$

$$+ {}^5C_4 m + {}^5C_5] + (2/3)$$

$$[{}^3C_1 m^2 + {}^3C_2 m + {}^3C_3] - 1/105.$$

$$= k + (1/7)(\text{multiple of } 7) + (1/7)$$

$$+ (1/5)(\text{multiple of } 5) + (1/5)$$

$$+ (2/3)(\text{multiple of } 3) + 2/3 - (1/105)$$

$$= k + (\text{a +ive integer}) + (1/7)$$

$$+ (\text{a positive integer}) + (1/5)$$

$$+ (\text{a +ive integer}) + (2/3) - (1/105).$$

$$= (k+1) + (\text{a +ive integer})$$

$$[\because (1/7) + (1/5) + (2/3) - (1/105) = 1]$$

$= $ an integer

Hence $P(m)$ is an integer $\Rightarrow P(m+1)$ is an integer

∴ By mathematical induction $P(n)$ is an integer for all $n \in \mathbf{N}$.

(b) Proceed as in last part **Q. 39 (a)**.

(c) $P(0) = \dfrac{1}{1+x}$, $\dfrac{1}{x-1} + \dfrac{2}{1-x^2} = \dfrac{1}{x-1} - \dfrac{2}{x^2-1}$

$$= \frac{x+1-2}{(x^2-1)} = \frac{1}{x+1}$$

Thus $P(0)$ holds good. Assume $P(n)$

$$P(n+1) = P(n) + \frac{2^{n+1}}{1+x^{2^{n+1}}}$$

$$= \frac{1}{x-1} + \frac{2^{n+1}}{1-x^{2^{n+1}}} + \frac{2^{n+1}}{1+x^{2^{n+1}}}$$

$$= \frac{1}{x-1} + \frac{2^{n+1}(1+1)]}{1-\left(x^{2^{n+1}}\right)^2} = \frac{1}{x-1} + \frac{2^{n+2}}{1-x^{2^{n+2}}}$$

(d) $1^3, 2^3, \ldots n^3$ have $1, 2, \ldots n$ terms respectively in their expression and these are in A.P. of $d = 2$. Also the first terms of these are $1, 3, 7, 13, \ldots$ Hence first term of n^3 is t_n of above series, which by method of n^3 is t_n of above series, which by method of differences is $n^2 - n + 1$.

∴ $n^3 = (n^2 - n + 1) + (n^2 - n + 3) + \ldots n$ terms ...(1)

Clearly $P(1), P(2)$ hold good. Assume $P(n) = n^3$.

Replacing n by $(n+1)$ in (1),

$P(n+1)$

$= [(n+1)^2 - (n+1) + 1] + [(n+1)^2 - (n+1) + 3]$
$$+ \ldots (n+1) \text{ terms}$$

$= (n+1)^2 \cdot (n+1) - (n+1)(n+1)$
$$+ [1 + 3 + 5 + \ldots (n+1) \text{ terms}]$$

$= (n+1)^3 - (n+1)^2 + (n+1)^2$
$$[\text{Sum of an A.P. of } (n+1) \text{ terms}]$$

∴ $P(n+1) = (n+1)^3$.

For $k=1$ we will have two terms for $m=0$ and $m=1$ in the sigma.

L.H.S. $= (n-0)\dfrac{r!}{0!} + (n-1)\dfrac{(r+1)!}{1!}$

$= n[(r+1)! + r!] - (r+1)!$

$= r![n(r+2) - (r+1)]$

and R.H.S. $= \dfrac{(r+2)!}{1!}\left[\dfrac{n}{r+1} - \dfrac{1}{r+2}\right]$

$= (r+2)!\left[\dfrac{n(r+2) - (r+1)}{(r+2)(r+1)}\right]$

$= r![n(r+2) - (r+1)]$

Hence L.H.S. = R.H.S. for $k=1$

Now let the formula hold for $k=s$, that is,

Let $\displaystyle\sum_{m=0}^{s} \frac{(n-m)(r+m)!}{m!}$

$$= \frac{(r+s+1)!}{s!}\left[\frac{n}{r+1} - \frac{s}{r+2}\right] \qquad \ldots(1)$$

Add next term corresponding to $m=s+1$

Adding $\dfrac{(n-s-1)(r+s+1)!}{(s+1)!}$ to both sides, we get

$$\sum_{m=0}^{s+1} \frac{(n-m)(r+m)!}{m!} = \frac{(r+s+1)!}{s!}$$

$$\left[\frac{n}{r+1} - \frac{s}{r+2}\right] + \frac{(n-s-1)(r+s+1)!}{(s+1)!}$$

$$= \frac{(r+s+1)!}{(s+1)!}\left[\frac{(s+1)n}{r+1} - \frac{s(s+1)}{r+2} + n - s - 1\right]$$

$$= \frac{(r+s+1)!}{(s+1)!}\left[n\left\{\frac{s+1}{r+1}+1\right\} - (s+1)\left\{\frac{s}{r+2}+1\right\}\right]$$

$$= \frac{(r+s+2)(r+s+1)!}{(s+1)!}\left[\frac{n}{r+1} - \frac{s+1}{r+2}\right]$$

$$= \frac{(r+s+2)!}{(s+1)!}\left[\frac{n}{r+1} - \frac{s+1}{r+2}\right]$$

Hence the formula holds for $k = s+1$ and so by induction the formula holds for all natural numbers k.

41. (a) $y = \cot^{-1} x$ ∴ $x = \cot y$ ...(1)

$$y_1 = -\frac{1}{1+x^2} = -\frac{1}{1+\cot^2 y} = -\sin^2 y$$

∴ $y_1 = (-1)^1\, 0!\, \sin^1 y \sin 1 . y = P(1)$

Assume on the basis of $P(1)$ that $P(m)$ holds i.e.,

$$y_m = (-1)^m (m-1)! \sin^m y \sin my \qquad \ldots(2)$$

Now differentiate both sides w.r.t. x.

$$y_{m+1} = (-1)^m (m-1)!$$

$[m\sin^{m-1} y \cos y \sin my + \sin^m y . m\cos my]\, y_1$

$= (-1)^m (m-1)! \sin^{m-1} y . m$

$[\cos y \sin my + \sin y \cos my](-\sin^2 y)$

$= (-1)^{m+1} m! \sin^{m+1} y [\sin (m+1) y]$

Above shows that the statement is true for $n = m+1$. Hence it is universally true.

(b) $x = a\cot\theta$ ∴ $\dfrac{dx}{d\theta} = -a\,\mathrm{cosec}^2\theta$

$$y = \frac{x}{x^2+a^2} = \frac{a\cot\theta}{a^2\,\mathrm{cosec}^2\theta} = \frac{1}{a}\sin\theta\cos\theta$$

∴ $y_1 = \dfrac{dy}{dx} = \dfrac{dy}{d\theta} \cdot \dfrac{d\theta}{dx} = \dfrac{1}{a}(\cos^2\theta - \sin^2\theta)$

$$\left(-\frac{1}{a\,\mathrm{cosec}^2\theta}\right)$$

$$= -\frac{1}{a^2}\sin^2\theta\cos 2\theta$$

Thus $P(n)$ holds for $n = 1$.

Assume $P(n)$ holds good.

$$\therefore \quad y_n = \frac{(-1)^n\, n!}{a^{n+1}}\sin^{n+1}\theta\cos(n+1)\theta$$

Differentiate both sides w.r.t. x.

$$\therefore \quad y_{n+1} = \frac{(-1)^n\, n!}{a^{n+1}}$$

$$[(n+1)\sin^n\theta\cos\theta\cos(n+1)\theta$$

$$-\sin^{n+1}\theta\cdot(n+1)\sin(n+1)\theta]\frac{d\theta}{dx}$$

$$= \frac{(-1)^n\, n!\,(n+1)}{a^{n+1}}\sin^n\theta\,[\cos(n+1)\theta\cos\theta$$

$$-\sin\theta\sin(n+1)\theta]\frac{d\theta}{dx}$$

$$= \frac{((-1)^n\,(n+1)!}{a^{n+1}}\sin^n\theta\cos(n+1+1)\theta$$

$$\cdot\left(-\frac{1}{a\,\text{cosec}^2\theta}\right)$$

$$= \frac{(-1)^n\,(n+1)!}{a^{n+2}}\sin^{n+2}\theta\cos(n+2)\theta$$

Hence $P(n) \Rightarrow P(n+1)$.

(c) $\quad P(1) = y_1 = \dfrac{1}{x^2}(1 - \log x)$

$$= \frac{(-1)^1\, 1!}{x^{1+1}}(\log x - 1)$$

Assume $P(n)$; i.e.,

$$y_n = \frac{(-1)^n\,(n!)}{x^{n+1}}\left[\log x - 1 - \frac{1}{2} - \ldots - \frac{1}{n}\right] \quad \ldots(2)$$

Now $P(n+1) = y_{n+1} = \dfrac{d}{dx}(y_n)$

$$= \frac{d}{dx}\frac{(-1)^n\,(n!)}{x^{n+1}}\left[\log x - 1 - \frac{1}{2} - \ldots - \frac{1}{n}\right] \text{ by (2)}$$

Differentiating as product

$$y_{n+1} = (-1)^n\,(n!)$$

$$\times\left[\frac{-(n+1)}{n^{n+2}}\left\{\log x - 1 - \frac{1}{2} - \ldots - \frac{1}{n}\right\}\right.$$

$$\left. + \frac{1}{x^{n+1}}\cdot\frac{1}{x}\right]$$

$$= \frac{(-1)^{n+1}\,(n+1)!}{x^{n+2}}\times\left[\log x - 1 - \frac{1}{2} - \ldots - \frac{1}{n} - \frac{1}{n+1}\right]$$

Thus $P(n+1)$ also holds good.

(d) For $P(1)$ we have to prove

$$y_1 = 1!\,(\log x + 1)$$

where $y = x\log x$ for $n = 1$

$$y_1 = x\cdot\frac{1}{x} + 1\cdot\log x = (\log x + 1) = 1!\,(\log x + 1)$$

Thus $P(1)$ holds good.

Now assume $y_n = n!\left(\log x + 1 + \frac{1}{2} + \ldots + \frac{1}{n}\right)$

where $y = x^n\log x$ for $n = n$.

$P(n+1) = y_{n+1}$ of $x^{n+1}(\log x)$

$$= y_n \text{ of } \frac{d}{dx}\{x^{n+1}\log x\}$$

$$= y_n\left\{(n+1)x^n\log x + x^{n+1}\frac{1}{x}\right\}$$

$$= y_n\{(n+1)x^n\log x\} + y_n\,(x^n)$$

$$= (n+1)\,P(n) + n!$$

$$= (n+1)\,n!\left[\log x + 1 + \frac{1}{2} + \ldots + \frac{1}{n}\right]n!\frac{(n+1)}{(n+1)}$$

$$= (n+1)!\left[\log x + 1 + \frac{1}{2} + \frac{1}{3} + \ldots + \frac{1}{n+1}\right]$$

Hence $P(n+1)$ also holds good.

42. (a) $\quad P(1) = \displaystyle\int_0^{\pi/2}\cos x\sin x\,dx$

$$= \frac{1}{2}[\sin^2 x]_0^{\pi/2} = \frac{1}{2} = \frac{1}{2^{1+1}}\left[\frac{2}{1}\right]$$

Assume $P(m)$ to hold good.

$$P(m+1) = \int_0^{\pi/2}\cos^{m+1}x\sin(m+1)x\,dx$$

$$= \int_0^{\pi/2}\cos^m x\,[\sin(m+1)x\cos x]\,dx$$

$$= \int_0^{\pi/2}\cos^m x\,[\cos(m+1)x\sin x + \sin mx] \quad \ldots(1)$$

Using the formula of $\sin(A - B)$

i.e., $\sin mx = \sin[(m+1)x - x]$

$$= \sin(m+1)x\cos x - \cos(m+1)x\sin x \ldots(2)$$

$$\therefore \quad P(m+1) = \int_0^{\pi/2}(\cos^m x\sin x)\cos(m+1)x$$

$$+ P(m), \quad \text{by (1)}$$

Integrating by parts.

$$= \left[\frac{\cos^{m+1}x}{m+1}\cos(m+1)x\right]_0^{\pi/2}$$

$$+ \frac{1}{m+1}\int\cos^{m+1}x\times$$

$$-(m+1)\sin(m+1)x + P(m)$$

$$P(m+1) = \frac{1}{m+1} - P(m+1) + P(m)$$

$$2P(m+1) = \frac{1}{m+1} + \frac{1}{2^{m+1}}\left[2 + \frac{2^2}{2} + \ldots + \frac{2^m}{m}\right]$$

$$= \frac{1}{2^{m+1}} \left[2 + \frac{2^2}{2} + \ldots + \frac{2^m}{m} + \frac{2^{m+1}}{m+1} \right]$$

$$\therefore \quad P(m+1) = \frac{1}{2^{m+2}} \left[2 + \frac{2^2}{2} + \ldots + \frac{2^{m+1}}{m+1} \right]$$

(b) $P(1) = \int_0^\pi \frac{1-\cos x}{1-\cos x} dx = [x]_0^\pi = 1 \cdot \pi = \pi$

$$P(2) = \int_0^\pi \frac{1 - \cos 2x}{1 - \cos x} dx = \int_0^\pi \frac{2\sin^2 x}{2\sin^2 (x/2)}$$

$$= \int_0^\pi 4 \cdot \cos^2 \frac{x}{2} dx$$

$$= \int_0^\pi 2(1 + \cos x) dx = 2 \cdot \pi + 0 = 2\pi$$

Let us assume that $P(m) = m\pi$ and we will establish that $P(m+1) = (m+1)\pi$

$$\therefore \quad P(m+1) = \int_0^\pi \frac{1 - \cos(m+1)x}{1 - \cos x} dx \quad \ldots(1)$$

$$= (m+1)\pi$$

Now $\cos(m+1)x + \cos(m-1)x = 2\cos mx \cos x$

$$\therefore \quad -\cos(m+1)x$$

$$= \cos(m-1)x - 2\cos mx \cos x$$

or $\quad 1 - \cos(m+1)x$

$$= 1 + \cos(m-1)x - 2\cos mx \cos x$$

$$= -[1 - \cos(m-1)x] + 2\cos mx(1 - \cos x)$$

$$+ 2 - 2\cos mx$$

(Note this step)

Now divide throughout by $1 - \cos x$ and integrate

$$\therefore \quad P(m+1) \qquad \text{(by 1)}$$

$$= -P(m-1) + 2P(m) + \int_0^\pi 2\cos mx \, dx$$

$$= -(m-1)\pi + 2m\pi + 2[\sin mx]_0^\pi$$

$$= (m+1)\pi + 0 = (m+1)\pi.$$

(c) $P(1) = \int_0^\pi \frac{\sin 2x}{\sin x} dx = 2 \int_0^\pi \cos x \, dx$

$$= 2[\sin x]_0^\pi = 0.$$

Assume $P(n)$.

$$P(n+1) = \int_0^\pi \frac{\sin(2n+2)x}{\sin x} dx$$

$$= \int_0^\pi \frac{\sin 2nx \cos 2x + \cos 2nx \sin 2x}{\sin x} dx$$

$$= \int_0^\pi \frac{\sin 2nx(1 - 2\sin^2 x) + \cos 2nx(2\sin x \cos x)}{\sin x} dx$$

$$= \int_0^\pi \frac{\sin 2nx}{\sin x} dx$$

$$+ 2\int_0^\pi \frac{\sin x}{\sin x}(\cos 2nx \cos x - \sin 2nx \sin x) dx$$

$$= P(n) + 2\int_0^\pi \cos(2n+1)x \, dx$$

$$= 0 + 2\left[\frac{\sin(2n+1)x}{(2n+1)} \right]_0^\pi = 0 + 0 = 0$$

(d) As usual $P(1)$ holds good, $P(n)$ is assumed. We shall prove that $P(n+1)$ also holds good. Now

$$P(n+1) - P(n) = \int_0^{\pi/2} \frac{\sin^2(n+1)x - \sin^2 nx}{\sin x} dx$$

$$= \int_0^{\pi/2} \frac{\sin(2n+1)n \cdot \sin x}{\sin x} dx$$

$$= \int_0^{\pi/2} \sin(2n+1)x \, dx = \left[\frac{-\cos(2n+1)x}{2n+1} \right]_0^{\pi/2}$$

$$= \frac{1}{2n+1}[0-1] = \frac{1}{2n+1}$$

$$\therefore \quad P(n+1) = P(n) + \frac{1}{2n+1}$$

$$= 1 + \frac{1}{3} + \frac{1}{5} + \ldots + \frac{1}{2n-1} + \frac{1}{2n+1}$$

Thus $P(n+1)$ also holds good.

Note : The idea of $P(n+1) - P(n)$ is suggested by the formula of $\sin^2 A - \sin^2 B$.

(e) $P(1) = \int_0^{\pi/2} \cos^2 x \, dx = \frac{1}{2} \cdot \frac{\pi}{2} = \frac{\pi}{2^2} = \frac{\pi}{2^{1+1}}$

Assume $P(n) = \frac{\pi}{2^{n+1}}$

$$P(n+1) = \int_0^{\pi/2} \cos^{n+1} x \cos(n+1)x \, dx$$

Now

$$P(n+1) = \int_0^{\pi/2} [\cos^{n+1} x \cos(n+1)x] \, dx$$

$$= \int_0^{\pi/2} \cos^n x \{\cos x(\cos nx \cdot \cos x - \sin nx \cdot \sin x) \, dx$$

$$= \int_0^{\pi/2} \cos^n x \{\cos nx(1 - \sin^2 x)$$

$$- \sin nx \sin x \cos x\} \, dx$$

$$= P(n) + \int_0^{\pi/2} \cos^n x \{-\sin x \{\cos nx \sin x$$

$$+ \sin nx \cos x\} \, dx$$

$$= P(n) + \int_0^{\pi/2} \cos^n x \, (-\sin x) \sin(n+1)x \, dx$$

Integrating by parts

$$P(n) + \left[\frac{\cos^{n+1}}{n+1} \sin(n+1)x \right]_0^{\pi/2}$$

$$- \int_0^{\pi/2} \frac{\cos^{n+1}}{n+1} \cos(n+1)x \times (n+1) \, dx$$

$\therefore \quad P(n+1) = P(n) + 0 - P(n+1)$

or $\quad 2P(n+1) = P(n)$

$\therefore \quad P(n+1) = \frac{1}{2} P(n) = \frac{1}{2} \cdot \frac{\pi}{2^{n+1}} = \frac{\pi}{2^{n+2}}$

(f) $\quad P(1) = \int x e^x \, dx = x \cdot e^x - \int e^x \cdot 1 \, dx = e^x (x-1)$

$$\text{R.H.S.} = e^x \left(\frac{x}{1!} - \frac{1}{0!} \right) = e^x (x-1)$$

Thus $P(1)$ holds good. Assume $P(n)$.

$\therefore \quad P(n+1) = \int x^{n+1} e^x \, dx$

$$= x^{n+1} \cdot e^x - (n+1) \int x^n e^x \, dx$$

$$= x^{n+1} \cdot e^x - (n+1) \cdot P(n)$$

$$= x^{n+1} \cdot e^x - (n+1) \cdot n! \, e^x \left[\frac{x^n}{n!} - \frac{x^{n-1}}{(n-1)!} \right.$$

$$\left. + \frac{x^{n-2}}{(n-1)!} + \dots \right]$$

$$= (n+1)! \, e^x \left[\frac{x^{n+1}}{(n+1)!} - \frac{x^n}{n!} + \frac{x^{n+1}}{(n-1)!} - \dots \right]$$

Thus $P(n+1)$ also holds good.

43. Given $p \geq 3$ is an integer and α, β are the roots of
$$x^2 - (p+1)x + 1 = 0$$
so that $\alpha + \beta = p+1, \alpha\beta = 1$ ...(1)
$$\alpha^2 + \beta^2 = (\alpha+\beta)^2 - 2\alpha\beta$$
$$= (p+1)^2 - 2 = p^2 + 2p - 1 \quad \text{...(2)}$$

Now p is an integer greater or equal to 3, therefore from (1) and (2) we conclude that $P(1), P(2)$ hold good and assume that $P(n)$ also holds good i.e., they are all integers.

Now multiplying both sides of
$$x^2 - (p+1)x + 1 = 0 \text{ by } x^{n-1}, \text{ we get}$$
$$x^{n+1} = (p+1)x^n + x^{n-1}$$

Its roots are α and β also
$$\alpha^{n+1} + \beta^{n+1} = (p+1)(\alpha^n + \beta^n) + (\alpha^{n-1} + \beta^{n-1})$$
or $\quad P(n+1) = (p+1)P(n) + P(n-1) \quad \text{...(3)}$
Since $P(n)$ and $P(n-1)$ hold good, therefore $P(n+1)$ also holds good.

i.e., $\alpha^{n+1} + \beta^{n+1}$ is an integer.

Again $\dfrac{\alpha + \beta}{p} = \dfrac{p+1}{p} = 1 + \dfrac{1}{p}$

$$\frac{\alpha^2 + \beta^2}{p} = \frac{p^2 + 2p - 1}{p} = (p+2) - \frac{1}{p}$$

From above we conclude that $\alpha + \beta$ and $\alpha^2 + \beta^2$ are not divisible by p since $1/p$ is a proper fraction, therefore $P(1), P(2)$ hold good and assume $P(n)$ also holds good i.e., $P(n)$ is not divisible by p.

$\therefore \quad P(n+1) = (p+1)P(n) + P(n-1)$.] from (3)
Since each of $P(n)$ and $P(n-1)$ are not divisible by 3
$\therefore \quad P(n+1) = (p+1)P(n) + P(n-1)$ is also not divisible (3).
This proves the 2nd part.

44. To prove the assertion, we first assign to each hand shake a number in natural order. Then our assertion is equivalent to the following : "For every n, after a handshake with number n, the number of people who have made an odd number of handshakes is even." This statement depends on n and will be proved by induction. For convenience, we call the people who have made an odd number of handshakes type A and the rest type B, that is, type B are those people who had made an even number of handshakes.

After the handshake with number 1, we have two people of type A, an even number. After the mth handshake, let the number of people of type A be even and let the handshake number $m+1$ take place. Three cases arise : the handshake number $m+1$ will occur between (a) two people of type A (b) two people of type B, (c) a person of type A and a person type B.

In case (a), two persons of type A add one handshake to their odd number of handshakes and becomes of type B; in case (b) two persons of type B become of type A and in case (c) a person of type A becomes of type B and a person of type B is changed into type A. Thus the number of people of type A either decreases by two or increases by two or remains unchanged. In any case the number remains even and the proof is complete.

45. Let $A_n = n^p - n$.

For $n = 2$, we have
$$A_2 = 2^p - 2 = (1+1)^p - 2$$
$$= (1 + {}^pC_1 + {}^pC_2 + \dots + {}^pC_r + \dots$$
$$+ {}^pC_{p-1} + 1) - 2$$
$$= {}^pC_1 + {}^pC_2 + \dots + {}^pC_r + \dots + {}^pC_{p-1} \quad \text{...(1)}$$

Now $\quad {}^pC_r = \dfrac{p(p-1)(p-2)\dots(p-r+1)}{r!}$

where r is a positive integer $\leq p-1$.

Since p is prime, no factor of $r!$ can divide p. Also since $p > r$, p cannot divide any factor of $r!$.

But ^pC_r is positive integer.

It follows that $(p-1)(p-2)\ldots(p+r+1)$ must be divisible by $r!$.

Hence ^pC_r is divisible by p for all positive integer $r \le p-1$.

It then follows from (1) that A_2 is divisible by p.

Now assume A_m is divisible by p. We have

$$A_{m+1} - A_m = (m+1)^p - (m+1) - (m^p - m)$$

$$= pm^{p-1} + \frac{p(p-1)}{2!}m^{p-2} + \ldots + p_m.$$

Arguing as above, the expression on the right hand side is a multiple of p since p is prime.

Thus $A_{m+1} = A_m + $ a multiple of p

= a multiple of p by induction hypothesis on A_m.

Finally we conclude that $n^p - n$ is divisible by p.

Remark. This problem provides a proof of Fermat's theorem which states :

If p is a prime number and n is prime to p, then $n^{p-1} - 1$ is divisible by p.

For if n is prime to p, it follows from the above problem that $n^{p-1} - 1$ is a multiple of p.

46. the assertion given in the problem is obviously true for $n = 1$ since a single straight line divides the plane into 2 parts.

Now assume the assertion for $n = m$, that is, assume that m straight lines, divided the plane into $2m$ angles. The $(m+1)$ th line will clearly bisect two vertically opposite angles *i.e.* will increase the number of parts, into which the plane is divided, by two. Therefore the $(m+1)$ straight lines divide the plane into $2m + 2$ parts. The assertion of the problem is then proved by induction.

47. For $n = 1$, we have ...(1)
$$x^3 = x + 1 = 1.x + 1 + 0.x^{-1}$$

so that $a_1 = 1, b_1 = 1, c_1 = 0$.
For $n = 2$, $x^6 = (x^3)^2 = (x+1)^2$

$$= x^2 + 2x + 1 = \frac{x^3}{x} + 2x + 1$$

$$= \frac{x+1}{x} + 2x + 1 = 2x + 2 + 1.x^{-1} \quad \text{by (1)}$$

so that $a_2 = 2, b_2 = 2, c_2 = 1$.
Here $a_1 + b_1 = 1 + 1 = 2 = a_2$.
$$a_1 + b_1 + c_1 = 1 + 1 + 0 = 2 = b_2$$
and $\quad a_1 + c_1 = 1 + 0 = c_2$.
Hence the assertion is valid for $n = 2$.
Let us now assume that

$$x^{3m} = a_m x + b_m + c_m x^{-1}$$

where $a_{m+1} = a_m + b_m$;$b_{m+1} = a_m + b_m + c_m$,
$c_{m+1} = a_m + c_m.$ Then
$$x^{3(m+1)} = x^{3m}.x^3 = (a_m x + b_m + c_m x^{-1})(x+1)$$

$$= a_m x^2 + b_m x + c_m + a_m x + b_m + c_m x^{-1}$$

$$= a_m.\frac{x^3}{x} + (a_m + b_m)x + b_m + c_m + c_m x^{-1}$$

$$= a_m \frac{(x+1)}{x} + a_{m+1} x + b_m + c_m + c_m x^{-1}$$

$$= a_m + a_m x^{-1} + a_{m+1} x + b_m + c_m + c_m x^{-1}$$

$$= a_{m+1} x + (a_m + b_m + c_m) + (a_m + c_m)x^{-1}$$

$$= a_{m+1} x + b_{m+1} + c_{m+1} x^{-1}$$

Hence assertion holds for $n = m + 1$

Therefore by mathematical induction, the assertion holds for all natural numbers n.

48. If $x_1 x_2 = 1$, then
$$x_1 + x_2 = (\sqrt{x_1} - \sqrt{x_2})^2 + 2\sqrt{x_1 x_2} \ge 2\sqrt{x_1 x_2} = 2,$$

so that the inequality holds true for $n = 2$.

Now assume that the sum of any m positive numbers whose product is 1 is greater than or equal to m and let $x_1, x_2, \ldots, x_m, x_{m+1}$ be $(m+1)$ positive integers such that

$$x_1 . x_2 \ldots x_m . x_{m+1} = 1$$

We shall prove

$$x_1 + x_2 + \ldots + x_m + x_{m+1} \ge m + 1.$$

If each x_i $(i = 1, 2, \ldots m+1)$ is 1, then $x_1 + x_2 + \ldots x_m + x_{m+1} = m + 1$, so that in this case the inequality holds true.

If x_i's are not all 1, then among them there will be a number greater than 1 and a number less than 1. Let

$$x_m > 1 \text{ and } x_{m+1} < 1. \quad \ldots(1)$$

We have $x_1 x_2 \ldots x_{m-1} (x_m x_{m+1}) = 1.$

This is a product of m numbers and so by our induction hypothesis, we can say that

$$x_1 + x_2 + \ldots x_{m-1} + x_m x_{m+1} \ge m \quad \ldots(2)$$

But then

$$x_1 + x_2 + \ldots + x_{m-1} + x_m + x_{m+1}$$

$$\ge m - x_m x_{m+1} + x_m + x_{m+1} \text{ by (2)}$$

$$= m + 1 + (x_m - 1)(1 - x_{m+1}) > m + 1,$$

since $x_m - 1 > 0$ and $1 - x_{m+1} > 0$ by (1)

so that $(x_m - 1)(1 - x_{m+1}) > 0$.

This completes the proof.

49. Prove yourself.

50. $P(n) = 3^{2^n} - 1$ is $\div 2^{n+2}$ but $\ne \div$ by 2^{n+3}

$$P(1) = 3^2 - 1 = 8 \text{ is } \div 2^{1+2} \text{ } i.e., 8$$

but $\ne \div$ by 2^{1+3} i.e. 16

Also $n = 8.1$

$P(2) = 3^{2^2} - 1 = 80$ is $\div 2^{2+2}$ i.e., 16

but $\neq \div$ by 2^{2+3} i.e. 32

Also $80 = 16 \cdot 5$

Thus $P(1)$, $P(2)$ hold good

Let us suppose that

$\qquad P(m) = 3^{2^m} - 1$ is $\div$ by 2^{m+2}

but $\neq \div 2^{m+3}$

$\therefore \qquad 3^{2^m} - 1 = O \cdot 2^{m+2}$

where O is an odd integer

$\therefore \qquad 3^{2^m} = O \cdot 2^{m+2} + 1 \qquad \qquad \dots(1)$

$P(m+1) = 3^{2^{m+1}} - 1 = 3^{2^m \cdot 2^1} - 1$

$= (3^{2^m})^2 - 1 \quad \because \quad 3^{ab} = (3^a)^b$

$= (O\,2^{m+2} + 1)^2 - 1, \quad$ by (1)

$= O^2 \cdot 2^{2m+4} + 2 \cdot O \cdot 2^{m+2} + 1 - 1$

$= O^2 \cdot 2^{m+3} \cdot 2^{m+1} + O \cdot 2^{m+3}$

$= 2^{m+3} [O^2 \cdot 2^{m+1} + O]$

$\neq 2^{m+3} \cdot 2k \quad$ or $\quad \neq 2^{m+4} \cdot k$

Since O is odd $\therefore O^2 2^{m+1} + O$

$= \text{Even} + O = \text{odd} \neq 2k$

Above shows that $P(m+1)$ holds as it is divisible by 2^{m+1+2} i.e., 2^{m+3} but not by 2^{m+1+3} i.e., 2^{m+4}.

Fascinating Facts

- The statement which is either True or False is called proposition.
- If the proposition is not true even for one natural number it is False.
- If a proposition is true at each and every step then proposition must be true.

- To prove the truth of a statement $P(n)$ for all $n \in \mathbf{N}$, use the following procedure.

  Step (1) : (Basis step) Verify the truth of $P(1)$

  Step (2) : (Hypothesis) Assume that $P(m)$ is true, $m \in \mathbf{N}$

  Step (3) : (Inductive step) Prove that $P(m+1)$ is true (with the help of step (1) and step (2)).

❑

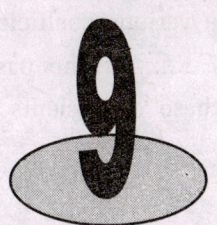

CHAPTER 9

Algebra

Binomial Theorem

§1. Binomial theorem for positive integral index.

$$(x+a)^n = x^n + {}^nC_1 x^{n-1} a^1 + {}^nC_2 x^{n-2} a^2 + \ldots$$
$$+ {}^nC_r x^{n-r} a^r + \ldots + {}^nC_{n-1} x a^{n-1} + {}^nC_n a^n$$

If the binomi ' be $x - a$ then the terms in the expansion of $(x-a)^n$ will be alternately + ive and − ive.

§2. General term, T_{r+1}

$$\quad {}^nC_r x^{n-r} . a^r \qquad \text{for} \quad (x+a)^n$$
$$\text{or} \quad {}^nC_r x^{n-r} (-a)^r \qquad \text{for} \quad (x-a)^n$$

The index of x is $n-r$ and that of a is r i.e. sum of the indices of x and a in each term is same i.e., n.

$$\mid {}^nC_r \, (I)^{n-r} \, (II)^r \mid$$

§3. Binomial coefficients

(a)* Binomial coefficients of terms equidistant from the beginning and the end are equal.

Since $\quad {}^nC_r = {}^nC_{n-r}$,

$$\therefore \quad {}^nC_0 = 1 = {}^nC_n, \, {}^nC_1 = {}^nC_{n-1},$$
$${}^nC_2 = {}^nC_{n-2} \text{ etc.}$$

(b) $\quad {}^nC_r + {}^nC_{r-1} = {}^{n+1}C_r$ \hfill (See P. 318)

(c) $\quad {}^nC_r = {}^nC_p \Rightarrow$ either $r = p$ or $r + p = n$

(d) $\quad \dfrac{{}^nC_r}{{}^{n-1}C_{r-1}} = \dfrac{n}{r}$ \hfill (See P. 319)

(e) $\quad {}^nC_r$ is greatest when $r = \dfrac{n}{2}$, (n being even)

(f) $\quad {}^nC_r$ is greatest when $r = \dfrac{n-1}{2}$ or $\dfrac{n+1}{2}$,

(n being odd) and ${}^nC_{(n+1)/2} = {}^nC_{(n-1)/2}$

§4. Number of terms and middle term.

The number of terms in the expansion of $(x+a)^n$ is $n+1$.

If $n = 6$ the number of terms will be $6 + 1 = 7$ and the middle will be only one i.e. 4th i.e. $\dfrac{6}{2} + 1 = 4$.

If $n = 7$ the number of terms will be $7 + 1 = 8$ and in this case there will be 2 middle terms i.e. 4th and 5th

$$\dfrac{7+1}{2} = 4 \quad \text{and} \quad \dfrac{7+3}{2} = 5.$$

Hence if **n is even** there will be only **one middle** term i.e., $\left(\dfrac{n}{2} + 1\right)$ th.

If n is **odd** then there will be two middle terms i.e., $\left(\dfrac{n+1}{2}\right)$ th and $\left(\dfrac{n+3}{2}\right)$ th.

§5. Values of Binomial Coefficients.

$${}^nC_0 = 1, \quad {}^nC_1 = \dfrac{n!}{(n-1)! \, . 1!} = n.$$

$${}^nC_2 = \dfrac{n!}{(n-2)! \, . 2!} = \dfrac{n(n-1)}{2!},$$

$${}^nC_3 = \dfrac{n(n-1)(n-2)}{3!}$$

and in general.

$${}^nC_r = \dfrac{n(n-1)(n-2)\ldots(n-r+1)}{r!}$$

$$(1+x)^n = 1 + {}^nC_1 x + {}^nC_2 x^2 + \ldots + {}^nC_r x^r$$
$$+ \ldots + {}^nC_n x^n.$$

§6. Term containing

Term containing x^r will occur in T_{r+1} for $(1+x)^n$ and it will be ${}^nC_r x^r$.

§7. $\dfrac{T_{r+1}}{T_r}$ for $(x+a)^n$

$$\dfrac{T_{r+1}}{T_r} = \dfrac{{}^nC_r x^{n-r} a^r}{{}^nC_{r-1} x^{n-r+1} . a^{r-1}}$$

$$= \dfrac{n!}{r!\,(n-r)!} \dfrac{(r-1)!\,(n-r+1)!}{n!} \dfrac{a}{x}$$

$$\ast \quad = \frac{n-r+1}{r} \cdot \frac{a}{x} \qquad \ldots(1)$$

*Greatest term in $(1+x)^n$, $n>0$

Putting $x=1$, $a=x$ in (1), we get

$$\ast \quad \frac{T_{r+1}}{T_r} = \frac{n-r+1}{r} x \qquad \textbf{(V. Imp.)}$$

For a given value of x we find as to when $\dfrac{T_{r+1}}{T_r} \geq 1$

or $\quad T_{r+1} \geq T_r$ where r is to be a positive integer.
This inequality will reduce either to the form

$$r \leq m+k \quad \text{or} \quad r \leq m$$

where m is a +ive integer and $0 \leq k < 1$. In the first case T_{m+1} is the greatest term and in the second case both T_m and T_{m+1} are *numerically* greatest terms.
The greatest term (numerically) in the expansion of $(1-x)^n$, $x>0$ is the same as the greatest term in the expansion of $(1+x)^n$. For greatest term in the expansion of $(a+x)^n$ write it as $a^n(1+x/a)^n$.

Another Method. Evaluate $m = \left(\dfrac{x}{x+1}\right)(n+1)$

In case m is an integer, then T_m and T_{m+1} will be equal and both these will be numerically the greatest terms.
In case m is not an integer, then evaluate $[m]$ i.e. greatest integer, then $T_{[m]+1}$ will be the greatest term.

§8. Term independent of x in the expansion

(i) **Term independent of x in the expansion of $(x+a)^n$.**

Let T_{r+1} be the term independent of x. Equate to zero the index of x and you will find the value of r.

(ii) **Terms equidistant from the beginning and end of the binomial expansion $(x+a)^n$.**

T_{r+1} from beginning of $(x+a)^n = {}^nC_r\, x^{n-r}\, a^r$

T_r from end of $(x+a)^n$ is T_{r+1} from beginning of $(a+x)^n$ (binomial reversed) and is equal to ${}^nC_r\, a^{n-r}\, x^r$.

General Terms

Expansion	General Term
$(1+x)^n$	$T_{r+1} = \dfrac{n(n-1)(n-2)\ldots(n-(r-1))}{r!} x^r$
$(1-x)^n$	$T_{r+1} = (-1)^r \dfrac{n(n-1)(n-2)\ldots(n-(r-1))}{r!} x^r$
$(1+x)^{-n}$	$T_{r+1} = (-1)^r \dfrac{n(n+1)(n+2)\ldots(n+(r-1))}{r!} x^r$
$(1-x)^{-n}$	$T_{r+1} = \dfrac{n(n+1)(n+2)\ldots(n+(r-1))}{r!} x^r$

§9. Pascal Triangle

In $(x+a)^n$ when expanded the various coefficients which occur are ${}^nC_0$, ${}^nC_1$, ${}^nC_2 \ldots\ldots$. The pascal triangle gives the values of these coefficients for $n=0,1,2,3,4,5,\ldots\ldots$

$n=0$					1					
$n=1$					1	1				
$n=2$				1	2	1				
$n=3$			1	3	3	1				
$n=4$		1	4	6	4	1				
$n=5$	1	5	10	10	5	1				
$n=6$	1	6	15	20	15	6	1			
$n=7$	1	7	21	35	35	21	7	1		
$n=8$	1	8	28	56	70	56	28	8	1	

Rule : It will be noted that the first and last terms in each row is 1. The terms equidistant from the beginning and end are equal. Any number in any row is obtained by adding the two numbers in the preceding row that are just at the left and just at the right of the given number e.g. The number 21 in the row for $n=7$ is the sum of 6 (left) and 15 (right) which occur in the preceding row for $n=6$

$n=3$	1	3	3	1
$n=4$	1	$1+3$	$3+3$	$3+1$	1
i.e.,	1	4	6	4	1

§10. Number of terms in the expansion

(a) **Number of terms in the expansion of $(x+y+z)^n$ where n is a +ive integer.**

$$(x+y+z)^n = x^n + {}^nC_1\, x^{n-1}(y+z)$$
$$+ {}^nC_2\, x^{n-2}(y+z)^2 + \ldots + {}^nC_n(y+z)^n$$

Now we know that the number of terms in the above expansion is

$$1+2+3+4+\ldots+(n+1) = \frac{(n+1)(n+2)}{2}$$

(b) Similarly number of terms in $(x+y+z+w)^n$ will be $\dfrac{(n+1)(n+2)(n+3)}{1.2.3} = {}^{n+3}C_3$ as shown below.

$$(x+y+z+w)^n = (x+y)^n + {}^nC_1(x+y)^{n-1}(z+w)$$
$$+ {}^nC_2(x+y)^{n-2}(z+w)^2 + \ldots + {}^nC_n(z+w)^n$$

Clearly the number of terms in R.H.S. is $(n+1).1 + n.2 + (n-1).3 + \ldots 1.(n+1)$
Refer Q. 19 P. 194-99.

$$= \sum_{r=1}^{n+1} \{n-(r-2)\}\, r$$

$$= \sum_{r=1}^{n+1} \{(n+2)r - r^2\}$$

$$= (n+2) \sum_{r=1}^{n+1} r - \sum_{r=1}^{n+1} r^2$$

$$= (n+2)\frac{N(N+1)}{2} - \frac{N(N+1)(2N+1)}{6},$$

$$\text{where } N = n+1$$

$$= \frac{(n+2)(n+1)(n+2)}{2} - \frac{(n+1)(n+2)(2n+3)}{6}$$

$$= \frac{(n+1)(n+2)}{6}[(3n+6)-(2n+3)]$$

$$= \frac{(n+1)(n+2)(n+3)}{1.2.3} = {}^{n+3}C_3.$$

Hence the number of terms in

$(x+y)^n, (x+y+z)^n, (x+y+z+w)^n$ are respectively.

$$\frac{n+1}{1}, \frac{(n+2)(n+1)}{1.2}, \frac{(n+3)(n+2)(n+1)}{1.2.3}$$

or $\quad {}^{n+1}C_1, \ {}^{n+2}C_2, \ {}^{n+3}C_3$

Problem Set (1)

Term independent of x. Coefficient of x^r in binomial expansion,
Sum of the coefficients in the expansion of $(1+x)^n$. Middle term.

In Q. 1 and 2 find the term independent of x in the expansion of

1. (a) $\left(3x - \dfrac{2}{x^2}\right)^{15}$ (b) $\left(\dfrac{3}{2}x^2 - \dfrac{1}{3x}\right)^9$

    (c) $\left(\sqrt{\dfrac{x}{3}} + \dfrac{3}{2x^2}\right)^{10}$

2. (a)* $(1 + x + 2x^3)\left(\dfrac{3}{2}x^2 - \dfrac{1}{3x}\right)^9$

    (b)* $\left(\dfrac{1}{2}x^{1/3} + x^{-1/5}\right)^8$ (c) $\left(x^3 - \dfrac{3}{x^2}\right)^{15}$

3. (a) Find the coefficient of x^{10} and x^9 in the expansion of $\left(2x^2 - \dfrac{1}{x}\right)^{20}$.

    (b) Find the coefficient of x^5 and x^{-15} in the expansion of $\left(3x^2 - \dfrac{b}{3x^3}\right)^{10}$.

    (c) Prove that the coefficient of x^3 in the expansion of $(1+x+2x^2)\left(2x^2 - \dfrac{1}{3x}\right)^9$ is $-\dfrac{224}{27}$.

    (d) Find the coefficient of x in the expansion of $(1 - 2x^3 + 3x^5)[1 + (1/x)]^8$.

4. (a) Prove that the ratio of the coefficient of x^{10} in $(1 - x^2)^{10}$ and the term independent of x in $\left(x - \dfrac{2}{x}\right)^{10}$ is $1 : 32$.

    (b)* Find (a) the coefficient of x^9, (b) the term independent of x in the expansion of $(x^2 - 1/3x)^9$.

    (c) If x is $+$ive, the first $-$ive term in the expansion of $(1+x)^{27/5}$ is :

    (a) T_7 (b) T_5
    (c) T_8 (d) T_6 **(AIEEE 2003)**

5. (a)* Find the coefficient of x^7 in $\left(ax^2 + \dfrac{1}{bx}\right)^{11}$ and of

x^{-7} in $\left(ax - \dfrac{1}{bx^2}\right)^{11}$.

and find the relation between a and b so that these coefficients are equal.

    (b) Given that the fourth term in the expansion of $\left(px + \dfrac{1}{x}\right)^n$ is $\dfrac{5}{2}$. Evaluate n and p.

6. (a)* Determine the value of x in the expression $(x + x^{\log_{10}(x)})^5$ if the third term in the expansion is $10,00,000$.   **(Roorkee 1992)**

    (b) If in the expansion of $(1+x)^m (1-x)^n$, the coefficients of x and x^2 are 3 and -6 respectively, then m is

    (a) 6   (b) 9
    (c) 12   (d) 24   **(I.I.T. 1999)**

7. Find the number of terms and the middle term or terms in the expansion of

    (a) $\left(\dfrac{a}{x} + bx\right)^{12}$ (b) $\left(\dfrac{x}{a} - \dfrac{a}{x}\right)^{10}$ (c) $\left(3x - \dfrac{x^3}{6}\right)^9$.

    (d) The number of terms in $(1+x)^{101}(1+x^2-x)^{100}$ is

    (a) 101   (b) 202
    (c) 301   (d) 302

8. (a) For what value of r the coefficients of $(r-1)$th and $(2r+3)$rd terms in the expansion of $(1+x)^{15}$ are equal ?

    (b)* If the coefficients of $(2r+1)$th term and $(r+2)$th term in the expansion of $(1+x)^{43}$ are equal, find r.

9. (a) If the coefficient of 4th and 13th terms in the expansion of $\left(x^2 + \dfrac{1}{x}\right)^n$ be equal then find the term which is independent of x.

    (b) If the coefficients of $(2r+4)$th and $(r-2)$th terms in the expansion of $(1+x)^{18}$ are equal, find r.

10. (a) In the binomial expansion of $(a-b)^n$, $n \le 5$, the sum of the 5th and 6th terms is zero. Then a/b equals

(a) $\dfrac{n-5}{6}$ (b) $\dfrac{n-4}{5}$

(c) $\dfrac{5}{n-4}$ (c) $\dfrac{6}{n-5}$ **(I.I.T. Sc. 2001)**

(b) Find the coefficient of x^r in the expansion of
$\left(x + \dfrac{1}{x}\right)^n$ if it occurs.

(Bihar C.E.E. 1999)

11. (a) If $\dfrac{1}{\sqrt{4x+1}}\left\{\left(\dfrac{1+\sqrt{4x+1}}{2}\right)^n - \left(\dfrac{1-\sqrt{4x+1}}{2}\right)^n\right\}$

$= a_0 + a_1 x + \ldots + a_5 x^5$, show that $n = 11$.

(b) Prove that the coefficient of the term independent of y in the expansion of

$\left(\dfrac{y+1}{y^{2/3} - y^{1/3} + 1} - \dfrac{y-1}{y - y^{1/2}}\right)^{10}$ is 210.

12. (a) Show that the coefficient of x^{50} in $(1+x)^{41}(1-x+x^2)^{40}$ is 0.

(b) The coefficient of x^8 in the expansion of
$1 + (1+x) + (1+x)^2 + \ldots + (1+x)^n \ (n \geq 8)$ is

(a) 1   (b) 2

(c) $^{n+1}C_{n-8}$ (d) $^nC_{n-8}$

(c) The coefficient of x^n in the expansion of $(1+x)(1-x)^n$ is

(a) $n-1$ (b) $(-1)^n (1-n)$

(c) $(-1)^{n-1} (n-1)^2$ (d) $(-1)^{n-1} n$ **(AIEEE 2004)**

13. (a) If x^p occurs in the expansion of $\left(x^2 + \dfrac{1}{x}\right)^{2n}$

prove that its coefficient is
$\dfrac{(2n)!}{\left[\dfrac{1}{3}(4n-p)\right]!\left[\dfrac{1}{3}(2n+p)\right]!}.$

(b) If x^{4r} occurs in the expansion of $\left(x + \dfrac{1}{x^2}\right)^{4n}$

prove that its coefficient is
$\dfrac{(4n)!}{\left[\dfrac{4}{3}(n-r)\right]!\left[\dfrac{4}{3}(2n+r)\right]!}.$

14. (a) Prove that the coefficient of $(r+1)$th term in the expansion of $(1+x)^{n+1}$ is equal to the sum of the coefficients of r th and $(r+1)$th terms in the expansion of $(1+x)^n$.

(b) Prove that the coefficient of middle term in the expansion of $(1+x)^{2n}$ is equal to the sum of the coefficients of two middle terms in $(1+x)^{2n-1}$.

15. For $2 \leq r \leq n$, $\begin{pmatrix} n \\ r \end{pmatrix} + 2\begin{pmatrix} n \\ r-1 \end{pmatrix} + \begin{pmatrix} n \\ r-2 \end{pmatrix} =$

(a) $\begin{pmatrix} n+1 \\ r-1 \end{pmatrix}$ (b) $2\begin{pmatrix} n+1 \\ r+1 \end{pmatrix}$

(c) $2\begin{pmatrix} n+2 \\ r \end{pmatrix}$ (d) $\begin{pmatrix} n+2 \\ r \end{pmatrix}$ **(I.I.T. Sc. 2000)**

16. (a) Prove that the coefficient of x^n in the expansion of $(1+x)^{2n}$ is double the coefficient of x^n in the expansion of $(1+x)^{2n-1}$.

(b)* Show that the coefficients of x^p and x^q (where p and q are positive integers) in the expansion of $(1+x)^{p+q}$ are equal.

17. (a) If the sum of the coefficients in the expansion of $(x+y)^n$ is 4096, then prove that the greatest coefficient in the expansion is 924. **(Roorkee 2000)**

(b) Sum of coefficients in the expansion of $(x+2y+z)^{10}$ is

(a) 2^{10} (b) 3^{10}

(c) 1   (d) none of these

(c) If the sum of the coefficients in the expansion of $(1-3x+10x^2)^n$ is A and if the sum of the coefficients in the expansion of $(1+x^2)^n$ is B, then

(a) $A = 3B$ (b) $A = B^3$

(c) $B = A^3$ (d) none of these

(d) If the sum of the coefficients in the expansion of $(\alpha x^2 - 2x + 1)^{35}$ is equal to sum of the coefficients in the expansion of $(x - \alpha y)^{35}$ then prove that $\alpha = 1$.

18. (a)* Show that the coefficient of x^5 in the expansion of $(1+x^2)^5 (1+x)^4$ is 60.

(b) The coefficient of x^4 in the expansion of $(1+x+x^2+x^3)^n$ is $^nC_4 + {}^nC_2 + {}^nC_1 \cdot {}^nC_2$

(D.C.E. 1998; M.N.R. 1993)

(c) The coefficient of t^{24} in $(1+t^2)^{12} (1+t^{12}) (1+t^{24})$ is

(a) $^{12}C_6 + 3$ (b) $^{12}C_6$

(c) $^{12}C_6 + 1$ (d) $^{12}C_6 + 2$

(Screening 2003)

(d) Given $(1+x^2)^2 (1+x)^n = \sum_{k=0}^{n+4} a_k x^k$.

If a_1, a_2 and a_3 are in A.P. then find the value of n.

(e) For natural numbers m, n if
$(1-y)^m (1+y)^n = 1 + a_1 y + a_2 y^2 + \ldots$
and $a_1 = a_2 = 10$, then (m, n) is

(a) $(35, 20)$ (b) $(45, 35)$

(c) $(35, 45)$ (d) $(20, 45)$

19. (a)* The coefficient of x^{53} in the expansion
$\sum_{m=0}^{100} {}^{100}C_m (x-3)^{100-m} \cdot 2^m$ is $-{}^{100}C_{53}$

(b) Find the coefficient of x^{301} in the expansion of
$(1+x)^{500} + x(1+x)^{499} + x^2 (1+x)^{498} + \ldots + x^{500}$

20. Find the coefficient of x^4 in the expansion of
    (a) $(1+x+x^2+x^3)^{11}$ (b) $(2-x+3x^2)^6$
    (c) Prove that the coefficient of x^5 in $(1+x+x^3)^9$ is 378.

21. (a)* Prove that coefficient of x^4 in $(1+x-2x^2)^6$ is -45 and if the complete expansion of the expression is $1+a_1x+a_2x^2+......+a_{12}x^{12}$ prove that $a_2+a_4+a_6+.......+a_{12}=31$.
    (b)* If $(1-x+x^2)^n=a_0+a_1x+a_2x^2+.....+a_{2n}x^{2n}$ then $a_0+a_2+a_4+........+a_{2n}$ equals $\dfrac{3^n+1}{2}$.
    (M.N.R. 1992)
    (c) If $(1-x+x^2)^n=a_0+a_1x+a_2x^2+...a_{2n}x^{2n}$ where $a_0,a_1,a_2,...a_{2n}$ are in A.P. then prove that $a_n=\dfrac{1}{2n+1}$.

22. (a) Show that the sum of odd coefficients in the expansion of $(1+2x-3x^2)^{1025}$ is an even integer.
    (b)* Coefficient of x^{11} in the expansion of $(2x^2+x-3)^6$ is
    (i) 384   (ii) 192
    (iii) 572   (iv) 64

23. (a) Find the coefficient of x^2yz in the expansion of $(x+y+z)^4$.
    (b) Find the coefficient of x^4 in the expansion of $(2-x+3x^2)^6$

24. (a)* Find the coefficient of x^5 in the expansion of $(1+3x-2x^3)^8$
    (b) Prove that the coefficient of x^5 in the expansion of $(2-x+3x^2)^6$ is -4692.
    (c) The coefficient of x^{10} in the expansion of $(1+x^2-x^3)^8$ is
    (a) 476   (b) 496
    (c) 506   (d) 528

25. If $(1+2x+3x^2)^{10}=b_0+b_1x+b_2x^2...+b_{20}x^{20}$, then $b_1=20,b_2=210,b_4=8085$ and $b_{20}=3^{10}$

26. Find the coefficient of the middle term in the expansion of $(1+x)^n$ when n is even and the coefficient of middle terms if n is odd. Your answer must not be in factorial notations.

27. (a) Prove that the middle term in the expansion of $(1+x)^{2n}$ is $\dfrac{1.3.5....(2n-1)}{n!}2^n.x^n$.
    (b) Show that the term independent of x in the expansion of $\left(x+\dfrac{1}{x}\right)^{2n}$ is $\dfrac{1.3.5.....(2n-1)}{n!}.2^n$.

28. (a)* Which term in the expansion of the binomial $\left[\sqrt[3]{\sqrt{\dfrac{a}{\sqrt{(b)}}}}+\sqrt{\dfrac{b}{\sqrt[3]{(a)}}}\right]^{21}$ contains a and b to one and the same power?
    (b) The last term in $(2^{1/3}+2^{-1/2})^n$ is $\left(\dfrac{1}{3(9)^{1/3}}\right)^{\log_3 8}$, then show that the fifth term is 210.

29. In the expansion of $(x+a)^n$ if the sum of odd terms be P and sum of even terms be Q, prove that
    (a) $P^2-Q^2=(x^2-a^2)^n$,
    (b) $4PQ=(x+a)^{2n}-(x-a)^{2n}$.

30. (a) Find the value of $\dfrac{(18^3+7^3+3.18.7.25)}{3^6+6.243.2+15.81.4+20.27.8+15.9.16+6.3.32+64}$.
    (b) The product of any r consecutive natural numbers is always divisible by $r!$.
    (i) True   (ii) False
    Hence prove that if n be a +ive integer then $n^5-5n^3+60n^2-56n$ is divisible by 120.

31. Use the Binomial theorem to find 999^3.

32. Evaluate $(0.99)^{15}$ and $(1.0025)^{10}$ correct to four decimal places.

33. (a)* Show that $(\sqrt2+1)^6+(\sqrt2-1)^6=198$.
    Hence show that the integral part of $(\sqrt2+1)^6$ is 197.
    (b) Evaluate $[x+\sqrt{(x^2-1)}]^6+[x-\sqrt{(x^2-1)}]^6$.

34. (a)* The expression $[x+(x^3-1)^{1/2}]^5+[x-(x^3-1)^{1/2}]^5$ is a polynomial of degree
    (a) 5   (b) 6
    (c) 7   (d) 8   (I.I.T. 1992)
    (b) The degree of the polynomial $[\sqrt{2y^2+1}+\sqrt{2y^2-1}]^6+\left[\dfrac{2}{\sqrt{2y^2+1}+\sqrt{2y^2-1}}\right]^6$ is equal to
    (a) 8   (b) 7
    (c) 6   (d) 5
    (c) Prove that $3^n+C_2.3^{n-2}+C_4.3^{n-4}+...=2^{n-1}(1+2^n)$

35. (a) Prove that $\sqrt{10}\{(\sqrt{10}+1)^{100}-(\sqrt{10}-1)^{100}\}$ is a whole number.
    (b) The positive integer which is just greater than $(1+0.0001)^{1000}$ is equal to

(a) 3   (b) 4

(c) 5   (d) 2

(c) Prove that the digit at unit place in the number $17^{1995} + 11^{1995} - 7^{1995}$ is 1.

36. (a) What is remainder when 5^{99} is divided by 13 ?

(b) Prove that $(106)^{85} - (85)^{106}$ is divisible by 7.

37. (a)* Larger of $99^{50} + 100^{50}$ and 101^{50} is ....

(b) Of the two numbers $(1000)^{1000}$ and $(1001)^{999}$ which one is greater ?

38. (a)* The sum of the coefficients of the polynomial $(1 + x - 3x^2)^{2143}$ is ....

(b) Find out the sum of the coefficients in the expansion of the binomial $(5p - 4q)^n$, where n is a + ive integer.

39. (a)* In the expansion of $(7^{1/3} + 11^{1/9})^{6561}$, prove that there will be only 730 terms which are free from radicals.

(b)* The sum of the rational terms in the expansion of $(\sqrt{2} + 3^{1/5})^{10}$ is ....   **(I.I.T. Re-ex. 1997)**

(c) Prove that there will be only three terms which will be free from radicals in the expansion of $(5^{1/2} + 7^{1/5})^{22}$.

40. (a)* If a_1, a_2, a_3, a_4 are the coefficients of any four consecutive terms in the expansion of $(1 + x)^n$, prove that $\dfrac{a_1}{a_1 + a_2} + \dfrac{a_3}{a_3 + a_4} = \dfrac{2a_2}{a_2 + a_3}$

Another form :

$\dfrac{a_1}{a_1 + a_2}, \dfrac{a_2}{a_2 + a_3}, \dfrac{a_3}{a_3 + a_4}$ are in A.P.

or $\dfrac{a_1 + a_2}{a_1}, \dfrac{a_2 + a_3}{a_2}, \dfrac{a_3 + a_4}{a_3}$ are in H.P.

(b) With the same notations as of part (a), prove that

$\left(\dfrac{a_2}{a_2 + a_3}\right)^2 > \dfrac{a_1 a_3}{(a_1 + a_2)(a_3 + a_4)}$

41.* If the 3rd, 4th, 5th and 6th terms in the expansion of $(x + \alpha)^n$ be respectively a, b, c and d, prove that $\dfrac{b^2 - ac}{c^2 - bd} = \dfrac{5a}{3c}$.

42.* (a) The 3rd, 4th and 5th terms in the expansion of $(x + a)^n$ are respectively 84, 280 and 560, find the values of x, a and n.

(b)* If the 2nd, 3rd and 4th terms in the expansion of $(x + a)^n$ are 240, 720 and 1080 respectively, find x, a and n.

43. (a)* The coefficients of 5th, 6th and 7th terms in the expansion of $(1 + x)^n$ are in A.P., find n.

(b) Let n be a positive integer. If the coefficients of 2nd, 3rd, 4th terms in the expansion of $(1 + x)^n$ are in A.P., then find the value of n.   **(I.I.T. 1994)**

44. (a) If the coefficients of second, third and fourth terms in the expansion of $(1 + x)^{2n}$ are in A.P., show that $2n^2 - 9n + 7 = 0$.

(b) The coefficients of the second, third and fourth terms in the expansion of $(1 + x)^n$ are in A.P., find n.

45. (a) If the coefficients of rth, $(r + 1)$th and $(r + 2)$th terms in the expansion of $(1 + x)^{14}$ are in A.P., find r.

(b) Prove that two + ive integers n, r cannot be found such that $^nC_r, {}^nC_{r+1}, {}^nC_{r+2}$ and $^nC_{r+3}$ are in A.P.

46. (a)* Show that no three consecutive binomial coefficients can be in

(i) G.P.   (ii) H.P.

(b) If the coefficients of rth, $(r + 1)$th and $(r + 2)$th terms in the expansion of $(1 + x)^n$ be in H.P. then prove that n is a root of the equation $x^2 - (4r - 1) x + 4r^2 = 0$

47. Find the two consecutive terms in the expansion of $(3 + 2x)^{74}$ whose coefficients are equal.

48.* Determine at what value of x the 6th term in the expansion of the binomial $[\sqrt{2^{\log(10 - 3^x)}} + \sqrt[5]{2^{(x-2)\log 3}}]^m$ is equal to 21 if it is known that the binomial coefficients of the 2nd, 3rd and 4th terms in the expansion represent respectively the first, third and fifth terms of an A.P. (the symbol log stands for logarithm to the base 10).   **(Roorkee 1993)**

49. (a)* Show that values of x for which the sixth term in the expansion of

$\left[2^{\log_2 \sqrt{9^{x-1}+7}} + \dfrac{1}{2^{(1/5)\log_2(3^{x-1}+1)}} \right]^7$

is 84 are 1 and 2.

(b) If the second term in the expansion

$\left(\sqrt[13]{x} + \dfrac{x}{\sqrt{x^{-1}}} \right)^n$

is $14x^{5/2}$ then find the value of $^nC_3 / {}^nC_2$.

50. (a) Find n in the binomial $\left[\sqrt[3]{2} + \dfrac{1}{\sqrt[3]{(3)}} \right]^n$ if the ratio of 7th term from the beginning to the 7th term from the end is 1/6.

(b)* The sixth term in the expansion of binomial $\left(\dfrac{1}{x^{8/3}} + x^2 \log_{10} x \right)^8$ is 5600. Prove that $x = 10$.

51. (a) If the fourth term in the expansion of $[\sqrt{\{x^{1/(\log x +1)}\}} + x^{1/12}]^6$ is equal to 200 and $x > 1$, then prove that $x = 10$.

(b) The third term in the expansion of $\left(\dfrac{1}{x} + x^{\log_{10} x}\right)^5$, $x > 1$ is 1000, then prove that $x = 100$.

52. (a) In the expansion of $\left(2^x + \dfrac{1}{4^x}\right)^n$ it is observed that

(i) $\dfrac{T_3}{T_2} = 7$

(ii) The sum of the co-efficients of 2nd and 3rd term is 36. Find the value of x.

(b) If the ninth term in the expansion of $[3^{\log_3 \sqrt{25^{x-1}+7}} + 3^{-1/8 \log_3 (5^{x-1}+1)}]^{10}$ is equal to 180 and $x > 1$ then show that x is equal to $\log_5 15$.

53.* Let $(1 + x^2)^2 (1 + x)^n = \displaystyle\sum_{k=0}^{n+4} a_k x^k$. If a_1, a_2 and a_3 are in arithmetic progression, find n. **(Roorkee 1996)**

54. (a)* In the expansion of $(1 + x)^n$ the binomial coefficients of three consecutive terms are respectively 220, 495 and 792, find the value of n.

(b) If the coefficients of three consecutive terms in the expansion of $(1 + x)^n$ be 165, 330 and 462, find n.

(c) The coefficients of three consecutive terms in the expansion of $(1 + x)^n$ are in the ratio $1 : 7 : 42$ then prove that $n = 55$.

55. If $x = \dfrac{1}{3}$, find the greatest term in the expansion of $(1 + 4x)^8$.

56. (a) Find the greatest term in the expansion of $(2 + 3x)^9$ when $x = 3/2$.

(b)* In the expansion of the expression $(x + a)^{15}$, if the eleventh term is the geometric mean of the eighth and twelfth terms, which term in the expansion is the greatest? **(Roorkee 1997)**

57.* Given that the 4th term in the expansion of $\left(2 + \dfrac{3}{8} x\right)^{10}$ has the maximum numerical value, find the range of value of x for which this will be true. **(Roorkee 1994)**

58. (a) Find numerically the greatest term in the expansion of $(3 - 5x)^{15}$ when $x = 1/5$.

(b) Find the value of greatest term in the expansion of $\sqrt{3}\left(1 + \dfrac{1}{\sqrt{(3)}}\right)^{20}$.

(c)* Find numerically the greatest term in the expansion of $(2 + 3x)^{12}$ when $x = 5/6$.

59.* Prove that greatest term in the expansion of $(1 + x)^{2n}$ will have the greatest coefficient if x lies between $\dfrac{n}{n+1}$ and $\dfrac{n+1}{n}$.

60. Show that

(a) $(1 + x)^n - nx - 1$ is divisible by x^2 when $n \in N$.

(b) $2^{3n} - 7n - 1$ is divisible by 49. Hence show that $2^{3n+3} - 7n - 8$ is divisible by 49, $n \in N$.

(c) If $\theta = \left\{\dfrac{3^{2n}}{8}\right\}$, where $\{x\}$ = Fractional part of x then the value of $\sec^{-1}(8\theta)$ is

(a) π (b) 2π
(c) 3π (d) 0

(d) The remainder left out when $8^{2n} - (62)^{2n+1}$ is divided by 9 is

(a) 8 (b) 0
(c) 2 (d) 7 **(AIEEE 2009)**

61. (a) $3^{2n+2} - 8n - 9$ is divisible by 64, $n \in N$.

(b)* Show that $2^{4n} - 15n - 1$ is divisible by 225.

62. (a)* If $(2 + \sqrt{3})^n = I + f$ where I and n are $+$ive integers and $0 < f < 1$, show that I is an odd integer and $(1 - f)(I + f) = 1$.

(b) If $(5 + 2\sqrt{6})^n = I + f$ where I and n are $+$ive integers and f is a $+$ive fraction less than one, show that I is an odd integer and $(I + f)(1 - f) = 1$.

(c)* If n be any positive integer, show that the integral part of $(7 + 4\sqrt{3})^n$ is an odd number. Also if $(7 + 4\sqrt{3})^n = I + f$ where I is a $+$ive integer and f is a proper fraction, show that $(1 - f)(I + f) = 1$.

63. (a)* Show that the integer next above $(\sqrt{3} + 1)^{2m}$ contains 2^{m+1} as a factor.

(b) If I is the integral part and f the fractional part of $(5\sqrt{2} + 7)^{2n+1}$ then prove that $f(I + f) = \ldots$

64. (a)* If $(6\sqrt{6} + 14)^{2n+1} = P$, prove that the integral part of P is an even integer and $PF = 20^{2n+1}$ where F is the fractional part of P.

(b)* Let $R = (5\sqrt{5} + 11)^{2n+1}$ and $f = R - [R]$ where $[\ ]$ denotes the greatest integer function, prove that $Rf = 4^{2n+1}$.

65. Using Binomial theorem, prove the inequality

$$2 \le \left(1 + \dfrac{1}{n}\right)^n < 3, n \ge 1,$$

$$n^{n+1} > (n+1)^n, \ n \ge 3, n \in N.$$

66. (a)* Find the coefficient of x^{50} in the expression

$(1 + x)^{1000} + 2x(1 + x)^{999} + 3x^2(1 + x)^{998} + \ldots$

$+ 1001 x^{1000}$. **(Roorkee 1990)**

(b) Prove that the coefficient of x^m in the expansion of $(1+x)^n + 2(1+x)^{n-1} + 3(1+x)^{n-2} + \ldots..$
$$+ (n-m+1)(1+x)^m$$
where $0 \le m \le n$ is $^{n+2}C_{m+2}$.

(c) If $C_r = (^{101}C_r)$, then $E = \sum\limits_{r=0}^{100} (-1)^r C_r C_{r+1} =$

    (a) $(^{100}C_{51})$ (b) $(^{100}C_{50})$

    (c) $(^{101}C_{50})$ (d) $-(^{100}C_{50})$

67. (a)* If n is a positive integer and $C_k = {}^nC_k$, find the

value of $\sum\limits_{k=1}^{n} k^3 \left(\dfrac{C_k}{C_{k-1}}\right)^2$.

                         (Roorkee 1991)

(b) $\sum\limits_{r=0}^{n-1} \dfrac{{}^nC_r}{{}^nC_r + {}^nC_{r+1}} =$

    (a) $\dfrac{n}{2}$ (b) $\dfrac{n+1}{2}$

    (c) $\dfrac{n(n-1)}{2(n+1)}$ (d) $\dfrac{n(n+1)}{2}$

68.* If $\sum\limits_{r=0}^{2n} a_r (x-2)^r = \sum\limits_{i=0}^{2n} b_r (x-3)^r$ and $a_k = 1$ for all

$k \ge n$, then show $b_n = {}^{2n+1}C_{n+1}$ **(I.I.T. 1992)**

69. Prove that $\sum\limits_{r=1}^{k} (-3)^{r-1} \, {}^{3n}C_{2r-1} = 0$, where $k = \dfrac{3n}{2}$

and n is an even positive integer.   **(I.I.T. 1993)**

70. If C_r stands for ${}^nC_r$, prove that
$C_1 \sin\alpha \cos(n-1)\alpha + C_2 \sin 2\alpha \cos(n-2)\alpha$
$$+ C_3 \sin 3\alpha \cos(n-3)\alpha + \ldots + C_n \sin n\alpha$$
$$= 2^{n-1} \sin n\alpha$$

71. Prove that ${}^nC_1 - \left(1 + \dfrac{1}{2}\right){}^nC_2 + \left(1 + \dfrac{1}{2} + \dfrac{1}{3}\right){}^nC_3$
$$+ \ldots + (-1)^{n-1}\left(1 + \dfrac{1}{2} + \dfrac{1}{3} + \ldots \dfrac{1}{n}\right){}^nC_n = \dfrac{1}{n}$$

72. Let $\left(\dfrac{2x^2 + x + 2}{x}\right)^n = \sum\limits_{r=m}^{r=t} a_r x^r$, then answer the

following :

(a) The values of m and t are $\ldots$

(b) The value of $\sum\limits_{r=m}^{r=t} a_r = \ldots$

(c) The value of $a_t = \ldots$

(d) The value of $a_m = \ldots$

(e) If $a_p = a_q$, then $p + q = \ldots$
$$E = \left[1 + 2\left(x + \dfrac{1}{x}\right)\right]^n = \sum\limits_{r=m}^{r=t} a_r x^r,$$
where $r = (m, m+1, \ldots, t)$
$$E = C_0 + C_1 \cdot 2\left(x + \dfrac{1}{x}\right) + C_2\left[2\left(x + \dfrac{1}{x}\right)\right]^2 + \ldots$$
$$\ldots + C_n\left[2\left(x + \dfrac{1}{x}\right)\right]^n = \sum\limits_{r=m}^{t} a_r x^r$$

Solutions to Problem Set (1)

1. (a) Let T_{r+1} be independent of x, i.e. index of x is zero.
$$\left(3x - \dfrac{2}{x^2}\right)^{15}$$
$$T_{r+1} = {}^{15}C_r (3x)^{15-r}\left(-\dfrac{2}{x^2}\right)^r$$
$$= (-1)^r \, {}^{15}C_r \, 3^{15-r} \cdot 2^r \cdot x^{15-r-2r}. \qquad \ldots(1)$$

The index of x is $15 - 3r = 0$ ∴ $r = 5$.

Hence the 6th term is the required term. Putting $r = 5$ in (1), we get
$$T_6 = (-1)^5 \, {}^{15}C_5 \, 3^{10} \, 2^5 \, x^0$$
$$= -3^{10} \, 2^5 \cdot \dfrac{15!}{5!\,(10)!}$$
$$= -3^{10} \, 2^5 \cdot \dfrac{15 \times 14 \times 13 \times 12 \times 11}{5.4.3.2.1}$$
$$= -(3003)\, 3^{10} \, 2^5.$$

(b) Here $r = 6$ and $T_7 = 7/18$.

(c) Here $r = 2$ and $T_3 = 5/4$.

2. (a) $(1 + x + 2x^3)\left(\dfrac{3}{2}x^2 - \dfrac{1}{3x}\right)^9$
$$= (1 + x + 2x^3)\left[\left(\dfrac{3}{2}x^2\right)^9 - 9C_1\left(\dfrac{3}{2}x^2\right)^8 \cdot \dfrac{1}{3x} \ldots\right.$$
$$\left. + {}^9C_6\left(\dfrac{3}{2}x^2\right)^3\left(\dfrac{1}{3x}\right)^6 - 9C_7\left(\dfrac{3}{2}x^2\right)^2\left(\dfrac{1}{3x}\right)^7 \ldots\right]$$

In the second bracket we have to search out terms of x^0 and $1/x^3$ which when multiplied with the terms 1 and $2x^3$ in the first bracket will give a term independent of x. The term containing $1/x$ will not occur in the 2nd bracket.

∴ Term independent of x
$$= 1 \cdot \left[{}^9C_6 \dfrac{3^3}{2^3} \cdot \dfrac{1}{3^6}\right] - 2x^3\left[{}^9C_7 \dfrac{3^2}{2^2} \cdot \dfrac{1}{3^7} \cdot \dfrac{1}{x^3}\right]$$
$$= \left[\dfrac{9.8.7}{1.2.3} \cdot \dfrac{1}{8.27}\right] - 2\left[\dfrac{9.8}{1.2} \cdot \dfrac{1}{4.243}\right] = \dfrac{7}{18} - \dfrac{2}{27} = \dfrac{17}{54}.$$

(b) $T_6 = 7$.

(c) 10th term, i.e., $r = 9$
$$\therefore \quad \text{Value} = {}^{15}C_9 (-3)^9.$$

3. (a) $T_{r+1} = {}^{20}C_r (2x^2)^{20-r} (-1/x)^r$
$$= (-1)^r \, {}^{20}C_r \, 2^{20-r} \, x^{40-2r-r}$$
$$\therefore \quad 40 - 3r = 10 \quad \text{or} \quad 9$$
$$\therefore \quad 3r = 30 \quad \text{or} \quad 31.$$
∴ $r = 10$, the other value does not give integral value of r so that there will be no term of x^9.

Putting $r = 10$,

$$T_{11} = (-1)^{10}\ ^{20}C_{10}\ 2^{20-10}\ x^{40-30}$$

$$= \frac{(20)!}{(10)!(10)!}\ 2^{10}\ x^{10}$$

Hence the required coefficient is $\dfrac{(20)!}{(10)!(10)!} \cdot 2^{10}$.

(b) $T_{r+1} = {}^{10}C_r\ 3^{10-r}(-b)^r \cdot x^{20-2r-3r}$

∴ $20 - 5r = 5$ or -15

∴ $r = 3$ or $r = 7$.

∴ Coeff. of x^5 is $-9720\,b^3$ and that of x^{-15} is $-\dfrac{40}{27}b^7$.

(c) T_{r+1} in $\left(2x^2 - \dfrac{1}{3x}\right)^9 = {}^9C_r\ (2x^2)^{9-r}\left(-\dfrac{1}{3x}\right)^r$

$$= {}^9C_r\ 2^{9-r}\left(-\dfrac{1}{3}\right)^r x^{18-2r-r} \qquad \ldots(1)$$

This has got to be multiplied by the terms of first factor i.e., $1 + x + 2x^2 = x^0 + x + 2x^2$

Hence the power of x in (1) after multiplication with the terms of first factor will be $18 - 3r, 18 - 3r + 1, 18 - 3r + 2$

Each should be equal to 3

∴ $18 - 3r = 3 \Rightarrow r = 5$

$18 - 3r + 1 = 3$ ∴ $r = \dfrac{16}{3}$ rejected,

$18 - 3r + 2 = 3$ ∴ $r = \dfrac{17}{3}$ rejected.

Putting $r = 5, T_{r+1} = {}^9C_5\ 2^4\left(-\dfrac{1}{3}\right)^5 x^3$

$$= \frac{9.8.7.6.5}{1.2.3.4.5}\cdot\left(-\frac{16}{243}\right)x^3 = -\frac{224}{7}x^3$$

This when multiplied with (1) of first factor will give the term of x^3.

Hence coefficient of x^3 in the product is $-\dfrac{224}{7}$.

(d) Coefficient of $x = 154$.

4. (a) Coefficient of x^{10} i.e. $(x^2)^5$ will be in 6th term $= -\ ^{10}C_5$.

The term independent of x in the 2nd binomial will be 6th term $= -2^5\ ^{10}C_5$.

Hence their ratio is $1:2^5$ or $1:32$.

(b) The term of x^9 in $\left(x^2 - \dfrac{1}{3x}\right)^9$ will occur in 4th term i.e. $r = 3$ and its coefficient will be

$${}^9C_3\ (x^2)^6\left(-\frac{1}{3x}\right)^3 = -\frac{9!}{6!.3!}\cdot\frac{1}{3^3}$$

$$= -\frac{9\times8\times7}{3.2.1}\times\frac{1}{27} = -\frac{28}{9}.$$

Similarly term independent of x will be 7th i.e., $r = 6$ and $T_7 = \dfrac{28}{243}$.

(c) Ans. (c).

$$T_{r+1} = \frac{\dfrac{27}{5}\left(\dfrac{27}{5}-1\right)\left(\dfrac{27}{5}-2\right)\cdots\left(\dfrac{27}{5}-r+1\right)}{r!}\ x^r$$

∴ $\dfrac{27}{5} - r + 1 < 0$ or $\dfrac{32}{5} < r$

or $r > 6\dfrac{2}{5}$ ∴ $r = 7$

Hence $T_{r+1} = T_8$ is the first – ive term.

5. (a) Coefficient of x^7 in $\left(ax^2 + \dfrac{1}{bx}\right)^{11}$ is $^{11}C_5\ \dfrac{a^6}{b^5}$

Coefficient of x^{-7} in $\left(ax - \dfrac{1}{bx^2}\right)^{11}$ is $^{11}C_6\ \dfrac{a^5}{b^6}$

In case these coefficients are equal, then

$\dfrac{a^6}{b^5} = \dfrac{a^5}{b^6}$ or $a = \dfrac{1}{b}$ or $ab = 1$

∵ $^{11}C_5 = {}^{11}C_6$

(b) Ans. $n = 6, p = 1/2$.

6. (a) Put $\log_{10} x = z$.

Given expression is $(x + x^z)^5$.

$T_3 = {}^5C_2\ x^3\ (x^z)^2 = 10x^{3+2z} = 10^6$

∴ $x^{3+2z} = 10^5$. Taking log, we get

$(3 + 2z)\log_{10} x = 5\log_{10} 10$

or $(3 + 2z)z = 5$ or $2z^2 + 3z - 5 = 0$

∴ $(z - 1)(2z + 5) = 0$ ∴ $z = 1, -5/2$

∴ $\log_{10} x = 1$ or $-5/2$

∴ $x = 10^1$ or $10^{-5/2}$.

(b) Ans. (c).

$(1 + {}^mC_1 x + {}^mC_2 x^2 + \ldots)(1 - {}^nC_1 x + {}^nC_2 x^2 - \ldots)$

${}^mC_1 - {}^nC_1 = 3 \Rightarrow m - n = 3$

${}^mC_2 + {}^nC_2 - {}^mC_1\ {}^nC_1 = -6$

$m(m-1) + n(n-1) - 2mn = -12$

or $(m-n)^2 - (m+n) = -12$

or $9 - (2m-3) = -12$ ∴ $m = 12$

7. (a) $\left(\dfrac{a}{x} + bx\right)^{12}$ will have $12 + 1 = 13$ terms and middle term will be

$12/2 + 1$ i.e. 7th ∴ $T_7 = 924\,a^6b^6$

(b) Middle term will be $10/2 + 1$ i.e. 6th and $T_6 = -252$.

(c) Here $n = 9$ the number of terms will be 10 and there will be two middle terms

$\dfrac{n+1}{2}$ and $\dfrac{n+3}{2}$ i.e. 5th and 6th

$$T_5 = \frac{189}{8} x^{17}, \quad T_6 = -\frac{21}{16} x^{19}.$$

(d) Ans. (b).

$$E = (1+x)^1 [(1+x)(1+x^2-x)]^{100}$$
$$= (1+x)(1+x^3)^{100}$$
$$= (1+x) [101 \text{ terms in } (1+x^3)^{100}]$$
$$= 101 + 101 = 202 \text{ terms in } E.$$

8. (a) $T_{r-1} = {}^nC_{r-2} \cdot x^{r-2}$ ∴ Coeff. is ${}^nC_{r-2}$

$T_{2r+3} = {}^nC_{2r+2} \cdot x^{2r+2}$ ∴ Coeff. is ${}^nC_{2r+2}$.

Now ${}^nC_{r-2} = {}^nC_{2r+2}$.

But if ${}^nC_p = {}^nC_q$ then $p + q = n$

∴ $(r-2) + (2r+2) = n = 15$

or $3r = 15$ ∴ $r = 5$.

(b) ${}^{43}C_{2r} = {}^{43}C_{r+1}$ ∴ $2r + r + 1 = 43$

or $3r = 42$ ∴ $r = 14$.

9. (a) ${}^nC_3 = {}^nC_{12} \Rightarrow n = 15$

$\left(x^2 + \dfrac{1}{x}\right)^{15}$. We have to find the term independent

of x. It will be 11th term

$$T_{11} = {}^{15}C_{10} (x^2)^5 \left(\frac{1}{x}\right)^{10} = {}^{15}C_5 = 3003.$$

(b) Ans. $r = 6$.

10. (a) Ans. (b).

$$T_5 + T_6 = 0$$
$$\Rightarrow \quad {}^nC_4 \, a^{n-4} (-b)^4 + {}^nC_5 \, a^{(n-5)} (-b)^5 = 0$$
$$\therefore \quad \frac{{}^nC_5}{{}^nC_4} = -\frac{a^{n-4}}{a^{n-5}} \cdot \frac{b^4}{-b^5} = \frac{a}{b}$$
$$\text{or} \quad \frac{n-4}{5} = \frac{a}{b}$$
$$\left[\frac{{}^nC_5}{{}^nC_4} = \text{coeff. of } \frac{T_6}{T_5} = \frac{n-r+1}{r} = \frac{n-4}{5} \text{ for } r = 5\right]$$

(b) $T_{p+1} = {}^nC_p \, x^{n-p} (1/x)^p$

Index of x is $n - p - p = r$ ∴ $p = \dfrac{n-r}{2}$

∴ Coeff. of x^r is

$${}^nC_{(n-r)/2} = \frac{n!}{\{(n-r)/2\}! \, \{(n+r)/2\}!}.$$

11. (a) Let $\sqrt{4x+1} = y$ ∴ $4x + 1 = y^2$

or $x^5 = \left(\dfrac{y^2 - 1}{4}\right)^5$ i.e., the power of y is 10

$$E = \frac{1}{y} \left[\left(\frac{1+y}{2}\right)^n - \left(\frac{1-y}{2}\right)^n \right]$$
$$= \frac{1}{y} \cdot \frac{1}{2^n} [2({}^nC_1 \, y + {}^nC_3 \, y^3 + \dots + {}^nC_n \, y^n)]$$

For x^5, E should contain y^{10} or the numerator of E should have the term of y^{11}. Hence $n = 11$

(b) $T_1 = \dfrac{y+1}{y^{2/3} - y^{1/3} + 1} = \dfrac{t^3 + 1}{t^2 - t + 1}$ where $t = y^{1/3}$

or $T_1 = t + 1 = y^{1/3} + 1$

$$T_2 = \frac{y-1}{y - y^{1/2}} = \frac{z^2 - 1}{z^2 - z} \text{ where } z = y^{1/2}$$

$$T_2 = \frac{1}{z}(z+1) = 1 + z^{-1} = 1 + y^{-1/2}$$

∴ $E = (T_1 - T_2)^{10} = (y^{1/3} - y^{-1/2})^{10}$

$$T_{r+1} = {}^{10}C_r (-1)^r (y)^{\frac{10-r}{3}} (y^{-1/2})^r \quad \dots(1)$$

The power of y is $\dfrac{10-r}{3} - \dfrac{r}{2} = 0$

$\Rightarrow 5r = 20 \Rightarrow r = 4$

Hence the coefficient is

$${}^{10}C_4 (-1)^4 = \frac{10!}{6! \, 4!} = 210$$

12. (a) $E = (1+x) [(1+x)(1-x+x^2)]^{40}$

$= (1+x)(1+x^3)^{40}$

$T_{r+1} = (1+x) \, {}^{40}C_r \, (x^3)^r$

The power of x will be $3r$ or $3r + 1$.

If $3r = 50$ or $3r + 1 = 50$ then both do not give integral value of r and hence no term will be of the type λx^{50}.

Hence coefficient of x^{50} is 0 (zero).

(b) Ans. (c).

$E = $ Sum of a G.P. of $(n+1)$ terms

$$1 \cdot \left[\frac{(1+x)^{n+1} - 1}{1 + x - 1}\right] = \frac{1}{x} [(1+x)^{n+1} - 1]$$

Coefficient of x^8 in E is coefficient of x^9 in $(1+x)^{n+1}$ which is

$${}^{n+1}C_9 = {}^{n+1}C_{(n+1)-9} = {}^{n+1}C_{n-8} \Rightarrow \text{(c)}$$

as ${}^nC_r = {}^nC_{n-r}$

(c) Ans. (b).

T_{r+1} in $(1-x)^n = {}^nC_r (-x)^r = (-1)^r \, {}^nC_r \, x^r$

∴ Required coefficient of x^n in $(1+x)(1-x)^n$ is

$(-1)^n \, {}^nC_n + 1 \cdot (-1)^{n-1} \, {}^nC_{n-1} = (-1)^n [1-n] \Rightarrow \text{(b)}$

∴ ${}^nC_n = 1, \, {}^nC_{n-1} = {}^nC_1 = n$

13. (a) $T_{r+1} = {}^{2n}C_r (x^2)^{2n-r} \cdot (1/x)^r$

Index of x is $4n - 2r - r = p$

∴ $r = \dfrac{4n-p}{3}$ which should be an integer.

∴ Coefficient is

$$^{2n}C_{(4n-p)/3} = \frac{(2n)!}{[(2n+p)/3]![(4n-p)/3]!}.$$

(b) Proceed as above.

14. (a) In other words we have to prove that

$$^{n+1}C_r = {}^nC_{r-1} + {}^nC_r$$

which we have proved already in the chapter of permutation and combination. **See Q. 6, P. 319-321.**

(b) Do yourself as in last question.

15. Ans. (d).

$$^nC_r + 2\,{}^nC_{r-1} + {}^nC_{r-2}$$

$$= ({}^nC_r + {}^nC_{r-1}) + ({}^nC_{r-1} + {}^nC_{r-2})$$

$$= {}^{n+1}C_r + {}^{n+1}C_{r-1} = {}^{n+2}C_r \Rightarrow \text{(d)}.$$

16. (a) x^n will occur in $(n+1)$th term and their coefficients will be $^{2n}C_n$ and $^{2n-1}C_n$ and we have to find their ratio

$$\frac{(2n)!}{n!.n!} \cdot \frac{n!(n-1)!}{(2n-1)!} = \frac{2n.(2n-1)!}{n.(n-1)!} \cdot \frac{(n-1)!}{(2n-1)!} = 2.$$

Hence first coefficient is double the other.

(b) Prove yourself.

17. (a) Putting $x = y = 1$ the sum of the coefficients is

$$2^n = 4096 = 16^3 = (2^4)^3 \quad \therefore \ n = 12$$

If $^nC_r = {}^{12}C_r$ will be greatest when $r = \dfrac{n}{2} = 6$ as n is even. Hence $^{12}C_6 = 924$.

(b) Ans. (d).

As sum of coeff. is 4^{10} on putting

$$x = y = z = 1$$

(c) Ans. (b).

$$A = 8^n, B = 2^n \quad \therefore \quad B^3 = 8^n = A$$

(d) The sum of the coefficients is obtained by putting $x = 1 = y$ in the two binomials

$$\therefore \quad (\alpha - 2 + 1)^{35} = (1 - \alpha)^{35}$$

or $\quad (\alpha - 1)^{35} = -(\alpha - 1)^{35}$

or $\quad 2(\alpha - 1)^{35} = 0$ or $\alpha - 1 = 0$ ∴ $\alpha = 1$

18. (a) We have to find the coefficient of x^5 and hence in the expansion terms of x^6, x^7, etc. be rejected

$$(1 + x^2)^5 (1 + x)^4$$

$$= (1 + {}^5C_1 x^2 + {}^5C_2 x^4 + ...)(1 + {}^4C_1 x + {}^4C_2 x^2 + {}^4C_3 x^3 + {}^4C_4 x^4)$$

$$= (1 + 5x^2 + 10x^4 + ...)(1 + 4x + 6x^2 + 4x^3 + x^4)$$

The terms giving x^5 in the above product is

$$(5x^2)(4x^3) + (10x^4)(4x) = (20 + 40)x^5 = 60x^5.$$

Hence the coefficient is 60.

(b) $(1 + x + x^2 + x^3)^n = (1 + x)^n (1 + x^2)^n$

$$= (C_0 + C_1 x + C_2 x^2 + C_3 x^3 + C_4 x^4 + ...)$$

$$[C_0 + C_1 (x^2) + C_2 (x^2)^2 + ...]$$

∴ Coeff. of $x^4 = C_0 C_2 + C_2 C_1 + C_4 C_0$

$$= {}^nC_2 + {}^nC_2 \cdot {}^nC_1 + {}^nC_4$$

(c) Ans. (d). $E = (1 + t^2)^{12}(1 + t^{12} + t^{24} + t^{36})$

$$= [C_0 + C_1 (t^2) + C_2 (t^2)^2 + ... C_6 (t^2)^6 + ... + C_{12}(t^2)^{12}] \cdot [1 + t^{12} + t^{24} + t^{36}]$$

∴ Coefficient of t^{24} is

$$1.C_{12} + 1.C_6 + C_0 = 2 + {}^{12}C_6$$

as $C_0 = C_{12} = 1$.

(d) $(1 + 2x^2 + x^4)(c_0 + c_1 x + c_2 x^2 + c_3 x^3 ...)$

$$= a_0 + a_1 x + a_2 x^2 + a_3 x^3 + ...$$

Equating the coefficients of x, x^2 and x^3 we have

$$a_1 = c_1, \ a_2 = 2c_0 + c_2, \ a_3 = 2c_1 + c_3$$

Also $2a_2 = a_1 + a_3$ as a_1, a_2, a_3 are in A.P.

∴ $\quad 2(2c_0 + c_2) = c_1 + 2c_1 + c_3$

or $\quad 4 + 2.\dfrac{n(n-1)}{1.2} = 3n + \dfrac{n(n-1)(n-2)}{1.2.3}$

$$6(n^2 - n + 4) = n[18 + n^2 - 3n + 2]$$

or $\quad n^3 - 9n^2 + 26n - 24 = 0$

By trial $n = 2$ satisfies it

∴ $\quad (n-2)(n^2 - 7n + 12) = 0$

$$(n-2)(n-3)(n-4) = 0$$

∴ $\quad n = 2, 3, 4.$

(e) Ans. (c).

$$\left(1 - my + \frac{m(m-1)}{2}y^2 - ...\right)$$

$$\left(1 + ny + \frac{n(n-1)}{2}y^2 + ...\right)$$

$$a_1 = \text{coeff. of } y = n - m = 10 \qquad ...(1)$$

$$a_2 = \text{Coeff. of } y^2 = \frac{m(m-1)}{2} + \frac{n(n-1)}{2} - mn = 10$$

$$(m^2 + n^2) - (m + n) - 2mn = 20$$

or $\quad (n - m)^2 - 20 = m + n$

or $\quad m + n = 10^2 - 20 = 80$ by (1) $\qquad ...(2)$

Solving (1) and (2), $n = 45, m = 35$.

19. (a) The given sum is expansion of

$$[(x - 3) + 2]^{100} = (x - 1)^{100} = (1 - x)^{100}$$

∴ $\quad x^{53}$ will occur in T_{54}.

$$T_{54} = {}^{100}C_{53}(-x)^{53} \quad \therefore \text{ Coefficient is } - {}^{100}C_{53}.$$

(b) $S = (1 + x)^{500} \times$

$$\left[1 + \left(\frac{x}{1+x}\right) + \left(\frac{x}{1+x}\right)^2 + ... \left(\frac{x}{1+x}\right)^{500}\right]$$

$$= (1+x)^{500} \times$$

$$\left[\text{Sum of a G.P. of 501 terms whose } a = 1, r = \frac{x}{1+x}\right]$$

$$= (1+x)^{500} \left[\frac{1 \cdot \left\{1 - \left(\frac{x}{1+x}\right)^{501}\right\}}{1 - \frac{x}{1+x}}\right]$$

$$= (1+x)^{500} \left[\frac{(1+x)^{501} - x^{501}}{(1+x)^{500}}\right] = [(1+x)^{501} - x^{501}]$$

Now coefficient of x^r in $(1+x)^n$ is ^nC_r

∴ Coefficient of x^{301} is $^{501}C_{301}$

20. (a) $1 + x + x^2 + x^3 = (1+x) + x^2(1+x)$

$$= (1+x)(1+x^2)$$

∴ $(1 + x + x^2 + x^3)^{11} = (1+x)^{11}(1+x^2)^{11}$.

We want the coeff. of x^4.

$$= (1 + {}^{11}C_1 \, x + {}^{11}C_2 \, x^2 + {}^{11}C_3 \, x^3 + {}^{11}C_4 \, x^4 + ...)$$
$$\times (1 + {}^{11}C_1 \, x^2 + {}^{11}C_2 \, x^4 + ...)$$

Collect terms which give x^4.

$$1 \cdot {}^{11}C_2 \, x^4 + {}^{11}C_2 \, x^2 \cdot {}^{11}C_1 \, x^2 + {}^{11}C_4 \, x^4 \cdot 1.$$

Hence the coefficient of x^4 is

$${}^{11}C_2 + {}^{11}C_2 \times {}^{11}C_1 + {}^{11}C_4$$

$$= \frac{11 \times 10}{1.2} + \frac{11 \times 10}{1.2} \times \frac{11}{1} + \frac{11 \times 10 \times 9 \times 8}{4.3.2.1}$$

$$= 55 + 605 + 330 = 990.$$

(b) $(2 - x + 3x^2)^6 = [2 - x(1 - 3x)]^6$

$$= 2^6 - {}^6C_1 \, 2^5 \, x(1 - 3x) + {}^6C_2 \, 2^4 \, x^2 (1-3x)^2$$
$$- {}^6C_3 \, 2^3 \, x^3 (1-3x)^3 + {}^6C_4 \cdot 2^2 \, x^4 (1-3x)^4 ...$$

Only 3rd, 4th and 5th terms will give the terms of x^4

In 3rd it is $\quad {}^6C_2 \cdot 2^4 \, x^2 (9x^2); \quad {}^6C_2 = \frac{6.5}{1.2} = 15$

In 4th it is $\quad - {}^6C_3 \cdot 2^3 \, x^3 (-3.3x);$

$$\qquad\qquad\qquad {}^6C_3 = \frac{6.5.4}{1.2.3} = 20$$

In 5th it is $\quad {}^6C_4 \, 2^3 \, x^4 \cdot 1; \quad {}^6C_4 = {}^6C_2 = 15.$

Hence the total coefficient of x^4 is

$$(15 \times 16 \times 9 + 20 \times 8 \times 9 + 15 \times 4)$$
$$= (2160 + 1440 + 60) = 3660.$$

Note : For alternative method, see **Q. 23 (b)** below.

(c) $\{(1+x) + x^3\}^9$

$$= (1+x)^9 + {}^9C_1 \, (1+x)^8 \cdot (x^3) + ...$$

Other forms will contain powers of x greater than 5

∴ Co-efficient of x^5 in $^9C_5 + 9 \cdot {}^8C_2$

$$= \frac{9.8.7.6.5}{1.2.3.4.5} + 9 \cdot \frac{8.7}{1.2} = 126 + 252 = 378$$

21. (a) $(1 + x - 2x^2)^6 = (1-x)^6 (1+2x)^6$

$$= (1 - 6x + 15x^2 - 20x^3 + 15x^4 ....) \times$$
$$[1 + 6(2x) + 15(2x)^2 + 20(2x)^3 + 15(2x)^4 + ...]$$
$$^6C_1 = 6, \ ^6C_2 = 15, \ ^6C_3 = 20, \ ^6C_4 = 15 \text{ etc.}$$

Multiply and the term of x^4 will be

$$[1 . 15 . 2^4 - 6 . 20 . 2^3 + 15 . 15 . 2^2$$
$$- 20.6.2 + 15.1] \, x^4.$$

Hence the coefficient of x^4 is

$$240 - 960 + 900 - 240 + 15 = -60 + 15 = -45$$

$$(1 + x - 2x^2)^6 = 1 + a_1 x + a_2 x^2 + ... + a_{12} \, x^{12}$$

Putting, $x = 1$, we get

$$0 = 1 + a_1 + a_2 + ... + a_{12} \qquad ...(1)$$

Putting, $x = -1$, we get

$$64 = 1 - a_1 + a_2 - .... + a_{12} \qquad ...(2)$$

Adding (1) and (2), we get

$$64 = 2(1 + a_2 + a_4 + ...)$$

∴ $a_2 + a_4 + a_6 + ... + a_{12} = 31$

(b) Put $x = 1, -1$ successively in the given equation and add.

(c) $a_n = T_{n+1}$ of A.P. $= a_0 + nd \qquad ...(1)$

Putting $x = 1$ in the given relation, we have

$$a_0 + a_1 + a_2 + ... a_{2n} = 1^n$$

or $S_{2n+1} = \dfrac{2n+1}{2} [a_0 + a_{2n}] = 1$

or $a_0 + T_{2n+1} = \dfrac{2}{2n+1} \quad \because a_{2n} = T_{2n+1}$

or $a_0 + (a_0 + 2nd) = \dfrac{2}{2n+1}$

or $2(a_0 + nd) = \dfrac{2}{2n+1}$ or $a_0 + nd = \dfrac{1}{2n+1}$

or $T_{n+1} = a_0 + nd = a_n = \dfrac{1}{2n+1}$

22. (a) Let $(1 + 2x - 3x^2)^{1025} = a_0 + a_1 x + a_2 x^2 + ...$

Putting $x = 1$, we get $0 = a_0 + a_1 + a_2 + a_3 + ...$

Putting $x = -1$, we get

$$(-4)^{1025} = a_0 - a_1 + a_2 - a_3 + ...$$

Adding $a_0 + a_2 + a_4 + ... = -\dfrac{1}{2}(4)^{1025}$

$$= -2(4)^{1024} \ i.e., \text{even}$$

(b) Ans. (b).

$$(x - 1)^6 (2x + 3)^6$$

$$= (x^6 - 6x^5 + 15 x^4 - 20 x^3 ...)$$
$$\cdot \{(2x)^6 + 6.(2x)^5 . 3 + 15(2x)^4 . 3^2 + ...\}$$

Coeff. of x^{11} is

$$18.2^5 - 6.2^6 = 2^5(18-12) = 192.$$

23. (a) **1st Method :** $[x+(y+z)]^4$. Expand binomially and proceed as above.

Ans. 12

2nd Method : If $p+q+r = n$ then the coefficient of $x^p y^q z^r$ in $(x+y+z)^n$ is $\dfrac{n!}{p!q!r!}$.

Here $2+1+1 = 4$

∴ Coefficient of $x^2 yz = \dfrac{4!}{2!1!2!} = 12$.

In general $(x+y+z)^n = \Sigma \dfrac{n!}{p!q!r!} x^p y^q z^r$

such that $p+q+r = n$ and the summation is taken over all **non-negative integers** p, q, r which satisfy the above condition.

(b) We have already done this question in **Q. 20 (b)**.

$$(x+y+z)^n = \Sigma \dfrac{n!}{p!q!r!} x^p y^q z^r$$

where $p+q+r = 6$ ...(1)

∴ $(2-x+3x^2)^6 = \Sigma \dfrac{6!}{p!q!r!} 2^p (-x)^q (3x^2)^r$ ...(2)

For the term of x^4 we must have

$$q+2r = 4 \quad ...(3)$$

Now we have to solve (1) and (3) and find non-negative integral values of p, q, r.

From (2) we have the following :

$$r = 0, q = 4 \quad \therefore \quad p = 2$$
$$r = 1, q = 2 \quad \therefore \quad p = 3$$
$$r = 2, q = 0 \quad \therefore \quad p = 4$$

Putting the above values in (2), the coefficient of x^4 is

$$\dfrac{6!}{2!4!0!}.2^2.1.1 + \dfrac{6!}{3!2!1!}.2^3.1.3 + \dfrac{6!}{4!0!2!}.2^4.1.3^2$$

$$= (15 \times 4) + (60 \times 24) + (15 \times 144)$$
$$= 15(4+96+144) = 15 \times 244 = 3660.$$

24. (a) $(1+3x-2x^3)^8$

$$= \Sigma \dfrac{n!}{(p!)(q!)(r!)} (1)^p (3x)^q (-2x^3)^r \quad ...(A)$$

where $p+q+r = n = 8$ ...(I)

for x^5, we have $q+3r = 5$

∴ $r = 0, q = 5 \quad \therefore \quad p = 3$ by (I)

or $r = 1, q = 2 \quad \therefore \quad p = 5$ by (I)

Putting the above values in (A), we have

$$\dfrac{8!}{(3!)(5!)(0!)}.1^3.3^5(-2)^0$$

$$+ \dfrac{8!}{(5!)(2!)(1!)}.1^5.3^2.(-2)^1$$

$$= 56(243) + 8.7.6(-9) = 56(243-54) = 56(189)$$

(b) Proceed exactly as in part (a).

(c) Ans. (a).

$$E = [1+x^2(1-x)]^8$$

$$= {}^8C_0 + {}^8C_1 x^2(1-x) + {}^8C_2 x^4 (1-x)^2$$
$$+ {}^8C_3 x^6(1-x)^3 + {}^8C_4 x^8(1-x)^4$$
$$+ {}^8C_5 x^{10}(1-x)^5 + ...$$

In the above expansion we have to find the coefficient of x^{10} which will occur in the following two terms :

$$= {}^8C_4 x^8(1-x)^4 + {}^8C_5 x^{10}(1-x)^5$$

${}^8C_4$ coeff. of x^2 in $(1-x)^4 + {}^8C_5 x^{10}.1$

$$= {}^8C_4 . {}^4C_2 + {}^8C_5.1$$

$$= \dfrac{8!}{4!4!}.6 + \dfrac{8.7.6}{1.2.3} + \dfrac{8.7.6.5}{1.2.3.4}.6 + 8.7 = \dfrac{7.6.5}{3}.6 + 56$$

$$= (70).6 + 56 = 420 + 56 = 476$$

25. $(x+y+z)^n = \Sigma \dfrac{n!}{p!q!r!} x^p . y^q . z^r$

where $p+q+r = n$

∴ $(1+2x+3x^2)^{10} = \Sigma \dfrac{10!}{p!q!r!} 1^p.(2x)^q (3x^2)^r$

$$= \Sigma \dfrac{10!}{p!q!r!} 2^q .3^r x^{q+2r}$$

where $p+q+r = 10$ ...(1)

Now b_1, b_2, b_4, b_{20} are coefficients of x, x^2, x^4 and x^{20} respectively. Hence we must have

$$q+2r = 1 \text{ or } 2 \text{ or } 4 \text{ or } 20 \quad ...(2)$$

We will now solve (1) with each of the four equations given in (2) to get the non-negative integral values of p, q and r.

$$p+q+r = 10, q+2r = 1$$

∴ $r = 0, q = 1, p = 9$

∴ $b_1 = \dfrac{10!}{9!1!0!} 1^9.(2)^1 (3)^0 = \dfrac{10.9! \times 2}{9! \times 1 \times 1} = 20$

Again solving for non-negative integral values

$$p+q+r = 10 \text{ and } q+2r = 2$$

∴ $r = 0, q = 2, p = 8, r = 1$ or $q = 0, p = 9$

∴ $b_2 = \dfrac{10!}{8!2!0!} (1)^8.(2)^2 .!(3)^0$

$$+ \dfrac{10!}{9!1!0!} 1^9.(2)^0 (3)^1$$

$b_2 = (45)(4) + (10)(3) = 180 + 30 = 210$

Again solving $p+q+r = 10$ and $q+2r = 4$

∴ $r = 0, q = 4 \ p = 6$, or $r = 1, q = 2, p = 6$

or $r = 2, q = 0, p = 8$

∴ $b_4 = \dfrac{10!}{6!4!0!} 1^6.2^4.3^0 + \dfrac{10!}{6!2!1!}$

$$1^6.2^2.3^1 + \dfrac{10!}{8!0!2!} 1^8.2^0.3^2$$

$b_4 = 3360 + 4320 + 405 = 8085$

Again solving

$p + q + r = 10$ and $q + 2r = 20$

We have $r = 10, q = 0, p = 0$. All other values of r from 0 to 9 and corresponding values of q will make $q + r > 10$ whereas $p + q + r = 10$

$\therefore \quad b_{20} = \dfrac{10!}{10!} 1^0 . 2^0 . 3^{10} = 3^{10}$

26. If n is even, then middle term is $[(n/2) + 1]$th. Hence

$T_{n/2 + 1} = {}^nC_{n/2} \, x^{n/2}$

$\therefore$ Coefficient is ${}^nC_{n/2} = \dfrac{n!}{(n/2)! . (n/2)!}$ (n is even)

$= \dfrac{n(n-1)(n-2)\ldots 3.2.1}{(n/2)! . (n/2)!}$

$= [n(n-2)\ldots 4.2][(n-1)(n-3)\ldots 3.1] \div (n/2)! . (n/2)!$

Even Num.   Odd. Num.

Each bracket contains $n/2$ numbers and the first contains all even numbers and 2nd all odd. You can take 2 common from each of the $n/2$ even numbers.

$= 2^{n/2} \left[\dfrac{n}{2} \left(\dfrac{n}{2} - 1 \right) \ldots 2.1 \right]$

$\qquad [(n-1)(n-3)\ldots 5.3.1] \div (n/2)! . (n/2)!$

$= 2^{n/2} . (n/2)! [(n-1)(n-3)\ldots 5.3.1] \div (n/2)! . (n/2)!$

$= 2^{n/2} \dfrac{[(n-1)(n-3)\ldots 5.3.1]}{[1.2.3\ldots n/2]}$

2nd Part : If n is odd, then the two middle terms are

$\left(\dfrac{n+1}{2} \right)$th and $\left(\dfrac{n+3}{2} \right)$th

i.e. $T_{(n+1)/2} = T_{(n-1)/2 + 1} = {}^nC_{(n-1)/2} \, x^{(n-1)/2}$

and $T_{(n+3)/2} = T_{(n+1)/2 + 1} = {}^nC_{(n+1)/2} \, x^{(n+1)/2}$

$\therefore$ The coefficients are

${}^nC_{(n-1)/2}$ and ${}^nC_{(n+1)/2}$.

But as ${}^nC_r = {}^nC_{n-r}$ therefore the above two coefficients are equal. It should be noted when n is odd then both

$\dfrac{n-1}{2}$ and $\dfrac{n+1}{2}$ are integers.

Now proceeding as above the coefficient is

$2^{(n-1)/2} \dfrac{1.3.5 \ldots n}{1.2 \ldots [(n+1)/2]}$

27. (a) The middle term is $\dfrac{2n}{2} + 1$, i.e. T_{n+1}

in the expansion of $(1 + x)^{2n}$

$T_{n+1} = {}^{2n}C_n \, x^n = \dfrac{(2n)!}{n! \, n!} x^n$.

$= x^n [2n (2n-1)(2n-2)(2n-3)\ldots$

$\qquad\qquad\qquad\qquad 5.4.3.2.1] \div n! . n!$

$= x^n [2n (2n-2)\ldots 4.2][(2n-1)(2n-3)\ldots$

$\qquad\qquad\qquad\qquad\qquad 5.3.1] \div n! . n!$

even   odd

$= x^n \, 2^n \, n! [(2n-1)(2n-3)\ldots 5.3.1] \div n! . n!$

$= 2^n [1.3.5\ldots (2n-1)] x^n \div n!$

(b) The term independent of x will be T_{n+1}

$\therefore \quad T_{n+1} = {}^{2n}C_n \, x^n . \dfrac{1}{x^n} = {}^{2n}C_n$

which can be shown as given by part (a).

28. (a) On simplification, we easily get

$T_{r+1} = {}^{21}C_r \, a^{7 - r/2} . b^{2r/3 - 7/2}$

Since the powers of a and b are the same, we have

$7 - \dfrac{1}{2} r = \dfrac{2}{3} r - \dfrac{7}{2}$ or $r = 9$.

Hence $(9 + 1)$th, i.e., 10th term is the required term.

(b) The last term $= T_{n+1}$

$= {}^nC_n (2^{1/3})^0 (2^{-1/2})^n = \left[\dfrac{1}{3 \, (9)^{1/3}} \right]^{\log_3 8}$

or $2^{-n/2} = (3^{-5/3})^{\log_3 8} = 3^{\log_3 8^{-5/3}}$

$\because \quad a^{\log_a n} = n$

or $2^{-n/2} = 8^{-5/3} = (2^3)^{-5/3} = 2^{-5} \quad \therefore n = 10$

$\therefore \quad T_5 = {}^{10}C_4 (2^{1/3})^6 (2^{-1/2})^4$

$= 210 \, (2^2)(2^{-2}) = 210.$

29. (a) $(x + a)^n = x^n + {}^nC_1 x^{n-1} a + {}^nC_2 x^{n-2} a^2$

$\qquad\qquad\qquad\qquad + {}^nC_3 x^{n-3} a^3 + \ldots$

$= (x^n + {}^nC_2 x^{n-2} a^2 + \ldots)$

$\qquad\qquad + ({}^nC_1 x^{n-1} a + {}^nC_3 x^{n-3} a^3 + \ldots)$

$= P + Q$

$\therefore \quad (x - a)^n = P - Q$, as the terms are alt. +ive and $-$ive.

$\therefore \quad P^2 - Q^2 = (P + Q)(P - Q)$

$\qquad\qquad = (x + a)^n (x - a)^n = (x^2 - a^2)^n$

(b) $4PQ = (P + Q)^2 - (P - Q)^2 = (x + a)^{2n} - (x - a)^{2n}$

30. (a) The numerator is of the form

$a^3 + b^3 + 3ab(a + b) = (a + b)^3$,

where $a = 18$ and $b = 7$

$\therefore \quad N^r = (18 + 7)^3 = 25^3$.

For D^r, $3^1 = 3$, $3^2 = 9$, $3^3 = 27$,

$3^4 = 81$, $3^5 = 243$

${}^6C_1 = 6$, ${}^6C_2 = 15$, ${}^6C_3 = 20$,

${}^6C_4 = {}^6C_2 = 15$, ${}^6C_5 = {}^6C_1 = 6$, ${}^6C_6 = 1$

$\therefore \quad D^r = 3^6 + {}^6C_1 \, 3^5 . 2^1 + {}^6C_2 \, 3^4 . 2^2$

$\qquad + {}^6C_3 \, 3^3 . 2^3 + {}^6C_4 \, 3^2 . 2^4 + {}^6C_5 \, 3 . 2^5 + {}^6C_6 \, 2^6$

This is clearly the expansion of

$$(3+2)^6 = 5^6 = (25)^3$$

$$\therefore \quad \frac{N^r}{D^r} = \frac{(25)^3}{(25)^3} = 1.$$

(b) Ans. (i). We prove it by induction.

$$\frac{(n+1)(n+2)....(n+r)}{r!} = P, \text{ say} \quad ...(1)$$

$$\therefore \quad \frac{1.2.3......n}{n!} \cdot P = \frac{(n+r)!}{n! \, r!}, \text{ by (1)}$$

$$= {}^{n+r}C_r = \text{an integer. Hence from (1)}$$

$(n+1)(n+2).....(n+r)$ is divisible by $r!$.

Now $n(n^4 - 5n^2 + 60n - 56)$

$$= n[(n^4 - 5n^2 + 4) + 60n - 60]$$

$$= n(n^2 - 1)(n^2 - 4) + 60n(n-1)$$

$$= n(n+1)(n-1)(n+2)(n-2) + 60n(n-1)$$

$$= (n+2)(n+1)n(n-1)(n-2) + 60n(n-1)$$

$$= 120k$$

The first term being the product of 5 consecutive numbers has a factor $5! = 120$ in it. In the second, $60n(n-1)$ has $60.2! = 120$.

Hence the given expression is divisible by 120.

31. $(999)^3 = (10^3 - 1)^3 = (10^9 - 1) - 3.10^3 . 1(10^3 - 1)$

$$[\because (a-b)^3 = a^3 - b^3 - 3ab(a-b)]$$

$$= 10^3 [10^6 - 3(10^3 - 1)] - 1$$

$$= 1000[1000000 - 2997] - 1$$

$$= 1000 \times 997003 - 1 = 997002999.$$

32. $(.99)^{15} = (1 - .01)^{15}$

$$= 1 - {}^{15}C_1 (.01) + {}^{15}C_2 (.01)^2 - {}^{15}C_3 (.01)^3 + ...$$

We want the answer correct to only 4 decimal places and as such we have left further expansion.

$$\therefore \quad (.99)^{15} = (1 - .01)^{15}$$

$$= 1 - 15(.01) + \frac{15.14}{1.2}(.0001) - \frac{15.14.13}{1.2.3}(.000001)$$

$$= 1 - .15 + .0105 - .000455$$

$$= 1.0105 - (.150455) = 1.0105 - .1504 = .8601,$$

correct to four places of decimal.

33. (a) $(x+a)^n + (x-a)^n = 2(x^n + {}^nC_2 x^{n-2} a^2$

$$+ {}^nC_4 x^{n-4} a^4 + {}^nC_6 x^{n-6} a^6 + ...)$$

Here $n = 6$, ${}^6C_2 = 15$, ${}^6C_4 = 15$, ${}^6C_6 = 1$,

$$x = \sqrt{2}, a = 1$$

$$\therefore \quad (\sqrt{2}+1)^6 + (\sqrt{2}-1)^6 = 2[(\sqrt{2})^6$$

$$+ 15(\sqrt{2})^4 .1 + 15(\sqrt{2})^2 .1 + 1.1]$$

$$= 2[8 + 15.4 + 15.2 + 1] = 2(99) = 198$$

$$\therefore \quad (\sqrt{2}+1)^6 = 198 - (\sqrt{2}-1)^6 \quad ...(1)$$

Now $\sqrt{2} - 1 = 1.4 - 1 = .4 < 1$

$$\therefore \quad (\sqrt{2}-1)^6 < 1, \text{ and it is certainly } +\text{ive}$$

$$\therefore \quad 0 < (\sqrt{2}-1)^6 < 1. \quad ...(2)$$

Hence from (1) by the help of (2), we get

$(\sqrt{2}+1)^6 = 198 - (\text{something} + \text{ive but} < 1)$

$$= 197 . (\text{something})$$

Therefore the integral part of $(\sqrt{2}+1)^6$ is 197.

(b) As above $x = x, a = \sqrt{x^2 - 1}$

$$\therefore \quad [(x+\sqrt{x^2-1})]^6 + [(x-\sqrt{x^2-1})]^6$$

$$= 2[x^6 + 15x^4 \sqrt{(x^2-1)^2} + 15x^2 \sqrt{(x^2-1)^4}$$

$$+ \sqrt{(x^2-1)^6}]$$

$$= 2[x^6 + 15x^4 (x^2-1) + 15x^2 (x^2-1)^2$$

$$+ (x^2-1)^3]$$

$$= 2[x^6 + 15(x^6 - x^4) + 15(x^6 - 2x^4 + x^2)$$

$$+ (x^6 - 3x^4 + 3x^2 - 1)]$$

$$= 64x^6 - 96x^4 + 36x^2 - 2.$$

34. (a) Ans. (c).

L.H.S.

$$= 2[x^5 + 10x^3 \{(x^3 - 1)^{1/2}\}^2 + 5x \{(x^3 - 1)^{1/2}\}^4]$$

$$= 2[x^5 + 10x^3 (x^3 - 1) + 5x (x^3 - 1)^2].$$

(b) Ans. (c).

$$\text{Second term} = \left[\frac{2(\sqrt{2y^2 + 1} - \sqrt{2y^2 - 1})}{2} \right]^6$$

$$\therefore \quad E = (a+b)^6 + (a-b)^6 = 2[T_1 + T_3 + T_5 + T_7]$$

$$= 2[a^6 + {}^6C_2 a^4 b^2 + {}^6C_4 a^2 b^4 + {}^6C_6 b^6]$$

$$E = 2[a^6 + b^6 + 15a^2 b^2 (a^2 + b^2)]$$

Now put $a^2 = 2y^2 + 1$ and $b^2 = 2y^2 - 1$

$$\therefore \quad a^2 + b^2 = 4y^2$$

$$\therefore \quad E = 2[(2y^2 + 1)^3 + (2y^2 - 1)^3$$

$$+ 15(2y^2 + 1)(2y^2 - 1)(4y^2)]$$

Hence the degree of E is $6 \Rightarrow$ (c).

(c) L.H.S. $= \frac{1}{2}[(3+1)^n + (3-1)^n] = \frac{1}{2}[4^n + 2^n]$

$$= 2^{n-1}[2^n + 1]$$

35. (a) $x[(x+1)^n - (x-1)^n]$ where $x = \sqrt{10}$, $n = 100$.

$$= x.2[C_1 x^{n-1} + C_3 x^{n-3} + C_5 x^{n-5} + ...]$$

$$= 2[C_1 x^n + C_3 x^{n-2} + C_5 x^{n-4} + ...]$$

Now $n = 100$, $n-2, n-4, ...$ are all even.

$x = \sqrt{10}$ $\therefore x^n, x^{n-2}, x^{n-4}, ...$ are all integers,

and $C_1, C_3, C_5, ...$ are also integers.

Hence given expression is a whole number.

(b) Ans. (d).

$$E = \left(1 + \frac{1}{10^4}\right)^{1000}$$

$$= 1 + 1000\left(\frac{1}{10^4}\right) + (1000)\frac{(999)}{2}\left(\frac{1}{10^4}\right)^2 + \ldots$$

$$< 1 + \frac{1}{10} + \frac{1}{10^2} + \frac{1}{10^3} + \ldots \infty$$

$$= \frac{1}{1 - \frac{1}{10}} = \frac{10}{9} = 1\frac{1}{9}$$

Hence the integer which is just greater than E is 2.

(c) If a number is 532, then the digit in unit place is 2. In the above number 3 stands for $3 \cdot 10 = 30$, 5 stands for $5 \cdot 10^2 = 500$ so that $532 = 500 + 30 + 2$

$$E = (10 + 7)^N + (1 + 10)^N - 7^N \text{ where } N = 1995$$

$$= 10^N + {}^N C_1 10^{N-1} 7 + {}^N C_2 10^{N-2} 7^2 + \ldots + 7^N$$

$$+ 1 + {}^N C_1 10 + {}^N C_2 10^2 + \ldots - 7^N$$

$1 +$ All integers being multiple of 10.
Hence the digit at unit place is 1.

36. (a) $5^{99} = 5^3 \cdot 5^{96} = (125)(625)^{24}$

$$= [13 \times 9 + 8](1 + 48 \times 13)^{24}$$

$$= (13 \times 9 + 8)[1 + {}^{24}C_1 \times (48 \times 13)$$

$$+ {}^{24}C_2 (48 \times 13)^2 + \ldots + (48 \times 13)^{24}]$$

$$= 8 + \text{terms including powers of 13.}$$

Hence remainder $= 8$.

Alternative Method : $5^{99} = 5 \cdot 5^{98} = 5 \cdot (5^2)^{49}$

$$= 5(26 - 1)^{49} = 5(13 \times 2 - 1)^{49}.$$

All the terms will contain 13 as a factor except the last *i.e.*

$$5(-1) = -5 = -13 + 8$$

∴ Remainder is 8.

(b) L.H.S. $= (1 + 105)^{85} - (1 + 84)^{106}$

1, 1 will cancel and both 105 and 84 are divisible by 7 and binomial coefficients which occur are all integers and hence L.H.S. is divisible by 7.

37. (a) We have $101^{50} = (100 + 1)^{50}$

$$= 100^{50} + 50 \cdot 100^{49} + \frac{50 \cdot 49}{1 \cdot 2} \cdot 100^{48} + \ldots$$

and $99^{50} = (100 - 1)^{50}$

$$= 100^{50} - 50 \cdot 100^{49} + \frac{50 \cdot 49}{1 \cdot 2} \cdot 100^{48} - \ldots$$

Subtracting, we get
$$101^{50} - 99^{50} = 2[50 \cdot 100^{49}$$

$$+ \frac{50 \cdot 49 \cdot 48}{1 \cdot 2 \cdot 3} \cdot 100^{47} + \ldots]$$

$$= 100^{50} + 2 \cdot \frac{50 \cdot 49 \cdot 48}{1 \cdot 2 \cdot 3} \cdot 100^{47} + \ldots > 100^{50}$$

Hence $101^{50} > 99^{50} + 100^{50}$.

(b) $(1000)^{1000}$ is greater than $(1001)^{999}$.

38. (a) Putting $x = 1$ in $(1 + x - 3x^2)^{2143}$ we get sum of the coefficients as $(1 + 1 - 3)^{2143} = (-1)^{2143} = -1$.

(b) Sum of the coefficient is obtained by putting $p = q = 1$.

Required sum $= (5 - 4)^n = 1^n = 1$.

39. (a) $T_{r+1} = {}^{6561}C_r (7^{1/3})^{6561-r} (11^{1/9})^r$

$$T'_{r+1} = {}^{6561}C_r (7^{1/3})^{6561-r} 11^{1/9})^r$$

$$= {}^{6561}C_r 7^{2187} \cdot 7^{-r/3} \cdot 11^{r/9}, 0 \le r \le 6561$$

Now T_{r+1} will be integral if $r/3$ and $r/9$ both are integers in the span $0 \le r \le 6561$. It will be possible if r is a multiple of 9. In other words, we have to find the number of those numbers lying between 0 to 6561 which are multiple of 9 *i.e.* those which form an A.P. of common difference 9.

$$0, 9, 18, 27, \ldots 6561.$$

Note that 6561 is divisible by 9. If it were not divisible by 9 we would have chosen just the preceding number which is divisible by 9.

$$T_n = 6561 = a + (n - 1)d = 0 + (n - 1)9$$

∴ $n = 1 + \frac{6561}{9} = 1 + 729 = 730$

Hence there will be 730 terms which will be free from radicals.

(b) Ans. 41.

$$T_{r+1} = {}^{10}C_r (\sqrt{2})^{10-r} (3^{1/5})^r$$

where r varies from 0 to 10 as there will be only 11 terms.

In T_{r+1} the powers of 2 and 3 are $\frac{10-r}{2}$ and $\frac{r}{5}$ where $0 \le r \le 10$.

$\frac{r}{5}$ will be an integer for $r = 0, 5, 10$ but $\frac{10-r}{2}$ will not be an integer for $r = 5$.

Thus both powers are integers for $r = 0$ and 10. Hence T_1 and T_{11} will have rational coefficients whose sum is

$${}^{10}C_1 (\sqrt{2})^{10} \cdot 1 + {}^{10}C_{10} \cdot 1 \cdot 3^2 = 32 + 9 = 41$$

(c) Do yourself.

40. (a) Let the coefficients of $T_r, T_{r+1}, T_{r+2}, T_{r+3}$ be a_1, a_2, a_3, a_4 respectively in the expansion of $(1 + x)^n$.

The question can be written as

$$\frac{1}{1 + \frac{a_2}{a_1}} + \frac{1}{1 + \frac{a_4}{a_3}} = 2 \cdot \frac{1}{1 + \frac{a_3}{a_2}}$$

Hence we evaluate $1 + \frac{a_2}{a_1}$ etc.

$$\frac{a_2}{a_1} = \frac{T_{r+1}}{T_r} = \frac{n-r+1}{r}$$

$$\therefore \quad 1 + \frac{a_2}{a_1} = \frac{n+1}{r}.$$

Similarly $1 + \dfrac{a_3}{a_2} = \dfrac{n+1}{r+1}$, $1 + \dfrac{a_4}{a_3} = \dfrac{n+1}{r+2}$

L.H.S. $= \dfrac{r}{n+1} + \dfrac{r+2}{n+1} = \dfrac{2(r+1)}{n+1} =$ R.H.S.

(b) From part (a),

$$\frac{a_2}{a_2+a_3} = \frac{1}{2}\left[\frac{a_1}{a_1+a_2} + \frac{a_3}{a_3+a_4}\right] = \text{A.M. of } P \text{ and } Q$$

which is greater than the G.M., *i.e.*, $\sqrt{PQ}$.

Hence squaring we get the result.

41. $\dfrac{T_{r+1}}{T_r} = \dfrac{n-r+1}{r} \cdot \dfrac{\alpha}{x} : T_3 = a, T_4 = b, T_5 = c, T_6 = d$

Putting $r = 3, 4, 5$ in the above, we get

$$\frac{T_4}{T_3} = \frac{n-2}{3} \cdot \frac{\alpha}{x} = \frac{b}{a} \qquad \qquad \dots(1)$$

$$\frac{T_5}{T_4} = \frac{n-3}{4} \cdot \frac{\alpha}{x} = \frac{c}{b} \qquad \qquad \dots(2)$$

$$\frac{T_6}{T_5} = \frac{n-4}{5} \cdot \frac{\alpha}{x} = \frac{d}{c} \qquad \qquad \dots(3)$$

Now dividing (1) by 2 and (2) by 3 respectively, we get

$$\frac{4}{3} \cdot \frac{(n-2)}{(n-3)} = \frac{b^2}{ac} \qquad \qquad \dots(4)$$

$$\frac{5}{4} \cdot \frac{(n-3)}{(n-4)} = \frac{c^2}{bd} \qquad \qquad \dots(5)$$

Subtracting 1 from both sides of (4) and (5),

$$\frac{1}{3} \cdot \frac{(n+1)}{(n-3)} = \frac{b^2-ac}{ac} \qquad \qquad \dots(6)$$

$$\frac{1}{4} \cdot \frac{(n+1)}{(n-4)} = \frac{c^2-bd}{bd} \qquad \qquad \dots(7)$$

Dividing (6) and (7), we get

$$\frac{4}{3} \cdot \frac{(n-4)}{(n-3)} = \frac{b^2-ac}{c^2-bd} \cdot \frac{bd}{ac}$$

or $\dfrac{4}{3} \cdot \dfrac{5}{4} \dfrac{bd}{c^2} = \dfrac{b^2-ac}{c^2-bd} \cdot \dfrac{bd}{ac}$. \hfill by (5)

$$\therefore \quad \frac{b^2-ac}{c^2-bd} = \frac{5a}{3c}$$

42. (a) As in **Q. 41.**

$$T_3 = \frac{n(n-1)}{1.2} x^{n-2} a^2 = 84 \qquad \dots(1)$$

$$T_4 = \frac{n(n-1)(n-2)}{1.2.3} x^{n-3} a^3 = 280 \qquad \dots(2)$$

$$T_5 = \frac{n(n-1)(n-2)(n-3)}{1.2.3.4} x^{n-4} a^4 = 560 \qquad \dots(3)$$

In order to eliminate x and a we multiply (1) and (3) and divide by square of (2).

$$\therefore \quad \frac{T_3 \times T_5}{(T_4)^2} = \frac{84 \times 560}{280 \times 280} = \frac{3}{5}$$

or $\left(\dfrac{T_5}{T_4} \cdot \dfrac{T_3}{T_4}\right) = \dfrac{3}{5}$

Now $\dfrac{T_{r+1}}{T_r} = \dfrac{{}^nC_r}{{}^nC_{r-1}} = \dfrac{n-r+1}{r}$

Putting $r = 4$ and 3, we get

$$\frac{n-3}{4} \cdot \frac{3}{n-2} = \frac{3}{5}$$

or $5n - 15 = 4n - 8$ or $n = 7$.

$$\frac{T_4}{T_3} = \frac{n-2}{3} \cdot \frac{a}{x} = \frac{280}{84}$$

or $\dfrac{5}{3} \cdot \dfrac{a}{x} = \dfrac{10}{3}$ $\therefore$ $x = \dfrac{a}{2}$.

Hence $T_3 = \dfrac{7.6}{1.2} x^5 \cdot a^2 = 84$ $\because$ $n = 7$

or $\left(\dfrac{a}{2}\right)^5 \cdot a^2 = 84 \times \dfrac{2}{7.6} = 4$

or $a^7 = 2^5 \cdot 2^2 = 2^7$ $\therefore$ $a = 2$

Hence $x = \dfrac{a}{2} = 1$ $\therefore$ $x = 1$, $a = 2$, $n = 7$.

(b) Proceed as above $n = 5$, $x = 2$ and $a = 3$.

43. (a) Coefficients of T_5, T_6, T_7 are in A.P.

or of $T_5/T_6, 1, T_7/T_6$ are in A.P.

or $\dfrac{1}{T_6/T_5}, 1, T_7/T_6$ are in A.P.

Now use $\dfrac{T_{r+1}}{T_r} = \dfrac{n-r+1}{r}, r = 5, 6$

Above implies $n^2 - 21n + 98 = 0$

or $(n-7)(n-14) = 0$ $\therefore$ $n = 7, 14$.

(b) $n^2 - 9n + 14 = 0$ $\therefore$ $n = 7$ as n cannot be 2.

44. (a) $T_2 = {}^{2n}C_1 \cdot x$, $T_3 = {}^{2n}C_2 x^2$, $T_4 = {}^{2n}C_3 x^3$.

The coefficients are given to be in A.P.

$\therefore$ $2 \cdot {}^{2n}C_2 = {}^{2n}C_1 + {}^{2n}C_3$

$\therefore$ $2 \cdot \dfrac{2n(2n-1)}{1.2} = \dfrac{2n}{1} + \dfrac{2n(2n-1)(2n-2)}{1.2.3}$

Cancel the factor $2n$ and multiplying by 6, we get

$2n^2 - 9n + 7 = 0$

(b) $n = 7$ or 2. But if $n = 2$ then there will be only 3 terms and hence $n = 7$.

45. (a) The coefficients of T_r, T_{r+1}, T_{r+2} are in A.P. or

coefficients of $\dfrac{T_r}{T_{r+1}}, 1, \dfrac{T_{r+2}}{T_{r+1}}$ are in A.P.

$$\qquad \qquad \dots(1)$$

$$\frac{T_{r+1}}{T_r} = \frac{n-r+1}{r}x$$

∴ coefficient of $\dfrac{T_{r+1}}{T_r} = \dfrac{14-r+1}{r} = \dfrac{15-r}{r}$

Now put $r+1$ for r ...(2)

∴ coefficient of $\dfrac{T_{r+2}}{T_{r+1}} = \dfrac{15-(r+1)}{r+1} = \dfrac{14-r}{r+1}$ ...(3)

Also on taking reciprocal of (2) coefficient of

$$\frac{T_r}{T_{r+1}} = \frac{r}{15-r}. \qquad ...(4)$$

Hence from (1) by (3) and (4) $\dfrac{r}{15-r}, 1, \dfrac{14-r}{r+1}$ are in

A.P.

∴ $\quad 2 = \dfrac{r}{15-r} + \dfrac{14-r}{r+1}$

∴ $\quad 2(15+14r-r^2) = r^2 + r + 210 - 29r + r^2$

or $\quad 4r^2 - 56r + 180 = 0$ or $r^2 - 14r + 45 = 0$

∴ $\quad (r-5)(r-9) = 0$ ∴ $r = 5$ or 9.

The two answers are justified because
$^{14}C_5 = {}^{14}C_9$ i.e. $^{14}C_r = {}^{14}C_{14-r}$.

(b) The first three being in A.P. implies that
$2\,{}^nC_{r+1} = {}^nC_r + {}^nC_{r+2}$

The given terms are the coefficients of T_{r+1}, T_{r+2}, T_{r+3}, T_{r+4}. The first three being in A.P. implies

$$2T_{r+2} = T_{r+1} + T_{r+3} \quad \text{or} \quad 2 = \frac{T_{r+1}}{T_{r+2}} + \frac{T_{r+3}}{T_{r+2}}$$

or $\quad 2 = \dfrac{1}{{}^nC_{r+1} / {}^nC_r} + \dfrac{{}^nC_{r+2}}{{}^nC_{r+1}}$ ...(1)

Now $\dfrac{{}^nC_{r+1}}{{}^nC_r} = \dfrac{n!}{(n-r-1)!\,(r+1)!} \cdot \dfrac{(n-r)!\,r!}{n!} = \dfrac{n-r}{r+1}$

...(2)

Replacing r by $r+1$, we have

$$\frac{{}^nC_{r+2}}{{}^nC_{r+1}} = \frac{n-r-1}{r+2} \qquad ...(3)$$

Hence from (1) by the help of (2) and (3), we have

$$2 = \frac{r+1}{n-r} + \frac{n-r-1}{r+2}$$

or $\quad (n-r)(2r+4) = (r^2 + 3r + 2) + (n-r)^2 - (n-r)$

or $\quad (n-r)^2 - (n-r)(2r+5) + (r+1)(r+2) = 0$

...(4)

Above is the condition for first three terms to be in A.P. Again replacing r by $r+1$, we shall get the condition for the last three terms to be in A.P. as
$(n-r-1)^2 - (n-r-1)(2r+7) + (r+2)(r+3) = 0$

or $\quad (n-r)^2 + 1 - 2(n-r) - (n-r)(2r+7)$
$$\qquad\qquad + (2r+7) + r^2 + 5r + 6 = 0$$

or $\quad (n-r)^2 - (n-r)(2r+9) + (r^2 + 7r + 13) = 0$

...(5)

Comparing (4) and (5), we have

$$\frac{1}{1} = \frac{2r+5}{2r+9} = \frac{r^2+3r+2}{r^2+7r+13}$$

1st and 2nd give $9 = 5$ and 1st and 3rd give $-$ive value of r. Both are not possible. Hence the given four terms cannot be in A.P.

46. **(a)** **(i)** T_r, T_{r+1}, T_{r+2} are in G.P.

∴ $\quad \dfrac{T_r}{T_{r+1}}, 1, \dfrac{T_{r+2}}{T_{r+1}}$ are in G.P.

$\quad \dfrac{r}{n-r+1}, 1, \dfrac{n-r}{r+1}$ are in G.P.

∴ $\quad 1^2 = \dfrac{r(n-r)}{(n-r+1)(r+1)}$

$\quad n(r+1) - (r^2 - 1) = nr - r^2$

⇒ $\quad n+1 = 0$

∴ $\quad n = -1$. This is not possible.

(ii) T_r, T_{r+1}, T_{r+2} are in H.P.

$\quad \dfrac{1}{T_r}, \dfrac{1}{T_{r+1}}, \dfrac{1}{T_{r+2}}$ are in A.P.

∴ $\quad \dfrac{T_{r+1}}{T_r}, 1, \dfrac{T_{r+1}}{T_{r+2}}$ are in A.P.

$$2 = \frac{n-r+1}{r} + \frac{r+1}{n-r}$$

or $\quad 2r(n-r) = (n-r)^2 + (n-r) + r^2 + r$

or $\quad 2rn - 2r^2 = n^2 - 2nr + r^2 + n - r + r^2 + r$

or $\quad n^2 + 4r^2 - 4nr + n = 0$ ...(1)

or $\quad (n-2r)^2 + n = 0$

This is not possible as both $(n-2r)^2$ and n are $+$ive.

(b) We have done in part **(a) (ii) R (1)** that
$$n^2 + 4r^2 - 4nr + n = 0$$

∴ $\quad n$ is a root of the equation
$$x^2 - (4r - 1)x + 4r^2 = 0$$

47. $(3+2x)^{74} = 3^{74} \cdot \left(1 + \dfrac{2x}{3}\right)^{74}$

$$\frac{T_{r+1}}{T_r} = \frac{n-r+1}{r}\left(\frac{2x}{3}\right)$$

Coeff. $= \dfrac{n-r+1}{r} \cdot \dfrac{2}{3} = 1,$ by given condition

or $\quad 2(74 - r + 1) = 3r$ or $150 = 5r,$ $r = 30.$

Hence 30th and 31st terms will have their coefficients equal.

48. Since $^mC_1$, $^mC_2$ and $^mC_3$ are the first, third and fifth terms of an A.P., which will also be in A.P. of common difference $2d$.

Hence $\quad 2.\,^mC_2 = {}^mC_1 + {}^mC_3$

or $\quad m(m-1) = m + \dfrac{m(m-1)(m-2)}{1.2.3}$

or $\quad 6m - 6 = 6 + m^2 - 3m + 2 \qquad [\because m \neq 0]$

or $\quad m^2 - 9m + 14 = 0$

or $\quad (m-2)(m-7) = 0$.

Since 6th term is 21, $m = 2$ is ruled out and we have $m = 7$ and

$21 = {}^7C_5 \left[\sqrt{2^{\log(10 - 3^x)}}\right]^{7-5} \times \left[\sqrt[5]{2^{(x-2)\log 3}}\right]^5$

$= \dfrac{7.6}{1.2} 2^{\log(10 - 3^x)} . 2^{(x-2)\log 3}$

or $\quad 21 = 21.2^{\log(10 - 3^x) + \log 3^{x-2}}$

Hence $\quad 2^{\log[(10 - 3^x).3^{x-2}]} = 1$.

or $\quad \log[(10 - 3^x).3^{x-2}] = 0 \qquad \because 2^0 = 1$

or $\quad (10 - 3^x).3^{x-2} = 1 \qquad \because \log 1 = 0$

or $\quad 3^{2x-2} - 10.3^{x-2} + 1 = 0$

or $\quad 3^{2x} - 10.3^x + 9 = 0$

or $\quad (3^x - 1)(3^x - 9) = 0$

$\therefore \quad 3^x - 1 = 0$ which gives $x = 0$

or $\quad 3^x = 9 = 3^2$ which gives $x = 2$.

Hence $\quad x = 0$ or 2.

49. (a) $T_6 = {}^7C_5 (I)^{7-5} (II)^5 = 84$

or $\dfrac{7.6}{1.2}\left[\sqrt{9^{x-1} + 7}\right]^2 . \dfrac{1}{\left[2^{(1/5)}.\log_2(3^{x-1}+1)\right]^5} = 84$

or $\dfrac{3^{2(x-1)} + 7}{3^{x-1} + 1} = 4 \qquad \because a^{\log_a n} = n$

Put $3^{x-1} = t \qquad \therefore \quad t^2 + 7 = 4(t+1)$

or $\quad t^2 - 4t + 3 = 0 \ \therefore \ t = 3^{x-1} = 3, 1$ i.e. $3^1, 3^0$

$\therefore \quad x - 1 = 1, 0 \quad$ or $\quad x = 2$ or 1.

(b) $T_2 = {}^nC_1 \, x^{\frac{n-1}{13}} (x\sqrt{x})^1 = 14x^{5/2}$

or $\quad n\, x^{\frac{n-1}{13} + \frac{3}{2}} = 14x^{5/2}$

$\therefore \quad \dfrac{n-1}{13} + \dfrac{3}{2} = \dfrac{5}{2} \ \Rightarrow \ \dfrac{n-1}{13} = 1 \ $ or $\ n = 14$

Now $\dfrac{^nC_r}{^nC_{r-1}} = \dfrac{n-r+1}{r}$ for $r = 3, n = 14$

$\therefore \quad \dfrac{^nC_3}{^nC_2} = \dfrac{14 - 3 + 1}{3} = 4$

50. (a) Ans. $n = 9$.

T_7 from end of $\left(\sqrt[3]{2} + \dfrac{1}{\sqrt[3]{3}}\right)^n$ is T_7 from beginning of

$\left(\dfrac{1}{\sqrt[3]{3}} + \sqrt[3]{2}\right)^n$

$\dfrac{1}{6} = \dfrac{^nC_6 (2^{1/3})^{n-6} (3^{-1/3})^6}{^nC_6 (3^{-1/3})^{n-6} (2^{1/3})^6} = (2.3)^{\frac{n-6}{3} - \frac{6}{3}}$

or $\quad 6^{-1} = 6^{\frac{n-12}{3}}$

$\therefore \quad n/3 - 4 = -1$ giving $n = 9$.

(b) $T_6 = {}^8C_5 (x^{-8/3})^{8-5} (x^2 \log_{10} x)^5 = 5600$

$= \dfrac{8.7.6}{1.2.3} x^{-8} . x^{10} (\log_{10} x)^5 = 5600$

or $\quad x^2 (\log_{10} x)^5 = 10^2$.

Clearly $x = 10$ satisfies as $\log_{10} 10 = 1$.

$x > 10$ or $x < 10$ will result in inequality.

51. (a) $T_4 = {}^6C_3 \left(x^{\frac{1}{\log x + 1}}\right)^{3/2} . (x^{1/12})^3 = 200$

$= \dfrac{6.5.4}{1.2.3} x^{\frac{3}{2(\log x + 1)} + \frac{1}{4}} = 200$

$\therefore \quad \dfrac{3}{2(\log x + 1)} + \dfrac{1}{4} = \log_x 10 = \dfrac{1}{\log x}$

If $\log_{10} x = z$ then $\dfrac{3}{2(z+1)} + \dfrac{1}{4} = \dfrac{1}{z}$

or $\quad 7z + z^2 = 4z + 4 \quad$ or $\quad z^2 + 3z - 4 = 0$

$\therefore \quad (z+4)(z-1) = 0 \ \therefore \ z = \log_{10} x = -4, 1$

$\therefore \quad x = 10^{-4}, 10^1$. Since $x > 1 \ \therefore \ x = 10$ only.

(b) Proceed as above $2z^2 - 3z - 2 = 0$

or $\quad (2z+1)(z-2) = 0 \ \therefore \ z = \log_{10} x = -1/2, 2$

or $\quad x = 10^2$ only as $x > 1 \quad \because \ 10^{-1/2} < 1$

52. (a) $\dfrac{T_3}{T_2} = 7 \Rightarrow \dfrac{n-r+1}{r} \dfrac{a}{x} = 7$

for $(x + a)^n$. **See Rule 7, P. 365**

Put $r = 2, x = 2^x, a = \dfrac{1}{4^x} = 2^{-2x} \ \therefore \ \dfrac{a}{x} = 2^{-3x}$

$\therefore \quad \dfrac{n-1}{2}(2^{-3x}) = 7 \qquad \qquad ...(1)$

Also $^nC_1 + {}^nC_2 = 36 \ \Rightarrow \ n + \dfrac{n(n-1)}{2} = 36$

or $\quad n^2 + n - 72 = 0$

or $\quad (n+9)(n-8) = 0 \ \therefore \ n = 8$

Putting the value of n in (1), we get

$\dfrac{7}{2}(2^{-3x}) = 7 \quad$ or $\quad 2^{-3x} = 2^1$

$\therefore \quad -3x = 1 \quad$ or $\quad x = -\dfrac{1}{3}$

(b)   In $(A+B)^n, T_9 = {}^nC_8 A^{n-8} B^8 = 180$

We know that $a^{\log_a n} = n$

$\therefore \quad A = \sqrt{25^{x-1}+7} = \sqrt{5^{2(x-1)}+7}$

$\quad B = [(5^{x-1}+1)]^{-1/8}, n = 10$

$\quad T_9 = {}^{10}C_8 A^2 B^8 = 180$

$\therefore \quad {}^{10}C_8 (5^{2(x-1)}+7)[(5^{x-1}+1)]^{-1} = 180$

Now put $5^{x-1} = t$

$\therefore \quad \dfrac{10 \cdot 9}{1 \cdot 2}(t^2+7)(t+1)^{-1} = 180$

$\therefore \quad t^2 + 7 = 4(t+1) \quad \text{or} \quad t^2 - 4t + 3 = 0$

or $(t-3)(t-1) = 0 \quad \therefore \quad t = 3, 1$

$\therefore \quad 5^{x-1} = 3, 1 \quad \text{or} \quad 5^x = 15, 5$

$\therefore \quad x = \log_5 15 \quad \text{or} \quad x = 1$

But $x > 1 \qquad \therefore \quad x = \log_5 15$

53. L.H.S. $= (1 + 2x^2 + x^4)(1 + c_1 x + c_2 x^2 + c_3 x^3 + ...)$

R.H.S. $= a_0 + a_1 x + a_2 x^2 + a_3 x^3 + ...$

Comparing the coefficients of $x, x^2, x^3, ...$

$\quad a_1 = c_1, a_2 = c_2 + 2, a_3 = c_3 + 2c_1 \qquad ...(1)$

Now $2a_2 = a_1 + a_3$ (A.P.)

$2({}^nC_2 + 2) = {}^nC_1 + ({}^nC_3 + 2\,{}^nC_1) \qquad \text{by (1)}$

$2\dfrac{n(n-1)}{2} + 4 = 3n + \dfrac{n(n-1)(n-2)}{6}$

or $n^3 - 9n^2 + 26n - 24 = 0$

Clearly $n = 2$ is a root as $8 + 52 = 36 + 24$

$\therefore \quad (n-2)(n^2 - 7n + 12) = 0$

or $(n-2)(n-3)(n-4) = 0$

$\therefore \quad n = 2, 3, 4.$

54. (a) Let the successive terms be T_r, T_{r+1}, T_{r+2} whose coefficents are 220, 495 and 792 respectively.

$\dfrac{T_{r+1}}{T_r} = \dfrac{n-r+1}{r} x$

$\therefore \quad \dfrac{n-r+1}{r} = \dfrac{495}{220} = \dfrac{9}{4}$

Putting $r+1$ for r,

$\dfrac{T_{r+2}}{T_{r+1}} = \dfrac{n-r}{r+1} x \quad \therefore \quad \dfrac{n-r}{r+1} = \dfrac{792}{495} = \dfrac{8}{5}$

$\therefore \quad 4n - 13r + 4 = 0$

$\quad 5n - 13r - 8 = 0$

Subtracting, we get $n = 12 \quad \therefore \quad r = 4.$

(b) Proceed as above.

$\quad n - 3r + 1 = 0, 5n - 12r - 1 = 0.$

Solve $n = 5, r = 2.$

(c) Proceed as in part **(a)**, $n = 55.$

55. In the expansion of $(1+x)^n$ **(by 7, P. 365)**

$\dfrac{T_{r+1}}{T_r} = \dfrac{n-r+1}{r} x.$ Here $n = 8, \; x = 4 \cdot \dfrac{1}{3}$

$\therefore \quad \dfrac{T_{r+1}}{T_r} = \dfrac{9-r}{r} \cdot \dfrac{4}{3}$

$\therefore \quad T_{r+1} \ge T_r$ if $36 - 4r \ge 3r$

or $36 \ge 7r$ or $r \le 5\dfrac{1}{7}$

Now if r is less than or equal to $5\dfrac{1}{7}, T_{r+1}$ is the greatest term. But r is an integer.

Hence $r = 5,$ and T_{r+1} *i.e.,* 6th term is greatest.

$\therefore \quad T_6 = {}^8C_5 (4x)^5 = \dfrac{8!}{5!\,3!} \cdot \left(\dfrac{4}{3}\right)^5$

$\quad = \dfrac{8 \times 7 \times 6}{6}\left(\dfrac{4}{3}\right)^5 = 56\left(\dfrac{4}{3}\right)^5$

Another Method :

$m = \left(\dfrac{x}{x+1}\right)(n+1) \quad n = 8, x = 4x = 4 \cdot \dfrac{1}{3}$

$m = \dfrac{4}{7} \cdot 9 = \dfrac{36}{7} = 5\dfrac{1}{7} \quad \therefore [m] = 5$

$\therefore \quad T_{5+1} = T_6$ is the greatest term.

Note : We can also say $T_{r+1} \ge T_{r+2}$

or $\dfrac{T_{r+1}}{T_{r+2}} \ge 1$ or $\dfrac{T_{r+2}}{T_{r+1}} \le 1$

or $\dfrac{n-(r+1)+1}{r+1} x \le 1$

or $\dfrac{8-r}{r+1} \cdot \dfrac{4}{3} \le 1$ or $29 \le 7r$ or $r \ge 4\dfrac{1}{7}$

$\therefore \quad r = 5.$ Hence T_6 is greatest as found above.

56. (a) Proceed as in **Q. 55.** We have

$\quad (2 + 3x)^9 = 2^9 \left(1 + \dfrac{3x}{2}\right)^9.$

Here $\dfrac{T_{r+1}}{T_r} = \dfrac{n-r+1}{r} x$

$\quad = \dfrac{10-r}{r} \cdot \left(\dfrac{3x}{2}\right) \qquad \because \; n = 9$

$\quad = \dfrac{10-r}{r} \cdot \dfrac{3}{2} \cdot \dfrac{3}{2} = \dfrac{10-r}{r} \cdot \dfrac{9}{4}.$

$\therefore \quad T_{r+1} \ge T_r$ if $90 - 9r \ge 4r$ or $90 > 13r$

or $13r < 90$ or $r \le 6\dfrac{12}{13} \quad \therefore \; r = 6.$

Hence $T_{r+1} = T_7 = 2^9 \cdot {}^9C_6 \left(\dfrac{3x}{2}\right)^6$

$\quad = 2^9 \cdot \dfrac{9!}{3!\,6!} \cdot \dfrac{3^{12}}{2^{12}} \qquad \because \; x = \dfrac{3}{2}$

$\quad = \dfrac{9 \times 8 \times 7}{1 \cdot 2 \cdot 3} \cdot \dfrac{3^{12}}{2^3} = \dfrac{3^{13} \cdot 7}{2}$

Alt. $m = \left(\dfrac{x}{x+1}\right)(n+1)$

$$n = 9, \quad x = \frac{3x}{2} = \frac{3}{2} \cdot \frac{3}{2} = \frac{9}{4}$$

$$\therefore \quad m = \frac{9}{13} \cdot 10 = \frac{90}{13} = 6\frac{12}{13} \quad \therefore [m] = 6$$

$$\therefore \quad T_{[m]+1} \quad \text{or} \quad T_{6+1} = T_7 \text{ is greatest term.}$$

(b) $(T_{11})^2 = T_8 \cdot T_{12}$

$$({}^{15}C_{10} \, x^5 a^{10})^2 = ({}^{15}C_7 \, x^8 a^7)({}^{15}C_{11} \, x^4 a^{11})$$

$$\therefore \quad \left(\frac{a}{x}\right)^2 = \frac{{}^{15}C_7 \cdot {}^{15}C_4}{{}^{15}C_5 \cdot {}^{15}C_5} = \frac{10!\,5!\,10!\,5!}{8!\,7!\,11!\,4!}$$

$$= \frac{10 \cdot 9}{7 \cdot 6} \cdot \frac{5}{11} = \frac{75}{77} \qquad \ldots(1)$$

Now if T_{r+1} is the greatest term, then

$$\frac{T_{r+1}}{T_r} = \left| \frac{n-r+1}{r} \cdot \frac{a}{x} \right| \geq 1 \qquad \text{where, } n = 15$$

$$\frac{16-r}{r} \cdot \frac{a}{x} \geq 1 \quad \text{by 7 (i), P. 366}$$

or $\dfrac{a}{x} \geq \dfrac{r}{16-r}$ or $\sqrt{\dfrac{75}{77}} \geq \dfrac{r}{16-r}$, by (1) $\ldots(2)$

Now $\sqrt{\dfrac{77}{77}} > \sqrt{\dfrac{75}{77}} > \dfrac{r}{16-r}$

or $(16 - r) \cdot 1 > r$ or $16 > 2r$ or $r < 8$

$\therefore \quad r = 7$ (integer).

Hence T_{r+1} i.e., T_8 is the greatest term.

57. Let T_4 be numerically the greatest term in the expansion of $2^{10}\left(1 + \dfrac{3x}{16}\right)^{10}$

$$\therefore \quad \left| \frac{T_4}{T_3} \right| \geq 1 \quad \text{and} \quad \left| \frac{T_4}{T_5} \right| \geq 1$$

$$\text{or} \quad \left| \frac{T_4}{T_3} \right| \geq 1 \quad \text{and} \quad \left| \frac{T_5}{T_4} \right| \leq 1$$

Now $\dfrac{T_{r+1}}{T_r} = \dfrac{n-r+1}{r} \cdot x$

Taking $r = 3$ and $r = 4$ and x by $\dfrac{3x}{16}$ and $n = 10$, in the above two, we get

$$\left| \frac{11-3}{3} \cdot \frac{3x}{16} \right| \geq 1 \quad \text{and} \quad \left| \frac{11-4}{4} \cdot \frac{3x}{16} \right| \leq 1$$

or $|x| \geq 2$ and $|x| \leq \dfrac{64}{21}$ $\qquad \ldots(A)$

$$\therefore \quad x^2 \geq 4 \text{ and } x^2 \leq \left(\frac{64}{21}\right)^2$$

$$\therefore \quad 4 \leq x^2 \leq \left(\frac{64}{21}\right)^2 \quad \textbf{Double inequality}$$

$$\therefore \quad 2 \leq x \leq \frac{64}{21} \quad \text{and} \quad -\frac{64}{21} \leq x \leq -2$$

Note : $a^2 < x^2 < b^2$ leads to two inequalities $a \leq x < b$ and $-b \leq x \leq -a$

58. (a) $\dfrac{T_{r+1}}{T_r} = \dfrac{n-r+1}{r} \cdot \left(\dfrac{5}{3}x\right)$

$$\because \quad (3-5x)^{15} = 3^{15}\left(1 - \frac{5}{3}x\right)^{15}$$

$$= \frac{15-r+1}{r}\left(\frac{5}{3} \cdot \frac{1}{5}\right) \geq 1 \quad \because x = \frac{1}{5}$$

$$\therefore \quad 16 - r \geq 3r \qquad \therefore 4r \leq 16 \quad \therefore r \leq 4.$$

$$\therefore \quad r = 3, r = 4.$$

$\therefore \quad T_4$ and T_5 are numerically equal to each other and greater than any other term.

$$T_4 = 3^{15} \; {}^{15}C_3 \left(-\frac{5}{3} \cdot \frac{1}{5}\right)$$

$$= 3^{15} \cdot \frac{(15)!}{(12)!\,.3!} \cdot \frac{1}{3^3} \qquad \text{numerically}$$

$$\text{or} \quad T_4 = 3^{12} \frac{15 \times 14 \times 13}{1.2.3} = 455\,(3^{12}).$$

$$T_5 = 3^{15} \cdot {}^{15}C_4 \, (-5/3 \, . \, 1/5)^4$$

$$= 3^{15} \cdot \frac{(15)!}{(11)!\,4!} \cdot \frac{1}{3^4} = 3^{11} \times \frac{15 \times 14 \times 13 \times 12}{1.2.3.4}$$

$$= 3^{12} \times 5 \times 7 \times 13 = 455 \times (3)^{12}.$$

(b) $T_8 = \dfrac{25840}{9}.$

(c) $T_8 = {}^{12}C_7 \, 2^7 \cdot (5/2)^5$

59. We know that ${}^N C_r$ is greatest when

$$r = \frac{N}{2} (N \text{ even}). \text{ Here } N = 2n \text{ (even)}.$$

Let T_{r+1} have greatest coefficient in $(1+x)^{2n}$

$\therefore \quad {}^{2n}C_r$ is greatest. It will be so if $r = \dfrac{N}{2} = \dfrac{2n}{2} = n.$

Hence T_{n+1} will have greatest coefficient. It will be greatest term if

$$\frac{T_{n+1}}{T_n} \geq 1 \quad \text{and} \quad \frac{T_{n+1}}{T_{n+2}} \geq 1.$$

$$\text{or} \quad \frac{T_{n+1}}{T_n} \geq 1 \quad \text{and} \quad \frac{T_{n+2}}{T_{n+1}} \leq 1 \qquad \textbf{(Note)}$$

Now $\dfrac{T_{r+1}}{T_r} = \dfrac{n-r+1}{r} x$

Putting $r = n, n+1$ and $n = 2n$, we get

$$\frac{2n-n+1}{n} x \geq 1 \text{ and } \frac{2n-(n+1)+1}{n+1} x \leq 1$$

$$\frac{n+1}{n} x \geq 1 \text{ and } \frac{n}{n+1} x \leq 1$$

$$\therefore \quad x \leq \frac{n+1}{n} \quad \text{and} \quad x \geq \frac{n}{n+1}$$

$$\text{or} \quad \frac{n}{n+1} \leq x \leq \frac{n+1}{n}$$

In other words, x lies between $\dfrac{n}{n+1}$ and $\dfrac{n+1}{n}$.

60. (a) $(1+x)^n = 1 + nx + \dfrac{n(n-1)}{1.2}x^2$

$$+ \dfrac{n(n-1)(n-2)}{1.2.3}x^3 + \ldots.$$

$$\therefore \quad (1+x)^n - nx - 1$$

$$= x^2\left[\dfrac{n(n-1)}{1.2} + \dfrac{n(n-1)(n-2)}{1.2.3}x + \ldots..\right]$$

From above it is clear that $(1+x)^n - nx - 1$ is divisible by x^2. ...(1)

(b) We have to prove that $2^{3n} - 7n - 1$ is divisible by 49.

or $(1+7)^n - n.7 - 1$ is divisible by 7^2.

Choosing, $x = 7$ in (1), we prove the result.

Again $2^{3n+3} - 7n - 8 = 8^{n+1} - 7(n+1) - 1$.

$= (1+7)^N - 7N - 1$, where $N = n+1$

which is divisible by 49 by the above case.

(c) Ans. (d).

$\dfrac{3^{2n}}{8} = \dfrac{9^n}{8} = \dfrac{(1+8)^n}{8} = \dfrac{[1 + C_1.8 + C_2.8^2 + \ldots + C_n.8^n]}{8}$

$= \dfrac{1}{8} + [C_1 + C_2.8 + C_3.8^2 + \ldots + C_n.8^{n-1}]$

$= \dfrac{1}{8} + \text{integer}$

$\therefore \quad \left\{\dfrac{3^{2n}}{8}\right\} = \text{Fractional part} = \dfrac{1}{8}$

$\therefore \quad \theta = \dfrac{1}{8}$ or $8\theta = 1$

$\therefore \quad \sec^{-1}(8\theta) = \sec^{-1}(1) = 0$

(d) Ans. (c).

$E = 8^{2n} - (62)^{2n+1} = (9-1)^{2n} - (63-1)^{2n+1}$

$= ({}^nC_0\, 9^{2n} - {}^{2n}C_1\, 9^{2n-1} + \ldots)$

$\qquad - [{}^{2n+1}C_0\,(63)^{2n+1} - {}^{2n+1}C_1\,(63)^{2n} + \ldots.]$

The last term in each bracket being

$(-1)^{2n} - (-1)^{2n+1} = 1 + 1 = 2$

All other terms will have 9 and $63 = 9.7$ as factors.

$\therefore \quad E$ is of the form $9k + 2$

Hence, when given expression is divided by 9 the remainder is 2.

61. (a) $(1+x)^n - nx - 1$ is divisible by x^2.

Choose $x = 8$

$\therefore \quad 9^n - 8n - 1$ is divisible by 64.

Choosing, $n+1$ in place of n, we can say

$9^{n+1} - 8(n+1) - 1$ is divisible by 64.

or $3^{2n+2} - 8n - 9$ is divisible by 64.

(b) $2^{4n} = (2^4)^n = (16)^n = (1+15)^n$

$\therefore \quad 2^{4n} = 1 + {}^nC_1.15 + {}^nC_2\,15^2 + {}^nC_3\,15^3 + \ldots..$

$\therefore \quad 2^{4n} - 1 - 15n = 15^2[{}^nC_2 + {}^nC_3.15 + \ldots...]$

$= 225\,K$, where K is an integer.

Hence $2^{4n} - 15n - 1$ is divisible by 225.

62. (a) $(2+\sqrt{3})^n = I + f$.

or $I + f = 2^n + {}^nC_1\, 2^{n-1}\sqrt{3} + {}^nC_2\, 2^{n-2}(\sqrt{3})^2$

$\qquad + {}^nC_3\, 2^{n-3}(\sqrt{3})^3 + \ldots.$ ...(1)

Now, $0 < 2 - \sqrt{3} < 1$. $\therefore \quad 0 < (2-\sqrt{3})^n < 1$.

Let $(2-\sqrt{3})^n = f'$ where $0 < f' < 1$

$\therefore \quad f' = 2^n - {}^nC_1\, 2^{n-1}\sqrt{3} + {}^nC_2\, 2^{n-2}(\sqrt{3})^2$

$\qquad - {}^nC_3\, 2^{n-3}(\sqrt{3})^3 + \ldots$ ...(2)

Adding (1) and (2),

$I + f + f' = 2[2^n + {}^nC_2\, 2^{n-2}.3 + \ldots..]$

or $I + f + f' = \text{even integer}$. ...(3)

Now $0 < f < 1$ and $0 < f' < 1$.

$\therefore \quad 0 < f + f' < 2$.

Hence from (3) we conclude that $f + f'$ is an integer between 0 and 2.

$\therefore \quad f + f' = 1 \qquad \therefore \quad f' = 1 - f.$ ...(4)

From (3) and (4) we get $I + 1 = $ even integer.

$\therefore \quad I$ is an odd integer.

Now $I + f = (2+\sqrt{3})^n$, $f' = 1 - f = (2-\sqrt{3})^n$

$\therefore \quad (I+f)(1-f) = [(2+\sqrt{3})(2-\sqrt{3})]^n$

$= (4-3)^n = 1$

$\therefore \quad (I+f)(1-f) = 1$

(b) Proceed exactly as above.

(c) Proceed as above in part (a).

63. (a) Let $(\sqrt{3}+1)^{2m} = I + f$

and $(\sqrt{3}-1)^{2m} = f'$ where $0 < f' < 1$

and $0 < f' < 1$ and I is an integer.

Thus $I + f + f' = (\sqrt{3}+1)^{2m} + (\sqrt{3}-1)^{2m}$

$= (4+2\sqrt{3})^m + (4-2\sqrt{3})^m$

$= 2^m[(2+\sqrt{3})^m + (2-\sqrt{3})^m]$

$= 2^{m+1}[2^m + {}^mC_2.2^{m-2}.(\sqrt{3})^2 + \ldots..]$ ...(1)

Now as in part (a) $f + f' = 1$ and so $I + f + f'$ is an integer next above $(\sqrt{3}+1)^{2m}$ which by (1) contains 2^{m+1} as a factor.

(b) It is exactly as part (a).

$(5\sqrt{2}+7)^{2n+1} = I + f \quad 0 < f < 1$

$(5\sqrt{2}-7)^{2n+1} = f' \quad 0 < f' < 1$

Subtracting $I + f - f' = $ Even integer

It will be possible only when $f - f' = 0$ as both lie between 0 and 1. $\therefore \quad f = f'$

$\therefore \quad f(I+f) = f'(I+f)$

$\quad = [(5\sqrt{2}-7)(5\sqrt{2}+7)]^{2n+1}$

$\quad = [50-49]^{2n+1} = 1.$

64. (a) Let $(6\sqrt{6}+14)^{2n+1} = P = I + F$

where I is a positive integer and $0 < F < 1$

clearly $(6\sqrt{6}-14)^{2n+1} = F'$ where $0 < F' < 1$

Subtracting, we get

$2\,[^{2n+1}C_1\,(6\sqrt{6})^{2n} \times 14 + {}^{2n+1}C_3\,(6\sqrt{6})^{2n-2}$

$\qquad\qquad\qquad \times 14^3 + \dots]$

$\quad = I + F - F'$

$\therefore \quad I + F - F' =$ an even integer.

But since $0 < F < 1$ and $0 < F' < 1$, the only possibility is that $F - F' = 0$ or $F = F'$.

Hence I is an even integer.

Also $PF = PF' = (6\sqrt{6}+14)^{2n+1}\,(6\sqrt{6}-14)^{2n+1}$

$\quad = (216-196)^{2n+1} = 20^{2n+1}.$

(b) Let I and F denote respectively the integral and the fractional part of R. Then by definition of $[R]$.
$R - [R]$ is the fractional part of R.

$\therefore \quad F = f.$

$R = I + f = (5\sqrt{5}+11)^{2n+1}, \ 0 < f < 1$

$f' = (5\sqrt{5}-11)^{2n+1}, \ 0 < f' < 1.$

Subtracting, $I + f - f' = 2\,[^{2n+1}C_1\,(5\sqrt{5})^{2n} \times 11$

$\qquad\qquad + {}^{2n+1}C_3\,(5\sqrt{5})^{2n-2}\,11^3 + \dots]$

$\quad =$ an even integer

Since I is an integer $\therefore f - f'$ must also be an integer. But $0 < f < 1, 0 < f' < 1$ it follows that

$f - f' = 0$ or $f' = f.$

Now, $Rf = Rf' = (5\sqrt{5}+11)^{2n+1}\cdot(5\sqrt{5}-11)^{2n+1}$

$\quad = (125-121)^{2n+1} = 4^{2n+1}$

65. By use of Binomial theorem, we have

$\left(1+\frac{1}{n}\right)^n = 1 + n\cdot\frac{1}{n} + \frac{n(n-1)}{2!}\cdot\frac{1}{n^2}$

$\qquad + \frac{n(n-1)(n-2)}{3!}\cdot\frac{1}{n^3} + \dots$

$\qquad + \frac{n(n-1)(n-2)\dots[n-(n-1)]}{n!}\cdot\frac{1}{n^n}$

$= 1 + 1 + \frac{1}{2!}\left(1-\frac{1}{n}\right) + \frac{1}{3!}\left(1-\frac{1}{n}\right)\left(1-\frac{2}{n}\right)$

$\qquad + \frac{1}{4!}\left(1-\frac{1}{n}\right)\left(1-\frac{2}{n}\right)\left(1-\frac{3}{n}\right)$

$\qquad + \dots + \frac{1}{n!}\left(1-\frac{1}{n}\right)\left(1-\frac{2}{n}\right)\dots\left(1-\frac{n-1}{n}\right)$

$< 1 + 1 + \frac{1}{2!} + \frac{1}{3!} + \dots + \frac{1}{n!}$

$< 1 + 1 + \frac{1}{2} + \frac{1}{2^2} + \frac{1}{2^3} + \dots + \frac{1}{2^{n-1}}$ ...(1)

$= 1 + 1\cdot\dfrac{\left\{1-\left(\frac{1}{2}\right)^n\right\}}{1-\frac{1}{2}} = 1 + 2\left\{1-\left(\frac{1}{2}\right)^n\right\}$

$= 3 - \dfrac{1}{2^{n-1}}.$ ...(2)

$\therefore$ from (1) and (2) we prove the first part

i.e. $2 \le \left(1+\frac{1}{n}\right)^n < 3, \ n \ge 1$

Again, $\left(1+\frac{1}{n}\right)^n < 3$, by (2) ...(3)

Since $n \ge 3$, we have $\left(1+\frac{1}{n}\right)^n < n$, by (3)

or $(n+1)^n < n^{n+1}$ or $n^{n+1} > (n+1)^n$.

66. (a) Let $S = (1+x)^{1000} + 2x(1+x)^{999}$

$\qquad + 3x^2\,(1+x)^{998} + \dots +$

$\qquad\qquad 1000\,x^{999}\,(1+x) + 1001\cdot x^{1000}$

Above is A.G.S. of common ratio $r = \dfrac{x}{1+x}$

$\therefore \ [x/(1+x)]S = x(1+x)^{999} + 2x^2\,(1+x)^{998}$

$\qquad\qquad + \dots + 1000\cdot x^{1000} + \dfrac{1001\,x^{1001}}{1+x}$

Subtracting,

$\left(1-\dfrac{x}{1+x}\right)S = (1+x)^{1000} + x(1+x)^{999}$

$\qquad + x^2\,(1+x)^{998} + \dots + x^{1000} - \dfrac{1001\,x^{1001}}{1+x}$

or $S = (1+x)^{1001} + x(1+x)^{1000} + x^2\,(1+x)^{999}$

$\qquad + \dots + x^{1000}\,(1+x) - 1001\,x^{1001}.$

$= \dfrac{(1+x)^{1001}\,[1-\{x/(1+x)\}^{1001}]}{1-x/(1+x)} - 1001\,x^{1001}$

Sum G.P.

$= (1+x)^{1002}\,[1-\{x/(1+x)\}^{1001}] - 1001\,x^{1001}$

$= (1+x)^{1002} - x^{1001}\,(1+x) - 1001\,x^{1001}$

$= (1+x)^{1002} - x^{1002} - 1002\,x^{1001}$ ...(1)

Now the coefficient of x^{50} on the R.H.S. of (1)

$= {}^{1002}C_{50}$ Ans.

(b) The given series is an A.G.S. with $d = 1$ and

$r = \dfrac{1}{(1+x)}.$

$S = (1+x)^n + 2(1+x)^{n-1} + 3(1+x)^{n-2}$

$\qquad \dots(n-m+1)$ terms

$\therefore \ S\dfrac{1}{(1+x)} = (1+x)^{n-1} + 2(1+x)^{n-2}$

$\qquad + \dots + (n-m+1)(1+x)^{m-1}$

Subtracting,

$$S\left\{1 - \frac{1}{1+x}\right\} = \{(1+x)^n + (1+x)^{n-1}$$

$$+ (1+x)^{n-2} \ldots\}$$

or $\quad \dfrac{x}{1+x} S = (1+x)^n \left\{\dfrac{1 - \left(\dfrac{1}{(1+x)}\right)^{n-m+1}}{1 - 1/(1+x)}\right\}$

$$- (n-m+1)(1+x)^{m-1}$$

$$\therefore \quad \frac{Sx}{1+x} = (1+x)^n \frac{(1+x)^{n-m+1} - 1}{x.(1+x)^{n-m}}$$

$$- (n-m+1)(1+x)^{m-1}$$

or $\quad \dfrac{Sx}{1+x} = \dfrac{(1+x)^m}{x}\{(1+x)^{n-m+1} - 1\}$

$$- (n-m+1)(1+x)^{m-1}$$

$$\therefore \quad \frac{Sx}{1+x} = \frac{1}{x}\left\{(1+x)^{n+1} - (1+x)^m\right\}$$

$$- (n-m+1)(1+x)^{m-1}$$

$$\therefore \quad S = \frac{1}{x^2}\left\{(1+x)^{n+2} - (1+x)^{m+1}\right\}$$

$$- (n-m+1)\frac{(1+x)^m}{x}$$

$$= \frac{1}{x^2}(1+x)^{n+2} - \frac{1}{x^2}(1+x)^{m+1}$$

$$- (n-m+1)\frac{(1+x)^m}{x}$$

$$= T_1 + T_2 + T_3$$

There will be no term of x^m in T_2 and T_3 as the highest degree term in both will be x^{m-1}

The term of x^m in T_1 will be the term of x^{m+2} in $(1+x)^{n+2}$ which will be $^{n+2}C_{m+2}$.

(c) Ans. (c).

$$(1+x)^{101} = C_0 + C_1 x + C_2 x^2 + \ldots$$

$$(x-1)^{101} = C_0 x^{101} - C_1 x^{100} + C_2 x^{99} - \ldots$$

Multiplying both sides,

$$(x^2 - 1)^{101} = (C_0 + C_1 x + C_2 x^2 + \ldots)$$

$$(C_0 x^{101} - C_1 x^{100} + C_2 x^{99} - \ldots) \qquad \ldots(1)$$

Now $E = C_0 C_1 - C_1 C_2 + C_2 C_3 - \ldots$

$$= - [\text{Coefficient of } x^{100} \text{ in the product of}$$
$$\text{R.H.S. of (1)}]$$

or $\quad = - [\text{Coefficient of } (x^2)^{50} \text{ in the product of}$
$$\text{R.H.S. of (1)}] \qquad \ldots(2)$$

Now

$$(x^2 - 1)^{101} = (-1)^{101}(1 - x^2)^{101} = -(1 - x^2)^{101}$$

$$\therefore \quad \text{Coefficient of } (x^2)^{50}$$

$$= -(-1)^{50} \, {}^{101}C_{50} = - \, {}^{101}C_{50} \qquad \ldots(3)$$

$$\therefore \quad E = (-)(-) \, {}^{101}C_{50} = {}^{101}C_{50} \text{ by (2) and (3)}.$$

67. (a) $\displaystyle\sum_{k=1}^{n} k^3 \left(\frac{C_k}{C_{k-1}}\right)^2 = \sum_{k=1}^{n} k^3 \left(\frac{n-k+1}{k}\right)^2$

$$\left[\because \frac{{}^nC_k}{{}^nC_{k-1}} = \frac{n-k+1}{k}\right]$$

$$= \sum_{k=1}^{n} k(n-k+1)^2$$

$$= \sum_{k=1}^{n} k[(n+1)^2 - 2k(n+1) + k^2]$$

$$= (n+1)^2 \sum_{k=1}^{n} k - 2(n+1)\sum_{k=1}^{n} k^2 + \sum_{k=1}^{n} k^3$$

$$= (n+1)^2 \cdot \frac{n(n+1)}{2} - 2(n+1) \cdot$$

$$\frac{n(n+1)(2n+1)}{6} + \frac{n^2(n+1)^2}{4}$$

$$= \frac{n(n+1)^2}{12}[6(n+1) - 4(2n+1) + 3n]$$

$$= \frac{n(n+1)^2}{12} \cdot (n+2) = \frac{n(n+2)(n+1)^2}{12}.$$

(b) Ans. (a).

$$\frac{{}^nC_r}{{}^nC_r + {}^nC_{r+1}} = \frac{{}^nC_r}{{}^{n+1}C_{r+1}}$$

$$= \frac{n!}{(n-r)! \, r!} \cdot \frac{(n-r)!(r+1)!}{(n+1)!} = \frac{r+1}{n+1}$$

$$\sum_{r=0}^{n-1} = \frac{1}{n+1}[1+2+3+\ldots+n] = \frac{n(n+1)}{2(n+1)} = \frac{n}{2}$$

68. Put $x - 3 = t$ so that $x - 2 = t + 1$.

$$\therefore \quad \sum_{r=0}^{2n} a_r (1+t)^r = \sum_{r=0}^{2n} b_r t^r$$

b_n is coefficient of t^n in R.H.S. so that it will be coefficient of t^n in the L.H.S. But for $r = 0$ to $n - 1$ no term will have the term of t^n and for $r \geq n, a_r = 1$

$$\therefore \quad \text{L.H.S.} = \sum_{r=n}^{2n} 1.(1+t)^r$$

$$= (1+t)^n + (1+t)^{n+1} + (1+t)^{n+2}$$

$$+ \ldots + (1+t)^{n+n}$$

Above is a G.P. of $n+1$ terms with common ratio $1+t$.

$$\text{L.H.S.} = (1+t)^n \left[\frac{(1+t)^{n+1} - 1}{(1+t) - 1}\right]$$

$$= \frac{(1+t)^{2n+1} - (1+t)^n}{t}$$

We have to search the coefficient of t^n in L.H.S. or coefficient of t^{n+1} in numerator of L.H.S. *i.e.*,

$(1+t)^{2n+1} - (1+t)^n$. It is $^{2n+1}C_n$ in T_{n+2} of 1st only, as the 2nd term will not have t^{n+1}

$\therefore \quad ^{2n+1}C_n = b_n$

69. $k = 3n/2$ where n is an even integer. Choose $n = 2m$ so that $k = 3m$.

or $\displaystyle\sum_{r=1}^{k} (-3)^{r-1} \, ^{3n}C_{2r-1}$

$= \displaystyle\sum_{r=1}^{3m} (-3)^{r-1} \, ^{6m}C_{2r-1}$

$= \,^{6m}C_1 - 3\,^{6m}C_3 + 3^2\,^{6m}C_5 - 3^3\,^{6m}C_7 + ...$

Consider $(\cos\theta - i\sin\theta)^{6m}$

$= \cos^{6m}\theta - \,^{6m}C_1 \cos^{6m-1}\theta\, i\sin\theta$
$\quad + \,^{6m}C_2 \cos^{6m-2}\theta\, i^2 \sin^2\theta$
$\quad\quad - \,^{6m}C_3 \cos^{6m-3}\theta\, i^3 \sin^3\theta + ...$

$\therefore$ L.H.S. $= \cos 6m\theta - i\sin 6m\theta$
(De-Moivre's Theorem)

Equating imaginary parts, we get

$\sin 6m\theta = \,^{6m}C_1 \cos^{6m-1}\theta \sin\theta$
$\quad\quad - \,^{6m}C_3 \cos^{6m-3}\theta \sin^3\theta + ...$

Now put $\theta = \pi/3 \quad \therefore \quad 6\theta = 2\pi$

or $\sin 6m\theta = \sin 2m\pi = 0$

$\therefore \quad 0 = \,^{6m}C_1 \dfrac{\sqrt3}{2}\left(\dfrac12\right)^{6m-1}$
$\quad\quad - \,^{6m}C_3 \left(\dfrac{\sqrt3}{2}\right)^3 \left(\dfrac12\right)^{6m-3} + ...$

or $0 = \dfrac{\sqrt3}{2^{6m}}\left[\,^{6m}C_1 - 3\,^{6m}C_3 + 3^2\,^{6m}C_5 - ...\right]$

$\therefore \,^{6m}C_1 - 3\,^{6m}C_3 + 3^2\,^{6m}C_5 - ... = 0$

70. Let the given series be denoted by

$E = S + C_n \sin n\alpha$ ...(1)

where $S = C_1 \sin\alpha \cos(n-1)\alpha + C_2 \sin 2\alpha$
$\quad\quad\quad\quad\quad \cos(n-2)\alpha + ...$

Writing the above in reverse order, we get

$S = C_n \cos\alpha \sin(n-1)\alpha$
$\quad\quad + C_{n-1} \cos 2\alpha \sin(n-2)\alpha + ...$

Adding, $2S = (C_1 + C_n)\sin(n\alpha - \alpha + \alpha)$
$\quad\quad + (C_2 + C_{n-1})\sin(n\alpha - 2\alpha + 2\alpha) + ...$

or $2S = (C_1 + C_2 + C_3 + ... + C_{n-1})\sin n\alpha$

$\therefore \sin A \cos B + \cos A \sin B = \sin(A+B) = \sin n\alpha$

Add and substract $(C_0 + C_1)\sin n\alpha$

$\therefore \quad 2S = \left(\displaystyle\sum_{i=0}^{n} C_i\right)\sin n\alpha - (1+1)\sin n\alpha$

$= (2^n - 2)\sin n\alpha$

$\therefore \quad S = (2^{n-1} - 1)\sin n\alpha$ ...(2)

$\therefore \quad E = S + \,^nC_n \sin n\alpha$

$= S + \sin n\alpha = 2^{n-1}\sin n\alpha$, by (2).

71. $T_r = (-1)^{r-1}\left[1 + \dfrac12 + \dfrac13 + ... \dfrac1r\right]\,^nC_r$

Consider $(-1)^{r-1}[1 + x + x^2 + ... x^{r-1}]\,^nC_r$

$= (-1)^{r-1}\left[\dfrac{1-x^r}{1-x}\right]\,^nC_r$

$\therefore \quad S = \dfrac{1}{1-x}[\Sigma(-1)^{r-1}\,^nC_r - \Sigma(-1)^{r-1}x^r\,^nC_r]$

$= \dfrac{1}{1-x}[(-1)\Sigma(-1)^r\,^nC_r + \Sigma(-1)^r x^r\,^nC_r]$

$= \dfrac{1}{1-x}[(-1)\{(1-1)^0 - 1\} + \{(1-x)^n - 1\}]$

$= \dfrac{1}{1-x}[0 + 1 + (1-x)^n - 1] = (1-x)^{n-1}$

Now integrate both sides with limits as 0 to 1 etc.

72. **(a)** Clearly $m = -n, t = n$ as the highest power of x will be n and lowest will be $-n$.

(b) $\Sigma a_r =$ Sum of binomial coefficients is obtained by putting $x = 1$ and hence $\Sigma a_r = 5^n$.

(c) $a_t = a_n =$ coefficient of $x^n = \,^nC_n 2^n = 2^n$.

(d) $a_m = a_{-n} =$ coefficient of $x^{-n} = \,^nC_n 2^n = 2^n$.

(e) $a_p = a_q$, then if $p = \lambda$ then $q = -\lambda$
$\therefore \quad p + q = 0 \quad\quad$ by (d).

§11. Properties of Binomial Coefficients.

The binomial coefficients are generally written as $C_0, C_1, C_2, ... C_n$ instead of $^nC_0, \,^nC_1, \,^nC_2, ...$

(a) **Sum of the binomial coefficients $= 2^n$.**

We know that

$(1+x)^n = C_0 + C_1 x + C_2 x^2 + ... + C_n x^n.$ ...(A)

Putting $x = 1$ in the above, we get

$2^n = C_0 + C_1 + C_2 + ... + C_n$ ...(1)

or $C_1 + C_2 + C_3 + ... + C_n = 2^n - 1$

$\because \quad C_0 = \,^nC_0 = 1$.

Again putting $x = -1$ in the above, we get

$0 = C_0 - C_1 + C_2 - C_3 + C_4 - C_5 + ...$

or $C_0 + C_2 + C_4 + ... = C_1 + C_3 + C_5 + ...$

i.e. $A = B$.

Also from (1), $A + B = 2^n \quad \therefore \quad 2A = 2^n$

or $A = 2^{n-1} = B$.

*Hence

$C_0 + C_2 + C_4 + ... = C_1 + C_3 + C_5 + ... = 2^{n-1}$ ...(2)

Thus sum of all the binomial coefficients $= 2^n$.

and sum of odd binomial coefficients = sum of even binomial coefficients $= 2^{n-1}$.

(b) **Some Important Results**

Differentiating (A), we get

$n(1+x)^{n-1} = C_1 + 2C_2 x + 3C_3 x^2 + ... + nC_n x^{n-1}$

Putting $x = 1, -1$, we get

* $\quad n\,2^{n-1} = C_1 + 2C_2 + 3C_3 + \ldots + nC_n \qquad \ldots(3)$

* $\quad 0 = C_1 - 2C_2 + 3C_3 + \ldots + (-1)^{n-1}\, nC_n \qquad \ldots(4)$

Integrating (A), we get

$$\frac{(1+x)^{n+1}}{n+1} + C = C_0\, x + C_1\,\frac{x^2}{2} + C_2\,\frac{x^3}{3} + \ldots + C_n\,\frac{x^{n+1}}{n+1}$$

Putting $x = 0$, we get $C = -\dfrac{1}{n+1}$

$$\therefore \quad \frac{(1+x)^{n+1} - 1}{n+1} = C_0\, x + C_1\,\frac{x^2}{2} + \ldots\ldots + C_n\,\frac{x^{n+1}}{n+1}$$

Putting $n = 1, -1$ and 2, we get

* $\dfrac{2^{n+1} - 1}{n+1} = C_0 + \dfrac{C_1}{2} + \dfrac{C_2}{3} + \ldots\ldots + \dfrac{C_n}{n+1} \qquad \ldots(5)$

$\dfrac{1}{n+1} = C_0 - \dfrac{C_1}{2} + \dfrac{C_2}{3} - \ldots\ldots \qquad \ldots(6)$

* $\dfrac{3^{n+1} - 1}{n+1} = 2C_0 + \dfrac{2^2}{2}C_1 + \dfrac{2^3}{3}C_2 + \ldots + \dfrac{2^{n+1}}{n+1}C_n \qquad \ldots(7)$

Above (5), (6) and (7) are solutions of **Q. 16, 17, 19, P. 391-98.**

Problem Set (2)

Binomial coefficients $C_0, C_1, C_2, \ldots C_n$. Relations between binomial coefficients obtained by differentiation or integration of the expansion of $(1 + x)^n$.

Prove that :

1. (a) $C_1 + 2C_2 + 3C_3 + \ldots\ldots + nC_n = n \cdot 2^{n-1}$.

   (b) $C_1 - 2C_2 + 3C_3 - 4C_4 + \ldots\ldots = 0$.

   (c) Sum of the last 30 coefficients in the expansion of $(1 + x)^{59}$ when expanded in ascending powers of x is

       (a) 2^{28} (b) 2^{29}

       (c) 2^{58} (d) $^{60}C_{30} - 2^{19}$

2. (a) In the usual notations prove that

   $$C_1 + 2C_2\, x + 3C_3\, x^2 + \ldots\ldots + nC_n\, x^{n-1}$$
   $$= n\,(1 + x)^{n-1}$$

   (b) $C_0 + 3C_1 + 5C_2 + \ldots\ldots (2n+1)\, C_n = (n+1)\, 2^n$

   (c) Prove that

   $$1 - 2n + \frac{2n\,(2n-1)}{2!} - \frac{2n\,(2n-1)\,(2n-2)}{3!} + \ldots$$
   $$+ (-1)^{n-1}\,\frac{2n\,(2n-1)\ldots(n+2)}{(n-1)!}$$
   $$= (-1)^{n+1}\,\frac{(2n)!}{2\,(n!)^2}, \text{ where } n \text{ is a +ive integer.}$$

3. (a)* $1^2 \cdot C_1 + 2^2 \cdot C_2 + 3^2 \cdot C_3 + \ldots\ldots + n^2 \cdot C_n$
   $$= n\,(n+1)\,2^{n-2}$$

   (b) $1^2\, C_1 - 2^2\, C_2 + 3^2\, C_3 - \ldots + (-1)^{n-1}\, n^2 C_n = 0$

   (c) $1^3\, C_1 + 2^3\, C_2 + 3^3\, C_3 + \ldots + n^3\, C_n$
   $$= n^2\,(n+3)\,2^{n-3}$$

4.* $C_0 - 2^2\, C_1 + 3^2\, C_2 + \ldots + (-1)^n\,(n+1)^2\, C_n = 0, \quad n > 2.$

5. Sum the series

   $$ab\, C_0 - (a-1)\,(b-1)\, C_1 + (a-2)\,(b-2)\, C_2 + \ldots$$
   $$+ (-1)^n\,(a-n) \cdot (b-n)\, C_n$$

   where a, b are real numbers and $C_r = {}^nC_r, n > 3$.

6. (a)* If $n > 2$, then prove that

   $$C_1\,(a-1)^2 - C_2\,(a-2)^2 + \ldots + (-1)^{n-1}$$
   $$C_n\,(a-n)^2 = a^2$$

   (b) If C_r be the coefficient of x^r in $(1 + x)^n$, then the value of $\displaystyle\sum_{r=0}^{n} (r+1)^2\, C_r$ is

       (a) $(n+1)\,(n+4)\,2^{n-2}$

       (b) $(n+1)\,(n+4)\,2^{n-1}$

       (c) $(n+1)^2\,2^{n-2}$

       (d) $(n+4)^2\,2^{n-2}$

7. (a) If n is an integer greater than 1, show that

   $$a - {}^nC_1\,(a-1) + {}^nC_2\,(a-2) - \ldots + (-1)^n\,(a-n) = 0.$$

   (b) If $a_1, a_2, a_3, \ldots$ are in A.P. then show that

   $$a_1 C_0 - a_2 C_1 + a_3 C_2 - \ldots + (-1)^n\, a_{n+1}\, C_n = 0.$$

   Hence deduce that

   $$3\,C_0 - 8\,C_1 + 13\,C_2 - 18\,C_3 + \ldots = 0$$

8. (a)* Find the sum of

   $$3 \cdot {}^nC_0 - 8 \cdot {}^nC_1 + 13 \cdot {}^nC_2 - 18 \cdot {}^nC_3 + \ldots$$
   $$+ \text{ upto } (n+1) \text{ terms.}$$

   (b)* Prove that

   $$3C_1 + 7C_2 + 11C_3 + \ldots + (4n-1)\, C_n$$
   $$= 1 + (2n-1) \cdot 2^n.$$

   (c) If $\Delta = a + (a+d) + (a+2d) + \ldots + (a+nd)$

   and $S = a + (a+d)\, C_1 + (a+2d)\, C_2 + \ldots$
   $$+ (a+nd)\, C_n$$

   then prove that $(n+1)\, S = 2^n\, \Delta$

9. (a) $\dfrac{C_1}{C_0} + 2\dfrac{C_2}{C_1} + 3\dfrac{C_3}{C_2} + \ldots + n\dfrac{C_n}{C_{n-1}} = \dfrac{n\,(n+1)}{2}$.

   (b)* If $C_0, C_1, C_2, \ldots\ldots C_{15}$ are the binomial coefficients in the expansion of $(1 + x)^{15}$, prove that

$$\frac{C_1}{C_0} + 2\frac{C_2}{C_1} + 3\frac{C_3}{C_2} + \dots + 15\frac{C_{15}}{C_{14}} = 120$$

10. (a) Find the coefficient of x^{49} in the polynomial

$$\left(x - \frac{C_1}{C_0}\right)\left(x - 2^2\frac{C_2}{C_1}\right)\left(x - 3^2\frac{C_3}{C_2}\right)\dots\left(x - 50^2\frac{C_{50}}{C_{49}}\right),$$

where $C_r = {}^{50}C_r$. **(Roorkee 2001)**

(b) $\dfrac{1}{1!\,(n-1)!} + \dfrac{1}{3!\,(n-3)!} + \dfrac{1}{5!\,(n-5)!} + \dots = \dfrac{2^{n-1}}{n!}$

11.* If $(1+x)^n = C_0 + C_1 x + C_2 x^2 + \dots + C_n x^n$, $x \in N$, then prove that $C_0 - C_1 + C_2 - \dots + (-1)^{m-1} C_{m-1}$

$$= (-1)^{m-1}\frac{(n-1)(n-2)\dots(n-m+1)}{(m-1)!}$$

12. (a) $C_0 + 2C_1 + 3C_2 + \dots + (n+1)C_n$
$$= 2^n + n\,2^{n-1} = (n+2)\,2^{n-1}$$

(b) $C_0 + 3C_1 + 5C_2 + \dots + (2n+1)C_n = (n+1)\,2^n$.

13.* Prove that

$$1 - {}^nC_1\frac{1+x}{1+nx} + {}^nC_2\frac{1+2x}{(1+nx)^2} - {}^nC_3\frac{1+3x}{(1+nx)^3}$$
$$+ \dots (n+1)\text{ terms} = 0.$$

14. Evaluate $\displaystyle\sum_{r=0}^{n} (r+1)^3\, C_r$ where $C_r = {}^nC_r$

15. (a) If $p + q = 1$, then show that
$$\sum_{r=0}^{n} r^2 C_r\, p^r \cdot q^{n-r} = npq + n^2 p^2.$$

(b) If $(1+x)^n = C_0 + C_1 x + C_2 x^2 + \dots + C_n x^n$; find the value of $3C_3 + 8C_4 + 15C_5 + 24C_6 + \dots (n-2)$ terms.

16. (a) $\dfrac{C_0}{1} + \dfrac{C_2}{3} + \dfrac{C_4}{5} + \dfrac{C_6}{7} + \dots = \dfrac{2^n}{n+1}$.

(b)* Prove that $\dfrac{C_1}{2} + \dfrac{C_3}{4} + \dfrac{C_5}{6} + \dots = \dfrac{2^n - 1}{n+1}$

17. (a) $C_0 + \dfrac{C_1}{2} + \dfrac{C_2}{3} + \dots + \dfrac{C_n}{n+1} = \dfrac{2^{n+1}-1}{n+1}$.

(b)* $C_0 - \dfrac{C_1}{2} + \dfrac{C_2}{3} - \dfrac{C_3}{4} + \dots = \dfrac{1}{n+1}$.

18. Prove that
$$\frac{1}{2}C_1 - \frac{2}{3}C_2 + \frac{3}{4}C_3 - \frac{4}{5}C_4 + \dots + (-1)^{n+1}\cdot\frac{n}{n+1} = \frac{1}{n+1}$$

19. (a)* $2C_0 + 2^2\dfrac{C_1}{2} + 2^3\dfrac{C_2}{3} + 2^4\dfrac{C_3}{4} + \dots$
$$+ 2^{n+1}\cdot\frac{C_n}{n+1} = \frac{3^{n+1}-1}{n+1}$$

(b) In the usual notation prove that
$$2C_0 + \frac{2^2}{2}C_1 + \frac{2^3}{3}C_2 + \dots + \frac{2^{11}}{11}C_{10} = \frac{3^{11}-1}{11}$$
(M.P. C.E.E. 1999)

(c) In the usual notation prove that
$$C_0 + \frac{C_1}{2}x + \frac{C_2}{3}x^2 + \dots + \frac{C_n}{n+1}x^n$$
$$= \frac{(1+x)^{n+1}-1}{(n+1)x}$$

(d) $3C_0 + 3^2\dfrac{C_1}{2} + 3^3\dfrac{C_2}{3} + \dots + 3^{n+1}\cdot\dfrac{C_n}{n+1} = \dfrac{4^{n+1}-1}{n+1}$

20. (a)* Prove that
$$\frac{C_0}{2} + \frac{C_1}{3} + \frac{C_2}{4} + \dots + \frac{C_n}{n+2} = \frac{1+n\cdot 2^{n+1}}{(n+1)(n+2)}$$

(b) Prove that
$$\frac{C_0}{2} - \frac{C_1}{3} + \frac{C_2}{4} - \frac{C_3}{5} + \dots = \frac{1}{(n+1)(n+2)}.$$

(c) If $(1+x)^n = \displaystyle\sum_{r=0}^{n} C_r x^r$ and
$$\sum_{r=0}^{n} (-1)^r \frac{C_r}{(r+1)^2} = k\sum_{r=0}^{n}\frac{1}{r+1}, \text{ then } k \text{ is equal}$$
to :

(a) $\dfrac{1}{n}$ (b) $\dfrac{1}{n+1}$

(c) $\dfrac{n}{n+1}$ (d) none

21.* If $(1+x)^n = \displaystyle\sum_{r=0}^{n} C_r x^r$, prove that
$$\frac{2^2 \cdot C_0}{1.2} + \frac{2^3 \cdot C_1}{2.3} + \dots + \frac{2^{n+2}\cdot C_n}{(n+1)(n+2)} = \frac{3^{n+2}-2n-5}{(n+1)(n+2)}.$$

22. $\dfrac{C_1}{1} - \dfrac{C_2}{2} + \dfrac{C_3}{3} - \dfrac{C_4}{4} + \dots + \dfrac{(-1)^{n-1}}{n}C_n$
$$= 1 + \frac{1}{2} + \frac{1}{3} + \dots + \frac{1}{n}.$$

23.* Prove that $\dfrac{C_0}{1} - \dfrac{C_1}{4} + \dfrac{C_2}{9} - \dots + \dfrac{(-1)^n C_n}{n^2+2n+1}$
$$= \frac{1}{n+1} + \frac{1}{2n+2} + \dots + \frac{1}{n^2+2n+1}$$

24.* $\dfrac{C_0}{1} - \dfrac{C_1}{5} + \dfrac{C_2}{9} - \dfrac{C_3}{13} + \dots (-1)^n\dfrac{C_n}{4n+1} = \dfrac{4^n\,n!}{1.5.9\dots(4n+1)}$

25. (a)* $C_0^2 + C_1^2 + C_2^2 + \dots + C_n^2 = \dfrac{(2n)!}{n!\,n!}$.

(b) $C_0 C_n + C_1 C_{n-1} + \dots + C_n C_0 = \dfrac{(2n)!}{n!\,n!}$.

(c)* If $(1+x)^n = C_0 + C_1 x + C_2 x^2 + \dots + C_n x^n$, then show that the sum of the products of the $C_i's$ taken two at a time represented by $\Sigma\Sigma\, C_i C_j$ is equal to $0 \le i < j \le n$.
$$2^{2n-1} - \frac{(2n)!}{2\cdot(n!)^2}.$$
(M.N.R 1992)

26. (a)* $C_0C_1 + C_1C_2 + ... + C_{n-1}C_n = \dfrac{(2n)!}{(n-1)!\,(n+1)!}$

(b)* $C_0C_2 + C_1C_3 + C_2C_4 + ... + C_{n-2}C_n$

$$= \dfrac{(2n!)}{(n-2)!\,(n+2)!}$$

(c)* $C_0C_r + C_1C_{r+1} + C_2C_{r+2} + ... + C_{n-r}C_n.$

$= C_0C_r + C_1C_{r+1} + C_2C_{r+2} + ... + C_rC_0$

$$= \dfrac{(2n)!}{(n-r)!\,(n+r)!}.$$

27. (a) The sum

$$\sum_{i=0}^{m} \binom{10}{i}\binom{20}{m-i}, \quad \left(\text{where } \binom{p}{q} = 0 \text{ if } p < q\right)$$

is maximum when m is

(a) 5
(b) 10
(c) 15
(d) 20   **(I.I.T. Sc. 2002)**

(b) If $s_n = C_0C_1 + C_1C_2 + ... + C_{n-1}C_n$ and

$\dfrac{s_{n+1}}{s_n} = \dfrac{15}{4}$, then prove that $n = 2, 4$.

28. Prove that

$(C_0 + C_1 + C_2 + ... + C_n)^2 = 1 + {}^{2n}C_1 + {}^{2n}C_2 + ...$

$$+ {}^{2n}C_n.$$

29. Prove that

$\dfrac{1}{m!}C_0 + \dfrac{n}{(m+1)!}C_1 + \dfrac{n(n-1)}{(m+2)!}C_2$

$$+ ... + \dfrac{n(n-1)...2.1}{(m+n)!}C_n$$

$$= \dfrac{(m+n+1)(m+n+2)...(m+2n)}{(m+n)!}$$

30. (a) By expanding $\{(1+x)^n - 1\}^m$ in two ways, prove that ${}^mC_1\,{}^nC_m - {}^mC_2\,{}^{2n}C_m + {}^mC_3\,{}^{3n}C_m - ...$

$$= (-1)^{m-1}n^m$$

(b) Prove that

$C_0\,{}^{2n}C_n - C_1\,{}^{2n-2}C_n + C_2\,{}^{2n-4}C_n - ... = 2^n$

where $C_r = {}^nC_r$

31. (a)* Prove that according as n is odd or even the value of $C_0^2 - C_1^2 + C_2^2 - ..... + (-1)^n (C_n)^2$

$$= 0 \quad \text{or} \quad (-1)^{n/2}\dfrac{n!}{(n/2)!\,(n/2)!}.$$

(b) $({}^{2n}C_0)^2 - ({}^{2n}C_1)^2 + ({}^{2n}C_2)^2 - .... + ({}^{2n}C_{2n})^2$

$$= (-1)^n \cdot {}^{2n}C_n.$$

(c)* Evaluate $C_0^2 - C_1^2 + C_2^2 - .... + (-1)^n C_n^2$

for $n = 10$ and $n = 11$.

32. (a) Prove that

${}^{m+n}C_r = {}^mC_r + {}^mC_{r-1} \cdot {}^nC_1$

$$+ {}^mC_{r-2} \cdot {}^nC_2 + ... + {}^nC_r$$

where $r < m, r < n$ and m, n, r are + ive integers.

(b) Find the coefficient of $x^n y^n$ in the expansion of $[(1+x)(1+y)(x+y)]^n$.

33. (a) The coefficient of x^r in the expansion of $1 + (1+x) + (1+x)^2 + ... + (1+x)^n$ is ${}^{n+1}C_{r+1}$

(b)* The coefficient of x^r $(0 \le r \le n-1)$ in the expansion of

$(x+2)^{n-1} + (x+2)^{n-2}(x+1)$

$$+ (x+2)^{n-3}(x+1)^2 + ... + (x+1)^{n-1}$$

is ${}^nC_r (2^{n-r} - 1)$.

34. Prove that the coefficient of x^r $(0 \le r \le (n-1))$ in the expansion of

$(x+3)^{n-1} + (x+3)^{n-2}(x+2) + (x+3)^{n-3}$

$(x+2)^2 + ... + (x+2)^{n-1}$ is ${}^nC_r (3^{n-r} - 2^{n-r})$

35. (a) For any positive integers m, n (with $n \ge m$), let

$$\binom{n}{m} = {}^nC_m .$$

Prove that

$$\binom{n}{m} + \binom{n-1}{m} + \binom{n-2}{m} + ... + \binom{m}{m} = \binom{n+1}{m+1}$$

Hence or otherwise, prove that

$$\binom{n}{m} + 2\left\{\binom{n-1}{m}\right\} + 3\binom{n-2}{m} + ...$$

$$+ (n-m+1)\binom{m}{m} = \binom{n+2}{m+2}$$

(I.I.T. 2000)

(b) Prove $2^k \binom{n}{0}\binom{n}{k} - 2^{k-1}\binom{n}{1}\binom{n-1}{k-1}...$

$$(-1)^k \binom{n}{k}\binom{n-k}{0} = \binom{n}{k}$$

where $\binom{n}{m} = {}^nC_m$

(IIT 2003)

36. Prove that $C_1^2 - 2.C_2^2 + 3.C_3^2 - ...... - 2n\,C_{2n}^2$

$$= (-1)^{n-1}\,nC_n.$$

37. $[1 + (n+1)x](1+x)^{n-1}$

$$= C_0 + 2C_1x + 3C_2x^2 + ... + (n+1)C_nx^n$$

and $C_0^2 + 2C_1^2 + 3C_2^2 + ... + (n+1)C_n^2$

$$= \dfrac{(n+2)(2n-1)!}{n!(n-1)!}$$

38.* If C_r stands for ${}^nC_r$ then the sum of the series

$\dfrac{2(n/2)!(n/2)!}{n!}[C_0^2 - 2C_1^2 + 3C_2^2 - .....$

$$+ (-1)^n (n+1)C_n^2],$$

where n is an even positive integer, is equal to $(-1)^{n/2}(n+2)$.

39. If $(1+x)^{15} = C_0 + C_1 x + C_2 x^2 + ... + C_{15} x^{15}$, find the value of $C_2 + 2C_3 + 3C_4 + ... + 14C_{15}$

40. (a)* In the usual notations prove that
$$(C_0 + C_1)(C_1 + C_2)\ldots\ldots(C_{n-1} + C_n)$$
$$= \frac{(n+1)^n}{n!} C_1 C_2 C_3 \ldots C_n.$$

(b)* In the expansion of $(1+x)^n$, $P(n)$ stands for the product of all the binomial coefficients then prove that $\dfrac{P(n+1)}{P(n)} = \dfrac{(n+1)^n}{n!}$

41. (a) If n is an odd natural number then show that
$$\sum_{r=0}^{n} \frac{(-1)^r}{^nC_r} = 0.$$

(b) If $(1+x)^n = C_0 + C_1 x + C_2 x^2 + \ldots + C_n x^n$ then prove that
$$C_0 + (C_0 + C_1) + (C_0 + C_1 + C_2) + \ldots$$
$$+ (C_0 + C_1 + C_2 + \ldots + C_{n-1})$$
is equal to $n \cdot 2^{n-1}$.

42.* Given $s_n = 1 + q + q^2 + \ldots\ldots + q^n$,
$$S_n = 1 + \frac{q+1}{2} + \left(\frac{q+1}{2}\right)^2 + \ldots + \left(\frac{q+1}{2}\right)^n, q \neq 1$$

Prove that
$$^{n+1}C_1 + {}^{n+1}C_2 \, s_1 + {}^{n+1}C_3 \, s_2 + \ldots\ldots$$
$$+ {}^{n+1}C_{n+1} \, s_n = 2^n \, S_n.$$

43.* Find the sum of the series :
$$\sum_{r=0}^{n} (-1)^r \; {}^nC_r \left[\frac{1}{2^r} + \frac{3^r}{2^{2r}} + \frac{7^r}{2^{3r}} + \frac{15^r}{2^{4r}} + \ldots \text{upto } m \text{ terms}\right]$$

44. Prove that
$$\frac{C_0}{x} - \frac{C_1}{x+1} + \frac{C_2}{x+2} - \ldots + (-1)^n \frac{C_n}{x+n}$$
$$= \frac{n!}{x(x+1)\ldots(x+n)}$$
where n is a +ive integer and x is not a negative integer. Hence prove that
$$\frac{C_0}{1} - \frac{C_1}{4} + \frac{C_2}{7} - \ldots + (-1)^n \frac{C_n}{3n+1}$$
$$= \frac{3^n \cdot n!}{1.4.7\ldots(3n+1)}$$

45.* Prove independently that
$$\frac{C_0}{1} - \frac{C_1}{4} + \frac{C_2}{7} - \ldots + (-1)^n \frac{C_n}{3n+1} = \frac{3^n \cdot n!}{1.4.7\ldots(3n+1)}$$

46. Evaluate the integral $\int_0^1 x^{n-1}(1-x)^n \, dx$ and hence find the sum of the series
$$\frac{C_0}{n} - \frac{C_1}{n+1} + \frac{C_2}{n+2} - \ldots + (-1)^n \frac{C_n}{2n} = \frac{(n!)(n-1)!}{(2n)!}$$

47. If $T_0, T_1, T_2, \ldots\ldots, T_n$ represent the terms in the expansion of $(x+a)^n$, then

$$(T_0 - T_2 + T_4 - \ldots\ldots)^2 + (T_1 - T_3 + T_5 - \ldots\ldots)^2$$
$$= (x^2 + a^2)^n.$$

In Q. 48 to 51 if $a_0, a_1, a_2, \ldots$ be the coefficients in the expansion of $(1 + x + x^2)^n$ in ascending powers of x, then prove that :

48. (a)* $a_r = a_{2n-r}$,

(b) $a_0 + a_1 + a_2 + \ldots + a_{n-1} = \frac{1}{2}(3^n - a_n)$,

49. $(r+1) a_{r+1} = (n-r) a_r + (2n-r+1) a_{r-1}, (0 < r < 2n)$

50. (a) $a_0^2 - a_1^2 + a_2^2 - a_3^2 + \ldots - a_{2n-1}^2 + a_{2n}^2 = a_n$
    (I.I.T. 1994)

(b) $a_0^2 - a_1^2 + a_2^2 - a_3^2 + \ldots + (-1)^{n-1} a_{n-1}^2$
$$= \frac{1}{2} a_n \{1 - (-1)^n a_n\}$$

51. $(a_0 + a_3 + a_6 + \ldots) = (a_1 + a_4 + a_7 + \ldots)$
$$= (a_2 + a_5 + a_8 + \ldots) = 3^{n-1}$$

52. If k and n be +ive integers and $s_k = 1^k + 2^k + 3^k + \ldots + n^k$, then show that
$$\sum_{r=1}^{m} {}^{m+1}C_r \, s_r = (n+1)^{m+1} - (n+1).$$
Hence evaluate s_4.

53.* Find the sum of the infinite series
$$a_1 + a_2 + a_3 + \ldots, \text{ where}$$
$$a_n = (\log 3)^n \sum_{k=1}^{n} \frac{2k+1}{k!(n-k)!}$$
    (Roorkee 1995)

54.* Prove that $\displaystyle\sum_{r=0}^{n} r(n-r) \, C_r^2 = n^2 \, ({}^{2n-2}C_n)$

55. (a)* Prove that $\dfrac{3!}{2(n+3)} = \displaystyle\sum_{r=0}^{n} (-1)^r \left(\dfrac{{}^nC_r}{{}^{r+3}C_r}\right)$
    (I.I.T. 1997; J.E.E.W.B. 2000)

(b) Find the sum of $\displaystyle\sum_{r=0}^{n} (-1)^r \dfrac{{}^nC_r}{{}^{r+2}C_r}$

(c) Prove that
$$\sum_{r=0}^{n} \cdot (-2)^r \cdot \frac{{}^nC_r}{{}^{r+2}C_r} = \begin{bmatrix} 1/(n+1), n \text{ even} \\ 1/(n+2), n \text{ odd} \end{bmatrix}$$

56. Prove that $\displaystyle\sum_{r=1}^{k} (-3)^{r-1} \; {}^{3n}C_{2r-1} = 0$
where $k = \dfrac{3n}{2}$ and n is an even + ive integer.

Solutions to Problem Set (2)

Procedure for Q. 1 to 9 by differentiation.
$$(1+x)^n = C_0 + C_1 x + C_2 x^2 + \ldots + C_n x^n \qquad \ldots(1)$$

The coefficient of x^r is C_r. Putting $x = 1, -1$ in (1)
$$C_0 + C_1 + C_2 + \ldots + C_n = 2^n \qquad \ldots(2)$$
$$C_0 - C_1 + C_2 - C_3 + \ldots = 0 \qquad \ldots(3)$$

Adding and subtracting (2) and (3),

$$C_0 + C_2 + C_4 + \ldots = C_1 + C_3 + C_5 + \ldots = 2^{n-1} \quad \ldots(4)$$

$T_{r+1} = C_r \, x^r$. Now concentrate on the term $C_2 x^2$ in the expansion of $(1+x)^n$.

If in a question, you find the terms of the type given below then follow the procedure suggested below on both sides of (1).

['×' means multiply, '→' means it becomes]

$2C_2 x \to$ Diff. both sides of (1), $2C_2 \to$ Diff. and put $x = 1$.

$-2C_2 \to$ Diff. and put $x = -1$,

$\pm 2^2 C_2. \to$ Diff. both sides of (1) $\to 2C_2 x \to \times$ by $x \to$

$2C_2 x^2$, Diff. $\to 2^2 C_2 x$.

Put $x = \pm 1 \to \pm 2^2 C_2$

$3^2 C_2 \to \times$ both sides of (1) by $x \to C_2 x^3$, Diff. $\to 3C_2 x^2$.

Again $\times$ by $x \to 3C_2 x^3$. Agian diff. $\to 3^2 C_2 x^2$.

Now put $x = 1$ or -1

$$\frac{T_{r+1}}{T_r} = \frac{n-r+1}{r} = \frac{C_r}{C_{r-1}}$$

This procedure will be adopted for Q. 1 to 9.

1. (a) $C_1 + 2C_2 + 3C_3 + \ldots + nC_n$

$$= n + 2 \cdot \frac{n(n-1)}{2!} + 3 \cdot \frac{n(n-1)(n-2)}{3!} + \ldots + n \cdot 1$$

$$= n\left[1 + \frac{n-1}{1!} + \frac{(n-1)\cdot(n-2)}{2!} + \ldots 1\right]$$

Put $n - 1 = N$.

$$\therefore \quad \text{R.H.S.} = n\left[1 + N + \frac{N(N-1)}{2!} + \ldots 1\right]$$

$$= n[{}^N C_0 + {}^N C_1 + {}^N C_2 + \ldots + {}^N C_N]$$

$$= n2^N = n \cdot 2^{n-1}$$

(b) On putting for C_1, C_2 etc.

$$\text{L.H.S.} = n - 2 \cdot \frac{n(n-1)}{2!} + 3 \cdot \frac{n(n-1)(n-2)}{3!} - \ldots$$

$$= n\left[1 - (n-1) + \frac{(n-1)(n-2)}{2!} - \ldots\right]$$

$$= n\left[1 - N + \frac{N(N-1)}{2!} - \ldots\right],$$

where $n - 1 = N$

$$= n[{}^N C_0 - {}^N C_1 + {}^N C_2 - \ldots]$$

$$= n \cdot 0 = 0 \quad \therefore \quad C_0 - C_1 + C_2 - C_3 + \ldots = 0$$

(c) Ans. (c).

There will be 60 terms in the expansion of $(1+x)^{59}$. Last thirty terms will be

$$T_{31}, T_{32}, \ldots, T_{60}$$

$$\therefore \quad S = {}^{59}C_{30} + {}^{59}C_{31} + \ldots + {}^{59}C_{59}$$

Applying ${}^n C_r = {}^n C_{n-r}$

$$S = {}^{59}C_{29} + {}^{59}C_{28} + \ldots + {}^{59}C_1 + {}^{59}C_0$$

$$\therefore \quad 2S = {}^{59}C_0 + {}^{59}C_1 + \ldots + {}^{59}C_{59} = 2^{59}$$

or $\quad S = 2^{58} \Rightarrow$ (c)

2. (a) **Alt. Method :**

$$(1+x)^n = C_0 + C_1 x + C_2 x^2 + C_3 x^3 \ldots + C_n x^n.$$

Differentiate both sides w.r.t. x.

$$n(1+x)^{n-1} = C_1 + 2C_2 x + 3C_3 x^2 + \ldots$$

$$+ nC_n x^{n-1}. \quad \ldots(1)$$

This proves the result.

Putting $x = 1$, we get

$$n \cdot 2^{n-1} = C_1 + 2C_2 + 3C_3 + \ldots + nC_n. \quad \ldots(A)$$

This is Q. 1 (a) done above.

Putting $x = -1$ we get

$$0 = C_1 - 2C_2 + 3C_3 - \ldots \quad \ldots(B)$$

This is Q. 1 (b) done above.

(b) Split into two $\sum_{r=0}^{n} C_r + 2 \sum_{r=1}^{n} r C_r$.

$$= 2^n + 2 \cdot n \, 2^{n-1} = (n+1) \, 2^n \quad \text{by Q. 1 (a)}$$

(c) L.H.S.

$$= S = 1 - {}^{2n}C_1 + {}^{2n}C_2 - \ldots + (-1)^{n-1} \, {}^{2n}C_{n-1}$$

$$\textbf{\textit{n} terms}$$

Now we know that ${}^{2n}C_0 = 1 = {}^{2n}C_{2n}$,

${}^{2n}C_1 = {}^{2n}C_{2n-1}$ etc.

$$\therefore \quad 2S = ({}^{2n}C_0 + {}^{2n}C_{2n}) - ({}^{2n}C_1 + {}^{2n}C_{2n-1}) + \ldots$$

$$+ (-1)^{n-1}({}^{2n}C_{n-1} + {}^{2n}C_{n+1})$$

$$2S = {}^{2n}C_0 - {}^{2n}C_1 + {}^{2n}C_2 - \ldots - {}^{2n}C_{2n-1} + {}^{2n}C_{2n}$$

$$\textbf{2\textit{n} terms}$$

Add $(-1)^n \, {}^{2n}C_n$ to both sides to make $(2n+1)$ terms

$$2S + (-1)^n \, {}^{2n}C_n = C_0 - C_1 + C_2 - \ldots + C_{2n} = 0$$

[on putting $x = -1$ in the expansion of $(1+x)^{2n}$ which contain $(2n+1)$ terms]

$$\therefore \quad S = -\frac{1}{2}(-1)^n \, {}^{2n}C_n = (-1)^{n+1} \frac{(2n)!}{2(n!)^2} = \text{R.H.S.}$$

3. (a) $C_0 + C_1 x + C_2 x^2 + \ldots C_n x^n = (1+x)^n$

$C_2 x^2$ occurs in $(1+x)^n$. We want $2^2 C_2$ in the L.H.S. Diff. to get $2C_2 x$ but we want $2^2 C_2$. Again multiply by x to get $2C_2 x^2$. Again diff. to get $2^2 C_2 x$ and finally put $x = 1$. The operations done in L.H.S. should also be done in R.H.S. All this is exhibited below.

Differentiating the expansion of $(1+x)^n$ we get

$$n(1+x)^{n-1} = C_1 + 2C_2 x + 3C_3 x^2 + \ldots$$

$$+ nC_n x^{n-1} \quad \ldots(1)$$

Keeping in view the form of question we multiply both sides of (1) by x.

$$nx(1+x)^{n-1} = C_1 x + 2C_2 x^2 + 3C_3 x^3 + \dots + nC_n x^n.$$

Now differentiate w.r.t. x

$$n[1.(1+x)^{n-1} + x.(n-1)(1+x)^{n-2}] \quad \dots(2)$$
$$= C_1 + 2^2 C_2 x + 3^2 C_3 x^2 + \dots + n^2 C_n x^{n-1}.$$

Now put $x = 1$

$$n[2^{n-1} + (n-1)(2^{n-2})] = C_1 + 2^2 C_2 + 3^2 C_3 + \dots + n^2 C_n$$
$$= n 2^{n-2}[2+n-1] = n(n+1)2^{n-2}.$$

(b) Put $x = -1$ in (2) to prove (b).

(c) $(1+x)^n = C_0 + C_1 x + C_2 x^2 + \dots C_n x^n$

keeping in view $2^3 C_2$ or $3^3 C_3$

Differentiate and multiply by x

$$n(1+x)^{n-1} x = C_1 x + 2C_2 x^2 + 3C_3 x^3 + \dots$$

Again differentiate and multiply by x

$$nx\{(n-1)(1+x)^{n-2}.x + 1(1+x)^{n-1}\}$$
$$= C_1 x + 2^2 C_2 x^2 + 3^2 C_3 x^3 + \dots$$

or $n(n-1)(1+x)^{n-2} x^2 + nx(1+x)^{n-1}$
$$= C_1 x + 2^2 C_2 x^2 + 3^2 C_3 x^3 + \dots$$

Differentiate again w.r.t. x

$$n(n-1)\{(n-2).(1+x)^{n-3}.x^2 + (1+x)^{n-2}.2x\}$$
$$+ n\{(n-1)x(1+x)^{n-2} + 1(1+x)^{n-1}\}$$
$$= C_1 + 2^3 C_2 x + 3^3 C_3 x^2 + \dots$$

Now put $x = 1$

$$n(n-1)\{(n-2)2^{n-3} + 2^{n-2}.2\}$$
$$+ n(n-1)2^{n-2} + n.2^{n-1}$$

$$2^{n-3}\{n(n-1)(n-2) + 4n(n-1) + 2n(n-1) + 4n\}$$
$$= 2^{n-3} n(n^2 - 3n + 2 + 4n - 4 + 2n - 2 + 4)$$
$$= 2^{n-3} n(n^2 + 3n) = n^2(n+3)2^{n-3}$$

Remark : In view of Ex. 1, 2, 3 the following results be noted.

(A) $\sum_{r=0}^{n} {}^n C_r = 2^n$, (B) $\sum_{r=0}^{n} r . {}^n C_r = n.2^{n-1}$

(C) $\sum_{r=0}^{n} r^2 . {}^n C_r = n(n+1)2^{n-2}$,

(D) $\sum_{r=0}^{n} r^3 {}^n C_r = n^2(n+3)2^{n-3}$

4. $C_0 + C_1 x + C_2 x^2 + \dots + C_n x^n = (1+x)^n$

We want $3^2 C_2$ whereas we get the term of $C_2 x^2$.
Multiply by x to get $C_2 x^3$. Diff. to get $3C_2 x^2$. Again multiply by x to get $3C_2 x^3$. Again diff. to get $3C_2 x^2$.

Finally put $x = -1$ as the terms are **alternately +ive and – ive**. The operations done in L.H.S. should also be done in R.H.S. Now proceed as in part (a).

5. L.H.S. $= (-1)^r \sum_{r=0}^{n} (a-r)(b-r) C_r$

$$= (-1)^r \sum_{r=0}^{n} [ab - (a+b)r + r^2]C_r$$

$$= (-1)^r \left[ab \sum_{r=0}^{n} C_r - (a+b) \sum_{r=0}^{n} r C_r + \sum_{r=0}^{n} r^2 C_r \right] = 0$$

Because of $(-1)^r$ the terms in each sum are alternately +ive and – ive.

Hence by Q. 1, as in Q. 3 (b) on putting $x = -1$ and **result (A) P. 389.**

6. (a) $T_r = (-1)^{r-1} C_r (a-r)^2$

$$\therefore S_n = \sum_{r=1}^{n} T_r = \sum_{r=1}^{n} (-1)^{r-1}$$
$$C_r(a^2 - 2ar + r^2)$$

$$= (-1)^{r-1} \left\{ a^2 \sum_{r=1}^{n} C_r - 2a \sum_{r=1}^{n} r C_r + a^2 \sum_{r=1}^{n} r^2 C_r \right\}$$

The last two sums are zeros by Q. 3 (a) and (b) if we put $x = -1$ because of alt. +ive and – ive signs.
The first sum

$$C_1 - C_2 + C_3 - C_4 + \dots = C_0 = 1$$
by R. 11 (a) P. 389.

$$\therefore S_n = a^2 . 1 + 0 + 0 = a^2$$

(b) Ans. (a).

$$E = \sum_{r=0}^{n} C_r + 2 \sum_{r=0}^{n} r C_r + \sum_{r=0}^{n} r^2 C_r$$

Putting $x = 1$ in (1), (2) and (3) of last question,
$$E = 2^n + 2.(n.2^{n-1}) + n(n+1)2^{n-2}$$
$$= 2^{n-2}[4 + 4n + n^2 + n] = 2^{n-2}(n^2 + 5n + 4)$$
$$E = 2^{n-2}(n+1)(n+4) \Rightarrow (a)$$

7. (a) $a - C_1(a-1) + C_2(a-2) - C_3(a-3)$
$$+ \dots + (-1)^n (a-n) = 0$$

Now $C_0 = 1$, $C_n = 1$. Collect terms of a in one bracket and without a in the other.

L.H.S. $= a[C_0 - C_1 + C_2 - C_3 + \dots (-1)^n . C_n]$
$$+ [C_1 - 2C_2 + 3C_3 \dots + (-1)^{n-1} nC_n]$$

$\because \quad -(-1)^n = (-1)(-1)(-1)^{n-1} = (-1)^{n-1}$

L.H.S. $= a0 + 0 = 0$ **by Q. 1 and result (A) P. 389.**

(b) Let $a_1 = a, a_2 = a+d, \dots, a_{n+1} = a+nd$.
L.H.S. $= aC_0 - (a+d)C_1 + (a+2d)C_2 - \dots$
$$+ (-1)^n (a+nd) C_n$$

$$= a\{C_0 - C_1 + C_2 - \dots\} - d\{C_1 - 2C_2 + 3C_3 - \dots\}$$
$$= a.0 - d.0 = 0, \text{ by Q. 1 and } \textbf{result (A) P. 389.}$$

Deduction : 3, 8, 13, 18, … form an A.P. whose $a = 3, d = 5$.
Putting $a = 3, d = 5$ we get the result $3.0 - 5.0 = 0$.

8. **(a)** This is Q. 7 (b). Let S denote the sum of the series. General term of the series is given by

$$T_r = (-1)^r (3+5r) \, {}^nC_r, \text{ (nth term of A.P.)}$$

where $r = 0, 1, 2, \ldots\ldots n$.

$$\therefore \quad S = \sum_{r=0}^{n} (-1)^r (3+5r) \, {}^nC_r$$

$$= 3 \sum_{r=0}^{n} (-1)^r \, {}^nC_r + 5 \sum_{r=0}^{n} (-1)^r \, r \, {}^nC_r$$

$$= 3(C_0 - C_1 + C_2 - C_3 + C_4 \ldots..)$$
$$+ 5(-C_1 + 2C_2 - 3C_3 + 4C_4 \ldots.)$$

$$= 0 + 0 \quad \text{by Q. 2 or 4, P. 390-94}$$

(b) L.H.S.

$$= \sum_{r=1}^{n} (4r-1) \, C_r = 4 \sum_{r=1}^{n} rC_r - \sum_{r=1}^{n} C_r$$

$$= 4[n \, 2^{n-1}] - (2^n - 1) \quad \text{by Q. 2 or 4, P. 390-94}$$

$$= 2n \cdot 2^n - 2^n + 1 = 1 + (2n-1) \, 2^n$$

(c) Δ = sum of $(n+1)$ terms of an A.P.

$$\Delta = \frac{n+1}{2} [2a + nd] \qquad \ldots(1)$$

$$S = a[C_0 + C_1 + C_2 + \ldots.. C_n]$$
$$+ d[C_1 + 2C_2 + \ldots + nC_n]$$

$$= a \cdot 2^n + d \cdot n \cdot 2^{n-1}$$

$$= 2^{n-1} \cdot [2a + nd] = 2^{n-1} \frac{2\Delta}{n+1} \quad \text{by (1)}$$

$$\therefore \quad (n+1) S = 2^n \cdot \Delta$$

9. **(a)** $\dfrac{C_1}{C_0} + 2\dfrac{C_2}{C_1} + 3\dfrac{C_3}{C_2} + \ldots\ldots + n\dfrac{C_n}{C_{n-1}}$

$$\frac{T_{r+1}}{T_r} = \frac{C_r}{C_{r-1}} = \frac{n-r+1}{r}$$

$$\therefore \quad r \cdot \frac{C_r}{C_{r-1}} = n - r + 1$$

Now put $r = 1, 2, 3, \ldots n$ and add.

L.H.S. $= n + (n-1) + (n-2) + \ldots.. + 1$

$$= \Sigma n = \frac{n(n+1)}{2}$$

(b) Putting $n = 15$ in part (a), we get

$$\text{L.H.S.} = \frac{15 \cdot 16}{2} = 120 = \text{R.H.S.}$$

Procedure for Q. 10 to 16 by integration.

$$(1+x)^n = C_0 + C_1 x + C_2 x^2 + \ldots + C_r x^r + \ldots C_n x^n$$

The term $\dfrac{C_2}{3}$ in Question $\rightarrow$ Integrate $C_2 x^2$ and

put $x = 0$ for constant of integration and finally put $x = 1, -1, 2$ or x etc. depending upon the question. You may directly say

Integrate within proper limits as

$\int_0^{1,2} dx$, if the terms are all +ive.

or $\int_{-1,-2}^{0} dx$, if the terms are alt. +ive and – ive.

or $\int_{-1}^{1} dx$, if the sum contains even

coefficients $i.e. C_0, C_2, C_4, \ldots$

as $\int_{-1}^{1} C_3 \cdot x^3 \, dx = 0$ **Odd**

and $\int_{-1}^{1} C_4 \cdot x^4 \, dx = 2\int_0^1 C_4 \, x^4 \, dx$ etc. **Even**

Note : If only even or only odd coefficients are involved then use expansion of $\dfrac{1}{2}[(1+x)^n \pm (1-x)^n]$

$\dfrac{C_2}{4} \rightarrow \times$ both sides by x so that $C_2 \, x^2 \rightarrow C_2 \, x^3$

Now integrate $\rightarrow C_2 \dfrac{x^4}{4}$ and then put $x = 1$ etc.

10. **(a)** We know that $(x-a)(x-b)(x-c) \ldots 50$

factors $= x^{50} - x^{49} \cdot S_1 + x^{48} \cdot S_2 - \ldots$

The coefficient of x^{49} is

$$S_1 = -\left[\frac{C_1}{C_0} + 2^2 \frac{C_2}{C_1} + 3^2 \frac{C_3}{C_2} + \ldots r^2 \frac{C_r}{C_{r-1}} \right]$$

Now $r^2 \cdot \dfrac{C_r}{C_{r-1}} = r^2 \cdot \dfrac{n-r+1}{r}$

$$= r(51-r) = 51r - r^2 \qquad \text{as } n = 50$$

$$\therefore \quad \sum_{r=1}^{50} r^2 \frac{C_r}{C_{r-1}} = 51 \sum_{r=1}^{50} r - \sum_{r=1}^{50} r^2$$

$$= 51 \cdot \frac{N(N+1)}{2} - \frac{N(N+1)(2N+1)}{6}$$

$$= 51 \cdot \frac{50 \cdot 51}{2} - \frac{50 \cdot 51 \cdot (101)}{6}$$

$$= \frac{1}{6} 50 \cdot 51 [3 \times 51 - 101] = 25 \times 17 \times 52$$

(b) Multiplying both sides by $n!$ the question reduces to

$$\frac{n!}{1! \, (n-1)!} + \frac{1}{3!} \cdot \frac{n!}{(n-3)!} + \frac{1}{5!} \cdot \frac{n!}{(n-5)!} + \ldots\ldots = 2^{n-1}$$

or $C_1 + C_3 + C_5 + \ldots.. = 2^{n-1}$,

which is true. **R. 11 (a), P. 389**

11. R.H.S. $= (-1)^{m-1} \dfrac{(n-1)(n-2)\ldots(n-m+1)}{(m-1)!}$

$$\cdot \frac{(n-m)(n-m-1)\ldots 2.1}{(n-m)(n-m-1)\ldots 2.1}$$

$$= (-1)^{m-1} \frac{(n-1)!}{(m-1)!(n-m)!}$$

$$= (-1)^{m-1} \, {}^{n-1}C_{m-1}$$

Now $(-1)^{m-1} \, {}^{n-1}C_{m-1} = $ Coeff. of x^{m-1} in the

expansion of $(1-x)^{n-1}$

or in $(1-x)^n (1-x)^{-1}$

or in $\quad[C_0 - C_1 x + C_2 x^2 - \ldots +$

$$(-1)^{(m-1)} C_{m-1} x^{m-1} \ldots]$$

$$.[1 + x + x^2 + \ldots + x^{m-1} + \ldots]$$

$$S_\infty \text{ of a G.P.}$$

Coeff. of x^{m-1} in the above product is clearly

$C_0 - C_1 + C_2 - \ldots + (-1)^{m-1} C_{m-1}$

12. (a) $C_0 + 2C_1 + 3C_2 + \ldots + (n+1) C_n$

$= (C_0 + C_1 + C_2 + \ldots + C_n)$

$$+ (C_1 + 2C_2 + \ldots + nC_n)$$

$= 2^n + n \cdot 2^{n-1} = 2^{n-1} \cdot 2 + n \, 2^{n-1}, \qquad$ by Q. 1

$= 2^{n-1} (n+2).$

(b) $C_0 + 3C_1 + 5C_2 + \ldots + (2n+1) C_n$

$= (C_0 + C_1 + C_2 + \ldots + C_n)$

$$+ 2(C_1 + 2C_2 + \ldots + nC_n),$$

$= 2^n + 2(n \cdot 2^{n-1}) = 2^n + n \cdot 2^n = 2^n (n+1),$ by Q. 1

13. Put $\dfrac{1}{1 + nx} = t$ and spilt into two.

$(C_0 - C_1 t + C_2 t^2 - C_3 t^3 + \ldots) + x\{-C_1 t + 2C_2 t^2$

$$- 3C_3 t^3 + \ldots\} = A + x B$$

$A = C_0 - C_1 t + C_2 t^2 - C_3 t^3 + \ldots \qquad \ldots(1)$

$$= (1-t)^n = \left(1 - \frac{1}{1+nx}\right)^n = \left(\frac{nx}{1+nx}\right)^n$$

In order to get B, we differentiate (1)

$$- n(1-t)^{n-1} = -C_1 + 2C_2 t - 3C_3 t^2 + \ldots$$

Multiply both sides by t

$$- nt(1-t)^{n-1} = -C_1 t + 2C_2 t^2 - 3C_3 t^3 + \ldots$$

$$= B$$

$\therefore \quad B = -n \dfrac{1}{1+nx} \left[1 - \dfrac{1}{1+nx}\right]^{n-1}$

$$= -\frac{n}{1+nx} \left(\frac{nx}{1+nx}\right)^{n-1} \qquad \ldots(2)$$

$\therefore \quad A + xB$

$$= \left(\frac{nx}{1+nx}\right)^n - \frac{nx}{1+nx} \left(\frac{nx}{1+nx}\right)^{n-1}$$

$$= \left(\frac{nx}{1+nx}\right)^n - \left(\frac{nx}{1+nx}\right)^n = 0.$$

14. $\displaystyle\sum_{r=0}^{n} (r+1)^3 C_r = C_0 + 2^3 C_1 + 3^3 C_2 + \ldots + (n+1)^3 C_n$

Now $(1+x)^n = C_0 + C_1 x + C_2 x^2 + \ldots$

We have the term $C_2 x^2$ whereas we want the term of $C_2 . 3^3$. Hence multiply by x to make $C_2 x^2 \to C_2 x^3$. Now differentiate it and we get $3 C_2 x^2$. Again multiply by x to make it $3 C_2 x^3$. Again differentiate to make $3^2 C_2 x^2$. Again multiply by x to make $3^2 C_2 x^3$ and

differentiate it to get $3^3 C_2 x^2$ and finally put $x = 1$. The above procedure is shown below.

Multiply by x

$$x(1+x)^n = C_0 x + C_1 x^2 + C_2 x^3 + \ldots$$

Differentiate w.r.t. x

$$(1+x)^n + x \cdot n(1+x)^{n-1} = C_0 + 2C_1 x + 3C_2 x^2 + \ldots$$

or $\quad (1+x)^{n-1} [1 + (n+1) x] = C_0 + 2C_1 x + 3C_2 x^2 + \ldots$

Again multiply by x

$(1+x)^{n-1} [x + (n+1) x^2] = C_0 x + 2C_1 x^2 + 3C_2 x^3 + \ldots$

Differentiate w.r.t. x

$(n-1)(1+x)^{n-2} [x + (n+1) x^2]$

$$+ (1+x)^{n-1} [1 + 2(n+1) x]$$

$$= C_0 + 2^2 C_1 x + 3^2 C_2 x^2 + \ldots$$

L.H.S. $= (1+x)^{n-2} [(n-1) x + (n^2 - 1) x^2$

$$+ (1+x) + 2(n+1)(x + x^2)]$$

$$= (1+x)^{n-2} [1 + (3n+2) x + (n^2 + 2n + 1) x^2]$$

R.H.S. $= C_0 + 2^2 C_1 x + 3^2 C_2 x^2 + \ldots$

Again multiply both sides by x and differentiate and lastly put $x = 1$.

$\therefore \quad \displaystyle\sum_{r=0}^{n} (r+1)^3 C_r = (n-2) 2^{n-3} (4 + 5n + n^2)$

$$+ 2^{n-2} (8 + 12n + 3n^2)$$

15. (a) $\displaystyle\sum_{r=0}^{n} r^2 C_r \, p^r q^{n-r} = 0 + 1^2 C_1 \, pq^{n-1}$

$$+ 2^2 C_2 \, p^2 q^{n-2} + \ldots + n^2 C_n p^n. \quad \ldots(1)$$

Because of factor $2^2 C_2$ we follow the procedure of 3 (a).

We have done above in **Q. 3. (a) R (2), P. 394.**

$$C_1 + 2^2 C_2 x + 3^2 C_3 x^2 + \ldots + n^2 C_n x^{n-1}$$

$$= n(1+x)^{n-2} [1 + x + x(n-1)]$$

$$= n(1+x)^{n-2} (1 + nx) \qquad \ldots(2)$$

Comparing (1) and (2) and keeping in view that $p + q = 1$, we put $x = p/q$ in both sides of (1)

$$C_1 + 2^2 C_2 \frac{p}{q} + 3^2 C_3 \frac{p^2}{q^2} + \ldots + n^2 C_n \frac{p^{n-1}}{q^{n-1}}$$

$$= n \frac{(p+q)^{n-2}}{q^{n-2}} \left(\frac{q + np}{q}\right) = \frac{nq + n^2 p}{q^{n-1}} \quad \because \quad p + q = 1$$

Multiply by q^{n-1}

$$C_1 q^{n-1} + 2^2 C_2 \, pq^{n-2} + 3^2 C_3 \, p^2 q^{n-3} \ldots$$

$$= nq + n^2 p$$

Multiplying both sides by p, we get

$$C_1 pq^{n-1} + 2^2 C_2 p^2 q^{n-2} + 3^2 C_3 p^3 q^{n-3} + \ldots$$

$$= npq + n^2 p^2$$

(b) $T_1 = (2^2 - 1) C_3 ; T_2 = (3^2 - 1) C_4 ; T_3 = (4^2 - 1) C_5 \ldots$

$$\therefore \quad E = \sum_{r=3}^{n} [(r-1)^2 - 1] C_r = \sum_{r=3}^{n} [(r^2 - 2r)] C_r$$

$$= \sum_{r=3}^{n} r^2 C_r - 2 \sum_{r=3}^{n} r C_r$$

We shall convert $\sum_{r=3}^{n}$ to $\sum_{r=0}^{n}$ by subtracting three terms corresponding to $r = 0, 1, 2$. For $r = 0$, the terms will be zero.

$$\therefore \quad E = \sum_{r=0}^{n} . r^2 C_r - (1^2 . C_1 + 2^2 C_2)$$

$$- 2 \left\{ \sum_{r=0}^{n} r C_r - (1 . C_1 + 2C_2) \right\}$$

$$= n(n+1) 2^{n-2} - 1 - 4C_2 - 2\{n 2^{n-1} - 1 - 2C_2\}$$

by Q. 2 and 3, **P. 390**

$$= \{n(n+1) 2^{n-2} - 1 - 4C_2\} - \{4n . 2^{n-2} - 2 - 4C_2\}$$

$$= 2^{n-2} n(n+1-4) + 1 = 2^{n-2} n(n-3) + 1$$

16. (a) (b) $(1+x)^n + (1-x)^n = 2[C_0 + C_2 x^2 + C_4 x^4 + \ldots]$

$(1+x)^n - (1-x)^n = 2[C_1 x + C_3 x^3 + C_5 x^5 + \ldots]$

Now integrate both sides within limits 0 to 1 to get the desired results as given

$$\left[\frac{(1+x)^{n+1}}{n+1} \pm \frac{(1-x)^{n+1}}{n+1} \right]_0^1$$

$$= 2 \left[C_0 x + C_2 \frac{x^3}{3} + C_4 \frac{x^5}{5} + \ldots \right]_0^1$$

or $2 \left[C_1 \frac{x^2}{2} + C_3 \frac{x^4}{4} + C_5 \frac{x^6}{6} + \ldots \right]_0^1$

or $\dfrac{1}{2(n+1)} [(2^{n+1} - 1) \pm (0 - 1)] = \begin{matrix} 16 \text{ (a)} \\ 16 \text{ (b)} \end{matrix}$

or $\dfrac{2^n}{n+1} = 16$ (a), $\dfrac{2^n - 1}{n+1} = 16$ (b)

For Q. 16, 17, 18, 19. See method of § 11 (b), P. 389.

$(1+x)^n = C_0 + C_1 x + C_2 x^2 + \ldots + C_n x^n$.

Integrating w.r.t. x

$$\frac{(1+x)^{n+1}}{n+1} = C_0 x + C_1 \frac{x^2}{2} + C_2 \frac{x^3}{3} + \ldots$$

$$+ C_n \frac{x^{n+1}}{n+1} + A$$

where A is a constant of integration and on putting $x = 0$ in both sides, we get

$A = \dfrac{1}{n+1}$.

$$\therefore \quad \frac{(1+x)^{n+1}}{n+1} - \frac{1}{n+1}$$

$$= C_0 x + C_1 \frac{x^2}{2} + C_2 \frac{x^3}{3} + \ldots \qquad \ldots(1)$$

Now putting $x = 1$ and -1 in above, we get

$$\frac{2^{n+1} - 1}{n+1} = C_0 + \frac{C_1}{2} + \frac{C_2}{3} + \ldots + \frac{C_n}{n+1} ; (x = 1)$$

$$\ldots(2)$$

This is **Q. 17 (a)**.

and $-\dfrac{1}{n+1} = -C_0 + \dfrac{C_1}{2} - \dfrac{C_2}{3} + \ldots ; (x = -1)$

or $\dfrac{1}{1+n} = C_0 - \dfrac{C_1}{2} + \dfrac{C_2}{3} - \dfrac{C_3}{4} + \ldots \qquad \ldots(3)$

This is **Q. 17 (b)**.

Adding the two results of **Q. 17 (a) and Q. 17 (b)**, we get

$$\frac{2^{n+1} - 1 + 1}{n+1} = 2 \left(C_0 + \frac{C_2}{3} + \frac{C_4}{5} + \ldots \right)$$

or $\dfrac{2^n}{n+1} = C_0 + \dfrac{C_2}{3} + \dfrac{C_4}{5} + \ldots$

This is **Q. 16 (a)**.

18. L.H.S. $= \left(1 - \dfrac{1}{2}\right) C_1 - \left(1 - \dfrac{1}{3}\right) C_2 + \left(1 - \dfrac{1}{4}\right) C_3 + \ldots$

$= (C_1 - C_2 + C_3 - C_4 + \ldots) - \left(\dfrac{C_1}{2} - \dfrac{C_2}{3} + \dfrac{C_3}{4} - \ldots \right)$

Now $C_0 - C_1 + C_2 - C_3 + \ldots = 0$

and $\dfrac{C_1}{2} - \dfrac{C_2}{3} + \dfrac{C_3}{4} - \ldots = C_0 - \dfrac{1}{n+1}$, by 3 last page

$$\therefore \quad \text{L.H.S.} = C_0 - \left(C_0 - \frac{1}{n+1} \right) = \frac{1}{n+1}$$

19. (a) $(1+x)^n = C_0 + C_1 x + C_2 x^2 + C_3 x^3 + \ldots$

Integrate both sides w.r.t. x with limits 0 to 2.

$$\left[\frac{(1+x)^{n+1}}{n+1} \right]_0^2 = \left[C_0 x + C_1 \frac{x^2}{2} + C_2 \frac{x^3}{3} + \ldots \right]_0^2 \text{ etc.}$$

(b) $(1+x)^n$

$= C_0 + C_1 x + C_2 x^2 + C_3 x^3 + \ldots + C_n x^n \qquad \ldots(1)$

We have to prove that

$$2C_0 + \frac{2^2}{2} C_1 + \frac{2^3}{3} C_2 + \ldots + \frac{2^{11}}{11} C_{10} = \frac{3^{11} - 1}{11}$$

$1 + x = 3$ for $x = 2$. All the terms are $+$ive hence we integrate both sides of (1) with limits as 0 to 2.

Integrating both sides of (1) w.r.t. x

$$\left[\frac{(1+x)^{n+1}}{n+1} \right]_0^2 = \left[C_0 x + C_1 . \frac{x^2}{2} + C_2 \frac{x^3}{3} + \ldots \right.$$

$$\left. + C_n \frac{x^{n+1}}{n+1} \right]_0^2 \qquad \ldots(2)$$

Now putting $x = 2$ and $n = 10$ in (2), we get the result.

(c) If we take x from R.H.S. to L.H.S. the question reduces to

$$C_0\, x + C_1\, \frac{x^2}{2} + C_2\, \frac{x^3}{3} + \ldots\ldots + C_n\, \frac{x^{n+1}}{n+1}$$

$$= \frac{(1+x)^{n+1} - 1}{n+1}.$$

This we have proved in result (2) of Part (a).

(d) Integrate $(1+x)^n$ with limits as 0 to 3 as in (a), (b), (c).

20. (a) $(1+x)^n = C_0 + C_1\, x + C_2\, x^2 + C_3\, x^3 + \ldots$

$\dfrac{C_2}{4}$ is desired. We have a term of $C_2\, x^2$.

Multiply by x, it becomes $C_2\, x^3$ and on integrating with limits 0 to 1 it becomes $\dfrac{C_2}{4}$.

Multiply both sides by x

$x(1+x)^n = C_0\, x + C_1\, x^2 + C_2\, x^3 + C_3\, x^4 + \ldots\ldots$

Now integrate w.r.t. x within limits 0 to 1.

$$x \cdot \frac{(1+x)^{n+1}}{n+1} - \int 1 \cdot \frac{(1+x)^{n+1}}{n+1}\, dx$$

$$= \left[\frac{x(1+x)^{n+1}}{n+1} - \frac{(1+x)^{n+2}}{(n+1)(n+2)} \right]_0^1.$$

$$= \left[C_0\, \frac{x^2}{2} + C_1\, \frac{x^3}{3} + C_2\, \frac{x^4}{4} + \ldots\ldots \right]_0^1$$

$$\frac{2^{n+1}}{n+1} - \frac{2^{n+2}}{(n+1)(n+2)} - \left\{ 0 - \frac{1}{(n+1)(n+2)} \right\}$$

$$= \frac{C_0}{2} + \frac{C_1}{3} + \frac{C_2}{4} + \frac{C_3}{5} + \ldots\ldots + \frac{C_n}{n+2}$$

$$\text{L.H.S.} = \frac{2^{n+1}(n+2-2)}{(n+1)(n+2)} + \frac{1}{(n+1)(n+2)}$$

$$= \frac{n \cdot 2^{n+1} + 1}{(n+1)(n+2)}$$

This proves the result.

(b) Proceed exactly as in part (a) but start with expansion of $(1-x)^n$ because of alternative $+$ and $-$ signs or integrate with limits as -1 to 0.

(c) Ans. (b).

Integrating both sides of the given relation,

$$\frac{(1+x)^{n+1}}{n+1} + c = \sum_{r=0}^{n} C_r\, \frac{x^{r+1}}{r+1}.$$

When $x = 0$, we have $\dfrac{1}{n+1} + c = 0$

$$\therefore \quad c = -\frac{1}{n+1} \quad \therefore \quad \frac{(1+x)^{n+1} - 1}{n+1} = \sum_{r=0}^{n} \frac{C_r}{r+1}\, x^{r+1}$$

Divide both sides by $x = (1+x) - 1$

or $\dfrac{1}{n+1} \left[\dfrac{(1+x)^{n+1} - 1}{(1+x) - 1} \right] = \displaystyle\sum_{r=0}^{n} \dfrac{C_r}{r+1}\, x^r$

Above is sum of a G.P.

or $\dfrac{1}{n+1}[(1+x) + (1+x)^2 + (1+x)^3 + \ldots]$

$$= \sum_{r=0}^{n} \frac{C_r}{r+1}\, x^r$$

Integrating both sides with limits -1 to 0,

$$\frac{1}{n+1} \left[\frac{(1+x)^2}{2} + \frac{(1+x)^3}{3} + \ldots \right]_{-1}^{0}$$

$$= \sum_{r=0}^{n} \frac{C_r}{r+1} \left[\frac{x^{r+1}}{r+1} \right]_{-1}^{0}$$

$$\frac{1}{n+1} \left[\frac{1}{2} + \frac{1}{3} + \ldots + \frac{1}{n+1} \right]$$

$$= \Sigma\, C_r \left[\frac{0 - (-1)^{r+1}}{(r+1)^2} \right]$$

$$= \frac{1}{n+1} \sum_{r=0}^{n} \frac{1}{r+1} = \sum_{r=0}^{n} (-1)^r \frac{C_r}{(r+1)^2}$$

$$\therefore \quad k = \frac{1}{n+1}$$

21. $(1+x)^n = C_0 + C_1\, x + C_2\, x^2 + \ldots\ldots + C_n\, x^n.$ ...(1)

We have to prove that

$$\frac{2^2 \cdot C_0}{1.2} + \frac{2^3 C_1}{2.3} + \ldots\ldots + \frac{2^{n+2} C_n}{(n+1)(n+2)} = \frac{3^{n+2} - 2n - 5}{(n+1)(n+2)}$$

$2^3\, \dfrac{C_1}{2.3}$ is desired. We have a term of $C_1\, x$.

Integrating once it becomes $C_1\, \dfrac{x^2}{2}$ and again integrating but with limits 0 to 2 it becomes $C_1\, \dfrac{x^3}{2.3}$ or $2^3 \cdot \dfrac{C_1}{2.3}$.

Integrating both sides of (1), we get

$$\frac{(1+x)^{n+1}}{(n+1)} = C_0\, x + C_1\, \frac{x^2}{2} + C_2\, \frac{x^3}{3} + \ldots + C_n\, \frac{x^{n+1}}{n+1} + A$$

...(2)

where A is arbitrary constant.

Putting $x = 0$, we get $\dfrac{1}{n+1} = A.$

Integrating (2) again w.r.t. x within limits 0 to 2, we get

$$\left[\frac{(1+x)^{n+2}}{(n+1)(n+2)} - \frac{1}{n+1} \cdot x \right]_0^2 = \left[C_0\, \frac{x^2}{2} + C_1\, \frac{x^3}{2.3} \right.$$

$$\left. + C_2\, \frac{x^4}{3.4} + \ldots + \frac{C_n\, x^{n+2}}{(n+1)(n+2)} \right]_0^2$$

$$\frac{3^{n+2} - 1}{(n+1)(n+2)} - \frac{2}{n+1} = C_0 \cdot \frac{2^2}{2} + C_1\, \frac{2^3}{2.3}$$

$$+ C_2\, \frac{2^4}{3.4} + \ldots\ldots \frac{C_n\, 2^{n+2}}{(n+2)(n+1)}.$$

R.H.S. is $\dfrac{3^{n+2}-1-2(n+2)}{(n+1)(n+2)} \neq \dfrac{3^{n+2}-2n-5}{(n+1)(n+2)} = $ L.H.S.

22. $(1-x)^n = 1 - C_1 x + C_2 x^2 - C_3 x^3 + \dots + (-1)^n C_n x^n.$

or $\dfrac{(1-x)^n}{x} - \dfrac{1}{x} = -C_1 + C_2 x - C_3 x^2 \div \dots$

$$+ (-1)^n C_n x^{n-1}$$

or $\dfrac{1-(1-x)^n}{1-(1-x)} = C_1 - C_2 x + C_3 x^2 + \dots$

$$+ (-1)^{n-1} C_n x^{n-1}$$

L.H.S. = Sum of a G.P.

∴ $1 + (1-x) + (1-x)^2 + \dots + (1-x)^{n-1}$

$$= C_1 - C_2 x + C_3 x^2 \dots + (-1)^{n-1} C_n x^{n-1}$$

Integrating both sides, we get

$x - \dfrac{(1-x)^2}{2} - \dfrac{(1-x)^3}{3} - \dfrac{(1-x)^4}{4} - \dots + C$

$$= C_1 x - C_2 \dfrac{x^2}{2} + C_3 \dfrac{x^3}{3} - \dots \quad \dots(1)$$

Putting $x = 0$, we get

$-\dfrac{1}{2} - \dfrac{1}{3} - \dots - \dfrac{1}{n} + C = 0$

∴ $C = \dfrac{1}{2} + \dfrac{1}{3} + \dots + \dfrac{1}{n}$ ....(2)

Now putting $x = 1$ in both sides of (1)

$1 + C = C_1 - \dfrac{C_2}{2} + \dfrac{C_3}{3} - \dfrac{C_4}{4} + \dots$

Now put for C from (2).

or $1 + \dfrac{1}{2} + \dfrac{1}{3} + \dots + \dfrac{1}{n}$

$$= C_1 - \dfrac{C_2}{2} + \dfrac{C_3}{3} - \dots + (-1)^{n-1} \dfrac{C_n}{n}.$$

Note : The result could be directly obtained if we say that integrate both sides within limits 0 to 1.

23. L.H.S. $= \dfrac{C_0}{1^2} - \dfrac{C_1}{2^2} + \dfrac{C_2}{3^2} - \dots + (-1)^n \dfrac{C_n}{(n+1)^2}$

Since the terms are $+, -$ we consider the expansion of
$(1-x)^n = C_0 - C_1 x + C_2 x^2 - \dots + (-1)^n C_n x^n$

Integrating we get

$\dfrac{-(1-x)^{n+1}}{n+1} + k = C_0 x - C_1 \dfrac{x^2}{2} + C_2 \dfrac{x^3}{3} - \dots$

$x = 0$ gives $k = \dfrac{1}{n+1}$

∴ $\dfrac{1}{n+1}[1 - (1-x)^{n+1}] = C_0 x - C_1 \dfrac{x^2}{2} + C_2 \dfrac{x^3}{3} - \dots$

We have $C_2 \dfrac{x^3}{3}$ and we want $\dfrac{C_2}{3^2}$. Hence we divide by x

and integrate again within limits 0 to 1

∴ $\dfrac{1}{n+1}\left[\dfrac{1-(1-x)^{n+1}}{1-(1-x)}\right] = C_0 - C_1 \dfrac{x}{2} + C_2 \dfrac{x^2}{3} - \dots$

L.H.S. is a G.P. whose $r = 1 - x$

∴ $\dfrac{1}{n+1}[1 + (1-x) + (1-x)^2 + \dots]$

$$= C_0 - C_1 \dfrac{x}{2} + C_2 \dfrac{x^2}{3} - \dots$$

Now integrate both sides within limits 0 to 1 and you get the desired result.

24. We require $\dfrac{C_2}{9}$. Usually we have $C_2 x^2$ which on integration becomes $C_2 \cdot \dfrac{x^3}{3}$. In order to get $\dfrac{C_2}{9}$ we must have $C_2 (x^4)^2 = C_2 x^8$ which on integration becomes $C_2 \dfrac{x^9}{9}$. Also the terms are alternately $+$ and $-$. Hence we must have the expansion of $(1 - x^4)^n$ which is to be integrated within limits 0 to 1.

Now $(1-x^4)^n = C_0 - C_1 x^4 + C_2 x^8 - C_3 x^{12} + \dots$

$$+ (-1)^n C_n x^{4n} \quad \dots(1)$$

Integrate both sides within limits 0 to 1 and you get the result.

Let $I_n = \int_0^1 (1-x^4)^n dx$ Integrate by parts

$= [x(1-x^4)^n dx]_0^1 - \int x \cdot n(1-x^4)^{n-1}(-4x^3) dx$

$= 0 - 4n \int (1-x^4)^{n-1}(1 - x^4 - 1) dx$

or $I_n = -4n I_n + 4n I_{n-1}$ or $I_n (4n+1) = 4n I_{n-1}$

∴ $I_n = \dfrac{4n}{4n+1} I_{n-1} = \dfrac{4n}{4n+1} \cdot \dfrac{4n-4}{4n-3} \dots \dfrac{8}{9} \dfrac{4}{5} \cdot I_0$

$$= \dfrac{4^n (1.2.3 \dots n)}{1.5.9 \dots (4n+1)} I_0 \quad \dots(2)$$

where $I_0 = \int_0^1 (1-x^4)^0 dx = \int_0^1 1 dx = 1$

Hence from (1) and (2) we get the required result.

Procedure for Q. 25 to 32.

$(1+x)^n = C_0 + C_1 x + C_2 x^2 + \dots + C_r x^r + \dots C_n x^n$

$$\dots(1)$$

$\left(1 + \dfrac{1}{x}\right)^n = C_0 + C_1 \dfrac{1}{x} + C_2 \dfrac{1}{x^2} + \dots + C_r \dfrac{1}{x^r} + \dots C_n \dfrac{1}{x^n}$

$$\dots(2)$$

If we multiply both sides, we get

$\dfrac{(1+x)^{2n}}{x^n}$

$$= \Sigma C_0^2 + x \Sigma C_0 C_1 + x^2 \Sigma C_0 C_2 + \dots x^r \Sigma C_0 C_r + \dots$$

The various sums are the coefficients of $x^0, x, x^2, \dots, x^r$

in L.H.S. $\dfrac{(1+x)^{2n}}{x^n}$

or Coefficients of $x^n, x^{n+1}, x^{n+2}, ..., x^{n+r}$ in the expansion of $(1+x)^{2n}$ which occur in $T_{n+1}, T_{n+2}, \cdots$ and are $^{2n}C_n, {}^{2n}C_{n+1}, {}^{2n}C_{n+2}, ..., {}^{2n}C_{n+r}$ etc.

25. (a) Clearly the coefficient of x^n in $(1+x)^{2n}$ is in T_{n+1} and equal to $^{2n}C_n = \dfrac{(2n)!}{n!\,n!}$.

∴ $C_0^2 + C_1^2 + C_2^2 + ... + C_n^2 = \dfrac{(2n)!}{n!\,n!}$

(b) We know that $C_n = C_0, C_{n-1} = C_1, C_{n-2} = C_2$
Hence the question reduces to
$C_0^2 + C_1^2 + C_2^2 + ... + C_n^2$
i.e. part (a), and its value is $\dfrac{(2n)!}{n!.n!}$.

(c) $\displaystyle\sum\sum_{0 \le i < j \le n} C_i C_j = \dfrac{1}{2}[(\Sigma C_i)^2 - \Sigma C_i^2]$

$= \dfrac{1}{2}\left[(2^n)^2 - \dfrac{(2n)!}{(n!)^2}\right]$, by part (a)

$= 2^{2n-1} - \dfrac{(2n)!}{2(n!)^2}$.

26. (a), (b), (c). Multiplying eqns. (1) and (2) of **P. 400**, L.H.S. are respectively the coefficients of x, x^2 and x^r in $\dfrac{1}{x^n}(1+x)^{2n}$, or the coefficients of $x^{n+1}, x^{n+2}, x^{n+r}$ in $(1+x)^{2n}$. These are $^{2n}C_{n+1}, {}^{2n}C_{n+2}, {}^{2n}C_{n+r}$ respectively

or $\dfrac{(2n)!}{(n-1)!\,(n+1)!}, \dfrac{(2n)!}{(n-2)!\,(n+2)!}$

and $\dfrac{(2n)!}{(n-r)!\,(n+r)!}$

27. (a) Ans. (c).
$^{10}C_i$ is coefficient of x^i in $(1+x)^{10}$
$^{20}C_{m-i}$ is coefficient of x^{m-i} in $(1+x)^{20}$.

$\displaystyle\sum_{i=0}^{m} {}^{10}C_i \cdot {}^{20}C_{m-i}$ is coefficient of x^{m-i+i} *i.e.* of x^m in the product $(1+x)^{10+20} = (1+x)^{30} = {}^{30}C_m$

Now $^{30}C_m$ is maximum when $m = \dfrac{30}{2} = 15$.

(b) $s_n = C_0 C_1 + C_1 C_2 + ... + C_{n-1} C_n$
$= \dfrac{(2n)!}{(n-1)!\,(n+1)!}$, as proved in Q. 26 (a).

∴ $s_{n+1} = \dfrac{(2n+2)!}{n!\,(n+2)!}$, replacing n by $n+1$

∴ $\dfrac{s_{n+1}}{s_n} = \dfrac{15}{4}$

$\dfrac{(2n+2)!}{n!\,(n+2)!} \cdot \dfrac{(n-1)!\,(n+1)!}{(2n)!} = \dfrac{15}{4}$.

or $\dfrac{(2n+2)(2n+1)}{n.(n+2)} = \dfrac{15}{4}$

or $4(4n^2 + 6n + 2) = 15n^2 + 30n$

or $n^2 - 6n + 8 = 0$ or $(n-2)(n-4) = 0$

∴ $n = 2$ or 4.

28. $(1+x)^n (1+x)^n = (1+x)^{2n}$
Expand both sides and put $x = 1$.

29. Multiply both sides by $\dfrac{(m+n)!}{n!}$ so that
R.H.S. is $\dfrac{1}{n!}\dfrac{(m+2n)!}{(m+n)!} = {}^{m+2n}C_n$
$=$ Coeff. of x^n in the expansion of $(1+x)^{m+2n}$
or in $(1+x)^n (1+x)^{m+n}$ ...(1)
or coefficient of x^n in
$(^nC_0 + {}^nC_1 x + {}^nC_n x^2 + ... {}^nC_n x^n) \times$
$[^{m+n}C_0 + {}^{m+n}C_1 x + ... {}^{m+n}C_{n-1} x^{n-1}$
$+ {}^{m+n}C_n x^n + ...]$

Collect the coefficients of x^n in the above and write ^nC_r as C_r only.

$^{m+n}C_n C_0 + {}^{m+n}C_{n-1} C_1 + {}^{m+n}C_{n-2} C_2 + ...$

$= \dfrac{(m+n)!}{m!\,n!} C_0 + \dfrac{(m+n)!}{(m+1)!\,(n-1)!} C_1$

$+ \dfrac{(m+n)!}{(m+2)!\,(n-2)!} C_2 + ...$

$=$ L.H.S. $\left(\text{obtained after multiplication by } \dfrac{(m+n)!}{n!}.\right)$

30. (a) $[(1+x)^n - 1]^m = [1 + {}^nC_1 x + {}^nC_2 x^2 + ... - 1]^m$
$= x^m [^nC_1 + {}^nC_2 x + ...]^m$
$= x^m [n + {}^nC_2 x + ...]^m$

Coeff. of x^m is n^m ...(1)
Again the given expression can be written as
$(-1)^m [1 - (1+x)^n]^m$
$= (-1)^m [1 - {}^mC_1 (1+x)^n + {}^mC_2 (1+x)^{2n}$
$- {}^mC_3 (1+x)^{3n} + ...]$

Now we know that coefficients of x^r in $(1+x)^n$ is ^nC_r as it occurs in T_{r+1}

Hence coefficient of x^m in the above expansion is
$(-1)^m [- {}^mC_1 {}^nC_m + {}^mC_2 {}^{2n}C_m - {}^mC_3 {}^{3n}C_m + ...]$ ...(2)

Equating the coefficients of x^m from (1) and (2), we get the result $(-1)^m = -(-1)^{m-1}$ etc.

(b) Consider the expansion of
$(2x + x^2)^n = [(1+x)^2 - 1]^n$
or $x^n (2+x)^n = [(1+x)^2 - 1]^n$

The coefficient of x^n in L.H.S. is 2^n and it should be equal to coefficient of x^n in R.H.S.

$$[(1+x)^2 - 1]^n = C_0(1+x)^{2n} - C_1(1+x)^{2n-2}$$
$$+ C_2(1+x)^{2n-4} - \ldots$$
$$= C_0\,{}^{2n}C_n - C_1\,{}^{2n-2}C_n + C_2\,{}^{2n-4}C_n - \ldots$$

We know that coefficient of x^r in $(1+x)^n$ is ${}^nC_r$.

31. (a) $(1+x)^n = C_0 + C_1 x + C_2 x^2 + \ldots + C_n x^n$
$$(x-1)^n = C_0 x^n - C_1 x^{n-1} + C_2 x^{n-2} + \ldots$$
$$+ (-1)^n C_n$$

Multiplying both sides,
$$(-1)^n(1-x^2)^n = (\quad)(\quad)$$

Now $C_0^2 - C_1^2 + C_2^2 - \ldots$ is the coefficient of x^n in the product in R.H.S. Hence it is the coeff. of x^n in $(-1)^n(1-x^2)^n$ or coeff. of $(x^2)^{n/2}$ in $(1-x^2)^n$ which will appear in $T_{\frac{n}{2}+1}$

$$\therefore \quad (-1)^n\,{}^nC_{n/2}(-1)^{n/2}(x^2)^{n/2}$$

Above is possible only when $\frac{n}{2}$ is an integer i.e. n is even and in case n is odd, then the term x^n will not occur. Also when n is even, then $(-1)^n = 1$.

$$\therefore \quad (-1)^{n/2} \cdot \frac{n!}{\frac{n}{2}!\frac{n}{2}!} \text{ is the required answer.}$$

(b) This is just like part (a) if we take into consideration $(1+x)^{2n}$ and $(x-1)^{2n}$ and multiply their corresponding expansions and equate the coefficient of x^{2n} on both sides.

$$(x-1)^{2n} = {}^{2n}C_0\, x^{2n} - {}^{2n}C_1\, x^{2n-1} \ldots \quad \ldots(2)$$

(c) Proceed as in Q. 31.
For $n = 10$, the value
$$= (-1)^{10/2}\,{}^{10}C_5 = (-1)^5 \frac{(10)!}{5!.5!}$$
$$= (-1)^5 \frac{10 \times 9 \times 8 \times 7 \times 6}{5.4.3.2.1} = -252.$$

And for $n = 11$, the value $= 0$ as $11/2$ is not an integer.

32. (a) Multiply $(1+x)^m$ and $(1+x)^n$ and the expression on R.H.S. is coefficient of x^r in the product.
Now coeff. of x^r in $(1+x)^{m+n}$ is ${}^{m+n}C_r$.

(b) $(1+x)^n = C_0 + C_1 x + C_2 x^2 + \ldots + C_n x^n$
$$(y+1)^n = C_0 y^n + C_1 y^{n-1} + C_2 y^{n-2} + \ldots + C_n$$
Note $(y+1)$
$$(x+y)^n = C_0 x^n + C_1 x^{n-1} y + C_2 x^{n-2} y^2 + \ldots$$
$$+ C_n y^n$$

If we multiply them, each vertical column will be the term of $x^n y^n$

$\therefore \ (1+x)^n (1+y)^n (x+y)^n$, the coefficient of $x^n y^n$ is
$$C_0^3 + C_1^3 + C_2^3 + \ldots + C_n^3.$$

33. (a) The given series is a G.P. of $(n+1)$ terms whose sum is
$$\frac{(1+x)^{n+1} - 1}{1 + x - 1} = \frac{(1+x)^{n+1} - 1}{x}$$

$\therefore$ Coefficient of x^r in $\dfrac{(1+x)^{n+1} - 1}{x}$ means coefficient of x^{r+1} in $[(1+x)^{n+1} - 1]$.
It is clearly ${}^{n+1}C_{r+1}$.

(b) As above the given series is a G.P. of n terms where $a = (x+2)^{n-1}$ and $r = \dfrac{x+1}{x+2}$

$$S = \frac{a(r^n - 1)}{r - 1} = (x+2)^{n-1}\left[\left(\frac{x+1}{x+2}\right)^n - 1\right]$$
$$\div \left[\frac{x+1}{x+2} - 1\right]$$
$$= \frac{(x+1)^n - (x+2)^n}{-1} = (2+x)^n - (1+x)^n$$

x^r will occur in T_{r+1} of both.
$${}^nC_r\, 2^{n-r} \cdot x^r - {}^nC_r \cdot x^r$$

$\therefore$ Coefficient of x^r is ${}^nC_r\,(2^{n-r} - 1)$.

34. E is a G.P. of $A = (x+3)^{n-1}$, $R = \dfrac{x+2}{x+3}$ and $N = n$.
$$E = \frac{A(1-R^n)}{1-R} = (x+3)^{n-1}\left[\frac{(x+3)^n - (x+2)^n}{(x+3) - (x+2)}\right]$$
$$\cdot \frac{x+3}{(x+3)^n}$$

$\therefore \ E = (x+3)^n - (x+2)^n = (3+x)^n - (2+x)^n$

$\therefore$ Coefficient of x^r is ${}^nC_r\,[3^{n-r} - 2^{n-r}]$

35. (a) We know that ${}^nC_r$ is the coefficient of x^r in the expansion of $(1+x)^n$.
Hence ${}^nC_m + {}^{n-1}C_m + {}^{n-2}C_m + \ldots + {}^mC_m$ is the coefficient of x^m in the series $(n > m)$
$$(1+x)^n + (1+x)^{n-1} + (1+x)^{n-2} + \ldots (1+x)^m,$$
$$= (1+x)^m[1 + (1+x) + (1+x)^2 + \ldots (1+x)^{n-m}]$$
Above is a G.P. of $a = 1$, $r = 1+x$ and number of terms is $n - m + 1$.
$$S = (1+x)^m \cdot \frac{[1 - (1+x)^{n-m+1}]}{1 - (1+x)}$$
$$= \frac{(1+x)^{n+1} - (1+x)^m}{x}$$

Coefficient of x^m in the above is coefficient of x^{m+1} in the N^r. The first term in N^r will have $^{n+1}C_{m+1}$ as the coefficient of x^{m+1} and there will be no term of x^{m+1} in $(1+x)^m$.

$\therefore \quad ^nC_m + {}^{n-1}C_m + \ldots {}^mC_m = {}^{n+1}C_{m+1} \quad \ldots(1)$

2nd part : We have to prove the following
$^nC_m + 2\,^{n-1}C_m + 3\,^{n-2}C_m + \ldots(n-m+1)\,^mC_m$
$= {}^{n+2}C_{m+2} \qquad \ldots(2)$

We rewrite the L.H.S. as
$[\,^nC_m + {}^{n-1}C_m + \ldots {}^mC_m\,]$
$\quad [\,^{n-1}C_m + {}^{n-2}C_m + \ldots {}^mC_m\,]$
$\qquad + [\,^{n-2}C_m + \ldots {}^mC_m\,]\ldots + {}^mC_m$

By repeated application of result (1), we have
$^{n+1}C_{m+1} + {}^nC_{m+1} + {}^{n-1}C_{m+1} + \ldots + {}^{m+1}C_{m+1}$
$\qquad [\because {}^mC_m = {}^{m+1}C_{m+1}]$

$= {}^{n+2}C_{m+2}$ by (1) again by replacing n and m by $(n+1)$ and $(m+1)$ respectively.

(b) $2^k\,^nC_k = $ coeff. of x^k in $(1+2x)^n$

$2^{k-1}\,^{n-1}C_{k-1} = $ coeff. of x^{k-1} in $(1+2x)^{n-1}$

$= $ coeff. of x^k in $x(1+2x)^{n-1}$ and so on.

Hence the given expression is coefficient of x^k in
$^nC_0(1+2x)^n - {}^nC_1\,x(1+2x)^{n-1}$
$\qquad\qquad + {}^nC_2\,x^2(1+2x)^{n-2} - \ldots$

Form $[A-B]^n$
$= $ coeff. of x^k in $[1+2x-x]^n$ or of x^k in $(1+x)^n$
which is $^nC_k = \begin{pmatrix} n \\ k \end{pmatrix}$.

36. $(1+x)^{2n} = C_0 + C_1 x + C_2 x^2 + \ldots + C_{2n}x^{2n} \qquad \ldots(1)$

Differentiating the expansion of $(1+x)^{2n}$, we get
$2n(1+x)^{2n-1} = C_1 + 2C_2 x + 3C_3 x^2 + \ldots$
$\qquad\qquad\qquad + 2n\,C_{2n}x^{2n-1} \quad \ldots(2)$

$\left(1 - \dfrac{1}{x}\right)^{2n} = C_0 - C_1 \cdot \dfrac{1}{x} + C_2 \cdot \dfrac{1}{x^2} - \ldots + C_{2n} \cdot \dfrac{1}{x^{2n}} \quad \ldots(3)$

where $C_r = {}^{2n}C_r$.

Multiplying (2) and (3), we get
$2n(1+x)^{2n-1}\left(1 - \dfrac{1}{x}\right)^{2n}$

$= (C_1 + 2C_2 x + 3C_3 x^2 + \ldots + 2n\,C_{2n}x^{2n-1})$

$\qquad \times \left(C_0 - C_1 \cdot \dfrac{1}{x} + C_2 \cdot \dfrac{1}{x^2} - \ldots + C_{2n}\dfrac{1}{x^{2n}}\right)$

The coefficient of $1/x$ in R.H.S. is
$-(C_1^2 - 2C_2^2 + 3C_3^2 - \ldots - 2n\,C_{2n}^2) \qquad \ldots(4)$

Also the coefficient of $\dfrac{1}{x}$ in
$2n(1+x)^{2n-1}\left(1 - \dfrac{1}{x}\right)^{2n}$

$= $ coefficient of $\dfrac{1}{x}$ in $2n\dfrac{(1+x)^{2n-1}(x-1)^{2n}}{x^{2n}}$

$= $ coeff. of $\dfrac{1}{x}$ in $\dfrac{2n}{x^{2n}}(1-x^2)^{2n-1}(1-x)$

$= $ coeff. of x^{2n-1} in $2n(1-x^2)^{2n-1}(1-x)$

$= $ coeff. of x^{2n-2} in $2n(1-x^2)^{2n-1}$
$\qquad\qquad\qquad \times$ coeff. of x in $(1-x)$

$= $ coeff. of $(x^2)^{n-1}$ in $2n(1-x^2)^{2n-1} \times$ coeff. of x in $(1-x)$.

$= 2n(-1)^{n-1}\,{}^{2n-1}C_{n-1}(-1)$

$= (-1)^n\,2n \cdot \dfrac{(2n-1)!}{(n-1)!\,n!} = (-1)^n\,\dfrac{(2n)!}{n \cdot (n-1)!\,n!} \cdot n$

$= (-1)^n\,\dfrac{(2n)!}{n!\,n!} \cdot n = -(-1)^{n-1}\,nC_n;\,[C_n = {}^{2n}C_n] \quad \ldots(5)$

$\therefore$ From (4) and (5), we get
$C_1^2 - 2C_2^2 + 3C_3^2 - \ldots - 2nC_{2n}^2 = (-1)^{n-1}\,nC_n$.

37. $(1+x)^n = C_0 + C_1 x + C_2 x^2 + \ldots$

$x(1+x)^n = C_0 x + C_1 x^2 + C_2 x^3 + \ldots$

Diff. both sides
$1.(1+x)^n + n \cdot x(1+x)^{n-1} = C_0 + 2C_1 x + 3C_2 x^2 + \ldots$

or $[1+(n+1)x](1+x)^{n-1} = C_0 + 2C_1 x + 3C_2 x^2 + \ldots$
$\qquad\qquad\qquad\qquad\qquad\qquad \ldots(1)$

2nd Part : We have to evaluate
$C_0^2 + 2C_1^2 + 3C_2^2 + \ldots + (n+1)C_n^2 \qquad \ldots(2)$

Consider $\left(1 + \dfrac{1}{x}\right)^n = C_0 + C_1\dfrac{1}{x} + C_2\dfrac{1}{x^2} + \ldots \qquad \ldots(3)$

If we multiply (1) and (3) then (2) occurs as the term independent of x in this product.

Hence we have to search the term which is independent of x in

$[1+(n+1)x](1+x)^{n-1}\left(1 + \dfrac{1}{x}\right)^n$

or $\dfrac{[1+(n+1)x](1+x)^{2n-1}}{x^n}$

or the coefficient of x^n in the numerator
$[1+(n+1)x](1+x)^{2n-1}$

or coeff. of x^n in $(1+x)^{2n-1} + (n+1)$
$\qquad\qquad$ coeff. of x^{n-1} in $(1+x)^{2n-1}$

$= {}^{2n-1}C_n + (n+1) \cdot {}^{2n-1}C_{n-1}$

$= \dfrac{(2n-1)!}{n!\,(n-1)!} + (n+1)\dfrac{(2n-1)!}{(n-1)!\,n!}$

$$= \frac{(2n-1)!}{n!(n-1)!}[1+(n+1)] = \frac{(n+2)(2n-1)!}{n!(n-1)!}.$$

38. We have $C_0^2 - 2C_1^2 + 3C_2^2 - ..... + (-1)^n(n+1)C_n^2$

$$= [C_0^2 - C_1^2 + C_2^2 - ..... + (-1)^n C_n^2]$$

$$\quad - [C_1^2 - 2C_2^2 + 3C_3^2 ...... - (-1)^n nC_n^2]$$

$$= (-1)^{n/2} \cdot \frac{n!}{(n/2)! \cdot (n/2)!} - (-1)^{(n/2)-1} \cdot \frac{1}{2} n \cdot {}^nC_{\frac{n}{2}}$$

$$= (-1)^{n/2} \cdot \frac{n!}{(n/2)! \cdot (n/2)!} \cdot \left(1 + \frac{1}{2}n\right)$$

[See Q. 31 and 36, P. 392-402].

$$\therefore \quad \text{L.H.S.} = \frac{2(n/2)! \cdot (n/2)!}{n!}.$$

$$(-1)^{n/2} \cdot \frac{1}{2}(n+2) \cdot \frac{n!}{(n/2)! \cdot (n/2)!}$$

$$= (-1)^{n/2}(n+2)$$

39. $(1+x)^{15} = C_0 + C_1 x + C_2 x^2 + ... + C_{15} x^{15}.$

$$\therefore \quad \frac{(1+x)^{15}}{x} = \frac{C_0}{x} + C_1 + C_2 x + C_3 x^2 + ... + C_{15} x^{14}.$$

Differentiate both sides w.r.t. x

$$\frac{x \cdot 15(1+x)^{14} - 1 \cdot (1+x)^{15}}{x^2}$$

$$= -\frac{C_0}{x^2} + C_2 + 2C_3 x + 3C_4 x^2 + ... + 14C_{15} x^{13}$$

Putting $x = 1$ on both sides

$$15 \cdot 2^{14} - 2^{15} = -C_0 + C_2 + 2C_3 + 3C_4 + ... + 14C_{15}$$

$$2^{14}(15-2) + 1 = C_2 + 2C_3 + 3C_4 + ... + 14C_{15}$$

The given series $= 2^{14} \cdot 13 + 1 = 219923.$

40. (a) We have to prove that

$$\frac{(c_0 + c_1)}{c_1} \frac{c_1 + c_2}{c_2} .... \frac{c_{n-1} + c_n}{c_n} = \frac{(n+1)^n}{n!}$$

or $\left(\frac{c_0}{c_1} + 1\right)\left(\frac{c_1}{c_2} + 1\right) .... \left(\frac{c_{n-1}}{c_n} + 1\right) = \frac{(n+1)^n}{n!}$

Now $\dfrac{{}^nc_r}{{}^nc_{r-1}} = \dfrac{n-r+1}{r} = \dfrac{(n+1)}{r} - 1$

$$\therefore \quad \frac{c_r}{c_{r-1}} + 1 = \frac{(n+1)}{r} \quad \text{or} \quad \frac{c_r + c_{r-1}}{c_{r-1}} = \frac{(n+1)}{r}$$

...(1)

Putting $r = 1, 2, 3, ... n$ in both sides and multiply etc.

$$c_n = c_0 \cdot$$

(b) L.H.S. $= \dfrac{{}^{n+1}C_0 \cdot {}^{n+1}C_1 \cdot {}^{n+1}C_2 \quad ... \quad {}^{n+1}C_r ... {}^{n+1}C_{n+1}}{{}^nC_0 \cdot {}^nC_1 \cdot {}^nC_2 ... {}^nC_r ... {}^nC_n}$

Put ${}^{n+1}C_0 = {}^nC_0 = 1$ and ${}^{n+1}C_{n+1} = 1$

$$\therefore \quad \frac{P(n+1)}{P(n)} = \frac{{}^{n+1}C_1}{{}^nC_1} \cdot \frac{{}^{n+1}C_2}{{}^nC_2} ... \frac{{}^{n+1}C_r}{{}^nC_r}$$

$$... \frac{{}^{n+1}C_n}{{}^nC_n} \quad ...(1)$$

Now $\dfrac{{}^{n+1}C_r}{{}^nC_r} = \dfrac{(n+1)!}{r!(n-r+1)!} \cdot \dfrac{r!(n-r)!}{n!}$

$$= \frac{n+1}{n-r+1} \quad ...(2)$$

where r varies from 1 to n.

Putting $r = 1, 2, 3, ... n$ and multiplying

$$\frac{P(n+1)}{P(n)} = \frac{(n+1)(n+1)...}{n(n-1)...2.1} = \frac{(n+1)^n}{n!}$$

41. (a) Since n is odd, the number of terms will be $n+1$ i.e. even, so that $\dfrac{n+1}{2}$ is an integer so we make pairs of terms equidistant from the beginning and end

$$\therefore \quad \sum_{r=0}^{n} \frac{(-1)^r}{{}^nC_r} = \sum_{r=0}^{(n+1)/2} \left[\frac{(-1)^r}{{}^nC_r} + \frac{(-1)^{n-r}}{{}^nC_{n-r}}\right]$$

$$= (-1)^r \sum_{r=0}^{(n+1)/2} \left[\frac{1}{{}^nC_r} + \frac{(-1)^{n-2r}}{{}^nC_r}\right] = 0$$

because n being odd, $n - 2r = $ odd

$$\therefore \quad (-1)^{n-2r} = -1$$

(b) Combining brackets equidistant from beginning and end, $C_0 + (C_0 + C_1 + C_2 + ... C_{n-1})$

Replace one C_0 by C_n and it becomes

$$\sum_{r=0}^{n} C_r = 2^n.$$

Similarly combine others and each will be 2^n.

There will be $\dfrac{n}{2}$ such combinations.

$$\therefore \quad \frac{n}{2} \cdot 2^n = n \cdot 2^{n-1}$$

42. We have $s_n = \dfrac{1 - q^{n+1}}{1-q}$ ...(1)

and $S_n = \dfrac{1 - \left(\dfrac{q+1}{2}\right)^{n+1}}{1 - \dfrac{q+1}{2}} = \dfrac{2^{n+1} - (q+1)^{n+1}}{2^n(1-q)}$ ...(2)

Now

$${}^{n+1}C_1 + {}^{n+1}C_2 s_1 + {}^{n+1}C_3 s_2 + ... + {}^{n+1}C_{n+1} \cdot s_n$$

$$= \frac{1}{1-q}[{}^{n+1}C_1(1-q) + {}^{n+1}C_2(1-q^2)$$

$$+ {}^{n+1}C_3(1-q^3) + ... + {}^{n+1}C_{n+1}(1-q^{n+1})], \text{ by (1)}$$

$$= \frac{1}{1-q} [(^{n+1}C_1 + {}^{n+1}C_2 + ... + {}^{n+1}C_{n+1})$$
$$- (^{n+1}C_1 q + {}^{n+1}C_2 q^2 + ... + {}^{n+1}C_{n+1} q^{n+1})]$$

$$= \frac{1}{1-q} [(2^{n+1} - 1) - \{(1+q)^{n+1} - 1\}]$$

$$= \frac{2^{n+1} - (1+q)^{n+1}}{(1-q)} = 2^n S_n, \text{ by (2)}.$$

43. Series $= \sum_{r=0}^{n} (-1)^r \, {}^nC_r \left[\left(\frac{1}{2}\right)^r + \left(\frac{3}{4}\right)^r + \left(\frac{7}{8}\right)^r \right.$

$$\left. + \left(\frac{15}{16}\right)^r + ... \text{to } m \text{ terms} \right]$$

Now $\sum_{r=0}^{n} (-1)^r \, {}^nC_r \left(\frac{1}{2}\right)^r$

$$= 1 - {}^nC_1 \cdot \frac{1}{2} + {}^nC_2 \cdot \frac{1}{2^2} - {}^nC_3 \cdot \frac{1}{2^3} + ...$$

$$= \left(1 - \frac{1}{2}\right)^n = \frac{1}{2^n}$$

Similarly $\sum_{r=0}^{n} (-1)^r \, {}^nC_r \left(\frac{3}{4}\right)^r = \left(1 - \frac{3}{4}\right)^n = \frac{1}{4^n}$ etc.

Hence the given series

$$= \frac{1}{2^n} + \frac{1}{4^n} + \frac{1}{8^n} + \frac{1}{16^n} + ... \text{to } m \text{ terms}$$

$$= \frac{\dfrac{1}{2^n}\left[1 - \left(\dfrac{1}{2^n}\right)^m\right]}{1 - \dfrac{1}{2^n}} \quad \text{[summing the G.P.]}$$

$$= \frac{2^{mn} - 1}{2^{mn} (2^n - 1)}.$$

44. Splitting the right hand side into partial fractions by the method of suppression *i.e.* by putting $x = 0, -1, -2, ..., -n$, we get

$$A_0 = \frac{n!}{n!} = 1 = C_0 ,$$

$$A_1 = \frac{n!}{-2.3...(n-1)} = \frac{-n!}{(n-1)!} = -C_1$$

$$A_2 = \frac{n!}{(-2)(-1).1.2.3...(n-2)} = \frac{n!}{2!(n-2)!} = C_2$$

$$A_n = (-1)^n C_n.$$

Hence we prove the first part. Putting $x = 1/3$ in the first part we get the second part.

45. $\dfrac{C_1}{4}$ suggests $\displaystyle\int_0^1 C_1 x^3 \, dx, \dfrac{C_2}{7}$ suggests

$\int_0^1 C_2 (x^3)^2 \, dx$. Hence consider $\int_0^1 (1-x^3)^n \, dx$.

$$= \int_0^1 [1 - C_1 x^3 + C_2 (x^3)^2 + ... (-1)^n C_n (x^3)^n] dx$$

$$= C_0 - \frac{C_1}{4} + \frac{C_2}{7} - ... + (-1)^n \frac{C_n}{3n+1} = \text{L.H.S.}$$

Again $I_n = \int_0^1 1 \cdot (1-x^3)^n \, dx$

$$= [x(1-x^3)^n]_0^1 - n \int_0^1 x(1-x^3)^{n-1} (-3x^2) \, dx$$

We have integrated by parts

or $I_n = 0 + 3n \int x^3 (1-x^3)^{n-1} \, dx$

$$= 3n \int \{1 - (1-x^3)\} (1-x^3)^{n-1} \, dx$$

$$= 3n [I_{n-1} - I_n]$$

$\therefore \quad I_n (3n+1) = 3n I_{n-1}$

$\therefore \quad I_n = \dfrac{3n}{3n+1} I_{n-1} = \dfrac{3n}{3n+1} \dfrac{3(n-1)}{3n-2} \cdot I_{n-2}$

$$= \frac{3n}{3n+1} \frac{3(n-1)}{3n-2} ... \frac{3.1}{3.1+1} \cdot I_0$$

$$= \frac{3^n \cdot n!}{(3n+1)...7.4.1} 1 = \text{R.H.S.}$$

as $I_0 = \int_0^1 (1-x^3)^0 \, dx = \int_0^1 1 . dx = [x]_0^1 = 1.$

46. $I = \int_0^1 x^{n-1} (1-x)^n \, dx$

$$= \int_0^1 x^{n-1} [C_0 - C_1 x + C_2 x^2 - ... + (-1)^n C_n x^n] dx$$

$$= \int_0^1 [C_0 x^{n-1} - C_1 x^n + C_2 x^{n+1}$$
$$+ ... + (-1)^n C_n x^{2n-1}] dx$$

$$= \left[C_0 \frac{x^n}{n} - C_1 \frac{x^{n+1}}{n+1} + C_2 \frac{x^{n+2}}{n+2} - ... + (-1)^n C_n \frac{x^{2n}}{2n}\right]_0^1$$

$$= \frac{C_0}{n} - \frac{C_1}{n+1} + \frac{C_2}{n+2} - ... + (-1)^n \frac{C_n}{2n} = \text{L.H.S.}$$

Again putting $x = \sin^2 \theta$

$\therefore \quad dx = 2\sin\theta\cos\theta \, d\theta$ and adjust the limits as 0 to $\pi/2$.

$I = \int_0^{\pi/2} 2\sin^{2n-2}\theta\cos^{2n}\theta . 2\sin\theta\cos\theta \, d\theta$

$$= \int_0^{\pi/2} 2\sin^{2n-1}\theta\cos^{2n+1}\theta \, d\theta$$

$$= 2 \frac{\Gamma\left(\dfrac{2n-1+1}{2}\right)\Gamma\left(\dfrac{2n+1+1}{2}\right)}{2\Gamma\left(\dfrac{4n+2}{2}\right)} = \frac{\Gamma n \Gamma(n+1)}{\Gamma(2n+1)}$$

$$= \frac{(n-1)! \, n!}{(2n)!}, \text{ as } \Gamma(n+1) = n!$$

47. Given $(x+a)^n = T_0 + T_1 + T_2 + ... + T_n$ ...(1)

Replacing a by ai and $-ai$ respectively in (1), we get

$(x+ai)^n = (T_0 - T_2 + T_4 - ......) + i(T_1 - T_3 + T_5 - .....)$ ...(2)

and $(x-ai)^n = (T_0 - T_2 + T_4 - ....)$
$$- i(T_1 - T_3 + T_5 - ....) \quad ...(3)$$

Multiplying (2) and (3), we get

$(x^2 + a^2)^n = (T_0 - T_2 + T_4 - ....)^2$
$$+ (T_1 - T_3 + T_5 - ....)^2.$$

48. (a) $(1 + x + x^2)^n = a_0 + a_1 x + a_2 x^2 + ...$
$$+ a_{2n} x^{2n} = \sum_{r=0}^{2n} a_r x^r \quad ...(1)$$

Replace x by $1/x$.

$$\left(1 + \frac{1}{x} + \frac{1}{x^2}\right)^n = a_0 + a_1\left(\frac{1}{x}\right) + a_2\left(\frac{1}{x^2}\right) + \ldots$$

or $\quad \dfrac{(1 + x + x^2)^n}{x^{2n}} = a_0 + a_1\left(\dfrac{1}{x}\right) + \ldots + a_r\left(\dfrac{1}{x^r}\right) + \ldots$

or $\quad (1 + x + x^2)^n = a_0 x^{2n} + a_1 x^{2n-1} + \ldots$
$$+ a_r x^{2n-r} + \ldots \quad \ldots(2)$$

$$\sum_{r=0}^{2n} a_r x^r = \sum_{r=0}^{2n} a_r x^{2n-r}, \text{ by (1) and (2)}$$

Equating the coefficients of x^{2n-r} in both sides, we get $a_{2n-r} = a_r$ or $a_r = a_{2n-r}$, where $0 < r < 2n$

(b) Putting $x = 1$ in (1), we get

$$a_0 + a_1 + a_2 + \ldots + a_r + \ldots + a_{2n} = 3^n \quad \ldots(2)$$

Since $a_r = a_{2n-r}$ i.e. $a_0 = a_{2n}$, $a_1 = a_{2n-1}$ etc.

$$2(a_0 + a_1 + a_2 + \ldots + a_{n-1}) + a_n = 3^n$$

$$\therefore \quad a_0 + a_1 + a_2 + \ldots + a_{n-1} = \frac{1}{2}(3^n - a_n).$$

49. Differentiating both sides of (1) w.r.t. x, we get

$$n(1 + x + x^2)^{n-1}(1 + 2x) = \sum_{r=0}^{2n} r a_r x^{r-1}$$

Multiplying both sides by $1 + x + x^2$ and replacing $(1 + x + x^2)^n$ by $\displaystyle\sum_{r=0}^{2n} a_r x^r$, we get

$$n(2x + 1)\sum_{r=0}^{2n} a_r x^r = (1 + x + x^2)\sum_{r=0}^{2n} r a_r x^{r-1}$$

Equating the coefficients of x^r in both sides
$$n\{2a_{r-1} + a_r\} = \{(r+1)a_{r+1} + r a_r + (r-1)a_{r-1}\}$$
or $\quad (r+1)a_{r+1} = (n-r)a_r + (2n-r+1)a_{r-1},$
$$(0 < r < 2n)$$

This proves the third part.

50. (a) Replacing x by $-x$ in (1), we get
$$(1 - x + x^2)^n$$
$$= a_0 - a_1 x + a_2 x^2 \ldots + (-1)^n a_n x^n \ldots + a_{2n} x^{2n}$$
$$= a_{2n} - a_{2n-1} x + \ldots - a_1 x^{2n-1} + a_0 x^{2n} \quad \ldots(3)$$

Multiplying (1) and (3), we get
$$[(1 + x^2)^2 - x^2]^n = [1 + x^2 + x^4]^n$$

The term of x^{2n} will have its coefficients as $a_0^2 - a_1^2 + a_2^2 - \ldots + a_{2n}^2$ or the coefficient of x^{2n} or $(x^2)^n$ is $a_0^2 - a_1^2 + a_2^2 - \ldots + a_{2n}^2$

Put $x^2 = t$

$$\therefore \quad a_0^2 - a_1^2 + \ldots + a_{2n}^2$$
$$= \text{Coeff. of } t^n \text{ in } (1 + t + t^2)^n = a_n$$

(b) Now $a_{2n} = a_0, a_{2n-1} = a_1$
$$\therefore \quad 2[a_0^2 - a_1^2 + \ldots + (-1)^{n-1}a_{n-1}^2] + (-1)^n a_n^2 = a_n$$

or $\quad a_0^2 - a_1^2 + \ldots + (-1)^{n-1}a_{n-1}^2$
$$= \frac{1}{2}a_n[1 - (-1)^n a_n]$$

This proves the second part.

51. Put $x = \omega$ and note that $1 + \omega + \omega^2 = 0$

where $\omega = -\dfrac{1}{2} + i\dfrac{\sqrt{3}}{2}$ and $\omega^2 = -\dfrac{1}{2} - i\dfrac{\sqrt{3}}{2}$

$$\Delta = (a_0 + a_3 + a_6 + \ldots) + \omega(a_1 + a_4 + \ldots)$$
$$+ \omega^2(a_2 + a_5 + \ldots)$$

or $\quad \Delta = A + B\omega + C\omega^2 = 0$

Equating real and imaginary parts on both sides
$$A - \frac{B}{2} - \frac{C}{2} = 0, \quad \frac{\sqrt{3}}{2}(B - C) = 0$$

$\therefore \quad B = C$ and hence $A = B$

$\therefore \quad A = B = C$

Again putting $x = 1$ in the given relation, we get
$$3^n = \text{Sum of all the coefficients}$$
$$= A + B + C$$

or $\quad 3^n = 3A \quad \therefore \quad A = 3^{n-1} = B = C.$

52. $(1 + x)^{m+1} = {}^{m+1}C_0 + {}^{m+1}C_1 x + {}^{m+1}C_2 x^2 + \ldots$
$$+ {}^{m+1}C_{m+1} x^{m+1}$$

$\therefore \quad \{(1 + x)^{m+1} - x^{m+1}\} - 1 = \displaystyle\sum_{r=1}^{m} {}^{m+1}C_r x^r$

Now put $x = 1, 2, 3, \ldots, n$ and add and put
$$1^r + 2^r + 3^r + \ldots n^r = s_r$$

L.H.S. is
$$(2^{m+1} - 1^{m+1}) + (3^{m+1} - 2^{m+1})$$
$$+ (4^{m+1} - 3^{m+1}) + \ldots[(n+1)^{m+1}$$
$$- n^{m+1}] - \sum 1 = (n+1)^{m+1} - 1 - \sum 1$$

and R.H.S. $= \displaystyle\sum_{r=1}^{m} {}^{m+1}C_r s_r$

Put $\sum 1 = n$

$\therefore \quad (n+1)^{m+1} - (n+1) = \displaystyle\sum_{r=1}^{m} {}^{m+1}C_r s_r \quad \ldots(1)$

Now putting $m = 1$ in (1),
$$(n+1)^2 - (n+1) = \sum_{r=1}^{1} {}^2C_r s_r = {}^2C_1 \cdot s_1 = 2s_1$$

$\therefore \quad (n+1)\cdot n\cdot\dfrac{1}{2} = s_1 = 1 + 2 + 3 + \ldots n \quad \ldots(2)$

Again putting $m = 2$ in (1)

$$(n+1)^3 - (n+1) = \sum_{r=1}^{2} {}^3C_r s_r = {}^3C_1 s_1 + {}^3C_2 s_2$$

or $\quad (n+1)[(n+1)^2 - 1] = 3\cdot\dfrac{n(n+1)}{2} + 3s_2$

or $\quad (n+1)n\cdot(n+2) - \dfrac{3}{2}n(n+1) = 3s_2$

or $\quad n(n+1)\left(n+2-\dfrac{3}{2}\right)=3s_2$

or $\quad \dfrac{n(n+1)(2n+1)}{6}=s_2$ $\qquad$ ...(3)

Now putting $m=3$ in (1), we get

$$(n+1)^4-(n+1)=\sum_{r=1}^{3}\ {}^4C_r\,s_r$$

$$={}^4C_1 s_1+{}^4C_2 s_2+{}^4C_3 s_3$$

$$=4\,\dfrac{n(n+1)}{2}+\dfrac{4.3}{1.2}\,\dfrac{n(n+1)(2n+1)}{6}+4s_3$$

or $\quad (n+1)[(n+1)^3-1-2n-n(2n+1)]=4s_3$

or $\quad (n+1)(n^3+3n^2+3n+1-1-2n-2n^2-n)=4s_3$

or $\quad (n+1)(n^3+n^2)=4s_3$

$\therefore\quad s_3=\dfrac{1}{4}n^2(n+1)^2=\left[\dfrac{n(n+1)}{2}\right]^2$

Lastly putting $m=4$ in (1), we have

$$(n+1)^5-(n+1)=\sum_{r=1}^{4}\ {}^5C_r\,s_r$$

$$={}^5C_1 s_1+{}^5C_2 s_2+{}^5C_3 s_3+{}^5C_4 s_4$$

$$=5.\dfrac{n(n+1)}{2}+10.\dfrac{n(n+1)(2n+1)}{6}$$

$$+10.\dfrac{n^2(n+1)^2}{4}+5.s_4$$

or $\quad (n+1)^5-(n+1)-\dfrac{5}{2}n(n+1)$

$$-\dfrac{5}{3}n(n+1)(2n+1)-\dfrac{5}{2}n^2(n+1)^2=5s_4$$

$\dfrac{(n+1)}{6}[6(n+1)^4-6-15n+10(2n^2+n)$

$$-15(n^3+n^2)]=5s_4$$

$\therefore\quad s_4=\dfrac{1}{30}(n+1)[6(n^4+4n^3+6n^2+4n+1)$

$$-6-15n-20n^2-10n-15n^3-15n^2]$$

$$=\dfrac{1}{30}(n+1)[6n^4+9n^3+n^2-n]$$

$$=\dfrac{1}{30}n(n+1)(6n^3+9n^2+n-1)$$

$$=\dfrac{1}{30}n(n+1)(2n+1)(3n^2+3n-1)$$

53. $a_n=\dfrac{(\log 3)^n}{n!}\sum_{k=1}^{n}\ (2k+1)\dfrac{n!}{k!(n-k)!}$

$$=\dfrac{(\log 3)^n}{n!}\sum_{k=1}^{n}\ (2k+1)\ {}^nC_k$$

$$=\dfrac{(\log 3)^n}{n!}\left[\sum_{k=1}^{n}\ 2k\ {}^nC_k+\sum_{k=1}^{n}\ {}^nC_k\right]$$

$$=\dfrac{(\log 3)^n}{n!}[2.(n.2^{n-1})+(2^n-1)]$$

Result (1), (3) Page 389.

$$=\dfrac{(2\log 3)^n}{(n-1)!}+\dfrac{(2\log 3)^n}{n!}-\dfrac{(\log 3)^n}{n!}$$

$\therefore\quad \sum_{1}^{\infty}\ a_n=\sum_{n=1}^{\infty}\left[\dfrac{x^n}{(n-1)!}+\dfrac{y^n}{n!}-\dfrac{z^n}{n!}\right]$

$$=\sum_{n=1}^{\infty}\left[x.\dfrac{x^{n-1}}{(n-1)!}+\dfrac{y^n}{n!}-\dfrac{z^n}{n!}\right]$$

$e^x=1+\dfrac{x}{1!}+\dfrac{x^2}{2!}+...+\dfrac{x^n}{n!}+...$

$\therefore\quad e^x-1=\sum_{n=1}^{\infty}\ \dfrac{x^n}{n!}$

$\therefore\quad \sum_{1}^{\infty}\ a_n=x.e^x+(e^y-1)+(e^z-1)$

$$=2\log 3.e^{2\log 3}+(e^{2\log 3}-1)-(e^{\log 3}-1)$$

$$=(2\log 3)e^{\log 9}+(e^{\log 9}-1)-(e^{\log 3}-1)$$

$$=9(2\log 3)+(9-1)-(3-1)$$

$$=18\log 3+6\ .$$

54. $(1+x)^n=C_0+C_1 x+C_2 x^2+...+C_r x^r+...+C_n x^n$

$$\qquad\qquad ...(1)$$

Now the term $r(n-r)C_r^2$ suggests the factors

$$r(C_r)(n-r)C_r$$

By complementary rule $C_r=C_{n-r}$

Again rC_r suggests differentiation. The second factor suggests that (1) should be written as

$(x+1)^n=C_0 x^n+C_1 x^{n-1}+...C_r x^{n-r}+...+C_n$ $\quad$ ...(2)

and the second factor $(n-r)C_r$ suggests again differentiation of (2).

Differentiate both (1) and (2).

$n(1+x)^{n-1}=C_1+2C_2 x+...+rC_r x^{r-1}+...$ $\qquad$ ...(3)

$n(x+1)^{n-1}=nC_0 x^{n-1}+(n-1)C_1 x^{n-2}$

$$+...+(n-r)C_r x^{n-r-1}+...\qquad ...(4)$$

Multiplying (3) and (4), we get

$n^2(1+x)^{2n-2}=\sum\ (rC_r)(n-r)C_r x^{r-1}\,x^{n-r-1}$

$$=\sum r(n-r)C_r^2\,x^{n-2}$$

Hence we should search the coefficient of x^{n-2} in L.H.S. and it will be $n^2.\,{}^{2n-2}C_{n-2}=n^2({}^{2n-2}C_n)$ by complementary rule.

55. (a) On putting $r=0,1,2,...n$, the given sum is equal to

$$\dfrac{{}^nC_0}{{}^3C_0}-\dfrac{{}^nC_1}{{}^4C_1}+\dfrac{{}^nC_2}{{}^5C_2}+...+(-1)^n\dfrac{{}^nC_n}{{}^{n+3}C_n}$$

$$=1-\dfrac{n}{4}+\dfrac{n(n-1)}{5.4}-\dfrac{n(n-1)(n-2)}{6.5.4}$$

$$+...+(-1)^n\dfrac{3!}{(n+3)(n+2)(n+1)}$$

$$= \frac{3!}{(n+3)(n+2)(n+1)} \left[\frac{(n+3)(n+2)(n+1)}{3!} \right.$$

$$- \frac{(n+3)(n+2)(n+1)n}{(3!)\,4}$$

$$\left. + \frac{(n+3)(n+2)(n+1)n(n-1)}{(3!)\,5\cdot4} + \dots + (-1)^n \right]$$

Now put $n+3 = N$

$$\therefore \quad \text{L.H.S.} = \frac{3!}{N(N-1)(N-2)}$$

$$\times \left[\frac{N(N-1)(N-2)}{3!} - \frac{N(N-1)(N-2)(N-3)}{4!} \right.$$

$$\left. + \frac{N(N-1)(N-2)(N-3)(N-4)}{5!} + \dots (-1)^{N-3} \right]$$

$$= \frac{3!}{N(N-1)(N-2)}$$

$$\times [\, ^N C_3 - {}^N C_4 + {}^N C_5 - \dots + (-1)^{N-3}\,] \quad \dots(1)$$

Now $C_0 - C_1 + C_2 - C_3 + \dots = (1-1)^N = 0$

$$\therefore \quad C_0 - C_1 + C_2 = C_3 - C_4 + C_5 \dots$$

$$\text{where, } C_3 = {}^N C_3$$

$$1 - N + \frac{N(N-1)}{2} = C_3 - C_4 + C_5 \dots$$

Putting in (1), we get

$$\text{L.H.S.} = \frac{3!}{N(N-1)(N-2)} \left[\frac{2 - 2N + N^2 - N}{2} \right]$$

$$= \frac{3!}{2N(N-1)(N-2)}(N^2 - 3N + 2)$$

$$= \frac{3!}{2N(N-1)(N-2)}(N-1)(N-2) = \frac{3!}{2N}$$

$$= \frac{3!}{2(n+3)} = \text{R.H.S.} \quad \therefore \ N = n+3.$$

(b) You may proceed exactly as in part (a).
Alternate method is given below :

$$\frac{{}^n C_r}{{}^{r+2} C_r} = \frac{n!}{(n-r)!\,r!} \cdot \frac{(r+2)!}{2!\,r!} = \frac{2(n)!}{(n-r)!\,(r+2)!}$$

$$= \frac{2}{(n+2)(n+1)} \cdot \left[\frac{(n+2)!}{[(n+2)-(r+2)]!\,(r+2)!} \right]$$

$$= \frac{2}{(n+2)(n+1)} \, {}^{n+2} C_{r+2} \quad \dots(A)$$

Now put $r+2 = s$, when $r = 0, s = 2$, when $r = n$, $s = n+2$.

$$\therefore \quad \sum = \frac{2}{(n+2)(n+1)} \sum_{s=2}^{n+2} (-1)^{s+2} \cdot {}^{n+2} C_s$$

$$= \frac{2}{(n+2)(n+1)}$$

$$\left[\sum_{s=0}^{n+2} (-1)^s \, {}^{n+2} C_s - \{{}^{n+2} C_0 - {}^{n+2} C_1\} \right]$$

$$= \frac{2}{(n+2)(n+1)} [0 - \{1 - (n+2)\}]$$

$$= \frac{2}{(n+2)(n+1)}(n+1) = \frac{2}{(n+2)}$$

(c) As in last part by (A) we have,

$$\frac{{}^n C_r}{{}^{r+2} C_r} = \frac{2}{(n+2)(n+1)} \, {}^{n+2} C_{r+2} \quad \dots(1)$$

$$\sum = \frac{2}{(n+2)(n+1)} \cdot \left[\sum (-2)^r \cdot {}^{n+2} C_{r+2} \right]$$

Now put $r+2 = s$ $\therefore$ $r = s-2$

$$\therefore \quad (-2)^r = (-2)^s (-2)^{-2} = \frac{1}{4}(-2)^s$$

$$\sum = \frac{1}{2(n+2)(n+1)} \left[\sum_{s=0}^{n+2} (-2)^s \, {}^{n+2} C_s \right.$$

$$\left. - \{(-2)^0 \, {}^{n+2} C_0 + (-2)^1 \, {}^{n+2} C_1\} \right]$$

$$= \frac{1}{2(n+2)(n+1)} [(1-2)^{n+2} - 1 + 2(n+2)]$$

$$= \frac{1}{2(n+2)(n+1)} [(-1)^{n+2} + 2n + 3]$$

Now if n is even then $N^r = 2n+4 = 2(n+2)$

when n is odd then $N^r = 2n+2 = 2(n+1)$ etc.

56. n being an even integer

$$\therefore \quad n = 2m \quad \therefore \quad k = \frac{3n}{2} = 3m$$

$$\therefore \quad \text{L.H.S.} = \sum_{r=1}^{3m} (-3)^{r-1} \, {}^{6m} C_{2r-1}$$

$$= {}^{6m} C_1 - 3 \, {}^{6m} C_3 + 9 \, {}^{6m} C_5 + \dots (-3)^{3m-1} \, {}^{6m} C_{6m-1}$$

$$\dots(1)$$

Now consider $(1+x)^{6m} - (1-x)^{6m}$

$$= 2 [{}^{6m} C_1 x + {}^{6m} C_3 x^3 + \dots + {}^{6m} C_{6m-1} x^{6m-1}]$$

$$\therefore \quad \frac{(1+x)^{6m} - (1-x)^{6m}}{2x}$$

$$= {}^{6m} C_1 + {}^{6m} C_3 x^2 + \dots {}^{6m} C_{6m-1} x^{6m-2} \quad \dots(2)$$

Comparing (1) and (2) we get the idea that put $x = i\sqrt{3}$

$$\therefore \quad 1 + x = 1 + i\sqrt{3} = r(\cos\theta + i\sin\theta) = re^{i\theta}$$

$$r = \sqrt{a^2 + b^2} = 2, \tan\theta = \sqrt{3} \quad \therefore \quad \theta = \frac{\pi}{3}$$

$$\therefore \quad \text{L.H.S.} = r^6 \frac{e^{i\,6m\theta} - e^{-i\,6m\theta}}{2\sqrt{3}i}$$

$$= 2^{6m} \cdot \frac{2i \sin 6m\theta}{2\sqrt{3}i} = \frac{2^{6m}}{\sqrt{3}} \sin 2m\pi = 0$$

R.H.S. on putting $x = -i\sqrt{3}$ gives R.H.S. of (1).

Hence proved.

Problem Set (3)

▶ **Objective Questions**

1. Sum of coefficients in the expansion of $(x + 2y + z)^{10}$ is
   (a) 2^{10}
   (b) 3^{10}
   (c) 1
   (d) None of these.

2. The number of terms in the expansion of $(x + y + z)^{10}$ is
   (a) 11
   (b) 33
   (c) 66
   (d) None of these.

3. The total number of terms in the expansion of $(x + a)^{100} + (x - a)^{100}$ after simplification is
   (a) 202
   (b) 51
   (c) 50
   (d) None of these.

4. The coefficient of middle term in the expansion of $(1 + x)^{10}$ is
   (a) $10! / 5! 6!$
   (b) $10! / 5!^2$
   (c) $10! / 5! . 7!$
   (d) None of these.

5. The coefficient of $1/x$ in the expansion of $(1 + x)^n (1 + 1/x)^n$ is
   (a) $n! / [(n-1)! . (n+1)!]$.
   (b) $2n! / [(n-1)! . (n+1)]$,
   (c) $n! / [(2n-1)! . (2n+1)!]$
   (d) $2n! / [(2n-1)! . (2n+1)!]$.

6. Coefficient of x^4 in $\left(\dfrac{x}{2} - \dfrac{3}{x^2}\right)^{10}$ is
   (a) $\dfrac{405}{256}$
   (b) $\dfrac{504}{259}$
   (c) $\dfrac{450}{263}$
   (d) None of these.

7. The coefficient of y in the expansion of $\left(y^2 + \dfrac{c}{y}\right)^5$ is
   (a) $20c$
   (b) $10c$
   (c) $10c^3$
   (d) $20c^2$

8. The coefficients of x^p and x^q (p and q are positive integers) in the expansion of $(1 + x)^{p+q}$ are
   (a) equal
   (b) equal with opposite signs
   (c) reciprocals to each other
   (d) none of these

9. Given positive integers $i > 1$, $n > 2$ and that the coefficients of $(3r)^{th}$ and $(r + 2)^{th}$ terms in the binomial expansion of $(1 + x)^{2n}$ are equal, then
   (a) $n = 2r$
   (b) $n = 3r$
   (c) $n = 2r + 1$
   (d) None of these.

10. (i) The term independent of x in $\left(x^2 - \dfrac{1}{x}\right)^9$ is
    (a) 1
    (b) −1
    (c) 48
    (d) None

(ii) The term independent of x in the expansion of $\left(2x + \dfrac{1}{3x}\right)^6$ is
   (a) $160/9$
   (b) $80/9$
   (c) $160/27$
   (d) $80/3$ **(M.N.R. 1995)**

11. The term independent of x in $\left[\sqrt{\left(\dfrac{x}{3}\right)} + \sqrt{\left(\dfrac{3}{2x^2}\right)}\right]^{10}$ is
   (a) None
   (b) $^{10}C_1$
   (c) $\dfrac{5}{12}$
   (d) 1
   (B.I.T.S. 1993)

12. If the coefficients of x^7 and x^8 in $\left(2 + \dfrac{x}{3}\right)^n$ are equal, then n is
   (a) 56
   (b) 55
   (c) 45
   (d) 15

13. In the expansion of $(1 + x)^{50}$ the sum of the coefficients of odd powers of x is
   (a) 0
   (b) 2^{49}
   (c) 2^{50}
   (d) 2^{51}

14. For $r = 0, 1, \ldots 10$, let A_r, B_r and C_r denote respectively the coefficient of x^r in the expansions of $(1 + x)^{10}, (1 + x)^{20}$ and $(1 + x)^{30}$. Then
   $$\sum_{r=1}^{10} A_r (B_{10}B_r - C_{10}A_r) \text{ is equal to}$$
   (a) $B_{10} - C_{10}$
   (b) $A_{10}(B_{10}^2 - C_{10}A_{10})$
   (c) 0
   (d) $C_{10} - B_{10}$ **(IIT JEE 2010)**

Solutions to Problem Set (3)

1. Ans. (d).
   [**Hint** : Sum of coeff. $= 4^{10}$].

2. Ans. (c).

3. Ans. (b).

4. Ans. (b).

5. Ans. (b).

6. Ans. (a).

7. Ans. (c).

8. Ans. (a).

9. Ans. (a).

10. (i) Ans. (d). It is 7th term $= 84$

(ii) Ans. (c). $T_4 = {}^6C_3 (2x)^3 \cdot \dfrac{1}{(3x)^3} = \dfrac{160}{27}$

11. Ans. (a). $r = 10/3$ which is not possible.

12. Ans. (b). Coefficients of T_8 and T_9 are equal

$\therefore \quad {}^nC_7 2^{n-7} \left(\dfrac{1}{3}\right)^7 = {}^nC_8 2^{n-8} \cdot \left(\dfrac{1}{3}\right)^8$

$\dfrac{n!}{7!(n-7)!} \cdot 2 = \dfrac{n!}{8!(n-8)!} \cdot \dfrac{1}{3}$ or $\dfrac{2}{(n-7)} = \dfrac{1}{8.3}$

$\therefore \quad 48 = n - 7$ or $n = 55$

13. Ans. (b).

$(1+x)^{50} = C_0 + C_1 x + C_2 x^2 + C_3 x^3 + \ldots + C_{50} x^{50}$

Putting $x = 1$ and -1 and subtracting, we get

$2^{50} + 0 = 2[C_1 + C_3 + C_5 + \ldots]$

$\therefore \quad C_1 + C_3 + C_5 + \ldots = 2^{49}$

or Sum of coefficients of odd powers of $x = 2^{49}$.

14. Ans. (d).

$$B_{10} \sum_{r=1}^{10} A_r B_r - C_{10} \sum_{r=1}^{10} (A_r)^2$$

$$= {}^{20}B_{10}({}^{30}C_{20} - 1) - {}^{30}C_{10}({}^{20}C_{10} - 1)$$

$$= {}^{30}C_{10} - {}^{20}C_{10} = C_{10} - B_{10}$$

MISCELLANEOUS EXERCISE

Matching Entries

▶ *Match the entries of List-A and List-B.*

1.   **List-A**   **List-B**

(a) The expansion $[x + (x^3 - 1)^{1/2}]^5 + [x - (x^3 - 1)^{1/2}]^5$ is a polynomial
of degree ...

1. 5, 9

(b) The number of terms free from radicals in the expansion of
$[7^{1/3} + 11^{1/9}]^{6561}$ is ...

2. 30, 31

(c) If the coefficients of T_r, T_{r+1}, T_{r+2} terms in the expansion of
$(1+x)^{14}$ are in A.P., then $r =$

3. 7

(d) The two consecutive terms in the expansion of $(3 + 2x)^{74}$ whose
coefficients are equal are ...

4. 730

2.   **List-A**   **List-B**

If $(1+x)^n = C_0 + C_1 x + C_2 x^2 + \ldots + C_n x^n$, then

(a) $\left(1 + \dfrac{C_1}{C_0}\right)\left(1 + \dfrac{C_2}{C_1}\right) \ldots \left(1 + \dfrac{C_n}{C_{n-1}}\right)$

1. $2^{n-1}(n+2)$

(b) $\sum\limits_{r=0}^{n} (r+1) C_r$

2. $\dfrac{n}{2}$

(c) $\sum\limits_{r=0}^{n} (r+1)^2 C_r$

3. $\dfrac{(n+1)^n}{n!}$

(d) $\sum\limits_{r=0}^{n-1} \dfrac{{}^nC_r}{{}^nC_r + {}^nC_{r+1}}$

4. $(n+1)(n+4) 2^{n-2}$

3.   **List-A**   **List-B**

(a) Sum of the coefficients in the expansion of $(x + 2y + z)^{10}$ is

1. $\dfrac{(n+1)(n+2)}{2}$

(b) The number of terms in the expansion of $(x + y + z)^n$ is

2. 50

(c) The number of irrational terms in the expansion of $(x^{1/5} + y^{1/10})^{55}$ is

3. 4^{10}

Hints / Solutions

1. (a) → 3. **Q. 34 (a) P. 369**

(b) → 4. **Q. 39 (a) P. 370**

(c) → 1. **Q. 45 (a) P. 370**

(d) → 2. **Q. 47 P. 370**

2. (a) → 3. **Q. 40 (a) P. 393**

(b) → 1. **Q. 12 (a) P. 391**

(c) → 4. **Q. 6 (b) P. 390**

(d) → 2.

$$\frac{{}^nC_r}{{}^nC_r + {}^nC_{r+1}} = \frac{{}^nC_r}{{}^{n+1}C_{r+1}}$$

$$= \frac{n!}{(n-r)! \, r!} \cdot \frac{(n-r)!(r+1)!}{(n+1)!} = \frac{r+1}{n+1}$$

$$\sum_{r=0}^{n-1} = \frac{1}{n+1}[1 + 2 + 3 + \ldots + n] = \frac{n(n+1)}{2(n+1)} = \frac{n}{2}$$

3. (a) → 3.

As sum of coeff. is 4^{10} on putting $x = y = z = 1$

(b) → 1. **10 (a) P. 366**

(c) → 2.

$$\sum_{r=0}^{55} T_{r+1} = \Sigma \, ^{55}C_r \frac{x^{55-r}}{5}$$

$$= \Sigma \, ^{55}C_r \, x^{11} \, x^{-r/5} \, y^{r/10} \qquad \qquad ...(1)$$

The terms which are free from radical will correspond to those values of r for which the radicals sign disappear i.e., $\frac{r}{5}$ and $\frac{r}{10}$. Clearly from (1) r should be a multiple of 10 in the range 0 to 55.

∴ $r = 0, 10, 20, 30, 40, 50$. Thus there will be 6 terms free from radical sign.

Total – integral = 56 – 6 = 50.

Fascinating Facts

• $^{n}C_r$ is greatest if $r = \begin{cases} \dfrac{n}{2} & \text{if} \quad n = \text{even} \\[2mm] \dfrac{n-1}{2} \text{ or } \dfrac{n+1}{2} & \text{if} \quad n = \text{odd} \end{cases}$

• The number of terms in the expansion of $(x + y + z)^n$, where n is a positive integer is $\frac{1}{2}(n+1)(n+2)$

• $^{n}C_0 - \,^{n}C_1 + \,^{n}C_2 - \,^{n}C_3 + ... + (-1)^n \cdot \,^{n}C_n = \dfrac{1}{n+1}$

• $^{n}C_0 + \dfrac{^{n}C_1}{2} + \dfrac{^{n}C_2}{3} + \dfrac{^{n}C_3}{4} + ... + \dfrac{^{n}C_n}{(n+1)} = \dfrac{2^{n+1}-1}{n+1}$

• $^{n}C_1 - 2 \cdot \,^{n}C_2 + 3 \,^{n}C_3 - ... + n \, (-1)^{n-1} \cdot \,^{n}C_n = 0$

• $^{n}C_1 + 2 \cdot \,^{n}C_2 + 3 \,^{n}C_3 + ... + n \,^{n}C_n = n \cdot 2^{n-1}$

• $^{n}C_0 + \,^{n}C_2 + \,^{n}C_4 + ... = \,^{n}C_1 + \,^{n}C_3 + \,^{n}C_5 + ... = 2^{n-1}$

• The binominal coefficients $^{n}C_0, \,^{n}C_1, \,^{n}C_2, ...$ equidistant from begining and end are equal i.e., $^{n}C_r = \,^{n}C_{n-r}$

• The number of terms in the expansion of $(x + y)^n$ are $(n + 1)$ but there are infinite number of terms in the expansion if n is negative integer or fraction.

• If n is odd, then $(x + y)^n + (x - y)^n$ and $(x + y)^n - (x - y)^n$ both have the same number of terms equal to $\dfrac{n+1}{2}$

• If coefficients of rth, $(r + 1)$th, $(r + 2)$th terms in the expansion of $(1 + x)^n$ are in A.P. then $n^2 - n(4r + 1) + 4r^2 - 2 = 0$

• If the coefficients of rth, $(r + 1)$th and $(r + 2)$th terms in the expansion of $(1 + x)^n$ are in H.P. then $n + (n - 2r)^2 = 0$

❑

CHAPTER

Algebra

Determinants

§1. Introduction

Consider the equations

$$a_1 x + b_1 y = 0, \quad a_2 x + b_2 y = 0.$$

These give

$$-\frac{a_1}{b_1} = \frac{y}{x} = -\frac{a_2}{b_2},$$

Hence $\dfrac{a_1}{b_1} = \dfrac{a_2}{b_2}$ or $a_1 b_2 - a_2 b_1 = 0$.

We shall express the above eliminant as

$$\begin{vmatrix} a_1 & b_1 \\ a_2 & b_2 \end{vmatrix} = 0. \qquad ...(A)$$

We have suppressed the letters x and y to be eliminated and enclosed their coefficients as above in two parallel lines. The left hand member of (A) is called a determinant of second order and its value as we have seen is $a_1 b_2 - a_2 b_1$.

Aid to memory

$$\begin{matrix} a_1 & \searrow & b_1 \\ -a_2 & \nearrow & b_2 \end{matrix}$$

Similarly a determinant of 3rd order will consist of 3 rows and 3 columns enclosed in two vertical lines and is thus of the form

$$\begin{vmatrix} a_1 & b_1 & c_1 \\ a_2 & b_2 & c_2 \\ a_3 & b_3 & c_3 \end{vmatrix} \qquad ...(B)$$

It can be seen that this determinant is the eliminant of x, y, z from the equations

$$a_1 x + b_1 y + c_1 z = 0$$
$$a_2 x + b_2 y + c_2 z = 0$$
$$a_3 x + b_3 y + c_3 z = 0.$$

The value of determinant (B) is

$$a_1 \begin{vmatrix} b_2 & c_2 \\ b_3 & c_3 \end{vmatrix} - b_1 \begin{vmatrix} a_2 & c_2 \\ a_3 & c_3 \end{vmatrix} + c_1 \begin{vmatrix} a_2 & b_2 \\ a_3 & b_3 \end{vmatrix}$$

$$= a_1 (b_2 c_3 - b_3 c_2) - b_1 (a_2 c_3 - a_3 c_2) + c_1 (a_2 b_3 - a_3 b_2)$$
$$...(1)$$

Rule : a_1 (determinant obtained by removing the row and column intersecting at a_1)

$-b_1$ (determinant obtained by removing the row and column intersecting at b_1)

$+c_1$ (determinant obtained by removing the row and column intersecting at c_1)

Above is called expansion of the determinant w.r.t. first row.

Expansion with respect to first column.

$$a_1 \begin{vmatrix} b_2 & c_2 \\ b_3 & c_3 \end{vmatrix} - a_2 \begin{vmatrix} b_1 & c_1 \\ b_3 & c_3 \end{vmatrix} + a_3 \begin{vmatrix} b_1 & c_1 \\ b_2 & c_2 \end{vmatrix}$$

$$= a_1 (b_2 c_3 - b_3 c_2) - a_2 (b_1 c_3 - b_3 c_1) + a_3 (b_1 c_2 - b_2 c_1)$$
$$...(2)$$

If you compare (1) and (2) term by term you will observe that they are same.

▶ Aid To Memory

1.	Always expand a determinant along a row or column with maximum number of zeros.
2.	The value of determinant is same when expanded by any row or any column.
3.	If each element above or below the main diagonal of a determinant is zero, then the value of the determinant is the product of elements along the main diagonal.

§ 2. Properties of the determinants

1. **The value of determinant is not altered by changing rows into columns and columns into rows.**

$$e.g. \begin{vmatrix} 1 & 1 & 1 \\ x & y & z \\ x^2 & y^2 & z^2 \end{vmatrix} = \begin{vmatrix} 1 & x & x^2 \\ 1 & y & y^2 \\ 1 & z & z^2 \end{vmatrix}$$

2. **If any two adjacent rows or two adjacent columns of a determinant are interchanged the determinant retains its absolute value but changes its sign**

$$e.g. \begin{vmatrix} 1 & 1 & 1 \\ x & y & z \\ x^2 & y^2 & z^2 \end{vmatrix} = - \begin{vmatrix} x & y & z \\ 1 & 1 & 1 \\ x^2 & y^2 & z^2 \end{vmatrix}$$

Here we have interchanged 1st and 2nd rows and hence changed the sign.

3. **If any line of a determinant Δ be passed over p parallel lines the resultant determinant is $(-1)^p \Delta$.**

e.g. $\begin{vmatrix} 1 & 1 & 1 & 1 \\ x & y & z & u \\ x^2 & y^2 & z^2 & u^2 \\ x^3 & y^3 & z^3 & u^3 \end{vmatrix}$

$= (-1)^3 \begin{vmatrix} x^3 & y^3 & z^3 & u^3 \\ 1 & 1 & 1 & 1 \\ x & y & z & u \\ x^2 & y^2 & z^2 & u^2 \end{vmatrix}$

$= (-1)^2 \begin{vmatrix} x^2 & y^2 & z^2 & u^2 \\ 1 & 1 & 1 & 1 \\ x & y & z & u \\ x^3 & y^3 & z^3 & u^3 \end{vmatrix}$

$= (-1)^1 \begin{vmatrix} x & y & z & u \\ 1 & 1 & 1 & 1 \\ x^2 & y^2 & z^2 & u^2 \\ x^3 & y^3 & z^3 & u^3 \end{vmatrix}$

In the first we have crossed fourth row over three parallel rows and hence $(-1)^3$ and in the second we have crossed 3rd row over two parallel rows and hence $(-1)^2$ and in the last we have crossed 2nd row over one parallel row and hence $(-1)^1$. Similarly is the rule for crossing any column over other columns.

4. **If any two rows or two columns of a determinant are identical then the determinant vanishes. Thus**

$$\begin{vmatrix} a_1 & c_1 & c_1 \\ a_2 & c_2 & c_2 \\ a_3 & c_3 & c_3 \end{vmatrix} = 0.$$

5. **If each constituent in any row or in any column be multiplied by the same factor then the determinant is multiplied by that factor**

$$\begin{vmatrix} pa_1 & b_1 & c_1 \\ pa_2 & b_2 & c_2 \\ pa_3 & b_3 & c_3 \end{vmatrix} = p\begin{vmatrix} a_1 & b_1 & c_1 \\ a_2 & b_2 & c_2 \\ a_3 & b_3 & c_3 \end{vmatrix}$$

We have taken p common from 1st column.

$$\begin{vmatrix} a_1 & b_1 & c_1 \\ qa_2 & qb_2 & qc_2 \\ ra_3 & rb_3 & rc_3 \end{vmatrix} = qr\begin{vmatrix} a_1 & b_1 & c_1 \\ a_2 & b_2 & c_2 \\ a_3 & b_3 & c_3 \end{vmatrix}$$

We have taken q and r from 2nd and 3rd rows respectively.

6. **If each constituent in any row or column consists of r terms then the determinant can be expressed as the sum of r determinants. Thus**

$$\begin{vmatrix} a_1 + \alpha_1 & b_1 & c_1 \\ a_2 + \alpha_2 & b_2 & c_2 \\ a_3 + \alpha_3 & b_3 & c_3 \end{vmatrix} = \begin{vmatrix} a_1 & b_1 & c_1 \\ a_2 & b_2 & c_2 \\ a_3 & b_3 & c_3 \end{vmatrix} + \begin{vmatrix} \alpha_1 & b_1 & c_1 \\ \alpha_2 & b_2 & c_2 \\ \alpha_3 & b_3 & c_3 \end{vmatrix}$$

and $\begin{vmatrix} a_1 & b_1 & c_1 + \alpha_1 + \beta_1 \\ a_2 & b_2 & c_2 + \alpha_2 + \beta_2 \\ a_3 & b_3 & c_3 + \alpha_3 + \beta_3 \end{vmatrix}$

$$= \begin{vmatrix} a_1 & b_1 & c_1 \\ a_2 & b_2 & c_2 \\ a_3 & b_3 & c_3 \end{vmatrix} + \begin{vmatrix} a_1 & b_1 & \alpha_1 \\ a_2 & b_2 & \alpha_2 \\ a_3 & b_3 & \alpha_3 \end{vmatrix} + \begin{vmatrix} a_1 & b_1 & \beta_1 \\ a_2 & b_2 & \beta_2 \\ a_3 & b_3 & \beta_3 \end{vmatrix}$$

7. **If from each constituent of a row (or column) of a determinant are added or subtracted the equi-multiples of the corresponding constituent of any other row (or column) the determinant remains unaltered.**

e.g. consider $\Delta = \begin{vmatrix} a_1 & b_1 & c_1 \\ a_2 & b_2 & c_2 \\ a_3 & b_3 & c_3 \end{vmatrix}$

Now suppose we add to 1st column, p times the corresponding elements of 2nd column and subtract q times of the corresponding elements of 3rd column then the value of the determinant remains unaltered

Thus $\begin{vmatrix} a_1 + pb_1 - qc_1 & b_1 & c_1 \\ a_2 + pb_2 - qc_2 & b_2 & c_2 \\ a_3 + pb_3 - qc_3 & b_3 & c_3 \end{vmatrix} = \Delta$

$$= \begin{vmatrix} a_1 & b_1 & c_1 \\ a_2 & b_2 & c_2 \\ a_3 & b_3 & c_3 \end{vmatrix} + p.0 - q.0 \qquad \text{by (4)}$$

Notation. The above changes will be expressed as

$$C_1 + (pC_2 - qC_3)$$

Similarly $R_1 + (pR_2 - qR_3)$ would stand for the corresponding alteration with respect to rows.

$C_1 + (C_2 + C_3)$ would mean add to the first column the corresponding elements of 2nd and 3rd columns.

$R_2 + (3R_1 - 6R_3)$ would mean add 3 times the elements of first row and subtract 6 times the elements of third row from the corresponding elements of second row.

In particular if there is a column which contains all elements same (e.g. 1 or a) then applying

$$R_2 - R_1, \ R_3 - R_1, \ R_4 - R_1$$

we will have three zeros in that column. Similarly for rows.

General rule. It is always desired that we should try to bring in as many zeros as possible in any row or any column and then expand the determinant with respect to that column

Thus $\begin{vmatrix} a & x & y \\ 0 & p & q \\ 0 & r & s \end{vmatrix} = a\begin{vmatrix} p & q \\ r & s \end{vmatrix} - 0 + 0 = a(ps - qr)$

If $\Delta = \begin{vmatrix} a & x & y \\ b & 0 & q \\ c & 0 & s \end{vmatrix}$, we would like to expand with respect to second column as it has two zeros.

In order to make 2nd column first we have to make it cross over one column and hence we shall attach $(-1)^1$.

$\therefore \ \Delta = (-1)^1 \left[x\begin{vmatrix} b & q \\ c & s \end{vmatrix} - 0 + 0 \right] = (-1) x(bs - cq) \ \ldots(2)$

In order to bring zeros in any row or column we have to use property 7 for alteration. More expansion should be avoided as far as possible.

Changing the order of a determinant.
As shown above if any line (row or column) consists of all zero elements except one element then the order of the determinant is reduced by one as shown in (1) and (2).

Similarly we can increase the order of a determinant by boardering it with a row and column of 1, 0, 0 e.g.
$\begin{vmatrix} 2 & 7 \\ 5 & 9 \end{vmatrix}$ is of order 2 and it can be written as a determinant of 3rd order as

$\begin{vmatrix} 1 & 0 & 0 \\ 0 & 2 & 7 \\ 0 & 5 & 9 \end{vmatrix}$ or $\dfrac{1}{\lambda}\begin{vmatrix} \lambda & 0 & 0 \\ 0 & 2 & 7 \\ 0 & 5 & 9 \end{vmatrix}$.

8. Special Determinants.

(1) Symmetric determinant
$\begin{vmatrix} a & h & g \\ h & b & f \\ g & f & c \end{vmatrix} = abc + 2fgh - af^2 - bg^2 - ch^2,$

In this the elements $a_{ij} = a_{ji}$ or the elements situated at equal distance from the diagonal are equal both in magnitude and sign.

(2) Skew symmetric determinant of odd order
$\begin{vmatrix} 0 & b & -c \\ -b & 0 & a \\ c & -a & 0 \end{vmatrix} = 0.$ **See proof. Q. 8 (a), P. 415-19.**

All the diagonal elements are zero and $a_{ij} = -a_{ji}$ or the elements situated at equal distance from the diagonal are equal in magnitude but opposite in sign. Its value is zero.

(3) Circulant :
$\begin{vmatrix} a & b & c \\ b & c & a \\ c & a & b \end{vmatrix} = -(a^3 + b^3 + c^3 - 3abc)$

See Q. 16, P. 440

The three rows or columns are in cyclic arrangement of the letters a, b, c, i.e. a, b, c ; b, c, a and c, a, b respectively.

Problem Set (1)

Determinants whose value is zero.

Evaluate the following determinants without expansion as far as possible.

1. (a) $\begin{vmatrix} 43 & 1 & 6 \\ 35 & 7 & 4 \\ 17 & 3 & 2 \end{vmatrix}$

(b) $\begin{vmatrix} 1 & 2 & 3 \\ 3 & 5 & 7 \\ 8 & 14 & 20 \end{vmatrix}$

2. (a) $\begin{vmatrix} 1 & \omega & \omega^2 \\ \omega & \omega^2 & 1 \\ \omega^2 & 1 & \omega \end{vmatrix}$

(M.N.R 1991)

where ω is an imaginary cube root of unity.

(b) If $\Delta = \begin{vmatrix} x_1 + y_1\omega & x_1\omega^2 + y_1 & x_1 + y_1\omega + z_1\omega^2 \\ x_2 + y_2\omega & x_2\omega^2 + y_2 & x_2 + y_2\omega + z_2\omega^2 \\ x_3 + y_3\omega & x_3\omega^2 + y_3 & x_3 + y_3\omega + z_3\omega^2 \end{vmatrix}$

where $1, \omega, \omega^2$ are cube roots of unity then Δ is equal to

(a) 0   (b) 1
(c) – 1   (d) none of these

(c) Let $\omega = -\dfrac{1}{2} + i\dfrac{\sqrt{3}}{2}$. Then the value of the

determinant $\begin{vmatrix} 1 & 1 & 1 \\ 1 & -1-\omega^2 & \omega^2 \\ 1 & \omega^2 & \omega^4 \end{vmatrix}$ is

(a) 3ω (b) $3\omega(\omega - 1)$
(c) $3\omega^2$ (d) $3\omega(1-\omega)$ **(I.I.T. Sc. 2002)**

(d) If Δ_1 and Δ_2 be the determinants

$\begin{vmatrix} 1 & 1 & 1 \\ 1 & \omega & \omega^2 \\ 1 & \omega^2 & \omega \end{vmatrix}$ and $\begin{vmatrix} 1 & 1 & \omega \\ 1 & 1 & \omega^2 \\ \omega^2 & \omega & 1 \end{vmatrix}$,

then prove that $\dfrac{\Delta_1}{\Delta_2} = \sqrt{3}\, i$ where ω, ω^2 are the imaginary cube roots of unity.

(e) If ω is imaginary cube root of unity then prove that the value of

$\begin{vmatrix} 1+\omega & \omega^2 & -\omega \\ 1+\omega^2 & \omega & -\omega^2 \\ \omega^2 + \omega & \omega & -\omega^2 \end{vmatrix}$ is equal to $-3\omega^2$.

3. (a) $\begin{vmatrix} a-b & b-c & c-a \\ b-c & c-a & a-b \\ c-a & a-b & b-c \end{vmatrix}$

(b) $\begin{vmatrix} a-b & b-c & c-a \\ x-y & y-z & z-x \\ p-q & q-r & r-p \end{vmatrix}$

4. (a) $\begin{vmatrix} 1 & a & b+c \\ 1 & b & c+a \\ 1 & c & a+b \end{vmatrix}$

(b)* $\begin{vmatrix} 1 & bc & bc(b+c) \\ 1 & ca & ca(c+a) \\ 1 & ab & ab(a+b) \end{vmatrix}$

5. (a) Prove that $\begin{vmatrix} 1 & ab & \dfrac{1}{a}+\dfrac{1}{b} \\ 1 & bc & \dfrac{1}{b}+\dfrac{1}{c} \\ 1 & ca & \dfrac{1}{c}+\dfrac{1}{a} \end{vmatrix} = 0$

(b)* Evaluate $\begin{vmatrix} b^2c^2 & bc & b+c \\ c^2a^2 & ca & c+a \\ a^2b^2 & ab & a+b \end{vmatrix}$.

6. (a)* Find the value of the determinant without expansion

$$\begin{vmatrix} b^2-ab & b-c & bc-ac \\ ab-a^2 & a-b & b^2-ab \\ bc-ac & c-a & ab-a^2 \end{vmatrix}$$

(b) If a, b, c be all + ive and $p, q, r \in R$ then evaluate the determinant

$$\Delta = \begin{vmatrix} (a^p + a^{-p}) & (a^p - a^{-p}) & 1 \\ (b^q + b^{-q}) & (b^q - b^{-q}) & 1 \\ (c^r + c^{-r}) & (c^r - c^{-r}) & 1 \end{vmatrix}$$

7. Evaluate :

$$\begin{vmatrix} \dfrac{1}{z} & \dfrac{1}{z} & -\dfrac{(x+y)}{z^2} \\ -\dfrac{(y+z)}{x^2} & \dfrac{1}{x} & \dfrac{1}{x} \\ -\dfrac{y(y+z)}{x^2 z} & \dfrac{x+2y+z}{xz} & -\dfrac{y(x+y)}{xz^2} \end{vmatrix}$$

8. Skew Symmetric determinant of odd order is zero.

(a)* $\begin{vmatrix} 0 & b & -c \\ -b & 0 & a \\ c & -a & 0 \end{vmatrix}$

(b) $\begin{vmatrix} 0 & a-b & a-c \\ b-a & 0 & b-c \\ c-a & c-b & 0 \end{vmatrix}$

9. If $ax^4 + bx^3 + cx^2 + dx + e$

$\equiv \begin{vmatrix} x^3+3x & x-1 & x+3 \\ x+1 & -2x & x-4 \\ x-3 & x+4 & 3x \end{vmatrix}$ then $e = 0$.

10. (a) The determinants

$\begin{vmatrix} 1 & a & bc \\ 1 & b & ca \\ 1 & c & ab \end{vmatrix}$ and $\begin{vmatrix} 1 & a & a^2 \\ 1 & b & b^2 \\ 1 & c & c^2 \end{vmatrix}$

are not identically equal.
   (i) True,   (ii) False.

(a$_1$) Prove that $\begin{vmatrix} 1 & a & a^2 \\ 1 & b & b^2 \\ 1 & c & c^2 \end{vmatrix} = \begin{vmatrix} 1 & bc & b+c \\ 1 & ca & c+a \\ 1 & ab & a+b \end{vmatrix}$

(b) Evaluate : $\begin{vmatrix} \dfrac{1}{a} & a^2 & bc \\ \dfrac{1}{b} & b^2 & ca \\ \dfrac{1}{c} & c^2 & ab \end{vmatrix}$

(c) Find the value of the determinant,

$$\begin{vmatrix} 1 & a & a^2-bc \\ 1 & b & b^2-ca \\ 1 & c & c^2-ab \end{vmatrix}$$

11. (a)* Evaluate : $\begin{vmatrix} 1 & a & a^2 & a^3+bcd \\ 1 & b & b^2 & b^3+cda \\ 1 & c & c^2 & c^3+abd \\ 1 & d & d^2 & d^3+abc \end{vmatrix}$

(b) Without expanding prove that the determinant
$\begin{vmatrix} \sin A & \cos A & \sin(A+\theta) \\ \sin B & \cos B & \sin(B+\theta) \\ \sin C & \cos C & \sin(C+\theta) \end{vmatrix} = 0.$

12. (a)* Evaluate : $\begin{vmatrix} 1 & \log_x y & \log_x z \\ \log_y x & 1 & \log_y z \\ \log_z x & \log_z y & 1 \end{vmatrix}$

x, y, z being + ive. **(I.I.T. 1993)**

(b) Evaluate $\begin{vmatrix} \log_x xyz & \log_x y & \log_x z \\ \log_y xyz & 1 & \log_y z \\ \log_z xyz & \log_z y & 1 \end{vmatrix}$.

In Q. 13 to 15 evaluate the determinants :

(c) If ω be imaginary cube root of unity then evaluate
$\begin{vmatrix} 2+3\omega^{100}+\omega^{203} & 2\omega^2 & 1 \\ 1 & 1+\omega^{100}+3\omega^{203} & 2\omega \\ 2\omega & 2\omega^2 & 3+\omega^{100}+\omega^{203} \end{vmatrix}$

13. (a) $\begin{vmatrix} 1^2 & 2^2 & 3^2 & 4^2 \\ 2^2 & 3^2 & 4^2 & 5^2 \\ 3^2 & 4^2 & 5^2 & 6^2 \\ 4^2 & 5^2 & 6^2 & 7^2 \end{vmatrix}$

(b) $\begin{vmatrix} 265 & 240 & 219 \\ 240 & 225 & 198 \\ 219 & 198 & 181 \end{vmatrix}$

14. (a) $\begin{vmatrix} 18 & 40 & 89 \\ 40 & 89 & 198 \\ 89 & 198 & 440 \end{vmatrix}$

(b) $\begin{vmatrix} 38 & 7 & 63 \\ 16 & 3 & 29 \\ 27 & 5 & 46 \end{vmatrix}$

15. (a) $\begin{vmatrix} 21 & 17 & 7 & 10 \\ 24 & 22 & 6 & 10 \\ 6 & 8 & 2 & 3 \\ 5 & 7 & 1 & 2 \end{vmatrix}$

(b) $\begin{vmatrix} 1 & 1 & 1 & 1 & 1 \\ 1 & 2 & 3 & 4 & 5 \\ 1 & 3 & 6 & 10 & 15 \\ 1 & 4 & 10 & 20 & 35 \\ 1 & 5 & 15 & 35 & 69 \end{vmatrix}$

16. (a)* Prove that
$$\begin{vmatrix} a & b & c & d \\ a & a+b & a+b+c & a+b+c+d \\ a & 2a+b & 3a+2b+c & 4a+3b+2c+d \\ a & 3a+b & 6a+3b+c & 10a+6b+3c+d \end{vmatrix} = a^4$$

(b) Let $\Delta = \begin{vmatrix} a & a+b & a+b+c \\ 3a & 4a+3b & 5a+4b+3c \\ 6a & 9a+6b & 11a+9b+6c \end{vmatrix}$,

where $a = i, b = \omega$, and $c = \omega^2$, then prove that Δ equals i.

(c) Prove that $\begin{vmatrix} a^2+2a & 2a+1 & 1 \\ 2a+1 & a+2 & 1 \\ 3 & 3 & 1 \end{vmatrix} > = < 0$

according as $a > = < 1$

17.* Find the value of the determinant
$$\begin{vmatrix} \sqrt{13}+\sqrt{3} & 2\sqrt{5} & \sqrt{5} \\ \sqrt{15}+\sqrt{26} & 5 & \sqrt{10} \\ 3+\sqrt{65} & \sqrt{15} & 5 \end{vmatrix}$$

(Roorkee 1992)

18. (a) If a, b, c (all + ive) are the pth, qth and rth terms respectively of a geometric progression, then prove that
$$\begin{vmatrix} \log a & p & 1 \\ \log b & q & 1 \\ \log c & r & 1 \end{vmatrix} = 0$$

(b)* If T_p be the pth term of a G.P. of +ive terms then evaluate
$$\begin{vmatrix} \log T_{p+1} & \log T_{p+3} & \log T_{p+5} \\ \log T_{p+3} & \log T_{p+5} & \log T_{p+7} \\ \log T_{p+5} & \log T_{p+7} & \log T_{p+9} \end{vmatrix}.$$

19.* If the pth, qth and rth terms of an H.P. be a, b, c respectively, then prove that
$$\Delta = \begin{vmatrix} bc & ca & ab \\ p & q & r \\ 1 & 1 & 1 \end{vmatrix} = 0$$

(I.I.T. 1997)

20. (a) Prove that for all values of θ,
$$\begin{vmatrix} \sin\theta & \cos\theta & \sin 2\theta \\ \sin\left(\theta+\frac{2\pi}{3}\right) & \cos\left(\theta+\frac{2\pi}{3}\right) & \sin\left(2\theta+\frac{4\pi}{3}\right) \\ \sin\left(\theta-\frac{2\pi}{3}\right) & \cos\left(\theta-\frac{2\pi}{3}\right) & \sin\left(2\theta-\frac{4\pi}{3}\right) \end{vmatrix} = 0$$

(I.I.T. 2000)

(b) $\Delta = \begin{vmatrix} 1 & \sin 3\theta & \sin^3\theta \\ 2\cos\theta & \sin 6\theta & \sin^3 2\theta \\ 4\cos^2\theta-1 & \sin 9\theta & \sin^3 3\theta \end{vmatrix}$ equals

(a) -2 (b) -1
(c) 1 (d) 0

(c) Let ABC be an equilateral triangle inscribed in the circle $x^2 + y^2 = a^2$. Suppose perpendiculars from

A, B, C to the major axis of the ellipse $\frac{x^2}{a^2} + \frac{y^2}{b^2} = 1$, $(a > b)$ meet the ellipse respectively at P, Q, R so that P, Q, R lie on the same side of the major axis as A, B, C respectively. Prove that the normals to the ellipse drawn at the points P, Q and R are concurrent. **(I.I.T. 2000)**

21. (a)* If $D_r = \begin{vmatrix} r & x & \frac{n(n+1)}{2} \\ 2r-1 & y & n^2 \\ 3r-2 & z & \frac{n(3n-1)}{2} \end{vmatrix}$

then prove that $\sum_{r=1}^{n} D_r = 0$

(b) If $D_r = \begin{vmatrix} 2r-1 & {}^nC_r & 1 \\ n^2-1 & 2^n & n+1 \\ \cos^2(n^2) & \cos^2(n) & \cos^2(n+1) \end{vmatrix}$,

$$n \geq r \geq 0,$$

then evaluate $\sum_{r=0}^{n} D_r$.

22. (a)* If $D_r = \begin{vmatrix} 2^{r-1} & 2(3^{r-1}) & 4(5^{r-1}) \\ x & y & z \\ 2^n-1 & 3^n-1 & 5^n-1 \end{vmatrix}$

then prove that $\sum_{r=1}^{n} D_r = 0$.

(b)* If
$$\Delta_r = \begin{vmatrix} x & y & z \\ 2^r & 2 \times 3^r & 3 \times 4^r \\ 2.(2^n-1) & 3.(3^n-1) & 4.(4^n-1) \end{vmatrix}$$

Find the value of $\sum_{r=1}^{n} \Delta_r$. **(M.N.R. 1996)**

23. (a)* Let $\Delta_a = \begin{vmatrix} a-1 & n & 6 \\ (a-1)^2 & 2n^2 & 4n-2 \\ (a-1)^3 & 3n^3 & 3n^2-3n \end{vmatrix}$.

show that $\sum_{a=1}^{n} \Delta_a = c$, a constant.

(b) Evaluate $\sum_{n=1}^{N} U_n$ if

$$U_n = \begin{vmatrix} n & 1 & 5 \\ n^2 & 2N+1 & 2N+1 \\ n^3 & 3N^2 & 3N \end{vmatrix}$$

(M.N.R. 1994)

(c) If f, g, h are polynomials of second degree in n having $(n+2)$ a common factor then prove that $\sum_{r=1}^{n} \Delta_r$ is independent of n where

$$\Delta_r = \begin{vmatrix} 2r+1 & 6n(n+2) & f \\ 2^{r-1} & 3.2^{n+1}-6 & g \\ r(n-r+1) & n(n+1)(n+2) & h \end{vmatrix}$$

24. (a) Prove that $\begin{vmatrix} x+1 & x+2 & x+a \\ x+2 & x+3 & x+b \\ x+3 & x+4 & x+c \end{vmatrix} = 0$

where a, b, c are given to be in A.P.

(b) If

$$f(x) = \begin{vmatrix} 1 & x & x+1 \\ 2x & x(x-1) & (x+1)x \\ 3x(x-1) & x(x-1)(x-2) & (x+1)x(x-1) \end{vmatrix}$$

then $f(100)$ is equal to

(a) 0 (b) 1
(c) 100 (d) -100 **(I.I.T. 1999)**

25. (a) Evaluate $\begin{vmatrix} \sin^2 A & \cot A & 1 \\ \sin^2 B & \cot B & 1 \\ \sin^2 C & \cot C & 1 \end{vmatrix}$,

where A, B, C are the angles of a triangle.

(b) Prove that $\begin{vmatrix} \sin^3 A & \sin^3 B & \sin^3 C \\ \sin A & \sin B & \sin C \\ \cos A & \cos B & \cos C \end{vmatrix}$

$= -\sin(A-B)\sin(B-C)\sin(C-A)$
$$\sin(A+B+C)$$

where A, B, C are any three angles such that $A+B+C \neq n\pi$.

(c) Prove that $\Delta = \begin{vmatrix} \sin A & \sin B & \sin C \\ \cos A & \cos B & \cos C \\ \cos^3 A & \cos^3 B & \cos^3 C \end{vmatrix}$

$= \sin(A-B)\sin(B-C)\sin(C-A)\cos(A+B+C)$
Also determine when $\Delta = 0$.

26. (a) $f(x) = \begin{vmatrix} \cos^2 x & \cos x \cdot \sin x & -\sin x \\ \cos x \sin x & \sin^2 x & \cos x \\ \sin x & -\cos x & 0 \end{vmatrix}$

Prove that $f(x) = 1$ is an identity.

(b) If $\Delta = \begin{vmatrix} 2\cos^2 x & \sin 2x & -\sin x \\ \sin 2x & 2\sin^2 x & \cos x \\ \sin x & -\cos x & 0 \end{vmatrix}$,

then prove that $\int_0^{\pi/2} [\Delta + \Delta'] dx = \pi$
where $\Delta' = d/dx (\Delta)$.

(c) If the max. and min. values of

$$\Delta = \begin{vmatrix} 1+\sin^2 x & \cos^2 x & \sin 2x \\ \sin^2 x & 1+\cos^2 x & \sin 2x \\ \sin^2 x & \cos^2 x & 1+\sin x \end{vmatrix}$$

are α and β, then

(a) $\alpha + \beta^{99} = 4$

(b) $\alpha^3 - \beta^{17} = 26$

(c) $\alpha^{2n} - \beta^{2n}$ is always an even integer for $n \in N$

(d) $\exists$ a triangle having sides as α, β and $\alpha - \beta$.

27. If the number of distinct real roots of

$$\begin{vmatrix} \sin x & \cos x & \cos x \\ \cos x & \sin x & \cos x \\ \cos x & \cos x & \sin x \end{vmatrix} = 0$$

in the interval $-\dfrac{\pi}{4} \leq x \leq \dfrac{\pi}{4}$ is

(a) 0 (b) 2
(c) 1 (d) 3 **(I.I.T. Sc. 2001)**

28. If A, B, C be the angles of a triangle, then prove that

(a) $\begin{vmatrix} -1 & \cos C & \cos B \\ \cos C & -1 & \cos A \\ \cos B & \cos A & -1 \end{vmatrix} = 0$

(b) $\begin{vmatrix} -1+\cos B & \cos C+\cos B & \cos B \\ \cos C+\cos A & -1+\cos A & \cos A \\ \cos B-1 & \cos A-1 & -1 \end{vmatrix} = 0$

29.* If a, b, c be the sides of a triangle ABC, then prove that

$$\Delta = \begin{vmatrix} a^2 & b\sin A & c\sin A \\ b\sin A & 1 & \cos A \\ c\sin A & \cos A & 1 \end{vmatrix} = 0$$

30.* If Δ_1, Δ_2 be the areas of two triangles with vertices $(b,c), (c,a), (a,b)$ and $(ac-b^2, ab-c^2), (ba-c^2, bc-a^2), (cb-a^2, ca-b^2)$, then evaluate $\dfrac{\Delta_1}{\Delta_2}$.

31. (a) Given $\Delta = \begin{vmatrix} -1 & 2+3i & 5-4i \\ 2-3i & 8 & 1+i \\ 5+4i & 1-i & 3 \end{vmatrix}$

Without expanding prove that Δ is real.

(b) If x, y, z are complex numbers, then

$$\Delta = \begin{vmatrix} 0 & -y & -z \\ \bar{y} & 0 & -x \\ \bar{z} & \bar{x} & 0 \end{vmatrix} \text{ is equal to}$$

(a) purely real (b) purely imaginary
(c) complex (d) 0

32.* If $\begin{vmatrix} 6i & -3i & 1 \\ 4 & 3i & -1 \\ 20 & 3 & i \end{vmatrix} = x+iy$, then

(a) $x=3, y=1$ (b) $x=1, y=3$
(c) $x=0, y=3$ (d) $x=0, y=0$ **(I.I.T. 1998)**

33. (a) If the two determinants D_1 and D_2 given below be equal, then prove that

$\cos^2\theta + \cos^2\phi + \cos^2\psi = 1$ where

$$D_1 = \begin{vmatrix} 1 & \cos\theta & \cos\phi \\ \cos\theta & 1 & \cos\psi \\ \cos\phi & \cos\psi & 1 \end{vmatrix},$$

$$D_2 = \begin{vmatrix} 0 & \cos\theta & \cos\phi \\ \cos\theta & 0 & \cos\psi \\ \cos\phi & \cos\psi & 0 \end{vmatrix},$$

(b) If $D = \begin{vmatrix} a_1 & b_1 & c_1 \\ a_2 & b_2 & c_2 \\ a_3 & b_3 & c_3 \end{vmatrix}$

and $D' = \begin{vmatrix} a_1 + pb_1 & b_1 + qc_1 & c_1 + ra_1 \\ a_2 + pb_2 & b_2 + qc_2 & c_2 + ra_2 \\ a_3 + pb_3 & b_3 + qc_3 & c_3 + ra_3 \end{vmatrix}$, then

prove that $D' = D(1 + pqr)$.   (Karnataka C.E.E. 1993)

(c) Let a, b, c be such that $b(a+c) \neq 0$. If

$\begin{vmatrix} a & a+1 & a-1 \\ -b & b+1 & b-1 \\ c & c-1 & c+1 \end{vmatrix}$

$+ \begin{vmatrix} a+1 & b+1 & c+1 \\ a-1 & b-1 & c+1 \\ (-1)^{n+2}a & (-1)^{n+1}b & (-1)^n c \end{vmatrix} = 0,$

then the value of n is

(a) any integer   (b) zero

(c) any even integer   (d) any odd integer

(AIEEE 2009)

34.* $\Delta = \begin{vmatrix} x & y & y \\ z & x & y \\ z & z & x \end{vmatrix} = \dfrac{z(x-y)^3 - y(x-z)^3}{z-y}$.

35. (a) Let $\Delta = \begin{vmatrix} 1 & \sin\alpha & 1 \\ -\sin\alpha & 1 & \sin\alpha \\ -1 & -\sin\alpha & 1 \end{vmatrix}$, then

show that Δ lies in the interval $(2, 4)$.

(b) If $\Delta = \begin{vmatrix} \cos\alpha & -\sin\alpha & 1 \\ \sin\alpha & \cos\alpha & 1 \\ \cos(\alpha+\theta) & -\sin(\alpha+\theta) & 1 \end{vmatrix}$, then prove

that $\Delta \in [1 - \sqrt{2}, 1 + \sqrt{2}]$.

36. (a) If t_1, t_2, t_3, t_4, t_5 be in A.P. of common difference d then the value of

$D = \begin{vmatrix} t_2 t_3 & t_2 & t_1 \\ t_3 t_4 & t_3 & t_2 \\ t_4 t_5 & t_4 & t_3 \end{vmatrix}$ is $2d^4$. True/False ?

(b) If t_1, t_2, t_3 are in A.P. and T_1, T_2, T_3 are in H.P. then prove that the value of

$\Delta = \begin{vmatrix} t_1 - T_1 & t_1 - T_2 & t_1 - T_3 \\ t_2 - T_1 & t_2 - T_2 & t_2 - T_3 \\ t_3 - T_1 & t_3 - T_2 & t_3 - T_3 \end{vmatrix}$ is zero.

(c) If a, b, c are three non-zero distinct numbers in A.P., then prove that

$\Delta = \begin{vmatrix} (b-c)(c-a) & (a-b)(c-a) & (a-b)(b-c) \\ (c-a)(a-b) & (b-c)(a-b) & (b-c)(c-a) \\ (a-b)(b-c) & (c-a)(b-c) & (c-a)(a-b) \end{vmatrix}$

is always +ive.

37. (a) If A, B, C be the angles of a triangle, then prove that

$\Delta = \begin{vmatrix} \sin 2A & \sin C & \sin B \\ \sin C & \sin 2B & \sin A \\ \sin B & \sin A & \sin 2C \end{vmatrix} = 0.$

(b) The value of Δ

$= \begin{vmatrix} 2 & a+r+2 & a+r \\ a+r+2 & 2(a+1)(r+1) & a(r+1)+r(a+1) \\ a+r & a(r+1)+r(a+1) & 2ar \end{vmatrix}$

(a) 0   (b) $-2a(r+1)$

(c) $a(ar+r+a)$ (d) -1

Solutions to Problem Set (1)

1. (a) $\Delta = \begin{vmatrix} 7.6+1 & 1 & 6 \\ 7.4+7 & 7 & 4 \\ 7.2+3 & 3 & 2 \end{vmatrix}$

$= 7\begin{vmatrix} 6 & 1 & 6 \\ 4 & 7 & 4 \\ 2 & 3 & 2 \end{vmatrix} + \begin{vmatrix} 1 & 1 & 6 \\ 7 & 7 & 4 \\ 3 & 3 & 2 \end{vmatrix}$

$= 7.0 + 0 = 0.$

Both the determinants are zero because of identical columns.

Aliter : Apply $C_1 - 7C_3$ then C_1 and C_2 are identical $\therefore \Delta = 0$

(b) Apply $C_3 - C_2, C_2 - C_1$ and two columns are identical. $\therefore \quad \Delta = 0$

2. (a) We know that if ω is a cube root of unity then $1 + \omega + \omega^2 = 0$ and $\omega^3 = 1$ and $\omega^4 = \omega^3 \cdot \omega = \omega$ etc.

Hence applying $C_1 + C_2 + C_3$ we see that each element of the first column becomes $1 + \omega + \omega^2$ i.e. zero. $\therefore \quad \Delta = 0.$

(b) Ans. (a).

Multiply each element of C_1 by ω^2 and hence divide Δ by ω^2. Thus C_1 and C_2 become identical.

$\therefore \quad \Delta = 0 \Rightarrow$ (a)

(c) Ans. (b).

The basic formula involved is $1 + \omega + \omega^2 = 0$ or $\omega = -1 - \omega^2$ and making as many zeros in a particular line of the determinant,

$\Delta = \begin{vmatrix} 1 & 1 & 1 \\ 1 & \omega & \omega^2 \\ 1 & \omega^2 & \omega \end{vmatrix}$ Apply $C_1 + C_2 + C_3$.

$= \begin{vmatrix} 3 & 1 & 1 \\ 0 & \omega & \omega^2 \\ 0 & \omega^2 & \omega \end{vmatrix} = 3(\omega^2 - \omega)$
$= 3\omega(\omega - 1).$

(d) Applying $R_1 + R_2 + R_3$, putting $1 + \omega + \omega^2 = 0$ and $\omega^4 = \omega$.

$\Delta_1 = 3(\omega^2 - \omega) = 3\left[\dfrac{-1 - i\sqrt{3}}{2} - \dfrac{-1 + i\sqrt{3}}{2} \right]$

$= -3\sqrt{3}\, i$

Apply $R_1 - R_2$ thus making two zeros.

$\Delta_2 = (\omega - \omega^2)^2 = \omega^2 + \omega^4 - 2\omega^3$

$= \omega^2 + \omega + 1 - 3 = -3$

∴ $\dfrac{\Delta_1}{\Delta_2} = \sqrt{3}\, i$.

(e) Apply $C_1 + C_2, C_2 - C_3$ and put $1 + \omega + \omega^2 = 0$ or
$\omega + \omega^2 = -1$

$$\Delta = \begin{vmatrix} 0 & -1 & -\omega \\ 0 & -1 & -\omega^2 \\ \omega^2 + 2\omega & -1 & -\omega^2 \end{vmatrix}$$

$= (\omega^2 + 2\omega)(\omega^2 - \omega)$

$= \omega^4 + 2\omega^3 - \omega^3 - 2\omega^2$

$= 1 + \omega - 2\omega^2 = -\omega^2 - 2\omega^2 = -3\omega^2$

3. (a) Apply $C_1 + C_2 + C_3$ each element of first column is zero ∴ $\Delta = 0$.

(b) $\Delta = 0$

4. (a) Apply $C_3 + C_2$ etc., $\Delta = 0$

(b) Ans. 0.

Multiply R_1, R_2, R_3 by a, b and c respectively and divide by abc. Now take out abc from C_3 and question reduces to form of Q. 4 (a). Apply $C_1 + C_3$.

5. (a) $\dfrac{1}{a} + \dfrac{1}{b} = \dfrac{a+b}{ab} = \dfrac{c(a+b)}{abc}$

∴ $\Delta = \dfrac{1}{abc}\begin{vmatrix} 1 & ab & bc+ca \\ 1 & bc & ca+ab \\ 1 & ca & ab+bc \end{vmatrix} = 0$

by $C_3 + C_2$ and taking $\Sigma(ab)$ out thus making C_1 and C_3 identical.

(b) Multiply R_1, R_2, R_3 by a, b, c respectively and hence divide by abc.

∴ $\Delta = \dfrac{1}{abc}\begin{vmatrix} (abc)\,bc & abc & a(b+c) \\ (abc)\,ca & abc & b(c+a) \\ (abc)\,ab & abc & c(a+b) \end{vmatrix}$

$= \dfrac{(abc)^2}{abc}\begin{vmatrix} bc & 1 & ab+ac \\ ca & 1 & bc+ba \\ ab & 1 & ca+cb \end{vmatrix}$

Apply $C_3 + C_1$ and take out $\Sigma\, ab$ and then C_2 and C_3 become identical.

∴ $\Delta = 0$.

6. (a) Taking out $(b - a)$ from C_1 and C_3, we get

$$\Delta = (b-a)^2\begin{vmatrix} b & b-c & c \\ a & a-b & b \\ c & c-a & a \end{vmatrix}.$$

Now operating $C_1 - C_3$, we get C_1 and C_2 identical in the newly formed determinant. Hence $\Delta = 0$.

(b) $(x+y)^2 - (x-y)^2 = 4xy = 4a^p a^{-p} = 4$

Apply $C_1 - C_2$ and take 4 common.

∴ $\Delta = 0$.

7. Multiply C_1, C_2, C_3 by x, y and z respectively and hence divide by xyz

∴ $\Delta = \dfrac{1}{xyz}\begin{vmatrix} \dfrac{x}{z} & \dfrac{y}{z} & -\dfrac{(x+y)}{z} \\ -\dfrac{(y+z)}{x} & \dfrac{y}{x} & \dfrac{z}{x} \\ -\dfrac{y(y+z)}{xz} & \dfrac{y(x+2y+z)}{xz} & -\dfrac{y(x+y)}{xz} \end{vmatrix}$

Apply $C_1 + C_2 + C_3$ then C_1 becomes a column of zeros.

∴ $\Delta = 0$

8. (a) Take (-1) common from each row

∴ $\Delta = (-1)^3\begin{vmatrix} 0 & -b & c \\ b & 0 & -a \\ -c & a & 0 \end{vmatrix}$.

Now change rows into columns and columns into rows

∴ $\Delta = -\begin{vmatrix} 0 & b & -c \\ -b & 0 & a \\ c & -a & 0 \end{vmatrix} = -\Delta$.

∴ $2\Delta = 0$ or $\Delta = 0$.

(b) Applying $R_1 - R_2$ and $R_2 - R_3$, we get

$$\Delta = \begin{vmatrix} a-b & a-b & a-b \\ b-c & b-c & b-c \\ c-a & c-b & 0 \end{vmatrix}$$

or R_1 and R_2 are identical.

Note : We can say that Δ is a skew-symmetric determinant of odd order and hence zero by part (a).

9. Now e is obtained by putting $x = 0$ in L.H.S. Hence putting $x = 0$ on both sides of the given equation,

we get $e = \begin{vmatrix} 0 & -1 & 3 \\ 1 & 0 & -4 \\ -3 & 4 & 0 \end{vmatrix} = 0$ being a skew-symmetric

determinant of odd order.

10. (a) Ans. (ii). False.

Multiplying R_1, R_2, R_3 by a, b, c respectively and hence dividing Δ by abc. Take abc common from C_3. Δ_1 and Δ_2 are identical.

(a$_1$) We have to prove $D = D_1$ where D

$$D_1 = \begin{vmatrix} 1 & bc & \Sigma a - a \\ 1 & ca & \Sigma a - b \\ 1 & ab & \Sigma a - c \end{vmatrix}$$

Split into two determinants one of which will be zero because of identical lines

∴ $D_1 = -\begin{vmatrix} 1 & bc & a \\ 1 & ca & b \\ 1 & ab & c \end{vmatrix}$

Multiply R_1, R_2, R_3 by a, b, c respectively and divide by abc and then take out abc ∴ $D_1 = D$.

(b) Ans. 0.

(c) Ans. 0.

Here $\Delta = \Delta_1 - \Delta_2$ and Δ_2 can be shown to be equal to Δ_1.

11. (a) Split into two determinants

$$\therefore \quad \Delta = \begin{vmatrix} 1 & a & a^2 & a^3 \\ 1 & b & b^2 & b^3 \\ 1 & c & c^2 & c^3 \\ 1 & d & d^2 & d^3 \end{vmatrix} + \begin{vmatrix} 1 & a & a^2 & bcd \\ 1 & b & b^2 & cda \\ 1 & c & c^2 & dab \\ 1 & d & d^2 & abc \end{vmatrix}$$

$$= \Delta_1 + \Delta_2$$

In Δ_2 multiply R_1, R_2, R_3, R_4 by a, b, c, d respectively and hence divide it by $abcd$

$$\therefore \quad \Delta_2 = \frac{1}{abcd} \begin{vmatrix} a & a^2 & a^3 & abcd \\ b & b^2 & b^3 & abcd \\ c & c^2 & c^3 & abcd \\ d & d^2 & d^3 & abcd \end{vmatrix}$$

$$= \frac{abcd}{abcd} \begin{vmatrix} a & a^2 & a^3 & 1 \\ b & b^2 & b^3 & 1 \\ c & c^2 & c^3 & 1 \\ d & d^2 & d^3 & 1 \end{vmatrix}$$

Now cross the 4th column over three columns and hence write $(-1)^3$

$$\therefore \quad \Delta_2 = (-1)^3 \begin{vmatrix} 1 & a & a^2 & a^3 \\ 1 & b & b^2 & b^3 \\ 1 & c & c^2 & c^3 \\ 1 & d & d^2 & d^3 \end{vmatrix} = -\Delta_1$$

$$\therefore \quad \Delta = \Delta_2 + \Delta_1 = 0.$$

(b) Consider $\sin(A + \theta)$ in C_3.

$$\sin(A + \theta) = \sin A \cos \theta + \cos A \sin \theta$$

Hence apply $C_3 - \cos \theta . C_1 - \sin \theta . C_2$

Then each element in C_3 is zero. $\therefore \Delta = 0.$

12. (a) Ans. Zero. $\log_n m = \dfrac{\log m}{\log n}.$

Hence each row becomes

$\log x \ \log y \ \log z$ *i.e.* identical.

(b) $1 = \log_y y = \log_z z$

$$\Delta = \begin{vmatrix} \log_x xyz & \log_x y & \log_x z \\ \log_y xyz & \log_y y & \log_y z \\ \log_z xyz & \log_z y & \log_z z \end{vmatrix}$$

As in (b) write $\log_n m = \dfrac{\log m}{\log n}$ then each row

becomes identical $\log xyz, \log y, \log z$

(c) $\omega^{100} = (\omega^3)^{33} . \omega = \omega, \ \omega^{203} = (\omega^{100})^2 . \omega^3$

$$= \omega^2 . 1 = \omega^2$$

Apply $C_1 + C_2 + C_3$ then new C_1 becomes a column of zeros as $3(1 + \omega + \omega^2) = 0$

13. (a) Apply $C_4 - C_3, C_3 - C_2, C_2 - C_1$ **(Note)** **The reverse operations** for making smaller numbers

$$\Delta = \begin{vmatrix} 1 & 3 & 5 & 7 \\ 4 & 5 & 7 & 9 \\ 9 & 7 & 9 & 11 \\ 16 & 9 & 11 & 13 \end{vmatrix}$$

Again apply $C_4 - C_3$ and $C_3 - C_2$

$$\Delta = \begin{vmatrix} 1 & 3 & 2 & 2 \\ 4 & 5 & 2 & 2 \\ 9 & 7 & 2 & 2 \\ 16 & 9 & 2 & 2 \end{vmatrix} = 0$$

$[\because C_4$ and C_3 are identical columns]

(b) In order to make smaller numbers we apply $C_1 - C_2$ and $C_2 - C_3$

$$\therefore \quad \Delta = \begin{vmatrix} 25 & 21 & 219 \\ 15 & 27 & 198 \\ 21 & 17 & 181 \end{vmatrix}$$

Now applying $C_1 - C_2$ and $C_3 - 10C_2$, we get

$$\Delta = \begin{vmatrix} 4 & 21 & 219 - 210 \\ -12 & 27 & 198 - 270 \\ 4 & 17 & 181 - 170 \end{vmatrix}$$

$$= 4 \begin{vmatrix} 1 & 21 & 9 \\ -3 & 27 & -72 \\ 1 & 17 & 11 \end{vmatrix}$$

Now make two zeros by $R_2 + 3R_1, \ R_3 - R_1$

$$\Delta = 4 \begin{vmatrix} 1 & 21 & 9 \\ 0 & 90 & -45 \\ 0 & -4 & 2 \end{vmatrix} = 4(180 - 180) = 0.$$

14. (a) Applying $R_2 - 2R_1, \ R_3 - 5R_1$, we get

$$\Delta = \begin{vmatrix} 18 & 40 & 89 \\ 4 & 9 & 20 \\ -1 & -2 & -5 \end{vmatrix} \quad [\text{Apply } C_3 - 2C_2]$$

$$\Delta = \begin{vmatrix} 18 & 40 & 9 \\ 4 & 9 & 2 \\ -1 & -2 & -1 \end{vmatrix}$$

Now apply $C_1 - 2C_3$ to make zeros in C_1

$$\Delta = \begin{vmatrix} 0 & 40 & 9 \\ 0 & 9 & 2 \\ 1 & -2 & -1 \end{vmatrix} = 1 \begin{vmatrix} 40 & 9 \\ 9 & 2 \end{vmatrix} = 80 - 81 = -1.$$

(b) Apply $C_1 - 5C_2, \ C_3 - 9C_2$ to reduce the numbers

$$\Delta = \begin{vmatrix} 3 & 7 & 0 \\ 1 & 3 & 2 \\ 2 & 5 & 1 \end{vmatrix} \quad \text{Apply } R_2 - 2R_3$$

$$\Delta = \begin{vmatrix} 3 & 7 & 0 \\ -3 & -7 & 0 \\ 2 & 5 & 1 \end{vmatrix} = 0,$$

as R_1 and R_2 are identical.

15. (a) Here we shall try to make three zeros in any line and keeping this in view we apply the following operations :

$$R_1 - (R_2 + R_4), \ R_2 - 3R_3, \ R_3 - 2R_4$$

and it will make three zeros in column no. 3

$$\Delta = \begin{vmatrix} -8 & -12 & 0 & -2 \\ 6 & -2 & 0 & 1 \\ -4 & -6 & 0 & -1 \\ 5 & 7 & 1 & 2 \end{vmatrix}$$

$$= (-2)(-1)\begin{vmatrix} 4 & 6 & 0 & 1 \\ 6 & -2 & 0 & 1 \\ 4 & 6 & 0 & 1 \\ 5 & 7 & 1 & 2 \end{vmatrix} = 0$$

as R_1 and R_3 are identical.

(b) Here we apply reverse order operation $R_5 - R_4, R_4 - R_3, R_3 - R_2, R_2 - R_1$. Note that as in Q. 13 (a) we have started changing from the last row so that the numbers are reduced and then we expand with 1st column and we are left with a determinant of 4th order as under

$$\Delta = \begin{vmatrix} 1 & 2 & 3 & 4 \\ 1 & 3 & 6 & 10 \\ 1 & 4 & 10 & 20 \\ 1 & 5 & 15 & 34 \end{vmatrix}$$

Again apply reverse order operation $R_4 - R_3$, $R_3 - R_2$, $R_2 - R_1$ and expand

$$\Delta = \begin{vmatrix} 1 & 3 & 6 \\ 1 & 4 & 10 \\ 1 & 5 & 14 \end{vmatrix}$$

Again apply $R_3 - R_2, R_2 - R_1$ and expand

$$\Delta = \begin{vmatrix} 1 & 4 \\ 1 & 4 \end{vmatrix} = 4 - 4 = 0.$$

16. (a) Apply reverse operation for making smaller numbers

$R_5 - R_4, R_4 - R_3, R_3 - R_2, R_2 - R_1$.

$$\Delta = \begin{vmatrix} a & b & c & d \\ 0 & a & a+b & a+b+c \\ 0 & a & 2a+b & 3a+2b+c \\ 0 & a & 3a+b & 6a+3b+c \end{vmatrix} = a| \quad |.$$

Again apply $R_3 - R_2, R_2 - R_1$, etc.

(b) Apply $R_3 - 2R_2, R_2 - 3R_1$ thus making two zeros and expand.

$$\Delta = -a^3 = -(i)^3 = i$$

(c) Apply $R_1 - R_2$ and $R_2 - R_3$ thus making two zeros.

$$\therefore \quad \Delta = \begin{vmatrix} a^2 - 1 & a-1 & 0 \\ 2(a-1) & a-1 & 0 \\ 3 & 3 & 1 \end{vmatrix}$$

or $\quad \Delta = (a-1)^2 \begin{vmatrix} a+1 & 1 \\ 2 & 1 \end{vmatrix} = (a-1)^3$

Clearly $\Delta > = < 0$ according as $a > = < 1$.

17. Take $\sqrt{5}$ and $\sqrt{5}$ common from each of C_2 and C_3 and rearrange the elements of first column.

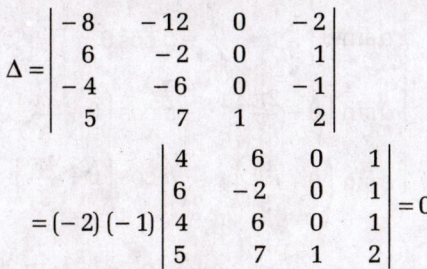

$$\Delta = \sqrt{5} \cdot \sqrt{5} \begin{vmatrix} \sqrt{13} + \sqrt{3} & 2 & 1 \\ \sqrt{26} + \sqrt{15} & \sqrt{5} & \sqrt{2} \\ \sqrt{65} + 3 & \sqrt{3} & \sqrt{5} \end{vmatrix}$$

Split into two determinants, the first of which will vanish. Take $\sqrt{13}$ common from Δ_1 and $\sqrt{3}$ from Δ_2

$$\therefore \quad \Delta = 0 + 5\sqrt{3} \begin{vmatrix} 1 & 2 & 1 \\ \sqrt{5} & \sqrt{5} & \sqrt{2} \\ \sqrt{3} & \sqrt{3} & \sqrt{5} \end{vmatrix}.$$

Apply $C_1 - C_2$

$$\Delta = 5\sqrt{3} \begin{vmatrix} -1 & 2 & 1 \\ 0 & \sqrt{5} & \sqrt{2} \\ 0 & \sqrt{3} & \sqrt{5} \end{vmatrix} = -5\sqrt{3}(5 - \sqrt{6})$$
$$= 5\sqrt{3}(\sqrt{6} - 5)$$

18. (a) Let A be the 1st term and R the common ratio of G.P., then

$$a = T_p = AR^{p-1}$$

$\therefore \quad \log a = \log A + (p-1)\log R.$

Similarly $b = T_q$, $c = T_r$ etc.

$$\therefore \quad \Delta = \begin{vmatrix} \log A + (p-1)\log R & p & 1 \\ \log A + (q-1)\log R & q & 1 \\ \log A + (r-1)\log R & r & 1 \end{vmatrix}$$

Split into two determinants and in the first take $\log A$ common and in the second take $\log R$ common

$$\Delta = \log A \begin{vmatrix} 1 & p & 1 \\ 1 & q & 1 \\ 1 & r & 1 \end{vmatrix} + \log R \begin{vmatrix} p-1 & p & 1 \\ q-1 & q & 1 \\ r-1 & r & 1 \end{vmatrix}$$

Apply $C_1 - C_2 + C_3$ in the second

$$\Delta = 0 + \log R \begin{vmatrix} 0 & p & 1 \\ 0 & q & 1 \\ 0 & r & 1 \end{vmatrix} = 0.$$

(b) In a G.P., $\dfrac{T_{p+3}}{T_{p+1}} = \dfrac{ar^{p+2}}{ar^p} = r^2$

Apply $C_3 - C_2$ and $C_2 - C_1$ and $\log m - \log n = \log \dfrac{m}{n}$

$$\therefore \quad \Delta = \begin{vmatrix} \log T_{p+1} & \log r^2 & \log r^2 \\ \log T_{p+3} & \log r^2 & \log r^2 \\ \log T_{p+5} & \log r^2 & \log r^2 \end{vmatrix} = 0.$$

19. Take abc common from R_1

$$\therefore \quad \Delta = abc \begin{vmatrix} 1/a & 1/b & 1/c \\ p & q & r \\ 1 & 1 & 1 \end{vmatrix}$$

Now $a = T_p$ of H.P. or $\dfrac{1}{a} = T_p$ of A.P. $= A + (p-1)D$.

$$\therefore \quad \Delta = abc \times$$
$$\begin{vmatrix} A + (p-1)D & A + (q-1)D & A + (r-1)D \\ p & q & r \\ 1 & 1 & 1 \end{vmatrix}$$

Apply $R_1 - DR_2 + DR_3$

$$\Delta = abc \begin{vmatrix} A & A & A \\ p & q & r \\ 1 & 1 & 1 \end{vmatrix} = 0.$$

Identical rows R_1 and R_3.

20. (a) Apply $R_2 + R_3$ so that new R_2 becomes

$2 \sin \theta \cos \dfrac{2\pi}{3}$ $2 \cos \theta \cos \dfrac{2\pi}{3}$ $2 \sin 2\theta \cos \dfrac{4\pi}{3}$

Now put $\cos \dfrac{2\pi}{3} = -\dfrac{1}{2}$

and $\cos \dfrac{4\pi}{3} = \cos 240° = -\dfrac{1}{2}$

Then R_1 and new R_2 become identical and hence $\Delta = 0$.

(b) Ans. (d).

Multiply C_1 by $3 \sin \theta$ and divide Δ by $3 \sin \theta$. This is done keeping in view that $\sin 3\theta = 3 \sin \theta - 4 \sin^3 \theta$. The elements of column are changed.

$$\therefore \quad \Delta = \dfrac{1}{3 \sin \theta} = \begin{vmatrix} 3 \sin \theta & \sin 3\theta & \sin^3 \theta \\ 3 \sin 2\theta & \sin 6\theta & \sin^3 2\theta \\ 3 \sin 3\theta & \sin 9\theta & \sin^3 3\theta \end{vmatrix}$$

$\because \quad 3 \sin \theta (4 \cos^2 \theta - 1) = 3 \sin \theta (3 - 4 \sin^2 \theta)$

$= 3 (\sin \theta - 4 \sin^3 \theta) = 3 \sin 3\theta$

Now apply $C_1 - 4C_3$ so that new C_1 becomes identical with C_2 and hence $\Delta = 0$.

(c) If the eccentric angle of P be θ then those of Q and R are $\theta + \dfrac{2\pi}{3}$ and $\theta + \dfrac{4\pi}{3}$ respectively.

Now normal at any point P 'θ' is

$$\dfrac{ax}{\cos \theta} - \dfrac{by}{\sin \theta} = a^2 - b^2$$

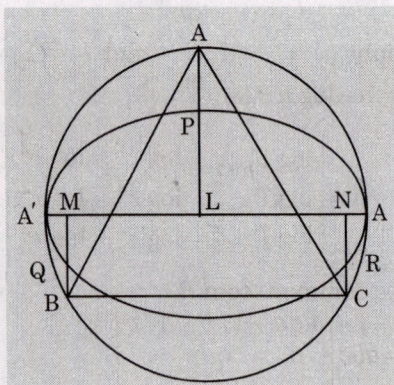

Fig. 1

or $ax \sin \theta - by \cos \theta - \dfrac{1}{2}(a^2 - b^2) \sin 2\theta = 0$

...(1)

Replace θ by $\theta + \dfrac{2\pi}{3}$ and $\theta + \dfrac{4\pi}{3}$ in (1).

We get the equations of the normals at Q and R. These three normals will be concurrent if the determinant of coefficients $\Delta = 0$.

$$\begin{vmatrix} a \sin \theta & -b \cos \theta & -\dfrac{1}{2}(a^2 - b^2)\sin 2\theta \\ a \sin\left(\theta + \dfrac{2\pi}{3}\right) & -b \cos\left(\theta + \dfrac{2\pi}{3}\right) & -\dfrac{1}{2}(a^2 - b^2)\sin 2\left(\theta + \dfrac{2\pi}{3}\right) \\ a \sin\left(\theta + \dfrac{4\pi}{3}\right) & -b \cos\left(\theta + \dfrac{4\pi}{3}\right) & -\dfrac{1}{2}(a^2 - b^2)\sin 2\left(\theta + \dfrac{4\pi}{3}\right) \end{vmatrix} = 0$$

or $$\begin{vmatrix} \sin \theta & \cos \theta & \sin 2\theta \\ \sin\left(\theta + \dfrac{2\pi}{3}\right) & \cos\left(\theta + \dfrac{2\pi}{3}\right) & \sin 2\left(\theta + \dfrac{2\pi}{3}\right) \\ \sin\left(\theta + \dfrac{4\pi}{3}\right) & \cos\left(\theta + \dfrac{4\pi}{3}\right) & \sin 2\left(\theta + \dfrac{4\pi}{3}\right) \end{vmatrix} = 0$$

Now apply $R_2 + R_3$ and new R_2 becomes identical to R_1 as in part (a).

Hence $\Delta = 0$ so the normals are concurrent.

21. (a) $\displaystyle\sum_{r=1}^{n} r = 1 + 2 + 3 + \ldots + n = \dfrac{n(n+1)}{2}$

$\displaystyle\sum_{r=1}^{n} (2r - 1) = 1 + 3 + 5 + \ldots + (2n - 1)$

$= \dfrac{n}{2}[1 + (2n - 1)] = n^2$

$\displaystyle\sum_{r=1}^{n} (3r - 2) = 1 + 4 + 7 + \ldots + (3n - 2)$

$= \dfrac{n}{2}[1 + 3n - 2] = \dfrac{n(3n - 1)}{2}.$

We have used the formula for A.P.

$$S_n = \dfrac{n}{2}[a + l].$$

$$\therefore \quad \sum_{r=1}^{n} D_r = \begin{vmatrix} \Sigma r & x & \dfrac{n(n+1)}{2} \\ \Sigma(2r - 1) & y & n^2 \\ \Sigma(3r - 2) & z & \dfrac{n(3n - 1)}{2} \end{vmatrix}$$

$\displaystyle\sum_{r=1}^{n} D_r$ consists of n determinants in L.H.S. in each of which elements of 1st column vary but elements of 2nd and 3rd column remain the same. Hence adding all such determinants, we have sigma in 1st column and no change in 2nd and 3rd column.

Now putting the values of various sigmas as given in the beginning, we get

$$\sum_{r=1}^{n} D_r = \begin{vmatrix} \dfrac{n(n+1)}{2} & x & \dfrac{n(n+1)}{2} \\ n^2 & y & n^2 \\ \dfrac{n(3n-1)}{2} & z & \dfrac{n(3n-1)}{2} \end{vmatrix} = 0.$$

$$[\because C_1 \text{ and } C_3 \text{ are identical}]$$

(b) Putting $r = 0, 1, 2, \ldots n$ and adding all the determinants, the first row will become

$$\sum_{r=0}^{n} \underset{\text{A.P.}}{(2r-1)}, \quad \sum_{r=0}^{n} {}^nC_r, \quad \sum_{r=0}^{n} 1$$

or $\dfrac{n+1}{2}[-1 + 2n - 1], C_0 + C_1 + \ldots C_n,$

$1 + 1 + 1 + \ldots (n+1)$ times for $r = 0$ to n

or $n^2 - 1, 2^n, n + 1$

R_2 and R_3 remain the same.

Thus R_1 becomes identical with R_2 $\therefore$ $\Delta = 0$.

22. (a) $\displaystyle\sum_{r=1}^{n} 2^{r-1} = 1 + 2 + 2^2 + 2^3 + \ldots + 2^{n-1}$

$$= 1 \cdot \dfrac{(2^n - 1)}{2 - 1} = 2^n - 1,$$

$\sum 2(3^{r-1}) = 2(1 + 3 + 3^2 + \ldots + 3^{n-1})$

$$= 2 \cdot 1 \cdot \dfrac{(3^n - 1)}{3 - 1} = 3^n - 1,$$

$\sum 4(5^{r-1}) = 4(1 + 5 + 5^2 + \ldots + 5^{n-1})$

$$= 4 \cdot 1 \cdot \dfrac{(5^n - 1)}{5 - 1} = 5^n - 1.$$

We have used the formula for G.P.

$$S_n = \dfrac{a(r^n - 1)}{r - 1} \quad (r > 1)$$

Rest is as in Q. 16.

(b) Ans. 0. Proceed as in part (a).

23. (a) As in Q. 21 and 22 putting $(n-1)$ for n in the values of Σn, Σn^2 and Σn^3 as for $a = 1, a - 1 = 0$,

$\therefore$ $D_1 = 0$ for $a = n, a - 1 = n - 1$

$\therefore$ Sigma will be sum of only $(n-1)$ determinants and not n.

$$\sum_{a=1}^{n} \Delta_a = \begin{vmatrix} \dfrac{(n-1)n}{2} & n & 6 \\ \dfrac{1}{6}(n-1)n(2n-1) & 2n^2 & 4n-2 \\ \dfrac{1}{4}(n-1)^2 n^2 & 3n^3 & 3n^2 - 3n \end{vmatrix}$$

Taking $\dfrac{(n-1)n}{12}$ common from C_1 it becomes identical with C_3 and hence $\Sigma \Delta_a = 0$ i.e. constant.

(b) Exactly as part (a). After taking $\dfrac{n(n+1)}{12}$ common from C_1 and then applying $C_1 - C_2$ it becomes identical with C_3. $\therefore$ $\Delta = 0$.

(c) $3 + 5 + 7 + \ldots = \dfrac{n}{2}[2 \cdot 3 + (n-1) \cdot 2] = n(n+2)$

$2^0 + 2^1 + 2^2 + \ldots 2^{n-1} = \dfrac{1 \cdot (2^n - 1)}{2 - 1} = 2^n - 1$

$$= \dfrac{1}{6}(6 \cdot 2^n - 6) = \dfrac{1}{6}(3 \cdot 2^{n+1} - 6)$$

$1 \cdot n + 2(n-1) + 3(n-2) + \ldots n \cdot (n-1)$

$= 1 \cdot (n+1-1) + 2(n+1-2) + 3(n+1-3) + \ldots$

$= (n+1)(1 + 2 + 3 + \ldots) - (1^2 + 2^2 + 3^2 + \ldots)$

$= (n+1)\dfrac{n(n+1)}{2} - \dfrac{n(n+1)(2n+1)}{6}$

$= \dfrac{n(n+1)}{6}[3n + 3 - (2n+1)]$

$= \dfrac{1}{6}n(n+1)(n+2)$

Thus putting $r = 1, 2, 3, \ldots, n$, we have $\displaystyle\sum_{r=1}^{n} \Delta_r$

becomes a determinant in which C_1 and C_2 become identical.

Hence $\displaystyle\sum_{r=0}^{n} \Delta_r = 0$.

24. (a) Apply $R_1 + R_3 - 2R_2$

$$\Delta = \begin{vmatrix} 0 & 0 & a+c-2b \\ x+2 & x+3 & x+b \\ x+3 & x+4 & x+c \end{vmatrix} = 0.$$

Since a, b, c are in A.P.

$\therefore$ $a + c = 2b$ or $a + c - 2b = 0$

and as such R_1 is a row of zeros only.

(b) Ans. (a). Take $x(x-1)$ from R_3 and x from R_2 common and $(x+1)$ from C_3.

$$f(x) = \Delta = x^2(x^2 - 1)\begin{vmatrix} 1 & x & 1 \\ 2 & x-1 & 1 \\ 3 & x-2 & 1 \end{vmatrix}$$

Apply $R_1 + R_3 - 2R_2$ $\therefore$ $\Delta = 0$

as R_1 becomes a row of zeros.

$f(x) = 0 \; \forall \; x$ $\therefore$ $f(100) = 0$.

25. (a) To make two zeros apply $R_2 - R_1$ and $R_3 - R_1$, and use $\sin^2 x - \sin^2 y = \sin(x+y)\sin(x-y)$

and $\cot x - \cot y = \dfrac{\sin(y-x)}{\sin x \sin y}$,

$\sin(A+B) = \sin C$ in a triangle.

$$\therefore \; \Delta = \begin{vmatrix} \sin^2 A & \cot A & 1 \\ \sin C \sin(B-A) & \dfrac{\sin(A-B)}{\sin A \sin B} & 0 \\ \sin B \sin(C-A) & \dfrac{\sin(A-C)}{\sin A \sin C} & 0 \end{vmatrix}$$

$$= \dfrac{\sin(A-B)\sin(A-C)}{\sin A}\begin{vmatrix} -\sin C & \dfrac{1}{\sin B} \\ -\sin B & \dfrac{1}{\sin C} \end{vmatrix}$$

$$= -\frac{\sin(A-B)\sin(A-C)}{\sin A}\left[\frac{\sin C}{\sin C} - \frac{\sin B}{\sin B}\right] = 0$$

(b) Taking $\sin A, \sin B, \sin C$ common from C_1, C_2 and C_3

$$\Delta = \sin A \sin B \sin C \begin{vmatrix} \sin^2 A & \sin^2 B & \sin^2 C \\ 1 & 1 & 1 \\ \cot A & \cot B & \cot C \end{vmatrix}$$

Now proceed as in part (b) but note that
$$A + B + C \neq n\pi.$$
Making two zeros by $C_1 - C_2$ and $C_2 - C_3$, we get
$$\Delta = -\sin A \sin B \sin C \sin(A-B)\sin(B-C)$$
$$\times \begin{vmatrix} \sin(A+B) & \sin(B+C) \\ -1 & -1 \\ \dfrac{}{\sin A \sin B} & \dfrac{}{\sin B \sin C} \end{vmatrix}$$

$$= \sin(A-B)\sin(B-C)$$
$$[\sin(A+B)\sin A - \sin(B+C)\sin C]$$
$$= \sin(A-B)\sin(B-C)$$
$$[(\sin A \cos B + \cos A \sin B)\sin A$$
$$- (\sin B \cos C + \cos B \sin C)\sin C]$$
$$= \sin(A-B)\sin(B-C)[\cos B(\sin^2 A - \sin^2 C)$$
$$+ \frac{1}{2}\sin B(\sin 2A - \sin 2C)]$$
$$= \sin(A-B)\sin(B-C)\sin(A-C)$$
$$[\cos B \sin(A+C) + \sin B \cos(A+C)]$$
$$= \sin(A-B)\sin(B-C)\sin(C-A)\sin(A+B+C).$$

(c) Proceed as in part (b). $\Delta = 0$ when any two of A, B, C are equal or $A+B+C = \pi/2$.

26. (a) Apply $C_1 - \sin x\, C_3$ and $C_2 + \cos x\, C_3$
$$\therefore \quad f(x) = \begin{vmatrix} 1 & 0 & -\sin x \\ 0 & 1 & \cos x \\ \sin x & -\cos x & 0 \end{vmatrix}$$

Now expand and put $\sin^2 x + \cos^2 x = 1$ for all x. Thus $f(x) = 1$ is an identity.

(b) It is exactly as part (a).
Apply $C_1 - 2\sin x\, C_3$, $C_2 + 2\cos x\, C_3$
$$\Delta = \begin{vmatrix} 2 & 0 & -\sin x \\ 0 & 2 & \cos x \\ \sin x & -\cos x & 0 \end{vmatrix}$$
$$= 2(\cos^2 x + \sin^2 x) = 2.$$
$$\therefore \quad \Delta' = 0 \quad \text{and} \quad \Delta + \Delta' = 2.$$
$$\therefore \quad \int_0^{\pi/2}(\Delta + \Delta')\,dx = \int_0^{\pi/2} 2\,dx = [2x]_0^{\pi/2} = \pi.$$

(c) Ans. (a), (b), (c).
Apply $R_1 - R_2$ and $R_2 - R_3$ and expanding
$$\Delta = 2 + \sin 2x.$$
$$\therefore \quad \text{Max. value} = 2 + 1 = 3 = \alpha$$
and min. value $= 2 - 1 = 1 = \beta$
Hence (a), (b), (c) are correct.
(d) option is not possible as the sides will be 3, 1 and 2. Sum of two sides $2 + 1 = 3 = $ 3rd side whereas in a triangle sum of two sides is always greater than the third side.

27. Ans. (c).
Apply $C_1 + C_2 + C_3$
$$\Delta = (2\cos x + \sin x)\begin{vmatrix} 1 & \cos x & \cos x \\ 1 & \sin x & \cos x \\ 1 & \cos x & \sin x \end{vmatrix}$$
Make two zeros by $R_1 - R_3$ and expand
$$\Delta = (2\cos x + \sin x)(\cos x - \sin x)^2 = 0$$
$$\therefore \quad \tan x = 1 \quad \text{or} \quad -2$$
Since $x \in \left[-\dfrac{\pi}{4}, \dfrac{\pi}{4}\right]$ $\therefore$ $\tan x = -2$ is rejected and hence
there is only one solution $x = \dfrac{\pi}{4}$ in the given interval.

28. (a) In a triangle
$$\cos(A+B) = \cos(\pi - C) = -\cos C \qquad \text{...(1)}$$
$$\therefore \quad \cos A \cos B + \cos C = \sin A \sin B \text{ etc.}$$
$$\sin(A+B) = \sin C \text{ etc.}$$
Expanding the given determinant, we get
$$\Delta = -(1 - \cos^2 A) + \cos C[\cos C + \cos A \cos B]$$
$$+ \cos B[\cos B + \cos A \cos C]$$
$$= -\sin^2 A + \cos C(\sin A \sin B)$$
$$+ \cos B(\sin A \sin C)$$
$$= -\sin^2 A + \sin A \sin(B+C)$$
$$= -\sin^2 A + \sin^2 A = 0.$$

(b) Just expand and use the result of Part (a).

29. By sine rule $\dfrac{\sin A}{a} = k$
$$\Delta = \begin{vmatrix} a^2 & bak & cak \\ bak & 1 & \cos A \\ cak & \cos A & 1 \end{vmatrix}$$
Take a common from each R_1 and C_1
$$\therefore \quad \Delta = a^2 \begin{vmatrix} 1 & \sin B & \sin C \\ \sin B & 1 & \cos A \\ \sin C & \cos A & 1 \end{vmatrix}$$
Make two zeros by $C_2 - (\sin B)C_1$, $C_3 - (\sin C)C_1$
$$\Delta = a^2 \begin{vmatrix} 1 & 0 & 0 \\ \sin B & 1 - \sin^2 B & \cos A - \sin B \sin C \\ \sin C & \cos A - \sin B \sin C & 1 - \sin^2 C \end{vmatrix}$$
$$= a^2 \begin{vmatrix} \cos^2 B & -\cos B \cos C \\ -\cos B \cos C & \cos^2 C \end{vmatrix}$$
$$= a^2[\cos^2 B \cos^2 C - \cos^2 B \cos^2 C] = 0$$
$$\therefore \cos A = -\cos(B+C) = -\cos B \cos C + \sin B \sin C \text{ etc.}$$

30. $\Delta_1 = \dfrac{1}{2}\begin{vmatrix} b & c & 1 \\ c & a & 1 \\ a & b & 1 \end{vmatrix} = \dfrac{1}{2}(\Sigma ab - \Sigma a^2)$

by expansion with third column.

$$\Delta_2 = \dfrac{1}{2}\begin{vmatrix} ac - b^2 & ab - c^2 & 1 \\ ba - c^2 & bc - a^2 & 1 \\ cb - a^2 & ca - b^2 & 1 \end{vmatrix}$$

Make two zeros by $R_3 - R_2, R_2 - R_1$ and take $a+b+c$ common from each R_3 and R_2.

$$\Delta_2 = \frac{1}{2}(a+b+c)^2 \begin{vmatrix} ac-b^2 & ab-c^2 & 1 \\ b-c & c-b & 0 \\ c-a & a-b & 0 \end{vmatrix}$$

Expand with 3rd column.

$$= \frac{1}{2}(a+b+c)^2 (\Sigma ab - \Sigma a^2)$$

$$\therefore \quad \frac{\Delta_1}{\Delta_2} = (a+b+c)^2$$

31. (a) Take conjugate and then change rows into columns and columns into rows. This gives $\overline{\Delta} = \Delta$. Hence Δ must be real.

(b) Ans. (b).

$$\overline{\Delta} = \begin{vmatrix} 0 & -\overline{y} & -\overline{z} \\ y & 0 & -\overline{x} \\ z & x & 0 \end{vmatrix}$$

Now change rows into columns and columns into rows and take (-1) common from each row

$$\therefore \quad \overline{\Delta} = (-1)^3 \Delta = -\Delta \quad \therefore \quad \overline{\Delta} + \Delta = 0$$

$$\Rightarrow \quad 2 \text{ (real part)} = 0$$

$$\therefore \quad \Delta \text{ is purely imaginary.}$$

32. Ans. (d).

Apply $R_1 + R_2$ and expand $x + iy = (6i+4)(-3+3) = 0$

$$\Rightarrow \quad x = 0, y = 0.$$

33. (a) Expand both

$$D_1 = 1 - \Sigma \cos^2 \theta + 2 \cos \theta \cos \phi \cos \psi$$

$$D_2 = 2 \cos \theta \cos \phi \cos \psi$$

$$D_1 = D_2 \text{ implies the result.}$$

(b) Split into eight determinants out of which six will vanish because of identical lines and only two will remain $D' = D + pqr . D = (1+pqr)D$

(c) Ans. (d). $\Delta = \Delta_1 + \Delta_2$ where

$$\Delta_2 = (-1)^n \begin{vmatrix} a+1 & b+1 & c-1 \\ a-1 & b-1 & c+1 \\ a & -b & c \end{vmatrix}$$

$$\Delta_2 = (-1)^n \begin{vmatrix} a & -b & c \\ a+1 & b+1 & c-1 \\ a-1 & b-1 & c+1 \end{vmatrix}$$

$$= (-1)^n \begin{vmatrix} a & a+1 & a-1 \\ -b & b+1 & b-1 \\ c & c-1 & c+1 \end{vmatrix} \text{by } R \to C \text{ and } C \to R$$

$$\therefore \quad \Delta_2 = (-1)^n \Delta_1$$

$$\therefore \quad \Delta = \Delta_1 + \Delta_2 = \Delta_1 [1+(-1)^n] = 0 \text{ given. Above}$$

is possible only when n is an odd integer.

34. Expansion of $\Delta \Rightarrow x^3 - 3xyz + yz(z+y) = \text{L.H.S.}$

$$\text{R.H.S.} = \frac{1}{z-y}[x^3(z-y) - 3x^2 yz + 3x^2 yz$$

$$+ 3zxy^2 - 3yxz^2 - zy^3 + yz^3]$$

$$= \frac{1}{z-y}[x^3(z-y) - 3xyz(z-y) + yz(z^2 - y^2)]$$

$$= x^3 - 3xyz + yz(z+y) = \text{L.H.S.}$$

35. (a) By expansion

$$\Delta = 2 + 2\sin^2 \alpha \in (2,4) \text{ as } \sin^2 \alpha \in (0,1)$$

(b) Apply $R_3 - \cos\theta R_1 + \sin\theta R_2$ thus making two zeros in R_3, we get

$$\Delta = (1 + \sin\theta - \cos\theta)(\cos^2 \alpha + \sin^2 \alpha)$$

$$\Delta = 1 + \sqrt{2} \sin\left(\theta - \frac{\pi}{4}\right)$$

Now $-1 \le \sin\left(\theta - \frac{\pi}{4}\right) \le 1$ etc.

36. (a) True.

Apply $R_3 - R_2, R_2 - R_1$

$$t_5 - t_3 = t_4 - t_2 = 2d$$

$$D = \begin{vmatrix} t_2 t_3 & t_2 & t_1 \\ t_3(2d) & d & d \\ t_4(2d) & d & d \end{vmatrix}$$

$$= d^2 \begin{vmatrix} t_2 t_3 & t_2 & t_1 \\ 2t_3 & 1 & 1 \\ 2t_4 & 1 & 1 \end{vmatrix} \text{ Apply } R_3 - R_2$$

$$= d^2 \begin{vmatrix} t_2 t_3 & t_2 & t_1 \\ 2t_3 & 1 & 1 \\ 2d & 0 & 0 \end{vmatrix} = d^2 . 2d(t_2 - t_1)$$

$$= 2d^4$$

(b) $t_1 - t_2 = t_2 - t_3 = -d$ ...(1)

Apply $R_1 - R_2$ and $R_2 - R_3$ and using (1) two rows become identical $\therefore \Delta = 0$.

(c) If d be the common difference of A.P. then $a - b = -d, b - c = -d, c - a = 2d$

$$\therefore \quad \Delta = \begin{vmatrix} -2d^2 & -2d^2 & d^2 \\ -2d^2 & d^2 & -2d^2 \\ d^2 & -2d^2 & -2d^2 \end{vmatrix}$$

$$= d^2 \begin{vmatrix} -2 & -2 & 1 \\ -2 & 1 & -2 \\ 1 & -2 & -2 \end{vmatrix}$$

Make two zeros and expand $\therefore \Delta = 27d^2 > 0$.

37. (a) We know that $\dfrac{a}{\sin A} = \dfrac{b}{\sin B} = \dfrac{c}{\sin C} = 2R$

and $\cos A = \dfrac{b^2 + c^2 - a^2}{2bc} = a \dfrac{(b^2 + c^2 - a^2)}{2abc}$

$$\therefore \quad \sin 2A = 2\sin A \cos A$$

$$= 2 . \frac{a}{2R} . \frac{(b^2 + c^2 - a^2)}{2bc}$$

Hence the elements of R_1 in Δ are

$$\frac{a(b^2 + c^2 - a^2)}{2Rbc} \qquad \frac{c}{2R} \qquad \frac{b}{2R}$$

or $\dfrac{1}{2Rbc}\{a(b^2 + c^2 - a^2) \quad bc^2 \quad b^2c\}$

$$\therefore \quad \Delta = \frac{1}{(2R\,bc)\,(2R\,ca)\,(2R\,ab)}$$

$$\begin{vmatrix} a(b^2+c^2-a^2) & bc^2 & b^2c \\ c^2a & b(c^2+a^2-b^2) & a^2c \\ b^2a & ba^2 & c(a^2+b^2-c^2) \end{vmatrix}$$

Take a, b, c common from C_1, C_2 and C_3 respectively

$$\therefore \quad \Delta =$$

$$\frac{1}{8R^3\,abc}\begin{vmatrix} b^2+c^2-a^2 & c^2 & b^2 \\ c^2 & c^2+a^2-b^2 & a^2 \\ b^2 & a^2 & a^2+b^2-c^2 \end{vmatrix}$$

Now apply $R_1 - R_2$ and $R_2 - R_3$ and take $b^2 - a^2$ and $c^2 - b^2$ common from R_1 and R_2.

$$\therefore \quad \Delta = \frac{(b^2-a^2)\,(c^2-b^2)}{8R^3\,abc}\begin{vmatrix} 1 & 1 & 1 \\ 1 & 1 & 1 \\ b^2 & a^2 & a^2+b^2-c^2 \end{vmatrix} = 0$$

as two rows are identical.

(b) Ans. (a).

$R_2 - R_1$ makes new R_2 identical with R_3 and hence $\Delta = 0$

Problem Set (2)

Evaluation of determinant, by row-column operations.

Prove the following :

1. (a)* $\begin{vmatrix} b+c & c+a & a+b \\ a+b & b+c & c+a \\ c+a & a+b & b+c \end{vmatrix} = 2\begin{vmatrix} a & b & c \\ c & a & b \\ b & c & a \end{vmatrix}$

(b). $\begin{vmatrix} 2ab & a^2 & b^2 \\ a^2 & b^2 & 2ab \\ b^2 & 2ab & a^2 \end{vmatrix} = -(a^3+b^3)^2.$

2. (a) $\begin{vmatrix} y+z & z & y \\ z & z+x & x \\ y & x & x+y \end{vmatrix} = 4xyz$

(b) $\begin{vmatrix} y+z & x & x \\ y & z+x & y \\ z & z & x+y \end{vmatrix} = 4xyz$

(Karnatak C.E. 1999)

3. (a) $\begin{vmatrix} \dfrac{a^2+b^2}{c} & c & c \\ a & \dfrac{b^2+c^2}{a} & a \\ b & b & \dfrac{c^2+a^2}{b} \end{vmatrix} = 4abc$

(b) $\begin{vmatrix} a & b & ax+by \\ b & c & bx+cy \\ ax+by & bx+cy & 0 \end{vmatrix}$

$$= (b^2-ac)\,(ax^2+2bxy+cy^2).$$

4. (a) $\begin{vmatrix} a^2 & bc & ac+c^2 \\ a^2+ab & b^2 & ac \\ ab & b^2+bc & c^2 \end{vmatrix} = 4a^2b^2c^2.$

(b)* $\begin{vmatrix} b^2+c^2 & ab & ac \\ ab & c^2+a^2 & bc \\ ca & cb & a^2+b^2 \end{vmatrix}$

$$= \begin{vmatrix} b^2+c^2 & a^2 & a^2 \\ b^2 & c^2+a^2 & b^2 \\ c^2 & c^2 & a^2+b^2 \end{vmatrix} = 4a^2b^2c^2$$

(c) One factor of $\Delta = \begin{vmatrix} a^2+\lambda & ab & ac \\ ab & b^2+\lambda & cb \\ ca & cb & c^2+\lambda \end{vmatrix}$ is

(a) λ^2

(b) $1/\lambda$

(c) $(a^2+\lambda)(b^2+\lambda)(c^2+\lambda)$

(d) none

5. $\begin{vmatrix} a & b & c \\ a-b & b-c & c-a \\ b+c & c+a & a+b \end{vmatrix} = a^3+b^3+c^3-3abc.$

6. (a) $\begin{vmatrix} a-b-c & 2a & 2a \\ 2b & b-c-a & 2b \\ 2c & 2c & c-a-b \end{vmatrix} = (a+b+c)^3.$

(b)* $\begin{vmatrix} a+b+2c & a & b \\ c & b+c+2a & b \\ c & a & c+a+2b \end{vmatrix}$

$$= 2(a+b+c)^3.$$

7. (a) $\begin{vmatrix} 1+a^2-b^2 & 2ab & -2b \\ 2ab & 1-a^2+b^2 & 2a \\ 2b & -2a & 1-a^2-b^2 \end{vmatrix}$

$$= (1+a^2+b^2)^3.$$

(b)* $\begin{vmatrix} a^2 & b^2 & c^2 \\ (a+1)^2 & (b+1)^2 & (c+1)^2 \\ (a-1)^2 & (b-1)^2 & (c-1)^2 \end{vmatrix}$

$$= 4\begin{vmatrix} a^2 & b^2 & c^2 \\ a & b & c \\ 1 & 1 & 1 \end{vmatrix}.$$

8. (a) $\begin{vmatrix} 1+a_1 & a_2 & a_3 & a_4 \\ a_1 & 1+a_2 & a_3 & a_4 \\ a_1 & a_2 & 1+a_3 & a_4 \\ a_1 & a_2 & a_3 & 1+a_4 \end{vmatrix}$

$$= 1+a_1+a_2+a_3+a_4.$$

(b)* $\begin{vmatrix} 1+a & 1 & 1 & 1 \\ 1 & 1+b & 1 & 1 \\ 1 & 1 & 1+c & 1 \\ 1 & 1 & 1 & 1+d \end{vmatrix}$

$= abcd \left(1 + \dfrac{1}{a} + \dfrac{1}{b} + \dfrac{1}{c} + \dfrac{1}{d}\right) = s - r$

if a, b, c, d are the roots of
$$x^4 + px^3 + qx^2 + rx + s = 0.$$

9.* Prove that if $\alpha, \beta, \gamma \neq 0$, then

$\begin{vmatrix} \alpha + a_1 b_1 & a_1 b_2 & a_1 b_3 \\ a_2 b_1 & \beta + a_2 b_2 & a_2 b_3 \\ a_3 b_1 & a_3 b_2 & \gamma + a_3 b_3 \end{vmatrix}$

$= \alpha\beta\gamma \left[1 + \dfrac{a_1 b_1}{\alpha} + \dfrac{a_2 b_2}{\beta} + \dfrac{a_3 b_3}{\gamma}\right]$

10. (a) $\begin{vmatrix} 1+x & 2 & 3 & 4 \\ 1 & 2+x & 3 & 4 \\ 1 & 2 & 3+x & 4 \\ 1 & 2 & 3 & 4+x \end{vmatrix} = x^3 (x+10).$

(b) $\begin{vmatrix} x & a & a & a \\ a & x & a & a \\ a & a & x & a \\ a & a & a & x \end{vmatrix} = (x+3a)(x-a)^3.$

11.* Let $\Delta = \begin{vmatrix} \Sigma a^2 & \Sigma ab & \Sigma ab \\ \Sigma ab & \Sigma a^2 & \Sigma ab \\ \Sigma ab & \Sigma ab & \Sigma a^2 \end{vmatrix}$

Prove that Δ is non-negative and establish the relation between a, b and c if $\Delta = 0$.

12. (a) $\begin{vmatrix} a^2+1 & ab & ac & ad \\ ab & b^2+1 & bc & bd \\ ac & bc & c^2+1 & cd \\ ad & bd & cd & d^2+1 \end{vmatrix}$

$= \begin{vmatrix} a^2+1 & b^2 & c^2 & d^2 \\ a^2 & b^2+1 & c^2 & d^2 \\ a^2 & b^2 & c^2+1 & d^2 \\ a^2 & b^2 & c^2 & d^2+1 \end{vmatrix}$

$= 1 + a^2 + b^2 + c^2 + d^2 .$

(b)* Prove that
$\begin{vmatrix} a^2+x & ab & ac \\ ab & b^2+x & bc \\ ac & bc & c^2+x \end{vmatrix} = x^2 (a^2 + b^2 + c^2 + x)$

13. (a) $\begin{vmatrix} ax & by & cz \\ x^2 & y^2 & z^2 \\ 1 & 1 & 1 \end{vmatrix} = \begin{vmatrix} a & b & c \\ x & y & z \\ yz & zx & xy \end{vmatrix}$

(b) If $\Sigma a^2 = -2$ and

$f(x) = \begin{vmatrix} 1+a^2 x & (1+b^2) x & (1+c^2) x \\ (1+a^2) x & 1+b^2 x & (1+c^2) x \\ (1+a^2) x & (1+b^2) x & 1+c^2 x \end{vmatrix}$

then $f(x)$ is a polynomial of degree

(a) 3   (b) 2
(c) 1   (d) 0   **(AIEEE 2005)**

(c) $\begin{vmatrix} bc & bc' + b'c & b'c' \\ ca & cd' + c'd & c'd' \\ ab & ab' + d'b & d'b' \end{vmatrix}$

$= (bc' - b'c)(cd' - c'd)(ab' - d'b)$

14. Prove that
$\begin{vmatrix} 0 & a^2 & b^2 & c^2 \\ a^2 & 0 & \gamma^2 & \beta^2 \\ b^2 & \gamma^2 & 0 & \alpha^2 \\ c^2 & \beta^2 & \alpha^2 & 0 \end{vmatrix} = \begin{vmatrix} 0 & a\alpha & b\beta & c\gamma \\ a\alpha & 0 & c\gamma & b\beta \\ b\beta & c\gamma & 0 & a\alpha \\ c\gamma & b\beta & a\alpha & 0 \end{vmatrix}$

15. (a)* If $p + q + r = 0$, prove that
$\begin{vmatrix} pa & qb & rc \\ qc & ra & pb \\ rb & pc & qa \end{vmatrix} = pqr \begin{vmatrix} a & b & c \\ c & a & b \\ b & c & a \end{vmatrix}$

(b)* If $a \neq p, b \neq q, c \neq r$ and $\begin{vmatrix} p & b & c \\ a & q & c \\ a & b & r \end{vmatrix} = 0,$

then find the value of $\dfrac{p}{p-a} + \dfrac{q}{q-b} + \dfrac{r}{r-c}$

                               (I.I.T. 1991)

(c) If $\begin{vmatrix} a & b-y & c-z \\ a-x & b & c-z \\ a-x & b-y & c \end{vmatrix} = 0,$ then $\dfrac{a}{x} + \dfrac{b}{y} + \dfrac{c}{z} = \ldots\ldots$

16. (a)* $\begin{vmatrix} x^3 & 3x^2 & 3x & 1 \\ x^2 & x^2+2x & 2x+1 & 1 \\ x & 2x+1 & x+2 & 1 \\ 1 & 3 & 3 & 1 \end{vmatrix} = (x-1)^6$

(b) $\begin{vmatrix} x^2+2x & 2x+1 & 1 \\ 2x+1 & x+2 & 1 \\ 3 & 3 & 1 \end{vmatrix} = (x-1)^3.$

17. $\begin{vmatrix} (x-2)^2 & (x-1)^2 & x^2 \\ (x-1)^2 & x^2 & (x+1)^2 \\ x^2 & (x+1)^2 & (x+2)^2 \end{vmatrix} = -8.$

18. (a)* $\begin{vmatrix} 0 & x & y & z \\ -x & 0 & c & b \\ -y & -c & 0 & a \\ -z & -b & -a & 0 \end{vmatrix} = (ax - by + cz)^2.$

(b) $\Delta = \begin{vmatrix} 5 & 6 & 7 & a \\ 6 & 7 & 8 & b \\ 7 & 8 & 9 & c \\ a & b & c & 0 \end{vmatrix} = (a - 2b + c)^3.$

Is this statement true or false ?

19. $\begin{vmatrix} a & b-c & c+b \\ a+c & b & c-a \\ a-b & b+a & c \end{vmatrix} = (a+b+c)(a^2+b^2+c^2).$

20.* $\begin{vmatrix} (b+c)^2 & a^2 & a^2 \\ b^2 & (c+a)^2 & b^2 \\ c^2 & c^2 & (a+b)^2 \end{vmatrix} = 2\,abc\,(a+b+c)^3.$

21. (a)
$$\begin{vmatrix} (a+b)^2 & ca & cb \\ ca & (b+c)^2 & ab \\ bc & ab & (c+a)^2 \end{vmatrix}$$
$$= 2\,abc\,(a+b+c)^3.$$

(b)* If $2s = a+b+c$, prove that
$$\begin{vmatrix} a^2 & (s-a)^2 & (s-a)^2 \\ (s-b)^2 & b^2 & (s-b)^2 \\ (s-c)^2 & (s-c)^2 & c^2 \end{vmatrix}$$
$$= 2s^3\,(s-a)\,(s-b)\,(s-c).$$

22.* Without expanding at any stage show that
$$\begin{vmatrix} x^2+x & x+1 & x-2 \\ 2x^2+3x-1 & 3x & 3x-3 \\ x^2+2x+3 & 2x-1 & 2x-1 \end{vmatrix} = xA+B$$

where A and B are determinants of order 3 not involving x.

23. (a)* Without expanding as far as possible, evaluate
$$\begin{vmatrix} \sin^2 A & \sin A\cos A & \cos^2 A \\ \sin^2 B & \sin B\cos B & \cos^2 B \\ \sin^2 C & \sin C\cos C & \cos^2 C \end{vmatrix}$$

given that $A+B+C = \pi$

(b)* If A, B, C be the angles of a triangle and
$$\begin{vmatrix} \cos(A-B) & \cos(B-C) & \cos(C-A) \\ \cos(A+B) & \cos(B+C) & \cos(C+A) \\ \sin(A+B) & \sin(B+C) & \sin(C+A) \end{vmatrix} = 0,$$

then prove that the triangle is an isosceles triangle.

24. (a) If A, B, C be the angles of a triangle and
$$\begin{vmatrix} 1 & 1 & 1 \\ 1+\sin A & 1+\sin B & 1+\sin C \\ \sin A+\sin^2 A & \sin B+\sin^2 B & \sin C+\sin^2 C \end{vmatrix} = 0$$

then prove that Δ must be isosceles.

(b)* Prove that
$$\begin{vmatrix} 1 & \cos\alpha & \cos^2\alpha \\ 1 & \cos\beta & \cos^2\beta \\ 1 & \cos\gamma & \cos^2\gamma \end{vmatrix}$$
$$= 2\sin\frac{\alpha+\beta}{2}\sin\frac{\beta+\gamma}{2}\sin\frac{\gamma+\alpha}{2}$$
$$[\sin(\alpha-\beta)+\sin(\beta-\gamma)+\sin(\gamma-\alpha)]$$

25. (a) Prove that
$$\begin{vmatrix} \sin\alpha & \sin 2\alpha & \sin 3\alpha \\ \sin\beta & \sin 2\beta & \sin 3\beta \\ \sin\gamma & \sin 2\gamma & \sin 3\gamma \end{vmatrix}$$
$$= 16\,(\sin\alpha\sin\beta\sin\gamma)\sin\frac{\alpha+\beta}{2}\sin\frac{\beta+\gamma}{2}$$
$$\sin\frac{\gamma+\alpha}{2}[\sin(\alpha-\beta)+\sin(\beta-\gamma)+\sin(\gamma-\alpha)]$$

(b) If $y = \sin px$, prove that
$$\Delta = \begin{vmatrix} y & y_1 & y_2 \\ y_3 & y_4 & y_5 \\ y_6 & y_7 & y_8 \end{vmatrix} = 0.$$

where y_r means r-th differential coefficient of y.

26.* Prove that
$$\begin{vmatrix} -bc & b^2+bc & c^2+bc \\ a^2+ac & -ac & c^2+ac \\ a^2+ab & b^2+ab & -ab \end{vmatrix} = (bc+ca+ab)^3.$$

27. (a) $\Delta = \begin{vmatrix} ax-by-cz & ay+bx & cx+az \\ ay+bx & by-cz-ax & bz+cy \\ cx+az & bz+cy & cz-ax-by \end{vmatrix}$

$$= (x^2+y^2+z^2)(a^2+b^2+c^2)(ax+by+cz).$$

(b) Let a,b,c be real numbers with $a^2+b^2+c^2 = 1$. Show that the equation
$$\begin{vmatrix} ax-by-c & bx+ay & cx+a \\ bx+ay & -ax+by-c & cy+b \\ cx+a & cy+b & -ax-by+c \end{vmatrix} = 0$$

represents a straight line. **(I.I.T. 2001)**

28. (a) The value of n for which the determinant
$$\Delta = \begin{vmatrix} {}^8C_3 & {}^9C_5 & {}^{10}C_7 \\ {}^8C_4 & {}^9C_6 & {}^{10}C_8 \\ {}^9C_n & {}^{10}C_{n+2} & {}^{11}C_{n+4} \end{vmatrix} = 0 \text{ is}$$

(a) 2   (b) 3
(c) 4   (d) none

(b)* Show that
$$\begin{vmatrix} {}^xC_r & {}^xC_{r+1} & {}^xC_{r+2} \\ {}^yC_r & {}^yC_{r+1} & {}^yC_{r+2} \\ {}^zC_r & {}^zC_{r+1} & {}^zC_{r+2} \end{vmatrix}$$
$$= \begin{vmatrix} {}^xC_r & {}^{x+1}C_{r+1} & {}^{x+2}C_{r+2} \\ {}^yC_r & {}^{y+1}C_{r+1} & {}^{y+2}C_{r+2} \\ {}^zC_r & {}^{z+1}C_{r+1} & {}^{z+2}C_{r+2} \end{vmatrix}$$

(c)* If both n and r be greater than 1, find the value of x if
$$\Delta = \begin{vmatrix} {}^xC_r & {}^{n-1}C_r & {}^{n-1}C_{r-1} \\ {}^{x+1}C_r & {}^nC_r & {}^nC_{r-1} \\ {}^{x+2}C_r & {}^{n+1}C_r & {}^{n+1}C_{r-1} \end{vmatrix} = 0$$

(d) If n and p be two +ive integers such that $n \geq p+2$ and
$$D(n,p)\begin{vmatrix} {}^nC_p & {}^nC_{p+1} & {}^nC_{p+2} \\ {}^{n+1}C_p & {}^{n+1}C_{p+1} & {}^{n+1}C_{p+2} \\ {}^{n+2}C_p & {}^{n+1}C_{p+1} & {}^{n+2}C_{p+2} \end{vmatrix}$$

then prove that $D(n,p) = \dfrac{{}^{n+2}C_3}{{}^{p+2}C_3}\,D(n-1,\,p-1)$

29. (a) If $n > 2$ then sum the series

$$\sum_{r=2}^{n} (-2)^r \begin{vmatrix} {}^{n-2}C_{r-2} & {}^{n-2}C_{r-1} & {}^{n-2}C_r \\ -3 & 1 & 1 \\ 2 & -1 & 0 \end{vmatrix}$$

(b) If 3^n is a factor of the determinant

$$\begin{vmatrix} 1 & 1 & 1 \\ {}^nC_1 & {}^{n+3}C_1 & {}^{n+6}C_2 \\ {}^nC_2 & {}^{n+3}C_2 & {}^{n+6}C_2 \end{vmatrix},$$

then the maxium value of n is 3.

30.* Evaluate $\begin{vmatrix} {}^xC_1 & {}^xC_2 & {}^xC_3 \\ {}^yC_1 & {}^yC_2 & {}^yC_3 \\ {}^zC_1 & {}^zC_2 & {}^zC_3 \end{vmatrix}$.

(Roorkee 1990)

31. (a)* Suppose three digit numbers $A28, 3B9$ and $62C$ where A, B and C are integers between 0 and 9, are divisible by a fixed integer k. Prove that determinant $\begin{vmatrix} A & 3 & 6 \\ 8 & 9 & C \\ 2 & B & 2 \end{vmatrix}$ is also divisible by k.

(I.I.T. 1990)

(b) If abc, lmn and pqr be any three-digit numbers each of which is divisible by k, then show that $\Delta = \begin{vmatrix} a & b & c \\ l & m & n \\ p & q & r \end{vmatrix}$ is also divisible by k.

32. (a)* For a fixed positive integer n, if

$$D = \begin{vmatrix} n! & (n+1)! & (n+2)! \\ (n+1)! & (n+2)! & (n+3)! \\ (n+2)! & (n+3)! & (n+4)! \end{vmatrix}$$

then show that $\left[\dfrac{D}{(n!)^3} - 4 \right]$ is divisible by n.

(b) For a fixed +ive integer n, let $D = $

$$\begin{vmatrix} (n-1)! & (n+2)! & (n+3)!/n(n+1) \\ (n+1)! & (n+3)! & (n+5)!/(n+2)(n+3) \\ (n+3)! & (n+5)! & (n+7)!/(n+4)(n+5) \end{vmatrix}$$

then $\dfrac{D}{(n-1)!(n+1)!((n+3)!}$ is equal to

(a) -8 (b) -16
(c) -32 (d) -64 **(I.I.T. 1992)**

33.* Let $a > 0, d > 0$. Find the value of the determinant

$$\begin{vmatrix} \dfrac{1}{a} & \dfrac{1}{a(a+d)} & \dfrac{1}{(a+d)(a+2d)} \\ \dfrac{1}{(a+d)} & \dfrac{1}{(a+d)(a+2d)} & \dfrac{1}{(a+2d)(a+3d)} \\ \dfrac{1}{(a+2d)} & \dfrac{1}{(a+2d)(a+3d)} & \dfrac{1}{(a+3d)(a+4d)} \end{vmatrix}$$

(I.I.T. 1996)

34. If $f(x) = (x-a)(x-b)(x-c)(x-d)$ then prove that

$$\Delta = \begin{vmatrix} a & x & x & x \\ x & b & x & x \\ x & x & c & x \\ x & x & x & d \end{vmatrix} = f(x) - x f'(x).$$

Solutions to Problem Set (118)

1. (a) Operating $C_1 + (C_2 + C_3)$ and taking out 2 from newly formed C_1, we get

$$\Delta = 2 \begin{vmatrix} a+b+c & c+a & a+b \\ a+b+c & b+c & c+a \\ a+b+c & a+b & b+c \end{vmatrix}$$

Apply $C_2 - C_1$ and $C_3 - C_1$

$$\therefore \quad \Delta = 2 \begin{vmatrix} a+b+c & -b & -c \\ a+b+c & -a & -b \\ a+b+c & -c & -a \end{vmatrix},$$

$$= 2(-1)^2 \begin{vmatrix} a+b+c & b & c \\ a+b+c & a & b \\ a+b+c & c & a \end{vmatrix}$$

$$= 2 \begin{vmatrix} a & b & c \\ c & a & b \\ b & c & a \end{vmatrix}, \text{ applied } C_1 - (C_2 + C_3).$$

(b) Apply $C_1 + C_2 + C_3$ and take out $(a+b)^2$ common from C_1

$$\Delta = (a+b)^2 \begin{vmatrix} 1 & a^2 & b^2 \\ 1 & b^2 & 2ab \\ 1 & 2ab & a^2 \end{vmatrix}$$

Apply $R_2 - R_1$, $R_3 - R_1$ to make two zeros.

$$\Delta = (a+b)^2 \begin{vmatrix} 1 & a^2 & b^2 \\ 0 & b^2 - a^2 & b(2a-b) \\ 0 & a(2b-a) & a^2 - b^2 \end{vmatrix}$$

$$= (a+b)^2 \begin{vmatrix} b^2 - a^2 & b(2a-b) \\ a(2b-a) & a^2 - b^2 \end{vmatrix}$$

$$= (a+b)^2 [-(a^2-b^2)^2 - ab(2b-a)(2a-b)]$$

$$= -(a+b)^2 [(a^2-b^2)^2 + 4a^2b^2$$
$$\qquad\qquad - 2ab(a^2+b^2) + a^2b^2]$$

$$= -(a+b)^2 [(a^2+b^2)^2 - 2ab(a^2+b^2) + a^2b^2]$$

$$= -(a+b)^2 [a^2+b^2-ab]^2 = -(a^3+b^3)^2.$$

2. (a) Apply $C_1 - (C_2 + C_3)$ to make one zero we get

$$\Delta = \begin{vmatrix} 0 & z & y \\ -2x & z+x & x \\ -2x & x & x+y \end{vmatrix}$$

Take out $-2x$ from C_1 and then apply $R_2 - R_3$

$$\Delta = -2x \begin{vmatrix} 0 & z & y \\ 0 & z & -y \\ 1 & x & x+y \end{vmatrix}$$

$$= -2x [-zy - zy] = 4xyz.$$

(b) Apply $R_1 - R_2 - R_3$ etc.

3. (a) Multiply R_1, R_2 and R_3 by c, a and b respectively and hence divide Δ by abc

$$\therefore \quad \Delta = \frac{1}{abc} \begin{vmatrix} a^2+b^2 & c^2 & c^2 \\ a^2 & b^2+c^2 & a^2 \\ b^2 & b^2 & c^2+a^2 \end{vmatrix}$$

Now apply $R_1 - (R_2 + R_3)$

$$\therefore \quad \Delta = \frac{1}{abc}\begin{vmatrix} 0 & -2b^2 & -2a^2 \\ a^2 & b^2+c^2 & a^2 \\ b^2 & b^2 & c^2+a^2 \end{vmatrix}$$

$$= -\frac{2}{abc}\begin{vmatrix} 0 & b^2 & a^2 \\ a^2 & b^2+c^2 & a^2 \\ b^2 & b^2 & c^2+a^2 \end{vmatrix}$$

Apply $R_2 - R_1$ and $R_3 - R_1$

$$= -\frac{2}{abc}\begin{vmatrix} 0 & b^2 & a^2 \\ a^2 & c^2 & 0 \\ b^2 & 0 & c^2 \end{vmatrix} \text{ Expand.}$$

$$= -\frac{2}{abc}[0 - b^2(a^2c^2 - 0) + a^2(0 - b^2c^2)]$$

$$= -\frac{2}{abc}(-2a^2b^2c^2) = 4abc.$$

(b) Apply $R_3 - (xR_1 + yR_2)$.

4. (a) Take out a, b, c from C_1, C_2 and C_3 respectively

$$\Delta = abc\begin{vmatrix} a & c & a+c \\ a+b & b & a \\ b & b+c & c \end{vmatrix}$$

Apply $C_1 + (C_2 - C_3)$ and take $2b$ common from C_1

$$\Delta = abc \cdot 2b\begin{vmatrix} 0 & c & a+c \\ 1 & b & a \\ 1 & b+c & c \end{vmatrix}$$

Apply $R_2 - R_3$

$$\Delta = 2ab^2c\begin{vmatrix} 0 & c & a+c \\ 0 & -c & a-c \\ 1 & b+c & c \end{vmatrix}$$

$$= 2ab^2c\{c(a-c) + c(a+c)\}$$

$$= 2ab^2c(2ac) = 4a^2b^2c^2.$$

(b) Multiply C_1 by a, C_2 by b and C_3 by c and hence divide by abc

$$\Delta = \frac{1}{abc}\begin{vmatrix} a(b^2+c^2) & ab^2 & ac^2 \\ a^2b & b(c^2+a^2) & bc^2 \\ a^2c & cb^2 & c(a^2+b^2) \end{vmatrix}$$

Take out a, b, c common from R_1, R_2 and R_3 respectively

$$\therefore \quad \Delta = \frac{abc}{abc}\begin{vmatrix} b^2+c^2 & b^2 & c^2 \\ a^2 & c^2+a^2 & c^2 \\ a^2 & b^2 & a^2+b^2 \end{vmatrix}$$

Apply $C_1 - C_2 - C_3$.

$$\Delta = \begin{vmatrix} 0 & b^2 & c^2 \\ -2c^2 & c^2+a^2 & c^2 \\ -2b^2 & b^2 & a^2+b^2 \end{vmatrix}$$

$$= -2\begin{vmatrix} 0 & b^2 & c^2 \\ c^2 & a^2 & 0 \\ b^2 & 0 & a^2 \end{vmatrix}$$

[Operating $C_2 - C_1$ and $C_3 - C_1$ after taking -2 common from C_1].

$$= -2[0 - b^2(c^2a^2 - 0) + c^2(0 - a^2b^2)] = 4a^2b^2c^2.$$

(c) Ans. (a).

Consider $f(x) = 0$. If $f(a) = 0$, then $(x-a)$ is a factor of $f(x)$. On putting $\lambda = 0$ in Δ, it becomes

$$\begin{vmatrix} a^2 & ba & ca \\ ab & b^2 & cb \\ ac & bc & c^2 \end{vmatrix} = abc\begin{vmatrix} a & a & a \\ b & b & b \\ c & c & c \end{vmatrix} = 0$$

Hence λ or λ^2 both being zero is a factor of Δ. Since λ is not given in choice, we choose λ^2.

5. Applying $R_2 - R_1$, we get

$$\Delta = \begin{vmatrix} a & b & c \\ -b & -c & -a \\ b+c & c+a & a+b \end{vmatrix}.$$

Now apply $R_3 + R_2$

$$\therefore \quad \Delta = -\begin{vmatrix} a & b & c \\ b & c & a \\ c & a & b \end{vmatrix} \text{ Circulant.}$$

$$= -[a(bc - a^2) - b(b^2 - ca) + c(ab - c^2)]$$

$$= -(3abc - a^3 - b^3 - c^3) = a^3 + b^3 + c^3 - 3abc$$

6. (a) Apply $C_1 - C_2$ and $C_2 - C_3$ and take $(a+b+c)$ common from each of C_1 and C_2.

$$\therefore \quad \Delta = (a+b+c)^2\begin{vmatrix} -1 & 0 & 2a \\ 1 & -1 & 2b \\ 0 & 1 & c-a-b \end{vmatrix}$$

Apply $R_1 + R_2 + R_3$

$$= (a+b+c)^2\begin{vmatrix} 0 & 0 & a+b+c \\ 1 & -1 & 2b \\ 0 & 1 & c-a-b \end{vmatrix}$$

Expand with 1st row

$$\Delta = (a+b+c)^3\begin{vmatrix} 1 & -1 \\ 0 & 1 \end{vmatrix} = (a+b+c)^3.$$

(b) Apply $C_1 + C_2 + C_3$ and take out $2(a+b+c)$ from C_1

$$\Delta = 2(a+b+c) \times \begin{vmatrix} 1 & a & b \\ 1 & b+c+2a & b \\ 1 & a & c+a+2b \end{vmatrix}$$

Apply $R_2 - R_1$ and $R_3 - R_1$

$$= 2(a+b+c)\begin{vmatrix} 1 & a & b \\ 0 & b+c+a & 0 \\ 0 & 0 & c+a+b \end{vmatrix}$$

$$= 2(a+b+c)^3$$

Aliter : Operate $R_1 - R_2$ and $R_2 - R_3$ etc.

7. (a) Apply $C_1 - bC_3, C_2 + aC_3$ and take out $1 + a^2 + b^2$ each common from both new C_1 and C_2

$$\therefore \quad \Delta = (1 + a^2 + b^2)^2 \begin{vmatrix} 1 & 0 & -2b \\ 0 & 1 & 2a \\ b & -a & 1 - a^2 - b^2 \end{vmatrix}$$

Again apply $R_3 - b R_1$

$$\therefore \quad \Delta = (1 + a^2 + b^2)^2 \begin{vmatrix} 1 & 0 & -2b \\ 0 & 1 & 2a \\ 0 & -a & 1 - a^2 + b^2 \end{vmatrix}$$

$$= (1 + a^2 + b^2)^2 (1 - a^2 + b^2 + 2a^2)$$

$$= (1 + a^2 + b^2)^3$$

(b) Apply $R_2 - R_3$ and note that

$$(x + y)^2 - (x - y)^2 = 4xy$$

$$\therefore \quad \Delta = 4 \begin{vmatrix} a^2 & b^2 & c^2 \\ a & b & c \\ (a-1)^2 & (b-1)^2 & (c-1)^2 \end{vmatrix}$$

$$= 4 \begin{vmatrix} a^2 & b^2 & c^2 \\ a & b & c \\ 1 & 1 & 1 \end{vmatrix}$$

[Applying $R_3 - (R_1 - 2R_2)$]

8. (a) Apply $C_1 + C_2 + C_3 + C_4$ and take out $1 + a_1 + a_2 + a_3 + a_4$

$$\therefore \quad \Delta = (1 + \Sigma a_1) \times \begin{vmatrix} 1 & a_2 & a_3 & a_4 \\ 1 & 1+a_2 & a_3 & a_4 \\ 1 & a_2 & 1+a_3 & a_4 \\ 1 & a_2 & a_3 & 1+a_4 \end{vmatrix}$$

Apply $R_2 - R_1, R_3 - R_1, R_4 - R_1$

$$\Delta = (1 + \Sigma a_1) \begin{vmatrix} 1 & a_2 & a_3 & a_4 \\ 0 & 1 & 0 & 0 \\ 0 & 0 & 1 & 0 \\ 0 & 0 & 0 & 1 \end{vmatrix}$$

Expand with first column

$$\Delta = (1 + \Sigma a_1) \begin{vmatrix} 1 & 0 & 0 \\ 0 & 1 & 0 \\ 0 & 0 & 1 \end{vmatrix} = 1 + \Sigma a_1.$$

$$= 1 + a_1 + a_2 + a_3 + a_4.$$

(b) Divide C_1, C_2, C_3, C_4 by a, b, c, d respectively and hence multiply Δ by $abcd$

$$\Delta = abcd \begin{vmatrix} \frac{1}{a} + 1 & \frac{1}{b} & \frac{1}{c} & \frac{1}{d} \\ \frac{1}{a} & \frac{1}{b} + 1 & \frac{1}{c} & \frac{1}{d} \\ \frac{1}{a} & \frac{1}{b} & \frac{1}{c} + 1 & \frac{1}{d} \\ \frac{1}{a} & \frac{1}{b} & \frac{1}{c} & \frac{1}{d} + 1 \end{vmatrix}$$

Now apply $C_1 + C_2 + C_3 + C_4$ as in part (a) etc.

$$\therefore \quad \Delta = abcd \left(1 + \frac{1}{a} + \frac{1}{b} + \frac{1}{c} + \frac{1}{d} \right) = abcd + \Sigma abc$$

$$= s_4 - s_3 = s - r.$$

9. Take α, β, γ from R_1, R_2 and R_3

$$\Delta = \alpha\beta\gamma \begin{vmatrix} 1 + \frac{a_1 b_1}{\alpha} & \frac{a_1 b_2}{\alpha} & \frac{a_1 b_3}{\alpha} \\ 0 + \frac{a_2 b_1}{\beta} & 1 + \frac{a_2 b_2}{\beta} & \frac{a_2 b_3}{\beta} \\ 0 + \frac{a_3 b_1}{\gamma} & \frac{a_3 b_2}{\gamma} & 1 + \frac{a_3 b_3}{\gamma} \end{vmatrix}$$

Split into two determinants say $\Delta_1 + \Delta_2$

$$\Delta_1 = 1 . \begin{vmatrix} 1 + \frac{a_2 b_2}{\beta} & \frac{a_2 b_3}{\beta} \\ \frac{a_3 b_2}{\gamma} & 1 + \frac{a_3 b_3}{\gamma} \end{vmatrix}$$

$$= 1 + \frac{a_2 b_2}{\beta} + \frac{a_3 b_3}{\gamma} \qquad \qquad \dots(1)$$

$$\Delta_2 = b_1 \begin{vmatrix} \frac{a_1}{\alpha} & \frac{a_1 b_2}{\alpha} & \frac{a_1 b_3}{\alpha} \\ \frac{a_2}{\beta} & 1 + \frac{a_2 b_2}{\beta} & \frac{a_2 b_3}{\beta} \\ \frac{a_3}{\gamma} & \frac{a_3 b_2}{\gamma} & 1 + \frac{a_3 b_3}{\gamma} \end{vmatrix}$$

Apply $C_2 - b_2 C_1, C_3 - b_3 C_1$

$$\Delta_2 = b_1 \begin{vmatrix} \frac{a_1}{\alpha} & 0 & 0 \\ \frac{a_2}{\beta} & 1 & 0 \\ \frac{a_3}{\gamma} & 0 & 1 \end{vmatrix} = \frac{a_1 b_1}{\alpha}$$

$$\therefore \quad \Delta = \alpha\beta\gamma \left[1 + \frac{a_1 b_1}{\alpha} + \frac{a_2 b_2}{\beta} + \frac{a_3 b_3}{\gamma} \right]$$

10. (a) Apply $C_1 + (C_2 + C_3 + C_4)$ and take out $x + 1 + 2 + 3 + 4$ *i.e.* $x + 10$ common from new C_1; rest as in Q. 8.

(b) Apply $C_1 + (C_2 + C_3 + C_4)$ and take out $x + 3a$ common from new C_1 and rest as in Q. 8.

11. Apply $C_1 + C_2 + C_3$ and $\Sigma a^2 + 2\Sigma ab = (\Sigma a)^2$ be taken out from new C_1

$$\Delta = (\Sigma a)^2 \begin{vmatrix} 1 & \Sigma ab & \Sigma ab \\ 1 & \Sigma a^2 & \Sigma ab \\ 1 & \Sigma ab & \Sigma a^2 \end{vmatrix}$$

Now making two zeros by $R_2 - R_1$ and $R_3 - R_1$

$$\Delta = (\Sigma a)^2 [\Sigma a^2 - \Sigma ab]^2$$

Δ being perfect square of real quantities is always +ive.

$\Delta = 0$ if either $\Sigma a = 0$ or $\Sigma a^2 - \Sigma ab = 0$

i.e. $1/2 [(a-b)^2 + (b-c)^2 + (c-a)^2] = 0$

Above will hold only when $a - b = 0, b - c = 0, c - a = 0$ or $a = b = c$.

12. (a) Multiply C_1, C_2, C_3 dend C_4 by a, b, c and d respectively and hence divide by $abcd$.

$$\therefore \quad \Delta = \frac{1}{abcd}$$

$$\times \begin{vmatrix} a(a^2+1) & ab^2 & ac^2 & ad^2 \\ a^2b & b(b^2+1) & bc^2 & bd^2 \\ a^2c & b^2c & c(c^2+1) & cd^2 \\ a^2d & b^2d & c^2d & d(d^2+1) \end{vmatrix}$$

Now take out a, b, c and d common from $R_1, R_2,$ R_3 and R_4

$$\therefore \quad \Delta = \frac{abcd}{abcd} \begin{vmatrix} a^2+1 & b^2 & c^2 & d^2 \\ a^2 & b^2+1 & c^2 & d^2 \\ a^2 & b^2 & c^2+1 & d^2 \\ a^2 & b^2 & c^2 & d^2+1 \end{vmatrix}$$

Now proceeding exactly as in Q. 8 or 10 by
$C_1 + (C_2 + C_3 + C_4)$, we get
$\Delta = 1 + a^2 + b^2 + c^2 + d^2$.

Note : The above method is important.

(b) Proceed exactly as in part (a).

13. (a) Multiply R_3 by xyz and divide by xyz

$$\Delta = \frac{1}{xyz} \begin{vmatrix} ax & by & cz \\ x^2 & y^2 & z^2 \\ xyz & xyz & xyz \end{vmatrix}$$

Now take out x, y, z form C_1, C_2 and C_3

$$\therefore \quad \Delta = \frac{xyz}{xyz} \begin{vmatrix} a & b & c \\ x & y & z \\ yz & zx & xy \end{vmatrix} = \begin{vmatrix} a & b & c \\ x & y & z \\ yz & zx & xy \end{vmatrix}$$

(b) Ans. (b).
Apply $R_2 - R_1, R_3 - R_1$ and take $(x-1)$ common.

$$\Delta = (x-1)^2 \begin{vmatrix} 1+a^2x & (1+b^2)x & (1+c^2)x \\ 1 & -1 & 0 \\ 0 & 1 & -1 \end{vmatrix}$$

Expand with first row.
$= (x-1)^2 \{(1+a^2x).1 - (1+b^2)x(-1) + (1+c^2)x.1\}$
$= (x-1)^2 \{1 + x(\Sigma a^2 + 2)\}$
$= (x-1)^2 \{1\} = (x-1)^2 \quad \because \Sigma a^2 = -2$

(c) **Hint** : Multiply R_1, R_2, R_3 by a, b, c respectively and divide the det. by abc.

Now operate $R_2 - R_1$ and $R_3 - R_1$. This will give

$$\Delta = \frac{1}{abc} \begin{vmatrix} abc & abc' + ab'c & ab'c' \\ 0 & c(a'b - b'a) & c'(ba' - ab') \\ 0 & b(a'c - c'a) & b'(ca' - ac') \end{vmatrix}$$

$$= (ba' - ab')(a'c - c'a) \begin{vmatrix} c & c' \\ b & b' \end{vmatrix}$$

$= (ba' - ab')(a'c - c'a)(cb' - bc')$
$= (bc' - cb')(c'a - ac')(ab' - ba').$

14. Multiply C_1, C_2, C_3, C_4 of R.H.S. by abc, a, b, c respectively and hence divide by $(abc)^2$.

$$\Delta = \frac{1}{(abc)^2} \begin{vmatrix} 0 & a^2\alpha & b^2\beta & c^2\gamma \\ a^2bc\alpha & 0 & bc\gamma & bc\beta \\ ab^2c\beta & ac\gamma & 0 & ac\alpha \\ abc^2\gamma & ab\beta & ab\alpha & 0 \end{vmatrix}$$

Now multiply R_2, R_3, R_4 by $\beta\gamma, \gamma\alpha, \alpha\beta$ and hence divide by $(\alpha\beta\gamma)^2$

$$\therefore \quad \Delta = \frac{1}{(abc)^2 (\alpha\beta\gamma)^2} \times$$

$$\begin{vmatrix} 0 & a^2\alpha & b^2\beta & c^2\gamma \\ a^2bc\alpha\beta\gamma & 0 & bc\beta\gamma^2 & bc\gamma\beta^2 \\ ab^2c\alpha\beta\gamma & ac\alpha\gamma^2 & 0 & ac\gamma\alpha^2 \\ abc^2\alpha\beta\gamma & ab\alpha\beta^2 & ab\beta\alpha^2 & 0 \end{vmatrix}$$

Now take bc, ca and ab common from R_2, R_3 and R_4 respectively. Also take out $\alpha\beta\gamma, \alpha, \beta, \gamma$ from C_1, C_2, C_3 and C_4 and you get L.H.S. Δ.

15. (a) By expansion
L.H.S. $= pa(qra^2 - p^2bc) - qb(q^2ac - prb^2)$
$\qquad\qquad\qquad + rc(pqc^2 - r^2ab)$
$= pqr(a^3 + b^3 + c^3) - abc(p^3 + q^3 + r^3)$ ...(1)
Now $p + q = r = 0 \quad \therefore p^3 + q^3 + r^3 = 3pqr$
Putting in (1), we get
$\Delta = pqr(a^3 + b^3 + c^3 - 3abc)$
Again R.H.S.
$= pqr[a(a^2 - bc) - b(ca - b^2) + c(c^2 - ab)]$
$= pqr[a^3 + b^3 + c^3 - 3abc] = $ L.H.S.

(b) Applying $R_1 - R_2$ and $R_2 - R_3$, we have kept $p - a, q - b$ and $r - c$ as desired

$$\begin{vmatrix} p-a & -(q-b) & 0 \\ 0 & q-b & -(r-c) \\ a & b & r \end{vmatrix} = 0.$$

Expand w.r.t. C_1.
$\therefore \quad (p-a)\{(q-b)r + b(r-c)\}$
$\qquad\qquad\qquad + a\{(q-b)(r-c)\} = 0$
or $(p-a)(q-b)r + (p-a)(r-c)b$
$\qquad\qquad\qquad + a(q-b)(r-c) = 0$
Dividing throughout by $(p-a)(q-b)(r-c)$ which is justified
since $a \neq p, b \neq q, c \neq r$ is given
$$\frac{r}{r-c} + \frac{b}{q-b} + \frac{a}{p-a} = 0$$
Add $1 + 1$ on both sides to get the desired form
$$\frac{r}{r-c} + \left(\frac{b}{q-b} + 1\right) + \left(\frac{a}{p-a} + 1\right) = 1 + 1$$
or $$\frac{r}{r-c} + \frac{q}{q-b} + \frac{p}{p-a} = 2$$
$$\therefore \quad \Sigma \frac{p}{p-a} = 2$$

(c) Ans. (2). Apply $R_1 - R_2$ and $R_2 - R_3$. **(I.I.T. 1991)**

$$\Delta = \begin{vmatrix} x & -y & 0 \\ 0 & y & -z \\ a-x & b-y & c \end{vmatrix} = 0$$

or $x\{cy + z(b-y)\} + y\{z(a-x)\} = 0$

or $xyc + zxb + yza = 2xyz$

∴ $\dfrac{c}{z} + \dfrac{b}{y} + \dfrac{a}{x} = 2.$

16. (a) Keeping in view that $x^3 - 3x^2 + 3x - 1 = (x-1)^3$, we apply $C_1 - C_2 + C_3 - C_4$.

∴ $\Delta = \begin{vmatrix} (x-1)^3 & 3x^2 & 3x & 1 \\ 0 & x^2 + 2x & 2x+1 & 1 \\ 0 & 2x+1 & x+2 & 1 \\ 0 & 3 & 3 & 1 \end{vmatrix}$

$= (x-1)^3 \begin{vmatrix} x^2+2x & 2x+1 & 1 \\ 2x+1 & x+2 & 1 \\ 3 & 3 & 1 \end{vmatrix}$

Now make two zeros by $R_1 - R_2$ and $R_2 - R_3$

$\Delta = (x-1)^3 \begin{vmatrix} x^2-1 & x-1 & 0 \\ 2(x-1) & x-1 & 0 \\ 3 & 3 & 1 \end{vmatrix}$

$= (x-1)^3 (x-1)^2 \begin{vmatrix} x+1 & 1 \\ 2 & 1 \end{vmatrix}$

$= (x-1)^5 (x+1-2) = (x-1)^6.$

(b) Already done in part (a).

17. Apply $R_1 + R_3 - 2R_2$ and take 2 common from R_1

$\Delta = 2 \begin{vmatrix} 1 & 1 & 1 \\ (x-1)^2 & x^2 & (x+1)^2 \\ x^2 & (x+1)^2 & (x+2)^2 \end{vmatrix}$

Make two zeros by $C_2 - C_1$ and $C_3 - C_1$

$\Delta = 2 \begin{vmatrix} 1 & 0 & 0 \\ (x-1)^2 & 2x-1 & 4x \\ x^2 & 2x+1 & 4x+4 \end{vmatrix}$

$= 2 \times 4 \begin{vmatrix} 2x-1 & x \\ 2x+1 & x+1 \end{vmatrix}$

$= 8 [(2x-1)(x+1) - x(2x+1)]$

$= 8 [2x^2 + x - 1 - 2x^2 - x] = -8.$

18. (a) Keeping in view the answer involving $ax - by + cz$ we multiply C_2, C_3 and C_4 by a, b, c respectively and divide Δ by abc

∴ $\Delta = \dfrac{1}{abc} \begin{vmatrix} 0 & ax & by & cz \\ -x & 0 & bc & bc \\ -y & -ac & 0 & ac \\ -z & -ab & -ab & 0 \end{vmatrix}$

Apply $C_2 - C_3 + C_4$

$\Delta = \dfrac{1}{abc} \begin{vmatrix} 0 & ax-by+cz & by & cz \\ -x & 0 & bc & bc \\ -y & 0 & 0 & ac \\ -z & 0 & -ab & 0 \end{vmatrix}$

Expand with 2nd column hence – ive sign.

∴ $\Delta = \dfrac{-(ax-by+cz)}{abc} \begin{vmatrix} -x & bc & bc \\ -y & 0 & ac \\ -z & -ab & 0 \end{vmatrix}$

Take $-1, b$ and c common from C_1, C_2 and C_3 respectively.

∴ $\Delta = \dfrac{ax-by+cz}{a} \begin{vmatrix} x & c & b \\ y & 0 & a \\ z & -a & 0 \end{vmatrix}$

$= \dfrac{ax-by+cz}{a} [x(0+a^2) - y(0+ab) + z(ac+0)]$

$= (ax-by+cz)^2$

Note : A skew-symmetric Δ of even order is a perfect square but of odd order is zero.

[See Q. 8 P. 415-429]

(b) False. Correct is $(a-2b+c)^2$.

$8 + 6 - 2(7) = 0, 7 + 9 - 2(8) = 0, 5 + 7 - 2(6) = 0$

Above suggests that we should apply $C_1 + C_3 - 2C_2$.

$\Delta = \begin{vmatrix} 0 & 6 & 7 & a \\ 0 & 7 & 8 & b \\ 0 & 8 & 9 & c \\ a+c-2b & b & c & 0 \end{vmatrix}$

$= -(a+c-2b) \begin{vmatrix} 6 & 7 & a \\ 7 & 8 & b \\ 8 & 9 & c \end{vmatrix}$

Again apply $R_1 + R_3 - 2R_2$ and expand

∴ $\Delta = (a+c-2b)^2.$

19. Multiply C_1, C_2 and C_3 by a, b, c respectively and divide by abc

$\Delta = \dfrac{1}{abc} \begin{vmatrix} a^2 & b^2-bc & c^2+cb \\ a^2+ac & b^2 & c^2-ac \\ a^2-ab & a^2+ab & c^2 \end{vmatrix}$

Apply $C_1 + C_2 + C_3$ and take out $a^2 + b^2 + c^2$

$\Delta = \dfrac{a^2+b^2+c^2}{abc} \begin{vmatrix} 1 & b^2-bc & c^2+cb \\ 1 & b^2 & c^2-ac \\ 1 & b^2+ab & c^2 \end{vmatrix}$

Take b and c common from R_2 and R_3

$= \dfrac{a^2+b^2+c^2}{abc} \cdot bc \begin{vmatrix} 1 & b-c & c+b \\ 1 & b & c-a \\ 1 & b+a & c \end{vmatrix}$

Apply $R_2 - R_1$ and $R_3 - R_1$

$\Delta = \dfrac{a^2+b^2+c^2}{a} \begin{vmatrix} 1 & b-c & c+b \\ 0 & c & -a-b \\ 0 & a+c & -b \end{vmatrix}$

$= \dfrac{a^2+b^2+c^2}{a} [-bc + (a+c)(a+b)]$

$= \dfrac{a^2+b^2+c^2}{a} [-bc + a^2 + ac + ab + bc]$

$$= \frac{a^2+b^2+c^2}{a} \cdot a(a+b+c)$$

$$= (a+b+c)(a^2+b^2+c^2).$$

20. Apply $C_2 - C_1$ and $C_3 - C_1$.

$$\therefore \quad \Delta = \begin{vmatrix} (b+c)^2 & a^2-(b+c)^2 & a^2-(b+c)^2 \\ b^2 & (c+a)^2-b^2 & 0 \\ c^2 & 0 & (a+b)^2-c^2 \end{vmatrix}$$

Take out $(a+b+c)$ common from each of C_2 and C_3

$$\therefore \quad \Delta = (a+b+c)^2 \times \begin{vmatrix} (b+c)^2 & a-b-c & a-b-c \\ b^2 & c+a-b & 0 \\ c^2 & 0 & a+b-c \end{vmatrix}$$

Apply $R_1 - (R_2 + R_3)$. Then

$$\Delta = (a+b+c)^2 \begin{vmatrix} 2bc & -2c & -2b \\ b^2 & c+a-b & 0 \\ c^2 & 0 & a+b-c \end{vmatrix}$$

Apply $C_2 + \frac{1}{b} C_1$, $C_3 + \frac{1}{c} C_1$ to make two zeros in R_1

$$\therefore \quad \Delta = (a+b+c)^2 \begin{vmatrix} 2bc & 0 & 0 \\ b^2 & c+a & \frac{b^2}{c} \\ c^2 & \frac{c^2}{b} & a+b \end{vmatrix}$$

$$= 2bc(a+b+c)^2 [(a+c)(a+b) - bc]$$

$$= 2bc(a+b+c)^2 (a^2+ab+ac+bc-bc)$$

$$= 2abc(a+b+c)^3.$$

21. (a) Multiplying R_1, R_2 and R_3 by c, a and b respectively and hence dividing by abc, we get

$$\Delta = \frac{1}{abc} \begin{vmatrix} c(a+b)^2 & c^2a & c^2b \\ a^2c & a(b+c)^2 & a^2b \\ b^2c & b^2a & b(c+a)^2 \end{vmatrix}$$

Now take c, a, b common from C_1, C_2 and C_3 respectively

$$\therefore \quad \Delta = \frac{abc}{abc} \begin{vmatrix} (a+b)^2 & c^2 & c^2 \\ a^2 & (b+c)^2 & a^2 \\ b^2 & b^2 & (c+a)^2 \end{vmatrix}$$

It is of the same form as **Q. 20.**

(b) Let $s-a=A$, $s-b=B$, $s-c=C$.
Then $A+B+C = 3s - (a+b+c) = 3s - 2s = s$
$B+C = 2s - b - c = a$, $C+A = b$, $A+B = c$

$$\therefore \quad \Delta = \begin{vmatrix} (B+C)^2 & A^2 & A^2 \\ B^2 & (C+A)^2 & B^2 \\ C^2 & C^2 & (A+B)^2 \end{vmatrix}$$

It is of the form of **Q. 20.**

$$\therefore \quad \Delta = 2ABC(A+B+C)^3$$

$$= 2(s-a)(s-b)(s-c)s^3.$$

22. Apply $R_2 - (R_1 + R_3)$

$$\Delta = \begin{vmatrix} x^2+x & x+1 & x-2 \\ -4 & 0 & 0 \\ x^2+2x+3 & 2x-1 & 2x-1 \end{vmatrix}$$

Now apply $R_1 + \frac{1}{4} x^2 R_2$, $R_3 + \frac{1}{4} x^2 R_2$

$$\Delta = \begin{vmatrix} x & x+1 & x-2 \\ -4 & 0 & 0 \\ 2x+3 & 2x-1 & 2x-1 \end{vmatrix}$$

Apply $R_3 - 2R_1$

$$\Delta = \begin{vmatrix} x+0 & x+1 & x-2 \\ -4 & 0 & 0 \\ 3 & -3 & 3 \end{vmatrix}$$

$$\Delta = \begin{vmatrix} x & x & x \\ -4 & 0 & 0 \\ 3 & -3 & 3 \end{vmatrix} + \begin{vmatrix} 0 & 1 & -2 \\ -4 & 0 & 0 \\ 3 & -3 & 3 \end{vmatrix}$$

$$= x \begin{vmatrix} 1 & 1 & 1 \\ -4 & 0 & 0 \\ 3 & -3 & 3 \end{vmatrix} + \begin{vmatrix} 0 & 1 & -2 \\ -4 & 0 & 0 \\ 3 & -3 & 3 \end{vmatrix}$$

which is of the form $xA + B$.

23. (a) Apply $C_1 + C_3$ and then multiply C_2 and C_3 by 2 each and divide Δ by 4 and write $2\sin A \cos A = \sin 2A$ and $2\cos^2 A = 1 + \cos 2A$

$$\therefore \quad \Delta = \frac{1}{4} \begin{vmatrix} 1 & \sin 2A & 1+\cos 2A \\ 1 & \sin 2B & 1+\cos 2B \\ 1 & \sin 2C & 1+\cos 2C \end{vmatrix}$$

Split into two determinants one of which will vanish

$$\Delta = \frac{1}{4} \begin{vmatrix} 1 & \sin 2A & \cos 2A \\ 1 & \sin 2B & \cos 2B \\ 1 & \sin 2C & \cos 2C \end{vmatrix}.$$

Expanding we get

$$\Delta = \frac{1}{4}[\sin 2(B-C) + \sin 2(C-A) + \sin 2(A-B)]$$

$$= \frac{1}{4}[\sin 2X + \sin 2Y + \sin 2Z]$$

where $X+Y+Z = 0$

$$\therefore \quad \sin(X+Y) = -\sin Z, \cos(X+Y) = \cos Z$$

$$= \frac{1}{4} \cdot -4\sin X \sin Y \sin Z \text{ as in Q. 1 (i) identities of}$$

Trigonometry

$$= -\sin(A-B)\sin(B-C)\sin(C-A).$$

(b) Expand the determinant w.r.t. Ist row

$$\Delta = \cos(A-B)\{\sin(C+A-B-C) + \ldots + \ldots$$

$$= \cos(A-B)\sin(A-B) + \ldots + \ldots$$

$$= \frac{1}{2}[\sin(2A-2B) + \sin(2B-2C) + \sin(2C-2A)]$$

$$= \frac{1}{2}(-4)\sin(A-B)\sin(B-C)\sin(C-A),$$

as in part (a)

$$= -2\sin(A-B)\sin(B-C)\sin(C-A) = 0$$

$$\Rightarrow \quad \text{either } A=B \text{ or } B=C \text{ or } C=A$$

i.e. if A, B, C be the angles of a triangle then the triangle must be isosceles.

24. (a) Apply $R_2 - R_1$ and then $R_3 - R_2$ (new).

$\Delta = (\sin A - \sin B)(\sin B - \sin C)(\sin C - \sin A) = 0$

Hence Δ is isosceles as in part (b).

(b) $(\cos \alpha - \cos \beta)(\cos \beta - \cos \gamma)(\cos \gamma - \cos \alpha)$

$= -\left(2 \sin \dfrac{(\alpha+\beta)}{2} \sin \dfrac{(\alpha-\beta)}{2}\right)(\quad)(\quad)$

$= 2 \sin \dfrac{\alpha+\beta}{2} \sin \dfrac{\beta+\gamma}{2} \sin \dfrac{\gamma+\alpha}{2}$

$\left[-4 \sin \dfrac{\alpha-\beta}{2} \sin \dfrac{\beta-\gamma}{2} \sin \dfrac{\gamma-\alpha}{2}\right]$

Let $\dfrac{\alpha-\beta}{2} = X$ etc. $X + Y + Z = 0$

and $\sin 2X + \sin 2Y + \sin 2Z$

$= -4 \sin X \sin Y \sin Z$

as proved in **Q. 23 (a) above.**

25. (a) $\Delta = \begin{vmatrix} \sin \alpha & 2 \sin \alpha \cos \alpha & \sin \alpha (4 \cos^2 \alpha - 1) \\ \sin \beta & 2 \sin \beta \cos \beta & \sin \beta (4 \cos^2 \beta - 1) \\ \sin \gamma & 2 \sin \gamma \cos \gamma & \sin \gamma (4 \cos^2 \gamma - 1) \end{vmatrix}$

$\because$ $\sin 3\alpha = 3 \sin \alpha - 4 \sin^3 \alpha$

$= \sin \alpha [3 - 4(1 - \cos^2 \alpha)]$

$= 4 \cos^2 \alpha - 1$

Take $\sin \alpha, \sin \beta, \sin \gamma$ common from R_1, R_2 and R_3.

$\Delta = \sin \alpha \sin \beta \sin \gamma \begin{vmatrix} 1 & 2 \cos \alpha & 4 \cos^2 \alpha - 1 \\ 1 & 2 \cos \beta & 4 \cos^2 \beta - 1 \\ 1 & 2 \cos \gamma & 4 \cos^2 \gamma - 1 \end{vmatrix}$

$= 8 \sin \alpha \sin \beta \sin \gamma \begin{vmatrix} 1 & \cos \alpha & \cos^2 \alpha \\ 1 & \cos \beta & \cos^2 \beta \\ 1 & \cos \gamma & \cos^2 \gamma \end{vmatrix}$

etc. by Q. 24 (b).

(b) $\Delta = \begin{vmatrix} \sin px & p \cos px & -p^2 \sin px \\ -p^3 \cos px & p^4 \sin px & p^5 \cos px \\ -p^6 \sin px & -p^7 \cos px & p^8 \sin px \end{vmatrix}$

$= -p^3 \begin{vmatrix} \sin px & \cos px & \sin px \\ -p^3 \cos px & p^3 \sin px & -p^3 \cos px \\ -p^6 \sin px & -p^6 \cos px & -p^6 \sin px \end{vmatrix}$

$= 0$, since C_1, C_3 are identical.

26. Multiply R_1, R_2, R_3 by a, b, c respectively and then take out a, b, c common from C_1, C_2 and C_3.

$\therefore$ $\Delta = \dfrac{abc}{abc} \begin{vmatrix} -bc & ab+ac & ac+ab \\ ab+bc & -ac & bc+ab \\ ac+bc & bc+ca & -ab \end{vmatrix}$

Now apply $C_3 - C_1$ and $C_2 - C_1$ and take out Σab common from each of C_3 and C_2

$\therefore$ $\Delta = (\Sigma ab)^2 \begin{vmatrix} -bc & 1 & 1 \\ ab+bc & -1 & 0 \\ ac+bc & 0 & -1 \end{vmatrix}$

Now expand with third column

$\therefore$ $\Delta = (\Sigma ab)^2 [1 \cdot (0 + ac + bc) - 1(bc - ab - bc)]$

$= (ab + bc + ca)^3$

27. (a) Operations are suggested by the form of factors required.

Multiply C_1 by x and hence divide by x and then apply

$C_1 + (y C_2 + z C_3)$, we get

$\Delta = \dfrac{1}{x} \begin{vmatrix} a(x^2 + y^2 + z^2) & ay + bx & cx + az \\ b(x^2 + y^2 + z^2) & by - cz - ax & bz + cy \\ c(x^2 + y^2 + z^2) & bz + cy & cz - ax - by \end{vmatrix}$

Take Σx^2 from C_1 and then again multiply R_1 by a and divide Δ by a. Now operate $R_1 + (bR_2 + cR_3)$

$\Delta = \dfrac{1}{ax}(x^2 + y^2 + z^2)$

$\begin{vmatrix} a^2 + b^2 + c^2 & y(a^2 + b^2 + c^2) & z(a^2 + b^2 + c^2) \\ b & by - cz - ax & bz + cy \\ c & bz + cy & cz - ax - by \end{vmatrix}$

$= \dfrac{1}{ax}(x^2 + y^2 + z^2)(a^2 + b^2 + c^2)$

$\times \begin{vmatrix} 1 & y & z \\ b & by - cz - ax & bz + cy \\ c & bz + cy & cz - ax - by \end{vmatrix}$

Now make two zeros by applying $R_2 - bR_1$ and $R_3 - CR_1$

$\therefore$ $\Delta = \begin{vmatrix} 1 & y & z \\ 0 & -(cz + ax) & cy \\ 0 & bz & -(ax + by) \end{vmatrix}$

$= (cz + ax)(ax + by) - bcyz$

$= ax(ax + by + cz)$ $\therefore$ $\Delta = \Sigma x^2 \cdot \Sigma a^2 \cdot \Sigma ax$

(b) Put $z = 1$

$\therefore$ $\Delta = (x^2 + y^2 + 1)(a^2 + b^2 + c^2)$

$(ax + by + c) = 0$

$\Rightarrow$ $ax + by + c = 0$ as $x^2 + y^2 + 1 \neq 0$

and $a^2 + b^2 + c^2 = 1$ given.

Hence $\Delta = 0$ represents the line $ax + by + c = 0$.

28. (a) Ans. (c).

Apply $R_2 + R_1$ then R_2 becomes $^9C_4$ $^{10}C_6$ $^{11}C_8$

$\therefore$ $n = 4, n + 2 = 6, n + 4 = 8$.

(b) **Hint :** First observe that

$^x C_r + {}^x C_{r+1} = {}^{x+1} C_{r+1}$

and $^x C_{r+1} + {}^x C_{r+2} = {}^{x+1} C_{r+2}$.

Now applying $C_3 + C_2$ and $C_2 + C_1$, we get

$$\Delta = \begin{vmatrix} {}^{x}C_r & {}^{x+1}C_{r+1} & {}^{x+1}C_{r+2} \\ {}^{y}C_r & {}^{y+1}C_{r+1} & {}^{y+1}C_{r+2} \\ {}^{z}C_r & {}^{z+1}C_{r+1} & {}^{z+1}C_{r+2} \end{vmatrix}$$

Again applying $C_3 + C_2$, we get

$$\Delta = \begin{vmatrix} {}^{x}C_r & {}^{x+1}C_{r+1} & {}^{x+2}C_{r+2} \\ {}^{y}C_r & {}^{y+1}C_{r+1} & {}^{y+2}C_{r+2} \\ {}^{z}C_r & {}^{z+1}C_{r+1} & {}^{z+2}C_{r+2} \end{vmatrix}$$

by the same rule.

(c) Apply $C_3 + C_2$ and note that
$${}^{n-1}C_{r-1} + {}^{n-1}C_r = {}^{n}C_r$$

$$\therefore \quad \Delta = \begin{vmatrix} {}^{x}C_r & {}^{n-1}C_r & {}^{n}C_r \\ {}^{x+1}C_r & {}^{n}C_r & {}^{n+1}C_r \\ {}^{x+2}C_r & {}^{n+1}C_r & {}^{n+2}C_r \end{vmatrix}$$

Now $\Delta = 0$ if two columns are identical.
Comparing C_1 and C_3 we get $x = n$
Comparing C_1 and C_2 we get $x = n - 1$. **(P. 467)**

(d) We know that $\dfrac{{}^{n}C_r}{{}^{n-1}C_{r-1}} = \dfrac{n}{r}$

$$R_1 = \frac{n}{p}{}^{n-1}C_{p-1}, \ \frac{n}{p+1}{}^{n-r}C_p, \ \frac{n}{p+2}{}^{n-1}C_{p+1}$$

Similarly we can write

$$R_2 = \frac{n+1}{p}{}^{n}C_{p-1}, \ \frac{n+1}{p+1}{}^{n}C_p, \ \frac{n+1}{p+2}{}^{n}C_{p+1}$$

$$R_3 = \frac{n+2}{p}{}^{n+1}C_{p-1}, \ \frac{n+2}{p+1}{}^{n+1}C_p, \ \frac{n+2}{p+2}{}^{n+1}C_{p+1}$$

Taking $n, n+1, n+2$ common from R_1, R_2 and R_3 and $\dfrac{1}{p}, \dfrac{1}{p+1}, \dfrac{1}{p+2}$ common from C_1, C_2 and C_3

$$D(n, p) = \frac{(n+2)(n+1)n}{(p+2)(p+1)p} \cdot D(n-1, p-1)$$

$$= \frac{{}^{n+2}C_3}{{}^{(p+2)}C_3} \cdot D(n-1, p-1)$$

29. (a) Applying $C_1 + C_3 + 2C_2$ thus making two zeros in C_1
Also ${}^{n-2}C_{r-2} + {}^{n-2}C_r + 2 \cdot {}^{n-2}C_{r-1}$

$$= [{}^{n-2}C_{r-2} + {}^{n-2}C_{r-1}] + [{}^{n-2}C_{r-1} + {}^{n-2}C_r]$$

$$= {}^{n-1}C_{r-1} + {}^{n-1}C_r = {}^{n}C_r$$

$$\therefore \quad \Delta = \sum_{r=2}^{n} (-2)^r \, {}^{n}C_r$$

$$= C_2 (-2)^2 + C_3 (-2)^3 + C_4 (-2)^4 + \ldots$$
$$\qquad\qquad\qquad\qquad + C_n (-2)^n$$

$$= (1+x)^n - [C_0 + C_1 x], \text{ where } x = -2$$

$$= (1-2)^n - [1 + n(-2)] = 2n - 1 + (-1)^n.$$

(b) $\quad {}^{n}C_1 = n, \ {}^{n}C_2 = \dfrac{n(n-1)}{2}$

Making two zeros and expanding $\Delta = 27 = 3^3$

If 3^n is to be a factor of Δ, then max. value of n is 3.

30. $\Delta = \begin{vmatrix} X & X(X-1)/1.2 & X(X-1)(X-2)/1.2.3 \\ Y & Y(Y-1)/1.2 & Y(Y-1)(Y-2)/1.2.3 \\ Z & Z(Z-1)/1.2 & Z(Z-1)(Z-2)/1.2.3 \end{vmatrix}$

$$= \frac{XYZ}{2.6} \begin{vmatrix} 1 & (X-1) & (X-1)(X-2) \\ 1 & (Y-1) & (Y-1)(Y-2) \\ 1 & (Z-1) & (Z-1)(Z-2) \end{vmatrix}$$

[Operate $R_2 - R_1$ and $R_3 - R_1$ and expand with C_1]

$$= \frac{XYZ}{12} \begin{vmatrix} 1 & (X-1) & (X-1)(X-2) \\ 0 & (Y-X) & (Y-X)(Y+X-3) \\ 0 & (Z-X) & (Z-X)(Z+X-3) \end{vmatrix}$$

$$= \frac{XYZ}{12} \cdot (Y-X)(Z-X) \begin{vmatrix} 1 & Y+X-3 \\ 1 & Z+X-3 \end{vmatrix}$$

$$= \frac{XYZ}{12} (Y-X)(Z-X)[(Z+X-3) - (Y+X-3)]$$

$$= \frac{XYZ}{12} (Y-X)(Z-X)(Z-Y)$$

$$= \frac{1}{12} XYZ (Y-Z)(Z-X)(X-Y).$$

31. (a) Since $A28$, $3B9$ and $62C$ are divisible by k, we can write

$$A28 = 100A + 20 + 8 = n_1 k \qquad \ldots(1)$$
$$3B9 = 300 + 10B + 9 = n_2 k \qquad \ldots(2)$$
$$62C = 600 + 20 + C = n_3 k \qquad \ldots(3)$$

Now $\Delta = \begin{vmatrix} A & 3 & 6 \\ 8 & 9 & C \\ 2 & B & 2 \end{vmatrix}$

$$= \begin{vmatrix} A & 3 & 6 \\ 100A+20+8 & 300+10B+9 & 600+20+C \\ 2 & B & 2 \end{vmatrix}$$

[By operating $R_2 + (100 R_1 + 10 R_3)$]

$$= \begin{vmatrix} A & 3 & 6 \\ n_1 k & n_2 k & n_3 k \\ 2 & B & 2 \end{vmatrix}, \text{ by (1), (2) and (3)}$$

$$= k \begin{vmatrix} A & 3 & 6 \\ n_1 & n_2 & n_3 \\ 2 & B & 2 \end{vmatrix} = k \text{ (an integer)}.$$

Hence Δ is also divisible by k.

(b) $abc = 100a + 10b + c = n_1 k$ etc.
Apply $C_3 + 10 C_2 + 100 C_1$

$$\Delta = \begin{vmatrix} a & b & n_1 k \\ l & m & n_2 k \\ p & q & n_3 k \end{vmatrix} = k | \ | = k\Delta_1$$

where Δ_1 is a determinant consisting of integers.
$\therefore \ k\Delta_1$ is also an integer. Hence Δ is divisible by k

32. (a) From the given value we have

$$\frac{D}{(n!)^3} = \begin{vmatrix} 1 & (n+1) & \\ (n+1) & (n+2)(n+1) & \\ (n+2)(n+1) & (n+3)(n+2)(n+1) & \end{vmatrix}$$

$$\begin{vmatrix} & & (n+2)(n+1) \\ & & (n+3)(n+2)(n+1) \\ & & (n+4)(n+3)(n+2)(n+1) \end{vmatrix}$$

Take $(n+1)$ and $(n+1)(n+2)$ common from C_2 and C_3.

$$\therefore \quad \Delta = (n+1)\cdot(n+1)(n+2)$$

$$\begin{vmatrix} 1 & 1 & 1 \\ n+1 & n+2 & n+3 \\ (n+2)(n+1) & (n+3)(n+2) & (n+4)(n+3) \end{vmatrix}$$

Apply $C_3 - C_2$ and $C_2 - C_1$

$$\Delta = (n+1)^2(n+2) \begin{vmatrix} 1 & 0 & 0 \\ n+1 & 1 & 1 \\ (n+2)(n+1) & 2(n+2) & 2(n+3) \end{vmatrix}$$

$$= (n+1)^2(n+2)\cdot 2\cdot 1 = (n^2+2n+1)(n+2)\cdot 2$$

$$= 2(n^3+4n^2+5n+2)$$

$$\therefore \quad \frac{D}{(n!)^3} - 4 = 2n(n^2+4n+5).$$

Hence divisible by n.

(b) Ans. (d).

Take $(n-1)!, (n+1)!, (n+3)!$ common from R_1, R_2, R_3 respectively

$$\therefore \quad \frac{D}{(n-1)!(n+1)!((n+3)!}$$

$$= \begin{vmatrix} 1 & (n+1)n & (n+3)(n+2) \\ 1 & (n+3)(n+2) & (n+5)(n+4) \\ 1 & (n+5)(n+4) & (n+7)(n+6) \end{vmatrix}$$

Making two zeros in column I by applying $R_3 - R_2$ and $R_2 - R_1$, we have

$$E = \begin{vmatrix} 1 & (n+1)n & (n+3)(n+2) \\ 0 & 4n+6 & 4n+14 \\ 0 & 4n+14 & 4n+22 \end{vmatrix}$$

or $E = \begin{vmatrix} 4n+6 & 8 \\ 4n+14 & 8 \end{vmatrix}$ by $C_2 - C_1$

$$= 8[4n+6-4n-14] = 8[-8] = -64 \Rightarrow (d)$$

33. Multiplying R_1 by $a(a+d)(a+2d)$ to remove fractions and hence divide Δ by the same.

Similarly clear fractions in R_2 and R_3

If $k = a(a+d)(a+2d)(a+d)(a+2d)(a+3d)$
$$(a+2d)(a+3d)(a+4d)$$

or $k = a(a+d)^2(a+2d)^2(a+3d)^2(a+4d)$

then $\Delta = \dfrac{1}{k} \begin{vmatrix} (a+d)(a+2d) & a+2d & a \\ (a+2d)(a+3d) & a+3d & a+d \\ (a+3d)(a+4d) & a+4d & a+2d \end{vmatrix}$

Apply $C_2 - C_3$ and take $2d$ common from C_2

$$\Delta = \frac{2d}{k} \begin{vmatrix} (a+d)(a+2d) & 1 & a \\ (a+2d)(a+3d) & 1 & a+d \\ (a+3d)(a+4d) & 1 & a+2d \end{vmatrix}$$

Now make two zeros by $R_3 - R_2$ and $R_2 - R_1$

$$\Delta = \frac{2d}{k} \begin{vmatrix} (a+d)(a+2d) & 1 & a \\ (a+2d)\cdot 2d & 0 & d \\ (a+3d)\cdot 2d & 0 & d \end{vmatrix}$$

Expanding with 2nd column after taking $2d$ and d common

$$\Delta = -\frac{2d}{k}\times 2d^2 \begin{vmatrix} a+2d & 1 \\ a+3d & 1 \end{vmatrix} = \frac{4d^4}{k}$$

$$= \frac{4d^4}{a(a+d)^2(a+2d)^2(a+3d)^2(a+4d)}$$

34. $f(x) = (x-a)(x-b)(x-c)(x-d)$

$\log f(x) = \Sigma \log(x-a)$

$\dfrac{1}{f(x)}\cdot f'(x) = \dfrac{1}{x-a} + ...$

Our answer is

$$f(x) - xf'(x) = f(x)\left[1 - x\cdot\frac{f'(x)}{f(x)}\right]$$

$$= f(x)\left[1 - x\left\{\frac{1}{x-a} + ...\right\}\right]$$

$$= ()()()() - x\{()()() + ... + ... + ...\} \quad ...(1)$$

Apply $C_1 - C_2$, $C_2 - C_3$, $C_3 - C_4$

$$\Delta = \begin{vmatrix} -(x-a) & 0 & 0 & x \\ (x-b) & -(x-b) & 0 & x \\ 0 & (x-c) & -(x-c) & x \\ 0 & 0 & (x-d) & d \end{vmatrix}$$

Expand with first row.

$$\Delta = (x-a)\begin{vmatrix} -(x-b) & 0 & x \\ (x-c) & -(x-c) & x \\ 0 & (x-d) & d \end{vmatrix}$$

$$- x\begin{vmatrix} (x-b) & -(x-b) & 0 \\ 0 & (x-c) & -(x-c) \\ 0 & 0 & (x-d) \end{vmatrix}$$

$$= (x-a)\{(x-b)(x-c)d + (x-b)(x-d)x$$
$$+ x(x-c)(x-d)\} - x(x-b)(x-c)(x-d)$$

Now write d as $x - (x-d)$.   **(Note)**

It takes the form of (1) i.e.

$(x-a)(x-b)(x-c)(x-d)$
$$- x\{(x-a)(x-b)(x-c) + ... + ... + ...\}$$

i.e. $\Delta = f(x) - xf'(x)$.

1.* Mutiplication of two determinants of same order.

$\Delta \Delta' = D$ say.

Rule. Take the first row of Δ and multiply it successively with 1st, 2nd and 3rd rows of Δ'. The three expressions thus obtained will be elements of 1st row of D. In a similar manner the elements of 2nd and 3rd rows of D are obtained.

Thus $\begin{vmatrix} a_1 & b_1 & c_1 \\ a_2 & b_2 & c_2 \\ a_3 & b_3 & c_3 \end{vmatrix} \times \begin{vmatrix} \alpha_1 & \beta_1 & \gamma_1 \\ \alpha_2 & \beta_2 & \gamma_2 \\ \alpha_3 & \beta_3 & \gamma_3 \end{vmatrix}$

$$= \begin{vmatrix} R_1R_1' & R_1R_2' & R_1R_3' \\ R_2R_1' & R_2R_2' & R_2R_3' \\ R_3R_1' & R_3R_2' & R_3R_3' \end{vmatrix}$$

$$= \begin{vmatrix} a_1\alpha_1 + b_1\beta_1 + c_1\gamma_1 & a_1\alpha_2 + b_1\beta_2 + c_1\gamma_2 \\ a_2\alpha_1 + b_2\beta_1 + c_2\gamma_1 & a_2\alpha_2 + b_2\beta_2 + c_2\gamma_2 \\ a_3\alpha_1 + b_3\beta_1 + c_3\gamma_1 & a_3\alpha_2 + b_3\beta_2 + c_3\gamma_2 \end{vmatrix}$$

$$\begin{vmatrix} a_1\alpha_3 + b_1\beta_3 + c_1\gamma_3 \\ a_2\alpha_3 + b_2\beta_3 + c_2\gamma_3 \\ a_3\alpha_3 + b_3\beta_3 + c_3\gamma_3 \end{vmatrix}$$

Similarly it could be written with respect to columns as

$$\begin{vmatrix} C_1 C_1' & C_2 C_1' & C_3 C_1' \\ C_1 C_2' & C_2 C_2' & C_3 C_2' \\ C_1 C_3' & C_2 C_3' & C_3 C_3' \end{vmatrix}$$

2.* (a) Cofactors and Minors.

Let $\Delta = \begin{vmatrix} a_1 & a_2 & a_3 \\ b_1 & b_2 & b_3 \\ c_1 & c_2 & c_3 \end{vmatrix}$

Then cofactor of $a_1 = \begin{vmatrix} b_2 & b_3 \\ c_2 & c_3 \end{vmatrix} = A_1$, say,

cofactor of $a_2 = -\begin{vmatrix} b_1 & b_3 \\ c_1 & c_3 \end{vmatrix} = A_2$, say etc.

Thus cofactor of an element of Δ is the determinant obtained by omitting the row and column to which that element belongs with proper sign.

Minor of $a_1 = A_1$, Minor of $a_2 = -A_2$.
Minor of $a_3 = A_3$ etc.

Remark. It is easy to see that

$$\Delta = a_1 A_1 + a_2 A_2 + a_3 A_3$$
$$= b_1 B_1 + b_2 B_2 + b_3 B_3$$
$$= a_1 A_1 + b_1 B_1 + c_1 C_1$$

that is, the value of a determinant is obtained by multiplying the elements of any row (or column) with the corresponding cofactors and adding the resulting products.

Also it can be easily verified that if we multiply the elements of any row (or column) with the corresponding cofactors of any other row (or column) and add them, then the result is zero.

*Theorem. If Δ' is the determinant formed by replacing the elements of a determinant Δ by their corresponding cofactors, then $\Delta' = \Delta^2$.

Proof. It suffices to prove the theorem for a determinant of third order. So let

$$\Delta = \begin{vmatrix} a_1 & a_2 & a_3 \\ b_1 & b_2 & b_3 \\ c_1 & c_2 & c_3 \end{vmatrix}.$$

Then $\Delta' = \begin{vmatrix} A_1 & A_2 & A_3 \\ B_1 & B_2 & B_3 \\ C_1 & C_2 & C_3 \end{vmatrix}$

Then in view of the remark preceding this theorem, we have

$$\Delta \Delta' = \begin{vmatrix} \Delta & 0 & 0 \\ 0 & \Delta & 0 \\ 0 & 0 & \Delta \end{vmatrix} = \Delta^3$$

or $\Delta' = \Delta^2$

(b) Differentiation of a determinant

We know that if X, Y, Z be functions of x then

$$\frac{d}{dx}(XYZ) = X'YZ + XY'Z + XYZ'$$

$$\frac{d}{dx}\begin{vmatrix} R_1 \\ R_2 \\ R_3 \end{vmatrix} = \begin{vmatrix} R_1' \\ R_2 \\ R_3 \end{vmatrix} + \begin{vmatrix} R_1 \\ R_2' \\ R_3 \end{vmatrix} + \begin{vmatrix} R_1 \\ R_2 \\ R_3' \end{vmatrix}$$

where R_1' stands for differentiation of elements of first row.

Similarly we can say

$$\frac{d}{dx}|C_1 \ C_2 \ C_3| = |C_1' \ C_2 \ C_3| + |C_1 \ C_2' \ C_3|$$
$$+ |C_1 \ C_2 \ C_3'|$$

Ex. 1. If $D = \begin{vmatrix} x & x^2 & x^3 \\ 1 & 2x & 3x^2 \\ 0 & 2 & 6x \end{vmatrix}$ then prove that $\frac{d}{dx}(D) = 6x^2$

$$\frac{d}{dx}(D) = \begin{vmatrix} 1 & 2x & 3x^2 \\ 1 & 2x & 3x^2 \\ 0 & 2 & 6x \end{vmatrix} + \begin{vmatrix} x & x^2 & x^3 \\ 0 & 2 & 6x \\ 0 & 2 & 6x \end{vmatrix}$$

$$+ \begin{vmatrix} x & x^2 & x^3 \\ 1 & 2x & 3x^2 \\ 0 & 0 & 6 \end{vmatrix}$$

$$= 0 + 0 + 6(2x^2 - x^2) = 6x^2$$

The first two determinants are zero because of idntical lines R_1, R_2 in Ist and R_2, R_3 in 2nd.

Integration of a determinant.

If $\Delta = \begin{vmatrix} f(x) & g(x) & h(x) \\ a & b & c \\ p & q & r \end{vmatrix}$ where a, b, c, p, q, r are all constants, then

$$\int_a^b \Delta \, dx = \begin{vmatrix} \int_a^b f(x)\,dx & \int_a^b g(x)\,dx & \int_a^b h(x)\,dx \\ a & b & c \\ p & q & r \end{vmatrix}$$

Factors of certain standard determinants. Remember the results.

3* (A) $\begin{vmatrix} 1 & 1 & 1 \\ a & b & c \\ a^2 & b^2 & c^2 \end{vmatrix} = (a-b)(b-c)(c-a)$

(B) $\begin{vmatrix} 1 & 1 & 1 \\ a & b & c \\ a^3 & b^3 & c^3 \end{vmatrix} = (a-b)(b-c)(c-a)(a+b+c)$

(C) $\begin{vmatrix} 1 & 1 & 1 \\ a^2 & b^2 & c^2 \\ a^3 & b^3 & c^3 \end{vmatrix} = (a-b)(b-c)(c-a)(ab+bc+ca)$

For proof see Q. 1, 6 (a), 9 (a), Set 119 P. 439.

Problem Set (3)

Factors of a determinant, Circulant.
$(a-b)(b-c)(c-a)$, $(a-b)(b-c)(c-a)(a+b+c)$, $(a-b)(b-c)(c-a)(ab+bc(ca)$.
Multiplication of determinants and Differentiation of determinants.

1. **(a)** Prove the following :

$$\begin{vmatrix} 1 & a & a^2 \\ 1 & b & b^2 \\ 1 & c & c^2 \end{vmatrix} = \begin{vmatrix} 1 & 1 & 1 \\ a & b & c \\ a^2 & b^2 & c^2 \end{vmatrix}$$

$$= (a-b)(b-c)(c-a)$$ **(Bihar 1999)**

(b) Prove that

$$\begin{vmatrix} \lambda a & \lambda^2 + a^2 & 1 \\ \lambda b & \lambda^2 + b^2 & 1 \\ \lambda c & \lambda^2 + c^2 & 1 \end{vmatrix} = \lambda (a-b)(b-c)(c-a).$$

2.* If $f(x)$ is a polynomial of degree < 3, prove that

$$\begin{vmatrix} 1 & a & f(a)/(x-a) \\ 1 & b & f(b)/(x-b) \\ 1 & c & f(c)/(x-c) \end{vmatrix} \div \begin{vmatrix} 1 & a & a^2 \\ 1 & b & b^2 \\ 1 & c & c^2 \end{vmatrix}$$

$$= \frac{f(x)}{(x-a)(x-b)(x-c)}$$

3. **(a)** $\begin{vmatrix} a & b+c & a^2 \\ b & c+a & b^2 \\ c & a+b & c^2 \end{vmatrix} = -(a+b+c)(a-b)$
$(b-c)(c-a)$

(b) Without expanding at any stage prove that

$$\begin{vmatrix} 1 & a & a^2 \\ 1 & b & b^2 \\ 1 & c & c^2 \end{vmatrix} = \begin{vmatrix} 1 & bc & b+c \\ 1 & ca & c+a \\ 1 & ab & a+b \end{vmatrix}$$

4. **(a)** $\begin{vmatrix} 1 & (m+n-l-p)^2 & (m+n-l-p)^4 \\ 1 & (n+l-m-p)^2 & (n+l-m-p)^4 \\ 1 & (l+m-n-p)^2 & (l+m-n-p)^4 \end{vmatrix}$

$$= 64(l-m)(l-n)(l-p)(m-n)(m-p)(n-p)$$

(b) $\begin{vmatrix} 1 & 1 & 1 \\ b+c & c+a & a+b \\ b^2+c^2 & c^2+a^2 & a^2+b^2 \end{vmatrix} = (b-c)(c-a)(a-b)$

5. $\begin{vmatrix} 1 & bc+ad & b^2c^2+a^2d^2 \\ 1 & ca+bd & c^2a^2+b^2d^2 \\ 1 & ab+cd & a^2b^2+c^2d^2 \end{vmatrix}$

$$= (a-b)(a-c)(a-d)(b-c)(b-d)(c-d).$$

6. **(a)** $\begin{vmatrix} 1 & 1 & 1 \\ a & b & c \\ a^3 & b^3 & c^3 \end{vmatrix} = (a-b)(b-c)(c-a)(a+b+c)$

(b) If a,b,c are different then the determinant

$$\begin{vmatrix} 1 & 1 & 1 \\ (x-a)^2 & (x-b)^2 & (x-c)^2 \\ (x-b)(x-c) & (x-c)(x-a) & (x-a)(x-b) \end{vmatrix}$$

vanishes when $x = \frac{1}{3}(a+b+c)$

7.* Prove that

$$\begin{vmatrix} bc-a^2 & ca-b^2 & ab-c^2 \\ -bc+ca+ab & bc-ca+ab & bc+ca-ab \\ (a+b)(a+c) & (b+c)(b+a) & (c+a)(c+b) \end{vmatrix}$$

$$= 3(a-b)(b-c)(c-a)(a+b+c) \cdot (bc+ca+ab)$$

8. $\begin{vmatrix} -2a & a+b & c+a \\ b+a & -2b & b+c \\ c+a & c+b & -2c \end{vmatrix} = 4(b+c)(c+a).$
$\cdot (a+b)$

9. **(a)*** $\begin{vmatrix} x & y & z \\ x^2 & y^2 & z^2 \\ yz & zx & xy \end{vmatrix} = \begin{vmatrix} 1 & 1 & 1 \\ x^2 & y^2 & z^2 \\ x^3 & y^3 & z^3 \end{vmatrix}$

$$= (x-y)(y-z)(z-x)(xy+yz+zx)$$

(b) Find x, when

$$\begin{vmatrix} x+a & a^2 & a^3 \\ x+b & b^2 & b^3 \\ x+c & c^2 & c^3 \end{vmatrix} = 0$$

(M.N.R 1991)

10. **(a)*** If x, y and z are all different and given that

$$\begin{vmatrix} x & x^2 & 1+x^3 \\ y & y^2 & 1+y^3 \\ z & z^2 & 1+z^3 \end{vmatrix} = 0, \text{ prove } 1+xyz=0$$

(M.N.R. 1993)

(b) If $\begin{vmatrix} x^k & x^{k+2} & x^{k+3} \\ y^k & y^{k+2} & y^{k+3} \\ z^k & z^{k+2} & z^{k+3} \end{vmatrix}$

$$= (x-y)(y-z)(z-x)\left(\frac{1}{x}+\frac{1}{y}+\frac{1}{z}\right), \text{ then } k =$$

(a) – 3   (b) 3
(c) –1   (d) 1

11. **(a)*** If x, y and z are all different given that

$$\begin{vmatrix} x & x^3 & x^4-1 \\ y & y^3 & y^4-1 \\ z & z^3 & z^4-1 \end{vmatrix} = 0, \text{ prove that}$$

$$xyz(xy+yz+zx) = x+y+z.$$

(b)* If x, y, z be non-zero and different quantities such

that $\begin{vmatrix} x & x^3 & x^4-1 \\ y & y^3 & y^4-1 \\ z & z^3 & z^4-1 \end{vmatrix} = 0$ then prove the

following :

(i) $xyz(xy+yz+zx)=x+y+z$

(ii) $2xy^2z=3-x^2z^2$ if x,y,z are in A.P.

(iii) $y^4=1$ if x,y,z are in G.P.

(iv) $x+z=y(3x^2z^2-1)$ if x,y,z are in H.P.

12. If x,y,z be all different and

$$\begin{vmatrix} x^3 & (x+k)^3 & (x-k)^3 \\ y^3 & (y+k)^3 & (y-k)^3 \\ z^3 & (z+k)^3 & (z-k)^3 \end{vmatrix}=0,$$

then prove that $k^2(x+y+z)=3xyz$.

13. If a,b,c are all different and the points $\left(\dfrac{r^3}{r-1},\dfrac{r^2-3}{r-1}\right)$ where $r=a,b,c$ are collinear, then prove

that $3(a+b+c)=ab+bc+ca-abc$

14. (a)* If $x<y<z$ then determine whether

$$\Delta=\begin{vmatrix} 1 & x & x^4 \\ 1 & y & y^4 \\ 1 & z & z^4 \end{vmatrix}\text{ is }+\text{ive or -ive.}$$

(b) If the points $(t_i,2at_i+at_i^3),i=1,2,3$ be collinear and t_1,t_2,t_3 are distinct then prove that $t_1+t_2+t_3=0$

15.* $\begin{vmatrix} x^2 & x^2-(y-z)^2 & yz \\ y^2 & y^2-(z-x)^2 & zx \\ z^2 & z^2-(x-y)^2 & xy \end{vmatrix}$

$=(x-y)(y-z)(z-x)(x+y+z)(x^2+y^2+z^2)$

16.* Prove that

$$\begin{vmatrix} a & b & c \\ b & c & a \\ c & a & b \end{vmatrix}^2=\begin{vmatrix} 2bc-a^2 & c^2 & b^2 \\ c^2 & 2ca-b^2 & a^2 \\ b^2 & a^2 & 2ab-c^2 \end{vmatrix}$$

$=(a^3+b^3+c^3-3abc)^2.$

17. (a) Let a,b,c be positive and not all equal. Show that the value of the determinant $\begin{vmatrix} a & b & c \\ b & c & a \\ c & a & b \end{vmatrix}$ is negative.

(b) If a,b,c are the roots of $x^3+px^2+q=0$, then prove that $\begin{vmatrix} a & b & c \\ b & c & a \\ c & a & b \end{vmatrix}=p^3.$

18. (a) If $\begin{vmatrix} x & y & z \\ y & z & x \\ z & x & y \end{vmatrix}$

$=-(x+y+z)(x+yk+zk^2)(x+yk^2+zk)$

then show that $k=\omega$, where ω is a complex cube root of unity.

(b) If $a=\cos\theta+i\sin\theta,b=\cos2\theta-i\sin2\theta,$

$c=\cos3\theta+i\sin3\theta$ and if $\begin{vmatrix} a & b & c \\ b & c & a \\ c & a & b \end{vmatrix}=0$ then $\theta=2n\pi,n\in N.$

19. If $\begin{vmatrix} x & 1 & 5 \\ 1 & 5 & x \\ 5 & x & 1 \end{vmatrix}=\begin{vmatrix} x & 2 & 4 \\ 2 & 4 & x \\ 4 & x & 2 \end{vmatrix}=\begin{vmatrix} x & -1 & 7 \\ -1 & 7 & x \\ 7 & x & -1 \end{vmatrix}=0$ then

$x=$

(a) 6

(b) -6

(c) 0

(d) none of these

20.* Express $\Delta=\begin{vmatrix} (a-x)^2 & (a-y)^2 & (a-z)^2 \\ (b-x)^2 & (b-y)^2 & (b-z)^2 \\ (c-x)^2 & (c-y)^2 & (c-z)^2 \end{vmatrix}$

or $\begin{vmatrix} (1+ax)^2 & (1+ay)^2 & (1+az)^2 \\ (1+bx)^2 & (1+by)^2 & (1+bz)^2 \\ (1+cx)^2 & (1+cy)^2 & (1+cz)^2 \end{vmatrix}$

as the product of two determinants and evaluate it.

Solve for x (Q. 21 to Q. 24) :

21. $\begin{vmatrix} a & a & x \\ x & x & x \\ b & x & b \end{vmatrix}=0$

22. (a) $\begin{vmatrix} 15-2x & 11 & 10 \\ 11-3x & 17 & 16 \\ 7-x & 14 & 13 \end{vmatrix}=0$

(b) $\begin{vmatrix} x-2 & 2x-3 & 3x-4 \\ x-4 & 2x-9 & 3x-16 \\ x-8 & 2x-27 & 3x-64 \end{vmatrix}=0$

23. (a)* $\begin{vmatrix} 4x & 6x+2 & 8x+1 \\ 6x+2 & 9x+3 & 12x \\ 8x+1 & 12x & 16x+2 \end{vmatrix}=0$

(b) $\begin{vmatrix} 3x-8 & 3 & 3 \\ 3 & 3x-8 & 3 \\ 3 & 3 & 3x-8 \end{vmatrix}=0$

24. (a) $\begin{vmatrix} x+2 & 2x+3 & 3x+4 \\ 2x+3 & 3x+4 & 4x+5 \\ 3x+5 & 5x+8 & 10x+17 \end{vmatrix}=0$

(b) $\begin{vmatrix} x+2 & x+6 & x-1 \\ x+6 & x-1 & x+2 \\ x-1 & x+2 & x+6 \end{vmatrix}=0$

25. (a) Show that $x=2$ is a root of

$$\begin{vmatrix} x & -6 & -1 \\ 2 & -3x & x-3 \\ -3 & 2x & x+2 \end{vmatrix}=0$$

and solve it completely.

(b) If $\begin{vmatrix} 1 & 3 & 9 \\ 1 & x & x^2 \\ 4 & 6 & 9 \end{vmatrix}=0$, then

(a) $x=3$

(b) $x=3$ or $x=6$

(c) $x = 3$ or $3/2$ (d) None of these

(c) Show that $x = -9$ is a root of
$$\begin{vmatrix} x & 3 & 7 \\ 2 & x & 2 \\ 7 & 6 & x \end{vmatrix} = 0,$$

other two roots are .... and .... **(M.N.R. 1992)**

26.* Given $a + b + c = 0$, solve
$$\begin{vmatrix} a-x & c & b \\ c & b-x & a \\ b & a & c-x \end{vmatrix} = 0$$

27. If $\begin{vmatrix} x^2-a^2 & x^2-b^2 & x^2-c^2 \\ (x-a)^3 & (x-b)^3 & (x-c)^3 \\ (x+a)^3 & (x+b)^3 & (x+c)^3 \end{vmatrix} = 0,$

and a, b, c are all distinct, then prove that $x = 0$,
$$\pm \sqrt{\frac{1}{3}(\Sigma\, ab)}.$$

28.* If $\Delta = \begin{vmatrix} \sin x & \sin(x+\delta x) & \sin(x+2\delta x) \\ \sin(x+2\delta x) & \sin x & \sin(x+\delta x) \\ \sin(x+\delta x) & \sin(x+2\delta x) & \sin x \end{vmatrix}$

then prove that $\underset{\delta x \to 0}{\text{Lt}}\ \dfrac{\Delta}{(\delta x)^2} = 9 \sin x \cos^2 x$.

29. (a) If $(b-c)^2 \neq (a-b)(c-a)$, solve for x
$$\begin{vmatrix} a+x & b+x & c+x \\ b+x & c+x & a+x \\ c+x & a+x & b+x \end{vmatrix} = 0$$

(b) If $a \neq b \neq c$, one value of x which satisfies the
equation $\begin{vmatrix} 0 & x-a & x-b \\ x+a & 0 & x-c \\ x+b & x+c & 0 \end{vmatrix} = 0$ is given by

(i) $x = a$ (ii) $x = b$

(iii) $x = c$ (iv) $x = 0$

30. The vertices of a triangle are the points $[p(p+1), p+1]$, $[(p+1)(p+2), p+2]$ and $[(p+2)(p+3), p+3]$. Prove that the area is independent of p.

31. The vertices of three triangles are given as under :
$\Delta_1 : (0,0), (a \tan\theta, b \cot\theta), (a \sin\theta, b \cos\theta)$
$\Delta_2 : (a,b), (a \sec^2\theta, b \operatorname{cosec}^2\theta),$
$$(a + a \sin^2\theta, b + b \cos^2\theta)$$
$\Delta_3 : (0,0), (a \tan\theta, -b \cot\theta), (a \sin\theta, b \cos\theta)$
If $\Delta_1, \Delta_2, \Delta_3$ represent the areas of the triangles then find the value of θ so that these areas may be in G.P.

32.* If (a_r, b_r), $r = 1, 2, 3$ be the vertices of a triangle, then prove that
$$\begin{vmatrix} a_2-a_3 & b_2-b_3 & a_1(a_2-a_3) + b_1(b_2-b_3) \\ a_3-a_1 & b_3-b_1 & a_2(a_3-a_1) + b_2(b_3-b_1) \\ a_1-a_2 & b_1-b_2 & a_3(a_1-a_2) + b_3(b_1-b_2) \end{vmatrix} = 0$$
and hence prove that the altitudes of a triangle are concurrent.

33. If α and β are the roots of the equation $x^2 - px + q = 0$, then evaluate

$$\begin{vmatrix} 1 & \cos(\beta-\alpha) & \cos\alpha \\ \cos(\alpha-\beta) & 1 & \cos\beta \\ \cos\alpha & \cos\beta & 1 \end{vmatrix}$$

34. If a, b, c, d are in A.P. and
$$f(x) = \begin{vmatrix} x+a & x+b & x+a-c \\ x+b & x+c & x-1 \\ x+c & x+d & x-b+d \end{vmatrix}$$
such that $\int_0^2 f(x)\, dx = -4$, then prove that common difference of A.P. is ± 1.

35.* The value of θ lying between $\theta = 0$ and $\pi/2$ and satisfying the equation
$$\begin{vmatrix} 1+\sin^2\theta & \cos^2\theta & 4\sin 4\theta \\ \sin^2\theta & 1+\cos^2\theta & 4\sin 4\theta \\ \sin^2\theta & \cos^2\theta & 1+4\sin 4\theta \end{vmatrix} = 0 \text{ are}$$

(a) $7\pi/24$ (b) $5\pi/24$
(c) $11\pi/24$ (d) $\pi/24$ **(M.N.R. 1992)**

36. (a)* The parameter, on which the value of the determinant
$$\begin{vmatrix} 1 & a & a^2 \\ \cos(p-d)x & \cos px & \cos(p+d)x \\ \sin(p-d)x & \sin px & \sin(p+d)x \end{vmatrix}$$
does not depend upon is
(a) a (b) p
(c) d (d) x **(I.I.T. Re-ex. 1997)**

(b) If $\Delta = \begin{vmatrix} 1 & a & a^2 \\ \cos(n-1)x & \cos nx & \cos(n+1)x \\ \sin(n-1)x & \sin nx & \sin(n+1)x \end{vmatrix}$,

then Δ is independent of x or a or n or none.

(c) Solve for x the equation
$$\begin{vmatrix} a^2 & a & 1 \\ \sin(n+1)x & \sin nx & \sin(n-1)x \\ \cos(n+1)x & \cos nx & \cos(n-1)x \end{vmatrix} = 0$$

(Roorkee 2001)

37.* Show that the value of the determinant
$$\begin{vmatrix} \cos(\theta+\alpha) & \cos(\theta+\beta) & \cos(\theta+\gamma) \\ \sin(\theta+\alpha) & \sin(\theta+\beta) & \sin(\theta+\gamma) \\ \sin(\beta-\gamma) & \sin(\gamma-\alpha) & \sin(\alpha-\beta) \end{vmatrix}$$
is independent of θ.

38. (a) The determinant
$$\begin{vmatrix} \cos(\theta+\varphi) & -\sin(\theta+\varphi) & \cos 2\varphi \\ \sin\theta & \cos\theta & \sin\varphi \\ -\cos\theta & \sin\theta & \cos\varphi \end{vmatrix} \text{ is}$$
independent of θ or φ or both.

(b)* If
$$\Delta = \begin{vmatrix} a^2+(b^2+c^2)\cos\theta & ab(1-\cos\theta) & ac(1-\cos\theta) \\ ba(1-\cos\theta) & b^2+(c^2+a^2)\cos\theta & bc(1-\cos\theta) \\ ca(1-\cos\theta) & cb(1-\cos\theta) & c^2+(a^2+b^2)\cos\theta \end{vmatrix}$$

where $a^2 + b^2 + c^2 = 1$, then find whether Δ is dependent on a, b, c or θ.

Differentiation of a Determinant.

39.* If $f_r(x)$, $g_r(x)$, $h_r(x)$, $r = 1, 2, 3$ are polynomials in x such that

$$f_r(a) = g_r(a) = h_r(a), r = 1, 2, 3.$$

and $F(x) = \begin{vmatrix} f_1(x) & f_2(x) & f_3(x) \\ g_1(x) & g_2(x) & g_3(x) \\ h_1(x) & h_2(x) & h_3(x) \end{vmatrix}$,

then F' at $x = a$ is ....

40. (a) If u, v, w be functions of x and if suffixes denote differentiation w.r.t. x, prove that

$$\frac{d}{dx}\begin{vmatrix} u_1 & v_1 & w_1 \\ u_2 & v_2 & w_2 \\ u_3 & v_3 & w_3 \end{vmatrix} = \begin{vmatrix} u_1 & v_1 & w_1 \\ u_2 & v_2 & w_2 \\ u_4 & v_4 & w_4 \end{vmatrix}$$

(b) If $F(x), G(x)$ and $H(x)$ are three polynomials of degree 2, then show that

$$\phi(x) = \begin{vmatrix} F(x) & G(x) & H(x) \\ F'(x) & G'(x) & H'(x) \\ F''(x) & G''(x) & H''(x) \end{vmatrix}$$

is a polynomial of degree zero.

(c) If $f(x) = \begin{vmatrix} \cos(x+\alpha) & \cos(x+\beta) & \cos(x+\gamma) \\ \sin(x+\alpha) & \sin(x+\beta) & \sin(x+\gamma) \\ \sin(\beta-\gamma) & \sin(\gamma-\alpha) & \sin(\alpha-\beta) \end{vmatrix}$,

then $f(\theta) - 2f(\phi) + f(\psi)$ is ...

41. (a)* If f, g and h are differentiable functions of x and

$$\Delta = \begin{vmatrix} f & g & h \\ (xf)' & (xg)' & (xh)' \\ (x^2 f)'' & (x^2 g)'' & (x^2 h)'' \end{vmatrix}$$

prove that

$$\Delta' = \begin{vmatrix} f & g & h \\ f' & g' & h' \\ (x^3 f'')' & (x^3 g'')' & (x^3 h'')' \end{vmatrix}$$

(Roorkee 1991)

(b) If $\Delta(x) = \begin{vmatrix} e^{x^2} & \log(1+x) \\ \tan x & \sin x \end{vmatrix}$, then $\underset{x \to 0}{\text{Lt}} \dfrac{\Delta(x)}{x} =$

(a) -1 (b) 0
(c) 1 (d) none

42. (a) $f(x) = \begin{vmatrix} \cos(x+x^2) & \sin(x+x^2) & -\cos(x+x^2) \\ \sin(x-x^2) & \cos(x-x^2) & \sin(x-x^2) \\ \sin 2x & 0 & \sin 2x^2 \end{vmatrix}$

$f'(0) =$

(a) 4   (b) 2
(c) 3   (d) 0

(b)* Let $f(x) = \begin{vmatrix} x^3 & \sin x & \cos x \\ 6 & -1 & 0 \\ p & p^2 & p^3 \end{vmatrix}$,

where p is a constant. Then $\dfrac{d^3}{dx^3}[f(x)]$ at $x = 0$ is

(a) p (b) $p + p^2$
(c) $p + p^3$ (d) independent of p

(I.I.T. 1997)

(c) If $\Delta = \begin{vmatrix} x^2 - 5x + 3 & 2x - 5 & 3 \\ 3x^2 + x + 4 & 6x + 1 & 9 \\ 7x^2 - 6x + 9 & 14x - 6 & 21 \end{vmatrix}$

$= ax^3 + bx^2 + cx + d$ then $\Delta' =$

(a) 6   (b) 5
(c) 4   (d) 0

(d) If $f(x) = \begin{vmatrix} x + a^2 & x^4 + 1 & 3 \\ x + b^2 & 2x^4 + 2 & 3 \\ x + c^2 & 3x^4 + 7 & 3 \end{vmatrix}$

where $x \neq 0$ and $f'(x) = 0$, then a^2, b^2, c^2 are in :

(a) A.P.   (b) G.P.
(c) H.P.   (d) none

43. (a)* If $f(x) = \begin{vmatrix} x^n & \sin x & \cos x \\ n! & \sin \dfrac{n\pi}{2} & \cos \dfrac{n\pi}{2} \\ p & p^2 & p^3 \end{vmatrix}$,

then $\dfrac{d^n}{dx^n}(f(x))$ at $x = 0$ is

(a) 0   (b) p
(c) p^3 (d) independent of p.

(b) If $f(x) = \begin{vmatrix} 1 + x^2 \cos x & 2 - \sin^2 x \\ 1 - x^2 \cos x & 2 + \sin^2 x \end{vmatrix}$, find $f'(x)$.

44. (a)* If

$$f(x) = \begin{vmatrix} (1+x)^{a_1 b_1} & (1+x)^{a_1 b_2} & (1+x)^{a_1 b_3} \\ (1+x)^{a_2 b_1} & (1+x)^{a_2 b_2} & (1+x)^{a_2 b_3} \\ (1+x)^{a_3 b_1} & (1+x)^{a_3 b_2} & (1+x)^{a_3 b_3} \end{vmatrix},$$

then prove that coefficient of x in $f(x) = 0$.

(b) If $f(x) = \begin{vmatrix} x^2 + x & 2x - 1 & x + 3 \\ 3x + 1 & 2 + x^2 & x^3 - 3 \\ x - 3 & x^2 + 4 & 2x \end{vmatrix}$

$= a_0 x^7 + a_1 x^6 + a_2 x^5 + \ldots + a_6 x + a_7$

then prove that $(a_6, a_7) = (75, 21)$.

45.* Let α be a repeated root of quadratic equation $f(x) = 0$ and $A(x)$, $B(x)$, $C(x)$ be polynomials of degree 3, 4 and 5 respectively, then show that

$$\begin{vmatrix} A(x) & B(x) & C(x) \\ A(\alpha) & B(\alpha) & C(\alpha) \\ A'(\alpha) & B'(\alpha) & C'(\alpha) \end{vmatrix}$$

is divisible by $f(x)$, where dash denotes the derivative.

46. (a) If $\Delta = \begin{vmatrix} \cos(\theta+\alpha) & \cos(\theta+\beta) & \cos(\theta+\gamma) \\ \sin(\theta+\alpha) & \sin(\theta+\beta) & \sin(\theta+\gamma) \\ p + \theta\sin\alpha & q + \theta\sin\beta & r + \theta\sin\gamma \end{vmatrix}$,

then prove that Δ is independent of θ.

(b)* If $\Delta = \begin{vmatrix} \cos(\theta+\alpha) & \cos(\theta+\beta) & \cos(\theta+\gamma) \\ \sin(\theta+\alpha) & \sin(\theta+\beta) & \sin(\theta+\gamma) \\ \sin(\beta-\gamma) & \sin(\gamma-\alpha) & \sin(\alpha-\beta) \end{vmatrix}$,

then prove that Δ is independent of θ.

Multiplication of Determinants.

47. (a) Prove that
$$\begin{vmatrix} a_1\alpha_1+b_1\beta_1 & a_1\alpha_2+b_1\beta_2 & a_1\alpha_3+b_1\beta_3 \\ a_2\alpha_1+b_2\beta_1 & a_2\alpha_2+b_2\beta_2 & a_2\alpha_3+b_2\beta_3 \\ a_3\alpha_1+b_3\beta_1 & a_3\alpha_2+b_3\beta_2 & a_3\alpha_3+b_3\beta_3 \end{vmatrix} = 0.$$

(b) If z is a complex number and all a_i's and b_i's are real numbers, then
$$\Delta = \begin{vmatrix} a_1 z+b_1\bar{z} & a_2 z+b_2\bar{z} & a_3 z+b_3\bar{z} \\ b_1 z+a_1\bar{z} & b_2 z+a_2\bar{z} & b_3 z+a_3\bar{z} \\ b_1 z+a_1 & b_2 z+a_2 & b_3 z+a_3 \end{vmatrix} =$$

(a) $(a_1 a_2 a_3 + b_1 b_2 b_3)^2 |z|^2$

(b) 0

(c) $(a_1 a_2 a_3 - b_1 b_2 b_3)^2 |z|^2$

(d) none

48. (a)* For all values of A, B, C and P, Q, R show that
$$\begin{vmatrix} \cos(A-P) & \cos(A-Q) & \cos(A-R) \\ \cos(B-P) & \cos(B-Q) & \cos(B-R) \\ \cos(C-P) & \cos(C-Q) & \cos(C-R) \end{vmatrix} = 0$$

(I.I.T. 1994)

(b)* If A, B, C are real numbers, then prove without expansion that $\Delta = 0$ where
$$\Delta = \begin{vmatrix} 1 & \cos(B-A) & \cos(C-A) \\ \cos(A-B) & 1 & \cos(C-B) \\ \cos(A-C) & \cos(B-C) & 1 \end{vmatrix}.$$

49.* Evaluate
$$\begin{vmatrix} 2 & a+b+c+d & ab+cd \\ a+b+c+d & 2(a+b)(c+d) & ab(c+d)+cd(a+b) \\ ab+cd & ab(c+d)+cd(a+b) & 2abcd \end{vmatrix}$$

50. If a, b, c be the sides of a triangle ABC, opposite to the angles A, B, C respectively, then evaluate
$$\Delta = \begin{vmatrix} a^2 & b\sin A & c\sin A \\ b\sin A & 1 & \cos(B-C) \\ c\sin A & \cos(B-C) & 1 \end{vmatrix}$$

51. If $ax^2+2hxy+by^2+2gx+2fy+c$
$$\equiv (lx+my+n)(l'x+m'y+n'),$$
then prove $\begin{vmatrix} a & h & g \\ h & b & f \\ g & f & c \end{vmatrix} = 0.$

52. If $\Delta = \begin{vmatrix} py+qz & rz-px & qx+ry \\ bp+cq & -ap+cr & aq+br \\ mp+nq & nr-lp & lq+mr \end{vmatrix}$ then $\Delta = \ldots$

53.* If $\alpha_1\gamma_1+\alpha_2\gamma_2+\alpha_3\gamma_3 = \beta_1\gamma_1+\beta_2\gamma_2+\beta_3\gamma_3 = 0$
$\gamma_1^2+\gamma_2^2+\gamma_3^2 = 1$ and $\alpha_1\beta_1+\alpha_2\beta_2+\alpha_3\beta_3$

$= \dfrac{\sqrt{3}}{2}\sqrt{(\alpha_1^2+\alpha_2^2+\alpha_3^2)(\beta_1^2+\beta_2^2+\beta_3^2)}$,

then show that
$$\begin{vmatrix} \alpha_1 & \alpha_2 & \alpha_3 \\ \beta_1 & \beta_2 & \beta_3 \\ \gamma_1 & \gamma_2 & \gamma_3 \end{vmatrix}^2 = \frac{1}{4}(\alpha_1^2+\alpha_2^2+\alpha_3^2)$$
$$\cdot (\beta_1^2+\beta_2^2+\beta_3^2)$$

54. (a) Evaluate $\Delta = \begin{vmatrix} l_1 & m_1 & n_1 \\ l_2 & m_2 & n_2 \\ l_3 & m_3 & n_3 \end{vmatrix}$

under the conditions that

$l_1^2+m_1^2+n_1^2 = 1, \Sigma\, l_2^2 = 1, \Sigma\, l_3^2 = 1,$

$l_1 l_2+m_1 m_2+n_1 n_2 = 0, \Sigma\, l_2 l_3 = 0, \Sigma l_3 l_1 = 0$

(b) If $ax_1^2+by_1^2+cz_1^2 = \Sigma\, ax_2^2 = \Sigma\, ax_3^2 = d$ and

$ax_2 x_3+by_2 y_3+cz_2 z_3 = \Sigma\, ax_3 x_1 = \Sigma\, ax_1 x_2 = f$

then show that
$$\begin{vmatrix} x_1 & y_1 & z_1 \\ x_2 & y_2 & z_2 \\ x_3 & y_3 & z_3 \end{vmatrix} = (d-f)\left\{\frac{d+2f}{abc}\right\}^{1/2}.$$

55.* If $a_1, a_2, a_3; b_1, b_2, b_3$ all $\in R$ such that product of any member of first set with any member of the other set is not equal to 1, then evaluate the determinant
$$\begin{vmatrix} \dfrac{1-a_1^3 b_1^3}{1-a_1 b_1} & (a_1, b_2) & (a_1, b_3) \\ (a_2, b_1) & (a_2, b_2) & (a_2, b_3) \\ (a_3, b_1) & (a_3, b_2) & (a_3, b_3) \end{vmatrix}$$

where $(a_i, b_j) = \dfrac{1-a_i^3 b_j^3}{1-a_i b_j}$.

56. Show that $\begin{vmatrix} a+ib & c+id \\ -c+id & a-ib \end{vmatrix}\begin{vmatrix} -\alpha-i\beta & \gamma-i\delta \\ -\gamma-i\delta & -\alpha+\beta i \end{vmatrix}$

can be expressed in the form
$$\begin{vmatrix} A-iB & C-iD \\ -C-iD & A+iB \end{vmatrix}$$

Hence show that the product of two sums, each of four squares, can be expressed as the sum of four squares.

57. (a) If α, β be the roots of the equation $ax^2+bx+c = 0$ and $s_n = \alpha^n+\beta^n$, evaluate
$$\begin{vmatrix} 3 & 1+s_1 & 1+s_2 \\ 1+s_1 & 1+s_2 & 1+s_3 \\ 1+s_2 & 1+s_3 & 1+s_4 \end{vmatrix}.$$

(b) By squaring the determinant
$$\begin{vmatrix} 1 & 1 & 1 & 1 \\ \alpha & \beta & \gamma & \delta \\ \alpha^2 & \beta^2 & \gamma^2 & \delta^2 \\ \alpha^3 & \beta^3 & \gamma^3 & \delta^3 \end{vmatrix},$$

show that
$$\begin{vmatrix} s_0 & s_1 & s_2 & s_3 \\ s_1 & s_2 & s_3 & s_4 \\ s_2 & s_3 & s_4 & s_5 \\ s_3 & s_4 & s_5 & s_6 \end{vmatrix}$$

$$= [(\alpha - \beta)(\alpha - \gamma)(\alpha - \delta)(\beta - \gamma)(\beta - \delta)(\gamma - \delta)]^2$$

where $s_r = \alpha^r + \beta^r + \gamma^r + \delta^r$.

58. (a)* Prove $\begin{vmatrix} yz - x^2 & zx - y^2 & xy - z^2 \\ zx - y^2 & xy - z^2 & yz - x^2 \\ xy - z^2 & yz - x^2 & zx - y^2 \end{vmatrix}$

$$= \begin{vmatrix} r^2 & u^2 & u^2 \\ u^2 & r^2 & u^2 \\ u^2 & u^2 & r^2 \end{vmatrix}$$

where $r^2 = x^2 + y^2 + z^2$ and $u^2 = yz + zx + xy$.

(b) Prove that
$$\begin{vmatrix} a^2 + \lambda^2 & ab + c\lambda & ca - b\lambda \\ ab - c\lambda & b^2 + \lambda^2 & bc + a\lambda \\ ca + b\lambda & bc - a\lambda & c^2 + \lambda^2 \end{vmatrix} \times \begin{vmatrix} \lambda & c & -b \\ -c & \lambda & a \\ b & -a & \lambda \end{vmatrix}$$

$$= \lambda^3 (\lambda^2 + a^2 + b^2 + c^2)^3.$$

59. Show that :
$$\begin{vmatrix} a^2 + x^2 & ab - cx & ac + bx \\ ab + cx & b^2 + x^2 & bc + ax \\ ac - bx & bc - ax & c^2 + x^2 \end{vmatrix} = \begin{vmatrix} x & c & -b \\ -c & x & a \\ b & -a & x \end{vmatrix}^2$$

60. * Use the determinant (circulant) $\begin{vmatrix} a & b & c \\ b & c & a \\ c & a & b \end{vmatrix}$ to prove

that the product of two expressions of the type $(a^3 + b^3 + c^3 - 3abc)$ is of the same type.

61. Prove that the area of the triangle enclosed by the lines $a_1 x + b_1 y + c_1 = 0$, $a_2 x + b_2 y + c_2 = 0$, $a_3 x + b_3 y + c_3 = 0$ is

$$\frac{1}{2} \begin{vmatrix} a_1 & b_1 & c_1 \\ a_2 & b_2 & c_2 \\ a_3 & b_3 & c_3 \end{vmatrix}^2 \div (a_1 b_2 - a_2 b_1)(a_2 b_3 - a_3 b_2) (a_3 b_1 - a_1 b_3)$$

62. (a)* Let

$$f(x) = \begin{vmatrix} \sec x & \cos x & \sec^2 x + \cot x . \csc x \\ \cos^2 x & \cos^2 x & \csc^2 x \\ 1 & \cos^2 x & \cos^2 x \end{vmatrix}$$

then $\int_0^{\pi/2} f(x) \, dx = -\left(\frac{\pi}{4} + \frac{8}{15} \right)$

(b) Evaluate

$$\Delta = \begin{vmatrix} 4 \sin^2 \theta & 1 & 1 \\ (\sin \theta - 1)^2 & (\sin \theta + 2)^2 & (\sin \theta - 1)^2 \\ (\sin \theta + 1)^2 & (\sin \theta + 1)^2 & \sin^2 \theta \end{vmatrix}$$

Hence show that $\int_{-\pi/2}^{\pi/2} \Delta \, d\theta = -4\pi$.

63. (a) If $A_n = \int_0^{\pi/2} \frac{1 - \cos 2nx}{1 - \cos 2x} \, dx$, then evaluate

$$\Delta = \begin{vmatrix} \pi/2 & A_2 & A_3 \\ A_4 & A_5 & A_6 \\ A_7 & A_8 & A_9 \end{vmatrix}.$$

(b) If $f(\theta) = \begin{vmatrix} \sec^2 \theta & 1 & 1 \\ \cos^2 \theta & \cos^2 \theta & \csc^2 \theta \\ 1 & \cos^2 \theta & \cot^2 \theta \end{vmatrix}$

then $\int_0^{\pi/4} f(\theta) \, d\theta = \frac{3\pi + 8}{32}$.

Solutions to Problem Set (3)

1. (a) Changing rows into columns and columns into rows, we get the two forms.

Applying $R_2 - R_1$ and $R_3 - R_1$ thus making two zeros we get

$$\begin{vmatrix} 1 & a & a^2 \\ 0 & b - a & b^2 - a^2 \\ 0 & c - a & c^2 - a^2 \end{vmatrix}$$

$$= (b - a)(c - a) \begin{vmatrix} 1 & b + a \\ 1 & c + a \end{vmatrix}$$

$$= (b - a)(c - a)(c + a - b - a)$$

$$= (b - a)(c - a)(c - b)$$

$$= (a - b)(b - c)(c - a).$$

(b) $\Delta = \Delta_1 + \Delta_2$

$$= \lambda \times \lambda^2 \begin{vmatrix} a & 1 & 1 \\ b & 1 & 1 \\ c & 1 & 1 \end{vmatrix} + \lambda \begin{vmatrix} a & a^2 & 1 \\ b & b^2 & 1 \\ c & c^2 & 1 \end{vmatrix}$$

$$= 0 + \lambda (a - b)(b - c)(c - a), \text{ as in part (a)}.$$

2. L.H.S. on expanding with third column is

$$\left[\frac{f(a)}{(x - a)} (c - b) - \frac{f(b)}{(x - b)} (c - a) + \frac{f(c)}{(x - c)} (b - a) \right] \div \Delta_1$$

or $\left[\Sigma - \frac{f(a)}{(x - a)} \right] \div (b - c)\ (a - b)(b - c)(c - a)$

or $\Sigma \frac{-f(a)}{(x - a)(a - b)(c - a)} = \Sigma \frac{f(a)}{(a - b)(a - c)(x - a)}$

R.H.S. will also be the same if we split it into partial fractions by the method of suppression by putting $x = a, b, c$ successively. Also R.H.S. is a proper fraction as degree of N^r is < 3, the degree of D^r.

3. (a) Apply $C_2 + C_1$ and take $a + b + c$ common from C_2 etc.

(b) Applying $C_3 - (a + b + c) C_1$ on R.H.S.,

$$\therefore \quad \Delta = \begin{vmatrix} 1 & bc & -a \\ 1 & ca & -b \\ 1 & ab & -c \end{vmatrix}$$

Now multiply R_1, R_2 and R_3 by a, b, c respectively and divide Δ by abc

$$\therefore \quad \Delta = -\frac{1}{abc} \begin{vmatrix} a & abc & a^2 \\ b & abc & b^2 \\ c & abc & c^2 \end{vmatrix}$$

$$= -\frac{abc}{abc} \begin{vmatrix} a & 1 & a^2 \\ b & 1 & b^2 \\ c & 1 & c^2 \end{vmatrix}$$

$$= \begin{vmatrix} 1 & a & a^2 \\ 1 & b & b^2 \\ 1 & c & c^2 \end{vmatrix} = \text{L.H.S.}$$

We have interchanged C_1 and C_3 and hence changed the sign.

4. (a) **Hint :** Put $(m+n-l-p)^2 = A$ etc.

   (b) Apply $C_3 - C_2, C_2 - C_1$ and take out $b-c$ and $a-b$ common and then expand.

5. Subtract R_1 from R_2 and R_3, and expand.

   Alternative : Put $bc + ad = x$

   $\therefore \quad b^2 c^2 + a^2 d^2 = x^2 - 2abcd.$

   Split into two and $\Delta = (x-y)(y-z)(z-x) + 0$

   where $x - y = (a-b)(d-c)$ etc.

6. (a) Applying $C_2 - C_1, C_3 - C_1$ as in Q. (1) thus making two zeros

   $$\Delta = (b-a)(c-a) \begin{vmatrix} 1 & 1 \\ b^2 + a^2 + ab & c^2 + a^2 + ca \end{vmatrix}$$

   $$= (b-a)(c-a)[(c^2 + a^2 + ca) - (b^2 + a^2 + ab)]$$

   $$= (b-a)(c-a)[(c^2 - b^2) + a(c-b)]$$

   $$= (b-a)(c-a)(c-b)(c+b+a)$$

   $$= (a-b)(b-c)(c-a)(a+b+c).$$

   (b) Put $x - a = A, x - b = B, x - c = C$

   $$\Delta = \begin{vmatrix} 1 & 1 & 1 \\ A^2 & B^2 & C^2 \\ BC & CA & AB \end{vmatrix} = \frac{1}{ABC} \begin{vmatrix} A & B & C \\ A^3 & B^3 & C^3 \\ ABC & ABC & ABC \end{vmatrix}$$

   $$= \begin{vmatrix} 1 & 1 & 1 \\ A & B & C \\ A^3 & B^3 & C^3 \end{vmatrix}$$

   $$= (A-B)(B-C)(C-A)(A+B+C) \text{ by (a)}$$

   $$= (a-b)(b-c)(c-a)(3x - a - b - c) = 0$$

   Since a, b, c are different $\therefore x = \frac{1}{3}(a+b+c).$

7. We rewrite the given determinant as

   $$\begin{vmatrix} bc - a^2 & ca - b^2 & ab - c^2 \\ \Sigma ab - 2bc & \Sigma ab - 2ca & \Sigma ab - 2ab \\ \Sigma ab + a^2 & \Sigma ab + b^2 & \Sigma ab + c^2 \end{vmatrix}$$

   Apply $R_1 - R_2 + R_3$, we get

   $$\Delta = 3 \begin{vmatrix} bc & ca & ab \\ -2bc + \Sigma ab & -2ca + \Sigma ab & -2ab + \Sigma ab \\ a^2 + \Sigma ab & b^2 + \Sigma ab & c^2 + \Sigma ab \end{vmatrix}$$

Apply $R_3 - R_2$ and $R_2 + 2R_1$

$$\Delta = 3\Sigma ab \begin{vmatrix} bc & ca & ab \\ 1 & 1 & 1 \\ a^2 + 2bc & b^2 + 2ca & c^2 + 2ab \end{vmatrix} = \Delta_1 + \Delta_2$$

$$\therefore \quad \Delta = 3\Sigma ab \begin{vmatrix} bc & ca & ab \\ 1 & 1 & 1 \\ a^2 & b^2 & c^2 \end{vmatrix} + 0$$

Multiply C_1, C_2, C_3 by a, b, c respectively and divide by abc

$$= \frac{3\Sigma ab}{abc} \begin{vmatrix} abc & abc & abc \\ a & a & b \\ a^3 & b^3 & c^3 \end{vmatrix}$$

$$= 3\Sigma ab \begin{vmatrix} 1 & 1 & 1 \\ a & b & c \\ a^3 & b^3 & c^3 \end{vmatrix}$$

$$= 3\Sigma ab (a-b)(b-c)(c-a)(a+b+c) \text{ by Q. 6 (a)}$$

8. Putting $b + c = 0$ or $b = -c$, we have

   $$\Delta = \begin{vmatrix} -2a & a-c & a+c \\ a-c & 2c & 0 \\ c+a & 0 & -2c \end{vmatrix}$$

   Apply $c_1 + c_3$ and $c_2 - c_3$

   $$\Delta = \begin{vmatrix} c-a & -2c & a+c \\ -(c-a) & 2c & 0 \\ -(c-a) & 2c & -2c \end{vmatrix}$$

   $$= (-2c)(c-a) \begin{vmatrix} 1 & 1 & a+c \\ -1 & -1 & 0 \\ -1 & -1 & -2c \end{vmatrix} = 0$$

   $\therefore b + c$ is a factor. Similarly $(c+a)$ and $(a+b)$ are also its factors

   The Δ being a cubic there will be only three factors. If there be any other factor it will be constant.

   $\therefore \quad \Delta = \lambda (a+b)(b+c)(c+a)$

   For λ, we give numerical values $a = 0, b = 1, c = 2$

   $$\therefore \quad \begin{vmatrix} 0 & 1 & 2 \\ 1 & -2 & 3 \\ 2 & 3 & -4 \end{vmatrix} = \lambda (1)(3)(2)$$

   or $24 = 6\lambda$ or $\lambda = 4$

   $\therefore \quad \Delta = 4(b+c)(c+a)(a+b)$

9. (a) Multiplying C_1, C_2 and C_3 by x, y and z and hence dividing by xyz we get

   $$\Delta = \frac{1}{xyz} \begin{vmatrix} x^2 & y^2 & z^2 \\ x^3 & y^3 & z^3 \\ xyz & xyz & xyz \end{vmatrix}$$

   $$= \frac{xyz}{xyz} \begin{vmatrix} x^2 & y^2 & z^2 \\ x^3 & y^3 & z^3 \\ 1 & 1 & 1 \end{vmatrix} .$$

   Now cross R_3 over two rows and hence $(-1)^2$ i.e. $+1$

$$\therefore \quad \Delta = \begin{vmatrix} 1 & 1 & 1 \\ x^2 & y^2 & z^2 \\ x^3 & y^3 & z^3 \end{vmatrix}$$

Apply $C_2 - C_1$ and $C_3 - C_1$ thus making two zeros.

$$\therefore \quad \Delta = \begin{vmatrix} 1 & 0 & 0 \\ x^2 & y^2 - x^2 & z^2 - x^2 \\ x^3 & y^3 - x^3 & z^3 - x^3 \end{vmatrix}$$

$$= (y-x)(z-x) \begin{vmatrix} y+x & z+x \\ y^2 + xy + x^2 & z^2 + xz + x^2 \end{vmatrix}$$

Apply $C_2 - C_1$.

$\Delta = (y-x)(z-x)$
$$\begin{vmatrix} y+x & z-y \\ y^2 + xy + x^2 & z^2 - y^2 + x(z-y) \end{vmatrix}$$

$$= (y-x)(z-x)(z-y) \begin{vmatrix} y+x & 1 \\ y^2 + xy + x^2 & z+y+x \end{vmatrix}$$

$= (x-y)(y-z)(z-x)[(x+y)^2 + z(x+y)$
$\qquad\qquad\qquad\qquad\qquad - y^2 - xy - x^2]$

$= (x-y)(y-z)(z-x)[xy + yz + zx].$

(b) Split into two determinants and take x common from 1st and abc from 2nd.

$\therefore \quad \Delta = x\Delta_1 + abc\,\Delta_2 = 0.$

Now refer **Q.1 and 9, P. 439-445** for Δ_2 and Δ_1

$x(a-b)(b-c)(c-a)(ab+bc+ca)$
$\qquad\qquad + abc(a-b)(b-c)(c-a) = 0$

$\therefore \quad x = -abc/(ab+bc+ca)$

10. (a) Splitting into two determinants, we get

$$0 = \begin{vmatrix} 1 & x & x^2 \\ 1 & y & y^2 \\ 1 & z & z^2 \end{vmatrix} + xyz \begin{vmatrix} 1 & x & x^2 \\ 1 & y & y^2 \\ 1 & z & z^2 \end{vmatrix}$$

$$= (1 + xyz)[(x-y)(y-z)(z-x)] \text{ by Q. 1.}$$

Since x, y, z are all different

$\therefore \quad x - y \neq 0,\ y - z \neq 0,\ z - x \neq 0$

$\therefore \quad 1 + xyz = 0.$

(b) Ans. (c).

$$\Delta = x^k . y^k . z^k \begin{vmatrix} 1 & x^2 & x^3 \\ 1 & y^2 & y^3 \\ 1 & z^2 & z^3 \end{vmatrix}$$

$$= x^k y^k z^k (x-y)(y-z)(z-x)(xy+yz+zx)$$

$\qquad\qquad\qquad\qquad\qquad \text{**by Q. 9 P 439**}$

$$= x^{k+1} y^{k+1} z^{k+1}$$

$$(x-y)(y-z)(z-x)\left(\frac{1}{x} + \frac{1}{y} + \frac{1}{z}\right)$$

$\therefore \quad k+1 = 0 \Rightarrow k = -1$

11. (a) Proceed as above and use the result of Q. 6 (a) and Q. 9.

(b) (i) For the first part see **part (a) above** of deteriminants

$\qquad x\,y\,z\,(xy + yz + zx) = x + y + z \qquad \dots(1)$

(ii) $2y = x + z$, putting in (1)

$\qquad xyz\{y(x+z) + zx\} = 2y + y$

or $\quad xyz\{2y^2 - xz\} = 3y$ Divide by y

$\therefore \quad 2y^2 xz = 3 - x^2 z^2$

(iii) $y^2 = xz$ Putting in (1),

$\qquad yy^2(xy + yz + y^2) = x + y + z$

$\qquad y^4(x + y + z) = x + y + z \quad \therefore \quad y^4 = 1.$

(iv) $y = \dfrac{2xz}{x+z}$, putting in (1) etc.

$\qquad xyz[2xz + xz] = x + z + y$

or $\quad y.3x^2 z^2 - y = x + z$ etc.

12. Apply $C_2 - C_3$ and take 2 common

$$\Delta = 2\begin{vmatrix} x^3 & 3x^2 k + k^3 & (x-k)^3 \\ y^3 & 3y^2 k + k^3 & (y-k)^3 \\ z^3 & 3z^2 k + k^3 & (z-k)^3 \end{vmatrix} = 0$$

Apply $C_3 - C_1 + C_2$ and take $3k^2$ common.

$$\Delta = 2 \times 3k^2 \begin{vmatrix} x^3 & 3x^2 k + k^3 & x \\ y^3 & 3y^2 k + k^3 & y \\ z^3 & 3z^2 k + k^3 & z \end{vmatrix} = 0$$

Cancel $6k^2$ and split into two determinants.

$$\Delta = 3k\begin{vmatrix} x^3 & x^2 & x \\ y^3 & y^2 & y \\ z^3 & z^2 & z \end{vmatrix} + k^3 \begin{vmatrix} x^3 & 1 & x \\ y^3 & 1 & y \\ z^3 & 1 & z \end{vmatrix} = 0$$

$$3xyz\begin{vmatrix} x^2 & x & 1 \\ y^2 & y & 1 \\ z^2 & z & 1 \end{vmatrix} + k^2 \begin{vmatrix} 1 & x & x^3 \\ 1 & y & y^3 \\ 1 & z & z^3 \end{vmatrix} = 0$$

or $\quad -3xyz\begin{vmatrix} 1 & x & x^2 \\ 1 & y & y^2 \\ 1 & z & z^2 \end{vmatrix} + k^2 \begin{vmatrix} 1 & x & x^3 \\ 1 & y & y^3 \\ 1 & z & z^3 \end{vmatrix} = 0$

Now use the results of Q. 1 and Q. 6 done above

or $\quad 3xyz(x-y)(y-z)(z-x)$
$\qquad\qquad = k^2(x-y)(y-z)(z-x)(x+y+z)$

Since x, y, z are all different

$\therefore \quad 3xyz = k^2(x+y+z).$

13. If the points are collinear then $\Delta = 0$

$\therefore \quad \begin{vmatrix} \dfrac{a^3}{a-1} & \dfrac{a^2 - 3}{a-1} & 1 \\ \cdots & & \end{vmatrix} = 0$

or $\quad \begin{vmatrix} a^3 & a^2 - 3 & a-1 \\ \cdots & & \end{vmatrix} = 0$

$$\begin{vmatrix} a^3 & a^2 & a-1 \\ \cdots\cdots\cdots\cdots \\ \end{vmatrix} + \begin{vmatrix} a^3 & -3 & a-1 \\ \cdots\cdots\cdots\cdots \\ \end{vmatrix} = 0$$

Split each into two determinants.

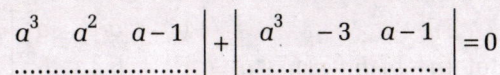

$$\begin{vmatrix} a^3 & a^2 & a \\ \cdots\cdots\cdots \\ \end{vmatrix} - \begin{vmatrix} a^3 & a^2 & 1 \\ \cdots\cdots\cdots \\ \end{vmatrix} + \begin{vmatrix} a^3 & -3 & a \\ \cdots\cdots\cdots \\ \end{vmatrix} + 0 = 0$$

$$abc\begin{vmatrix} a^2 & a & 1 \\ b^2 & b & 1 \\ c^2 & c & 1 \end{vmatrix} - \begin{vmatrix} a^3 & a^2 & 1 \\ b^3 & b^2 & 1 \\ c^3 & c^2 & 1 \end{vmatrix} + 3\begin{vmatrix} a^3 & a & 1 \\ b^3 & b & 1 \\ c^3 & c & 1 \end{vmatrix} = 0$$

Now refer **Q. 6, 9 (P. 439-445)** for factors of above determinants

$(a-b)(b-c)(c-a)[abc-(ab+bc+ca)$
$$+3(a+b+c)]=0$$

Since a,b,c are all different, we have from above

$3(a+b+c)=(ab+bc+ca)-abc$

14. (a) Making two zeros by $R_2 - R_1$ and $R_3 - R_1$ and expanding

$$\Delta = (y-x)(z-x)\begin{vmatrix} 1 & y^3 + y^2x + yx^2 + x^3 \\ 1 & z^3 + z^2x + zx^2 + x^3 \end{vmatrix}$$

$$= (y-x)(z-x)(z-y)(x^2 + y^2 + z^2$$
$$+ xy + yz + zx)$$

$$= \frac{1}{2}(x-y)(y-z)(z-x)[(x+y)^2 + (y+z)^2$$
$$+ (z+x)^2]$$

$$= \frac{1}{2}(-)(-)(+)(+) = +\text{ive as } x < y < z$$

(b) As above in 13 we have $\Delta = 0$ for collinear

$$\therefore \quad \Delta = \begin{vmatrix} t_1 & 2at_1 + at_1^3 & 1 \\ t_2 & 2at_2 + at_2^3 & 1 \\ t_3 & 2at_3 + at_3^3 & 1 \end{vmatrix} = 0$$

Apply $C_2 - 2aC_1$ and take a common.

$$\therefore \quad \Delta = a(t_1 - t_2)(t_2 - t_3)(t_3 - t_1)$$
$$(t_1 + t_2 + t_3) = 0 \quad \text{by 6.}$$

$\Rightarrow t_1 + t_2 + t_3 = 0$ as t_1, t_2 and t_3 are all different.

15. Split into two determinants first of which vanishes as C_1 and C_2 are identical.

$$\therefore \quad \Delta = 0 - \begin{vmatrix} x^2 & (y^2 + z^2) - 2yz & yz \\ y^2 & (z^2 + x^2) - 2zx & zx \\ z^2 & (x^2 + y^2) - 2xy & xy \end{vmatrix}$$

Again split into two determinants the second of which vanishes because C_2 and C_3 will be identical

$$\therefore \quad \Delta = -\begin{vmatrix} x^2 & y^2 + z^2 & yz \\ y^2 & z^2 + x^2 & zx \\ z^2 & x^2 + y^2 & xy \end{vmatrix}$$

Apply $C_2 + C_1$ **(Note).**
We have not applied $C_1 + C_2$ and taking out $x^2 + y^2 + z^2$, we get

$$\Delta = -(x^2 + y^2 + z^2)\begin{vmatrix} x^2 & 1 & yz \\ y^2 & 1 & zx \\ z^2 & 1 & xy \end{vmatrix}$$

Multiply R_1, R_2, R_3 by x, y and z respectively and hence divide by xyz

$$\therefore \quad \Delta = -\frac{(x^2 + y^2 + z^2)}{xyz}\begin{vmatrix} x^3 & x & xyz \\ y^3 & y & xyz \\ z^3 & z & xyz \end{vmatrix}$$

$$= -\frac{(x^2 + y^2 + z^2)}{xyz}\cdot(xyz)\begin{vmatrix} x^3 & x & 1 \\ y^3 & y & 1 \\ z^3 & z & 1 \end{vmatrix}$$

Interchanging C_1 and C_3 and hence change the sign

$$\Delta = +(x^2 + y^2 + z^2)\begin{vmatrix} 1 & x & x^3 \\ 1 & y & y^3 \\ 1 & z & z^3 \end{vmatrix}$$

$$= (x^2 + y^2 + z^2)(x-y)(y-z)(z-x)(x+y+z)$$

by Q. 6.

16. If we expand the first determinant, we get

$$a(bc - a^2) - b(b^2 - ca) + c(ab - c^2)$$
$$= 3abc - a^3 - b^3 - c^3.$$

$$\therefore \quad \Delta = (3abc - a^3 - b^3 - c^3)^2$$
$$= (a^3 + b^3 + c^3 - 3abc)^2$$

2nd part : $\Delta^2 = \begin{vmatrix} a & b & c \\ b & c & a \\ c & a & b \end{vmatrix}\begin{vmatrix} a & b & c \\ b & c & a \\ c & a & b \end{vmatrix}$

If we multiply them in the present form then the first element of first row will be $a^2 + b^2 + c^2$ whereas we want it to be $2bc - a^2$. Therefore we interchange C_2 and C_3 of first determinant and hence change of sign. Again we want $-a^2$ in the result therefore we multiply the first column of first determinant by -1.

$$\therefore \quad \Delta = \begin{vmatrix} -a & c & b \\ -b & a & c \\ -c & b & a \end{vmatrix}\begin{vmatrix} a & b & c \\ b & c & a \\ c & a & b \end{vmatrix}$$

Elements of first row after multiplication are

$-aa + cb + bc, \quad -ab + cc + ba, \quad -ac + ca + bb$

or $\quad 2bc - a^2 \qquad c^2 \qquad b^2$

which is R_1 of 2nd determinant.
Similarly we can find the elements of R_2 and R_3.

17. (a) $\Delta = -(a^3 + b^3 + c^3 - 3abc)$

$$= -(a+b+c)(a^2 + b^2 + c^2 - ab - bc - ca)$$

$$= -\frac{1}{2}(a+b+c)[(a-b)^2 + (b-c)^2 + (c-a)^2].$$

Above is clearly negative because of given conditions.

(b) $\Delta = -(a^3 + b^3 + c^3 - 3abc)$

$\Delta = -(a+b+c)(a^2+b^2+c^2-ab-bc-ca)$

$\Delta = -(a+b+c)[(a+b+c)^2 - 3(ab+bc+ca)]$

$\qquad = -S_1(S_1^2 - 3S_2)$

$\qquad = -S_1^3 \text{ as } S_2 = 0$

$\qquad = -(-p)^3 = p^3 \text{ as } S_1 = -p$

18. (a) Δ is circulant whose value is

$$-(x^3 + y^3 + z^3 - 3xyz)$$
$$= -(x+y+z)(x+y\omega+z\omega^2)(x+y\omega^2+z\omega)$$

$\therefore \quad k = \omega$

(b) $\Delta = -(a^3+b^3+c^3-3abc) = 0$

$\therefore \quad a^3 + b^3 + c^3 - 3abc = 0$

$\frac{1}{2}(a+b+c)[(a-b)^2 + (b-c)^2 + (c-a)^2] = 0$

Above relation implies that either $a+b+c = 0$

or $\quad a = b = c$.

If $a+b+c = 0$, then we must have

$\cos\theta + \cos 3\theta + \cos 2\theta = 0$

$\sin\theta + \sin 3\theta - \sin 2\theta = 0$

or $\quad \cos 2\theta(2\cos\theta + 1) = 0$

and $\sin 2\theta(2\cos\theta - 1) = 0$

The above equations do not hold simultaneously because $\cos 2\theta = 0$ *i.e.* $\theta = 45^\circ$ then second equation is not satisfied and if $2\cos\theta + 1 = 0$

or $\cos\theta = -\frac{1}{2}$ *i.e.* $\theta = 120^\circ$ then also second

equation is not satisfied.

Therefore the only possibility is $a = b = c$.

or $\quad e^{i\theta} = e^{-2i\theta} = e^{3i\theta}$

Above is satisfied only when $e^{i\theta} = 1$.

i.e. $\cos\theta + i\sin\theta = 1$

$\therefore \quad \cos\theta = 1$ and $\sin\theta = 0$ $\therefore$ $\theta = 2n\pi$.

19. Ans. (b).

A careful look at all the three determinants shows that each is a circulant and we know that $a+b+c$ is a factor of circulant.

Hence $x+1+5 = x+2+4 = x-1+7 = 0$

i.e. $x+6 = 0 \implies x = -6 \implies$ (b).

20. If we put $x = y$ then C_1 and C_2 are identical so that $\Delta = 0$ and hence $x-y$ is a factor of Δ. Similarly $y-z$ and $z-x$ are its factors.

But $(x-y)(y-z)(z-x) = \begin{vmatrix} 1 & x & x^2 \\ 1 & y & y^2 \\ 1 & z & z^2 \end{vmatrix}$

by Q. 1.

Similarly if we put $a = b$ then R_1 and R_2 are identical so that $\Delta = 0$ and hence $(a-b)$ is a factor of Δ. Similarly $b-c$ and $c-a$ are its factors.

But $(a-b)(b-c)(c-a) = \begin{vmatrix} 1 & a & a^2 \\ 1 & b & b^2 \\ 1 & c & c^2 \end{vmatrix}$ by Q. 1.

$\therefore \quad \Delta = k \begin{vmatrix} 1 & x & x^2 \\ 1 & y & y^2 \\ 1 & z & z^2 \end{vmatrix} \begin{vmatrix} 1 & a & a^2 \\ 1 & b & b^2 \\ 1 & c & c^2 \end{vmatrix}$ ...(2)

where k is constant.

If we multiply in the present form then first element of first row will be $1 + ax + a^2 x^2$ where as we want it $a^2 + x^2 - 2ax$.

Therefore we interchange C_1 and C_3 of first determinant and hence $-$ive sign since it means three interchanges of adjacent columns.

$\Delta = -k \begin{vmatrix} x^2 & x & 1 \\ y^2 & y & 1 \\ z^2 & z & 1 \end{vmatrix} \begin{vmatrix} 1 & a & a^2 \\ 1 & b & b^2 \\ 1 & c & c^2 \end{vmatrix}$

Now the first element will be $x^2 + ax + a^2$ where as we want it $x^2 - 2ax + a^2$.

Choose $k = 2$ and then take -2 with 2nd column of first determinant

$\therefore \quad \Delta = \begin{vmatrix} x^2 & -2x & 1 \\ y^2 & -2y & 1 \\ z^2 & -2z & 1 \end{vmatrix} \begin{vmatrix} 1 & a & a^2 \\ 1 & b & b^2 \\ 1 & c & c^2 \end{vmatrix}$

Now after multiplication the elements of first row will be

$$x^2 - 2ax + a^2, \ x^2 - 2bx + b^2, \ x^2 - 2cx + c^2$$

or $(a-x)^2, \quad (b-x)^2$ and $(c-x)^2$.

Similarly other rows can be formed, as

$(a-y)^2 \quad (b-y)^2 \quad (c-y)^2$

$(a-z)^2 \quad (b-z)^2 \quad (c-z)^2$

Changing rows into columns and columns into rows we shall get the required form. Hence from (1) on choosing $k = 2$ the factors of Δ are

$2 \begin{vmatrix} 1 & x & x^2 \\ 1 & y & y^2 \\ 1 & z & z^2 \end{vmatrix} \begin{vmatrix} 1 & a & a^2 \\ 1 & b & b^2 \\ 1 & c & c^2 \end{vmatrix}$

$= 2(x-y)(y-z)(z-x)(a-b)(b-c)(c-a)$ by Q. 1.

21. Apply $R_1 - R_2, R_2 - R_3$.

$\Delta = \begin{vmatrix} a-x & a-x & 0 \\ x-b & 0 & x-b \\ b & x & b \end{vmatrix}$

$= (a-x)(x-b)\begin{vmatrix} 1 & 1 & 0 \\ 1 & 0 & 1 \\ b & x & b \end{vmatrix}$

$= -x(a-x)(x-b),$ by expansion

$\therefore \quad \Delta = 0 \implies x = 0, a, b.$

22. (a) Apply $C_3 - C_2$ and cancel -1, we get

$$\Delta = \begin{vmatrix} 15-2x & 11 & 1 \\ 11-3x & 17 & 1 \\ 7-x & 14 & 1 \end{vmatrix} = 0$$

Apply $R_2 - R_1$ and $R_3 - R_1$.

$$\Delta = \begin{vmatrix} 15-2x & 11 & 1 \\ -(x+4) & 6 & 0 \\ (x-8) & 3 & 0 \end{vmatrix} = 0$$

or $\begin{vmatrix} -x-4 & 2 \\ x-8 & 1 \end{vmatrix} = 0$

or $-x-4-2x+16 = 0$

∴ $-3x+12 = 0$ ∴ $x = 4$.

(b) Apply $R_2 - R_1$ and $R_3 - R_1$, we get

$$\begin{vmatrix} x-2 & 2x-3 & 3x-4 \\ -2 & -6 & -12 \\ -6 & -24 & -60 \end{vmatrix}$$

or $\begin{vmatrix} x-2 & 2x-3 & 3x-4 \\ 1 & 3 & 6 \\ 1 & 4 & 10 \end{vmatrix} = 0$

Expand with 1st row

or $(x-2).6 - (2x-3).4 + (3x-4).1 = 0$

or $x-4 = 0$ ∴ $x = 4$.

23. (a) Apply $C_2 - 3/2.C_1$ and $C_3 - 2C_1$ to remove x form C_2 and C_3

$$\Delta = \begin{vmatrix} 4x & 2 & 1 \\ 6x+2 & 0 & -4 \\ 8x+1 & -\dfrac{3}{2} & 0 \end{vmatrix} = 0$$

Expand with 1st column

$$4x(-6) - (6x+2).\dfrac{3}{2} + (8x+1)(-8) = 0$$

or $24x + 9x + 3 + 64x + 18 = 0$

or $97x + 11 = 0$ ∴ $x = -\dfrac{11}{97}$.

(b) Apply $C_1 + C_2 + C_3$ and take $3x-2$ out,

$$\Delta = (3x-2)\begin{vmatrix} 1 & 3 & 3 \\ 1 & 3x-8 & 3 \\ 1 & 3 & 3x-8 \end{vmatrix} = 0$$

Apply $R_2 - R_1$ and $R_3 - R_1$ to make two zeros

$$\Delta = (3x-2)\begin{vmatrix} 1 & 3 & 3 \\ 0 & 3x-11 & 0 \\ 0 & 0 & 3x-11 \end{vmatrix}$$

$= (3x-2)(3x-11)^2 = 0$

∴ $x = \dfrac{2}{3}$ or $\dfrac{11}{3}, \dfrac{11}{3}$.

24. (a) Apply $R_3 - R_2$ and $R_2 - R_1$

$$\Delta = \begin{vmatrix} x+2 & 2x+3 & 3x+4 \\ x+1 & x+1 & x+1 \\ x+2 & 2(x+2) & 6(x+2) \end{vmatrix} = 0$$

∴ $\Delta = (x+1)(x+2)\begin{vmatrix} x+2 & 2x+3 & 3x+4 \\ 1 & 1 & 1 \\ 1 & 2 & 6 \end{vmatrix} = 0$

∴ $\Delta = (x+1)(x+2)[(x+2).4 - (2x+3).5 + (3x+4).1] = 0$

$\Delta = (x+1)(x+2)(-3x-3) = 0$

or $(x+1)^2(x+2) = 0$ ∴ $x = -1, -1, -2$.

Note : You can apply $C_1 + C_3 - 2C_2$. It will make two zeros.

(b) Apply $C_1 + C_2 + C_3$ and take $3x-7$ common.

∴ $\Delta = (3x-7)\begin{vmatrix} 1 & x+6 & x-1 \\ 1 & x-1 & x+2 \\ 1 & x+2 & x+6 \end{vmatrix} = 0$

Apply $R_2 - R_1$, $R_3 - R_1$

∴ $\Delta = (3x-7)\begin{vmatrix} 1 & x+6 & x-1 \\ 0 & -7 & 3 \\ 0 & -4 & 7 \end{vmatrix} = 0$

or $(3x-7)(-49+12) = 0$

∴ $3x-7 = 0$ or $x = \dfrac{7}{3}$.

25. (a) Apply $R_1 - R_2$ and take $(x-2)$ common from R_1. Clearly $x = 2$ is a root.

$$\Delta = (x-2)\begin{vmatrix} 1 & 3 & -1 \\ 2 & -3x & x-3 \\ -3 & 2x & x+2 \end{vmatrix} = 0$$

Apply $C_2 - 3C_1$, $C_3 + C_1$

$$\Delta = (x-2)\begin{vmatrix} 1 & 0 & 0 \\ 2 & -3x-6 & x-1 \\ -3 & 2x+9 & x-1 \end{vmatrix} = 0$$

or $(x-2)(x-1)\begin{vmatrix} -3x-6 & 1 \\ 2x+9 & 1 \end{vmatrix} = 0$

or $(x-2)(x-1)(-5x-15) = 0$

∴ $x = 1, 2, -3$.

(b) If we put $x = 3$ then R_1 and R_2 become identical. Again if we take 4 common from R_3 it becomes $1 \quad \dfrac{3}{2} \quad \left(\dfrac{3}{2}\right)^2$ and hence by taking $x = \dfrac{3}{2}$, R_2 and R_3 are identical. ∴ $x = 3$ or $\dfrac{3}{2}$ are the roots.

(c) Applying $R_1 + R_2 + R_3$,

$$\Delta = (x+9)\begin{vmatrix} 1 & 1 & 1 \\ 2 & x & 2 \\ x & 3 & 7 \end{vmatrix} \quad \text{Apply } C_3 - C_1$$

$$\Delta = (x+9)\begin{vmatrix} 1 & 1 & 0 \\ 2 & x & 0 \\ x & 3 & 7-x \end{vmatrix}$$

$= (x+9)(7-x)(x-2) = 0$

∴ $x = -9$ is a root and other roots are 2 and 7.

26. Apply $C_1 + C_2 + C_3$ and take out $a+b+c-x$ i.e. $0-x$ or $-x$ common as $a+b+c = 0$ given .

∴ $\Delta = -x\begin{vmatrix} 1 & c & b \\ 1 & b-x & a \\ 1 & a & c-x \end{vmatrix} = 0$

Apply $R_2 - R_1$ and $R_3 - R_1$ for making two zeros

$$\therefore \quad \Delta = -x \begin{vmatrix} 1 & c & b \\ 0 & b-c-x & a-b \\ 0 & a-c & c-b-x \end{vmatrix} = 0$$

or $\quad -x[-(b-c-x)(b-c+x)-(a-c)(a-b)]=0$

or $\quad -x[-(b-c)^2+x^2-(a^2-ac-ab+bc)]=0$

or $\quad -x[-b^2-c^2+2bc+x^2-a^2+ac+ab-bc]=0$

or $\quad -x[x^2-(a^2+b^2+c^2-ab-bc-ca)]=0$

But $a+b+c=0 \quad \therefore \quad (a+b+c)^2=0$

or $\quad \Sigma a^2 + 2\Sigma bc = 0$

$$\therefore \quad -x[x^2 - \Sigma a^2 - \frac{1}{2}\Sigma a^2] = 0$$

$$\because \quad \Sigma bc = -\frac{1}{2}\Sigma a^2$$

$$\therefore \quad -x[x^2 - \frac{3}{2}(a^2+b^2+c^2)] = 0$$

$$\therefore \quad x = 0, \pm\sqrt{\frac{3}{2}(a^2+b^2+c^2)}.$$

27. Operate $R_3 - R_2$ and take 2 common

$$\Delta = 2\begin{vmatrix} x^2-a^2 & x^2-b^2 & x^2-c^2 \\ (x-a)^3 & (x-b)^3 & (x-c)^3 \\ 3x^2a+a^3 & 3x^2b+b^3 & 3x^2c+c^3 \end{vmatrix}$$

Apply $R_2 + R_3$ and take x common from R_2

$$\Delta = 2x\begin{vmatrix} x^2-a^2 & x^2-b^2 & x^2-c^2 \\ x^2+3a^2 & x^2+3b^2 & x^2+3c^2 \\ 3x^2a+a^3 & 3x^2b+b^3 & 3x^2c+c^3 \end{vmatrix}$$

Apply $C_3 - C_1, C_2 - C_1$ thereby removing x^2

$$\Delta = 2x\begin{vmatrix} x^2-a^2 & a^2-b^2 \\ x^2+3a^2 & -3(a^2-b^2) \\ 3x^2a+a^3 & -3x^2(a-b)-(a^3-b^3) \end{vmatrix}$$

$$\begin{vmatrix} a^2-c^2 \\ -3(a^2-c^2) \\ -3x^2(a-c)-(a^3-c^3) \end{vmatrix}$$

$$= 2x(a-b)(a-c) \times \begin{vmatrix} x^2-a^2 & a+b \\ x^2+3a^2 & -3(a+b) \\ 3x^2a+a^3 & -3x^2-(a^2+b^2+ab) \end{vmatrix}$$

$$\begin{vmatrix} a+c \\ -3(a+c) \\ -3x^2-(a^2+c^2+ac) \end{vmatrix}$$

Now make two zeros by $R_2 + 3R_1, R_3 + aR_1$

$$\Delta = 2x(a-b)(a-c)$$

$$\times \begin{vmatrix} x^2-a^2 & a+b & a+c \\ 4x^2 & 0 & 0 \\ 4x^2a & -(3x^2+b^2) & -(3x^2+c^2) \end{vmatrix}$$

$$= 8x^3(a-b)(a-c)\begin{vmatrix} a+b & a+c \\ -(3x^2+b^2) & -(3x^2+c^2) \end{vmatrix}$$

$$= -8x^3(a-b)(a-c)\{(3x^2+c^2)(a+b)$$
$$\qquad\qquad -(3x^2+b^2)(a+c)\}$$

$$= 8x^3(a-b)(c-a)\{3x^2(b-c)+bc(c-b)+a(c^2-b^2)\}$$

$$= 8x^3(a-b)(c-a)(b-c)\{3x^2 - \Sigma\, ab\}$$

Hence when $\Delta = 0$, then $x = 0$ or $x^2 = \frac{1}{3}(\Sigma\, ab)$.

In case $\Sigma\, ab = +$ive, then $x = 0$, $x = \pm\sqrt{\frac{1}{3}(\Sigma\, ab)}$

In case $\Sigma\, ab = -$ive, then $x = 0$ is the only real root.

28. If you interchange R_2 and R_3, then Δ becomes circulant and its value is

$$(a^3+b^3+c^3-3abc)=(a+b+c)\frac{1}{2}[\Sigma(a-b)^2]$$

$$a = \sin x, b = \sin(x+\delta x), c = \sin(x+2\delta x)$$

$$\therefore \quad a+b+c = 3\sin x \quad \text{when} \quad \delta x \to 0$$

$$(a-b)^2 = [\sin x - \sin(x+\delta x)]^2$$

$$= \left[2\sin\left(-\frac{\delta x}{2}\right)\cos\left(x+\frac{\delta x}{2}\right)\right]^2$$

$$= \left[2\left(-\frac{\delta x}{2}\right)\cos x\right]^2 = (\delta x)^2\cos^2 x \text{ when } \delta x \to 0$$

$$\therefore \quad \Delta = 3\sin x.(\delta x)^2[3\cos^2 x]$$

or $\quad \dfrac{\Delta}{(\delta x)^2} = 9\sin x\cos^2 x.$

29. (a) Apply $C_1 + C_2 + C_3$ and take out $a+b+c+3x$ common

$$\therefore \quad \Delta = [3x+(a+b+c)]\begin{vmatrix} 1 & b+x & c+x \\ 1 & c+x & a+x \\ 1 & a+x & b+x \end{vmatrix} = 0$$

Apply $R_2 - R_1$ and $R_3 - R_1$

$$\Delta = [3x+(a+b+c)]\begin{vmatrix} 1 & b+x & c+x \\ 0 & c-b & a-c \\ 0 & a-b & b-c \end{vmatrix} = 0$$

or $[3x+(a+b+c)][-(b-c)^2-(a-c)(a-b)]=0$

or $[3x+(a+b+c)][(b-c)^2-(c-a)(a-b)]=0$.

It is given that $(b-c)^2 \neq (a-b)(c-a)$ and hence from above

$$3x+a+b+c=0 \quad \therefore \quad x = -\frac{1}{3}(a+b+c).$$

(b) On putting $x = a$,

$$\Delta = \begin{vmatrix} 0 & 0 & a-b \\ 2a & 0 & a-c \\ a+b & a+c & 0 \end{vmatrix}$$

Clearly $\Delta \neq 0$ on expansion with 2nd column, so that $x = a$ does not satisfy. Similarly $x = b$ and $x = c$ also do not satisfy. Now put $x = 0$

$$\therefore \quad \Delta = \begin{vmatrix} 0 & -a & -b \\ a & 0 & -c \\ b & c & 0 \end{vmatrix}$$

Above is a skew symmetric determinant of odd order which is zero as shown in **Q. 8 (a), Page 414-419.** Hence $x = 0$ satisfies.

∴ (iv) is correct.

30. $\Delta = \dfrac{1}{2}\begin{vmatrix} p(p+1) & p+1 & 1 \\ (p+1)(p+2) & p+2 & 1 \\ (p+2)(p+3) & p+3 & 1 \end{vmatrix}$

Apply $R_3 - R_2, R_2 - R_1$

$\Delta = \dfrac{1}{2}\begin{vmatrix} p(p+1) & p+1 & 1 \\ 2(p+1) & 1 & 0 \\ 2(p+2) & 1 & 0 \end{vmatrix}$

Expand with 3rd column.

$\Delta = \dfrac{1}{2}.2[(p+1)-(p+2)] = -1$

$\Delta = |-1| = 1$

31. We know that area of a triangle whose one vertex is at the origin is $\dfrac{1}{2}(x_1 y_2 - x_2 y_1)$

∴ $\Delta_1 = \dfrac{1}{2}ab[\tan\theta\cos\theta - \sin\theta\cot\theta]$

or $\Delta_1 = \dfrac{1}{2}ab(\sin\theta - \cos\theta)$

Similarly

$\Delta_3 = \dfrac{1}{2}(\sin\theta + \cos\theta)$

$\Delta_2 = \dfrac{1}{2}\begin{vmatrix} a & b & 1 \\ a\sec^2\theta & b\cosec^2\theta & 1 \\ a+a\sin^2\theta & b+b\cos^2\theta & 1 \end{vmatrix}$

Apply $C_1 - aC_3, C_2 - bC_3$

$\Delta_2 = \dfrac{1}{2}\begin{vmatrix} 0 & 0 & 1 \\ a\tan^2\theta & b\cot^2\theta & 0 \\ a\sin^2\theta & b\cos^2\theta & 0 \end{vmatrix}$

$= \dfrac{1}{2}ab(\tan^2\theta\cos^2\theta - \cot^2\theta\sin^2\theta)$

$\Delta_2 = \dfrac{1}{2}ab(\sin^2\theta - \cos^2\theta)$ ...(1)

Now $\Delta_2^2 = \Delta_1\Delta_3$ as they are in G.P.

or $\Delta_2^2 = \dfrac{1}{4}a^2b^2(\sin^2\theta - \cos^2\theta) = \dfrac{1}{2}ab\,\Delta_2$, by (1)

∴ $\Delta_2 = \dfrac{1}{2}ab$

or $\dfrac{1}{2}ab(\sin^2\theta - \cos^2\theta) = \dfrac{1}{2}ab$, by (1)

or $\cos 2\theta = -1 = \cos\pi$

∴ $2\theta = \pi$ or $\theta = \pi/2$

But when $\theta = \pi/2$ the vertices of the triangle are not defined. Thus we can say that for no value of θ the areas can be in G.P.

32. Apply $R_1 + R_2 + R_3$ and we get $\Delta = 0$
Altitude through A is AD which is perpendicular to BC.

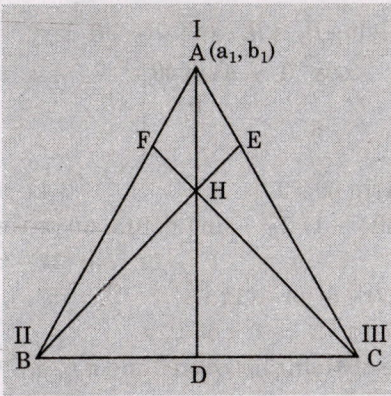

Fig. 2

Slope of BC is $\dfrac{b_2 - b_3}{a_2 - a_3}$

∴ Slope of altitude $AD = -\dfrac{a_2 - a_3}{b_2 - b_3}$

∴ Eq. of AD is $y - b_1 = -\dfrac{a_2 - a_3}{b_2 - b_3}(x - a_1)$

or $x(a_2 - a_3) + y(b_2 - b_3)$
$\qquad\qquad = a_1(a_2 - a_3) + b_1(b_2 - b_3)$

Similarly write down the equations of altitudes, BE and CF by symmetry. The altitudes will be concurrent if $\Delta = $ given determinant $= 0$ which is true.

33. $\alpha + \beta = p, \alpha\beta = q$. Now by expansion,

$\Delta = (1 - \cos^2\beta) - \cos(\alpha - \beta)\{\cos(\beta - \alpha) - \cos\alpha\cos\beta\}$
$\qquad + \cos\alpha[\cos\beta\cos(\alpha - \beta) - \cos\alpha]$

$= \sin^2\beta - \cos(\alpha - \beta)\sin\alpha\sin\beta + \cos(\alpha - \beta)$
$\qquad\qquad\qquad .\cos\alpha\cos\beta - \cos^2\alpha$

$= \cos(\alpha - \beta)\cos(\alpha + \beta) - (\cos^2\alpha - \sin^2\beta)$

$= (\cos^2\alpha - \sin^2\beta) - (\cos^2\alpha - \sin^2\beta) = 0$

34. Let D be the common difference of A.P. a, b, c, d then $a - c = -2D, d - b = 2D,\ 2b = a + c,\ 2c = b + d$. Apply $R_1 + R_3 - 2R_2$ and use the above relations.

∴ $f(x) = \begin{vmatrix} 0 & 0 & 2 \\ x+b & x+c & x-1 \\ x+c & x+d & x-b+d \end{vmatrix}$

$= 2[(x+b)(x+d) - (x+c)^2]$

$= 2[x(b+d-2c) + (bd - c^2)]$

$= 2[0 + (a+D)(a+3D) - (a+2D)^2]$

$= 2[-D^2]$

∴ $\int_0^2 f(x)\,dx = \int_0^2 -2D^2\,dx = [-2D^2 x]_0^2$

or $-4 = -4D^2$

∴ $D^2 = 1$ or $D = \pm 1$

35. Ans. (a) and (c). Adding C_2 to C_1, we get

$\begin{vmatrix} 2 & \cos^2\theta & 4\sin 4\theta \\ 2 & 1+\cos^2\theta & 4\sin 4\theta \\ 1 & \cos^2\theta & 1+4\sin 4\theta \end{vmatrix} = 0$

Now applying $R_2 - R_1$ and $R_3 - R_1$,

$$\begin{vmatrix} 2 & \cos^2\theta & 4\sin 4\theta \\ 0 & 1 & 0 \\ -1 & 0 & 1 \end{vmatrix} = 0$$

or $2 + 4\sin 4\theta = 0$

or $\sin 4\theta = -1/2 = -\sin(\pi/6) = \sin(\pi + \pi/6)$

$\qquad\qquad$ or $\sin(2\pi - \pi/6)$

$\therefore \quad 4\theta = 7\pi/6$ or $11\pi/6$

$\quad 0 < \theta < \pi/2 \Rightarrow 0 < 4\theta < 2\pi$

The value of θ lying between 0 and $\pi/2$ are $7\pi/24$ and $11\pi/24$.

36. (a) Ans. (b).

Apply $C_1 + C_3 - (2\cos d)C_2$

$$\Delta = \begin{vmatrix} 1 + a^2 - 2a\cos d & a & a^2 \\ 0 & \cos px & \cos(p+d)x \\ 0 & \sin px & \sin(p+d)x \end{vmatrix}$$

$= (1 + a^2 - 2a\cos d)\sin(px + dx - px)$

$= (1 + a^2 - 2a\cos d)\sin dx$

It does not depend upon p.

(b) Ans. Independent of n.

Apply $C_1 + C_3 - (2\cos x)C_2$

(c) Proceed as in (b).

37. Expand with R_3

$\therefore \quad \Delta = \sin(\beta - \gamma)[\sin(\gamma - \beta)...]$

$\qquad = -\Sigma\sin^2(\beta - \gamma)$ *i.e.* independent of θ.

38. (a) $\cos(\theta + \varphi)\cos(\theta + \varphi)$

$\quad + \sin(\theta + \varphi).\sin(\theta + \varphi) + \cos 2\varphi(\sin^2\theta + \cos^2\theta)$

$= 1 + \cos 2\varphi = 2\cos^2\varphi$

Above is independent of θ.

(b) **Refer Q. 12 (a) P. 415-420.**

Multiplying C_1, C_2, C_3 by a, b, c respectively and then taking a, b, c common from R_1, R_2, R_3 respectively so that we have only a^2, b^2 and c^2.

$$\Delta = \frac{abc}{abc}\begin{vmatrix} a^2 + (b^2 + c^2)\cos\theta \\ a^2(1 - \cos\theta) \\ a^2(1 - \cos\theta) \end{vmatrix}$$

$$\begin{vmatrix} b^2(1 - \cos\theta) & c^2(1 - \cos\theta) \\ b^2 + (c^2 + a^2)\cos\theta & c^2(1 - \cos\theta) \\ b^2 + (1 - \cos\theta) & c^2 + (a^2 + b^2)\cos\theta \end{vmatrix}$$

Apply $C_1 + C_2 + C_3$ and take out $a^2 + b^2 + c^2$ which is given to be 1.

$$\Delta = \begin{vmatrix} 1 & ... & ... \\ 1 & ... & ... \\ 1 & ... & ... \end{vmatrix}$$

Now make two zeros and expand $\Delta = \cos^2\theta$. Thus Δ depends upon θ.

39. Ans. $F'(x)$ at $x = a$ is **0**.

$$F'(x) = \begin{vmatrix} f_1'(x) & f_2'(x) & f_3'(x) \\ g_1(x) & g_2(x) & g_3(x) \\ h_1(x) & h_2(x) & h_3(x) \end{vmatrix}$$

$$+ \begin{vmatrix} f_1(x) & f_2(x) & f_3(x) \\ g_1'(x) & g_2'(x) & g_3'(x) \\ h_1(x) & h_2(x) & h_3(x) \end{vmatrix}$$

$$+ \begin{vmatrix} f_1(x) & f_2(x) & f_3(x) \\ g_1(x) & g_2(x) & g_3(x) \\ h_1'(x) & h_2'(x) & h_3'(x) \end{vmatrix}$$

Hence $F'(a) = 0$, since two rows in each determinant are identical by virtue of the relations

$\qquad f_r(a) = g_r(a) = h_r(a), \quad r = 1, 2, 3.$

40. (a) As above we will have three determinants out of which two will be zero beacuse of identical lines.

(b) Differentiate as explained above. The first two determinants will be zero because of identical lines.

$$\phi'(x) = 0 + 0 + \begin{vmatrix} F & G & H \\ F' & G' & H' \\ F'' & G'' & H''' \end{vmatrix} = 0$$

Each element in R_3 is zero as F, G, H are polynomials of degree 2 and hence F''', G''', H''' each is zero.

Since $\phi'(x) = 0$, therefore $\phi(x) = $ constant and hence a polynomial of zero degree.

(c) Ans. Zero.

$f'(x) = \Delta_1 + \Delta_2 + \Delta_3 = 0$, where both Δ_1, Δ_2 are zero because of identical lines and $\Delta_3 = 0$ because of a line of zeros.

Since $f'(x) = 0$ $\therefore f(x) = $ constant $= \lambda$ say

$\therefore \quad E = \lambda - 2\lambda + \lambda = 0$

41. (a) $\Delta = \begin{vmatrix} f & g & h \\ (xf)' & (xg)' & (xh)' \\ (x^2f)'' & (x^2g)'' & (x^2h)'' \end{vmatrix}$

$= \begin{vmatrix} f & g \\ xf' + f & xg' + g \\ x^2f'' + 4xf' + 2f & x^2g'' + 4xg' + 2g \end{vmatrix}$

$\begin{vmatrix} h \\ xh' + h \\ x^2h'' + 4xh' + 2h \end{vmatrix}$

$= \begin{vmatrix} f & g & h \\ xf' & xg' & xh' \\ x^2f'' + 4xf' & x^2g'' + 4xg' & x^2h'' + 4xh' \end{vmatrix}$

by $R_3 - 2R_2$ and $R_2 - R_1$

Now apply $R_3 - 4R_2$

$\Delta = x.x^2\begin{vmatrix} f & g & h \\ f' & g' & h' \\ f'' & g'' & h'' \end{vmatrix} = \begin{vmatrix} f & g & h \\ f' & g' & h' \\ x^3f'' & x^3g'' & x^3h'' \end{vmatrix}$

Now differentiate as explained in (b).

$$\therefore \quad \Delta' = \begin{vmatrix} f' & g' & h' \\ f' & g' & h' \\ x^3 f'' & x^3 g'' & x^3 h'' \end{vmatrix}$$

$$+ \begin{vmatrix} f & g & h \\ f'' & g'' & h'' \\ x^3 f'' & x^3 g'' & x^3 h'' \end{vmatrix}$$

$$+ \begin{vmatrix} f & g & h \\ f' & g' & h' \\ (x^3 f'')' & (x^3 g'')' & (x^3 h'')' \end{vmatrix}$$

$$= 0 + 0 + \begin{vmatrix} f & g & h \\ f' & g' & h' \\ (x^3 f'')' & (x^3 g'')' & (x^3 h'')' \end{vmatrix}$$

In the second det. R_2, R_3 become identical after taking x^3 common from R_3.

(b) Ans. (c).

$\dfrac{\Delta x}{x}$ is of the form $\left(\dfrac{0}{0}\right)$ as $x \to 0$.

Hence by L'Hospital's rule, $Lt = \underset{x \to 0}{Lt} \dfrac{\Delta'(x)}{1}$

$$= \underset{x \to 0}{Lt} \begin{vmatrix} 2xe^{x^2} & \dfrac{1}{1+x} \\ \tan x & \sin x \end{vmatrix} + \begin{vmatrix} e^{x^2} & \log(1+x) \\ \sec^2 x & \cos x \end{vmatrix}$$

(by rule for differentiation of a determinant)

$$= \begin{vmatrix} 0 & 1 \\ 0 & 0 \end{vmatrix} + \begin{vmatrix} 1 & 0 \\ 1 & 1 \end{vmatrix} = 1.$$

42. (a) Ans. (b).

$f'(0) = \Delta_1 + \Delta_2 + \Delta_3$ on putting $x = 0$

$$\begin{vmatrix} 0 & 1 & 0 \\ 0 & 1 & 0 \\ 0 & 0 & 0 \end{vmatrix} + \begin{vmatrix} 1 & 0 & -1 \\ 0 & 0 & 1 \\ 0 & 0 & 0 \end{vmatrix} + \begin{vmatrix} 1 & 0 & -1 \\ 0 & 1 & 0 \\ 2 & 0 & 0 \end{vmatrix} = 2$$

(b) Ans. (d).

$$\frac{d}{dx} f(x) = \begin{vmatrix} 3x^2 & \cos x & -\sin x \\ \cdots & \cdots & \cdots \\ \cdots & \cdots & \cdots \end{vmatrix} + 0 + 0$$

$$\frac{d^3}{dx^3} f(x) \text{ at } x = 0 \begin{vmatrix} 6 & -1 & 0 \\ 6 & -1 & 0 \\ p & p^2 & p^3 \end{vmatrix} = 0$$

i.e. independent of p.

(c) Ans. (d). By rule for differentiation of a determinant $\Delta' = \Delta_1 + \Delta_2 + \Delta_3$

Δ_1 is zero because of identical columns and $\Delta_3 = 0$ because of a column of all zeros. $\Delta_2 = 0$ because C_3 in Δ_2 is $\dfrac{3}{2} C_2$.

(d) Ans. (a).

Differentiating columnwise,

$$f'(x) = \Delta_1 + \Delta_2 + \Delta_3$$

where $\Delta_1 = 0$ because of identical columns C_1 and C_3 and $\Delta_3 = 0$ because of a column C_3 of zeros and

$$\Delta_2 = \begin{vmatrix} x+a^2 & 4x^3 & 3 \\ x+b^2 & 8x^3 & 3 \\ x+c^2 & 12x^3 & 3 \end{vmatrix}$$

$$= 12x^3 \begin{vmatrix} x+a^2 & 1 & 1 \\ x+b^2 & 2 & 1 \\ x+c^2 & 3 & 1 \end{vmatrix}$$

Apply $R_1 + R_3 - 2R_2$

$$\Delta = 12x^3 \begin{vmatrix} a^2 + c^2 - 2b^2 & 0 & 0 \\ x+b^2 & 2 & 1 \\ x+c^2 & 3 & 1 \end{vmatrix} = 0$$

or $-12x^3 (a^2 + c^2 - 2b^2) = 0$

Since $x \neq 0$

$\therefore \quad a^2 + c^2 = 2b^2 \Rightarrow a^2, b^2, c^2$ are in A.P.

43. (a) Ans. (a), (d).
Proceed as in Q. 42 (b).

$$\frac{d^n}{dx^n}(x^n) = n!$$

$$\frac{d^n}{dx^n}\begin{Bmatrix} \sin x \\ \cos x \end{Bmatrix} = \begin{aligned} &\sin\left(x + \frac{n\pi}{2}\right) \\ &\cos\left(x + \frac{n\pi}{2}\right) \end{aligned}$$

(b) $f(x) = 2\sin^2 x + 4x^2 \cos x$

$f'(x) = 4\sin x \cos x - 4x^2 \sin x + 8x \cos x$

44. (a) If $f(x) = a_0 x^n + a_1 x^{n-1} + \ldots a_{n-1} x + a_n$

then a_{n-1} is coefficient of x

$f'(x) = na_0 x^{n-1} + (n-1) a_1 x^{n-2} + \ldots + a_{n-1}$

$\therefore \quad f'(0) = a_{n-1}$

Therefore we have to differentiate the given determinant and then put $x = 0$ in it.

$$f'(0) = \begin{vmatrix} a_1 b_1 & a_1 b_2 & a_1 b_3 \\ 1 & 1 & 1 \\ 1 & 1 & 1 \end{vmatrix} + \begin{vmatrix} & & \end{vmatrix} + \begin{vmatrix} & & \end{vmatrix}$$

$= 0 + 0 + 0 = 0$

(b) Put $x = 0$, then $a_7 = \begin{vmatrix} 0 & -1 & 3 \\ 1 & 2 & -3 \\ -3 & 4 & 0 \end{vmatrix} = 21$

Now differentiate both sides and put $x = 0$

$$a_6 = \begin{vmatrix} R_1' \\ R_2 \\ R_3 \end{vmatrix} + \begin{vmatrix} R_1 \\ R_2' \\ R_3 \end{vmatrix} + \begin{vmatrix} R_1 \\ R_2 \\ R_3' \end{vmatrix} = 40 + 36 - 1 = 75$$

45. Set $P(x) = \begin{vmatrix} A(x) & B(x) & C(x) \\ A(\alpha) & B(\alpha) & C(\alpha) \\ A'(\alpha) & B'(\alpha) & C'(\alpha) \end{vmatrix}$ ...(1)

Then $P'(x) \begin{vmatrix} A'(x) & B'(x) & C'(x) \\ A(\alpha) & B(\alpha) & C(\alpha) \\ A'(\alpha) & B'(\alpha) & C'(\alpha) \end{vmatrix} + 0 + 0$ ...(2)

See rule for $P'(x)$

Since $f(x) = 0$ is a quadratic having a repeated root α, we can write $f(x) = a(x - \alpha)^2$ where a is a constant.

Now $P(x)$ will be divisible by $\Sigma(x)$ if $P(x)$ and $P'(x)$ are divisible by $(x - \alpha)$ i.e. $P(\alpha) = 0$ and $P'(\alpha) = 0$ which is obvious by (1) and (2) because of two identical rows.

46. (a) $\Delta = f(\theta)$. It will be independent of θ if $\Delta'(\theta) = 0$

$$\Delta' = 0 + 0 + \begin{vmatrix} \cos(\theta + \alpha) & \cos(\theta + \beta) & \cos(\theta + \gamma) \\ \sin(\theta + \alpha) & \sin(\theta + \beta) & \sin(\theta + \gamma) \\ \sin\alpha & \sin\beta & \sin\gamma \end{vmatrix}$$

$\Delta' = \Sigma \sin\alpha \sin(\theta + \gamma - \theta - \beta)$

$\quad = \Sigma \sin\alpha \sin(\beta - \gamma) = 0$

$\therefore \quad \Delta = $ constant $i.e.$ independent of θ.

(b) Proceed as in part (a).

47. (a) We write the given determinant Δ, say, as the product of two determinants as follows

$$\Delta = \begin{vmatrix} a_1 & b_1 & 0 \\ a_2 & b_2 & 0 \\ a_3 & b_3 & 0 \end{vmatrix} \times \begin{vmatrix} \alpha_1 & \beta_1 & 0 \\ \alpha_2 & \beta_2 & 0 \\ \alpha_3 & \beta_3 & 0 \end{vmatrix}$$

Since value of each det. on R.H.S. is zero, we have $\Delta = 0$.

(b) Ans. (b).

A careful look at the question suggests that Δ is product of the following two determinants :

$$\begin{vmatrix} a_1 & b_1 & 1 \\ a_2 & b_2 & 1 \\ a_3 & b_3 & 1 \end{vmatrix} \cdot \begin{vmatrix} z & \bar{z} & 0 \\ \bar{z} & z & 0 \\ 1 & z & 0 \end{vmatrix} = 0$$

48. (a) As in Q. 47 multiply the two zero determinants

$$\begin{vmatrix} \cos A & \sin A & 0 \\ \cos B & \sin B & 0 \\ \cos C & \sin C & 0 \end{vmatrix}, \begin{vmatrix} \cos P & \sin P & 0 \\ \cos Q & \sin Q & 0 \\ \cos R & \sin R & 0 \end{vmatrix}$$

(b) Multiply two zero-determinants :

$$\Delta = \begin{vmatrix} \cos A & \sin A & 0 \\ \cos B & \sin B & 0 \\ \cos C & \sin C & 0 \end{vmatrix} \begin{vmatrix} \cos A & \sin A & 0 \\ \cos B & \sin B & 0 \\ \cos C & \sin C & 0 \end{vmatrix} = 0$$

49. $\Delta = \Delta_1 \Delta_2 = \begin{vmatrix} 1 & 1 & 0 \\ a+b & c+d & 0 \\ ab & cd & 0 \end{vmatrix} \cdot \begin{vmatrix} 1 & 1 & 0 \\ c+d & a+b & 0 \\ cd & ab & 0 \end{vmatrix} = 0.$

50. By sine rule $\sin A = ak$

$$\Delta = \begin{vmatrix} a^2 & abk & cak \\ abk & 1 & \cos(B-C) \\ ack & \cos(B-C) & 1 \end{vmatrix}$$

Take a common from each R_1 and C_1

$$\Delta = a^2 \begin{vmatrix} 1 & \sin B & \sin C \\ \sin B & 1 & \cos(B-C) \\ \sin C & \cos(B-C) & 1 \end{vmatrix}$$

Now in a triangle,

$\sin B = \sin(C + A), \sin C = \sin(A + B)$

$$\therefore \quad \Delta = a^2 \begin{vmatrix} \sin A & \cos A & 0 \\ \cos C & \sin C & 0 \\ \cos B & \sin B & 0 \end{vmatrix} \begin{vmatrix} \sin A & \cos A & 0 \\ \cos C & \sin C & 0 \\ \cos B & \sin B & 0 \end{vmatrix} = 0$$

51. Equating coefficients of like terms, in the given identity, we get

$$a = ll', \; b = mm', \; c = nn'.$$
$$2h = lm' + l'm, \; 2g = ln' + l'n, \; 2\Sigma = mn' + m'n.$$

Consider the product $\Delta_1 \Delta_2$ where each of them is zero determinant

$$\therefore \quad \begin{vmatrix} l & l' & 0 \\ m & m' & 0 \\ n & n' & 0 \end{vmatrix} \begin{vmatrix} l' & l & 0 \\ m' & m & 0 \\ n' & n & 0 \end{vmatrix} = 0$$

or $\begin{vmatrix} 2ll' & lm' + l'm & ln' + l'n \\ lm' + l'm & 2mm' & mn' + m'n \\ nl' + n'l & mn' + m'n & 2nn' \end{vmatrix} = 0$

or $\begin{vmatrix} 2a & 2h & 2g \\ 2h & 2b & 2f \\ 2g & 2f & 2c \end{vmatrix} = 8 \begin{vmatrix} a & h & g \\ h & b & f \\ g & f & c \end{vmatrix} = 0$

52. Ans. 0.

$$\Delta = -\begin{vmatrix} x & y & z \\ a & b & c \\ l & m & n \end{vmatrix} \cdot \begin{vmatrix} 0 & p & q \\ -p & 0 & r \\ -q & -r & 0 \end{vmatrix} = 0$$

as the second factor is a skew symmetric determinant of odd order which we know is zero always.

53. We have

$$\Delta^2 = \begin{vmatrix} \alpha_1 & \alpha_2 & \alpha_3 \\ \beta_1 & \beta_2 & \beta_3 \\ \gamma_1 & \gamma_2 & \gamma_3 \end{vmatrix} \begin{vmatrix} \alpha_1 & \alpha_2 & \alpha_3 \\ \beta_1 & \beta_2 & \beta_3 \\ \gamma_1 & \gamma_2 & \gamma_3 \end{vmatrix}$$

$$= \begin{vmatrix} \Sigma \alpha_1^2 & \Sigma \alpha_1\beta_1 & \Sigma \alpha_1\gamma_1 \\ \Sigma \beta_1\alpha_1 & \Sigma \beta_1^2 & \Sigma \beta_1\gamma_1 \\ \Sigma \gamma_1\alpha_1 & \Sigma \gamma_1\beta_1 & \Sigma \gamma_1^2 \end{vmatrix}$$

$$= \begin{vmatrix} \Sigma \alpha_1^2 & \frac{\sqrt{3}}{2}\sqrt{()()} & 0 \\ \frac{\sqrt{3}}{2}\sqrt{()()} & \Sigma \beta_1^2 & 0 \\ 0 & 0 & 1 \end{vmatrix}$$

(Using the given relations)

$= (\alpha_1^2 + \alpha_2^2 + \alpha_3^2)(\beta_1^2 + \beta_2^2 + \beta_3^2)$

$\quad - \frac{3}{4}(\alpha_1^2 + \alpha_2^2 + \alpha_3^2)(\beta_1^2 + \beta_2^2 + \beta_3^2)$

$= \frac{1}{4}(\alpha_1^2 + \alpha_2^2 + \alpha_3^2)(\beta_1^2 + \beta_2^2 + \beta_3^2)$

54. (a) $\Delta^2 = \begin{vmatrix} l_1 & m_1 & n_1 \\ l_2 & m_2 & n_2 \\ l_3 & m_3 & n_3 \end{vmatrix} \begin{vmatrix} l_1 & m_1 & n_1 \\ l_2 & m_2 & n_2 \\ l_3 & m_3 & n_3 \end{vmatrix} = \begin{vmatrix} 1 & 0 & 0 \\ 0 & 1 & 0 \\ 0 & 0 & 1 \end{vmatrix} = 1,$

using given relations.

$\therefore \quad \Delta = \pm 1.$

(b) Squaring both sides we have to prove that

$$abc \begin{vmatrix} x_1 & y_1 & z_1 \\ x_2 & y_2 & z_2 \\ x_3 & y_3 & z_3 \end{vmatrix}^2 = (d - f)^2 (d + 2f)$$

Write $D^2 = D.D$ and take $a, b, c,$ with C_1, C_2, C_3 respectively.

$$\text{L.H.S.} = \begin{vmatrix} ax_1 & by_1 & cz_1 \\ ax_2 & by_2 & cz_2 \\ ax_3 & by_3 & cz_3 \end{vmatrix} \begin{vmatrix} x_1 & y_1 & z_1 \\ x_2 & y_2 & z_2 \\ x_3 & y_3 & z_3 \end{vmatrix}$$

$$= \begin{vmatrix} d & f & f \\ f & d & f \\ f & f & d \end{vmatrix} \text{ by virtue of given relations}$$

Apply $C_1 + C_2 + C_3$ and take out $d + 2f$.

$$= (d + 2f) \begin{vmatrix} 1 & f & f \\ 1 & d & f \\ 1 & f & d \end{vmatrix}.$$

Now make two zeros and expand; we get

$$(d + 2f)(d - f)^2.$$

55. $\dfrac{1 - x^3}{1 - x} = 1 + x + x^2$

$$\begin{vmatrix} 1 + a_1 b_1 + a_1^2 b_1^2 & 1 + a_1 b_2 + a_1 b_2^2 & 1 + a_1 b_3 + a_1 b_3^2 \\ (a_2, b_1) & (a_2, b_2) & (a_2, b_3) \\ (a_3, b_1) & (a_3, b_2) & (a_3, b_3) \end{vmatrix}$$

Consider the product

$$\Delta_1 \Delta_2 = \begin{vmatrix} 1 & a_1 & a_1^2 \\ 1 & a_2 & a_2^2 \\ 1 & a_3 & a_3^3 \end{vmatrix} \begin{vmatrix} 1 & b_1 & b_1^2 \\ 1 & b_2 & b_2^2 \\ 1 & b_3 & b_3^2 \end{vmatrix}$$

$$= (a_1 - a_2)(a_2 - a_3)(a_3 - a_1)(b_1 - b_2)$$
$$(b_2 - b_3)(b_3 - b_1)$$

by Q. 1 (a) P. 349-444.

56. Do yourself.

57. (a) $3 = 1 + 1 + 1$

$$\begin{vmatrix} 1+1+1 & 1+\alpha+\beta & 1+\alpha^2+\beta^2 \\ 1+\alpha+\beta & 1+\alpha^2+\beta^2 & 1+\alpha^3+\beta^3 \\ 1+\alpha^2+\beta^2 & 1+\alpha^3+\beta^3 & 1+\alpha^4+\beta^4 \end{vmatrix}$$

$$\begin{vmatrix} 1 & 1 & 1 \\ 1 & \alpha & \beta \\ 1 & \alpha^2 & \beta^2 \end{vmatrix} \begin{vmatrix} 1 & 1 & 1 \\ 1 & \alpha & \beta \\ 1 & \alpha^2 & \beta^2 \end{vmatrix} = \Delta^2$$

Apply $R_2 - R_1, R_3 - R_1$ on Δ

$$\Delta = \begin{vmatrix} 1 & 1 & 1 \\ 0 & \alpha - 1 & \beta - 1 \\ 0 & \alpha^2 - 1 & \beta^2 - 1 \end{vmatrix}$$

$$= (\alpha - 1)(\beta - 1) \begin{vmatrix} 1 & 1 \\ \alpha + 1 & \beta + 1 \end{vmatrix}$$

$$= [\alpha\beta - (\alpha + \beta) + 1][(\beta + \alpha)^2 - 4\alpha\beta]^{1/2}$$

$$= \left[\frac{c}{a} + \frac{b}{a} + 1\right] \left[\frac{b^2 - 4ac}{a^2}\right]^{1/2}$$

$$\therefore \quad D = \Delta^2 = \frac{1}{a^4}(a + b + c)^2 (b^2 - 4ac).$$

(b) Do yourself.

58. (a) **Hint :** Det. on L.H.S. is the det. formed by the cofactors of the det.

$$\begin{vmatrix} x & y & z \\ y & z & x \\ z & x & y \end{vmatrix} = \Delta \text{ , say.}$$

$$\text{L.H.S. det.} = \Delta^2 = \begin{vmatrix} x & y & z \\ y & z & x \\ z & x & y \end{vmatrix} \begin{vmatrix} x & y & z \\ y & z & x \\ z & x & y \end{vmatrix}$$

$$= \begin{vmatrix} r^2 & u^2 & u^2 \\ u^2 & r^2 & u^2 \\ u^2 & u^2 & r^2 \end{vmatrix}, \text{ by given relations.}$$

(b) In accordance with the rule for multiplication the constituents of first row of product determinant will be as below

1st constituent
$$= \lambda(a^2 + \lambda^2) + c(ab + c\lambda) - b(ca - b\lambda)$$
$$= \lambda(a^2 + b^2 + c^2 + \lambda^2)$$

2nd constituent
$$= -c(a^2 + \lambda^2) + \lambda(ab + c\lambda) + a(ca - b\lambda) = 0$$

3rd constituent
$$= b(a^2 + \lambda^2) - a(ab + c\lambda) - \lambda(ca - b\lambda) = 0$$

Similarly we can find the constituent of R_2 and R_3

$$\therefore \quad \Delta = \begin{vmatrix} \lambda(\Sigma a^2 + \lambda^2) & 0 & 0 \\ 0 & \lambda(\Sigma a^2 + \lambda^2) & 0 \\ 0 & 0 & \lambda(\Sigma a^2 + \lambda^2) \end{vmatrix}$$

$$= \lambda^3 (a^2 + b^2 + c^2 + \lambda^2)^3$$

Alternative : If we denote the second det. by Δ and first by Δ' so that Δ' is det. formed by cofactors of Δ. Hence by the Theorem of P. 437 we get

$$\Delta' = \Delta^2$$

$$\Delta' \Delta = \Delta^2 . \Delta = \Delta^3 = \begin{vmatrix} \lambda & c & -b \\ -c & \lambda & a \\ b & -a & \lambda \end{vmatrix}^3$$

$$= [\lambda(a^2 + \lambda^2) + c(ab + c\lambda) - b(ca - b\lambda)]^3$$
$$= \lambda^3 (\lambda^2 + a^2 + b^2 + c^2)^3$$

on expansion by R_1.

59. After changing R^s to C^s and C^s to R^s

Δ' of L.H.S. = Determinant of cofactors of elements of Δ of R.H.S.

$$\therefore \quad \Delta' = \Delta^2.$$

60. We know that $\begin{vmatrix} a & b & c \\ b & c & a \\ c & a & b \end{vmatrix} = -(a^3 + b^3 + c^3 - 3abc)$

Now $\begin{vmatrix} a & b & c \\ b & c & a \\ c & a & b \end{vmatrix} \begin{vmatrix} x & y & z \\ y & z & x \\ z & x & y \end{vmatrix}$

$$= \begin{vmatrix} ax+by+cz & ay+bz+cx & az+bx+cy \\ = P & = Q & = R \\ R & P & Q \\ Q & R & P \end{vmatrix}$$

$$= -\begin{vmatrix} P & Q & R \\ Q & R & P \\ R & P & Q \end{vmatrix} = +(P^3 + Q^3 + R^3 - 3PQR)$$

L.H.S. $= (a^3 + b^3 + c^3 - 3abc)(x^3 + y^3 + z^3 - 3xyz)$

$$= (P^3 + Q^3 + R^3 - 3PQR).$$

61. Consider the determinant $\Delta = \begin{vmatrix} a_1 & b_1 & c_1 \\ a_2 & b_2 & c_2 \\ a_3 & b_3 & c_3 \end{vmatrix}$

If Δ' is the det. formed by the cofactors of Δ, then we know that $\Delta' = \Delta^2$ *i.e.,* **Theorem, P. 438**

$$\begin{vmatrix} A_1 & B_1 & C_1 \\ A_2 & B_2 & C_2 \\ A_3 & B_3 & C_3 \end{vmatrix} = \begin{vmatrix} a_1 & b_1 & c_1 \\ a_2 & b_2 & c_2 \\ a_3 & b_3 & c_3 \end{vmatrix}^2 \qquad \ldots(1)$$

Now solving $a_2 x + b_2 y + c_2 = 0$ and
$$a_3 x + b_3 y + c_3 = 0, \text{ we get}$$

$$\frac{x_1}{\begin{vmatrix} b_2 & c_2 \\ b_3 & c_3 \end{vmatrix}} = \frac{y_1}{\begin{vmatrix} c_2 & a_2 \\ c_3 & a_3 \end{vmatrix}} = \frac{1}{\begin{vmatrix} a_2 & b_2 \\ a_3 & b_3 \end{vmatrix}}$$

i.e., $\dfrac{x_1}{A_1} = \dfrac{y_1}{B_1} = \dfrac{1}{C_1}$

Hence point of intersection of the above two lines is $\left[\dfrac{A_1}{C_1}, \dfrac{B_1}{C_1} \right]$.

This gives one of the vertices of the triangle.

Similarly other two vertices are $\left[\dfrac{A_2}{C_2}, \dfrac{B_2}{C_2} \right]$ and

$\left[\dfrac{A_3}{C_3}, \dfrac{B_3}{C_3} \right]$. Hence area of triangle

$$= \frac{1}{2} \begin{vmatrix} A_1/C_1 & B_1/C_1 & 1 \\ A_2/C_2 & B_2/C_2 & 1 \\ A_3/C_3 & B_3/C_3 & 1 \end{vmatrix}$$

$$= \frac{1}{2} \begin{vmatrix} A_1 & B_1 & C_1 \\ A_2 & B_2 & C_2 \\ A_3 & B_3 & C_3 \end{vmatrix} \div (C_1 C_2 C_3)$$

$$= \frac{1}{2} \begin{vmatrix} a_1 & b_1 & c_1 \\ a_2 & b_2 & c_2 \\ a_3 & b_3 & c_3 \end{vmatrix}^2 \div \begin{array}{l} (a_2 b_3 - a_3 b_2)(a_3 b_1 - a_1 b_3) \\ (a_1 b_2 - a_2 b_1) \end{array}$$

[Using (1) and substituting the values of C_1, C_2, C_3]

62. (a) Applying $R_1 - \sec x \cdot R_3$ thereby making two zeros in R_1, we get $f(x) =$

$$\begin{vmatrix} 0 & 0 & \dfrac{1}{\cos^2 x} + \dfrac{\cos x}{\sin^2 x} - \cos x \\ \cos^2 x & \cos^2 x & \operatorname{cosec}^2 x \\ 1 & \cos^2 x & \cos^2 x \end{vmatrix}$$

$$= \left[\frac{1}{\cos^2 x} + \frac{\cos x}{\sin^2 x} (1 - \sin^2 x) \right] (\cos^4 x - \cos^2 x)$$

$$= \left(\frac{1}{\cos^2 x} + \frac{\cos^3 x}{\sin^2 x} \right) \cos^2 x (-\sin^2 x)$$

$$= -\sin^2 x - \cos^5 x$$

$$\therefore \int_0^{\pi/2} f(x)\, dx = \int_0^{\pi/2} (-\sin^2 x - \cos^5 x)\, dx$$

$$= -\left[\frac{1}{2} \cdot \frac{\pi}{2} + \frac{4.2}{5.3.1} \right] = -\left[\frac{\pi}{4} + \frac{8}{15} \right].$$

(b) Let us put $\sin \theta = s$ and now apply $C_1 - C_2$ and $C_2 - C_3$ and use the formula $a^2 - b^2 = (a+b)(a-b)$. Also take out $2\sin\theta + 1$ *i.e.* $2s + 1$ common from each of new C_1 and C_2.

$$\therefore \quad \Delta = (2s+1)^2 \begin{vmatrix} 2s-1 & 0 & 1 \\ -3 & 3 & (s-1)^2 \\ 0 & 1 & s^2 \end{vmatrix}$$

Again apply $R_2 - 3R_3$ in order to make two zeros.

$$\Delta = (2s+1)^2 \begin{vmatrix} 2s-1 & 0 & 1 \\ -3 & 0 & -(2s^2+2s-1) \\ 0 & 1 & s^2 \end{vmatrix}$$

$$= -(2s+1)^2 \begin{vmatrix} 2s-1 & 1 \\ -3 & -(2s^2+2s-1) \end{vmatrix}$$

$$= (2s+1)^2 \{(2s-1)(2s^2+2s-1) - 3\}$$

$$= (2s+1)^2 [4s^3 + 2s^2 - 4s - 2]$$

$$= (2s+1)^2 [2s^2(2s+1) - 2(2s+1)]$$

$$= (2s+1)^2 (2s+1)(2s^2 - 2)$$

$$= -2(2s+1)^3 (1-s^2)$$

Now $1 - s^2 = 1 - \sin^2\theta = \cos^2\theta = c^2$

$$\therefore \quad \Delta = -2(8s^3 + 3.4s^2 + 3.2s + 1)c^2$$

$$= -16\sin^3\theta\cos^2\theta - 24\sin^2\theta\cos^2\theta$$
$$\qquad\quad - 12\sin\theta\cos^2\theta - 2\cos^2\theta$$

Now we know that
$$\int_{-a}^{a} f(x)\, dx = 0 \text{ if } f(x) \text{ is odd}$$
$$= 2\int_0^a \text{ if } f(x) \text{ is even (Prop. V)}$$

$$\therefore \int_{-\pi/2}^{\pi/2} \Delta\, d\theta = 0 - 24.2\int_0^{\pi/2} \sin^2\theta\cos^2\theta\, d\theta - 0$$
$$\qquad\qquad\qquad - 2.2\int_0^{\pi/2}\cos^2\theta\, d\theta$$

$$= -48 \cdot \frac{1}{4} \cdot \frac{1}{2} \cdot \frac{\pi}{2} - 4 \cdot \frac{1}{2} \cdot \frac{\pi}{2} \text{ (Gamma } f^n)$$

$$= -3\pi - \pi = -4\pi.$$

63. (a) $A_n + A_{n+2} - 2A_{n+1}$

$$= \int_0^{\pi/2} \frac{(1 - \cos 2nx) + [1 - \cos(2n+4)x]}{-2[1 - \cos(2n+2)x]} \Big/ (1 - \cos 2x)\, dx$$

$$= \int_0^{\pi/2} \frac{-2\cos(2n+2)x\cos 2x + 2\cos(2n+2)x}{(1 - \cos 2x)}\, dx$$

$$= \int_0^{\pi/2} 2\cos(2n+2)x\, dx$$

$$= 2\left[\frac{\sin(2n+2)x}{2n+2}\right]_0^{\pi/2} = 0.$$

$$\therefore \quad A_n + A_{n+2} - 2A_{n+1} = 0 \qquad \dots(1)$$

Again $A_1 = \displaystyle\int_0^{\pi/2} \frac{1-\cos 2x}{1-\cos 2x}\,dx = [x]_0^{\pi/2} = \frac{\pi}{2}$

Now in the given determinant write A_1 in place of $\pi/2$ in the first element in R_1.

Apply $C_1 + C_3 - 2C_2$, then by virtue of relation (1) each element in new C_1 will be zero corresponding to $n = 1, 4, 7$. $\therefore \quad \Delta = 0$

(b) In order to make two zeros, apply $C_2 - \cos^2\theta\, C_1$ and then expand with C_2.

$$\therefore \quad f(\theta) = \cos^4\theta = \left(\frac{1+\cos 2\theta}{2}\right)^2$$

$$\therefore \quad \int_0^{\pi/4} f(\theta)\,d\theta$$

$$= \frac{1}{4}\int_0^{\pi/4} (1 + 2\cos 2\theta + \cos^2 2\theta)\,d\theta.$$

Put $2\theta = t$ and adjust the limits

$$I = \frac{1}{4}\int_0^{\pi/2} (1 + 2\cos t + \cos^2 t)\frac{1}{2}\,dt$$

$$= \frac{1}{8}\left[\frac{\pi}{2} + 2 + \frac{1}{2}\cdot\frac{\pi}{2}\right] = \frac{3\pi + 8}{32}.$$

§ 2. System of linear Equations.

Definition 1. *A system of linear equations in n unknowns* $x_1, x_2, x_3, \dots x_n$ *is of the form :*

$$\left.\begin{array}{l} a_{11}x_1 + a_{12}x_2 + \dots + a_{1n}x_n = b_1 \\ a_{21}x_1 + a_{22}x_2 + \dots + a_{2n}x_n = b_2 \\ \dots\dots\dots\dots\dots\dots\dots\dots\dots\dots\dots \\ \dots\dots\dots\dots\dots\dots\dots\dots\dots\dots\dots \\ a_{n1}x_1 + a_{n2}x_2 + \dots + a_{nn}x_n = b_n \end{array}\right\} \quad \dots(A)$$

If $b_1, b_2, \dots\dots\dots, b_n$ are all zero, the system is called **homogeneous** and non-homogeneous if at least one b_i is non-zero.

Definition 2. *The* **solution set** *of the system (A) is an n tuple* $(\alpha_1, \alpha_2, \dots, \alpha_n)$ *of real numbers (or complex numbers if the coefficients are complex) which satisfy each of the equations of the system.*

Definition 3. *A system of equations is called* **consistent** *if it has at least one solution;* **inconsistent** *if it does not have any solution;* **determinate** *if it has a unique solution;* **indeterminate** *if it has more than one solution.*

(A) Non-homogeneous Equations in two unknowns.

Consider the system of equations

$$\left.\begin{array}{l} a_1 x + b_1 y = c_1 \\ a_2 x + b_2 y = c_2 \end{array}\right\} \quad \dots(1)$$

We consider the following cases :

1. $a_i, b_i, c_i\ (i = 1, 2)$ **are all zero.** Then any pair of numbers (x, y) is a solution of the system (1) since in this case equation reduces to an identity. So in this case equations are always **consistent** and **indeterminate.**

2. $a_i, b_i\ (i = 1, 2)$ are all zero, but at least one of c_1 and c_2 is non-zero. Then the system has no solution *i.e.* the equations are **inconsistent.**

3. **At least one of** $a_i, b_i\ (i = 1, 2)$ **is non-zero.**

Suppose $b_2 \neq 0$. Then system (1), is equivalent to the system

$$\left.\begin{array}{l} a_1 x + b_1 y = c_1 \\ \dfrac{a_2}{b_2} x + y = \dfrac{c_2}{b_2} \end{array}\right\} \quad \dots(2)$$

i.e., if the pair (x_0, y_0) is a solution of system (1), then it is also a solution of system (2), and vice-versa.

Multiplying the second equation of system (2) by b_1 and subtracting from first, we get

$$\left(a_1 - \frac{a_2}{b_2}b_1\right)x = c_1 - \frac{c_2}{b_2}\cdot b_1. \quad \dots(3)$$

Now replacing the first equation of system (2) by equation (3), we obtain the system

$$\left.\begin{array}{l} \left(a_1 - \dfrac{a_2}{b_2}b_1\right)x = c_1 - \dfrac{c_2}{b_2}\cdot b_1 \\ \dfrac{a_2}{b_2}x + y = \dfrac{c_2}{b_2} \end{array}\right\} \quad \dots(4)$$

which is evidently equivalent to system (2).

(a) If $a_1 - \dfrac{a_2}{b_2}b_1 \neq 0$ *i.e.*, if $a_1 b_2 - a_2 b_1 \neq 0$,

then we find from the first equation of system (4) that

$$x = \frac{c_1 b_2 - c_2 b_1}{a_1 b_2 - a_2 b_1} \quad \dots(5)$$

Substituting this value of x into the second equation of system (4), we obtain

$$y = \frac{a_1 c_2 - a_2 c_1}{a_1 b_2 - a_2 b_1}$$

For convenience, we write

$$\Delta = \begin{vmatrix} a_1 & b_1 \\ a_2 & b_2 \end{vmatrix}, \quad \Delta_x = \begin{vmatrix} c_1 & b_1 \\ c_2 & b_2 \end{vmatrix},$$

$$\Delta_y = \begin{vmatrix} a_1 & c_1 \\ a_2 & c_2 \end{vmatrix} \quad \dots(6)$$

[Note that Δ_x and Δ_y are obtained by replacing the first and second columns in Δ by the column of c_1 and c_2 respectively].

Then (5) and (6) can be written as

$$x = \frac{\Delta_x}{\Delta}, \quad y = \frac{\Delta_y}{\Delta} \quad \dots(7)$$

This is known as **Crammer's rule.** If $a_1 b_2 - a_2 b_1 \neq 0$ *then the system (4) or system (1)* has the unique solution given by (7). Hence in this case, the equations are **consistent and determinate.**

(b) Now let $\Delta = a_1 b_2 - a_2 b_1 = 0$.
Then the system (4) has the form

$$\begin{cases} 0 \cdot x = c_1 b_2 - c_2 b_1 \\ \dfrac{a_2}{b_2} x + y = \dfrac{c_2}{b_2} \end{cases} \quad ...(9)$$

Obviously this system has no solution if

$$c_1 b_2 - c_2 b_1 = \Delta_x \neq 0$$

thus in this case, the equations are **inconsistent.**
But if $\Delta_x = 0$, then any pair of numbers (x, y),

where $y = \dfrac{c_2}{b_2} - \dfrac{a_2}{b_2} x$, $x \in \mathbf{R}$, is a solution of

system (9).
So in this case, the equations are **consistent** and **indeterminate.**

We summarize the whole discussion given in (A) as follows :

(i) If $\Delta \neq 0$, then the system is **consistent** and **determinate** and its solution is given by

$$x = \frac{\Delta_x}{\Delta}, \quad y = \frac{\Delta_y}{\Delta} \qquad \text{(i.e. unique solution)}$$

(ii) If $\Delta = 0$, but at least one of the numbers Δ_x, Δ_y is non-zero, then the system is **inconsistent** i.e., it has no solution.

(iii) If $\Delta = 0$, and $\Delta_x = \Delta_y = 0$ but at least one of the numbers a_1, b_1, a_2, b_2 is non-zero, then the system has infinite number of solutions and hence it is **consistent** and **indeterminate.**

(iv) If $a_i = b_i = c_i = 0$ $(i = 1, 2)$, then the system has infinite number of solutions and so it is **consistent** and **indeterminate.**

(B) Homogeneous linear equations in two unknowns.
Consider the system of equations

$$\begin{cases} a_1 x + b_1 y = 0 \\ a_2 x + b_2 y = 0 \end{cases} \quad ...(10)$$

The system always has the solution $x = 0, y = 0$.
It follows from the discussion in part (A) that if $\Delta \neq 0$, then the system (10) has the unique solution $x = 0$, $y = 0$.
And if $\Delta = 0$, and at least one of a_1, a_2, b_1, b_2 is non-zero, then system (10) reduces to the single equation so that any pair of numbers (x, y) is a solution. Thus system (10) is always **consistent.**

(C) Non-homogeneous linear equations in three unknowns.
Consider the system of equations

$$\begin{cases} a_1 x + b_1 y + c_1 z = d_1 \\ a_2 x + b_2 y + c_2 z = d_2 \\ a_3 x + b_3 y + c_3 z = d_3 \end{cases} \quad ...(1)$$

Let us introduce the following notations

$$\Delta = \begin{vmatrix} a_1 & b_1 & c_1 \\ a_2 & b_2 & c_2 \\ a_3 & b_3 & c_3 \end{vmatrix}, \quad \Delta_x = \begin{vmatrix} d_1 & b_1 & c_1 \\ d_2 & b_2 & c_2 \\ d_3 & b_3 & c_3 \end{vmatrix}$$

$$\Delta_y = \begin{vmatrix} a_1 & d_1 & c_1 \\ a_2 & d_2 & c_2 \\ a_3 & d_3 & c_3 \end{vmatrix}, \quad \Delta_z = \begin{vmatrix} a_1 & b_1 & d_1 \\ a_2 & b_2 & d_2 \\ a_3 & b_3 & d_3 \end{vmatrix}$$

Without going into details, we give the following rule for testing the consistency of the system (1).

1. Let $a_i = b_i = c_i = d_i = 0$, $i = 1, 2, 3$.
   In this case any triplet (x, y, z) is a solution of the system.
   Hence equations are **consistent and indeterminate.**

2. If $a_i = b_i = c_i = 0$, $i = 1, 2, 3$ and at least one d_i $(i = 1, 2, 3)$ is non-zero, then the system has no solution, i.e., the equations in this case are **inconsistent.**

3. Let $\Delta \neq 0$. In this case the system (1) has the unique solution.

$$x = \frac{\Delta_x}{\Delta}, \quad y = \frac{\Delta_y}{\Delta}, \quad z = \frac{\Delta_z}{\Delta} \qquad ...(2)$$

This is known as **Crammer's rule.** So equations in this case are **consistent and determinate.**

4. If $\Delta = 0$, $\Delta_x \neq 0$ (or $\Delta_y \neq 0$ or $\Delta_z \neq 0$), then the system has no solution so that equations are **inconsistent.**

5. If $\Delta = \Delta_x = \Delta_y = \Delta_z = 0$ and at least one of the cofactors of Δ is non-zero, then the system will have an infinite number of solutions. In this case, any one of the variables can be given arbitrary value and other variables can be expressed in terms of that variable.
   In such cases, the three equations reduce to two equations.
   If all the cofactors $\Delta, \Delta_x, \Delta_y, \Delta_z$ are zero but elements of Δ are not all zero, then in this case the system will reduce to single equation and any two variables can be given arbitrary values. So equations are **consistent and indeterminate.**

(D) Homogeneous linear equations.
If in (1), we take $d_i = 0$ $(i = 1, 2, 3)$ then the system is called the homogeneous system of equations.
For such a system if $\Delta \neq 0$, then it has the unique solution $x = 0$, $y = 0$, $z = 0$. **(Trivial)**
If $\Delta = 0$, then the system has an infinite number of solutions.
So such system of equations is **always consistent.**

§ 4. Three equations in two unknowns.

Consider the equations

$$\begin{cases} a_1 x + b_1 y = c_1 \\ a_2 x + b_2 y = c_2 \\ a_3 x + b_3 y = c_3 \end{cases} \quad ...(3)$$

The system (3) will be **consistent** if the solutions set of any two satisfies the third equation, i.e., if

$$\begin{vmatrix} a_1 & b_1 & c_1 \\ a_2 & b_2 & c_2 \\ a_3 & b_3 & c_3 \end{vmatrix} = 0.$$

Note : The factors of the following two determinants be remembered.

$$\begin{vmatrix} 1 & 1 & 1 \\ a & b & c \\ a^2 & b^2 & c^2 \end{vmatrix} = \begin{vmatrix} 1 & a & a^2 \\ 1 & b & b^2 \\ 1 & c & c^2 \end{vmatrix}$$

$$= (a-b)(b-c)(c-a)$$

$$\begin{vmatrix} 1 & 1 & 1 \\ a & b & c \\ a^3 & b^3 & c^3 \end{vmatrix} = \begin{vmatrix} 1 & a & a^3 \\ 1 & b & b^3 \\ 1 & c & c^3 \end{vmatrix}$$

$$= (a-b)(b-c)(c-a)(a+b+c)$$

*§ 5. Gist of discussion in simple language :

1. **Consistent :** Solution exists whether unique or infinite number of solutions.
2. **Inconsistent :** Solution does not exist.
3. **Homogeneous Equations :** Constant terms zero.
4. **Trivial solution :** All variables zero *i.e.* $x = 0, y = 0, z = 0$
5. **Non-trivial Solution :** Infinite number of solutions.
   Illustration : $a_1 x + b_1 y = c_1$ $a_2 x + b_2 y = c_2$
   $$\Delta = \begin{vmatrix} a_1 & b_1 \\ a_2 & b_2 \end{vmatrix}, \Delta_1 \text{ or } \Delta_x = \begin{vmatrix} c_1 & b_1 \\ c_2 & b_2 \end{vmatrix},$$
   $$\Delta_2 \text{ or } \Delta_y = \begin{vmatrix} a_1 & c_1 \\ a_2 & c_2 \end{vmatrix}$$

6. **Case I. Intersecting lines**
   $2x + 3y = 10$ and $x + y = 4$
   $\therefore$ $x = 2, y = 2$
   $$\Delta = \begin{vmatrix} 2 & 3 \\ 1 & 1 \end{vmatrix} = -1, \Delta \neq 0.$$
   Solution is unique, consistent.

7. **Case II. Only one line** $2x + 3y = 10$ $4x + 6y = 20$

Here $\Delta = \begin{vmatrix} 2 & 3 \\ 4 & 6 \end{vmatrix} = 0,$

but $\Delta_1 = \begin{vmatrix} 10 & 2 \\ 20 & 4 \end{vmatrix} = 0, \Delta_2 = 0$

As a matter of fact on division by 2 the second equation reduces to first. Thus we have got only one line $2x + 3y = 10$ on which lie infinite number of points. Thus there are **infinite number of solutions and the system is consistent.** $\left(k, \dfrac{10 - 3k}{2} \right)$ are infinite number of solutions by giving different values to k.

8. **Case III.** $\begin{array}{l} 2x + 3y = 10 \\ 4x + 6y = 15 \end{array}$ or $\begin{array}{l} 2x + 3y = 10 \\ 2x + 3y = 15/2 \end{array}$

i.e. **parallel lines** which we know do not intersect and hence no solution
i.e. **inconsistent.** Here $\Delta = 0$ but $\Delta_1 \neq 0, \Delta_2 \neq 0$

Summary :
(i) $\Delta \neq 0$ Unique (Intersecting lines) Consistent
(ii) $\Delta = 0, \Delta_1 = 0, \Delta_2 = 0$ (Identical lines) Consistent, Infinite solution.
(iii) $\Delta = 0, \Delta_1 \neq 0, \Delta_2 \neq 0$ (Parallel lines) Inconsistent. No solution.

9. **Homogeneous :** $a_1 x + b_1 y = 0$ $a_2 x + b_2 y = 0$
   $\Delta \neq 0$, Unique $x = 0, y = 0$, **Trivial**.
   $\Delta = 0$, Identical line through origin, **Non-trivial** solution.

10.* **Concurrent lines : Two variables, three equations**
   $a_1 x + b_1 y = c_1$, $a_2 x + b_2 y = c_2$, $a_3 x + b_3 y = c_3$
   The point of intersection of any two lines should satisfy the third.
   $$\therefore \quad D = \begin{vmatrix} a_1 & b_1 & c_1 \\ a_2 & b_2 & c_2 \\ a_3 & b_3 & c_3 \end{vmatrix} = 0$$
   is the required condition.

11.* **Crammer's rule :** $\dfrac{x}{\Delta_1} = \dfrac{y}{\Delta_2} = \dfrac{z}{\Delta_3} = \dfrac{1}{\Delta}$ $(\Delta \neq 0)$

Problem Set (4)

Solution of equations both homogeneous and non-homogeneous. Crammer's rule, Trivial and non-trivial solutions.

(A) Concurrent Lines $D = 0$.

1. Find the value of λ if the following equations are consistent
   $$x + y - 3 = 0$$
   $$(1 + \lambda) x + (2 + \lambda) y - 8 = 0$$
   $$x - (1 + \lambda) y + (2 + \lambda) = 0$$

2.* If the equations
   $$ax + hy + g = 0,\ hx + by + f = 0,$$
   $$gx + fy + c = \lambda$$
   are consistent, show that
   $$\lambda = \frac{abc + 2fgh - af^2 - bg^2 - ch^2}{ab - h^2}.$$

Another Form :
If the system of equations $ax + hy + g = 0$, $hx + by + f = 0$ and $ax^2 + 2hxy + by^2 + 2gx + 2fy + c = \lambda$ are consistent, then prove that λ is as given above.

3. If the equations
   $$(b + c) x + (c + a) y + (a + b) = 0, cx + ay + b = 0$$
   and $ax + by + c = 0$ are consistent, then show that either
   $$a + b + c = 0 \quad \text{or} \quad a = b = c.$$

4. (a)* If a, b, c are all different and the equations
   $$ax + a^2 y + (a^3 + 1) = 0$$
   $$bx + b^2 y + (b^3 + 1) = 0$$

$$cx + c^2 y + (c^3 + 1) = 0$$

are consistent then prove that $abc + 1 = 0$.

(b)* Find those values of c for which the equations :

$$2x + 3y = 3$$
$$(c + 2) x + (c + 4) y = c + 6$$
$$(c + 2)^2 x + (c + 4)^2 y = (c + 6)^2$$

are consistent. Also solve above equations for these values of c. **(Roorkee 1996)**

5.* Find the value of a if the three equations are consistent

$$(a + 1)^3 x + (a + 2)^3 y = (a + 3)^3$$
$$(a + 1) x + (a + 2) y = a + 3$$
$$x + y = 1.$$

6. If $bc + qr = ca + rp = ab + pq = -1$, show that

$$\begin{vmatrix} ap & a & p \\ bq & b & q \\ cr & c & r \end{vmatrix} = 0$$

(B) Homogeneous Equations.

$\Delta \neq 0$ **for Trivial Solution**

$\Delta = 0$ **for Non-Trivial Solution**

7. (a) For what value of k do the following system of equations possess a non-tirvial solution over the set of rationals

$$x + ky + 3z = 0$$
$$3x + ky - 2z = 0$$
$$2x + 3y - 4z = 0$$

For that value of k, find all the solutions of the system.

(b) Find all values of k for which the following system possesses a non-trivial solution

$$x + ky + 3z = 0, \quad kx + 2y + 2z = 0,$$
$$2x + 3y + 4z = 0. \quad \textbf{(Dhanbad 1992)}$$

8. (a)* If the system of equations

$$(k - 1) x + (3k + 1) y + 2kz = 0$$
$$(k - 1) x + (4k - 2) y + (k + 3) z = 0$$
$$2x + (3k + 1) y + 3 (k - 1) z = 0$$

has a non-zero solution, then prove that $k = 0, 3$

(b) If the system of equations $x - ky - z = 0$, $kx - y - z = 0$, $x + y - z = 0$ has a non zero solution, then the possible values of k are

(a) $-1, 2$ (b) $1, 2$

(c) $0, 1$ (d) $-1, 1$ **(I.I.T. Sc. 2000)**

(c) $x + ay = 0, y + az = 0, z + ax = 0$. The value of a for which the system of equation has infinitely many solutions is

(a) $a = 1$ (b) $a = 0$

(c) $a = -1$ (d) no value

(Screening 2003)

9. Find the real values of r for which the following system of linear equations has a non-trivial solution. Also find the non-trivial solutions :

$$2rx - 2y + 3z = 0$$
$$x + ry + 2z = 0$$

$$2x + rz = 0 \qquad \textbf{(Roorkee 2000)}$$

10. (a) Given $x = cy + bz$, $y = az + cx$, $z = bx + ay$ where x, y, z are not all zero, prove that $a^2 + b^2 + c^2 + 2abc = 1$.

(b)* If x, y, z are not all zeros and

$$ax + y + z = 0, \quad x + by + z = 0, \quad x + y + cz = 0,$$

then prove that $\dfrac{1}{1-a} + \dfrac{1}{1-b} + \dfrac{1}{1-c} = 1$.

(c) If the system of equations $x = a(y + z)$, $y = b(z + x)$, $z = c(x + y), (a, b, c \neq -1)$ has a non-zero solution, then the value of $\dfrac{a}{1+a} + \dfrac{b}{1+b} + \dfrac{c}{1+c}$ is

(a) 2   (b) 1

(c) 0   (d) -1

11.* If the system of equations

$$(a - \lambda) x + by + cz = 0$$
$$bx + (c - \lambda) y + az = 0$$
$$cx + ay + (b - \lambda) z = 0$$

have non-trivial solution, then there will be three values of λ whose product is the circulant

$$\begin{vmatrix} a & b & c \\ b & c & a \\ c & a & b \end{vmatrix}.$$

12.* If x, y, z are not all zero and if

$$ax + by + cz = 0$$
$$bx + cy + az = 0$$
$$cx + ay + bz = 0$$

prove that $x : y : z = 1 : 1 : 1$ or $1 : \omega : \omega^2$ or $1 : \omega^2 : \omega$ where ω is one of the imaginary roots of unity.

13. (a) If $a > b > c$ and the system of equations $ax + by + cz = 0$, $bx + cy + az = 0$, $cx + ay + bz = 0$ has a non-trivial solution then prove that both the roots of the quadratic equation $at^2 + bt + c = 0$ are real.

(b) If $a = \dfrac{x}{y - z}$, $b = \dfrac{y}{z - x}$ and $c = \dfrac{z}{x - y}$ where x, y, z are not all zero, prove that $1 + ab + bc + ca = 0$.

14. If $\dfrac{ax}{y} + \dfrac{by}{x} = c$, $\dfrac{by}{z} + \dfrac{cz}{y} = a$, $\dfrac{cz}{x} + \dfrac{ax}{z} = b$, then find the values of

(a) $\dfrac{yz}{x^2} + \dfrac{zx}{y^2} + \dfrac{xy}{z^2}$ (b) $a^3 + b^3 + c^3$

15. (a)* Consider the system of linear equations in x, y, z

$$(\sin 3\theta) x - y + z = 0$$
$$(\cos 2\theta) x + 4y + 3z = 0$$
$$2x + 7y + 7z = 0.$$

Find the value of θ for which this system has non-trivial solutions.

(b)* Let λ and α be real. Find the set of all values of λ for which the system of linear equations

$\lambda x + (\sin \alpha) y + (\cos \alpha) z = 0$

$x + (\cos \alpha) y + (\sin \alpha) z = 0$

$- x + (\sin \alpha) y - (\cos \alpha) z = 0$

has a non-trivial solution. For $\lambda = 1$, find all values of α. **(I.I.T. 1993)**

16. (a)* Let α_1, α_2 and β_1, β_2 be the roots of $ax^2 + bx + c = 0$ and $px^2 + qx + r = 0$ respectively. If the system of equations $\alpha_1 y + \alpha_2 z = 0$ and $\beta_1 y + \beta_2 z = 0$ has non-trivial solution, then prove that $\dfrac{b^2}{q^2} = \dfrac{ac}{pr}$.

   (b) If a, b, c are in G.P. with common ratio r_1 and α, β, γ also form a G.P. with common ratio r_2, then find the conditions that r_1 and r_2 must satisfy so that the equations $ax + \alpha y + z = 0$, $bx + \beta y + z = 0$, $cx + \gamma y + z = 0$ have only zero solution.

17. If A, B, C are the angles of a triangle show that system of equations

   $x \sin 2A + y \sin C + z \sin B = 0$

   $x \sin C + y \sin 2B + z \sin A = 0$

   $x \sin B + y \sin A + z \sin 2C = 0$

   possesses non-trivial solution.

18. If A, B, C are the angles of a triangle, then show that the system of equations

   $- x + y \cos C + z \cos B = 0$,

   $x \cos C - y + z \cos A = 0$

   and $x \cos B + y \cos A - z = 0$

   has non-zero solution.

19.* If the equations

   $(f^2 - bc) x + (ch - fg) y + (bg - hf) z = 0$

   $(ch - fg) x + (g^2 - ca) y + (af - gh) z = 0$

   $(bg - hf) x + (af - gh) y + (h^2 - ab) z = 0$

   possess a non-trivial solution, then

   $\begin{vmatrix} a & h & g \\ h & b & f \\ g & f & c \end{vmatrix} = 0.$

20. Three vectors $\mathbf{a}, \mathbf{b}, \mathbf{c}$ are given by

   (a) $\mathbf{a} = \mathbf{i} - 3\mathbf{j} + 2\mathbf{k}, \mathbf{b} = 2\mathbf{i} - 4\mathbf{j} - 4\mathbf{k}, \mathbf{c} = 3\mathbf{i} + 2\mathbf{j} - \mathbf{k}$

   (b) $\mathbf{a} = \mathbf{i} + \mathbf{j} + \mathbf{k}, \mathbf{b} = 2\mathbf{i} + 3\mathbf{j} - \mathbf{k}, \mathbf{c} = -\mathbf{i} - 2\mathbf{j} + 2\mathbf{k}$

   Determine whether the systems of vectors in (i) and (ii) are linearly independent or dependent.

(C) Crammer's rule.

$$\frac{x}{\Delta_1} = \frac{y}{\Delta_2} = \frac{z}{\Delta_3} = \frac{1}{\Delta}$$

21. (a) $x + y + z = 1$

   $ax + by + cz = k$

   $a^2 x + b^2 y + c^2 z = k^2$

   (b)* $ax + by + cz = k$

   $a^2 x + b^2 y + c^2 z = k^2$

   $a^3 x + b^3 y + c^3 z = k^3$ **(M.N.R. 1995)**

22. (a) $x + 2y + 3z = 6$

   $2x + 4y + z = 7$

   $3x + 2y + 9z = 14.$

   (b)* $x + 2y + 3z = 6$

   $2x + 4y + z = 17$

   $3x + 2y + 9z = 2$ **(Roorkee 1994)**

   (c) Solve by Crammer rule the equation

   $\dfrac{1}{x} + \dfrac{2}{y} + \dfrac{1}{z} = 2, \dfrac{3}{x} - \dfrac{4}{y} - \dfrac{2}{z} = 1, \dfrac{2}{x} + \dfrac{5}{y} - \dfrac{2}{z} = 3.$

23. $x + y + z = 11$

   $2x - 6y - z = 0$

   $3x + 4y + 2z = 0.$

24. $x + y + z = 6$

   $x - y + z = 2$

   $2x + y - z = 1.$

25. (a) $5x - 6y + 4z = 15$

   $7x + 4y - 3z = 19$

   $2x + y + 6z = 46.$

   (b) $x + y + z = 1$

   $3x + 5y + 6z = 4$

   $9x + 2y - 36z = 17.$

26. Find a, b, c when $f(x) = ax^2 + bx + c = 0$ and

   $f(0) = 6, \ f(2) = 11, \ f(-3) = 6.$

   Determine $f(x)$ and find the value of $f(1)$.

27.* $x \cos \theta - y \sin \theta + z = 1 + \cos \phi$

   $x \sin \theta + y \cos \theta + z = 1 - \sin \phi$

   $x \cos (\theta + \phi) - y \sin (\theta + \phi) + z = 2$

   where $\phi \neq \pi / 4$, find x, y, z and hence the value of $x^2 + y^2 + z^2$.

(D) $\Delta = 0, \ \Delta_1 \neq 0.$ **Inconsistent.**

$\Delta = 0,$ **any of** $\Delta_1, \Delta_2, \Delta_3$ **is zero.**

Infinite solutions.

28. (a) Show that there is no solution for the equations

   $x + 4y - 2z = 3$

   $3x + y + 5z = 7$

   $2x + 3y + z = 5.$

   (b) $2x - y - 2z = 2, x - 2y + z = -4, x + y + \lambda z = 4$ then the value of λ such that system of equations has no solution, is

   (a) 1   (b) 2

   (c) 3   (d) $- 3$ **(IIT-Screening 2004)**

29.* Find k for which the set of equations

   $x + y - 2z = 0$

   $2x - 3y + z = 0$

   $x - 5y + 4z = k$

   are consistent and find the solutions for all such values of k.

30. (a) For what values of m does the system of equations $3x + my = m$ and $2x - 5y = 20$ has a solution satisfying the conditions $x > 0, \ y > 0$.

(b) The number of values of k for which the system of equations

$$(k+1)x + 8y = 4k$$
$$kx + (k+3)y = 3k-1$$

has infinitely many solutions is

(a) 0   (b) 1

(c) 2   (d) infinite   (I.I.T. Sc. 2002)

31.* Show that the system of equations

$$3x - y + 4z = 3$$
$$x + 2y - 3z = -2$$
$$6x + 5y + \lambda z = -3$$

has at least one solution for any real number λ. Find the set of solutions if $\lambda = -5$.

32. Test the consistency and solve them when consistent, the following system of equations for all values of λ :

$$x + y + z = 1, \quad x + 3y - 2z = \lambda,$$
$$3x + (\lambda + 2)y - 3z = 2\lambda + 1. \quad \textbf{(Roorkee 2001)}$$

33.* For what real values of k, the system of equations

$$x + 2y + z = 1; x + 3y + 4z = k; x + 5y + 10z = k^2$$

has solution ? Find the solution in each case.

                                 (Roorkee 1997)

34. (a)* For what values of p and q, the system of equations

$$2x + py + 6z = 8$$
$$x + 2y + qz = 5$$
$$x + y + 3z = 4$$

has (i) no solution (ii) a unique solution (iii) infinitely many solutions.   **(Roorkee 1995)**

(b) The system of equations

$$\alpha x + y + z = \alpha - 1$$
$$x + \alpha y + z = \alpha - 1$$
$$x + y + \alpha z = \alpha - 1$$

has no solution if $\alpha = $

(a) not -2 (b) 1

(c) -2 (d) either -2 or 1

                                 (AIEEE 2005)

35. (a)* Using matrix method find the values of λ and μ so that the system of equations

$$2x - 3y + 5z = 12$$
$$3x + y + \lambda z = \mu$$
$$x - 7y + 8z = 17$$

has (i) a unique solution; (ii) infinite solutions; and (iii) no solution.   **(Roorkee 1998)**

(b)* For what values of p and q the system of equations

$$2x + 5y + pz = q$$
$$x + 2y + 3z = 14$$
$$x + y + z = 6 \text{ are consistent ?}$$

36. For all values of λ, find the rank of the matrix

$$\begin{bmatrix} 1 & 4 & 5 \\ \lambda & 8 & 8\lambda - 6 \\ 1 + \lambda^2 & 8\lambda + 4 & 2\lambda + 21 \end{bmatrix}$$

                                 (Roorkee 1999)

37. $A = \begin{bmatrix} a & 0 & 1 \\ 1 & c & b \\ 1 & d & b \end{bmatrix}, B = \begin{bmatrix} a & 1 & 1 \\ 0 & d & c \\ f & g & h \end{bmatrix}, U = \begin{bmatrix} f \\ g \\ h \end{bmatrix}, V = \begin{bmatrix} a^2 \\ 0 \\ 0 \end{bmatrix}.$

If there is vector matrix X, such that $AX = U$ has infinitely many solutions, then prove that $BX = V$ cannot have a unique solution. If $afd \neq 0$ then prove that $BX = V$ has no solution.   **(I.I.T. 2004)**

Solutions to Problem Set (4)

1. For the equations to be consistent, $D = 0$.

$$\therefore \quad D = \begin{vmatrix} 1 & 1 & -3 \\ 1+\lambda & 2+\lambda & -8 \\ 1 & -1-\lambda & 2+\lambda \end{vmatrix} = 0$$

Here the equations are in two variables x and y. If they are consistent then the values of x and y obtained from first two should satisfy the third and hence $D = 0$

Apply $C_2 - C_1, C_3 + 3C_1$

$$D = \begin{vmatrix} 1 & 0 & 0 \\ 1+\lambda & 1 & -5+3\lambda \\ 1 & -2-\lambda & 5+\lambda \end{vmatrix} = 0$$

or $(5 + \lambda) + (2 + \lambda)(-5 + 3\lambda) = 0$

or $5 + \lambda + (-10 + \lambda + 3\lambda^2) = 0$

or $3\lambda^2 + 2\lambda - 5 = 0$ or $(\lambda - 1)(3\lambda + 5) = 0$

$$\therefore \quad \lambda = 1, -5/3.$$

2. As in Q. (1) for consistency, we must have $D = 0$ i.e.

$$\begin{vmatrix} a & h & g \\ h & b & f \\ g & f & c-\lambda \end{vmatrix} = 0$$

or $\begin{vmatrix} a & h & g+0 \\ h & b & f+0 \\ g & f & c-\lambda \end{vmatrix} = 0$

or $\begin{vmatrix} a & h & g \\ h & b & f \\ g & f & c \end{vmatrix} + \begin{vmatrix} a & h & 0 \\ h & b & 0 \\ g & f & -\lambda \end{vmatrix} = 0,$

Expand

$a(bc - f^2) - h(ch - gf) + g(hf - bg) - \lambda(ab - h^2) = 0.$

$$\therefore \quad \lambda = \frac{abc + 2fgh - af^2 - bg^2 - ch^2}{ab - h^2}$$

Another Form :

The last equation is

$x(ax + hy + g) + y(hx + by + f) + (gx + by + c - \lambda) = 0$

or $gx + fy + c = \lambda$

Hence the three equations are same as of part (a). Hence same value of λ.

3. For consistency of three equations in two unknowns as in Q. 1, we must have $D = 0$

$$\Delta = \begin{vmatrix} b+c & c+a & a+b \\ c & a & b \\ a & b & c \end{vmatrix} = 0$$

or $\begin{vmatrix} b & c & a \\ c & a & b \\ a & b & c \end{vmatrix} = 0,$ by $R_1 - R_2$

or $3abc - a^3 - b^3 - c^3 = 0$

or $a^3 + b^3 + c^3 - 3abc = 0$

or $(a + b + c)(a^2 + b^2 + c^2 - ab - bc - ca) = 0$

or $\frac{1}{2}(a + b + c)[(b - c)^2 + (c - a)^2 + (a - b)^2] = 0$.

Hence either $a + b + c = 0$

or $b - c = 0$, $c - a = 0$, $a - b = 0$, i.e. $a = b = c$.

Hence the conditions are either

$a + b + c = 0$ or $a = b = c$.

4. (a) For consistency $D = 0$

$\therefore \begin{vmatrix} a & a^2 & a^3 + 1 \\ b & b^2 & b^3 + 1 \\ c & c^2 & c^3 + 1 \end{vmatrix} = 0$

Hence as in **Q. 10, Page 439-446**, we have
$1 + abc = 0$.

(b) As in **(A), P. 457**, the equation will be consistent (concurrent) if

$\begin{vmatrix} 2 & 3 & 3 \\ c + 2 & c + 4 & c + 6 \\ (c + 2)^2 & (c + 4)^2 & (c + 6)^2 \end{vmatrix} = 0$

Apply $C_3 - C_2$ and use formula $P^2 - Q^2$ and expand.

$\therefore c^2 + 10c = 0$ $\therefore c = 0, -10$.

$c = 0 \quad \begin{matrix} 2x + 3y = 3 \\ 2x + 4y = 6 \end{matrix} \}$

$\therefore x = -3, y = 3$.

$c = -10 \quad 2x + 3y = 3$
$\qquad\qquad -8x - 6y = -4$

or $4x + 3y = 2$ $\therefore x = -\frac{1}{2}, y = \frac{4}{3}$

These values also satisfy the third equation

$4x + 16y = 36$ or $64x + 36y = 16$.

5. The three equations in two unknowns will be consistent if $D = 0$

or $\begin{vmatrix} (a + 1)^3 & (a + 2)^3 & -(a + 3)^3 \\ (a + 1) & (a + 2) & -(a + 3) \\ 1 & 1 & -1 \end{vmatrix} = 0$

Cancel minus from third column

Now put $u = (a + 1)$, $v = a + 2$, $w = a + 3$.

Then $u - v = -1$, $v - w = -1$.

$w - u = 2$ and $u + v + w = 3a + 6$. ...(1)

Also $D = 0$ reduces to

$\begin{vmatrix} u^3 & v^3 & w^3 \\ u & v & w \\ 1 & 1 & 1 \end{vmatrix} = 0$

or $(u - v)(v - w)(w - u)(u + v + w) = 0$

by Q. 6 (a) P. 439-447,

or $(-1)(-1)(2)(3a + 6) = 0$

or $(a + 2) = 0$ or $a = -2$

6. Rewriting the given equations, we have

$1 + bc + qr = 0$

$1 + ca + rp = 0$

$1 + ab + pq = 0$.

Multiply 1st by ap, 2nd by bq and 3rd by cr, we get

$ap + (abc)p + (pqr)a = 0$

$bq + (abc)q + (pqr)b = 0$

$cr + (abc)r + (pqr)c = 0$.

Put $abc = x$ and $pqr = y$

$\therefore$ The above equations are

$px + ay + ap = 0$

$qx + by + bq = 0$

$rx + cy + cr = 0$.

These equations in x and y will be consistent if $D = 0$

or $\begin{vmatrix} p & a & ap \\ q & b & bq \\ r & c & cr \end{vmatrix} = 0$

Interchange C_1 and C_3

$\therefore \begin{vmatrix} ap & a & p \\ bq & b & q \\ cr & c & r \end{vmatrix} = 0$

7. (a) For non-trivial solution $D = 0$

or $\begin{vmatrix} 1 & k & 3 \\ 3 & k & -2 \\ 2 & 3 & -4 \end{vmatrix} = 0$

Apply $R_2 - 3R_1$, $R_3 - 2R_1$.

$\therefore \Delta = \begin{vmatrix} 1 & k & 3 \\ 0 & -2k & -11 \\ 0 & 3 - 2k & -10 \end{vmatrix} = 0$

or $20k + 11(3 - 2k) = 0$

or $33 - 2k = 0$ $\therefore k = 33/2$.

Putting the value of k, the equations are

$x + \frac{33}{2}y + 3z = 0$ ...(1)

$3x + \frac{33}{2}y - 2z = 0$ ...(2)

$2x + 3y - 4z = 0$. ...(3)

Multiply (1) by (3) and subtract from (2) and similarly multiply (1) by 2 and subtract from (3).

Thus we get the equivalent system of equations as

$x + \frac{33}{2}y + 3z = 0$

$-33y - 11z = 0$

$-30y - 10z = 0$.

From any of the last two, we get $3y = -z$,

or $\frac{y}{1} = \frac{z}{-3} = \lambda$, say. $\therefore y = \lambda$, $z = -3\lambda$.

From 1st $x + \frac{33}{2}y + 3z = 0$, we get

$x + \frac{33}{2}\lambda - 9\lambda = 0$ $\therefore x = -\frac{15}{2}\lambda$

$\therefore \quad x:y:z :: -\dfrac{15}{2}:1:-3$

(b) Ans. $k = 2, 5/4$

8. (a) For non-trivial solution $\Delta = 0$

$$\begin{vmatrix} k-1 & 3k+1 & 2k \\ k-1 & 4k-2 & k+3 \\ 2 & 3k+1 & 3k-3 \end{vmatrix} = 0$$

Apply $R_2 - R_1, R_3 - R_1$.

$$\Delta = \begin{vmatrix} k-1 & 3k+1 & 2k \\ 0 & k-3 & -(k-3) \\ -(k-3) & 0 & k-3 \end{vmatrix} = 0.$$

$$= (k-3)^2 \begin{vmatrix} k-1 & 3k+1 & 2k \\ 0 & 1 & -1 \\ -1 & 0 & 1 \end{vmatrix}$$

Apply $C_2 + C_3$.

$$= (k-3)^2 \begin{vmatrix} k-1 & 5k+1 & 2k \\ 0 & 0 & -1 \\ -1 & 1 & 1 \end{vmatrix} = 0$$

Expanding with 2nd row,

$(k-3)^2 \, 6k = 0 \quad \therefore \quad k = 0$ or 3.

*(b) Ans. (d). Set of homogeneous equations will have non-trivial solution if $\Delta = 0$

$$\Rightarrow \begin{vmatrix} 1 & -k & -1 \\ k & -1 & -1 \\ 1 & 1 & -1 \end{vmatrix} = 0$$

Apply $R_2 - R_1, R_3 - R_1$ and expand.

$k^2 - 1 = 0 \quad \therefore \quad k = \pm 1$.

(c) Ans. (c).

$$\Delta = 0 \Rightarrow \begin{vmatrix} 1 & a & 0 \\ 0 & 1 & a \\ a & 0 & 1 \end{vmatrix} = 0 \text{ or } 1 + a^3 = 0$$

or $(1+a)(1-a+a^2) = 0 \quad \therefore \quad a = -1$.

The other factor does not give real value of a.

9. $\Delta = 0 \Rightarrow r^3 - 2r - 4 = 0 \Rightarrow (r-2)(r^2 + 2r + 2) = 0$

$\therefore \quad r = 2$ as other factor gives imaginary roots.

Putting $r = 2$, the equation reduces to $4x - 2y + 3z = 0$,
$x + 2y + 2z = 0$ and $x + z = 0$

Putting $x + z = 0$, they reduce to $x - 2y = 0, 2y + z = 0$ and $x + z = 0$

Choosing $x = k$, we get $y = \dfrac{k}{2}, z = -k$ which give the required solutions.

10. (a) The given equations are
$$x - cy - bz = 0$$
$$cx - y + az = 0$$
$$bx + ay - z = 0$$

Since x, y, z are not all zero, the system will have non-trivial solution if

$$\Delta = \begin{vmatrix} 1 & -c & -b \\ c & -1 & a \\ b & a & -1 \end{vmatrix} = 0$$

or $1.(1-a^2) + c(-c-ab) - b(ac+b) = 0$

or $1 - a^2 - c^2 - abc - abc - b^2 = 0$

or $a^2 + b^2 + c^2 + 2abc = 1$.

(b) $\Delta = \begin{vmatrix} a & 1 & 1 \\ 1 & b & 1 \\ 1 & 1 & c \end{vmatrix} = 0$

Apply $C_1 - C_2, C_2 - C_3$ and expand.

(c) Ans. (b).

For non-trivial solution $\Delta = 0$

$$\therefore \quad \begin{vmatrix} 1 & -a & -a \\ b & -1 & b \\ c & c & -1 \end{vmatrix} = 0$$

Apply $C_1 - C_2, C_2 - C_3$

$$\Delta = \begin{vmatrix} 1+a & 0 & -a \\ 1+b & -(1+b) & b \\ 0 & (1+c) & -1 \end{vmatrix} = 0$$

$(1+a)\{(1+b) - b(1+c)\} - (1+b)a(1+c) = 0$

Divide by $(1+a)(1+b)(1+c)$

$$\therefore \quad \frac{1}{1+c} - \frac{b}{1+b} - \frac{a}{1+a} = 0$$

Subract 1 from both sides

$$-\frac{c}{1+c} - \frac{b}{1+b} - \frac{a}{1+a} = -1$$

$$\therefore \quad \Sigma \, \frac{a}{1+a} = 1 \Rightarrow \text{(b)}.$$

11. For non-trivial solution $\Delta = 0$

$$\therefore \quad \begin{vmatrix} a-\lambda & b & c \\ b & c-\lambda & a \\ c & a & b-\lambda \end{vmatrix} = 0$$

Above is a cubic in λ which will give three values of λ. If $p\lambda^3 + q\lambda^2 + r\lambda + s = 0$ and the roots be λ_1, λ_2 and λ_3 then $\lambda_1 \lambda_2 \lambda_3 = -\dfrac{s}{p}$ where s is the constant term in the given equation and p is the coefficient of λ^3. Clearly the coefficient of λ^3 is $-1 = p$.

The constant term is obtained by putting $\lambda = 0$ and it is

$$\begin{vmatrix} a & b & c \\ b & c & a \\ c & a & b \end{vmatrix} = D = \text{circulant}.$$

$$\therefore \quad \lambda_1 \lambda_2 \lambda_3 = -\frac{D}{-1} = D = \text{circulant}.$$

12. For non-trivial solution, we must have

$$\begin{vmatrix} a & b & c \\ b & c & a \\ c & a & b \end{vmatrix} = 0$$

or $3abc - a^3 - b^3 - c^3 = 0$

or $(a+b+c)(a^2+b^2+c^2-bc-ca-ab) = 0$

or $\dfrac{1}{2}(a+b+c)[(b-c)^2 + (c-a)^2 + (a-b)^2] = 0$.

Thus for non-trivial solution we have

$$a+b+c=0 \quad \text{or} \quad a=b=c.$$

When $a+b+c=0$,

then 1st two given equations can be written as

$$ax+by-(a+b)z=0$$

and $bx-(a+b)y+az=0$

Solving these equations, we get

$$\frac{x}{ab+(a+b)^2}=\frac{y}{-b(a+b)-a^2}=\frac{z}{-a(a+b)-b^2}$$

or $\frac{x}{1}=\frac{y}{1}=\frac{z}{1}=k.$

When $a=b=c$, the three equations reduce to a single equation

$$x+y+z=0.$$

Since $1+\omega+\omega^2=0$, the solution set can be written as

$$(k,k\omega,k\omega^2) \quad \text{or} \quad (k,k\omega^2,k\omega).$$

Thus in this case, we have $\dfrac{x}{1}=\dfrac{y}{w}=\dfrac{z}{w^2}=k$

or $\dfrac{x}{1}=\dfrac{y}{w^2}=\dfrac{z}{w}=k.$

13. (a) For non-trivial solution,

$$\Delta=\begin{vmatrix} a & b & c \\ b & c & a \\ c & a & b \end{vmatrix}=0$$

$$\Rightarrow -(a^3+b^3+c^3-3abc)=0$$

$$\Rightarrow a+b+c=0 \text{ or } b=-(a+c)$$

$$at^2+bt+c=0$$

$$\Delta=b^2-4ac=(a+c)^2-4ac$$

or $\Delta=(a-c)^2$ i.e. +ive ∴ Real.

(b) The given equations can be written as

$$x-ay+az=0$$
$$bx+y-bz=0$$
$$cx-cy-z=0$$

For a non-trivial solution we have

$$\therefore \begin{vmatrix} 1 & -a & a \\ b & 1 & -b \\ c & -c & -1 \end{vmatrix}=0$$

or $1(-1-bc)+a(-b+bc)+a(-bc-c)=0$

or $-1-ab-bc-ca+abc-abc=0$

or $1+ab+bc+ca=0.$

14. Writing the equations in a,b,c as under

(a) $a\left(\dfrac{x}{y}\right)+b\left(\dfrac{y}{x}\right)-c=0$

$a-b\left(\dfrac{y}{z}\right)-c\left(\dfrac{z}{y}\right)=0$

$a\left(\dfrac{x}{z}\right)-b+c\left(\dfrac{z}{x}\right)=0$

Eliminating a,b,c to get relation in x,y,z

$$\begin{vmatrix} \dfrac{x}{y} & \dfrac{y}{x} & -1 \\ 1 & -\dfrac{y}{z} & -\dfrac{z}{y} \\ \dfrac{x}{z} & -1 & \dfrac{z}{x} \end{vmatrix}=0$$

Expanding we get $\dfrac{yz}{x^2}+\dfrac{zx}{y^2}+\dfrac{xy}{z^2}=-1$

(b) Again putting $\dfrac{x}{y}=p,\dfrac{y}{z}=q,\dfrac{z}{x}=r$, so that

$pqr=1$, we get

$$ap+\frac{b}{p}=c, \; bq+\frac{c}{q}=a, \; cr+\frac{a}{r}=b \qquad ...(1)$$

We have to eliminate p,q,r to get a relation in a,b,c

Multiplying the relations in (1) we get

$$\left(ap+\frac{b}{p}\right)\left(bq+\frac{c}{q}\right)\left(cr+\frac{a}{r}\right)=abc$$

$$\left(abpq+\frac{bc}{pq}+b^2\frac{q}{p}+ac\frac{p}{q}\right)\left(cr+\frac{a}{r}\right)=abc$$

$$\left(abcpqr+bc^2\frac{r}{pq}+b^2c\frac{qr}{p}+ac^2\frac{pr}{q}\right.$$

$$\left.+\left(a^2b\frac{pq}{r}+\frac{abc}{pqr}+ab^2\frac{q}{pr}+a^2c\frac{p}{qr}\right)\right)=abc$$

Now put $pqr=1$ or $p=\dfrac{1}{qr}$ etc.

$$\therefore \quad 2abc+\Sigma\left(bc^2r^2+\frac{a^2b}{r^2}\right)=abc$$

or $b\left(c^2r^2+\dfrac{a^2}{r^2}\right)+c\left(a^2p^2+\dfrac{b^2}{p^2}\right)$

$$+a\left(b^2q^2+\frac{c^2}{q^2}\right)=-abc$$

Now $ap+\dfrac{b}{p}=c \Rightarrow a^2p^2+\dfrac{b^2}{p^2}+2ab=c^2$ etc.

$\therefore \quad c(c^2-2ab)+a(a^2-2bc)+b(b^2-2ca)$

$$=-abc.$$

or $a^3+b^3+c^3=5abc.$

15. (a) The system will have a non-trivial solution if

$$\begin{vmatrix} \sin 3\theta & -1 & 1 \\ \cos 2\theta & 4 & 3 \\ 2 & 7 & 7 \end{vmatrix}=0.$$

or $(28-21)\sin 3\theta-(-7-7)\cos 2\theta$

$$+2(-3-4)=0$$

or $7\sin 3\theta+14\cos 2\theta-14=0$

or $\sin 3\theta+2\cos 2\theta-2=0$

or $3\sin\theta-4\sin^3\theta+2(1-2\sin^2\theta)-2=0$

or $4\sin^3\theta+4\sin^2\theta-3\sin\theta=0$

or $\sin\theta(2\sin\theta-1)(2\sin\theta+3)=0$

$\therefore \quad \sin\theta = 0$ which gives $\theta = n\pi$,

or $\quad \sin\theta = \dfrac{1}{2}$ which gives $\theta = n\pi + (-1)^n \cdot \pi/6$,

where n is an integer.

[Note that $\sin\theta \neq -3/2$]

(b) For non-trivial solution **see (12) Page 460.**

$$\Delta = \begin{vmatrix} \lambda & \sin\alpha & \cos\alpha \\ 1 & \cos\alpha & \sin\alpha \\ -1 & \sin\alpha & -\cos\alpha \end{vmatrix} = 0.$$

Expanding, we get

$$\lambda(-1) - 1(-2\sin\alpha\cos\alpha) - 1(\sin^2\alpha - \cos^2\alpha) = 0$$

$\therefore \quad \lambda = \sin 2\alpha + \cos 2\alpha$. If $\lambda = 1$, then

$$\sin 2\alpha + \cos 2\alpha = 1$$

or $\quad \cos\left(2\alpha - \dfrac{\pi}{4}\right) = \dfrac{1}{\sqrt{2}} = \cos\dfrac{\pi}{4}$

$\therefore \quad 2\alpha - \dfrac{\pi}{4} = 2n\pi \pm \dfrac{\pi}{4}$ or $2\alpha = 2n\pi \pm \dfrac{\pi}{4} + \dfrac{\pi}{4}$ etc.

16. (a) We have the following relations

$$\alpha_1 + \alpha_2 = -\dfrac{b}{a}, \ \alpha_1\alpha_2 = \dfrac{c}{a} \qquad \ldots(1)$$

$$\beta_1 + \beta_2 = -\dfrac{q}{p}, \ \beta_1\beta_2 = \dfrac{r}{p} \qquad \ldots(2)$$

Since the given system has non-trivial solution

$$\Delta = \begin{vmatrix} \alpha_1 & \alpha_2 \\ \beta_1 & \beta_2 \end{vmatrix} = 0 \quad \text{or} \quad \alpha_1\beta_2 - \alpha_2\beta_1 = 0$$

or $\quad \dfrac{\alpha_1}{\beta_1} = \dfrac{\alpha_2}{\beta_2} = \dfrac{\alpha_1 + \alpha_2}{\beta_1 + \beta_2} = \sqrt{\left(\dfrac{\alpha_1\alpha_2}{\beta_1\beta_2}\right)}$

or $\quad \dfrac{pb}{qa} = \sqrt{\left(\dfrac{pc}{ra}\right)} \quad$ Square

or $\quad \dfrac{b^2}{q^2} = \dfrac{ac}{pr}$

(b) By given conditions,

$$a = a, b = ar_1, c = ar_1^2.$$

$$\alpha = \alpha, \beta = \alpha r_2, \gamma = \alpha r_2^2$$

Since the system possesses only zero (trivial) solution, therefore $\Delta \neq 0$.

$$\therefore \quad \begin{vmatrix} a & \alpha & 1 \\ ar_1 & \alpha r_2 & 1 \\ ar_1^2 & \alpha r_2^2 & 1 \end{vmatrix} \neq 0$$

$a\alpha(r_1 - r_2)(r_2 - r_3)(r_3 - r_1)$ where $r_3 = 1$

Refer factors **Q. 1 P. 439-44.**

or $\quad a\alpha(r_1 - 1)(r_2 - 1)(r_2 - r_1) \neq 0$

Since a and α are the first terms of two G.P's, are non-zero. Hence the required condition is

$$r_1 - 1 \neq 0, r_2 - 1 \neq 0, r_2 - r_1 \neq 0$$

i.e. $r_1 \neq 1, r_2 \neq 1$ and $r_1 \neq r_2$.

17. Write $\sin 2A = 2\sin A \cos A = 2ka\dfrac{b^2 + c^2 - a^2}{2bc}$

(By sin-cosine rule)

$$\Delta = k^3 \begin{vmatrix} \dfrac{a(b^2 + c^2 - a^2)}{bc} & c & b \\ c & \dfrac{b(c^2 + a^2 - b^2)}{ca} & a \\ b & a & \dfrac{c(a^2 + b^2 - c^2)}{ab} \end{vmatrix}$$

Now multiply R_1, R_2 and R_3 by bc, ca, ab respectively and hence divide Δ by $a^2b^2c^2$. Then take out a, b, c common from C_1, C_2 and C_3 respectively.

$$\Delta = \dfrac{k^3}{abc} \times \begin{vmatrix} b^2 + c^2 - a^2 & c^2 & b^2 \\ c^2 & c^2 + a^2 - b^2 & a^2 \\ b^2 & a^2 & a^2 + b^2 - c^2 \end{vmatrix}$$

Apply $C_2 - C_1$ and $C_3 - C_1$

$$\Delta = \dfrac{k^3}{abc}(a^2 - b^2)(a^2 - c^2) \times \begin{vmatrix} b^2 + c^2 - a^2 & 1 & 1 \\ c^2 & 1 & 1 \\ b^2 & 1 & 1 \end{vmatrix} = 0.$$

Since $\Delta = 0$, the system has non-trivial solution.

18. For non-trivial solution we must have $\Delta = 0$

or $\quad \Delta = \begin{vmatrix} -1 & \cos C & \cos B \\ \cos C & -1 & \cos A \\ \cos B & \cos A & -1 \end{vmatrix} = 0$

When $A + B + C = \pi$

i.e. $\cos(A + B) = -\cos C, \sin(A + B) = \sin C$

$\Delta = -1(1 - \cos^2 A) - \cos C(-\cos C - \cos A\cos B)$

$\qquad + \cos B(\cos A\cos C + \cos B) = 0$

$= -\sin^2 A - \cos C[\cos(A + B) - \cos A\cos B]$

$\qquad + \cos B[\cos A\cos C - \cos(A + C)]$

$= -\sin^2 A + \cos C\sin A\sin B + \cos B\sin A\sin C$

$= -\sin^2 A + \sin A . \sin(B + C)$

$= -\sin^2 A + \sin A . \sin A = 0$

19. For non-trivial solution $\Delta = 0$

$$\Delta = \begin{vmatrix} f^2 - bc & ch - fg & bg - hf \\ ch - fg & g^2 - ca & af - gh \\ bg - hf & af - gh & h^2 - ab \end{vmatrix} = 0$$

Now consider $\Delta_1 = \begin{vmatrix} a & h & g \\ h & b & f \\ g & f & c \end{vmatrix}$

Cofactor of a is $(bc - f^2) = A$

Cofactor of h is $-(ch - fg) = H$

Cofactor of g is $(hf - bg) = G$

$$\therefore \quad \Delta = \begin{vmatrix} -A & -H & -G \\ -H & -B & -F \\ -G & -F & -C \end{vmatrix} = -\begin{vmatrix} A & H & G \\ H & B & F \\ G & F & C \end{vmatrix} = -\Delta_1^2$$

by Th. P. 438

$\therefore \quad \Delta = 0 \Rightarrow \Delta_1 = 0.$

20. Consider the linear relation

$$x\mathbf{a} + y\mathbf{b} + z\mathbf{c} = 0 \qquad \ldots(i)$$

If x, y z are all zero, then it is L.I. and if x, y, z are not all zero, then it is L.D.

On Putting the values of **a**, **b**, **c** as given and combining the terms of **i**, **j**, **k**, we have

(a) $(x + 2y + 3z)\,\mathbf{i} + (-3x - 4y + 2z)\,\mathbf{j}$
$$+ (2x - 4y - z)\,\mathbf{k} = 0$$

We know that **i**, **j**, **k** being non-coplanar represent a L.I. system. Hence all the scalars in the above must be zero.

∴ $\qquad x + 2y + 3z = 0$
$$-3x - 4y + 2z = 0$$
$$2x - 4y - z = 0$$

Above represents a homogeneous system of equations

Its $\Delta = \begin{vmatrix} 1 & 2 & 3 \\ -3 & -4 & 2 \\ 2 & -4 & -1 \end{vmatrix}$ Apply $C_2 - 2C_1$ and $C_3 - 3C_1$

$= \begin{vmatrix} 1 & 0 & 0 \\ -3 & 2 & 11 \\ 2 & -8 & -7 \end{vmatrix} = -14 + 88$
$= 74 \neq 0$

Hence the above system has only trivial solution *i.e.* all x, y, z will be zero. Hence the vectors **a**, **b**, **c** are L.I.

(b) In this case proceeding as above

$\Delta = \begin{vmatrix} -1 & 2 & 1 \\ -2 & 3 & 1 \\ 2 & -1 & 1 \end{vmatrix}$ Apply $C_3 - C_2$

Two columns C_1 and C_3 become identical so that $\Delta = 0$. Hence the system has non-trivial solution *i.e.* all x, y, z are not zero. Hence the vectors **a**, **b**, **c** are L.D.

21. (a) By Crammer's rule,

$\dfrac{x}{D_1} = \dfrac{y}{D_2} = \dfrac{z}{D_3} = \dfrac{1}{D}$ or $xD = D_1$ etc.

∴ $x \begin{vmatrix} 1 & 1 & 1 \\ a & b & c \\ a^2 & b^2 & c^2 \end{vmatrix} = \begin{vmatrix} 1 & 1 & 1 \\ k & b & c \\ k^2 & b^2 & c^2 \end{vmatrix}$

or $x(a-b)(b-c)(c-a) = (k-b)(b-c)(c-k)$.
[See Ex. 1 P. 439-44]

$x = \dfrac{(k-b)(b-c)(c-k)}{(a-b)(b-c)(c-a)} = \dfrac{(k-b)(k-c)}{(a-b)(a-c)}$.

Similarly $y = \dfrac{(k-c)(k-a)}{(b-c)(b-a)}$, $z = \dfrac{(k-a)(k-b)}{(c-a)(c-b)}$

(b) Just as in Ex. 1.

$x = \dfrac{k(k-b)(k-c)}{a(a-b)(a-c)}$ and similarly for y and z.

22. (a) $x \begin{vmatrix} 1 & 2 & 3 \\ 2 & 4 & 1 \\ 3 & 2 & 9 \end{vmatrix} = \begin{vmatrix} 6 & 2 & 3 \\ 7 & 4 & 1 \\ 14 & 2 & 9 \end{vmatrix}$

or $xD = D_1$

Operating $C_1 - (C_2 + C_3)$ on D_1, we get

$D_1 = \begin{vmatrix} 1 & 2 & 3 \\ 2 & 4 & 1 \\ 3 & 2 & 9 \end{vmatrix} = D.$

Hence $xD = D$ or $x = 1$

Similarly $y = 1$, $z = 1$.

(b) $D = -20$, $D_1 = -20$ etc. $1, 4, -1$

(c) Put $\dfrac{1}{x} = a$, $\dfrac{1}{y} = b$, $\dfrac{1}{z} = c$, and solve by

Crammer rule. $a = 1$, $b = 1/3$, $c = 1/3$.

∴ $x = 1$, $y = 3$, $z = 3$.

23. Here $\dfrac{x}{D_1} = \dfrac{y}{D_2} = \dfrac{z}{D_3} = \dfrac{1}{D}$, by Crammer's rule.

or $\dfrac{x}{-88} = \dfrac{y}{-77} = \dfrac{z}{286} = \dfrac{1}{11}$

∴ $x = -8$, $y = -7$, $z = 26$.

24. $\dfrac{x}{D_1} = \dfrac{y}{D_2} = \dfrac{z}{D_3} = \dfrac{1}{D}$

By Crammer's rule. Now calculate D_1, D_2 D_3 and D yourself.

Then $\dfrac{x}{6} = \dfrac{y}{12} = \dfrac{z}{18} = \dfrac{1}{6}$

∴ $x = 1$, $y = 2$, $z = 3$.

25. (a) Here $D = \begin{vmatrix} 5 & -6 & 4 \\ 7 & 4 & -3 \\ 2 & 1 & 6 \end{vmatrix}$

Apply $C_1 - 2C_2$, $C_3 - 6C_2$

∴ $D = \begin{vmatrix} 17 & -6 & 40 \\ -1 & 4 & -27 \\ 0 & 1 & 0 \end{vmatrix} = -\begin{vmatrix} 17 & 40 \\ -1 & -27 \end{vmatrix}$

$= -[-459 + 40] = 419 \neq 0$.

Since $D \neq 0$, therefore the equations are consistent.

$D_1 = \begin{vmatrix} 15 & -6 & 4 \\ 19 & 4 & -3 \\ 46 & 1 & 6 \end{vmatrix}$

$= 15(27) - 19(-40) + 46(2) = 1257$.

Similarly, $D_2 = 1676$, $D_3 = 2514$

∴ $\dfrac{x}{1257} = \dfrac{y}{1676} = \dfrac{z}{2514} = \dfrac{1}{419}$

∴ $x = 3$, $y = 4$, $z = 6$.

(b) Ans. $x = \dfrac{1}{3}$, $y = 1$, $z = -\dfrac{1}{3}$.

26. Since $f(x) = ax^2 + bx + c$

where a, b, c are unknown.

$f(0) = a.0 + b.0 + c = 6$ ...(1)
$f(2) = a.4 + b.2 + c = 11$ ...(2)
$f(-3) = a.9 - b.3 + c = 6$ ...(3)

Thus we have got three equations in a, b, c and on solving them we shall find the values of a, b, c and hence of $f(x)$ and $f(1)$

$\dfrac{a}{D_1} = \dfrac{b}{D_2} = \dfrac{c}{D_3} = \dfrac{1}{D}$.

Now $D = \begin{vmatrix} 0 & 0 & 1 \\ 4 & 2 & 1 \\ 9 & -3 & 1 \end{vmatrix} = -12 - 18 = -30$

$$D_1 = \begin{vmatrix} 6 & 0 & 1 \\ 11 & 2 & 1 \\ 6 & -3 & 1 \end{vmatrix} = \begin{vmatrix} 6 & 0 & 1 \\ 5 & 2 & 0 \\ 0 & -3 & 1 \end{vmatrix} = -15$$

Similarly $D_2 = -45$, $D_3 = -180$

$$\therefore \quad \frac{a}{-15} = \frac{b}{-45} = \frac{c}{-180} = \frac{1}{-30}$$

$$\therefore \quad a = \frac{1}{2},\ b = \frac{3}{2},\ c = 6$$

Hence $f(x) = ax^2 + bx + c = \frac{1}{2}x^2 + \frac{3}{2}x + 6$.

$$\therefore \quad f(1) = \frac{1}{2} + \frac{3}{2} + 6 = 2 + 6 = 8.$$

Alternative :

From 1st equation, $c = 6$

Putting for c in (2) and (3), we get

$$4a + 2b = 5,\ 9a - 3b = 0$$

Solving, $a = 1/2$, $b = 3/2$.

Putting for a, b, c, we get

$$f(x) = \frac{1}{2}x^2 + \frac{3}{2}x + 6 \text{ and } f(1) = 8.$$

27. $D = \begin{vmatrix} \cos\theta & -\sin\theta & 1 \\ \sin\theta & \cos\theta & 1 \\ \cos(\theta+\phi) & -\sin(\theta+\phi) & 1 \end{vmatrix}$

Apply $R_3 - \cos\phi\,R_1 + \sin\phi\,R_2$ thus making two zeros in R_3.

$$\therefore \quad D = \begin{vmatrix} \cos\theta & -\sin\theta & 1 \\ \sin\theta & \cos\theta & 1 \\ 0 & 0 & 1-\cos\phi+\sin\phi \end{vmatrix}$$

$$= (1-\cos\phi+\sin\phi).1$$

Similarly calculate

$$D_1 = (1-\cos\phi+\sin\phi)\cos(\theta+\phi)$$
$$D_2 = -(1-\cos\phi+\sin\phi)\sin(\theta+\phi)$$
$$D_3 = 1-\cos\phi+\sin\phi$$

$$\therefore \quad x = \frac{D_1}{D},\ y = \frac{D_2}{D},\ z = \frac{D_3}{D}$$

$$x = \cos(\theta+\phi),\ y = \sin(\theta+\phi),\ z = 1$$

$$\therefore \quad x^2 + y^2 + z^2 = 1 + 1 = 2.$$

28. (a) Here $\Delta = \begin{vmatrix} 1 & 4 & -2 \\ 3 & 1 & 5 \\ 2 & 3 & 1 \end{vmatrix}$

$$= 1(1-15) - 3(4+6) + 2(20+2)$$
$$= -14 - 30 + 44 = 0$$

And $\Delta_x = \begin{vmatrix} 3 & 4 & -2 \\ 7 & 1 & 5 \\ 5 & 3 & 1 \end{vmatrix}$

$$= 3(1-15) - 7(4+6) + 5(20+2)$$
$$= -2 \neq 0$$

Since $\Delta = 0$ and $\Delta_x \neq 0$, the equations are not consistent and hence there is no solution of the given system of equations.

(b) Ans. (d) For the system to have no solution we must have $\Delta = 0$

$$\therefore \quad \begin{vmatrix} 2 & -1 & -2 \\ 1 & -2 & 1 \\ 1 & 1 & \lambda \end{vmatrix} = 0$$

$$\therefore \quad 2(-2\lambda - 1) + 1(\lambda - 1) - 2(3) = 0$$

or $-3\lambda - 9 = 0$ $\therefore$ $\lambda = -3$

Alt : Subtracting first two equations we have $x + y - 3z = 6$ and it will be parallel to $x + y + \lambda z = 4$ if $\lambda = -3$. We know that two parallel planes do not intersect.

29. Here

$$\Delta = \begin{vmatrix} 1 & 1 & -2 \\ 1 & -3 & 1 \\ 1 & -5 & 4 \end{vmatrix}$$

$$= 1(-12+5) - 1(8-1) - 2(-10+3)$$
$$= -7 - 7 + 14 = 0$$

Thus $\Delta = 0$. Hence if the equations are to be consistent, then we must have

$$\Delta_x = \Delta_y = \Delta_z = 0$$

$$\Delta_x = \begin{vmatrix} 0 & 1 & -2 \\ 0 & -3 & 1 \\ k & -5 & 4 \end{vmatrix} = 0$$

if $5k = 0$ $\therefore$ $k = 0$.

But when $k = 0$, the equations become homogeneous. Since $\Delta = 0$ for $k = 0$ the system has non-trivial solution.

Also from 1st two

$$\frac{x}{1-6} = \frac{y}{-4-1} = \frac{z}{-3-2}$$

or $\frac{x}{1} = \frac{y}{1} = \frac{z}{1} = \lambda$

$\therefore$ $x = y = z = \lambda$. Thus there are infinite number of solutions.

30. (a) Here $\Delta = \begin{vmatrix} 3 & m \\ 2 & -5 \end{vmatrix} = -15 - 2m$,

$$\Delta_x = \begin{vmatrix} m & m \\ 20 & -5 \end{vmatrix} = -5m - 20m = -25m$$

and $\Delta_y = \begin{vmatrix} 3 & m \\ 2 & 20 \end{vmatrix} = 60 - 2m$

If $\Delta = 0$, then $m = -\frac{15}{2}$ and for this value of m, $\Delta_x \neq 0$ and $\Delta_y \neq 0$. Hence when $m = -\frac{15}{2}$, the given system of equations has no solution.

If $\Delta \neq 0$, that is, if $m \neq -\frac{15}{2}$, the system has the unique solution given by

$$x = \frac{\Delta_x}{\Delta} = \frac{-25m}{-15-2m} = \frac{25m}{15+2m}$$

$$= \frac{25.2\left\{m - \left(-\frac{15}{2}\right)\right\}(m-0)}{(15+2m)^2}$$

$$y = \frac{\Delta_y}{\Delta} = \frac{60 - 2m}{-15 - 2m} = \frac{2m - 60}{2m + 15}$$

$$= \frac{2.2\left\{m - \left(-\frac{15}{2}\right)\right\}(m - 30)}{(2m + 15)^2}$$

Now $x > 0$ if $m > 0$ or $m < -\dfrac{15}{2}$ ...(1)

and $y > 0$ if $m > 30$ or $m < -\dfrac{15}{2}$ ...(2)

Both the inequalities (1) and (2) are satisfied if

$$m < -\frac{15}{2} \quad \text{or} \quad m > 30$$

Hence the given system of equations has a solution satisfying the conditions $x > 0$, $y > 0$ if $m < -\dfrac{15}{2}$ or $m > 30$.

(b) Ans. (b). For infinitely many solutions, $\Delta = 0$, and $\Delta_1 = 0, \Delta_2 = 0$

$\Delta = 0 \Rightarrow (k+1)(k+3) - 8k = 0$

or $k^2 - 4k + 3 = 0$ $\therefore k = 3, 1$

$\Delta_1 = 0 \Rightarrow k^2 - 3k + 2 = 0$ or $k = 1, 2$

$\Delta_2 = 0 \Rightarrow k = 1$

Hence $k = 1$ is only common value for which each $\Delta, \Delta_1, \Delta_2$ is zero.

32. (a) After simple calculations, it is easy to see that

$$\Delta = \begin{vmatrix} 3 & -1 & 4 \\ 1 & 2 & -3 \\ 6 & 5 & \lambda \end{vmatrix} = 7\lambda + 35,$$

$$\Delta_x = \begin{vmatrix} 3 & -1 & 4 \\ -2 & 2 & -3 \\ -3 & 5 & \lambda \end{vmatrix} = 4\lambda + 20.$$

$$\Delta_y = \begin{vmatrix} 3 & 3 & 4 \\ 1 & -2 & -3 \\ 6 & -3 & \lambda \end{vmatrix} = -9\lambda - 45$$

and $\Delta_z = \begin{vmatrix} 3 & -1 & 3 \\ 1 & 2 & -2 \\ 6 & 5 & -3 \end{vmatrix} = 0$

If $\Delta \neq 0$, that is, if $\lambda \neq -5$, the system of equations has the unique solution

$$x = \frac{4\lambda + 20}{7\lambda + 35} = \frac{4}{7}$$

$$y = -\frac{9\lambda + 45}{7\lambda + 35} = -\frac{9}{7} \text{ and } z = 0.$$

If $\Delta = 0$, that is, if $\lambda = -5$, then we also have $\Delta_x = \Delta_y = \Delta_z = 0$. So in this case, the system has infinite number of solutions.

Eliminating x between (1) and (2) and then between (1) and (3), we get

$$7y - 13z = -9$$
$$7y - 13z = -9$$

i.e. only one equation. Put $z = c$.

$\therefore$ $y = \dfrac{13c - 9}{7}$ and hence from any, $x = \dfrac{4 - 5c}{7}$.

32. After making two zeros and expanding, we get

$$\Delta = \begin{vmatrix} 1 & 1 & 1 \\ 1 & 3 & -2 \\ 3 & \lambda + 2 & -3 \end{vmatrix} = 3(\lambda - 5)$$

$$\Delta_x = \begin{vmatrix} 1 & 1 & 1 \\ \lambda & 3 & -2 \\ 2\lambda + 1 & 2\lambda + 2 & -3 \end{vmatrix} = (\lambda - 5)(\lambda + 2)$$

$$\Delta_y = \begin{vmatrix} 1 & 1 & 1 \\ 1 & \lambda & -2 \\ 3 & 2\lambda + 1 & -3 \end{vmatrix} \begin{matrix} = 0 \\ R_3 - R_1, \text{identical} \end{matrix}$$

$$\Delta_z = \begin{vmatrix} 1 & 1 & 1 \\ 1 & 3 & \lambda \\ 3 & \lambda + 2 & 2\lambda + 1 \end{vmatrix} = -(\lambda - 1)(\lambda - 5)$$

$\Delta \neq 0$ i.e, $\lambda \neq 5$, the system has unique solution given by

$$\frac{x}{\Delta_x} = \frac{y}{\Delta_y} = \frac{z}{\Delta_z} = \frac{1}{\Delta}$$

If $\Delta = 0$ i.e., $\lambda = 5$ then $\Delta_x = \Delta_y = \Delta_z = 0$

Hence the system has infinite solutions.

Putting $\lambda = 5$ and eliminating z, we have $3x + 5y = 7$ i.e. only one equation in two variables.

Putting $x = c$, $y = \dfrac{7 - 3c}{5}$ and hence from any

$$z = -\frac{2(1 + c)}{5}.$$

33. $\Delta = \begin{vmatrix} 1 & 2 & 1 \\ 1 & 3 & 4 \\ 1 & 5 & 10 \end{vmatrix} = 0$ after making two zeros.

$\therefore$ Solution is not unique.

The system will have infinite solutions if $\Delta_1 = 0, \Delta_2 = 0,$ $\Delta_3 = 0$

$\Delta_1 = 0 \Rightarrow k^2 - 3k + 2 = 0$ $\therefore k = 1, 2$

For these values Δ_2 and Δ_3 are also zero.

Now take $z = \lambda, k = 1$ then $x = 1 + 5\lambda, y = -3\lambda$

$z = \lambda, k = 2$ then $x = -1 + 5\lambda, y = 1 - 3\lambda$

34. (a) $\Delta \neq 0$ unique

$\Delta = 0$ and if Δ_1, Δ_2 and Δ_3 be all $= 0$ also then infinite solutions.

$\Delta = 0$ and if any of Δ_1, Δ_2 and $\Delta_3 \neq 0$ then no solution.

$$\Delta = \begin{vmatrix} 2 & p & 6 \\ 1 & 2 & q \\ 1 & 1 & 3 \end{vmatrix} = pq - 3p - 2q + 6 = 0$$

or $(p - 2)(q - 3) = 0$

$\Delta_1 = 30 - 8q - 15p + 4pq, \Delta_2 = 0,$

$\Delta_3 = p - 2$

(i) $\Delta \neq 0$ i.e. $p \neq 2$ and $q \neq 3$. Then the system has unique solution given by

$$\frac{x}{\Delta_1} = \frac{y}{\Delta_2} = \frac{z}{\Delta_3} = \frac{1}{\Delta}$$

(ii) If $\Delta = 0$ *i.e.* $p = 2$ or $q = 3$. Then if all of $\Delta_1, \Delta_2, \Delta_3$ are zero then the system has infinite solutions but if any of the three is not zero then no solution.

∴ If $p = 2$, $\Delta = 0$ and also $\Delta_1, \Delta_2, \Delta_3$ each is zero and hence the system has infinite solution.

If $p \neq 2$ but $q = 3$ then $\Delta = 0$ but $\Delta_3 \neq 0$ and hence the system has no solution.

(b) Ans. (d).
$$\Delta = 0 \Rightarrow (\alpha + 2)(\alpha - 1) = 0 \quad \therefore \quad \alpha = -2 \text{ or } 1.$$

35. (a) Here $\Delta = 11(\lambda - 2) = 0 \Rightarrow \lambda = 2$,
$\Delta_1 = 11(3\lambda - \mu + 1) = 11(7 - \mu)$
$\Delta_2 = 11(-2\lambda + \mu - 3) = 11(\mu - 7)$.
$\Delta_3 = 11(\mu - 7)$
$\Delta \neq 0$ *i.e.* $\lambda \neq 2$ unique solution;
$\Delta = 0$ *i.e.* $\lambda = 2, \mu = 7$,
then infinite solution as $\Delta, \Delta_1, \Delta_2, \Delta_3$ are all zero;
$\lambda = 2$ but $\mu \neq 7$ then no solution.

(b) $p \neq 8$, $\Delta \neq 0$, unique
$p = 8$, $q = 36$, infinite solutions
as $\Delta = 0$, $\Delta_1 = 0$, $\Delta_2 = 0$ and $\Delta_3 = 0$.

36. Apply $R_3 - (R_1 + \lambda R_2)$
$$A = \begin{bmatrix} 1 & 4 & 5 \\ \lambda & 8 & 8\lambda - 6 \\ 0 & 0 & 16 - 8\lambda^2 + 8\lambda \end{bmatrix}$$

Case I. If $16 - 8\lambda^2 + 8\lambda \neq 0$, then rank $A = 3$, the number of non-zero rows

If $16 - 8\lambda^2 + 8\lambda = 0$ or $\lambda^2 - \lambda - 2 = 0$
or $(\lambda - 2)(\lambda + 1) = 0$ ∴ $\lambda = 2, -1$

Case II. $\lambda = 2$.
$$A = \begin{bmatrix} 1 & 4 & 5 \\ 2 & 8 & 10 \\ 0 & 0 & 0 \end{bmatrix} = \begin{bmatrix} 1 & 4 & 5 \\ 0 & 0 & 0 \\ 0 & 0 & 0 \end{bmatrix} \text{ by } R_2 - 2R_1$$

∴ Rank $A = 1$, the number of non-zero rows

Case III. $\lambda = -1$
$$A = \begin{bmatrix} 1 & 4 & 5 \\ -1 & 8 & -14 \\ 0 & 0 & 0 \end{bmatrix}$$

∴ Rank $A = 2$, the number of non-zero rows.

37. **Refer Summary P. 459.**
$\Delta \neq 0$, Unique solution (Intersecting lines)
$\Delta = 0, \Delta_1 = 0, \Delta_2 = 0$, Infinite solutions (Identical lines)
$\Delta = 0, \Delta_1 \neq 0, \Delta_2 \neq 0$, No solution (Parallel lines)
$AX = U$ has infinite many solutions.

∴ $\Delta = 0, \Delta_1 = 0, \Delta_2 = 0, \Delta_3 = 0$,
$|A| = 0, |A_1| = 0, |A_2| = 0, |A_3| = 0$.

$$|A| = 0 \Rightarrow \begin{vmatrix} a & 0 & 1 \\ 1 & c & b \\ 1 & d & b \end{vmatrix} = 0$$

or $ab(c - d) + 1(d - c) = 0$
or $(c - d)(ab - 1) = 0$
∴ $ab = 1$ or $c = d$ ...(1)

$$|A_1| = 0 \Rightarrow \begin{vmatrix} f & 0 & 1 \\ g & c & b \\ h & d & b \end{vmatrix} = 0$$

Above is possible if $g = h$ and $c = d$ ...(2)
as in that case R_2 and R_3 become identical.

$$|A_2| = 0 \Rightarrow \begin{vmatrix} a & f & 1 \\ 1 & g & b \\ 1 & h & b \end{vmatrix} = 0$$

Above is possible if $g = h$ ...(3)
as in that case R_2 and R_3 become identical.

$$|A_3| = 0 \Rightarrow \begin{vmatrix} a & 0 & f \\ 1 & c & g \\ 1 & d & h \end{vmatrix} = 0$$

by virtue of relations in (2).
$BX = V$
$|B| \neq 0$ for unique solution
and $|B| = 0$ for no unique solution.

$$|B| = \begin{vmatrix} a & 1 & 1 \\ 0 & d & c \\ f & g & h \end{vmatrix} = 0 \text{ as } C_2 \text{ and } C_3 \text{ are identical by}$$

virtue of relations in (2).
$BX = V$ has no solution, then $|B| = 0, |B_1| = 0$ but
$|B_2| = a^2 cf = a^2 df = a(adf) \neq 0$ as $adf \neq 0$.
Similarly $|B_3| = a^2 df \neq 0$.
Hence there is no solution.

Problem Set (5)

▶ **Multiple Choice Questions**

1. Let a_{ij} denote the element of the ith row and jth column in a 3×3 determinant
$(1 \leq i \leq 3, 1 \leq j \leq 3)$ and let $a_{ij} = -a_{ij}$ for every i and j. Then the determinant has all the principal diagonal elements as

(a) 1   (b) -1

(c) 0   (d) none of these.

2. If each element of a determinant of third order with value A is multiplied by 3, then the value of newly formed determinant is

(a) $3A$ (b) $9A$

(c) $27A$ (d) none of these.

3.* For $a > 0, b > 0, c > 0$, the value of the determinant
$$\begin{vmatrix} a & b & c \\ b & c & a \\ c & a & b \end{vmatrix}$$
is always positive.

(a) True

(h) False.

4. The value of the determinant

$$\begin{vmatrix} a+b & a+2b & a+3b \\ a+2b & a+3b & a+4b \\ a+4b & a+5b & a+6b \end{vmatrix} \text{ is ....}$$

5. The value of determinant
$$\begin{vmatrix} x+1 & x+2 & x+4 \\ x+3 & x+5 & x+8 \\ x+7 & x+10 & x+14 \end{vmatrix} \text{ is}$$

(a) -2 (b) $x^2 + 2$

(c) 2 (d) none of these.

6. If $\begin{vmatrix} x_1 & y_1 & 1 \\ x_2 & y_2 & 1 \\ x_3 & y_3 & 1 \end{vmatrix} = \begin{vmatrix} a_1 & b_1 & 1 \\ a_2 & b_2 & 1 \\ a_3 & b_3 & 1 \end{vmatrix}$,

then the two triangles with vertices (x_1, y_1), (x_2, y_2), (x_3, y_3) and (a_1, b_1), (a_2, b_2), (a_3, b_3) must be congruent.

(a) True (b) False.

7. * If $\Delta_1 = \begin{vmatrix} x & b & b \\ a & x & b \\ a & a & x \end{vmatrix}$ and $\Delta_2 = \begin{vmatrix} x & b \\ a & x \end{vmatrix}$

are the given determinants, then

(i) $\Delta_1 = 3(\Delta_2)^2$

(ii) $(d/dx)\,\Delta_1 = 3\Delta_2$,

(iii) $(d/dx)\,\Delta_1 = 3(\Delta_2)^2$

(iv) $\Delta_1 = 3\,\Delta_2^{3/2}$

8 (i)* The determinant
$$\begin{vmatrix} a & b & a\alpha+b \\ b & c & b\alpha+c \\ a\alpha+b & b\alpha+c & 0 \end{vmatrix}$$

is equal to zero, if

(a) a, b, c are in A.P

(b) a, b, c are in G.P.

(c) a, b, c are in H.P.

(d) α is a root of the equation $ax^2 + bx + c = 0$

(e) $(x - \alpha)$ is a factor of $ax^2 + 2bx + c$.

(ii)* The determinant
$$\begin{vmatrix} xp+y & x & y \\ yp+z & y & z \\ 0 & xp+y & yp+z \end{vmatrix} = 0.$$

if

(a) x, y, z are in A.P. (b) x, y, z are in G.P.

(c) x, y, z are in H.P. (d) xy, yz, zx are in A.P.

(I.I.T. 1997)

9. Let $\vec{a} = a_1\mathbf{i} + a_2\mathbf{j} + a_3\mathbf{k}$, $\vec{b} = b_1\mathbf{i} + b_2\mathbf{j} + b_3\mathbf{k}$,

and $\vec{c} = c_1\mathbf{i} + c_2\mathbf{j} + c_3\mathbf{k}$

be three non-zero vectors such that $\vec{c}$ is a unit vector perpendicular to both the vectors $\vec{a}$ and $\vec{b}$. If the angle between $\vec{a}$ and $\vec{b}$ is $\pi/6$, then

$$\begin{vmatrix} a_1 & a_2 & a_3 \\ b_1 & b_2 & b_3 \\ c_1 & c_2 & c_3 \end{vmatrix}^2 \text{ is equal to}$$

(a) 0

(b) 1

(c) $\dfrac{1}{4}(a_1^2 + a_2^2 + a_3^2)(b_1^2 + b_2^2 + b_3^2)$

(d) $\dfrac{3}{4}(a_1^2 + a_2^2 + a_3^2)(b_1^2 + b_2^2 + b_3^2)$

$\cdot (c_1^2 + c_2^2 + c_3^2)$

(e) none of these

10.* If ω is a cube root of unity, then a root of the following equation is

$$\begin{vmatrix} x+1 & \omega & \omega^2 \\ \omega & x+\omega^2 & 1 \\ \omega^2 & 1 & x+\omega \end{vmatrix}$$

(a) $x = 1$ (b) $x = \omega$

(c) $x = \omega^2$ (d) $x = 0$

11. If $A + B + C = \pi$, then
$$\begin{vmatrix} \sin(A+B+C) & \sin B & \cos C \\ -\sin B & 0 & \tan A \\ \cos(A+B) & -\tan A & 0 \end{vmatrix} = \text{......}$$

12. If a, b, c are different and
$$\begin{vmatrix} 0 & x-a & x-b \\ x+a & 0 & x-c \\ x+b & x+c & 0 \end{vmatrix} = 0,$$

then x is equal to

(a) a (b) b (c) c (d) 0

13. Let a, b, c be such that $b(a+c) \neq 0$. If
$$\begin{vmatrix} a & a+1 & a-1 \\ -b & b+1 & b-1 \\ c & c-1 & c+1 \end{vmatrix}$$
$$+ \begin{vmatrix} a+1 & b+1 & c-1 \\ a-1 & b-1 & c+1 \\ (-1)^{n+2}a & (-1)^{n+1}b & (-1)^n c \end{vmatrix} = 0$$

Then the value of n is

(a) 0 (b) any even integer

(c) any odd integer (d) any integer

(AIEEE 2009)

Solutions to Problem Set (5)

1. Ans. (c).

2. Ans. (c).

3. Ans. (b).

4. Ans. 0.

   [**Hint.** Operate $R_3 - R_2$ and $R_2 - R_1$].

5. Ans. (a).

   Operating $C_3 - C_2$ and $C_2 - C_1$, we get

$$\Delta = \begin{vmatrix} x+1 & 1 & 2 \\ x+3 & 2 & 3 \\ x+7 & 3 & 4 \end{vmatrix}$$

Apply $R_3 - R_2$, $R_2 - R_1$

$$\Delta = \begin{vmatrix} x+1 & 1 & 2 \\ 2 & 1 & 1 \\ 4 & 1 & 1 \end{vmatrix}$$ Apply $C_3 - C_2$

$$\begin{vmatrix} x+1 & 1 & 1 \\ 2 & 1 & 0 \\ 4 & 1 & 0 \end{vmatrix} = 1.(2-4) = -2.$$

6. Ans. (b).

The two determinants denote twice the area of Δ^s whose vertices are $(x_1,y_1),(x_2,y_2),(x_3,y_3)$ and $(a_1,b_1),(a_2,b_2),(a_3,b_3)$. Thus the equality of two determinants implies that their areas are equal. But equality of the areas of two triangles does not imply that they are congruent.

7. Ans. (b).

$$\frac{d}{dx}\Delta_1 = \begin{vmatrix} 1 & 0 & 0 \\ a & x & b \\ a & a & x \end{vmatrix} + \begin{vmatrix} x & b & b \\ 0 & 1 & 0 \\ a & a & x \end{vmatrix} + \begin{vmatrix} x & b & b \\ a & x & b \\ 0 & 0 & 1 \end{vmatrix}$$

$$= \begin{vmatrix} x & b \\ a & x \end{vmatrix} + \begin{vmatrix} x & b \\ a & x \end{vmatrix} + \begin{vmatrix} x & b \\ a & x \end{vmatrix} = 3\Delta_2$$

8. (i) Ans. (b) and (e).

Opearating $R_3 - (\alpha R_1 + R_2)$ and expanding, we shall easily get

$$\Delta = -(a\alpha^2 + 2b\alpha + c)(ac - b^2).$$

Hence Δ is zero if $ac - b^2 = 0$

or $a\alpha^2 + 2b\alpha + c = 0$, i.e. a, b, c

are in G.P. or $x - \alpha$ is a factor of $ax^2 + 2bx + c$.

(ii) Ans. (b).

$$\Delta = (y^2 - xz)(p^2x + 2py + z) = 0$$

9. Ans. (c).

$\because |\vec{c}| = 1$ we have $|\vec{c}|^2 = 1$

$$c_1^2 + c_2^2 + c_3^2 = 1 \qquad ...(1)$$

Again since $\vec{c} \perp \vec{a}$ and $\vec{c} \perp \vec{b}$, we have

$$\vec{c}.\vec{a} = 0 \Rightarrow a_1c_1 + a_2c_2 + a_3c_3 = 0 \qquad ...(2)$$

and $\vec{c}.\vec{b} = 0 \Rightarrow b_1c_1 + b_2c_2 + b_3c_3 = 0 \qquad ...(3)$

Also since angle between $\vec{a}$ and $\vec{b}$ is $\pi/6$ we have

$$\mathbf{a}.\mathbf{b} = (a_1\mathbf{i} + a_2\mathbf{j} + a_3\mathbf{k}).(b_1\mathbf{i} + b_2\mathbf{j} + b_3\mathbf{k})$$

or $|\mathbf{a}||\mathbf{b}|\cos\frac{\pi}{6} = (a_1b_1 + a_2b_2 + a_3b_3)$

or $(a_1^2 + a_2^2 + a_3^2)(b_1^2 + b_2^2 + b_3^2).\frac{3}{4}$

$$= (a_1b_1 + a_2b_2 + a_3b_3)^2 \qquad ...(4)$$

Now with condition (1), (2), (3) and (4) it reduces to **Q. 53. P. 443-64.**

10. Ans. (d).

$$\text{Let } \Delta = \begin{vmatrix} x+1 & \omega & \omega^2 \\ \omega & x+\omega^2 & 1 \\ \omega^2 & 1 & x+\omega \end{vmatrix}$$

Apply $R_1 + R_2 + R_3$

$$\Delta = \begin{vmatrix} x+1+\omega+\omega^2 & x+1+\omega+\omega^2 & x+1+\omega+\omega^2 \\ \omega & x+\omega^2 & 1 \\ \omega^2 & 1 & x+\omega \end{vmatrix}$$

$$= x\begin{vmatrix} 1 & 1 & 1 \\ \omega & x+\omega^2 & 1 \\ \omega^2 & 1 & x+\omega \end{vmatrix} \quad [\because 1+\omega+\omega^2 = 0]$$

$\therefore \quad \Delta = 0 \Rightarrow x = 0$.

11. Ans. zero

Above is skew symmetric determinant of odd order because $\cos(A+B) = -\cos C$ etc.

Refer R. 8 (2) P. 414 or Q. 8 P. 415-19.

12. Ans. (d).

Expand with R_1 and you get

$$2x[x^2 + (ac - ab - bc)] = 0$$

13. Ans. (c).

$$\begin{vmatrix} a & a+1 & a-1 \\ -b & b+1 & b-1 \\ c & c-1 & c+1 \end{vmatrix} + \begin{vmatrix} (-1)^{n+2}a & a+1 & a-1 \\ (-1)^{n+1}b & b+1 & b-1 \\ (-1)^n c & c-1 & c+1 \end{vmatrix}$$

$$= \begin{vmatrix} a+(-1)^{n+2}a & a+1 & a-1 \\ -b+(-1)^{n+1}b & b+1 & b-1 \\ c+(-1)^n c & c-1 & c+1 \end{vmatrix}$$

$= 0$ if n is an odd integer.

MISCELLANEOUS EXERCISE

Matching Entries

♦ *Match the entries of List-A and List-B.*

1.   List-A   List-B

(a) $\begin{vmatrix} 1 & a & a^2 - bc \\ 1 & b & b^2 - ca \\ 1 & c & c^2 - ab \end{vmatrix}$ 1.   0

(b) If $D_r = \begin{vmatrix} 2^{r-1} & 2(3^{r-1}) & 4(5^{r-1}) \\ x & y & z \\ 2^n - 1 & 3^n - 1 & 5^n - 1 \end{vmatrix}$ then $\sum\limits_{r=1}^{n} D_r = \dots$ 2.   0

(c) In an H.P., $T_p = a, T_q = b, T_r = c$, then $\Delta = \begin{vmatrix} bc & ca & ab \\ p & q & r \\ 1 & 1 & 1 \end{vmatrix} = \dots$ 3.   0

(d) If a, b, c be in A.P., then $\Delta = \begin{vmatrix} x+1 & x+2 & x+a \\ x+2 & x+3 & x+b \\ x+3 & x+4 & x+c \end{vmatrix} = \dots$ 4.   0

2.   List-A   List-B

(a) If x, y, z are all different and $\begin{vmatrix} x & x^2 & 1+x^3 \\ y & y^2 & 1+y^3 \\ z & z^2 & 1+z^3 \end{vmatrix} = 0$ then $xyz = \dots$ 1.   1

(b) $\Delta = \begin{vmatrix} \cos(A-P) & \cos(A-Q) & \cos(A-R) \\ \cos(B-P) & \cos(B-Q) & \cos(B-R) \\ \cos(C-P) & \cos(C-Q) & \cos(C-R) \end{vmatrix} = \dots$ 2. -1

(c) If $\Delta = \begin{vmatrix} x^2 - 5x + 3 & 2x - 5 & 3 \\ 3x^2 + x + 4 & 6x + 1 & 9 \\ 7x^2 - 6x + 9 & 14x - 6 & 21 \end{vmatrix}$ then $\dfrac{d}{dx}(\Delta) = \dots$ 3.   0

(d) If system of equations $x = a(y + z), y = b(z + x), z = c(x + y)$ have a non-trivial solution and $(a, b, c \neq -1)$ then $\dfrac{a}{1+a} + \dfrac{b}{1+b} + \dfrac{c}{1+c} = \dots$ 4.   0

3.   Consider the following linear equations $ax + by + cz = 0$, $bx + cy + az = 0$, $cx + ay + bz = 0$.

   Column-I

   (a) $a + b + c \neq 0$ and $a^2 + b^2 + c^2 = ab + bc + ca$

   (b) $a + b + c = 0$ and $a^2 + b^2 + c^2 \neq ab + bc + ca$

   (c) $a + b + c \neq 0$ and $a^2 + b^2 + c^2 \neq ab + bc + ca$

   (d) $a + b + c = 0$ and $a^2 + b^2 + c^2 = ab + bc + ca$

   Column-II

   (p) the equations represent planes meeting only at a single point

   (q) the equations represent the line $x = y = z$

   (r) the equations represent identical planes

   (s) the equations represent the whole of the three dimensional space

Hints / Solutions

1.   Each goes to 0.

   (a) **Q. 10 (c) P. 415**

   (b) **Q. 22 (a) P. 416**

   (c) **Q. 19 P. 416**

   (d) **Q. 24 P. 417**

2.   (a) $\to$ 2. **Q. 10 P. 439**

   (b) $\to$ 3. **Q. 48 P. 443**

   (c) $\to$ 4. **Q. 42 (c) P. 442**

   (d) $\to$ 1. **Q. 10 (c) P. 460**

3.   Ans. a $\to$ r, b $\to$ q, c $\to$ p, d $\to$ s

Refer **Q. 16 P. 422.**

$$\Delta = \begin{vmatrix} a & b & c \\ b & c & a \\ c & a & b \end{vmatrix} = -(a^3 + b^3 + c^3 - 3abc)$$

$$\Delta = -(a+b+c)[a^2 + b^2 + c^2 - ab - bc - ca]$$

$$= -(a+b+c) \cdot \frac{1}{2}[(a-b)^2 + (b-c)^2 + (c-a)^2]$$

$$a \Rightarrow \frac{1}{2}[(a-b)^2 + (b-c)^2 + (c-a)^2] = 0$$

$$\Rightarrow \quad a - b = 0, b - c = 0, c - a = 0$$

$$\Rightarrow \quad a = b = c$$

Hence the equation represent identical planes

$$\therefore \quad a \to r$$

$b \Rightarrow \Delta = 0$ as $a + b + c = 0$ and hence the equations have infinitely many solutions.

$$\therefore \quad ax + by = -cz = (a+b)z \qquad \ldots(1)$$
$$bx + cy = -az = (b+c)z \qquad \ldots(2)$$

Multiply 1 by (b) and (2) by (a) and subtract

$$\therefore \quad (b^2 - c^2) y = (b^2 - c^2) z \quad \therefore \quad y = z$$

Similarly $x = z$ $\therefore$ $x = y = z$ which represents the equation of a line.

$$c \to p \quad \because \quad \Delta \neq 0$$
$$d \to s \quad \therefore \quad \text{Here } a = 0, b = 0, c = 0.$$

Hence the equations represent the whole of three dimensional space.

Fascinating Facts

- The sum and the product of the elements of any row with their corresponding cofactors is equal to the value of the determinant.
- The value of a determinant of order α is equal to the product of the elements along the principal diagonal minus the product of the off diagonal elements
- If a row or a column of a determinant consists of all zeros, the value of the determinant is zero.
- If $D \neq 0$, then system is consistant and has a unique solution.

- If $D = 0$ and $D_1 = D_2 = D_3 = 0$ then system is consistant and dependent and has infinitely many solutions.
- If $D = 0$ and atleast one of the determinants D_1, D_2, D_3 is non-zero, the given system is inconsistent i.e. has no solution.
- If $D_1 = D_2 = D_3 = 0$, then the system is said to be homogeneous, otherwise it is called non-homogeneous.
- If any two rows or columns of a determinant are proportional then its value is zero.

❑

CHAPTER

11

Algebra

Matrices

§1. Introduction.

A set of mn numbers arranged in the form of an ordered set of m rows and n columns is called $m \times n$ matrix (to be read as m by n matrix.)

Thus $m \times n$ matrix A is written as

$$A = \begin{bmatrix} a_{11} & a_{12} & \cdots & a_{1n} \\ a_{21} & a_{22} & \cdots & a_{2n} \\ a_{31} & a_{32} & \cdots & a_{3n} \\ \cdots & \cdots & \cdots & \cdots \\ a_{m1} & a_{m2} & \cdots & a_{mn} \end{bmatrix}$$

or $A = [a_{ij}]$; $i = 1, 2, \ldots m$ and $j = 1, 2, \ldots n$

or $A = [a_{ij}]_{m \times n}$

where a_{ij} represents the element at the intersection of ith row and jth column.

In case the order of a matrix is established or known then we shall simply write

$A = [a_{ij}]$ of type $m \times n$.

§2. Various Types of Matrices

(a) **Square Matrix :** A matrix in which the number of rows is equal to the number of columns is called a Square Matrix. Thus $m \times n$ matrix A will be a square matrix if $m = n$, and it will be termed as a **square matrix of order n or n-rowed square matrix.**

(b) **Diagonal Elements :** In a square matrix all those elements a_{ij} for which $i = j$ i.e. all those elements which occur in the same row and same column namely a_{11}, a_{22}, a_{33} are called the diagonal elements and the line along which they lie is called the **principal diagonal.** Also the **sum of the diagonal elements** of a square matrix A is called **trace of A,**

i.e., $a_{11} + a_{22} + a_{33} + \ldots = $ Trace of A.

In general $a_{11}, a_{22}, \ldots a_{nn}$ are the diagonal elements of n-rowed square matrix and

$a_{11} + a_{22} + \ldots a_{nn} = $ Trace of A.

(c) **Diagonal Matrix :** A square matrix A is said to be a diagonal matrix if all its non-diagonal elements be zero.

Thus $\begin{bmatrix} 1 & 0 & 0 \\ 0 & 4 & 0 \\ 0 & 0 & 8 \end{bmatrix}$ or $\begin{bmatrix} d_1 & 0 & 0 \\ 0 & d_2 & 0 \\ 0 & 0 & d_3 \end{bmatrix}$

Above are diagonal matrices of the type 3×3. These are in short written as

Diag $[1, 4, 8]$ or Diag $[d_1, d_2, d_3]$

(d) **Scalar Matrix :** A diagonal matrix [i.e. all non-diagonal elements being zero] whose all the **diagonal elements** are **equal** is called a scalar matrix.

Thus, $\begin{bmatrix} 3 & 0 & 0 \\ 0 & 3 & 0 \\ 0 & 0 & 3 \end{bmatrix}$ or $\begin{bmatrix} d & 0 & 0 \\ 0 & d & 0 \\ 0 & 0 & d \end{bmatrix}$

are both scalar matrices of type 3×3.

In general for a scalar matrix,

$a_{ij} = 0$ for $i \neq j$ and $a_{ij} = d$ for $i = j$

(e) **Unit Matrix :** A square matrix A all of whose non-diagonal elements are zero (i.e. it is a diagonal matrix) and also all the **diagonal elements are unity** is called a **unit matrix** or an **identity matrix.**

Thus $\begin{bmatrix} 1 & 0 & 0 \\ 0 & 1 & 0 \\ 0 & 0 & 1 \end{bmatrix}$ and $\begin{bmatrix} 1 & 0 & 0 & 0 \\ 0 & 1 & 0 & 0 \\ 0 & 0 & 1 & 0 \\ 0 & 0 & 0 & 1 \end{bmatrix}$

are unit matrices of order 3 and 4 respectively.

In general for a unit matrix,

$a_{ij} = 0$ for $i \neq j$ and $a_{ij} = 1$ for $i = j$.

They are generally denoted by I_3, I_4 or I_n where 3, 4, n denote the order of the square matrix. In case the order be known then we may simply denote it by I.

(f) **Zero matrix or Null Matrix :** Any $m \times n$ matrix in which all the elements are zero is called a zero matrix or null matrix of the type $m \times n$ and is denoted by $O_{m \times n}$.

Thus $\begin{bmatrix} 0 & 0 \\ 0 & 0 \\ 0 & 0 \end{bmatrix}, \begin{bmatrix} 0 & 0 & 0 \\ 0 & 0 & 0 \\ 0 & 0 & 0 \end{bmatrix}, \begin{bmatrix} 0 & 0 & 0 & 0 \\ 0 & 0 & 0 & 0 \end{bmatrix}$

All the above are zero or null matrices of the type $3 \times 2, 3 \times 3$ and 2×4 respectively.

(g) **Determinant of a Square Matrix :** If we have a square matrix having same number of rows and columns it will have $n \times n = n^2$ arrays of numbers. These n^2 numbers also determine a determinant having n rows and n columns and is denoted by Det A or $|A|$.

(h) **Equality of Matrices :** Two matrices $A = [a_{ij}]_{m \times n}$, $B = [b_{ij}]_{m \times n}$ are said to be equal and written as $A = B$ if and only if they **have the same order** or are of the same type *i.e.* each has as many rows and columns as the other [**In this case they are said to be comparable** and also **each element of one is equal to the corresponding element of the other** *i.e.* $a_{ij} = b_{ij}$ for each pair of subscripts i and j where $i = 1, 2, \dots m$ and $j = 1, 2, \dots n.$]

Hence we can say that two matrices are equal if and only if one is duplicate of the other.

(i) **Sum of Matrices.**
Let $A = [a_{ij}]$ and $B = [b_{ij}]$ be two matrices of the same type $m \times n$. Then their sum (or difference) $A + B$ (or $A - B$) is defined as another matrix of the same type, say $C = [c_{ij}]$ such that any element of C is the sum (or difference) of the corresponding elements of A and B.

$\therefore \quad C = A \pm B = [a_{ij} \pm b_{ij}]$

e.g. $A = \begin{bmatrix} 1 & 2 & 4 \\ 0 & 5 & 3 \end{bmatrix}$ and $B = \begin{bmatrix} 7 & 3 & 2 \\ 5 & 1 & 9 \end{bmatrix}$

Here both A and B are 2×3 matrices.

$\therefore \quad A + B = \begin{bmatrix} 1+7 & 2+3 & 4+2 \\ 0+5 & 5+1 & 3+9 \end{bmatrix}$

$= \begin{bmatrix} 8 & 5 & 6 \\ 5 & 6 & 12 \end{bmatrix}$

and $A - B = \begin{bmatrix} 1-7 & 2-3 & 4-2 \\ 0-5 & 5-1 & 3-9 \end{bmatrix}$

$= \begin{bmatrix} -6 & -1 & 2 \\ -5 & 4 & -6 \end{bmatrix}$

(j) **Negative of a Matrix :** If A be a given matrix then $-A$ is called the negative of matrix A and all its elements are the corresponding elements of A multiplied by -1.

Thus if $A = \begin{bmatrix} 2 & 3 & -1 \\ 6 & -4 & 2 \end{bmatrix}$

then $-A = \begin{bmatrix} -2 & -3 & 1 \\ -6 & 4 & -2 \end{bmatrix}$

(k) **Scalar Multiple of a Matrix :** If A be a given matrix and k is any scalar number real or complex. [We call it scalar k to disintiguish it from matrix $[k]$ which is 1×1 matrix] then by matix $kA = Ak$ is meant the matrix all of whose elements are k times of the corresponding elements of A.

If $A = \begin{bmatrix} 2 & 3 & 1 \\ 5 & 2 & 4 \end{bmatrix}$

then $3A = \begin{bmatrix} 3.2 & 3.3 & 3.1 \\ 3.5 & 3.2 & 3.4 \end{bmatrix}$

or $3A = \begin{bmatrix} 6 & 9 & 3 \\ 15 & 6 & 12 \end{bmatrix}$

Similarly $-4A = \begin{bmatrix} -4.2 & -4.3 & -4.1 \\ -4.5 & -4.2 & -4.4 \end{bmatrix}$

$= \begin{bmatrix} -8 & -12 & -4 \\ -20 & -8 & -16 \end{bmatrix}$

§3. Properties of Matrix Addition

(i) **Matrix addition is commutative**
i.e., $A + B = B + A$.

(ii) **Matrix addition is associative.**
i.e., $A + (B + C) = (A + B) + C$.

§ 4. Matrix Multiplication

If $A = [a_{ij}]_{m \times p}$
$B = [b_{jk}]_{p \times n}$ and then $C = AB = [C_{ik}]_{m \times n}$

where $C_{ik} = \sum_{j=1}^{p} a_{ij} b_{jk}$

i.e., $C_{ik} = a_{i1} b_{1k} + a_{i2} b_{2k} + \dots a_{ip} b_{pk}$
In other words $C_{ik} =$ Sum of the products of ith row of A (having p elements) with kth column of B (having p elements). This is known as row by column multiplication of matrices.

It may be noted that in determinants we have row by row or column by column multiplication.

Illustration. If $A = \begin{bmatrix} 1 & -2 & 3 \\ -4 & 2 & 5 \end{bmatrix}_{2 \times 3}$

and $B = \begin{bmatrix} 2 & 3 \\ 4 & 5 \\ 2 & 1 \end{bmatrix}_{3 \times 2}$

compute AB and show that $AB \neq BA$.

A is 2×3 type and B is 3×2 type and hence both AB and BA are defined because the number of columns in pre-factor is equal to the number of rows in post-factor.

$AB = \begin{bmatrix} 1.2 - 2.4 + 3.2 & 1.3 - 2.5 + 3.1 \\ -4.2 + 2.4 + 5.2 & -4.3 + 2.5 + 5.1 \end{bmatrix}$

$= \begin{bmatrix} 0 & -4 \\ 10 & 3 \end{bmatrix}_{2 \times 2}$

$BA = \begin{bmatrix} 2 & 3 \\ 4 & 5 \\ 2 & 1 \end{bmatrix}_{3 \times 2} \begin{bmatrix} 1 & -2 & 3 \\ -4 & 2 & 5 \end{bmatrix}_{2 \times 3}$

$= \begin{bmatrix} -10 & 2 & 21 \\ -16 & 2 & 37 \\ -2 & -2 & 11 \end{bmatrix}_{3 \times 3}$

Hence $AB \neq BA$

If A and B be two matrices then their product is defined or in other words A is **conformable** to B for multiplication if **the number of columns of A is the same as the number of rows in B. i.e. If A be $m \times p$ and B be $p \times n$, the matrix AB will be of the type $m \times n$.**

It may also be noted that if A is conformable to B for multiplication *i.e.* AB is defined then it does not necessarily mean that B is conformable to A *i.e.* the product BA is also defined as B is $p \times n$ and A is $m \times p$, and the number of columns in B (*i.e. n*) is not the same as the number of rows in A (*i.e. m*). Hence BA is not defined.

Now let us suppose that A is $m \times n$ and B is $n \times m$ then in this case AB is defined and is a matrix of $m \times m$ type. On the other hand BA is also defined but it will be a matrix of $n \times n$ type. Hence, even though both AB and BA are defined but $AB \neq BA$ as they are of different order.

In the case when both A and B are square matrices of the same type then also both AB and BA are defined and the product matrix is also a matrix of the same type but still $AB \neq BA$.

§5. Properties of matrix multiplication.

(a) **Multiplication of matrices is distributive with respect to addition of matrices**
   i.e., $A(B + C) = AB + AC$.

(b) **Matrix multiplication is associative if conformability is assured.**
   i.e. $A(BC) = (AB)C$.

(c) **The multiplication of matrices is not always commutative.** *i.e.* AB is not always equal to BA.

(d) **Multiplication of a matrix A by a null matrix conformable with A for multiplication is a null matrix**
   i.e., $AO = O$.

   In particular if A be a square matrix and O be square null matrix of the same order, then $AO = OA = O$.

(e) If $AB = O$ then it does not necessarily mean that $A = O$ or $B = O$ or both are O as shown below.
$$\begin{bmatrix} 0 & 1 \\ 0 & 0 \end{bmatrix} \begin{bmatrix} 1 & 0 \\ 0 & 0 \end{bmatrix} = \begin{bmatrix} 0 & 0 \\ 0 & 0 \end{bmatrix}$$

None of the matrices on the left is a null matrix whereas their poroduct is a null matrix.

(f) **Multiplication of matrix A by a unit matrix I** : Let A be a $m \times n$ matrix and I be a square unit matrix of order n, so that A and I are conformable for multiplication, then
$$AI_n = A.$$
Similarly for IA to exist I should be square unit matrix of order m and in that case $I_m A = A$.

Ex. 1. If $A = \begin{bmatrix} 2 \\ 3 \end{bmatrix}$ and $B = \begin{bmatrix} 4 & 5 \\ 6 & 2 \end{bmatrix}$

Here A is 2×1 type and B is 2×2 type *i.e.*, the number of columns in A is not the same as the number of rows in B and hence the product AB is not defined or we say A is not conformable to B for multiplication. However B is 2×2 and A is 2×1. Hence the number of columns of B is equal to the number of rows of A. Therefore B is conformable to A for multiplication and BA will be a 2×1 matrix :

$$BA = \begin{bmatrix} 4 & 5 \\ 6 & 2 \end{bmatrix} \begin{bmatrix} 2 \\ 3 \end{bmatrix} = \begin{bmatrix} 4.2 + 5.3 \\ 6.2 + 2.3 \end{bmatrix} = \begin{bmatrix} 23 \\ 18 \end{bmatrix}_{2 \times 1}$$

Ex. 2. If $A = \begin{Bmatrix} 1 & -1 & 1 \\ -3 & 2 & -1 \\ -2 & 1 & 0 \end{Bmatrix}, B = \begin{Bmatrix} 1 & 2 & 3 \\ 2 & 4 & 6 \\ 1 & 2 & 3 \end{Bmatrix}$

compute AB and BA.

Here A is 3×3 and B is 3×3. Hence both AB and BA are defined and each will be 3×3 matrix.

Let $AB = C = \begin{bmatrix} C_{11} & C_{12} & C_{13} \\ C_{21} & C_{22} & C_{23} \\ C_{31} & C_{32} & C_{33} \end{bmatrix}$

where C_{ij} means that take the product of ith row of A with jth column of B.

e.g., C_{23} = product of 2nd row of A with 3rd column of B.

i.e., $[-3 \; 2 \; -1] \begin{bmatrix} 3 \\ 6 \\ 3 \end{bmatrix} = -3 \cdot 3 + 2 \cdot 6 - 1 \cdot 3 = 0$

Similarly we can find other elements of C.

We can also say that take the product of first row of A with the three columns of B and we shall get the three elements of first row of C.

i.e., $R_1 C_1, R_1 C_2, R_1 C_3$

and similarly take the second row of A and multiply with all the columns of B and you will get the three elements of 2nd row of C *i.e.* $R_2 C_1, R_2 C_2, R_2 C_3$ and elements of 3rd row of C will be $R_3 C_1, R_3 C_2, R_3 C_3$.

$\therefore AB = \begin{bmatrix} 1.1 - 1.2 + 1.1 & 1.2 - 1.4 + 1.2 & 1.3 - 1.6 + 1.3 \\ -3.1 + 2.2 - 1.1 & -3.2 + 2.4 - 1.2 & -3.3 + 2.6 - 1.3 \\ -2.1 + 1.2 + 0.1 & -2.2 + 1.4 + 0.2 & -2.3 + 1.6 + 0.3 \end{bmatrix}$

$= \begin{bmatrix} 0 & 0 & 0 \\ 0 & 0 & 0 \\ 0 & 0 & 0 \end{bmatrix} = O$ (*i.e.*, null matrix).

The above will be more clear as shown below :

R_1, R_2, R_3 are rows of A and C_1, C_2, C_3 are columns of B.

$\therefore AB = \begin{bmatrix} R_1 C_1 & R_1 C_2 & R_1 C_3 \\ R_2 C_1 & R_2 C_2 & R_2 C_3 \\ R_3 C_1 & R_3 C_2 & R_3 C_3 \end{bmatrix}$

For convenience of multiplication, you may just write the rows written within rectangles as columns.

$$\left[\begin{array}{c}1\\-1\\1\end{array}\right]\times\left[\begin{array}{c}1\\2\\1\end{array}\right]\quad\left[\begin{array}{c}1\\-1\\1\end{array}\right]\times\left[\begin{array}{c}2\\4\\2\end{array}\right]\quad\left[\begin{array}{c}1\\-1\\1\end{array}\right]\left[\begin{array}{c}3\\6\\3\end{array}\right]$$

$$\left[\begin{array}{c}-3\\2\\-1\end{array}\right]\times\left[\begin{array}{c}1\\2\\1\end{array}\right]\quad\left[\begin{array}{c}-3\\2\\-1\end{array}\right]\times\left[\begin{array}{c}2\\4\\2\end{array}\right]\quad\left[\begin{array}{c}-3\\2\\-1\end{array}\right]\left[\begin{array}{c}3\\6\\3\end{array}\right]$$

$$\left[\begin{array}{c}-2\\1\\0\end{array}\right]\left[\begin{array}{c}1\\2\\1\end{array}\right]\quad\left[\begin{array}{c}-2\\1\\0\end{array}\right]\left[\begin{array}{c}2\\4\\2\end{array}\right]\quad\left[\begin{array}{c}-2\\1\\0\end{array}\right]\left[\begin{array}{c}3\\6\\3\end{array}\right]$$

$$=\left[\begin{array}{ccc}1.1-1.2+1.1 & 1.2-1.4+1.2 & 1.3-1.6+1.3\\-3.1+2.2-1.1 & -3.2+2.4-1.2 & -3.3+2.6-1.3\\-2.1+1.2+0.1 & -2.2+1.4+0.2 & -2.3+1.6+0.3\end{array}\right]$$

$$=\left[\begin{array}{ccc}1-2+1 & 2-4+2 & 3-6+3\\-3+4-1 & -6+8-2 & -9+12-3\\-2+2+0 & -4+4+0 & -6+6+0\end{array}\right]=\left[\begin{array}{ccc}0 & 0 & 0\\0 & 0 & 0\\0 & 0 & 0\end{array}\right]$$

$$BA=\left[\begin{array}{ccc}1 & 2 & 3\\2 & 4 & 6\\1 & 2 & 3\end{array}\right]\left[\begin{array}{ccc}1 & -1 & 1\\-3 & 2 & -1\\-2 & 1 & 0\end{array}\right]$$

$$=\left[\begin{array}{ccc}1.1+2(-3)+3(-2) & 1(-1)+2(2)+3(1) & \\2.1+4(-3)+6(-2) & 2(-1)+4(2)+6(1) & \\1.1+2(-3)+3(-2) & 1(-1)+2(2)+3(1) & \end{array}\right.$$

$$\left.\begin{array}{c}1.1+2(-1)+3(0)\\2(1)+4(-1)+6(0)\\1(1)+2(-1)+3(0)\end{array}\right]$$

$$=\left[\begin{array}{ccc}-11 & 6 & -1\\-22 & 12 & -2\\-11 & 6 & -1\end{array}\right]$$

From above we observe that $AB\ne BA$ and we would say that A and B do not commute, whereas in algebra we know that ab is always equal to ba where a and b are any two numbers.

Again we know that when $ab=0$ it means that either a or b (or both) is zero. But $AB=O$ i.e. a null matrix does not necessarily imply that either A or $B=O$ as shown above because neither A, nor B is null matrix whereas AB is a null matrix.

Problem Set (1)

Addition and multiplication of matrices.

1. Prove the following
$$\left[\begin{array}{cccc}1 & 3 & 2 & 0\\4 & 1 & 5 & 9\\3 & 2 & 1 & 3\end{array}\right]\pm\left[\begin{array}{cccc}1 & 0 & 5 & 8\\2 & 3 & 4 & 5\\1 & -5 & 2 & 3\end{array}\right]$$

$$=\left[\begin{array}{cccc}2 & 3 & 7 & 8\\6 & 4 & 9 & 14\\4 & -3 & 3 & 6\end{array}\right]\text{ for plus.}$$

$$=\left[\begin{array}{cccc}0 & 3 & -3 & -8\\2 & -2 & 1 & 4\\0 & 7 & -1 & 0\end{array}\right]\text{ for minus.}$$

2. Can the following two matrices be added
$$\left[\begin{array}{ccc}1 & 2 & 3\\3 & 4 & 5\\5 & 6 & 8\end{array}\right]\text{ and }\left[\begin{array}{cc}4 & 3\\5 & 6\\9 & 8\end{array}\right]$$

Ans. No. Two matrices are conformable for addition if they are of the same type and the above are of different types i.e. 3×3 and 3×2.

3. If $A=\left[\begin{array}{cc}1 & 3\\3 & 2\\2 & 5\end{array}\right]$, $B=\left[\begin{array}{cc}-1 & -2\\0 & 5\\3 & 1\end{array}\right]$

find the matrix D such that $A+B-D=O$ i.e. zero matrix.

Let the matrix D be $\left[\begin{array}{cc}a & b\\c & d\\e & f\end{array}\right]$

$$\therefore\quad A+B-D\left[\begin{array}{cc}1-1-a & 4-2-b\\3+0-c & 2+5-d\\2+3-e & 5+1-f\end{array}\right]$$

$$=\left[\begin{array}{cc}-a & 2-b\\3-c & 7-d\\5-e & 6-f\end{array}\right]=\left[\begin{array}{cc}0 & 0\\0 & 0\\0 & 0\end{array}\right]\text{ given.}$$

From the definition of equality of matrices., we know that one should be duplicate of the other.

$\therefore\quad -a=0$ i.e. $a=0$, $2-b=0$.

$\therefore\quad b=2$, $3-c=0$ $\therefore c=3$ etc.

$$\therefore\quad D=\left[\begin{array}{cc}0 & 2\\3 & 7\\5 & 6\end{array}\right]\text{ which is clearly equal to }A+B.$$

4. If a matrix has 13 elements, then the possible dimension (order) it can have are
   (a) 1×13 or 13×1 (b) 1×26 or 26×1
   (c) 2×13 or 13×2 (d) None of these
   Ans. (a). The number of elements in $A_{m\times n}=mn$.

5. If $A=\left[\begin{array}{ccc}2 & 3 & 1\\0 & -1 & 5\end{array}\right]$, $B=\left[\begin{array}{ccc}1 & 2 & -1\\0 & -1 & 3\end{array}\right]$, find $2A-3B$.

   Ans. $\left[\begin{array}{ccc}1 & 0 & 5\\0 & 1 & 1\end{array}\right]$.

6. If $A=\left[\begin{array}{ccc}0 & 1 & 2\\2 & 3 & 4\\4 & 5 & 6\end{array}\right]$, $B=\left[\begin{array}{ccc}1 & 0 & 0\\0 & 1 & 0\\0 & 0 & 1\end{array}\right]$, find $3A-4B$.

Ans. $\begin{bmatrix} -4 & 3 & 6 \\ 6 & 5 & 12 \\ 12 & 15 & 14 \end{bmatrix}$.

7. If $A + B = \begin{bmatrix} 1 & 0 & 2 \\ 2 & 2 & 2 \\ 1 & 1 & 2 \end{bmatrix}$ and $A - B = \begin{bmatrix} 1 & 4 & 4 \\ 4 & 2 & 0 \\ -1 & -1 & 2 \end{bmatrix}$

then prove that

$A = \begin{bmatrix} 1 & 2 & 3 \\ 3 & 2 & 1 \\ 0 & 0 & 2 \end{bmatrix}$ and $B = \begin{bmatrix} 0 & -2 & -1 \\ -1 & 0 & 1 \\ 1 & 1 & 0 \end{bmatrix}$

Ans. Adding and subtracting we get $2A$ and $2B$. Hence A and B are as given.

8. $A = \begin{bmatrix} 1 & 2 & -3 \\ 5 & 0 & 2 \\ 1 & -1 & 1 \end{bmatrix}$ and $B = \begin{bmatrix} 3 & -1 & 2 \\ 4 & 2 & 5 \\ 2 & 0 & 3 \end{bmatrix}$

find the matrix C satisfying the relation $A + 2C = B$

Ans. $C = \dfrac{1}{2}(B - A) = \begin{bmatrix} 1 & -2 & 5/2 \\ -1/2 & 1 & 3/2 \\ 1/2 & 1/2 & 1 \end{bmatrix}$

9. If $2X - Y = \begin{bmatrix} 3 & -3 & 0 \\ 3 & 3 & 2 \end{bmatrix}$ and $2Y + X = \begin{bmatrix} 4 & 1 & 5 \\ -1 & 4 & -4 \end{bmatrix}$,

then find X and Y.

Ans. Eliminate Y and find X. Put for X and find Y. $X = \begin{bmatrix} 2 & -1 & 1 \\ 1 & 2 & 0 \end{bmatrix}, Y = \begin{bmatrix} 1 & 1 & 2 \\ -1 & 1 & -2 \end{bmatrix}$

10. If $A = \begin{bmatrix} 1 & 2 \\ 3 & 4 \end{bmatrix}, B = \begin{bmatrix} 2 & 3 \\ 4 & 5 \end{bmatrix}$, and $4A - 3B + C = O$, then $C =$

(a) $\begin{bmatrix} 2 & -1 \\ 0 & 1 \end{bmatrix}$ (b) $\begin{bmatrix} 2 & 1 \\ 0 & -1 \end{bmatrix}$

(c) $\begin{bmatrix} -2 & 1 \\ 0 & -1 \end{bmatrix}$ (d) None

Ans. (b).

11. Prove that a 3×4 matrix A whose element a_{ij} is given by $\dfrac{(i+j)^2}{2}$ is

$\begin{bmatrix} 2 & 9/2 & 8 & 25/2 \\ 9/2 & 8 & 25/2 & 18 \\ 8 & 25/2 & 18 & 49/2 \end{bmatrix}$

12. Is it possible to define the matrix $A + B$ when
(a) A has 3 rows and B has 2 rows ....
(b) A has 2 columns and B has 4 columns ....
(c) A has 3 rows and B has 2 columns ....
(d) Both A and B are square matrices of the same order ....

Ans. (a). No. For matrix addition the matrix should be of the same type.
(a) No. As above.
(b) Ans. Yes. Only when A has 2 columns and B has 3 rows for in that case both will be of the same type.
(c) Ans. Yes. Always.

13. Show that product of two given matrices can be a zero matrix without either of the matrices being a zero matrix.

$AB = \begin{bmatrix} 0 & 1 \\ 0 & 0 \end{bmatrix} \begin{bmatrix} 1 & 0 \\ 0 & 0 \end{bmatrix} = \begin{bmatrix} 0 & 0 \\ 0 & 0 \end{bmatrix} = O$

i.e. $AB = O$

Neither A nor B is null matrix but AB is a null matrix.

But $BA = \begin{bmatrix} 0 & 1 \\ 0 & 0 \end{bmatrix} \neq O$

Another Example :

Let us choose two non-zero matrices A and B as under

$A = \begin{bmatrix} 1 & 1 \\ 3 & 3 \end{bmatrix}_{2 \times 2}$ and $B = \begin{bmatrix} -1 & 1 \\ 1 & -1 \end{bmatrix}_{2 \times 2}$

$AB = \begin{bmatrix} 1(-1) + 1.1 & 1.1 + 1(-1) \\ 3(-1) + 3.1 & 3(1) + 3(-1) \end{bmatrix} = \begin{bmatrix} 0 & 0 \\ 0 & 0 \end{bmatrix} = O$

Thus we observe that the matrix AB is null matrix whereas neither A nor B is a null matrix.

But $BA = \begin{bmatrix} 2 & 2 \\ -2 & -2 \end{bmatrix} \neq O$

14. If $A = \begin{bmatrix} 1 & 2 \\ 3 & 0 \\ 4 & 1 \end{bmatrix}$ and $B = \begin{bmatrix} 0 & 1 & 0 \\ 0 & 2 & 1 \\ 2 & 3 & 1 \end{bmatrix}$ find BA. Can we find AB also ?

$A = 3 \times 2$ and $B = 3 \times 3$. Since the number of columns of A is not equal to number of rows of B as such the matrix AB is not defined. But the matrix BA is defined because the number of columns in B is equal to the number of rows in A each being equal to 3.

$BA = \begin{bmatrix} 0 & 1 & 0 \\ 0 & 2 & 1 \\ 2 & 3 & 1 \end{bmatrix} \begin{bmatrix} 1 & 2 \\ 3 & 0 \\ 4 & 1 \end{bmatrix}$

$= \begin{bmatrix} 0.1 + 1.3 + 0.4 & 0.2 + 1.0 + 0.1 \\ 0.1 + 2.3 + 1.4 & 0.2 + 2.0 + 1.1 \\ 2.1 + 3.3 + 1.4 & 2.2 + 3.0 + 1.1 \end{bmatrix} = \begin{bmatrix} 3 & 0 \\ 10 & 1 \\ 15 & 5 \end{bmatrix}$

Verification for the Product to be correct.
We have proved above that

$BA = \begin{bmatrix} 0 & 1 & 0 \\ 0 & 2 & 1 \\ 2 & 3 & 1 \end{bmatrix} \begin{bmatrix} 1 & 2 \\ 3 & 0 \\ 4 & 1 \end{bmatrix} = \begin{bmatrix} 3 & 0 \\ 10 & 1 \\ 15 & 5 \end{bmatrix}$

Sum   2 6 2   28 6

Multiply the row of sum i.e. 2, 6, 2 with the columns of 2nd matrix and the result should come out to be row of sum of product matrix on the right i.e., 28 ,6 as shown below.

i.e. $2.1 + 6.3 + 2.4 = 2 + 18 + 8 = 28$

and $2.2 + 6.0 + 2.1 = 4 + 0 + 2 = 6$

Hence correct.

15. (a) $A = \begin{bmatrix} 2 & 3 & 4 \\ 1 & 2 & 3 \\ -1 & 1 & 2 \end{bmatrix}, B = \begin{bmatrix} 1 & 3 & 0 \\ -1 & 2 & 1 \\ 0 & 0 & 2 \end{bmatrix}$

Show that

$$AB = \begin{bmatrix} -1 & 12 & 11 \\ -1 & 7 & 8 \\ -2 & -1 & 5 \end{bmatrix} \text{ and } BA = \begin{bmatrix} 5 & 9 & 13 \\ -1 & 2 & 4 \\ -2 & 2 & 4 \end{bmatrix}$$

Hence $AB \neq BA$.

It is easy to compute both AB and BA.

Let us verify the product AB to be correct.

$$\qquad\qquad\qquad\qquad\qquad\qquad\qquad \text{Product}$$

$$AB = \begin{bmatrix} 2 & 3 & 4 \\ 1 & 2 & 3 \\ -1 & 1 & 2 \end{bmatrix} \begin{bmatrix} 1 & 3 & 0 \\ -1 & 2 & 1 \\ 0 & 0 & 2 \end{bmatrix} = \begin{bmatrix} -1 & 12 & 11 \\ -1 & 7 & 8 \\ -2 & -1 & 5 \end{bmatrix}$$

Sum $\quad\overline{2\quad 6\quad 9}\qquad\qquad\qquad$ Sum $\overline{-4\quad 18\quad 24}$

$2.1 + 6. - 1 + 9.0 = 2 - 6 + 0 = -4$

$2.3 + 6.2 + 9.0 = 6 + 12 + 0 = 18$

$2.0 + 6.1 + 9.2 = 0 + 6 + 18 = 24.$

Hence correct.

Similarly we can verify the product BA.

(b) The value of λ for which the matrix product
$$\begin{bmatrix} 2 & 0 & 7 \\ 0 & 1 & 0 \\ 1 & -2 & 1 \end{bmatrix} \begin{bmatrix} -\lambda & 14\lambda & 7\lambda \\ 0 & 1 & 6 \\ \lambda & -4\lambda & -2\lambda \end{bmatrix}$$ is an identity matrix.

(a) $\dfrac{1}{2}$ (b) $\dfrac{1}{3}$

(c) $\dfrac{1}{4}$ (d) $\dfrac{1}{5}$ **(C.E.T. Delhi 1993)**

Ans. (d).

$AB = I$ if $a_{ij} = 0, i \neq j$ and $a_{ij} = 1$ for $i = j$.

$a_{11} = 5\lambda = 1 \Rightarrow \lambda = 1/5, a_{12} = 28\lambda - 28\lambda = 0,$

$a_{13} = 14\lambda - 14\lambda = 0$

You may verify other elements will also satisfy the criteria.

16. If $\begin{bmatrix} 4 \\ 1 \\ 3 \end{bmatrix} A = \begin{bmatrix} -1 & 8 & 4 \\ -1 & 2 & 1 \\ -3 & 6 & 3 \end{bmatrix}$ find A.

Ans. We have $XA = 3 \times 3$ matrix where X is 3×1. Now XA is conformable for multiplication if the number of columns in pre-factor is equal to the number of rows in the post factor. Keeping in view that the product is 3×3 matrix, we must have matrix A of 1×3 type i.e. A has one row and 3 columns i.e. A is a row matrix.

Let $A = [p \quad q \quad r]$ say of 1×3 type.

Now $\begin{bmatrix} 4 \\ 1 \\ 3 \end{bmatrix} [p \quad q \quad r] = \begin{bmatrix} 4p & 4q & 4r \\ p & q & r \\ 3p & 3q & 3r \end{bmatrix} = \begin{bmatrix} -4 & 8 & 4 \\ -1 & 2 & 1 \\ -3 & 6 & 3 \end{bmatrix}$

clearly $p = -1, q = 2$ and $r = 1$ satisfy above.

Hence matrix $A = [-1 \quad 2 \quad 1]$.

17. The order of $[x \; y \; z] \begin{bmatrix} a & h & g \\ h & b & f \\ g & f & c \end{bmatrix} \begin{bmatrix} x \\ y \\ z \end{bmatrix}$ is

(a) 3×1 (b) 1×1 (c) 1×3 (d) 3×3

Ans. (b). $A_{1 \times 3} \; B_{3 \times 3} \; C_{3 \times 1} = P_{1 \times 3} C_{3 \times 1} = D_{1 \times 1}$

18. Is it possible to define the matrix AB and BA when :

(a) A has 3 rows and B has 2 rows.

Ans.   Let $AB = A_{3 \times p} \, B_{2 \times q}$.

The product AB is defined only when the number of columns in prefactor A i.e. p is the same as the number of rows in post factor B i.e. 2. Since B has 2 rows therefore A should have 2 columns for AB to be defined i.e. $p = 2$.

Also for BA to be defined the number of columns in prefactor B i.e. q should be same as number of rows in post-factor A i.e. 3 and hence B should have 3 columns.

(b) A has 3 columns and B has 4 columns.

$AB = A_{p \times 3} \, B_{q \times 4}$ and $B_{q \times 4} \, A_{p \times 3}$

for AB. B should have three rows i.e., $q = 3$.

for BA. A should have four rows i.e., $p = 4$.

(c) A has 4 rows and B has 4 columns.

$AB = A_{4 \times p} \, B_{q \times 4}$ and $BA = B_{q \times 4} \, A_{4 \times p}$

for AB. It depends on the number of columns of A and number of rows of B i.e. p, q and both should be equal.

for BA. It is always defined because the number of columns in prefactor B is the same as the number of rows in post-factor A i.e. $4 = 4$.

19. If A and B be matrices such that both AB and $A + B$ are defined. Prove that both A and B are square matrices of the same order.

We know that two matrices A and B are conformable for addition if they are of the same type. Thus if A be $m \times n$ then B should also be $m \times n$ as $A + B$ is defined. Again since AB is also defined therefore number of columns in A i.e., n should be equal to number of rows in B i.e. m. Hence $n = m$ and in that case both A and B will be square matrices of order equal to $m = n$.

20. If A be any $m \times n$ matrix and both AB and BA are defined prove that B should be $n \times m$ matrix.

Since A is $m \times n$ and AB defined therefore B should be $n \times p$ because the number of columns of A should be equal to number of rows of B.

Again B is now $n \times p$ and A is $m \times n$.

And since BA is also defined therefore p should be equal to m by the same argument as above i.e. $p = m$.

$\therefore$ B is $n \times m$ matrix.

21. (a) If A and B are two matrices such that $AB = B$ and $BA = A$, then $A^2 + B^2 =$

(a) $2AB$ (b) $2BA$

(c) $A + B$ (d) AB

Ans. (c).

We have to make use of given relations $AB = B$ and $BA = A$

$A^2 + B^2 = AA + BB = A(BA) + B(AB)$

$= (AB)A + (BA)B = BA + AB$

$= A + B \Rightarrow (c).$

(b) If A and B are square matrices of size $n \times n$ such that $A^2 - B^2 = (A-B)(A+B)$, then which of the following will be always true

(a) $AB = BA$ (b) $A = B$

(c) A or $B = O$ (d) A or $B = I$ **(AIEEE 2006)**

Ans. (a).

$$A^2 - B^2 = (A-B)(A+B) = A^2 + AB - BA - B^2$$

$$\Rightarrow \quad AB - BA = O \text{ or } AB = BA$$

(c) If $A = \begin{bmatrix} 1 & 2 \\ 3 & 4 \end{bmatrix}, B = \begin{bmatrix} a & 0 \\ 0 & b \end{bmatrix}$ where $a, b \in N$.

If $AB = BA$, then there exists

(a) only one B

(b) infinitely many B's

(c) more than one but finite B's

(d) no B exists   **(AIEEE 2006)**

Ans. (c).

$$AB = \begin{bmatrix} a & 2b \\ 3a & 4b \end{bmatrix}$$

$$BA = \begin{bmatrix} a & 2a \\ 3b & 4b \end{bmatrix}$$

Since $AB = BA$ $\therefore$ $2b = 2a$ and $3a = 3b$.

$\therefore \quad a = b \; \forall \; n \in \mathbf{N}$.

22. If α and β differ by an odd multiple of $\pi/2$ prove that the product of the two matrices given below is a null matrix.

$$A = \begin{bmatrix} \cos^2 \alpha & \cos \alpha \sin \alpha \\ \cos \alpha \sin \alpha & \sin^2 \alpha \end{bmatrix}$$

$$B = \begin{bmatrix} \cos^2 \beta & \cos \beta \sin \beta \\ \cos \beta \sin \beta & \sin^2 \beta \end{bmatrix}$$

$$AB = \begin{bmatrix} \cos \alpha \cos \beta \cos(\alpha-\beta) & \cos \alpha \sin \beta \cos(\alpha-\beta) \\ \sin \alpha \cos \beta \cos(\alpha-\beta) & \sin \alpha \sin \beta \cos(\alpha-\beta) \end{bmatrix}$$

$$= \begin{bmatrix} 0 & 0 \\ 0 & 0 \end{bmatrix}$$

$\because \quad \alpha - \beta = $ odd multiple of $\pi/2$

$\therefore \quad \cos(\alpha - \beta) = 0$.

23. If $A = \begin{bmatrix} a & b \\ -b & a \end{bmatrix}, B = \begin{bmatrix} c & d \\ -d & c \end{bmatrix}$, show that A and B commute *i.e.* $AB = BA$. Also verify that $|AB| = |A| \cdot |B|$

Here we can easily show that

$$AB = BA = \begin{bmatrix} ac - bd & ad + bc \\ -bc - ad & -bd + ac \end{bmatrix}$$

$\therefore$ Det $AB = |AB| = (ac - bd)^2 + (ad + bc)^2$

$$= a^2 c^2 + b^2 d^2 + a^2 d^2 + b^2 c^2$$

$$= (a^2 + b^2)(c^2 + d^2) = |A||B| = \text{Det } A \cdot \text{Det } B.$$

24. Find the form of all the matrices which commute with the matrix $A = \begin{bmatrix} 1 & 3 \\ 2 & 4 \end{bmatrix}$

If B be the required matrix then both AB and BA should be defined and also $AB = BA$

$A_{2 \times 2}$ $\therefore$ B should be $2 \times p$

$\therefore \quad AB = 2 \times p$

$B_{2 \times p} A_{2 \times 2}$ will be defined if $p = 2$

Hence, B must be a 2×2 matrix and let it be $\begin{bmatrix} p & q \\ r & s \end{bmatrix}$

$$AB = \begin{bmatrix} 1 & 3 \\ 2 & 4 \end{bmatrix} \begin{bmatrix} p & q \\ r & s \end{bmatrix} = \begin{bmatrix} p + 3r & q + 3s \\ 2p + 4r & 2q + 4s \end{bmatrix}$$

$$BA = \begin{bmatrix} p & q \\ r & s \end{bmatrix} \begin{bmatrix} 1 & 3 \\ 2 & 4 \end{bmatrix} = \begin{bmatrix} p + 2q & 3p + 4q \\ r + 2s & 3r + 4s \end{bmatrix}$$

By definition of equality of matrices we have

$p + 3r = p + 2q$ $\therefore$ $r = \dfrac{2q}{3}$

$q + 3s = 3p + 4q$ $\therefore$ $s = p + q$

$2p + 4r = r + 2s = r + 2(p+q)$ $\therefore$ $r = \dfrac{2q}{3}$

$2q + 4s = 3r + 4s$ $\therefore$ $r = \dfrac{2q}{3}$

Let us put $\dfrac{q}{3} = \lambda$

$\therefore \quad q = 3\lambda, r = 2\lambda, \; s = p + 3\lambda$

$\therefore$ The family of matrices which conmmute with the given matrix are of the type

$$\begin{bmatrix} p & 3\lambda \\ 2\lambda & p + 3\lambda \end{bmatrix}$$

where p and λ are arbitrary constants.

25. Prove in two ways

$$[x \; y \; z] \begin{bmatrix} a & h & g \\ h & b & f \\ g & f & c \end{bmatrix} \begin{bmatrix} x \\ y \\ z \end{bmatrix}$$

$$= [ax^2 + by^2 + cz^2 + 2fyz + 2gzx + 2hxy].$$

Let us call the matrices as A, B, C which are of $1 \times 3, 3 \times 3, 3 \times 1$, so that the matrix ABC will be 1×1. Evidently they are conformable for multiplication

$ABC = A(BC)$ or $(AB)C$

$$(BC) = \begin{bmatrix} ax + hy + gz \\ hx + by + fz \\ gx + fy + cz \end{bmatrix}_{3 \times 1}$$

$$\therefore \quad ABC = A(BC) = [x, y, z]_{1 \times 3} \begin{bmatrix} ax + hy + gz \\ hx + by + fz \\ gx + fy + cz \end{bmatrix}_{3 \times 1}$$

$$= [x(ax + hy + gz) + y(hx + by + fz)$$
$$+ z(gx + fy + cz)]_{1 \times 1}$$

$$= [ax^2 + by^2 + cz^2 + 2fyz + 2gzx + 2hxy]_{1 \times 1}$$

Similarly we can find ABC as $(AB)C$ where AB will be 1×3 and C being 3×1, $(AB)C$ will be 1×1 matrix which will be same as above.

26. If $A_\alpha = \begin{bmatrix} \cos \alpha & \sin \alpha \\ -\sin \alpha & \cos \alpha \end{bmatrix}$, then prove the following

(a) $(A_\alpha)^n = \begin{bmatrix} \cos n\alpha & \sin n\alpha \\ -\sin n\alpha & \cos n\alpha \end{bmatrix}$

(b) $A_\alpha A_\beta = A_{\alpha + \beta} = A_\beta A_\alpha$.

(a) $(A_\alpha)^2 = A_\alpha A_\alpha = \begin{bmatrix} \cos\alpha & \sin\alpha \\ -\sin\alpha & \cos\alpha \end{bmatrix}$

$\begin{bmatrix} \cos\alpha & \sin\alpha \\ -\sin\alpha & \cos\alpha \end{bmatrix}$

$= \begin{bmatrix} \cos^2\alpha - \sin^2\alpha & 2\sin\alpha\cos\alpha \\ -2\sin\alpha\cos\alpha & -\sin^2\alpha + \cos^2\alpha \end{bmatrix}$

$= \begin{bmatrix} \cos 2\alpha & \sin 2\alpha \\ -\sin 2\alpha & \cos 2\alpha \end{bmatrix}$

Similarly, $(A_\alpha)^3 = (A_\alpha)^2 A_\alpha$

$= \begin{bmatrix} \cos 2\alpha & \sin 2\alpha \\ -\sin 2\alpha & \cos 2\alpha \end{bmatrix} \begin{bmatrix} \cos\alpha & \sin\alpha \\ -\sin\alpha & \cos\alpha \end{bmatrix}$

$= \begin{bmatrix} \cos(2\alpha + \alpha) & \sin(2\alpha + \alpha) \\ -\sin(2\alpha + \alpha) & \cos(2\alpha + \alpha) \end{bmatrix}$

$= \begin{bmatrix} \cos 3\alpha & \sin 3\alpha \\ -\sin 3\alpha & \cos 3\alpha \end{bmatrix}$

In the light of above let us assume that

$(A_\alpha)^n = \begin{bmatrix} \cos n\alpha & \sin n\alpha \\ -\sin n\alpha & \cos n\alpha \end{bmatrix}$

$\therefore \quad (A_\alpha)^{n+1} = (A_\alpha)^n A_\alpha$

$= \begin{bmatrix} \cos n\alpha & \sin n\alpha \\ -\sin n\alpha & \cos n\alpha \end{bmatrix} \begin{bmatrix} \cos\alpha & \sin\alpha \\ -\sin\alpha & \cos\alpha \end{bmatrix}$

$= \begin{bmatrix} \cos(n+1)\alpha & \sin(n+1)\alpha \\ -\sin(n+1)\alpha & \cos(n+1)\alpha \end{bmatrix}$

Thus we observe that our assumption for $(A_\alpha)^n$ is true for $n = n + 1$ and it was shown to be true for $n = 2, 3, \ldots$ and hence it is true universally.

(b) $A_\alpha A_\beta = \begin{bmatrix} \cos\alpha & \sin\alpha \\ -\sin\alpha & \cos\alpha \end{bmatrix} \begin{bmatrix} \cos\beta & \sin\beta \\ -\sin\beta & \cos\beta \end{bmatrix}$

$= \begin{bmatrix} \cos(\alpha+\beta) & \sin(\alpha+\beta) \\ -\sin(\alpha+\beta) & \cos(\alpha+\beta) \end{bmatrix} = A_{\alpha+\beta}$

Also $A_\beta \cdot A_\alpha = A_{\alpha+\beta}$ which can be shown as above. **Hence proved.**

27. (a) If $A = \begin{bmatrix} 3 & -4 \\ 1 & -1 \end{bmatrix}$ then $A^k = \begin{bmatrix} 1+2k & -4k \\ k & 1-2k \end{bmatrix}$

where k is any + ive integer.

$A = \begin{bmatrix} 3 & -4 \\ 1 & -1 \end{bmatrix}$ then $A^1 = \begin{bmatrix} 1+2.1 & -4.1 \\ 1 & 1-2.1 \end{bmatrix}_{k=1}$

Also $A^2 = AA$

$= \begin{bmatrix} 3 & -4 \\ 1 & -1 \end{bmatrix} \begin{bmatrix} 3 & -4 \\ 1 & -1 \end{bmatrix} = \begin{bmatrix} 9-4 & -12+4 \\ 3-1 & -4+1 \end{bmatrix}$

or $A^2 = \begin{bmatrix} 5 & -8 \\ 2 & -3 \end{bmatrix} = \begin{bmatrix} 1+2.2 & -4.2 \\ 2 & 1-2.2 \end{bmatrix}_{k=2}$

Now assume that $A^k = \begin{bmatrix} 1+2k & -4k \\ k & 1-2k \end{bmatrix}_{k=k}$

$\therefore A^{k+1} = AA^k = \begin{bmatrix} 3 & -4 \\ 1 & -1 \end{bmatrix} \begin{bmatrix} 1+2k & -4k \\ k & 1-2k \end{bmatrix}$

$= \begin{bmatrix} 3+6k-4k & -12k-4+8k \\ 1+2k-k & -4k-1+2k \end{bmatrix}$

$= \begin{bmatrix} 3+2k & -4k-4 \\ 1+k & -2k-1 \end{bmatrix}$

$= \begin{bmatrix} 1+2(k+1) & -4(k+1) \\ k+1 & 1-2(k+1) \end{bmatrix}$

We observe that our assumption is true for $k = k+1$ and it was true when $k = 1$ or 2. Hence, it is true for all +ive intergral values of k.

(b) If $A = \begin{bmatrix} \alpha & 0 \\ 1 & 1 \end{bmatrix}$, $B = \begin{bmatrix} 1 & 0 \\ 5 & 1 \end{bmatrix}$ whenever $A^2 = B$,

then the value of α is

(a) 1   (b) -1

(c) 4   (d) no real value of α

(IIT-Screening 2003)

Ans. (d).

$A^2 = B \Rightarrow \begin{bmatrix} \alpha & 0 \\ 1 & 1 \end{bmatrix} \begin{bmatrix} \alpha & 0 \\ 1 & 1 \end{bmatrix} = \begin{bmatrix} 1 & 0 \\ 5 & 1 \end{bmatrix}$

$\Rightarrow \begin{bmatrix} \alpha^2 & 0 \\ \alpha+1 & 1 \end{bmatrix} = \begin{bmatrix} 1 & 0 \\ 5 & 1 \end{bmatrix}$

$\Rightarrow \alpha^2 = 1, \alpha + 1 = 5$

$\therefore \quad \alpha = \pm 1, \alpha = 4$

There is no real value of α which satisfies both.

(c) If $A = \begin{bmatrix} \alpha & 2 \\ 2 & \alpha \end{bmatrix}$ and $|A^3| = 125$ then α is

(a) ± 1 (b) $+2$

(c) ± 3 (d) ± 5 **(IIT-Screening 2004)**

Ans. (c). $|A| = 5 \Rightarrow \alpha^2 - 4 = 5 \therefore \alpha = \pm 3$

(d) There are two column vectors $X = \begin{pmatrix} x \\ 1 \end{pmatrix}$ and $\begin{pmatrix} 1 & 4 \\ 5 & 2 \end{pmatrix} X$ is parallel to X. If θ is the angle between them, then $\tan\theta$ is

(a) 3   (b) 5

(c) 7   (d) 9

Ans. (d).

$\begin{bmatrix} 1 & 4 \\ 5 & 2 \end{bmatrix} \begin{bmatrix} x \\ 1 \end{bmatrix} = \lambda \begin{bmatrix} x \\ 1 \end{bmatrix}$

$\begin{bmatrix} x+4 \\ 5x+2 \end{bmatrix} = \begin{bmatrix} \lambda x \\ \lambda \end{bmatrix}$

$\therefore \quad x+4 = \lambda x$ and $5x+2 = \lambda$

Eliminating λ, we get $\dfrac{x+4}{x} = 5x+2$

or $5x^2 + x - 4 = 0$ or $(x+1)(5x-4) = 0$

$\therefore \quad x = \dfrac{4}{5}, -1$

Hence the two column vectors are

$\begin{bmatrix} 4/5 \\ 1 \end{bmatrix}$ and $\begin{bmatrix} -1 \\ 1 \end{bmatrix}$ i.e. $\begin{bmatrix} a_1 \\ b_1 \end{bmatrix}$, $\begin{bmatrix} a_2 \\ b_2 \end{bmatrix}$

$\therefore \quad \tan\theta = \dfrac{a_1 b_2 - a_2 b_1}{a_1 a_2 + b_1 b_2}$ or $\tan\theta = \dfrac{\dfrac{4}{5}+1}{-\dfrac{4}{5}+1} = 9$

28. (a) If ω be the complex cube root of unity and $A = \begin{bmatrix} \omega & 0 \\ 0 & \omega \end{bmatrix}$, then A^{70} is equal to

(a) 0 (b) A

(c) $-A$ (d) none

Ans. (b) $A^2 = \begin{bmatrix} \omega & 0 \\ 0 & \omega \end{bmatrix} \begin{bmatrix} \omega & 0 \\ 0 & \omega \end{bmatrix} = \begin{bmatrix} \omega^2 & 0 \\ 0 & \omega^2 \end{bmatrix}$

$A^3 = A^2 \cdot A = \begin{bmatrix} \omega^2 & 0 \\ 0 & \omega^2 \end{bmatrix} \begin{bmatrix} \omega & 0 \\ 0 & \omega \end{bmatrix} = \begin{bmatrix} \omega^3 & 0 \\ 0 & \omega^3 \end{bmatrix}$

Since ω is complex cube root of unity $\therefore \omega^3 = 1$

$\therefore \quad A^3 = \begin{bmatrix} 1 & 0 \\ 0 & 1 \end{bmatrix} = I$

$\therefore \quad A^{70} = A^{69} \cdot A = (A^3)^{23} \cdot A = I^{23} \cdot A = I \cdot A = A$

(b) If $A = \text{diag}\ [d_1, d_2, d_3]$, then A^n is equal to

(a) $\text{diag}\ [d_1^{n-1}, d_2^{n-1}, d_3^{n-1}]$

(b) A

(c) $\text{diag}\ [d_1^{\ n}, d_2^{\ n}, d_3^{\ n}]$

(d) none

Ans. (c).

$A = \begin{bmatrix} d_1 & 0 & 0 \\ 0 & d_2 & 0 \\ 0 & 0 & d_3 \end{bmatrix}$

then $A^2 = \begin{bmatrix} d_1 & 0 & 0 \\ 0 & d_2 & 0 \\ 0 & 0 & d_3 \end{bmatrix} \begin{bmatrix} d_1 & 0 & 0 \\ 0 & d_2 & 0 \\ 0 & 0 & d_3 \end{bmatrix}$

$= \begin{bmatrix} d_1^2 & 0 & 0 \\ 0 & d_2^2 & 0 \\ 0 & 0 & d_3^2 \end{bmatrix}$

$A^3 = A^2 \cdot A = \begin{bmatrix} d_1^3 & 0 & 0 \\ 0 & d_2^3 & 0 \\ 0 & 0 & d_3^3 \end{bmatrix}$

Hence continuing like this

$A^n = \text{diag}\ [d_1^{\ n}, d_2^{\ n}, d_3^{\ n}]$.

29. If $A = \begin{bmatrix} 0 & -\tan \alpha/2 \\ \tan \alpha/2 & 0 \end{bmatrix}$

and I is a 2×2 unit matrix, then prove that

$I + A = (I - A) \begin{bmatrix} \cos \alpha & -\sin \alpha \\ \sin \alpha & \cos \alpha \end{bmatrix}$

L.H.S. $I + A = \begin{bmatrix} 1 & -\tan \alpha/2 \\ \tan \alpha/2 & 1 \end{bmatrix}$

as $I = \begin{bmatrix} 1 & 0 \\ 0 & 1 \end{bmatrix}$ ...(1)

R.H.S. $= \begin{bmatrix} 1 & \tan \alpha/2 \\ -\tan \alpha/2 & 1 \end{bmatrix} \begin{bmatrix} \cos \alpha & -\sin \alpha \\ \sin \alpha & \cos \alpha \end{bmatrix}$

$= \begin{bmatrix} \cos \alpha + \sin \alpha \tan \alpha/2 & -\sin \alpha + \cos \alpha \tan \alpha/2 \\ (-\tan \alpha/2) \cos \alpha + \sin \alpha & (\tan \alpha/2) \sin \alpha + \cos \alpha \end{bmatrix}$

Now changing $\tan \alpha/2$ into $\sin \alpha/2 / \cos \alpha/2$ and applying the formula for $\sin (A \pm B)$ and $\cos (A \pm B)$

R.H.S. $= \dfrac{1}{\cos \alpha/2} \begin{bmatrix} \cos (\alpha - \alpha/2) & -\sin (\alpha - \alpha/2) \\ \sin (\alpha - \alpha/2) & \cos (\alpha - \alpha/2) \end{bmatrix}$

$= \dfrac{1}{\cos \alpha/2} \begin{bmatrix} \cos \alpha/2 & -\sin \alpha/2 \\ \sin \alpha/2 & \cos \alpha/2 \end{bmatrix}$

$= \begin{bmatrix} 1 & -\tan \alpha/2 \\ \tan \alpha/2 & 1 \end{bmatrix} = I + A$ by (1)

30. If A and B are matrices given below :

$A = \begin{bmatrix} 0 & c & -b \\ -c & 0 & a \\ b & -a & 0 \end{bmatrix}$ and $B = \begin{bmatrix} a^2 & ab & ac \\ ab & b^2 & bc \\ ac & bc & c^2 \end{bmatrix}$

then AB is a unit matrix. Is this statement true ?

Ans. False.

Correct is that AB is null matrix.

31. Compute $A^3 - 2A^2 + 3A - I$ where I is a unit matrix.

and $A = \begin{bmatrix} 1 & 3 & 2 \\ 2 & 0 & 3 \\ 1 & -1 & 1 \end{bmatrix}$

The matrices A^3 and A^2 can be computed as usual.

$\therefore \quad A^3 - 2A^2 + 3A - I$

$\begin{bmatrix} 24 & 14 & 34 \\ 18 & 8 & 26 \\ 4 & 0 & 6 \end{bmatrix} - 2 \begin{bmatrix} 9 & 1 & 13 \\ 5 & 3 & 7 \\ 0 & 2 & 0 \end{bmatrix}$

$+ 3 \begin{bmatrix} 1 & 3 & 2 \\ 2 & 0 & 3 \\ 1 & -1 & 1 \end{bmatrix} - \begin{bmatrix} 1 & 0 & 0 \\ 0 & 1 & 0 \\ 0 & 0 & 1 \end{bmatrix}$

$= \begin{bmatrix} 24 & 14 & 34 \\ 18 & 8 & 26 \\ 4 & 0 & 6 \end{bmatrix} - \begin{bmatrix} 18 & 2 & 26 \\ 10 & 6 & 14 \\ 0 & 4 & 0 \end{bmatrix}$

$+ \begin{bmatrix} 3 & 9 & 6 \\ 6 & 0 & 9 \\ 3 & -3 & 3 \end{bmatrix} - \begin{bmatrix} 1 & 0 & 0 \\ 0 & 1 & 0 \\ 0 & 0 & 1 \end{bmatrix}$

$= \begin{bmatrix} 24-18+3-1 & 14-2+9-0 & 34-26+6-0 \\ 18-10+6-0 & 8-6+0-1 & 26-14+9-0 \\ 4-0+3-0 & 0-4-3-0 & 6-0+3-1 \end{bmatrix}$

$= \begin{bmatrix} 8 & 21 & 14 \\ 14 & 1 & 21 \\ 7 & -7 & 8 \end{bmatrix}$

32. Compute $A^2 - 4A - 5I$ where

$A = \begin{bmatrix} 1 & 2 & 2 \\ 2 & 1 & 2 \\ 2 & 2 & 1 \end{bmatrix}$ and I is a unit matrix.

As in last question,

$A^2 = \begin{bmatrix} 9 & 6 & 6 \\ 6 & 9 & 6 \\ 6 & 6 & 9 \end{bmatrix}$

$\therefore \quad A^2 - 4A - 5I$

$= \begin{bmatrix} 9 & 6 & 6 \\ 6 & 9 & 6 \\ 6 & 6 & 9 \end{bmatrix} - \begin{bmatrix} 4 & 8 & 8 \\ 8 & 4 & 8 \\ 8 & 8 & 4 \end{bmatrix} - \begin{bmatrix} 5 & 0 & 0 \\ 0 & 5 & 0 \\ 0 & 0 & 5 \end{bmatrix}$

$$= \begin{bmatrix} 0 & -2 & -2 \\ -2 & 0 & -2 \\ -2 & -2 & 0 \end{bmatrix} = -2 \begin{bmatrix} 0 & 1 & 1 \\ 1 & 0 & 1 \\ 1 & 1 & 0 \end{bmatrix}$$

33. Let $F(\alpha) = \begin{bmatrix} \cos\alpha & -\sin\alpha & 0 \\ \sin\alpha & \cos\alpha & 0 \\ 0 & 0 & 1 \end{bmatrix}$ then $F(\alpha) \cdot F(\beta)$ is

equal to

(a) $F(\alpha\beta)$ (b) $F\left(\dfrac{\alpha}{\beta}\right)$

(c) $F(\alpha+\beta)$ (d) $F(\alpha-\beta)$

Ans. (c).

$$F(\alpha) \cdot F(\beta) = \begin{bmatrix} \cos\alpha & -\sin\alpha & 0 \\ \sin\alpha & \cos\alpha & 0 \\ 0 & 0 & 1 \end{bmatrix} \begin{bmatrix} \cos\beta & -\sin\beta & 0 \\ \sin\beta & \cos\beta & 0 \\ 0 & 0 & 1 \end{bmatrix}$$

$$F(\alpha) \cdot F(\beta) = \begin{bmatrix} \cos(\alpha+\beta) & -\sin(\alpha+\beta) & 0 \\ \sin(\alpha+\beta) & \cos(\alpha+\beta) & 0 \\ 0 & 0 & 1 \end{bmatrix}$$

$$= F(\alpha+\beta) \implies (c).$$

34. If A is a diagonal matrix diag $(d_1, d_2 \ldots\ldots d_n)$, then $A^n, n \in R$ is diag $(d_1^n, d_2^n \ldots\ldots d_n^n)$

Let $A = \begin{bmatrix} d_1 & 0 & 0 \\ 0 & d_2 & 0 \\ 0 & 0 & d_3 \end{bmatrix}$

$$A^2 = A \cdot A = \begin{bmatrix} d_1^2 & 0 & 0 \\ 0 & d_2^3 & 0 \\ 0 & 0 & d_3^3 \end{bmatrix}$$

by actual multiplication

Similarly, $A^3 = A^2 \cdot A = \begin{bmatrix} d_1^3 & 0 & 0 \\ 0 & d_2^3 & 0 \\ 0 & 0 & d_3^3 \end{bmatrix}$

The same procedure be followd for nature of nth order.

PASSAGE

$A = \begin{bmatrix} 2 & 0 & 1 \\ 1 & 1 & 0 \\ 1 & 0 & 1 \end{bmatrix}_{3\times3}$; $AU_1 = \begin{bmatrix} 1 \\ 0 \\ 0 \end{bmatrix}_{3\times1}$; $AU_2 = \begin{bmatrix} 2 \\ 3 \\ 0 \end{bmatrix}_{3\times1}$

and $AU_3 = \begin{bmatrix} 3 \\ 2 \\ 1 \end{bmatrix}_{3\times1}$.

If U_1, U_2, U_3 are columns of matrix U, then **(I.I.T. 2006)**

35. (a) Determinant of U is :

(a) 13   (b) 15

(c) 3   (d) 2

Ans. (c).

Let $U_1 = \begin{bmatrix} x_1 \\ y_1 \\ z_1 \end{bmatrix}$

$$AU_1 = \begin{bmatrix} 2 & 0 & 1 \\ 1 & 1 & 0 \\ 1 & 0 & 1 \end{bmatrix}_{3\times3} \begin{bmatrix} x_1 \\ y_1 \\ z_1 \end{bmatrix}_{3\times1} = \begin{bmatrix} 1 \\ 0 \\ 0 \end{bmatrix}_{3\times1}$$

$\therefore \quad 2x_1 + z_1 = 1, \ x_1 + y_1 = 0, \ x_1 + z_1 = 0$

Solving $x_1 = 1, y_1 = -1, z_1 = -1$

$\therefore \quad U_1 = \begin{bmatrix} 1 \\ -1 \\ -1 \end{bmatrix}, \ U_2 = \begin{bmatrix} 2 \\ 1 \\ -2 \end{bmatrix}$ and $U_3 = \begin{bmatrix} 2 \\ 0 \\ -1 \end{bmatrix}$

and $U = \begin{bmatrix} 1 & 2 & 2 \\ -1 & 1 & 0 \\ -1 & -2 & -1 \end{bmatrix}$

$\therefore \quad$ Det $U = \begin{vmatrix} 1 & 2 & 2 \\ -1 & 1 & 0 \\ -1 & -2 & -1 \end{vmatrix} = \begin{vmatrix} 1 & 2 & 2 \\ 0 & 3 & 2 \\ 0 & 0 & 1 \end{vmatrix}$

by $R_2 + R_1$ and $R_3 + R_1$

$\therefore \quad$ Det $(U) = 3$.

(b) Sum of elements of U^{-1} is :

(a) $\dfrac{1}{3}$ (b) $\dfrac{1}{12}$

(c) $\dfrac{1}{4}$ (d) 0

Ans. (d).

$$U^{-1} = \frac{\text{Adj } U}{\text{Det } U} = \frac{1}{3}(\text{Adj } U)$$

Now $U = \begin{bmatrix} 1 & 2 & 2 \\ -1 & 1 & 0 \\ -1 & -2 & -1 \end{bmatrix}$

$\therefore \quad$ Adj U is found by the **rule (b), Page 487.**

Adj $U = \begin{bmatrix} 1 & -2 & -2 \\ 1 & 1 & -2 \\ 0 & 0 & 3 \end{bmatrix}$

$\therefore \quad \dfrac{\text{Adj } U}{\text{Det } U} = \dfrac{1}{3}(\text{Adj } U) = \begin{bmatrix} 1/3 & -2/3 & -2/3 \\ 1/3 & 1/3 & -2/3 \\ 0 & 0 & 1 \end{bmatrix}$

$\therefore \quad$ Sum of the elements of

$$U^{-1} = \left(3 \cdot \frac{1}{3} + 1\right) + 3\left(-\frac{2}{3}\right) = 0$$

(c) $[3 \ 2 \ 0] U \begin{bmatrix} 3 \\ 2 \\ 0 \end{bmatrix}_{3\times1} = [a]_{1\times1}$,

then a equals :

(a) 12   (b) 21

(c) 19   (d) 24

Ans. (c).

$$[3 \ 2 \ 0]_{1\times3} \begin{bmatrix} 1 & 2 & 2 \\ -1 & 1 & 0 \\ -1 & -2 & -1 \end{bmatrix}_{3\times3} \begin{bmatrix} 3 \\ 2 \\ 0 \end{bmatrix}_{3\times1}$$

$$= [1 \ 8 \ 6]_{1\times3} \begin{bmatrix} 3 \\ 2 \\ 0 \end{bmatrix}_{3\times1} = [3 + 16 + 0]_{1\times1} = [19]_{1\times1}$$

$\therefore \quad a = 19$.

§ 6. Various Kinds of Matrices

1. **Idempotent Matrix**

   A matrix A such that $A^2 = A$ is called Idempotent matrix.

2. **Periodic Matrix**

   A matrix A will be called a periodic matrix if $A^{k+1} = A$ where k is +ive integer. If, however, k is the least +ive integer for which $A^{k+1} = A$, then k is said to be the period of A.

3. **Nilpotent Matrix**

   A matrix A will be called a nilpotent matrix if $A^k = O$ (null matrix) where k is a +ive integer. If, however, k is the least +ive integer for which $A^k = O$, then k is the index of the nilpotent matrix A.

4. **Involuntary Matrix.**

   A matrix A will be called an involuntary matrix if $A^2 = I$ (unit matrix).

   Since $I^2 = I$ always.

   ∴ Unit Matrix I is involuntary.

Gist

$A^2 = A$ (Idempotent), $A^2 = I$ (Involuntary)

$A^{k+1} = A$ (Periodic of period k)

$A^k = O$ (Nilpotent of index k)

where k is the least + ive integer satisfying the above conditions.

Problem Set (2)

Idempotent, periodic and nilpotent matrices.

1. Prove that the matrix $A = \begin{bmatrix} 2 & -2 & -4 \\ -1 & 3 & 4 \\ 1 & -2 & -3 \end{bmatrix}$ is idempotent.

   It is easy to show that $A^2 = A \cdot A = A$ by actual multiplication.

   Hence, A is idempotent.

2. Find all the idempotent diagonal matrices of order 3.

   Let $A = \begin{bmatrix} d_1 & 0 & 0 \\ 0 & d_2 & 0 \\ 0 & 0 & d_3 \end{bmatrix}$,

   then $A^2 = A \cdot A = \begin{bmatrix} d_1^2 & 0 & 0 \\ 0 & d_2^2 & 0 \\ 0 & 0 & d_3^2 \end{bmatrix}$.

   For idempotent matrix, $A^2 = A$.

   ∴ $d_i^2 = d_i$ $(i = 1, 2, 3)$

   or $d_i (d_i - 1) = 0$ or $d_i = 0$ or 1 for $i = 1, 2, 3$

   ∴ $A = \begin{bmatrix} 0 & 0 & 0 \\ 0 & 0 & 0 \\ 0 & 0 & 0 \end{bmatrix}$ or $\begin{bmatrix} 1 & 0 & 0 \\ 0 & 1 & 0 \\ 0 & 0 & 1 \end{bmatrix}$

   Both are diagonal and idempotent.

3. Prove that the matrix $A = \begin{bmatrix} -5 & -8 & 0 \\ 3 & 3 & 0 \\ 1 & 2 & -1 \end{bmatrix}$ is involuntary.

   Evaluate $A^2 = A \cdot A = I_3$ by actual multiplication and hence A is involuntary.

4. Determine the condition that the matrix

   $A = \begin{bmatrix} a & b \\ c & -a \end{bmatrix}$ be involuntry $i.e., A^2 = I$

   $A^2 = A \cdot A = \begin{bmatrix} a^2 + bc & ab - ab \\ ac - ac & bc + a^2 \end{bmatrix}$

   $= \begin{bmatrix} a^2 + bc & 0 \\ 0 & a^2 + bc \end{bmatrix}$

   $A^2 = I$ if $a^2 + bc = 1$ is the required condition.

5. Show that $A = \begin{bmatrix} 1 & -3 & -4 \\ -1 & 3 & 4 \\ 1 & -3 & -4 \end{bmatrix}$ is nilpotent of index 2.

   If $A^k = O$, then A is nilpotent of index k (least +ive integer)

   Evaluate $A^2 = A \cdot A = O_{3 \times 3}$ by actual calculation and hence A is nilpotent of index 2.

6. Show that $A = \begin{bmatrix} ab & b^2 \\ -a^2 & -ab \end{bmatrix}$ is nilpotent of index 2.

   Show as above that

   $A^2 = A \cdot A = \begin{bmatrix} a^2b^2 - a^2b^2 & ab^3 - ab^3 \\ -a^3b + a^3b & -a^2b^2 + a^2b^2 \end{bmatrix} = \begin{bmatrix} 0 & 0 \\ 0 & 0 \end{bmatrix} = O$

   Hence, A is nilpotent of index 2.

7. Prove that the matrix $A = \begin{bmatrix} 1 & -2 & -6 \\ -3 & 1 & 9 \\ 2 & 0 & -3 \end{bmatrix}$ is periodic whose period is 2.

   If $A^{k+1} = A$ then A is periodic of period k (least + ive integer). By actual calculation first find A^2 and then $A^3 = A^2 \cdot A = A$ by calculation since $A^{2+1} = A$.

   ∴ A is periodic of period 2.

8. If B is idempotent, show that $A = I - B$ is also idempotent and that $AB = BA = O$.

   Since B is idempotent ∴ $B^2 = B$ given

   $A^2 = (I - B)^2 = I^2 - 2IB + B^2$

$\because$ I and B commute i.e., $IB = BI = B$

$$= I - 2B + B = I - B = A$$

Since $A^2 = A$ $\therefore$ A is also idempotent.

Again $AB = (I - B) B = IB - B^2 = B - B = O$

Similarly $BA = B (I - B) = BI - B^2 = B - B = O$

9. If A and B are idempotent matrices, then show that AB is idempotent if A and B commute.

    Given $A^2 = A, B^2 = B$ and $AB = BA$ ...(1)

$$(AB)^2 = (AB)(AB) = A(BA) B = A (AB) B \text{ by } (1)$$

$$= (AA)(BB) = A^2 B^2 = AB \text{ by } (1)$$

Hence, AB is idempotent under given condition.

10. If A and B are idempotent then $A + B$ will be idempotent if $AB = BA = O$ where O is the null matrix.

$$(A + B)^2 = (A + B)(A + B) = A^2 + AB + BA + B^2$$

$$= A + O + O + B = A + B.$$

Hence, idempotent if $AB = BA = O$

11. Show that $A = \begin{bmatrix} 1 & 1 & 3 \\ 5 & 2 & 6 \\ -2 & -1 & -3 \end{bmatrix}$ is nilpotent of index 3.

$$A^2 = AA = \begin{bmatrix} 0 & 0 & 0 \\ 3 & 3 & 9 \\ -1 & -1 & -3 \end{bmatrix}$$

$$A^3 = A^2 A = \begin{bmatrix} 0 & 0 & 0 \\ 3 & 3 & 9 \\ -1 & -1 & -3 \end{bmatrix} \begin{bmatrix} 1 & 1 & 3 \\ 5 & 2 & 6 \\ -2 & -1 & 3 \end{bmatrix}$$

$$= \begin{bmatrix} 0 & 0 & 0 \\ 0 & 0 & 0 \\ 0 & 0 & 0 \end{bmatrix} = O.$$

$\therefore$ $A^3 = O$ i.e., $A^p = O$

$\therefore$ nilpotent of index 3.

Similarly we can show that $A = \begin{bmatrix} 1 & 2 & 3 \\ 1 & 2 & 3 \\ -1 & -2 & -3 \end{bmatrix}$

is a nilpotent matrix of order 2.

12. If A and B are n-square matrices then prove that A and B will commute if and only if $A - kI$ and $B - kI$ commute for every scalar k.

   Let us suppose that A and B commute i.e., $AB = BA$ then

$$(A - kI)(B - kI) = AB - k(AI + IB) + k^2 I^2.$$

$$= AB - k(A + B) + k^2 I$$

$IB = B, AI = A, I^2 = I.$

Similarly $(B - kI)(A - kI) = BA - k(A + B) + k^2 I$

But $AB = BA$ given, $\therefore$ $A - kI$ and $B - kI$ commute.

Converse : If $A - kI$ and $B - kI$ commute, then

$$(A - kI)(B - kI) = (B - kI)(A - kI).$$

$\therefore$ $AB - k(A + B) + k^2 I = BA - k(A + B) + k^2 I.$

$\therefore$ $AB = BA$ and hence A and B commute.

§ 7. The Transpose of a Matrix

If A be a given matrix of the type $m \times n$ then the matrix obtained by changing the rows of A into columns and columns of A into rows is called Transpose of matrix A and is denoted by A'. As there are m rows in A therefore there will be m columns in A' and similarly as there are n columns in A there will be n rows in A'.

Hence the matrix A' is $\boldsymbol{n \times m}$ type.

e.g. If $A = \begin{bmatrix} 3 & 4 \\ 2 & 1 \\ 5 & 9 \end{bmatrix}_{3 \times 2}$, then $A' = \begin{bmatrix} 3 & 2 & 5 \\ 4 & 1 & 9 \end{bmatrix}_{2 \times 3}$

§ 8. Properties of Transpose

(1) $(A')' = A.$ (2) $(KA)' = KA'.$ K being a scalar.

(3) $(A + B)' = A' + B'.$ (4) $(AB)' = B' A'.$

(5) $(ABC)' = C' B' A'$

§ 9. Symmetric Matrices

A square matrix $A = [a_{ij}]$ will be called symmetric if for all values of i and j, $a_{ij} = a_{ji}$.

i.e. every i-jth element = j-ith element.

e.g. $A = \begin{bmatrix} a & h & g \\ h & b & f \\ g & f & c \end{bmatrix}_{3 \times 3}$ is a symmetric matrix.

Property $A' = A$

§ 10. Skew Symmetric Matrix

A square matrix $A = [a_{ij}]$ will be called skew symmetric if its i-jth element is $-$ ive of $j - i$th element for all values of i and j i.e. $a_{ij} = -a_{ji}$ for all values of i and j. Since diagonal elements will be of the type $a_{11}, a_{22}, a_{33}, \ldots a_{ii}$ and by given condition $a_{ii} = -a_{ii}$ for all values of i

or $2a_{ii} = 0$ $\therefore$ $a_{ii} = 0.$

Hence the diagonal elements of a skew symmetric matrix are zero.

e.g. $\begin{bmatrix} 0 & h & g \\ -h & 0 & f \\ -g & -f & 0 \end{bmatrix}$ is a skew symmetric matrix.

Property : $A' = - A.$

§ 11. Adjoint of a Matrix

If $A = [a_{ij}]$ be a $\boldsymbol{n\text{-squared matrix}}$, then the matrix

$B = [b_{ij}]$ *such that b_{ij} is the co-factor of the element a_{ji} in the determinant $|A|$ is called the adjoint of matrix A and is written as adj. A.*

In simple language we can say that adj. A is the transpose of the matrix formed by the co-factors of elements of $|A|$.

Working rule for finding the adjoint of A.

Write down the determinant $|A|$ and the co-factors of various rows which will be columns of adj. A or replace each element in A by its co-factors and then take transpose to get adj. A.

▶ **Rule to write the cofactors of an element a_{ij}.**

Cross the row and column intersecting at the element a_{ij} and the determinant which is left be denoted by D, then

$$\left[\begin{array}{l} \textbf{Cofactor of } a_{ij} = D \quad \textbf{if } i+j = \textbf{even} \\ \qquad\qquad\qquad = -D \quad \textbf{if } i+j = \textbf{odd} \end{array}\right]$$

Illustration : $A = \begin{bmatrix} \alpha & \beta \\ \gamma & \delta \end{bmatrix}$ find adj. A and show that adj. (adj. A) = A.

Co-factor of α is δ and co-factor of β is $-\gamma$.
Co-factor of γ is $-\beta$ and co-factor of δ is α.

∴ Matrix formed by co-factors is $\begin{bmatrix} \delta & -\gamma \\ -\beta & \alpha \end{bmatrix}$ ...(1)

Adj. A = transpose of matrix (1)

$$= \begin{bmatrix} \delta & -\beta \\ -\gamma & \alpha \end{bmatrix} \qquad ...(2)$$

You may see that $\delta, -\gamma$ are the co-factors of first row of A and it forms the first column of adj. A, $-\beta, \alpha$ are the co-factors of 2nd row of A and it forms the second column of adj. A.

▶ **Rule for adjoint of 2 × 2 matrix**

If A be 2 × 2 then adj. A is written by interchanging the elements of leading diagonal and changing the sign of the elements of other diagonal *i.e.* if

$$A = \begin{bmatrix} 3 & 4 \\ -5 & 7 \end{bmatrix} \text{ then adj. } A = \begin{bmatrix} 7 & -4 \\ 5 & 3 \end{bmatrix} \qquad ...(3)$$

i.e. elements 3, 7 of leading diagonal have been interchanged and the sign of 4, –5 in the other diagonal have been changed. **(Note the rule)**

(b) Prove from above that if A be a square matrix then adj. (adj. A) = A. You have to show that adj. of matrix (2) in above examples is matrix A.
Both (2) and (3) give adjoint $(A) = B$ where A is a 2 × 2 matrix.

∴ adj (adj. A) = adj. B where B is 2 × 2 matrix given by 2 and 3

∴ adj. $(B) = \begin{vmatrix} \alpha & \gamma \\ \beta & \delta \end{vmatrix}$ or $\begin{vmatrix} 3 & 4 \\ -5 & 7 \end{vmatrix} = A$

by rule for adjoint of 2 × 2 matrix.
or adj (adj. A) = A

Ex. 1. Find the adjoint of matrix

(a) $A = \begin{bmatrix} 0 & 1 & 1 \\ 1 & 2 & 0 \\ 3 & -1 & 4 \end{bmatrix}$ (b) $A = \begin{bmatrix} 1 & 1 & 1 \\ 1 & 2 & -3 \\ 2 & -1 & 3 \end{bmatrix}$

(a) Co-factors of elements of 1st row are respectively

of a_{11} of a_{12} of a_{13}

$\begin{vmatrix} 2 & 0 \\ -1 & 4 \end{vmatrix} = 8, -\begin{vmatrix} 1 & 0 \\ 3 & 4 \end{vmatrix} = -4, \begin{vmatrix} 1 & 2 \\ 3 & -1 \end{vmatrix} = -7$

Co-factors of elements of 2nd row are respectively.

of a_{21} of a_{22} of a_{23}

$-\begin{vmatrix} 1 & 1 \\ -1 & 4 \end{vmatrix} = -5, \begin{vmatrix} 0 & 1 \\ 3 & 4 \end{vmatrix} = -3, -\begin{vmatrix} 0 & 1 \\ 3 & -1 \end{vmatrix} = 3$

Co-factors of elements of 3rd row are respectively

of a_{31} of a_{32} of a_{33}

$\begin{vmatrix} 1 & 1 \\ 2 & 0 \end{vmatrix} = -2, -\begin{vmatrix} 0 & 1 \\ 1 & 1 \end{vmatrix} = 1, \begin{vmatrix} 0 & 1 \\ 1 & 0 \end{vmatrix} = -1$

Form a matrix by replacing the elements of A by the co-factors of $|A|$.

i.e. $\begin{bmatrix} 8 & -4 & -7 \\ -5 & -3 & 3 \\ -2 & 1 & -1 \end{bmatrix}$

∴ Adj. A = Transpose of above

$= \begin{bmatrix} 8 & -5 & -2 \\ -4 & -3 & 1 \\ -7 & 3 & -1 \end{bmatrix}$

(b) Ans. $\begin{bmatrix} 3 & -4 & -5 \\ -9 & 1 & 4 \\ -5 & 3 & 1 \end{bmatrix}$

Ex. 2. Find the adjoints of the following matrices :

(a) $\begin{bmatrix} -1 & -2 & 3 \\ -2 & 2 & 1 \\ 4 & -5 & 2 \end{bmatrix}$ (b) $\begin{bmatrix} 1 & 2 & 3 \\ 0 & 1 & 2 \\ 0 & 0 & 1 \end{bmatrix}$

(c) $\begin{bmatrix} 1 & 2 & 3 \\ 1 & 3 & 4 \\ 1 & 4 & 3 \end{bmatrix}$ (d) $\begin{bmatrix} 2 & 1 & 0 \\ 0 & -3 & 1 \\ -1 & -1 & 3 \end{bmatrix}$

Ans.

(a) $\begin{bmatrix} 9 & -11 & -8 \\ 8 & -14 & -5 \\ 2 & -13 & -6 \end{bmatrix}$ (b) $\begin{bmatrix} 1 & -2 & 1 \\ 0 & 1 & -2 \\ 0 & 0 & 1 \end{bmatrix}$

(c) $\begin{bmatrix} -7 & 6 & -1 \\ 1 & 0 & -1 \\ 1 & -2 & 1 \end{bmatrix}$ (d) $\begin{bmatrix} -8 & -3 & 1 \\ -1 & 6 & -2 \\ -3 & 1 & -6 \end{bmatrix}$

Ex. 3. If $A = \begin{bmatrix} -1 & -2 & -2 \\ 2 & 1 & -2 \\ 2 & -2 & 1 \end{bmatrix}$ show that Adj. $A = 3A'$

Adj. $A = \begin{bmatrix} -3 & 6 & 6 \\ -6 & 3 & -6 \\ -6 & -6 & 3 \end{bmatrix} = 3 \begin{bmatrix} -1 & 2 & 2 \\ -2 & 1 & -2 \\ -2 & -2 & 1 \end{bmatrix} = 3A'$

∵ A' = Transpose of $A = \begin{bmatrix} -1 & 2 & 2 \\ -2 & 1 & -2 \\ -2 & -2 & 1 \end{bmatrix}$

Ex. 4. If A is 3 × 4 matrix and B is a matrix such that $A'B$ and BA' are both defined. Then B is of the type

(a) 3 × 4   (b) 3 × 3

(c) 4 × 4   (d) 4 × 3

Ans. (a).

$A_{3 \times 4} \Rightarrow A'_{4 \times 3}$

Now $A'B$ defined $\Rightarrow B$ is 3 × p

Again $B_{3 \times p} A'_{4 \times 3}$ defined $\Rightarrow p = 4$

∴ B is 3 × 4.

§ 12. Properties of adjoint A.

The product of a matrix and its adjoint is commutative.

(a)   If A be n-rowed square matrix, then

$$(\text{adj. } A) A = A (\text{adj. } A) = |A| . I_n$$

$$= |A| \begin{bmatrix} 1 & 0 & 0 \\ 0 & 1 & 0 \\ 0 & 0 & 1 \end{bmatrix} = \begin{bmatrix} |A| & 0 & 0 \\ 0 & |A| & 0 \\ 0 & 0 & |A| \end{bmatrix} \quad …(I)$$

where $|A|$ is determinant A and I_n is the n-rowed unit matrix.

Deduction (a). If A is a n-squared singular matrix i.e., $|A| = 0$, then

$A (\text{adj. } A) = (\text{adj. } A) A = O$ (null matrix) by (I)
A matrix is said to be **Singular** if its determinant is zero i.e., $|A| = 0$

Deduction (b). $|\text{adj. } A| = |A|^{n-1}$ if $|A|$ is not zero.

If clearly follows from above on taking determinants of both sides in (I) in (a) that

$$|A| . |\text{adj. } A| = |A|^n = |\text{adj. } A| . |A|$$

$$|\text{adj. } A| = |A|^{n-1} \text{ provided } |A|$$

is not zero.
If $|A|$ is not zero, then A is said to be non-singular matrix.

Verification of the rule

$$(\text{adj. } A) A = A (\text{Adj. } A) = |A| I_n$$

We have proved above is Ex. 1 (a) that if

$$A = \begin{bmatrix} 0 & 1 & 1 \\ 1 & 2 & 0 \\ 3 & -1 & 4 \end{bmatrix}$$

then $\text{Adj } A = \begin{bmatrix} 8 & -5 & -2 \\ -4 & -3 & 1 \\ -7 & 3 & -1 \end{bmatrix}$

Also $|A| = -11$ by calculation.

∴ $A (\text{adj. } A)$ by actual multiplication

$$= \begin{bmatrix} -11 & 0 & 0 \\ 0 & -11 & 0 \\ 0 & 0 & -11 \end{bmatrix} = \begin{bmatrix} |A| & 0 & 0 \\ 0 & |A| & 0 \\ 0 & 0 & |A| \end{bmatrix}$$

$$= \text{diag } [|A|, |A|, |A|]$$

Taking determinants of both sides, we get

$$|A \text{ adj. } A| = |\text{diag.} [|A|, |A|, |A|]|$$

or $|A||\text{adj. } A| = |A|^n$

∴ $|\text{adj. } A| = |A|^{n-1}$ provided

$|A| \neq 0$ i.e., A is non-singular.

(b) $\text{Adj. (Adj. } A) = |A|^{n-2} A$ if A be non-singular

Put $\text{Adj. } A = B$, then

$B \text{ adj. } B = |B| I_n = \text{diag.} [|B|, |B| … |B|]$

∴ $A (B \text{ adj. } B) = A \text{ diag } [|B|, |B| …. |B|] = |B| A$

$$…(I)$$

Now put $B = \text{adj. } A$ in (I)

∴ $|B| = |\text{adj. } A| = |A|^{n-1}$

∴ $A (\text{adj. } A) \text{ adj. (adj. } A) = |A|^{n-1} A$

$|A| I_n \text{ adj. (adj. } A) = |A|^{n-1} A$

∴ $\text{adj. (adj. } A) = |A|^{n-2} A$

Particular Case

If A be 3×3 matrix, then
$\text{adj. (adj. } A) = |A|^{n-2} A = |A|^{3-2} A = |A| \cdot A.$

§ 13. The Inverse of a Matrix.

Definition : If A and B be two n-squared matrices such that $AB = BA = I$ then we shall say that $B = A^{-1}$. i.e. B is equal to inverse of A. Also the matrix B has an inverse. We shall say that $A = B^{-1}$ i.e. A is equal to inverse of B. It will be seen that every square matrix does not possess an inverse.

▸ **Properties of inverse**

Inverse of a matrix is unique.

(a)   We shall show below that **if a matrix A has an inverse, then it is unique.**

(b)   **Condition for a square matrix A to possess an inverse is that A is non-singular.**
i.e., $|A| \neq 0.$

(c)   **Inverse by the help of adjoint.**
$$A^{-1} = \frac{1}{|A|} (\text{adj. } A)$$

(d)   **If A be non-singular and $AB = AC$, then $B = C$, where B and C are square matrices of the same order.**

(e)   **Reversal Law for the inverse of product.**
i.e., $(AB)^{-1} = B^{-1} A^{-1}$.

In other words it means that inverse of the product is the product of the inverses in the reverse order.

(f)   **The operation of transposing and inverting are commutative.**
i.e., $(A')^{-1} = (A^{-1})'$.

(g)   **Adj. AB = Adj. B Adj. A**
i.e., Adjoint of product = Product of adjoints in reverse order

We know that $A^{-1} = \dfrac{\text{Adj. } A}{|A|}, |A| \neq 0$ by (c)

or $\text{adj. } A = |A| A^{-1}$ …(I)

∴ $\text{Adj. } (AB) = |AB| (AB)^{-1}$

$= |A||B|(B^{-1} A^{-1})$ by (e)

$= |B|(B^{-1})(|A| A^{-1})$

$= (\text{adj. } B)(\text{adj. } A)$ by (I)

Illustration :   Find the adjoint and inverse of the following matrix :

$$\begin{bmatrix} 1 & 2 & 1 \\ 3 & 2 & 3 \\ 1 & 1 & 2 \end{bmatrix}$$

$|A| = 1(4-3) - 3(4-1) + 1(6-2) = 1 - 9 + 4 = -4$

Hence matrix A is non-singular $i.e. |A| \neq 0$.

The co-factors of elements of various rows of $|A|$ are

$$(4-3),\quad -(6-3),\quad (3-2)\ i.e.\quad 1,\ -3,\ 1$$
$$-(4-1),\quad (2-1),\quad -(1-2)\ i.e.\quad -3,\ 1,\ 1$$
$$(6-2),\quad -(3-3),\quad (2-6)\ i.e.\quad 4,\ 0,\ -4$$

Therefore the matrix formed by co-factors of $|A|$ is

$$C = \begin{bmatrix} 1 & -3 & 1 \\ -3 & 1 & 1 \\ 4 & 0 & -4 \end{bmatrix}$$

∴ Adj. A = Transpose of C

$i.e.$ change rows into columns and columns into rows in C.

$$\therefore\ \text{Adj.}\ A = \begin{bmatrix} 1 & -3 & 4 \\ -3 & 1 & 0 \\ 1 & 1 & -4 \end{bmatrix}$$

$$\therefore\ A^{-1} = \frac{1}{|A|}\text{adj.}\ A = -\frac{1}{4}\begin{bmatrix} 1 & -3 & 4 \\ -3 & 1 & 0 \\ 1 & 1 & -4 \end{bmatrix}$$

Multiply each element of the matrix by $-\frac{1}{4}$

$$\text{or}\quad A^{-1} = \begin{bmatrix} -\frac{1}{4} & \frac{3}{4} & -1 \\ \frac{3}{4} & -\frac{1}{4} & 0 \\ -\frac{1}{4} & -\frac{1}{4} & 1 \end{bmatrix}$$

$$AA^{-1} = \begin{bmatrix} 1 & 2 & 1 \\ 3 & 2 & 3 \\ 1 & 1 & 2 \end{bmatrix} \times -\frac{1}{4}\begin{bmatrix} 1 & -3 & 4 \\ -3 & -1 & 0 \\ 1 & 1 & -4 \end{bmatrix}$$

Verification. $A A^{-1} = A^{-1} A = I$

$$= -\frac{1}{4}\begin{bmatrix} 1-6+1 & -3+2+1 & 4+0-4 \\ 3-6+3 & -9+2+3 & 12+0-12 \\ 1-3+2 & -3+1+2 & 4+0-8 \end{bmatrix}$$

$$= -\frac{1}{4}\begin{bmatrix} -4 & 0 & 0 \\ 0 & -4 & 0 \\ 0 & 0 & -4 \end{bmatrix}$$

$$= -\frac{1}{4}(-4)\begin{bmatrix} 1 & 0 & 0 \\ 0 & 1 & 0 \\ 0 & 0 & 1 \end{bmatrix} = \begin{bmatrix} 1 & 0 & 0 \\ 0 & 1 & 0 \\ 0 & 0 & 1 \end{bmatrix}$$

Similarly we can show that $A^{-1}A = 1$.

Problem Set (3)

Symmetric and skew symmetric matrices.

1. (a) If A is n squared matrix, then prove that $A + A'$ is symmetric and $A - A'$ is skew symmetric.

   Ans. For any matrix to be symmetric $A' = A$ and to be skew symmetric $A' = -A$.

   Now $(A + A')' = A' + (A')' = A' + A = A + A'$

   The condition $A' = A$ is satisfied by the matrix $A + A'$ which therefore is symmetric.

   Again $(A - A')' = A' - (A')' = A' - A = -(A - A')$.

   The condition $A' = -A$ is satisfied by the matrix $A - A'$ which therefore is skew symmetric.

   (b) If A be a skew symmetric matrix, then $|A|$ is

   (a) 1   (b) -1
   (c) 0   (d) none

   Ans. (c)

   Let $A = \begin{bmatrix} 0 & h & g \\ -h & 0 & f \\ -g & -f & 0 \end{bmatrix}$

   Clearly $|A| = \begin{vmatrix} 0 & h & g \\ -h & 0 & f \\ -g & -f & 0 \end{vmatrix} = 0$

   because a skew symmetric determinant of odd order is zero **(see page .....)**

   (c) Find the symmetric and skew symmetric parts of the matrix

   $$A = \begin{bmatrix} 1 & 2 & 4 \\ 6 & 8 & 1 \\ 3 & 5 & 7 \end{bmatrix}$$

   $$A' = \begin{bmatrix} 1 & 6 & 3 \\ 2 & 8 & 5 \\ 4 & 1 & 7 \end{bmatrix}$$

   Hence, the symmetric and skew symmetric parts are

   $$\frac{1}{2}(A + A') = \begin{bmatrix} 1 & 4 & 7/2 \\ 4 & 8 & 3 \\ 7/2 & 3 & 7 \end{bmatrix}$$

   which is symmetric and

   $$\frac{1}{2}(A - A') = \begin{bmatrix} 0 & -2 & 1/2 \\ 2 & 0 & -2 \\ -1/2 & 2 & 0 \end{bmatrix}$$

   which is skew symmetric.

   Clearly the given matrix is the sum of above two matrices.

2. If A and B are n squared symmetric matrices then prove that AB is symmetric if and only if A and B commute.

   Ans. $A' = A, B' = B$ given as both A and B are symmetric. Let us choose that A and B commute $i.e.\ AB = BA.$ ...(I)

   AB will be symmetric if $(AB)' = AB$

   Now $(AB)' = B'A' = BA = AB$ by (I)

   ∴ AB is symmetric.

   Converse : Choose that AB is symmetric.

   ∴ $(AB)' = AB$ or $B'A' = AB$ or $BA = AB.$

   ∴ A and B commute.

3. If A and B are n squared skew symmetric matrices then AB is symmetric if and only if A and B commute.

Ans. Here $A' = -A$ and $B' = -B$ given as both A and B are skew symetric. Rest is as above.

4. If A is n squared matrix then AA' and $A'A$ are symmetric.

Ans. $(AA')' = (A')'A = AA'$ and hence symmetric.

$(A'A)' = A'(A')' = A'A$ and hence symmetric.

5. Show that the matrix KA is symmetric or skew symmetric according as A is symmetric or skew symmetric.

Ans. $(KA)' = KA' = KA$ if A is symmetric.

∴ KA is symmetric.

$(KA)' = KA' = K(-A) = -KA$ if A is skew symmetric.

∴ KA is skew symmetric.

6. Show that matrix $A + B$ is symmetric or skew symmetric according as A and B are symmetric or skew symmetric.

Ans. $(A + B)' = A' + B' = A + B$ if both A and B are symmetric.

∴ $A + B$ is symmetric.

$(A + B)' = A' + B' = -A - B = -(A + B)$ if both A and B are skew symmetric.

∴ $A + B$ is skew symmetric.

7. Prove that all + ive integral powers of a symmetric matrix are symmetric.

Ans. Let A be symmetric i.e. $A' = A$.

$$A^P = AAA \ldots p \text{ times}$$

or $(A^P)' = (AAA \, . \, p \text{ times})'$

$$= (A'A'A' \ldots p \text{ times})$$
$$= (AAA \ldots p \text{ times}) \qquad \because A' = A$$
$$= A^P$$

Hence A^P is symmetric.

8. Prove that + ive odd integral powers of a skew symmetric matrix are skew symmetric but + ive even integral powers are symmetric.

Ans. Proceeding as above we can show that

$$(A^P)' = (A \, . \, A \, . \, A \ldots p \text{ times})'$$
$$= (A'A'A' \ldots p \text{ times})$$
$$= (-1)^P A^P$$

because $A' = -A$ when A is skew symmetric.

∴ $(A^P)' = A^P$ when p is even and hence A^P is symmetric.

and $(A^P)' = -A^P$ when p is odd and hence skew symmetric.

9. Prove that the matrix $B'AB$ is symmetric or skew symmetric according as A is symmetric or skew symmetric.

Ans. If A be symmetric i.e. $A' = A$, then

$(B'AB)' = [B'(AB)]' = (AB)'(B')'$

$\qquad = (B'A')B = B'AB = B'AB.$

Hence $B'AB$ is symmetric.

If A is skew symmetric i.e. $A' = -A$ then

$(B'AB)' = [B'(AB)]' = (AB)'(B')'$

$\qquad = (B'A')B = B'(-A)B = -(B'AB).$

∴ $B'AB$ is skew symmetric.

10. If $AB = A$ and $BA = B$, then $B'A' = A'$ and $A'B' = B'$ and prove that A' and B' are idempotent.

Ans. $B'A' = (AB)' = A'$ and $A'B' = (BA)' = B'$.

Now A' is idempotent if $A'^2 = A'$,

Then $A'^2 = A'A' = A'(B'A') = (A'B')A' = B'A' = A'.$

∴ A' is idempotent. Similarly B' is idempotent.

11. If $A = \begin{pmatrix} a & b & c \\ b & c & a \\ c & a & b \end{pmatrix}$, $abc = A^T A = 1$, then find the value of $a^3 + b^3 + c^3$.   **(IIT 2003)**

$A = \begin{bmatrix} a & b & c \\ b & c & a \\ c & a & b \end{bmatrix}$, $A^T = \begin{bmatrix} a & b & c \\ b & c & a \\ c & a & b \end{bmatrix}$

Given $AA^T = I$ ∴ $|AA^T| = |I| = 1$

or $\begin{vmatrix} a & b & c \\ b & c & a \\ c & a & b \end{vmatrix}^2 = 1$ or $\begin{vmatrix} a & b & c \\ b & c & a \\ c & a & b \end{vmatrix} = \pm 1$

or $3abc - a^3 - b^3 - c^3 = \pm 1$

or $3 \mp 1 = a^3 + b^3 + c^3$

∴ $a^3 + b^3 + c^3 = 2$ or   4.

12. If M is a 3×3 matrix, where $M^T M = I$ and $\det(M) = 1$, then prove that $\det(M - I) = 0$.   **(I.I.T. 2004)**

Refer properties of Transpose of matrix A § 8 P. 486.

Also we know that in a determinant, rows can be changed into columns and columns into rows.

Hence if there be a square matrix A, then

$\qquad \det(A^T) = \det A$ or $|A^T| = |A|$.

Also if I be a square matrix then $I^T = I$ and $|I| = 1$ and $(A \pm B)^T = A^T \pm B^T$.

Given M is 3×3 square matrix such that $M^T M = I$ and $\det M = |M| = 1$.

We have to prove that $\det(M - I) = 0$.

Now $(M - I)^T = M^T - I^T = M^T - I$

$\qquad = M^T - M^T M$ (as given) $= M^T(I - M)$

Taking determinant of both sides,

$\qquad |(M - I)^T| = |M^T||I - M|$

or $|M - I| = |M||I - M|$ $\because$ $|A^T| = |A|$

or $|M - I| = 1 . (-1)^3 |M - I|$ $\because |M| = 1$

or $2|M - I| = 0$ ∴ $|M - I| = 0$

or $\det(M - I) = 0.$

Problem Set (4)

1. Find the inverse of the matrix

$$A = \begin{bmatrix} 0 & 1 & 2 \\ 1 & 2 & 3 \\ 3 & 1 & 1 \end{bmatrix}.$$

Sol. $|A| = 0 - 1(1-2) + 3(3-4) = 1 - 3 = -2 \neq 0.$

Hence matrix A is non-singular.

Co-factors of the 1st, 2nd and 3rd rows of $|A|$ are

$-1, 8, -5; \quad 1, -6, 3; \quad -1, 2, -1.$

Therefore the matrix formed by co-factors of $|A|$ is

$$C = \begin{bmatrix} -1 & 8 & -5 \\ 1 & -6 & 3 \\ -1 & 2 & -1 \end{bmatrix}$$

∴ Adj. A = Transpose of C

∴ Adj. $A = \begin{bmatrix} -1 & 1 & -1 \\ 8 & -6 & 2 \\ -5 & 3 & -1 \end{bmatrix}$

∴ $A^{-1} = \dfrac{1}{|A|}$ Adj. $A = -\dfrac{1}{2}\begin{bmatrix} -1 & 1 & -1 \\ 8 & -6 & 2 \\ -5 & 3 & -1 \end{bmatrix}$

Multiply each element of the matrix by $-\dfrac{1}{2}$

or $A^{-1} = \begin{bmatrix} \dfrac{1}{2} & -\dfrac{1}{2} & \dfrac{1}{2} \\ -4 & 3 & -1 \\ \dfrac{5}{2} & -\dfrac{3}{2} & \dfrac{1}{2} \end{bmatrix}$

Verification. $A A^{-1} = A^{-1} A = 1$

$$\begin{bmatrix} 0 & 1 & 2 \\ 1 & 2 & 3 \\ 3 & 1 & 1 \end{bmatrix} \times -\dfrac{1}{2}\begin{bmatrix} -1 & 1 & -1 \\ 8 & -6 & 2 \\ -5 & 3 & -1 \end{bmatrix}$$

$$= -\dfrac{1}{2}\begin{bmatrix} -2 & 0 & 0 \\ 0 & -2 & 0 \\ 0 & 0 & -2 \end{bmatrix} = \begin{bmatrix} 1 & 0 & 0 \\ 0 & 1 & 0 \\ 0 & 0 & 1 \end{bmatrix} = I_3$$

2. Find the inverse of the matrix $\begin{bmatrix} 1 & 2 & 3 \\ 4 & 1 & 5 \\ 3 & 6 & 9 \end{bmatrix}$

Sol. $|A| = \begin{vmatrix} 1 & 2 & 3 \\ 4 & 1 & 5 \\ 3 & 6 & 9 \end{vmatrix} = 3\begin{vmatrix} 1 & 2 & 3 \\ 4 & 1 & 5 \\ 1 & 2 & 3 \end{vmatrix} = 0$

as two rows are identical.

Since $|A| = 0$ hence matrix A is singular and therefore it does not possess any inverse. **For a matrix to possess an inverse it should be non-singular i.e., $|A| \neq 0$ Prop. (b).**

3. (a) If $A = \begin{bmatrix} 1 & -1 & 1 \\ 2 & -1 & 0 \\ 1 & 0 & 0 \end{bmatrix}$ find A^2 and show that

$A^2 = A^{-1}.$

Sol. Ans. $A^2 = AA = \begin{bmatrix} 0 & 0 & 1 \\ 0 & -1 & 2 \\ 1 & -1 & 1 \end{bmatrix}$

Now evaluate A^{-1} and show $A^{-1} = A^2$

(b) Let $A = \begin{bmatrix} 0 & 0 & -1 \\ 0 & -1 & 0 \\ -1 & 0 & 0 \end{bmatrix}$. Then the only correct statement A is :

(a) $A = O$

(b) $A = (-1) I$

(c) A^{-1} does not exist

(d) $A^2 = I$ **(AIEEE 2004)**

Sol. Ans. (d). It is easy to observe that $A^2 = I$

$$A^2 = \begin{bmatrix} 0 & 0 & -1 \\ 0 & -1 & 0 \\ -1 & 0 & 0 \end{bmatrix}\begin{bmatrix} 0 & 0 & -1 \\ 0 & -1 & 0 \\ -1 & 0 & 0 \end{bmatrix} = \begin{bmatrix} 1 & 0 & 0 \\ 0 & 1 & 0 \\ 0 & 0 & 1 \end{bmatrix}$$

(c) If $A = \begin{bmatrix} 1 & -1 & 1 \\ 2 & 1 & -3 \\ 1 & 1 & 1 \end{bmatrix}$ and $B = \begin{bmatrix} 4 & 2 & 2 \\ -5 & 0 & \alpha \\ 1 & 2 & 3 \end{bmatrix}$,

If B is the inverse of A, then α is

(a) -2 (b) -1

(c) 2 (d) 5 **(AIEEE 2004)**

Sol. Ans. (d).

If B is the inverse of A, then by definition

$B = A^{-1} = \dfrac{\text{Adj } A}{|A|}$

Matrix of cofactors of the elements of various rows of A are

$C = \begin{bmatrix} 4 & -5 & 1 \\ 2 & 0 & 2 \\ 2 & 5 & 3 \end{bmatrix}$ and $|A| = 10$

∴ $A^{-1} = \dfrac{\text{Adj } A}{|A|} = \dfrac{\text{Transpose of } C}{10}$

$A^{-1} = \dfrac{1}{10}\begin{bmatrix} 4 & 2 & 2 \\ -5 & 0 & 5 \\ 1 & 2 & 3 \end{bmatrix} = B$ ∴ $\alpha = 5$

(d) If $A^2 - A + I = O$, the inverse of A is

(a) $A - I$ (b) $I - A$

(c) $A + I$ (d) A **(AIEEE 2005)**

Sol. Ans. (b).

$A^2 - A + I = O \Rightarrow A - A^2 = I$

or $A(I - A) = I$ ∴ $A^{-1} = I - A$

4. Find the inverse of the matrix.

$$\begin{bmatrix} 14 & 3 & -2 \\ 6 & 8 & -1 \\ 0 & 2 & -7 \end{bmatrix}.$$

Sol. Co-factors of elements of first row of A are

$$\begin{vmatrix} 8 & -1 \\ 2 & -7 \end{vmatrix} = -54, -\begin{vmatrix} 6 & -1 \\ 0 & 7 \end{vmatrix} = 42, \begin{vmatrix} 6 & 8 \\ 0 & 2 \end{vmatrix} = 12$$

Similarly co-factors of 2nd row are $17, -98, -28$ whereas co-factors of 3rd row are $13, 2, 94$.

Adj. A = Transpose of the matrix formed by replacing each element by its co-factors.

$$\therefore \quad \text{Adj. } A = \begin{bmatrix} -54 & 17 & 13 \\ 42 & -98 & 2 \\ 12 & -28 & 94 \end{bmatrix}$$

Also $|A| = \begin{vmatrix} 14 & 3 & -2 \\ 6 & 8 & -1 \\ 0 & 2 & -7 \end{vmatrix}$

$$= 14(-56+2) - 6(-21+4) = -654$$

$$\therefore \quad A^{-1} = \frac{1}{|A|} \text{ adj. } A = -\frac{1}{654} \begin{bmatrix} -54 & 17 & 13 \\ 42 & -98 & 2 \\ 12 & -28 & 94 \end{bmatrix}$$

You can easily verify at $AA^{-1} = A^{-1}A = I$.

5. Find the inverses of the following matrices :

(a) $\begin{bmatrix} 2 & -4 & -2 \\ 4 & 6 & 2 \\ 0 & 10 & -4 \end{bmatrix}$ (b) $\begin{bmatrix} \cos\theta & -\sin\theta & 0 \\ \sin\theta & \cos\theta & 0 \\ 0 & 0 & 1 \end{bmatrix}$

(c) $\begin{bmatrix} 2 & 2 & 2 \\ 2 & 5 & 5 \\ 2 & 5 & 11 \end{bmatrix}$ (d) $\begin{bmatrix} 1 & 2 & 3 \\ 2 & 4 & 5 \\ 3 & 5 & 6 \end{bmatrix}$

(e) $\begin{bmatrix} 1 & 4 & 0 \\ -1 & 2 & 2 \\ 0 & 0 & 2 \end{bmatrix}$

Ans.

(a) $A^{-1} = -\frac{1}{58} \begin{bmatrix} -11 & -9 & 1 \\ 4 & -2 & -3 \\ 10 & -5 & 7 \end{bmatrix}$

(b) $A^{-1} = \begin{bmatrix} \cos\theta & \sin\theta & 0 \\ \sin\theta & \cos\theta & 0 \\ 0 & 0 & 1 \end{bmatrix}$

(c) $A^{-1} = \frac{1}{6} \begin{bmatrix} 5 & -2 & 0 \\ -2 & 3 & -1 \\ 0 & -1 & 1 \end{bmatrix}$

(d) $A^{-1} = \begin{bmatrix} 1 & -3 & 2 \\ -3 & 3 & -1 \\ 2 & -1 & 0 \end{bmatrix}$

(e) $A^{-1} = \frac{1}{6} \begin{bmatrix} 2 & -4 & 4 \\ 1 & 1 & -1 \\ 0 & 0 & 3 \end{bmatrix}$

6. If $A^3 = O$ then $1 + A + A^2$ is equal to

(a) $I + A$ (b) $(I + A)^{-1}$

(c) $I - A$ (d) $(I - A)^{-1}$

Ans. (d) $(I - A)(I + A + A^2) = I - A^3 = I - O = I$

$AB = I \Rightarrow B$ is A^{-1}

$$\therefore \quad I + A + A^2 = (I - A)^{-1}$$

7. If A and B are two square matrices such that $B = -A^{-1}BA$, then prove that $(A + B)^2 = A^2 + B^2$

$B = -A^{-1}BA \Rightarrow AB = -AA^{-1}BA = -BA$

$$\because \quad AA^{-1} = I$$

$$\therefore \quad AB + BA = 0 \qquad \qquad \dots(I)$$

Now $(A + B)^2 = (A + B)(A + B)$

$$= AA + (AB + BA) + BB = A^2 + B^2 \text{ by (I)}$$

8. If $\omega = e^{2i\pi/3}$ find the inverse of the matrix.

$$A = \begin{bmatrix} 1 & 1 & 1 \\ 1 & \omega & \omega^2 \\ 1 & \omega^2 & \omega \end{bmatrix}$$

Sol. Clearly $\omega^3 = e^{2\pi i} = 1$

$\therefore \quad \omega$ is complex cube root of unity

and $1 + \omega + \omega^2 = 0$ or $\omega + \omega^2 = -1$

$|A| = (\omega^2 - \omega^4) - (\omega - \omega^2) + (\omega^2 - \omega)$

$$= 3\omega(\omega - 1) \neq 0 \qquad \dots(I)$$

The co-factors of elements of various rows of $|A|$ are

$(\omega^2 - \omega^4), -(\omega - \omega^2), (\omega^2 - \omega)$

$-(\omega - \omega^2), (\omega - 1), -(\omega^2 - 1)$

$(\omega^2 - \omega), -(\omega^2 - 1), (\omega - 1)$

Put $\omega^4 = \omega^3, \omega = \omega$

$$-(\omega^2 - 1) = -(\omega + 1)(\omega - 1) = \omega^2(\omega - 1)$$

$\therefore$ The matrix formed by cofactors of $|A|$ is

$$C = \begin{bmatrix} \omega(\omega-1) & \omega(\omega-1) & \omega(\omega-1) \\ \omega(\omega-1) & \omega^3(\omega-1) & \omega^2(\omega-1) \\ \omega(\omega-1) & \omega^2(\omega-1) & \omega^3(\omega-1) \end{bmatrix}$$

$\therefore$ Adj. A = Transpose of matric C of co-factors

$$= \omega(\omega - 1) \begin{bmatrix} 1 & 1 & 1 \\ 1 & \omega^2 & \omega \\ 1 & \omega & \omega^2 \end{bmatrix}$$

$$\therefore \quad A^{-1} = \frac{1}{|A|} \text{ Adj. } A = \frac{1}{3} \begin{bmatrix} 1 & 1 & 1 \\ 1 & \omega^2 & \omega \\ 1 & \omega & \omega^2 \end{bmatrix} \text{ by (I)}$$

You can easily verify using $1 + \omega + \omega^2 = 0$ that

$$AA^{-1} = A^{-1}A = I_3$$

9. If α, β, γ are three real numbers then the matrix A given below is $\begin{bmatrix} 1 & \cos(\alpha-\beta) & \cos(\alpha-\gamma) \\ \cos(\beta-\alpha) & 1 & \cos(\beta-\gamma) \\ \cos(\gamma-\alpha) & \cos(\gamma-\beta) & 1 \end{bmatrix}$ is

(a) singular   (b) symmetric

(c) invertible   (d) none

Ans. (a), (b)

Since $a_{ij} = a_{ji} \ \forall i, j$. $\therefore \ A$ is symmetric

Put $\beta - \gamma = A$, $\gamma - \alpha = B$, $\alpha - \beta = C$

so that $A + B + C = 0$

or $B + C = -A$

$\therefore \quad \cos(B+C) = \cos(-A) = \cos A$

$\quad \sin(B+C) = -\sin A$ ...(I)

$|A| = (1 - \cos^2 A) - \cos C(\cos C - \cos A \cos B)$
$\qquad\qquad + \cos B[\cos C \cos A - \cos B]$

$= \sin^2 A - \cos C[\cos(A+B) - \cos A \cos B]$
$\qquad\qquad + \cos B[\cos C \cos A - \cos(C+A)]$ by (I)

$= \sin^2 A - \cos C[-\sin A \sin B]$
$\qquad\qquad\qquad + \cos B(\sin C \sin A)$

$= \sin^2 A + \sin A(\sin B \cos C + \cos B \sin C)$

$= \sin^2 A + \sin A \sin(B+C)$

$= \sin^2 A + \sin A(-\sin A) = 0$ by (I)

Since $|A| = 0$, the matrix A is singular.

10. Show that $\begin{bmatrix} \cos\theta & -\sin\theta \\ \sin\theta & \cos\theta \end{bmatrix}$

$= \begin{bmatrix} 1 & -\tan\theta/2 \\ \tan\theta/2 & 1 \end{bmatrix}\begin{bmatrix} 1 & \tan\theta/2 \\ -\tan\theta/2 & 1 \end{bmatrix}^{-1}$

Sol. We know that **(See rule P. 487).**

$B^{-1} = \dfrac{\text{Adj.}\,B}{|B|} = \dfrac{1}{\sec^2\theta/2}\begin{bmatrix} 1 & -\tan\theta/2 \\ \tan\theta/2 & 1 \end{bmatrix}$

$\therefore \quad \text{R.H.S.} = \cos^2\dfrac{\theta}{2}\begin{bmatrix} 1 & -\tan\theta/2 \\ \tan\theta/2 & 1 \end{bmatrix}$

$\qquad\qquad\qquad \cdot \begin{bmatrix} 1 & -\tan\theta/2 \\ \tan\theta/2 & 1 \end{bmatrix}$

$= \cos^2\dfrac{\theta}{2}\begin{bmatrix} 1 - \tan^2\theta/2 & -2\tan\theta/2 \\ 2\tan\theta/2 & -\tan^2\theta/2 + 1 \end{bmatrix}$

$= \begin{bmatrix} \cos^2\theta/2 - \sin^2\theta/2 & -2\sin\theta/2\cos\theta/2 \\ 2\sin\theta/2\cos\theta/2 & \cos^2\theta/2 - \sin^2\theta/2 \end{bmatrix}$

$= \begin{bmatrix} \cos\theta & -\sin\theta \\ \sin\theta & \cos\theta \end{bmatrix} = \text{L.H.S.}$

11. Show that commutative law holds good for the product of the two matrices

$A = \begin{bmatrix} a & b \\ -b & a \end{bmatrix}$ and $B = \begin{bmatrix} x & y \\ -y & x \end{bmatrix}$

If a, b, x, y are all different from zero, find the inverse of A, B and verify that

$(AB)^{-1} = B^{-1} A^{-1}$.

Sol. It is easy to verify that

$AB = BA = \begin{bmatrix} ax - by & ay + bx \\ -(ay+bx) & ax - by \end{bmatrix}$

Adjoint of a 2×2 matrix is written by the rule given on **Page 487.**

$\therefore \quad \text{Adj. } A = \begin{bmatrix} a & -b \\ b & a \end{bmatrix}, \text{Adj. } B = \begin{bmatrix} x & -y \\ y & x \end{bmatrix}$

$\text{Adj. } AB = \begin{bmatrix} ax - by & -(ay+bx) \\ (ay+bx) & ax - by \end{bmatrix}$

$A^{-1} = \dfrac{1}{|A|}\text{Adj. }A = \dfrac{1}{(a^2+b^2)}\begin{bmatrix} a & -b \\ b & a \end{bmatrix}$ ...(1)

$B^{-1} = \dfrac{1}{|B|}\text{Adj. }B = \dfrac{1}{x^2+y^2}\begin{bmatrix} x & -y \\ y & x \end{bmatrix}$ ...(2)

$(AB)^{-1} = \dfrac{1}{|AB|}\text{Adj. }(AB) = \dfrac{1}{(ax-by)^2 + (ay+bx)^2}$

$\begin{bmatrix} ax - by & -(ay+bx) \\ ay + bx & ax - by \end{bmatrix}$

But $(ax-by)^2 + (ay+bx)^2$

$= a^2(x^2+y^2) + b^2(x^2+y^2) = (a^2+b^2)(x^2+y^2)$

$\therefore \quad (AB)^{-1} = \dfrac{1}{(a^2+b^2)(x^2+y^2)}$

$\begin{bmatrix} ax - by & -(ay+bx) \\ (ay+bX) & ax - by \end{bmatrix}$ ...(3)

Also $B^{-1}A^{-1} = \dfrac{1}{(a^2+b^2)(x^2+y^2)}$

$\begin{bmatrix} x & -y \\ y & x \end{bmatrix}\begin{bmatrix} a & -b \\ b & a \end{bmatrix}$

$= \dfrac{1}{(a^2+y^2)(x^2+y^2)}\begin{bmatrix} ax - by & -(ay+bx) \\ ay + bx & ax - by \end{bmatrix}$ ...(4)

From (3) and (4) we verify that $(AB)^{-1} = B^{-1}A^{-1}$.

12. If $\begin{bmatrix} 2 & 1 \\ 3 & 2 \end{bmatrix}A\begin{bmatrix} -3 & 2 \\ 5 & -3 \end{bmatrix} = \begin{bmatrix} 1 & 0 \\ 0 & 1 \end{bmatrix}$, then the matrix A is equal to

(a) $\begin{bmatrix} 1 & 1 \\ 1 & 0 \end{bmatrix}$ ____ (b) $\begin{bmatrix} 1 & 1 \\ 0 & 1 \end{bmatrix}$

(c) $\begin{bmatrix} 1 & 0 \\ 1 & 1 \end{bmatrix}$ ____ (d) $\begin{bmatrix} 0 & 1 \\ 1 & 1 \end{bmatrix}$

Ans. (a).

If $CAB = D$, then premultiplying by C^{-1} and post-multiplying by B^{-1} in both sides, we get

$A = C^{-1}DB^{-1}$ ...(1)

Now use $C^{-1} = \dfrac{1}{|C|}$ adj. (C) **by (C) P. 488**

$C^{-1} = \dfrac{1}{|C|}\begin{bmatrix} 2 & -1 \\ -3 & 2 \end{bmatrix} = 1\begin{vmatrix} 2 & -1 \\ -3 & 2 \end{vmatrix}$

See Rule Page 487 for adjoint of 2×2 matrix.

$B^{-1} = \dfrac{1}{|B|}\begin{bmatrix} -3 & -2 \\ -5 & -3 \end{bmatrix} = \dfrac{-1}{-1}\begin{bmatrix} 3 & 2 \\ 5 & 3 \end{bmatrix}$

$\therefore \quad A = \begin{bmatrix} 2 & -1 \\ -3 & 2 \end{bmatrix}\begin{bmatrix} 1 & 0 \\ 0 & 1 \end{bmatrix}\begin{bmatrix} 3 & 2 \\ 5 & 3 \end{bmatrix}$ by (1)

$= \begin{bmatrix} 2 & -1 \\ -3 & 2 \end{bmatrix}\begin{bmatrix} 3 & 2 \\ 5 & 3 \end{bmatrix}$ ____ $[\because IA = A]$

$= \begin{bmatrix} 1 & 1 \\ 1 & 0 \end{bmatrix} \Rightarrow$ (a)

13. Let $F(\alpha) = \begin{bmatrix} \cos\alpha & -\sin\alpha & 0 \\ \sin\alpha & \cos\alpha & 0 \\ 0 & 0 & 1 \end{bmatrix}$ where $\alpha \in R$.

Prove that $F(\alpha).F(-\alpha)=I_3$ hence show that $[F(\alpha)]^{-1}=F(-\alpha)$

$$F(\alpha).F(-\alpha)=\begin{bmatrix} \cos\alpha & -\sin\alpha & 0 \\ \sin\alpha & \cos\alpha & 0 \\ 0 & 0 & 1 \end{bmatrix}$$

$$\cdot\begin{bmatrix} \cos(-\alpha) & -\sin(-\alpha) & 0 \\ \sin(-\alpha) & \cos(-\alpha) & 0 \\ 0 & 0 & 1 \end{bmatrix}$$

$$F(\alpha).F(-\alpha)=\begin{bmatrix} \cos\alpha & -\sin\alpha & 0 \\ \sin\alpha & \cos\alpha & 0 \\ 0 & 0 & 1 \end{bmatrix}$$

$$\cdot\begin{bmatrix} \cos\alpha & \sin\alpha & 0 \\ -\sin\alpha & \cos\alpha & 0 \\ 0 & 0 & 1 \end{bmatrix}$$

$$=\begin{bmatrix} \cos^2\alpha+\sin^2\alpha+0 & \cos\alpha.\sin\alpha-\cos\alpha.\sin\alpha+0 & 0+0+0 \\ \sin\alpha\cos\alpha-\sin\alpha.\cos\alpha+0 & \sin^2\alpha+\cos^2\alpha+0 & 0+0+0 \\ 0+0+0 & 0+0+0 & 0+0+1 \end{bmatrix}$$

$$=\begin{bmatrix} 1 & 0 & 0 \\ 0 & 1 & 0 \\ 0 & 0 & 1 \end{bmatrix}=I \quad \because \cos^2\alpha+\sin^2\alpha=1$$

$$F(\alpha).F(-\alpha)=I$$

$$\therefore \quad [F(\alpha)]^{-1}=F(-\alpha) \Rightarrow (a).$$

14. If $F(\alpha)=\begin{bmatrix} \cos\alpha & -\sin\alpha & 0 \\ \sin\alpha & \cos\alpha & 0 \\ 0 & 0 & 1 \end{bmatrix}$ and

$$G(\beta)=\begin{bmatrix} \cos\beta & 0 & \sin\beta \\ 0 & 1 & 0 \\ -\sin\beta & 0 & \cos\beta \end{bmatrix},$$

then $[F(\alpha)\,G(\beta)]^{-1}$ is equal to

(a) $F(-\alpha)\,G(-\beta)$ (b) $F(\alpha^{-1})\,G(\beta^{-1})$

(c) $G(-\beta)\,F(-\alpha)$ (d) $G(\beta^{-1})\,F(\alpha^{-1})$

Ans. (c).

$$[F(\alpha)\,G(\beta)]^{-1}=[G(\beta)]^{-1}\,[F(\alpha)]^{-1}$$

$$=G(-\beta)\,F(-\alpha), \text{ as shown in last question.}$$

15. If $A=\begin{bmatrix} a & 0 & 0 \\ 0 & a & 0 \\ 0 & 0 & a \end{bmatrix}$, then the value of

(i) $|A||\text{Adj. }A|$ and

(ii) $|\text{Adj. }A|$ is equal to

   (a) a^3 (b) a^6

   (c) a^9 (d) a^{27}

Ans. (c) for (i) and (b) for (ii).

$$A(\text{Adj. }A)=|A|I_3=|A|\begin{bmatrix} 1 & 0 & 0 \\ 0 & 1 & 0 \\ 0 & 0 & 1 \end{bmatrix}$$

$$=\begin{bmatrix} |A| & 0 & 0 \\ 0 & |A| & 0 \\ 0 & 0 & |A| \end{bmatrix} \text{ where } |A|=a^3$$

See I P. 488 Col 1.

Take determinant of both sides.

$$|A|.|\text{Adj. }A|=\begin{vmatrix} |A| & 0 & 0 \\ 0 & |A| & 0 \\ 0 & 0 & |A| \end{vmatrix}$$

or $|A|.|\text{Adj. }A|=|A|^3=(a^3)^3=a^9 \Rightarrow (c)$

Also $|\text{Adj. }A|=|A|^{n-1}=|A|^2=a^6 \Rightarrow (b)$

16. For a 3×3 matrix A, if $\det A=4$, then $\det(\text{Adj. }A)$ equals

(a) -4 (b) 4 (c) 16 (d) 64

Ans. (c).

Refer last question.

$|\text{Adj. }A|=|A|^{n-1}=|A|^2=4^2=16 \Rightarrow (c)$

17. If A and B be two square matrices of the same order then $|AB|=0$ implies

(a) $A=O$ or $B=O$

(b) $A=O$ and $B=O$

(c) $|A|=0$ and $|B|=0$

(d) $|A|=0$ or $|B|=0$

Ans. (d).

$A=O$ means that A is a null matrix

$|A|=0$ means that $\det(A)$ is a scalar zero

$$|AB|=|A||B|=0 \qquad\qquad\qquad ...(I)$$

$\Rightarrow$ either $|A|=0$ or $|B|=0 \Rightarrow (d)$

Note : Answer given in (c) also satisfies (I) but it is not necessary for both $|A|$ and $|B|$ to be zero to satisfy (I).

18. If A and B are two non-zero square matrices of the same order then $AB=O$ implies that both A and B must be singular.

Let us assume that A is non-singular i.e., $|A|\neq0$ and hence A^{-1} exists such that $AA^{-1}=I$.

$$\therefore \quad AB=O$$

$$\Rightarrow A^{-1}(AB)=(A^{-1}A)B=IB=B=O$$

Above shows that B is a null matrix which is a contradiction.

Similarly if B is non-singular then as above we will have $A=O$ which is again a contradiction. Hence, both A and B must be singular.

19. If $A=\begin{bmatrix} a \\ b \\ -a \end{bmatrix}_{3\times1}$ $[a \quad b \quad -a]_{1\times3}$ then find whether

A^{-1} exists or not.

A will be 3×3 matrix.

$$\therefore \quad A=\begin{bmatrix} a^2 & ab & -a^2 \\ ba & b^2 & ba \\ -a^2 & -ab & a^2 \end{bmatrix}$$

Clearly $|A| = 0$ because R_1 and R_3 are identical. Therefore A is singular and hence its inverse does not exist.

20. If $A = \text{diag}(a, b, c) = \begin{bmatrix} a & 0 & 0 \\ 0 & b & 0 \\ 0 & 0 & c \end{bmatrix}$ such that $abc \neq 0$

then $A^{-1} = \text{diag}\left(\dfrac{1}{a}, \dfrac{1}{b}, \dfrac{1}{c}\right) = \begin{bmatrix} \dfrac{1}{a} & 0 & 0 \\ 0 & \dfrac{1}{b} & 0 \\ 0 & 0 & \dfrac{1}{c} \end{bmatrix}$

$|A| = abc \neq 0$ and hence A is non-singular whose inverse will exit. Now $A^{-1} = \dfrac{\text{adj.}(A)}{|A|}$

If C be the matrix formed by cofactors of the elements of A then $C = \begin{bmatrix} bc & 0 & 0 \\ 0 & ca & 0 \\ 0 & 0 & ab \end{bmatrix}$

$\therefore$ adj. $A = $ Transpose of $C = \begin{bmatrix} bc & 0 & 0 \\ 0 & ca & 0 \\ 0 & 0 & ab \end{bmatrix}$

Rows $\rightarrow$ col and Col $\rightarrow$ rows

$\therefore \quad A^{-1} = \dfrac{1}{|A|} \text{ Adj. } A = \dfrac{1}{abc} \begin{bmatrix} bc & 0 & 0 \\ 0 & ca & 0 \\ 0 & 0 & ab \end{bmatrix}$

$= \begin{bmatrix} \dfrac{1}{a} & 0 & 0 \\ 0 & \dfrac{1}{b} & 0 \\ 0 & 0 & \dfrac{1}{c} \end{bmatrix}$

§ 14. Rank of a matrix

Consider the matrix $A = \begin{bmatrix} 1 & 3 & 4 \\ 2 & 6 & 8 \end{bmatrix}_{2 \times 3}$

Above is 2×3 matrix.

Sub-matrix of order r : If we retain any r rows and equal number of r columns we will have a square submatrix of order r whose determinant is called minor of order r.

In the above matrix we cannot have a square sub matrix of order 3 because there are no 3 rows though 3 columns are there. We can at the most have minors of order 2 say

$\begin{vmatrix} 1 & 3 \\ 2 & 6 \end{vmatrix}, \quad \begin{vmatrix} 3 & 4 \\ 6 & 8 \end{vmatrix}, \quad \begin{vmatrix} 1 & 4 \\ 2 & 8 \end{vmatrix}$

or we can have minors of order 1 which means each element of the matrix is a minor of order 1.

Similarly if a matrix A is 3×4 then we can have minors of order 3, 2 and 1 only.

The rank of a given matrix A is said to be r if

(a) Every minor of A of order $r + 1$ is zero.

(b) There is at least one minor of A of order r which does not vanish.

The rank r of matrix A is written as $\rho(A) = r$

Note : From above it clearly follows that the rank of a null matrix i.e., zero matrix all of whose elements are zeros is zero.

Also the rank of a **singular square matrix** of order n cannot be n because minor of highest order i.e., $|A| = 0$ and there is only one minor of highest order.

Working rule. Calculate the minors of highest possible order of a given matix A. If it is not zero then the order of the minor is the rank. If it is zero and all other minors of the same order be also zero then calculate minors of next lower order and if at least one of them is not zero then this next lower order will be the rank. If, however, all the minors of next lower order are zero then calculate minors of still next lower order and so on.

Problem Set (5)

Rank of a matrix.

1. Find the rank of the following matrices :

(a) $A = \begin{bmatrix} 1 & 3 & 4 \\ 2 & 6 & 8 \end{bmatrix}$

(b) $A = \begin{bmatrix} 3 & -1 & 2 \\ -6 & 2 & -4 \\ -3 & 1 & -2 \end{bmatrix}$

(a) A is 2×3 matrix and we can have minors of order 1 and 2. Minor of order 2.

$\begin{vmatrix} 1 & 3 \\ 2 & 6 \end{vmatrix} = 6 - 6 = 0$

Other minors of order 2 are

$\begin{vmatrix} 3 & 4 \\ 6 & 8 \end{vmatrix} = 0$ and $\begin{vmatrix} 1 & 4 \\ 2 & 8 \end{vmatrix} = 0$

Thus all minors of order 2 are zero, because of identical lines.

Hence, we have only minors of order 1, which will be elements of the given matrix and are not all equal to zero or at least one of them is not equal to zero. Hence, the rank of A is 1.

(b) Proceed as above. The minors of order 3 and 2 are all zero because of identical lines.

$R_2 = -2R_1, R_3 = -R_1 \quad \therefore \quad \text{Rank } A = 1$

2. (a) $A = \begin{bmatrix} 1 & 2 & 3 \\ 2 & 4 & 7 \\ 3 & 6 & 10 \end{bmatrix}$

(b) $A = \begin{bmatrix} 1 & 2 & 3 \\ 2 & 3 & 4 \\ 4 & 10 & 18 \end{bmatrix}$

(a) A is 3×3 matrix and we can have minors of order 1, 2, 3.

Minor of order 3.

$\begin{vmatrix} 1 & 2 & 3 \\ 2 & 4 & 7 \\ 3 & 6 & 10 \end{vmatrix}$ Apply $R_3 - (R_1 + R_2)$.

$= \begin{vmatrix} 1 & 2 & 3 \\ 2 & 4 & 7 \\ 0 & 0 & 0 \end{vmatrix} = 0$

Minor of order 2.

$\begin{vmatrix} 1 & 2 \\ 2 & 4 \end{vmatrix} = 0, \begin{vmatrix} 2 & 4 \\ 3 & 6 \end{vmatrix} = 0$

$\begin{vmatrix} 2 & 3 \\ 4 & 7 \end{vmatrix} = 14 - 12 = 2 \neq 0$

Hence, there is at least one minor of order 2 which is not zero whereas all the minors of order $2 + 1$ *i.e.* 3 are zero. Hence $\rho(A) = 2$.

(b) In this case minors of order $3 = -2 \neq 0$

∴ $\rho(A) = 3$

3. (a) $A = \begin{bmatrix} 1 & 5 & 9 \\ 4 & 8 & 12 \\ 7 & 11 & 15 \end{bmatrix}$ (b) $A = \begin{bmatrix} 4 & 5 & 6 \\ 1 & 2 & 3 \\ 3 & 4 & 4 \end{bmatrix}$

Minor of highest order 3 is $\begin{vmatrix} 1 & 5 & 9 \\ 4 & 8 & 12 \\ 7 & 11 & 15 \end{vmatrix} = 0$

by $R_1 + R_3 - 2R_2$

Minor of order 2 is $\begin{bmatrix} 1 & 5 \\ 4 & 8 \end{bmatrix} = 8 - 20 = -12 \neq 0$

Hence $\rho(A) = 2$

Note. Rank of unit matrix, I_3 is 3 as minor of highest order 3 is $|I_3| = 1 \neq 0$. Similarly rank $I_n = n$.

4. Find the rank of the following matrices :

(a) $\begin{bmatrix} 1 & 2 & 3 \\ 2 & 5 & 8 \\ 4 & 10 & 18 \end{bmatrix}$ (b) $\begin{bmatrix} 1 & 3 & 2 \\ 1 & 2 & 3 \\ 1 & 5 & 4 \end{bmatrix}$

(c) $\begin{bmatrix} 1 & 2 & 3 \\ 2 & 3 & 4 \\ 4 & 5 & 6 \end{bmatrix}$ (d) $\begin{bmatrix} 1 & 2 & 3 \\ 2 & 3 & 1 \\ -2 & -3 & -1 \end{bmatrix}$

(e) $\begin{bmatrix} 13 & 16 & 19 \\ 14 & 17 & 20 \\ 15 & 18 & 21 \end{bmatrix}$ (f) $\begin{bmatrix} 1 & -3 & 2 \\ 3 & -9 & 6 \\ -2 & 6 & -4 \end{bmatrix}$

Ans.

(a) $|A| = 2 \neq 0$ ∴ $\rho(A) = 3$

(b) Apply $R_2 - R_1, R_3 - R_1$ ∴ $|A| = -4 \neq 0$

∴ $\rho(A) = 3$

(c) $R_3 - R_2, R_2 - R_1$ makes two rows identical.

∴ $|A| = 0$

minor of order 2 is not zero

∴ $\rho(A) = 2$

(d) $R_2 + R_3$ gives $|A| = 0$

∴ $\rho(A) = 2$ as above

(e) $\rho(A) = 2$ exactly as in part (c)

(f) $R_3 + 2R_1$ makes R_3 a row of zeros.

∴ $|A| = 0$

∴ $\rho(A) = 2$ as above.

§15 Solution of Equations

We have already introduced the following terms in relation to solution of equations.

i.e., **Consistent** (having solution), **Inconsistent** (having no solution), **unique** (only one solution) **infinite** (many solutions), **Trivial** (all variables zero *i.e.*, unique.

▸ **Representation of equations in matrix form.**

I. **Intersecting lines. Unique solution. Consistent**

$x + 2y = 4$

$3x + y = 2$

or $\begin{bmatrix} 1 & 2 \\ 3 & 1 \end{bmatrix} \begin{bmatrix} x \\ y \end{bmatrix} = \begin{bmatrix} 4 \\ 2 \end{bmatrix}$ or $AX = B$

A is called **coefficient matrix** and $C = [A, B] = \begin{bmatrix} 1 & 2 & 4 \\ 3 & 1 & 2 \end{bmatrix}$ is 2×3 matrix. C is called **augmented matrix.**

▸ **Nature of solution.**

(a) Rank A = Rank $C = n = 2$ the number of unknown. Solution is unique and is obtained as under.

Here $|A| = \begin{vmatrix} 1 & 2 \\ 3 & 1 \end{vmatrix} = 1 - 6 = -5 \neq 0$

∴ A is non-singular and A^{-1} exists and

$A^{-1} = \frac{1}{|A|}(\text{adj. } A) = \frac{1}{-5}\begin{bmatrix} 1 & -2 \\ -3 & 1 \end{bmatrix}$

by rule **page 487**.

Multiplying both sides by A^{-1} we have

$A^{-1}(AX) = A^{-1}B$ or $X = A^{-1}B$

or $\begin{bmatrix} x \\ y \end{bmatrix} = -\frac{1}{5}\begin{bmatrix} 1 & -2 \\ -3 & 1 \end{bmatrix}\begin{bmatrix} 4 \\ 2 \end{bmatrix}$

$= -\frac{1}{5}\begin{bmatrix} 0 \\ -10 \end{bmatrix} = \begin{bmatrix} 0 \\ 2 \end{bmatrix}$

∴ $x = 0$

$y = 2$

2nd Method by Cramer's rule

$\frac{x}{D_1} = \frac{y}{D_2} = \frac{1}{D}$

or $\frac{x}{\begin{vmatrix} 4 & 2 \\ 2 & 1 \end{vmatrix}} = \frac{y}{\begin{vmatrix} 1 & 4 \\ 3 & 2 \end{vmatrix}} = \frac{1}{\begin{vmatrix} 1 & 2 \\ 3 & 1 \end{vmatrix}}$

or $\frac{x}{0} = \frac{y}{-10} = \frac{1}{-5}$

∴ $x = 0$ and $y = 2$

(b) **Homogeneous equations. Unique solution. Trivial.**

$$\begin{matrix} x + 2y = 0 \\ 3x + y = 0 \end{matrix} \quad \text{or} \quad \begin{bmatrix} 1 & 2 \\ 3 & 1 \end{bmatrix} \begin{bmatrix} x \\ y \end{bmatrix} = \begin{bmatrix} 0 \\ 0 \end{bmatrix}$$

$$AX = B$$

$$C = [A, B] = \begin{bmatrix} 1 & 2 & 0 \\ 3 & 1 & 0 \end{bmatrix}$$

Here as above Rank A = Rank $C = n = 2$ the number of unknown variables and hence the solution will be unique and is given by $X = A^{-1} B$

or $\begin{bmatrix} x \\ y \end{bmatrix} = -\dfrac{1}{5} \begin{bmatrix} 1 & -2 \\ -3 & 1 \end{bmatrix} \begin{bmatrix} 0 \\ 0 \end{bmatrix} = \begin{bmatrix} 0 \\ 0 \end{bmatrix}$

∴ $x = 0, y = 0$

By Cramer's rule

or $\dfrac{x}{D_1} = \dfrac{y}{D_2} = \dfrac{1}{D}$ or $\dfrac{x}{0} = \dfrac{y}{0} = -\dfrac{1}{5}$

∴ $x = 0, y = 0$

II. Coincident lines. Infinite solutions. Consistent

(c) $x + 2y = 4$
$3x + 6y = 12$

or $\begin{bmatrix} 1 & 2 \\ 3 & 6 \end{bmatrix} \begin{bmatrix} x \\ y \end{bmatrix} = \begin{bmatrix} 4 \\ 12 \end{bmatrix}$

or $AX = B$ $\quad C = [A,B] = \begin{bmatrix} 1 & 2 & 4 \\ 3 & 6 & 12 \end{bmatrix}$

Here $|A| = \begin{bmatrix} 1 & 2 \\ 3 & 6 \end{bmatrix} = 0$

so that matrix A is singular and A^{-1} will not exist
Apply $R_2 - 3R_1$

$$C = \begin{bmatrix} 1 & 2 & 4 \\ 0 & 0 & 0 \end{bmatrix} \text{ and } A = \begin{bmatrix} 1 & 2 \\ 0 & 0 \end{bmatrix}$$

Clearly Rank C = Rank $A = 1$ which is less than $n = 2$ the number of variables and hence the system of equations are consistent and will have infinite solutions. As a matter of fact we have only one equation on two variables $x + 2y = 4$ (The second equation on dividing by 3 becomes the same as $x + 2y = 4$)

∴ We can have infinite number of points on a line Choosing $x = c$ we have $y = \dfrac{4 - c}{2}$

(d) **Homogeneous equations**

$$\begin{matrix} x + 2y = 0 \\ 3x + 6y = 0 \end{matrix} \quad \text{or} \quad \begin{bmatrix} 1 & 2 \\ 3 & 6 \end{bmatrix} \begin{bmatrix} x \\ y \end{bmatrix} = \begin{bmatrix} 0 \\ 0 \end{bmatrix}$$

or $Ax = B$

Arguing as in (c) Rank C = Rank $A = 1$, $|A| = 0$. As a matter of fact we have only one equation $x + 2y = 0$. Rank C = Rank $A = 1$, $< n = 2$ the number of variables.

Choosing $y = c, x = -2c$ ∴ $(c, -2c)$ constitute infinite solutions.

III. Parallel lines. Inconsistent. No solution.

(e) $x + 2y = 4$
$3x + 6y = 7$

or $\begin{bmatrix} 1 & 2 \\ 3 & 6 \end{bmatrix} = \begin{bmatrix} 4 \\ 7 \end{bmatrix}$

or $AX = B$ $\quad C = \begin{bmatrix} 1 & 2 & 4 \\ 3 & 6 & 7 \end{bmatrix}$

$|A| = 0$ *i.e.*, A is singular.
Clearly Rank $A = 1$ but Rank $C = 2$
Rank $A <$ Rank C ∴ Inconsistent
As a matter of fact the two equations are $x + 2y = 4$
and $x + 2y = \dfrac{7}{3}$ which are clearly inconsistent and have no solution.

Gist

I.	Rank A = Rank $C = n$ the number of variables then equations are consistent and have unique solution, $A \neq 0$ see (a), (b).
II.	Rank A = Rank $C = r < n$ the number of variables, the equations are consistent and have infinite solutions, $|A| = 0$ see (c), (d).
III	Rank $A <$ Rank C
.	∴ Inconsistent, $|A| = 0$ see (e).
	Non-homogenous equation
	We will illustrate the method by two examples. We have discussed this topic in determinants. Here we illustate the method by use of matrices.

Problem Set (6)

Solution of equations.

1. Solve the following equations
   $5x - 6y + 4z = 15$
   $7x + 4y - 3z = 19$
   $2x + y + 6z = 46$

Sol. The above equations can be written in matrix form as

$$\begin{bmatrix} 5 & -6 & 4 \\ 7 & 6 & -3 \\ 2 & 1 & 6 \end{bmatrix} \begin{bmatrix} x \\ y \\ z \end{bmatrix} = \begin{bmatrix} 15 \\ 19 \\ 46 \end{bmatrix}$$

or $AX = B$.

$$|A| = D = \begin{vmatrix} 5 & -6 & 4 \\ 7 & 4 & -3 \\ 2 & 1 & 6 \end{vmatrix}$$

Apply $C_1 - 2C_2, C_3 - 6C_2$ to make two zeros in R_3

$$D = \begin{vmatrix} 17 & -6 & 40 \\ -1 & 4 & -27 \\ 0 & 1 & 0 \end{vmatrix} = - \begin{vmatrix} 17 & 40 \\ -1 & -27 \end{vmatrix}$$

$$= -[-459 + 40] = 419 \neq 0.$$

∴ The matrix A is non-singular or rank of matrix A is 3. We will have a unique solution and the equations are consistent.

By Crammer's rule.

$$\frac{x}{D_1} = \frac{y}{D_2} = \frac{z}{D_3} = \frac{1}{D}$$

where D_1 is obtained from D by replacing the first column of D by b's i.e., 15, 19, 46

$$D_1 = \begin{vmatrix} 15 & -6 & 4 \\ 19 & 4 & -3 \\ 46 & 1 & 6 \end{vmatrix}$$

$$= 15(27) - 19(-40) + 46(2) = 1257$$

$$D_2 = \begin{vmatrix} 5 & 15 & 4 \\ 7 & 19 & -3 \\ 2 & 46 & 6 \end{vmatrix} = -\begin{vmatrix} 15 & 5 & 4 \\ 19 & 7 & -3 \\ 46 & 2 & 6 \end{vmatrix}$$

$$= -\{15(48) - 19(22) + 46(-43) = 1676$$

$$D_3 = \begin{vmatrix} 5 & -6 & 15 \\ 7 & 4 & 19 \\ 2 & 1 & 46 \end{vmatrix}$$

$$= 15(-1) - 19(17) + 46(62) = 2514$$

∴ $$\frac{x}{1257} = \frac{y}{1676} = \frac{z}{2514} = \frac{1}{419}$$

∴ $x = 3, y = 4, z = 6$.

2nd Method.

$AX = B$.

Since A is non-singular and hence its inverse exists. Multiplying both sides by A^{-1} we get

$$A^{-1} AX = A^{-1} B \quad \text{or} \quad IX = A^{-1} B$$

or $X = A^{-1} B$

Now $A^{-1} = \dfrac{\text{adj.} A}{|A|}$ where

$$|A| = \begin{vmatrix} 5 & -6 & 4 \\ 7 & 4 & -3 \\ 2 & 1 & 6 \end{vmatrix} = 419$$

Cofactors of elements of first row of $|A|$ are $27, -48, -1$
Cofactors of elements of 2nd row of $|A|$ are $40, 22, -17$
Cofactors of elements or 3rd row of $|A|$ are $2, 43, 62$
Above will be respective columns of adj. A.

∴ Adj. $A = \begin{bmatrix} 27 & 40 & 2 \\ -48 & 22 & 43 \\ -1 & -17 & 62 \end{bmatrix}$

∴ $A^{-1} = \dfrac{\text{Adj.} A}{|A|} = \dfrac{1}{419}\begin{vmatrix} 27 & 40 & 2 \\ -48 & 22 & 43 \\ -1 & -17 & 62 \end{vmatrix}$

∴ $X = A^{-1} B$

or $\begin{bmatrix} x \\ y \\ z \end{bmatrix} = \dfrac{1}{419}\begin{bmatrix} 27 & 40 & 2 \\ -48 & 22 & 43 \\ -1 & -17 & 62 \end{bmatrix}\begin{bmatrix} 15 \\ 19 \\ 46 \end{bmatrix}$

or $\begin{bmatrix} x \\ y \\ z \end{bmatrix} = \dfrac{1}{419}\begin{bmatrix} 27.15 + 40.19 + 2.46 \\ -48.15 + 22.19 + 43.46 \\ -1.15 - 17.19 + 62.46 \end{bmatrix}$

$$= \frac{1}{419}\begin{bmatrix} 1257 \\ 1676 \\ 2514 \end{bmatrix} = \begin{bmatrix} 3 \\ 4 \\ 6 \end{bmatrix}$$

∴ $x = 3, y = 4, z = 6$.

2. Solve the equations

$x + y + z = 6$
$x - y + z = 2$
$2x + y - z = 1$

Sol. In matrix form the given equations are

$$\begin{bmatrix} 1 & 1 & 1 \\ 1 & -1 & 1 \\ 2 & 1 & -1 \end{bmatrix}\begin{bmatrix} x \\ y \\ z \end{bmatrix} = \begin{bmatrix} 6 \\ 2 \\ 1 \end{bmatrix} \quad \text{or} \quad AX = B$$

$$A = \begin{bmatrix} 1 & 1 & 1 \\ 1 & -1 & 1 \\ 2 & 1 & -1 \end{bmatrix}$$

∴ $|A| = D = \begin{vmatrix} 1 & 1 & 1 \\ 1 & -1 & 1 \\ 2 & 1 & -1 \end{vmatrix}$

Apply $R_2 - R_1, R_3 - 2R_1$.

$$= \begin{vmatrix} 1 & 1 & 1 \\ 0 & -2 & 0 \\ 0 & -1 & -3 \end{vmatrix} = 6 \neq 0.$$

i.e. matrix A is non-singular.

We will have unique solution and the equations are consistent.

∴ By Crammer's rule, $\dfrac{x}{D_1} = \dfrac{y}{D_2} = \dfrac{z}{D_3} = \dfrac{1}{D}$

where D_1 is obtained from D by replacing the first column of D by b's i.e., 6, 2, 1

∴ $D_1 = \begin{vmatrix} 6 & 1 & 1 \\ 2 & -1 & 1 \\ 1 & 1 & -1 \end{vmatrix} = \begin{vmatrix} 6 & 1 & 1 \\ -4 & -2 & 0 \\ 7 & 2 & 0 \end{vmatrix}$

By $R_2 - R_1$ and $R_3 + R_1$

∴ $D_1 = \begin{vmatrix} -4 & -2 \\ 7 & 2 \end{vmatrix} = -8 + 14 = 6$

$D_2 = \begin{vmatrix} 1 & 6 & 1 \\ 1 & 2 & 1 \\ 2 & 1 & -1 \end{vmatrix} = \begin{vmatrix} 1 & 6 & 1 \\ 0 & -4 & 0 \\ 0 & -11 & -3 \end{vmatrix}$

$$= \begin{vmatrix} -4 & 0 \\ -11 & -3 \end{vmatrix} = 12$$

$D_3 = \begin{vmatrix} 1 & 1 & 6 \\ 1 & -1 & 2 \\ 2 & 1 & 1 \end{vmatrix} = \begin{vmatrix} 1 & 1 & 6 \\ 0 & -2 & -4 \\ 0 & -1 & -11 \end{vmatrix}$

$$= \begin{vmatrix} -2 & -4 \\ -1 & -11 \end{vmatrix} = 22 - 4 = 18.$$

∴ $\dfrac{x}{6} = \dfrac{y}{12} = \dfrac{z}{18} = \dfrac{1}{6}$

∴ $x = 1, y = 2, z = 3$.

Above gives the unique solution.

2nd Method.

$AX = B$

We have seen that coefficient matrix A is non-singular and hence its inverse i.e. A^{-1} exists and $A^{-1} AX = A^{-1} B$ or $IX = A^{-1} B$ or $X = A^{-1} B$

Now we should calculate A^{-1} as in last question.

$$A^{-1} = \begin{vmatrix} 0 & \dfrac{1}{3} & \dfrac{1}{3} \\ \dfrac{1}{2} & -\dfrac{1}{2} & 0 \\ \dfrac{1}{2} & \dfrac{1}{6} & -\dfrac{1}{3} \end{vmatrix} \text{ by } \dfrac{adj.\,A}{|A|}$$

∴ $AX = B$ implies $X = A^{-1} B$

$$\begin{bmatrix} x \\ y \\ z \end{bmatrix} = \begin{bmatrix} 0 & \dfrac{1}{3} & \dfrac{1}{3} \\ \dfrac{1}{2} & -\dfrac{1}{2} & 0 \\ \dfrac{1}{2} & \dfrac{1}{3} & -\dfrac{1}{3} \end{bmatrix} \begin{bmatrix} 6 \\ 2 \\ 1 \end{bmatrix}$$

or $\begin{bmatrix} x \\ y \\ z \end{bmatrix} = \begin{bmatrix} 6.0 + 2/3 + 1/3 \\ 6/2 - 1 + 0 \\ 6/2 + 1/3 - 1/3 \end{bmatrix} = \begin{bmatrix} 1 \\ 2 \\ 3 \end{bmatrix}$

∴ $x = 1, y = 2, z = 3$.

3. Solve the following equations
$x + y + z = 9$
$3x + 5y + 7z = 52$
$2x + y - z = 0$
Ans. $x = 1, y = 3, z = 5$

4. Solve the equations
$x + 2y + 3z = 14$
$2x - y + 5z = 15$
$3x - 2y - 4z = -13$
Ans. $x = 1, y = 2, z = 3$

5. For what values of λ the equations :
$x + y + z = 1$
$x + 2y + 4z = \lambda$
$x + 4y + 10z = \lambda^2$

Sol. In matrix form the given equations are

$$\begin{bmatrix} 1 & 1 & 1 \\ 1 & 2 & 4 \\ 1 & 4 & 10 \end{bmatrix} \begin{bmatrix} x \\ y \\ z \end{bmatrix} = \begin{bmatrix} 1 \\ \lambda \\ \lambda^2 \end{bmatrix}$$

has a solution and solve them completely in each case.

Augmented Matrix $C = [A\,B] = \begin{bmatrix} 1 & 1 & 1 & 1 \\ 1 & 2 & 4 & \lambda \\ 1 & 4 & 10 & \lambda^2 \end{bmatrix}$

$C \sim \begin{bmatrix} 1 & 1 & 1 & 1 \\ 0 & 1 & 3 & \lambda - 1 \\ 0 & 3 & 9 & \lambda^2 - 1 \end{bmatrix}$ by $R_2 - R_1, R_3 - R_1$

$\sim \begin{bmatrix} 1 & 1 & 1 & 1 \\ 0 & 1 & 3 & \lambda - 1 \\ 0 & 0 & 0 & \lambda^2 - 3\lambda + 2 \end{bmatrix}$ by $R_3 - 3R_2$ ...(A)

∴ $A \sim \begin{bmatrix} 1 & 1 & 1 \\ 0 & 1 & 3 \\ 0 & 0 & 0 \end{bmatrix}$. Its rank is 2.

The system will be consistent if Rank $A =$ Rank C. But rank of C is 3 as there are three non-zero rows. It will be 2 only when $\lambda^2 - 3\lambda + 2 = 0$ or $(\lambda - 2)(\lambda - 1) = 0$.

$$\lambda = 2, 1.$$

In either case Rank $A =$ Rank $C = r = 2 < n = 3$, the number of variables and as such $3 - 2 = 1$ variable will be assigned arbitrary values and the remaining $r = 2$ variables shall be found in terms of these values.

The equivalent system of equations for $\lambda = 2$

$$\begin{bmatrix} 1 & 1 & 1 \\ 0 & 1 & 3 \\ 0 & 0 & 0 \end{bmatrix} \begin{bmatrix} x \\ y \\ z \end{bmatrix} = \begin{bmatrix} 1 \\ 1 \\ 0 \end{bmatrix} \text{ from (A)}$$

$x + y + z = 1, y + 3z = 1, 0 = 0$,

Choose $z = k$, ∴ $y = 1 - 3k$ and $x = 2k$.

The equivalent system of equations for $\lambda = 1$

$$\begin{bmatrix} 1 & 1 & 1 \\ 0 & 1 & 3 \\ 0 & 0 & 0 \end{bmatrix} \begin{bmatrix} x \\ y \\ z \end{bmatrix} = \begin{bmatrix} 1 \\ 0 \\ 0 \end{bmatrix} \text{ from (A)}$$

$x + y + z = 1, y + 3z = 0, 0 = 0$

Choose $z = c$, ∴ $y = -3c, x = 1 + 2c$.

6. Investigate for what values of λ, μ the simultaneous equations
$x + y + z = 6$
$x + 2y + 3z = 10$
$x + 2y + \lambda z = \mu$

or $\begin{bmatrix} 1 & 1 & 1 \\ 1 & 2 & 3 \\ 1 & 2 & \lambda \end{bmatrix} \begin{bmatrix} x \\ y \\ z \end{bmatrix} = \begin{bmatrix} 6 \\ 10 \\ \mu \end{bmatrix}$

have, (a) no solution. (b) a unique solution, (c) an infinite number of solutions.

Sol. (a) For no solution
Rank $A \neq$ Rank C

(b) For unique solution *i.e.*, coefficient matrix is non-singular.
Rank $A =$ Rank $C = n$

(c) For infinite number of solutions.
Rank $A =$ Rank $C = r$ where $r < n$.

Augmented Matrix

$C = [A, B] = \begin{bmatrix} 1 & 1 & 1 & 6 \\ 1 & 2 & 3 & 10 \\ 1 & 2 & \lambda & \mu \end{bmatrix}$ Apply $R_3 - R_2$

or $\begin{bmatrix} 1 & 1 & 1 & 6 \\ 1 & 2 & 3 & 10 \\ 0 & 0 & \lambda - 3 & \mu - 10 \end{bmatrix}$ Apply $R_2 - R_1$

$\sim \begin{bmatrix} 1 & 1 & 1 & 6 \\ 0 & 1 & 2 & 4 \\ 0 & 0 & \lambda - 3 & \mu - 10 \end{bmatrix}$

Also $A \sim \begin{bmatrix} 1 & 1 & 1 \\ 0 & 1 & 2 \\ 0 & 0 & \lambda - 3 \end{bmatrix}$

(a) $\lambda = 3, \mu \neq 10$.

In this case Rank $A = 2$ whereas Rank $C = 3$

∴ Rank $A \neq$ Rank C and hence no solution.

(b) In case $\lambda \neq 3$ then coefficient matrix A is non-singular Rank $A = $ Rank $C = 3$, the number of variables. Hence we have a unique solution which can be found by Crammer's rule or by the help of inverse or by equivalent system of equations.

(c) In case $\lambda = 3$ and $\mu = 10$ then the ranks of both A and C will be $2 < n = 3$ and the equations will be consistent. We shall assign arbitrary value to $3 - 2 = 1$ variable and remaining $r = 2$ variables shall be found in terms of these.

The equivalent system of equations when $\lambda = 3$ and $\mu = 10$ are

$$\begin{bmatrix} 1 & 1 & 1 \\ 0 & 1 & 2 \\ 0 & 0 & 0 \end{bmatrix} \begin{bmatrix} x \\ y \\ z \end{bmatrix} = \begin{bmatrix} 6 \\ 4 \\ 0 \end{bmatrix}$$

or $x + y + z = 6, y + 2z = 4, 0 = 0$

Choose $z = k$ ∴ $y = 4 - 2k$

∴ $x = 6 - y - z = 6 - (4 - 2k) - k = 2 + k$.

Homogeneous Equations :

Refer chapter of determinants. If $D = |A| \neq 0$ then the system of homogenous equations have trivial solution i.e., $x = 0, y = 0,$ and $z = 0$. If however $|A| = 0$ then the system of equations will have non-trivial solution. We will illustrate the same by following examples.

7. Solve completely the equations

$x + 3y - 2z = 0$

$2x - y + 4z = 0$

$x - 11y + 14z = 0$

Sol. $AX = O$

$$A = \begin{bmatrix} 1 & 3 & -2 \\ 2 & -1 & 4 \\ 1 & -11 & 14 \end{bmatrix}$$

Reduce the matrix to Echelon form by applying elementary row-column operation.

$$|A| = \begin{vmatrix} 1 & 3 & -2 \\ 0 & -7 & 8 \\ 0 & -14 & 16 \end{vmatrix} = -112 + 112 = 0$$

by $R_2 - 2R_1, R_3 - R_1$

Since $|A| = 0$ the system of equations will have non-trivial solution.

Above is Echelon form of A and its rank is 2 the number of non-zero rows. Rank $A = r < n$ where $n = 3$. Hence the system has non-trivial solution. We shall assign arbitrary values to $n - r = 3 - 2 = 1$ variable and remaining $r = 2$ variables shall be found in terms of these.

The equivalent system of equations is $AX = O$

$$\begin{bmatrix} 1 & 3 & -2 \\ 0 & -7 & 8 \\ 0 & -14 & 16 \end{bmatrix} \begin{bmatrix} x \\ y \\ z \end{bmatrix} = O$$

$x + 3y - 2z = 0, -7y + 8z = 0$ and $-14y + 16z = 0$

The last two are identical.

Thus we have only two equations in three variables i.e., $x + 3y - 2z = 0$ and $y = 8z/7$.

We choose $z = k$ ∴ $y = 8k/7$

and hence $x = 2z - 3y = 2k - \dfrac{24}{7}k = \dfrac{10}{7}k$.

8. Discuss for all values of k the system of equations

$x + (k + 4)y + (4k + 2)z = 0$

$2x + 3ky + (3k + 4)z = 0$ or $AX = O$

$x + 2(k + 1)y + (3k + 4)z = 0$

Sol. The given equations can be written as

$$\begin{bmatrix} 1 & k + 4 & 4k + 2 \\ 2 & 3k & 3k + 4 \\ 1 & 2k + 2 & 3k + 4 \end{bmatrix} \begin{bmatrix} x \\ y \\ z \end{bmatrix} = O$$

$$|A| = \begin{vmatrix} 1 & k + 4 & 4k + 2 \\ 2 & 3k & 3k + 4 \\ 1 & 2k + 2 & 3k + 4 \end{vmatrix}$$

Apply $R_2 - 2R_1, R_3 - R_1$

∴ $$|A| = \begin{vmatrix} 1 & k + 4 & 4k + 2 \\ 0 & k - 8 & -5k \\ 0 & k - 2 & -k + 2 \end{vmatrix}$$

$= (k - 8)(-k + 2) + 5k(k - 2)$

or $-k^2 + 2k + 8k - 16 + 5k^2 - 10k = 4k^2 - 16$

Now $|A| = 0$ when $k^2 = 4$ ∴ $k = \pm 2$.

Hence when $k = \pm 2$ then $|A| = 0$ so that the matrix A is singular and hence the system will have non-trivial solution. But when $k \neq \pm 2$ then $|A| \neq 0$ that the system will have only trivial solution i.e. $x = 0, y = 0, z = 0$.

For $k = 2$ the equivalent system of equations will be

$$\begin{bmatrix} 1 & 6 & 10 \\ 0 & -6 & -10 \\ 0 & 0 & 0 \end{bmatrix} \begin{bmatrix} x \\ y \\ z \end{bmatrix} = O$$

Clearly rank of A is 2 and we will assign arbitrary values to $n - r$ i.e. $3 - 2 = 1$ variable and remaining $r = 2$ variables shall be found in terms of these

$x + 6y + 10z = 0, -6y - 10z = 0, 0 = 0$

Only two equations in three variables.

Choose $z = c$ ∴ $y = -5c/3$ and $x = 0$

For $k = -2$ the equivalent system of equations will be

$$\begin{bmatrix} 1 & 2 & -6 \\ 0 & -10 & 10 \\ 0 & -4 & 4 \end{bmatrix} \begin{bmatrix} x \\ y \\ z \end{bmatrix} = 0$$

or $$\begin{bmatrix} 1 & 2 & -6 \\ 0 & 1 & -1 \\ 0 & 1 & -1 \end{bmatrix} \begin{bmatrix} x \\ y \\ z \end{bmatrix} = 0$$

$x + 2y - 6z = 0, y - z = 0$ and $y - z = 0$

As above two equations in three variables

Choose $z = k$ ∴ $y = k$ and $x = 4k$

9. $x + y + z = 0, 2x + 5y + 7z = 0, 2x - 5y + 3z = 0$

Ans. Trivial solution $x = y = z = 0$

10. $x + 2y + 3z = 0, 2x + 3y + 4z = 0,$
$7x + 13y + 19z = 0$

Ans. Non-trivial solution.
$x = c, y = -2c, z = c$

11. $2x - 3y + z = 0, x + 2y - 3z = 0,$
$4x - y - 2z = 0$

Ans. Trivial solution
$x = y = z = 0.$

Problem Set (7)

Multiple Choice Questions

1. The numbers of 3×3 matrices A whose entries are either 0 or 1 and for which the system $A \begin{bmatrix} x \\ y \\ z \end{bmatrix} = \begin{bmatrix} 1 \\ 0 \\ 0 \end{bmatrix}$ has exactly two distinct solutions is

(a) 10   (b) $2^9 - 1$

(c) 168   (d) 2   **(IIT JEE 2010)**

2. If P is a 3×3 matrix such that $P^T = 2P + I$ where P^T is the transpose of P and I is the 3×3 identity matrix, then there exists a column matrix $X = \begin{bmatrix} x \\ y \\ z \end{bmatrix} \neq \begin{bmatrix} 0 \\ 0 \\ 0 \end{bmatrix}$ such that

(a) $PX = \begin{bmatrix} 0 \\ 0 \\ 0 \end{bmatrix}$ (b) $PX = X$

(c) $PX = 2X$ (d) $PX = -X$ **(IIT-JEE 2012)**

3. Let $A = \begin{bmatrix} 1 & 0 & 0 \\ 2 & 1 & 0 \\ 3 & 2 & 1 \end{bmatrix}$. If u_1 and u_2 are column matrices such that $Au_1 = \begin{bmatrix} 1 \\ 0 \\ 0 \end{bmatrix}$ and $Au_2 = \begin{bmatrix} 0 \\ 1 \\ 0 \end{bmatrix}$. Then $u_1 + u_2$ is equal to

(a) $\begin{pmatrix} -1 \\ 1 \\ 0 \end{pmatrix}$ (b) $\begin{pmatrix} -1 \\ 1 \\ -1 \end{pmatrix}$ (c) $\begin{pmatrix} -1 \\ -1 \\ 0 \end{pmatrix}$ (d) $\begin{pmatrix} 1 \\ -1 \\ -1 \end{pmatrix}$

(AIEEE 2012)

4. Let $P = [a_{ij}]$ be a 3×3 matrix and let $Q = (b_{ij})$ where $b_{ij} = 2^{i+j} a_{ij}$ for $1 \leq i, j \leq 3$. If the determinant of P is 2 then the determinant of the matrix Q is

(a) 2^{10} (b) 2^{11} (c) 2^{12} (d) 2^{13}

(IIT-JEE 2012)

5. Le. P and Q be 3×3 matrices such that $P \neq Q$. If $P^3 = Q^3$ and $P^2 Q = Q^2 P$ then determinant of $(P^2 + Q^2)$ is equal to

(a) -2 (b) 1   (c) 0   (d) -1

(AIEEE 2012)

6. Let M and N be two even order non-singular skew symmetric matrices such that $MN = NM$. If P^T denotes the transpose of P, then $M^2 N^2 (M^T N)^{-1} (MN^{-1})^T$ is equal to

(a) M^2 (b) $-N^2$ (c) $-M^2$ (d) MN

(IIT-JEE 2011)

7. Let $w \neq 1$ be a cube roots of unity and S be the set of all non-singular matrices of the form $\begin{bmatrix} 1 & a & b \\ \omega & 1 & c \\ \omega^2 & \omega & 1 \end{bmatrix}$ where each a, b and c is either ω or ω^2. Then the number of distinct matrices in the set S is

(a) 2   (b) 6   (c) 4   (d) 8

(IIT-JEE 2011)

8. If the adjoint of a 3×3 matrix P is $\begin{bmatrix} 1 & 4 & 4 \\ 2 & 1 & 7 \\ 1 & 1 & 3 \end{bmatrix}$ then the possible values of the determinant of P is

(a) -2 (b) -1 (c) 1   (d) 2

(IIT-JEE 2012)

9. The number of 3×3 non-singular matrices with four entries as 1 and all other entries as 0 is

(a) < 4 (b) 5   (c) 6   (d) at least 7

(AIEEE 2010)

10. Let ω be the complex number $\cos\dfrac{2\pi}{3} + i\sin\dfrac{2\pi}{3}$. Then the number of distinct complex numbers z satisfying $\begin{vmatrix} z+1 & \omega & \omega^2 \\ \omega & z+\omega^2 & 1 \\ \omega^2 & 1 & z+\omega \end{vmatrix} = 0$ is equal to

(a) 1   (b) 2   (c) 0   (d) 4

(IIT-JEE 2010)

11. Let k be a positive real number and let

$A = \begin{bmatrix} 2k-1 & 2\sqrt{k} & 2\sqrt{k} \\ 2\sqrt{k} & 1 & -2k \\ -2\sqrt{k} & 2k & -1 \end{bmatrix}$,

$B = \begin{bmatrix} 0 & 2k-1 & \sqrt{k} \\ 1-2k & 0 & 2\sqrt{k} \\ -\sqrt{k} & -2\sqrt{k} & 0 \end{bmatrix}$

If det (Adj (A)) + det (Adj (B)) = 10^6 then $[k]$ is equal to

(a) 4   (b) 6
(c) 0   (d) 1   **(IIT-JEE 2010)**

12. Let M be a 3×3 matrix satisfying

$$M\begin{bmatrix} 0 \\ 1 \\ 0 \end{bmatrix} = \begin{bmatrix} -1 \\ 2 \\ 3 \end{bmatrix}, M\begin{bmatrix} 1 \\ -1 \\ 0 \end{bmatrix} = \begin{bmatrix} 1 \\ 1 \\ -1 \end{bmatrix} \text{ and } M\begin{bmatrix} 1 \\ 1 \\ 1 \end{bmatrix} = \begin{bmatrix} 0 \\ 0 \\ 12 \end{bmatrix} \text{ then}$$

The sum of the diagonal entries of M is

(a) 9   (b) 4
(c) 1   (d) 10   **(IIT-JEE 2011)**

Solution to Problem set (7)

1. Ans. (a).

$$A_{3 \times 3} \cdot B_{3 \times 1} = C_{3 \times 1} \qquad \ldots(1)$$

A is a matrix whose entries are either 0 or 1

∴ AB will be a 3×1 matrix with entries x, y, z.

Thus, equation (1) represents the equation of three planes. We know that three planes can not intersect at two distinct points. Hence the number of solutions is zero.

2. Ans. (d).

$$P^T = 2P + I$$

$$\Rightarrow \quad (P^T)^T = (2p + I)^T = 2P^T + I$$

$$\Rightarrow \quad P = 2P^T + I \qquad (\because (P^T)^T = P)$$

$$\Rightarrow \quad P = 2(2p + I) + I$$

$$\Rightarrow \quad 3P = -3I \quad \Rightarrow \quad P = -I$$

$$\Rightarrow \quad PX = -IX = -X$$

3. Ans. (d).

$$A(u_1 + u_2) = \begin{bmatrix} 1 \\ 1 \\ 0 \end{bmatrix} |A| = 1$$

$$A^{-1} = \frac{1}{|A|} adj (A) \qquad u_1 + u_2 = A^{-1}\begin{bmatrix} 1 \\ 1 \\ 0 \end{bmatrix},$$

$$A^{-1} = \begin{bmatrix} 1 & 0 & 0 \\ -2 & 1 & 0 \\ 1 & -2 & 1 \end{bmatrix} = \begin{bmatrix} 1 \\ -1 \\ -1 \end{bmatrix}$$

4. Ans. (d).

$$P = [a_{ij}]_{3 \times 3}, \quad b_{ij} = 2^{i+j} \cdot a_{ij}, \quad Q = [b_{ij}]_{3 \times 3}$$

$$P = \begin{bmatrix} a_{11} & a_{12} & a_{13} \\ a_{21} & a_{22} & a_{23} \\ a_{31} & a_{32} & a_{33} \end{bmatrix}, |P| = 2$$

$$Q = \begin{bmatrix} b_{11} & b_{12} & b_{13} \\ b_{21} & b_{22} & b_{23} \\ b_{31} & b_{32} & b_{33} \end{bmatrix} = \begin{bmatrix} 4a_{11} & 8a_{12} & 16a_{13} \\ 8a_{21} & 16a_{22} & 32a_{23} \\ 16a_{31} & 32a_{32} & 64a_{33} \end{bmatrix}$$

$$= 4 \times 8 \times 16 \begin{vmatrix} a_{11} & a_{12} & a_{13} \\ 2a_{21} & 2a_{22} & 2a_{23} \\ 4a_{31} & 4a_{32} & 4a_{33} \end{vmatrix}$$

$$= 4 \times 8 \times 16 \times 2 \times 4 \begin{vmatrix} a_{11} & a_{12} & a_{13} \\ a_{21} & a_{22} & a_{23} \\ a_{31} & a_{32} & a_{33} \end{vmatrix}$$

$$= 2^2 . 2^3 . 2^4 . 2^1 . 2^2 . 2^1 = 2^{13}$$

5. Ans. (c). On sustracting, we get

$$P^3 - P^2 Q = Q^3 - Q^2 P$$

$$\Rightarrow \quad P^2 (P - Q) + Q^2 (P - Q) = 0$$

$$\Rightarrow \quad (P^2 + Q^2)(P - Q) = 0$$

If $|P^2 + Q^2| \neq 0$; then $P^2 + Q^2$ is invertible

$$\Rightarrow \quad P - Q = 0, \text{ contradition}$$

∴ $|P^2 + Q^2| = 0$

6. Ans. (c).

$$M^2 N^2 (M^T N)^{-1} (MN^{-1})^T$$

$$= M^2 N^2 N^{-1} (M^T)^{-1} (N^{-1})^T M^T$$

$$= -M^2 N^2 N^{-1} M^{-1} N^{-1} M$$

$$= -M^2 N M^{-1} N^{-1} M$$

$$= -MNN^{-1}m = -M^2$$

7. Ans. (a). $a, b, c \in \{w, w^2\}$

Let $A = \begin{bmatrix} 1 & a & b \\ \omega & 1 & < \\ \omega^2 & \omega & 1 \end{bmatrix}$

$$\Rightarrow \quad |A| = 1 - (a + c)\omega + ac\omega^2$$

Now $|A|$ will be non-zero only when $a = c = w$

∴ $(a, b, c) = (\omega, \omega, \omega)$ or $(\omega, \omega^2, \omega)$

Hence, number of nm-singular matrices = 2

8. Ans. (a) and (d).

Let $A = [a_{ij}]_{3 \times 3}$

$$adj (A) = \begin{bmatrix} 1 & 4 & 4 \\ 2 & 1 & 7 \\ 1 & 1 & 3 \end{bmatrix}$$

$$\Rightarrow \quad |adj (A)| = 1(3 - 7) - 4(6 - 7) + 4(2 - 1) = 4$$

$$\Rightarrow \quad |A|^{3-1} = 4 \quad \Rightarrow \quad |A|^2 = 4 \quad \Rightarrow \quad |A| = \pm 2$$

9. Ans. (d).

For non-singular matrix $|A| \neq 0$

$$A = \begin{bmatrix} 1 & - & - \\ - & 1 & - \\ - & - & 1 \end{bmatrix} \text{There are 6 vacant places when 5 zero's}$$

and one 1 are be placed for $|A| \neq 0$

∴   No. of ways = 6

$$|A| = \begin{vmatrix} 0 & 0 & 1 \\ 1 & 1 & 0 \\ 1 & 0 & 0 \end{vmatrix} \neq 0 = \begin{vmatrix} 1 & 0 & 1 \\ 0 & 1 & 0 \\ 1 & 0 & 0 \end{vmatrix} \neq 0$$

Hence, at least 7 matrices are possible.

10. Ans. (a).

$$\omega = \cos \frac{2\pi}{3} + i \sin \frac{2\pi}{3}$$

Apply $C_1 \to C_1 + C_2 + C_3$, we get

$$\begin{vmatrix} z & \omega & \omega^2 \\ z & z+\omega^2 & 1 \\ z & 1 & z+\omega \end{vmatrix} = 0$$

$$\Rightarrow \quad z \begin{vmatrix} 1 & \omega & \omega^2 \\ 1 & z+\omega^2 & 1 \\ 1 & 1 & z+\omega \end{vmatrix} = 0$$

$$\Rightarrow \quad z \begin{vmatrix} 1 & \omega & \omega^2 \\ 0 & z+\omega^2-\omega & 1-\omega^2 \\ 0 & 1-\omega & z+\omega-\omega^2 \end{vmatrix} = 0$$

by $R_2 \to R_2 - R_1$
   $R_3 \to R_3 - R_1$

$$= (z+\omega^2-\omega)(z+\omega-\omega^2) - (1-\omega)(1-\omega^2) = 0$$

$$\Rightarrow \quad z^2 = 0$$

$\Rightarrow$ only one solution

11. Ans. (a)

$$\det(A) = \begin{vmatrix} 2k-1 & 2\sqrt{k} & 2\sqrt{k} \\ 2\sqrt{k} & 1 & -2k \\ -2\sqrt{k} & 2k & -1 \end{vmatrix}$$

$$= \begin{vmatrix} 2k-1 & 0 & 2\sqrt{k} \\ 2\sqrt{k} & 1+2k & -2k \\ -2\sqrt{k} & 2k+1 & -1 \end{vmatrix}$$

(By $C_2 \to C_2 - C_3$)

$$= \begin{vmatrix} 2k-1 & 0 & 2\sqrt{k} \\ 4\sqrt{k} & 0 & 1-2k \\ -2\sqrt{k} & 2k+1 & -1 \end{vmatrix} (R_2 \to R_2 - R_1)$$

$$= (2k+1)^3$$

$\because$ B is a skew symmetric matrix of odd order therefore det $(B) = 0$

Now det $(\text{Adj}(A)) + \det(\text{adj}(B)) = 10^6$

$\Rightarrow \quad \{(2k+1)^3\}^2 + 0 = 10^6$

$\Rightarrow \quad 2k+1 = 0 \Rightarrow k = 4,5 \Rightarrow [k] = 4$

12. Ans. (a).

Let $M = \begin{bmatrix} a_{11} & a_{12} & a_{13} \\ a_{21} & a_{22} & a_{23} \\ a_{31} & a_{32} & a_{33} \end{bmatrix}$ Then $a_{12} = -1$

$a_{11} - a_{12} = 1 \Rightarrow a_{11} = 0$
$a_{11} + a_{12} + a_{13} = 0 \Rightarrow a_{13} = 1,$
$a_{22} = 2, a_{21} - a_{22} = 1 \Rightarrow a_{21} = 3$
$a_{21} + a_{22} + a_{23} = 0 \Rightarrow a_{23} = -5$
$a_{32} = 3, a_{35} - a_{32} = 1 \Rightarrow a_{31} = 2$
$a_{31} + a_{32} + a_{33} = 12 \Rightarrow a_{33} = 7$

Hence, sum of diagonal of the matrix M is
$a_1 + a_{22} + a_{33} = 0 + 2 + 7 = 9$

Comprehension

Paragraph for Question 1 to 3 : Let p be an odd prime number and T_p be the following set of 2×2 matrices

$$T_p = \left\{ A = \begin{bmatrix} a & b \\ c & a \end{bmatrix} : a,b,c \in [0,1,2,\dots p-1] \right\}$$

1. The number of A in T_p such that A is either symmetric or skew symmetric or both and let det (A) divisible by p is

(a) $(p-1)^2$

(b) $2(p-1)$

(c) $(p-1)^2 + 1$

(d) $2p-1$ **(IIT-JEE 2010)**

2. The number of A is T_p such that the trace of A is not divisible by p but det (A) is divisible by p is

(a) $(p-1)(p^2-p+1)$

(b) $p^3 - (p-1)^2$

(c) $(p-1)^2$

(d) $(p-1)(p^2-2)$

(IIT-JEE 2010)

3. The number of A in T_p such that det (A) is not divisible by p is

(a) $2p^2$

(b) $p^3 - 5p$

(c) $p^3 - 3p$

(d) $p^3 - p^2$ **(IIT-JEE 2010)**

Paragraph for Question Nos. 4 to 6 : Let $\mathcal{A}$ be the set of all 3×3 symmetric matrices all of whose entries are either 0 or 1. Five of these entries are 1 and four of them are 0.

4. The number of matrices in $\mathcal{A}$ is

(a) 12

(b) 6

(c) 9

(d) 3   **(IIT-JEE 2009)**

5. The number of matrices A in A for which the system of linear equations $A \begin{bmatrix} x \\ y \\ z \end{bmatrix} = \begin{bmatrix} 1 \\ 0 \\ 0 \end{bmatrix}$ has a unique solution, is

(a) less than 4

(b) at least 4 but less than 7

(c) at least 7 but less than 10

(d) at least 10

6. The number of matrices A in $\mathcal{A}$ for which the system of linear equations $A \begin{bmatrix} x \\ y \\ z \end{bmatrix} = \begin{bmatrix} 1 \\ 0 \\ 0 \end{bmatrix}$ is inconsistent, is

(a) 0

(b) more than 2

(c) 2

(d) 1

Hints / Solution

1. Ans. (d). $\quad A = \begin{bmatrix} a & b \\ c & a \end{bmatrix}$

Case I If A is symmetric $\Rightarrow b = c$

$\Rightarrow \quad \det(A) = a^2 - b^2$ is divisible by p

$\Rightarrow \quad (a - b)(a + b)$ is divisible by p

(i) $a - b$ is divisible by p if $a = b$, then p cases are possible

(ii) $a + b$ is divisible by p if $a + b = p$ then $\dfrac{p-1}{2} \times 2 = (p-1)$ cases are possible

Case II If A is skew symmetric

It $a = 0$, $b + c = 0$, then $\det(A) = b^2$

$\Rightarrow \quad b^2$ can never be divisible by p

$\Rightarrow \quad$ No case is possible

Hence total no. of A possible $= 2p - 1$

2. Ans. (c).

$(a^2 - bc) \div p$, a can be chosen in $p - 1$ ways $(a \neq 0)$

Let a be 4 and $p = 5$

$\therefore \quad a^2 = 16$ and so bc should be chosen such that $a^2 - bc \div p$

Now p can be chosen in $p - 1$ ways and c is only 1.

because If $b = 1 \Rightarrow c = 1; b = 2 \Rightarrow c = 3$

$\quad\quad b = 3 \quad \Rightarrow \quad c = 2; b = 4 \Rightarrow c = 4$

$\therefore \quad a$ can be chosen in $p - 1$ ways and b can be chosen in $(p - 1)$ ways and c can be chosen in 1 way.

Hence, total no. of ways $= (p - 1)^2$

3. Ans. (d).

A's = Total cases $- (a \neq 0$ and $|A|$ is divisible by $p]$
$\quad\quad\quad\quad - (a = 0$ and $|A|$ is divisible by $p]$

$\quad = p^3 - (p - 1)^2 - (2p - 1)$

$= p^3 - p^2 - bc + p$ ($\because b$ and c both be coprime to p)

$\Rightarrow \quad$ one of them must be 0.

If $b = 0 \Rightarrow c$ can be chosen in $\{0, 1, \dots p - 1\}$

If $c = 0 \Rightarrow b$ can be chosen in $\{0, 1, \dots p - 1\}$

4. Ans. (a).

We have five entries of 1 and four are 0. For symmetric matrix, we have $a_{ij} = a_{ji}$

Case I. Diagonal having two zeros and one 1. Other elements will be two zeros and four 1, subject to the condition $a_{ij} = a_{ji}$

$\begin{bmatrix} 0 & 1 & 1 \\ 1 & 0 & 0 \\ 1 & 0 & 1 \end{bmatrix}, \begin{bmatrix} 0 & 1 & 0 \\ 1 & 0 & 1 \\ 0 & 1 & 1 \end{bmatrix}, \begin{bmatrix} 0 & 0 & 1 \\ 0 & 0 & 1 \\ 1 & 1 & 1 \end{bmatrix}$

$\begin{bmatrix} 0 & 1 & 1 \\ 1 & 1 & 0 \\ 1 & 0 & 0 \end{bmatrix}, \begin{bmatrix} 0 & 1 & 0 \\ 1 & 1 & 1 \\ 0 & 1 & 0 \end{bmatrix}, \begin{bmatrix} 0 & 0 & 1 \\ 0 & 1 & 1 \\ 1 & 1 & 0 \end{bmatrix}$

$\begin{bmatrix} 1 & 1 & 1 \\ 1 & 0 & 0 \\ 1 & 0 & 0 \end{bmatrix}, \begin{bmatrix} 1 & 1 & 0 \\ 1 & 0 & 1 \\ 0 & 1 & 0 \end{bmatrix}, \begin{bmatrix} 1 & 0 & 1 \\ 0 & 0 & 1 \\ 1 & 1 & 0 \end{bmatrix}$ 9 matrices

Case II. When all diagonal elements are 1.

$\begin{bmatrix} 1 & 0 & 0 \\ 0 & 1 & 1 \\ 0 & 1 & 1 \end{bmatrix}, \begin{bmatrix} 1 & 0 & 1 \\ 0 & 1 & 0 \\ 1 & 0 & 1 \end{bmatrix}, \begin{bmatrix} 1 & 1 & 0 \\ 1 & 1 & 0 \\ 0 & 0 & 1 \end{bmatrix}$ 3 matrices

Total $= 9 + 3 = 12 \Rightarrow$ (a)

5. (b).

The system of equations will have unique solution if $|A| \neq 0$.

Case I. All diagonal elements are 1. There will be 3 such cases as shown in case II and $|A| \neq 0$. It is easy to observe that out of the remaining 9 matrices of case I $|A| \neq 0$ in three cases marked by $(\sqrt{})$. Thus there will be 6 cases when $|A| \neq 0$.

6. Ans. (b).

MISCELLANEOUS EXERCISE

Matching Entries

▶ *Match the entries of List-A and List-B.*

1.

List-A

(a) If $\begin{bmatrix} 2 & 0 & 7 \\ 0 & 1 & 0 \\ 1 & -2 & 1 \end{bmatrix} \begin{bmatrix} -\lambda & 14\lambda & 7\lambda \\ 0 & 1 & 6 \\ \lambda & -4\lambda & -2\lambda \end{bmatrix} = I_3$ then $\lambda = \dots$

(b) Classify the type of matrix $\begin{bmatrix} 0 & 5 & -7 \\ -5 & 0 & 11 \\ 7 & -11 & 0 \end{bmatrix}$

(c) If $A = \begin{bmatrix} a & b \\ c & d \end{bmatrix}$ such that $ad - bc \neq 0$, then $A^{-1} = \dots$

List-B

1. Skew symmetric

2. $\dfrac{1}{(ad - bc)} \begin{bmatrix} d & -b \\ -c & a \end{bmatrix}$

3. $\dfrac{1}{5}$

(d) If $A = \text{diag}[d_1, d_2, d_3]$, then $A^n = ...$

(e) If $F(\alpha) = \begin{bmatrix} \cos\alpha & -\sin\alpha & 0 \\ \sin\alpha & \cos\alpha & 0 \\ 0 & 0 & 1 \end{bmatrix}$, then

   (i) $F(\alpha) \cdot F(\beta) = ...$

   (ii) $[F(\alpha)]^{-1} = ...$

4. (i) $F(\alpha + \beta)$

   (ii) $F(-\alpha)$

5. $\text{diag}[d_1^n, d_2^n, d_3^n]$

Answers

1. (a) → 3. **Q. 15 (b) P. 480**
(b) → 1. **§ 10 P. 486**
(c) → 2. **See rule P. 487 & (b) 488**

(d) → 5. **Q. 28 (b) P. 484**
(e) (i), (ii) → 4. **Q. 33 P. 484, Q. 13 P. 493**

Assertion / Reason

1. Let A be a 2×2 matrix.   **(AIEEE 2009)**
Statement-1 : $adj\,(adj\,A) = A$.
Statement-2 : $|adj\,A| = |A|$.

Sol. Both are true but statement (2) is not the correct explanation of (1).

$$A = \begin{bmatrix} a & b \\ c & d \end{bmatrix}$$

$\therefore$ $Adj\,A = \begin{bmatrix} d & -b \\ -c & a \end{bmatrix}$ **See Rule P. 487**

$\therefore$ $Adj\,(Adj\,A) = \begin{bmatrix} a & b \\ c & d \end{bmatrix} = A$

$|Adj\,A| = \begin{vmatrix} d & -b \\ -c & a \end{vmatrix} = ad - bc = |A|$

2. Let A and B be two symmetric matric of order 3
Statement 1. $A(BA)$ and $(AB)A$ are symmetric
Statement 2. AB is symmetric if matrix multiplication of A and B is commutative.   **(AIEEE 2011)**

Sol. Ans.(b).

$A' = A$, $B' = A$, $P = A(BA)$
$\Rightarrow$ $P' = (A(BA))' = (BA)'\,A' = (A'\,B')A'$
    $= (AB)A = A(BA)$

$\Rightarrow$ $A(BA)$ is symmetric

$\Rightarrow$ statement-2 is correct but not correct explanation of statement-1.

3. Let A be a 2×2 matrix with non-zero entries and let $A^2 = I$, where I is a 2×2 identify matrix. Define $Tr(A) = $ sum of diagonal elements of A and $|A| = \det(A)$
Statement 1 : $Tr(A) = 0$
Statement 2 : $|A| = 1$ **(AIEEE 2010)**

Sol. Ans. (c).

Statement-1. Let $A = \begin{bmatrix} a & b \\ c & d \end{bmatrix}$,

$A^2 = I \Rightarrow \begin{bmatrix} a^2 + bc & ab + bd \\ ac + cd & bc + d^2 \end{bmatrix} = \begin{bmatrix} 1 & 0 \\ 0 & 1 \end{bmatrix}$

$\Rightarrow$ $a + d = 0$ $(\because\ b \neq 0, c \neq 1)$
$\Rightarrow$ $Tr(A) = 0 \Rightarrow$ statement 1 is true.
Statement 2 : $A^2 = I$

$A = A^{-1}$ But for $A = A^{-1}$, A should be I, but I is not possible because all entries are not zero.
Hence, statement-2 is not true.

Fascinating Facts

- The concept of diagonal applies only to square matrix
- Every triangular matrix is square amtrix, but every square matrix is not triangular.
- For any matrix to be symmetric or skew symmetric it must be a square matrix.
- If A is a square matrix then AA^T or A^TA is a symmetric matrix.
- Minimum number of zeroes in a triangular matrix is $\frac{n(n-1)}{2}$, where n is the order of matrix.
- Number of zeros in a diagonal matrix is given by $n^2 - n$, where n is the order of the matrix.
- The rank of a singular square matrix of order n can not be n.
- A homogeneous system of equation is never inconsistent.
- No element of a principal diagonal in a diagonal matrix is zero.
- The rank of the null matrix is not defined and the rank of every non-null matrix is greater than or equal to 1.

CHAPTER 12

Trigonometry Ratios and Identities

§ 1. Measurement of angles.

There are two common systems of measuring angles :
(1) **Sexagesimal Measure.**
(2) **Circular Measure.**

According to sexagesimal system of measurement, we divide a right angle into 90 equal parts called **degrees**. Each degree is divided into sixty equal parts called **minutes**, and each minute is divided into sixty equal parts called **seconds**. We denote one degree, one minute and one second by the symbols 1°, $1'$ and $1''$ respectively. Thus 60 seconds (60") = 1', 60 minutes (60') = 1° and 90 degrees (90°) = a right angle.

In second system, the unit of measurement is called a **radian** whose definition is as follows :

Take any circle whose centre is O. In this, measure an arc AB equal in length of the radius. Join O to A and B. Then $\angle AOB$ is the measurement of one radian. We shall denote one radian by the symbol 1^c. This is the unit of circular measure. We denote the ratio of the circumference to the diameter of a circle by the Greek letter π.

Thus $\dfrac{\textbf{Circumference}}{\textbf{Diameter}} = \pi.$

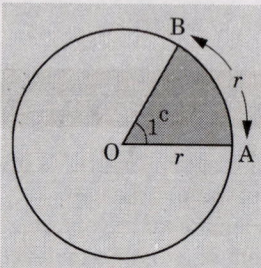

Fig. 1

It can be proved that π is an irrational number. Its approximate value is often taken as 22 / 7. This value is correct only to two places of decimals. Its value correct to 5 decimal places is 3·14159... Sometimes, we require the value of $1/\pi$ which is given by

$$\frac{1}{\pi} = 0 \cdot 3183098862$$

Relation between degree and radian. Students must remember that

$$\textbf{1 Radian} = 180^\circ \times \frac{1}{\pi} = 180^\circ \times 0 \cdot 3183098862$$

$$= 57 \cdot 2957795^\circ = \textbf{57}^\circ\,\textbf{17}'\,\textbf{44}\cdot\textbf{8}''$$

Again $\quad 1^\circ = \dfrac{\pi}{180}$ radian.

The length s of an arc PQ of a circle of radius r subtending an angle θ radians at the centre is given by $s = r\,\theta$.

Example 1. *(i) Convert angles of $60^\circ, 75^\circ$ and 120° in radians.*

(ii) Convert angles of $\dfrac{\pi}{12}, \dfrac{\pi}{4}, \dfrac{5\pi}{6}$ and $\dfrac{11\pi}{12}$ radians in degrees.

Sol. (i) $\quad 60^\circ = 60 \times \dfrac{\pi}{180}$ radians $= \dfrac{\pi}{3}$ radians,

$\qquad 75^\circ = 75 \times \dfrac{\pi}{180}$ radians $= \dfrac{5\pi}{12}$ radians,

and $120^\circ = 120 \times \dfrac{\pi}{180}$ radians $= \dfrac{2\pi}{3}$ radians .

(ii) $\dfrac{\pi}{12}$ radians $= \dfrac{\pi}{12} \times \dfrac{180}{\pi}$ degrees $= 15^\circ$,

$\quad \dfrac{\pi}{4}$ radians $= \dfrac{\pi}{4} \times \dfrac{180}{\pi}$ degrees $= 45^\circ$,

$\quad \dfrac{5\pi}{6}$ radians $= \dfrac{5\pi}{6} \times \dfrac{180}{\pi}$ degrees $= 150^\circ$,

and $\dfrac{11\pi}{12}$ radians $= \dfrac{11\pi}{12} \times \dfrac{180}{\pi}$ degrees $= 165^\circ$.

Example 2. *The angles of a quadrilateral are in A.P. and the greatest angle is 120°. Express the angles in radians.*

Sol. Let the angles in degrees be :

$$\alpha - 3\delta,\ \alpha - \delta,\ \alpha + \delta,\ \alpha + 3\delta .$$

sum of the angles $= 4\alpha = 360^\circ$

$\therefore \quad \alpha = 90^\circ.$

Also greatest angle $= \alpha + 3\delta = 120^\circ$ (given)

Hence $\quad 3\delta = 120^\circ - \alpha = 120^\circ - 90^\circ = 30^\circ$

$\therefore \quad \delta = 10^\circ.$

Hence the angles are :

$90° - 30°, 90° - 10°, \quad 90° + 10°$ and $90° + 30°$.

That is, the angles in degrees are :

$60°, 80°, 100°$ and $120°$.

∴ In terms of radians the angles are

$60 \times \dfrac{\pi}{180}, 80 \times \dfrac{\pi}{180}, 100 \times \dfrac{\pi}{180}$ and $120 \times \dfrac{\pi}{180}$ that is,

$\dfrac{\pi}{3}, \dfrac{4\pi}{9}, \dfrac{5\pi}{9}$ and $\dfrac{2\pi}{3}$.

Example 3. *The angles of a triangle are in A.P. and the number of degrees in the least is to the number of radians in the greatest as* $60 : \pi$, *find the angles of the triangle in radians.*

Sol. Let the angles of the triangle in degrees be

$\alpha - \delta, \alpha, \alpha + \delta$.

Then $\quad (\alpha - \delta) + \alpha + (\alpha + \delta) = 180°$

which gives $\quad \alpha = 60°$.

Now the greatest angle of the triangle $= (\alpha + \delta)°$

$\qquad = \dfrac{\pi}{180}(\alpha + \delta)$ radians.

∴ As given in the question, we have

$\dfrac{\alpha - \delta}{(\pi/180)(\alpha + \delta)} = \dfrac{60}{\pi}$ or $3(\alpha - \delta) = \alpha + \delta$

This gives $\quad \delta = \dfrac{1}{2}\alpha = \dfrac{1}{2} \times 60° = 30°$.

Hence the angles are $30°, 60°$ and $90°$, *i.e.* $\pi/6, \pi/3$ and $\pi/2$ radians.

Example 4. *The minute hand of a clock is 10 cm long. How far does the tip of the hand move in 20 minutes ?*

Sol. We know that the tip of the minute hand makes one complete round in one hour *i.e.* 60 minutes since the length of the hand is 10 cm., the distance moved by its tip in 60 minutes $= 2\pi \times 10$ cm $= 20 \pi$ cm.

Hence the distance in 20 minutes

$= \dfrac{20\pi}{60} \times 20$ cm $= \dfrac{20\pi}{3}$ cm.

Problem Set (1)

1. The arc of a circle of radius 21 cm subtends an angle of $60°$ at the centre, find the length of the arc. (Take $\pi = 22/7$).

2. The angles of a triangle are in A.P. and the least angle is $30°$; express the greatest angle in radians.

3. The angles of a quadrilateral are in A.P. and the greatest angle is double the least ; express the angles in radians.

4. The number of sides in two regular polygons are as $5 : 4$ and the difference between their angles is $6°$, find the number of sides in the polygons.

5. The perimeter of a certain sector of a circle is equal to the length of the arc of a semi-circle having the same radius ; express the angle of the sector in degrees, minutes and seconds.

Solutions to Problem Set (29)

1. $l = r\theta = 21 \cdot \dfrac{\pi}{3} = 7\pi = 22$ cm.

2. $(A - D) + A + (A + D) = 3A = 180°$ ∴ $A = 60°$

Also $A - D = 30°$ ∴ $D = 30°$

Hence $A + D = 90° = \dfrac{\pi}{2}$ radians.

3. $(A - 3D) + (A - D) + (A + D) + (A + 3D) = 360°$

∴ $A = 90°$

Also $(A + 3D) = 2(A - 3D)$

∴ $9D = A = 90°$ ∴ $D = 10°$

Hence the angles are $60°, 80°, 100°, 120°$

or $\dfrac{\pi}{3}, \dfrac{4\pi}{9}, \dfrac{5\pi}{9}, \dfrac{2\pi}{3}$.

4. Let $N, n (N > n)$ be the sides of regular polygons so that each interior angle is $\dfrac{2N - 4}{N} \dfrac{\pi}{2}$ and $\dfrac{2n - 4}{n} \dfrac{\pi}{2}$ where as

given $\dfrac{2N - 4}{N} \dfrac{\pi}{2} - \dfrac{2n - 4}{n} \dfrac{\pi}{2} = 6° = \dfrac{\pi}{30}$

or $\left(1 - \dfrac{2}{N}\right) - \left(1 - \dfrac{2}{n}\right) = \dfrac{1}{30}$ or $\dfrac{1}{n} - \dfrac{1}{N} = \dfrac{1}{60}$ ...(1)

Also it is given that $\dfrac{N}{n} = \dfrac{5}{4}$ or $\dfrac{N}{5} = \dfrac{n}{4} = k$, say. ...(2)

∴ $\dfrac{1}{4k} - \dfrac{1}{5k} = \dfrac{1}{60}$ or $\dfrac{1}{20k} = \dfrac{1}{60}$ ∴ $k = 3$

Hence the sides are 15 and 12 by (2).

5. Let r be the radius of the circle and θ the number of radians in the angle.

Then $r\theta + 2r = \pi r$ or $\theta = (\pi - 2)$ radians

or $\theta = (\pi - 2) \times \dfrac{180°}{\pi}$

or $= 180° - 2 \times 57° \, 17' \, 44 \cdot 8''$

or $\theta = 180° - 114° \, 35' \, 29 \cdot 6'' = 65° \, 24' \, 30 \cdot 4''$.

§ 2. Basic Formulae :

1. $\sin^2 A + \cos^2 A = 1$

or $\sin^2 A = 1 - \cos^2 A$ or $\cos^2 A = 1 - \sin^2 A$.

2. $1 + \tan^2 A = \sec^2 A$ or $\sec^2 A - \tan^2 A = 1$

or $\sec A + \tan A = \dfrac{1}{\sec A - \tan A}$ **(Imp.)**

$\left(A \neq n\pi + \dfrac{1}{2}\pi, \ n \in I\right)$

3. $1 + \cot^2 A = \mathrm{cosec}^2 A$ or $\mathrm{cosec}^2 A - \cot^2 A = 1$

or $(\mathrm{cosec} \, A - \cot A)(\mathrm{cosec} \, A + \cot A) = 1$

or $\quad$ cosec $A + \cot A = \dfrac{1}{\text{cosec } A - \cot A}$ $\quad$ **(Imp.)**

$\quad (A \neq n\pi, \ n \in \mathbf{I})$

4. Since $\sin^2 A + \cos^2 A = 1$, hence each of $\sin A$ and $\cos A$ is numerically less than or equal to unity, that is,

$\quad |\sin A| \leq 1$ and $|\cos A| \leq 1$

or $\quad -1 \leq \sin A \leq 1$ and $-1 \leq \cos A \leq 1$

Note that modulus of real number x is defined as :

$|x| = x$ if $x \geq 0$ and $|x| = -x$ if $x \leq 0$

(Note carefully)

5. Since sec A and cosec A are respectively reciprocals of cos A and sin A, therefore the values of sec A and cosec A are always numerically greater than or equal to unity. That is

$\quad$ sec $A \geq 1$ or sec $A \leq -1$

and $\quad$ coesc $A \geq 1$ or cosec $A \leq -1$

In other words, **we never have**

$\quad -1 < \text{cosec } A < 1$ and $-1 < \text{sec } A < 1$.

6. To determine the values of other trigonometrical ratios in terms of a given ratio. (The following method is valid only for acute angles).

Let $\quad \sin \theta = s = \dfrac{s}{1} = \dfrac{\text{Perp.}}{\text{Hyp.}} = \dfrac{p}{h}$.

Construct a triangle whose $p = s$ and $h = 1$ and hence the other side is $\sqrt{1-s^2}$. Now from the adjoining triangle, we can find the values of all the remaining ratios. Thus,

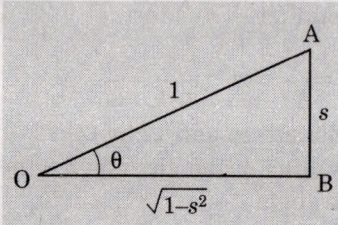

Fig. 2

$\cos \theta = \sqrt{1-s^2} = \sqrt{1-\sin^2 \theta}$,

$\tan \theta = \dfrac{s}{\sqrt{(1-s^2)}} = \dfrac{\sin \theta}{\sqrt{(1-\sin^2 \theta)}}$.

The remaining three ratios are reciprocals of the above three ratios.

Similarly if

$\quad \cos \theta = c = \dfrac{c}{1} = \dfrac{\text{Base}}{\text{Hyp.}} = \dfrac{b}{h}$,

we construct a triangle where $b = c$ and $h = 1$

so that $\quad p = \sqrt{1-c^2}$

Now from the triangle we can find the values of all the remaining ratios. Thus

$\quad \sin \theta = \sqrt{1-c^2} = \sqrt{1-\cos^2 \theta}$

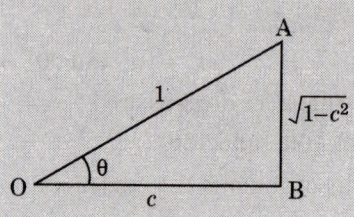

Fig. 3

$\tan \theta = \dfrac{\sqrt{1-c^2}}{c} = \dfrac{\sqrt{1-\cos^2 \theta}}{\cos \theta}$.

The remaining three ratios are reciprocals of the above three ratios.

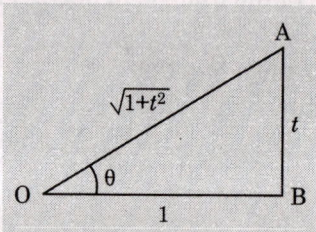

Fig. 4

In a similar manner if $\tan \theta = t = \dfrac{t}{1} = \dfrac{\text{Perp.}}{\text{Base}} = \dfrac{p}{b}$, we construct a triangle where $p = t, b = 1$ so that

$\quad h = \sqrt{1+t^2}$

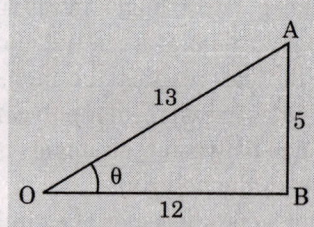

Fig. 5

$\therefore \quad \sin \theta = \dfrac{t}{\sqrt{(1+t^2)}} = \dfrac{\tan \theta}{\sqrt{(1+\tan^2 \theta)}}$

$\quad \cos \theta = \dfrac{1}{\sqrt{(1+t^2)}} = \dfrac{1}{\sqrt{(1+\tan^2 \theta)}}$ etc.

For example if $\sin \theta = 5/13$, then taking $p = 5$ and $h = 13$, the base

$\quad b = \sqrt{13^2 - 5^2} = 12$.

Hence $\quad \cos \theta = \dfrac{12}{13}$, $\tan \theta = \dfrac{5}{12}$ etc.

7. The following formulae of Algebra must be noted.

$a^2 + b^2 = (a+b)^2 - 2ab,$

$a^3 + b^3 = (a+b)^3 - 3ab\,(a+b),$

$a^3 - b^3 = (a-b)^3 + 3ab\,(a-b),$

$(a+b)\,(a-b) = a^2 - b^2$

$* \quad a+b+c = 0 \ \Rightarrow \ a^3 + b^3 + c^3 = 3abc$

Method of componendo and dividendo.

If $p/q = a/b$ then by componendo and dividendo we can write

$$\frac{p-q}{p+q} = \frac{a-b}{a+b} \quad \text{or} \quad \frac{q-p}{q+p} = \frac{b-a}{b+a}$$

or $\dfrac{p+q}{p-q} = \dfrac{a+b}{a-b}$ or $\dfrac{q+p}{q-p} = \dfrac{b+a}{b-a}$.

Note : Reference of the above formulae will be given in the solutions of problems.

Problem Set (2)

Questions based on three fundamental formulae $\sin^2 A + \cos^2 A = 1, 1 + \tan^2 A = \sec^2 A,$
$1 + \cot^2 A = \csc^2 A, \sin A$ **or** $\cos A \in [-1, 1], \sec A$ **or** $\csc A \notin\ ]-1, 1[.$ **Elimination of variable.**

1. (a) $2(\sin^6 A + \cos^6 A) - 3(\sin^4 A + \cos^4 A) + 1 = 0.$

Another form :
The expression

$$3\left[\sin^4\left(\frac{3}{2}\pi - \alpha\right) + \sin^4(3\pi + \alpha)\right]$$
$$- 2\left[\sin^6\left(\frac{1}{2}\pi + \alpha\right) + \sin^6(5\pi - \alpha)\right]$$

is equal to

(a) 0   (b) 1

(c) 3   (d) $\sin 4\alpha + \sin 6\alpha$

(e) none of these

(b) $\sin^6 A + \cos^6 A + 3\sin^2 A \cos^2 A = 1.$

2. (a)* $3(\sin x - \cos x)^4 + 6(\sin x + \cos x)^2$
$$+ 4(\sin^6 x + \cos^6 x)$$

is independent of x.

(b) $(\sin^8 A - \cos^8 A)$
$$= (\sin^2 A - \cos^2 A)(1 - 2\sin^2 A \cos^2 A).$$

3. (a) $(3 + \cos 4\theta)\cos 2\theta = 4(\cos^8 \theta - \sin^8 \theta)$

(J.E.W.B. 1995)

(b) If $\sin\theta + \cos\theta = a$, then find the values of $|\sin\theta - \cos\theta|$ and $\cos^4\theta + \sin^4\theta$.

4. (a) If $\sin\theta + \csc\theta = 2$, then
$\sin^2\theta + \csc^2\theta$ is equal to 2. T or F. *(M.N.R. 1990)*

(b) $f(x) = \cos^2 x + \sec^2 x \geq 2$. True or False.
or   Min. value of $f(x)$ is 2.

5. (a) Given $A = \sin^2\theta + \cos^4\theta$, then for all real θ,

(a) $1 \leq A \leq 2$ (b) $3/4 \leq A \leq 1$

(c) $13/16 \leq A \leq 1$ (d) $3/4 \leq A \leq 13/16$

(D.C.E. 1997)

(b) Let $A = \sin^8\theta + \cos^{14}\theta$, then for all real θ

(a) $A \geq 1$ (b) $0 < A \leq 1$

(c) $1/2 < A \leq 3/2$ (d) None of these.

(c) If θ, ϕ are acute, $\sin\theta = 1/2, \cos\phi = 1/3,$ then $(\theta + \phi) \in$

(a) $(\pi/3, \pi/2)$ (b) $(\pi/2, 2\pi/3)$

(c) $(2\pi/3, 5\pi/6)$ (d) $(5\pi/6, \pi)$

(Screening 2004)

6. (a) $(\tan A + \cot A)^2 = \sec^2 A + \csc^2 A$
$$= \sec^2 A \csc^2 A.$$

(b) $(1 + \tan\alpha\tan\beta)^2 + (\tan\alpha - \tan\beta)^2 = \sec^2\alpha\sec^2\beta$

(c) $\dfrac{\sec A - \tan A}{\sec A + \tan A} = 1 - 2\sec A\tan A + 2\tan^2 A.$

7. (a) $\dfrac{1}{\sec x - \tan x} - \dfrac{1}{\cos x} = \dfrac{1}{\cos x} - \dfrac{1}{\sec x + \tan x}$

(b) $(\sec A + \tan A - 1)(\sec A - \tan A + 1) - 2\tan A = 0$

8. (a) If $(\sec A + \tan A)(\sec B + \tan B)(\sec C + \tan C)$
$$= (\sec A - \tan A)(\sec B - \tan B)(\sec C - \tan C)$$
prove that each of the side is equal to ± 1.

(b) If $(1 + \sin A)(1 + \sin B)(1 + \sin C)$
$$= (1 - \sin A)(1 - \sin B)(1 - \sin C),$$
show that each side is equal to $\pm\cos A\cos B\cos C$.

9. (a) Let $f(\theta) = \sin\theta(\sin\theta + \sin 3\theta)$. Then $f(\theta)$

(a) ≥ 0 only when $\theta \geq 0$

(b) ≤ 0 for all real θ

(c) ≥ 0 for all real θ

(d) ≤ 0 only when $\theta \leq 0$ *(I.I.T. Sc. 2000)*

(b) The maximum value of
$$(\cos\alpha_1).(\cos\alpha_2)\ldots(\cos\alpha_n),$$
under the restrictions $0 \leq \alpha_1, \alpha_2, \ldots \alpha_n \leq \dfrac{\pi}{2}$ and
$(\cot\alpha_1).(\cot\alpha_2)\ldots(\cot\alpha_n) = 1$ is

(a) $\dfrac{1}{2^{n/2}}$ (b) $\dfrac{1}{2^n}$

(c) $\dfrac{1}{2n}$ (d) 1   *(I.I.T. Sc. 2001)*

10. (a) $\sqrt{\left(\dfrac{1 - \sin A}{1 + \sin A}\right)} = \sec A - \tan A,$

(b) $\sqrt{\left(\dfrac{1 + \cos\theta}{1 - \cos\theta}\right)} = \csc\theta + \cot\theta.$

11. (a)* If $\sin\theta + \sin^2\theta = 1$, then prove that
$$\cos^{12}\theta + 3\cos^{10}\theta + 3\cos^8\theta + \cos^6\theta - 1 = 0$$

(b)* If $\sin\theta + \sin^2\theta + \sin^3\theta = 1$, then
$$\cos^6\theta - 4\cos^4\theta + 8\cos^2\theta = \ldots\ldots$$

12. (a) $\sec^4 A(1 - \sin^4 A) - 2\tan^2 A = 1.$

(b) $\tan^2 A - \sin^2 A = \sin^4 A\sec^2 A = \tan^2 A\sin^2 A.$

(c) $\dfrac{\cot A + \tan B}{\cot B + \tan A} = \cot A\tan B.$

13. (a) $(\sin A + \cos A)(\tan A + \cot A) = \sec A + \operatorname{cosec} A$

(b) $\dfrac{\cos A \operatorname{cosec} A - \sin A \sec A}{\cos A + \sin A} = \operatorname{cosec} A - \sec A.$

14. (a) $(1 + \cot A - \operatorname{cosec} A)(1 + \tan A + \sec A) = 2$

(b) $(\operatorname{cosec} \theta - \sin \theta)(\sec \theta - \cos \theta)(\tan \theta + \cot \theta) = 1$

15. (a) $\dfrac{\tan A + \sec A - 1}{\tan A - \sec A + 1} = \dfrac{1 + \sin A}{\cos A}.$

(b) $\dfrac{\cot^2 \theta (\sec \theta - 1)}{1 + \sin \theta} = \sec^2 \theta \cdot \dfrac{1 - \sin \theta}{1 + \sec \theta}.$

16. (a) $\dfrac{\sec x + 1 - \tan x}{\tan x - \sec x + 1} = \dfrac{1 + \cos x}{\sin x}.$

(b) $\dfrac{\cos A}{1 - \tan A} + \dfrac{\sin A}{1 - \cot A} = \sin A + \cos A.$

17.* If $t_n = \sin^n \theta + \cos^n \theta$, then $\dfrac{t_3 - t_5}{t_1} = \dfrac{t_5 - t_7}{t_3}$

18. (a) $\dfrac{\tan A}{1 - \cot A} + \dfrac{\cot A}{1 - \tan A} = \sec A \operatorname{cosec} A + 1.$

(b) $(\sin \alpha + \operatorname{cosec} \alpha)^2 + (\cos \alpha + \sec \alpha)^2$
$$= \tan^2 \alpha + \cot^2 \alpha + 7$$

19. (a) $(1 + \cot A + \tan A)(\sin A - \cos A)$
$$= \dfrac{\sec A}{\operatorname{cosec}^2 A} - \dfrac{\operatorname{cosec} A}{\sec^2 A}$$

(b) $(\sec A - \operatorname{cosec} A)(1 + \tan A + \cot A)$
$$= \tan A \sec A - \cot A \operatorname{cosec} A.$$

20. $\dfrac{2 \sin \theta \tan \theta (1 - \tan \theta) + 2 \sin \theta \sec^2 \theta}{(1 + \tan \theta)^2} = \dfrac{2 \sin \theta}{(1 + \tan \theta)}$

21. $(\tan \theta + \operatorname{cosec} \phi)^2 - (\cot \phi - \sec \theta)^2$
$$= 2 \tan \theta \cot \phi (\operatorname{cosec} \theta + \sec \phi)$$

22. (a) $\left(\dfrac{1 + \sin \theta - \cos \theta}{1 + \sin \theta + \cos \theta}\right)^2 = \dfrac{1 - \cos \theta}{1 + \cos \theta}.$

(b) If $\dfrac{2 \sin \theta}{1 + \cos \theta + \sin \theta} = y$, then
$$\dfrac{1 - \cos \theta + \sin \theta}{1 + \sin \theta} \text{ is also } y.$$

23. (a)* $\left(\dfrac{1}{\sec^2 \alpha - \cos^2 \alpha} + \dfrac{1}{\operatorname{cosec}^2 \alpha - \sin^2 \alpha}\right)$
$$\times \sin^2 \alpha \cos^2 \alpha = \dfrac{1 - \sin^2 \alpha \cos^2 \alpha}{2 + \sin^2 \alpha \cos^2 \alpha}$$

(b) $(\operatorname{cosec} \theta - \sec \theta)(\cot \theta - \tan \theta)$
$$= (\operatorname{cosec} \theta + \sec \theta)(\sec \theta \operatorname{cosec} \theta - 2)$$

24. (a) If $\tan A + \sin A = m$ and $\tan A - \sin A = n,$ then show that $m^2 - n^2 = 4\sqrt{mn}.$

(b)* Eliminate θ from the relations $a \sec \theta = 1 - b \tan \theta$ and $a^2 \sec^2 \theta = 5 + b^2 \tan^2 \theta$

25. (a)* If $\operatorname{cosec} \theta - \sin \theta = m,$ $\sec \theta - \cos \theta = n,$ eliminate $\theta.$

*Another form :

If $\operatorname{cosec} \theta - \sin \theta = a^3,$ $\sec \theta - \cos \theta = b^3,$ then
$$a^2 b^2 (a^2 + b^2) = 1.$$

(b)* If $\cot \theta + \tan \theta = x,$ $\sec \theta - \cos \theta = y,$ eliminate $\theta.$

(c)* If $c \cos^3 \theta + 3c \cos \theta \sin^2 \theta = m,$
$c \sin^3 \theta + 3c \cos^2 \theta \sin \theta = n,$ then prove that
$(m + n)^{2/3} + (m - n)^{2/3} = 2c^{2/3}.$

26. (a) If $\cos x + \sin x = \sqrt{2} \cos x,$ prove that
$\cos x - \sin x = \sqrt{2} \sin x.$

(b) If $3 \sin \theta + 5 \cos \theta = 5,$ show that
$5 \sin \theta - 3 \cos \theta = \pm 3.$

(c) If $a \cos \theta + b \sin \theta = p,$ $a \sin \theta - b \cos \theta = q,$ prove that $a^2 + b^2 = p^2 + q^2.$ **(Remember)**

27. (a)* If $a \cos \theta - b \sin \theta = c,$ show that
$$a \sin \theta + b \cos \theta = \pm \sqrt{a^2 + b^2 - c^2}$$

(b) If $a \sin \theta + b \cos \theta = c,$ then prove that
$$\dfrac{a - b \tan \theta}{b + a \tan \theta} = \pm \dfrac{\sqrt{a^2 + b^2 - c^2}}{c}$$

28. If $\tan^2 \theta = (1 - e^2),$ prove that
$$\sec \theta + \tan^3 \theta \operatorname{cosec} \theta = (2 - e^2)^{3/2}.$$

29.* If $\dfrac{ax}{\cos \theta} + \dfrac{by}{\sin \theta} = (a^2 - b^2),$ and
$\dfrac{ax \sin \theta}{\cos^2 \theta} - \dfrac{by \cos \theta}{\sin^2 \theta} = 0,$ show that
$(ax)^{2/3} + (by)^{2/3} = (a^2 - b^2)^{2/3}.$

30. (a) If $\sin \theta = \dfrac{m^2 - n^2}{m^2 + n^2},$ determine the values of $\tan \theta, \sec \theta$ and $\operatorname{cosec} \theta.$

(b) If $\tan \theta = \dfrac{2x(x + 1)}{2x + 1},$ determine $\sin \theta$ and $\cos \theta.$

31. (a) If $\cos \theta = \dfrac{2x}{1 + x^2},$ find the values of $\tan \theta$ and $\operatorname{cosec} \theta.$

(b) If $\sec x = p + 1/4p,$ then $\sec x + \tan x = 2p$ or $1/2p$

(c) If $\sec \theta + \tan \theta = p,$ obtain the values of $\sec \theta, \tan \theta, \sin \theta$ in terms of $p.$

32. If $\dfrac{\cos \alpha}{\cos \beta} = a,$ $\dfrac{\sin \alpha}{\sin \beta} = b,$ then $(a^2 - b^2) \sin^2 \beta = a^2 - 1$

33. If $\tan \theta = p/q,$ show that
$$\dfrac{p \sin \theta - q \cos \theta}{p \sin \theta + q \cos \theta} = \dfrac{p^2 - q^2}{p^2 + q^2}.$$

34.* Is the equation $\sec^2 \theta = \dfrac{4xy}{(x + y)^2}$ possible for real values of x and y ?
If not, then find out a relation between x and y so that it may be possible.

35.* If $m^2 + m'^2 + 2mm' \cos \theta = 1,$
$n^2 + n'^2 + 2nn' \cos \theta = 1,$
and $mn + m'n' + (mn' + m'n) \cos \theta = 0,$
prove that $m^2 + n^2 = \operatorname{cosec}^2 \theta.$

36. (a) If $\tan\theta = \dfrac{p}{q}$ and $\theta = 3\phi\ \left(0 < \theta < \dfrac{\pi}{2}\right)$, prove

that $\dfrac{p}{\sin\phi} - \dfrac{q}{\cos\phi} = 2\sqrt{(p^2 + q^2)}$

(b) If $\dfrac{\sin^4 x}{2} + \dfrac{\cos^4 x}{3} = \dfrac{1}{5}$, then

(I.I.T. 2009)

(a) $\tan^2 x = \dfrac{2}{3}$

(b) $\dfrac{\sin^8 x}{8} + \dfrac{\cos^8 x}{27} = \dfrac{1}{125}$

(c) $\tan^2 x = \dfrac{1}{3}$

(d) $\dfrac{\sin^8 x}{8} + \dfrac{\cos^8 x}{27} = \dfrac{2}{125}$

Solutions to Problem Set (2)

1. (a) We know that $\sin^2\theta + \cos^2\theta = 1$ and

$a^3 + b^3 = (a+b)^3 - 3ab(a+b)$,

$a^2 + b^2 = (a+b)^2 - 2ab$,

$\therefore$ L.H.S. $= 2\{(\sin^2 A + \cos^2 A)^3$

$\qquad - 3\sin^2 A\cos^2 A(\sin^2 A + \cos^2 A)\}$

$\qquad - 3\{(\sin^2 A + \cos^2 A)^2 - 2\sin^2 A\cos^2 A\} + 1$

$= 2 - 6\sin^2 A\cos^2 A - 3 + 6\sin^2 A\cos^2 A + 1$

$= 3 - 3 = 0$.

Another form :

Ans. (b). by part (a).

L.H.S. $= 3[\cos^4\alpha + \sin^4\alpha] - 2[\cos^6\alpha + \sin^6\alpha]$

(b) Proceed as in (a).

2. (a) We have as in Q. 1 (a) and (b), L.H.S.

$= 3[(1 - 2\sin x\cos x)^2] + 6(1 + 2\sin x\cos x)$

$\qquad + 4[(\sin^2 x + \cos^2 x)^2 - 3\sin^2 x\cos^2 x]$

$= 3(1 - 2\sin x\cos x)^2 + 6(1 + 2\sin x\cos x)$

$\qquad\qquad + 4(1 - 3\sin^2 x\cos^2 x)$

$= 3(1 - 4\sin x\cos x + 4\sin^2 x\cos^2 x) + 6$

$\qquad + 12\sin x\cos x + 4 - 12\sin^2 x\cos^2 x$

$= 13$, which is independent of x.

(b) Do yourself.

3. (a) R.H.S. $= 4.1.(\cos^2\theta - \sin^2\theta)(\cos^4\theta + \sin^4\theta)$

$= 4\cos 2\theta(1 - 2\sin^2\theta\cos^2\theta)$

$= 4\cos 2\theta\left[1 - \dfrac{1}{2}\sin^2 2\theta\right]$

$= 4\cos 2\theta\left[1 - \dfrac{1}{2}\dfrac{(1 - \cos 4\theta)}{2}\right]$

$= \cos 2\theta[3 + \cos 4\theta]$

(b) Squaring, we get

$1 + \sin 2\theta = a^2 \quad\therefore\quad \sin 2\theta = a^2 - 1$

$|\sin\theta - \cos\theta| = \sqrt{(\sin\theta - \cos\theta)^2}$

$\qquad = \sqrt{1 - \sin 2\theta} = \sqrt{2 - a^2}$

$\sin^4\theta + \cos^4\theta = 1 - 2\sin^2\theta\cos^2\theta$

$\qquad = 1 - \dfrac{1}{2}\sin^2 2\theta = 1 - \dfrac{1}{2}(a^2 - 1)^2$

4. (a) Ans. True.

$\sin^2\theta + \text{cosec}^2\theta = (\sin\theta + \text{cosec}\,\theta)^2$

$\qquad\qquad\qquad\qquad - 2\sin\theta\,\text{cosec}\,\theta$

$\qquad = 2^2 - 2.1 = 2. \qquad [\because \sin\theta + \text{cosec}\,\theta = 2]$

(b) Ans. True.

L.H.S. $= (\cos x - \sec x)^2 + 2\cos x.\sec x$

$\qquad = 2 + (\cos x - \sec x)^2$

$\therefore \quad f(x) \geq 2$

Similarly, min. value of $\text{cosec}^2 x + \sin^2 x$ and $\cot^2 x + \tan^2 x$ is also 2.

5. (a) Ans. (b).

$\sin^2\theta + \cos^4\theta = \sin^2\theta + \cos^2\theta.\cos^2\theta$

$\qquad \leq \sin^2\theta + \cos^2\theta = 1 \qquad [\because \cos^2\theta \leq 1]$

Thus $A = \sin^2\theta + \cos^4\theta \leq 1$.

Again $A = \sin^2\theta + \cos^4\theta = 1 - \cos^2\theta + \cos^4\theta$

$\qquad = 1 + (\cos^4\theta - \cos^2\theta) = 1 + \left(\cos^2\theta - \dfrac{1}{2}\right)^2 - \dfrac{1}{4}$

$\qquad = \dfrac{3}{4} + \left(\cos^2\theta - \dfrac{1}{2}\right)^2 \geq \dfrac{3}{4}$

Hence $3/4 \leq A \leq 1 \implies$ (b).

(b) Ans. (b). Evidently $A > 0$ ...(1)

Again $\sin^2\theta < 1 \quad\therefore\quad \sin^4\theta < \sin^2\theta$

$\sin^6\theta < \sin^4\theta < \sin^2\theta$

$\sin^8\theta < \sin^4\theta < \sin^2\theta$ ...(2)

Similarly, $\cos^{14}\theta < \cos^2\theta$ ...(3)

Adding (2) and (1), we get

$\sin^8\theta + \cos^{14}\theta < \sin^2\theta + \cos^2\theta = 1$ ...(4)

(c) Ans. (b).

$\sin\theta = \dfrac{1}{2} \qquad\qquad \therefore\quad \dfrac{\pi}{6} = \theta = \dfrac{\pi}{6}$ ...(1)

$\cos\phi = \dfrac{1}{3}$

Now $\dfrac{1}{2} > \dfrac{1}{3} > 0$ or $\cos\dfrac{\pi}{3} > \cos\phi > \cos\dfrac{\pi}{2}$

$\therefore \qquad \dfrac{\pi}{3} < \phi < \dfrac{\pi}{2}$ ...(2)

Adding (1) and (2), $\dfrac{\pi}{2} < \theta + \phi < \dfrac{2\pi}{3}$

6. (a), (b), (c). Do yourself.

In part (c), multiply by conjugate of D^r.

7. (a) We have to prove that

$\dfrac{1}{\sec x - \tan x} + \dfrac{1}{\sec x + \tan x} = \dfrac{2}{\cos x}$

L.H.S. $= (\sec x + \tan x) + (\sec x - \tan x)$

$= 2 \sec x = \dfrac{2}{\cos x} = $ R.H.S. by § 2 (2), P. 506

(b) L.H.S. $= [\sec A + (\tan A - 1)].$

$[\sec A - (\tan A - 1)] - 2 \tan A$

$= \sec^2 A - (\tan A - 1)^2 - 2 \tan A$

$= \sec^2 A - \tan^2 A - 1 + 2 \tan A - 2 \tan A$

$= 1 - 1 = 0 = $ R.H.S.

8. (a) Denoting the left hand and right hand sides by x and y,

we have $x = y \;\Rightarrow\; x^2 = xy$

or $x^2 = (\sec^2 A - \tan^2 A)(\sec^2 B - \tan^2 B)$

$(\sec^2 C - \tan^2 C) = 1.$

∴ $x = \pm 1 = y.$

(b) If $x = y$, then $x^2 = xy.$

∴ $x^2 = (1 - \sin^2 A)(1 - \sin^2 B)(1 - \sin^2 C)$

$= \cos^2 A \cos^2 B \cos^2 C$

∴ $x = \pm \cos A \cos B \cos C = y.$

9. (a) Ans. (c).

$f(\theta) = \dfrac{1}{2} [(1 - \cos 2\theta) + (\cos 2\theta - \cos 4\theta)]$

$= \dfrac{1}{2}(1 - \cos 4\theta) = \sin^2 2\theta \geq 0 \;\forall\;$ real $\theta.$

(b) Ans. (a).

The given relation implies that

$\displaystyle\prod_{i=1}^{n} \cos \alpha_i = \prod_{i=1}^{n} \sin \alpha_i$

∴ $\displaystyle\prod_{i}^{n} \cos^2 \alpha_i = \prod_{i=1}^{n} \cos \alpha_i \sin \alpha_i$

$= \displaystyle\prod_{i=1}^{n} \left(\dfrac{\sin 2\alpha_i}{2}\right)$

where $0 \leq \alpha_i < \dfrac{\pi}{2}$ or $0 \leq 2\alpha_i \leq \pi$

∴ $\displaystyle\prod_{i=1}^{n} \cos^2 \alpha_i = \dfrac{1}{2^n}$ as max value of $\sin \theta = 1$

or $\displaystyle\prod_{i=1}^{n} \cos \alpha_i = \dfrac{1}{2^{n/2}}$

10. (a) L.H.S.

$= \sqrt{\dfrac{(1 - \sin A)^2}{(1 - \sin^2 A)}} = \dfrac{1 - \sin A}{\cos A} = \dfrac{1}{\cos A} - \dfrac{\sin A}{\cos A}$

$= \sec A - \tan A$

(b) Do yourself.

11. (a) Given $\sin \theta = 1 - \sin^2 \theta = \cos^2 \theta.$ ...(1)

L.H.S. $= \cos^6 \theta [\cos^2 \theta + 1]^3 - 1$

$= \sin^3 \theta (1 + \sin \theta)^3 - 1$ by (1)

$= (\sin \theta + \sin^2 \theta)^3 - 1 = 1^3 - 1 = 0.$ by (1)

(b) Ans. 4.

$\sin \theta (1 + \sin^2 \theta) = 1 - \sin^2 \theta = \cos^2 \theta$

Square and change in terms of $\cos \theta.$

$(1 - c^2)(2 - c^2)^2 = c^4.$ Simplify.

12 to 14. Do yourself.

Change in terms of $\sin A$ and $\cos A.$

15. (a) We know that $\sec^2 A - \tan^2 A = 1$; hence

L.H.S. $= \dfrac{(\tan A + \sec A) - (\sec^2 A - \tan^2 A)}{\tan A - \sec A + 1}$

$= \dfrac{(\tan A + \sec A)[1 - (\sec A - \tan A)]}{\tan A - \sec A + 1}$

$= \tan A + \sec A = \dfrac{\sin A + 1}{\cos A}.$

(b) L.H.S. $= \cot^2 \theta . \dfrac{\sec \theta - 1}{1 + \sin \theta} . \dfrac{\sec \theta + 1}{\sec \theta + 1}$

$= \dfrac{\cot^2 \theta (\sec^2 \theta - 1)}{(\sec \theta + 1)(1 + \sin \theta)}$

$= \dfrac{\cot^2 \theta \tan^2 \theta}{(\sec \theta + 1)} . \dfrac{1 - \sin \theta}{1 - \sin^2 \theta}$

$= \dfrac{1}{1 + \sec \theta} . \dfrac{1 - \sin \theta}{\cos^2 \theta} = \sec^2 \theta . \dfrac{1 - \sin \theta}{1 + \sec \theta}.$

16. (a) Change in terms of sin and cos .

(b) Do yourself. Change in terms of $\sin A$ and $\cos A.$

17. L.H.S. $= [(\sin^3 \theta + \cos^3 \theta) - (\sin^5 \theta + \cos^5 \theta)]$

$\div (\sin \theta + \cos \theta)$

$= [\sin^3 \theta (1 - \sin^2 \theta) + \cos^3 \theta (1 - \cos^2 \theta)]$

$\div (\sin \theta + \cos \theta)$

$= \sin^2 \theta \cos^2 \theta [\sin \theta + \cos \theta] \div (\sin \theta + \cos \theta)$

$= \sin^2 \theta \cos^2 \theta.$

Similarly, R.H.S. $= \sin^2 \theta \cos^2 \theta.$

18. (a) L.H.S.

$= \dfrac{\sin^2 A}{\cos A (\sin A - \cos A)} - \dfrac{\cos^2 A}{\sin A (\sin A - \cos A)}$

$= \dfrac{\sin^3 A - \cos^3 A}{\sin A \cos A (\sin A - \cos A)}$

$= \dfrac{\sin^2 A + \cos^2 A + \sin A \cos A}{\sin A \cos A}$

$= \left(\dfrac{1 + \sin A \cos A}{\sin A \cos A}\right)$

$= \dfrac{1}{\sin A \cos A} + 1 = \sec A \operatorname{cosec} A + 1.$

(b) Do yourself. Open, $\sec^2 \alpha = 1 + \tan^2 \alpha$, etc.

19. (a) L.H.S. $= (\sin A - \cos A)\left(1 + \dfrac{\cos A}{\sin A} + \dfrac{\sin A}{\cos A}\right)$

$= \dfrac{1}{\sin A \cos A}(\sin A - \cos A)$

$(\sin^2 A + \cos^2 A + \sin A \cos A)$

$$= \frac{\sin^3 A - \cos^3 A}{\sin A \cos A} = \frac{\sin^2 A}{\cos A} - \frac{\cos^2 A}{\sin A}$$

$$= \frac{\sec A}{\text{cosec}^2 A} - \frac{\text{cosec } A}{\sec^2 A}.$$

(b) Change in terms of sin A and cos A.

20. L.H.S. $= \dfrac{2\sin\theta\,[\tan\theta - \tan^2\theta + \sec^2\theta]}{(1+\tan\theta)^2}$

$$= \frac{2\sin\theta\,(\tan\theta + 1)}{(1+\tan\theta)^2} = \frac{2\sin\theta}{1+\tan\theta}$$

21. L.H.S. $= (\tan^2\theta + \text{cosec}^2\phi + 2\tan\theta\,\text{cosec}\,\phi)$

$$- (\cot^2\phi + \sec^2\theta - 2\cot\phi\sec\theta)$$

$$= (\text{cosec}^2\phi - \cot^2\phi) - (\sec^2\theta - \tan^2\theta)$$

$$+ 2\tan\theta\cot\phi\left(\frac{\text{cosec}\,\phi}{\cot\phi} + \frac{\sec\theta}{\tan\theta}\right)$$

$$= 1 - 1 + 2\tan\theta\cot\phi\,[1/\cos\phi + 1/\sin\theta]$$

$$= 2\tan\theta\cot\phi\,(\sec\phi + \text{cosec}\,\theta).$$

22. (a) L.H.S.

$$= \frac{(1+\sin\theta)^2 + \cos^2\theta - 2\cos\theta\,(1+\sin\theta)}{(1+\sin\theta)^2 + \cos^2\theta + 2\cos\theta\,(1+\sin\theta)}$$

$$= \frac{\begin{array}{c}1+\sin^2\theta + \cos^2\theta + 2\sin\theta\\ -2\cos\theta\,(1+\sin\theta)\end{array}}{\begin{array}{c}1+\sin^2\theta + \cos^2\theta + 2\sin\theta\\ +2\cos\theta\,(1+\sin\theta)\end{array}}$$

$$= \frac{2\,(1+\sin\theta) - 2\cos\theta\,(1+\sin\theta)}{2\,(1+\sin\theta) + 2\cos\theta\,(1+\sin\theta)} = \frac{1-\cos\theta}{1+\cos\theta}$$

We have cancelled $2\,(1+\sin\theta)$ from N^r and D^r.

(b) Multiply and divide T_2 by $(1+\cos\theta + \sin\theta)$

$$\therefore\quad T_2 = \frac{(1+\sin\theta)^2 - \cos^2\theta}{(1+\sin\theta)\,(1+\cos\theta + \sin\theta)}$$

$$= \frac{(1+\sin\theta)\,[1+\sin\theta - (1-\sin\theta)]}{(1+\sin\theta)\,(1+\cos\theta + \sin\theta)}$$

$$= T_1 = y.$$

Note : You may multiply and divide T_1 by $1-\cos\theta + \sin\theta$.

23. (a) $\dfrac{1}{\sec^2\alpha - \cos^2\alpha} = \dfrac{\cos^2\alpha}{1-\cos^4\alpha}$

$$= \frac{\cos^2\alpha}{(1-\cos^2\alpha)\,(1+\cos^2\alpha)}$$

$$= \frac{\cos^2\alpha}{\sin^2\alpha\,(1+\cos^2\alpha)}$$

Similarly,

$$\frac{1}{\text{cosec}^2\alpha - \sin^2\alpha} = \frac{\sin^2\alpha}{\cos^2\alpha\,(1+\sin^2\alpha)}$$

Hence,

L.H.S. $= \Bigg[\dfrac{\cos^2\alpha}{\sin^2\alpha\,(1+\cos^2\alpha)}$

$$+ \frac{\sin^2\alpha}{\cos^2\alpha\,(1+\sin^2\alpha)}\Bigg]\sin^2\alpha\cos^2\alpha$$

$$= \frac{\cos^4\alpha}{1+\cos^2\alpha} + \frac{\sin^4\alpha}{1+\sin^2\alpha}$$

$$= [\sin^2\alpha\cos^2\alpha\,(\sin^2\alpha + \cos^2\alpha)$$

$$+ (\cos^4\alpha + \sin^4\alpha)]$$

$$\div (1+\cos^2\alpha + \sin^2\alpha + \cos^2\alpha\sin^2\alpha)$$

$$= \frac{\sin^2\alpha\cos^2\alpha + (\cos^2\alpha + \sin^2\alpha)^2 - 2\sin^2\alpha\cos^2\alpha}{2+\cos^2\alpha\sin^2\alpha}$$

$$= \frac{1-\sin^2\alpha\cos^2\alpha}{2+\cos^2\alpha\sin^2\alpha} = \text{R.H.S.}$$

(b) L.H.S. $= \dfrac{\cos\theta - \sin\theta}{\sin\theta\cos\theta} \cdot \dfrac{\cos^2\theta - \sin^2\theta}{\sin\theta\cos\theta}$,

on changing to sin θ and cos θ,

$$= \frac{(\cos\theta - \sin\theta)^2}{\sin\theta\cos\theta} \cdot \frac{\cos\theta + \sin\theta}{\sin\theta\cos\theta}.$$

$$= \frac{1-2\sin\theta\cos\theta}{\sin\theta\cos\theta}\left[\frac{1}{\sin\theta} + \frac{1}{\cos\theta}\right]$$

$$= (\text{cosec}\,\theta\sec\theta - 2)\,(\text{cosec}\,\theta + \sec\theta) = \text{R.H.S.}$$

24. (a) $m^2 - n^2 = (m+n)\,(m-n)$

$$= 2\tan A \,.\, 2\sin A = 4\tan A\sin A,$$

$$4\sqrt{(mn)} = 4\sqrt{(\tan^2 A - \sin^2 A)}$$

$$= 4\sin A\sqrt{(\sec^2 A - 1)} = 4\sin A\tan A.$$

$$\therefore\quad m^2 - n^2 = 4\sqrt{(mn)}.$$

(b) Squaring first relation and putting in 2nd,

$$1-2b\tan\theta + b^2\tan^2\theta = 5 + b^2\tan^2\theta$$

which gives $\tan\theta = -2/b$.

Putting this value of $\tan\theta$ in the second given relation , we get

$$a^2\,[1+(4/b^2)] = 5 + b^2 \,.\,(4/b^2) = 9$$

or $\quad a^2 b^2 + 4a^2 = 9b^2$.

25. (a) $\text{cosec}\,\theta - \sin\theta = m$ and $\sec\theta - \cos\theta = n$.

or $\quad (1/\sin\theta) - \sin\theta = m$ and $(1/\cos\theta) - \cos\theta = n$

or $\quad \dfrac{\cos^2\theta}{\sin\theta} = m$ and $\dfrac{\sin^2\theta}{\cos\theta} = n$.

$$mn = \cos\theta\sin\theta \text{ and } \cos^2\theta = m\sin\theta$$

$$\therefore\quad \cos^3\theta = m\sin\theta\cos\theta = m\,(mn)$$

$$\therefore\quad m^2 n = \cos^3\theta \text{ and } mn^2 = \sin^3\theta$$

Since $\quad \sin^2\theta + \cos^2\theta = 1$

$$\therefore\quad (m^2 n)^{2/3} + (mn^2)^{2/3} = 1$$

Another form :

Put $m = a^3, n = b^3$ in part (a).

(b) $(1/\tan\theta) + \tan\theta = x, (1/\cos\theta) - \cos\theta = y.$

or $\quad \dfrac{\sec^2\theta}{\tan\theta} = x, \dfrac{\sin^2\theta}{\cos\theta} = y.$

$\quad x = \dfrac{1}{\sin\theta\cos\theta}, y = \dfrac{\sin^2\theta}{\cos\theta}$

$\therefore \quad x^2 y = \dfrac{1}{\cos^3\theta} = \sec^3\theta, \quad xy^2 = \tan^3\theta$

Since $\quad \sec^2\theta - \tan^2\theta = 1$

$\therefore \quad (x^2 y)^{2/3} - (xy^2)^{2/3} = 1.$

(c) Adding the given relations, we get

$\quad c(\sin\theta + \cos\theta)^3 = m + n$

or $\quad c^{2/3}(\sin\theta + \cos\theta)^2 = (m+n)^{2/3}.$ ...(1)

Similarly, by subtracting, we shall get

$\quad c^{2/3}(\sin\theta - \cos\theta)^2 = (m-n)^{2/3}$ ...(2)

Now add (1) and (2).

26. (a) Squaring, $1 + 2\sin x\cos x = 2(1 - \sin^2 x)$

or $\quad 2\sin^2 x = 1 - 2\sin x\cos x = (\cos x - \sin x)^2$

$\therefore \quad \sqrt{2}\sin x = \cos x - \sin x.$

(b) Squaring $3\sin\theta + 5\cos\theta = 5$, we get

$\quad 9\sin^2\theta + 25\cos^2\theta + 30\sin\theta\cos\theta = 25$

or $\quad 9(1 - \cos^2\theta) + 25(1 - \sin^2\theta)$
$$\qquad\qquad\qquad + 30\sin\theta\cos\theta = 25$$

or $\quad 9 = 9\cos^2\theta + 25\sin^2\theta - 30\sin\theta\cos\theta$

$\quad = (5\sin\theta - 3\cos\theta)^2$

$\therefore \quad 5\sin\theta - 3\cos\theta = \pm 3.$

(c) Square and add and put $\sin^2\theta + \cos^2\theta = 1.$

27. (a) Square $a\cos\theta - b\sin\theta = c.$ Then

$\therefore \quad a^2\cos^2\theta + b^2\sin^2\theta - 2ab\sin\theta\cos\theta = c^2$

or $\quad a^2(1 - \sin^2\theta) + b^2(1 - \cos^2\theta)$
$$\qquad\qquad\qquad - 2ab\sin\theta\cos\theta = c^2$$

$\therefore \quad a^2 + b^2 - c^2 = a^2\sin^2\theta + b^2\cos^2\theta$
$$\qquad\qquad\qquad + 2ab\sin\theta\cos\theta$$

or $\quad (a\sin\theta + b\cos\theta)^2 = a^2 + b^2 - c^2$

$\therefore \quad a\sin\theta + b\cos\theta = \pm\sqrt{(a^2 + b^2 - c^2)}$

(b) L.H.S. $= \dfrac{a\cos\theta - b\sin\theta}{a\sin\theta + b\cos\theta} = \dfrac{N^r}{c}$ by part (a).

28. $\tan^2\theta = 1 - e^2$ (given).

Now $\sec\theta + \tan^3\theta\,\mathrm{cosec}\,\theta$

$\quad = \sec\theta(1 + \tan^3\theta\,\mathrm{cosec}\,\theta/\sec\theta)$

$\quad = \sec\theta(1 + \tan^3\theta\cot\theta) = \sec^3\theta$

$\quad = (1 + \tan^2\theta)^{3/2} = (1 + 1 - e^2)^{3/2} = (2 - e^2)^{3/2}.$

29. From the second relation, we get

$\dfrac{\sin^2\theta\sin\theta}{\cos^2\theta\cos\theta} = \dfrac{by}{ax}$

$\tan^3\theta = by/ax \therefore \tan\theta = (by)^{1/3}/(ax)^{1/3}$

$\therefore \quad \sin\theta = \dfrac{(by)^{1/3}}{[(ax)^{2/3} + (by)^{2/3}]^{1/2}},$

$\quad \cos\theta = \dfrac{(ax)^{1/3}}{[(ax)^{2/3} + (by)^{2/3}]^{1/2}}$

Putting for $\sin\theta$ and $\cos\theta$ in

$\dfrac{ax}{\cos\theta} + \dfrac{by}{\sin\theta} = a^2 - b^2,$ we get

$[(ax)^{2/3} + (by)^{2/3}]^{1/2}[ax/(ax)^{1/3} + by/(by)^{1/3}]$
$$\qquad\qquad\qquad\qquad = a^2 - b^2$$

or $[(ax)^{2/3} + (by)^{2/3}]^{1/2}[(ax)^{2/3} + (by)^{2/3}] = a^2 - b^2$

or $[(ax)^{2/3} + (by)^{2/3}]^{3/2} = a^2 - b^2$

or $(ax)^{2/3} + (by)^{2/3} = (a^2 - b^2)^{2/3}.$

30. (a) We know that

$(m^2 + n^2)^2 - (m^2 - n^2)^2 = 4m^2 n^2.$

$\therefore \quad \tan\theta = \dfrac{m^2 - n^2}{2mn}, \quad \sec\theta = \dfrac{m^2 + n^2}{2mn},$

$\quad \mathrm{cosec}\,\theta = \dfrac{m^2 + n^2}{m^2 - n^2}.$

You have to make a triangle whose height is $m^2 - n^2$ and hypotenuse is $m^2 + n^2$ so that its base is $2mn$ etc. as explained in § 2 (6), P. 508.

(b) $\tan\theta = \dfrac{2x(x+1)}{2x+1}.$

Make a triangle whose height is

$\quad PM = 2x(x+1)$ and base $OM = 2x + 1.$

$\therefore \quad$ hypotenuse $OP = \sqrt{(OM^2 + PM^2)},$

$\quad = [4x^2(x+1)^2 + (2x+1)^2]^{1/2}$

or $\quad OP = [4x^4 + 8x^3 + 8x^2 + 4x + 1]^{1/2}$

or $\quad OP = [(2x^2)^2 + (2x)^2 + 1^2 + 2(2x)(2x^2)$
$$\qquad\qquad + 2(2x).1 + 2.1(2x^2)]^{1/2}$$

$\quad = [(2x^2 + 2x + 1)^2]^{1/2} = 2x^2 + 2x + 1.$

$\sin\theta = PM/OP$ and $\cos\theta = OM/OP$ gives

$\sin\theta = \dfrac{2x(x+1)}{2x^2 + 2x + 1}, \cos\theta = \dfrac{2x+1}{2x^2 + 2x + 1}.$

31. (a) $\tan\theta = \dfrac{1 - x^2}{2x}, \mathrm{cosec}\,\theta = \dfrac{1 + x^2}{1 - x^2}.$

(b) $\tan x = \sqrt{(\sec^2 x - 1)} = \pm(p - 1/4p)$ etc.

(c) We know that $\sec^2\theta - \tan^2\theta = 1.$

Also $\sec\theta + \tan\theta = p$ (given).

$\therefore \quad \sec\theta - \tan\theta = 1/(\sec\theta + \tan\theta) = 1/p.$

Adding, we get $\quad \sec\theta = \dfrac{1}{2}\left(p + \dfrac{1}{p}\right);$

Subtracting, we get $\tan\theta = \dfrac{1}{2}\left(p - \dfrac{1}{p}\right)$.

Dividing, we get $\sin\theta = \dfrac{p^2 - 1}{p^2 + 1}$.

32. Eliminate α by $\sin^2\alpha + \cos^2\alpha = 1$ and change $\cos^2\beta$ to $\sin^2\beta$.

33. $\dfrac{p\sin\theta - q\cos\theta}{p\sin\theta + q\cos\theta} = \dfrac{p\tan\theta - q}{p\tan\theta + q}$, on dividing by $\cos\theta$.

$= \dfrac{p(p/q) - q}{p(p/q) + q} = \dfrac{p^2 - q^2}{p^2 + q^2}$ $\quad\left(\because \tan\theta = \dfrac{p}{q}\right)$.

34. Since $\sec^2\theta \geq 1$, we have from the given relation,

$\dfrac{4xy}{(x+y)^2} \geq 1$ or $(x+y)^2 \leq 4xy$.

or $(x+y)^2 - 4xy \leq 0$ or $(x-y)^2 \leq 0$.

Above is possible only when $x = y$ but $x \neq 0$.

35. The given relation can be written as
$(m' + m\cos\theta)^2 + m^2 - m^2\cos^2\theta = 1$

or $(m' + m\cos\theta)^2 = 1 - m^2\sin^2\theta$ ....(1)

Similarly $(n' + n\cos\theta)^2 = 1 - n^2\sin^2\theta$ ....(2)

Now $(m' + m\cos\theta)(n' + n\cos\theta)$
$= m'n' + (mn' + m'n)\cos\theta + mn\cos^2\theta$
$= -mn + mn\cos^2\theta$ by given relation
$= -mn(1 - \cos^2\theta) = -mn\sin^2\theta$

Now squaring both sides, we get

or $(m' + m\cos\theta)^2 (n' + n\cos\theta)^2 = m^2 n^2 \sin^4\theta$ ....(3)

Hence substituting from (1) and (2) in (3), we get
$(1 - m^2\sin^2\theta)(1 - n^2\sin^2\theta) = m^2 n^2 \sin^4\theta$

or $(m^2 + n^2)\sin^2\theta = 1$ *i.e.* $m^2 + n^2 = \operatorname{cosec}^2\theta$.

36. (a) From given relation

$\dfrac{\sin\theta}{p} = \dfrac{\cos\theta}{q} = \sqrt{\dfrac{\sin^2\theta + \cos^2\theta}{p^2 + q^2}} = \dfrac{1}{\sqrt{p^2 + q^2}}$

Now putting for p and q in the L.H.S., we have

$\text{L.H.S.} = \sqrt{(p^2 + q^2)}\left[\dfrac{\sin\theta}{\sin\phi} - \dfrac{\cos\theta}{\cos\phi}\right]$

$= \sqrt{(p^2 + q^2)}\,\dfrac{\sin(\theta - \phi)}{\sin\phi\cos\phi}$

$= \sqrt{(p^2 + q^2)}\cdot 2\,\dfrac{\sin(3\phi - \phi)}{\sin 2\phi} = \sqrt{p^2 + q^2}$ $\because \theta = 3\phi$

(b) Ans. (a), (b).

$3\sin^4 x + 2(1 - \sin^2 x)^2 = 6/5$

or $5\sin^4 x - 4\sin^2 x + \dfrac{4}{5} = 0$

or $25\sin^4 x - 20\sin^2 x + 4 = 0$

or $(5\sin^2 x - 2)^2 = 0$ $\therefore \sin^2 x = \dfrac{2}{5}$

$\therefore \cos^2 x = 1 - \sin^2 x = \dfrac{3}{5}$ $\therefore \tan^2 x = \dfrac{2}{3}$

Also $\dfrac{\sin^8 x}{8} + \dfrac{\cos^8 x}{27} = \dfrac{1}{8}\left(\dfrac{2}{5}\right)^4 + \dfrac{1}{27}\left(\dfrac{3}{5}\right)^4$

$= \dfrac{1}{5^4}(2 + 3) = \dfrac{1}{5^3} = \dfrac{1}{125}$

Problem Set (3)

▶ Multiple Choice Questions

1. The value of $\sin^6\theta + \cos^6\theta + 3\sin^2\theta\cos^2\theta$ is

   (a) 0   (b) 1   (c) 2   (d) 3

2. The least value of $2\sin^2\theta + 3\cos^2\theta$ is

   (a) 1   (b) 2   (c) 3   (d) 5

3. The greatest value of $\sin^4\theta + \cos^4\theta$ is

   (a) 1/2   (b) 1   (c) 2   (d) 3

4. The value of $\sin^2\theta\cos^2\theta(\sec^2\theta + \operatorname{cosec}^2\theta)$ is

   (a) 2   (b) 4   (c) 1   (d) 0

5. * If $\sin\theta + \operatorname{cosec}\theta = 2$, then $\sin^2\theta + \operatorname{cosec}^2\theta$ is equal to

   (a) 1   (b) 4   (c) 2   (d) none

   (M.N.R. 1990)

6. For how many values of x between 0 and 2π is the equation $2\operatorname{cosec}2x\cot x - \cot^2 x = 1$ valid ?

   (a) 0   (b) 2   (c) 1   (d) none

7. (a) Incorrect statement is

   (a) $\sin\theta = -1/5$ (b) $\cos\theta = 1$
   (c) $\sec\theta = 1/2$ (d) $\tan\theta = 20$ **(M.N.R. 1993)**

(b) If A lies in 2nd quadrant and $3\tan A + 4 = 0$ then prove that the value of

   $2\cot A - 5\cos A + \sin A$ is $\dfrac{23}{10}$.

8. (a) $\sec^2\theta = \dfrac{4xy}{(x+y)^2}$ is true if and only if

   (a) $x + y \neq 0$ (b) $x = y, x \neq 0$
   (c) $x = y$ (d) $x \neq 0, y \neq 0$ **(I.I.T. 1996)**

(b) The equation $\cos 2x + a\sin x = 2a - 7$ has a solution if

   (a) $a < 2$ (b) $2 \leq a \leq 6$
   (c) $a > 6$ (d) none

True and false type questions :
State whether the following statements are true or false .

9. * If $x = a\cos^2\theta\sin\theta$ and $y = a\sin^2\theta\cos\theta$,
   then $(x^2 + y^2)^3 / (x^2 y^2)$ is independent of θ.

10. The inequality $2^{\sin^2\theta} + 2^{\cos^2\theta} \geq 2\sqrt{2}$ holds for all real θ.

11. The equation $\sin\theta = x + (1/x)$ holds true for all real θ.

Fill in the blanks :

12. The least value of $\tan^2\theta + \cot^2\theta$ is ....

13. The value of $\sin\theta\cos\theta(\tan\theta + \cot\theta)$ is ....

14. If for real x, the equation
$x + (1/x) = 2\cos\theta$ holds, then $\cos\theta = ...$

15. If $\csc\theta - \cot\theta = q$, then the value of $\csc\theta =$ ....

Hints/Answers to Problem Set (3)

1. Ans. (b). We have
$$\sin^6\theta + \cos^6\theta + 3\sin^2\theta\cos^2\theta = \sin^6\theta + \cos^6\theta$$
$$+ 3\sin^2\theta\cos^2\theta(\sin^2\theta + \cos^2\theta)$$
$$= (\sin^2\theta + \cos^2\theta)^3 = 1.$$

2. Ans. (b). We have
$$2\sin^2\theta + 3\cos^2\theta = 2(\sin^2\theta + \cos^2\theta) + \cos^2\theta$$
$$= 2 + \cos^2\theta \geq 2 \qquad [\because \cos^2\theta \geq 0]$$

3. Ans. (b). $\sin^4\theta + \cos^4\theta = (\sin^2\theta + \cos^2\theta)^2$
$$-2\sin^2\theta\cos^2\theta$$
$$= 1 - 2\sin^2\theta\cos^2\theta \leq 1$$

4. Ans. (c).

5. Ans. (c). **See Q. 4 (a) P. 509-511.**

6. Ans. (d). The given equation is $\dfrac{2}{\sin 2x} - \cot x = \tan x$.

We have divided by $\cot x$

or $\dfrac{1}{\sin x\cos x} = \dfrac{\sin x}{\cos x} + \dfrac{\cos x}{\sin x}$

or $1 = \sin^2 x + \cos^2 x$

Above is an identity which is true for all values of x
($\sin x \neq 0, \cos x \neq 0$)

7. (a) Ans. (c). $\sec\theta \geq 1$

(b) $\tan A = -\dfrac{4}{3}$ and since A lies in 2nd quadrant,

$\cos A = -$ive and $\sin A = +$ive

$\sec A = \pm\sqrt{1 + \tan^2 A} = \pm\dfrac{5}{3} \quad \therefore \quad \cos A = -\dfrac{3}{5}$

$\sin A = \pm\sqrt{1 - \cos^2 A} = \pm\dfrac{4}{5} \quad \therefore \quad \sin A = \dfrac{4}{5}$

$\therefore \quad E = 2\left(-\dfrac{3}{4}\right) - 5\left(-\dfrac{3}{5}\right) + \dfrac{4}{5}$

$$= -\dfrac{3}{2} + 3 + \dfrac{4}{5} = \dfrac{3}{2} + \dfrac{4}{5} = \dfrac{23}{10}$$

8. (a) Ans. (b). If both $x = y = 0$ then it takes indeterminate form.

(b) Ans. (b).
The given equation can be written as
$$1 - 2\sin^2 x + a\sin x = 2a - 7$$

or $2\sin^2 x - a\sin x + 2(a - 4) = 0$

$\therefore \quad \sin x = \dfrac{a \pm \sqrt{a^2 - 16(a-4)}}{4}$

$$= \dfrac{a \pm (a-8)}{4} = 2, \dfrac{a-4}{2}$$

The first value is rejected as $|\sin x| \leq 1$.

Hence, $-1 \leq \dfrac{a-4}{2} < 1$. $\therefore \quad 2 \leq a \leq 6 \Rightarrow$ (b)

9. True $(x^2 + y^2)^3 = (a^2\cos^2\theta\sin^2\theta)^3 = a^2 x^2 y^2$

10. Ans. True. [**Hint :** Apply A.M. $\geq$ G.M.]

11. Ans. False. We have $x + \dfrac{1}{x} \geq 2\left(x \cdot \dfrac{1}{x}\right)^{1/2} = 2$

i.e. A.M. $\geq$ G.M.

$\therefore \quad \sin\theta \geq 2$. This is not possible.

12. Ans. 2. [**Hint :** Apply A.M. $\geq$ G.M.]

13. Ans. 1.

14. Ans. $\cos\theta = \pm 1$. We have

$x + (1/x) = 2\cos\theta \Rightarrow x^2 - 2x\cos\theta + 1 = 0$

Now for real x, we must have $4\cos^2\theta - 4 \geq 0$ or $\cos^2\theta \geq 1$. But $\cos^2\theta > 1$ is impossible.

Hence we must have $\cos^2\theta = 1$, that is, $\cos\theta = \pm 1$.

15. Ans. $\csc\theta - \cot\theta = q$ ...(1)

$\therefore \quad \csc\theta + \cot\theta = \dfrac{1}{q}$ [**§ 2 (3), P. 507**]

as the two expressions are reciprocal.

$\therefore \quad \csc\theta = \dfrac{1}{2}[q + (1/q)]$, on adding.

§ 3. Trigonometrical ratios for sum and difference.

1. $\sin(A + B) = \sin A\cos B + \cos A\sin B$.

2. $\sin(A - B) = \sin A\cos B - \cos A\sin B$.

3. $\cos(A + B) = \cos A\cos B - \sin A\sin B$.

4. $\cos(A - B) = \cos A\cos B + \sin A\sin B$.

5. $\tan(A + B) = \dfrac{\tan A + \tan B}{1 - \tan A\tan B}$

6. $\tan(A - B) = \dfrac{\tan A - \tan B}{1 + \tan A\tan B}$

$A \neq n\pi + \pi/2, \quad B \neq m\pi + \pi/2$
$A \pm B \neq k\pi + \pi/2$ for 5 and 6.

Deductions :

(a) $\tan\left(\dfrac{\pi}{4} + \theta\right) = \dfrac{1 + \tan\theta}{1 - \tan\theta}$ **(Imp.)**

(b) $\tan\left(\dfrac{\pi}{4} - \theta\right) = \dfrac{1 - \tan\theta}{1 + \tan\theta}$ **(Imp.)**

7. $\cot(A + B) = \dfrac{\cot A\cot B - 1}{\cot A + \cot B}$

$(A \neq n\pi, B \neq m\pi, A + B \neq k\pi)$

8. $\cot(A - B) = \dfrac{\cot A\cot B + 1}{\cot B - \cot A}$

$(A \neq n\pi, B \neq m\pi, A - B \neq k\pi)$

9.* $\sin(A + B)\sin(A - B) = \sin^2 A - \sin^2 B$

$$= \cos^2 B - \cos^2 A$$

10.* $\cos(A+B)\cos(A-B) = \cos^2 A - \sin^2 B$

$$= \cos^2 B - \sin^2 A$$

11. (a) $\sin 2\theta = 2\sin\theta\cos\theta = 2\tan\theta/(1+\tan^2\theta)$

(b)* $(\cos A \pm \sin A)^2 = 1 \pm \sin 2A$

12.* $\cos 2\theta = \cos^2\theta - \sin^2\theta = (1-\tan^2\theta)/(1+\tan^2\theta)$

$$= 1 - 2\sin^2\theta = 2\cos^2\theta - 1.$$

13.* $1 + \cos 2\theta = 2\cos^2\theta,\ 1-\cos 2\theta = 2\sin^2\theta.$

or $\cos^2\theta = \dfrac{1}{2}(1+\cos 2\theta),$

$\sin^2\theta = \dfrac{1}{2}(1-\cos 2\theta).$

14. (a) $\tan 2\theta = \dfrac{2\tan\theta}{1-\tan^2\theta}\quad [\theta \neq (2n+1)\,\pi/4]$

(b) $\dfrac{(1-\cos\theta)}{\sin\theta} = \tan\dfrac{\theta}{2}\quad [\theta \neq (2n+1)\,\pi].$

(c) $\dfrac{(1+\cos\theta)}{\sin\theta} = \cot\dfrac{\theta}{2}\quad [\theta \neq 2n\pi].$

(d) $\dfrac{(1-\cos\theta)}{(1+\cos\theta)} = \tan^2\dfrac{\theta}{2}\quad [\theta \neq (2n+1)\,\pi].$

(e) $\dfrac{(1+\cos\theta)}{(1-\cos\theta)} = \cot^2\dfrac{\theta}{2}\quad [\theta \neq 2n\pi].$

Triple angles :

15. $\sin 3x = 3\sin x - 4\sin^3 x$

or $\sin^3 x = \dfrac{1}{4}(3\sin x - \sin 3x).$

16. $\cos 3x = 4\cos^3 x - 3\cos x$

or $\cos^3 x = \dfrac{1}{4}(3\cos x + \cos 3x).$

17. $\tan 3x = \dfrac{3\tan x - \tan^3 x}{1 - 3\tan^2 x}\quad (x \neq n\pi + \pi/6).$

▶ Sum and difference into products :

18. $\sin C + \sin D = 2\sin\{(C+D)/2\}\cos\{(C-D)/2\}$

19. $\sin C - \sin D = 2\cos\{(C+D)/2\}\sin\{(C-D)/2\}$

20. $\cos C + \cos D = 2\cos\{(C+D)/2\}\cos\{(C-D)/2\}$

21.* $\cos C - \cos D = 2\sin\{(C+D)/2\}\sin\{(D-C)/2\}$

(Note $(D-C)/2$)

22.* $\tan A \pm \tan B = \dfrac{\sin A}{\cos A} \pm \dfrac{\sin B}{\cos B}$

$$= \dfrac{\sin A\cos B \pm \cos A\sin B}{\cos A\cos B}$$

$$= \dfrac{\sin(A \pm B)}{\cos A\cos B}\quad \left(A \neq n\pi + \dfrac{\pi}{2}, B \neq m\pi\right)$$

23. $\cot A \pm \cot B = \dfrac{\sin(B \pm A)}{\sin A\sin B}\quad \left(A \neq n\pi, B \neq m\pi + \dfrac{\pi}{2}\right)$

24. (i)* $\cos A \pm \sin A = \sqrt{2}\sin(\pi/4 \pm A)$

$$= \sqrt{2}\cos(\pi/4 \mp A)$$

(ii) $\tan A + \cot A = 1/(\sin A\cos A)$ **(Imp.)**

Product into sum or difference :

25. $2\sin A\cos B = \sin(A+B) + \sin(A-B).$

26. $2\cos A\sin B = \sin(A+B) - \sin(A-B)$

27. $2\cos A\cos B = \cos(A+B) + \cos(A-B)$

28. $2\sin A\sin B = \cos(A-B) - \cos(A+B)$ **(Note)**

29. Values of Trigonometrical ratios for particular angles :

θ	0°	30°	45°	60°	90°
$\sin\theta$	$\sqrt{\dfrac{0}{4}}$	$\sqrt{\dfrac{1}{4}}$	$\sqrt{\dfrac{2}{4}}$	$\sqrt{\dfrac{3}{4}}$	$\sqrt{\dfrac{4}{4}}$
$\cos\theta$	$\sqrt{\dfrac{4}{4}}$	$\sqrt{\dfrac{3}{4}}$	$\sqrt{\dfrac{2}{4}}$	$\sqrt{\dfrac{1}{4}}$	$\sqrt{\dfrac{0}{4}}$
$\tan\theta$	0	$\dfrac{1}{\sqrt{3}}$	1	$\sqrt{3}$	undefined

The table of values, shown on the next page, is useful and be remembered.

30. Sign of Trigonometrical Ratios :

Quadrant	$\sin\theta$	$\cos\theta$	$\tan\theta$	$\cot\theta$	$\sec\theta$	$\operatorname{cosec}\theta$
I	+	+	+	+	+	+
II	+	−	−	−	−	+
III	−	−	+	+	−	−
IV	−	+	−	−	+	−

Aid to Memory : First of all remember the following sentence :

Add Sugar to Coffee : This sentence consists of four words. Write down the first letter of each word in the same order as :

A, S, T, C

Taking the meaning of A as "All ratios are + ive". Second letter S means "sine, ∴ cosec + ive and rest − ive". Third letter T means : "tan, ∴ cot + ive and rest − ive" and the fourth letter C means : "cos, ∴ sec + ive and rest − ive".

Note. How to remember the Reduction Formulae. (See next page). Suppose $X'OX$ and $Y'OY$ divide the plane in four quadrants. Then

(1) First determine the name of the trigonometrical ratio by the following rule : If θ is measured from $X'OX$, that is, $(\pi \pm \theta, 2\pi - \theta)$, then retain the original name of the ratio and if θ is measured from $Y'OY$, that is, $(\pi/2 \pm \theta, 3\pi/2 \pm \theta)$, then change sine to cosine, cosine to sine, tangent to cotangent, cotangent to tangent, sec to cosec and cosec to sec.

(2) Determine the sign of the trigonometrical ratio as follows : Regarding θ as lying in the first quadrant, find the quadrant in which $n\pi/2 \pm \theta$ is situated and then determine the sign of the given ratio in this quadrant. For example

$$\cot(19\pi/6) = \cot(3\pi + \pi/6) = \cot(\pi + \pi/6).$$
$$= \cot(\pi/6) = \sqrt{3}.$$

Note that by rule (1), the ratio in $\cot(\pi + \pi/6)$ will remain cot and by rule (2), the sign will be positive since $\pi + \pi/6$ lies in the third quadrant. Hence $\cot(\pi + \pi/6) = \cot(\pi/6)$.

Again $\tan\left(\dfrac{3\pi}{2} - \dfrac{\pi}{3}\right) = \cot\dfrac{\pi}{3} = \dfrac{1}{\sqrt{3}}$, since by rule (1) the

ratio tan is changed to cot and by rule (2), sign is + ive. Hence

$$\tan\left(\frac{3\pi}{2} - \frac{\pi}{3}\right) = \cot\frac{\pi}{3}.$$

31. Table for Reduction Formulae :

θ	$\frac{\pi}{2}-\theta$	$\frac{\pi}{2}+\theta$	$\pi-\theta$	$\pi+\theta$	$\frac{3\pi}{2}-\theta$	$\frac{3\pi}{2}+\theta$	$2\pi-\theta$	$-\theta$
$\sin\theta$	$\cos\theta$	$\cos\theta$	$\sin\theta$	$-\sin\theta$	$-\cos\theta$	$-\cos\theta$	$-\sin\theta$	$-\sin\theta$
$\cos\theta$	$\sin\theta$	$-\sin\theta$	$-\cos\theta$	$-\cos\theta$	$-\sin\theta$	$\sin\theta$	$\cos\theta$	$\cos\theta$
$\tan\theta$	$\cot\theta$	$-\cot\theta$	$-\tan\theta$	$\tan\theta$	$\cot\theta$	$-\cot\theta$	$-\tan\theta$	$-\tan\theta$
$\cot\theta$	$\tan\theta$	$-\tan\theta$	$-\cot\theta$	$\cot\theta$	$\tan\theta$	$-\tan\theta$	$-\cot\theta$	$-\cot\theta$

θ	0	$\pi/6$	$\pi/4$	$\pi/3$	$\pi/2$	$2\pi/3$	$3\pi/4$	$5\pi/6$	π	$3\pi/2$
$\sin\theta$	0	$1/2$	$1/\sqrt{2}$	$\sqrt{3}/2$	1	$\sqrt{3}/2$	$1/\sqrt{2}$	$1/2$	0	-1
$\cos\theta$	1	$\sqrt{3}/2$	$1/\sqrt{2}$	$1/2$	0	$-1/2$	$-1/\sqrt{2}$	$-\sqrt{3}/2$	-1	0
$\tan\theta$	0	$1/\sqrt{3}$	1	$\sqrt{3}$	undefined	$-\sqrt{3}$	-1	$-1/\sqrt{3}$	0	undefined
$\cot\theta$	undefined	$\sqrt{3}$	1	$1/\sqrt{3}$	0	$-1/\sqrt{3}$	-1	$-\sqrt{3}$	undefined	0
$\sec\theta$	1	$2/\sqrt{3}$	$\sqrt{2}$	2	undefined	-2	$-\sqrt{2}$	$-2/\sqrt{3}$	-1	undefined
$\operatorname{cosec}\theta$	undefined	2	$\sqrt{2}$	$2/\sqrt{3}$	1	$2/\sqrt{3}$	$\sqrt{2}$	2	undefined	-1

32. Complementary and Supplementary Rules :

If θ be any angle, then $\dfrac{\pi}{2} - \theta$ is its complement and $\pi - \theta$ is its supplement.

C.R. sin of any angle = cos of its complement. This is true of all the six trigonometrical ratios.

S.R. sin of any angle = sin of its supplement;

cos of any angle = – cos of its supplement

tan of any angle = – tan of its supplement.

$\sin 30° = \cos 60°, \tan 20° = \cot 70°,$

$\sec 10° = \operatorname{cosec} 80°, \sin 30° = \sin 150°$

$\cos 20° = -\cos 160°, \tan 110° = -\tan 70°$

33. Values of trigonometrical ratios of some important angles : $15° = 45° - 30°$

(i) $\sin 15° = (\sqrt{3} - 1)/2\sqrt{2} = \cos 75°$

(ii) $\cos 15° = (\sqrt{3} + 1)/2\sqrt{2} = \sin 75°$

(iii) $\tan 15° = 2 - \sqrt{3} = \cot 75°$

(iv) $\cot 15° = 2 + \sqrt{3} = \tan 75°$

If $A = 22\dfrac{1}{2}°$ then $2A = 45°$,

$$\cos 2A = 2\cos^2 A - 1 = 1 - 2\sin^2 A$$

(v) $\sin 22\dfrac{1}{2}° = \dfrac{1}{2}\sqrt{2 - \sqrt{2}}$

(vi) $\cos 22\dfrac{1}{2}° = \dfrac{1}{2}\sqrt{2 + \sqrt{2}}$

(vii) $\tan 22\dfrac{1}{2}° = \sqrt{2} - 1$

(viii) $\cot 22\dfrac{1}{2}° = \sqrt{2} + 1$

(ix) $\sin 18° = \dfrac{1}{4}(\sqrt{5} - 1) = \cos 72°$

(x) $\cos 18° = \dfrac{1}{4}\sqrt{10 + 2\sqrt{5}} = \sin 72°$

(xi) $\sin 36° = \dfrac{1}{4}\sqrt{10 - 2\sqrt{5}} = \cos 54°$

(xii) $\cos 36° = \dfrac{1}{4}(\sqrt{5} + 1) = \sin 54°$.

34. Expression of $\sin(A/2)$ and $\cos(A/2)$ in terms of $\sin A$:

It is easy to see that

$$\left(\sin\frac{A}{2} + \cos\frac{A}{2}\right)^2 = 1 + \sin A$$

$$\left(\sin\frac{A}{2} - \cos\frac{A}{2}\right)^2 = 1 - \sin A$$

so that $\quad \sin\dfrac{A}{2} + \cos\dfrac{A}{2} = \pm\sqrt{1 + \sin A}$ ...(1)

and $\quad \sin\dfrac{A}{2} - \cos\dfrac{A}{2} = \pm\sqrt{1 - \sin A}$ ...(2)

By addition and subtraction, we have

$$\mathbf{2\sin\frac{A}{2} = \pm\sqrt{1 + \sin A} \pm \sqrt{1 - \sin A}}\quad\text{...(3)}$$

$$\text{and } \mathbf{2\cos\frac{A}{2} = \pm\sqrt{1 + \sin A} \pm \sqrt{1 - \sin A}}\quad\text{...(4)}$$

The ambiguities of sign in relations (1) and (2) is determined by the following diagram.

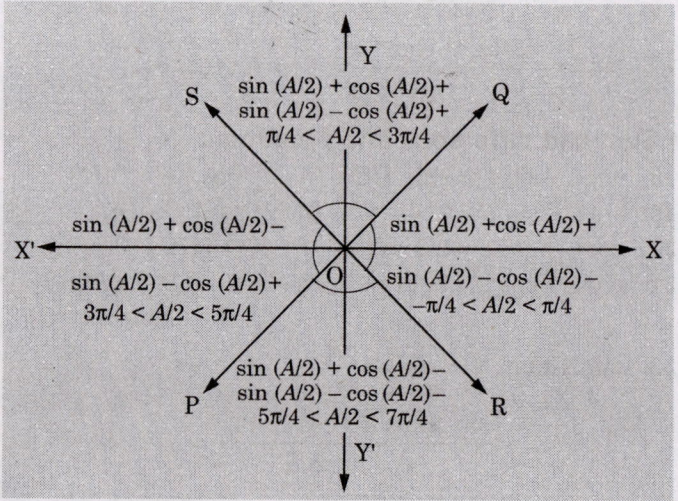

Fig. 6

35. (i) Sign of $\sin\dfrac{A}{2} + \cos\dfrac{A}{2}$ and $\sin\dfrac{A}{2} - \cos\dfrac{A}{2}$

$$\sin\frac{A}{2} + \cos\frac{A}{2} = \sqrt{2}\sin\left(\frac{A}{2} + \frac{\pi}{4}\right)$$

+ ive if $\quad 0 \le \dfrac{A}{2} + \dfrac{\pi}{4} \le \pi$

$-$ive if $\quad \pi \le \dfrac{A}{2} + \dfrac{\pi}{4} \le 2\pi$

or $\qquad -\dfrac{\pi}{4} \le \dfrac{A}{2} \le \dfrac{3\pi}{4} \quad$ for $+$ ive $\qquad$ ...(1)

$\qquad \dfrac{3\pi}{4} \le \dfrac{A}{2} \le \dfrac{7\pi}{4} \quad$ for $-$ ive $\qquad$ ...(2)

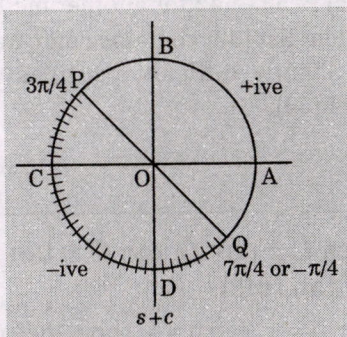

Fig. 7

(ii) Similarly

$$\sin \dfrac{A}{2} - \cos \dfrac{A}{2} = \sqrt{2}\,\sin\left(\dfrac{A}{2} - \dfrac{\pi}{4}\right)$$

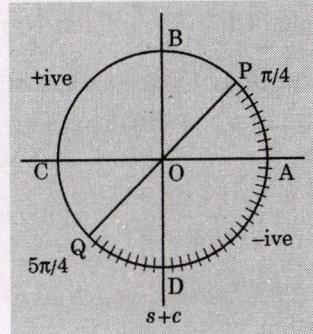

Fig. 8

$+$ ive if $\quad 0 \le \dfrac{A}{2} - \dfrac{\pi}{4} \le \pi$

$-$ ive if $\quad \pi \le \dfrac{A}{2} - \dfrac{\pi}{4} \le 2\pi$

or $\quad \dfrac{\pi}{4} \le \dfrac{A}{2} \le \dfrac{5\pi}{4} \quad$ for $+$ ive $\qquad$ ...(3)

or $\quad \dfrac{5\pi}{4} \le \dfrac{A}{2} \le \dfrac{9\pi}{4} \quad$ for $-$ ive

or $\quad \dfrac{5\pi}{4} \le \dfrac{A}{2} \le \dfrac{\pi}{4} \quad$ for $-$ ive $\qquad$ ...(4)

36. To find the greatest and least values of the expression $a\sin\theta + b\cos\theta$: $\qquad$ **(M.N.R. 1991)**

Let $\qquad a = r\cos\alpha, b = r\sin\alpha,$

then $\qquad a^2 + b^2 = r^2 \quad$ or $\quad r = \sqrt{a^2 + b^2}$

$\therefore \quad a\sin\theta + b\cos\theta$

$\qquad = r\,(\sin\theta\cos\alpha + \cos\theta\sin\alpha)$

$\qquad = r\sin(\theta + \alpha)$

But $-1 \le \sin(\theta + \alpha) \le 1$ so that $-r \le r\sin(\theta+\alpha) \le r$

Hence $-\sqrt{a^2+b^2} \le a\sin\theta + b\cos\theta \le \sqrt{a^2+b^2}$

Thus the greatest and least values of $a\sin\theta + b\cos\theta$ are respectively $\sqrt{(a^2+b^2)}$ and $-\sqrt{(a^2+b^2)}$.

Similarly maximum value of

$\qquad a\sin\theta - b\cos\theta$ is $\sqrt{(a^2+b^2)}$. $\qquad$ **(M.N.R. 1991)**

37.* $\cos A \cos 2A \cos 4A \cos 8A \dots \cos 2^{n-1} A$

$\qquad = \dfrac{1}{2^n \sin A}\sin(2^n A)$. **(V. Imp.)** **(Remember)**

(Each angle being double of preceding)

Multiply above and below by $2^n \sin A$

$\therefore \quad$ L.H.S.

$= \dfrac{2^{n-1}}{2^n \sin A}[2\sin A \cos A \cos 2A \cos 4A \dots \cos 2^{n-1} A]$

$= \dfrac{2^{n-2}}{2^n \sin A}[2\sin 2A \cos 2A \cos 4A \dots \cos 2^{n-1} A]$

$= \dfrac{2^{n-3}}{2^n \sin A}[2\sin 4A \cos 4A \dots \cos 2^{n-1} A]$

$= \dfrac{1}{2^n \sin A}[2\sin 2^{n-1} A \cos 2^{n-1} A]$

$= \dfrac{1}{2^n \sin A}\sin(2 \cdot 2^{n-1} A) = \dfrac{\sin(2^n A)}{2^n \sin A}.$

[See Q. 31, P. 533-543]

38. Sum of the sin and cosine series when the angles are in A.P.

$\sin\alpha + \sin(\alpha+\beta) + \sin(\alpha+2\beta) + \dots n$ terms

$\cos\alpha + \cos(\alpha+\beta) + \cos(\alpha+2\beta) + \dots n$ terms

$$= \dfrac{\sin n \cdot \frac{\text{diff}}{2}}{\sin \frac{\text{diff}}{2}} \cdot \begin{matrix}\sin \\ \text{or} \\ \cos\end{matrix}\left[\dfrac{\text{1st angle} + \text{last angle}}{2}\right]$$

(Remember the above rule)

$$= \dfrac{\sin(n\beta/2)}{\sin(\beta/2)}\begin{matrix}\sin \\ \text{or} \\ \cos\end{matrix}\left[\dfrac{\alpha + \alpha + (n-1)\beta}{2}\right]$$

$$= \dfrac{\sin(n\beta/2)}{\sin\beta/2}\begin{matrix}\sin \\ \text{or} \\ \cos\end{matrix}\left[\alpha + (n-1)\dfrac{\beta}{2}\right] \qquad \text{...(A)}$$

Note : β is not an even multiple of π, i.e. $\beta \ge 2n\pi$ because in that case sum will take the form $\dfrac{0}{0}$.

Particular case : Both the sums will be zero if $\sin\dfrac{n\beta}{2} = 0$ i.e. $\dfrac{n\beta}{2} = r\pi$ or $\beta = \dfrac{2r\pi}{n}$

or $\quad \beta =$ even multiple of π/n then $S = 0$

Proof :

Let $S = \sin\alpha + \sin(\alpha+\beta) + \sin(\alpha+2\beta) + \dots$

Multiply both sides by $2\sin(\beta/2)$ and write

$\qquad 2\sin A \sin B = \cos(A-B) - \cos(A+B)$

$\therefore \quad 2\sin(\beta/2)\,S = [\cos(\alpha - \beta/2) - \cos(\alpha + \beta/2)]$

$\qquad\qquad\qquad + [\cos(\alpha + \beta/2) - \cos(\alpha + 3\beta/2)]$

$+ [\cos (\alpha + 3\beta/2) - \cos (\alpha + 5\beta/2)]$

....

$+ [\cos \{\alpha + (2n - 3) \beta/2\} - \cos \{\alpha + (2n - 1) \beta/2\}]$

$\therefore \quad 2 \sin \dfrac{\beta}{2} . S = \cos (\alpha - \beta/2) - \cos [\alpha + (2n - 1) \beta/2]$

$= 2 \sin \{\alpha + (n - 1) \beta/2\} \sin (n\beta/2)$

$\therefore \quad S = $ etc. as given in (A).

Ex. $\cos \dfrac{\pi}{7} + \cos \dfrac{2\pi}{7} + \cos \dfrac{3\pi}{7} + ... \cos \dfrac{6\pi}{7} = 0$

Angles are in A.P.

Here $n = 6, \alpha = \pi/7, \beta = \pi/7$.

$S = \dfrac{\sin (6 . \pi/14)}{\sin (\pi/14)} \cos \dfrac{1}{2} \left(\dfrac{\pi}{7} + \dfrac{6\pi}{7} \right)$

$= \dfrac{\sin (3\pi/7)}{\sin (\pi/14)} \cos \dfrac{\pi}{2} = 0$

See **Q. 27 (c) P. 533-542** for another method.

Note : Problem Set (32) contains comparatively easier questions. Slightly difficult questions are given in problems set (33).

Problem Set (4)

Max. and min. value of $a \cos \theta + b \sin \theta$; $\sin C \pm \sin D, \cos C \pm \cos D, \tan C \pm \tan D$;
$1 \pm \cos 2\theta; \sin \theta, \cos \theta, \tan \theta$ in terms of $\tan (\theta/2)$.

1. (a) Prove that $\tan 1° \tan 2° \tan 3° ....\tan 89° = 1$

(b) $\sin^2 5° + \sin^2 10° + \sin^2 15° + ...$

$\qquad\qquad + \sin^2 85° + \sin^2 90° = 9\dfrac{1}{2}$

(Karnataka C.E.E. 1999)

(c) One of the roots of the equation $8x^3 - 6x + 1 = 0$ is

(a) $\cos 10°$ (b) $\cos 30°$

(c) $\sin 30°$ (d) $\cos 80°$

2. (a) Prove : $\cot \theta - \cot 2\theta = \mathrm{cosec} \, 2\theta$

(b) $\tan 70° - \tan 20° = 2 \tan 50°$.

3. (a) $\dfrac{\sin (A - B)}{\sin A \sin B} + \dfrac{\sin (B - C)}{\sin B \sin C} + \dfrac{\sin (C - A)}{\sin C \sin A} = 0$

(b) $\dfrac{\sin (A - B)}{\cos A \cos B} + \dfrac{\sin (B - C)}{\cos B \cos C} + \dfrac{\sin (C - A)}{\cos C \cos A} = 0$.

4. (a) $\dfrac{\sin (B + A) + \cos (B - A)}{\sin (B - A) + \cos (B + A)} = \dfrac{\cos A + \sin A}{\cos A - \sin A}$.

(b) $\dfrac{\tan (A + B)}{\cot (A - B)} = \dfrac{\sin^2 A - \sin^2 B}{\cos^2 A - \sin^2 B}$.

5. (a) $\sin^2 (\pi/8 + A/2) - \sin^2 (\pi/8 - A/2) = (1/\sqrt{2}) \sin A$

(b) $\sin^2 (n + 1) A - \sin^2 nA = \sin (2n + 1) A . \sin A$.

6. (a) $\sin^2 24° - \sin^2 6° = (\sqrt{5} - 1)/8$.

(b) $\sin^2 42° - \cos^2 78° = (\sqrt{5} + 1)/8$.

7. (a)* $\cos 2\theta \cos 2\phi + \sin^2 (\theta - \phi) - \sin^2 (\theta + \phi)$

$\qquad\qquad\qquad\qquad = \cos 2 (\theta + \phi)$

(b) $\mathrm{cosec} \, (\pi/4 + \theta) \, \mathrm{cosec} \, (\pi/4 - \theta)$

$\qquad\qquad = \sec (\pi/4 + \theta) \sec (\pi/4 - \theta) = 2 \sec 2\theta$.

8. (a)* $\tan 3A \tan 2A \tan A = \tan 3A - \tan 2A - \tan A$.

(b) $\tan 15° + \tan 30° + \tan 15° \tan 30° = 1$.

9. If $A + B = 45°$, prove that

(a) $(1 + \tan A) (1 + \tan B) = 2$.

(b) $(\cot A - 1) (\cot B - 1) = 2$.

(c) If $A + B = 225°$, prove that

$\dfrac{\cot A}{1 + \cot A} . \dfrac{\cot B}{1 + \cot B} = \dfrac{1}{2}$.

10. (a) If $\tan \alpha = m/(m + 1), \tan \beta = 1/(2m + 1)$, show that $\alpha + \beta = \pi/4$.

(b) If $\tan \alpha = \dfrac{1}{2}$, $\tan \beta = \dfrac{1}{3}$, show that $\alpha + \beta = \pi/4$

11. Prove that

(a) $\tan (\pi/4 + \theta) - \tan (\pi/4 - \theta) = 2 \tan 2\theta$.

(b) $\tan (\pi/4 + \theta) + \tan (\pi/4 - \theta) = 2 \sec 2\theta$.

(c) $\tan (\pi/4 + \theta) \times \tan (\pi/4 - \theta) = 1$.

(d) In a triangle $PQR, \angle R = \dfrac{\pi}{2}$. If $\tan \dfrac{P}{2}$ and $\tan \dfrac{Q}{2}$

are the roots of $ax^2 + bx + c = 0, a \neq 0$, then

(a) $b = c$ (b) $b = a + c$

(c) $a = b + c$ (d) $c = a + b$ **(AIEEE 2005)**

12. (a) $\tan \left(\dfrac{\pi}{4} + \dfrac{\theta}{2} \right) = \sqrt{\left(\dfrac{1 + \sin \theta}{1 - \sin \theta} \right)} = \tan \theta + \sec \theta$

(b) $\dfrac{\tan^2 2\theta - \tan^2 \theta}{1 - \tan^2 2\theta \tan^2 \theta} = \tan 3\theta \tan \theta$.

(c) If $f (x) = \tan 2x \tan 3x \tan 5x$, then prove that $f ' (x) = 5 \sec^2 5x - 3 \sec^2 3x - 2 \sec^2 2x$.

13. (a) $\dfrac{\cos 9° + \sin 9°}{\cos 9° - \sin 9°} = \tan 54°$.

(b) $\tan A + \cot A = 2 \, \mathrm{cosec} \, 2A$.

(c) $(\tan \alpha \sec^2 \alpha + \cot \alpha \, \mathrm{cosec}^2 \alpha) - (\tan \alpha + \cot \alpha)$

$\qquad\qquad = 2 \, \mathrm{cosec} \, 2\alpha [\sec^2 \alpha + \mathrm{cosec}^2 \alpha - 3]$

14. (a) $\cot A - \tan A = 2 \cot 2A$.

(b)* $\tan A + 2 \tan 2A + 4 \tan 4A + 8 \cot 8A = \cot A$

15. (a) $\mathrm{cosec} \, A - 2 \cot 2A \cos A = 2 \sin A$.

(b) $\mathrm{cosec} \, 2A - \cot 2A = \tan A$.

16. (a) $\dfrac{1 - \cos A}{\sin A} = \tan \dfrac{A}{2}$.

(b) $\dfrac{1 + \cos A}{\sin A} = \cot \dfrac{A}{2}$.

(c) $2 \sin A \cos^3 A - 2 \sin^3 A \cos A = \dfrac{1}{2} \sin 4A$

17. (a) $\dfrac{1 + \sin 2\theta - \cos 2\theta}{1 + \sin 2\theta + \cos 2\theta} = \tan \theta$

(b) $\dfrac{\sin \theta + \sin 2\theta}{1 + \cos \theta + \cos 2\theta} = \tan \theta$

(c) $2\cos\theta = \sqrt{2 + \sqrt{(2 + 2\cos 4\theta)}}$

18. (a) If $2\tan\beta + \cot\beta = \tan\alpha$, then $\cot\beta = 2\tan(\alpha - \beta)$.
    (b) If $\tan\theta = b/a$, then prove that
    $a\cos 2\theta + b\sin 2\theta = a$.

19. Prove :
    (a) $\sin A \sin(60° - A)\sin(60° + A) = \frac{1}{4}\sin 3A$
    (b) $\cos A \cos(60° - A)\cos(60° + A) = \frac{1}{4}\cos 3A$

20. $\dfrac{\sin^2 A - \sin^2 B}{\sin A \cos A - \sin B \cos B} = \tan(A + B)$.

21. (a) $\dfrac{\sin A + \sin 3A + \sin 5A + \sin 7A}{\cos A + \cos 3A + \cos 5A + \cos 7A} = \tan 4A$
    (b) $\dfrac{\sin 3\theta + \sin 5\theta + \sin 7\theta + \sin 9\theta}{\cos 3\theta + \cos 5\theta + \cos 7\theta + \cos 9\theta} = \tan 6\theta$
    (c) $\dfrac{2(\sin 2\theta + 2\cos^2\theta - 1)}{\cos\theta - \sin\theta - \cos 3\theta + \sin 3\theta} = \dfrac{1}{\sin\theta}$

22. (a) $\dfrac{\cos 3A + 2\cos 5A + \cos 7A}{\cos A + 2\cos 3A + \cos 5A} = \dfrac{\cos 5A}{\cos 3A}$
    $= \cos 2A - \sin 2A \tan 3A$.
    (b) $\dfrac{\cos 6\theta + 6\cos 4\theta + 15\cos 2\theta + 10}{\cos 5\theta + 5\cos 3\theta + 10\cos\theta} = 2\cos\theta$.

23. (a) $2\cos x - \cos 3x - \cos 5x = 16\cos^3 x \sin^2 x$
    (b) $1 + \cos 2x + \cos 4x + \cos 6x$
    $= 4\cos x \cos 2x \cos 3x$.
    (c) $\cos^3\theta \sin^2\theta = (1/16)(2\cos\theta - \cos 3\theta - \cos 5\theta)$

24. (a) $(\cos\alpha + \cos\beta)^2 + (\sin\alpha + \sin\beta)^2$
    $= 4\cos^2\{(\alpha - \beta)/2\}$.
    (b) $(\cos\alpha - \cos\beta)^2 + (\sin\alpha - \sin\beta)^2$
    $= 4\sin^2\{(\alpha - \beta)/2\}$.

25. (a)* $\cos\alpha + \cos\beta + \cos\gamma + \cos(\alpha + \beta + \gamma)$
    $= 4\cos\{(\alpha + \beta)/2\}\cos\{(\beta + \gamma)/2\}\cos\{(\gamma + \alpha)/2\}$
    (b) $\left(\dfrac{\cos A + \cos B}{\sin A - \sin B}\right)^n + \left(\dfrac{\sin A + \sin B}{\cos A - \cos B}\right)^n$
    $= 2\cot^n\left(\dfrac{A - B}{2}\right)$
    or 0 according as n is even or odd positive integer.

26. (a) If three angles A, B and C are in A.P., prove that
    $\cot B = \dfrac{\sin A - \sin C}{\cos C - \cos A}$.
    (b) If A, B, C and D are angles of a cyclic quadrilateral, prove that
    $\cos A + \cos B + \cos C + \cos D = 0$
    (c) If in a triangle ABC, $\sin A \cdot \cos B = 1/4$ and $3\tan A = \tan B$, then the triangle is
    (a) right angled   (b) equilateral
    (c) isosceles   (d) none of these

27. (a) $\dfrac{\cos 2A \cos 3A - \cos 2A \cos 7A + \cos A \cos 10A}{\sin 4A \sin 3A - \sin 2A \sin 5A + \sin 4A \sin 7A}$
    $= \cot 6A \cot 5A$
    (b) $\dfrac{\cos 8A \cos 5A - \cos 12A \cos 9A}{\sin 8A \cos 5A + \cos 12A \sin 9A} = \tan 4A$.
    (c) If in a ΔABC, $\cos A = \dfrac{\sin B}{2\sin C}$,
    prove that it is an isosceles triangle.

28. (a) If $\tan A - \tan B = x$ and $\cot B - \cot A = y$, prove that $\cot(A - B) = (1/x) + (1/y)$.
    (b)* If $2\cos A = x + 1/x$, $2\cos B = y + 1/y$, show that $2\cos(A - B) = x/y + y/x$.
    (c) If $\tan\theta = p/q$ and $\theta = 3\phi$ where θ lies in Ist quadrant, then prove that
    $\dfrac{p}{\sin\phi} - \dfrac{q}{\cos\phi} = 2\sqrt{p^2 + q^2}$
    (d) If $p = \tan 27\theta - \tan\theta$ and
    $q = \dfrac{\sin\theta}{\cos 3\theta} + \dfrac{\sin 3\theta}{\cos 9\theta} + \dfrac{\sin 9\theta}{\cos 27\theta}$, then
    prove that $\dfrac{p}{q} = 2$.

29. If α and β are the solutions of $a\cos\theta + b\sin\theta = c$, then show that
    (a) $\sin\alpha + \sin\beta = 2bc/(a^2 + b^2)$,
    $\sin\alpha \sin\beta = (c^2 - a^2)/(a^2 + b^2)$
    (b) $\cos\alpha + \cos\beta = 2ac/(a^2 + b^2)$,
    $\cos\alpha \cos\beta = (c^2 - b^2)/(a^2 + b^2)$
    (c) If α and β are the solutions of the equation $a\tan\theta + b\sec\theta = c$, then show that
    $\tan(\alpha + \beta) = 2ac/(a^2 - c^2)$
    (d)* If $a\cos 2\theta + b\sin 2\theta = c$ has α and β as its solutions, then prove that
    $\tan\alpha + \tan\beta = 2b/(c + a)$,
    $\tan\alpha \tan\beta = (c - a)/(c + a)$
    (e)* If $\theta_1, \theta_2, \theta_3, \theta_4$ be the four values of θ which satisfy the equation $3\tan 3\theta = \tan(45° + \theta)$, then prove that
    $\Sigma\tan\theta_1 = 0$.
    (f) If $\tan\theta_1, \tan\theta_2, \tan\theta_3, \tan\theta_4$ are the roots of the equation
    $x^4 - x^3\sin 2\beta + x^2\cos 2\beta - x\cos\beta - \sin\beta = 0$,
    then prove that
    $\tan(\theta_1 + \theta_2 + \theta_3 + \theta_4) = \cot\beta$

30. (a) If $f(x) = \dfrac{1.\cos x + 5\cos 3x + \cos 5x}{\cos 6x + 6\cos 4x + 15\cos 2x + 10}$
    then $f(0) + f'(0) + f''(0) =$
    (a) $-\dfrac{1}{2}$ (b) 0
    (c) $\dfrac{1}{2}$ (d) 1
    (b) The value of $\sin^3 10° + \sin^3 50° - \sin^3 70° =$

(a) $-\dfrac{3}{2}$ (b) $\dfrac{3}{4}$

(c) $-\dfrac{3}{4}$ (d) $-\dfrac{3}{8}$

(c) If $x = \dfrac{4\lambda}{1+\lambda^2}$ and $y = \dfrac{2-2\lambda^2}{1+\lambda^2}$ where λ is a real

parameter then $Z = x^2 - xy + y^2$ lies between

(a) $[2,6]$ (b) $[2,4]$
(c) $[4,6]$ (d) none

(d) Let α, β be such that $\pi < \alpha - \beta < 3\pi$. If $\sin\alpha + \sin\beta = -\dfrac{21}{65}$ and $\cos\alpha + \cos\beta = -\dfrac{27}{65}$ then the value of $\cos\dfrac{\alpha-\beta}{2}$ is

(a) $-\dfrac{3}{\sqrt{130}}$ (b) $\dfrac{3}{\sqrt{130}}$

(c) $\dfrac{6}{65}$ (d) $-\dfrac{6}{65}$ **(AIEEE 2004)**

31. (a) Find the max. and min. value of
$7\cos\theta + 24\sin\theta$

(b) Show that the max. and min. values of
$8\cos\theta - 15\sin\theta$
are 17 and -17 respectively.

(c) Determine the max. value of
$(5\sin x - 12\cos x)(5\cos x + 12\sin x)$

(d) The number of integral values of k for which the equation $7\cos x + 5\sin x = 2k+1$ has a solution is

(a) 4 (b) 8 (c) 10 (d) 12
(I.I.T. Sc. 2002)

32. (a)* Prove that $5\cos\theta + 3\cos(\theta + \pi/3) + 3$
lies between -4 and 10.

(b) Max. value of $\sin x + \cos x$ is

(a) 1 (b) 2 (c) $\sqrt{2}$ (d) $1/\sqrt{2}$

(c) The value of $\sqrt{3}\sin x + \cos x$ is max. when x is equal to

(a) $30°$ (b) $90°$ (c) $60°$ (d) $45°$

(d)* Find a and b such that the inequality $a \le 3\cos x + 5\sin(x - \pi/6) \le b$ holds good for all x.

33. (a)* If $\tan\dfrac{\theta}{2} = \sqrt{\left(\dfrac{1-e}{1+e}\right)}\tan\dfrac{\phi}{2}$, prove that

$$\cos\phi = \dfrac{\cos\theta - e}{1 - e\cos\theta}.$$

(b)* If $\cos\theta = \dfrac{a\cos\phi + b}{a + b\cos\phi}$, prove that
$\tan(\theta/2) = \sqrt{[(a-b)/(a+b)]}\tan(\phi/2)$

(c) If $\cos\theta = \dfrac{2\cos\phi - 1}{2 - \cos\phi}$, prove that
$\tan(\theta/2) = \sqrt{3}\tan(\phi/2)$

and hence show that $\sin\phi = \dfrac{\sqrt{3}\sin\theta}{2 + \cos\theta}$.

34. (a) If $\cos\theta = \dfrac{\cos\alpha - \cos\beta}{1 - \cos\alpha\cos\beta}$, then prove that
$\tan(\theta/2) = \pm\tan(\alpha/2)\cot(\beta/2)$.

(b) If $\tan\beta = \cos\theta\tan\alpha$, then prove that
$\sin(\alpha - \beta) = \tan^2(\theta/2)\sin(\alpha + \beta)$.

(c) If $\tan^2\theta = 2\tan^2\phi + 1$, then $\cos 2\theta + \sin^2\phi = 0$.

35. (a)* If an angle θ be divided into two parts such that the tangent of one part is m times the tangent of the other, then prove that their difference ϕ is obtained from the equation
$\sin\phi = [(m-1)/(m+1)]\sin\theta$.

(b) If $m\cos(\theta + \alpha) = n\cos(\theta - \alpha)$, show that
$(m-n)\cot\theta = (m+n)\tan\alpha$.

(c) If $\cos x = k\cos(x - 2y)$, show that
$\tan(x - y)\tan y = (1-k)/(1+k)$.

36. (a) If $\cos A = m\cos B$, then prove that
$$\cot\left(\dfrac{A+B}{2}\right) = \left(\dfrac{m+1}{m-1}\right)\tan\left(\dfrac{B-A}{2}\right)$$
(I.I.T. 1990)

(b) If $\sin\theta = n\sin(\theta + 2\alpha)$, show that
$\tan(\theta + \alpha) = [(1+n)/(1-n)]\tan\alpha$

37. (a) If $m\tan(\theta - 30°) = n\tan(\theta + 120°)$, show that
$\cos 2\theta = (m+n)/2(m-n)$

(b) If $\cos(\alpha + \beta)\sin(\gamma + \delta) = \cos(\alpha - \beta)\sin(\gamma - \delta)$, prove that $\cot\alpha\cot\beta\cot\gamma = \cot\delta$.   **(D.C.E. 1998)**

(c) If $\cos 2\alpha = \dfrac{3\cos 2\beta - 1}{3 - \cos 2\beta}$, then $\tan\alpha = \sqrt{2}\tan\beta$.

(d) If A and B are acute +ive angles satisfying the equation $3\sin^2 A + 2\sin^2 B = 1$ and $3\sin 2A - 2\sin 2B = 0$, then prove that
$A + 2B = \pi/2$

38. (a) If $\sin(y + z - x), \sin(z + x - y), \sin(x + y - z)$ be in A.P., prove that $\tan x\tan y, \tan z$ are also in A.P.

(b) If $\tan B = 2\sin A\sin C\operatorname{cosec}(A + C)$,
then prove that $\cot A, \cot B, \cot C$ are in A.P.

(c) If $\sec(\phi - \alpha), \sec\phi, \sec(\phi + \alpha)$ are in A.P., prove that $\cos\phi = \sqrt{2}\cos(\alpha/2)$.

39. (a)* If $\tan\dfrac{x-y}{2}, \tan z, \tan\dfrac{x+y}{2}$ are in G.P., then show that $\cos x = \cos y \cdot \cos 2z$

(b) If $\sin\theta$ is G.M. of $\sin\phi$ and $\cos\phi$, then prove that
$\cos 2\theta = 2\cos^2\left(\dfrac{\pi}{4} + \phi\right)$

(c) The sides of a right angled triangle are in G.P. Find the cosines of the acute angles of the triangle.

40. If $\cot A, \cot B, \cot C$ are in A.P., then prove that $\cot(B - A), \cot B, \cot(B - C)$ are also in A.P. where A, B, C are any angles.

41. (a) Prove that $\tan\alpha + \tan\beta + \tan\gamma - \tan\alpha\tan\beta\tan\gamma$
$$= \dfrac{\sin(\alpha + \beta + \gamma)}{\cos\alpha\cos\beta\cos\gamma}.$$

(b) If $0 < \alpha, \beta, \gamma < \pi/2$, prove that
$$\sin \alpha + \sin \beta + \sin \gamma > \sin (\alpha + \beta + \gamma)$$

42. If $\sin x + \sin y = 3 (\cos y - \cos x)$, prove that $\sin 3x + \sin 3y = 0$.

43. If $x = \dfrac{\sqrt{1 - \sin 4\theta} + 1}{\sqrt{1 + \sin 4\theta} - 1}$ then one of the values of x is

(a) $-\tan \theta$ (b) $\cot \theta$

(c) $\tan \left(\dfrac{\pi}{4} + \theta \right)$ (d) $-\cot \left(\dfrac{\pi}{4} + \theta \right)$

44. If A, B, C, D are the smallest positive angles in ascending order of magnitude which have their sines equal to the positive quantity k, then show that the value of
$$4 \sin \frac{A}{2} + 3 \sin \frac{B}{2} + 2 \sin \frac{C}{2} + \sin \frac{D}{2} \text{ is equal to } 2 \sqrt{1 + k}.$$

45. (a) $\dfrac{2 \sec \theta + 3 \tan \theta + 5 \sin \theta - 7 \cos \theta + 5}{2 \tan \theta + 3 \sec \theta + 5 \cos \theta + 7 \sin \theta + 8} =$

(a) $\tan \dfrac{\theta}{2}$ (b) $\cot \dfrac{\theta}{2}$

(c) $\sec \dfrac{\theta}{2}$ (d) $\operatorname{cosec} \dfrac{\theta}{2}$

(b) The minimum value of $\tan B \tan C$ in an acute angled triangle ABC is

(a) $\tan \dfrac{A}{2}$ (b) $\cot \dfrac{A}{2}$

(c) $\operatorname{cosec}^2 \dfrac{A}{2}$ (d) $\cot^2 \dfrac{A}{2}$

46. (a) The roots of both the equations
$$\sin^2 x + p \sin x + q = 0$$
and $\cos^2 x + r \cos x + s = 0$
are α and β. Then the value of $\sin (\alpha + \beta) =$

(a) $\dfrac{2qs}{q^2 + s^2}$ (b) $\dfrac{2ps}{p^2 + s^2}$

(c) $\dfrac{2pr}{p^2 + r^2}$ (d) $\dfrac{2qr}{q^2 + r^2}$

(b) If
$$u = \sqrt{a^2 \cos^2 \theta + b^2 \sin^2 \theta} + \sqrt{a^2 \sin^2 \theta + b^2 \cos^2 \theta}$$
then the difference between maximum and minimum values of u^2 is given by

(a) $2 (a^2 + b^2)$ (b) $2 \sqrt{a^2 + b^2}$

(c) $(a + b)^2$ (d) $(a - b)^2$ **(AIEEE 2004)**

(c) If $\cos x + \cos y = a, \cos 2x + \cos 2y = b$, $\cos 3x + \cos 3y = c$, then

(a) $\cos^2 x + \cos^2 y = 1 + \dfrac{b}{2}$

(b) $\cos x \cos y = \dfrac{a^2}{2} - \left(\dfrac{b + 2}{4} \right)$

(c) $2a^3 + c = 3a (1 + b)$

(d) $a + b + c = 3abc$

Solutions to Problem Set (4)

1. (a) By complementary rule
$(\tan 1° \cot 1°) (\tan 2° \cot 2°) (\tan 3° \cot 3°) \ldots$
$(\tan 44° \cot 44°) (\tan 45°) = 1$

(b) $8 + 1 + \dfrac{1}{2} = 9\dfrac{1}{2}$. The angles are in A.P. of 18 terms of which $\sin^2 90° = 1$,

$\sin^2 45° = \dfrac{1}{2}$ and 16 terms form 8 pairs like

$\sin^2 5° + \sin^2 85° = \sin^2 5° + \cos^2 5° = 1$

             by Complementary Rule.

(c) Ans. (d). From given equation $4x^3 - 3x = -1/2$
If $x = \sin \theta$, then $-\sin 3\theta = -1/2$ or $3\theta = 30°$
or $\theta = 10°$
$\therefore \quad x = \sin 10° = \cos 80° \Rightarrow$ (d)

2. (a) Changing to $\sin \theta$ and $\cos \theta$, we get
$$\cot \theta - \cot 2\theta = \frac{\cos \theta}{\sin \theta} - \frac{\cos 2\theta}{\sin 2\theta}$$
$$= \frac{\sin 2\theta \cos \theta - \cos 2\theta \sin \theta}{\sin \theta \sin 2\theta}$$
$$= \frac{\sin (2\theta - \theta)}{\sin \theta \sin 2\theta} = \operatorname{cosec} 2\theta.$$

(b) $\because \quad 70° = 50° + 20°$,
$$\therefore \quad \tan 70° = \frac{\tan 50° + \tan 20°}{1 - \tan 50° \tan 20°}$$

or $\tan 70° - \tan 70° \tan 50° \tan 20°$
$$= \tan 50° + \tan 20°$$

or $\tan 70° - \tan 20° = \tan 50° + \tan 50°$
$$= 2 \tan 50°$$

$[\because \tan 70° \tan 20° = \tan (90° - 20°) \tan 20°$
$$= \cot 20° \tan 20° = 1]$$

Alt. $\tan 70° - \tan 20° = \dfrac{\sin (70° - 20°)}{\cos 70° \cos 20°}$

$$= \frac{2 \sin 50°}{2 \sin 20° \cos 20°} \qquad \textbf{(Comp. Rule)}$$

$$= \frac{2 \sin 50°}{\sin 40°} = \frac{2 \sin 50°}{\cos 50°} = 2 \tan 50°$$

3. (a) $\dfrac{\sin (A - B)}{\sin A \sin B} = \dfrac{\sin A \cos B}{\sin A \sin B} - \dfrac{\cos A \sin B}{\sin A \sin B}$

$$= \cot B - \cot A.$$

L.H.S. $= (\cot B - \cot A) + (\cot C - \cot B)$
$$+ (\cot A - \cot C) = 0.$$

(b) Proceed as above.

4. (a) Do yourself. Expand $\sin (B \pm A)$ etc.

(b) On changing into sin and cos, we get

L.H.S. $= \dfrac{\sin (A + B) \sin (A - B)}{\cos (A - B) \cos (A + B)} = \dfrac{\sin^2 A - \sin^2 B}{\cos^2 A - \sin^2 B}$

5. (a) Using
$\sin^2 A - \sin^2 B = \sin (A + B) \sin (A - B)$,

we get

L.H.S. $= \sin (\pi/8 + A/2 + \pi/8 - A/2)$

$\qquad \sin (\pi/8 + A/2 - \pi/8 + A/2)$

$\qquad = \sin (\pi/4) \sin A = (1/\sqrt{2}) \sin A = $ R.H.S.

(b) Proceed as above.

6. (a) L.H.S. $= \sin (24° + 6°) \sin (24° - 6°)$

$\qquad = \sin 30° \sin 18° = \dfrac{1}{2} [(\sqrt{5} - 1)/4]$

(b) L.H.S. $= -(\cos^2 78° - \sin^2 42°)$

$\qquad = -\cos (78° + 42°) \cos (78° - 42°)$

$\qquad = -\cos 120° \cos 36° = -\left(-\dfrac{1}{2}\right) \dfrac{(\sqrt{5} + 1)}{4}$

$\qquad = (\sqrt{5} + 1) / 8$.

7. (a) L.H.S. $= \cos 2\theta \cos 2\phi$

$\qquad + [\sin (\theta - \phi + \theta + \phi) \sin (\theta - \phi - \theta - \phi)]$

$\qquad = \cos 2\theta \cos 2\phi + \sin 2\theta \sin (-2\phi)$

$\qquad = \cos 2\theta \cos 2\phi - \sin 2\theta \sin 2\phi = \cos 2 (\theta + \phi)$.

(b) L.H.S. $= \dfrac{1}{\sin (45° + \theta) \sin (45° - \theta)}$

$\qquad = \dfrac{1}{\sin^2 45° - \sin^2 \theta}$

$\qquad = \dfrac{2}{1 - 2\sin^2 \theta} = \dfrac{2}{\cos 2\theta} = 2 \sec 2\theta$.

Similarly, $\sec \left(\dfrac{\pi}{4} + \theta\right) \sec \left(\dfrac{\pi}{4} - \theta\right)$

$\qquad = \dfrac{1}{\cos^2 45° - \sin^2 \theta} = 2 \sec 2\theta$

as above.

8. (a) Rearranging the given relation, we have to prove that

$\qquad \tan A + \tan 2A = \tan 3A (1 - \tan A \tan 2A)$

or $\dfrac{\tan A + \tan 2A}{1 - \tan A \tan 2A} = \tan 3A$

or $\tan (A + 2A) = \tan 3A$, which is true.

(b) $\tan 15° + \tan 30° = 1 - \tan 15° \tan 30°$

or $\dfrac{\tan 15° + \tan 30°}{1 - \tan 15° \tan 30°} = 1$

or $\tan (15° + 30°) = 1$

or $\tan 45° = 1$, which is true.

9. (a) $(1 + \tan A) (1 + \tan B) = 2$,

or $1 + \tan A + \tan B + \tan A \tan B = 2$

or $\tan A + \tan B = 1 - \tan A \tan B$,

or $\dfrac{\tan A + \tan B}{1 - \tan A \tan B} = 1$ or $\tan (A + B) = 1$.

This is true as $A + B = 45°$

(b) Change cot in terms of tan and proceed as above.

(c) Changing cot in terms of tan we have to prove that

$\qquad \dfrac{1}{1 + \tan A} \cdot \dfrac{1}{1 + \tan B} = \dfrac{1}{2}$

or $2 = 1 + \tan A + \tan B + \tan A \tan B$

or $\tan A + \tan B = (1 - \tan A \tan B)$

or $\dfrac{\tan A + \tan B}{1 - \tan A \tan B} = 1$ or $\tan (A + B) = 1$.

or $\tan 225° = 1$.

But $\tan 225° = \tan (180° + 45°) = \tan 45° = 1$.

10. (a) $\tan (\alpha + \beta) = \dfrac{\tan \alpha + \tan \beta}{1 - \tan \alpha \tan \beta}$

$\qquad = \dfrac{\{m/(m + 1)\} + \{1/(2m + 1)\}}{1 - \{m/(m + 1)\} \cdot \{1/(2m + 1)\}}$

$\qquad = \dfrac{2m^2 + 2m + 1}{2m^2 + 3m + 1 - m} = 1, \quad \therefore \quad \alpha + \beta = \dfrac{\pi}{4}$

(b) Proceed as above.

11. (a) $\tan \left(\dfrac{\pi}{4} + \theta\right) = \dfrac{\tan (\pi/4) + \tan \theta}{1 - \tan (\pi/4) \tan \theta} = \dfrac{1 + \tan \theta}{1 - \tan \theta}$.

Similarly, $\tan \left(\dfrac{\pi}{4} - \theta\right) = \dfrac{1 - \tan \theta}{1 + \tan \theta}$.

$\therefore$ L.H.S. $= \dfrac{1 + \tan \theta}{1 - \tan \theta} - \dfrac{1 - \tan \theta}{1 + \tan \theta}$

$\qquad = \dfrac{(1 + \tan \theta)^2 - (1 - \tan \theta)^2}{1 - \tan^2 \theta}$

$\qquad = \dfrac{4 \tan \theta}{1 - \tan^2 \theta} = 2 \cdot \dfrac{2 \tan \theta}{1 - \tan^2 \theta} = 2 \tan 2\theta$.

(b) Proceed as above.

L.H.S. $= 2 \cdot \dfrac{1 + \tan^2 \theta}{1 - \tan^2 \theta} = 2 \cdot \dfrac{1}{\cos 2\theta} = 2 \cdot \sec 2\theta$.

(c) It is clear from part (a).

(d) Ans. (d).

$\qquad \Rightarrow R = 90° \Rightarrow P + Q = 90°$

$\therefore \quad \dfrac{P}{2} + \dfrac{Q}{2} = 45° \quad \therefore \quad \tan \left(\dfrac{P}{2} + \dfrac{Q}{2}\right) = 1$

or $\dfrac{S}{1 - P} = 1$ or $S = 1 - P$

or $-\dfrac{b}{a} = 1 - \dfrac{c}{a}$ or $-b = a - c \quad \therefore \quad c = a + b$

12. (a) L.H.S. $= \dfrac{1 + \tan (\theta/2)}{1 - \tan (\theta/2)} = \dfrac{\cos (\theta/2) + \sin (\theta/2)}{\cos (\theta/2) - \sin (\theta/2)}$

$\qquad = \left[\dfrac{\{\cos (\theta/2) + \sin (\theta/2)\}^2}{\{\cos (\theta/2) - \sin (\theta/2)\}^2}\right]^{1/2}$

$\qquad = \left[\dfrac{\cos^2 (\theta/2) + \sin^2 (\theta/2) + 2 \sin (\theta/2) \cos (\theta/2)}{\cos^2 (\theta/2) + \sin^2 (\theta/2) - 2 \sin (\theta/2) \cos (\theta/2)}\right]^{1/2}$

$\qquad = \sqrt{\left(\dfrac{1 + \sin \theta}{1 - \sin \theta}\right)} = \dfrac{1 + \sin \theta}{\sqrt{[(1 + \sin \theta) (1 - \sin \theta)]}}$

$\qquad = \dfrac{1 + \sin \theta}{\sqrt{(1 - \sin^2 \theta)}} = \dfrac{1 + \sin \theta}{\cos \theta}$

$\qquad = \dfrac{1}{\cos \theta} + \dfrac{\sin \theta}{\cos \theta} = \sec \theta + \tan \theta$

(b) Use $a^2 - b^2 = (a + b)(a - b)$.

Do yourself.

(c) $\tan 5x = \tan(2x + 3x) = \dfrac{\tan 2x + \tan 3x}{1 - \tan 2x \tan 3x}$

$\therefore \quad f(x) = \tan 5x - \tan 2x - \tan 3x$ etc.

13. (a) On dividing by $\cos 9°$.

L.H.S. $= \dfrac{1 + \tan 9°}{1 - \tan 9°} = \tan(45° + 9°) = \tan 54°$

as in **Q. 11 (a)**

(b) L.H.S. $= \dfrac{\sin A}{\cos A} + \dfrac{\cos A}{\sin A} = \dfrac{\sin^2 A + \cos^2 A}{\cos A \sin A}$

$= \dfrac{2}{2 \sin A \cos A} = \dfrac{2}{\sin 2A} = 2 \operatorname{cosec} 2A$.

(c) L.H.S. $= \left(\dfrac{\sin \alpha}{\cos^3 \alpha} + \dfrac{\cos \alpha}{\sin^3 \alpha} \right) - \dfrac{2}{\sin 2\alpha}$

$= \dfrac{1 - 2 \sin^2 \alpha \cos^2 \alpha}{\sin^2 \alpha \cos^2 \alpha} \cdot \dfrac{2}{2 \sin \alpha \cos \alpha} - \dfrac{2}{\sin 2\alpha}$

$= 2 \operatorname{cosec} 2\alpha \left[\dfrac{\sin^2 \alpha + \cos^2 \alpha}{\sin^2 \alpha \cos^2 \alpha} - 3 \right]$ etc.

14. (a) L.H.S. $= \dfrac{\cos A}{\sin A} - \dfrac{\sin A}{\cos A} = \dfrac{\cos^2 A - \sin^2 A}{\sin A \cos A}$

$= 2 \cos 2A / \sin 2A = 2 \cot 2A$.

(b) Transfer $\tan A$ to R.H.S.

$\therefore \quad 2 \tan 2A + 4 \tan 4A + 8 \cot 8A = \cot A - \tan A$
$= 2 \cot 2A$ by (a)

$\therefore \quad 4 \tan 4A + 8 \cot 8A = 2 (\cot 2A - \tan 2A)$
$= 2 . 2 . \cot 4A$ as in (a)

$\therefore \quad 8 \cot 8A = 4 [\cot 4A - \tan 4A] = 4 . 2 \cot 8A$,
as in (a)

$= 8 \cot 8A$, which is true .

15. (a) Transposing, we have to prove that
$\operatorname{cosec} A - 2 \sin A = 2 \cot 2A \cos A$

L.H.S. $= \dfrac{1}{\sin A} - 2 \sin A$

$= \dfrac{1 - 2 \sin^2 A}{\sin A} \times \dfrac{2 \cos A}{2 \cos A}$ **(Note)**

$= \dfrac{\cos 2A}{\sin 2A} . 2 \cos A = 2 \cot 2A \cos A$.

(b) L.H.S. $= \dfrac{1}{\sin 2A} - \dfrac{\cos 2A}{\sin 2A} = \dfrac{1 - \cos 2A}{\sin 2A}$

$= \dfrac{2 \sin^2 A}{2 \sin A \cos A} = \tan A$.

16. (a) and (b).

Proceed as above .

(c) $2 \sin A \cos A (\cos^2 A - \sin^2 A)$

$= \sin 2A \cos 2A = \dfrac{1}{2} \sin 4A$.

17. (a) L.H.S. $= \dfrac{(1 - \cos 2\theta) + \sin 2\theta}{(1 + \cos 2\theta) + \sin 2\theta}$

$= \dfrac{2 \sin^2 \theta + 2 \sin \theta \cos \theta}{2 \cos^2 \theta + 2 \sin \theta \cos \theta}$

$= \dfrac{2 \sin \theta (\sin \theta + \cos \theta)}{2 \cos \theta (\cos \theta + \sin \theta)} = \tan \theta$.

(b) Proceed as above .

(c) L.H.S. $= \sqrt{2 + \sqrt{(2 + 2 \cos 4\theta)}}$

$= \sqrt{2 + \sqrt{[2 (1 + \cos 4\theta)]}}$

$= \sqrt{2 + \sqrt{(2 . 2 \cos^2 2\theta)}}$

$= \sqrt{2 + 2 \cos 2\theta} = \sqrt{2 (1 + \cos 2\theta)}$

$= \sqrt{2 . 2 \cos^2 \theta} = 2 \cos \theta$.

18. (a) We have to prove that $\cot \beta = 2 \dfrac{(\tan \alpha - \tan \beta)}{1 + \tan \alpha \tan \beta}$

or $\cot \beta + \tan \alpha = 2 \tan \alpha - 2 \tan \beta$

or $\cot \beta + 2 \tan \beta = \tan \alpha$, which is given .

(b) $b \sin 2\theta = a (1 - \cos 2\theta)$ (given)

or $\dfrac{b}{a} = \dfrac{2 \sin^2 \theta}{2 \sin \theta \cos \theta} = \tan \theta$. True.

19. (a) L.H.S. $= \sin A [\sin^2 60° - \sin^2 A]$

$= \sin A [3/4 - \sin^2 A]$

$= \dfrac{1}{4} (3 \sin A - 4 \sin^3 A) = \dfrac{1}{4} \sin 3A$.

(b) Proceed as above .

20. L.H.S. $= \dfrac{\sin(A + B) \sin(A - B)}{\dfrac{1}{2} (\sin 2A - \sin 2B)}$

$= \dfrac{2 \sin(A + B) \sin(A - B)}{2 \sin(A - B) \cos(A + B)} = \tan(A + B)$.

21. (a) $7 + 1 = 3 + 5$

L.H.S. $= \dfrac{(\sin A + \sin 7A) + (\sin 3A + \sin 5A)}{(\cos A + \cos 7A) + (\cos 3A + \cos 5A)}$

$= \dfrac{2 \sin 4A \cos 3A + 2 \sin 4A \cos A}{2 \cos 4A \cos 3A + 2 \cos 4A \cos A}$

$= \dfrac{\sin 4A (\cos 3A + \cos A)}{\cos 4A (\cos 3A + \cos A)} = \tan 4A$.

(b) Proceed as in part (a).

(c) L.H.S. $= \dfrac{2 (\sin 2\theta + \cos 2\theta)}{2 \sin \theta \sin 2\theta + 2 \sin \theta \cos 2\theta} = \dfrac{1}{\sin \theta}$

22. (a) L.H.S. $= \dfrac{(\cos 3A + \cos 7A) + 2 \cos 5A}{(\cos A + \cos 5A) + 2 \cos 3A}$

$= \dfrac{2 \cos 5A \cos 2A + 2 \cos 5A}{2 \cos 3A \cos 2A + 2 \cos 3A} = \dfrac{\cos 5A}{\cos 3A}$

$= \dfrac{\cos(3A + 2A)}{\cos 3A} = \dfrac{\cos 3A \cos 2A}{\cos 3A} - \dfrac{\sin 3A \sin 2A}{\cos 3A}$

$= \cos 2A - \tan 3A \sin 2A$.

(b) In the N^r write 6 as $1 + 5$ and 15 as $10 + 5$

$N^r = \cos 6\theta + \cos 4\theta + 5\cos 4\theta + 5\cos 2\theta$

$\qquad\qquad\qquad + 10\cos 2\theta + 10$

$= 2\cos 5\theta \cos \theta + 5 . 2\cos 3\theta \cos \theta + 10 . 2\cos^2 \theta$

$= 2\cos \theta [\cos 5\theta + 5\cos 3\theta + 10\cos \theta]$

$= 2\cos \theta [D^r]$

$\therefore \quad \dfrac{N^r}{D^r} = 2\cos \theta.$

Alt. Bring $2\cos\theta$ from R.H.S. with D^r in L.H.S. and using

$2\cos A \cos B = \cos(A+B) + \cos(A-B),$

we get $D^r = (\cos 6\theta + \cos 4\theta)$

$\qquad\qquad + 5(\cos 4\theta + \cos 2\theta) + 10(1 + \cos 2\theta)$

$= \cos 6\theta + 6\cos 4\theta + 15\cos 2\theta + 10 = N^r$

$\therefore \quad N^r / D^r = 1$

23. (a) R.H.S.

$= 2\cos x - 2\cos 4x \cos x = 2\cos x (1 - \cos 4x)$

$= 2\cos x . 2\sin^2 2x = 4\cos x (2\sin x \cos x)^2$

$= 16\cos^3 x \sin^2 x .$

(b) Combine 1st two and last two.

(c) Proceed as above in part (a).

24. (a) L.H.S. $= (\cos^2 \alpha + \sin^2 \alpha) + (\cos^2 \beta + \sin^2 \beta)$

$\qquad\qquad\qquad + 2(\cos \alpha \cos \beta + \sin \alpha \sin \beta)$

$= 2[1 + \cos(\alpha - \beta)]$

$= 2 . 2\cos^2 \dfrac{\alpha - \beta}{2} = 4\cos^2 \dfrac{\alpha - \beta}{2} .$

(b) Proceed as above.

25. (a) L.H.S. $= 2\cos \dfrac{\alpha + \beta}{2} \cos \dfrac{\alpha - \beta}{2}$

$\qquad\qquad + 2\cos \dfrac{\alpha + \beta + 2\gamma}{2} \cos \dfrac{\alpha + \beta}{2}$

$= 2\cos \dfrac{\alpha + \beta}{2} \left[\cos \dfrac{\alpha - \beta}{2} + \cos \dfrac{\alpha + \beta + 2\gamma}{2} \right]$

$= 2\cos \dfrac{\alpha + \beta}{2} . 2\cos \dfrac{\alpha + \gamma}{2} \cos \left(- \dfrac{\gamma + \beta}{2} \right)$

$= 4\cos \dfrac{\alpha + \beta}{2} \cos \dfrac{\beta + \gamma}{2} \cos \dfrac{\gamma + \alpha}{2} ,$

$\qquad\qquad\qquad \because \cos(-\theta) = \cos \theta .$

(b) L.H.S.

$\left[\dfrac{2\cos \{(A+B)/2\} \cos \{(A-B)/2\}}{2\sin \{(A-B)/2\} \cos \{(A+B)/2\}} \right]^n$

$\qquad + \left[\dfrac{2\sin \{(A+B)/2\} \cos \{(A-B)/2\}}{2\sin \{(A+B)/2\} \sin \{(B-A)/2\}} \right]^n$

$= \cot^n \{(A-B)/2\} + [-\cot \{(A-B)/2\}]^n$

$= 2\cot^n \{(A-B)/2\}$ or 0

according as n is even or odd as

$\qquad\qquad (-1)^n = 1$ or -1

26. (a) R.H.S. $= \dfrac{2\sin \{(A-C)/2\} \cos \{(A+C)/2\}}{2\sin \{(C+A)/2\} \sin \{(A-C)/2\}}$

$= \cot \{(A+C)/2\} = \cot B$

$[\because A, B, C$ being in A.P. $\therefore B = (A+C)/2]$

(b) Since the quadrilateral $ABCD$ is cyclic, we have

$A + C = 180°$ and $B + D = 180°$ (Property)

Hence $\cos A = \cos(180° - C) = -\cos C$ ...(1)

and $\cos B = \cos(180° - D) = -\cos D$ ...(2)

Adding (1) and (2), we get

$\cos A + \cos B = -\cos C - \cos D$

or $\cos A + \cos B + \cos C + \cos D = 0.$

(c) Ans. (a).

$\dfrac{\tan A}{\tan B} = \dfrac{1}{3} \Rightarrow \dfrac{\sin A . \cos B}{\cos A . \sin B} = \dfrac{1}{3}$

Put $\sin A . \cos B = \dfrac{1}{4} \therefore \cos A . \sin B = \dfrac{3}{4}$

$\therefore \quad \sin(A+B) = \dfrac{1}{4} + \dfrac{3}{4} = 1$

or $\sin C = 1 = \sin \dfrac{\pi}{2}$

$\therefore \quad C = \dfrac{\pi}{2}$ hence triangle is right angled.

27. (a) Multiply above and below by 2 and apply

$2\cos A \cos B = \cos(A+B) + \cos(A-B)$ and

$2\sin A \sin B = \cos(A-B) - \cos(A+B) .$

$\therefore \quad$ L.H.S.

$= \dfrac{(\cos 5A + \cos A) - (\cos 9A + \cos 5A) + (\cos 11A + \cos 9A)}{(\cos A - \cos 7A) - (\cos 3A - \cos 7A) + (\cos 3A - \cos 11A)}$

$= \dfrac{\cos A + \cos 11A}{\cos A - \cos 11A} = \dfrac{2\cos 6A \cos 5A}{2\sin 6A \sin 5A}$

$= \cot 6A \cot 5A .$

(b) Proceed as above .

(c) We are given that $2\cos A \sin C = \sin B$

or $\sin(A+C) - \sin(A-C) = \sin B.$ ...(1)

But in a $\Delta , A + C = 180° - B$ so that

$\sin(A+C) = \sin B .$

$\therefore \quad \sin(A-C) = 0,$ by (1)

$\therefore \quad A - C = 0$ or $A = C .$

Hence the triangle is isosceles .

28. (a) $\cot B - \cot A = y,$

$\therefore \quad 1/(\tan B) - 1/(\tan A) = y$

or $\dfrac{\tan A - \tan B}{\tan A \tan B} = y . \therefore \dfrac{x}{y} = \tan A \tan B$

Now $\cot(A-B) = \dfrac{1}{\tan(A-B)} = \dfrac{1 + \tan A \tan B}{\tan A - \tan B}$

$= \dfrac{1 + (x/y)}{x} = \dfrac{1}{x} + \dfrac{1}{y} .$

(b) $2 \cos A = x + \dfrac{1}{x}$ ∴ $x^2 - 2x \cos A + 1 = 0$

∴ $x = \cos A + i \sin A = e^{iA}, \ y = e^{iB}$

$\dfrac{x}{y} + \dfrac{y}{x} = \dfrac{e^{iA}}{e^{iB}} + \dfrac{e^{iB}}{e^{iA}} = e^{i(A-B)} + e^{-i(A-B)}$

$\qquad = 2 \cos(A - B)$

∵ $e^{i\theta} = \cos\theta + i \sin\theta, \ e^{-i\theta} = \cos\theta - i \sin\theta$

(c) $\tan\theta = \dfrac{p}{q} \ \Rightarrow \ \sin\theta = \dfrac{p}{\sqrt{(p^2 + q^2)}}$,

$\cos\theta = \dfrac{q}{\sqrt{(p^2 + q^2)}}$

∴ $\dfrac{p}{\sin\phi} - \dfrac{q}{\cos\phi} = \sqrt{p^2 + q^2}\left[\dfrac{\sin\theta}{\sin\phi} - \dfrac{\cos\theta}{\cos\phi}\right]$

$= \sqrt{p^2 + q^2}\left[\dfrac{\sin(\theta - \phi)}{\sin\phi\cos\phi}\right] = \sqrt{p^2 + q^2}\left[\dfrac{\sin 2\phi}{\sin\phi\cos\phi}\right]$

$= 2\sqrt{p^2 + q^2}$ ∵ $\theta = 3\phi$ ∴ $\theta - \phi = 2\phi$

(d) Write $p = [\tan 27\theta - \tan 9\theta + \tan 9\theta - \tan 3\theta$

$\qquad\qquad\qquad + \tan 3\theta - \tan\theta]$

Now, $\tan A - \tan B = \dfrac{\sin(A - B)}{\cos A \cos B}$

∴ $p = \dfrac{\sin 18\theta}{\cos 27\theta \cos 9\theta} + \dfrac{\sin 6\theta}{\cos 9\theta \cos 3\theta}$

$\qquad\qquad\qquad + \dfrac{\sin 2\theta}{\cos 3\theta \cos\theta}$

$= \dfrac{2\sin 9\theta}{\cos 27\theta} + \dfrac{2\sin 3\theta}{\cos 9\theta} + \dfrac{2\sin\theta}{\cos 3\theta}$

or $p = 2(q)$ or $\dfrac{p}{q} = 2$.

29. (a) From the given relation, we have

$a\cos\theta = c - b\sin\theta$.

Square and change in terms of $\sin\theta$

$a^2(1 - \sin^2\theta) = c^2 - 2bc\sin\theta + b^2\sin^2\theta$.

∴ $(a^2 + b^2)\sin^2\theta - 2bc\sin\theta + (c^2 - a^2) = 0$.

Its roots are $\sin\alpha$ and $\sin\beta$ as α and β are the values of θ as given .

∴ $\sin\alpha + \sin\beta = $ sum of roots $= \dfrac{2bc}{a^2 + b^2}$

$\sin\alpha\sin\beta = $ product of roots $= \dfrac{c^2 - a^2}{a^2 + b^2}$.

(b) Here arrange as a quadratic in $\cos\theta$.

(c) Here $b\sec\theta = c - a\tan\theta$. Square

$b^2(1 + \tan^2\theta) = c^2 - 2ca\tan\theta + a^2\tan^2\theta$

$(a^2 - b^2)\tan^2\theta - 2ca\tan\theta + (c^2 - b^2) = 0$.

∴ $\tan\alpha + \tan\beta = \dfrac{2ca}{a^2 - b^2}, \ \tan\alpha\tan\beta = \dfrac{c^2 - b^2}{a^2 - b^2}$.

∴ $\tan(\alpha + \beta) = \dfrac{\tan\alpha + \tan\beta}{1 - \tan\alpha\tan\beta}$

$= \dfrac{2ca}{(a^2 - b^2) - (c^2 - b^2)} = \dfrac{2ac}{a^2 - c^2}$.

(d) Write $\cos 2\theta = \dfrac{1 - \tan^2\theta}{1 + \tan^2\theta}, \sin 2\theta = \dfrac{2\tan\theta}{1 + \tan^2\theta}$ etc.

(e) If $\tan\theta = t$, then the 4th degree equation in t is

$3t^4 - 6t^2 + 8t - 1 = 0$

∴ $\Sigma t_1 = 0$. The term of t^3 is missing.

(f) $\tan(\theta_1 + \theta_2 + \theta_3 + \theta_4) = \dfrac{S_1 - S_3}{1 - S_2 + S_4}$

where $S_1 = \sin 2\beta, S_2 = \cos 2\beta, S_3 = \cos\beta, S_4 = -\sin\beta$

∴ $\tan(\theta_1 + \theta_2 + \theta_3 + \theta_4) = \dfrac{\sin 2\beta - \cos\beta}{1 - \cos 2\beta - \sin\beta}$

$= \dfrac{\cos\beta(2\sin\beta - 1)}{2\sin^2\beta - \sin\beta} = \dfrac{\cos\beta}{\sin\beta} = \cot\beta$

30. (a) Ans. (d).

$6 = 1 + 5, 15 = 5 + 10$ and $1 + \cos\theta = 2\cos^2\dfrac{\theta}{2}$

∴ $f(x) = \dfrac{N^r}{2\cos x \cdot N^r} = \dfrac{1}{2}\sec x$

$f'(x) = \dfrac{1}{2}\sec x \tan x$

$f''(x) = \dfrac{1}{2}[\sec x \cdot \sec^2 x + \sec x \tan^2 x]$

∴ $f(0) + f'(0) + f''(0) = \dfrac{1}{2} + 0 + \dfrac{1}{2} = 1 \to$ (d)

(b) Ans. (d).

$\sin 3\theta = 3\sin\theta - 4\sin^3\theta$

∴ $E = \dfrac{1}{4}[(3\sin 10° - \sin 30°) + (3\sin 50° - \sin 150°)$

$\qquad\qquad\qquad\qquad - (3\sin 70° - \sin 210°)]$

$= \dfrac{1}{4}\left[3(\sin 10° + \sin 50° - \sin 70°) - \left\{\dfrac{1}{2} + \dfrac{1}{2} - \left(-\dfrac{1}{2}\right)\right\}\right]$

$= \dfrac{3}{4}[2\sin 30°\cos 20° - \sin 70°] - \dfrac{3}{8}$

$= \dfrac{3}{4} \cdot 0 - \dfrac{3}{8} = -\dfrac{3}{8}$ (∵ $\cos 20° = \sin 70°$)

(c) Ans. (a).

Choose $\lambda = \tan\alpha$ ∴ $x = 2\sin 2\alpha, y = 2\cos 2\alpha$

∴ $Z = x^2 - xy + y^2 = 4.1 - 2\sin 4\alpha$

Min. value of $Z = 4 - 2.1 = 2$ and max. value is $4 - 2(-1) = 6$.

∴ $Z \in [2, 6]$.

(d) Ans. (a).

Squaring and adding the given relations,

$1 + 1 + 2\cos(\alpha - \beta) = \dfrac{441 + 729}{65 \times 65}$

or $2[1 + \cos(\alpha - \beta)] = \dfrac{1170}{65 \times 65} = \dfrac{13 \times 5 \times 18}{65 \times 65}$

or $\quad 2.2\cos^2\dfrac{\alpha-\beta}{2}=\dfrac{18}{65}=\dfrac{36}{130}$

$\therefore\quad \cos\dfrac{\alpha-\beta}{2}=\pm\dfrac{3}{\sqrt{130}}$

Since $\pi<\alpha-\beta<3\pi\;\Rightarrow\;\dfrac{\pi}{2}<\dfrac{\alpha-\beta}{2}<\dfrac{3\pi}{2}$

In the above interval $\cos\dfrac{\alpha-\beta}{2}$ is $-$ive

$\therefore\quad \cos\dfrac{\alpha-\beta}{2}=-\dfrac{3}{\sqrt{130}}\Rightarrow$(a)

31. (a) In $7\cos\theta+24\sin\theta$,

take $\;7=r\cos\alpha$ and $24=r\sin\alpha$.

$\therefore\quad r=\sqrt{(7^2+24^2)}=25$.

$\therefore\quad$ L.H.S. $=r(\cos\theta\cos\alpha+\sin\theta\sin\alpha)$

$\qquad\qquad =25\cos(\theta-\alpha)$.

Now max. and min. values of $\cos(\theta-\alpha)$ are 1 and -1.

Therefore the max. and min. values of given expression are 25 and -25 respectively.

(b) Proceed as above.

(c) L.H.S. $=13\sin(x-\alpha).13\cos(x-\alpha)$

$\qquad\quad =\dfrac{169}{2}\sin 2(x-\alpha)$

$\therefore\quad$ Max. value is $169/2$.

(d) Ans. (b). $(7)^2+(5)^2=74=r^2$.

Dividing by r both sides, we have

$\cos(x-\alpha)=\dfrac{2k+1}{\sqrt{74}}$ where $\tan\alpha=\dfrac{5}{7}$

$\therefore\quad -1<\dfrac{2k+1}{\sqrt{74}}<1$ or $-\sqrt{74}<2k+1<\sqrt{74}$

or $\;-8<2k+1<8.\qquad$ For integral values.

$\therefore\quad k=-4,-3,-2,-1,0,1,2,3$

i.e., 8 values which will satisfy the above inequality.

32. (a) The given expression is

$5\cos\theta+3(\cos\theta\cos60°-\sin\theta\sin60°)+3$

$\qquad\qquad =\dfrac{1}{2}[(13\cos\theta-3\sqrt3\sin\theta)]+3$.

Put $13=r\cos\alpha,3\sqrt3=r\sin\alpha$.

$\therefore\quad r=\sqrt{169+27}=\sqrt{196}=14$,

$\therefore\quad$ Given expression

$\qquad =\dfrac{r}{2}[\cos(\theta+\alpha)]+3=7\cos(\theta+\alpha)+3$.

Hence max. and min. values of expression are $7+3$ and $-7+3$, *i.e.* 10 and -4 respectively.

(b) (c) is correct.

(c) (c) is correct.

(d) $a=-\sqrt{19}$ and $b=\sqrt{19}$.

Hint : Proceed as in part (a).

33. (a) We know that $\cos A=\dfrac{1-\tan^2(A/2)}{1+\tan^2(A/2)}$

$\therefore\quad \cos\phi=\dfrac{1-\tan^2(\phi/2)}{1+\tan^2(\phi/2)}$

$\qquad =\dfrac{1-\{(1+e)/(1-e)\}\tan^2(\theta/2)}{1+\{(1+e)/(1-e)\}\tan^2(\theta/2)}$,

from the given relation.

$\qquad =\dfrac{\{1-\tan^2(\theta/2)\}-e\{1+\tan^2(\theta/2)\}}{\{1+\tan^2(\theta/2)\}-e\{1-\tan^2(\theta/2)\}}$

Divide above and below by $1+\tan^2(\theta/2)$

$\therefore\quad \cos\phi=\dfrac{\cos\theta-e}{1-e\cos\theta}$.

(b) $\cos\theta=\dfrac{a\cos\phi+b}{a+b\cos\phi}\quad\therefore\quad \dfrac{1-\tan^2(\theta/2)}{1+\tan^2(\theta/2)}$

$\qquad =\dfrac{a\{1-\tan^2(\phi/2)\}+b\{1+\tan^2(\phi/2)\}}{a\{1+\tan^2(\phi/2)\}+b\{1-\tan^2(\phi/2)\}}$

or $\dfrac{1-\tan^2(\theta/2)}{1+\tan^2(\theta/2)}=\dfrac{(a+b)-(a-b)\tan^2(\phi/2)}{(a+b)+(a-b)\tan^2(\phi/2)}$

Apply componendo and dividendo

$\qquad \dfrac{2\tan^2(\theta/2)}{2}=\dfrac{2(a-b)\tan^2(\phi/2)}{2(a+b)}$

$\therefore\quad \tan(\theta/2)=\sqrt{(a-b)/(a+b)}\,\tan(\phi/2)$

(c) Proceed as above.

34. (a) $\tan^2\dfrac{\theta}{2}=\dfrac{1-\cos\theta}{1+\cos\theta}$

$\qquad =\left(1-\dfrac{\cos\alpha-\cos\beta}{1-\cos\alpha\cos\beta}\right)\Big/\left(1+\dfrac{\cos\alpha-\cos\beta}{1-\cos\alpha\cos\beta}\right)$

$\qquad =\dfrac{(1-\cos\alpha)+\cos\beta(1-\cos\alpha)}{(1+\cos\alpha)-\cos\beta(1+\cos\alpha)}$

$\qquad =\dfrac{(1-\cos\alpha)(1+\cos\beta)}{(1+\cos\alpha)(1-\cos\beta)}$

or $\;\tan^2\dfrac{\theta}{2}=\dfrac{2\sin^2(\alpha/2)}{2\cos^2(\alpha/2)}\cdot\dfrac{2\cos^2(\beta/2)}{2\sin^2(\beta/2)}$

$\qquad =\tan^2(\alpha/2).\cot^2(\beta/2)$

$\therefore\quad \tan(\theta/2)=\pm\tan(\alpha/2)\cot(\beta/2)$.

(b) The given relation is $\tan\alpha/\tan\beta=1/\cos\theta$.

Apply componendo and dividendo. Then

$\qquad \dfrac{\tan\alpha-\tan\beta}{\tan\alpha+\tan\beta}=\dfrac{1-\cos\theta}{1+\cos\theta}$

or $\;\dfrac{\sin(\alpha-\beta)}{\sin(\alpha+\beta)}=\dfrac{2\sin^2(\theta/2)}{2\cos^2(\theta/2)}=\tan^2\dfrac{\theta}{2}$ etc.

(c) $\cos2\theta=\dfrac{1-\tan^2\theta}{1+\tan^2\theta}=\dfrac{1-(2\tan^2\phi+1)}{1+(2\tan^2\phi+1)}$

$$= \frac{-2\tan^2\phi}{2(1+\tan^2\phi)} = -\frac{\sin^2\phi}{\cos^2\phi}\cdot\frac{1}{\sec^2\phi}$$

$$\therefore \quad \cos 2\theta + \sin^2\phi = 0.$$

35. (a) Let the two parts be A and B so that

$A+B=\theta$ and $A-B=\phi$ and $\tan A = m\tan B$.

$$\therefore \quad \frac{\tan A}{\tan B} = \frac{m}{1}.$$

Apply componendo and dividendo

$$\therefore \quad \frac{\tan A - \tan B}{\tan A + \tan B} = \frac{m-1}{m+1}$$

or $\quad \dfrac{\sin(A-B)}{\sin(A+B)} = \dfrac{m-1}{m+1}$

or $\quad \sin\phi = \{(m-1)/(m+1)\}\sin\theta$.

(b) From the given relation, we have

$$\frac{m}{n} = \frac{\cos(\theta-\alpha)}{\cos(\theta+\alpha)}.$$

Apply componendo and dividendo.

$$\therefore \quad \frac{m-n}{m+n} = \frac{\cos(\theta-\alpha)-\cos(\theta+\alpha)}{\cos(\theta-\alpha)+\cos(\theta+\alpha)}$$

$$= \frac{2\sin\theta\sin\alpha}{2\cos\theta\cos\alpha} = \frac{\tan\alpha}{\cot\theta}.$$

$$\therefore \quad (m-n)\cot\theta = (m+n)\tan\alpha.$$

(c) Proceed as above.

36. (a) and (b). Proceed as Q. 35 (b).

37. (a) $\quad \dfrac{m}{n} = \dfrac{\tan(\theta+120°)}{\tan(\theta-30°)} = \dfrac{\tan A}{\tan B} = \dfrac{\sin A\cos B}{\cos A\sin B}$

where $A = \theta+120°$ and $B = \theta-30°$.

Applying componendo and dividendo, we get

$$\frac{m+n}{m-n} = \frac{\sin(A+B)}{\sin(A-B)} = \frac{\sin(2\theta+90°)}{\sin 150°}$$

$$= \frac{\cos 2\theta}{\sin(180°-30°)} = \frac{\cos 2\theta}{\sin 30°} = 2\cos 2\theta.$$

$$\therefore \quad \cos 2\theta = \frac{m+n}{2(m-n)}.$$

(b) From the given relation, we have

$$\frac{\sin(\gamma+\delta)}{\sin(\gamma-\delta)} = \frac{\cos(\alpha-\beta)}{\cos(\alpha+\beta)}.$$

Now apply comp. and div.

$$\therefore \quad \frac{\sin(\gamma+\delta)+\sin(\gamma-\delta)}{\sin(\gamma+\delta)-\sin(\gamma-\delta)} = \frac{\cos(\alpha-\beta)+\cos(\alpha+\beta)}{\cos(\alpha-\beta)-\cos(\alpha+\beta)}$$

or $\quad \dfrac{2\sin\gamma\cos\delta}{2\cos\gamma\sin\delta} = \dfrac{2\cos\alpha\cos\beta}{2\sin\alpha\sin\beta}$

$$\therefore \quad \cot\delta = \cot\alpha\cot\beta\cot\gamma.$$

(c) We know that $\cos 2A = \dfrac{1-\tan^2 A}{1+\tan^2 A}$

Using this formula, we get

$$\frac{1-\tan^2\alpha}{1+\tan^2\alpha} = \frac{3\cdot\dfrac{1-\tan^2\beta}{1+\tan^2\beta} - 1}{3 - \dfrac{1-\tan^2\beta}{1+\tan^2\beta}} = \frac{1-2\tan^2\beta}{1+2\tan^2\beta}$$

Applying componendo and dividendo, we get

$$\frac{2\tan^2\alpha}{2} = \frac{4\tan^2\beta}{2} \quad \therefore \quad \tan^2\alpha = 2\tan^2\beta$$

or $\quad \tan\alpha = \sqrt{2}\tan\beta$.

(d) $3\sin^2 A = 1-2\sin^2 B = \cos 2B$

and $\quad \sin 2B = \dfrac{3}{2}\sin 2A$

Now, $\cos(A+2B) = \cos A\cos 2B - \sin A\sin 2B$

$$= \cos A\cdot 3\sin^2 A - \sin A\cdot\frac{3}{2}\sin 2A$$

$$= 3\cos A\sin^2 A - 3\cos A\sin^2 A = 0$$

$$\therefore \quad A+2B = 90° = \frac{\pi}{2}$$

38. (a) We know that if a,b,c are in A.P., then

$b-a = c-b$.

$$\therefore \quad \sin(z+x-y) - \sin(y+z-x)$$
$$= \sin(x+y-z) - \sin(z+x-y)$$

or $\quad 2\cos z\sin(x-y) = 2\cos x\sin(y-z)$

Divide both sides by $2\cos x\cos y\cos z$

$$\frac{\sin x\cos y - \cos x\sin y}{\cos x\cos y} = \frac{\sin y\cos z - \cos y\sin z}{\cos y\cos z}$$

or $\quad \tan x - \tan y = \tan y - \tan z$

or $\quad 2\tan y = \tan x + \tan z$.

$$\therefore \quad \tan x, \tan y, \tan z \text{ are also in A.P.}$$

(b) The given relation is rewritten as

$\sin B\sin(A+C) = 2\sin A\sin C\cos B$

Divide both sides by $\sin A\sin B\sin C$

$$\frac{\sin(A+C)}{\sin A\sin C} = 2\cot B$$

or $\quad \cot A + \cot C = 2\cot B$.

(c) Since $\sec(\phi-\alpha), \sec\phi, \sec(\phi+\alpha)$ are in A.P.,

$$\therefore \quad 2\sec\phi = \sec(\phi-\alpha) + \sec(\phi+\alpha)$$

or $\quad \dfrac{2}{\cos\phi} = \dfrac{\cos(\phi+\alpha)+\cos(\phi-\alpha)}{\cos(\phi-\alpha)\cos(\phi+\alpha)}$

or $\quad 2\cdot(\cos^2\phi-\sin^2\alpha) = \cos\phi[2\cos\phi\cos\alpha]$

or $\quad \cos^2\phi(1-\cos\alpha) = \sin^2\alpha = (1-\cos^2\alpha)$.

$$\therefore \quad \cos^2\phi = 1+\cos\alpha = 2\cos^2(\alpha/2).$$

$$\therefore \quad \cos\phi = \sqrt{2}\cos(\alpha/2).$$

39. (a) $b^2 = ac \Rightarrow \dfrac{\sin^2 z}{\cos^2 z} = \dfrac{\sin\dfrac{x+y}{2}\sin\dfrac{x-y}{2}}{\cos\dfrac{x+y}{2}\cos\dfrac{x-y}{2}}$

or $\quad \dfrac{\sin^2 z}{\cos^2 z} = \dfrac{\cos y - \cos x}{\cos y + \cos x}$

Cross multiply or by C and D.

$\cos x \cdot 1 = \cos y \, (\cos^2 z - \sin^2 z) = \cos y \cos 2z$

(b) $\sin^2 \theta = \sin \phi \cos \phi$ or $2 \sin^2 \theta = \sin 2\phi$

$\qquad 1 - \cos 2\theta = - \cos (\pi/2 + 2\phi)$

$\therefore \quad \cos 2\theta = 1 + \cos (\pi/2 + 2\phi)$

or $\cos 2\theta = 2 \cos^2 (\pi/4 + \phi)$

(c) a, b, c are in G.P. $\therefore \quad b^2 = ac$

$\qquad c^2 = a^2 + b^2 = a^2 + ac$

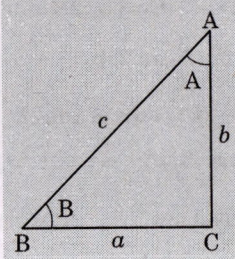

Fig. 9

or $\left(\dfrac{a}{c}\right)^2 + \dfrac{a}{c} - 1 = 0$

$\therefore \quad \dfrac{a}{c} = \cos B = \dfrac{-1 \pm \sqrt{5}}{2} = \dfrac{\sqrt{5} - 1}{2} \; \because \; \cos B \text{ is +ive}$

$\therefore \quad \cos A = \sin B = \sqrt{(1 - \cos^2 B)}$

$\qquad = \sqrt{\left(1 - \dfrac{6 - 2\sqrt{5}}{4}\right)} = \sqrt{\dfrac{\sqrt{5} - 1}{2}}$

40. Use $\cot x - \cot y = \dfrac{\sin (y - x)}{\sin x \sin y}$ etc.

41. (a) $\sin (\alpha + \beta + \gamma) = \sin (\alpha + \beta) \cos \gamma + \cos (\alpha + \beta) \sin \gamma$

$\qquad = \sin \alpha \cos \beta \cos \gamma + \cos \alpha \sin \beta \cos \gamma$

$\qquad\qquad + \cos \alpha \cos \beta \sin \gamma - \sin \alpha \sin \beta \sin \gamma .$

Now divide each term by $\cos \alpha \cos \beta \cos \gamma$ and you get L.H.S.

(b) On putting the value of $\sin (\alpha + \beta + \gamma)$, we get

$\sin \alpha + \sin \beta + \sin \gamma - \sin (\alpha + \beta + \gamma)$

$= \sin \alpha \, (1 - \cos \beta \cos \gamma) + \sin \beta \, (1 - \cos \gamma \cos \alpha)$

$\qquad + \sin \gamma \, (1 - \cos \alpha \cos \beta) + \sin \alpha \sin \beta \sin \gamma > 0$

$\because \quad \alpha, \beta, \gamma$ all lie in 1st quadrant.

$\therefore \quad \cos \alpha \cos \beta$ is +ive and less than 1 so that $1 - \cos \alpha \cos \beta$ is +ive and also $\sin \gamma$ is +ive . Thus every term in L.H.S. is +ive. $i.e.$ L.H.S. > 0

$\therefore \quad \sin \alpha + \sin \beta + \sin \gamma > \sin (\alpha + \beta + \gamma)$

42. From the given relation, we have

$\qquad 3 \cos x + \sin x = 3 \cos y - \sin y .$ \qquad ...(1)

Put $3 = r \cos \alpha, 1 = r \sin \alpha ,$

$\therefore \quad r = \sqrt{10} , \tan \alpha = \dfrac{1}{3} .$

$\therefore \quad r \cos (x - \alpha) = r \cos (y + \alpha)$

$\therefore \quad x - \alpha = \pm (y + \alpha)$

$\therefore \quad x = - y$ or $x = y + 2\alpha$

Clearly $x = - y$ satisfies (1)

$\therefore \quad 3x = - 3y$ or $\sin 3x = \sin (- 3y) = - \sin 3y$

or $\sin 3x + \sin 3y = 0 .$

43. Ans. (a), (b), (c), (d).

Refer **rule 34 P. 518**

$\qquad 1 \pm \sin \alpha = \left(\cos \dfrac{\alpha}{2} \pm \sin \dfrac{\alpha}{2}\right)^2$

$\therefore \quad x = \dfrac{\pm (\cos 2\theta - \sin 2\theta) + 1}{\pm (\cos 2\theta + \sin 2\theta) - 1}$

Now $1 - \cos 2\theta = 2 \sin^2 \theta, 1 + \cos 2\theta = 2 \cos^2 \theta$

Take $+, + ; + - ; - , + ;$ and $- , -$ and use above formula and you get all the four given answers.

44. $A < B < C < D$ are in ascending order \qquad ...(1)

$\sin A = \sin B = \sin C = \sin D = k$ (+ ive) \qquad ...(2)

$\therefore \quad B = \pi - A, C = 2\pi + A, D = 3\pi - A$

We have chosen the values so as to satisfy the conditions (1) and (2).

$E = 4 \sin \dfrac{A}{2} + 3 \sin \dfrac{\pi - A}{2} + 2 \sin \dfrac{2\pi + A}{2} + \sin \dfrac{3\pi - A}{2}$

$= 4 \sin \dfrac{A}{2} + 3 \cos \dfrac{A}{2} - 2 \sin \dfrac{A}{2} - \cos \dfrac{A}{2}$

$= 2 \left(\sin \dfrac{A}{2} + \cos \dfrac{A}{2}\right)$

$= 2 \sqrt{\sin^2 \dfrac{A}{2} + \cos^2 \dfrac{A}{2} + 2 \sin \dfrac{A}{2} \cos \dfrac{A}{2}}$

$= 2 \sqrt{1 + \sin A} = 2 \sqrt{1 + k}$

45. (a) Ans. (a).

Let $c = \cos \theta, s = \sin \theta$

$\therefore \quad E = \dfrac{2 + 3s + 5cs - 7c^2 + 5c}{2s + 3 + 5c^2 + 7cs + 8c}$

$= \dfrac{s (5c + 3) - (7c + 2) (c - 1)}{s (7c + 2) + (c + 1) (5c + 3)}$

Now $s^2 = 1 - c^2 = (1 + c) (1 - c)$

$\therefore \quad \dfrac{s}{1 - c} = \dfrac{1 + c}{s} = \lambda$ say

$\therefore \quad E = \dfrac{(1 - c) \lambda (5c + 3) + (1 - c) (7c + 2)}{s (7c + 2) + \lambda s (5c + 3)}$

$= \dfrac{1 - c}{s} \cdot \dfrac{(7c + 2) + \lambda (5c + 3)}{(7c + 2) + \lambda (5c + 3)}$

$= \dfrac{1 - c}{s} = \dfrac{2 \sin^2 \dfrac{\theta}{2}}{2 \sin \dfrac{\theta}{2} \cos \dfrac{\theta}{2}} = \tan \dfrac{\theta}{2}$

(b) Ans. (d).

$\tan (B + C) = \dfrac{\tan B + \tan C}{1 - \tan B \tan C} = - \tan A$

$\therefore \quad \tan A = \dfrac{\tan B + \tan C}{\tan B \tan C - 1} \geq \dfrac{2 \sqrt{\tan B \tan C}}{\tan B \tan C - 1}$

If $x = \tan B \tan C$, then

$\qquad x - 1 \geq 2 \sqrt{x} \cot A$ or $x - 2 \sqrt{x} \cot A \geq 1$

Add $\cot^2 A$ to both sides,

$(\sqrt{x} - \cot A)^2 \geq \operatorname{cosec}^2 A$

$\therefore \quad \sqrt{x} \geq \cot A + \operatorname{cosec} A = \dfrac{1 + \cos A}{\sin A} = \cot \dfrac{A}{2}$

$\therefore \quad x \geq \cot^2 \dfrac{A}{2} \Rightarrow (d)$

46. (a) Ans. (c).

We have the following relations :

$\sin \alpha + \sin \beta = -p, \quad \cos \alpha + \cos \beta = -r \qquad \ldots(A)$

$\sin \alpha \sin \beta = q, \quad \cos \alpha \cos \beta = s \qquad \ldots(B)$

Multiplying the relation in (A), we have

$\sin \alpha \cos \alpha + \sin \beta \cos \beta + \sin(\alpha + \beta) = pr$

$\therefore \quad \sin(\alpha + \beta) = pr - \dfrac{1}{2}(\sin 2\alpha + \sin 2\beta)$

$\qquad = pr - \dfrac{1}{2} . 2 \sin(\alpha + \beta) \cos(\alpha - \beta)$

$\therefore \quad \sin(\alpha + \beta)[1 + \cos(\alpha - \beta)] = pr \qquad \ldots(1)$

For finding the value of $\cos(\alpha - \beta)$, square and add relations in (A).

$1 + 1 + 2 \cos(\alpha - \beta) = p^2 + r^2$

or $\quad 1 + \cos(\alpha - \beta) = \dfrac{p^2 + r^2}{2} \qquad \ldots(2)$

$\therefore \quad \sin(\alpha + \beta) = \dfrac{2pr}{p^2 + r^2}$ by (1) and (2).

(b) Ans. (d).

$u^2 = a^2 . 1 + b^2 . 1 + 2\{a^2 b^2 (\cos^4 \theta + \sin^4 \theta)$

$\qquad + \sin^2 \theta \cos^2 \theta (a^4 + b^4)\}^{1/2}$

or $\quad u^2 = (a^2 + b^2) + 2\{a^2 b^2 (1 - 2 \sin^2 \theta \cos^2 \theta)$

$\qquad + \sin^2 \theta \cos^2 \theta (a^4 + b^4)\}^{1/2}$

$= (a^2 + b^2) + 2\{a^2 b^2 + \sin^2 \theta \cos^2 \theta (a^2 - b^2)^2\}^{1/2}$

$= (a^2 + b^2) + \{4a^2 b^2 + \sin^2 2\theta (a^2 - b^2)^2\}^{1/2}$

u^2 is max. when $\sin 2\theta = 1$ and min. when $\sin 2\theta = 0$

$\therefore \quad$ Max. $u^2 = (a^2 + b^2) + (a^2 + b^2) = 2(a^2 + b^2)$

$\qquad$ Min. $u^2 = a^2 + b^2 + 2ab$

Difference $= a^2 + b^2 - 2ab = (a - b)^2$.

(c) Ans. (a), (b), (c).

From 2nd relation,

$2 \cos^2 x - 1 + 2 \cos^2 y - 1 = b$

$\therefore \quad \cos^2 x + \cos^2 y = \dfrac{1}{2}(b + 2) = 1 + \dfrac{b}{2} \qquad \ldots(a)$

Squaring 1st relation,

$\cos^2 x + \cos^2 y + 2 \cos x \cos y = a^2$

or $\quad \left(1 + \dfrac{b}{2}\right) + 2 \cos x \cos y = a^2$

$\therefore \quad \cos x \cos y = \dfrac{a^2}{2} - \dfrac{b + 2}{4}$ by (a)

From last relation,

$4(\cos^3 x + \cos^3 y) - 3(\cos x + \cos y) = c$

or $\quad a[4(\cos^2 x + \cos^2 y - \cos x \cos y) - 3] = c$

Now put for $\cos^2 x + \cos^2 y$ and $\cos x \cos y$ from (a) and (b) and we get relation (c).

Problem Set (5)

The values of trigonometrical ratios of angles $18°, 36°, 54°, 72°$. Sum of sine or cosine series when angles are in A.P. Value of $\cos A \cos 2A \cos 4A \ldots \cos 2^{n-1} A = \dfrac{\sin(2^n A)}{2^n \sin A}$

1. Prove that

(a)* $\cot 7\frac{1}{2}° = (\sqrt{3} + \sqrt{2})(\sqrt{2} + 1) = \sqrt{2} + \sqrt{3} + \sqrt{4} + \sqrt{6}$

$\quad$ or $\quad \tan 82\frac{1}{2}° = (\sqrt{3} + \sqrt{2})(\sqrt{2} + 1)$

(b) $\tan(142° 30') = 2 + \sqrt{2} - \sqrt{3} - \sqrt{6}$

2. (a) $\cot 22\frac{1}{2}° = \sqrt{\left(\dfrac{2 + \sqrt{2}}{2 - \sqrt{2}}\right)} = \sqrt{\left(\dfrac{\sqrt{2} + 1}{\sqrt{2} - 1}\right)} = (\sqrt{2} + 1)$

(b)* $\tan\left(11\frac{1}{4}°\right) = \sqrt{4 + 2\sqrt{2}} - (\sqrt{2} + 1)$

3. Compute $\tan(\theta/4)$ if $\cos\theta = -0\cdot 8$ and $180° < \theta < 270°$.

4.* For $0 < \phi \leq \dfrac{\pi}{2}$, if $x = \sum\limits_{n=0}^{\infty} \cos^{2n} \phi$,

$\qquad y = \sum\limits_{n=0}^{\infty} \sin^{2n} \phi, z = \sum\limits_{n=0}^{\infty} \cos^{2n} \phi \sin^{2n} \phi,$

then $x + y = xy$ and $xyz = x + y + z = xy + z$.

$\qquad$ **(I.I.T. 1993)**

Prove the following :

5. (a) $\dfrac{1}{\tan 3A - \tan A} - \dfrac{1}{\cot 3A - \cot A} = \cot 2A$.

(b) $\dfrac{\sec\theta + \sec\phi + (\tan\theta - \tan\phi)}{\sec\theta + \sec\phi - (\tan\theta - \tan\phi)} = \dfrac{\tan\left(\dfrac{\pi}{4} + \dfrac{\theta}{2}\right)}{\tan\left(\dfrac{\pi}{4} + \dfrac{\phi}{2}\right)}$

6. (a)* $\cos 2\alpha = 2 \sin^2 \beta + 4 \cos(\alpha + \beta) \sin\alpha \sin\beta$

$\qquad\qquad\qquad + \cos 2(\alpha + \beta)$ **(M.N.R. 1993)**

(b) $\sin^2 A = \cos^2(A - B) + \cos^2 B$

$\qquad\qquad\qquad - 2 \cos(A - B) \cos A \cos B$

(c) $\sin^2 B = \sin^2 A + \sin^2(A - B)$

$\qquad\qquad\qquad - 2 \sin A \cos B \sin(A - B)$

7. (a) Show that

$\sin^2(\theta + A) + \sin^2(\theta + B)$

$\qquad\qquad - 2 \cos(A - B) \sin(\theta + A) \sin(\theta + B)$

is independent of θ or $= \sin^2(A - B)$

(b)* $\cos^2 A + \cos^2 B - 2\cos A \cos B \cos (A + B)$

$$= \sin^2 (A + B)$$

(c) $0 \le \cos^2 \alpha + \cos^2 (\alpha + \beta)$

$$- 2\cos \alpha \cos \beta \cos (\alpha + \beta) \le 1$$

8. (a) If θ lies in 4th quadrant and $\sin \dfrac{\theta}{2} + \cos \dfrac{\theta}{2} = -\dfrac{1}{2}$ then determine the value of $\sin 2\theta$.

(b) If $5\cos^2 \theta - 2\sin \theta - 2 = 0 \left(\dfrac{5\pi}{4} < \theta < \dfrac{7\pi}{4} \right)$

then prove that $\tan \dfrac{\theta}{2} = -1$.

(c) If $\alpha + \beta = \dfrac{\pi}{2}$ and $\beta + \gamma = \alpha$, then $\tan \alpha$ equals

(a) $2(\tan \beta + \tan \gamma)$ (b) $\tan \beta + \tan \gamma$

(c) $\tan \beta + 2\tan \gamma$ (d) $2\tan \beta + \tan \gamma$

(I.I.T. Sc. 2001)

9.* $\dfrac{\sin x}{\cos 3x} + \dfrac{\sin 3x}{\cos 9x} + \dfrac{\sin 9x}{\cos 27x} = \dfrac{1}{2}(\tan 27x - \tan x)$

10. (a)* Prove that

$$\left(\cot \dfrac{\theta}{2} - \tan \dfrac{\theta}{2} \right)^2 (1 - 2\tan \theta \cot 2\theta) = 4$$

(b)* If $\tan \alpha = \dfrac{1}{\sqrt{x(x^2 + x + 1)}}$, $\tan \beta = \dfrac{\sqrt{x}}{\sqrt{x^2 + x + 1}}$ and

$\tan \gamma = (x^{-3} + x^{-2} + x^{-1})^{1/2}$ then prove that
$\alpha + \beta = \gamma$.

11. $1 + \cos 56° + \cos 58° - \cos 66° = 4\cos 28° \cos 29° \sin 33°$

12. (a)* $\dfrac{\sec 8\theta - 1}{\sec 4\theta - 1} = \dfrac{\tan 8\theta}{\tan 2\theta}$

(b) $\tan A \sec 4A + \tan 4A = \tan A + \tan 4A \sec 2A$

13. (a) For a positive integer n, let

$$f_n (\theta) = \left(\tan \dfrac{\theta}{2} \right)(1 + \sec \theta)(1 + \sec 2\theta)$$

$$(1 + \sec 4\theta) \ldots (1 + \sec 2^n \theta)$$

Then

(a) $f_2 \left(\dfrac{\pi}{16} \right) = 1$ (b) $f_3 \left(\dfrac{\pi}{32} \right) = 1$

(c) $f_4 \left(\dfrac{\pi}{64} \right) = 1$ (d) $f_5 \left(\dfrac{\pi}{128} \right) = 1$

(I.I.T. 1999)

(b)* Match the following of C_1 and C_2

C_1 C_2

(a) $\log_3 2, \log_6 2, \log_{12} 2$

(b) $\cot 30°, \cot 45°, \cot 60°$ (i) A.P.

                                (ii) G.P.

                               (iii) H.P.

14.* If the angle A of a triangle ABC is given by the equation $5\cos A + 3 = 0$, then $\sin A$ and $\tan A$ are the roots of the equation $15 x^2 + 8 x - 16 = 0$.

15. (a) If $\cos \theta = \dfrac{1}{2} \left(a + \dfrac{1}{a} \right)$, then prove that

$$\cos 3\theta = \dfrac{1}{2} \left(a^3 + \dfrac{1}{a^3} \right).$$

(b)* If $\cos x + \cos y + \cos z = 0$, then find the value of $\cos 3x + \cos 3y + \cos 3z$.

16. Prove :

(a) $\cos 5\theta = 16\cos^5 \theta - 20\cos^3 \theta + 5\cos \theta$

(b) $\sin 5\theta = 5\cos^4 \theta \sin \theta - 10\cos^2 \theta \sin^3 \theta + \sin^5 \theta$

(c) Express $\sin 5\theta$ in terms of $\sin \theta$ and hence find the value of $\sin 36°$.

Prove the following :

17. (a) $\cos^3 \theta + \cos^3 (120° + \theta) + \cos^3 (240° + \theta)$

$$= \dfrac{3}{4} \cos 3\theta.$$

(b) $\cos^2 A + \cos^2 (A + 120°) + \cos^2 (A - 120°) = \dfrac{3}{2}$.

18. (a) $\cos^4 \dfrac{\pi}{8} + \cos^4 \dfrac{3\pi}{8} + \cos^4 \dfrac{5\pi}{8} + \cos^4 \dfrac{7\pi}{8} = \dfrac{3}{2}$.

(b)* $\sin^4 \dfrac{\pi}{8} + \sin^4 \dfrac{3\pi}{8} + \sin^4 \dfrac{5\pi}{8} + \sin^4 \dfrac{7\pi}{8} = \dfrac{3}{2}$.

19. (a)* $\tan^2 \dfrac{\pi}{16} + \tan^2 \dfrac{2\pi}{16} + \ldots + \tan^2 \dfrac{6\pi}{16} + \tan^2 \dfrac{7\pi}{16} = 35$

(b)* $\Sigma \sin^4 \dfrac{r\pi}{16} = \dfrac{3}{2}, r = 1, 3, 5, 7$

(c) Show that $\tan^6 \dfrac{\pi}{9} - 33\tan^4 \dfrac{\pi}{9} + 27\tan^2 \dfrac{\pi}{9} = 3$

20. (a)* $\tan \theta \tan (\theta + 60°) + \tan \theta \tan (\theta - 60°)$

$$+ \tan (\theta + 60°) \tan (\theta - 60°) = -3.$$

(b)* $\cot 16° \cot 44° + \cot 44° \cot 76°$

$$- \cot 76° \cot 16° = 3.$$

(c)* Prove that $\dfrac{3 + \cot 76° \cot 16°}{\cot 76° + \cot 16°} = \cot 44°$

21. (a) $\cot A \cot 2A + \cot 2A \cot 3A + 2$

$$= \cot A (\cot A - \cot 3A)$$

(J.E.E.W.B. 2000)

(b)* If $\cos (x - y) + \cos (y - z) + \cos (z - x) = -3/2$,
then prove that $\cos x + \cos y + \cos z = 0$ and
$\sin x + \sin y + \sin z = 0$.

22. (a) $\tan A + \tan (60° + A) - \tan (60° - A) = 3\tan 3A$

(b) $\cot \alpha + \cot (60° + \alpha) - \cot (60° - \alpha) = 3\cot 3\alpha$

23. (a)* If $x\sin \theta = y\sin \left(\theta + \dfrac{2\pi}{3} \right) = z\sin \left(\theta + \dfrac{4\pi}{3} \right)$ then

prove that $\Sigma xy = 0$

(b) If $a\cos \theta + b\sin \theta - c = 0$
$a\cos \phi + b\sin \phi - c = 0$, then prove that
$$\dfrac{a}{\cos \dfrac{\theta + \phi}{2}} = \dfrac{b}{\sin \dfrac{\theta + \phi}{2}} = \dfrac{c}{\cos \dfrac{\theta - \phi}{2}}$$

24. (a)* If β and γ are +ive angles less than two right angles
and $\cos \alpha + \cos (\alpha + \beta) + \cos (\alpha + \beta + \gamma) = 0$
and $\sin \alpha + \sin (\alpha + \beta) + \sin (\alpha + \beta + \gamma) = 0$
then $\beta = \gamma = 2\pi/3$.

(b) If $\dfrac{p\cos (x + \alpha) + q\sin (x + \beta)}{p'\sin (x + \alpha) + q'\cos (x + \beta)}$ has the

same value at $x = 0$ and $x = \pi/2$, then prove that

$$pp' - qq' = (p'q - pq') \sin(\alpha - \beta)$$

25. (a) $\cos 20° + \cos 100° + \cos 140° = 0.$

    (b) $\sin 10° + \sin 20° + \sin 40° + \sin 50°$
    $$- \sin 70° - \sin 80° = 0$$

    (c) $\sin 50° - \sin 70° + \sin 10° = 0$

26. (a) $\dfrac{\cos^2 33° - \cos^2 57°}{\sin 21° - \cos 21°} = -\dfrac{1}{\sqrt{2}}$

    (b) $2 \cos \dfrac{\pi}{13} \cos \dfrac{9\pi}{13} + \cos \dfrac{3\pi}{13} + \cos \dfrac{5\pi}{13} = 0.$

    (c) $\cos 20° \cos 100° + \cos 100° \cos 140°$
    $$- \cos 140° \cos 200° = -3/4$$

27. (a)* $\cos \dfrac{2\pi}{7} + \cos \dfrac{4\pi}{7} + \cos \dfrac{6\pi}{7} = -\dfrac{1}{2}$

    (b) $\cos \dfrac{\pi}{11} + \cos \dfrac{3\pi}{11} + \cos \dfrac{5\pi}{11} + \cos \dfrac{7\pi}{11} + \cos \dfrac{9\pi}{11} = \dfrac{1}{2}$

    (c) $\cos 0 + \cos \dfrac{\pi}{7} + \cos \dfrac{2\pi}{7} + \cos \dfrac{3\pi}{7}$
    $$+ \cos \dfrac{4\pi}{7} + \cos \dfrac{5\pi}{7} + \cos \dfrac{6\pi}{7} = 1$$

28. (a) $\tan 10° + \tan 70° - \tan 50° = \sqrt{3}.$

    (b)*   Show, without using tables or calculators, that
    $$\tan 9° - \tan 27° - \tan 63° + \tan 81° = 4$$

29. (a) $\cos^2 73° + \cos^2 47° + \cos 73° \cos 47° = \dfrac{3}{4}$

    (b)* $\sin^2 12° + \sin^2 21° + \sin^2 39° + \sin^2 48°$
    $$= 1 + \sin^2 9° + \sin^2 18°$$

30. $\dfrac{\cos 3\theta + \cos 3\phi}{2 \cos(\theta - \phi) - 1}$
    $$= (\cos \theta + \cos \phi) \cos(\theta + \phi) - (\sin \theta + \sin \phi) \sin(\theta + \phi).$$

31.   Prove that $\cos A \cos 2A \cos 4A \cos 8A = \dfrac{\sin 2^4 A}{2^4 \sin A}$

    Four angles, each double of preceding angle.

    (Remember and Note the form)

    Above can be used as a formula as given in and hence prove the following :   **(R. 37 P. 519)**

    (a)* $\cos 20° \cos 40° \cos 60° \cos 80° = \dfrac{1}{16}.$

    Another form (I) :

    $$\sin 10° \sin 30° \sin 50° \sin 70° = \dfrac{1}{16}$$

    (Complementary rule)

    Another form (II) :

    If $K = \sin(\pi/18) \sin(5\pi/18) \sin(7\pi/18)$,   then   the numerical value of K is ...., $\pi/18 = 10°$ **(I.I.T. 1993)**

    Another form (III) :

    $$\sin 70° + 8 \cos 20° \cos 40° \cos 80° = 2 \cos^2 10°$$

    (b) $\cos 7° \cos 14° \cos 28° \cos 56° = \dfrac{\sin 68°}{16 \cos 83°}.$

    (c)* $\cos \dfrac{2\pi}{15} \cos \dfrac{4\pi}{15} \cos \dfrac{8\pi}{15} \cos \dfrac{16\pi}{15} = \dfrac{1}{16}$

Another form :

$$\cos \dfrac{2\pi}{15} \cos \dfrac{4\pi}{15} \cos \dfrac{8\pi}{15} \cos \dfrac{14\pi}{15} = \dfrac{1}{16}$$

(d)   The value of $\cosec^2 \dfrac{\pi}{7} + \cosec^2 \dfrac{2\pi}{7} + \cosec^2 \dfrac{3\pi}{7}$ is

    (a) 2^3 (b) 2^2

    (c) 2^1 (d) 2^0

(e)   Prove that
$$\cot^2(\pi/9) + \cot^2(2\pi/9) + \cot^2(4\pi/9) = 9$$

32. (a) $\cos \dfrac{\pi}{7} \cos \dfrac{2\pi}{7} \cos \dfrac{4\pi}{7} = -\dfrac{1}{8}.$

    (b) $\cos \dfrac{\pi}{5} \cos \dfrac{2\pi}{5} = \dfrac{1}{4}$ and $\cos \dfrac{\pi}{5} + \cos \dfrac{3\pi}{5} = \dfrac{1}{2}$

    without using standard values .

33. (a) $\sin \dfrac{\pi}{14} \sin \dfrac{3\pi}{14} \sin \dfrac{5\pi}{14} = \dfrac{1}{8}.$

    (b)* $\sin \dfrac{\pi}{14} \sin \dfrac{3\pi}{14} \sin \dfrac{5\pi}{14} \sin \dfrac{7\pi}{14} = \dfrac{1}{8}$ **(M.N.R. 1992)**

    (c)* $\sin \dfrac{\pi}{14} \sin \dfrac{3\pi}{14} \sin \dfrac{5\pi}{14} \sin \dfrac{7\pi}{14}$
    $$\sin \dfrac{9\pi}{14} \sin \dfrac{11\pi}{14} \sin \dfrac{13\pi}{14} = \dfrac{1}{64}$$
    (I.I.T. 1991)

34.* (a) $\cos \dfrac{\pi}{15} \cos \dfrac{2\pi}{15} \cos \dfrac{3\pi}{15} \cos \dfrac{4\pi}{15} \cos \dfrac{5\pi}{15}$
    $$\cos \dfrac{6\pi}{15} \cos \dfrac{7\pi}{15} = \dfrac{1}{128}$$

    (b) $\cos \dfrac{\pi}{33} \cos \dfrac{2\pi}{33} \cos \dfrac{4\pi}{33} \cos \dfrac{8\pi}{33} \cos \dfrac{16\pi}{33} = \dfrac{1}{32}$

    (c)*   Find the value of :

    $\cos \dfrac{\pi}{65} \cdot \cos \dfrac{2\pi}{65} \cdot \cos \dfrac{4\pi}{65} \cdot \cos \dfrac{8\pi}{65} \cdot \cos \dfrac{16\pi}{65} \cdot \cos \dfrac{32\pi}{65}$
    (M.N.R. 1997)

    (d)*   If $\theta = \dfrac{\pi}{2^n + 1}$, prove that

    $$2^n \cos \theta \cos 2\theta \cos 2^2 \theta \ldots \cos 2^{n-1} \theta = 1.$$

35. (a)* $\sin 20° \sin 40° \sin 60° \sin 80° = \dfrac{3}{16}$

    (b) $\tan 20° \tan 40° \tan 60° \tan 80° = 3.$

36.* If $p_{n+1} = \sqrt{\dfrac{1}{2}(1 + p_n)}$, then $\cos\left(\dfrac{\sqrt{1 - p_0^2}}{p_1 \, p_2 \, p_3 \ldots \text{to} \infty}\right) = p_0$

37.* $(2 \cos \theta - 1)(2 \cos 2\theta - 1)(2 \cos 2^2 \theta - 1)$
    $$\ldots (2 \cos 2^{n-1} \theta - 1)$$
    $$= \dfrac{2 \cos 2^n \theta + 1}{2 \cos \theta + 1}$$

38. (a) $\sin 12° \sin 48° \sin 54° = \dfrac{1}{8}.$ **(D.C.E. 1997)**

    (b) $\sin \dfrac{\pi}{10} \sin \dfrac{13\pi}{10}$ is equal to

    (i) $\dfrac{1}{2}$ (ii) $-\dfrac{1}{2}$

    (iii) $-\dfrac{1}{4}$ (iv) 1

(c)* $(\sin 55° - \sin 19°) + (\sin 53° - \sin 17°) = \cos 1°$

(J.E.E.W.B. 1993)

39. (a)* $\left(1 + \cos \dfrac{\pi}{10}\right)\left(1 + \cos \dfrac{3\pi}{10}\right)$

$$\left(1 + \cos \dfrac{7\pi}{10}\right)\left(1 + \cos \dfrac{9\pi}{10}\right) = \dfrac{1}{16}$$

(b)* $\left(1 + \cos \dfrac{\pi}{8}\right)\left(1 + \cos \dfrac{3\pi}{8}\right)$

$$\left(1 + \cos \dfrac{5\pi}{8}\right)\left(1 + \cos \dfrac{7\pi}{8}\right) = \dfrac{1}{8}$$

40. (a)* $\cos 60° \cos 36° \cos 42° \cos 78° = 1/16$

(b)* $\sin 6° \sin 42° \sin 66° \sin 78° = 1/16$

and $\cos 6° \cos 42° \cos 66° \cos 78° = 1/16$

(c) $\tan 6° \tan 42° \tan 66° \tan 78° = 1.$

41. (a)* $\sin 36° \sin 72° \sin 108° \sin 144° = 5/16$

(b) $4 \sin 27° = \sqrt{(5 + \sqrt 5)} - \sqrt{(3 - \sqrt 5)}.$

42. (a)* If $\cos(\alpha + \beta) = (4/5)$ and $\sin(\alpha - \beta) = (5/13)$ and α, β lie between 0 and $\pi/4$ find $\tan 2\alpha$.

(b) If $\cos \alpha = (3/5), \cos \beta = (5/13)$, prove that $\sin^2(\alpha - \beta)/2 = 1/65, \cos^2(\alpha - \beta)/2 = 64/65$

43. If $\sin x + \sin y = a$ and $\cos x + \cos y = b$, show that

(a) $\sin(x + y) = 2ab/(a^2 + b^2)$

(b) $\cos(x - y) = (a^2 + b^2 - 2)/2$

(c)* $\tan\left(\dfrac{x - y}{2}\right) = \pm \sqrt{\dfrac{4 - a^2 - b^2}{a^2 + b^2}}$

44. (a)* If $\sin x + \cos x = a$, evaluate $\sin^6 x + \cos^6 x$.

(b)* If $\sin A + \sin 2A = x, \cos A + \cos 2A = y$, then prove that $(x^2 + y^2)(x^2 + y^2 - 3) = 2y$.

45. (a)* Eliminate x and y from the equations
$\cos x + \cos y = a, \cos 2x + \cos 2y = b,$
$$\cos 3x + \cos 3y = c.$$

(b) Eliminate x and y from the equations
$\sin x + \sin y = a,$ $\cos x + \cos y = b,$
$\tan x + \tan y = c$

46. (a) Eliminate x between the equations
$\sin x - \cos x = a$ and $\csc x - \sin x = b$

(b) If $a \sin \theta + b \cos \theta = a \csc \theta - b \sec \theta = 1$, prove that $a^2 + b^2 = 1 + b^{2/3} - b^{4/3}$

47. (a) Eliminate θ between the equations
$a \sec \theta + b \tan \theta + c = 0$
and $p \sec \theta + q \tan \theta + r = 0$

(b) Eliminate x from the equations
$m \tan x + n \cot 2x = p$
and $n \cot x - n \tan 2x = p$.

48. (a)* If $a \cos \theta + b \sin \theta = c$ and
$a \cos^2 \theta + 2a \sin \theta \cos \theta + b \sin^2 \theta = c$,
where a, b, c are all unequal quantities, then eliminate θ.

(b)* If $a \sin^2 \alpha + b \cos^2 \alpha = p, b \sin^2 \beta + a \cos^2 \beta = q$
and $a \tan \alpha = b \tan \beta$, then show that $\dfrac{1}{a} + \dfrac{1}{b} = \dfrac{1}{p} + \dfrac{1}{q}$
where $a \ne p, b \ne q$ and all the four are non-zero.

(c) If $x \cos \alpha + y \sin \alpha = 2a$,
$x \cos \beta + y \sin \beta = 2a$
and $2 \sin(\alpha/2) \sin(\beta/2) = 1$
then prove that $y^2 = 4a(a - x)$.

49. (a) If $\dfrac{\sin(x - \alpha)}{\sin(x - \beta)} = \dfrac{a}{b}, \dfrac{\cos(x - \alpha)}{\cos(x - \beta)} = \dfrac{A}{B}$
and $aB + bA \ne 0$, then prove that
$$\cos(\alpha - \beta) = \dfrac{aA + bB}{aB + bA}.$$

(b) If A and B be acute +ive angles satisfying the equalities $3 \sin^2 A + 2 \sin^2 B = 1$ and $3 \sin 2A - 2 \sin 2B = 0$, prove that $A + 2B = \pi/2$.

(c) If $\tan^3 \theta = \tan \phi$ and $\tan 2\theta = 2 \tan \alpha$, prove that $\theta + \phi = n\pi + \alpha$.

50. (a)* If α, β are two values of θ satisfying the equation $\dfrac{\cos \theta}{a} + \dfrac{\sin \theta}{b} = \dfrac{1}{c}$, then prove

(i) $\cot\left(\dfrac{\alpha + \beta}{2}\right) = \dfrac{b}{a}$ (ii) $\dfrac{\cos\left(\dfrac{\alpha + \beta}{2}\right)}{\cos\left(\dfrac{\alpha - \beta}{2}\right)} = \dfrac{c}{a}$

(b)* If $\dfrac{\sin A}{\sin B} = p, \dfrac{\cos A}{\cos B} = q$, then prove that
$$\tan A = \pm \dfrac{p}{q}\sqrt{\dfrac{1 - q^2}{p^2 - 1}}, \tan B = \pm \sqrt{\dfrac{1 - q^2}{p^2 - 1}}$$

(c) In a triangle ABC if $\tan \dfrac{A}{2} = p$ and $\tan \dfrac{B}{2} = q$,
prove that $\sin C = \dfrac{2(p + q)(1 - pq)}{(1 + p^2)(1 + q^2)}$.

51. (a) If $\tan \theta = \dfrac{p^2 - q^2}{2pq}$, then
$$\tan \dfrac{\theta}{2} = \dfrac{p - q}{p + q} \quad \text{or} \quad -\dfrac{p + q}{p - q}$$

(b)* If α and β are the two different values of θ lying between 0 and 2π which satisfy $3 \cos \theta + 4 \sin \theta = 6$. Find the value of $\sin(\alpha + \beta)$. In case the given equation be wrong then try it with 9/2 in place of 6 in R.H.S.

52. (a) If $\tan x = \dfrac{2b}{a - c} \ (a \ne c)$
$y = a \cos^2 x + 2b \sin x \cos x + c \sin^2 x$
$z = a \sin^2 x - 2b \sin x \cos x + c \cos^2 x$, then prove that
(i) $y + z = a + c$ (ii) $y - z = a - c$

(b) If x and y are acute angles such that $x + y$ and $x - y$ satisfy the equation $\tan^2 \theta - 4 \tan \theta + 1 = 0$, then $x = \ldots$, $y = \ldots$

(c) If $2 \tan A = 3 \tan B$, prove that
$$\tan (A - B) = \frac{\sin 2B}{5 - \cos 2B}.$$

53. (a) Prove that $\dfrac{1}{\sin 10°} - \dfrac{\sqrt{3}}{\cos 10°} = 4$

(b)* Prove that $\sqrt{3} \csc 20° - \sec 20° = 4$.

54. (a) Evaluate $4 \cos 20° - \sqrt{3} \cot 20°$ and

(b) $\dfrac{2 \cos 40° - \cos 20°}{\sin 20°}$.

(c) Find the value of $4 \cos 20° - \sqrt{3} \cot 20°$.

55. (a) Max. value of $y = \cos^2 (45° + x) + (\sin x - \cos x)^2$ is $\ldots$

(b)* Prove that minimum value of $a \sec x - b \tan x$ is $\sqrt{a^2 - b^2}$ where a and b are $+$ive, $a > b$.

56. (a) Determine a and b such that
$$a \le \cos 2x + 3 \sin x \le b$$

(b)* Show that for all real values of θ, the expression
$$a \sin^2 \theta + b \sin \theta \cos \theta + c \cos^2 \theta$$
lies between $\dfrac{1}{2}(a + c) - \dfrac{1}{2}\sqrt{b^2 + (a - c)^2}$
and $\dfrac{1}{2}(a + c) + \dfrac{1}{2}\sqrt{b^2 + (a - c)^2}$.

57. (a) If $a^2 + b^2 = 1$, $m^2 + n^2 = 1$, prove $|am + bn| \le 1$

(b)* If $f(x) = \sin^2 x + \sin^2 \left(x + \dfrac{\pi}{3}\right) + \cos x \cos \left(x + \dfrac{\pi}{3}\right)$
and $g\left(\dfrac{5}{4}\right) = 1$, then $(g \circ f)(x) = \ldots$
(I.I.T. 1996)

(c) Prove that $1 + \sin^2 \theta + \sin^2 \phi > \sin \theta$
$$+ \sin \phi + \sin \theta \sin \phi$$

(d) In a triangle ABC, prove that
$\dfrac{b + c}{a} \le \csc \dfrac{A}{2}$ and hence show that
$$\csc^n \dfrac{A}{2} \csc^n \dfrac{B}{2} \csc^n \dfrac{C}{2} \ge 2^{3n}$$
for all integers $n \ge 1$.

58.* If $\cos^2 \theta = \dfrac{1}{2}(a^2 - 1)$ and $\tan^2 \left(\dfrac{\theta}{2}\right) = \tan^{2/3} \alpha$,
prove that $\cos^{2/3} \alpha + \sin^{2/3} \alpha = (2/a)^{2/3}$.

59. (a)* If $\cot^2 \theta = \cot (\theta - \alpha) \cot (\theta - \beta)$,
show that $\cot 2\theta = \dfrac{1}{2}(\cot \alpha + \cot \beta)$,

(b)* If $\dfrac{\tan (\theta + x)}{a} = \dfrac{\tan (\theta + y)}{b} = \dfrac{\tan (\theta + z)}{c}$, then
$$\dfrac{a + b}{a - b} \sin^2 (x - y) + \dfrac{b + c}{b - c} \sin^2 (y - z)$$
$$+ \dfrac{c + a}{c - a} \sin^2 (z - x) = 0.$$

60. (a)* If $\dfrac{\tan (\alpha + \beta - \gamma)}{\tan (\alpha - \beta + \gamma)} = \dfrac{\tan \gamma}{\tan \beta}$, then prove that either
$\sin (\beta - \gamma) = 0$ or $\sin 2\alpha + \sin 2\beta + \sin 2\gamma = 0$.

(b)* If $\cos (\beta - \gamma) + \cos (\gamma - \alpha) + \cos (\alpha - \beta) = -3/2$,
then prove that $\Sigma \cos \alpha = 0, \Sigma \sin \alpha = 0$.

61.* If $\tan \beta = \dfrac{\tan \alpha + \tan \gamma}{1 + \tan \alpha \tan \gamma}$, prove that
$$\sin 2\beta = \dfrac{\sin 2\alpha + \sin 2\gamma}{1 + \sin 2\alpha \sin 2\gamma}$$

62.* If $\dfrac{\tan (\alpha - \beta)}{\tan \alpha} + \dfrac{\sin^2 \gamma}{\sin^2 \alpha} = 1$, then prove that $\tan \gamma$ is
geometric mean of $\tan \alpha$ and $\tan \beta$.
i.e., $\tan \alpha \tan \beta = \tan^2 \gamma$.

63.* Prove :
$$\dfrac{1 + \sin A}{\cos A} + \dfrac{\cos B}{1 - \sin B} = \dfrac{2 \sin A - 2 \sin B}{\sin (A - B) + \cos A - \cos B}$$

64.* If $\tan \left(\dfrac{\pi}{4} + \dfrac{y}{2}\right) = \tan^3 \left(\dfrac{\pi}{4} + \dfrac{x}{2}\right)$, prove that
$$\sin y = \sin x . \dfrac{3 + \sin^2 x}{1 + 3 \sin^2 x}.$$

65.* $\sin 3x \sin^3 x + \cos 3x \cos^3 x = \cos^3 2x$.

66. Let $\cos \alpha = \cos \beta \cos \phi = \cos \gamma \cos \theta$,
$\sin \alpha = 2 \sin (\phi/2) \sin (\theta/2)$.
Prove that $\tan^2 (\alpha/2) = \tan^2 (\beta/2) . \tan^2 (\gamma/2)$.

67. If $\cos (A + B + C) = \cos A \cos B \cos C$, then
$8 \sin (B + C) \sin (C + A) \sin (A + B)$
$$+ \sin 2A \sin 2B \sin 2C = 0$$

68.* If $\dfrac{\sin (\theta + A)}{\sin (\theta + B)} = \sqrt{\left(\dfrac{\sin 2A}{\sin 2B}\right)}$, prove that
$$\tan^2 \theta = \tan A \tan B$$

69.* If $\dfrac{\tan 3A}{\tan A} = k$, then prove that $\dfrac{\sin 3A}{\sin A} = \dfrac{2k}{k - 1}$ and that
k cannot lie between $\dfrac{1}{3}$ and 3.

70. If A, B, C be the angles of a triangle ABC, such that
$A = \pi/4$ and $\tan B \tan C = \lambda$, then prove that
$\lambda < (\sqrt{2} - 1)^2$ or $\lambda > (\sqrt{2} + 1)^2$.

71.* If $\cos x = \tan y, \cos y = \tan z, \cos z = \tan x$; prove that
$\sin x = \sin y = \sin z = 2 \sin 18°$.

72.* Prove that $\tan 18°$ is a root of the equation
$5x^4 - 10x^2 + 1 = 0$ and hence prove that
$\tan^2 18° = 0 \cdot 1056$

73.* Determine the smallest positive value of x (in degrees)
for which
$\tan (x + 100°) = \tan (x + 50°) \tan (x) \tan (x - 50°)$
(I.I.T. 1993)

74.* Given that the angles α, β, γ are connected by the
relation

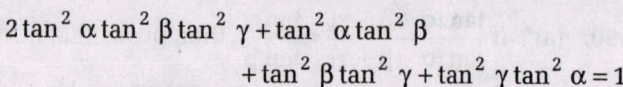

$$2\tan^2\alpha\tan^2\beta\tan^2\gamma+\tan^2\alpha\tan^2\beta$$
$$+\tan^2\beta\tan^2\gamma+\tan^2\gamma\tan^2\alpha=1$$

find the value of $\sin^2\alpha+\sin^2\beta+\sin^2\gamma$.

75.* If $\quad\tan\theta\tan\phi=\sqrt{(a-b)/(a+b)}$, prove that $(a-b\cos2\theta)(a-b\cos2\phi)$ is independent of θ and ϕ.

76. If $\dfrac{\cos^4 x}{\cos^2 y}+\dfrac{\sin^4 x}{\sin^2 y}=1$, prove that $\dfrac{\cos^4 y}{\cos^2 x}+\dfrac{\sin^4 y}{\sin^2 x}=1$.

77. (a)* Show that
$$\cos^3(\alpha+\theta)\sin^3(\beta-\gamma)+\cos^3(\beta+\theta)\sin^3(\gamma-\alpha)$$
$$+\cos^3(\gamma+\theta)\sin^3(\alpha-\beta)$$
$$=3\cos(\alpha+\theta)\cos(\beta+\theta)\cos(\gamma+\theta)$$
$$\times\sin(\alpha-\beta)\sin(\beta-\gamma)\sin(\gamma-\alpha).$$

(b)* Prove that
$$\sin^3(\beta-\gamma)\sin^3(\alpha-\delta)+\sin^3(\gamma-\alpha)\sin^3(\beta-\delta)$$
$$+\sin^3(\alpha-\beta)\sin^3(\gamma-\delta)$$
$$=3\sin(\alpha-\beta)\sin(\beta-\gamma)\sin(\gamma-\delta)\sin(\alpha-\delta)$$
$$\sin(\beta-\delta)\sin(\gamma-\delta).$$

78. (a) If $\cos(\theta-\alpha)=x$ and $\sin(\theta-\beta)=y$, then
$$\cos^2(\alpha-\beta)+2xy\sin(\alpha-\beta)=x^2+y^2.$$

(b) Prove that
$$\sin(A+B+C)\cos A\sin B\sin C$$
$$+\cos(A+B+C)\sin A\sin B\sin C$$
$$-\sin(A+B+C)\cos A\cos B\cos C$$
$$-\cos(A+B+C)\sin A\cos B\cos C$$
$$+\sin(A+B)\cos(B+C)\cos(C+A)$$
$$+\cos(A+B)\cos(B+C)\sin(C+A)=0.$$

79.* If $\sqrt{2}\cos A=\cos B+\cos^3 B$ and
$$\sqrt{2}\sin A=\sin B-\sin^3 B$$
show that $\sin(A-B)=\pm\dfrac{1}{3}$.

80.* If $\dfrac{\sin^4 A}{a}+\dfrac{\cos^4 A}{b}=\dfrac{1}{a+b}$, then prove that
$$\dfrac{\sin^8 A}{a^3}+\dfrac{\cos^8 A}{b^3}=\dfrac{1}{(a+b)^3}.$$

81.* Find roots of the following cubic equation :
$$2x^3-3x^2\cos(A-B)-2x\cos^2(A+B)$$
$$+\sin 2A.\sin 2B\cos(A-B)=0$$
(M.N.R. 1996)

82. (a) For all real θ, prove $\cos(\cos\theta)>0$

(b) For all real θ, prove $\cos(\sin\theta)>\sin(\cos\theta)$

Sum the following series :

83. (a) $\dfrac{1}{\sin\theta\sin2\theta}+\dfrac{1}{\sin2\theta\sin3\theta}+\dfrac{1}{\sin3\theta\sin4\theta}$
$$+\ldots n\text{ terms}$$

(b)* $\sec\theta.\sec2\theta+\sec2\theta\sec3\theta+\ldots n\text{ terms}$

84. (a) $\tan y\sec2y+\tan2y\sec4y+\tan4y\sec8y$
$$+\ldots n\text{ terms}$$

(b)* $\tan\dfrac{y}{2}\sec y+\tan\dfrac{y}{2^2}\sec\dfrac{y}{2}+\tan\dfrac{y}{2^3}\sec\dfrac{y}{2^2}$
$$+\ldots n\text{ terms}$$

85. (a)* $\tan x+2\tan2x+2^2\tan2^2\,x+\ldots n\text{ terms}$

(b) $\tan x+\dfrac{1}{2}\tan\dfrac{x}{2}+\dfrac{1}{2^2}\tan\dfrac{x}{2^2}+\ldots n\text{ terms}$

86. (a) $\tan x\tan2x+\tan2x\tan3x+\tan3x\tan4x$
$$+\ldots n\text{ terms}$$

(b)* If B be the exterior angle of a regular polygon of n sides and A is any constant, then prove that

(i) $\sin A+\sin(A+B)+\sin(A+2B)+\ldots n\text{ terms}=0$

(ii) $\cos A+\cos(A+B)+\cos(A+2B)+\ldots n\text{ terms}=0$

Formation of equations whose roots are given :

87.* Find the equation whose roots are
$$\cos\dfrac{2\pi}{7},\cos\dfrac{4\pi}{7}\text{ and }\cos\dfrac{8\pi}{7}\qquad\ldots(1)$$
or $\quad\cos\dfrac{2\pi}{7},\cos\dfrac{4\pi}{7}\text{ and }\cos\dfrac{6\pi}{7}.\qquad\ldots(2)$

Deductions :
$$\cos\dfrac{2\pi}{4}\cos\dfrac{4\pi}{7}\cos\dfrac{8\pi}{7}=S_3=\dfrac{1}{8}$$
$$\cos\dfrac{2\pi}{4}+\cos\dfrac{4\pi}{7}+\cos\dfrac{8\pi}{7}=S_1=-\dfrac{1}{2}$$

The equation whose roots are
$$\sec\dfrac{2\pi}{7},\sec\dfrac{4\pi}{7},\sec\dfrac{8\pi}{7}\left(=\sec\dfrac{6\pi}{7}\right)$$

88. (a) The equation whose roots are
$$\sec^2\dfrac{2\pi}{7},\sec^2\dfrac{4\pi}{7},\sec^2\dfrac{8\pi}{7}\left(=\sec^2\dfrac{6\pi}{7}\right)$$

(b)* The equation whose roots are
$$\tan^2\dfrac{2\pi}{7},\tan^2\dfrac{4\pi}{7},\tan^2\dfrac{8\pi}{7}\left(=\tan^2\dfrac{6\pi}{7}\right)$$

89. (a)* The equation whose roots are
$$\cot^2\dfrac{2\pi}{7},\cot^2\dfrac{4\pi}{7},\cot^2\dfrac{8\pi}{7}\left(=\cot^2\dfrac{6\pi}{7}\right)$$

(b)* Prove that
$$\left(\tan^2\dfrac{\pi}{7}+\tan^2\dfrac{2\pi}{7}+\tan^2\dfrac{3\pi}{7}\right).$$
$$\left(\cot^2\dfrac{\pi}{7}+\cot^2\dfrac{2\pi}{7}+\cot^2\dfrac{3\pi}{7}\right)=105.$$

90. (a)* Prove that $\sin\dfrac{\pi}{14}$ is a root of the equation
$$8x^3-4x^2-4x+1=0.$$

(b) Prove that
$$1+\sin^2\theta+\sin^2\phi>\sin\theta+\sin\phi+\sin\theta\sin\phi$$

Solutions to Problem Set (5)

1. (a) $\tan82\dfrac{1}{2}°=\tan\left(90°-7\dfrac{1}{2}°\right)=\cot7\dfrac{1}{2}°=\cot A$, say

where $A=7\dfrac{1}{2}°$.

Now $\cot A=\dfrac{\cos A}{\sin A}=\dfrac{2\cos^2 A}{2\sin A\cos A}$

$$= \frac{1 + \cos 2A}{\sin 2A} = \frac{1 + \cos 15°}{\sin 15°}$$

Now put the values of $\cos 15°$ and $\sin 15°$ from **R. (33) P. 518**

$$\therefore \quad \cot 7\frac{1}{2}° = \frac{2\sqrt{2} + (\sqrt{3} + 1)}{\sqrt{3} - 1} \times \frac{\sqrt{3} + 1}{\sqrt{3} + 1}$$

$$= \frac{2\sqrt{2}(\sqrt{3} + 1) + (\sqrt{3} + 1)^2}{3 - 1}$$

$$= \frac{2\sqrt{6} + 2\sqrt{2} + 4 + 2\sqrt{3}}{2}$$

$$= \sqrt{6} + \sqrt{2} + 2 + \sqrt{3}$$

$$= \sqrt{2}(\sqrt{2} + 1) + \sqrt{3}(\sqrt{2} + 1)$$

$$= (\sqrt{2} + 1)(\sqrt{3} + \sqrt{2}).$$

(b) $\quad \tan(142° 30') = \tan\left(90° + 45° + 7\frac{1}{2}°\right)$

$$= -\cot\left(45° + 7\frac{1}{2}°\right)$$

$$= \frac{-1}{\tan\left(45° + 7\frac{1}{2}°\right)} = -\frac{1 - \tan 7\frac{1}{2}°}{1 + \tan 7\frac{1}{2}°}$$

$$= -\frac{\cos A - \sin A}{\cos A + \sin A} \quad \text{where} \quad A = 7\frac{1}{2}°$$

$$= -\frac{(\cos A - \sin A)^2}{\cos^2 A - \sin^2 A} = -\frac{1 - \sin 2A}{\cos 2A}$$

$$= -\frac{1 - \sin 15°}{\cos 15°} = \frac{\frac{\sqrt{3} - 1}{2\sqrt{2}} - 1}{(\sqrt{3} + 1)/2\sqrt{2}}$$

$$= \frac{(\sqrt{3} - 1) - 2\sqrt{2}}{(\sqrt{3} + 1)} \cdot \frac{(\sqrt{3} - 1)}{\sqrt{3} - 1}$$

$$= \frac{(\sqrt{3} - 1)^2 - 2\sqrt{6} + 2\sqrt{2}}{(3 - 1)}$$

$$= \frac{4 - 2\sqrt{3} - 2\sqrt{6} + 2\sqrt{2}}{2} = 2 + \sqrt{2} - \sqrt{3} - \sqrt{6}.$$

2. (a) Here choose $A = 22\frac{1}{2}°$, $\therefore 2A = 45°$ etc.

(b) $\quad \tan 22\frac{1}{2}° = (1 - \cos 45°)/\sin 45°$

$$= \sqrt{2} - 1 = 1/(\sqrt{2} + 1) \quad \text{...(I)}$$

$$A = 11\frac{1}{4}°, 2A = 22\frac{1}{2}°, \tan 2A = \frac{2t}{1 - t^2} = \frac{1}{\sqrt{2} + 1},$$

$$\text{by (I)}$$

$$t^2 + 2(\sqrt{2} + 1)t - 1 = 0$$

where $\quad t = \tan 11\frac{1}{4}° = + \text{ive}$

$$\therefore \quad t = \frac{-2(\sqrt{2} + 1) \pm 2\sqrt{(3 + 2\sqrt{2} + 1)}}{2}$$

$$= \sqrt{(4 + 2\sqrt{2})} - (\sqrt{2} + 1), \quad \text{as } t \text{ is + ive.}$$

3. From the given conditions, we see that $45° < \theta/4 < 67° 30'$ so that $\tan(\theta/4) > 0$ and $90° < \theta/2 < 135°$ $\therefore \tan(\theta/2) = -\text{ive}.$

$$\tan\frac{\theta}{2} = -\sqrt{\left(\frac{1 - \cos\theta}{1 + \cos\theta}\right)} = -\sqrt{\left(\frac{1 + (4/5)}{1 - (4/5)}\right)} = -3$$

$\therefore$ Now $\tan\frac{\theta}{2} = \frac{2t}{1 - t^2} = -3$, where $t = \tan\frac{\theta}{4}$

$$\therefore \quad 3t^2 - 2t - 3 = 0 \quad \therefore \quad t = \frac{2 \pm \sqrt{(4 + 36)}}{6}$$

$$\therefore \quad t = \tan\frac{\theta}{4} = \frac{1 + \sqrt{10}}{3} \text{ as } \tan\frac{\theta}{4} \text{ is + ive.}$$

4. All are infinite G.P.s with common ratio < 1.

$$x = \frac{1}{1 - \cos^2\phi} = \frac{1}{\sin^2\phi}, y = \frac{1}{1 - \sin^2\phi} = \frac{1}{\cos^2\phi}$$

$$\therefore \quad x + y = \frac{1}{\sin^2\phi\cos^2\phi} = xy \quad \text{...(1)}$$

$$z = \frac{1}{1 - \cos^2\phi\sin^2\phi}. \quad \text{...(2)}$$

$$(x + y) + z = \left(\frac{1}{\sin^2\phi} + \frac{1}{\cos^2\phi}\right) + \frac{1}{1 - \sin^2\phi\cos^2\phi}$$

$$= \frac{1}{\sin^2\phi\cos^2\phi} + \frac{1}{1 - \sin^2\phi\cos^2\phi}$$

$$= \frac{1}{\sin^2\phi\cos^2\phi} \cdot \frac{1}{(1 - \sin^2\phi\cos^2\phi)}$$

$$= xyz \text{ by (1) and (2)}$$

or $\quad xy + z = xyz \quad (\because \quad x + y = xy)$

5. (a) Changing into sin and cos, we get

$$\frac{\cos A\cos 3A}{\sin 3A\cos A - \cos 3A\sin A}$$

$$- \frac{\sin 3A\sin A}{\cos 3A\sin A - \sin 3A\cos A}$$

$$= \frac{\cos A\cos 3A}{\sin(3A - A)} + \frac{\sin 3A\sin A}{\sin(3A - A)}$$

$$= \frac{\cos(3A - A)}{\sin 2A} = \cot 2A$$

(b) L.H.S. $= \frac{(\cos\theta + \cos\phi) + \sin(\theta - \phi)}{(\cos\theta + \cos\phi) - \sin(\theta - \phi)}$

$$= \frac{\cos\frac{\theta + \phi}{2} + \sin\frac{\theta - \phi}{2}}{\cos\frac{\theta + \phi}{2} - \sin\frac{\theta - \phi}{2}} \quad \text{...(1)}$$

We have cancelled the common factor $2\cos\frac{\theta - \phi}{2}$.

Now replace $\cos\frac{\theta + \phi}{2}$ by $\sin\left[\frac{\pi}{2} - \left(\frac{\theta + \phi}{2}\right)\right]$ and apply $\sin C \pm \sin D$ etc.

6. (a) R.H.S.

$$= (1 - \cos 2\beta) + 4\cos(\alpha + \beta)\sin\alpha\sin\beta$$
$$+ 2\cos^2(\alpha + \beta) - 1.$$

$$= -\cos 2\beta + 2\cos(\alpha+\beta)[2\sin\alpha\sin\beta + \cos(\alpha+\beta)]$$
$$= -\cos 2\beta + 2\cos(\alpha+\beta)[2\sin\alpha\sin\beta$$
$$+ \cos\alpha\cos\beta - \sin\alpha\sin\beta]$$
$$= -\cos 2\beta + 2\cos(\alpha+\beta)\cos(\alpha-\beta)$$
$$= -\cos 2\beta + (\cos 2\alpha + \cos 2\beta)$$
$$= \cos 2\alpha = \text{L.H.S.}$$

(b) R.H.S. $= \cos(A-B)[\cos(A-B)$
$$-2\cos A\cos B] + \cos^2 B$$
$$= \cos(A-B)[\cos A\cos B + \sin A\sin B$$
$$-2\cos A\cos B] + \cos^2 B$$
$$= -\cos(A-B)[\cos A\cos B - \sin A\sin B] + \cos^2 B$$
$$= -\cos(A-B)\cos(A+B) + \cos^2 B$$
$$= -[\cos^2 A - \sin^2 B] + \cos^2 B$$
$$= -\cos^2 A + (\sin^2 B + \cos^2 B)$$
$$= 1 - \cos^2 A = \sin^2 A.$$

(c) Proceed as in Q. 6 (b).

7. (a) Let $\theta + A = x, \theta + B = y$
$$\therefore \quad A - B = x - y \qquad\qquad \dots(1)$$
$$\text{L.H.S.} = \sin^2 x + \sin^2 y - 2\sin x\sin y\cos(x-y)$$
$$= \sin^2 x + \sin^2 y - 2\sin x\sin y(\cos x\cos y$$
$$+ \sin x\sin y)$$
$$= \sin^2 x(1-\sin^2 y) + \sin^2 y(1-\sin^2 x) - 2\sin x$$
$$\sin y\cos x\cos y$$
$$= \sin^2 x\cos^2 y + \cos^2 x\sin^2 y$$
$$- 2\sin x\sin y\cos x.\cos y$$
$$= (\sin x\cos y - \cos x\sin y)^2 = \sin^2(x-y)$$
$$= \sin^2(A-B), \text{ by (1)}.$$

(b) L.H.S. $= \cos^2 A + \cos^2 B$
$$- 2\cos A\cos B(\cos A\cos B - \sin A\sin B)$$
$$= (\cos^2 A - \cos^2 A\cos^2 B)$$
$$+ (\cos^2 B - \cos^2 A\cos^2 B)$$
$$+ 2\sin A\sin B\cos A\cos B$$
$$= \cos^2 A(1-\cos^2 B) + \cos^2 B(1-\cos^2 A)$$
$$+ 2\sin A\sin B\cos A\cos B$$
$$= \cos^2 A\sin^2 B + \cos^2 B\sin^2 A$$
$$+ 2\sin A\sin B\cos A\cos B$$
$$= (\sin A\cos B + \cos A\sin B)^2 = \sin^2(A+B)$$

(c) **Middle Term :**
$$= \cos^2\alpha - \cos(\alpha+\beta)[\cos\alpha\cos\beta + \sin\alpha\sin\beta]$$
$$= \cos^2\alpha - \cos(\alpha+\beta)\cos(\alpha-\beta)$$
$$= \cos^2\alpha - (\cos^2\alpha - \sin^2\beta) = \sin^2\beta,$$
which lies between 0 and 1.

8. (a) Squaring we have $1 + \sin\theta = \frac{1}{4}$ **(Rule 34, P. 324)**
$$\therefore \quad \sin\theta = -\frac{3}{4}$$

$$\therefore \quad \cos\theta = \sqrt{1 - \frac{9}{16}} = +\frac{\sqrt 7}{4} \qquad \text{(4th quadrant)}$$
$$\therefore \quad \sin 2\theta = 2\sin\theta\cos\theta = -\frac{3\sqrt 7}{8}.$$

(b) Changing to sine and factorizing, we have
$(\sin\theta + 1)(5\sin\theta - 3) = 0$. Since θ lies in the given interval, it must be – ive.
$$\therefore \quad \sin\theta = -1 \quad \text{or} \quad \theta = \frac{3\pi}{2} = \frac{6\pi}{4}$$
which lies in the given interval.
$$\therefore \quad \frac{\theta}{2} = \frac{3\pi}{4} \text{ and hence } \tan\frac{\theta}{2} = \tan\frac{3\pi}{4} = -1.$$

(c) Ans (c).
$$\alpha + \beta = \frac{\pi}{2} \quad \alpha = \frac{\pi}{2} - \beta \quad \text{or} \quad \tan\alpha = \cot\beta$$
$$\text{or} \quad \tan\alpha\tan\beta = 1 \qquad\qquad \dots(1)$$
Again $\beta + \gamma = \alpha \implies \gamma = \alpha - \beta$
$$\therefore \quad \tan\gamma = \frac{\tan\alpha - \tan\beta}{1 + \tan\alpha\tan\beta} = \frac{\tan\alpha - \tan\beta}{2} \quad \text{by (1)}$$
$$\therefore \quad \tan\alpha = \tan\beta + 2\tan\gamma \implies \text{(c)}.$$

9. $2 = 3 - 1, 6 = 9 - 3, 18 = 27 - 9$

Use $\tan A - \tan B = \dfrac{\sin(A-B)}{\cos A\cos B}$ **R. 22 P. 517**

$$T_1 = \frac{1}{2}\left[\frac{2\sin x\cos x}{\cos 3x\cos x}\right] = \frac{1}{2}\frac{\sin(3x-x)}{\cos 3x\cos x}$$
$$= \frac{1}{2}[\tan 3x - \tan x]$$
$$T_2 = \frac{1}{2}[\tan 9x - \tan 3x],$$
$$T_3 = \frac{1}{2}[\tan 27x - \tan 9x] \text{ etc.}$$

10. (a) $T_1 = \left(\dfrac{2\cos\theta}{\sin\theta}\right)^2, T_2 = 1 - 2\tan\theta\left(\dfrac{1-\tan^2\theta}{2\tan\theta}\right)$
$$\text{or} \quad T_1 = 4\cot^2\theta, T_2 = \tan^2\theta \quad \therefore \quad T_1 T_2 = 4$$

(b) $\tan(\alpha+\beta) = \dfrac{\tan\alpha + \tan\beta}{1 - \tan\alpha\tan\beta}$
$$= \frac{1}{\sqrt{(x^2 + x + 1)}} \cdot \frac{\left(\frac{1}{\sqrt x} + \sqrt x\right)}{1 - \dfrac{1}{(x^2 + x + 1)}}$$
$$= \frac{\sqrt{x^2 + x + 1}}{x(1 + x)} \cdot \frac{1 + x}{\sqrt x} = \sqrt{\left(\frac{x^2 + x + 1}{x^3}\right)}$$
$$= (x^{-1} + x^{-2} + x^{-3})^{1/2} = \tan\gamma$$
$$\therefore \quad \alpha + \beta = \gamma$$

11. L.H.S. $= 2\cos^2 28° + (2\sin 62°\sin 4°)$
$$= 2\cos^2 28° + 2\cos 28°\cos 86°$$
$$\because \sin\theta = \cos(90° - \theta)$$
$$= 2\cos 28°[\cos 28° + \cos 86°]$$

$$= 2\cos 28° \,(2\cos 57° \,\cos 29°)$$

$$= 4\cos 28° \,\cos 29° \,\sin 33°$$

$$[\because \cos 57° = \cos(90° - 33°) = \sin 33°]$$

12. (a) Changing in terms of cos, we get

$$\text{L.H.S.} = \frac{1 - \cos 8\theta}{\cos 8\theta} \cdot \frac{\cos 4\theta}{1 - \cos 4\theta}$$

$$= \frac{2\sin^2 4\theta \cdot \cos 4\theta}{\cos 8\theta \cdot 2\sin^2 2\theta}$$

$$= \frac{(2\sin 4\theta \cos 4\theta)\,(2\sin 2\theta \cos 2\theta)}{\cos 8\theta \cdot 2\sin^2 2\theta}$$

$$= \frac{\sin 8\theta}{\cos 8\theta} \cdot \frac{\cos 2\theta}{\sin 2\theta}$$

$$= \tan 8\theta \cdot \cot 2\theta = \frac{\tan 8\theta}{\tan 2\theta}.$$

(b) $\tan A\,(\sec 4A - 1) = \tan 4A\,(\sec 2A - 1)$

or $\dfrac{\sec 4A - 1}{\sec 2A - 1} = \dfrac{\tan 4A}{\tan A}$, as in (a).

13. (a) Ans. (a), (b), (c), (d).

$$E = f_n\,(\theta) = \frac{\sin(\theta/2)}{\cos(\theta/2)}\left[\frac{2\cos^2(\theta/2)}{\cos\theta} \cdot \frac{2\cos^2\theta}{\cos 2\theta}\right.$$

$$\left. \cdot \frac{2\cos^2 2\theta}{\cos 4\theta} \cdots\right]$$

Combine first two factors

$$f_n\,(\theta) = \frac{\sin\theta}{\cos\theta}\left[\frac{2\cos^2\theta}{\cos 2\theta} \cdot \frac{2\cos^2 2\theta}{\cos 4\theta} \cdots\right]$$

Again combine first two factors.

$$= \tan 2\theta\,[\quad] = \tan 2^n\theta.$$

$$\therefore \quad f_2\left(\frac{\pi}{16}\right) = \tan 4 \cdot \frac{\pi}{16} = \tan\frac{\pi}{4} = 1.$$

$$\because \quad n = 2, \theta = \frac{\pi}{16}$$

Similarly each other is $\tan\dfrac{\pi}{4} = 1$.

(b) Ans. (a) → (i), (b) → (ii)

$$\therefore \quad \frac{1}{\log_2 3}, \frac{1}{\log_2 2.3}, \frac{1}{\log_2 2^2.3} \qquad \ldots(1)$$

$$= \frac{1}{x}, \frac{1}{1+x}, \frac{1}{2+x} \quad \text{(H.P.)} \qquad \ldots(2)$$

where x is $\log_2 3$. They are in H.P. as their reciprocals are in A.P. Hence taking reciprocals of (1) and (2) we find that elements in (a) are in A.P.

Now $\sqrt{3}, 1, \dfrac{1}{\sqrt{3}}$ are clearly in G.P. $\therefore$ (b) → (ii)

14. We are given $5\cos A + 3 = 0$ so that $\cos A = -3/5 \to A$ being the angle of ΔABC, $\sin A$ cannot be negative so $\cos A = -3/5 \Rightarrow \sin A = 4/5$ and then $\tan A = -4/3$.

$$\therefore \quad \sin A + \tan A = -8/15 = S$$

and $\sin A \tan A = -16/15 = P$

$$\therefore \quad x^2 - xS + P = 0 \text{ is the required equation.}$$

15. (a) $\cos 3\theta = 4\cos^3\theta - 3\cos\theta$

$$= \cos\theta\,[4\cos^2\theta - 3]$$

$$= \frac{1}{2}\left(a + \frac{1}{a}\right)\left[4 \cdot \frac{1}{4}\left(a + \frac{1}{a}\right)^2 - 3\right]$$

$$= \frac{1}{2}\left(a + \frac{1}{a}\right)\left[a^2 + \frac{1}{a^2} - 1\right] = \frac{1}{2}\left[a^3 + \frac{1}{a^3}\right]$$

(b) $\Sigma\cos 3x = 4\Sigma\cos^3 x - 3\Sigma\cos x$

$$= 4\Sigma\,a^3 - 0$$

Now if $a + b + c = 0$ then $a^3 + b^3 + c^3 = 3abc$.

$$\therefore \quad \Sigma\cos 3x = 4.3\,(\cos x \cos y \cos z).$$

16. (a), (b), (c)

By De-Moivre's Theorem we know that

$$(\cos\theta + i\sin\theta)^5 = \cos 5\theta + i\sin 5\theta$$

L.H.S. on expansion by binomial theorem is

$$\cos^5\theta + 5\cos^4\theta\,(i\sin\theta) + 10\cos^3\theta\,(i\sin\theta)^2$$

$$+ 10\cos^2\theta\,(i\sin\theta)^3 + 5\cos\theta\,(i\sin\theta)^4 + (i\sin\theta)^5$$

Now equate real and imaginary parts and change $\sin^2\theta$ to $1 - \cos^2\theta$ and $\cos^2\theta$ to $1 - \sin^2\theta$ depending on the answer.

$$\therefore \quad \cos 5\theta = \cos\theta\,(16\cos^4\theta - 20\cos^2\theta + 5) \qquad \ldots(1)$$

$$\sin 5\theta = \sin\theta\,(16\sin^4\theta - 20\sin^2\theta + 5) \qquad \ldots(2)$$

Deduction : If $\theta = 36°$, then $5\theta = 180°$

$$\therefore \quad \sin 5\theta = 0$$

Also $\sin 36° < \sin 45°$ or $\sin^2 36° < \dfrac{1}{2}$

Now from (2), we get

$$0 = s\,(16s^4 - 20s^2 + 5), s = \sin 36° \ne 0$$

$$\therefore \quad s^2 = \frac{20 \pm \sqrt{400 - 320}}{32} = \frac{10 - 2\sqrt{5}}{16} \left(\because s^2 < \frac{1}{2}\right)$$

$$\therefore \quad s = \frac{\sqrt{10 - 2\sqrt{5}}}{4}$$

17. (a) We know that $\cos 3A = 4\cos^3 A - 3\cos A$

$$\therefore \quad \cos^3 A = \frac{1}{4}\,(\cos 3A + 3\cos A).$$

Also $\cos(2n\pi + \theta) = \cos\theta$.

Applying the above we have

$$\text{L.H.S.} = \frac{1}{4}\,[(3\cos\theta + \cos 3\theta) + 3\cos(120° + \theta)$$

$$+ \cos(360° + 3\theta) + 3\cos(240° + \theta)$$

$$+ \cos(720° + 3\theta)]$$

$$= \frac{1}{4}\,[3\cos 3\theta] + \frac{3}{4}\,[\cos\theta + \cos(120° + \theta)$$

$$+ \cos(240° + \theta)]$$

$$= \frac{3}{4}\cos 3\theta + \frac{3}{4}\,[\cos\theta + 2\cos(180° + \theta)\cos 60°]$$

$$= \frac{3}{4}\cos 3\theta + \frac{3}{4}\left[\cos\theta + 2 \cdot \frac{1}{2}(-\cos\theta)\right]$$

$$= \frac{3}{4}\cos 3\theta.$$

(b) L.H.S. $= \frac{1}{2}[(1 + \cos 2A) + 1$

$$+ \cos(2A + 240°) + 1 + \cos(2A - 240°)]$$

$$= \frac{1}{2}[3 + \cos 2A + 2\cos 2A \cos 240°]$$

$$= \frac{1}{2}[3 + \cos 2A - \cos 2A] = \frac{3}{2}$$

$$[\because \cos 240° = \cos(270° - 30°) - = -\sin 30° = -1/2]$$

18. (a) $\cos^4(7\pi/8) = \cos^4(\pi - \pi/8) = \cos^4(\pi/8)$

$$\cos^4(5\pi/8) = \cos^4(\pi/2 + \pi/8) = \sin^4(\pi/8)$$

$\therefore$ L.H.S. $= 2[\cos^4 A + \sin^4 A]$, where $A = \pi/8$

$$= 2[1 - 2\sin^2 A \cos^2 A] = 2 - (2\sin A \cos A)^2$$

$$= 2 - \left(\sin 2 \cdot \frac{\pi}{8}\right)^2 = 2 - \sin^2\left(\frac{\pi}{4}\right) = 2 - \frac{1}{2} = \frac{3}{2}$$

(b) Do yourself .

19. (a) $\left(\frac{\pi}{16} + \frac{7\pi}{16}\right) = \left(\frac{2\pi}{16} + \frac{6\pi}{16}\right) = \left(\frac{3\pi}{16} + \frac{5\pi}{16}\right) = \frac{\pi}{2}$

Thus these are complementary.

and $\frac{4\pi}{16} = \frac{\pi}{4}$. If we take $\theta = \frac{\pi}{16}$

L.H.S. $= (\tan^2\theta + \cot^2\theta) + (\tan^2 2\theta + \cot^2 2\theta)$

$$+ (\tan^2 3\theta + \cot^2 3\theta) + 1$$

Now 1st bracket $= (\tan\theta + \cot\theta)^2 - 2$

$$= \left(\frac{1}{\sin\theta\cos\theta}\right)^2 - 2 = \left(\frac{2}{\sin 2\theta}\right)^2 - 2$$

$$= \frac{8}{1 - \cos 4\theta} - 2 \text{ where } 4\theta = \frac{4\pi}{16} = \frac{\pi}{4}$$

$$= \frac{8\sqrt{2}}{(\sqrt{2} - 1)} - 2 = 8\sqrt{2}(\sqrt{2} + 1) - 2.$$

2nd bracket $= \frac{8}{1 - \cos 8\theta} - 2 = 8 - 2 = 6$

3rd bracket $= \frac{8}{1 - \cos 12\theta} = 8\sqrt{2}(\sqrt{2} - 1) - 2$

and $\tan^2\frac{\pi}{4} = 1$

$\therefore$ $S = 14 + 6 + 14 + 1 = 35$.

(b) $\left(\frac{7\pi}{16} + \frac{\pi}{16}\right) = \frac{\pi}{2}, \left(\frac{5\pi}{16} + \frac{3\pi}{16}\right) = \frac{\pi}{2}$

Hence by C.R.,

$$(\sin^4 x + \cos^4 x) + (\sin^4 y + \cos^4 y)$$

$$= 1 - 2\sin^2 x \cos^2 x + 1 - 2\sin^2 y \cos^2 y$$

$$= 2 - \frac{1}{2}[\sin^2 2x + \sin^2 2y]$$

$$= 2 - \frac{1}{2}\left[\sin^2\frac{\pi}{8} + \sin^2\frac{3\pi}{8}\right]$$

$$= 2 - \frac{1}{2}\left[\sin^2\frac{\pi}{8} + \cos^2\frac{\pi}{8}\right] = \frac{3}{2} \text{ by C.R.}$$

(c) Let $\alpha = \frac{\pi}{9}$ $\therefore$ $3\alpha = \frac{\pi}{3}$ and $\tan 3\alpha = \sqrt{3}$

If $\tan\frac{\pi}{9} = \tan\alpha = t$, then

$$\frac{3t - t^3}{1 - 3t^2} = \sqrt{3}, \text{ where } t = \tan\frac{\pi}{9}$$

Square both sides and simplify.

20. (a) We know that $\tan A \tan B + 1 = \left(\frac{\sin A \sin B}{\cos A \cos B} + 1\right)$

$$= \frac{\cos A \cos B + \sin A \sin B}{\cos A \cos B} = \frac{\cos(A - B)}{\cos A \cos B}$$

Now take -3 from R.H.S. to L.H.S. and write it as $1 + 1 + 1$.

Hence we have to prove that

$[\tan\theta\tan(\theta + 60°) + 1]$

$$+ [\tan\theta\tan(\theta - 60°) + 1]$$

$$+ [\tan(\theta + 60°)\tan(\theta - 60°) + 1] = 0$$

or $\frac{\cos(\theta - \theta - 60°)}{\cos\theta\cos(\theta + 60°)} + \frac{\cos(\theta - \theta + 60°)}{\cos\theta\cos(\theta - 60°)}$

$$+ \frac{\cos(\theta + 60° - \theta + 60°)}{\cos(\theta + 60°)\cos(\theta - 60°)}$$

$$= \frac{\cos 60°\cos(\theta - 60°) + \cos 60°\cos(\theta + 60°) + \cos 120°\cos\theta}{\cos\theta\cos(\theta + 60°)\cos(\theta - 60°)}$$

$$= \frac{\frac{1}{2}[\cos(\theta - 60°) + \cos(\theta + 60°)] + \cos(90° + 30°)\cos\theta}{D^r}$$

$$= \frac{\frac{1}{2} \cdot 2\cos\theta\cos 60° - \sin 30°\cos\theta}{D^r}$$

$$= \frac{1}{2}\frac{(\cos\theta - \cos\theta)}{D^r} = 0 .$$

(b) $\cot A \cot B - 1 = \frac{\cos(A + B)}{\sin A \sin B}$, and $3 = 1 + 1 + 1$

$44° + 16° = 60°$, $44° + 76° = 120°$, $76° - 16° = 60°$

$\therefore$ L.H.S.

$$= \frac{\cos 60°\sin 76° + \cos 120°\sin 16° - \cos 60°\sin 44°}{\sin 16°\sin 44°\sin 76°}$$

$$= \frac{1}{2}\left[\frac{\sin 76° - \sin 16° - \sin 44°}{D^r}\right]$$

$$= \frac{1}{2}\frac{(2\sin 30°\cos 46° - \sin 44°)}{D^r}$$

$$= \frac{1}{2D^r}(\cos 46° - \cos 46°), \text{ by comp. rule} = 0.$$

(c) Change in terms of sine and cos, $3 = 2 + 1$

$$\text{L.H.S.} = \frac{2\sin 76°\sin 16° + \cos(76° - 16°)}{\sin(76° + 16°)}$$

$$= \frac{\cos(76° - 16°) - \cos(76° + 16°) + \cos 60°}{\sin 92°}$$

$$= \frac{1 - \cos 92°}{\sin 92°} = \frac{2\sin^2 46°}{2\sin 46°\cos 46°}$$

$$= \tan 46° = \cot 44°, \text{ by C.R.}$$

21. (a) $\cot A \cdot \cot 2A + 1 = \dfrac{\cos(2A - A)}{\sin A \sin 2A} = \dfrac{\cos A}{\sin A \sin 2A}$

Similarly, $\cot 2A \cot 3A + 1 = \dfrac{\cos A}{\sin 2A \sin 3A}$

$$\therefore \text{ L.H.S.} = \frac{\cos A}{\sin 2A}\left[\frac{1}{\sin A} + \frac{1}{\sin 3A}\right]$$

$$= \frac{\cos A}{\sin 2A}\left[\frac{2\sin 2A \cos A}{\sin A \sin 3A}\right]$$

$$= \cot A \cdot \frac{2\cos A}{\sin 3A} = \cot A \cdot \frac{\sin 2A}{\sin A \sin 3A}$$

$$= \cot A \cdot \frac{\sin(3A - A)}{\sin A \sin 3A}$$

$$= \cot A(\cot A - \cot 3A)$$

(b) From the given relation,

$2\Sigma \cos x \cos y + 2\Sigma \sin x \sin y + 1 + 1 + 1 = 0$

Write $1 = \cos^2 x + \sin^2 x$ etc.

$$\therefore \quad (\Sigma \cos x)^2 + (\Sigma \sin x)^2 = 0$$

$$\Rightarrow \quad \Sigma \cos x = 0 \text{ and } \Sigma \sin x = 0$$

22. (a) We know that $\tan 60° = \sqrt{3}$,

$$\text{L.H.S.} = \tan A + \frac{\sqrt{3} + \tan A}{1 - \sqrt{3}\tan A} - \frac{\sqrt{3} - \tan A}{1 + \sqrt{3}\tan A}$$

$$= \tan A + \frac{\begin{array}{c}(\sqrt{3} + \tan A)(1 + \sqrt{3}\tan A)\\ -(\sqrt{3} - \tan A)(1 - \sqrt{3}\tan A)\end{array}}{1 - 3\tan^2 A}$$

$$= \tan A + \frac{8\tan A}{1 - 3\tan^2 A} = \frac{9\tan A - 3\tan^3 A}{1 - 3\tan^2 A}$$

$$= 3 \cdot \frac{(3\tan A - \tan^3 A)}{1 - 3\tan^2 A} = 3\tan 3A.$$

Note : You can also do it by changing into sine and cosine.

(b) $\text{L.H.S.} = \dfrac{\cos\alpha}{\sin\alpha} + \dfrac{\cos(60° + \alpha)}{\sin(60° + \alpha)} - \dfrac{\cos(60° - \alpha)}{\sin(60° - \alpha)}$

$$= \frac{\cos\alpha}{\sin\alpha} + \frac{-\cos(60° - \alpha)\sin(60° + \alpha)}{\sin^2 60° - \sin^2 \alpha}$$

$$\frac{\sin(60° - \alpha)\cos(60° + \alpha)}{}$$

$$= \frac{\cos\alpha\left(\dfrac{3}{4} - \sin^2 \alpha\right) + \sin\alpha \sin(60° - \alpha - 60° - \alpha)}{\sin\alpha\left(\dfrac{3}{4} - \sin^2 \alpha\right)}$$

$$= \frac{\cos\alpha(3 - 4\sin^2 \alpha) + 4\sin\alpha \sin(-2\alpha)}{4\sin\alpha\left(\dfrac{3 - 4\sin^2 \alpha}{4}\right)}$$

$$= \frac{\cos\alpha(3 - 4\sin^2 \alpha) - 4\sin\alpha \cdot 2\sin\alpha\cos\alpha}{3\sin\alpha - 4\sin^3 \alpha}$$

$$= \frac{\cos\alpha[3 - 12(1 - \cos^2 \alpha)]}{\sin 3\alpha}$$

$$= 3 \cdot \frac{[4\cos^3 \alpha - 3\cos\alpha]}{\sin 3\alpha} = 3 \cdot \frac{\cos 3\alpha}{\sin 3\alpha} = 3\cot 3\alpha.$$

23. (a) Let each be equal to $1/k$.

We have to prove that $xy + yz + zx = 0$

or $\dfrac{1}{x} + \dfrac{1}{y} + \dfrac{1}{z} = 0$, on dividing by xyz

On putting the values,

$$\Sigma\frac{1}{x} = k\left[\sin\theta + \sin\left(\theta + \frac{2\pi}{3}\right) + \sin\left(\theta + \frac{4\pi}{3}\right)\right]$$

Combine 1st and 3rd

$$= k\left[2\sin\left(\theta + \frac{2\pi}{3}\right)\cos\frac{2\pi}{3} + \sin\left(\theta + \frac{2\pi}{3}\right)\right] = 0$$

$$\because \quad 2\cos\frac{2\pi}{3} = 2\left(-\frac{1}{2}\right) = -1$$

$$\therefore \quad \frac{1}{x} + \frac{1}{y} + \frac{1}{z} = 0 \quad \text{or} \quad xy + yz + zx = 0$$

(b) Use cross-multiplication.

24. (a) Transpose the last term and then square and add.

$$1 + 1 + 2\cos(\alpha + \beta - \alpha) = 1$$

$$\therefore \quad \cos\beta = -\frac{1}{2} \quad \therefore \quad \beta = \frac{2\pi}{3}$$

Again $2\cos\left(\alpha + \dfrac{\beta}{2}\right)\cos\dfrac{\beta}{2} = -\cos(\alpha + \beta + \gamma)$

$$2\sin\left(\alpha + \frac{\beta}{2}\right)\cos\frac{\beta}{2} = -\sin(\alpha + \beta + \gamma)$$

$$\therefore \quad \tan\left(\alpha + \frac{\beta}{2}\right) = \tan(\alpha + \beta + \gamma)$$

$$\therefore \quad \alpha + \beta + \gamma = \alpha + \frac{\beta}{2} = \pi + \left(\alpha + \frac{\beta}{2}\right)$$

The first gives as $\gamma = -\dfrac{\beta}{2} = -\dfrac{\pi}{3}$ rejected as γ is $+$ive

$$\therefore \quad \text{From 2nd, } \gamma = \pi - \frac{\beta}{2} = \pi - \frac{\pi}{3} = \frac{2\pi}{3}.$$

(b) Equate the values for $x = 0$ and $x = \pi/2$ and cross-multiply.

$$\frac{p\cos\alpha + q\sin\beta}{p'\sin\alpha + q'\cos\beta} = \frac{-p\sin\alpha + q\cos\beta}{p'\cos\alpha - q'\sin\beta}$$

25. (a) $\cos 20° + \cos 100° + \cos 140°$

$$= (\cos 20° + \cos 140°) + \cos(90° + 10°)$$

$$= 2\cos 80° \cos 60° - \sin 10° = \cos 80° - \sin 10°$$

$$= \sin 10° - \sin 10° = 0. \qquad \textbf{(Comp. Rule)}$$

(b) L.H.S. $= (\sin 10° + \sin 50° - \sin 70°) + (\quad)$

$\qquad = (2 \sin 30° \cos 20° - \sin 70°) + (\quad)$

$\qquad = \sin 70° - \sin 70° + (\quad) = 0 + 0 = 0$ by C.R.

(c) Proceed as above .

26. (a) L.H.S. $= \dfrac{\sin^2 57° - \sin^2 33°}{-(\cos 21° - \cos 69°)}$, by complementary

rule

$\qquad = \dfrac{\sin 90° \sin 24°}{-2 \sin 45° \sin 24°} = -\dfrac{1}{\sqrt{2}}.$

(b) L.H.S. $= 2 \cos \dfrac{\pi}{13} \cos \dfrac{9\pi}{13} + 2 \cos \dfrac{4\pi}{13} \cos \dfrac{\pi}{13}$

$\qquad = 2 \cos \dfrac{\pi}{13} \left[\cos \dfrac{9\pi}{13} + \cos \dfrac{4\pi}{13} \right]$

$\qquad = 2 \cos \dfrac{\pi}{13} . 2 \cos \dfrac{\pi}{2} \cos \dfrac{5\pi}{26} = 0. \quad \because \cos (\pi/2) = 0$

(c) $2 \cos A \cos B = \cos (A + B) + \cos (A - B)$

L.H.S. $= \dfrac{1}{2} [(\cos 120° + \cos 80°) + (\cos 240° + \cos 40°)$

$\qquad\qquad\qquad\qquad - (\cos 340° + \cos 60°)]$

$\qquad = \dfrac{1}{2} \left[-\dfrac{1}{2} + \cos 80° - \dfrac{1}{2} + \cos 40° - \cos 20° - \dfrac{1}{2} \right]$

See §3 (31) P. 518

$\qquad = \dfrac{1}{2} \left[-\dfrac{3}{2} + 2 \cos 60° \cos 20° - \cos 20° \right]$

$\qquad = -\dfrac{3}{4} + \dfrac{1}{2} (\cos 20° - \cos 20°) = -\dfrac{3}{4}.$

27. (a) Apply **R. 38 P. 519** angles being in A.P. of three

terms $\alpha = 2\pi/7 = \beta, n = 3, \beta/2 = \pi/7$

$S = \dfrac{\sin (3\pi/7)}{\sin (\pi/7)} \cos \dfrac{1}{2} \left(\dfrac{2\pi}{7} + \dfrac{6\pi}{7} \right)$

$\quad = \dfrac{\sin (4\pi/7)}{\sin (\pi/7)} \cos \dfrac{4\pi}{7}$ **(Supp. R)**

$\quad = \dfrac{1}{2} \dfrac{\sin (8\pi/7)}{\sin (\pi/7)} = \dfrac{1}{2} \dfrac{\sin (\pi + \pi/7)}{\sin (\pi/7)} = -\dfrac{1}{2}.$

Alternative Method :

$\cos \dfrac{6\pi}{7} = \cos \left(2\pi - \dfrac{6\pi}{7} \right) = \cos \dfrac{8\pi}{7}$

Now apply rule (36) as each angle is double of the
preceding one.

(b) Here the angles are in A.P. of 5 terms.

$n = 5, \alpha = \dfrac{\pi}{11}, \beta = \dfrac{2\pi}{11} \qquad \therefore \dfrac{\beta}{2} = \dfrac{\pi}{11}$

Formula 38 P. 519.

$S = \dfrac{\sin 5 \cdot \dfrac{\pi}{11}}{\sin \dfrac{\pi}{11}} \cdot \cos \dfrac{1}{2} \left[\dfrac{\pi}{11} + \dfrac{9\pi}{11} \right]$

$\quad = \dfrac{2 \sin \dfrac{5\pi}{11} \cos \dfrac{5\pi}{11}}{2 \sin \dfrac{\pi}{11}} = \dfrac{\sin \dfrac{10\pi}{11}}{2 \sin \dfrac{\pi}{11}} = \dfrac{\sin \left(\pi - \dfrac{\pi}{11} \right)}{2 \sin \dfrac{\pi}{11}} = \dfrac{1}{2}.$

(c) **Hint :** $\cos 0 = 1, \cos \dfrac{6\pi}{7} = -\cos \dfrac{\pi}{7},$

$\cos \dfrac{5\pi}{7} = -\cos \dfrac{2\pi}{7}, \cos \dfrac{3\pi}{7} = -\cos \dfrac{4\pi}{7}$ by Supp. rule

Note : You may apply formula for angles in A.P.

28. (a) We know that

$\tan A + \tan B = \dfrac{\sin (A + B)}{\cos A \cos B}$

Here we have to prove that

$\tan 10° + \tan 70° = \tan 60° + \tan 50°$

$\qquad\qquad\qquad\qquad\qquad \because \tan 60° = \sqrt{3}$

or $\quad \dfrac{\sin 80°}{\cos 10° \cos 70°} = \dfrac{\sin 110°}{\cos 60° \cos 50°}.$

But $\sin 80° = \cos 10°, \sin 110° = \cos 20°$

$\therefore \quad \dfrac{1}{\sin 20°} = \dfrac{2 \cos 20°}{\cos 50°} \qquad \because \cos 60° = \dfrac{1}{2}$

or $\quad \cos 50° = 2 \sin 20° \cos 20° = \sin 40°$

$\qquad\qquad = \cos 50°$ by C.R.

(b) The given expression

$\qquad = \tan 9° - \tan 27° - \cot 27° + \cot 9°$

$\qquad = (\tan 9° + \cot 9°) - (\tan 27° + \cot 27°)$

$\qquad = \dfrac{1}{\sin 9° \cos 9°} - \dfrac{1}{\sin 27° \cos 27°}$

$\qquad = \dfrac{2}{\sin 18°} - \dfrac{2}{\sin 54°} = \dfrac{2}{\sin 18°} - \dfrac{2}{\cos 36°}$

by complementary rule

$\qquad = 2 \left[\dfrac{4}{\sqrt{(5)} - 1} - \dfrac{4}{\sqrt{(5)} + 1} \right] = 8 \cdot \dfrac{2}{4} = 4$

29. (a) L.H.S. $= \dfrac{1}{2} [1 + \cos 146° + 1 + \cos 94°$

$\qquad\qquad\qquad\qquad\qquad + \cos 120° + \cos 26°]$

$\qquad = \dfrac{1}{2} \left[2 - \dfrac{1}{2} + \cos 146° + \cos 94° + \cos 26° \right],$

$\qquad\qquad\qquad\qquad\qquad \because \cos 120° = -\dfrac{1}{2}$

$\qquad = \dfrac{1}{2} \left[\dfrac{3}{2} + \cos 146° + 2 \cos 60° \cos 34° \right]$

$\qquad = \dfrac{1}{2} \left[\dfrac{3}{2} - \cos 34° + \cos 34° \right] = \dfrac{3}{4}.$

(b) $39° - 9° = 30°, 48° - 18° = 30°.$

Multiplying both sides by 2, we have to prove

$2 \sin^2 12° + 2 \sin^2 21° + 2 (\sin^2 39° - \sin^2 9°)$

$\qquad\qquad\qquad + 2 (\sin^2 48° - \sin^2 18°) = 2$

or $\quad 1 - \cos 24° + 1 - \cos 42°$

$\qquad\qquad + 2 \sin 48° \sin 30° + 2 \sin 66° \sin 30° = 2$

Above is true as $\sin 30° = \dfrac{1}{2}$ and by compleme-

ntary rule.

$\sin 66° = \cos 24°; \sin 48° = \cos 42°$

30. Take D^r from L.H.S. to R.H.S.

R.H.S. $= (\cos\theta + \cos\phi)\,[(\cos 2\theta + \cos 2\phi) - \cos(\theta + \phi)]$

$\qquad - (\sin\theta + \sin\phi)\,[(\sin 2\theta + \sin 2\phi) - \sin(\theta + \phi)]$

$= T_1 + T_2$ each of which will have 6 terms on multiplication and then use

$\qquad \cos A \cos B - \sin A \sin B = \cos(A + B)$

$\therefore$ R.H.S. $= (\cos 2\theta \cos\theta - \sin 2\theta \sin\theta)$

$\qquad\qquad\qquad + (\cos 2\phi \cos\phi - \sin 2\phi \sin\phi)$

$\qquad + \cos(2\theta + \phi) + \cos(2\phi + \theta) - \cos(2\theta + \phi) - \cos(2\phi + \theta)$

$= \cos 3\theta + \cos 3\phi$, other terms cancel.

31. Here there are four angles each being double of the preceding one.

We multiply above and below by $2^4 \sin A$. **(Rule)**

L.H.S. $= \{1/(16 \sin A)\}\,[(2 \sin A \cos A)$

$\qquad\qquad\qquad (2 \cos 2A)(2 \cos 4A)(2 \cos 8A)]$

$= \{1/(16 \sin A)\}\,[\sin 2A . 2 \cos 2A\,(2 \cos 4A)(2 \cos 8A)]$

$= \{1/(16 \sin A)\}\,[(\sin 4A . 2 \cos 4A)(2 \cos 8A)]$

$= \{1/(16 \sin A)\}\,[(\sin 8A . 2 \cos 8A)]$

$= \{1/(16 \sin A)\}\,.\,[\sin 16A]$

$= \dfrac{1}{2^4 \sin A}\,.\,\sin(2^4\,A)$ \qquad **See R. 37, P. 519**

(a) L.H.S. $= \dfrac{1}{2}\cos 20° \cos 40° \cos 80°$

$\because \quad \cos 60° = \dfrac{1}{2}$

$= \dfrac{1}{2}\left[\dfrac{1}{2^3 \sin 20°}\right]\sin(2^3\,20°)$ As above

$= \dfrac{1}{16 \sin 20°}\sin 160°$

$= \dfrac{1}{16 \sin 20°}\sin(180° - 20°)$

$= (1/16).(\sin 20°)/(\sin 20°) = 1/16$.

Another form (I):

By complement rule $\sin\theta = \cos(90° - \theta)$ and hence the question reduces to (a).

Another form (II):

$\sin \pi/18 = \sin 10° = \cos 80°$

Ans. $K = \dfrac{1}{8}$ as $K = \sin 10° \sin 50° \sin 70°$

$= \cos 20° \cos 40° \cos 80° = \dfrac{1}{8}$

Another method is given below

$= \sin 10° \sin(60° - 10°) \sin(60° + 10°)$

$= \sin 10° (\sin^2 60° - \sin^2 10°)$

$= \sin 10°\left(\dfrac{3}{4} - \sin^2 10°\right)$

$= \dfrac{1}{4}(3 \sin 10° - 4 \sin^3 10°)$

$= \dfrac{1}{4}\sin 3.10° = \dfrac{1}{4}\sin 30° = \dfrac{1}{8}$.

Another form (III): Put $\sin 70° = \cos 20°$

$\cos 20° + 8 . 1/8$ by (a) $= 2 \cos^2 10°$

Use R. 32, P. 518; R. 36, P. 519.

(b) L.H.S. $= \dfrac{1}{2^4 \sin 7°}\sin(2^4 . 7°)$

$= \dfrac{1}{16 \sin 7°}.\sin(112°)$

$= \dfrac{1}{16}.\dfrac{\sin(180° - 68°)}{\sin(90° - 83°)} = \dfrac{1}{16}.\dfrac{\sin 68°}{\cos 83°}$.

(c) Here $A = (2\pi/15) = 24°$.

$\therefore$ L.H.S. $= \dfrac{1}{2^4 \sin 24°}.\sin(2^4 . 24°)$.

$= \dfrac{1}{16 \sin 24°}.\sin 384° = \dfrac{1}{16}$

$\because \quad \sin 384° = \sin(360° + 24°) = \sin 24°$.

Another form:

Again we know $\cos(2\pi - \theta) = \cos\theta$.

$\therefore \quad \cos\dfrac{16\pi}{15} = \cos\left(2\pi - \dfrac{14\pi}{15}\right) = \cos\dfrac{14\pi}{15}$.

and hence the question reduces to (c).

(d) Ans. (a). $\operatorname{cosec}^2\theta = \dfrac{2}{2 \sin^2\theta} = \dfrac{2}{1 - \cos 2\theta}$

where $\quad 2\theta = \dfrac{2\pi}{7}, \dfrac{4\pi}{7}, \dfrac{6\pi}{7}$

Let us put $a = \cos\dfrac{2\pi}{7}, b = \cos\dfrac{4\pi}{7}, c = \cos\dfrac{6\pi}{7}$

$\therefore \quad E = 2\left[\dfrac{1}{1-a} + \dfrac{1}{1-b} + \dfrac{1}{1-c}\right]$

$= 2\left[\dfrac{\Sigma(1-b)(1-c)}{1 - \Sigma a + \Sigma ab - abc}\right]$

$= 2\left[\dfrac{3 - 2\Sigma a + \Sigma ab}{1 - \Sigma a + \Sigma ab - abc}\right]$

$\Sigma a = \cos\dfrac{2\pi}{7} + \cos\dfrac{4\pi}{7} + \cos\dfrac{6\pi}{7} = -\dfrac{1}{2}$ by Q. 27

$\Sigma ab = \dfrac{1}{2}\left[\cos\dfrac{6\pi}{7} + \cos\dfrac{2\pi}{7} + \cos\dfrac{10\pi}{7} + \cos\dfrac{2\pi}{7}\right.$

$\left.\qquad\qquad\qquad + \cos\dfrac{8\pi}{7} + \cos\dfrac{4\pi}{7}\right]$

$\cos\dfrac{10\pi}{7} = \cos\left(2\pi - \dfrac{4\pi}{7}\right) = \cos\dfrac{4\pi}{7}$

$\cos\dfrac{8\pi}{7} = \cos\left(2\pi - \dfrac{6\pi}{7}\right) = \cos\dfrac{6\pi}{7}$

$\therefore \quad \Sigma ab = \dfrac{1}{2}.2\left(\cos\dfrac{2\pi}{7} + \cos\dfrac{4\pi}{7} + \cos\dfrac{6\pi}{7}\right)$

$= -\dfrac{1}{2}$ \qquad as in Q. 27.

$abc = \cos\dfrac{2\pi}{7}\cos\dfrac{4\pi}{7}\cos\dfrac{6\pi}{7}$

$= \cos\dfrac{2\pi}{7}\cos\dfrac{4\pi}{7}\cos\dfrac{8\pi}{7}$

$\because \quad \cos\dfrac{6\pi}{7} = \cos\left(2\pi - \dfrac{8\pi}{7}\right) = \cos\dfrac{8\pi}{7}$

$= \dfrac{\sin 2^3 (2\pi/7)}{2^3 \sin(2\pi/7)} = \dfrac{\sin(16\pi/7)}{8 \sin(2\pi/7)} = \dfrac{1}{8}$

$\because \quad \sin \dfrac{16\pi}{7} = \sin\left(2\pi + \dfrac{2\pi}{7}\right) = \sin \dfrac{2\pi}{7}$

$\therefore \quad E = \dfrac{2\,[3 - 2(-1/2) - 1/2]}{1 - (-1/2) + (-1/2) - 1/8} = 8$

(e) We know that $\operatorname{cosec}^2 \theta = 1 + \cot^2 \theta$.

Hence we have to prove that

$\operatorname{cosec}^2 \dfrac{\pi}{9} + \operatorname{cosec}^2 \dfrac{2\pi}{9} + \operatorname{cosec}^2 \dfrac{4\pi}{9} = 12$

Now proceed as in last part

$\operatorname{cosec}^2 \theta = \dfrac{2}{2\sin^2 \theta} = \dfrac{2}{1 - \cos 2\theta}$

where $2\theta = 2\pi/9,\, 4\pi/9,\, 8\pi/9$

$\therefore \quad E = 2\left[\dfrac{1}{1-a} + \dfrac{1}{1-b} + \dfrac{1}{1-c}\right]$

$= \dfrac{2\,[3 - 2\Sigma a + \Sigma ab]}{1 - \Sigma a + \Sigma ab - abc}$

$a = \cos \dfrac{2\pi}{9},\, b = \cos \dfrac{4\pi}{9},\, c = \cos \dfrac{8\pi}{9}$

$a + b + c = 2\cos \dfrac{3\pi}{9} \cos \dfrac{\pi}{9} + \cos\left(\pi - \dfrac{\pi}{9}\right)$

$= 2 \cdot \dfrac{1}{2} \cos \dfrac{\pi}{9} - \cos \dfrac{\pi}{9} = 0$

$abc = \cos \dfrac{2\pi}{9} \cos \dfrac{4\pi}{9} \cos \dfrac{8\pi}{9}$

$= \dfrac{\sin 2^3 (2\pi/9)}{2^3 \sin (2\pi/9)} = \dfrac{\sin (16\pi/9)}{8 \sin (2\pi/9)} = \dfrac{\sin (2\pi - 2\pi/9)}{8 \sin (2\pi/9)}$

$= -\dfrac{\sin (2\pi/9)}{8 \sin (2\pi/9)} = -\dfrac{1}{8}$

$ab + bc + ca$

$= \dfrac{1}{2}\left[\cos \dfrac{6\pi}{9} + \cos \dfrac{2\pi}{9} + \cos \dfrac{12\pi}{9} + \cos \dfrac{4\pi}{9}\right.$

$\left. + \cos \dfrac{10\pi}{9} + \cos \dfrac{6\pi}{9}\right]$

Combine 2nd and 4th and rewrite 5th.

$= \dfrac{1}{2}\left[\cos 120° + \cos 240° + \cos 120°\right.$

$\left. + 2\cos \dfrac{3\pi}{9} \cos \dfrac{\pi}{9} + \cos\left(\pi + \dfrac{\pi}{9}\right)\right]$

$= \dfrac{1}{2}\left[-\dfrac{1}{2} - \dfrac{1}{2} - \dfrac{1}{2} + 2 \cdot \dfrac{1}{2} \cos \dfrac{\pi}{9} - \cos \dfrac{\pi}{9}\right] = -\dfrac{3}{4}$

$\therefore \quad E = \dfrac{2\,[3 - 0 - 3/4]}{1 - 0 - 3/4 + 1/8} = \dfrac{9}{2} \div \dfrac{3}{8} = 12$

32. (a) L.H.S. $= \dfrac{1}{2^3 \sin (\pi/7)} \cdot \sin\left(2^3 \cdot \dfrac{\pi}{7}\right)$.

$= \dfrac{1}{8 \sin (\pi/7)} \cdot \sin\left(\pi + \dfrac{\pi}{7}\right) = -\dfrac{1}{8}$

$\because \quad \sin (\pi + \theta) = -\sin \theta.$

(b) L.H.S. $= \dfrac{1}{2^2 \sin (\pi/5)}\left[\sin 2^2 \cdot \dfrac{\pi}{5}\right]$

$= \dfrac{1}{4 \sin (\pi/5)} \cdot \sin\left\{\pi - \dfrac{\pi}{5}\right\} = \dfrac{1}{4}$ \quad ...(1)

Also $\quad \cos \dfrac{\pi}{5} + \cos \dfrac{3\pi}{5} = 2 \cdot \cos \dfrac{\pi}{5} \cos \dfrac{2\pi}{5}$

$= 2 \cdot \dfrac{1}{4} = \dfrac{1}{2},$ \quad by (1)

33. (a) $\sin \dfrac{\pi}{14} = \sin\left(\dfrac{\pi}{2} - \dfrac{6\pi}{14}\right) = \cos \dfrac{6\pi}{14}$

$= \cos\left(\pi - \dfrac{8\pi}{14}\right) = -\cos \dfrac{8\pi}{14}$

$\sin \dfrac{3\pi}{14} = \sin\left(\dfrac{\pi}{2} - \dfrac{4\pi}{14}\right) = \cos \dfrac{4\pi}{14}$

$\sin \dfrac{5\pi}{14} = \sin\left(\dfrac{\pi}{2} - \dfrac{2\pi}{14}\right) = \cos \dfrac{2\pi}{14}$

$\therefore \quad$ L.H.S. $= -\cos \dfrac{2\pi}{14} \cos \dfrac{4\pi}{14} \cos \dfrac{8\pi}{14}$

$= -\dfrac{1}{2^3 \sin A} \cdot \sin (2^3 A),\, A = \dfrac{2\pi}{14}$

$= -\dfrac{1}{8 \sin \dfrac{\pi}{7}} \sin \dfrac{8\pi}{7} = -\dfrac{1}{8 \sin \dfrac{\pi}{7}} \sin\left(\pi + \dfrac{\pi}{7}\right)$

$= -\dfrac{1}{8}(-1) = \dfrac{1}{8}$

$\because \quad \sin (\pi + \theta) = -\sin \theta$

(b) It is part (a) as $\sin \dfrac{7\pi}{14} = \sin \dfrac{\pi}{2} = 1$

(c) $\sin \dfrac{7\pi}{14} = \sin \dfrac{\pi}{2} = 1,$

$\sin \dfrac{13\pi}{14} = \sin\left(\pi - \dfrac{\pi}{14}\right) = \sin \dfrac{\pi}{14}$

Similarly, $\sin \dfrac{11\pi}{14} = \sin \dfrac{3\pi}{14}$ and $\sin \dfrac{9\pi}{14} = \sin \dfrac{5\pi}{14}$

Hence the question reduces to square of part (a)

$\therefore \quad$ Ans. $= \left(\dfrac{1}{8}\right)^2 = \dfrac{1}{64}$

34. (a) $\cos \dfrac{5\pi}{15} = \cos \dfrac{\pi}{3} = \dfrac{1}{2},\, \cos \dfrac{7\pi}{15} = -\cos \dfrac{8\pi}{15}$

L.H.S. $= \left[\cos \dfrac{\pi}{15} \cos \dfrac{2\pi}{15} \cos \dfrac{4\pi}{15}\left(-\cos \dfrac{8\pi}{15}\right)\right]$

$\left(\cos \dfrac{3\pi}{15} \cos \dfrac{6\pi}{15}\right) \cdot \dfrac{1}{2}$

Applying **R. 37, P. 519** on each bracket

$= -\dfrac{1}{2} \cdot \dfrac{\sin\left(2^4 \dfrac{\pi}{15}\right)}{2^4 \sin \dfrac{\pi}{15}} \cdot \dfrac{\sin\left(2^2 \dfrac{3\pi}{15}\right)}{2^2 \sin \dfrac{3\pi}{15}}$

$= -\dfrac{1}{128} \dfrac{\sin\left(\pi + \dfrac{\pi}{15}\right)}{\sin \dfrac{\pi}{15}} \cdot \dfrac{\sin\left(\pi - \dfrac{3\pi}{15}\right)}{\sin \dfrac{3\pi}{15}}$

$= \dfrac{1}{128},$ as $\sin (\pi + \theta) = -\sin \theta$

(b) $\dfrac{\sin (2^5 \cdot \pi/33)}{2^5 \cdot \sin (\pi/33)} = \dfrac{\sin\left(\pi - \dfrac{\pi}{33}\right)}{32 \cdot \sin (\pi/33)} = \dfrac{1}{32}.$

(c) Let $\theta = \dfrac{\pi}{65}$, $n = 6$

$$\text{L.H.S.} = \dfrac{\sin 2^6 \theta}{2^6 \sin \theta} = \dfrac{1}{64} \cdot \dfrac{\sin 64 \cdot \dfrac{\pi}{65}}{\sin \dfrac{\pi}{65}}$$

$$= \dfrac{1}{64} \cdot \dfrac{\sin\left(\pi - \dfrac{\pi}{65}\right)}{\sin \dfrac{\pi}{65}} = \dfrac{1}{64}. \qquad \text{as } \sin(\pi - \theta) = \sin \theta$$

(d) By R. 37 P. 519

$$\text{L.H.S.} = 2^n \cdot \dfrac{\sin 2^n \theta}{2^n \sin \theta} \text{ where } \theta = \dfrac{\pi}{2^n + 1}$$

$$= \left[\sin \dfrac{2^n \pi}{2^n + 1}\right] \div \left(\sin \dfrac{\pi}{2^n + 1}\right)$$

$$= \sin(\pi - \alpha) \div \sin \alpha = 1$$

35. (a) $\text{L.H.S.} = (\sqrt{3}/2) \sin 20° \sin(60° - 20°)$

$$\sin(60° + 20°).$$

$$= (\sqrt{3}/2) \sin 20° (\sin^2 60° - \sin^2 20°)$$

$$= (\sqrt{3}/2) \sin 20° [(3/4) - \sin^2 20°].$$

$$= (\sqrt{3}/8) [3 \sin 20° - 4 \sin^3 20°]$$

$$= (\sqrt{3}/8) \sin(3 \cdot 20°)$$

$$= (\sqrt{3}/8) \sin 60° = (\sqrt{3}/8) \cdot (\sqrt{3}/2) = 3/16.$$

(b) It follows from Q. 31 (a) and 35 (a) as

$$3/16 \div 1/16 = 3$$

Another method for (b) : Since $\tan 60° = \sqrt{3}$.

$\text{L.H.S.} = \sqrt{3} \tan 20° \tan 40° \tan 80°$

$$= \sqrt{3} \tan 20° \tan(60° - 20°) \tan(60° + 20°)$$

$$= \sqrt{3} \tan 20° \cdot \dfrac{\sqrt{3} - \tan 20°}{1 + \sqrt{3} \tan 20°} \cdot \dfrac{\sqrt{3} + \tan 20°}{1 - \sqrt{3} \tan 20°}$$

$$= \sqrt{3} \tan 20° \cdot \dfrac{3 - \tan^2 20°}{1 - 3 \tan^2 20°}$$

$$= \sqrt{3} \cdot \dfrac{3 \tan 20° - \tan^3 20°}{1 - 3 \tan^2 20°}$$

$$= \sqrt{3} \tan\{3(20°)\} = \sqrt{3} \tan 60° = \sqrt{3} \cdot \sqrt{3} = 3.$$

We have used the formula for $\tan 3A$.

36. Putting $n = 0, 1, 2, 3, \ldots$ in the given relation, we get

$$p_1 = \sqrt{\dfrac{1}{2}(1 + p_0)} = \sqrt{\dfrac{1}{2}(1 + \cos \theta)}$$

$$= \cos \dfrac{\theta}{2} \text{ where } p_0 = \cos \theta$$

$$p_2 = \sqrt{\dfrac{1}{2}(1 + p_1)} = \sqrt{\dfrac{1}{2}\left(1 + \cos \dfrac{\theta}{2}\right)} = \cos \dfrac{\theta}{2^2}$$

$$\therefore \quad p_3 = \cos \dfrac{\theta}{2^3}, \ldots \ldots p_n = \cos \dfrac{\theta}{2^n}$$

$$\therefore \quad p_1 p_2 p_3 \ldots \ldots \infty = \lim_{n \to \infty} p_1 p_2 \ldots p_n$$

$$= \lim_{n \to \infty} \cos \dfrac{\theta}{2} \cdot \cos \dfrac{\theta}{2^2} \ldots \cos \dfrac{\theta}{2^n}$$

Choose $\dfrac{\theta}{2^n} = A$ $\therefore$ $2^n A = \theta$

as $n \to \infty, A \to 0$

$$\therefore \quad \lim_{A \to 0} \cos A \cdot \cos 2A \cdot \cos 2^2 A \ldots n \text{ terms}$$

$$\lim_{A \to 0} \dfrac{\sin 2^n (A)}{2^n \sin A} = \lim_{A \to 0} \dfrac{\sin \theta}{2^n \cdot A} = \dfrac{\sin \theta}{\theta} \qquad \ldots(1)$$

Also $\sqrt{1 - p_0^2} = \sqrt{1 - \cos^2 \theta} = \sin \theta$ $\qquad \ldots(2)$

$$\therefore \quad \cos\left\{\dfrac{\sqrt{1 - p_0^2}}{p_1 \, p_2 \, p_3 \ldots \infty}\right\} = \cos\left[\dfrac{\sin \theta}{(\sin \theta)/\theta}\right] = \cos \theta = p_0$$

37. Take $2 \cos \theta + 1$ from R.H.S. to L.H.S.
and $4 \cos^2 \theta - 1 = 2(1 + \cos 2\theta) - 1$

$$= 2 \cos 2\theta + 1$$

and again multiply with 2nd factor and continue like this.

38. **Before doing this question remember the following**

$\sin 18° = \cos 72° = (\sqrt{5} - 1)/4$,
$\cos 36° = \sin 54° = (\sqrt{5} + 1)/4$
$\cos 18° = \sin 72° = \dfrac{1}{4} \cdot \sqrt{(10 + 2\sqrt{5})}$
$\sin 36° = \cos 54° = \dfrac{1}{4} \cdot \sqrt{(10 - 2\sqrt{5})}$

(a) $\text{L.H.S.} = \dfrac{1}{2} [2 (\sin 12° \sin 48°) \sin 54°]$

$$= \dfrac{1}{2} [(\cos 36° - \cos 60°) \cos 36°]$$

$$= \dfrac{1}{2} \left[\dfrac{\sqrt{5} + 1}{4} - \dfrac{1}{2}\right]\left(\dfrac{\sqrt{5} + 1}{4}\right)$$

$$= \dfrac{1}{2} \left[\dfrac{\sqrt{5} - 1}{4}\right]\left(\dfrac{\sqrt{5} + 1}{4}\right) = \dfrac{1}{32} \cdot 4 = \dfrac{1}{8}$$

(b) $\sin(13\pi/10) = \sin\{\pi + (3\pi)/10\}$

$$= -\sin(3\pi/10) = -\sin 54° = -\cos 36°.$$

and $\sin(\pi/10) = \sin 18°$

$$\therefore \quad \sin(\pi/10) \sin(13\pi/10) = \sin 18° (-\cos 36°)$$

$$= -\left(\dfrac{\sqrt{5} - 1}{4}\right)\left(\dfrac{\sqrt{5} + 1}{4}\right) = -\dfrac{1}{4}.$$

Hence (iii) is correct.

(c) $\text{L.H.S.} = 2 \sin 18° (\cos 37° + \cos 35°)$

$$= 2 \sin 18° \cdot 2 \cos 36° \cdot \cos 1°$$

$$= \cos 1°, \text{ as in last part.}$$

39. (a) By supplementary rule,
$\cos(\pi - A) = -\cos A$

$$\text{L.H.S.} = \left(1 + \cos \dfrac{\pi}{10}\right)\left(1 + \cos \dfrac{3\pi}{10}\right)\left(1 - \cos \dfrac{3\pi}{10}\right)$$

$$\left(1 - \cos \dfrac{\pi}{10}\right)$$

$$= \left(1 - \cos^2 \frac{\pi}{10}\right)\left(1 - \cos^2 \frac{3\pi}{10}\right) = \sin^2 18° \sin^2 54°$$

$$= \left(\frac{\sqrt{5}-1}{4} \cdot \frac{\sqrt{5}+1}{4}\right)^2 = \frac{1}{16}.$$

(b) $\cos \frac{3\pi}{8} = \cos\left\{\frac{\pi}{2} - \frac{\pi}{8}\right\} = \sin \frac{\pi}{8},$

$\cos \frac{5\pi}{8} = \cos\left\{\frac{\pi}{2} + \frac{\pi}{8}\right\} = -\sin \frac{\pi}{8},$

$\cos \frac{7\pi}{8} = \cos\left\{\pi - \frac{\pi}{8}\right\} = -\cos \frac{\pi}{8}.$

∴ L.H.S. $= (1 + \cos \pi/8)(1 + \sin \pi/8)$
$$(1 - \sin \pi/8)(1 - \cos \pi/8)$$

$$= (1 - \cos^2 \pi/8)(1 - \sin^2 \pi/8)$$

$$= \sin^2 \pi/8 \cos^2 \pi/8$$

$$= \frac{1}{4}\left[2 \sin \frac{\pi}{8} \cos \frac{\pi}{8}\right]^2$$

$$= \frac{1}{4}\left[\sin \frac{\pi}{4}\right]^2 = \frac{1}{4}\left\{\frac{1}{\sqrt{2}}\right\}^2 = \frac{1}{8}.$$

40. (a) L.H.S. $= \frac{1}{2} \cdot \frac{(\sqrt{5}+1)}{4} \cdot \frac{1}{2} \cdot (2 \cos 42° \cos 78°)$

$$= \frac{1}{16}(\sqrt{5}+1)(\cos 120° + \cos 36°)$$

$$= \frac{1}{16}(\sqrt{5}+1)\left(-\frac{1}{2} + \frac{\sqrt{5}+1}{4}\right)$$

$$= \frac{1}{16}(\sqrt{5}+1) \cdot \frac{\sqrt{5}-1}{4} = \frac{1}{16} \cdot \frac{5-1}{4} = \frac{1}{16}.$$

(b) L.H.S. $= \frac{1}{4}[(2 \sin 6° \sin 66°)(2 \sin 42° \sin 78°)]$

$$= \frac{1}{4}[(\cos 60° - \cos 72°)(\cos 36° - \cos 120°)]$$

$$= \frac{1}{4}\left[\left(\frac{1}{2} - \frac{\sqrt{5}-1}{4}\right)\left(\frac{\sqrt{5}+1}{4} + \frac{1}{2}\right)\right]$$

$$= \frac{1}{4} \cdot \frac{3-\sqrt{5}}{4} \cdot \frac{3+\sqrt{5}}{4} = \frac{1}{64} \cdot (9-5) = \frac{1}{16}.$$

(c) Changing in terms of sin and cos and then group 6° and 66° ; 42° and 78° as in part (a), (b).

41. (a) $\sin 36° = \sqrt{(10 - 2\sqrt{5})}/4,$

$\sin 72° = \cos 18° = \sqrt{(10 + 2\sqrt{5})}/4$

$\sin 108° = \cos 18°,$

$\sin 144° = \sin(180° - 36°) = \sin 36°$

L.H.S. $= (\sin 36° \sin 144°)(\sin 72° \sin 108°)$

$$= (\sin 36° \sin 36°)(\cos 18° \cos 18°)$$

$$= \sin^2 36° \cos^2 18°$$

$$= \frac{10 - 2\sqrt{5}}{16} \cdot \frac{10 + 2\sqrt{5}}{16} = \frac{100 - 20}{16 \times 16}$$

$$= \frac{80}{16 \times 16} = \frac{5}{16}.$$

(b) Squaring both sides, we get

L.H.S. $= 16 \sin^2 27° = 8(1 - \cos 54°)$

$$= 8(1 - \sin 36°)$$

$$= 8\left[1 - \frac{\sqrt{10 - 2\sqrt{5}}}{4}\right]$$

$$= 8 - 2\{\sqrt{10 - 2\sqrt{5}}\}$$

(R.H.S.)$^2 = 8 - 2[15 - 5 - 2\sqrt{5}] = 8 - 2[10 - 2\sqrt{5}]$

∴ L.H.S. = R.H.S.

42. (a) $\cos(\alpha + \beta) = 4/5$

∴ $\tan(\alpha + \beta) = \sqrt{(5^2 - 4^2)}/4 = 3/4$

$\sin(\alpha - \beta) = 5/13$

∴ $\tan(\alpha - \beta) = 5/\sqrt{(13^2 - 5^2)} = 5/12.$

$\tan 2\alpha = \tan(\alpha + \beta + \alpha - \beta)$

$$= \frac{\tan(\alpha + \beta) + \tan(\alpha - \beta)}{1 - \tan(\alpha + \beta)\tan(\alpha - \beta)}$$

$$= \frac{3/4 + 5/12}{1 - 3/4 \cdot 5/12} = \frac{56}{33}.$$

(b) $\sin^2 \frac{(\alpha - \beta)}{2} = \frac{1}{2}[1 - \cos(\alpha - \beta)],$

$\cos^2 \frac{(\alpha - \beta)}{2} = \frac{1}{2}[1 + \cos(\alpha - \beta)].$

where $\sin \alpha = 4/5, \sin \beta = 12/13$ etc.

43. (a) Dividing the given relations, we get

$$\frac{\sin x + \sin y}{\cos x + \cos y} = \frac{a}{b}$$

or $\dfrac{2 \sin\{(x+y)/2\} \cdot \cos\{(x-y)/2\}}{2 \cos\{(x+y)/2\} \cdot \cos\{(x-y)/2\}} = \dfrac{a}{b}.$

∴ $\tan\left(\frac{x+y}{2}\right) = \frac{a}{b}.$

Now $\sin A = \dfrac{2 \tan(A/2)}{1 + \tan^2(A/2)}$

∴ $\sin(x+y) = \dfrac{2 \cdot a/b}{1 + a^2/b^2} = \dfrac{2ab}{a^2 + b^2}.$

(b) Squaring and adding the given relations,
$(\sin^2 x + \sin^2 y + 2 \sin x \sin y)$
$\quad + (\cos^2 x + \cos^2 y + 2 \cos x \cos y) = a^2 + b^2$

or $2(\cos x \cos y + \sin x \sin y) = a^2 + b^2 - 2$

or $\cos(x - y) = (a^2 + b^2 - 2)/2.$

(c) ∵ $\tan^2\left(\frac{A}{2}\right) = \dfrac{1 - \cos A}{1 + \cos A},$

∴ $\tan^2\left(\frac{x-y}{2}\right) = \dfrac{1 - (a^2 + b^2 - 2)/2}{1 + (a^2 + b^2 - 2)/2}$ by (b).

or $\tan\left(\frac{x-y}{2}\right) = \pm\sqrt{\left(\dfrac{4 - a^2 - b^2}{a^2 + b^2}\right)}$

44. (a) $\sin^6 x + \cos^6 x$ **Refer Q. I (b)**

$$= 1 - 3 \sin^2 x \cos^2 x = \frac{1}{4}[4 - 3 \sin^2 2x] \quad ...(1)$$

Now $\sin x + \cos x = a$. Squaring,

$$1 + \sin 2x = a^2 \quad \therefore \quad \sin 2x = a^2 - 1$$

Putting in (1),

$$\therefore \quad \text{L.H.S.} = \frac{1}{4}[4 - 3(a^2 - 1)^2].$$

$$-1 \le \sin 2x \le 1 \quad \Rightarrow \quad -1 \le a^2 - 1 \le 1$$

or $\quad 0 \le a^2 \le 2 \quad \therefore \quad a^2 \ge 0$ and $a^2 \le 2$

which implies that $-\sqrt{2} \le a \le \sqrt{2}$.

(b) Squaring and adding the given relations, we get

$$1 + 1 + 2\cos(2A - A) = x^2 + y^2$$

$$\therefore \quad \cos A = \frac{1}{2}(x^2 + y^2 - 2) \qquad \ldots(1)$$

Now from second relation, we get

$$\cos A + 2\cos^2 A - 1 = y$$

or $\quad 2\cos^2 A + \cos A - 1 = y$

or $\quad (\cos A + 1)(2\cos A - 1) = y$.

Now put for $\cos A$ from (1).

45. (a) $c = 4[\cos^3 x + \cos^3 y] - 3(\cos x + \cos y)$, by 3rd

Cubing 1st.,

$$a^3 = \cos^3 x + \cos^3 y + 3\cos x \cos y \cdot a,$$

Equate $\cos^3 x + \cos^3 y$

$$\therefore \quad c + 3a = 4[a^3 - 3a\cos x \cos y]$$

$$4a^3 - c = 3a[1 + 4\cos x \cos y] \qquad \ldots(1)$$

From 2nd, $2(\cos^2 x + \cos^2 y) - 1 - 1 = b$

or $\quad 2[a^2 - 2\cos x \cos y] = b + 2$

$$\therefore \quad 2a^2 - b - 2 = 4\cos x \cos y = \frac{4a^3 - c}{3a} - 1 \text{ by (1)}$$

$$\therefore \quad 2a^3 + c = 3a(b + 1).$$

(b) $a^2 + b^2 = 1 + 1 + 2\cos(x - y) = 4\cos^2\dfrac{x - y}{2} \qquad \ldots(1)$

$$a = 2\sin\left(\frac{x + y}{2}\right)\cos\left(\frac{x - y}{2}\right)$$

$$\therefore \quad 4a^2 = 16\sin^2\left(\frac{x + y}{2}\right)\cos^2\left(\frac{x - y}{2}\right)$$

$$\therefore \quad (a^2 + b^2)^2 - 4a^2 = 16\cos^2\left(\frac{x - y}{2}\right)$$

$$\left[\cos^2\left(\frac{x - y}{2}\right) - \sin^2\left(\frac{x + y}{2}\right)\right]$$

$$= 16\cos^2\left(\frac{x - y}{2}\right)\cos x \cos y$$

$$\ldots(2)$$

Again $2ab = \sin 2x + \sin 2y + 2\sin(x + y)$

$$= 2\sin(x + y)\cos(x - y) + 2\sin(x + y)$$

$$= 2\sin(x + y)\left[2\cos^2\left(\frac{x - y}{2}\right)\right] \qquad \ldots(3)$$

Dividing (2) and (3),

$$\frac{(a^2 + b^2)^2 - 4a^2}{2ab} = \frac{4\cos x \cos y}{\sin(x + y)} = \frac{4}{c}$$

$$\therefore \quad \frac{\sin(x + y)}{\cos x \cos y} = c \qquad \text{from 3rd given relation.}$$

46. (a) Adding the given equations, we get

$$\operatorname{cosec} x - \cos x = a + b$$

$$\therefore \quad 1 - \sin x \cos x = (a + b)\sin x \qquad \ldots(1)$$

Squaring 1st equation, we get

$$1 - 2\sin x \cos x = a^2$$

$$\therefore \quad \frac{1 - a^2}{2} = \sin x \cos x. \quad \text{Put in (1)}$$

$$1 - \frac{1 - a^2}{2} = (a + b)\sin x$$

$$\frac{1 + a^2}{2(a + b)} = \sin x$$

Now put the value of $\sin x$ in 2nd equation

$$\operatorname{cosec} x - \sin x = b.$$

or $\quad \dfrac{2(a + b)}{1 + a^2} - \dfrac{1 + a^2}{2(a + b)} = b$

or $\quad 4(a + b)^2 - (1 + a^2)^2 = 2b(a + b)(1 + a^2)$

is required eliminant.

(b) $a\sin\theta + b\cos\theta = 1$

$a\cos\theta - b\sin\theta = \sin\theta \cdot \cos\theta \qquad$ Square and add

$$a^2 + b^2 = 1 + \sin^2\theta\cos^2\theta$$

$$= 1 + \cos^2\theta - \cos^4\theta \qquad \ldots(1)$$

Now we have to get only b in L.H.S.

Multiply the given equations by $\cos\theta$ and $\sin\theta$ and subtracting, we get

$$b(\cos^2\theta + \sin^2\theta) = \cos\theta - \cos\theta \cdot \sin^2\theta$$

or $\quad b = \cos^3\theta \quad \therefore \quad \cos\theta = b^{1/3} \qquad \text{Put in (1)}$

$$\therefore \quad a^2 + b^2 = 1 + b^{2/3} - b^{4/3}$$

47. (a) Solve by cross-multiplication for $\sec\theta$ and $\tan\theta$ and put in $\sec^2\theta - \tan^2\theta = 1$.

Ans. $(br - cq)^2 - (cp - ar)^2 = (aq - bp)^2$

(b) Subtracting the first from the second, we get

$$m(\cot x - \tan x) - n(\tan 2x + \cot 2x) = 0$$

or $\quad \dfrac{m\cos 2x}{\sin x \cos x} = \dfrac{n}{\sin 2x \cos 2x}$

which gives $\cos 2x = \sqrt{\left(\dfrac{n}{2m}\right)}$.

Now write the first equation as

$$p\sin 2x = 2m\sin^2 x + n\cos 2x$$

Change in double angles.

or $\quad p\sqrt{(1 - \cos^2 2x)} = m - (m - n)\cos 2x$

or $\quad p\sqrt{\left(1 - \dfrac{n}{2m}\right)} = m - (m - n)\sqrt{\left(\dfrac{n}{2m}\right)}$

or $\quad p\sqrt{(2m - n)} = m\sqrt{(2m)} - (m - n)\sqrt{n}$

48. (a) Square 1st equation and write
$$c^2 = c^2 (\cos^2 \theta + \sin^2 \theta)$$
Similarly in 2nd equation write
$$c = c (\cos^2 \theta + \sin^2 \theta)$$
Thus we have the following two equations :
$$(a^2 - c^2) x + 2abxy + (b^2 - c^2) y = 0$$
$$(a - c) x + 2axy + (b - c) y = 0,$$
$$\text{where } x = \cos^2 \theta, y = \sin^2 \theta$$
Solve by the method of cross-multiplication
$$\frac{x}{L} = \frac{2xy}{M} = \frac{y}{N} = \lambda \text{ say}$$
$$\therefore \quad (M)^2 = 4LN$$
or $(a - b)^2 (b - c)(c - a) = 4a^2 c (a + c - b)$

(b) From Ist, $a (1 - \cos^2 \alpha) + b \cos^2 \alpha = p$
$$\Rightarrow \quad \cos^2 \alpha = \frac{p - a}{b - a}$$
or $\tan^2 \alpha = \sec^2 \alpha - 1 = \frac{b - p}{p - a}$
Similarly, $\tan^2 \beta = \frac{a - q}{q - b}$
But $a^2 \tan^2 \alpha = b^2 \tan^2 \beta$
$$\therefore \quad a^2 \frac{(b - p)}{p - a} = b^2 \frac{(a - q)}{q - b}.$$
Cross-multiply and simplify
$$pq (a + b) = ab (p + q)$$
or $\frac{1}{a} + \frac{1}{b} = \frac{1}{p} + \frac{1}{q}$

(c) We are given that
$$4 \sin^2 (\alpha/2) \sin^2 (\beta/2) = 1$$
or $(1 - \cos \alpha)(1 - \cos \beta) = 1$
or $1 - (\cos \alpha + \cos \beta) + \cos \alpha \cos \beta = 1$
$$\therefore \quad \cos \alpha + \cos \beta = \cos \alpha \cos \beta$$
i.e., $S = P$ ...(I)
Now α and β satisfy the equation
$$y \sin \theta = 2a - x \cos \theta. \quad \text{Squaring}$$
$$y^2 (1 - \cos^2 \theta) = 4a^2 - 4ax \cos \theta + x^2 \cos^2 \theta$$
or $(x^2 + y^2) \cos^2 \theta - 4ax \cos \theta + 4a^2 - y^2 = 0$
Above is a quadratic in $\cos \theta$, whose roots are $\cos \alpha, \cos \beta$ by virtue of given relations.
Since $S = P$ by (I), we have
$$\frac{4ax}{x^2 + y^2} = \frac{4a^2 - y^2}{x^2 + y^2}$$
or $4a^2 - y^2 = 4ax$ or $y^2 = 4a(a - x)$

49. (a) Adding the given relations, we get
$$\frac{a}{b} + \frac{A}{B} = \frac{\sin (x - \alpha + x - \beta)}{\sin (x - \beta) \cos (x - \beta)}$$
$$\frac{aB + bA}{bB} = \frac{\sin (2x - \alpha - \beta)}{\sin (x - \beta) \cos (x - \beta)} \quad ...(1)$$

Multiplying the given relations and adding 1, we get
$$\frac{aA}{bB} + 1 = \frac{\begin{array}{c}\sin (x - \alpha) \cos (x - \alpha) \\ + \sin (x - \beta) \cos (x - \beta)\end{array}}{\sin (x - \beta) \cos (x - \beta)}$$
or $\dfrac{aA + bB}{bB}$
$$= \frac{1}{2} \cdot \frac{\sin (2x - 2\alpha) + \sin (2x - 2\beta)}{\sin (x - \beta) \cos (x - \beta)}$$
$$= \frac{1}{2} \cdot \frac{2 \sin (2x - \alpha - \beta) \cos (\alpha - \beta)}{\sin (x - \beta) \cos (x - \beta)} \quad ...(2)$$
Dividing (1) and (2), we get the result.

(b) $3 \sin^2 A = 1 - 2 \sin^2 B = \cos 2B$
Also $6 \sin A \cos A = 2 \sin 2B$.
Dividing, we get
$$2 \cot A = 2 \tan 2B$$
or $\tan 2B = \cot A = \tan \left(\dfrac{\pi}{2} - A \right)$ etc.

(c) $\tan (\theta + \phi) = \dfrac{\tan \theta + \tan \phi}{1 - \tan \theta \tan \phi}$
$$= \frac{\tan \theta (1 + \tan^2 \theta)}{1 - \tan^4 \theta} = \frac{1}{2} \cdot \frac{2 \tan \theta}{1 - \tan^2 \theta}$$
$$\therefore \quad \tan (\theta + \phi) = \frac{1}{2} \tan 2\theta = \frac{1}{2} \cdot 2 \tan \alpha = \tan \alpha$$
$$\therefore \quad \theta + \phi = n \pi + \alpha.$$

50. (a) $\tan \dfrac{\alpha}{2} = t_1, \tan \dfrac{\beta}{2} = t_2$ are the roots of t
quadratic $b (a + c) t^2 - 2act + b (a - c) = 0$
where $t = \tan (\theta / 2)$. Its roots are t_1, t_2.

(i) $\tan \left(\dfrac{\alpha + \beta}{2} \right) = \dfrac{t_1 + t_2}{1 - t_1 t_2} = \dfrac{S}{1 - P} = \dfrac{a}{b}$

(ii) By compo. and divi. on 2nd relation
$$\frac{2 \sin (\alpha/2) \sin (\beta/2)}{2 \cos (\alpha/2) \cos (\beta/2)} = \frac{a - c}{a + c}$$
or $t_1 t_2 = P$ which is true.

(b) Let $\tan A = t_1, \tan B = t_2$
Dividing the given relations,
$$\frac{\tan A}{\tan B} = \frac{p}{q} \quad \text{or} \quad \frac{t_1}{p} = \frac{t_2}{q} = k, \text{ say} \quad ...(1)$$
Multiplying the given relations, $\dfrac{\sin 2A}{\sin 2B} = pq$
or $\dfrac{2t_1}{1 + t_1^2} \cdot \dfrac{1 + t_2^2}{2t_2} = pq$
Now put for t_1 and t_2 from (1) and find k and hence
$$t_1 = \pm \frac{p}{q} \sqrt{\left(\frac{1 - q^2}{p^2 - 1} \right)}, t_2 = \pm \sqrt{\left(\frac{1 - q^2}{p^2 - 1} \right)}$$

(c) We have $\dfrac{2(p+q)(1-pq)}{(1+p^2)(1+q^2)}$

$= \dfrac{2[\tan(A/2)+\tan(B/2)][1-\tan(A/2)\tan(B/2)]}{[1+\tan^2(A/2)][1+\tan^2(B/2)]}$

$= \dfrac{2\sin\frac{1}{2}(A+B)\cos\frac{1}{2}(A+B)}{\left(\sin^2\frac{1}{2}A+\cos^2\frac{1}{2}A\right)\left(\sin^2\frac{1}{2}B+\cos^2\frac{1}{2}B\right)}$

$= 2\sin\dfrac{1}{2}(A+B)\cos\dfrac{1}{2}(A+B)$

$= \sin(A+B) = \sin(\pi-C) = \sin C.$

51. (a) $\dfrac{2t}{1-t^2} = \dfrac{p^2-q^2}{2pq}$

$t^2(p^2-q^2) + 4pqt - (p^2-q^2) = 0.$

Now solve for t by using $t = \dfrac{-b \pm \sqrt{b^2-4ac}}{2a}$

(b) Arrange as a quadratic in $\tan(\theta/2)$ as above
$9\tan^2(\theta/2) - 8\tan(\theta/2) + 3 = 0.$ Its roots are complex as

$64 - 4.3.9 = -ive$ *i.e.* $b^2-4ac < 0$.

Hence the given equation is wrong. If we choose $9/2$ in place of 6 in R.H.S., then it becomes

$15\tan^2(\theta/2) - 16\tan(\theta/2) + 3 = 0.$

∴ $\tan(\alpha/2) + \tan(\beta/2) = 16/15,$
$\tan(\alpha/2).\tan(\beta/2) = 1/5$

∴ $\tan(\alpha+\beta)/2 = \dfrac{\tan(\alpha/2)+\tan(\beta/2)}{1-\tan(\alpha/2)\tan(\beta/2)}$

$= \dfrac{16/15}{1-(1/5)} = \dfrac{4}{3}.$

Now $\sin(\alpha+\beta) = \dfrac{2\tan\{(\alpha+\beta)/2\}}{1+\tan^2\{(\alpha+\beta)/2\}}$

$= \dfrac{2.(4/3)}{1+(16/9)} = \dfrac{24}{25}.$

52. (a) Result (i) is obvious on adding y and z
Again $y - z = (a-c)\cos 2x + 2b\sin 2x$

$= \dfrac{(a-c)(1-t^2)+4bt}{1+t^2},$ where $t = \tan x$

Now as given put $t = \dfrac{2b}{a-c}$ in the above

$= \dfrac{(a-c)[(a-c)^2-4b^2]+8b^2(a-c)}{(a-c)^2+4b^2}$

$= (a-c)\left[\dfrac{(a-c)^2+4b^2}{(a-c)^2+4b^2}\right] = a-c.$

(b) $x = \pi/4, y = \pi/6$
The roots of quadratic in $\tan\theta$ are
$\tan(x+y)$ and $\tan(x-y)$
∴ $S = \tan(x+y) + \tan(x-y) = 4$ ...(1)
and $P = 1$

∴ $\tan 2x = \tan(x+y+x-y)$

$= \dfrac{S}{1-P} = \infty = \tan\dfrac{\pi}{2}$

∴ $2x = \dfrac{\pi}{2}$ or $x = \dfrac{\pi}{4}$

Now put $x = \dfrac{\pi}{4}$ in $S = 4$ *i.e.* in (1)

∴ $\dfrac{1+t}{1-t} + \dfrac{1-t}{1+t} = 4$ where $t = \tan y$

or $\dfrac{2(1+t^2)}{1-t^2} = 4$ ∴ $\cos 2y = \dfrac{1}{2}$

∴ $2y = \pi/3$ or $y = \pi/6$

(c) Expand $\tan(A-B)$ and put $\tan A = \dfrac{3}{2}, \tan B = \dfrac{3}{2}t$

∴ L.H.S. $= \dfrac{t}{2+3t^2}.$

Put $\sin 2B = \dfrac{2t}{1+t^2}, \cos 2B = \dfrac{1-t^2}{1+t^2}$ in R.H.S.

53. (a) L.H.S. $= \dfrac{1.\cos 10° - \sqrt{3}\sin 10°}{\sin 10°\cos 10°}.$

Put $1 = r\cos\alpha, \sqrt{3} = r\sin\alpha.$

∴ $r^2 = 1+3 = 4, ∴ r = 2$

and $\tan\alpha = \sqrt{3}, ∴ \alpha = 60°.$

L.H.S. $= \dfrac{r(\cos 60°\cos 10° - \sin 60°\sin 10°)}{\sin 10°\cos 10°}$

$= \dfrac{2\cos(60°+10°)}{\frac{1}{2}\sin 20°} = 4.\dfrac{\cos 70°}{\sin 20°} = 4.\dfrac{\sin 20°}{\sin 20°} = 4.$

(b) Proceed as in part (a).

54. (a) L.H.S. $= \dfrac{1}{\sin 20°}(4\cos 20°\sin 20° - \sqrt{3}\cos 20°)$

$= \dfrac{2}{\sin 20°}\left(\sin 40° - \dfrac{\sqrt{3}}{2}\cos 20°\right)$

$= \dfrac{1}{\sin 20°}(2\sin 40° - 2\sin 60°\cos 20°)$

$= \dfrac{1}{\sin 20°}[2\sin 40° - (\sin 80° + \sin 40°)]$

$= \dfrac{1}{\sin 20°}[\sin 40° - \sin 80°]$

$= \dfrac{1}{\sin 20°}[2\sin(-20°)\cos 60°] = -1$

(b) Ans. $\sqrt{3}$
$N^r = \cos 40° + (\cos 40° - \cos 20°)$

$= \cos 40° + 2\sin 30°\sin(-10°)$

$= \sin 50° - \sin 10° = 2\sin 20°\cos 30°$

∴ L.H.S. $= 2\cos 30° = \sqrt{3}.$

(c) Proceed as in Q 53 (a).

55. (a) $y = \left[\dfrac{1}{\sqrt{2}}(\cos x + \sin x)\right]^2 + (\sin x - \cos x)^2$

Ans. $\left(\dfrac{1}{2} + 1\right)(1 - \sin 2x) = \dfrac{3}{2} \cdot 2 = 3$.

∵   Max. value of $1 - \sin 2x = 1 - (-1) = 2$.

(b) If $u = a \sec x - b \tan x$

$(u + b \tan x)^2 = a^2(1 + \tan^2 x)$

or $\tan^2 x(a^2 - b^2) - 2bu \tan x + a^2 - u^2 = 0$

$\Delta \geq 0, -a^2(a^2 - b^2 - u^2) \geq 0$

or $a^2\{u^2 - a^2 + b^2\} \geq 0$

∴ $u^2 \geq (a^2 - b^2) \Rightarrow u \geq \surd(a^2 - b^2)$.

∴   Min. value of u is $\surd(a^2 - b^2)$

56. (a) **Note :** Here the angles are $2x$ and x

$y = \cos 2x + 3 \sin x = 1 - 2\sin^2 x + 3\sin x$

$= 1 - 2\left[s^2 - \dfrac{3s}{2} + \dfrac{9}{16} - \dfrac{9}{16}\right]$

$= \left(1 + \dfrac{9}{8}\right) - 2\left(s - \dfrac{3}{4}\right)^2$

Now y is greatest when $s - \dfrac{3}{4} = 0$ ∴ $s = \dfrac{3}{4}$

which is possible ∴ $b = 17/8$

Again y is least when $\left(s - \dfrac{3}{4}\right)^2$ is greatest and it

will be so when $s = -1$.

∴ $y = \dfrac{17}{8} - 2 \cdot \left(-\dfrac{7}{4}\right)^2 = \dfrac{17}{8} - \dfrac{49}{8} = -4$.

∴ $a = -4$.

(b) The given expression

$= \dfrac{1}{2}[a(1 - \cos 2\theta) + b \sin 2\theta + c(1 + \cos 2\theta)]$

$= \dfrac{1}{2}(a + c) + \dfrac{1}{2}b \sin 2\theta + \dfrac{1}{2}(c - a)\cos 2\theta$

Hence by **R. 36, P. 518** the least and greatest values of the given expression are respectively

$\dfrac{1}{2}(a + c) - \dfrac{1}{2}\sqrt{b^2 + (c - a)^2}$

and $\dfrac{1}{2}(a + c) + \dfrac{1}{2}\sqrt{\{b^2 + (c - a)^2\}}$

so that the value of the expression lies between these values as required.

57. (a) Since $a^2 + b^2 = 1$, we can find an angle α such that $a = \cos \alpha$ and $b = \sin \alpha$.

Similarly we can find an angle β such that $m = \cos \beta$ and $n = \sin \beta$.

We then have

$|am + bn| = |\cos \alpha \cos \beta + \sin \alpha \sin \beta|$

$= |\cos(\alpha - \beta)| \leq 1$.

(b) Ans. 1.

$f(x) = \sin^2 x + \dfrac{1}{4}(\sin x + \sqrt{3}\cos x)^2$

$\qquad + \dfrac{1}{2}\cos x(\cos x - \sqrt{3}\sin x)$

$= \dfrac{5}{4}(\sin^2 x + \cos^2 x) = \dfrac{5}{4}$

$(g \circ f)x = g[f(x)] = g(5/4) = 1$ (given)

(c) If $a = 1, b = \sin \theta, c = \sin \phi$, then we have to prove

$a^2 + b^2 + c^2 - ab - bc - ca > 0$

or $\dfrac{1}{2}[(a - b)^2 + (b - c)^2 + (c - a)^2] > 0$

Above is true.

(d) $\dfrac{b + c}{a} = \dfrac{\sin B + \sin C}{\sin A} = \dfrac{2\sin \dfrac{B+C}{2}\cos \dfrac{B-C}{2}}{2\sin \dfrac{A}{2}\cos \dfrac{A}{2}}$

$= \dfrac{\cos \dfrac{B-C}{2}}{\sin \dfrac{A}{2}} \leq \dfrac{1}{\sin \dfrac{A}{2}}$ (∵ $\cos \theta \leq 1$)

∴ $\operatorname{cosec}\dfrac{A}{2} \geq \dfrac{b+c}{a} = \dfrac{b}{a} + \dfrac{c}{a} \geq 2\sqrt{\dfrac{b}{a} \cdot \dfrac{c}{a}}$

∴ $\operatorname{cosec}^n \dfrac{A}{2} \geq 2^n \left(\dfrac{\sqrt{bc}}{a}\right)^n$

Write similar relations and multiply.

58. We have

$\tan^{2/3}\alpha = \tan^2 \dfrac{\theta}{2} = \dfrac{1 - \cos \theta}{1 + \cos \theta} = \dfrac{\sqrt{3} - \surd(a^2 - 1)}{\surd(3) + \surd(a^2 - 1)}$

∴ $\dfrac{\sin^{2/3}\alpha}{\surd(3) - \surd(a^2 - 1)} = \dfrac{\cos^{2/3}\alpha}{\surd(3) + \surd(a^2 - 1)}$

or $\dfrac{a}{p} = \dfrac{b}{q}$

Now apply the rule of ratio proportion

$\dfrac{a}{p} = \dfrac{b}{q} = \dfrac{a+b}{p+q} = \left(\dfrac{a^3 + b^3}{p^3 + q^3}\right)^{1/3}$ ...(2)

$p + q = 2\sqrt{3}$,

$p^3 + q^3 = 2[3\sqrt{3} + 3\sqrt{3}(a^2 - 1)] = 6\sqrt{3}\,a^2$

$a^3 + b^3 = \sin^2 \alpha + \cos^2 \alpha = 1$,

$a + b = \sin^{2/3}\alpha + \cos^{2/3}\alpha$

∴   From last two relations of (2), we have

$\sin^{2/3}\alpha + \cos^{2/3}\alpha$

$= 2\sqrt{3}\left[\dfrac{1}{6\sqrt{3}\,a^2}\right]^{1/3} = \left[\dfrac{24\sqrt{3}}{6\sqrt{3}\,a^2}\right]^{1/3}$

$= (4/a^2)^{1/3} = (2/a)^{2/3}$.

59. (a) From the given relation on changing to sin and cos, we have

$\dfrac{\cos^2 \theta}{\sin^2 \theta} = \dfrac{\cos(\theta - \alpha)\cos(\theta - \beta)}{\sin(\theta - \alpha)\sin(\theta - \beta)}$.

Apply compo. and divi.

$$\frac{\cos^2 \theta - \sin^2 \theta}{\cos^2 \theta + \sin^2 \theta} = \frac{\cos(\theta - \alpha + \theta - \beta)}{\cos(\theta - \alpha - \theta + \beta)},$$

using formula of $\cos(A \pm B)$

or $\cos 2\theta = \dfrac{\cos\{2\theta - (\alpha + \beta)\}}{\cos(\alpha - \beta)}$ $[\because \cos(-\theta) = \cos\theta]$

$\therefore$ $\cos 2\theta \cos(\alpha - \beta) = \cos 2\theta \cos(\alpha + \beta)$
$$+ \sin 2\theta \sin(\alpha + \beta)$$

or $\cos 2\theta \{\cos(\alpha - \beta) - \cos(\alpha + \beta)\}$
$$= \sin 2\theta \sin(\alpha + \beta)$$

$\therefore$ $\dfrac{\cos 2\theta}{\sin 2\theta} = \dfrac{\sin\alpha\cos\beta + \cos\alpha\sin\beta}{2\sin\alpha\sin\beta}$

or $\cot 2\theta = \dfrac{1}{2}[\cot\beta + \cot\alpha]$.

(b) $\dfrac{a}{b} = \dfrac{\tan(\theta + x)}{\tan(\theta + y)}$ Apply Compo. & Divi.

$\therefore$ $\dfrac{a+b}{a-b} = \dfrac{\sin(2\theta + x + y)}{\sin(x - y)}$

$\therefore$ $\dfrac{a+b}{a-b} \sin^2(x - y) = \sin(2\theta + x + y)\sin(x - y)$

$$= \frac{1}{2}[\cos(2\theta + 2y) - \cos(2\theta + 2x)]$$

$\therefore$ $\Sigma \dfrac{a+b}{a-b} \sin^2(x - y) = 0$ as the terms in R.H.S.

will cancel.

60. (a) Apply componendo and dividendo and remember

$$\tan A \pm \tan B = \frac{\sin(A \pm B)}{\cos A \cos B}$$

$\therefore$ $\dfrac{\sin 2\alpha}{\sin 2(\beta - \gamma)} = \dfrac{\sin(\beta + \gamma)}{-\sin(\beta - \gamma)}$

or $\sin(\beta - \gamma)[\sin 2\alpha + 2\cos(\beta - \gamma)\sin(\beta + \gamma)] = 0$

or $\sin(\beta - \gamma)[\sin 2\alpha + \sin 2\beta + \sin 2\gamma] = 0$ etc.

(b) $3 = 1 + 1 + 1 = (\cos^2\alpha + \sin^2\alpha) + (\ ) + (\ )$

or $(\cos^2\alpha + \cos^2\beta + \cos^2\gamma + 2\cos\beta\cos\gamma$
$$+ 2\cos\gamma\cos\alpha + 2\cos\alpha\cos\beta) + (\text{In sin}) = 0$$

or $(\cos\alpha + \cos\beta + \cos\gamma)^2 + (\ )^2 = 0$

$\therefore$ $\Sigma\cos\alpha = 0, \Sigma\sin\alpha = 0$

$[\because x^2 + y^2 = 0 \Rightarrow x = 0, y = 0]$

61. $\tan\beta = \dfrac{\sin(\alpha + \gamma)}{\cos(\alpha - \gamma)}$

on changing to sin and cos

$\therefore$ $\sin 2\beta = \dfrac{2\tan\beta}{1 + \tan^2\beta} = \dfrac{2\sin(\alpha + \gamma)\cos(\alpha - \gamma)}{\cos^2(\alpha - \gamma) + \sin^2(\alpha + \gamma)}$

$$= \frac{\sin 2\alpha + \sin 2\gamma}{\sin^2(\alpha + \gamma) + 1 - \sin^2(\alpha - \gamma)}$$

$$= \frac{\sin 2\alpha + \sin 2\gamma}{1 + \sin 2\alpha \sin 2\gamma}, \text{ by } \sin^2 A - \sin^2 B$$

using formula of $\sin^2 A - \sin^2 B$

62. We have $\dfrac{\sin^2\gamma}{\sin^2\alpha} = 1 - \dfrac{\tan(\alpha - \beta)}{\tan\alpha}$

or $\sin^2\gamma = \dfrac{\sin^2\alpha}{\tan\alpha}\left[\tan\alpha - \dfrac{\tan\alpha - \tan\beta}{1 + \tan\alpha\tan\beta}\right]$

or $\sin^2\gamma = \dfrac{\sin^2\alpha}{\tan\alpha}\left[\dfrac{\tan\beta(1 + \tan^2\alpha)}{1 + \tan\alpha\tan\beta}\right]$

or $\sin^2\gamma(1 + \tan\alpha\tan\beta) = \dfrac{\tan\beta}{\tan\alpha} \cdot \dfrac{\sin^2\alpha}{\cos^2\alpha}$

$$= \tan\alpha\tan\beta$$

or $\sin^2\gamma = \tan\alpha\tan\beta(1 - \sin^2\gamma)$

or $\tan^2\gamma = \tan\alpha\tan\beta$.

63. Let $A = 90° - x$, $B = 90° - y$ ...(1)

L.H.S. $= \dfrac{1 + \cos x}{\sin x} + \dfrac{\sin y}{1 - \cos y}$

$$= \cot\frac{x}{2} + \cot\frac{y}{2} = \frac{\sin\dfrac{x+y}{2}}{\sin\dfrac{x}{2}\sin\dfrac{y}{2}}$$

$$= \frac{2\sin\left(\dfrac{x+y}{2}\right)}{\cos\left(\dfrac{x-y}{2}\right) - \cos\left(\dfrac{x+y}{2}\right)}$$

$$= \frac{2\cos\dfrac{A+B}{2}}{\cos\dfrac{A-B}{2} - \sin\dfrac{A+B}{2}}, \text{ by (1)}$$

Keeping in view the form of R.H.S., multiplying above and below by $2\sin\dfrac{A-B}{2}$, we get

$$\frac{2(\sin A - \sin B)}{\sin(A - B) + (\cos A - \cos B)} = \text{R.H.S.}$$

64. We know that $\tan\left(\dfrac{\pi}{4} + \alpha\right) = \dfrac{1 + \tan\alpha}{1 - \tan\alpha} = \dfrac{\cos\alpha + \sin\alpha}{\cos\alpha - \sin\alpha}$

$\therefore$ $\tan^2\left(\dfrac{\pi}{4} + \alpha\right) = \dfrac{1 + \sin 2\alpha}{1 - \sin 2\alpha}$ $\because 2\sin\alpha\cos\alpha = \sin 2\alpha$

Squaring the given relation, we have to prove that

$\dfrac{1 + \sin y}{1 - \sin y} = \dfrac{(1 + \sin x)^3}{(1 - \sin x)^3}$. Apply comp. and divi.

$$\frac{2\sin y}{2} = \frac{2(3\sin x + \sin^3 x)}{2(1 + 3\sin^2 x)}.$$

$\therefore$ $\sin y = \dfrac{\sin x(3 + \sin^2 x)}{1 + 3\sin^2 x}$.

65. $\sin 3x = 3\sin x - 4\sin^3 x$

$\therefore$ $\sin^3 x = \dfrac{1}{4}(3\sin x - \sin 3x)$. ...(1)

Similarly, $\cos^3 x = \dfrac{1}{4}(3\cos x + \cos 3x)$ ...(2)

∴   L.H.S. $= \frac{1}{4}[\sin 3x (3\sin x - \sin 3x)$

$\qquad\qquad\qquad + \cos 3x (3\cos x + \cos 3x)]$

$= \frac{1}{4}[3\cos(3x-x) + (\cos^2 3x - \sin^2 3x)]$

$= \frac{1}{4}[3\cos 2x + \cos 6x] = \frac{1}{4}[3\cos A + \cos 3A]$

$= \cos^3 A$, by (2) $= \cos^3 2x$ $\qquad \because A = 2x$

66. We have to eliminate θ and φ.

$\sin^2 \alpha = 4\sin^2(\phi/2).\sin^2(\theta/2) = (1-\cos\phi)(1-\cos\theta)$

or $1 - \cos^2 \alpha = \left(1 - \frac{\cos\alpha}{\cos\beta}\right)\left(1 - \frac{\cos\alpha}{\cos\gamma}\right)$

$\qquad = 1 - \cos\alpha\left(\frac{1}{\cos\beta} + \frac{1}{\cos\gamma}\right) + \frac{\cos^2\alpha}{\cos\beta\cos\gamma}$

or $\cos\alpha\left(\frac{\cos\beta+\cos\gamma}{\cos\beta\cos\gamma}\right) = \cos^2\alpha.\frac{1+\cos\beta\cos\gamma}{\cos\beta\cos\gamma}$

∴ $\frac{\cos\beta+\cos\gamma}{1+\cos\beta\cos\gamma} = \frac{\cos\alpha}{1}.$

Apply compo. and divi.

$\frac{1-\cos\beta-\cos\gamma+\cos\beta\cos\gamma}{1+\cos\beta+\cos\gamma+\cos\beta\cos\gamma} = \frac{1-\cos\alpha}{1+\cos\alpha}$

or $\frac{(1-\cos\beta)(1-\cos\gamma)}{(1+\cos\beta)(1+\cos\gamma)} = \frac{1-\cos\alpha}{1+\cos\alpha}$

or $\frac{2\sin^2(\beta/2).2\sin^2(\gamma/2)}{2\cos^2(\beta/2).2\cos^2(\gamma/2)} = \frac{2\sin^2(\alpha/2)}{2\cos^2(\alpha/2)}$

or $\tan^2(\beta/2)\tan^2(\gamma/2) = \tan^2(\alpha/2)$

67. Given that

$\cos A \cos(B+C) - \sin A \sin(B+C) = \cos A \cos B \cos C$

∴ $\cos A[\cos(B+C) - \cos B \cos C] = \sin A \sin(B+C)$

or $\cos A(-\sin B \sin C) = \sin A \sin(B+C)$

∴ $\sin(B+C) = \frac{-\cos A \sin B \sin C}{\sin A}$

Write similar values of $\sin(C+A)$, $\sin(A+B)$ and multiply and put $\sin A \cos A = \frac{1}{2}\sin 2A$.

68. $\frac{\sin\theta\cos A + \cos\theta\sin A}{\sin\theta\cos B + \cos\theta\sin B} = \sqrt{\left\{\frac{2\sin A\cos A}{2\sin B\cos B}\right\}}$

or $\{\tan\theta\cos A + \sin A\}\sqrt{\sin B\cos B}$

$\qquad = (\tan\theta\cos B + \sin B)\sqrt{\sin A\cos A}.$

Collecting the terms of tan θ on one side and rest on the other, we get

$\tan\theta\{\cos A\sqrt{\sin B\cos B} - \cos B\sqrt{\sin A\cos A}\}$

$\qquad = \{\sin B\sqrt{\sin A\cos A} - \sin A\sqrt{\sin B\cos B}\}$

or $\tan\theta\sqrt{\cos A\cos B}\{\sqrt{\cos A\sin B} - \sqrt{\cos B\sin A}\}$

$\qquad = \sqrt{\sin A\sin B}\{\sqrt{\cos A\sin B} - \sqrt{\cos B\sin A}\}$

∴ $\tan\theta = \sqrt{\tan A\tan B}$ or $\tan^2\theta = \tan A\tan B$.

69. $k - 1 = \frac{\tan 3A - \tan A}{\tan A} = \frac{\sin 2A}{\cos 3A\sin A} = \frac{2\cos A}{\cos 3A}$

∴ $\frac{2k}{k-1} = \frac{2\tan 3A}{\tan A}.\frac{\cos 3A}{2\cos A} = \frac{\sin 3A}{\sin A}$

For 2nd part see **Q. 39 (b)** of quadratic equations.

70. Since $A = \frac{\pi}{4}$ ∴ $B + C = \frac{3\pi}{4}$

∴ $\tan B \tan C = \lambda$ ⇒ $\tan B\tan\left(\frac{3\pi}{4} - B\right) = \lambda$

or $\tan B\frac{(-1-\tan B)}{1-\tan B} = \lambda$ ∵ $\tan\frac{3\pi}{4} = -1$

or $\tan^2 B + (1-\lambda)\tan B + \lambda = 0$

$\Delta \geq 0 \Rightarrow (1-\lambda)^2 - 4\lambda \geq 0$

or $\lambda^2 - 6\lambda + 1 \geq 0$

Its roots are $a = 3 - 2\sqrt2$, $b = 3 + 2\sqrt2$

$(\lambda - a)(\lambda - b) \geq 0$, $a < b$

∴ $\lambda \leq a$ or $\lambda \geq b$

where $a = (\sqrt2 - 1)^2$, $b = (\sqrt2 + 1)^2$

71. Making use of given relations, we have

$\cos^2 x = \tan^2 y = \sec^2 y - 1 = \cot^2 z - 1.$

or $1 + \cos^2 x = \frac{\cos^2 z}{1-\cos^2 z} = \frac{\tan^2 x}{1-\tan^2 x}$

or $1 + \cos^2 x = \frac{\sin^2 x}{\cos^2 x - \sin^2 x}$

On changing to sin x, we get

$(2-\sin^2 x)(1-2\sin^2 x) = \sin^2 x$

or $2\sin^4 x - 6\sin^2 x + 2 = 0$

or $\sin^4 x - 3\sin^2 x + 1 = 0$

∴ $\sin^2 x = \frac{3\pm\sqrt{9-4}}{2} = \frac{3\pm\sqrt5}{2} = \frac{3-\sqrt5}{2}.$

We have rejected the value $\frac{3+\sqrt5}{2}$ as it is > 1.

or $\sin^2 x = \frac{6-2\sqrt5}{4} = \left(\frac{\sqrt5-1}{2}\right)^2.$

∴ $\sin x = \frac{\sqrt5-1}{2} = 2.\frac{(\sqrt5-1)}{4} = 2\sin 18°.$

By symmetry we can say that

$\sin x = \sin y = \sin z = 2\sin 18°.$

72. If θ = 18° then 5θ = 90° ∴ 3θ = 90° - 2θ

or $\tan 3\theta = \cot 2\theta$ or $\frac{3t - t^3}{1-3t^2} = \frac{1-t^2}{2t}$

∴ $5t^4 - 10t^2 + 1 = 0$ ∴ $t^2 = 1 \pm \sqrt{0.8}$

or $t^2 = 1 \pm .8944 = 1 - .8944 = 0.1056.$

$t^2 = \tan^2 18°$ is +ive and less than 1.

∵ $\tan 45° = 1$ ∴ $\tan 18° < \tan 45°$ or $t < 1$

and +ive. The other value being > 1 is rejected.

73. From the given relation, we have

$$\frac{\tan(x+100°)}{\tan(x-50°)} = \tan(x+50°)\tan x$$

We have chosen the combination as above because sum of the angles in both sides is $(2x+50°)$.

$$\frac{\sin(x+100°)\cos(x-50°)}{\cos(x+100°)\sin(x-50°)} = \frac{\sin(x+50°)\sin x}{\cos(x+50°)\cos x}$$

Apply componendo and dividendo

$$\frac{\sin(2x+50°)}{\sin 150°} = \frac{\cos 50°}{-(\cos 2x+50°)}$$

$$2\sin(2x+50°)\cos(2x+50°) = -\cos 50°$$

$\because \quad \sin 150° = \sin 30° = \frac{1}{2}$

$$\sin(4x+100°) = -\sin 40°$$
$$= \sin(180°+40°) = \sin 220°$$

or $\quad = \sin(2\pi - 40°) = \sin 320°$

$\therefore \quad 4x+100 = 220° \quad$ or $\quad 320°$

or $\quad 4x = 120°$ or $220°$ or $x = 30°$ or $55°$

74. We have $2 = 1+1$

$$\tan^2\beta\tan^2\gamma(1+\tan^2\alpha)$$
$$+\tan^2\gamma\tan^2\alpha(1+\tan^2\beta) = 1-\tan^2\alpha\tan^2\beta$$

or $\quad \dfrac{\sin^2\beta\sin^2\gamma + \sin^2\gamma\sin^2\alpha}{\cos^2\alpha\cos^2\beta\cos^2\gamma}$

$$= \frac{\cos^2\alpha\cos^2\beta - \sin^2\alpha\sin^2\beta}{\cos^2\alpha\cos^2\beta}$$

$$\sin^2\beta\sin^2\gamma + \sin^2\gamma\sin^2\alpha = (1-\sin^2\gamma).$$
$$[(1-\sin^2\alpha)(1-\sin^2\beta) - \sin^2\alpha\sin^2\beta]$$

or $\quad \sin^2\beta\sin^2\gamma + \sin^2\gamma\sin^2\alpha$
$$= (1-\sin^2\gamma)[1-\sin^2\alpha-\sin^2\beta]$$

or $\quad 0 = 1-\sin^2\gamma - \sin^2\alpha - \sin^2\beta$

or $\quad \Sigma\sin^2\alpha = 1.$

75. Let us put $\tan\theta = t_1$, $\tan\phi = t_2$

$\therefore \quad t_1^2 t_2^2 = \left(\dfrac{a-b}{a+b}\right)$

or $\quad (a+b)t_1^2 t_2^2 = a-b \qquad \qquad$ ...(1)

Also $\quad \cos 2\theta = \dfrac{1-\tan^2\theta}{1+\tan^2\theta} = \dfrac{1-t_1^2}{1+t_1^2}$ etc.

Now $\quad a-b\cos 2\theta = a-b\dfrac{(1-t_1^2)}{(1+t_1^2)}$

$$= \frac{(a-b)+(a+b)t_1^2}{(1+t_1^2)}$$

Put for $(a-b)$ from (1),

$$= \frac{a+b}{(1+t_1^2)}[t_1^2 t_2^2 + t_1^2] = \frac{(a+b)t_1^2(1+t_2^2)}{(1+t_1^2)},$$

Similarly, $\quad a-b\cos 2\phi = \dfrac{(a+b)}{1+t_2^2}t_2^2(1+t_1^2)$

$\therefore \quad (a-b\cos 2\theta)(a-b\cos 2\phi) = (a+b)^2 t_1^2 t_2^2$

$$= (a+b)^2 \cdot \{(a-b)/(a+b)\} = a^2-b^2, \qquad \text{by (1)}$$

which is independent of θ.

76. A careful look at the question suggests that we have to prove $x = y$. We know that

$$2\cos^2\theta = 1+\cos 2\theta,$$

and $\quad 2\sin^2\theta = 1-\cos 2\theta.$

Hence changing to double angles in the given relation $\dfrac{\cos^4 x}{\cos^2 y} + \dfrac{\sin^4 x}{\sin^2 y} = 1$, we get

$$\frac{\frac{1}{4}(1+\cos 2x)^2}{\frac{1}{2}(1-\cos 2y)}$$
$$+ \frac{\frac{1}{4}(1-\cos 2x)^2}{\frac{1}{2}(1+\cos 2y)}$$

$$= \frac{1}{2}(1+\cos 2y) \cdot \frac{1}{2}(1-\cos 2y)$$

or $\quad \{(1+\cos 2x)^2 + (1-\cos 2x)^2\}$
$$-\cos 2y\{(1+\cos 2x)^2 - (1-\cos 2x)^2\}$$
$$= 2(1-\cos^2 2y)$$

or $\quad 2(1+\cos^2 2x) - \cos 2y(4\cos 2x) = 2-2\cos^2 2y$

or $\quad \cos^2 2x + \cos^2 2y - 2\cos 2x\cos 2y = 0$

or $\quad (\cos 2x - \cos 2y)^2 = 0$

$\therefore \quad \cos 2x = \cos 2y \quad$ or $\quad y = n\pi \pm x$

$\therefore \quad \dfrac{\cos^4 y}{\cos^2 x} + \dfrac{\sin^4 y}{\sin^2 x} = \cos^2 x + \sin^2 x = 1$

(on putting $y = x$).

77. **(a)** Let us put $\cos(\alpha+\theta)\sin(\beta-\gamma) = a$, etc.

$\therefore \quad a+b+c = \Sigma(\cos\alpha\cos\theta - \sin\alpha\sin\theta)\sin(\beta-\gamma)$
$$= \cos\theta\Sigma\cos\alpha\sin(\beta-\gamma)$$
$$-\sin\theta\Sigma\sin\alpha\sin(\beta-\gamma) = 0$$

It is easy to observe on expansion that both the above sigmas are zero. Hence $a+b+c = 0$ so that from Algebra we know that

$$a^3+b^3+c^3 = 3abc.$$

On putting the values of a, b, c, we prove the given result.

(b) Let $a = \sin(\beta-\gamma)\sin(\alpha-\delta), b = ..., c = ...$

$a = \dfrac{1}{2}[\cos(\beta-\gamma-\alpha+\delta) - \cos(\beta-\gamma+\alpha-\delta)]$ etc.

It is easy to observe that $a+b+c = 0$.

$\therefore \quad a^3+b^3+c^3 = 3abc$, etc.

78. **(a)** Write $\alpha-\beta = (\theta-\beta) - (\theta-\alpha)$

$$\cos(\alpha-\beta) = x\sqrt{1-y^2} + y\sqrt{1-x^2}$$

$$\sin(\alpha-\beta) = xy - \sqrt{1-x^2}\sqrt{1-y^2}$$

Put in L.H.S. etc.

(b)   Combine (1, 3), (2, 4) and (5, 6).

L.H.S. $= -\sin(A+B+C)\cos A\cos(B+C)$

$-\cos(A+B+C)\sin A\cos(B+C)$

$+\cos(B+C)\sin(A+B+C+A)$.

Take out $\cos(B+C)$

L.H.S. $= \cos(B+C)[\sin(A+B+C+A)$

$-\sin(A+B+C+A)] = 0$

79. Multiplying the given relations by $\sin B$ and $\cos B$ and subtracting, we get

$-\sqrt{2}\,(\sin A\cos B - \cos A\sin B)$

$= \sin B\cos B\,(\cos^2 B + \sin^2 B)$

$\therefore$ $\sin(A-B) = -(1/2\sqrt{2})\sin 2B$ ...(1)

Again squaring and adding the given relations, we get

$2.1 = 1 + (\cos^6 B + \sin^6 B) + 2(\cos^4 B - \sin^4 B)$

$1 = 1.(\cos^4 B + \sin^4 B - \cos^2 B\sin^2 B)$

$+ 2.1.(\cos^2 B - \sin^2 B)$

or $1 = (1 - 3\cos^2 B\sin^2 B) + 2\cos 2B$

or $\dfrac{3}{4}(2\sin B\cos B)^2 = 2\cos 2B$

or $3\sin^2 2B = 8\cos 2B$

or $3\cos^2 2B + 8\cos 2B - 3 = 0$

or $3\cos^2 2B + 9\cos 2B - \cos 2B - 3 = 0$

or $(\cos 2B + 3)(3\cos 2B - 1) = 0$

$\therefore$ $\cos 2B = \dfrac{1}{3}$ as $\cos 2B \neq -3$.

$\therefore$ $\sin^2 2B = 1 - \cos^2 2B = 1 - \dfrac{1}{9} = \dfrac{8}{9}$

$\therefore$ $\sin 2B = \pm\dfrac{2\sqrt{2}}{3}$.

Hence from (1),

$\sin(A-B) = -\dfrac{1}{2\sqrt{2}}\sin 2B = \pm\dfrac{1}{3}$.

80. $(a+b)(b\sin^4 A + a\cos^4 A) - ab = 0$

or $ab[\sin^4 A + \cos^4 A - 1]$

$+ a^2\cos^4 A + b^2\sin^4 A = 0$

or $ab[1 - 2\sin^2 A\cos^2 A - 1]$

$+ a^2\cos^4 A + b^2\sin^4 A = 0$

or $(a\cos^2 A - b\sin^2 A)^2 = 0$

or $\dfrac{\cos^2 A}{b} = \dfrac{\sin^2 A}{a} = \dfrac{1}{a+b}$ ...(1)

$\therefore$ $\dfrac{\sin^8 A}{a^3} + \dfrac{\cos^8 A}{b^3} = \dfrac{1}{a^3}\cdot\dfrac{a^4}{(a+b)^4} + \dfrac{1}{b^3}\cdot\dfrac{b^4}{(a+b)^4}$

by (1)

$= \dfrac{(a+b)}{(a+b)^4} = \dfrac{1}{(a+b)^3}$

81. $\sin 2A\sin 2B = \dfrac{1}{2}[\cos(2A-2B) - \cos(2A+2B)]$

$= \dfrac{1}{2}[2\cos^2(A-B) - 1 - 2\cos^2(A+B) + 1]$

$\therefore$ $2x^3 - 3x^2\cos(A-B) - 2x\cos^2(A+B)$

$+ \cos^3(A-B) - \cos^2(A+B)\cos(A-B) = 0$

We write the above equation as under :

$\{2x^3 + x^2\cos(A-B)\} - 4x^2\cos(A-B)$

$+ \cos^3(A-B) - \cos^2(A+B)\{2x + \cos(A-B)\} = 0$

or $x^2\{2x + \cos(A-B)\} - \cos(A-B)\{4x^2 -$

$\cos^2(A-B)\} - \cos^2(A+B)\{2x + \cos(A-B)\} = 0$

Clearly $2x + \cos(A-B)$ is a factor.

$\therefore$ $\{2x + \cos(A-B)\}[x^2 - \cos(A-B).$

$\{2x - \cos(A-B)\} - \cos^2(A+B)] = 0$

or $\{2x + \cos(A-B)\}\{x^2 - 2x\cos(A-B)$

$+ \cos^2(A-B) - \cos^2(A+B)\} = 0$

The first factor gives $x = -\dfrac{1}{2}\cos(A-B) = 0$

Second factor by solving as a quadratic gives

$x = \dfrac{2\cos(A-B) \pm 2\cos(A+B)}{2}$

$= 2\cos A\cos B$ or $2\sin A\sin B$.

Hence the roots are

$2\cos A\cos B,\ 2\sin A\sin B$ and $-\dfrac{1}{2}\cos(A-B)$.

82. (a)   For all real θ, we have $-1 \leq \cos\theta \leq 1$.

Let $\cos\theta = A$ so that $-1 \leq A \leq 1$. Extend the interval.

Since $-\dfrac{\pi}{2} < -1$ and $1 < \dfrac{\pi}{2}$, it follows that

$-\dfrac{\pi}{2} < A < \dfrac{\pi}{2}$.

Hence $\cos A > 0$, that is, $\cos(\cos\theta) > 0$.

(b)   We have to prove

$\cos(\sin\theta) - \sin(\cos\theta) > 0$

or $\cos(\sin\theta) - \cos\left(\dfrac{\pi}{2} - \cos\theta\right) > 0$

or $2\sin\left(\dfrac{\pi}{4} + \dfrac{\sin\theta - \cos\theta}{2}\right)$

$\cdot\sin\left(\dfrac{\pi}{4} - \dfrac{\sin\theta + \cos\theta}{2}\right) > 0$ ...(1)

We now show that both the factors on the left hand side of (1) are positive. Since,

$|\sin\theta - \cos\theta| = \left|\sqrt{2}\sin\left(\theta - \dfrac{\pi}{4}\right)\right| \leq \sqrt{2} < \dfrac{\pi}{2}$

We have $-\dfrac{\pi}{2} < \sin\theta - \cos\theta < \dfrac{\pi}{2}$

or $-\dfrac{\pi}{4} < \dfrac{\sin\theta - \cos\theta}{2} < \dfrac{\pi}{4}$.

Add $\dfrac{\pi}{4}$ so that $0 < \dfrac{\pi}{4} + \dfrac{\sin\theta - \cos\theta}{2} < \dfrac{\pi}{2}$

and therefore $\sin\left(\dfrac{\pi}{4} + \dfrac{\sin\theta - \cos\theta}{2}\right) > 0$

Similarly we can prove $\sin\left(\dfrac{\pi}{4} - \dfrac{\sin\theta + \cos\theta}{2}\right) > 0$

Hence (1) holds which is what we wanted to prove.

83. (a) The difference of the angles is θ.
Multiply above and below by $\sin\theta$.

$$S = \dfrac{1}{\sin\theta}\left[\dfrac{\sin\theta}{\sin\theta\sin 2\theta} + \dfrac{\sin\theta}{\sin 2\theta\sin 3\theta} + \dots\right]$$

$$T_1 = \dfrac{\sin(2\theta - \theta)}{\sin\theta\sin 2\theta} = \cot\theta - \cot 2\theta$$

$$S_n = \dfrac{1}{\sin\theta}[(\cot\theta - \cot 2\theta) + (\cot 2\theta - \cot 3\theta) +$$

$$\dots + \{\cot n\theta - \cot(n+1)\theta\}]$$

$$= \dfrac{1}{\sin\theta}[\cot\theta - \cot(n+1)\theta]$$

(b) Change in cos and proceed as in part (a) by multiplying above and below by $\sin\theta$.

$$\therefore \quad S = \dfrac{1}{\sin\theta}[\tan(n+1)\theta - \tan n\theta]$$

Other forms of (a) and (b) :

(i) $\dfrac{1}{\cos\theta - \cos 3\theta} + \dfrac{1}{\cos\theta - \cos 5\theta}$

$$+ \dfrac{1}{\cos\theta - \cos 7\theta} + \dots n \text{ terms}$$

$$= \dfrac{1}{2\sin\theta}[\cot\theta - \cot(n+1)\theta]$$

(ii) $\dfrac{1}{\cos\theta + \cos 3\theta} + \dfrac{1}{\cos\theta + \cos 5\theta}$

$$+ \dfrac{1}{\cos\theta + \cos 7\theta} + \dots n \text{ terms}$$

$$= \dfrac{1}{2\sin\theta}[\tan(n+1)\theta - \tan\theta]$$

84. (a) $T_1 = \dfrac{\sin y}{\cos y\cos 2y} = \dfrac{\sin(2y - y)}{\cos y\cos 2y} = \tan 2y - \tan y$

$$T_2 = \tan 4y - \tan 2y$$

$$\dots\dots\dots\dots\dots\dots\dots\dots\dots$$

$$T_n = \tan 2^n y - \tan 2^{n-1} y$$

$$\therefore \quad S_n = \tan 2^n y - \tan y .$$

(b) $S_n = \tan y - \tan\dfrac{1}{2^n} y .$

85. (a) $T_1 = \dfrac{\sin x}{\cos x} = \dfrac{\sin^2 x}{\cos x\sin x} = \dfrac{\cos^2 x - \cos 2x}{\cos x\sin x}$

$$T_1 = \cot x - 2\cot 2x$$

$$T_2 = 2[\cot 2x - 2\cot 2^2 x]$$

$$= 2\cot 2x - 2^2\cot 2^2 x$$

and so on.

$$\therefore \quad S_n = \cot x - 2^n\cot 2^n x$$

(b) $S_n = \dfrac{1}{2^{n-1}}\cot\dfrac{1}{2^{n-1}} x - 2\cot 2x$

86. (a) $\tan x = \tan(2x - x) = \dfrac{\tan 2x - \tan x}{1 + \tan 2x\tan x}$

$$\therefore \quad T_1 = \tan 2x\tan x = \cot x(\tan 2x - \tan x) - 1$$

$$T_2 = \cot x(\tan 3x - \tan 2x) - 1 \text{ etc.}$$

$$\therefore \quad S_n = \cot x[\tan(n+1)x - \tan x] - n$$

$$= \cot x\tan(n+1)x - 1 - n .$$

(b) (i) We have $B = \dfrac{2\pi}{n}$

$$= \text{even multiple of } \dfrac{\pi}{n} \quad \therefore \quad \dfrac{nB}{2} = \pi$$

and $\sin\dfrac{nB}{2} = \sin\pi = 0 .$

(ii) Proceed as above.

87. (a) Let $\theta = \dfrac{2\pi}{7}, \cos\dfrac{4\pi}{7}$ and $\cos\dfrac{8\pi}{7}$

$$\therefore \quad 7\theta = \text{Even }\pi \quad \text{or} \quad 4\theta = \text{Even }\pi - 3\theta$$

$$\therefore \quad \cos 4\theta = \cos 3\theta$$

$$(2\cos^2 2\theta - 1) = 4\cos^3\theta - 3\cos\theta$$

Put $\cos\theta = x$

$$2(2x^2 - 1)^2 - 1 = 4x^3 - 3x$$

$$2(4x^4 - 4x^2 + 1) - 1 = 4x^3 - 3x$$

or $8x^4 - 4x^3 - 8x^2 + 3x + 1 = 0$

Clearly $x = 1$ is a root of above.

$$(x - 1)(8x^3 + 4x^2 - 4x - 1) = 0$$

$x = 1$ or $\cos\theta = 1 \Rightarrow \theta = 0$ or 2π rejected

$$\therefore \quad 8x^3 + 4x^2 - 4x - 1 = 0 \qquad \dots(3)$$

is the equation whose roots are given by (1) and (2) of the question.

Deductions : From (3), $S_1 = -\dfrac{4}{8} = -\dfrac{1}{2}, S_3 = \dfrac{1}{8} .$

$$\therefore \quad \sec\theta = \dfrac{1}{\cos\theta} . \text{ Hence putting } x = \dfrac{1}{y} \text{ in (3) the}$$

required equation is $y^3 + 4y^2 - 4y - 8 = 0 \quad \dots(4)$

88. (a) $y = \sec\theta \quad \therefore \quad z = \sec^2\theta = y^2$

Put in (4)

$$y \cdot y^2 + 4y^2 - 4y - 8 = 0$$

$$\sqrt{z}(z - 4) = -4(z - 2) . \text{ Square}$$

$$z(z^2 - 8z + 16) = 16(z^2 - 4z + 4)$$

or $z^3 - 24z^2 + 80z - 64 = 0 \qquad \dots(5)$

$$\therefore \quad \sec^2\dfrac{2\pi}{7} + \sec^2\dfrac{4\pi}{7} + \sec^2\dfrac{8\pi}{7} = 24 .$$

$$\sec^2\dfrac{2\pi}{7} \cdot \sec^2\dfrac{4\pi}{7} \cdot \sec^2\dfrac{8\pi}{7} = 64 .$$

(b) $z = \sec^2\theta = 1 + \tan^2\theta = 1 + t .$ Put in (5)

$$(t + 1)^3 - 24(t + 1)^2 + 80(t + 1) - 64 = 0$$

or $t^3 - 21t^2 + 35t - 7 = 0$ ...(6)

$\therefore \quad S_1 = \tan^2 \frac{2\pi}{7} + \tan^2 \frac{4\pi}{7} + \tan^2 \frac{8\pi}{7} = 21$

$S_3 = \tan^2 \frac{2\pi}{7} \cdot \tan^2 \frac{4\pi}{7} \cdot \tan^2 \frac{8\pi}{7} = 7.$

89. (a) $t = \tan^2 \theta \quad \therefore \quad u = \cot^2 \theta = \frac{1}{t}$ or $t = \frac{1}{u}$

Putting in (6), we get

$7u^3 - 35u^2 + 21u - 1 = 0$ ...(7)

$\therefore \quad S_1 = \cot^2 \frac{2\pi}{7} + \cot^2 \frac{4\pi}{7} + \cot^2 \frac{8\pi}{7} = \frac{35}{7} = 5$

$S_3 = \cot^2 \frac{2\pi}{7} \cdot \cot^2 \frac{4\pi}{7} \cdot \cot^2 \frac{8\pi}{7} = \frac{1}{7}.$

(b) It follows from (6) and (7) of last part.

as $21 \times 5 = 105.$

$\tan^2 \frac{3\pi}{7} = \tan^2 \left(\pi - \frac{4\pi}{7}\right) = \tan^2 \frac{4\pi}{7}$

$\tan^2 \frac{\pi}{7} = \tan^2 \left(\pi - \frac{6\pi}{7}\right) = \tan^2 \frac{6\pi}{7} = \tan^2 \frac{8\pi}{7}$ etc.

Independent Proof :

Let $\theta = \frac{n\pi}{7}, n = 1, 2, 3, \ldots 7$

$\therefore \quad 7\theta = n\pi \quad$ or $\quad 4\theta = n\pi - 3\theta$

$\therefore \quad \tan 4\theta = -\tan 3\theta$

Put $\tan\theta = t$, $\tan 2\theta = \frac{2t}{1 - t^2} = T$

$\tan 3\theta = \frac{3t - t^3}{1 - 3t^2}$

$\therefore \quad \frac{2T}{1 - T^2} = -\frac{t(3 - t^2)}{1 - 3t^2}$

or $\quad \frac{2 \cdot \frac{2t(1 - t^2)}{(1 - t^2)^2 - 4t^2}}{} = \frac{t(3 - t^2)}{1 - 3t^2}$

Cancel t as it corresponds to

$t = \tan \frac{7\pi}{7} = \tan \pi = 0$

Cross-multiplying, we get

$t^6 - 21t^4 + 35t^2 - 7 = 0$

Put $z = t^2 = \tan^2 \frac{n\pi}{7}, n = 1, 2, 3, 4, 5, 6$

$\tan^2 \frac{6\pi}{7} = \tan^2 \left(\pi - \frac{\pi}{7}\right) = \left(-\tan \frac{\pi}{7}\right)^2 = \tan^2 \frac{\pi}{7}$

         say z_1, z_2, z_3

Similarly, $\tan^2 \frac{5\pi}{7} = \tan^2 \frac{2\pi}{7}$, $\tan^2 \frac{4\pi}{7} = \tan^2 \frac{3\pi}{7}$

Hence the cubic equation

$z^3 - 21z^2 + 35z - 7 = 0$

has its roots $\tan^2 \frac{\pi}{7}, \tan^2 \frac{2\pi}{7}, \tan^2 \frac{3\pi}{7}.$

$\Sigma \tan^2 \frac{\pi}{7} = 21 = S_1$

$\Sigma \cot^2 \frac{\pi}{7} = \left(\frac{1}{z_1} + \frac{1}{z_2} + \frac{1}{z_3}\right)$

$= \frac{z_1 z_2 + z_2 z_3 + z_3 z_1}{z_1 z_2 z_3} = \frac{S_2}{S_3} = \frac{35}{7} = 5.$

$\therefore \quad \Sigma \tan^2 \frac{\pi}{7} \cdot \Sigma \cot^2 \frac{\pi}{7} = 21 \times 5 = 105.$

90. Let $\frac{\pi}{14} = \theta \Rightarrow 7\theta = \frac{\pi}{2} \Rightarrow 4\theta = \frac{\pi}{2} - 3\theta$

$\therefore \quad \sin 4\theta = \cos 3\theta$

or $2 \sin 2\theta \cos 2\theta = 4\cos^3 \theta - 3\cos\theta$

or $4 \sin\theta \cos\theta (1 - 2\sin^2 \theta) = \cos\theta [4(1 - \sin^2 \theta) - 3]$

$\cos\theta \neq 0$, cancel $\cos\theta$ and put $\sin\theta = x.$

(b) Apply $a^2 + b^2 + c^2 > ab + bc + ca$

$\therefore \quad a^2 + b^2 > 2ab, b^2 + c^2 > 2bc, c^2 + a^2 > 2ca$

         add etc.

Problem Set (6)

Multiple Choice Questions

1. The value of $\cos 10° - \sin 10°$ is
   (a) positive   (b) negative
   (c) 0   (d) 1

2. (a) The value of $\cos 1° \cos 2° \cos 3° \ldots\ldots \cos 179°$ is
   (a) $1/\sqrt{2}$ (b) 0
   (c) 1   (d) none of these

          (Karnataka C.C.E. 1999)

   (b) If $\sin x + \text{cosec } x = 2$, then
         $\sin^{3n} x + \text{cosec}^{3n} x$ equals
   (a) 2^{2n-1} (b) 2^{2n} (c) 2^{3n+1} (d) 2

3. Which of the following is correct ?
   (a) $\sin 1° > \sin 1$ (b) $\sin 1° < \sin 1$
   (c) $\sin 1° = \sin 1$ (d) $\sin 1° = \frac{\pi}{180} \sin 1.$

4. If $\tan\theta = -4/3$, then $\sin\theta$ is
   (a) $-4/5$ but not $4/5$ (b) $-4/5$ or $4/5$
   (c) $4/5$ but not $-4/5$ (d) none of these.

5. Which of the following number(s) is/are rational ?
   (a) $\sin 15°$ (b) $\cos 15°$
   (c) $\sin 15° \cos 15°$ (d) $\sin 15° \cos 75°$

          (I.I.T. 1998)

6. The value of $\tan 75° - \cot 75°$ is equal to
   (a) $2\sqrt{3}$ (b) $2 + \sqrt{3}$
   (c) $2 - \sqrt{3}$ (d) none of these.

7. The value of $\tan 3A - \tan 2A - \tan A$ is equal to
   (a) $\tan 3A \tan 2A \tan A$
   (b) $-\tan 3A \tan 2A \tan A$
   (c) $\tan A \tan 2A - \tan 2A \tan 3A - \tan 3A \tan A$
   (d) none of these

8. The value of $(\cos 11° + \sin 11°)/(\cos 11° - \sin 11°)$ is

(a) $\tan 45°$ (b) $\tan 56°$

(c) $\tan 60°$ (d) $\cot 11°$

9. (i) $\tan 54°$ can be expressed as

(a) $(\cos 9° - \sin 9°)/(\cos 9° + \sin 9°)$

(b) $(\sin 9° - \cos 9°)/(\sin 9° + \cos 9°)$

(c) $(\cos 9° + \sin 9°)/(\cos 9° - \sin 9°)$

(d) $(\sin 9° + \cos 9°)/(\sin 9° - \cos 9°)$.

(ii) If $4n\alpha = \pi$ then the value of $\tan \alpha \tan 2\alpha \tan 3\alpha \ldots \tan(2n-1)\alpha =$

(a) 1 (b) 0

(c) -1 (d) none

10. The value of $\sin(45° + \theta) - \cos(45° - \theta)$ is

(a) $2\cos\theta$ (b) $2\sin\theta$

(c) 1 (d) 0

11. If $\sin\theta = -4/5$ and θ lies in the third quadrant, then the value of $\cos(\theta/2)$ is

(a) $1/5$ (b) $-1/\sqrt{10}$

(c) $-1/\sqrt{5}$ (d) $1/\sqrt{10}$

12. If $\tan\theta = 3$ and θ lies in the third quadrant, then the value of $\sin\theta$ is

(a) $1/\sqrt{10}$ (b) $-1/\sqrt{10}$

(c) $-3/\sqrt{10}$ (d) $3/\sqrt{10}$

13. If $\sin\alpha = 12/13$ $(0 < \alpha < \pi/2)$ and $\cos\beta = -\dfrac{3}{5}$ $\left(\pi < \beta < \dfrac{3}{2}\pi\right)$, the value of $\sin(\alpha + \beta)$ is

(a) $-56/65$ (b) $16/65$

(c) $56/65$ (d) $-16/65$

14. If θ and ϕ are angles in the first quadrant such that $\tan\theta = 1/7$ and $\sin\phi = 1/\sqrt{10}$, then

(a) $\theta + 2\phi = 90°$ (b) $\theta + 2\phi = 30°$

(c) $\theta + 2\phi = 75°$ (d) $\theta + 2\phi = 45°$

15. The value of
$\cos(\pi/5)\cos(2\pi/5)\cos(4\pi/5)\cos(8\pi/5)$ is

(a) $1/16$ (b) 0

(c) $-1/8$ (d) $-1/16$

16. The value of $\sin 20° \sin 40° \sin 60° \sin 80°$ is equal to

(a) $-3/16$ (b) $5/16$

(c) $3/16$ (d) $-5/16$

17. The value of the expression $\sqrt{3}\operatorname{cosec} 20° - \sec 20°$ is equal to

(a) 2 (b) $2\sin 20°/\sin 40°$

(c) 4 (d) $4\sin 20°/\sin 40°$

18. Given $\pi/2 < \alpha < \pi$, then the expression
$\sqrt{(1 - \sin\alpha)/(1 + \sin\alpha)} + \sqrt{(1 + \sin\alpha)/(1 - \sin\alpha)} =$

(a) $1/\cos\alpha$ (b) $-2/\cos\alpha$

(c) $2/\cos\alpha$ (d) none of these

19. If $\tan x = b/a$, then
$\sqrt{(a+b)/(a-b)} + \sqrt{(a-b)/(a+b)}$ is equal to

(a) $2\sin x/\sqrt{\sin 2x}$ (b) $2\cos x/\sqrt{\cos 2x}$

(c) $2\cos x/\sqrt{\sin 2x}$ (d) $2\sin x/\sqrt{\cos 2x}$

20. (a) If $\cos(A - B) = 3/5$ and $\tan A \tan B = 2$, then

(a) $\cos A \cos B = 1/5$ (b) $\sin A \sin B = -2/5$

(c) $\cos(A + B) = -1/5$ (d) $\sin A \cos B = 4/5$

(b) If $A + B = \dfrac{\pi}{3}$ and $\cos A + \cos B = 1$, then which of the following are true :

(a) $\cos(A - B) = \dfrac{1}{3}$

(b) $\cos(A - B) = -\dfrac{1}{3}$

(c) $|\cos A - \cos B| = \sqrt{2/3}$

(d) $|\cos A - \cos B| = \dfrac{1}{\sqrt{3}}$

(c) If $\Sigma n^2 = \lambda \Sigma n$, then $\sin^{-1}\left(\dfrac{9\lambda^2 - 4n^2}{6\lambda + 4n}\right) =$

(a) $\dfrac{\pi}{6}$ (b) $\dfrac{\pi}{3}$

(c) $\dfrac{\pi}{2}$ (d) π

21. If $A = 580°$, then

(a) $\sin\dfrac{1}{2}A = \dfrac{1}{2}[\sqrt{(1 + \sin A)} - \sqrt{(1 - \sin A)}]$

(b) $\sin\dfrac{1}{2}A = -[\sqrt{(1 + \sin A)} - \sqrt{(1 - \sin A)}]$

(c) $\sin\dfrac{1}{2}A = \dfrac{1}{2}[-\sqrt{(1 + \sin A)} - \sqrt{(1 - \sin A)}]$

(d) $\cos\dfrac{1}{2}A = \sqrt{(1 + \sin A)} - \sqrt{(1 - \cos A)}$

22. If $2\cos(A/2) = \sqrt{(1 + \sin A)} - \sqrt{(1 - \sin A)}$, then

(a) $n\pi + (\pi/4) < A/2 < n\pi + (3\pi/4)$

(b) $n\pi - (\pi/4) < A/2 < 2n\pi - (3\pi/4)$

(c) $2n\pi - (3\pi/4) < A/2 < 2n\pi + (5\pi/4)$

(d) $2n\pi + (\pi/4) < A/2 < 2n\pi + (3\pi/4)$.

23. If $\cos(\alpha + \beta) = \dfrac{4}{5}$, $\sin(\alpha - \beta) = \dfrac{5}{13}$ and α, β lie between 0 and $\dfrac{\pi}{4}$ then $\tan 2\alpha =$

(a) $\dfrac{16}{63}$ (b) $\dfrac{56}{63}$

(c) $\dfrac{28}{33}$ (d) none of these

(AIEEE 2010)

24. In a ΔPQR if $3\sin P + 4\cos Q = 6$ and $4\sin Q + 3\cos P = 1$, then the angle R is equal to

(a) $\dfrac{5\pi}{6}$ (b) $\dfrac{\pi}{6}$ (c) $\dfrac{\pi}{4}$ (d) $\dfrac{3\pi}{4}$

(AIEEE 2012)

25. If $\dfrac{\sin^4 x}{2} + \dfrac{\cos^4 x}{3} = \dfrac{1}{5}$ then

(a) $\tan^2 x = \dfrac{2}{3}$ (b) $\dfrac{\sin^8 x}{8} + \dfrac{\cos^8 x}{27} = \dfrac{1}{125}$

(c) $\tan^2 x = \dfrac{1}{3}$ (d) $\dfrac{\sin^2 x}{8} + \dfrac{\cos^8 x}{27} = \dfrac{2}{125}$

(IIT-JEE 2009)

26. Let $\theta, \phi \in [0, 2\pi]$ be such that

$2 \cos(1 - \sin \phi) = \sin^2 \theta \left(\tan \dfrac{\theta}{2} + \cot \dfrac{\theta}{2} \right) \cos \phi + 1$,

$\tan(2\pi - \theta) > 0$ and $-1 < \sin \theta < \dfrac{\sqrt{3}}{2}$, then ϕ can not satisfy

(a) $0 < \phi < \dfrac{\pi}{2}$ (b) $\dfrac{\pi}{2} < \phi < \dfrac{4\pi}{3}$

(c) $\dfrac{4\pi}{3} < \phi < \dfrac{3\pi}{2}$ (d) $\dfrac{3\pi}{2} < \phi < 2\pi$

(IIT-JEE 2012)

27. The maximum value of the expresson

$\dfrac{1}{\sin^2 \theta + 3 \sin \theta \cos \theta + 5 \cos^2 \theta}$ is

(a) 2 (b) 3 (c) $\dfrac{1}{2}$ (c) $\dfrac{1}{3}$

(IIT-JEE 2004)

▶ True and False type Questions :

State whether the following statements are true or false.

28. If $\tan \theta = \tan 240°$, then the value of θ in the first quadrant is $30°$.

29. If θ lies in the third quadrant , then the expression $\sqrt{(4 \sin^4 \theta + \sin^2 2\theta)} + 4 \cos^2 \left(\dfrac{1}{4} \pi - \dfrac{1}{2} \theta \right)$ equals 2.

30. The equality $\sin A + \sin 2A + \sin 3A = 3$ holds for some real value of A.

31. (a) If $\theta = 160°$, then $\sin \theta + \cos \theta > 0$.

(b) $\cos 11° - \cos 2°$ is positive.

32. The value of $\cos(-1044°)$ is $(\sqrt{5} + 1)/4$.

33. If $\cos 2B = \dfrac{\cos(A + C)}{\cos(A - C)}$, then $\tan A, \tan B, \tan C$ are in G.P.

34. The inequality $2^{\sin \theta} + 2^{\cos \theta} \geq 2^{1 - (1/\sqrt{2})}$ holds for all real values of θ.

▶ Fill in the Blanks :

Fill in the blanks so that the following statements are correct.

35. The maximum distance of a point on the graph of the function $y = \sqrt{3} \sin x + \cos x$ from x-axis is ....

36. If $\theta + \phi = \pi/4$, then the value of
$(1 + \tan \theta)/(1 + \tan \phi)$ is ....

37. The larger of $\cos \log \theta$ and $\log \cos \theta$ if $e^{-\pi/2} < \theta < \pi/2$ is ....

38. (a) If $y = 4 \sin^2 \theta - \cos 2\theta$, then y lies in the interval ....

(b) The real roots of the equation $\cos^7 x + \sin^4 x = 1$ in the interval $(-\pi, \pi)$ are ...., ... and ....

(I.I.T. Re-ex. 1997)

39. Suppose that $\sin^3 x \sin 3x = \sum\limits_{m=0}^{n} c_m \cos mx$ is an identity in x where $c_0, c_1, ..., c_n$ are constants and $c_n \neq 0$ then the value of n is .... **(D.C.E. 1998)**

Hints and Solutions to Problem Set (6)

1. Ans. (a).

We know that for $0 \leq \theta < 45°$, we have $\cos \theta > \sin \theta$.

Hence $\cos 10° - \sin 10° > 0$

2. (a) Ans. (b). For, one of the factors of the given expression is $\cos 90°$ which has the value 0.

(b) Ans. (d).

Given relation $\Rightarrow (\sin x - 1)^2 = 0$

∴ $\sin x = 1 = \text{cosec } x$

3. Ans. (b). Since 1 radian $= 57° 30'$ approx. and $\sin 57° 30' > \sin 1°$, thus $\sin 1° < \sin 1$.

4. Ans. (b). Since $\tan \theta = -4/3$ which is negative. Hence θ either lies in the second quadrant or fourth quadrant. Hence $\sin \theta = 4/5$ (when θ is in the second quadrant) or $\sin \theta = -4/5$ (when θ is in fourth quadrant)

5. Ans. (c).

$\dfrac{1}{2} \cdot 2 \sin 15° \cos 15° = \dfrac{1}{2} \sin 30° = \dfrac{1}{4}$ i.e. rational.

6. Ans. (a). We have

$\tan 75° - \tan 15° = (2 + \sqrt{3}) - (2 - \sqrt{3}) = 2\sqrt{3}$

by R. 33 P. 518

7. Ans. (a). We have

$3A = 2A + A \Rightarrow \tan 3A = \tan(2A + A)$
$= (\tan 2A + \tan A)/(1 - \tan 2A \tan A)$

$\Rightarrow \tan 3A - \tan 3A \tan 2A \tan A = \tan 2A + \tan A$

$\Rightarrow \tan 3A - \tan 2A - \tan A = \tan 3A \tan 2A \tan A$

8. Ans. (b). We have

$(\cos 11° + \sin 11°)/(\cos 11° - \sin 11°)$
$= (1 + \tan 11°)/(1 - \tan 11°)$
$= (\tan 45° + \tan 11°)/(1 - \tan 45° \tan 11°)$
$= \tan(45° + 11°) = \tan 56°$

9. (i) Ans. (c).

(ii) Ans. (a).

$(2n - 1)\alpha = 2n\alpha - \alpha = \dfrac{\pi}{2} - \alpha$

or $\tan \alpha \tan(2n - 1)\alpha = 1$

∴ $\tan(2n - 1)\alpha = \cot \alpha$

Similarly, $\tan(2n - 2)\alpha = \cot 2\alpha$ etc.

Combine terms equidistant from the beginning and end and each product is 1.

10. Ans. (d).

[**Hint :** $\cos(45° - \theta) = \sin[\{90° - (45° - \theta)\}]$
$$= \sin(45° + \theta)]$$

11. Ans. (c). Since θ lies in the third quadrant,
$\cos\theta < 0$ so $\sin\theta = -4/5 \Rightarrow \cos\theta = -3/5$.

Now, $\cos^2(\theta/2) = \dfrac{1}{2}(1 + \cos\theta)$

$$= \dfrac{1}{2}\left(1 - \dfrac{3}{5}\right) = \dfrac{1}{5} \qquad \ldots(1)$$

since $180° < \theta < 270°$, we have $90° < \dfrac{\theta}{2} < 135°$ so that $\dfrac{\theta}{2}$

lies in the second quadrant.

Hence $\cos(\theta/2)$ is negative. Therefore (1) gives $\cos(\theta/2) = -1/\sqrt{5}$.

12. Ans. (c). Since θ lies in the third quadrant, we have $\sin\theta < 0$. Hence

$\tan\theta = 3 \Rightarrow \sin\theta = -3/\sqrt{(3^2 + 1^2)} = -3/\sqrt{10}$

13. Ans. (a). Since $0 < \alpha < \pi$ we have $\sin\alpha = 12/13$

$\Rightarrow \cos\alpha = \sqrt{[1 - (12/13)^2]} = 5/13$

and since $\pi < \beta < 3\pi/2$, we have

$\cos\beta = -3/5 \Rightarrow \sin\beta = -4/5$

Hence $\sin(\alpha + \beta) = \sin\alpha\cos\beta + \cos\alpha\sin\beta$

$$= \dfrac{12}{13}\left(-\dfrac{3}{5}\right) + \left(\dfrac{5}{13}\right)\left(-\dfrac{4}{5}\right) = -\dfrac{56}{65}.$$

14. Ans. (d).

Since $\tan\theta = 1/7$, we have $\sin\theta = 1/(5\sqrt{2})$ and $\cos\theta = 7/(5\sqrt{2})$

Also $\sin\phi = 1/\sqrt{10} \Rightarrow \tan\phi = 1/3$

$\therefore \sin 2\phi = (2\tan\phi)/(1 + \tan^2\phi)$

$$= (2/3)/[1 + (1/9)] = 3/5$$

and so $\cos 2\phi = 4/5$

Hence $\sin(\theta + 2\phi) = \sin\theta\cos 2\phi + \cos\theta\sin 2\phi$

$$= \dfrac{1}{5\sqrt{2}}\cdot\dfrac{4}{5} + \dfrac{7}{5\sqrt{2}}\cdot\dfrac{3}{5} = \dfrac{25}{25\sqrt{2}} = \dfrac{1}{\sqrt{2}}$$

$\therefore \quad \theta + 2\phi = 45°$

15. Ans. (d). We have by **Q. 34, P. 533-44**

$\cos(\pi/5)\cos(2\pi/5)\cos(4\pi/5)\cos(8\pi/5)$

$$= \dfrac{1}{2^4 \sin(\pi/5)}\sin\dfrac{2^4\pi}{5}$$

$$= -\dfrac{1}{16}\left[\because \sin\dfrac{16\pi}{5} = \sin\left(3\pi + \dfrac{\pi}{5}\right) = -\sin\dfrac{\pi}{5}\right]$$

16. Ans. (c). [**See Q. 35 (a), Problem set (33) P. 533-45**]

17. Ans. (c). [**See Q. 53 (a) P. 533-45**]

18. Ans. (b). The given expression

$$= \dfrac{(1 - \sin\alpha) + (1 + \sin\alpha)}{\sqrt{[(1 + \sin\alpha)(1 - \sin\alpha)]}}$$

$$= \dfrac{2}{\sqrt{(\cos^2\alpha)}} = \dfrac{2}{|\cos\alpha|} = -\dfrac{2}{\cos\alpha}$$

$[\because \pi/2 < \alpha < \pi \Rightarrow \cos\alpha < 0 \Rightarrow |\cos\alpha| = -\cos\alpha].$

19. Ans. (b). We have

$$\sqrt{\left(\dfrac{a+b}{a-b}\right)} + \sqrt{\left(\dfrac{a-b}{a+b}\right)} = \dfrac{a+b+a-b}{\sqrt{(a^2 - b^2)}}$$

$$= \dfrac{2a}{\sqrt{(a^2 - b^2)}} = \dfrac{2}{\sqrt{\{1 - (b/a)^2\}}}$$

$$= \dfrac{2}{\sqrt{(1 - \tan^2 x)}} = \dfrac{2\cos x}{\sqrt{(\cos^2 x - \sin^2 x)}} = \dfrac{2\cos x}{\sqrt{(\cos 2x)}}.$$

20. (a) Ans. (a) and (c).

$\cos(A - B) = 3/5$

$\therefore \quad 5\cos A\cos B + 5\sin A\sin B = 3$

But from 2nd relation

$\sin A\sin B = 2\cos A\cos B$

$\therefore \quad (5 + 10)\cos A\cos B = 3$

$\therefore \quad \cos A\cos B = 1/5$ *i.e.* (a)

or $5\left(\dfrac{1}{2} + 1\right)\sin A\sin B = 3$

$\therefore \quad \sin A\sin B = 2/5$ $\therefore$ (b) is not correct.

$\cos(A + B) = \cos A\cos B - \sin A\sin B$

$$= \dfrac{1}{5} - \dfrac{2}{5} = -\dfrac{1}{5}$$ *i.e.* (c).

(b) Ans. (b), (c).

From the given relation, we have

$$2\cos\dfrac{A+B}{2}\cos\dfrac{A-B}{2} = 1$$

or $2\cos 30°\cos\dfrac{A-B}{2} = 1$

$\therefore \quad \cos\dfrac{A-B}{2} = \dfrac{1}{\sqrt{3}}$

$\therefore \quad \cos(A - B) = 2\cos^2\dfrac{A-B}{2} - 1$

$$= 2\cdot\dfrac{1}{3} - 1 = -\dfrac{1}{3} \Rightarrow (b)$$

Again $|\cos A - \cos B| = 2\sin\dfrac{A+B}{2}\sin\dfrac{B-A}{2}$

$$= 2\sin 30°\sqrt{1 - \cos^2\dfrac{A-B}{2}} = 1\cdot\sqrt{1 - \dfrac{1}{3}} = \sqrt{\dfrac{2}{3}}$$

(c) Ans. (a).

$$\dfrac{n(n+1)(2n+1)}{6} = \lambda\cdot\dfrac{n(n+1)}{2}$$

$\therefore \quad 2n + 1 = 3\lambda \qquad \ldots(1)$

$\therefore \quad \dfrac{9\lambda^2 - 4n^2}{6\lambda + 4n} = \dfrac{(3\lambda - 2n)(3\lambda + 2n)}{2(3\lambda + 2n)} = \dfrac{1}{2}$ by (1)

$\therefore \quad E = \sin^{-1}\left(\dfrac{1}{2}\right) = \dfrac{\pi}{6}.$

21. Ans. (c).

Since $A/2 = 290°$, we have $225° < A/2 < 315°$

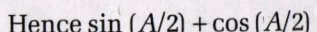

Hence $\sin (A/2) + \cos (A/2)$
and $\quad \sin (A/2) - \cos (A/2)$
are both negative [See **Rule 35 P. 518** and the figure on **P. 518**]

$\therefore \quad \sin (A/2) + \cos (A/2) = -\sqrt{(1 + \sin A)}$

and $\sin (A/2) - \cos (A/2) = -\sqrt{(1 - \sin A)}$

Adding these,

$2 \sin (A/2) = -\sqrt{(1 + \sin A)} - \sqrt{(1 - \sin A)}$

22. Ans. (d) . We know that

$\sin (A/2) + \cos (A/2) = \pm \sqrt{(1 + \sin A)}$ ...(1)

and $\sin (A/2) - \cos (A/2) = \pm \sqrt{(1 - \sin A)}$ ...(2)

But we are given,

$2 \cos (A/2) = \sqrt{(1 + \sin A)} - \sqrt{(1 - \sin A)}$ ...(3)

Now (3) will be obtained if we take positive sign both in (1) and (2) . But we know (**See 35, P. 519**) that $\sin (A/2) + \cos (A/2)$ and $\sin (A/2) - \cos (A/2)$ are both positive when $\pi/4 < A/2 < 3\pi/4$ or in general $2n\pi + \pi/4 < A/2 < 2n\pi + 3\pi/4$.

23. Ans. (b).

$\cos (\alpha + \beta) = \dfrac{4}{5}, \sin (\alpha - \beta) = \dfrac{5}{13}$

$\Rightarrow \quad \sin (\alpha + \beta) = \dfrac{3}{5}, \cos (\alpha - \beta) = \dfrac{12}{13}$

$\Rightarrow \quad 2\alpha = \sin^{-1}\dfrac{3}{5} + \sin^{-1}\dfrac{5}{13}$

$= \sin^{-1}\left[\dfrac{3}{5}\sqrt{1 - \dfrac{25}{169}} + \dfrac{5}{13}\sqrt{\left(1 - \dfrac{9}{25}\right)} \right]$

$= \sin^{-1}\left(\dfrac{56}{65}\right) \Rightarrow \sin 2\alpha = \dfrac{56}{65}$

$\therefore \quad \tan 2\alpha = \dfrac{\sin 22}{\cos 2\alpha} = \dfrac{56/65}{33/65} = \dfrac{56}{33}$

24. Ans. (b).

$3 \sin P + 4 \cos Q = 6$ ...(1)

$4 \sin Q + 3 \cos P = 1$ ...(2)

On squaring and adding we get $\sin (P + Q) = \dfrac{1}{2}$

$\Rightarrow \quad P + Q = \dfrac{\pi}{6}$ or $\dfrac{5\pi}{6} \quad \Rightarrow R = \dfrac{5\pi}{6}$ or $\dfrac{\pi}{6}$

If $R = \dfrac{5\pi}{6}$ then $0 < P, Q < \dfrac{\pi}{6}$

$\Rightarrow \quad \cos Q < 1$ and $\sin P < \dfrac{1}{2}$

$\Rightarrow \quad 3 \sin P + 4 \cos Q < \dfrac{11}{2} \quad$ Hence $R = \dfrac{\pi}{6}$

25. Ans. (a) and (b).

$\dfrac{\sin^4 x}{2} + \dfrac{\cos^4 x}{3} = \dfrac{1}{5}$

$\Rightarrow \quad \dfrac{\sin^4 x}{2} + \dfrac{(1 - \sin^2 x)^2}{3} = \dfrac{1}{5}$

$\Rightarrow \quad \dfrac{\sin 4x}{2} + \dfrac{1 + \sin^4 x - 2 \sin^2 x}{3} = \dfrac{1}{5}$

$\Rightarrow \quad 5 \sin^4 x - 4 \sin^2 x + 2 = \dfrac{6}{5}$

$\Rightarrow \quad (5 \sin^2 x - 2)^2 = 0$

$\Rightarrow \quad \sin^2 x = \dfrac{2}{5}, \cos^2 x = \dfrac{3}{5} \quad \Rightarrow \tan^2 x = \dfrac{2}{3}$

and $\quad \dfrac{\sin^8 x}{8} + \dfrac{\cos^8 x}{27} = \dfrac{1}{125}$

26. Ans. (a), (c) and (d).

$\tan (2\pi - \theta) > 0, -1 < \sin \theta < -\dfrac{\sqrt{3}}{2}, \theta \in [0, 2\pi]$

$\Rightarrow \quad \dfrac{3\pi}{2} < \theta < \dfrac{5\pi}{3}$

Now $2 \cos \theta (1 - \sin \phi) = \sin^2 \theta \left(\tan \dfrac{\theta}{2} + \cot \dfrac{\theta}{2} \right) \cos \phi - 1$

$\Rightarrow \quad 2 \cos \theta (1 - \sin \phi) = 2 \sin \theta \cos \phi - 1$

$\Rightarrow \quad 2 \cos \theta + 1 = 2 \sin (\theta + \phi)$

As $\theta \in \left(\dfrac{3\pi}{2}, \dfrac{5\pi}{3} \right) \Rightarrow 2 \cos \theta + 1 \in (1, 2)$

$\Rightarrow \quad 1 < 2 \sin (\theta + \phi) < 2 \Rightarrow \dfrac{1}{2} < \sin (\theta + \phi) < 1$

and as $\theta + \phi \in (0, 4\pi]$

$\theta + \phi \in \left] \dfrac{\pi}{6}, \dfrac{5\pi}{6} \right[\quad$ or $\quad \theta + \phi \in \left] \dfrac{13\pi}{6}, \dfrac{17\pi}{6} \right[$

$\Rightarrow \quad \dfrac{\pi}{6} - \theta < \phi < \dfrac{5\pi}{6} - \theta$ or $\dfrac{13\pi}{6} - \theta < \phi < \dfrac{17\pi}{6} - \theta$

$\Rightarrow \quad \phi \in \left] \dfrac{3\pi}{2}, \dfrac{-2\pi}{3} \right[\cup \left] \dfrac{2\pi}{3}, \dfrac{7\pi}{6} \right[\qquad \left[\because \theta \in \left] \dfrac{3\pi}{2}, \dfrac{5\pi}{3} \right[\right)$

27. Ans. Ans. (a).

$f(\theta) = \dfrac{1}{\sin^2 \theta + 3 \sin \theta \cos \theta + 5 \cos^2 \theta}$

$= \dfrac{1}{\dfrac{1 - \cos 2\theta}{2} + \dfrac{3}{2} \sin 2\theta + \dfrac{5(1 + \cos 2\theta)}{2}}$

$= \dfrac{2}{6 + 3 \sin 2\theta + 4 \cos 2\theta}$

Hence, $[f(\theta)]_{maximum} = \dfrac{2}{6 - 5} = 2$

28. Ans. False.

29. True. We have

$\sqrt{\{4 \sin^4 \theta + \sin^2 2\theta\}} = \sqrt{\{4 \sin^2 \theta (\sin^2 \theta + \cos^2 \theta)\}}$

$= \sqrt{(4 \sin^2 \theta)} = 2 |\sin \theta|$.

But since θ lies in the third quadrant, we have $\sin \theta < 0$ and $|\sin \theta| = -\sin \theta$.

Hence $\sqrt{\{4 \sin^4 \theta + \sin^2 2\theta\}} = -2 \sin \theta$.

and $4 \cos^2 (\pi/4 - \theta/2) = 2 [1 + \cos (\pi/2 - \theta)] = 2 + 2 \sin \theta$.

Hence the given expression

$= -2 \sin \theta + 2 + 2 \sin \theta = 2.$

[Note that $|x| = x$ if $x \geq 0$ and $= -x$ if $x \leq 0$]

30. Ans. False. Since $\sin A \leq 1$ for all real values of A, the given equation will hold true only if $\sin A = \sin 2A = \sin 3A = 1$. But this is clearly impossible for any real number A.

31. (a) Ans. Flase.

Since $\sin 160° = \sin(180° - 20°) = \sin 20°$

and $\cos 160° = \cos(180° - 20°) = -\cos 20°$,

we have

∴ $\sin 160° + \cos 160° = \sin 20° - \cos 20° < 0$

$[\because \sin 20° < \cos 20°]$

(b) False. $\cos 11° < \cos 2°$

32. Ans. True . We have

$\cos(-1044°) = \cos 1044° = \cos(3 \times 360° - 36°)$

$= \cos 36° = (\sqrt{5} + 1)/4$.

33. Ans. True. We have $\dfrac{\cos 2B}{1} = \dfrac{\cos(A+C)}{\cos(A-C)}$.

Applying componendo and dividendo,

$\dfrac{1 - \cos 2B}{1 + \cos 2B} = \dfrac{\cos(A-C) - \cos(A+C)}{\cos(A-C) + \cos(A+C)}$

$\Rightarrow \dfrac{2\sin^2 B}{2\cos^2 B} = \dfrac{2\sin A \sin C}{2\cos A \cos C}$

$\Rightarrow \tan^2 B = \tan A \tan C \Rightarrow \tan A, \tan B, \tan C$

are in G.P.

34. Ans. True. We have $\dfrac{1}{2}[2^{\sin\theta} + 2^{\cos\theta}] \geq \sqrt{2^{\sin\theta} \cdot 2^{\cos\theta}}$

$[\because A.M. \geq G.M.]$

$\Rightarrow 2^{\sin\theta} + 2^{\cos\theta} \geq 2 \cdot 2^{(\sin\theta + \cos\theta)/2}$ ...(1)

Now $(\sin\theta + \cos\theta) = \sqrt{2}\sin(\theta + \pi/4) \geq -\sqrt{2}$ for all real θ.

∴ $2^{\sin\theta} + 2^{\cos\theta} \geq 2 \cdot 2^{(\sin\theta + \cos\theta)/2}$

$> 2 \cdot 2^{-\sqrt{2}/2} = 2^{1-(1/\sqrt{2})}$

Thus $2^{\sin\theta} + 2^{\cos\theta} \geq 2^{1-(1/\sqrt{2})}$.

35. Ans. 2. We have ,

$y = \sqrt{3}\sin x + \cos x = 2\left[\dfrac{\sqrt{3}}{2}\sin x + \dfrac{1}{2}\cos x\right]$

$= 2[\cos(\pi/6)\sin x + \sin(\pi/6)\cos x]$

$= 2\sin(x + \pi/6)$

∴ Max. value of $y = 2$. or max. distance from x-axis is 2.

36. Ans. 2 .

We have $\pi/4 = \theta + \phi \Rightarrow \tan(\pi/4) = \tan(\theta + \phi)$

$\Rightarrow 1 = (\tan\theta + \tan\phi)/(1 - \tan\theta\tan\phi)$

$\Rightarrow \tan\theta + \tan\phi + \tan\theta\tan\phi = 1$

$\Rightarrow 1 + \tan\theta + \tan\phi + \tan\theta\tan\phi = 2$

$\Rightarrow (1 + \tan\theta)(1 + \tan\phi) = 2$.

37. Ans. $\cos\log\theta$.

For $e^{-\pi/2} < \theta < \pi/2$, we have

$-\dfrac{\pi}{2}\log e < \log\theta < \log\dfrac{\pi}{2}$

Now $\log_e e = 1, \dfrac{\pi}{2} < e$ ∴ $\log\dfrac{\pi}{2} < \log e = 1$

∴ $-\dfrac{\pi}{2} < \log\theta < 1 < \dfrac{\pi}{2}$

above shows that $\log\theta$ lies in 1st or 4th quadrant.

∴ $\cos(\log\theta) = +\text{ive}, i.e. > 0$ ...(1)

Now $0 < \cos\theta < 1$ ∴ $\log\cos\theta < \log 1 = 0$

∴ $\log\cos\theta = -\text{ive}, i.e. < 0$ ...(2)

From (1) and (2), we conclude that

$\cos\log\theta > \log\cos\theta$.

38. (a) Ans. $[-1, 5]$. We have

$y = 4\sin^2\theta - \cos 2\theta$

$= 4\sin^2\theta - (1 - 2\sin^2\theta) = 6\sin^2\theta - 1$

∴ $\dfrac{y+1}{6} = \sin^2\theta$

But $0 \leq \sin^2\theta \leq 1$. Hence $0 \leq \dfrac{y+1}{6} \leq 1$,

or $0 \leq y + 1 \leq 6$ or $-1 \leq y \leq 5 \Rightarrow y \in [-1, 5]$

(b) Ans. $-\pi/2, 0, \pi/2$

$\cos^7 x = 1 - \sin^4 x = (1 - \sin^2 x)(1 + \sin^2 x)$

$= \cos^2 x(1 + \sin^2 x)$

∴ $\cos x = 0$ or $x = \pi/2, -\pi/2$

or $\cos^5 x = 1 + \sin^2 x$ or $\cos^5 x - \sin^2 x = 1$

Now maximum value of each $\cos x$ or $\sin x$ is 1. Hence the above equation will hold when $\cos x = 1$ and $\sin x = 0$. Both these imply $x = 0$.

Hence $x = -\dfrac{\pi}{2}, \dfrac{\pi}{2}, 0$

39. Ans. $n = 6$. We have

$\sin^3 x \sin 3x = \dfrac{1}{4}(3\sin x - \sin 3x) \cdot \sin 3x$

$= \dfrac{3}{8} \cdot 2\sin x \sin 3x - \dfrac{1}{8} \cdot 2\sin^2 3x$

$= \dfrac{3}{8}(\cos 2x - \cos 4x) - \dfrac{1}{8}(1 - \cos 6x)$

$= -\dfrac{1}{8} + \dfrac{3}{8}\cos 2x - \dfrac{3}{8}\cos 4x + \dfrac{1}{8}\cos 6x$

∴ $-\dfrac{1}{8} + \dfrac{3}{8}\cos 2x - \dfrac{3}{8}\cos 4x + \dfrac{1}{8}\cos 6x$

$= \sum_{m=0}^{n} C_m \cos mx$

$= C_0 + C_1\cos x + C_2\cos 2x + C_3\cos 3x + \dots$

$+ \dots + C_n\cos nx$ ...(1)

Comparing both sides of (1), we see that $n = 6$.

We also have

$C_0 = -1/8, C_1 = 0, C_2 = 3/8, C_3 = 0,$

$C_4 = -3/8, C_5 = 0, C_6 = 1/8$

§ 4. The angles of a triangle and related identities.

1. If A, B, C are the angles of a triangle, then
$$A + B + C = 180°.$$
$$\therefore \quad B + C = 180° - A, C + A = 180° - B,$$
$$A + B = 180° - C,$$
Hence $\sin (B + C) = \sin (180° - A) = \sin A$.
Similarly,
$\sin (C + A) = \sin B$ and $\sin (A + B) = \sin C$.
Thus in a triangle, sine of any one angle is equal to the sine of the sum of the remaining angles.
Again $\cos (B + C) = \cos (180° - A) = - \cos A$. In the same manner,
$$\cos (C + A) = - \cos B \text{ and } \cos (A + B) = - \cos C.$$
Thus in a triangle, the cosine of any one angle is equal to minus times the cosine of the sum of the remaining two angles.

2. If A, B, C are the angles of a triangle, then
$$\frac{1}{2} (A + B + C) = 90°.$$
$$\sin \frac{1}{2} (B + C) = \sin (90° - \frac{1}{2} A) = \cos \frac{1}{2} A.$$
Similarly, $\quad \sin \frac{1}{2} (C + A) = \cos \frac{1}{2} B$
and $\quad \sin \frac{1}{2} (A + B) = \cos \frac{1}{2} C$
Again $\cos \frac{1}{2} (B + C) = \cos (90° - \frac{1}{2} A) = \sin \frac{1}{2} A$
$$\cos \frac{1}{2} (C + A) = \sin \frac{1}{2} B$$
and $\quad \cos \frac{1}{2} (A + B) = \sin \frac{1}{2} C.$

Thus the sine of half of any angle in a triangle is equal to the cosine of half the sum of the remaining two angles and similarly the cosine of half of any angle is equal to the sine of half the sum of the other two angles.

3. If $A + B + C = 180°$, then the following identities are useful to remember.

(i)	$\sin 2A + \sin 2B + \sin 2C = 4 \sin A \sin B \sin C$
(ii)	$\cos 2A + \cos 2B + \cos 2C = -1 - 4 \cos A \cos B \cos C.$
(iii)	$\sin A + \sin B + \sin C = 4 \cos \frac{1}{2} A \cos \frac{1}{2} B \cos \frac{1}{2} C.$
(iv)	$\cos A + \cos B + \cos C = 1 + 4 \sin \frac{1}{2} A \sin \frac{1}{2} B \sin \frac{1}{2} C.$
(v)	$\tan A + \tan B + \tan C = \tan A \tan B \tan C.$
(vi)	$\cot B \cot C + \cot C \cot A + \cot A \cot B = 1.$
(vii)	$\tan \frac{1}{2} B \tan \frac{1}{2} C + \tan \frac{1}{2} C \tan \frac{1}{2} A + \tan \frac{1}{2} A \tan \frac{1}{2} B = 1$
(viii)	$\cot \frac{1}{2} A + \cot \frac{1}{2} B + \cot \frac{1}{2} C = \cot \frac{1}{2} A \cot \frac{1}{2} B \cot \frac{1}{2} C$

The proofs of these identities will be given in Problem Set.

4. (a) For any angles A, B, C, we have

(i)	$\sin (A + B + C) = \sin A \cos B \cos C$ $+ \cos A \sin B \cos C + \cos A \cos B \sin C$ $- \sin A \sin B \sin C.$ $= \cos A \cos B \cos C [\tan A + \tan B + \tan C$ $- \tan A \tan B \tan C]$
(ii)	$\cos (A + B + C) = \cos A \cos B \cos C$ $- \cos A \sin B \sin C - \sin A \cos B \sin C$ $- \sin A \sin B \cos C.$ $= \cos A \cos B \cos C [1 - \Sigma \tan A \tan B]$
(iii)	On dividing (i) and (ii), we get $\tan (A + B + C)$ $= \dfrac{\tan A + \tan B + \tan C - \tan A \tan B \tan C}{1 - \tan A \tan B - \tan B \tan C - \tan C \tan A}$

The above result could also be obtained if we write
$$\tan (A + B + C) = \frac{\tan A + \tan (B + C)}{1 - \tan A . \tan (B + C)}$$
Again put the value of $\tan (B + C)$ and simplify. It can be expressed as
$$\tan (A + B + C) = \frac{S_1 - S_3}{1 - S_2}$$
where $S_1 = \Sigma \tan A, S_2 = \Sigma \tan A \tan B$
and $S_3 = \tan A \tan B \tan C$.

(b) **If A, B, C are the angles of a triangle, then**
$$\sin (A + B + C) = \sin \pi = 0,$$
and $\cos (A + B + C) = \cos \pi = -1$,
then (a) (i) gives
$\sin A \sin B \sin C = \sin A \cos B \cos C$
$\qquad + \cos A \sin B \cos C + \cos A \cos B \sin C$
(One sine and two cos)
and (a) (ii) gives
$1 + \cos A \cos B \cos C = \cos A \sin B \sin C$
$\qquad + \sin A \cos B \sin C + \sin A \sin B \cos C$
(One cos and two sine)
$$\tan (A + B + C) = \tan \pi = 0$$
$$\therefore \quad S_1 = S_3$$
$$\tan A + \tan B + \tan C = \tan A \tan B \tan C$$
On dividing by $\tan A \tan B \tan C$, we get
$$\cot A \cot B + \cot B \cot C + \cot C \cot A = 1$$
Above is Q. 26 (a) and (b).

Problem Set (7)

Trigonometrical identities. If *A*, *B*, *C* be the angles of a triangle, then the formulae for
$\Sigma \sin 2A$, $\Sigma \cos 2A$, $\Sigma \sin A$, $\Sigma \cos A$, $\Sigma \tan A$, $\Sigma \tan (A/2) \tan (B/2)$ etc.

If $A + B + C = 180°$, then prove the following identities :

1. (a) $\sin 2A + \sin 2B + \sin 2C = 4 \sin A \sin B \sin C$
   (b) $\sin 2A + \sin 2B - \sin 2C = 4 \cos A \cos B \sin C$

2. (a)* $\sin (B + C - A) + \sin (C + A - B)$
   $\qquad + \sin (A + B - C) = 4 \sin A \sin B \sin C.$
   (b) If $\sin^{-1} a + \sin^{-1} b + \sin^{-1} c = \pi$, then prove
   that $a\sqrt{1 - a^2} + b\sqrt{1 - b^2} + c\sqrt{1 - c^2} = 2abc.$

3.* If $A + B + C = 0$, (Note $0, \neq \pi$) then prove that
   $\sin 2A + \sin 2B + \sin 2C = 2 (\sin A + \sin B + \sin C)$
   $\qquad (1 + \cos A + \cos B + \cos C)$

4. (a)* $\cos 2A + \cos 2B + \cos 2C = -1 - 4 \cos A \cos B \cos C$
   (b) $\cos 2A + \cos 2B - \cos 2C = 1 - 4 \sin A \sin B \cos C$

5. If $A + B + C = 180°$, prove that
   (a)* $\sin A + \sin B + \sin C$
   $\qquad = 4 \cos (A/2) \cos (B/2) \cos (C/2).$
   (b) $\sin A + \sin B - \sin C$
   $\qquad = 4 \sin (A/2) \sin (B/2) \cos (C/2).$

6. (a) $\dfrac{\sin A + \sin B + \sin C}{\sin A + \sin B - \sin C} = \cot \dfrac{A}{2} \cot \dfrac{B}{2}.$
   (b) If A, B, C be the angles of a triangle and
   $\cos \theta (\sin B + \sin C) = \sin A$ then prove that
   $\qquad \tan^2 \dfrac{\theta}{2} = \tan \dfrac{B}{2} \tan \dfrac{C}{2}.$

7. (a) If A, B, C be the angles of a triangle ABC then
   $(\sin A + \sin B)(\sin B + \sin C)(\sin C + \sin A)$
   $\qquad\qquad > \sin A \sin B \sin C$
   (b) If $A + B + C = \pi$, prove that
   $(\sin A + \sin B + \sin C)(-\sin A + \sin B + \sin C)$
   $(\sin A - \sin B + \sin C)(\sin A + \sin B - \sin C)$
   $\qquad = 4 \sin^2 A \sin^2 B \sin^2 C.$

8. (a) $\dfrac{\sin 2A + \sin 2B + \sin 2C}{\sin A + \sin B + \sin C}$
   $\qquad = 8 \sin (A/2) \sin (B/2) \sin (C/2)$
   (b) $\dfrac{\cos A}{\sin B \sin C} + \dfrac{\cos B}{\sin C \sin A} + \dfrac{\cos C}{\sin A \sin B} = 2.$

9. (a) Express $\sin 3A + \sin 3B + \sin 3C$ as the product of
   three trigonometrical ratios where A, B, C are the
   angles of a triangle. If the given expression be
   zero, then at least one angle of the triangle is $60°$.
   (b) In a triangle prove that
   $\sin^3 A + \sin^3 B + \sin^3 C$
   $\qquad = 3 \cos (A/2) \cos (B/2) \cos (C/2)$
   $\qquad\qquad + \cos (3A/2) \cos (3B/2) \cos (3C/2)$
   (c) If $A + B + C = 2\pi$, prove that
   $\sin^3 A + \sin^3 B + \sin^3 C$
   $\quad = 3 \sin (A/2) \sin (B/2) \sin (C/2)$
   $\qquad\qquad - \sin (3A/2) \sin (3B/2) \sin (3C/2)$

10. (a)* **For any three angles *A*, *B*, *C*** prove that
    $\sin A + \sin B + \sin C - \sin (A + B + C)$
    $= 4 \sin \{(A + B)/2\} \sin \{(B + C)/2\} \sin \{(C + A)/2\}$
    (b) If $A + B + C = 180°$, show that
    $\sin (B + 2C) + \sin (C + 2A) + \sin (A + 2B)$
    $= 4 \sin [(B - C)/2] . \sin [(C - A)/2] . \sin [(A - B)/2]$

In any triangle *ABC* prove the identities in Q. 11 to 20.

11. (a)* $\cos A + \cos B + \cos C$
    $\qquad = 1 + 4 \sin (A/2) \sin (B/2) \sin (C/2).$
    (b) $\cos A + \cos B - \cos C$
    $\qquad = -1 + 4 \cos (A/2) \cos (B/2) \sin (C/2)$

12. (a) $\dfrac{1 - \cos A + \cos B + \cos C}{1 - \cos C + \cos A + \cos B} = \dfrac{\tan (A/2)}{\tan (C/2)}.$
    (b) $\dfrac{\sin 2A + \sin 2B + \sin 2C}{\cos A + \cos B + \cos C - 1}$
    $\qquad = 8 \cos (A/2) \cos (B/2) \cos (C/2)$

13. In a Δ, if $\tan \dfrac{(B + C - A)}{4} \cdot \tan \dfrac{(C + A - B)}{4}$
    $\qquad\qquad\qquad \cdot \tan \dfrac{(A + B - C)}{4} = 1$
    then $1 + \cos A + \cos B + \cos C = 0$.

14. In a triangle prove that
    (a)* $\cos A + \cos B + \cos C > 1$ but not greater than $3/2$
    (b) $\sin \dfrac{A}{2} \sin \dfrac{B}{2} \sin \dfrac{C}{2} \leq \dfrac{1}{8}$

15.* The vertices of a triangle are the points
    $(p, p \tan \alpha), (q, q \tan \beta), (r, r \tan \gamma)$ where $\alpha + \beta + \gamma = \pi$. If
    the circumcentre of the triangle is at the origin, then
    prove that its orthocentre lies on the line
    $x (4 \cos \alpha/2 \cos \beta/2 \cos \gamma/2)$
    $\qquad - y (1 + 4 \sin \alpha/2 \sin \beta/2 \sin \gamma/2) = 0$

16. (a) $\sin^2 A + \sin^2 B - \sin^2 C = 2 \sin A \sin B \cos C$
    (b)* $\cos^2 A + \cos^2 B - \cos^2 C = 1 - 2 \sin A \sin B \cos C.$

17. (a)* $\cos^2 A + \cos^2 B + \cos^2 C = 1 - 2 \cos A \cos B \cos C.$
    (b) $\sin^2 A + \sin^2 B + \sin^2 C = 2 + 2 \cos A \cos B \cos C.$

18. If $A + B + C = 2k$, then prove that
    $\cos^2 k + \cos^2 (k - A) + \cos^2 (k - B) + \cos^2 (k - C)$
    $\qquad = 2 + 2 \cos A \cos B \cos C.$

19. (a)* $\sin^2 (A/2) + \sin^2 (B/2) + \sin^2 (C/2)$
    $\qquad = 1 - 2 \sin (A/2) \sin (B/2) \sin (C/2).$
    (b) $\sin^2 (A/2) + \sin^2 (B/2) - \sin^2 (C/2)$
    $\qquad = 1 - 2 \cos (A/2) \cos (B/2) \sin (C/2).$

20. (a)* $\cos^2 (A/2) + \cos^2 (B/2) - \cos^2 (C/2)$
    $\qquad = 2 \cos (A/2) \cos (B/2) \sin (C/2).$
    (b) $\cos^2 (A/2) + \cos^2 (B/2) + \cos^2 (C/2)$
    $\qquad = 2 + 2 \sin (A/2) \sin (B/2) \sin (C/2).$

21. If $x + y + z = \pi/2$, show that

(a) $\sin^2 x + \sin^2 y + \sin^2 z = 1 - 2\sin x \sin y \sin z$

(b) $\cos^2 x + \cos^2 y + \cos^2 z = 2 + 2\sin x \sin y \sin z$

(c) $\sin 2x + \sin 2y + \sin 2z = 4\cos x \cos y \cos z$

22. If $A + B + C = \pi$, show that

(a)* $\cos(A/2) + \cos(B/2) + \cos(C/2)$
$= 4\cos\{(\pi - A)/4\}\cos\{(\pi - B)/4\}\cos\{(\pi - C)/4\}$
$= 4\cos\{(B + C)/4\}\cos\{(C + A)/4\}\cos\{(A + B)/4\}$

(b) $\sin(A/2) + \sin(B/2) + \sin(C/2)$
$= 1 + 4\sin\{(\pi - A)/4\}\sin\{(\pi - B)/4\}\sin\{(\pi - C)/4\}$.

(c)* $\cos(A/2) + \cos(B/2) - \cos(C/2)$
$= 4\cos\{(\pi + A)/4\}\cos\{(\pi + B)/4\}\cos\{(\pi - C)/4\}$.

23. (a) If $\alpha + \beta = \gamma$, then
$\cos^2 \alpha + \cos^2 \beta + \cos^2 \gamma = 1 + 2\cos \alpha \cos \beta \cos \gamma$

(b)* If $\alpha + \beta - \gamma = \pi$, show that
$\sin^2 \alpha + \sin^2 \beta - \sin^2 \gamma = 2\sin \alpha \sin \beta \cos \gamma$.

24. (a) $\sin 2(\alpha - \beta) + \sin 2(\beta - \gamma) + \sin 2(\gamma - \alpha)$
$= -4\sin(\alpha - \beta)\sin(\beta - \gamma)\sin(\gamma - \alpha)$.

(b)* $\Sigma \cos^2 \alpha \sin \beta \sin \gamma \sin(\beta - \gamma)$
$= -\sin(\beta - \gamma)\sin(\gamma - \alpha)\sin(\alpha - \beta)$

25. (a) $\sin x \sin y \sin(x - y)$
$+ \sin y \sin z \sin(y - z) + \sin z \sin x \sin(z - x)$
$+ \sin(x - y)\sin(y - z)\sin(z - x) = 0$

(b) $\sin(\beta + \gamma - \alpha) + \sin(\gamma + \alpha - \beta)$
$+ \sin(\alpha + \beta - \gamma) - \sin(\alpha + \beta + \gamma)$
$= 4\sin \alpha \sin \beta \sin \gamma$.

26. If A, B, C are the angles of a triangle, show that

(a) $\tan A + \tan B + \tan C = \tan A \tan B \tan C$.

(b) $\cot A \cot B + \cot B \cot C + \cot C \cot A = 1$.

(c) $\dfrac{\cot A + \cot B}{\tan A + \tan B} + \dfrac{\cot B + \cot C}{\tan B + \tan C} + \dfrac{\cot C + \cot A}{\tan C + \tan A} = 1$.

(d) If in ΔABC, $\cot A + \cot B + \cot C = \sqrt{3}$, prove that the triangle is equilateral.

(e) In a triangle ABC if $\tan A : \tan B : \tan C = 3 : 4 : 5$ then the value of $\sin A \sin B \sin C$ is

(a) $\dfrac{2}{\sqrt{5}}$ (b) $\dfrac{2\sqrt{5}}{3}$

(c) $\dfrac{2\sqrt{5}}{9}$ (d) $\dfrac{2}{3\sqrt{5}}$

27.* If $A + B + C = \pi$, prove that

(i) $\tan(A/2)\tan(B/2) + \tan(B/2)\tan(C/2)$
$\qquad + \tan(C/2)\tan(A/2) = 1$

(ii) $\cot(A/2) + \cot(B/2) + \cot(C/2)$
$\qquad = \cot(A/2)\cot(B/2)\cot(C/2)$.

(I.I.T. 2000)

Another Forms : If $x + y + z = \pi/2$, then

(i) $\tan y \tan z + \tan z \tan x + \tan x \tan y = 1$.

(ii) $\cot x + \cot y + \cot z = \cot x \cot y \cot z$.

28. If $x + y + z = xyz$, prove that

(a) $\dfrac{2x}{1 - x^2} + \dfrac{2y}{1 - y^2} + \dfrac{2z}{1 - z^2} = \dfrac{2x}{1 - x^2} \cdot \dfrac{2y}{1 - y^2} \cdot \dfrac{2z}{1 - z^2}$

Another form :

If $\log(x + y + z) = \log x + \log y + \log z$ then prove that

$$\log \frac{2x}{1 - x^2} + \log \frac{2y}{1 - y^2} + \log \frac{2z}{1 - z^2}$$
$$= \log\left(\frac{2x}{1 - x^2} + \frac{2y}{1 - y^2} + \frac{2z}{1 - z^2}\right)$$

(b)* $\dfrac{3x - x^3}{1 - 3x^2} + \dfrac{3y - y^3}{1 - 3y^2} + \dfrac{3z - z^3}{1 - 3z^2}$
$= \dfrac{3x - x^3}{1 - 3x^2} \cdot \dfrac{3y - y^3}{1 - 3y^2} \cdot \dfrac{3z - z^3}{1 - 3z^2}$

(c) $\dfrac{x + y}{1 - xy} + \dfrac{y + z}{1 - yz} + \dfrac{z + x}{1 - zx}$
$= \dfrac{x + y}{1 - xy} \cdot \dfrac{y + z}{1 - yz} \cdot \dfrac{z + x}{1 - zx}$

(d) For any three angles A, B, C, prove that
$\tan(B - C) + \tan(C - A) + \tan(A - B)$
$\qquad = \tan(B - C)\tan(C - A)\tan(A - B)$.

29. (a)* If $xy + yz + zx = 1$, prove that
$\dfrac{x}{1 - x^2} + \dfrac{y}{1 - y^2} + \dfrac{z}{1 - z^2} = \dfrac{4xyz}{(1 - x^2)(1 - y^2)(1 - z^2)}$

(b) If $xy + yz + zx = 1$, then prove that
$\dfrac{x}{1 + x^2} + \dfrac{y}{1 + y^2} + \dfrac{z}{1 + z^2}$

$$= \frac{2}{[(1 + x^2)(1 + y^2)(1 + z^2)]^{1/2}}$$

30. (a)* Given the product p of sines of the angles of a triangle and the product q of their cosines, find the cubic equation whose coefficients are functions of p and q and whose roots are the tangents of the angles of the triangle.

(Roorkee 1992)

(b) In a triangle ABC, prove that
$\sin A . \sin B . \sin C = \dfrac{1}{8}(3 + \sqrt{3})$ and
$\cos A . \cos B . \cos C = \dfrac{1}{8}(\sqrt{3} - 1)$.

Find the angles of ΔABC.

(c) A, B, C are the angles of a triangle such that $\tan A, \tan B, \tan C$ are three roots of the biquadratic $x^4 - px^3 + qx^2 - rx + s = 0$. Prove that the fourth root satisfies $x^2 - px + s = 0$.

31. (a)* Prove in ΔABC :
$\cot A + \cot B + \cot C = \cot A \cot B \cot C$
$\qquad + \operatorname{cosec} A \operatorname{cosec} B \operatorname{cosec} C$

(b) Prove that :

If $0 < \alpha, \beta, \gamma < \dfrac{\pi}{2}$, prove that

$\sin \alpha + \sin \beta + \sin \gamma > \sin (\alpha + \beta + \gamma)$

(c)* Prove in ΔABC :

$(\tan A + \tan B + \tan C) \cdot (\cot A + \cot B + \cot C)$
$= 1 + \sec A \sec B \sec C$

(d) If $A + B + C = 60°$, then prove that
$\sec A \sec B \sec C + 2 \Sigma \tan A \tan B = 2$

32. If $\alpha = \dfrac{2\pi}{7}$ then prove that

$\tan \alpha \tan 2\alpha + \tan 2\alpha \tan 4\alpha + \tan 4\alpha \tan \alpha = -7.$

33. (a)* Show $\tan^2 (A/2) + \tan^2 (B/2) + \tan^2 (C/2) \geq 1$
when $A + B + C = \pi$
Hence the minimum value of $\Sigma \tan^2 (A/2)$ is 1.

(b) If $A + B + C = \pi$, then prove that

$\cot A + \dfrac{\sin A}{\sin B \sin C}$ retains the same value when

any two of the angles A, B, C are interchanged.

(J.E.E.W.B. 1993)

(c) If angle C of a triangle ABC be obtuse, then prove
that $\tan A \tan B < 1$.

34. (a)* Prove that $\tan A \tan B \tan C > 3\sqrt{3}$

or $\cot A \cot B \cot C \leq \dfrac{1}{3\sqrt{3}}$ in a ΔABC.

(b)* Prove that a triangle ABC is equilateral if and only
if $\tan A + \tan B + \tan C = 3\sqrt{3}$. **(I.I.T. 1998)**

(c)* $\cot \dfrac{A}{2} \cot \dfrac{B}{2} \cot \dfrac{C}{2} \geq 3\sqrt{3}$

35. If $A + B + C = 2S$, show that

(a)* $\cos^2 S + \cos^2 (S - A) + \cos^2 (S - B)$
$\qquad + \cos^2 (S - C) = 2 + 2 \cos A \cos B \cos C$

(b) $\sin (S - A) + \sin (S - B) + \sin (S - C) - \sin S$
$\qquad = 4 \sin (A/2) \sin (B/2) \sin (C/2)$

36. (a) If $A + B + C + D = 2\pi$, show that

$\cos A - \cos B + \cos C - \cos D$

$\qquad = 4 \sin \dfrac{A+B}{2} \sin \dfrac{A+D}{2} \cos \dfrac{A+C}{2}$

(b) $\cos A + \cos B + \cos C + \cos D$

$\qquad = -4 \cos \dfrac{A+B}{2} \cos \dfrac{A+C}{2} \cos \dfrac{A+D}{2}$

(c) $\sin A - \sin B + \sin C - \sin D$

$\qquad = -4 \cos \dfrac{A+B}{2} \sin \dfrac{A+C}{2} \cos \dfrac{A+D}{2}$

37.* In a triangle ABC, prove that

$\sin^3 A \cos (B - C) + \sin^3 B \cos (C - A)$

$\qquad\qquad + \sin^3 C \cos (A - B)$

$\qquad = 3 \sin A \sin B \sin C$

38.* $\sin 3A \cos^3 (B - C) + \sin 3B \cos^3 (C - A)$

$\qquad\qquad + \sin 3C \cos^3 (A - B)$

$= \sin 3A \sin 3B \sin 3C$.

39.* In a ΔABC, prove that

(a) $\sin^4 A + \sin^4 B + \sin^4 C = \dfrac{3}{2} + 2 \cos A \cos B \cos C$

$\qquad\qquad + \dfrac{1}{2} \cos 2A \cos 2B \cos 2C.$

(b) $\cos^4 A + \cos^4 B + \cos^4 C = \dfrac{1}{2} - 2 \cos A \cos B \cos C$

$\qquad\qquad + \dfrac{1}{2} \cos 2A \cos 2B \cos 2C$

40. (a)* In a triangle if $\tan (A/2), \tan (B/2), \tan (C/2)$ are in
A.P., then $\cos A, \cos B, \cos C$ are also in A.P.

(b) If $A + B + C + D = 2\pi$, then
$\Sigma \tan A = \tan A \tan B \tan C \tan D \Sigma \cot A$

41. If A, B, C, D be four angles whose sum is π then prove
that the sum of the products of their cosines taken two
and two together is equal to the sum of the products of
their sines taken similarly.

42. If $A + B + C = \pi$, prove that

$$\begin{vmatrix} \sin^2 A & \cot A & 1 \\ \sin^2 B & \cot B & 1 \\ \sin^2 C & \cot C & 1 \end{vmatrix} = 0$$

43. In a triangle ABC, prove that

(a) $\sin 2mA + \sin 2mB + \sin 2mC$
$\qquad = (-1)^{m+1} 4 \sin mA \sin mB \sin mC,$
where m is any integer.

(b) $\cos mA + \cos mB + \cos mC - 1$
$\qquad = \pm 4 \sin \dfrac{mA}{2} \sin \dfrac{mB}{2} \sin \dfrac{mC}{2}$
according as m is of the form $4n + 1$ or $4n + 3$.

44. (a)* If A, B, C are the angles of a triangle and
$\sin^3 \theta = \sin (A - \theta) \sin (B - \theta) \sin (C - \theta)$, prove
that $\cot \theta = \cot A + \cot B + \cot C$ and conversely.

(Roorkee 1991)

(b) In a triangle ABC, if $\cot A + \cot B + \cot C = \cot \theta$,
then prove that

$\dfrac{\sin A \sin B \sin C}{1 + \cos A \cos B \cos C} = \tan \theta$

and the possible value of θ is $30°$

45. In a triangle ABC, if the angles are in the ratio $1 : 2 : 4$,

then $\dfrac{\Sigma \sec^2 A}{\Sigma \operatorname{cosec}^2 A} = \dots\dots$

46. If $t_1 = (\tan x)^{\cot x}, t_2 = (\cot x)^{\cot x}$,

$t_3 = (\tan x)^{\tan x}, t_4 = (\cot x)^{\tan x}, 0 < x < \dfrac{\pi}{4}$, then :

(a) $t_1 < t_2 < t_3 < t_4$ (b) $t_2 > t_4 > t_3 > t_1$

(c) $t_1 > t_4 > t_3 > t_2$ (d) $t_1 > t_2 > t_3 > t_4$

(I.I.T. 2006)

Solutions to Problem Set (7)

We shall make use of the formulae of
§ 3 P. 516-18 and § 4 (3) P. 562.

1. (a) L.H.S. $= 2\sin A \cos A + 2\sin(B+C)\cos(B-C)$
   $= 2\sin A \cos A + 2\sin A \cos(B-C)$
   $= 2\sin A[\cos A + \cos(B-C)],$
   $= 2\sin A[\cos(B-C) - \cos(B+C)]$
   $\qquad [\because \cos A = -\cos(B+C)]$
   $= 2\sin A . 2\sin B \sin C$
   $= 4\sin A \sin B \sin C.$

   (b) L.H.S. $= \sin 2A + \sin 2B - \sin 2C$
   $= 2\sin A \cos A + 2\sin(B-C)\cos(B+C)$
   $= 2\sin A \cos A - 2\sin(B-C)\cos A$
   $= 2\cos A[\sin A - \sin(B-C)]$
   $= 2\cos A[\sin(B+C) - \sin(B-C)]$
   $= 2\cos A[2\cos B \sin C] \quad \because \sin A = \sin(B \ C)$
   $= 4\cos A \cos B \sin C.$

2. (a) $B + C - A = 180° - A - A = 180° - 2A.$
   $\therefore \quad \sin(B+C-A) = \sin(180° - 2A) = \sin 2A$ etc.
   Hence the question reduces to
   $\sin 2A + \sin 2B + \sin 2C = 4\sin A \sin B \sin C.$
   To prove it, proceed as in Q. 1 (a).

   (b) Let $\sin^{-1} a = A, \therefore a = \sin A,$
   $a\sqrt{1-a^2} = \sin A \cos A = \frac{1}{2}\sin 2A.$

   It becomes Q. 1 (a).

3. By multiplication $(3 \times 4 = 12$ terms)
   $$\text{R.H.S.} = 2[\underset{3}{\Sigma \sin A} + \underset{3}{\Sigma \sin A \cos A} + \underset{6}{\Sigma \sin(A+B)}]$$
   Now $\sin(A+B) = \sin(0-C) = -\sin C$
   $= 0 + \Sigma \sin 2A = \text{L.H.S.}$

4. (a) In the answer we want -1 and as such we write $\cos 2A$ as $2\cos^2 A - 1$ and combine the other two terms.
   L.H.S. $= (2\cos^2 A - 1) + 2\cos(B+C)\cos(B-C)$
   $= -1 + 2\cos^2 A - 2\cos A \cos(B-C)$
   $= -1 + 2\cos A[\cos A - \cos(B-C)]$
   $= -1 + 2\cos A[-\cos(B+C) - \cos(B-C)]$
   $= -1 - 2\cos A(2\cos B \cos C)$
   $= -1 - 4\cos A \cos B \cos C.$

   (b) Here we want $+1$ and as such we write $\cos 2A = 1 - 2\sin^2 A$ and combine the other two terms.
   L.H.S. $= 1 - 2\sin^2 A + 2\sin(B+C)\sin(C-B)$ **(Note)**
   $= 1 - 2\sin^2 A - 2\sin A \sin(B-C)$
   $\qquad [\because \sin(-\theta) = -\sin\theta]$
   $= 1 - 2\sin A[\sin A + \sin(B-C)]$
   $= 1 - 2\sin A[\sin(B+C) + \sin(B-C)]$
   $= 1 - 2\sin A(2\sin B \cos C)$

   $= 1 - 4\sin A \sin B \cos C.$

5. (a) L.H.S.
   $= 2\sin(A/2)\cos(A/2) + 2\sin\{(B+C)/2\}\cos\{(B-C)/2\}$
   $= 2\sin(A/2)\cos(A/2) + 2\cos(A/2)\cos\{(B-C)/2\}$
   $= 2\cos(A/2)[\sin(A/2) + \cos\{(B-C)/2\}]$
   $= 2\cos(A/2)[\cos\{(B+C)/2\} + \cos\{(B-C)/2\}]$
   $= 2\cos(A/2)[2\cos(B/2)\cos(C/2)].$
   $= 4\cos(A/2)\cos(B/2)\cos(C/2).$

   (b) Proceed as above.

6. (a) **Hint :** Use the results of Q. 5 (a) and (b).

   (b) $\dfrac{\cos\theta}{1} = \dfrac{\sin A}{\sin B + \sin C}$

   Apply Comp. and Divi.

7. (a) We have proved in Q. (5)
   $$\sin A + \sin B - \sin C = 4\sin\frac{A}{2}\sin\frac{B}{2}\cos\frac{C}{2} > 0$$
   $\therefore \quad \sin A + \sin B > \sin C$
   Write similar expressions and multiply.

   (b) **Refer part (a)** then L.H.S.
   $$= \left[4\cos\frac{A}{2}\cos\frac{B}{2}\cos\frac{C}{2}\right]\left[4\sin\frac{B}{2}\sin\frac{C}{2}\cos\frac{A}{2}\right]$$
   $$\cdot\left[4\sin\frac{C}{2}\sin\frac{A}{2}\cos\frac{B}{2}\right]\left[4\sin\frac{A}{2}\sin\frac{B}{2}\cos\frac{C}{2}\right]$$
   $$= 4 \times 64\left(\sin^2\frac{A}{2}\cos^2\frac{A}{2}\right)(\ )(\ )$$
   $$= 4\left(2\sin\frac{A}{2}\cos\frac{A}{2}\right)^2 (\ )(\ )$$
   $$= 4\sin^2 A \sin^2 B \sin^2 C$$

8. (a) By the help of Q.1 (a) and Q. 5 (a), we have
   $$\text{L.H.S.} = \frac{4\sin A \sin B \sin C}{4\cos(A/2)\cos(B/2)\cos(C/2)}$$
   $$= \frac{\{2\sin(A/2)\cos(A/2)\}\{2\sin(B/2)\cos(B/2)\}}{\{(2\sin(C/2)\cos(C/2)\}}{\cos(A/2)\cos(B/2)\cos(C/2)}$$
   $= 8\sin(A/2)\sin(B/2)\sin(C/2).$

   (b) On simplification, we have to prove that
   $$\frac{\sin A \cos A + \sin B \cos B + \sin C \cos C}{\sin A \sin B \sin C} = 2.$$
   Multiplying both sides by 2, we get
   $\sin 2A + \sin 2B + \sin 2C = 4\sin A \sin B \sin C,$
   which is Q.1 (a)

9. (a) $A + B + C = \pi, \quad \therefore 3A + 3B + 3C = 3\pi$
   $$\frac{1}{2}(3A+3B) = \frac{3}{2}\pi - \frac{3}{2}C$$
   $\therefore \quad \sin\frac{1}{2}(3A+3B) = -\cos\frac{3}{2}C$
   and $\cos\frac{1}{2}(3A+3B) = -\sin\frac{3}{2}C.$ **(Note)**
   L.H.S. $= 2\sin\dfrac{3A+3B}{2}\cos\dfrac{3A-3B}{2} + 2\sin\dfrac{3C}{2}\cos\dfrac{3C}{2}$

$= -2\cos\dfrac{3C}{2}\cos\dfrac{3A - 3B}{2} + 2\sin\dfrac{3C}{2}\cos\dfrac{3C}{2}$

$= -2\cos\dfrac{3C}{2}\left[\cos\dfrac{3A - 3B}{2} - \sin\dfrac{3C}{2}\right]$

$= -2\cos\dfrac{3C}{2}\left[\cos\dfrac{3A - 3B}{2} + \cos\dfrac{3A + 3B}{2}\right]$

$= -4\cos\dfrac{3A}{2}\cos\dfrac{3B}{2}\cos\dfrac{3C}{2}$.

If it be zero then at least one factor is zero, hence

$3A/2 = 90°$ or $A = 60°$ etc.

(b) $\sin 3A = 3\sin A - 4\sin^3 A$.

$\therefore \quad \sin^3 A = \dfrac{1}{4}(3\sin A - \sin 3A)$.

Hence we have to find the value of

$\dfrac{3}{4}(\sin A + \sin B + \sin C) - \dfrac{1}{4}(\sin 3A + \sin 3B + \sin 3C)$

$= \dfrac{3}{4}\cdot 4\cos\dfrac{A}{2}\cos\dfrac{B}{2}\cos\dfrac{C}{2} + \dfrac{1}{4}\cdot 4\cos\dfrac{3A}{2}\cos\dfrac{3B}{2}\cos\dfrac{3C}{2}$

by Q. 5 (a) and 9 (b)

(c) Proceed as above. Note that $A + B + C = 2\pi$.

10. (a) **Note : Here A, B, C are not angles of a triangle *i.e.*
$A + B + C \neq 180°$.**

Combining the first two and last two, we get

L.H.S. $= 2\sin\dfrac{A + B}{2}\cos\dfrac{A - B}{2}$

$\qquad + 2\cos\dfrac{A + B + 2C}{2}\sin\left(-\dfrac{A + B}{2}\right)$

$= 2\sin\dfrac{A + B}{2}\left[\cos\dfrac{A - B}{2} - \cos\dfrac{A + B + 2C}{2}\right]$

$\qquad\qquad \because \quad \sin(-\theta) = -\sin\theta.$

$= 2\sin\dfrac{A + B}{2}\left[2\sin\dfrac{A + C}{2}\sin\dfrac{B + C}{2}\right]$

$= 4\sin\dfrac{A + B}{2}\sin\dfrac{B + C}{2}\sin\dfrac{C + A}{2}$.

(b) Here $A + B + C = 180°$.

$\therefore \quad B + 2C = B + C + C = 180° - A + C$

$\qquad\qquad = 180° + (C - A).$

$\therefore \quad \sin(B + 2C) = -\sin(C - A).$

$\therefore$ L.H.S. $= -[\sin(C - A) + \sin(A - B) + \sin(B - C)]$

$= -\left[2\sin\dfrac{C - A}{2}\cos\dfrac{C - A}{2}\right.$

$\qquad\qquad \left. + 2\sin\dfrac{A - C}{2}\cos\dfrac{A + C - 2B}{2}\right]$

$= -2\sin\dfrac{C - A}{2}\left[\cos\dfrac{C - A}{2} - \cos\dfrac{A + C - 2B}{2}\right]$

$= -2\sin\dfrac{C - A}{2}\left[2\sin\dfrac{C - B}{2}\sin\dfrac{A - B}{2}\right]$

$= 4\sin\dfrac{A - B}{2}\sin\dfrac{B - C}{2}\sin\dfrac{C - A}{2}$.

11. (a) Here we want $+1$ and so we write

$\cos A = 1 - 2\sin^2 (A/2)$

L.H.S. $= 1 - 2\sin^2 (A/2) + 2\cos\{(B + C)/2\}$

$\qquad\qquad\qquad \cos\{(B - C)/2\}$

$= 1 - 2\sin^2 (A/2) + 2\sin(A/2)\cos\{(B - C)/2\}$

$= 1 - 2\sin(A/2)[\sin(A/2) - \cos\{(B - C)/2\}]$

$= 1 - 2\sin(A/2)[\cos\{(B + C)/2\} - \cos\{(B - C)/2\}]$

$= 1 - 2\sin(A/2)[2\sin(B/2)\sin(-C/2)]$

$= 1 + 4\sin(A/2)\sin(B/2)\sin(C/2)$

$\qquad\qquad\qquad \because \quad \sin(-\theta) = -\sin\theta.$

(b) Here write $\cos A = 2\cos^2 (A/2) - 1$ and proceed as above.

12. (a) Do yourself.

(b) With the help of **Q.1 (a)** and **Q. 11 (a)** above.

L.H.S. $= \dfrac{4\sin A\sin B\sin C}{4\sin(A/2)\sin(B/2)\sin(C/2)}$

$= 8\cos(A/2)\cos(B/2)\cos(C/2)$.

$\qquad\qquad \because \quad \sin A = 2\sin(A/2)\cos(A/2)$ etc.

13. $\tan\dfrac{(B + C - A)}{4} = \dfrac{\sin\left(\dfrac{\pi - 2A}{4}\right)}{\cos\left(\dfrac{\pi - 2A}{4}\right)}$

Now given $P = 1 \Rightarrow P^2 = 1$

$\therefore \quad \sin^2\dfrac{\pi - 2A}{4}\cdot(\ )(\ ) = \cos^2\dfrac{\pi - 2A}{4}$ ....

or $\left[1 - \cos\dfrac{\pi - 2A}{2}\right]\ldots = \left[1 + \cos\dfrac{\pi - 2A}{2}\right]\ldots$

$= (1 - \sin A)(1 - \sin B)(1 - \sin C) = (1 + \sin A)$

$\qquad\qquad\qquad\qquad (1 + \sin B)(1 + \sin C)$

or $\Sigma\sin A + \sin A\sin B\sin C = 0$, other terms cancel.

Use result **Q. 5 (a)**

or $4\cos\dfrac{A}{2}\cos\dfrac{B}{2}\cos\dfrac{C}{2} + 8\left(\sin\dfrac{A}{2}\cos\dfrac{A}{2}\right)(\ )(\ ) = 0$

Cancel $2\cos A/2\cos B/2\cos C/2$

$\therefore \quad 2 + 4\sin\dfrac{A}{2}\sin\dfrac{B}{2}\sin\dfrac{C}{2} = 0$ ...(1)

or $2 + (\cos A + \cos B + \cos C - 1) = 0$ by Q. 11 (a)

or $\cos A + \cos B + \cos C + 1 = 0$. **Proved.**

14. (a) From Q. 11 (a),

$\cos A + \cos B + \cos C = 1 + 4\sin\dfrac{A}{2}\sin\dfrac{B}{2}\sin\dfrac{C}{2} > 1$ ...(1)

as neither of $\sin\dfrac{A}{2}, \sin\dfrac{B}{2}, \sin\dfrac{C}{2}$ is $-$ive or zero.

Again $\cos A + \cos B + \cos C$

$= 2\cos\dfrac{A + B}{2}\cos\dfrac{A - B}{2} + 1 - 2\sin^2\dfrac{C}{2}$

$\leq 2\sin\dfrac{C}{2}\cdot 1 + 1 - 2\sin^2\dfrac{C}{2}$

$\therefore \quad 0 \leq \cos\dfrac{A - B}{2} \leq 1$

$$= -2\left[s^2 - s - \frac{1}{2}\right], \text{ where } s = \sin\frac{C}{2}$$

$$= -2\left[\left(s - \frac{1}{2}\right)^2 - \frac{1}{2} - \frac{1}{4}\right]$$

$$= \frac{3}{2} - \left(s - \frac{1}{2}\right)^2 \le \frac{3}{2}$$

∴ $\cos A + \cos B + \cos C \le 3/2$ ...(2)

In other words, $\Sigma \cos A \not> 3/2$.

(b) Using result Q. 11 (a) in (2), we get

$$1 + 4\sin\frac{A}{2}\sin\frac{B}{2}\sin\frac{C}{2} \le \frac{3}{2}$$

∴ $\sin\frac{A}{2}\sin\frac{B}{2}\sin\frac{C}{2} \le \frac{1}{8}$

15. Since $OA = OB = OC = R$

⇒ $p^2(1 + \tan^2\alpha) = R^2$ ∴ $p\sec\alpha = R$

∴ $p = R\cos\alpha$ or $R\cos\beta$ or $R\cos\gamma$

∴ A is $(R\cos\alpha, R\sin\alpha)$ etc.

If $(\bar{x}, \bar{y})$ be the orthocentre, then O, H, G are collinear.

∴ slope of OH = slope of OG

$$\frac{\bar{x}}{\bar{y}} = \frac{\cos\alpha + \cos\beta + \cos\gamma}{\sin\alpha + \sin\beta + \sin\gamma}$$

Since $\alpha + \beta + \gamma = \pi$

∴ $\dfrac{\bar{x}}{\bar{y}} = \dfrac{1 + 4\sin\alpha/2\sin\beta/2\sin\gamma/2}{4\cos\alpha/2\cos\beta/2\cos\gamma/2}$

By Q. 5 (a), 11 (a) above.

Hence locus of $(\bar{x}, \bar{y})$ is as given.

16. (a) L.H.S. $= \sin^2 A + \sin(B + C)\sin(B - C)$

$$= \sin^2 A + \sin A \sin(B - C)$$

$$= \sin A[\sin A + \sin(B - C)]$$

$$= \sin A[\sin(B + C) + \sin(B - C)]$$

$$= \sin A(2\sin B\cos C)$$

$$= 2\sin A\sin B\cos C.$$

(b) Do yourself.

17. (a) We write $\cos^2 A = 1 - \sin^2 A$

L.H.S. $= 1 - \sin^2 A + \cos^2 B + \cos^2 C$

$$= 1 + (\cos^2 B - \sin^2 A) + \cos^2 C$$

$$= 1 + \cos(B + A)\cos(B - A) + \cos^2 C$$

$$= 1 - \cos C\cos(B - A) + \cos^2 C$$

$$= 1 - \cos C[\cos(B - A) - \cos C]$$

$$= 1 - \cos C[\cos(B - A) + \cos(B + A)]$$

$$= 1 - \cos C(2\cos A\cos B)$$

$$= 1 - 2\cos A\cos B\cos C.$$

(b) On changing $\sin^2 A$ to $1 - \cos^2 A$ etc., it reduces to part (a).

Proceeding directly as we need 2, we write

$\sin^2 A = 1 - \cos^2 A$ and $\sin^2 B = 1 - \cos^2 B$

L.H.S. $= 2 - \cos^2 A - \cos^2 B + \sin^2 C$

$$= 2 - (\cos^2 A - \sin^2 C) - \cos^2 B$$

$$= 2 - \cos(A + C)\cos(A - C) - \cos^2 B$$

$$= 2 + \cos B\cos(A - C) - \cos^2 B$$

$$= 2 + \cos B[\cos(A - C) - \cos B]$$

$$= 2 + \cos B[\cos(A - C) + \cos(A + C)]$$

$$= 2 + \cos B(2\cos A\cos C)$$

$$= 2 + 2\cos A\cos B\cos C.$$

18. $\cos^2 x - \sin^2 y = \cos(x + y)\cos(x - y)$

L.H.S. $= 2 + [\cos^2 k - \sin^2(k - A)]$

$$\qquad + [\cos^2(k - B) - \sin^2(k - C)]$$

$$= 2 + \cos(2k - A)\cos A$$

$$\qquad + \cos(2k - B - C)\cos(C - B)$$

Put $2k - A = B + C$ and $2k - B - C = A$

$$= 2 + \cos A[\cos(B + C) + \cos(C - B)]$$

$$= 2 + 2\cos A\cos B\cos C.$$

19. (a) We want $+1$ in R.H.S.

∴ L.H.S. $= 1 - \cos^2(A/2) + \sin^2(B/2) + \sin^2(C/2)$

$$= 1 - \{\cos^2(A/2) - \sin^2(B/2)\} + \sin^2(C/2)$$

$$= 1 - \cos\{(A + B)/2\}\cos\{(A - B)/2\} + \sin^2(C/2)$$

$$= 1 - \sin(C/2)\cos\{(A - B)/2\} + \sin^2(C/2)$$

$$= 1 - \sin(C/2)[\cos\{(A - B)/2\} - \sin(C/2)]$$

$$= 1 - \sin(C/2)[\cos\{(A - B)/2\} - \cos\{(A + B)/2\}]$$

$$= 1 - \sin(C/2)[2\sin(A/2)\sin(B/2)]$$

$$= 1 - 2\sin(A/2)\sin(B/2)\sin(C/2).$$

(b) We want $+1$ in R.H.S.

L.H.S. $= 1 - \cos^2(A/2) + \sin^2(B/2) - \sin^2(C/2)$

$$= 1 - \cos^2(A/2) + \sin\{(B + C)/2\}\sin\{(B - C)/2\}$$

$$= 1 - \cos(A/2)[\cos(A/2) + \sin\{(B - C)/2\}]$$

$$= 1 - \cos(A/2)[\sin\{(B + C)/2 - \sin(B - C)/2\}]$$

$$= 1 - \cos(A/2)[2\cos(B/2)\sin(C/2)]$$

$$= 1 - 2\cos(A/2)\cos(B/2)\sin(C/2).$$

20. (a) Do yourself.

(b) Either change $\cos^2$ to $\sin^2$ and it becomes Q. 19 (a) or proceed directly as in Q. 17 (b).

21. (a), (b) It is same as Q. 19. If we choose

$x = A/2$, $y = B/2$, $z = C/2$ so that

$x + y + z = \pi/2$ leads to $A + B + C = \pi$ and then both parts reduce to those of Q. 19 (a) and 20 (b). However, you should proceed directly.

(c) This is also to be proved by you.

22. (a) $A + B + C = \pi$ ∴ $\{(A + B)/4\} = \{(\pi - C)/4\}$ etc. for 2nd form ...(1)

L.H.S. $= 2\cos\dfrac{A + B}{4}\cos\dfrac{A - B}{4} + \sin\left(\dfrac{\pi}{2} - \dfrac{C}{2}\right)$ **(Note)**

$$= 2\cos\frac{\pi - C}{4}\cos\frac{A - B}{4} + 2\sin\frac{\pi - C}{4}\cos\frac{\pi - C}{4}$$

$$[\because \sin\theta = 2\sin(\theta/2)\cos(\theta/2)]$$

$= 2 \cos \dfrac{\pi - C}{4} \left[\cos \dfrac{A - B}{4} + \sin \dfrac{A + B}{4} \right]$, by (1)

$= 2 \cos \dfrac{\pi - C}{4} \left[\cos \dfrac{A - B}{4} + \cos \left(\dfrac{\pi}{2} - \dfrac{A + B}{4} \right) \right]$

$= 2 \cos \dfrac{\pi - C}{4} \left[2 \cos \dfrac{\pi - A}{4} \cos \dfrac{\pi - B}{4} \right]$

$= 4 \cos \dfrac{\pi - A}{4} \cos \dfrac{\pi - B}{4} \cos \dfrac{\pi - C}{4}$.

(b) L.H.S. $= 2 \sin \dfrac{A + B}{4} \cos \dfrac{A - B}{4} + \cos \left(\dfrac{\pi}{2} - \dfrac{C}{2} \right)$

$= 2 \sin \dfrac{\pi - C}{4} \cos \dfrac{A - B}{4} + 1 - 2 \sin^2 \dfrac{\pi - C}{4}$

$= 1 + 2 \sin \dfrac{\pi - C}{4} \left[\cos \dfrac{A - B}{4} - \sin \dfrac{A + B}{4} \right]$ by (1)

$= 1 + 2 \sin \dfrac{\pi - C}{4} \left[\cos \dfrac{A - B}{4} - \cos \left(\dfrac{\pi}{2} - \dfrac{A + B}{4} \right) \right]$

$= 1 + 2 \sin \dfrac{\pi - C}{4} \left[2 \sin \dfrac{\pi - B}{4} \sin \dfrac{\pi - A}{4} \right]$

$= 1 + 4 \sin \dfrac{\pi - A}{4} \sin \dfrac{\pi - B}{4} \sin \dfrac{\pi - C}{4}$.

(c) L.H.S. $= 2 \cos \dfrac{A + B}{4} \cos \dfrac{A - B}{4} - \sin \left(\dfrac{\pi}{2} - \dfrac{C}{2} \right)$.

$= 2 \cos \dfrac{\pi - C}{4} \cos \dfrac{A - B}{4} - 2 \sin \dfrac{\pi - C}{4} \cos \dfrac{\pi - C}{4}$

$= 2 \cos \dfrac{\pi - C}{4} \left[\cos \dfrac{A - B}{4} - \sin \dfrac{\pi - C}{4} \right]$

$= 2 \cos \dfrac{\pi - C}{4} \left[\cos \dfrac{A - B}{4} - \sin \left(\dfrac{A + B}{4} \right) \right]$

$= 2 \cos \dfrac{\pi - C}{4} \left[\cos \dfrac{A - B}{4} + \cos \left(\dfrac{\pi}{2} + \dfrac{A + B}{4} \right) \right]$

$\left[\because \cos \{ (\pi/2) + \theta \} = - \sin \theta \right]$

$= 2 \cos \dfrac{\pi - C}{4} \left[2 \cos \dfrac{\pi + A}{4} \cos \dfrac{\pi + B}{4} \right]$

$= 4 \cos \dfrac{\pi + A}{4} \cos \dfrac{\pi + B}{4} \cos \dfrac{\pi - C}{4}$.

23. (a) We want $+ 1$ in the R.H.S.
Also $\alpha + \beta = \gamma$.
L.H.S. $= \cos^2 \alpha + 1 - \sin^2 \beta + \cos^2 \gamma$

$= 1 + (\cos^2 \alpha - \sin^2 \beta) + \cos^2 \gamma$

$= 1 + \cos (\alpha + \beta) \cos (\alpha - \beta) + \cos^2 \gamma$

$= 1 + \cos \gamma [\cos (\alpha - \beta) + \cos (\alpha + \beta)]$

$\left[\because \gamma = \alpha + \beta \right]$

$= 1 + \cos \gamma [2 \cos \alpha \cos \beta]$

$= 1 + 2 \cos \alpha \cos \beta \cos \gamma$.

(b) L.H.S. $= \sin^2 \alpha + \sin^2 \beta - \sin^2 \gamma$

$= \sin^2 \alpha + \sin (\beta + \gamma) \sin (\beta - \gamma)$

$= \sin^2 \alpha + \sin (\beta + \gamma) \sin (\pi - \alpha)$

$\left[\because \alpha + \beta - \gamma = \pi \text{ gives } \beta - \gamma = \pi - \alpha \right]$

$= \sin^2 \alpha + \sin (\beta + \gamma) \sin \alpha$

$= \sin \alpha [\sin \alpha + \sin (\beta + \gamma)]$

$= \sin \alpha [\sin (\beta - \gamma) + \sin (\beta + \gamma)]$

$\left[\because \sin \alpha = \sin \{ \pi - (\beta - \gamma) \} = \sin (\beta - \gamma) \right]$

$= \sin \alpha . 2 \sin \beta \cos \gamma = 2 \sin \alpha \sin \beta \cos \gamma$

24. (a) Let $\alpha - \beta = x, \quad \beta - \gamma = y, \quad \gamma - \alpha = z$.

$x + y + z = 0 \quad \text{or} \quad x + y = - z$.

$\therefore \quad \sin (x + y) = - \sin z, \cos (x + y) = \cos z$ ...(1)
Hence we have to prove that

$\sin 2x + \sin 2y + \sin 2z = - 4 \sin x \sin y \sin z$.
L.H.S. $= 2 \sin (x + y) \cos (x - y) + 2 \sin z \cos z$
$\qquad\qquad\qquad$ by (1)

$= - 2 \sin z \cos (x - y) + 2 \sin z \cos z$

$= - 2 \sin z [\cos (x - y) - \cos z]$

$= - 2 \sin z [\cos (x - y) - \cos (x + y)]$, by (1)

$= - 2 \sin z (2 \sin x \sin y)$

$= - 4 \sin x \sin y \sin z$.

(b) $T_1 = \left(\dfrac{1 + \cos 2\alpha}{2} \right) . \dfrac{1}{2} [\cos (\beta - \gamma)$

$\qquad\qquad\qquad - \cos (\beta + \gamma)] \sin (\beta - \gamma)$

$\therefore \quad$ L.H.S. $= \dfrac{1}{8} (1 + \cos 2\alpha) [\sin 2 (\beta - \gamma)$

$\qquad\qquad\qquad - \{ \sin 2\beta - \sin 2\gamma \}]$

$= \dfrac{1}{8} [\Sigma \sin 2 (\beta - \gamma) - \Sigma (\sin 2\beta - \sin 2\gamma)$

$\quad + \Sigma \cos 2\alpha \sin 2 (\beta - \gamma) - \Sigma \cos 2\alpha (\sin 2\beta - \sin 2\gamma)]$
The second sigma is clearly zero.
The third sigma is of 6 terms which cancel in pairs.

$\Sigma \cos 2\alpha \{ \sin 2\beta \cos 2\gamma - \cos 2\beta \sin 2\gamma \} = 0$
The last sigma is of six terms and taken in pairs it is

$\{ \sin 2 (\beta - \gamma) + \sin 2 (\gamma - \alpha) + \sin 2 (\alpha - \beta) \}$
$\qquad = \Sigma \sin 2 (\beta - \gamma)$

$\therefore \quad$ L.H.S. $= \dfrac{1}{8} . 2 . \Sigma \sin 2 (\beta - \gamma)$

$= \dfrac{1}{4} \{ - 4 \sin (\beta - \gamma) \sin (\gamma - \alpha) \sin (\alpha - \beta) \}$

$= - \sin (\beta - \gamma) \sin (\gamma - \alpha) \sin (\alpha - \beta)$ as in part (a)

25. (a) Combining the 1st two and last two terms, we get
L.H.S. $= \sin y [\sin x \sin (x - y) + \sin z \sin (y - z)]$

$\quad + \sin (z - x) [\sin z \sin x + \sin (x - y) \sin (y - z)]$

$= \dfrac{1}{2} \sin y [\cos y - \cos (2x - y) + \cos (2z - y) - \cos y]$

$\quad + \dfrac{1}{2} \sin (z - x) [\cos (z - x) - \cos (z + x)$

$\quad + \cos (x - 2y + z) - \cos (x - z)]$

$$= \frac{1}{2}\sin y\,[\cos(2z-y) - \cos(2x-y)]$$

$$+ \frac{1}{2}\sin(z-x)\,[\cos(x-2y+z) - \cos(z+x)]$$

$$= \frac{1}{2}\sin y\,[2\sin(z+x-y)\sin(x-z)]$$

$$+ \frac{1}{2}\sin(z-x)\,[2\sin(z+x-y)\sin y] = 0$$

$$[\because \ \sin(x-z) = -\sin(z-x)]$$

(b) Combine the 1st two and last two terms as in part (a).

26. (a) $\because \quad \tan(A+B+C) = \tan \pi = 0$,

$$\therefore \quad \frac{S_1 - S_3}{1 - S_2} = 0 \ \text{ or } \ S_1 = S_3 \qquad \ldots(1)$$

or $\quad \tan A + \tan B + \tan C = \tan A \tan B \tan C$.

(b) Divide both sides by $\tan A \tan B \tan C$, we get

$$\frac{1}{\tan B \tan C} + \frac{1}{\tan C \tan A} + \frac{1}{\tan A \tan B} = 1$$

or $\quad \cot B \cot C + \cot C \cot A + \cot A \cot B = 1$.

(c) On changing cot in terms of tan,

$$\text{L.H.S.} = \frac{\tan A + \tan B}{\tan A \tan B\,(\tan A + \tan B)} + \ldots + \ldots = 1$$

or $\quad \dfrac{1}{\tan A \tan B} + \dfrac{1}{\tan B \tan C} + \dfrac{1}{\tan C \tan A} = 1$

or $\quad \tan C + \tan A + \tan B = \tan A \tan B \tan C$,

or $\quad S_1 = S_3 \quad$ which is true by (1).

(d) Squaring the given relation, we have

$$\Sigma \cot^2 A + 2\Sigma \cot A \cot B = 3\Sigma \cot A \cot B$$

because $\Sigma \cot A \cot B = 1$

or $\quad \Sigma \cot^2 A - \Sigma \cot A \cot B = 0$

Above is of form $x^2 + y^2 + z^2 - xy - yz - zx = 0$

or $\quad \dfrac{1}{2}\,[(x-y)^2 + (y-z)^2 + (z-x)^2] = 0$

Above is possible only when $x - y = 0, y - z = 0,$
$z - x = 0$

or $\quad x = y = z \ $ or $\ \cot A = \cot B = \cot C$

$\therefore \quad A = B = C \ \Rightarrow \ \Delta$ is equilateral.

(e) Ans. (b).

Let $\tan A = 3\lambda, \tan B = 4\lambda$ and $\tan C = 5\lambda$. In a triangle $S_1 = S_3$

$\therefore \quad (3+4+5)\lambda = (3.4.5)\lambda^3 \ \therefore 12\lambda - 60\lambda^3 = 0$

$$\therefore \quad \lambda = \pm \frac{1}{\sqrt 5}$$

$$\therefore \quad \tan A = \frac{3}{\sqrt 5}, \tan B = \frac{4}{\sqrt 5}, \tan C = \frac{5}{\sqrt 5}$$

$$\therefore \quad \sin A = \frac{3}{\sqrt{14}}, \sin B = \frac{4}{\sqrt{21}}, \sin C = \frac{5}{\sqrt{30}}$$

$$\therefore \quad \sin A \sin B \sin C = \frac{3.4.5}{7\sqrt{2.3.30}} = \frac{60}{7.6\sqrt 5} = \frac{2\sqrt 5}{7}$$

In a triangle, $\sin A, \sin B, \sin C$ are all +ive and hence we have chosen only + sign out of $\pm$.

27. (a) $\because \quad A + B + C = \pi$,

$\therefore \quad A/2 + B/2 + C/2 = \pi/2$.

$$\therefore \quad \tan\left(\frac{A}{2} + \frac{B}{2} + \frac{C}{2}\right) = \tan \frac{\pi}{2} = \infty\,.$$

or $\quad \dfrac{S_1 - S_3}{1 - S_2} = \infty \,. \ \therefore \ 1 - S_2 = 0 \ \text{ or } \ S_2 = 1$

or $\quad \tan \dfrac{A}{2} \tan \dfrac{B}{2} + \tan \dfrac{B}{2} \tan \dfrac{C}{2} + \tan \dfrac{C}{2} \tan \dfrac{A}{2} = 1$

(b) Dividing both sides by
$\tan(A/2)\tan(B/2)\tan(C/2)$, we get

$$\cot \frac{A}{2} + \cot \frac{B}{2} + \cot \frac{C}{2} = \cot \frac{A}{2} \cot \frac{B}{2} \cot \frac{C}{2}$$

28. (a) Put $x = \tan A, y = \tan B$ and $z = \tan C$
Since $\quad x + y + z = xyz$,

$\therefore \quad \tan A + \tan B + \tan C - \tan A \tan B \tan C = 0$

or $\quad S_1 - S_3 = 0$

Hence $\tan(A+B+C) = \dfrac{S_1 - S_3}{1 - S_2} = \dfrac{0}{1 - S_2} = 0$

$\therefore \quad A + B + C = 0 \ $ or $\ n\pi$

or $\quad 2A + 2B + 2C = 0 \ $ or $\ 2n\pi$

$\tan(2A + 2B + 2C) = 0$

$\dfrac{S_1 - S_3}{1 - S_2} = 0 \ \therefore \ S_1 = S_3$.

or $\quad \tan 2A + \tan 2B + \tan 2C = \tan 2A \tan 2B \tan 2C$

Now put $\tan 2A = \dfrac{2\tan A}{1 - \tan^2 A} = \dfrac{2x}{1 - x^2}$ etc.

Another from :
Put $x = \tan A$ etc., then by given relation $x + y + z = xyz$.

$\therefore \quad \tan A + \tan B + \tan C = \tan A \tan B \tan C$.

Hence $A + B + C = \pi \ $ or $\ 2A + 2B + 2C = 2\pi$ etc.

$\therefore \quad \tan 2A + \tan 2B + \tan 2C = \tan 2A \tan 2B \tan 2C$

(b) Proceeding as above $\tan(3A + 3B + 3C) = 0$.

$\therefore \quad \dfrac{S_1 - S_3}{1 - S_2} = 0 \quad$ so that $\quad S_1 = S_3$

or $\quad \tan 3A + \tan 3B + \tan 3C$
$\qquad = \tan 3A . \tan 3B . \tan 3C$

Now put $\tan 3A = \dfrac{3\tan A - \tan^3 A}{1 - 3\tan^2 A} = \dfrac{3x - x^3}{1 - 3x^2}$ etc.

(c) As above $A + B + C = 0$ or $n\pi$

$\tan A + \tan B + \tan C = \tan A \tan B \tan C \qquad \ldots(1)$

Now $A = \pi - (B + C)$

$\therefore \quad \tan A = -\tan(B + C)$

or $\quad \tan A = -\dfrac{\tan B + \tan C}{1 - \tan B \tan C} = -\left(\dfrac{y + z}{1 - yz}\right)$ etc.

Now put in (1) and cancel –ive sign from both sides.

(d) Put $B - C = p, C - A = q, A - B = r$.

$\therefore \quad p + q + r = 0$

or $\quad \tan(p + q + r) = \tan 0° = 0$

or $\dfrac{S_1 - S_3}{1 - S_2} = 0$ $\therefore$ $S_1 = S_3$.

or $\tan p + \tan q + \tan r = \tan p \tan q \tan r$

Now put the values of p, q and r.

29. (a) Put $x = \tan A, y = \tan B, z = \tan C$.

Then $xy + yz + zx = 1$ gives

$\tan A \tan B + \tan B \tan C + \tan C \tan A - 1 = 0$

or $S_2 - 1 = 0$ or $1 - S_2 = 0$

Now $\tan(A + B + C) = \dfrac{S_1 - S_3}{1 - S_2}$

$= \dfrac{S_1 - S_3}{0} = \infty = \tan \dfrac{\pi}{2}$

$\therefore$ $A + B + C = \pi/2$ or $2A + 2B + 2C = \pi$

$\therefore$ $\tan(2A + 2B + 2C) = \tan \pi = 0$

or $\dfrac{S_1 - S_3}{1 - S_2} = 0$ $\therefore$ $S_1 = S_3$

or $\tan 2A + \tan 2B + \tan 2C$

$= \tan 2A \tan 2B \tan 2C$.

or $\dfrac{2x}{1 - x^2} + \dfrac{2y}{1 - y^2} + \dfrac{2z}{1 - z^2}$

$= \dfrac{8xyz}{(1 - x^2)(1 - y^2)(1 - z^2)}$

or $\dfrac{x}{1 - x^2} + \dfrac{y}{1 - y^2} + \dfrac{z}{1 - z^2}$

$= \dfrac{4xyz}{(1 - x^2)(1 - y^2)(1 - z^2)}$

(b) Put $x = \tan \alpha$ etc.

so that $1 - S_2 = 0$, given.

$\therefore$ $\tan(\alpha + \beta + \gamma) = \dfrac{S_1 - S_3}{1 - S_2} = \infty$

$\therefore$ $\alpha + \beta + \gamma = \dfrac{\pi}{2}$.

Also $\dfrac{x}{1 + x^2} = \dfrac{\tan \alpha}{\sec^2 \alpha} = \sin \alpha \cos \alpha = \dfrac{1}{2} \sin 2\alpha$.

Hence we have to prove that

$\dfrac{1}{2}[\sin 2\alpha + \sin 2\beta + \sin 2\gamma] = \dfrac{2}{\sec \alpha \sec \beta \sec \gamma}$

or $\sin 2\alpha + \sin 2\beta + \sin 2\gamma = 4 \cos \alpha \cos \beta \cos \gamma$

when $\alpha + \beta + \gamma = \pi/2$

or $\sin(\beta + \gamma) = \sin\{(\pi/2) - \alpha\} = \cos \alpha$

Now above relation can be easily proved.

30. (a) $\sin A \sin B \sin C = p, \cos A \cos B \cos C = q$

$\therefore$ $\tan A \tan B \tan C = p/q = S_3$

$\therefore$ $S_1 = S_3 = \tan A + \tan B + \tan C$

If $S_2 = \tan A \tan B + \tan B \tan C + \tan C \tan A$

$= \dfrac{\sin A \sin B \cos C + \sin B \sin C \cos A}{\cos A \cos B \cos C}$
$\dfrac{+ \sin C \sin A \cos B}{\cos A \cos B \cos C}$

N^r is Σ (two sines one cos).

$= \dfrac{1 + \cos A \cos B \cos C}{\cos A \cos B \cos C} = \dfrac{1 + q}{q}$

by result 4 (b) ii P. 562.

Hence the required equation whose roots are $\tan A, \tan B, \tan C$ is

$x^3 - x^2 S_1 + x S_2 - S_3 = 0$

or $x^3 - \dfrac{p}{q} x^2 + \left(\dfrac{1 + q}{q}\right) x - \dfrac{p}{q} = 0$

or $q x^3 - p x^2 + (1 + q) x - p = 0$

(b) Dividing the given relations, we get

$\tan A . \tan B . \tan C = \dfrac{\sqrt{3}(\sqrt{3} + 1)}{(\sqrt{3} - 1)} = \dfrac{\sqrt{3}(\sqrt{3} + 1)^2}{2}$

or $\tan A . \tan B . \tan C = \sqrt{3}(2 + \sqrt{3}) = \Sigma \tan A$

$S_1 = S_3 = \sqrt{3}(2 + \sqrt{3})$

Now we have to find the value of

$S_2 = \Sigma \tan A . \tan B$ **by 4 (ii) P. 562.**

$\cos(A + B + C) = \cos A . \cos B . \cos C$
$(1 - \Sigma \tan A . \tan B)$

$-1 = \dfrac{1}{8}(\sqrt{3} - 1)[1 - S_2]$

or $S_2 = 1 + \dfrac{8}{\sqrt{3} - 1)}$

$\therefore$ $S_2 = 1 + 4(\sqrt{3} + 1) = 5 + 4\sqrt{3}$

Hence $\tan A, \tan B, \tan C$ are the roots of

$x^3 - x^2 S_1 + x S_2 - S_3 = 0$

or $x^3 - \sqrt{3}(2 + \sqrt{3}) x^2 + (5 + 4\sqrt{3}) x$
$\phantom{x^3 - \sqrt{3}(2 + \sqrt{3}) x^2} - \sqrt{3}(2 + \sqrt{3}) = 0$

Clearly $x = 1$ satisfies above.

$\therefore$ $(x - 1)[x^2 - 2(\sqrt{3} + 1) x + \sqrt{3}(2 + \sqrt{3})] = 0$

or $(x - 1)(x - \sqrt{3})[x - (2 + \sqrt{3})] = 0$

$\therefore$ $x = 1, \sqrt{3}, 2 + \sqrt{3}$

$\therefore$ $\tan \theta = \tan 45°, \tan 60°, \tan 75°$

$\therefore$ $A = 45°, B = 60°, C = 75°$

(c) Let the fourth root be α.

$\therefore$ $\tan A + \tan B + \tan C + \alpha = p$ ...(1)

$(\tan A \tan B \tan C) \alpha = s$ ...(2)

Also we know that in a triangle ABC

$\tan A + \tan B + \tan C = \tan A \tan B \tan C$ ...(3)

$\therefore$ $p - \alpha = \dfrac{s}{\alpha}$ or $\alpha^2 - p\alpha + s = 0$

$\therefore$ α is a root of $x^2 - px + s = 0$.

31. (a) We know from **P. 562 result 4 (b)** that

$\cos(A + B + C) = \cos \pi = -1$

$\therefore$ $-1 = \cos A \cos B \cos C - \cos A \sin B \sin C$
$ - \cos B \sin C \sin A - \cos C \sin A \sin B$

$\therefore \quad 1 + \cos A \cos B \cos C = \cos A \sin B \sin C$
$\qquad + \cos B \sin C \sin A + \cos C \sin A \sin B$

$\qquad\qquad$ **(one cos and two sines)**

Divide both sides by $\sin A \sin B \sin C$

$\therefore \quad \operatorname{cosec} A \operatorname{cosec} B \operatorname{cosec} C + \cot A \cot B \cot C$
$\qquad\qquad = \cot A + \cot B + \cot C$

(b) **Using result 4 (a) P. 562**, *i.e.* expansion of $\sin(\alpha + \beta + \gamma)$ we have to prove that

$\sin \alpha (1 - \cos \beta \cos \gamma) + \sin \beta (1 - \cos \gamma \cos \alpha)$
$\qquad + \sin \gamma (1 - \cos \alpha \cos \beta) + \sin \alpha \sin \beta \sin \gamma > 0$

Above is clearly true as $0 < \alpha, \beta, \gamma < \dfrac{\pi}{2}$ and each of

$1 - \cos \beta \cos \gamma$ is also +ive.

(c) We know in a triangle ABC

$\qquad \tan A + \tan B + \tan C = \tan A \tan B \tan C$

Hence the question reduces to

$\qquad \tan A \tan B \tan C \, (\cot A + \cot B + \cot C)$

$\qquad\qquad = 1 + \dfrac{1}{\cos A \cos B \cos C}$

or $\quad \tan B \tan C + \tan C \tan A + \tan A \tan B$

$\qquad\qquad = \dfrac{1 + \cos A \cos B \cos C}{\cos A \cos B \cos C}$

or $\quad \cos A \sin B \sin C + \cos B \sin C \cos A$
$\qquad\qquad\qquad\qquad + \cos C \sin A \sin B$

$\qquad\qquad = 1 + \cos A \cos B \cos C$

or $\quad -1 = \cos A \cos B \cos C - \Sigma \cos A \sin B \sin C$

or $\quad -1 = \cos(A + B + C) = \cos \pi,$

which is true by **R. 4 (b) P. 562.**

(d) Use $\cos(A + B + C) = \cos 60° = \dfrac{1}{2}$

Now expand as in last part and divide by $\cos A$ $\cos B \cos C.$

32. $\alpha = A,\ 2\alpha = B,\ 4\alpha = C$

$\therefore \quad A + B + C = 7\alpha = 2\pi$

$\text{L.H.S.} = \Sigma \tan A \tan B = \dfrac{\Sigma \sin A \sin B \cos C}{\cos A \cos B \cos C}$

Now by R. 4 (a) (ii) P. 367.

$\cos(A + B + C) = \cos A \cos B \cos C - \Sigma \sin A \sin B \cos C$

$\therefore \quad \text{L.H.S.} = \dfrac{\cos A \cos B \cos C - \cos 2\pi}{\cos A \cos B \cos C}$

$\qquad = 1 - \dfrac{1}{\cos \dfrac{2\pi}{7} \cos \dfrac{4\pi}{7} \cos \dfrac{8\pi}{7}}$

$\qquad = 1 - \dfrac{1}{\dfrac{\sin 2^3 (2\pi/7)}{2^3 \sin (2\pi/7)}}$ $\qquad$ **Rule 37 P. 519**

$\qquad = 1 - 8 = -7 .$

$\because \quad \sin \dfrac{16\pi}{7} = \sin\left(2\pi + \dfrac{2\pi}{7}\right) = \sin \dfrac{2\pi}{7}$

33. (a) We know from Q. 27 (a), that when
$\qquad A + B + C = \pi$, then

$\tan(A/2) \tan(B/2) + \tan(B/2) \tan(C/2)$
$\qquad\qquad + \tan(C/2) \tan(A/2) = 1 \quad ...(1)$

or $\quad yz + zx + xy = 1$, where $x = \tan(A/2)$ etc.

Now we know that

$\qquad (x - y)^2 + (y - z)^2 + (z - x)^2 \geq 0 .$

or $\quad 2\Sigma x^2 - 2\Sigma xy \geq 0 .$

or $\quad \Sigma x^2 \geq \Sigma xy \quad$ or $\quad \Sigma x^2 \geq 1. \qquad \because \Sigma xy = 1$

or $\quad \tan^2(A/2) + \tan^2(B/2) + \tan^2(C/2) \geq 1 .$

Note : For another method see the chapter on inequalities where we have proved that

$x^2 + y^2 + z^2 \geq xy + yz + zx = 1 \therefore x^2 + y^2 + z^2 \geq 1$

(b) $\dfrac{\sin A}{\sin B \sin C} = \dfrac{\sin(B + C)}{\sin B \sin C} = \cot B + \cot C$

$\therefore \quad$ Given expression $= \Sigma \cot A$. Hence proved by symmetry.

(c) Since $A + B = \pi - C$, we have

$\qquad \tan(A + B) = \tan(\pi - C)$

or $\quad \dfrac{\tan A + \tan B}{1 - \tan A \tan B} = -\tan C > 0, \qquad ...(1)$

$\qquad\qquad [\because \ C \text{ is obtuse angle implies } \tan C < 0]$

But since A and B are each less than $\pi/2$, it follows that $\tan A + \tan B > 0$

Hence (1) will hold if $1 - \tan A \tan B > 0$

or $\quad \tan A \tan B < 1$ as required.

34. (a) $\dfrac{\tan A + \tan B + \tan C}{3} > (\tan A \tan B \tan C)^{1/3}$

$\because \quad$ A.M. $>$ G.M.

But $S_1 = S_3$

or $\quad \tan A \tan B \tan C > 3 (\tan A \tan B \tan C)^{1/3}$

Cube both sides and take square root etc.

(b) Δ equilateral $\Rightarrow A = B = C = 60°$

$\therefore \quad \tan A + \tan B + \tan C = 3\sqrt{3}$

Converse $S_1 = 3\sqrt{3} = S_3$ in a triangle

Since $\tan A \tan B \tan C$ is +ive, each must be +ive as two of them cannot be – ive since two angles of Δ are not obtuse

$\therefore \quad$ A.M. $\geq$ G.M.

$\Rightarrow \quad \dfrac{\Sigma \tan A}{3} \geq (\tan A \tan B \tan C)^{1/3}$

$\therefore \quad S_1^3 \geq 27 S_3 \quad$ or $\quad S_1^3 \geq 27 S_1 \quad$ or $\quad S_1^2 \geq 27$

$\therefore \quad S_1 \geq 3\sqrt{3} \qquad$ but $S_1 = 3\sqrt{3}$ given.

Hence equality occurs when

$\tan A = \tan B = \tan C \quad$ or $\quad A = B = C$

$\therefore \quad \Delta$ is equilateral.

(c) By Q. 27 (b),

$\qquad \cot \dfrac{A}{2} + \cot \dfrac{B}{2} + \cot \dfrac{C}{2} = \cot \dfrac{A}{2} \cot \dfrac{B}{2} \cot \dfrac{C}{2}$

i.e., $S_1 = S_3$ for $\cot \dfrac{A}{2}, \cot \dfrac{B}{2}$ and $\cot \dfrac{C}{2}$

Apply A.M. $>$ G.M. as in part (b) and cube etc.

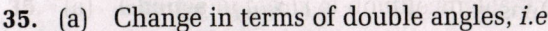

35. (a) Change in terms of double angles, *i.e.*

$$\cos^2 A = \frac{1}{2}(1 + \cos 2A)$$

Also $A + B + C = 2S$.

$$\text{L.H.S.} = \frac{1}{2}[1 + \cos 2S + 1 + \cos(2S - 2A) + 1$$

$$+ \cos(2S - 2B) + 1 + \cos(2S - 2C)].$$

$$= 2 + \frac{1}{2}[2\cos(2S - A)\cos A$$

$$+ 2\cos(2S - B - C)\cos(B - C)].$$

$$= 2 + \cos A[\cos(B + C) + \cos(B - C)],$$

$$\because 2S - A = B + C$$

$$= 2 + \cos A(2\cos B \cos C)$$

$$= 2 + 2\cos A \cos B \cos C.$$

Alternative :

$$\therefore \quad \text{L.H.S.} = 1 - \sin^2 S + 1 - \sin^2(S - A)$$

$$+ \cos^2(S - B) + \cos^2(S - C)$$

$$= 2 + [\cos^2(S - B) - \sin^2 S]$$

$$+ [\cos^2(S - C) - \sin^2(S - A)]$$

Now apply

$$\cos^2 A - \sin^2 B = \cos(A + B)\cos(A - B) \text{ etc.}$$

(b) $\text{L.H.S.} = 2\sin\dfrac{2S - A - B}{2}\cos\dfrac{B - A}{2}$

$$+ 2\cos\dfrac{2S - C}{2}\sin\left(-\dfrac{C}{2}\right)$$

$$= 2\sin\dfrac{C}{2}\left[\cos\dfrac{B - A}{2} - \cos\dfrac{A + B}{2}\right]\because 2S - C = A + B$$

$$= 2\sin\dfrac{C}{2}\left[2\sin\dfrac{A}{2}\sin\dfrac{B}{2}\right] = 4\sin\dfrac{A}{2}\sin\dfrac{B}{2}\sin\dfrac{C}{2}.$$

36. (a) $A + B + C + D = 2\pi$

$$\text{L.H.S.} = (\cos A + \cos C) - (\cos B + \cos D)$$

$$= 2\cos\dfrac{A + C}{2}\cos\dfrac{A - C}{2} - 2\cos\dfrac{B + D}{2}\cos\dfrac{B - D}{2}$$

Now $\dfrac{B + D}{2} = \pi - \dfrac{A + C}{2}$,

$$\therefore \quad \cos\dfrac{B + D}{2} = -\cos\dfrac{A + C}{2}$$

$$\therefore \quad \text{L.H.S.} = 2\cos\dfrac{A + C}{2}\left[\cos\dfrac{A - C}{2} + \cos\dfrac{B - D}{2}\right]$$

$$= 2\cos\left(\dfrac{A + C}{2}\right)\left[2\cos\left(\dfrac{A + B - C - D}{4}\right)\right.$$

$$\left.\cos\left(\dfrac{A + D - C - B}{4}\right)\right] \quad \text{...(1)}$$

Now $C + D = 2\pi - (A + B)$, $C + B = 2\pi - (A + D)$

$$\therefore \quad \dfrac{(A + B) - (C + D)}{4} = \dfrac{(A + B) - 2\pi + (A + B)}{4}$$

$$= \dfrac{A + B}{2} - \dfrac{\pi}{2}$$

$$\therefore \quad \cos\dfrac{(A + B) - (C + D)}{4} = \cos\left(\dfrac{A + B}{2} - \dfrac{\pi}{2}\right)$$

$$= \sin\dfrac{A + B}{2} \quad \text{...(2)}$$

Again $\dfrac{(A + D) - (C + B)}{4}$

$$= \dfrac{(A + D) - 2\pi + (A + D)}{4} = \left(\dfrac{A + D}{2} - \dfrac{\pi}{2}\right)$$

$$\therefore \quad \cos\dfrac{A + D - C - B}{4} = \cos\left(\dfrac{A + D}{2} - \dfrac{\pi}{2}\right)$$

$$= \sin\dfrac{A + D}{2} \quad \text{...(3)}$$

Hence from (1) with the help of (2) and (3), we get

$$\text{L.H.S.} = 4\cos\dfrac{A + C}{2} \cdot \sin\dfrac{A + B}{2} \cdot \sin\dfrac{A + D}{2}.$$

(b) & (c). Prove yourself.

37. $\sin^3 A \cos(B - C) = \sin^2 A \sin A \cos(B - C)$

$$= \frac{1}{2}\sin^2 A \cdot 2\sin(B + C)\cos(B - C)$$

$$= \frac{1}{2}\sin^2 A(\sin 2B + \sin 2C)$$

$$= \sin^2 A(\sin B \cos B + \sin C \cos C).$$

$$\therefore \quad \text{L.H.S.} = \Sigma \sin^3 A \cos(B - C)$$

$$= \sin^2 A(\sin B \cos B + \sin C \cos C)$$

$$+ \sin^2 B(\sin C \cos C + \sin A \cos A)$$

$$+ \sin^2 C(\sin A \cos A + \sin B \cos B)$$

$$= \sin A \sin B(\sin A \cos B$$

$$+ \cos A \sin B) + \dots + \dots$$

$$= \sin A \sin B \sin(A + B) + \dots + \dots$$

$$= \sin A \sin B \sin C + \dots + \dots$$

$$= 3\sin A \sin B \sin C.$$

38. $\cos 3\theta = 4\cos^3 \theta - 3\cos\theta$,

$$\therefore \quad \cos^3 \theta = \frac{1}{4}(\cos 3\theta + 3\cos\theta).$$

$$\therefore \quad \sin 3A \cos^3(B - C)$$

$$= \frac{1}{4}\sin 3A[\cos 3(B - C) + 3\cos(B - C)]$$

$$= \frac{1}{4}\sin 3(B + C)\cos 3(B - C)$$

$$+ \frac{3}{4}\sin(3B + 3C)\cos(B - C)$$

$$= \frac{1}{8}(\sin 6B + \sin 6C)$$

$$+ \frac{3}{8}\{\sin(4B + 2C) + \sin(2B + 4C)\}.$$

Now $4B + 2C = 2(B + C) + 2B = 2\pi - 2A + 2B$

$$\sin(4B + 2C) = \sin\{2\pi + 2(B - A)\} = \sin 2(B - A).$$

$$\therefore \quad \text{L.H.S.} = \frac{1}{8}\Sigma(\sin 6B + \sin 6C)$$

$$+ \frac{3}{8} \cdot \Sigma[\sin 2(b - A) + \sin 2(C - B)].$$

$$\therefore \quad \Sigma \sin 3A \cos^3(B - C) = \frac{1}{8} \cdot 2\Sigma \sin 6A + \frac{3}{8} \cdot 0$$

$$= \frac{1}{4}(\sin 6A + \sin 6B + \sin 6C)$$

$$= \frac{1}{4}.4\sin 3A \sin 3B \sin 3C, \quad \textbf{as in Q. 1, P. 562-66}$$

$$= \sin 3A \sin 3B \sin 3C.$$

39. (a) L.H.S.

$$= \left(\frac{1-\cos 2A}{2}\right)^2 + \left(\frac{1-\cos 2B}{2}\right)^2 + \left(\frac{1-\cos 2C}{2}\right)^2$$

$$= \frac{3}{4} + \frac{1}{4}(\cos^2 2A + \cos^2 2B + \cos^2 2C)$$

$$\qquad - \frac{1}{2}(\cos 2A + \cos 2B + \cos 2C)$$

$$= \frac{3}{4} + \frac{1}{4}\left\{\frac{1}{2}(1+\cos 4A) + \frac{1}{2}(1+\cos 4B)\right.$$

$$\left. + \frac{1}{2}(1+\cos 4C)\right\}$$

$$\qquad - \frac{1}{2}(\cos 2A + \cos 2B + \cos 2C)$$

$$= \frac{3}{4} + \frac{3}{8} + \frac{1}{8}(\cos 4A + \cos 4B + \cos 4C)$$

$$\qquad - \frac{1}{2}(\cos 2A + \cos 2B + \cos 2C)$$

$$= \frac{9}{8} + \frac{1}{8}[2\cos(2A+2B)\cos(2A-2B)$$

$$\qquad\qquad + 2\cos^2 2C - 1]$$

$$\qquad - \frac{1}{2}[2\cos(A+B)\cos(A-B) + 2\cos^2 C - 1]$$

$$= \frac{3}{2} + \frac{1}{4}[\cos(2\pi-2C)\cos(2A-2B) + \cos^2 2C]$$

$$\qquad - [\cos(\pi-C)\cos(A-B) + \cos^2 C]$$

$$\because \frac{9}{8} - \frac{1}{8} + \frac{1}{2} = \frac{3}{2}$$

$$[\because A+B+C = \pi \text{ gives } 2A+2B = 2\pi - 2C$$

$$\text{and } A+B = \pi - C]$$

$$= \frac{3}{2} + \frac{1}{4}\cos 2C[\cos(2A-2B) + \cos(2A+2B)]$$

$$\qquad - \cos C[-\cos(A-B) - \cos(A+B)]$$

$$= \frac{3}{2} + \frac{1}{4}\cos 2C.2\cos 2A\cos 2B$$

$$\qquad + \cos C.2\cos A\cos B$$

$$= \frac{3}{2} + 2\cos A\cos B\cos C + \frac{1}{2}\cos 2A\cos 2B\cos 2C$$

(b) Do yourself.

40. (a) $\tan(A/2) - \tan(B/2) = \tan(B/2) - \tan(C/2)$

or $\dfrac{\sin\{(A-B)/2\}}{\cos(A/2)\cos(B/2)} = \dfrac{\sin\{(B-C)/2\}}{\cos(B/2)\cos(C/2)}$

or $\sin\{(A-B)/2\}.\cos(C/2)$

$$= \sin\{(B-C)/2\}\cos(A/2)$$

or $2\sin\left(\dfrac{A-B}{2}\right)\sin\left(\dfrac{A+B}{2}\right)$

$$= 2\sin\left(\dfrac{B-C}{2}\right)\sin\left(\dfrac{B+C}{2}\right)$$

or $\cos B - \cos A = \cos C - \cos B$

$\therefore$ $\cos A$, $\cos B$, $\cos C$ are in A.P.

(b) $A+B = 2\pi - (C+D)$

$\therefore \tan(A+B) = -\tan(C+D)$

$$\frac{\tan A + \tan B}{1 - \tan A\tan B} = -\frac{\tan C + \tan D}{1 - \tan C\tan D}$$

Cross-multiply and transpose

$$\Sigma\tan A = \Sigma\tan A\tan B\tan C$$

or $\Sigma\tan A = \tan A\tan B\tan C\tan D\,\Sigma\cot A$.

41. AB, AC, AD, BC, BD, CD. Six in number.

$$A+B+C+D = \pi$$

$\therefore \quad A+B = \pi - (C+D) \qquad\qquad ...(1)$

or $\cos(A+B) = -\cos(C+D)$.

or $\cos A\cos B + \cos C\cos D$

$$= \sin A\sin B + \sin C\sin D \quad ...(2)$$

Similarly write relations in AC, BD and $AD; BC$ by taking

$$A+C = \pi - (B+D)$$

$$A+D = \pi - (B+C)$$

Adding these, we get

$$\Sigma\cos A\cos B = \Sigma\sin A\sin B$$

Six terms in each sigma.

42. Apply $R_1 - R_2$, $R_2 - R_3$ to make two zeros.

Use $\sin^2 A - \sin^2 B = \sin(A+B)\sin(A-B)$

$$= \sin C\sin(A-B)$$

and $\cot A - \cot B = \dfrac{\sin(B-A)}{\sin A\sin B}$

$$= \frac{-\sin C\sin(A-B)}{\sin A\sin B\sin C}$$

$$\Delta = \begin{vmatrix} -\sin C\sin(A-B) & -\sin C\sin(A-B) \\ -\sin A\sin(B-C) & -\sin A\sin(B-C) \end{vmatrix}$$

$$\div \sin A\sin B\sin C$$

Clearly $\Delta = 0$ as the two rows are identical, i.e.

$$\Delta = \lambda\begin{vmatrix} 1 & 1 \\ 1 & 1 \end{vmatrix} = 0.$$

43. (a) **Hint :** L.H.S.

$$= 2\sin(mA+mB)\cos(mA-mB)$$

$$+ 2\sin mC\cos mC$$

$$= 2\sin(m\pi - mC)\cos(mA-mB)$$

$$+ 2\sin mC\cos[m\pi - m(A+B)]$$

$$= 2(-1)^{m-1}\sin mC[\cos(mA-mB)$$

$$- \cos(mA+mB)]$$

$$= 4(-1)^{m-1}\sin mA\sin mB\sin mC.$$

(b) Do yourself.

44. (a) The given equation can be written as

$$\frac{\sin(A-\theta)}{\sin\theta} . \frac{\sin(B-\theta)}{\sin\theta} . \frac{\sin(C-\theta)}{\sin\theta} = 1$$

or $(\sin A\cot\theta - \cos A)(\sin B\cot\theta - \cos B)$

$$(\sin C\cot\theta - \cos C) = 1$$

$\sin A\sin B\sin C[(\cot\theta - \cot A)(\cot\theta - \cot B)$

$$(\cot\theta - \cot C)] = 1$$

Dividing by $\sin A \sin B \sin C$, we have

$$\cot^3 \theta - \cot^2 \theta S_1 + \cot \theta S_2 - S_3 = \frac{1}{\sin A \sin B \sin C}$$

where $S_2 = \Sigma \cot A \cot B = 1$

Also $S_1 = \cot A + \cot B + \cot C = \dfrac{\Sigma \cos A \sin B \sin C}{\sin A \sin B \sin C}$

$$S_3 = \cot A \cot B \cot C = \frac{\cos A \cos B \cos C}{\sin A \sin B \sin C}$$

$$\therefore \quad \cot \theta (1 + \cot^2 \theta) = \frac{\Sigma \cos A \sin B \sin C}{\sin A \sin B \sin C} \cdot \cot^2 \theta$$

$$+ \frac{1 + \cos A \cos B \cos C}{\sin A \sin B \sin C}$$

$$= \frac{\Sigma \cos A \sin B \sin C}{\sin A \sin B \sin C}(\cot^2 \theta + 1)$$

[We have used $\cos (A + B + C)$

$= \cos A \cos B \cos C - \Sigma \cos A \sin B \sin C = -1$]

Cancel $1 + \cot^2 \theta$.

$$\therefore \quad \cot \theta = \frac{\Sigma \cos A \sin B \sin C}{\sin A \sin B \sin C} = \cot A + \cot B + \cot C.$$

Converse :

Let $\sin^3 \theta = \sin (A - \theta) \sin (B - \theta) \sin (C - \theta)$

To prove : $\quad \cot \theta = \cot A + \cot B + \cot C$

$$\cot \theta - \cot A = \cot B + \cot C$$

or $\quad \dfrac{\sin (A - \theta)}{\sin \theta \sin A} = \dfrac{\sin (B + C)}{\sin B \sin C} = \dfrac{\sin A}{\sin B \sin C}$

$$\therefore \quad \sin (A - \theta) = \frac{\sin \theta \sin^2 A}{\sin B \sin C} \qquad ....(1)$$

Similarly, $\sin (B - \theta) = \dfrac{\sin \theta \sin^2 B}{\sin C \sin A} \qquad ...(2)$

$$\sin (C - \theta) = \frac{\sin \theta \sin^2 C}{\sin C \sin B} \qquad ...(3)$$

Multiplying (1), (2) and (3),

$$\sin (A - \theta) \sin (B - \theta) \sin (C - \theta) = \sin^3 \theta$$

(b) **Refer 4 (a) (ii) P. 562.**

$$1 + \cos A \cos B \cos C = \cos A \sin B \sin C$$

$$+ \cos B \sin C \sin A + \cos C \sin A \sin B$$

$$\therefore \quad E = \frac{\sin A \sin B \sin C}{\cos A \sin B \sin C + ... + ...}$$

Divide above and below by $\sin A \sin B \sin C$

$$\therefore \quad E = \frac{1}{\cot A + \cot B + \cot C} = \frac{1}{\cot \theta} = \tan \theta$$

2nd part.

$$\cot^2 \theta = \Sigma \cot^2 A + 2 \Sigma \cot B \cot C$$

$$= \frac{1}{2}[2 \Sigma \cot^2 A + 4 \Sigma \cot B \cot C]$$

$$= \frac{1}{2}[\Sigma (\cot A - \cot B)^2 + 2 \Sigma \cot B \cot C$$

$$+ 4 \Sigma \cot B \cot C]$$

$$= \frac{1}{2}[6 + \Sigma (\cot A - \cot B)^2]$$

$\because \quad \Sigma \cot B \cot C = 1 \qquad$ **(Q. 26 (b) and P. 564)**

$$= 3 + \text{something} + \text{ive}$$

$$\therefore \quad \cot^2 \theta \geq 3 \quad \text{or} \quad \tan \theta \leq \frac{1}{\sqrt{3}} \quad \therefore \quad \theta = 30°$$

45. Ans. 3.

$$\frac{A}{1} = \frac{B}{2} = \frac{C}{4} = \frac{A + B + C}{7} = \frac{\pi}{7}$$

$$A = \frac{\pi}{7}, B = \frac{2\pi}{7}, C = \frac{4\pi}{7}$$

$$\therefore \quad A = \alpha, B = 2\alpha, C = 4\alpha.$$

$$\therefore \quad \cos A \cos B \cos C = \cos \alpha \cos 2\alpha \cos 4\alpha$$

where $\alpha = \dfrac{\pi}{7}$

$$= \frac{\sin 2^3 \alpha}{2^3 \sin \alpha} = \frac{\sin (7\alpha + \alpha)}{8 \sin \alpha}$$

or $\quad \cos A \cos B \cos C = \dfrac{\sin (\pi + \alpha)}{8 \sin \alpha} = -\dfrac{1}{8}$

But $\cos (A + B + C) = \cos \pi = -1$

$\cos A \cos B \cos C (1 - S_2) = -1 \quad$ **by 4(a) (ii) P. 562**

$$\therefore \quad -\frac{1}{8}(1 - S_2) = -1 \quad \therefore \quad S_2 = 1 - 8 = -7$$

Also $\quad S_1 = \tan A + \tan B + \tan C = -\sqrt{7} = S_3 \quad$ in a triangle.

$$\therefore \quad \Sigma \tan^2 A = (\Sigma \tan A)^2 - 2S_2 = 7 - 2(-7) = 21$$

Now $\sec^2 A = 1 + \tan^2 A$

$$\therefore \quad \Sigma \sec^2 A = 3 + \Sigma \tan^2 A = 24 \qquad ...(1)$$

$$\Sigma \cot^2 A = \Sigma \frac{1}{\tan^2 A}$$

$$= \frac{\Sigma \tan^2 B \tan^2 C}{S_3^2} = \frac{(S_2)^2 - 2S_1 S_3}{S_3^2}$$

$$= \frac{49 - 2(-\sqrt{7})(-\sqrt{7})}{7} = \frac{35}{7} = 5$$

$$\therefore \quad \Sigma \operatorname{cosec}^2 A = 3 + \Sigma \cot^2 A = 3 + 5 = 8 \qquad ...(2)$$

$$\frac{\Sigma \sec^2 A}{\Sigma \operatorname{cosec}^2 A} = \frac{24}{8} = 3 \text{ by (1) and (2).}$$

46. Ans. (b).

Since $0 < x < \dfrac{\pi}{4} \quad \therefore \quad \tan x < 1$ and $\cot x > 1 \qquad ...(1)$

$\therefore \quad$ Choose $\tan x = 1 - k_1$ and $\cot x = 1 + k_2$, where k_1 and k_2 are very small $+$ ive quantitites.

$$\therefore \quad t_3 = (1 - k_1)^{1 - k_1}, t_1 = (1 - k_1)^{1 + k_2} \qquad ...(2)$$

$$t_4 = (1 + k_2)^{1 - k_1}, t_2 = (1 + k_2)^{1 + k_2} \qquad ...(3)$$

$$\therefore \quad t_4 > t_3 \text{ by (3) and (2)}, t_2 > t_4 \text{ by (2) and (3)}$$

$$\therefore \quad t_2 > t_4 > t_3. \text{ Also } t_3 > t_1$$

$$\therefore \quad t_2 > t_4 > t_3 > t_1.$$

MISCELLANEOUS EXERCISE

Matching Entries

▶ *Match the entries of Column-I and Column-II.*

1. **Column-I**   **Column-II**

(a) If $x \sin \theta = y \sin \left(\theta + \dfrac{2\pi}{3} \right) = z \sin \left(\theta + \dfrac{4\pi}{3} \right)$, then $\Sigma \, xy =$ 1. $1/2$

(b) $\cos^4 \dfrac{\pi}{8} + \cos^4 \dfrac{3\pi}{8} + \cos^4 \dfrac{5\pi}{8} + \cos^4 \dfrac{7\pi}{8} =$ 2. $\dfrac{1}{64}$

(c) $\cos \dfrac{\pi}{11} + \cos \dfrac{3\pi}{11} + \cos \dfrac{5\pi}{11} + \cos \dfrac{7\pi}{11} + \cos \dfrac{9\pi}{11} =$ 3. 1

(d) $\cos \dfrac{\pi}{65} \cos \dfrac{2\pi}{65} \cos \dfrac{4\pi}{65} \cos \dfrac{8\pi}{65} \cos \dfrac{16\pi}{65} \cos \dfrac{32\pi}{65} =$ 4. 0

(e) If $\theta = \dfrac{\pi}{2^n + 1}$, then $2^n \cos \theta \cos 2\theta \cos 2^2 \, \theta \ldots \cos 2^{n-1} \, \theta =$ 5. $3/2$

2. **Column-II**   **Column-II**

(a) $\sin \dfrac{\pi}{10} \sin \dfrac{3\pi}{10} =$ 1. 1

(b) $\cot 7 \dfrac{1}{2}^\circ =$ 2. $-\dfrac{1}{4}$

(c) $\sin^2 40^\circ + \cos^2 140^\circ$ 3. $3/4$

(d) $\cos^2 \dfrac{3\pi}{5} + \cos^2 \dfrac{4\pi}{5}$ 4. $\sqrt{2} + \sqrt{3} + \sqrt{4} + \sqrt{6}$

3. **Column-I**   **Column-II**

If A, B, C be the angles of a triangle, then

(a) $\sin (B + C - A) + \sin (C + A - B) + \sin (A + B - C) =$ 1. $1 - 2 \cos \dfrac{A}{2} \cos \dfrac{B}{2} \sin \dfrac{C}{2}$

(b) $\sin^2 \dfrac{A}{2} + \sin^2 \dfrac{B}{2} - \sin^2 \dfrac{C}{2} =$ 2. 1

(c) If $\tan^2 \dfrac{A}{2} + \tan^2 \dfrac{B}{2} + \tan^2 \dfrac{C}{2} = k$ then $k \geq$ 3. $4 \sin A \sin B \sin C$

4. $\cos A + \cos B = a, \;\; \sin A + \sin B = b$

     Column-I   **Column-II**

(a) $\tan \dfrac{A + B}{2}$ (p) $\dfrac{2ab}{a^2 + b^2}$

(b) $\cos (A + B)$ (q) $b \, / \, a$

(c) $\cos (A - B)$ (r) $\dfrac{a^2 - b^2}{a^2 + b^2}$

(d) $\sin (A + B)$ (s) $\dfrac{a^2 + b^2 - 2}{2}$

5. **Column-I**   **Column-II**

(a) $\cos 2\theta = \sin 3\theta$ (p) $22 \dfrac{1}{2}^\circ$

(b) $\cos 3\theta = \sin 7\theta$ (q) 30°

(c) $\tan \theta = \cot 3\theta$ (r) 9°

(d) $\cot \theta = \tan 2\theta$ (s) 18°

6. Given $\dfrac{\sin \alpha}{a} = \dfrac{\cos \alpha}{b} = \dfrac{\tan \alpha}{c} = k$

     Column-I   **Column-II**

(a) $a^2 + b^2$ (p) $\dfrac{1}{b^2 \, k^4}$

(b) $a^2 + b^2 + c^2$ (q) $\dfrac{1}{k^2}$

(c) bc

(r) $\dfrac{1}{ak}$

(d) $\dfrac{1}{ck}+\dfrac{ak}{1+bk}$

(s) $\dfrac{a}{k}$

Answers

1. (a) → (4), (b) → (5), (c) → (1), (d) → (2), (e) → (3)
2. (a) → (2), (b) → (4), (c) → (1), (d) → (3)
3. (a) → (3), (b) → (1), (c) → (2)
4. (a) → (q), (b) → (r), (c) → (s), (d) → (p)
5. (a) → (s), (b) → (r), (c) → (p), (d) → (q)
6. (a) → (q), (b) → (p), (c) → (s), (d) → (r)

Solutions

1. (a) **See Q. 23 P. 532-41**
   (b) **See Q. 18 (b) P. 532-40**
   (c) **See Q. 27 (b) P. 3532-42**
   (d) **See Q. 34 (c) P. 533-45**
   (e) **See Q. 34 (d) P. 533-45**
2. (a) **See Q. 38 (b) P. 339-35**
   (b) **See Q. 1 (a) P. 532-36**
   (c) $\sin^2 40° = \cos^2 50°, \cos^2 140° = \sin^2 50°$
   (d) $\cos^2 108° = \sin^2 18°, \cos^2 144° = \cos^2 36°$ etc.
3. (a) **See Q. 2 (a) P. 522-65**
   (b) **See Q. 19 (b) P. 653-68**
   (c) **See Q. 33 (a) P. 564-72**
4. Ans. (a) → (q), (b) → (r), (c) → (s), (d) → (p)

   (a) $\dfrac{b}{a}=\dfrac{\sin A+\sin B}{\cos A+\cos B}$

   $$=\dfrac{2\sin\dfrac{A+B}{2}\cos\dfrac{A-B}{2}}{2\cos\dfrac{A+B}{2}\cos\dfrac{A-B}{2}}=\tan\dfrac{A+B}{2}=T \text{ say}$$

   ∴ (a) → (q)

   (b) $\cos(A+B)=\dfrac{1-T^2}{1+T^2}=\dfrac{a^2-b^2}{a^2+b^2}$ ∴ (b) → (r)

   (c) $a^2+b^2=(\cos A+\cos B)^2+(\sin A+\sin B)^2$
   $=(\cos^2 A+\sin^2 A)+(\cos^2 B+\sin^2 B)$
   $+2(\cos A\cos B+\sin A\sin B)$

∴ $(a^2+b^2-2)=2\cos(A-B)$ ∴ (c) → (s)

(d) $\sin(A+B)=\dfrac{2T}{1+T^2}=\dfrac{2ab}{a^2+b^2}$ ∴ (d) → (p)

5. Ans. (a) → (s), (b) → (r), (c) → (p), (d) → (q)

   $\sin A=\cos B \Rightarrow A=90°-B$ ∴ $A+B=90°$

   ∴ $2\theta+3\theta=90° \Rightarrow \theta=18°$

       $7\theta+3\theta=90° \Rightarrow \theta=9°$

       $3\theta+\theta=90° \Rightarrow \theta=22\dfrac{1}{2}°$

       $2\theta+\theta=90° \Rightarrow \theta=30°$

6. Ans. (a) → (q), (b) → (p), (c) → (s), (d) → (r)

   (a) $a^2+b^2=\dfrac{1}{k^2}(\sin^2\alpha+\cos^2\alpha)=\dfrac{1}{k^2}$

   (b) $a^2+b^2+c^2=\dfrac{1}{k^2}+\dfrac{1}{k^2}\tan^2\alpha=\dfrac{1}{k^2}\sec^2\alpha$

   $$=\dfrac{1}{k^2}\cdot\dfrac{1}{b^2k^2}=\dfrac{1}{b^2k^4}$$

   (c) $bc=\dfrac{1}{k^2}\cos\alpha\cdot\tan\alpha=\dfrac{1}{k^2}\sin\alpha=\dfrac{1}{k^2}\cdot ak=\dfrac{a}{k}$

   (d) $\dfrac{1}{ck}+\dfrac{ak}{1+bk}=\cot\alpha+\dfrac{\sin\alpha}{1+\cos\alpha}$

   $$=\dfrac{\cos\alpha(1+\cos\alpha)+\sin^2\alpha}{\sin\alpha(1+\cos\alpha)}=\dfrac{\cos\alpha+1}{\sin\alpha(1+\cos\alpha)}$$

   $$=\dfrac{1}{\sin\alpha}=\dfrac{1}{ak}$$

Comprehension

1. If $y=\dfrac{\sqrt{1-\sin 4\theta}+1}{\sqrt{1+\sin 4\theta}-1}$ then one of the values of y is

   (a) $\cot\theta$
   (b) $-\tan\theta$
   (c) $\tan\left(\dfrac{\pi}{4}+\theta\right)$
   (d) $-\cot\left(\dfrac{\pi}{4}+\theta\right)$

   Sol. Ans. (a), (b), (c), (d).

   $1\pm\sin A=\cos^2\dfrac{A}{2}+\sin^2\dfrac{A}{2}\pm 2\cos\dfrac{A}{2}\sin\dfrac{A}{2}$

   $$=\left(\cos\dfrac{A}{2}\pm\sin\dfrac{A}{2}\right)^2$$

   ∴ $y=\dfrac{\pm\left(\cos\dfrac{A}{2}+\sin\dfrac{A}{2}\right)^2+1}{\pm\left(\cos\dfrac{A}{2}-\sin\dfrac{A}{2}\right)^2-1}$

   or $y_1=\dfrac{1+\cos\dfrac{A}{2}+\sin\dfrac{A}{2}}{-1+\cos\dfrac{A}{2}-\sin\dfrac{A}{2}}$, taking +, +

   $$=\dfrac{2\cos^2\dfrac{A}{4}+2\sin\dfrac{A}{4}\cos\dfrac{A}{4}}{-2\sin^2\dfrac{A}{4}-2\sin\dfrac{A}{4}\cos\dfrac{A}{4}}$$

   $$=-\dfrac{\cos\dfrac{A}{4}}{\sin\dfrac{A}{4}}=-\tan\dfrac{A}{4}=-\tan\theta, \text{ as } A=4\theta \Rightarrow \text{(b)}$$

   Take $+-;-+$; and $-,-$ you get the other forms

   $\dfrac{1+\tan\theta}{1-\tan\theta}=\tan\left(\dfrac{\pi}{4}+\theta\right)$ etc.

2. For $0 < \theta < \dfrac{\pi}{2}$ if $x = \sum\limits_{n=0}^{\infty} \cos^{2n}\theta$, $y = \sum\limits_{n=0}^{\infty} \sin^{2n}\theta$,

$$z = \sum\limits_{n=0}^{\infty} \cos^{2n}\theta \sin^{2n}\theta, \text{ then}$$

(a) $xyz = xz + y$ (b) $xyz = xy + z$

(c) $xyz = x + y + z$ (d) $xy^2 = y^2 + x$

Sol. Ans. (b), (c).

Sum of an infinite G.P. $= \dfrac{a}{1-r}$

$\therefore \quad x = \dfrac{1}{1-\cos^2\theta} = \dfrac{1}{\sin^2\theta}, y = \dfrac{1}{\cos^2\theta}$

$z = \dfrac{1}{1-\sin^2\theta\cos^2\theta}$ or $z = \dfrac{1}{1-\dfrac{1}{x}\cdot\dfrac{1}{y}}$

or $\quad z(xy-1) = xy \quad \therefore \quad xyz = xy + z \Rightarrow$ (b)

Again $x + y + z = \dfrac{1}{\sin^2\theta} + \dfrac{1}{\cos^2\theta} + \dfrac{1}{1-\sin^2\theta\cos^2\theta}$

$= \dfrac{1}{\sin^2\theta\cdot\cos^2\theta} + \dfrac{1}{1-\sin^2\theta\cos^2\theta}$

$= \dfrac{1}{\sin^2\theta\cdot\cos^2\theta(1-\sin^2\theta\cos^2\theta)}$

$= x \cdot y \cdot z \Rightarrow$ (a)

3. If $\cos(A-B) + \cos(B-C) + \cos(C-A) = -\dfrac{3}{2}$ then

(a) $\sum \cos A = 0$ (b) $\sum \sin A = 0$

(c) $\sum (\cos A + \sin A) = 0$ (d) $\sum \cos A \sin A = 0$

Sol. Ans. (a), (b), (c)

$2\sum \cos(A-B) + \sum(\cos^2 A + \sin^2 A) = 0$

$2[\cos A\cos B + \sin A\sin B] + ... + ... + (\cos^2 A + \sin^2 A)$

$+ ...... + ... = 0$

or $\quad (\sum \cos A)^2 + (\sum \sin A)^2 = 0$

$\Rightarrow \quad \sum \cos A = 0, \sum \sin A = 0$ and hence,

$\sum (\cos A + \sin A) = 0$

$\Rightarrow$ (a), (b), (c).

4. For a +ive integer, let

$f_n(\theta) = \tan\dfrac{\theta}{2}(1+\sec\theta)(1+\sec 2\theta)....(1+\sec 2^n\theta)$ then

(a) $f_2\left(\dfrac{\pi}{16}\right) = 1$ (b) $f_3\left(\dfrac{\pi}{32}\right) = 1$

(c) $f_4\left(\dfrac{\pi}{64}\right) = 1$ (d) $f_5\left(\dfrac{\pi}{128}\right) = 1$

Sol. Ans. (a), (b), (c), (d).

$f_n(\theta) = \dfrac{\sin\dfrac{\theta}{2}}{\cos\dfrac{\theta}{2}} \dfrac{1+\cos\theta}{\cos\theta}(\ )(\ )....$

$= \dfrac{\sin\dfrac{\theta}{2}}{\cos\dfrac{\theta}{2}} \dfrac{2\cos^2\dfrac{\theta}{2}}{\cos\theta}(\ )(\ )...$

$= \tan\theta(\ )(\ )(\ )...$

$= \dfrac{\sin\theta}{\cos\theta} \dfrac{1+\cos 2\theta}{\cos 2\theta}(\ )(\ )...$

$= \dfrac{\sin\theta}{\cos\theta} \dfrac{2\cos^2\theta}{\cos 2\theta}(\ )(\ )...$

$= \dfrac{\sin 2\theta}{\cos 2\theta}(1+\sec 2^2\theta)(\ )...$

$\therefore \quad f_n(\theta) = \tan 2\theta(\ )(\ )...$

$= \tan 2^n\theta$

Put $n = 2, \theta = \dfrac{\pi}{16}, \quad n = 3, \theta = \dfrac{\pi}{32}$

and $n = 4, \theta = \dfrac{\pi}{64}, \quad n = 5, \theta = \dfrac{\pi}{128}$

Then $f_n(\theta) = \tan\dfrac{\pi}{4} = 1$

Fascinating Facts

- Any formula that gives the value of $\sin\dfrac{A}{2}$ in terms of $\sin A$ shall also give the value of $\sin$ of $\dfrac{n\pi + (-1)^n \cdot A}{2}$.

- Any formula that gives the value of $\cos\dfrac{A}{2}$ in terms of $\cos A$ shall also give the value of $\cos$ of $\dfrac{2n\pi \pm A}{2}$.

- Any formula that gives the value of $\tan\dfrac{A}{2}$ in terms of $\tan A$ shall also give the value of $\tan$ of $\dfrac{n\pi \pm A}{2}$.

- The angle between two consecutive digits in a clock is 30. The hour hand rotates through an angle of 30° in one hour.

- The minute hand rotates through an angle of 6° in one minute.

- $\cos A \cdot \cos 2A \cdot \cos 2^2 \cdot \cos 2^3 \cos 2^3 A ... \cos 2^{n-1} \cdot A$

$$= \begin{cases} \dfrac{\sin 2^n A}{2^n \sin A} & \text{if} \quad A \neq n\pi \\ 1 & \text{if} \quad A = 2n\pi \\ 1 & \text{if} \quad A = (2n+1)\pi \end{cases}$$

CHAPTER

13

Trigonometrical Equations

§ 1. General Solutions of Trigonometrical Equations.

(i) **The equation** $\sin \theta = k$, $\quad (-1 \le k \le 1)$

(a) Let $-1 < k < 1$. In this case, there are two values of θ of the form α and $\pi - \alpha$, in the interval $0 \le \theta \le 2\pi$, which satisfy the equation. Adding $2r\pi$ $(r \in I)$, we get $2r\pi + \alpha$ and $(2r + 1)\pi - \alpha$. Both these solutions are included in $n\pi + (-1)^n \alpha, n \in I$, where I is the set of integers . Hence the general solution in this case is $\theta = n\pi + (-1)^n \alpha$, where $n \in I$, that is, $n = 0$, $\pm 1, \pm 2, \pm 3, \ldots$.

In particular if $k = 0$, then

$\sin \theta = 0 = \sin 0°$. $\quad \therefore \quad \theta = n\pi$.

(b) Let $k = 1$. In this case, there is only one value $\pi / 2$ in the interval $0 \le \theta \le 2\pi$ satisfying the given equation. Hence the general solution is given by

$\theta = 2n\pi + \pi/2, \quad (n \in I)$.

(c) Let $k = -1$. In this case, there is only one value $3\pi / 2$ in the interval $0 \le \theta \le 2\pi$ which satisfies the given equation. Hence the general solution in this case is :

$\theta = 2n\pi + 3\pi/2, \quad (n \in I)$

(ii) **The equation** $\cos \theta = k$, $\quad (-1 \le k \le 1)$

(a) Let $-1 < k < 1, k \ne 0$.

In this case , there are two values of θ of the form $\pm \alpha$, in the interval $-\pi < \theta \le \pi$ which satisfy the given equation . Hence the general solution is given by :

$\theta = 2n\pi \pm \alpha$.

(b) Let $k = 0$. The solution in this case is

$\theta = 2r\pi \pm \pi/2$

or $\quad \theta = (4r \pm 1)\pi/2, (r \in I)$

Thus in this case , the solution set consists of all odd multiples of $\pi/2$. Hence we may write the solution as

$\theta = (2n + 1)\pi/2$

or $\quad \theta = n\pi + \pi/2, n \in I$.

(c) Let $k = 1$. In this case there is only one value 0 of θ in the interval $-\pi < \theta \le \pi$ which satisfies the equation. Hence the solution in this case is :

$\theta = 2n\pi, n \in I$.

(d) $k = -1$. Here $\theta = \pi$ is the only solution in the interval $-\pi < \theta \le \pi$. Hence the general solution in this case is $\theta = (2n + 1)\pi, n \in I$.

(iii) **The equation** $\tan \theta = k$, $\quad (-\infty < k < \infty)$.

For any real value of k there are two values of the form α and $\pi + \alpha$, in the interval $0 \le \theta < 2\pi$ which satisfy the given equation. Adding $2r\pi$, we get $2r\pi + \alpha$ and $(2r + 1)\pi + \alpha, r \in I$. Both these solutions are included in the solution $\theta = n\pi + \alpha, n \in I$.

In particular, if $k = 0$, then the solution is $\theta = n\pi$.

(iv) **The equation** $\sin^2 \theta = k = \sin^2 \alpha$.

Since values of $\sin \theta$ are $\pm \sin \alpha$ and $-\sin \alpha = \sin(-\alpha)$, therefore $\theta = \pm \alpha, \pi \pm \alpha$.

Adding $2r\pi$, we get $2r\pi \pm \alpha$ and $(2r + 1)\pi \pm \alpha$, Both these solutions are included in $n\pi \pm \alpha$ $(n \in I)$. Hence the general solution in this case is given by $\theta = n\pi \pm \alpha$. But for $\sin^2 \theta = 1$, we have $\theta = n\pi + \pi/2$.

(v) **The equation** $\cos^2 \theta = k = \cos^2 \alpha$.

In this case also the solution is given by $\theta = n\pi \pm \alpha$. But for $\cos^2 \theta = 1$, we have $\theta = n\pi$

(vi) **The equation** $\tan^2 \theta = \tan^2 \alpha$.

The solution set is given by $\theta = n\pi \pm \alpha$

Note : Students are advised to derive the solution sets in (v) and (vi) .

§ 2. Some special type of equations

(a) **The equations** $a \cos \theta \pm b \sin \theta = c$ **are solved as follows**

Put $a = r \cos \alpha, b = r \sin \alpha$

so that $\quad r = \sqrt{a^2 + b^2}, \tan \alpha = b/a$

and $\quad \alpha = \tan^{-1}(b/a)$

The given equation becomes

$r[\cos \theta \cos \alpha \pm \sin \theta \sin \alpha] = c$

$\cos(\theta \pm \alpha) = c/r, \quad$ provided $|c/r| \le 1$.

(b) **Solution in Special Cases**

Common roots : Two equations are given and we have to find the values of variable θ which may satisfy both the given equations.

Rule : Find the common values of θ between 0 and 2π and then add $2n\pi$ to this common value.

Ex. 1. $\cos\theta = \dfrac{1}{\sqrt{2}}$ and $\tan\theta = -1$

$\theta = \dfrac{\pi}{4}, 2\pi - \dfrac{\pi}{4} = \dfrac{7\pi}{4}$ from 1st

$\tan\theta = -1 = -\tan(\pi/4)$

or $\theta = \pi - \dfrac{\pi}{4} = \dfrac{3\pi}{4}$ or $2\pi - \dfrac{\pi}{4} = \dfrac{7\pi}{4}$

The common value which satisfies both these equations is $\dfrac{7\pi}{4}$ and hence the general value is

$2n\pi + \dfrac{7\pi}{4}$.   **(General rule)**

Ex. 2.   If $\cos\theta = \dfrac{\sqrt{3}}{2}$ then by formula $\theta = 2n\pi \pm \dfrac{\pi}{6}$ ...(1)

Another method is find the values between 0 and 2π

from $\cos\theta = \dfrac{\sqrt{3}}{2}$ $\therefore$ $\theta = \dfrac{\pi}{6}$ or $2\pi - \dfrac{\pi}{6} = \dfrac{11\pi}{6}$

$\therefore$ General value is $2n\pi + \dfrac{\pi}{6}$ and $2n\pi + \dfrac{11\pi}{6}$ ...(2)

Both the answers given in (2) are included in (1) as

$2n\pi + \dfrac{11\pi}{6} = 2n\pi + 2\pi + \dfrac{11\pi}{6} - 2\pi$

$= (2n+2)\pi - \dfrac{\pi}{6} = $ Even $\pi - \dfrac{\pi}{6}$

Ex. 3.   Similarly, if $\sin\theta = \dfrac{\sqrt{3}}{2} = \sin\dfrac{\pi}{3}$ then

by formula $\theta = n\pi + (-1)^n \, \pi/3$ ...(1)

Another method is $\sin\theta = \dfrac{\sqrt{3}}{2}$

$\therefore$ $\theta = \dfrac{\pi}{3}$ and $\pi - \dfrac{\pi}{3} = \dfrac{2\pi}{3}$

$\therefore$ General value is $2n\pi + \dfrac{\pi}{3}$ and $2n\pi + \dfrac{2\pi}{3}$.   ...(2)

(1) and (2) give the same answers if we take $n = 2r, 2r+1$

Ex. 4. $\cos 5\theta = 0$, $\sin 4\theta = 0$

$5\theta = \left(n + \dfrac{1}{2}\right)\pi$, $4\theta = m\pi$

$\therefore$ $\theta = (2n+1)\dfrac{\pi}{10}$, $\theta = \dfrac{m\pi}{4}$ ...(A)

From the above two we shall find common values of θ between 0 and 2π and then generalise by adding $2n\pi$.

$\theta = (2n+1)\dfrac{\pi}{10}$

Now give n such values so that $(2n+1)$ does not exceed $10 \times 2 = 20$ as we have to find values between 0 and 2π.

$\theta = \dfrac{\pi}{10}$ (1, 3, 5, 7, 11, 13, 15, 17, 19)   ...(1)

Similarly from 2nd, i.e., $\theta = \dfrac{m\pi}{4}$

$\theta = \dfrac{\pi}{4}$ (0, 1, 2, 3, 4, 5, 6, 7)   ...(2)

From (1), $\dfrac{5\pi}{10} = \dfrac{\pi}{2}, \dfrac{15\pi}{10} = \dfrac{3\pi}{2}$

From (2), $\dfrac{2\pi}{4} = \dfrac{\pi}{2}, \dfrac{6\pi}{4} = \dfrac{3\pi}{2}$

The above two are the only two common values. Hence the general solution in

$2n\pi + \dfrac{\pi}{2}$ and $2n\pi + \dfrac{3\pi}{2}$ ...(3)

Note : We may also say that

$(2n+1)\dfrac{\pi}{10} = \dfrac{m\pi}{4}$ from (A)

$\therefore$ $m = \dfrac{(4n+2)}{5}$ where $m, n \in I$

Hence n should be so chosen so that $m \in I$

$\therefore$ $n = -8, -3, 2, 7, 12$ i.e. an A.P. of $d = 5$

or $n = 5k + 2$ where $k \in I$

$\therefore$ $\theta = (2n+1)\dfrac{\pi}{10} = [2(5k+2)+1]\dfrac{\pi}{10}$

$= (10k+5)\dfrac{\pi}{10} = (2k+1)\dfrac{\pi}{2}$

$= $ odd multiple of $\dfrac{\pi}{2}$

The answers found in (3) i.e., $2n\pi + \pi/2$ and $2n\pi + \dfrac{3\pi}{2}$ are

$(4n+1)\dfrac{\pi}{2}$ and $(4n+3)\dfrac{\pi}{2}$, i.e., odd multiple of $\dfrac{\pi}{2}$.

List of formulae :

(1)* $\sin\theta = 0, \theta = n\pi$, $\cos\theta = 0, \theta = \left(n + \dfrac{1}{2}\right)\pi$
$\tan\theta = 0, \theta = n\pi$
(2)* $\sin\theta = 1, -1, \theta = 2n\pi + \pi/2, \theta = 2n\pi + 3\pi/2$
$\cos\theta = 1, -1, \theta = 2n\pi,\ \ \theta = 2n\pi + \pi$
(3)* $\sin^2\theta = 1, \theta = n\pi + \pi/2$
$\cos^2\theta = 1, \theta = n\pi$
(4)* $\sin\theta = \sin\alpha, \theta = n\pi + (-1)^n \alpha$
$\cos\theta = \cos\alpha, \theta = 2n\pi \pm \alpha$
$\tan\theta = \tan\alpha, \theta = n\pi + \alpha$
(5)* $\sin\theta = -\sin\alpha, \theta = n\pi + (-1)^n (-\alpha)$
$\cos\theta = -\cos\alpha, \theta = 2n\pi + (\pi - \alpha)$
$\tan\theta = -\tan\alpha, \theta = n\pi - \alpha$
(6)* $\sin^2\theta = \sin^2\alpha, \theta = n\pi \pm \alpha$
$\cos^2\theta = \cos^2\alpha, \theta = n\pi \pm \alpha$
$\tan^2\theta = \tan^2\alpha, \theta = n\pi \pm \alpha$

(7)* If while solving an equation we have to square it, then the roots found after squaring must be checked whether they satisfy the original equation or not. e.g. Let $x = 3$. Squaring, we get $x^2 = 9$ $\therefore$ $x = 3$ and -3 but $x = -3$ does not satisfy the original equation $x = 3$.

Ex. $\sin x + \cos x = 1$

Square both sides, we get

$1 + \sin 2x = 1$ $\therefore$ $\sin 2x = 0$

$\therefore$ $2x = n\pi$ or $x = \dfrac{n\pi}{2}, n \in I$

∴ Roots are $..., \dfrac{-3\pi}{2}, \dfrac{-2\pi}{2}, \dfrac{-\pi}{2}, 0, \dfrac{\pi}{2}, \dfrac{2\pi}{2}, \dfrac{3\pi}{2}, ...$

We find that 0 and $\pi/2$ are roots but π and $3\pi/2$ do not satisfy the given equation as it leads to $-1 = 1$.

Similarly 0 and $\dfrac{-3\pi}{2}$ are roots but $-\dfrac{\pi}{2}$ and $-\pi$ are not roots as it will lead to $-1 = 1$.

As stated above, because of squaring we are solving the equations $\sin x + \cos x = 1$ and $\sin x + \cos x = -1$ both. The rejected roots are for $\sin x + \cos x = -1$

(8) Any value of x which makes both R.H.S. and L.H.S. equal will be a root but the value of x for which $\infty = \infty$ will not be a solution as it is an indeterminate form. Hence $\cos x \neq 0$ for those equations which involve $\tan x$ and $\sec x$ whereas $\sin x \neq 0$ for those which involve $\cot x$ and $\operatorname{cosec} x$.

Also exponential function is always +ive and $\log_a x$ is defined if $x > 0$, $x \neq 0$ and $a > 0$, $a \neq 1$ $\sqrt{\{f(x)\}} = +$ive always and not $\pm$ i.e. $\sqrt{(\tan^2 x)} = \tan x$ and not $\pm \tan x$

(9) (i) If $xy = xz$, then $x(y - z) = 0 \Rightarrow$ either $x = 0$ or $y = z$ or both. But $\dfrac{y}{x} = \dfrac{z}{x} \Rightarrow y = z$ only and not $x = 0$, as it will make $\infty = \infty$. Similarly if $ay = az$, then it will also imply $y = z$ only as $a \neq 0$ being a constant.

Similarly, $\quad x + y = x + z \Rightarrow y = z$
and $\quad\quad\quad x - y = x - z \Rightarrow y = z$.

Here we do not take $x = 0$ as in the above because x is an additive factor and not multiplicative factor.

(ii) When $\cos\theta = 0$, then $\sin\theta = 1$ or -1. We have to verify which value of $\sin\theta$ is to be chosen which satisfies the equation.

$$\cos\theta = 0 \Rightarrow \theta = \left(n + \dfrac{1}{2}\right)\pi.$$

Imp. If $\sin\theta = 1$, then obviously $n =$ even. But if $\sin\theta = -1$, then $n =$ odd.

Similarly, when $\sin\theta = 0$, then $\theta = n\pi$ and $\cos\theta = 1$ or -1. If $\cos\theta = 1$, then n is even and if $\cos\theta = -1$, then n is odd.

▶ **Cautions**
• While solving the equations squaring at any step should be avoided as for as possible. If squaring is necessary, check the solution for extra never values.

• Never cancel terms containing unknown quantities on the two sides, which are in product.
• Denominator should be non-zero at each and every stage of the solution.
• Exclude the repetitions of solution from the set of solutions and if two solution sets consist partly of common values, then common part must be occur only once.

(10) **Values of Trigonometrical Ratios for Certain Angles :**

$$\sin 15° = \cos 75° = \dfrac{\sqrt{3} - 1}{2\sqrt{2}}$$

$$\cos 15° = \sin 75° = \dfrac{\sqrt{3} + 1}{2\sqrt{2}}$$

$$\tan 15° = \cot 75° = \dfrac{\sqrt{3} - 1}{\sqrt{3} + 1} = 2 - \sqrt{3}$$

$$\tan 75° = \cot 15° = 2 + \sqrt{3}$$

$$\sin 18° = \cos 72° = \dfrac{\sqrt{5} - 1}{4}$$

$$\cos 36° = \sin 54° = \dfrac{\sqrt{5} + 1}{4}$$

$$\cos 18° = \sin 72° = \dfrac{\sqrt{10 + 2\sqrt{5}}}{4}$$

$$\sin 36° = \cos 54° = \dfrac{\sqrt{10 - 2\sqrt{5}}}{4}$$

$$*\sin 22\tfrac{1}{2}° = \sqrt{\dfrac{1 - \cos 45°}{2}} = \sqrt{\dfrac{\sqrt{2} - 1}{2\sqrt{2}}} = \dfrac{\sqrt{2 - \sqrt{2}}}{2}$$

$$*\cos 22\tfrac{1}{2}° = \sqrt{\dfrac{1 + \cos 45°}{2}} = \sqrt{\dfrac{\sqrt{2} + 1}{2\sqrt{2}}} = \dfrac{\sqrt{2 + \sqrt{2}}}{2}$$

Domain and range of some trigonometric functions

S.No.	Function	Domain	Range
1	$\sin x$	**R**	$[-1\ 1]$
2	$\cos x$	**R**	$[-1\ 1]$
3	$\tan x$	$\mathbf{R} - (2n + 1)\dfrac{\pi}{2}, n \in \mathbf{I}$	R
4	$\cot x$	$\mathbf{R} - n\pi, n \in I$	R
5	$\operatorname{cosec} x$	$\mathbf{R} - n\pi, n \in I$	$]-\infty, -1\,[\cup(\,\infty[$
6	$\sec x$	$\mathbf{R} - (2n + 1)\dfrac{\pi}{2}, n \in I$	$[-\infty, -1\,[\cup(1, \infty[$

Problem Set (1)

Questions based upon the solution of
$$\sin\theta = \sin\alpha, \cos\theta = \cos\alpha, \tan\theta = \tan\alpha, \sin\theta = 0, 1, -1, \cos\theta = 0, 1, -1.$$

1. (a) $2\sin^2 x + \sqrt{3}\cos x + 1 = 0$.

   (b) $\sin^2\theta - \cos\theta = \dfrac{1}{4}$ in the interval $0 \le \theta \le 2\pi$.

   (c) $2\sin^2\theta = 3\cos\theta$ in the interval $0 \le \theta \le 2\pi$.

   (d) The number of values of x in the interval $[0, 3\pi]$ satisfying the equation $2\sin^2 x + 5\sin x - 3 = 0$ is:

(a) 6   (b) 1

(c) 2   (d) 4   **(AIEEE 2006)**

(e) If $2\sin^2\theta - 5\sin\theta + 2 > 0, \theta \in (0, 2\pi)$, then $\theta \in$:

(a) $\left(\dfrac{5\pi}{6}, 2\pi\right)$ (b) $\left(0, \dfrac{\pi}{6}\right) \cup \left(\dfrac{5\pi}{6}, 2\pi\right)$

(c) $\left(0, \dfrac{\pi}{6}\right)$ (d) $\left(\dfrac{\pi}{80}, \dfrac{\pi}{6}\right)$ **(I.I.T. 2006)**

(f) The number of solutions of the pair of equations

$$2\sin^2\theta - \cos 2\theta = 0$$
$$2\cos^2\theta - 3\sin\theta = 0$$

in the interval $[0, 2\pi]$ is

(a) zero   (b) one

(c) two   (d) four   **(I.I.T. 2007)**

2. (a) $4\cos^2\theta + \sqrt{3} = 2[\sqrt{3}+1]\cos\theta$.

(b) $5\cos 2\theta + 2\cos^2\left(\dfrac{1}{2}\theta\right) + 1 = 0, -\pi < \theta < \pi$

(c)* If $32\tan^8\theta = 2\cos^2\alpha - 3\cos\alpha$ and $3\cos 2\theta = 1$, then find the general value of α.

3. (a) $4\cos\theta - 3\sec\theta = 2\tan\theta$.

(b)* $4\cos^2 x \sin x - 2\sin^2 x = 3\sin x$.

(c) $\cos(10x + 4) + 4\sqrt{2}\sin(5x + 2) = 4$.

4. (a) $\tan^2 x + [1 - \sqrt{3}]\tan x - \sqrt{3} = 0$.

(b) $3\cos^2\theta - 2\sqrt{3}\sin\theta\cos\theta - 3\sin^2\theta = 0$.

5. (a) $(1 - \tan\theta)(1 + \sin 2\theta) = 1 + \tan\theta$.

(b)* General value of θ satisfying the equation $\tan^2\theta + \sec 2\theta = 1$ is ....   **(I.I.T. 1996)**

(c) $1 + 2\operatorname{cosec} x = -\dfrac{\sec^2(x/2)}{2}$

6. (a) $\cos^2 x - 2\cos x = 4\sin x - \sin 2x, 0 \le x \le \pi$.

(b) $3(\cos\theta - \sin\theta) = 1 + \cos 2\theta - \sin 2\theta$.

7. (a)* $4\sin^4 x + \cos^4 x = 1$

(b) $\sin^2\theta = 1/4$

(c) $5\cos^2\theta + 7\sin^2\theta = 6$

8. (a) $2 + 7\tan^2 x = 3 \cdot 25\sec^2 x$

(b) If $\sin^2 x + \cos^2 y = 2\sec^2 z$ then x, y, z are ......

(c) $6\sin^2 x + 2\sin^2 2x = 5$.

9. (a) $2^{\cos 2x} = 3 \cdot 2^{\cos^2 x} - 4$

(b) $2^{\sin^2 x} + 5 \cdot 2^{\cos^2 x} = 7$

(c) $\sin^4 x + \cos^4 x = 5/8$.

(d) $\sin^6 2x + \cos^6 2x = 7/16$.

10. (a) If $0 \le x \le \pi$ and $81^{\sin^2 x} + 81^{\cos^2 x} = 30$, then x is equal to

(a) $\pi/6$ (b) $\pi/3$

(c) $5\pi/6$ (d) $2\pi/3$

(b) The smallest + ive x satisfying the equation $\log_{\cos x}\sin x + \log_{\sin x}\cos x = 2$ is $\pi/4$.

(c) If $\alpha, \beta, \gamma, \delta$ are the smallest +ive angles in ascending order of magnitude which have their sines equal to a +ive quantity λ then the value of $4\sin\dfrac{\alpha}{2} + 3\sin\dfrac{\beta}{2} + 2\sin\dfrac{\gamma}{2} + \sin\dfrac{\delta}{2} =$

(a) $2\sqrt{1 - \lambda}$ (b) $2\sqrt{1 + \lambda}$

(c) $2\sqrt{\lambda}$ (d) $2\sqrt{\lambda + 2}$

11. (a)* $(1 - \tan\theta)(1 + \tan\theta)\sec^2\theta + 2^{\tan^2\theta} = 0$ in the interval $(-\pi/2, \pi/2)$ **(I.I.T. 1996)**

(b) $6\tan^2 x - 2\cos^2 x = \cos 2x$.

12. (a) $1 + \sin 2x = (\sin 3x - \cos 3x)^2$.

(b) $\cos 4x = \cos^2 3x$.

13. (a) $\cos^{40}\theta + \sin^{58}\theta = 1$

(b) $1 - 2\sin\theta - 2\cos\theta + \cot\theta = 0$, $(0 < \theta < 2\pi)$

14. (a) $\tan^2\theta + \cot^2\theta = 2$.

(b)* $\cot\theta - \tan\theta = 2$.

(c) $\tan\theta + \cot\theta = 2$.

15. (a)* In a right angled triangle the hypotenuse is $2\sqrt{2}$ times the length of perpendicular drawn from the opposite vertex on the hypotenuse, then the other two angles are ....   **(M.N.R. 1994)**

(b) In a right angled ΔABC, the hypotenuse is four times the perpendicular distance of the opposite vertex from it. Determine the other two angles.

16. (a) $\tan\theta + \tan 2\theta + \sqrt{3}\tan 2\theta\tan\theta = \sqrt{3}$.

(b)* $\tan\theta + \tan 4\theta + \tan 7\theta = \tan\theta\tan 4\theta\tan 7\theta$.

17. (a)* $3\tan 2x - 4\tan 3x = \tan^2 3x\tan 2x$.

(b) $\sin^2 x(1 + \tan x) = 3\sin x(\cos x - \sin x) + 3$

18. (a) $\cot\theta + \tan\theta = 2\operatorname{cosec}\theta$.

(b)* $\cot\theta - \tan\theta = \sec\theta$.

19. (a) $2\sin 2x - \sin x = 0$.

(b) $2\sin^2 x + \sin^2 2x = 2$.

20. (a) $\sin 3\alpha = 4\sin\alpha\sin(x + \alpha)\sin(x - \alpha)$.

(b)* $\cot(x/2) - \operatorname{cosec}(x/2) = \cot x$..

21. (a) $3\tan^2\theta - 2\sin\theta = 0$.

(b) $\sin^3\theta\cos\theta - \cos^3\theta\sin\theta = 1/4$.

(c)* $\cos 3x\cos^3 x + \sin 3x\sin^3 x = 0$

22. (a) $\sec\theta - 1 = (\sqrt{2} - 1)\tan\theta$.

(b) $\sqrt{2}\sec\theta + \tan\theta = 1$.

(c)* $\cos 2\theta = (\sqrt{2} + 1)(\cos\theta - 1/\sqrt{2})$.

23. (a) $r\sin\theta = \sqrt{3}, r + 4\sin\theta = 2(\sqrt{3} + 1), 0 \le \theta \le 2\pi$

(b) $r\sin\theta = 3, r = 4(1 + \sin\theta), 0 \le \theta \le 2\pi$.

24. (a) $\sin 9\theta = \sin\theta$.

(b) $\sec x\cos 5x + 1 = 0; 0 < x < 2\pi$.

(c) $\sin m\theta + \sin n\theta = 0$.

25. (a) $\sin 5x = \cos 2x$, $0 \le x \le 180°$.

(b) $\sin 2\theta = \cos 3\theta$, $0 \le \theta \le 360°$.

Use this to find the value of sin 18° .

(c) Find the coordinates of the point of intersection of the curves
$$y = \cos x , y = \sin 3x \text{ if} - \pi /2 \le x \le \pi /2.$$

26. (a) $\tan p\theta = \cot q\theta.$
(b) $\tan mx + \cot nx = 0.$

27. (a) $\tan 3\theta = \cot \theta.$
(b)* $\tan 2\theta \tan \theta = 1.$

28. (a)* $\cos \theta + \cos 2\theta + \cos 3\theta = 0.$
(b) $\cos 6\theta + \cos 4\theta + \cos 2\theta + 1 = 0 ; 0 \le \theta \le \pi$
(c) $\sin \theta + \sin 3\theta + \sin 5\theta = 0 ; 0 \le \theta \le \frac{1}{2}\pi$

29. (a)* $\sin \theta + \sin 5\theta = \sin 3\theta ; 0 \le \theta \le \pi.$
(b) $4 \sin x \sin 2x \sin 4x = \sin 3x.$

30. (a) $\cos \theta \cos 2\theta \cos 3\theta = \frac{1}{4} ; \quad 0 \le \theta \le \pi.$
(b) $\cos \theta + \cos 7\theta + \cos 3\theta + \cos 5\theta = 0.$
(c)* $8 \cos x \cos 2x \cos 4x = \dfrac{\sin 6x}{\sin x}$

31. (a) $\cos \theta + \sin \theta = \cos 2\theta + \sin 2\theta$
(b) $\cos 3x + \cos 2x = \sin (3x/2) + \sin (x/2), 0 \le x < 2\pi.$

32. (a) $\sin 7\theta + \sin 4\theta + \sin \theta = 0 ; 0 \le \theta \le \pi/2$
(b) $\sin 6x = \sin 4x - \sin 2x.$
(c) $\cos \theta - \cos 2\theta = \sin 3\theta.$

33. (a)* $\sin 3\theta - \sin \theta = 4 \cos^2 \theta - 2.$
(b) $\sec 4\theta - \sec 2\theta = 2.$

34. (a) $\sin \theta + \sin 2\theta + \sin 3\theta + \sin 4\theta = 0.$
(b) $\sin \dfrac{n+1}{2}\theta = \sin \dfrac{n-1}{2}\theta + \sin \theta.$

35. (a) $\sin (3\theta + \alpha) + \sin (3\theta - \alpha) + \sin (\alpha - \theta)$
$$- \sin (\alpha + \theta) = \cos \alpha.$$
(b) $\sin^2 n\theta - \sin^2 (n-1)\theta = \sin^2 \theta.$

36. (a) $\sin x + \sqrt{3} \cos x = \sqrt{2}.$
(b) $\sin x + \sqrt{3} \cos x \ge 1$
(c) $\sqrt{3} \cos \theta + \sin \theta = 1$ for $-2\pi < \theta < 2\pi.$

37. (a) $\sqrt{3} \sin \theta - \cos \theta = \sqrt{2}.$
(b) Find real values of x for which $27^{\cos 2x} . 81^{\sin 2x}$ is minimum. Also find this minimum value.
(Roorkee 2000)

38. (a)* If $0 \le \theta \le 2\pi$ then solve the equation
$$(\sin 2\theta + \sqrt{3} \cos 2\theta)^2 - 5 = \cos \left(2\theta - \frac{\pi}{6}\right)$$
(b) $3 - 2 \cos \theta - 4 \sin \theta - \cos 2\theta + \sin 2\theta = 0$
(c)* $\sin x + \cos x = 1.$
(d) Solve the equation $\sin x + \cos x = \sin 2x - 1$

39. (a) $\operatorname{cosec} x = 1 + \cot x.$
(b) $\tan \theta + \sec \theta = \sqrt{3} ; 0 \le \theta \le 2\pi$
(c) $\cot \theta + \operatorname{cosec} \theta = \sqrt{3}.$
(d)* $(2 + \sqrt{3}) \cos \theta = 1 - \sin \theta.$

40. (a) $\tan \left(\dfrac{\pi}{2} \sin \theta\right) = \cot \left(\dfrac{\pi}{2} \cos \theta\right).$
(b)* If $\tan (\pi \cos \theta) = \cot (\pi \sin \theta)$, prove that
$$\cos \left(\theta - \frac{\pi}{4}\right) = \pm \frac{1}{2\sqrt{(2)}}.$$
(c) $\cos (\sin \theta) = \sin (\cos \theta)$
(d) $\cos \theta + \sqrt{3} \sin \theta = 2 \cos 2\theta$
(e) $\sin 8x - \cos 6x = \sqrt{3} (\sin 6x + \cos 8x)$

41. (a) $\tan \theta + \tan 2\theta + \tan 3\theta = 0.$
(b)* $\tan \theta + \tan 2\theta = \tan 3\theta.$
(c) $\tan 3\theta + \tan \theta = 2 \tan 2\theta.$

42. (a) $3 \tan (\theta - 15°) = \tan (\theta + 15°).$
(b)* $4 \cot 2\theta = \cot^2 \theta - \tan^2 \theta.$
(c)* $\tan \theta + \tan \left(\theta + \dfrac{\pi}{3}\right) + \tan \left(\theta + \dfrac{2\pi}{3}\right) = 3.$

43. (a) Solve $\tan 3x = \tan 5x .$
(b)* The set of values of x for which
$$\frac{\tan 3x - \tan 2x}{1 + \tan 3x \tan 2x} = 1 \text{ is ......}$$
(M.N.R. 1993)

44. (a)* $\left(\dfrac{\sin \theta}{\sin \phi}\right)^2 = \dfrac{\tan \theta}{\tan \phi} = 3 .$
(b) Solve for θ and ϕ the equation
$$\sec \theta = \sqrt{2} \sec \phi , \tan \theta = \sqrt{3} \tan \phi$$
(c)* $\dfrac{\tan x}{\tan 2x} + \dfrac{\tan 2x}{\tan x} + 2 = 0$

45. (a) $\sin^3 x + \sin x \cos x + \cos^3 x = 1.$
(b)* $1 + \sin^3 x + \cos^3 x = \dfrac{3}{2} \sin 2x$
(c) $\sqrt{3} (\cos \theta - \sqrt{3} \sin \theta) = 4 \sin 2\theta \cos 3\theta .$

46. (a)* $\dfrac{\sqrt{3}}{2} \sin x - \cos x = \cos^2 x .$
(b) $2 (\cos x + \cos 2x) + \sin 2x (1 + 2 \cos x)$
$$= 2 \sin x, - \pi \le \pi \le x \qquad \textbf{(J.E.E.W.B. 2000)}$$
(c) $2 (\sin x - \cos 2x) - \sin 2x (1 + 2 \sin x) + 2 \cos x = 0$

47. (a) $\sin 2x + 5 \cos x + 5 \sin x + 1 = 0$
(b) Find the range of y such that the equation in x, $y + \cos x = \sin x$ has a real solution . For $y = 1$, find x such that $0 < x < 2\pi .$

48. (a)* Solve $\sin x + \sin 2x + \sin 3x$
$$= \cos x + \cos 2x + \cos 3x$$
in the interval $0 \le x \le 2\pi .$
(b)* Prove that the general solution of
$$\sin x - 3 \sin 2x + \sin 3x$$
$$= \cos x - 3 \cos 2x + \cos 3x \text{ is } n\pi/2 + \pi/8$$

49. (a)* $\sin^2 x \tan x + \cos^2 x \cot x - \sin 2x$
$$= 1 + \tan x + \cot x$$
(b) $\sin 3x + \sin x + 2 \cos x = \sin 2x + 2 \cos^2 x$
(c)* $\sin^2 4x + \cos^2 x = 2 \sin 4x \cos^4 x$

50. What is most general value of θ which satisfies both the equations

(a)* $\sin\theta = -1/2$ and $\tan\theta = 1/\sqrt{3}$.

(b) $\cos\theta = -1/\sqrt{2}$, and $\tan\theta = 1$.

(c) $\cos\theta = 1/\sqrt{2}$, and $\tan\theta = -1$.

(d)* $\tan\theta = \sqrt{3}$ and $\csc\theta = -2/\sqrt{3}$.

(e) $\sin\theta = 1/2$ and $\cos\theta = \sqrt{3}/2$.

(f) If $\cos 3x + \sin\left(2x - \dfrac{7\pi}{6}\right) = -2$ then show that x is

of the form $\dfrac{\pi}{3}(6m+1)$.

Solutions to Problem Set (1)

1. (a) Changing $\sin^2 x$ into $1 - \cos^2 x$, we get

$$2(1 - \cos^2 x) + \sqrt{3}\cos x + 1 = 0$$

or $\quad 2\cos^2 x - \sqrt{3}\cos x - 3 = 0$

$\therefore \quad \cos x = \dfrac{\sqrt{3} \pm \sqrt{3 + 24}}{4}$

$= \dfrac{\sqrt{3} \pm 3\sqrt{3}}{4} = \sqrt{3}$ or $\dfrac{-\sqrt{3}}{2}$

Since $\sqrt{3}$ is greater than 1 it is not admissible as $\cos x$ can not be greater than 1.

$\therefore \quad \cos x = -\sqrt{3}/2 = -\cos(\pi/6)$

$\qquad = \cos(\pi - \pi/6) = \cos(5\pi/6)$

$\therefore \quad x = 2n\pi \pm (5\pi/6)$.

(b) As above the equation reduces to

$$4\cos^2\theta + 4\cos\theta - 3 = 0$$

or $\quad (2\cos\theta + 3)(2\cos\theta - 1) = 0$

But $\cos\theta = -3/2$ (rejected)

$\therefore \quad \cos\theta = \dfrac{1}{2} = \cos\dfrac{\pi}{3} \quad \therefore \quad \theta = 2n\pi \pm \pi/3$.

We have to choose values of θ s.t. $0 \le \theta \le 2\pi$.

$\therefore \quad \theta = \pi/3, \ 2\pi - \pi/3 = 5\pi/3$.

(c) As above $(\cos\theta + 2)(2\cos\theta - 1) = 0$.

Ans. $\theta = 2n\pi \pm \pi/3$ or $\pi/3, 5\pi/3$.

(d) Ans. (d).

$(\sin x + 3)(2\sin x - 1) = 0$

$\therefore \quad \sin x = \dfrac{1}{2}$ as $\sin x \ne -3$

$\therefore \quad x = \dfrac{\pi}{6}, \pi - \dfrac{\pi}{6} = \dfrac{5\pi}{6}$, i.e., two values in 0 to π.

No value in π to 2π as $\sin\theta$ will be $-$ive and two values again in 2π to 3π. Thus there will be only four values of x.

(e) Ans. (b).

$(2\sin\theta - 1)(\sin\theta - 2) > 0$

$\therefore \quad \sin\theta < \dfrac{1}{2} = \sin\dfrac{\pi}{6} = \sin\left(\pi - \dfrac{\pi}{6}\right) = \sin\dfrac{5\pi}{6}$

$\therefore \quad \theta \in \left(0, \dfrac{\pi}{6}\right)$ or $\theta \in \left(\dfrac{5\pi}{6}, 2\pi\right)$

$\therefore \quad \theta \in \left(0, \dfrac{\pi}{6}\right) \cup \left(\dfrac{5\pi}{6}, 2\pi\right)$

(f) Ans. (c).

From 1st, $\quad 2\sin^2\theta - (1 - 2\sin^2\theta) = 0$

$\therefore \quad 4\sin^2\theta = 1$ or $\sin\theta = \pm 1/2$

$\therefore \quad \theta = \pi/6, \ \pi + \pi/6$ in $[0, 2\pi]$

Also from 2nd equation, we have

$\qquad 2(1 - \sin^2\theta) - 3\sin\theta = 0$

or $\quad 2\sin^2\theta + 3\sin\theta - 2 = 0$

or $\quad (\sin\theta + 2)(2\sin\theta - 1) = 0$

$\therefore \quad \sin\theta = 1/2$ as -2 is rejected

$\therefore \quad \sin\theta = 1/2$ which in already included in 1st.

Hence there are only two solutions $\Rightarrow$ (c).

2. (a) $(2\cos\theta - 1)(2\cos\theta - \sqrt{3}) = 0$.

$\therefore \quad \cos\theta = 1/2 = \cos(\pi/3)$

$\qquad \cos\theta = \sqrt{3}/2 = \cos(\pi/6)$.

$\therefore \quad \theta = 2n\pi \pm \pi/3, \quad \theta = 2n\pi \pm \pi/6$.

(b) $5(2\cos^2\theta - 1) + (1 + \cos\theta) + 1 = 0$

or $\quad 10\cos^2\theta + \cos\theta - 3 = 0$

or $\quad (5\cos\theta + 3)(2\cos\theta - 1) = 0$.

$\therefore \quad \theta = \pi/3, -\pi/3, \pi - \cos^{-1}(3/5)$

$\because \quad -\pi < \theta < \pi$

(c) $\tan^2\theta = \dfrac{1 - \cos 2\theta}{1 + \cos 2\theta} = \dfrac{2}{4} = \dfrac{1}{2}$

$\therefore \quad \tan^8\theta = \dfrac{1}{16}$. Put for $\tan^8\theta$

$\therefore \quad 2\cos^2\alpha - 3\cos\alpha - 2 = 0$

$\therefore \quad \cos\alpha = -\dfrac{1}{2}, 2$ (rejected)

$\therefore \quad \cos\alpha = \cos\left(\pi - \dfrac{\pi}{3}\right) = \cos\dfrac{2\pi}{3}$

$\therefore \quad \alpha = 2n\pi \pm \dfrac{2\pi}{3}$.

3. (a) $4\cos\theta - \dfrac{3}{\cos\theta} = \dfrac{2\sin\theta}{\cos\theta}$

or $\quad 4(1 - \sin^2\theta) = 2\sin\theta + 3$

or $\quad 4\sin^2\theta + 2\sin\theta - 1 = 0$

$\therefore \quad \sin\theta = \dfrac{-2 \pm \sqrt{(4 + 16)}}{8}$

$= \dfrac{-2 \pm 2\sqrt{5}}{8} = \dfrac{\sqrt{5} - 1}{4}, -\left(\dfrac{\sqrt{5} + 1}{4}\right)$

or $\quad \sin\theta = \sin 18°$ i.e. $\sin(\pi/10)$,

$\therefore \quad \theta = n\pi + (-1)^n (\pi/10)$

or $\quad \sin\theta = -\cos 36° = -\sin 54°$

$\qquad = \sin(-3\pi/10)$

$\therefore \quad \theta = n\pi - (-1)^n (3\pi/10)$.

(b) $\sin x(4\cos^2 x - 2\sin x - 3) = 0$

or $-\sin x(4\sin^2 x + 2\sin x - 1) = 0$

Now see part (a).

(c) $1 - 2s^2 + 4\sqrt{2}\,s = 4$, where $s = \sin(5x + 2)$

or $2s^2 - 4\sqrt{2}\,s + 3 = 0$

or $(\sqrt{2}\,s - 3)(\sqrt{2}s - 1) = 0$

∴ $s = \dfrac{1}{\sqrt{2}}$ or $\sin(5x + 2) = \sin 45°$

∴ $5x + 2 = n\pi + (-1)^n \dfrac{\pi}{4}$ etc.

4. (a) $(\tan x + 1)(\tan x - \sqrt{3}) = 0$.

∴ $\tan x = -1 = -\tan(\pi/4) = \tan(-\pi/4)$.

∴ $x = n\pi - \pi/4$.

or $\tan x = \sqrt{3} = \tan(\pi/3)$, ∴ $x = n\pi + \pi/3$.

(b) Dividing by $\cos^2 \theta$, we get

$3 - 2\sqrt{3}\tan\theta - 3\tan^2\theta = 0$.

$\sqrt{3}\tan^2\theta + 2\tan\theta - \sqrt{3} = 0$

or $\sqrt{3}\tan^2\theta + 3\tan\theta - \tan\theta - \sqrt{3} = 0$,

$\sqrt{3}\tan\theta(\tan\theta + \sqrt{3}) - 1 \cdot (\tan\theta + \sqrt{3}) = 0$

or $(\tan\theta + \sqrt{3})(\sqrt{3}\tan\theta - 1) = 0$.

∴ $\tan\theta = -\sqrt{3} = -\tan(\pi/3) = \tan(-\pi/3)$.

∴ $\theta = n\pi - \pi/3$.

or $\tan\theta = 1/\sqrt{3} = \tan(\pi/6)$, ∴ $\theta = n\pi + \pi/6$.

Alt. The given equation is

$3(\cos^2\theta - \sin^2\theta) = \sqrt{3}(2\sin\theta\cos\theta)$

or $3\cos 2\theta = \sqrt{3}\sin 2\theta$

∴ $\tan 2\theta = \sqrt{3} = \tan(\pi/3)$

∴ $2\theta = n\pi + (\pi/3)$ or $\theta = n\pi/2 + \pi/6$.

5. (a) Replace $\sin 2\theta$ by $2\tan\theta/(1 + \tan^2\theta)$

$\dfrac{1 + \tan\theta}{1 - \tan\theta} = 1 + \dfrac{2\tan\theta}{1 + \tan^2\theta} = \dfrac{(1 + \tan\theta)^2}{1 + \tan^2\theta}$

or $(1 + \tan\theta)(2\tan^2\theta) = 0$

∴ $\tan\theta = 0, \tan\theta = -1 = \tan(-\pi/4)$

∴ $\theta = n\pi, n\pi - \pi/4$.

(b) Ans. $\theta = n\pi, n\pi \pm \pi/3$

$t^2 + \dfrac{1 + t^2}{1 - t^2} = 1$ where $t = \tan\theta$

∴ $t^2(t^2 - 3) = 0$ ∴ $\tan\theta = 0, \pm\sqrt{3}$

∴ $\theta = n\pi, n\pi \pm \pi/3$.

(c) $1 + 2 \cdot \dfrac{1 + t^2}{2t} = -\dfrac{1}{2}(1 + t^2)$ where $t = \tan\dfrac{x}{2}$

$t^3 + 2t^2 + 3t + 2 = 0$ or $(t + 1)(t^2 + t + 2) = 0$

∴ $t = -1$ only as other factor gives imaginary values.

∴ $\dfrac{x}{2} = n\pi + \left(-\dfrac{\pi}{4}\right)$ ∴ $x = 2n\pi - \dfrac{\pi}{2}$

6. (a) $\cos x(\cos x - 2) + 2\sin x(\cos x - 2) = 0$

$(\cos x + 2\sin x)(\cos x - 2) = 0$ but $\cos x \neq 2$

∴ $\tan x = -\dfrac{1}{2} = \tan\alpha$ ∴ $x = n\pi + \alpha$

$x = n\pi + \tan^{-1}\left(-\dfrac{1}{2}\right)$

∴ In the given interval $0 \leq x \leq \pi$

$\pi + \tan^{-1}\left(-\dfrac{1}{2}\right) = \pi - \tan^{-1}\left(\dfrac{1}{2}\right)$

(b) $3(\cos\theta - \sin\theta) = 2\cos\theta(\cos\theta - \sin\theta)$

∴ $\cos\theta - \sin\theta = 0$

or $\tan\theta = 1$ ∴ $\theta = n\pi + \dfrac{\pi}{4}$

$\cos\theta \neq 3/2$.

7. (a) The given equation can be put in the form

$4\sin^4 x = 1 - \cos^4 x = (1 - \cos^2 x)(1 + \cos^2 x)$

or $\sin^2 x[4\sin^2 x - 1 - (1 - \sin^2 x)] = 0$

or $\sin^2 x(5\sin^2 x - 2) = 0$

∴ $\sin x = 0$ or $\sin x = \pm\sqrt{2/5}$

or $x = n\pi$ or $x = n\pi \pm \alpha$,

where $\sin\alpha = \sqrt{2/5}$.

(b) The given equation is : $\sin^2\theta = 1/4$

or $\sin\theta = \pm 1/2$ ∴ $\theta = n\pi \pm \pi/6$.

(c) We write the given equation as

$5(1 - \sin^2\theta) + 7\sin^2\theta = 6$

or $2\sin^2\theta = 1$ or $\sin\theta = \pm\dfrac{1}{\sqrt{(2)}}$.

∴ $\theta = n\pi \pm (\pi/4)$.

8. (a) Ans. $n\pi \pm \dfrac{\pi}{6}$. Put $\sec^2 x = 1 + \tan^2 x$

and we get $\dfrac{15}{4}t^2 = \dfrac{5}{4}$

$\tan x = \pm\dfrac{1}{\sqrt{3}} = \pm\tan\dfrac{\pi}{6}$ etc.

(b) Ans. $\left(n + \dfrac{1}{2}\right)\pi$, $y = m\pi$, $z = r\pi$

Here L.H.S. ≤ 2 and R.H.S. ≥ 2.

The equation will hold when we have only sign of equality and in that case

$\sin^2 x = 1$, $\cos^2 y = \sec^2 z = 1$

or $\cos^2 x = 0$, $\sin^2 y = 0$, $\cos^2 z = 1$

or $\sin^2 z = 0$

∴ $x = \left(n + \dfrac{1}{2}\right)\pi$, $y = m\pi$, $z = r\pi$

(c) $6s^2 + 2 \cdot 4s^2 c^2 = 5$

or $6s^2 + 8s^2(1 - s^2) = 5$

or $8s^4 - 14s^2 + 5 = 0$

∴ $(4s^2 - 5)(2s^2 - 1) = 0$

∴ $s^2 = \dfrac{1}{2}$ or $\dfrac{5}{4}$ ∴ $\sin\theta = \pm\dfrac{1}{\sqrt{2}}$

$\therefore \quad \theta = n\pi \pm \dfrac{\pi}{4}.$ 2nd value rejected.

9. (a) $2^{2c^2-1} = 3.2^{c^2} - 4.$ Put $2^{c^2} = y$

or $y^2 = 2(3y - 4)$

or $y^2 - 6y + 8 = 0$ $\therefore$ $(y-4)(y-2) = 0$

$\therefore \quad y = 2c^2 = 2^2$ or 2^1

$\therefore \quad \cos^2 x = 2$ or $\cos^2 x = 1$

$\therefore \quad \sin^2 x = 0$ or $x = n\pi.$

(b) Ans. $n\pi + (\pi/2)$

(c) $1 - 2\sin^2 x \cos^2 x = 5/8$

or $2 - \sin^2 2x = 5/4$

$\therefore \quad \sin^2 2x = 3/4$

$\therefore \quad \sin 2x = \pm \sqrt{3}/2 = \pm \sin(\pi/2)$

$\therefore \quad 2x = n\pi \pm \dfrac{\pi}{3}$ or $x = \dfrac{n\pi}{2} \pm \dfrac{\pi}{6}.$

(d) The given equation can be rewritten as
$(1)^3 - 3\sin^2 2x \cos^2 2x (1) = 7/16$

or $3\sin^2 2x \cos^2 2x = 9/16$

or $4\sin^2 2x \cos^2 2x = 3/4$

or $\sin^2 4x = 3/4$

$\therefore \quad \sin 4x = \pm \dfrac{\sqrt{3}}{2} = \pm \sin \dfrac{\pi}{3}$

$\therefore \quad x = \dfrac{n\pi}{4} \pm \dfrac{\pi}{12}.$

10. (a) Ans. All correct.   Put $\cos^2 x = 1 - \sin^2 x$

If $y = 81^{\sin^2 x}$ then $y + \dfrac{81}{y} = 30$

$y^2 - 30y + 81 = 0, y = 27, 3$

$3^{4\sin^2 x} = 3^3, 3^1$ $\therefore$ $\sin^2 x = \dfrac{3}{4}, \dfrac{1}{4}$

$\therefore \quad \sin x = \dfrac{\sqrt{3}}{2}, \dfrac{1}{2}$

as $\sin x$ is + ive in the given interval $0 < x < \pi$

$\therefore \quad x = \dfrac{\pi}{3}, \pi - \dfrac{\pi}{3} = \dfrac{2\pi}{3}, \dfrac{\pi}{6}, \pi - \dfrac{\pi}{6} = \dfrac{5\pi}{6}$

(b) $y + \dfrac{1}{y} = 2$ $\Rightarrow$ $(y-1) = 0$ $\Rightarrow$ $y = 1$

$\therefore \quad \log_{\cos x} \sin x = 1$ or $\sin x = \cos x$

or $\tan x = 1$ $\therefore$ $x = \pi/4$

(c) Ans. (b).

$\sin \alpha = \lambda$

$\theta = n\pi + (-1)^n \alpha$

For + ive values, $n = 0, 1, 2, 3$

$\therefore \quad \alpha = \alpha, \beta = \pi - \alpha, \gamma = 2\pi + \alpha, \delta = 3\pi - \alpha$

$\therefore \quad E = 4\sin \dfrac{\alpha}{2} + 3\sin\left(\dfrac{\pi}{2} - \dfrac{\alpha}{2}\right)$

$+ 2\sin\left(\pi + \dfrac{\alpha}{2}\right) + \sin\left(\dfrac{3\pi}{2} - \dfrac{\alpha}{2}\right)$

$= 4\sin \dfrac{\alpha}{2} + 3\cos \dfrac{\alpha}{2} - 2\sin \dfrac{\alpha}{2} - \cos \dfrac{\alpha}{2}$

$= 2\left(\cos \dfrac{\alpha}{2} + \sin \dfrac{\alpha}{2}\right) = 2\sqrt{\left(\cos \dfrac{\alpha}{2} + \sin \dfrac{\alpha}{2}\right)^2}$

$= 2\sqrt{1 + \sin \alpha} = 2\sqrt{1 + \lambda}$

11. (a) Let us put $\tan^2 \theta = t$

$\therefore \quad (1 - t)(1 + t) + 2^t = 0$

or $1 - t^2 + 2^t = 0.$

It is clearly satisfied by $t = 3.$

as $-8 + 8 = 0$ $\therefore$ $\tan^2 \theta = 3$ or $\tan \theta = \pm\sqrt{3}$

$\therefore \quad \theta = \pm \pi/3$ in the given interval.

(b) $\dfrac{6(1-c)}{(1+c)} - (1+c) = c$, where $c = \cos 2x$

$\therefore \quad c = \dfrac{1}{2}, -5 \text{ (rej.)}$ $\therefore$ $2x = 2n\pi \pm \dfrac{\pi}{3}$ etc.

12. (a) $1 + \sin 2x = 1 - \sin 6x$

$\therefore \quad \sin 6x + \sin 2x = 0$

$\therefore \quad 2\sin 4x \cos 2x = 0$ $\therefore$ $\sin 4x = 0$

$\therefore \quad x = n\pi/4$

or $\cos 2x = 0$ $\therefore$ $2x = \left(n + \dfrac{1}{2}\right)\pi$

or $x = \left(n + \dfrac{1}{2}\right)\dfrac{\pi}{2}$

(b) Change in terms of $2x$.

$2\cos^2 2x - 1 = \dfrac{1}{2}(1 + \cos 6x)$

$\therefore \quad 4c^2 - 2 = 1 + 4c^3 - 3c$, where $c = \cos 2x$

or $4c^3 - 4c^2 - 3c + 3 = 0$

or $(c - 1)(4c^2 - 3) = 0$

$\therefore \quad \cos 2x = 1, \cos 2x = \pm \dfrac{\sqrt{3}}{2} = \pm \cos \dfrac{\pi}{6}$

$\therefore \quad 2x = 2n\pi$ or $2n\pi \pm (\pi/6)$

or $x = n\pi$ or $n\pi \pm (\pi/12)$

13. (a) Since both $\sin \theta$ and $\cos \theta$ are less than unity, both terms are + ive the above result is possible only if either

$\sin \theta = 1$ *i.e.*, $\cos \theta = 0$

or $\cos \theta = 1, \sin \theta = 0$

$\cos \theta = 0, \theta = \left(n + \dfrac{1}{2}\right)\pi = (2n+1)\dfrac{\pi}{2} = \text{odd } \dfrac{\pi}{2}$

...(1)

$\sin \theta = 0, \theta = n\pi = 2n.\dfrac{\pi}{2} = \text{even } \dfrac{\pi}{2}$ ...(2)

$\therefore \quad \theta = \dfrac{r\pi}{2}$, where $r \in I$, by (1) and (2).

(b) $(\cos \theta + \sin \theta)\left[\dfrac{1}{\sin \theta} - 2\right] = 0$

$\therefore \quad \sin \theta = \dfrac{1}{2}, \tan \theta = -1 = \tan\left(-\dfrac{\pi}{4}\right)$

$$\therefore \quad \theta = \frac{\pi}{6}, \pi - \frac{\pi}{6}, \pi + \left(-\frac{\pi}{4}\right), 2\pi + \left(-\frac{\pi}{4}\right)$$

$$\therefore \quad \theta = \frac{\pi}{6}, \frac{5\pi}{6}, \frac{3\pi}{4}, \frac{7\pi}{4} \text{ in the given range.}$$

14. (a) $\tan^2 \theta + (1/\tan^2 \theta) - 2 = 0$

or $\tan^4 \theta - 2\tan^2 \theta + 1 = 0$

$\therefore \quad (\tan^2 \theta - 1)^2 = 0 \quad \therefore \tan^2 \theta = 1$

or $\tan \theta = \pm 1 = \pm \tan (\pi/4)$

$\therefore \quad \theta = n\pi \pm \pi/4$.

(b) $\dfrac{\cos \theta}{\sin \theta} - \dfrac{\sin \theta}{\cos \theta} = 2$

or $\cos^2 \theta - \sin^2 \theta = 2 \sin \theta \cos \theta$

or $\cos 2\theta = \sin 2\theta \quad \therefore \tan 2\theta = 1 = \tan (\pi/4)$

$\therefore \quad 2\theta = n\pi + \dfrac{\pi}{4} \quad$ or $\quad \theta = \dfrac{n\pi}{2} + \dfrac{\pi}{8}$.

(c) The given equation can be written as

$$\dfrac{\sin \theta}{\cos \theta} + \dfrac{\cos \theta}{\sin \theta} = 2$$

or $(\sin^2 \theta + \cos^2 \theta)/(\sin \theta \cos \theta) = 2$

or $2 \sin \theta \cos \theta = 1$ or $\sin 2\theta = 1$

$\therefore \quad 2\theta = 2n\pi + \pi/2$ or $\theta = n\pi + (\pi/4), n \in \mathbf{I}$.

15. (a) $AB = AD + BD$.

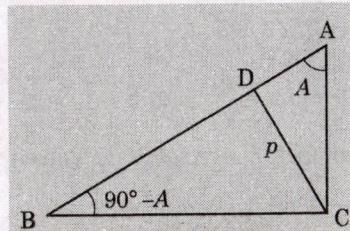

Fig. T-10

$2\sqrt{2}\, p = p \cot A + p \cot (90° - A)$

or $2\sqrt{2} = \cot A + \tan A$

or $2\sqrt{2} = \dfrac{1}{\sin A \cos A}$

or $\sin 2A = \dfrac{1}{\sqrt{2}} = \sin \dfrac{\pi}{4}$

$\therefore \quad A = \dfrac{\pi}{8}, B = \dfrac{\pi}{2} - A = \dfrac{\pi}{2} - \dfrac{\pi}{8} = \dfrac{3\pi}{8}$

(b) Here $\sin 2A = \dfrac{1}{2}$

$\therefore \quad A = 15°, B = 75°$

16. (a) $\tan \theta + \tan 2\theta = \sqrt{3} (1 - \tan \theta \tan 2\theta)$

or $\dfrac{\tan \theta + \tan 2\theta}{1 - \tan \theta \tan 2\theta} = \sqrt{3}$

or $\tan (\theta + 2\theta) = \tan (\pi/3)$

or $3\theta = n\pi + \pi/3$ or $\theta = n\pi/3 + \pi/9$.

(b) $\tan (A + B + C) = \dfrac{S_1 - S_3}{1 - S_2} = 0$

$\because \quad S_1 = S_3$ given

$\therefore \quad \tan (\theta + 4\theta + 7\theta) = 0$ or $\tan 12\theta = 0$

$\therefore \quad 12\theta = n\pi$ or $\theta = \dfrac{n\pi}{12}$.

Alternative solution :

We write the given equation as

$\tan \theta + \tan 4\theta = -\tan 7\theta (1 - \tan \theta \tan 4\theta)$

or $(\tan \theta + \tan 4\theta)/(1 - \tan \theta \tan 4\theta) = -\tan 7\theta$

or $\tan (\theta + 4\theta) = -\tan 7\theta$

or $\tan 5\theta = \tan (-7\theta)$

$\therefore \quad 5\theta = n\pi + (-7\theta)$ or $12\theta = n\pi$

$\therefore \quad \theta = n\pi/12, \quad n \in \mathbf{I}$.

17. (a) We write the given equation as :

$$3 \tan 2x - 3 \tan 3x = \tan 3x + \tan^2 3x \tan 2x$$

or $\dfrac{3 (\tan 2x - \tan 3x)}{1 + \tan 2x \tan 3x} = \tan 3x$

or $3 \tan (2x - 3x) = \tan 3x$

or $3 \tan x + \tan 3x = 0$

If we put $\tan x = t$, then from above we get

$$3t + \dfrac{3t - t^3}{1 - 3t^2} = 0 \text{ or } 6t - 10t^3 = 0$$

$\therefore \quad t = 0 \quad$ or $\quad t = \pm \sqrt{(3/5)}$

where $t = \tan x \quad \therefore x = n\pi \quad$ or $\quad n\pi \pm \alpha$

where $\alpha = \tan^{-1} \sqrt{(3/5)}$.

(b) $\sin^2 x (1 + \tan x) = 3 \sin x \cos x + 3 \cos^2 x$

Divide throughout by $\cos^2 x \ (\cos x \neq 0)$ and put $\tan x = t$.

$$t^2 (1 + t) = 3 (t + 1)$$

or $t + 1 = 0 \quad$ or $\quad t^2 = 3$

$\therefore \quad \tan x = -1 \quad$ or $\quad \pm \sqrt{3}$

$\therefore \quad x = n\pi - \dfrac{\pi}{4} \quad$ or $\quad n\pi \pm \dfrac{\pi}{3}$.

18. (a) $\dfrac{\cos \theta}{\sin \theta} + \dfrac{\sin \theta}{\cos \theta} = \dfrac{2}{\sin \theta}$

or $\dfrac{\cos^2 \theta + \sin^2 \theta}{\sin \theta \cos \theta} = \dfrac{2}{\sin \theta}$

or $\dfrac{1}{\sin \theta \cos \theta} = \dfrac{2}{\sin \theta}$

$\therefore \quad \cos \theta = \dfrac{1}{2} \quad (\sin \theta \neq 0)$ **(Note)**

$\therefore \quad \theta = 2n\pi \pm \pi/3$.

(b) $\dfrac{\cos \theta}{\sin \theta} - \dfrac{\sin \theta}{\cos \theta} = \dfrac{1}{\cos \theta}$

or $\dfrac{\cos 2\theta}{\sin \theta \cos \theta} = \dfrac{1}{\cos \theta}$

$\therefore \quad 1 - 2\sin^2 \theta = \sin \theta \quad (\cos \theta \neq 0)$

or $2 \sin^2 \theta + \sin \theta - 1 = 0$

or $(2 \sin \theta - 1)(\sin \theta + 1) = 0$

$\therefore \quad \sin \theta = \dfrac{1}{2} \quad \therefore \theta = n\pi + (-1)^n \dfrac{\pi}{6}$.

But $\sin \theta = -1$ implies $\cos \theta = 0$ but $\cos \theta \neq 0$.

Hence no value will be adimissible when $\sin\theta = -1$.

19. (a) $2\sin 2x - \sin x = 0$

$4\sin x\cos x - \sin x = 0$

$\therefore \quad \sin x(4\cos x - 1) = 0$

$\therefore \quad \sin x = 0 \quad \therefore \quad x = n\pi, \cos x = \dfrac{1}{4} = \cos\alpha,$ say.

$\therefore \quad x = 2n\pi \pm \alpha$ where $\alpha = \cos^{-1}(1/4)$.

(b) $\sin^2 2x = 2(1 - \sin^2 x)$

$(2\sin x\cos x)^2 = 2\cos^2 x$

or $\quad 2\sin^2 x\cos^2 x - \cos^2 x = 0$

$\therefore \quad \cos^2 x(2\sin^2 x - 1) = 0$

or $\quad \cos x = 0 \quad$ or $\quad \sin x = \pm 1/\sqrt{2}$

$\therefore \quad x = \left(n + \dfrac{1}{2}\right)\dfrac{\pi}{2}, n\pi \pm \dfrac{\pi}{4}$

20. (a) $3\sin\alpha - 4\sin^3\alpha = 4\sin\alpha(\sin^2 x - \sin^2\alpha)$

$\therefore \quad \sin^2 x = 3/4$

or $\quad \sin x = \pm\dfrac{\sqrt{3}}{2} = \pm\sin\dfrac{\pi}{3}$.

$\therefore \quad x = n\pi \pm \pi/3$.

(b) $\dfrac{\cos(x/2)}{\sin(x/2)} - \dfrac{\cos x}{2\sin(x/2)\cos(x/2)} = \dfrac{1}{\sin(x/2)}$

or $\quad 2\cos^2(x/2) - \cos x = 2\cos(x/2)$

or $\quad 1 + \cos x - \cos x = 2\cos(x/2)$

$\therefore \quad \cos(x/2) = 1/2 = \cos(\pi/3)$.

$\therefore \quad x/2 = 2n\pi \pm \pi/3 \quad$ or $\quad x = 4n\pi \pm 2\pi/3$.

21. (a) $3 \cdot \dfrac{\sin^2\theta}{\cos^2\theta} - 2\sin\theta = 0, \cos\theta \neq 0$.

Multiplying throughout by $\cos^2\theta$ and then changing it into $\sin^2\theta$, we get

$3\sin^2\theta - 2\sin\theta(1 - \sin^2\theta) = 0$

$\sin\theta(3\sin\theta - 2 + 2\sin^2\theta) = 0$

$\sin\theta(2\sin^2\theta + 4\sin\theta - \sin\theta - 2) = 0$

$\sin\theta(\sin\theta + 2)(2\sin\theta - 1) = 0$

$\therefore \quad \sin\theta = 0, \quad \therefore \quad \theta = n\pi$.

$\sin\theta = 1/2 = \sin(\pi/6)$,

$\therefore \quad \theta = n\pi + (-1)^n \pi/6$

$\sin\theta = -2$ (rejected as $\sin\theta$ cannot be greater than one numerically).

(b) We write the given equation as

$4\sin\theta\cos\theta(\sin^2\theta - \cos^2\theta) = 1$

or $\quad 2\sin 2\theta(-\cos 2\theta) = 1 \quad$ or $\quad -\sin 4\theta = 1$

or $\quad \sin 4\theta = -1$.

$\therefore \quad 4\theta = 2n\pi + (3\pi/2)$

or $\quad \theta = (n\pi/2) + (3\pi/8), \quad n \in \mathbf{I}$.

(c) **Refer Q. 65 P. 536-552**, we get

$4\cos^3 2x = 0 \quad \therefore \quad \cos 2x = 0$

or $\quad 2x = \left(n + \dfrac{1}{2}\right)\pi \quad$ or $\quad x = \left(n + \dfrac{1}{2}\right)\dfrac{\pi}{2}$

22. (a) $\sec\theta - 1 = (\sqrt{2} - 1)\tan\theta$

$\dfrac{1 - \cos\theta}{\cos\theta} = \dfrac{(\sqrt{2} - 1)\sin\theta}{\cos\theta}$

$\therefore \quad 2\sin^2(\theta/2) = (\sqrt{2} - 1) \cdot 2\sin(\theta/2)\cos(\theta/2)$

$\therefore \quad \sin(\theta/2) = 0 \quad \therefore \quad \theta/2 = n\pi \quad$ or $\quad \theta = 2n\pi$

or $\quad \tan(\theta/2) = (\sqrt{2} - 1) = \tan(\pi/8)$

$\dfrac{\theta}{2} = n\pi + \dfrac{\pi}{8} \quad$ or $\quad \theta = 2n\pi + \dfrac{\pi}{4}$

(b) $\sqrt{2}\sec\theta = 1 - \tan\theta$.

$\therefore \quad \sqrt{2} = \cos\theta - \sin\theta$

or $\quad 1 = \dfrac{1}{\sqrt{(2)}}\cos\theta - \dfrac{1}{\sqrt{(2)}}\sin\theta$

or $\quad \cos(\theta + \pi/4) = 1 = \cos 0°$

$\therefore \quad \theta + \pi/4 = 2n\pi \quad$ or $\quad \theta = 2n\pi - \pi/4$

(c) If $\cos\theta = c$, then

$2c^2 - 1 = \dfrac{\sqrt{2} + 1}{\sqrt{2}}(\sqrt{2}c - 1)$

or $\quad (\sqrt{2}c - 1)\left[(\sqrt{2}c + 1) - \left(1 + \dfrac{1}{\sqrt{2}}\right)\right] = 0$

or $\quad (\sqrt{2}c - 1)\sqrt{2}\left(c - \dfrac{1}{2}\right) = 0 \quad \therefore \quad c = \dfrac{1}{\sqrt{2}}, \dfrac{1}{2}$

$\therefore \quad \theta = 2n\pi \pm \dfrac{\pi}{4} \quad$ or $\quad 2n\pi \pm \dfrac{\pi}{3}$.

23. (a) Eliminating r between the given equations, we get

$\dfrac{\sqrt{3}}{\sin\theta} + 4\sin\theta = 2(\sqrt{3} + 1)$

or $\quad 4\sin^2\theta - 2\sqrt{3}\sin\theta - 2\sin\theta + \sqrt{3} = 0$

$2\sin\theta(2\sin\theta - \sqrt{3}) - 1 \cdot (2\sin\theta - \sqrt{3}) = 0$

$\therefore \quad (2\sin\theta - 1)(2\sin\theta - \sqrt{3}) = 0$

$\sin\theta = \dfrac{1}{2} = \sin\dfrac{\pi}{6} \quad$ or $\quad \sin\left(\pi - \dfrac{\pi}{6}\right)$

$\sin\theta = \dfrac{\sqrt{3}}{2} = \sin\dfrac{\pi}{3} \quad$ or $\quad \sin\left(\pi - \dfrac{\pi}{3}\right)$

$\therefore \quad \theta = \pi/6, \pi/3, 5\pi/6, 2\pi/3, 0 \leq \theta \leq 2\pi$

(b) Eliminating r, we get

$4\sin^2\theta + 4\sin\theta - 3 = 0$

or $\quad (2\sin\theta + 3)(2\sin\theta - 1) = 0$

$\therefore \quad \sin\theta = \dfrac{1}{2} = \sin\dfrac{\pi}{6}$.

$\theta = \pi/6, \pi - \pi/6 \quad$ for $\quad 0 \leq \theta \leq 2\pi$.

The other value is rejected as $\sin\theta$ cannot be greater than 1.

24. (a) $\sin 9\theta = \sin\theta$.

$\therefore \quad 9\theta = n\pi + (-1)^n \theta$. $\qquad \ldots(1)$

If n be even say $2r$ then $9\theta = 2r\pi + \theta \quad \therefore \quad \theta = r\pi/4$.

If n be odd say $2r + 1$ then $9\theta = (2r + 1)\pi - \theta$

or $\quad \theta = (2r + 1)\pi/10$.

(b) $\cos 5x = -\cos x = \cos(\pi - x)$ etc.

(c) $\sin m\theta = -\sin n\theta = \sin(-n\theta)$

$\therefore \quad m\theta = r\pi + (-1)^r (-n\theta) = r\pi - (-1)^r n\theta.$

If $r =$ even $= 2k$ say, then $m\theta = 2k\pi - n\theta.$

$\therefore \quad (m+n)\theta = 2k\pi \text{ or } \theta = \dfrac{2k\pi}{m+n}$

$r =$ odd $= (2k+1)$, say

then $m\theta = (2k+1)\pi + n\theta$

$\therefore \quad (m-n)\theta = (2k+1)\pi \text{ or } \theta = \dfrac{(2k+1)\pi}{m-n}$

25. (a) $\cos 2x = \sin 5x$

or $\cos 2x = \cos(\pi/2 - 5x).$

$\therefore \quad 2x = 2n\pi \pm (\pi/2 - 5x).$

$\therefore \quad 7x = (2n\pi + \pi/2) \text{ or } -3x = 2n\pi - \pi/2$

or $x = (4n+1)\pi/14 \text{ or } x = -(4n-1)\pi/6,$

$$n \in \mathbf{I}.$$

We have to find values of x lying between 0 and 180°.

Putting $n = 0, 1, 2, 3$ in the first, we get

$x = \dfrac{\pi}{14}, \dfrac{5\pi}{14}, \dfrac{9\pi}{14}, \dfrac{13\pi}{14}$ and other values will be greater than 180°.

Putting $n = 0, -1$ in the second, we get

$x = \dfrac{\pi}{6}, \dfrac{5\pi}{6}$ and values corresponding to other values of n will not lie between 0 and π.

(b) $\sin 2\theta = \cos 3\theta, 0 \le \theta < 2\pi$

or $\cos 3\theta = \cos(\pi/2 - 2\theta)$

$\therefore \quad 3\theta = 2n\pi \pm (\pi/2 - 2\theta)$

$\therefore \quad 3\theta = (4n+1)\pi/2 - 2\theta,$

and $3\theta = (4n-1)\pi/2 + 2\theta$

$\therefore \quad \theta = (4n+1)\pi/10 \text{ or } \theta = (4n-1)\pi/2.$

$(4n+1)\dfrac{\pi}{10} = (4n+1)\dfrac{2\pi}{20}.$

Now give n such values so that $4n+1$ is < 20.

Hence putting $n = 0, 1, 2, 3, 4$, we get

$$\theta = \dfrac{\pi}{10}, \dfrac{5\pi}{10}, \dfrac{9\pi}{10}, \dfrac{13\pi}{10}, \dfrac{17\pi}{10}.$$

or $\theta = 18°, 90°, 162°, 234°, 306°.$

The values of θ corresponding to other values of n will not lie between 0° and 360°.

From the second putting $n = 1$, we get $\theta = \dfrac{3\pi}{2}$ i.e.

270°.

2nd Part : Let $\theta = 18°$, then $2\theta = 90° - 3\theta = 36°$

$\therefore \quad \sin 2\theta = \sin(90° - 3\theta) = \cos 3\theta.$

or $2\sin\theta\cos\theta = 4\cos^3\theta - 3\cos\theta.$

$\cos\theta[2\sin\theta - 4(1 - \sin^2\theta) + 3] = 0$

$\therefore \quad \cos\theta = 0$ which gives $\theta = 90°$. But $\theta = 18°$ and hence $\cos\theta = 0$ is rejected .

or $4\sin^2\theta + 2\sin\theta - 1 = 0$

$\therefore \quad \sin\theta = \dfrac{-2 \pm \sqrt{4+16}}{8} = \dfrac{-1 \pm \sqrt{5}}{4} = \dfrac{\sqrt{5}-1}{4}$

The other value of $\sin\theta$ being $-$ive is rejected as $\sin 18°$ is $+$ive

$\therefore \quad \sin 18° = \dfrac{\sqrt{5}-1}{4}.$

(c) $\sin 3x = \cos x = \sin(\pi/2 - x)$

$\therefore \quad 3x = n\pi + (-1)^n (\pi/2 - x)$

n even $= 2r$

$\therefore \quad 3x = 2r\pi + \pi/2 - x \quad \therefore \quad x = (4r+1)\pi/8$

n odd $= 2r+1$

$\therefore \quad 3x = (2r+1)\pi - \pi/2 + x$

or $x = (4r+1)\pi/4.$

Also $-\pi/2 \le x \le \pi/2.$

$\therefore \quad x = \pi/8, \pi/4, -3\pi/8$

$\therefore$ The points of intersection are

$\left(\dfrac{\pi}{8}, \cos\dfrac{\pi}{8}\right), \left(\dfrac{\pi}{4}, \cos\dfrac{\pi}{4}\right)$

and $\left[-\dfrac{3\pi}{8}, \cos\left(-\dfrac{3\pi}{8}\right)\right]$

i.e. $\left(\dfrac{\pi}{8}, \dfrac{\sqrt{2+\sqrt{2}}}{2}\right), \left(\dfrac{\pi}{4}, \dfrac{1}{\sqrt{2}}\right)$

and $\left(-\dfrac{3\pi}{8}, \dfrac{\sqrt{2-\sqrt{2}}}{2}\right)$ **See 33 (v, vi) P. 511.**

since $\cos(\pi/8) = \sqrt{2+\sqrt{2}}/2$ and

$\cos\left(-\dfrac{3\pi}{8}\right) = \cos\dfrac{3\pi}{8} = \cos\left(\dfrac{\pi}{2} - \dfrac{\pi}{8}\right)$

$= \sin\dfrac{\pi}{8} = \dfrac{\sqrt{2-\sqrt{2}}}{2}.$

Note that $2\cos^2\dfrac{\pi}{8} = 1 + \cos\dfrac{\pi}{4} = 1 + \dfrac{1}{\sqrt{2}}$

$= \dfrac{\sqrt{2}+1}{\sqrt{2}} = \dfrac{2+\sqrt{2}}{2}.$

$\therefore \quad \cos\dfrac{\pi}{8} = \dfrac{\sqrt{2+\sqrt{2}}}{2}$

$\sin^2\dfrac{\pi}{8} = 1 - \cos^2\dfrac{\pi}{8} = 1 - \dfrac{2+\sqrt{2}}{4} = \dfrac{(2-\sqrt{2})}{4}$

$\therefore \quad \sin\dfrac{\pi}{8} = \dfrac{\sqrt{2-\sqrt{2}}}{2}.$

26. (a) $\dfrac{\sin p\theta}{\cos p\theta} = \dfrac{\cos q\theta}{\sin q\theta}$

or $\cos p\theta \cos q\theta - \sin p\theta \sin q\theta = 0$

or $\cos(p+q)\theta = 0$

$\therefore \quad (p+q)\theta = \left(n + \dfrac{1}{2}\right)\pi$

$\therefore \quad \theta = \dfrac{(2n+1)}{(p+q)}\left(\dfrac{\pi}{2}\right), n \in \mathbf{I}.$

(b) **Just as in part (e)**, $\cos(m-n)x = 0$

$\therefore \quad (m-n)x = \left(r + \dfrac{1}{2}\right)\pi$

or $\quad x = \dfrac{(2r+1)}{m-n}\cdot\dfrac{\pi}{2}, \quad r \in \mathbf{I}.$

27. (a) $\tan 3\theta = \cot\theta = \tan(\pi/2 - \theta)$

$\therefore \quad 3\theta = n\pi + (\pi/2 - \theta)$

or $\quad 4\theta = (2n+1)\pi/2, \therefore \theta = (2n+1)\pi/8.$

(b) $\dfrac{2\tan\theta}{1-\tan^2\theta}\cdot\tan\theta = 1, \quad \therefore \ 3\tan^2\theta = 1$

or $\quad \tan\theta = \pm 1/\sqrt{3} = \pm\tan(\pi/6)$

$\therefore \quad \theta = n\pi \pm \pi/6.$

28. (a) Combining $\cos\theta$ and $\cos 3\theta$.

$(\cos\theta + \cos 3\theta) + \cos 2\theta = 0$

$2\cos 2\theta\cos\theta + \cos 2\theta = 0$

or $\quad \cos 2\theta(2\cos\theta + 1) = 0.$

$\therefore \quad \cos 2\theta = 0 = \cos(\pi/2),$

$\therefore \quad 2\theta = \left(n + \dfrac{1}{2}\right)\pi,$

or $\quad \theta = (2n+1)\pi/4$

$2\cos\theta + 1 = 0$

$\therefore \quad \cos\theta = -1/2 = -\cos(\pi/3)$

$= \cos(\pi - \pi/3) = \cos(2\pi/3).$

$\therefore \quad \theta = 2n\pi \pm 2\pi/3.$

(b) $(\cos 6\theta + \cos 4\theta) + (1 + \cos 2\theta) = 0, 0 \le \theta \le \pi.$

$2\cos 5\theta\cos\theta + 2\cos^2\theta = 0.$

or $\quad 2\cos\theta(\cos 5\theta + \cos\theta) = 0$

or $\quad 4\cos\theta\cos 2\theta\cos 3\theta = 0.$

$\cos\theta = 0 \quad \therefore \ \theta = \left(n + \dfrac{1}{2}\right)\pi$

$n = 0, \qquad\qquad \theta = \pi/2$

$\cos 2\theta = 0 \quad \therefore \ 2\theta = \left(n + \dfrac{1}{2}\right)\pi$

$\therefore \quad \theta = (2n+1)\pi/4$

$n = 0, \theta = \pi/4, n = 1, \theta = 3\pi/4,$

$\cos 3\theta = 0 \quad \therefore \ 3\theta = n\pi + \pi/2$

$\therefore \quad \theta = (2n+1)\pi/6$

$n = 0, \theta = \pi/6, n = 1, \theta = \pi/2,$

$n = 2, \theta = 5\pi/6.$

$\therefore \quad \theta = 30°, 45°, 90°, 135°, 150°.$

(c) On simplification, $\sin 3\theta(2\cos 2\theta + 1) = 0$

$\therefore \quad \theta = n\pi/3, \theta = n\pi \pm \pi/3 \quad$ for given range

$\theta = 0, \pi/3 \quad \therefore \quad \theta = 0, \pi/3$

29. (a) On simplification, we have

$\sin 3\theta(2\cos 2\theta - 1) = 0$

$\theta = 0, \pi/6, \pi/3, 2\pi/3, 5\pi/6$ and $\pi.$

(b) The given equation can be written as

$4\sin x\sin(3x - x)\sin(3x + x) = 3\sin x - 4\sin^3 x$

or $\quad 4\sin x[\sin^2 3x - \sin^2 x] = 3\sin x - 4\sin^3 x$

or $\quad 4\sin x\sin^2 3x - 4\sin^3 x = 3\sin x - 4\sin^3 x$

or $\quad \sin x[4\sin^2 3x - 3] = 0.$

$\therefore \quad \sin x = 0° \quad \therefore \ x = n\pi$

and $4\sin^2 3x = 3$

or $\quad \sin 3x = \pm\sqrt{3}/2 = \pm\sin(\pi/3)$

$\therefore \quad 3x = n\pi \pm \pi/3 \ $ or $\ x = n\pi/3 \pm \pi/9.$

R. (iv), P. 579.

30. (a) Combining $\cos\theta$ and $\cos 3\theta$, we get

$\dfrac{1}{2}(2\cos\theta\cos 3\theta)\cos 2\theta = \dfrac{1}{4}$

or $\quad (\cos 2\theta + \cos 4\theta)\cos 2\theta = \dfrac{1}{2}$

or $\quad \dfrac{1}{2}[2\cos^2 2\theta + 2\cos 4\theta\cos 2\theta] = \dfrac{1}{2}$

or $\quad 1 + \cos 4\theta + 2\cos 4\theta\cos 2\theta = 1$

$\therefore \quad \cos 4\theta(1 + 2\cos 2\theta) = 0.$

$\cos 4\theta = 0 = \cos(\pi/2)$

$\therefore \quad 4\theta = \left(n + \dfrac{1}{2}\right)\pi \ \therefore \ \theta = (2n+1)\dfrac{\pi}{8}$

$n = 0, \ \theta = \dfrac{\pi}{8}, n = 1, \theta = \dfrac{3\pi}{8}, \ n = 2, \theta = \dfrac{5\pi}{8}$

$n = 3, \ \theta = (7\pi/8) \quad \because \ 0 \le \theta \le \pi$

From the second equation

$\cos 2\theta = -1/2 = -\cos(\pi/3)$

$= \cos(\pi - \pi/3) = \cos(2\pi/3).$

$\therefore \quad 2\theta = 2n\pi \pm 2\pi/3 \ \therefore \ \theta = n\pi \pm \pi/3$

$n = 0, \theta = \pi/3, n = 1, \theta = \pi - \pi/3 = 2\pi/3,$

$\therefore \quad \theta = \dfrac{\pi}{8}, \dfrac{\pi}{3}, \dfrac{3\pi}{8}, \dfrac{5\pi}{8}, \dfrac{2\pi}{3}, \dfrac{7\pi}{8} ; 0 \le \theta \le \pi.$

(b) Combining θ and $7\theta, 3\theta$ and 5θ, we get

$2\cos 4\theta(\cos 3\theta + \cos\theta) = 0$

$\therefore \quad 4\cos 4\theta\cos 2\theta\cos\theta = 0$

or $\quad 4\cdot\dfrac{1}{2^3\sin\theta}(\sin 2^3\theta) = 0 \qquad$ **(R. 37, P. 520)**

or $\quad \sin 8\theta = 0 \ \therefore \ \theta = n\pi/8$

(c) Multiplying by $\sin x(\sin x \ne 0)$, we get

$\sin 8x - \sin 6x = 0$

$2\sin x\cos 7x = 0$

$\therefore \quad \cos 7x = 0$ as $\sin x \ne 0$

$\therefore \quad 7x = \left(n + \dfrac{1}{2}\right)\pi \ \therefore \ x = \left(n + \dfrac{1}{2}\right)\dfrac{\pi}{7}$

You may use **R. 37 P. 520** for L.H.S.

31. (a) $(\cos\theta - \cos 2\theta) - (\sin 2\theta - \sin\theta) = 0$

$2\sin(3\theta/2)\sin(\theta/2) - 2\cos(3\theta/2)\sin(\theta/2) = 0$

or $\quad \sin(\theta/2)\{\sin(3\theta/2) - \cos(3\theta/2)\} = 0$

$\sin(\theta/2) = 0 \ \therefore \ \theta/2 = n\pi \ $ or $\ \theta = 2n\pi$

$\sin(3\theta/2) - \cos(3\theta/2) = 0$

$\therefore \quad \tan(3\theta/2) = 1 = \tan(\pi/4)$

$\therefore \quad \dfrac{3\theta}{2} = n\pi + \dfrac{\pi}{4} \ $ or $\ \theta = \dfrac{2n\pi}{3} + \dfrac{\pi}{6}.$

(b) $\cos 3x + \cos 2x = \sin(3x/2) + \sin(x/2)$

$\therefore \quad 2\cos\dfrac{5x}{2}\cos\dfrac{x}{2} - 2\sin x\cos\dfrac{x}{2} = 0$

∴ $2\cos(x/2)\,[\cos(5x/2) - \sin x] = 0$

$\cos\left(\dfrac{x}{2}\right) = 0$ ∴ $\dfrac{x}{2} = \left(n + \dfrac{1}{2}\right)\pi$

or $x = 2n\pi + \pi$,

$n = 0$, $x = \pi$ as $0 \le x \le 2\pi$.

$\cos\dfrac{5x}{2} = \sin x = \cos\left(\dfrac{\pi}{2} - x\right)$

$\dfrac{5x}{2} = 2n\pi \pm \left(\dfrac{\pi}{2} - x\right)$

Taking +ive sign $(5x/2) + x = 2n\pi + \pi/2$,

$(7x/2) = (4n + 1)(\pi/2)$

∴ $x = (4n + 1)\,\pi/7$.

$n = 0, x = \pi/7, n = 1, x = 5\pi/7, n = 2, x = 9\pi/7$,

$n = 3, x = 13\pi/7$.

Now taking – ive sign,

$(5x/2) - x = 2n\pi - \pi/2$

or $(3x/2) = (4n - 1)\pi/2$.

∴ $x = (4n - 1)\pi/3$, ∴ For $n = 1$, $x = \pi$.

∴ $x = \dfrac{\pi}{7}, \dfrac{5\pi}{7}, \pi, \dfrac{9\pi}{7}, \dfrac{13\pi}{7}$.

32. (a) Combining 7θ and θ, we get, $0 \le \theta \le \pi/2$.

$2\sin 4\theta\cos 3\theta + \sin 4\theta = 0$.

$\sin 4\theta\,(2\cos 3\theta + 1) = 0$.

$\sin 4\theta = 0 = \sin 0°$

∴ $4\theta = n\pi$ or $\theta = n\pi/4$.

$\theta = 0, \dfrac{\pi}{4}, \dfrac{\pi}{2}$ corresponding to $n = 0, 1, 2$.

$\cos 3\theta = -1/2 = -\cos(\pi/3)$

$= \cos(\pi - \pi/3) = \cos(2\pi/3)$

∴ $3\theta = 2n\pi \pm (2\pi/3)$

∴ $\theta = (6n \pm 2)(\pi/9)$

$n = 0, \theta = 2\pi/9$, $n = 1$, $\theta = 4\pi/9$ and all other values will be greater than $\pi/2$.

∴ $\theta = 0, \dfrac{\pi}{4}, \dfrac{\pi}{2}, \dfrac{2\pi}{9}, \dfrac{4\pi}{9}$

Note : You may use **result 38 P. 520**.

∴ $\dfrac{\sin 3\left(\dfrac{3\theta}{2}\right)}{\sin\left(\dfrac{3\theta}{2}\right)}\sin\left(\dfrac{\theta + 7\theta}{2}\right) = 0$

or $\dfrac{\sin\dfrac{9\theta}{2}\sin 4\theta}{\sin\left(\dfrac{3\theta}{2}\right)} = 0$

∴ $\sin 4\theta = 0$ ∴ $\theta = \dfrac{n\pi}{4}$

or $\sin\dfrac{9\theta}{2} = 0$ ∴ $\theta = \dfrac{2n\pi}{9}$ etc.

(b) $(\sin 6x + \sin 2x) - \sin 4x = 0$

or $2\sin 4x\cos 2x - \sin 4x = 0$

∴ $\sin 4x = 0$ or $\cos 2x = \dfrac{1}{2} = \cos\dfrac{\pi}{3}$

∴ $4x = n\pi$ or $2x = 2n\pi \pm \dfrac{\pi}{3}$

∴ $x = \dfrac{n\pi}{4}$ or $x = n\pi \pm \dfrac{\pi}{6}$.

(c) Do yourself.

33. (a) We have $2\sin\theta\cos 2\theta = 2(2\cos^2\theta - 1) = 2\cos 2\theta$

∴ $\cos 2\theta\,(\sin\theta - 1) = 0$

∴ $\sin\theta = 1, \cos 2\theta = 0$

∴ $\theta = n\pi + (-1)^n\,\pi/2, 2\theta = n\pi + \pi/2$

or $\theta = (2n + 1)\,\pi/4$.

(b) $\dfrac{1}{\cos 4\theta} - \dfrac{1}{\cos 2\theta} = 2$

$\cos 4\theta \ne 0, \cos 2\theta \ne 0$ ...(1)

∴ $\cos 2\theta - \cos 4\theta = 2\cos 2\theta\cos 4\theta$

$= \cos 2\theta + \cos 6\theta$

∴ $\cos 6\theta + \cos 4\theta = 0$

or $2\cos 5\theta\cos\theta = 0$

$\cos\theta = 0 = \cos(\pi/2)$ ∴ $\theta = n\pi + \pi/2$.

$\cos 5\theta = 0 = \cos(\pi/2)$ ∴ $5\theta = n\pi + \pi/2$

or $\theta = \dfrac{n\pi}{5} + \dfrac{\pi}{10}$.

Both these values satisfy conditions in (1).

34. (a) $(\sin\theta + \sin 3\theta) + (\sin 2\theta + \sin 4\theta) = 0$

$2\sin 2\theta\cos\theta + 2\sin 3\theta\cos\theta = 0$

$2\cos\theta\,(\sin 2\theta + \sin 3\theta) = 0$

$4\cos\theta\sin(5\theta/2)\cos(\theta/2) = 0$

$\cos\theta = 0 = \cos(\pi/2)$,

∴ $\theta = \left(n + \dfrac{1}{2}\right)\pi$

$\cos(\theta/2) = 0 = \cos(\pi/2)$,

∴ $\dfrac{\theta}{2} = \left(n + \dfrac{1}{2}\right)\pi$ or $\theta = (2n + 1)\pi$

$\sin(5\theta/2) = 0 = \sin 0$

∴ $(5\theta/2) = n\pi$ or $\theta = 2n\pi/5$.

(b) $\left[\sin\left(\dfrac{n+1}{2}\right)\theta - \sin\left(\dfrac{(n-1)}{2}\right)\theta\right] - \sin\theta = 0$

$2\cos\dfrac{n\theta}{2}\sin\dfrac{\theta}{2} - 2\sin\dfrac{\theta}{2}\cos\dfrac{\theta}{2} = 0$

$2\sin\dfrac{\theta}{2}\left[\cos\dfrac{n\theta}{2} - \cos\dfrac{\theta}{2}\right] = 0$

$\sin(\theta/2) = 0$

∴ $(\theta/2) = r\pi$ or $\theta = 2r\pi$

$\cos(n\theta/2) = \cos(\theta/2)$

∴ $(n\theta/2) = 2r\pi \pm \theta/2$

or $(n \pm 1)\theta/2 = 2r\pi$ ∴ $\theta = 4r\pi/(n \pm 1)$.   ...(1)

35. (a) Combining the first two and last two terms, we get

$2\sin 3\theta\cos\alpha + 2\cos\alpha\sin(-\theta) = \cos\alpha$

$2\sin 3\theta - 2\sin\theta = 1$

or $2(3\sin\theta - 4\sin^3\theta) - 2\sin\theta = 1$

or $8\sin^3\theta - 4\sin\theta + 1 = 0$.

Clearly $\sin \theta = \frac{1}{2}$ satisfies it

$\therefore$ $(2 \sin \theta - 1)(4 \sin^2 \theta + 2 \sin \theta - 1) = 0$

$\sin \theta = 1/2 = \sin (\pi /6)$

$\therefore$ $\theta = n\pi + (-1)^n \pi /6$

Also $\sin \theta = \dfrac{-2 \pm \sqrt{4 + 16}}{2} = \dfrac{\sqrt{5} - 1}{4}, -\dfrac{\sqrt{5} + 1}{4}$

$\sin \theta = \sin 18° = \sin (\pi /10)$

$\therefore$ $\theta = n\pi + (-1)^n \pi /10$

$\sin \theta = -\sin 54° = \sin \left(\dfrac{-3\pi}{10} \right)$

$\therefore$ $\theta = n\pi - (-1)^n \dfrac{3\pi}{10}.$

(b) $\because$ $\sin^2 A - \sin^2 B = \sin (A + B) \sin (A - B),$

we have $\sin (2n - 1) \theta . \sin \theta - \sin^2 \theta = 0$

$\sin \theta [\sin (2n - 1) \theta - \sin \theta] = 0$

$\sin \theta = 0$ $\therefore$ $\theta = r\pi$

$\sin (2n - 1) \theta = \sin \theta$

$\therefore$ $(2n - 1) \theta = r\pi + (-1)^r \theta$

r even $= 2k$, $(2n - 2) \theta = 2k\pi$ $\therefore$ $\theta = \dfrac{k\pi}{n - 1}.$

r odd $= 2k + 1, 2n\theta = (2k + 1) \pi$ $\therefore$ $\theta = \left(k + \dfrac{1}{2} \right) \dfrac{\pi}{n}.$

36. (a) Dividing both sides by $\sqrt{1 + 3} = 2$, we get

$\dfrac{\sqrt{3}}{2} \cos x + \dfrac{1}{2} \sin x = \dfrac{\sqrt{2}}{2} = \dfrac{1}{\sqrt{(2)}}$

$\cos x \cos \dfrac{\pi}{6} + \sin x \sin \dfrac{\pi}{6} = \cos \dfrac{\pi}{4}$

$\cos \left(x - \dfrac{\pi}{6} \right) = \cos \dfrac{\pi}{4}$

$\therefore$ $x - \dfrac{\pi}{6} = 2n\pi \pm \dfrac{\pi}{4}$ or $x = 2n\pi + \dfrac{\pi}{6} \pm \dfrac{\pi}{4}.$

(b) **Proceeding as in (a),** we get

$\cos \left(x - \dfrac{\pi}{6} \right) \geq \dfrac{1}{2} = \cos \dfrac{\pi}{3}$

$\therefore$ $-\pi /3 \leq x - (\pi /6) \leq \pi /3$

or $-\pi /6 \leq x \leq \pi /2.$

(c) As above, $\cos \left(\theta - \dfrac{\pi}{6} \right) = \dfrac{1}{2} = \cos \dfrac{\pi}{3}$

$\therefore$ $\theta - \dfrac{\pi}{6} = 2n\pi \pm \dfrac{\pi}{3}$

$\theta = 2n\pi + \dfrac{\pi}{6} + \dfrac{\pi}{3}$ or $2n\pi + \dfrac{\pi}{6} - \dfrac{\pi}{3}$

$= 2n\pi + \dfrac{\pi}{2}$ or $2n\pi - \dfrac{\pi}{6}$

$\theta = (4n + 1) \dfrac{\pi}{2}$ or $(12n - 1) \dfrac{\pi}{6}.$

or $\theta = \dfrac{4n + 1}{4} \cdot 2\pi$ or $\dfrac{12n - 1}{12} \cdot 2\pi$

Numerators are in A.P. of $d = 4$ and $d = 12$

$-2\pi < \theta < 2\pi$

$\therefore$ $\theta = \dfrac{(-7, -3, 1, 5, ...)}{4} \cdot 2\pi$

and $\theta = \dfrac{(-25, -13, -1, 11, 23, 35, ...)}{12} \cdot 2\pi$

$\therefore$ $\theta = \left(-\dfrac{3}{4}, \dfrac{1}{4} \right) 2\pi, \left(-\dfrac{1}{12}, \dfrac{11}{12} \right) . 2\pi$

$\therefore$ $\theta = \dfrac{-3\pi}{2}, \dfrac{-\pi}{6}, \dfrac{\pi}{2}$ and $\dfrac{11\pi}{6}.$

37. (a) **As in Q. 36 (a),** we have on dividing by 2,

$\dfrac{1}{2} \cos \theta - \dfrac{\sqrt{3}}{2} \sin \theta = -\dfrac{1}{\sqrt{(2)}}$

$\cos \theta \cos \dfrac{\pi}{3} - \sin \theta \sin \dfrac{\pi}{3}$

$= -\cos \dfrac{\pi}{4} = \cos \left(\pi - \dfrac{\pi}{4} \right)$

$\cos \left(\theta + \dfrac{\pi}{3} \right) = \cos \dfrac{3\pi}{4}$

$\therefore$ $\theta + \dfrac{\pi}{3} = 2n\pi \pm \dfrac{3\pi}{4}$ or $\theta = 2n\pi - \dfrac{\pi}{3} \pm \dfrac{3\pi}{4}.$

Another Method :

$\dfrac{\sqrt{3}}{2} \sin \theta - \dfrac{1}{2} \cos \theta = \dfrac{1}{\sqrt{(2)}}$

$\sin \theta \cos \dfrac{\pi}{6} - \cos \theta \sin \dfrac{\pi}{6} = \dfrac{1}{\sqrt{(2)}} = \sin \dfrac{\pi}{4}$

$\therefore$ $\sin \left(\theta - \dfrac{\pi}{6} \right) = \sin \dfrac{\pi}{4}$

$\therefore$ $\theta - \dfrac{\pi}{6} = n\pi + (-1)^n \dfrac{\pi}{4}$

$\therefore$ $\theta = n\pi + (-1)^n \dfrac{\pi}{4} + \dfrac{\pi}{6}.$

(b) $E = 3^{3 \cos 2x + 4 \sin 2x}$

Now $3 \cos 2x + 4 \sin 2x = r \cos (2x - \alpha)$

where $3 = r \cos \alpha, 4 = r \sin \alpha$

i.e. $r = 5, \tan \alpha = 4/3$

Its minimum value is $- r.$

When $\cos (2x - \alpha) = -1 = \cos \pi$

or $2x - \alpha = 2n\pi \pm \pi$

$\therefore$ $x = (2n \pm 1) \dfrac{\pi}{2} + \dfrac{1}{2} \tan^{-1} \dfrac{4}{3}$

and in this case min. value of E is

$3^{-r} = 3^{-5} = 1/243.$

38. (a) Ist term $= [2 \cos (2\theta - \pi /6)]^2$

$4 \cos^2 \left(2\theta - \dfrac{\pi}{6} \right) - 5 = \cos \left(2\theta - \dfrac{\pi}{6} \right)$

or $(4c - 5)(c + 1) = 0$

$\therefore$ $c = \cos \left(2\theta - \dfrac{\pi}{6} \right) = -1$ as $c \neq \dfrac{5}{4}$ i.e., > 1

$\therefore$ $2\theta - \dfrac{\pi}{6} = \pi, 3\pi$ only as $0 < 2\theta < 4\pi$

or $2\theta = \dfrac{7\pi}{6}, \dfrac{19\pi}{6}$ $\therefore$ $\theta = \dfrac{7\pi}{12}, \dfrac{19\pi}{12}$

(b) $3 - 2\cos\theta - 4\sin\theta - (1 - 2\sin^2\theta)$
$$+ 2\sin\theta\cos\theta = 0$$
$$2\sin^2\theta - 4\sin\theta + 2 - 2\cos\theta + 2\sin\theta\cos\theta = 0$$
$$(\sin^2\theta - 2\sin\theta + 1) + \cos\theta(\sin\theta - 1) = 0$$
$$(\sin\theta - 1)^2 + \cos\theta(\sin\theta - 1) = 0$$
$$\therefore \quad (\sin\theta - 1)(\sin\theta - 1 + \cos\theta) = 0$$
$$\sin\theta = 1 = \sin\frac{\pi}{2} \quad \therefore \quad \theta = n\pi + (-1)^n\frac{\pi}{2}$$
$$\cos\theta + \sin\theta = 1.$$
Divide by $\sqrt{1+1} = \sqrt{2}$
$$\frac{1}{\sqrt{2}}\cos\theta + \frac{1}{\sqrt{2}}\sin\theta = \frac{1}{\sqrt{2}}$$
or $\cos\theta\cos\frac{\pi}{4} + \sin\theta\sin\frac{\pi}{4} = \frac{1}{\sqrt{2}}$
or $\cos\left(\theta - \frac{\pi}{4}\right) = \cos\frac{\pi}{4} \quad \therefore \quad \theta - \frac{\pi}{4} = 2n\pi \pm \frac{\pi}{4}$
$$\therefore \quad \theta = 2n\pi \quad \text{or} \quad 2n\pi + \frac{\pi}{4} + \frac{\pi}{4} = 2n\pi + \frac{\pi}{2}$$

We could also write it as
$$\sin\left(\theta + \frac{\pi}{4}\right) = \frac{1}{\sqrt{2}} = \sin\frac{\pi}{4}$$
$$\therefore \quad \theta + \frac{\pi}{4} = n\pi + (-1)^n\frac{\pi}{4}$$
$$\therefore \quad \theta = n\pi + (-1)^n\frac{\pi}{4} - \frac{\pi}{4}.$$

(c) **We have already done it in part (b).**

(d) If $\sin x + \cos x = t$ then on squaring
$$1 + \sin 2x = t^2$$
$$\therefore \quad t = (t^2 - 1) - 1 \quad \text{or} \quad t^2 - t - 2 = 0$$
or $(t - 2)(t + 1) = 0 \quad \therefore \quad t = 2, -1$
$$\cos x + \sin x = 2 \quad \text{or} \quad -1$$
or $\frac{1}{\sqrt{2}}\cos x + \frac{1}{\sqrt{2}}\sin x = \sqrt{2} \quad \text{or} \quad -\frac{1}{\sqrt{2}}$
or $\cos\left(x - \frac{\pi}{4}\right) = \sqrt{2} \quad \text{or} \quad -\cos\frac{\pi}{4}$
The first option is rejected as $\sqrt{2} > 1$
$$\therefore \quad \cos\left(x - \frac{\pi}{4}\right) = \cos\left(\pi - \frac{\pi}{4}\right) = \cos\frac{3\pi}{4}$$
$$\therefore \quad x - \frac{\pi}{4} = 2n\pi \pm \frac{3\pi}{4}$$
$$\therefore \quad x = 2n\pi + \pi \quad \text{or} \quad 2n\pi - \frac{\pi}{2}$$

39. (a) The given equation can be written as
$$1/(\sin x) = 1 + (\cos x/\sin x),$$
provided $x \neq n\pi$ *i.e.* $\sin x \neq 0$
or $1 = \sin x + \cos x.$
or $\cos(x - \pi/4) = \cos(\pi/4)$
$$\therefore \quad x - \pi/4 = 2n\pi \pm (\pi/4)$$
Hence $x = 2n\pi$ or $x = 2n\pi + \pi/2, \quad n \in \mathbf{I}$
But $x = 2n\pi$ is ruled out $[\because x \neq n\pi]$

Hence we get the answer :
$$x = 2n\pi + (\pi/2), \quad n \in \mathbf{I}.$$

(b) $\tan\theta + \sec\theta = \sqrt{3}$
$$\frac{1 + \sin\theta}{\cos\theta} = \sqrt{3}$$
$$\frac{\left(\cos\frac{\theta}{2} + \sin\frac{\theta}{2}\right)^2}{\cos^2\frac{\theta}{2} - \sin^2\frac{\theta}{2}} = \sqrt{3}$$
or $\dfrac{\cos\frac{\theta}{2} + \sin\frac{\theta}{2}}{\cos\frac{\theta}{2} - \sin\frac{\theta}{2}} = \sqrt{3}$ or $\dfrac{1+t}{1-t} = \sqrt{3}$
or $\tan\left(\frac{\pi}{4} + \frac{\theta}{2}\right) = \tan\frac{\pi}{3}$
$$\therefore \quad \frac{\theta}{2} + \frac{\pi}{4} = n\pi + \frac{\pi}{3} \quad \therefore \quad \theta = 2n\pi + \frac{\pi}{6}$$

(c) Proceed as above. Ans. $\theta = 2n\pi + \pi/3$.

(d) $(2 + \sqrt{3})\cos\theta = 1 - \sin\theta$
$$\frac{1 - \sin\theta}{\cos\theta} = 2 + \sqrt{3}.$$
$$\frac{\left(\cos\frac{\theta}{2} - \sin\frac{\theta}{2}\right)^2}{\cos^2\frac{\theta}{2} - \sin^2\frac{\theta}{2}} = 2 + \sqrt{3}$$
or $\dfrac{1-t}{1+t} = \tan 75^\circ, \quad t = \tan\frac{\theta}{2}$
or $\tan\left(\frac{\pi}{4} - \frac{\theta}{2}\right) = \tan\frac{5\pi}{12}$
$$\therefore \quad \frac{\pi}{4} - \frac{\theta}{2} = n\pi + \frac{5\pi}{12}.$$
or $\theta = -2n\pi - \frac{2\pi}{3}$ or $\theta = 2r\pi - \frac{2\pi}{3}, \quad r \in I$

40. (a) $\tan\left(\frac{\pi}{2}\sin\theta\right) = \cot\left(\frac{\pi}{2}\cos\theta\right)$
$$\therefore \quad \tan\left(\frac{\pi}{2}\sin\theta\right) = \tan\left(\frac{\pi}{2} - \frac{\pi}{2}\cos\theta\right)$$
$$\therefore \quad \frac{\pi}{2}\sin\theta = n\pi + \frac{\pi}{2} - \frac{\pi}{2}\cos\theta$$
$$\therefore \quad \sin\theta + \cos\theta = 2n + 1$$
Divide by $\sqrt{1+1}$
$$\frac{1}{\sqrt{2}}\sin\theta + \frac{1}{\sqrt{2}}\cos\theta = \frac{2n+1}{\sqrt{2}}$$
$$\cos\left(\theta - \frac{\pi}{4}\right) = \frac{2n+1}{\sqrt{2}} = \cos\alpha, \text{say}$$
$$\theta - \frac{\pi}{4} = 2r\pi \pm \alpha$$
$$\therefore \quad \theta = 2r\pi + \frac{\pi}{4} \pm \cos^{-1}\frac{2n+1}{\sqrt{2}},$$
where $n = 0$ or -1 only as $\cos\alpha \leq 1; \ r \in \mathbf{I}$

$\therefore \quad \theta = 2r\pi + \pi/4 \pm \pi/4$

or $\quad 2r\pi + \pi/4 \pm 3\pi/4$

$\because \quad \cos^{-1}\left(-\frac{1}{\sqrt{2}}\right) = \frac{3\pi}{4}, r \in I.$

Hence the only solution is $\theta = 2r\pi$ or $2r\pi + \pi$. We reject other values as they will lead to $\infty = \infty$

(b) **Proceeding as in Q. 38 (c),** we get

$$\cos\left(\theta - \frac{\pi}{4}\right) = \frac{2n+1}{2\sqrt{(2)}}, \quad n = 0 \text{ or } -1$$

Hence $\quad \cos\left(\theta - \frac{\pi}{4}\right) = \pm\frac{1}{2\sqrt{(2)}}.$

(c) $\cos(\sin\theta) = \cos\left\{\frac{\pi}{2} - \cos\theta\right\}$

$\therefore \quad \sin\theta = 2n\pi \pm \left(\frac{\pi}{2} - \cos\theta\right)$

(i) Taking +ive sign, $\cos\theta + \sin\theta = (4n+1)\frac{\pi}{2}$

or $\quad \cos\left(\theta - \frac{\pi}{4}\right) = (4n+1)\frac{\pi}{2\sqrt{2}}, \frac{\pi}{2\sqrt{2}} > 1$

The R.H.S. is > 1 for $n \geq 0$ and < -1 for $n < 0$

Hence the equation does not possess any solution.

(ii) Taking $-$ive sign,

$$\sin\theta - \cos\theta = (4n-1)\frac{\pi}{2}$$

$\therefore \quad \sin\left(\theta - \frac{\pi}{4}\right) = (4n-1)\frac{\pi}{2\sqrt{2}}$

R.H.S. is either > 1 or < -1.

Hence the equation does not possess any solution in this case also.

(d) $\cos\left(\theta - \frac{\pi}{3}\right) = \cos 2\theta$ on dividing by 2

Ans. $(6n+1)\frac{\pi}{9}, (6n-1)\frac{\pi}{3}$

(e) Ans. $\frac{n\pi}{7} + \frac{\pi}{12}$ or $n\pi - \frac{3\pi}{4}$

$\sqrt{3}\cos 8x - \sin 8x = -(\cos 6x + \sqrt{3}\sin 6x)$

or $\frac{\sqrt{3}}{2}\cos 8x - \frac{1}{2}\sin 8x$

$\quad = -\left(\frac{1}{2}\cos 6x + \frac{\sqrt{3}}{2}\sin 6x\right)$

or $\cos\left(8x + \frac{\pi}{6}\right) = -\cos\left(6x - \frac{\pi}{3}\right)$

$\quad = \cos\left[\pi - \left(6x - \frac{\pi}{3}\right)\right]$

$\therefore \quad 8x + \frac{\pi}{6} = 2n\pi \pm \left(\frac{4\pi}{3} - 6x\right)$

$\therefore \quad 14x = 2n\pi + \frac{4\pi}{3} - \frac{\pi}{6}$

$\therefore \quad x = \frac{n\pi}{7} + \frac{\pi}{2}$ for +ive.

$\quad 2x = 2n\pi - \frac{4\pi}{3} - \frac{\pi}{6}$

$\therefore \quad x = n\pi - \frac{3\pi}{4}$ for $-$ive.

It can be written as $n\pi - \pi + \pi - \frac{3\pi}{4}$

or $\quad (n-1)\pi + \frac{\pi}{4} \quad$ or $\quad n\pi + \frac{\pi}{4}$

41. (a) $\tan\theta + \tan 2\theta + \tan(\theta + 2\theta) = 0$

$\quad (\tan\theta + \tan 2\theta) + \frac{\tan\theta + \tan 2\theta}{1 - \tan\theta\tan 2\theta} = 0$

or $\quad (\tan\theta + \tan 2\theta)(1 - \tan\theta\tan 2\theta + 1) = 0$

$\quad \tan 2\theta + \tan\theta = 0$

$\therefore \quad \tan 2\theta = -\tan\theta = \tan(-\theta)$

$\therefore \quad 2\theta = n\pi - \theta$ or $3\theta = n\pi \therefore \theta = n\pi/3$

From 2nd factor

$$\tan\theta\tan 2\theta = 2 \quad \text{or} \quad \tan\theta \cdot \frac{2\tan\theta}{1 - \tan^2\theta} = 2$$

or $\quad \tan^2\theta = 1 - \tan^2\theta$ or $2\tan^2\theta = 1$

$\therefore \quad \tan\theta = \pm\frac{1}{\sqrt{(2)}} = \pm\tan\alpha$

where $\quad \tan\alpha = \frac{1}{\sqrt{(2)}}$

$\therefore \quad \theta = n\pi \pm \alpha$, where $\alpha = \tan^{-1}\frac{1}{\sqrt{(2)}},$

$0 < \alpha < \pi/2.$

(b) $(\tan\theta + \tan 2\theta) - \frac{\tan\theta + \tan 2\theta}{1 - \tan\theta\tan 2\theta} = 0$

or $\quad (\tan\theta + \tan 2\theta)(1 - \tan\theta\tan 2\theta - 1) = 0$

or $\quad \tan\theta\tan 2\theta(\tan\theta + \tan 2\theta) = 0$

$\quad \tan\theta = 0, \therefore \theta = n\pi, \tan 2\theta = 0,$

$\therefore \quad 2\theta = n\pi$ or $\theta = n\pi/2$

$\quad \tan\theta + \tan 2\theta = 0$

or $\quad \sin(\theta + 2\theta) = 0 \quad \therefore \theta = n\pi/3.$

But for odd values of n, the values of θ given by $\theta = n\pi/2$ do not satisfy the given equation as it will lead to $\infty = \infty$

Hence the required solution is :

$$\theta = \frac{2m\pi}{2} = m\pi, \quad \theta = \frac{n\pi}{3}, m, n \in I.$$

(c) $\tan 3\theta + \tan\theta = 2\tan 2\theta$

$\quad \tan 3\theta - \tan 2\theta = \tan 2\theta - \tan\theta$

$\quad \frac{\sin(3\theta - 2\theta)}{\cos 3\theta\cos 2\theta} = \frac{\sin(2\theta - \theta)}{\cos 2\theta\cos\theta}$

or $\quad \sin\theta(\cos\theta - \cos 3\theta) = 0$

or $\quad \sin\theta \cdot 2\sin\theta\sin 2\theta = 0$

$\therefore \quad \sin\theta = 0, \therefore \theta = n\pi.$

$\quad \sin 2\theta = 0, \therefore 2\theta = n\pi$ or $\theta = \frac{n\pi}{2}.$

But $\theta = \frac{n\pi}{2}$ is rejected when n is odd as it makes

$\infty = \infty. \quad \therefore \quad \theta = n\pi$ as it will make $0 = 0.$

42. (a) $\dfrac{\tan A}{\tan B} = \dfrac{3}{1}$, where $A = \theta + 15°$, $B = \theta - 15°$

Apply componendo and dividendo

$\therefore \quad \dfrac{\tan A + \tan B}{\tan A - \tan B} = \dfrac{3+1}{3-1}$ or $\dfrac{\sin(A+B)}{\sin(A-B)} = 2$

or $\quad \sin 2\theta = 2 \sin 30° = 2 \cdot \dfrac{1}{2} = 1 = \sin \dfrac{\pi}{2}$

$\therefore \quad 2\theta = 2n\pi + \dfrac{\pi}{2}$ or $\theta = n\pi + \dfrac{\pi}{4}$ [§ **1(i) b, P. 580**]

(b) $\dfrac{4}{\tan 2\theta} = \dfrac{1}{\tan^2 \theta} - \tan^2 \theta$.

Put $\tan 2\theta = \dfrac{2\tan\theta}{1 - \tan^2\theta}$

$\therefore \quad \dfrac{4(1 - \tan^2\theta)}{2\tan\theta} = \dfrac{1 - \tan^4\theta}{\tan^2\theta}$

$(1 - \tan^2\theta)[2\tan\theta - (1 + \tan^2\theta)] = 0$

$(1 - \tan^2\theta)(\tan^2\theta - 2\tan\theta + 1) = 0$

$(1 - \tan^2\theta)(\tan\theta - 1)^2 = 0$

$\therefore \quad \tan\theta = 1, -1 \quad \therefore \quad \theta = n\pi \pm \dfrac{\pi}{4}$

(c) $\tan\dfrac{\pi}{3} = \sqrt{3}$, $\tan\dfrac{2\pi}{3} = \tan\left(\pi - \dfrac{\pi}{3}\right)$

$= -\tan\dfrac{\pi}{3} = -\sqrt{3}$

Now $\tan\theta + \tan\left(\theta + \dfrac{\pi}{3}\right) + \tan\left(\theta + \dfrac{2\pi}{3}\right)$

$= \tan\theta + \dfrac{\tan\theta + \sqrt{3}}{1 - \sqrt{3}\tan\theta} + \dfrac{\tan\theta - \sqrt{3}}{1 + \sqrt{3}\tan\theta}$

$= \dfrac{\tan\theta(1 - 3\tan^2\theta) + (\tan\theta + \sqrt{3})(1 + \sqrt{3}\tan\theta)}{\quad\quad\quad + (\tan\theta - \sqrt{3})(1 - \sqrt{3}\tan\theta)}{1 - 3\tan^2\theta}$

$= \dfrac{\tan\theta - 3\tan^3\theta + 2\tan\theta + \sqrt{3}(2\sqrt{3}\tan\theta)}{1 - 3\tan^2\theta}$

$= \dfrac{9\tan\theta - 3\tan^3\theta}{1 - 3\tan^2\theta}$

$= 3 \cdot \dfrac{(3\tan\theta - \tan^3\theta)}{1 - 3\tan^2\theta} = 3\tan 3\theta$.

Hence the given equation reduces to
$3\tan 3\theta = 3$

$\therefore \quad \tan 3\theta = 1 = \tan\dfrac{\pi}{4} \quad \therefore \quad 3\theta = n\pi + \dfrac{\pi}{4}$

or $\theta = \dfrac{n\pi}{3} + \dfrac{\pi}{12}$.

43. (a) We re-write the equation as

$\dfrac{\sin 3x}{\cos 3x} - \dfrac{\sin 5x}{\cos 5x} = 0$

or $\dfrac{\sin 3x \cos 5x - \sin 5x \cos 3x}{\cos 3x \cos 5x} = 0$

or $\dfrac{\sin 2x}{\cos 3x \cos 5x} = 0$.

Now solving the equation $\sin 2x = 0$, we get $x = \dfrac{1}{2}n\pi, n \in \mathbf{I}$. But we must discard extraneous solutions, that is, those for which the denominator $\cos 3x \cos 5x$ vanishes, which clearly happens when n is odd. Thus the solution of the given equation will be given by $x = \dfrac{1}{2}n\pi$, where n is even, say $n = 2m$, $m \in \mathbf{I}$.

Hence the required solution is $x = m\pi$, $m \in \mathbf{I}$.

Quite obviously, it is a serious error to take the solution as $x = \dfrac{1}{2}n\pi$, $n \in \mathbf{I}$.

(b) Ans. ϕ, $\tan(3x - 2x) = \tan x = 1$

$\therefore \quad x = n\pi + (\pi/4)$ but this value does not satisfy the given equation as $\tan 2x = \tan(\pi/2) = \infty$ and it reduces to indeterminate form.

44. (a) The given equation is

$\left(\dfrac{\sin\theta}{\sin\phi}\right)^2 = \dfrac{\sin\theta}{\sin\phi} \cdot \dfrac{\cos\phi}{\cos\theta}$

or $\dfrac{\sin\theta}{\sin\phi} = \dfrac{\cos\phi}{\cos\theta}$.

[Note $\sin\theta/\sin\phi \neq 0$, since its square is given to be 3]

or $2\sin\theta\cos\theta = 2\sin\phi\cos\phi$

$\Rightarrow \sin 2\theta = \sin 2\phi$

$\Rightarrow 2\tan\theta/(1 + \tan^2\theta) = 2\tan\phi/(1 + \tan^2\phi)$

$\Rightarrow 6\tan\phi/(1 + 9\tan^2\phi) = 2\tan\phi/(1 + \tan^2\phi)$

[$\because \tan\theta = 3\tan\phi$]

$\Rightarrow 3/(1 + 9\tan^2\phi) = 1/(1 + \tan^2\phi)$ [$\because \tan\phi \neq 0$]

$\Rightarrow 3 + 3\tan^2\phi = 1 + 9\tan^2\phi \Rightarrow 6\tan^2\phi = 2$

$\Rightarrow \tan\phi = \pm 1/\sqrt{3} \quad \therefore \quad \phi = n\pi \pm (\pi/6)$.

Now $\tan\theta = 3\tan\phi = 3(\pm 1/\sqrt{3}) = \pm\sqrt{3}$

$\therefore \quad \theta = n\pi \pm (\pi/3)$.

(b) Eliminating θ, we get $2\sec^2\phi - 3\tan^2\phi = 1$

$\therefore \quad \tan^2\phi = 1 = \tan^2\dfrac{\pi}{4}$ or $\phi = n\pi \pm \dfrac{\pi}{4}$

Eliminating ϕ, we get $\tan^2\theta = 3 = \tan^2\dfrac{\pi}{3}$

$\therefore \quad \theta = n\pi \pm \dfrac{\pi}{3}$.

(c) $u + \dfrac{1}{u} + 2 = 0$ where $u = \dfrac{\tan x}{\tan 2x}$

$(u + 1)^2 = 0 \quad \therefore \quad u = -1 = \dfrac{t(1 - t^2)}{2t}$,

where $t = \tan x$

$\therefore \quad -2 = 1 - t^2$ or $t^2 = 3$

$\therefore \quad t = \pm \sqrt{3} = \tan x \quad \therefore \quad x = n\pi \pm \dfrac{\pi}{3}$

45. (a) $(\sin^3 \theta + \cos^3 \theta) - (1 - \sin\theta\cos\theta) = 0$

or $\quad (\sin\theta + \cos\theta)(\sin^2\theta + \cos^2\theta$
$$- \sin\theta\cos\theta) - (1 - \sin\theta\cos\theta) = 0$$

or $\quad (\sin\theta + \cos\theta)(1 - \sin\theta\cos\theta)$
$$- (1 - \sin\theta\cos\theta) = 0$$

or $\quad (1 - \sin\theta\cos\theta)(\sin\theta + \cos\theta - 1) = 0$

$1 - \sin\theta\cos\theta = 0$

$\therefore \quad 2\sin\theta\cos\theta = 2 \quad$ or $\quad \sin 2\theta = 2.$

Above is not possible because $\sin 2\theta$ can never be greater than 1 .

Again $\sin\theta + \cos\theta = 1$. Divide by $\sqrt{1+1} = \sqrt{2}$

$$\dfrac{1}{\sqrt{(2)}} \sin\theta + \dfrac{1}{\sqrt{(2)}} \cos\theta = \dfrac{1}{\sqrt{(2)}}$$

or $\quad \cos\left(\theta - \dfrac{\pi}{4}\right) = \dfrac{1}{\sqrt{(2)}} = \cos\dfrac{\pi}{4}$

$\therefore \quad \theta - \dfrac{\pi}{4} = 2n\pi \pm \dfrac{\pi}{4}.$

$\therefore \quad \theta = 2n\pi + \dfrac{\pi}{4} + \dfrac{\pi}{4}, 2n\pi - \dfrac{\pi}{4} + \dfrac{\pi}{4}$

i.e. $\theta = 2n\pi + \pi/2,$ or $2n\pi.$

(b) $\sin^3 x + \cos^3 x + 1 - 3\sin x.\cos x.1 = 0$

Above is of the form $a^3 + b^3 + c^3 - 3abc = 0$

or $\quad (a + b + c)(a^2 + b^2 + c^2 - ab - bc - ca) = 0$

or $\quad \dfrac{1}{2}(a + b + c)[(a-b)^2 + (b-c)^2 + (c-a)^2] = 0$

$\therefore \quad a + b + c = 0$ only as other factor is not zero.

or $\quad \sin x + \cos x = -1$

$\cos\left(x - \dfrac{\pi}{4}\right) = -\dfrac{1}{\sqrt{2}} = \cos\dfrac{3\pi}{4}.$

$\therefore \quad x - \dfrac{\pi}{4} = 2n\pi \pm \dfrac{3\pi}{4}$

$\therefore \quad x = 2n\pi + \pi, 2n\pi - \dfrac{\pi}{2}$

(c) $\sqrt{3}\cos\theta - 3\sin\theta = 2(\sin 5\theta - \sin\theta)$

$\sqrt{3}\cos\theta - \sin\theta = 2\sin 5\theta.$

Divide by $\sqrt{3+1} = 2$.

$\therefore \quad \dfrac{\sqrt{3}}{2}\cos\theta - \dfrac{1}{2}\sin\theta = \sin 5\theta.$

$\sin\dfrac{\pi}{3}\cos\theta - \cos\dfrac{\pi}{3}\sin\theta = \sin 5\theta.$

$\therefore \quad \sin\left(\dfrac{\pi}{3} - \theta\right) = \sin 5\theta$

or $\quad \sin 5\theta = \sin\left(\dfrac{\pi}{3} - \theta\right)$

$\therefore \quad 5\theta = n\pi + (-1)^n (\pi/3 - \theta).$

n even $= 2r \quad \therefore \quad 5\theta = 2r\pi + \pi/3 - \theta$

or $\quad 6\theta = 2r\pi + \dfrac{\pi}{3} \quad \therefore \quad \theta = \dfrac{r\pi}{3} + \dfrac{\pi}{18}.$

n odd $= 2r + 1$

$\therefore \quad 5\theta = (2r+1)\pi - \pi/3 + \theta$

or $\quad 4\theta = 2r\pi + \pi - \pi/3 = 2r\pi + 2\pi/3.$

$\therefore \quad \theta = \dfrac{r\pi}{2} + \dfrac{\pi}{6}.$

46. (a) $\dfrac{1}{2}\sqrt{3}\sin x = \cos x + \cos^2 x.$ Square

$$3(1 - \cos^2 x) = 4(\cos^2 x + 2\cos^3 x + \cos^4 x)$$

or $\quad 4\cos^4 x + 8\cos^3 x + 7\cos^2 x - 3 = 0.$

Clearly $\cos x = -1$ satisfies above, hence it can be written as

$(\cos x + 1)(4\cos^3 x + 4\cos^2 x + 3\cos x - 3) = 0.$

Again $\cos x = \dfrac{1}{2}$ satisfies the 2nd factor

$(\cos x + 1)(2\cos x - 1)(2\cos^2 x + 3\cos x + 3) = 0.$

$\therefore \quad \cos x = -1 = \cos\pi$

$\therefore \quad x = 2n\pi + \pi = (2r+1)\pi$

$\cos x = 1/2 = \cos(\pi/3)$

$\therefore \quad x = 2n\pi \pm \pi/3$

$2\cos^2 x + 3\cos x + 3 = 0,$

$B^2 - 4AC = 9 - 4.2.3 = -$ ive .

Hence this factor does not give any real values of $\cos x.$

(b) $2(\cos x + 2\cos^2 x - 1) + 2\sin x\cos x.$
$$(1 + 2\cos x) - 2\sin x = 0$$

or $\quad 2(2\cos^2 x + \cos x - 1)$
$$+ 2\sin x(2\cos^2 x + \cos x - 1) = 0$$

$2(1 + \sin x)(\cos x + 1)(2\cos x - 1) = 0.$

We have to determine values of x ş. t. $-\pi \le x \le \pi$

$1 + \sin x = 0 \qquad \therefore \quad \sin x = -1$

$\therefore \quad x = 2n\pi + \dfrac{3\pi}{2} \quad \therefore \quad x = -\dfrac{\pi}{2},$

for $\quad n = -1 \quad \because \quad -\pi \le x < \pi$

$\cos x = -1 = \cos\pi \quad \therefore \quad x = 2n\pi \pm \pi$

$\therefore \quad x = -\pi, \pi$

$2\cos x - 1 = 0 \quad \therefore \quad \cos x = 1/2 = \cos(\pi/3)$

$\therefore \quad x = 2n\pi \pm \pi/3$

$\therefore \quad x = \pi/3, -\pi/3$

Hence the values of x s. t. $-\pi \le x \le \pi$ are

$-\pi, -\pi/2, -\pi/3, \pi/3, \pi.$

(c) As in part (a),

$2\{\sin x - (1 - 2\sin^2 x)\} + 2\cos x$
$$\{1 - \sin x(1 + 2\sin x)\} = 0$$

or $\quad (2\sin^2 x + \sin x - 1)(1 - \cos x) = 0$

or $\quad (\sin x + 1)(2\sin x - 1)(1 - \cos x) = 0$

$\therefore \quad \sin x = -1, \cos x = 1, \sin x = 1/2$

$\therefore \quad x = 2n\pi + \dfrac{3\pi}{2}, x = 2n\pi, n\pi + (-1)^n\dfrac{\pi}{6}$

47. (a) $1 + \sin 2x = (\sin x + \cos x)^2$ ∴ $u^2 + 5u = 0$

∴ $u = 0, -5,$ ∴ $u = 0 \Rightarrow \tan x = -1$

∴ $x = n\pi - \dfrac{\pi}{4}$

$u = -5$ *i.e.*, $\sin x + \cos x = -5$ (not possible)

(b) $y = \sin x - \cos x$

or $\dfrac{y}{\sqrt 2} = \dfrac{1}{\sqrt 2}\sin x - \dfrac{1}{\sqrt 2}\cos x$

or $\dfrac{y}{\sqrt 2} = \sin\left(x - \dfrac{\pi}{4}\right)$. For real solution

$-1 \le \left(x - \dfrac{\pi}{4}\right) \le 1$ or $-1 \le \dfrac{y}{\sqrt 2} \le 1$

If $y = 1$, then $\sin x - \cos x = 1$

or $\dfrac{1}{\sqrt 2} = \sin\left(x - \dfrac{\pi}{4}\right) = \sin\dfrac{\pi}{4}$

∴ $x - \dfrac{\pi}{4} = n\pi + (-1)^n \dfrac{\pi}{4}$

n even, $x = 2r\pi + \dfrac{\pi}{2}$; n odd, $x = (2r + 1)\pi$

∴ $x = \pi/2, \pi$ as $0 < x < 2\pi$

48. (a) We write the given equation as

$(\sin x + \sin 3x) + \sin 2x = (\cos x + \cos 3x) + \cos 2x$

or $2\sin 2x \cos x + \sin 2x = 2\cos 2x \cos x + \cos 2x$

or $\sin 2x(2\cos x + 1) = \cos 2x(2\cos x + 1)$

or $(\sin 2x - \cos 2x)(2\cos x + 1) = 0$

∴ $\sin 2x - \cos 2x = 0$ or $2\cos x + 1 = 0$.

If $\sin 2x - \cos 2x = 0$, then $\tan 2x = 1$,

Hence $2x = n\pi + \pi/4$

or $x = (4n + 1)\dfrac{\pi}{8}$ ...(1)

If $2\cos x + 1 = 0$, then $\cos x = -1/2$ ...(2)

∴ $x = 2n\pi \pm \dfrac{2\pi}{3}$ or $x = \dfrac{6n \pm 2}{3}\pi$

We seek values of x in the interval $0 \le x \le 2\pi$.

In this interval (1) gives

$x = \pi/8, 5\pi/8, 9\pi/8, 13\pi/8.$ $(n = 0, 1, 2, 3)$

and (2) gives $x = 2\pi/3, 4\pi/3.$ (for $n = 0, 1$)

Thus we get the answer :

$x = \pi/8, 5\pi/8, 2\pi/3, 9\pi/8, 4\pi/3, 13\pi/8$.

(b) The given equation can be written as

$\sin 3x + \sin x - 3\sin 2x$

$\qquad = \cos 3x + \cos x - 3\cos 2x$

$2\sin 2x \cos x - 3\sin 2x$

$\qquad = 2\cos 2x \cos x - 3\cos 2x$

$\sin 2x(2\cos x - 3) = \cos 2x(2\cos x - 3) = 0$

∴ $\sin 2x = \cos 2x$ as $2\cos x - 3 \ne 0$

$\qquad\qquad\qquad\qquad\qquad$ ∵ $\cos x \ne 3/2$

∴ $\tan 2x = 1 = \tan(\pi/4)$

∴ $2x = n\pi + \dfrac{\pi}{4}$ or $x = \dfrac{n\pi}{2} + \dfrac{\pi}{8}$

49. (a) It is clear that $\sin x \ne 0$ and $\cos x \ne 0$

i.e., $x \ne 0, x \ne \pi/2$

$\dfrac{\sin^4 x + \cos^4 x}{\sin x \cos x} - \sin 2x = 1 + \dfrac{\sin^2 x + \cos^2 x}{\sin x \cos x}$

$\dfrac{1 - 2\sin^2 x \cos^2 x - 1}{\sin x \cos x} - \sin 2x = 1$

or $-2\sin 2x = 1$

∴ $\sin 2x = -\dfrac{1}{2} = \sin\left(-\dfrac{\pi}{6}\right)$

$2x = n\pi + (-1)^n\left(-\dfrac{\pi}{6}\right)$ ∴ $x = $ etc.

(b) $2\sin 2x \cos x + 2\cos x = 2\sin x \cos x + 2\cos^2 x$

Cancel $2\cos x$ and $\cos x = 0$

gives $x = \left(n + \dfrac{1}{2}\right)\pi, n \in I$ ...(1)

∴ $\sin 2x + 1 = \sin x + \cos x$

or $(\sin x + \cos x)^2 = \sin x + \cos x$

∴ $\sin x + \cos x = 0$ or 1

$\sin x + \cos x = 0$ gives $\tan x = -1 = -\tan\dfrac{\pi}{4}$

∴ $x = n\pi - \dfrac{\pi}{4}$ ...(2)

$\sin x + \cos x = 1$ **Refer Q. 38 (c), P 583-92.**

∴ $x = 2n\pi$ or $\left(2n\pi + \dfrac{\pi}{2}\right)$ *i.e.* $\left(2n + \dfrac{1}{2}\right)\pi$ ...(3)

But the second form is included in (1). Hence the required answers are $\left(n + \dfrac{1}{2}\right)\pi, n\pi - \dfrac{\pi}{4}$ and $2n\pi$, from (1), (2), (3).

(c) The given equation can be re-written as

$\sin^2 4x - 2\sin 4x \cos^4 x + \cos^2 x = 0$

Add and subtract $\cos^8 x$

∴ $(\sin 4x - \cos^4 x)^2 + \cos^2 x(1 - \cos^6 x) = 0$

Since both the terms are + ive $(\cos^6 x \le 1)$, above is possible only when each term is zero for the same value of x

$\qquad \sin 4x - \cos^4 x = 0$ ...(1)

and $\cos^2 x(1 - \cos^6 x) = 0$ ...(2)

From (2) $\cos x = 0$ or $\cos^2 x = 1$

∵ $z^3 = 1 \Rightarrow z = 1$ only,

as other values will not be real.

Case I : If $\cos x = 0$ *i.e.*, $x = \left(n + \dfrac{1}{2}\right)\pi$, then from (1)

$\sin 4\left(n + \dfrac{1}{2}\right)\pi + 0 = 0$

or $\sin(4n + 2)\pi = 0$ which is true.

∴ $x = \left(n + \dfrac{1}{2}\right)\pi$ ...(3)

Case II : When $\cos^2 x = 1$ *i.e.*, $\sin x = 0$ ∴ $x = r\pi$

then from (1), $\sin 4r\pi - 1 = 0$ or $-1 = 0$ which is not true. Hence the only solution is given by (3).

50. (a) We shall first consider values of θ between 0 and 2π

$$\sin\theta = -\frac{1}{2} = -\sin\frac{\pi}{6} = \sin\left(\pi + \frac{\pi}{6}\right)$$

or $\sin(2\pi - \pi/6)$

∴ $\theta = 7\pi/6$; $11\pi/6$

$$\tan\theta = 1/\sqrt{3} = \tan(\pi/6) = \tan(\pi + \pi/6)$$

∴ $\theta = \pi/6, 7\pi/6$.

Hence the value of θ between 0 and 2π which satisfies both the equations is $7\pi/6$.

Hence the general value of θ is $2n\pi + 7\pi/6$, where $n \in \mathbf{I}$.

(b) $\cos\theta = -1/\sqrt{2} = -\cos(\pi/4)$

$\qquad = \cos(\pi - \pi/4)$ or $\cos(\pi + \pi/4)$

∴ $\theta = 3\pi/4, 5\pi/4$

$\tan\theta = 1 = \tan(\pi/4), \tan(\pi + \pi/4)$

∴ $\theta = \pi/4, 5\pi/4$.

Hence the value of θ between 0 and 2π which satisfies both the equations is $5\pi/4$.

∴ General value is

$$2n\pi + 5\pi/4 = (2n + 1)\pi + \pi/4.$$

(c) $2n\pi + 7\pi/4$.

(d) $\tan\theta = \sqrt{3} = \tan(\pi/3) = \tan(\pi + \pi/3)$

∴ $\theta = \pi/3, 4\pi/3$.

$\cosec\theta = -2/\sqrt{3}$

or $\sin\theta = -\sqrt{3}/2 = -\sin(\pi/3)$

or $\sin\theta = \sin(\pi + \pi/3)$

or $\sin(2\pi - \pi/3)$ as in part (a).

∴ $\theta = 4\pi/3, 5\pi/3$.

Hence the value of θ between 0 to 2π which satisfies both the equations is $4\pi/3$.

∴ General value is

$$\theta = 2n\pi + 4\pi/3 = (2n + 1)\pi + \pi/3.$$

(e) Ans. $2n\pi + \pi/6$.

(f) From the given relation we have

$$1 + \cos 3x + 1 - \cos\left[\frac{\pi}{2} + \left(2x - \frac{7\pi}{6}\right)\right] = 0$$

∵ $\sin\theta = -\cos\left(\dfrac{\pi}{2} + \theta\right)$

$$2\cos^2\frac{3x}{2} + 1 - \cos\left(2x - \frac{2\pi}{3}\right) = 0$$

or $2\cos^2\dfrac{3x}{2} + 2\sin^2\left(x - \dfrac{\pi}{3}\right) = 0$

Above will hold when we have both

$$\cos\frac{3x}{2} = 0 \text{ and } \sin\left(x - \frac{\pi}{3}\right) = 0$$

$$\frac{3x}{2} = \frac{\pi}{2}, \frac{3\pi}{2} \text{ and } x - \frac{\pi}{3} = 0, \pi, 2\pi, \dots$$

∴ $x = \dfrac{\pi}{3}, \pi$ and $x = \dfrac{\pi}{3}, \dfrac{4\pi}{3}, \dfrac{7\pi}{3}, \dots$

∴ $x = \dfrac{\pi}{3}$ is the common value which satisfies both

∴ $x = 2n\pi + \dfrac{\pi}{3} = (6n + 1)\dfrac{\pi}{3}$.

Problem Set (2)

Solution of equations $a\sin x \pm b\cos x = c$. General value satisfying two equations. Miscellaneous equations. Exponential and Logarithmic type.

1. Find all the solutions of the equation

$$\sin x + \sin\frac{\pi}{8}\sqrt{[(1-\cos x)^2 + \sin^2 x]} = 0$$

in the interval $\left[\dfrac{5\pi}{2}, \dfrac{7\pi}{2}\right]$.

2. (a)* Find all values of α for which the equation

$$\sin^4 x + \cos^4 x + \sin 2x + \alpha = 0$$

is valid. Also find the general solution of the equation. **(Roorkee 1990)**

(b) If $\sin^4 x + \cos^4 x = a$ has a real solution, then $\dfrac{1}{2} \le a \le 1$

(c) If the equation $\sin^6 x + \cos^6 x = \lambda$ is to have real solution, then determine the range of λ.

3. (a) $\sin^4 x + \cos^4 x = \dfrac{7}{2}\sin x \cos x$

(b) $\sin^4 x + \cos^4 x = \sin x \cos x$ $\qquad (0 \le x \le 2\pi)$

4. (a)* $\cos^4 x + \sin^4 x = 2\cos\left(2x + \dfrac{\pi}{6}\right)\cos\left(2x - \dfrac{\pi}{6}\right)$

(b)* Determine x such that $\sin^4\dfrac{x}{3} + \cos^4\dfrac{x}{3} > \dfrac{1}{2}$ for all real values of x.

5. $\sin^4 x + \sin^4\left(x + \dfrac{\pi}{4}\right) = \dfrac{1}{4}$

6.* The equation $(\cos p - 1)x^2 + (\cos p)x + \sin p = 0$, where x is a variable has real roots. Prove that p lies in the interval $(0, \pi)$. **(I.I.T. 1990)**

7. (a) Determine all values of a for which the equation $\cos^4 x - (a+2)\cos^2 x - (a+3) = 0$ has solutions and find these.

(b)* $\cos\left(x + \dfrac{\pi}{3}\right) + \cos x = a$

Determine all values of a so that the equation has a real solution. If $a = 1$ then find x in $(0, 2\pi)$. **(I.S.M. 1992)**

(c) The equation $a \sin x + \cos 2x = 2a - 7$ possesses a solution if

(a) $a > 6$ (b) $2 \le a \le 6$

(c) $a > 2$ (d) None of these.

8. (a) $\cos x \cos 6x = -1$.

(b) $\sin 3x + \cos 2x + 2 = 0$.

9. (a)* $\left(\cos \dfrac{\theta}{4} - 2 \sin \theta \right) \sin \theta$

$$+ \left(1 + \sin \dfrac{\theta}{4} - 2 \cos \theta \right) \cos \theta = 0$$

(b) $\cos 4\theta + \sin 5\theta = 2$

10. Solve the system of equations

(a)* $x + y = \pi/4$, $\tan x + \tan y = 1$,

(b)* The solution set of the system of equations

$x + y = 2\pi/3$, $\cos x + \cos y = 3/2$

where x and y are real is ....

11. (a) $2^{\sin x + \cos y} = 1$, $16^{\sin^2 x + \cos^2 y} = 4$.

(b)* $3^{\sin 2x + 2\cos^2 x} + 3^{1 - \sin 2x + 2\sin^2 x} = 28$

12. (a)* $3^{\sin x + \cos y} = 1$, $25^{\sin^2 x + \cos^2 y} = 5$

$0 < x < 2\pi$, $0 < y < 2\pi$

(b) Solve the following equations for x and y :

$5^{(\text{cosec}^2 x - 3 \sec^2 y)} = 1$,

$2^{(2 \, \text{cosec} x + \sqrt{3} \, |\sec y|)} = 64$.   **(Roorkee 2001)**

13. (a) $\sin x \sin y = \dfrac{\sqrt{3}}{4}$, $\cos x \cos y = \dfrac{\sqrt{3}}{4}$

(b) $\cos 2\theta = 0$ and $4 \sin \phi - 6 \sqrt{2} \cos \theta = 5 + 4 \cos^2 \phi$

14. (a) Find all values of k for which the system of equations $\sin x \cos 2y = (k^2 - 1)^2 + 1$

$\cos x \sin 2y = k + 1$

has a solution and determine all solutions.

                                   (Roorkee 1996)

(b)* Find the general values of x and y satisfying the equations

$5 \sin x \cos y = 1$, $4 \tan x = \tan y$.

                                     (Roorkee 1998)

15. (a) The general solution of the equation

$2^{\cos 2x} + 1 = 3.2^{-\sin^2 x}$ is $n\pi, \left(n \pm \dfrac{1}{2} \right) \pi$.

(b)* Find the general values of x and y satisfying the equation $(n^2 + 1) \sin x \cos y = 1$ and

$n^2 \tan x = \tan y$, n being a non-zero real number.

16. (a)* Find real θ such that $\dfrac{3 + 2i \sin \theta}{1 - 2i \sin \theta}$ is

(i) real (ii) purely imaginary.

(b) Does the equation $2 \cos^2 (x/2) \sin^2 x = x^2 + x^{-2}$,

$0 \le x \le \pi/2$ has a real solution ?

(c)* Show that $x = 0$ is the only solution satisfying the equation $1 + \sin^2 ax = \cos x$, where a is irrational.

17. (a)* The number of values of x in the interval $[0, 5\pi]$ satisfying the equation $3 \sin^2 x - 7 \sin x + 2 = 0$ is

(a) 0   (b) 5

(c) 6   (d) 10   **(I.I.T. 1998)**

(b) The number of solutions of the equation $\tan x . \tan 4x = 1$ for $0 < x < \pi$ is

(a) 1   (b) 2

(c) 5   (d) 8

18. (a) Prove that the equation $a \sin x + b \cos x = c$ where $|c| > \sqrt{a^2 + b^2}$ has no solution.

(b) Prove that the equation $\cos x + \sin x = 2$ has no solution.

19. (a)* The number of solutions of the equation $\tan x + \sec x = 2 \cos x$ lying in the interval $[0, 2\pi]$ is

(i) 0   (ii) 1

(iii) 2   (iv) 3   **(I.I.T. 1993)**

(b) The number of solutions of the equation $\sin 5x \cos 3x = \sin 6x \cos 2x$ in $[0, \pi]$ are ....

20. (a)* The equation

$3 (\sin \theta + \cos \theta) - 2 (\sin^3 \theta + \cos^3 \theta) = 8$

has no solution. Is it true or false ?

(b) Prove that there is no solution of the equation $\sin^3 x \cos x + \sin^2 x \cos^2 x + \sin x \cos^3 x = 1$

in the interval $[0, 2\pi]$.

21. (a) Prove that the equation

$\sin x + 2 \sin 2x = 3 + \sin 3x$

has no solution in the interval $0 < x < \pi$.

(b) $\sin^2 x + \dfrac{1}{4} \sin^2 3x = \sin x \sin^2 3x$

22. (a) Solve for x and y

$1 - 2x - x^2 = \tan^2 (x + y) + \cot^2 (x + y)$.

(b)* If $0 \le x \le 2\pi$, then solve the inequality

$2^{\frac{1}{\sin^2 x}} \sqrt{y^2 - 2y + 2} \le 2$

23. (a)* If $|\tan x| = \tan x + \dfrac{1}{\cos x}$ $(0 \le x \le 2\pi)$ then prove that $x = 7\pi/6, 11\pi/6$.

(b) If n be the number of solutions of the equation $|\cot x| = \cot x + \dfrac{1}{\sin x}$ $(0 < x < 2\pi)$, then $n =$

(a) 1   (b) 2

(c) 3   (d) 4

(c) The values of x between 0 and 2π which satisfy the equation $\sin x \sqrt{8 \cos^2 x} = 1$ are in A.P. The common difference of the A.P. is

(a) $\dfrac{\pi}{8}$ (b) $\dfrac{\pi}{4}$

(c) $\dfrac{3\pi}{8}$ (d) $\dfrac{5\pi}{8}$

24. (a) Find all the values of x lying in the interval $(-\pi, \pi)$ which satisfy the equation
$$8^{(1+|\cos x|+\cos^2 x+|\cos^3 x|+\ldots \text{ to }\infty)} = 4^3.$$

(b)* $|\cos x - 2\sin 2x - \cos 3x| = 1 - 2\sin x - \cos 2x$

(c)* If $|\cos x|^{\sin^2 x - \frac{3}{2}\sin x + \frac{1}{2}} = 1$ then find the general values of x.

25. (a)* $\sqrt{6 - \cos x - 7\sin^2 x} + \cos x = 0$

(b) $x^2 + 2x\sin(xy) + 1 = 0$

(c) Find the values of α and β, $0 < \alpha, \beta < \frac{\pi}{2}$; satisfying the following equation :
$$\cos \alpha \cos \beta \cos(\alpha + \beta) = -\frac{1}{8}.$$ **(Roorkee 1999)**

26. (a) Find the smallest positive values of x and y satisfying $x - y = \frac{\pi}{4}$, $\cot x + \cot y = 2$.

(Roorkee 2000)

(b) Solve the equation
$$2(\sin x + \sin y) - 2\cos(x - y) = 3$$
for smallest + ive values.

27. (a) Find the common roots of the equations
$$\cos 2x + \sin 2x = \cot x$$
and $\quad 2\cos^2 x + \cos^2 2x = 1$

(b) $4\cot 2x = 0$ and $\cos^2 x - \sin^2 x = 0$

(c)* Find the common roots of the equations
$$2\sin^2 x + \sin^2 2x = 2$$
and $\quad \sin 2x + \cos 2x = \tan x$

28. (a)* $\sqrt{\sin x \cos y} = 0$
$$2\sin^2 x - \cos 2y - 2 = 0$$

(b)* If exp
$$\{(\sin^2 x + \sin^4 x + \sin^6 x + \ldots \text{inf.})\log_e 2\}$$
satisfies the equation $x^2 - 9x + 8 = 0$, find the value of $\dfrac{\cos x}{\cos x + \sin x}$, $0 < x < \dfrac{\pi}{2}$.

(I.I.T. 1991)

(c) $\sqrt{(1 + \sin 2x)} - \sqrt{2}\cos 3x = 0$, $\pi \le x \le 3\pi/2$

29. (a) Show that the equation $e^{\sin x} - e^{-\sin x} - 4 = 0$ has no real solution.

Solve the following equations :

(b) $(\sin 10°)^{\tan x + \tan 3x}$
$$= \sin^2(2\pi - x) - \cos(\pi - x)\sin\left(\frac{\pi}{2} + x\right)$$

(c)* $\left(\sin \dfrac{\pi}{6}\right)^{\cot 3x + \cot x}$
$$= 2^{\cot x [\sin^2(2\pi - x) \cdot \cos(\pi - x)\sin(\pi/2 + x)]}$$

30. (a)* $\log_5 \tan \theta = \log_5 4 . \log_4 (3\sin \theta)$

(b)* Find the smallest positive number p for which the equation $\cos(p\sin x) = \sin(p\cos x)$ has a solution $x \in [0, 2\pi]$ **(I.I.T. 1995)**

(c)* The number of all possible triplets (a_1, a_2, a_3) such that $a_1 + a_2\cos 2x + a_3\sin^2 x = 0$ for all x is infinite. True or False ?

31. (a) Determine the number of solutions of the equation $\cos 3x \tan 5x = \sin 7x$ lying in the interval $0 \le x \le \pi/2$

(b) Determine the number of solutions if $\sin x + \cos x = \sqrt{2}\sin 5x$, $0 \le x \le \pi$

32. (a)* A triangle ABC is such that
$$\sin(2A + B) = \sin(C - A) = -\sin(B + 2C) = \frac{1}{2}$$
If A, B and C are in arithmetical progression, then find the values of A, B and C. **(I.I.T. 1990)**

(b)* In a triangle ABC, the angle B is greater than angle A. If the values of the angles A and B satisfy the equation $3\sin x - 4\sin^3 x - k = 0, 0 < k < 1$, then show that the value of C is $2\pi/3$. **(I.I.T. 1990)**

(c) The angle B and C $(B > C)$ of a triangle satisfy the equation $2\tan x - \lambda(1 + \tan^2 x) = 0$ then determine the angle A if $0 < \lambda < 1$.

33. (a)* One value of θ which satisfies the equation $\sin^4 \theta - 2\sin^2 \theta - 1 = 0$ lies between 0 and 2π. Is it true ?

(b)* The set of all values of x in the interval $[0, \pi]$ for which $2\sin^2 x - 3\sin x + 1 \ge 0$ is ....

(c) The set of all of θ in the interval $\left[\dfrac{\pi}{2}, \dfrac{3\pi}{2}\right]$ for which $2\cos^2 \theta + \sin \theta \le 2$

34. $A = \{\theta : \tan \theta - \tan^2 \theta > 0\}$
$$B = \left\{\theta : |\sin \theta| < \frac{1}{2}\right\}$$
Determine $A \cap B$.

35.* Choose correct answer from C_2 to match with C_1 $(\sin 3\alpha)/(\cos 2\alpha)$ is

C_1		C_2	
(a) positive	(i)	$\left(\dfrac{13\pi}{48}, \dfrac{14\pi}{48}\right)$	(ii) $\left(\dfrac{14\pi}{48}, \dfrac{18\pi}{48}\right)$
(b) negative	(iii)	$\left(\dfrac{18\pi}{48}, \dfrac{23\pi}{48}\right)$	(iv) $\left(0, \dfrac{\pi}{2}\right)$

(I.I.T. 1992)

36. (a)* Solve for x and y
$$x\cos^3 y + 3x\cos y \sin^2 y = 14$$
$$x\sin^3 y + 3x\cos^2 y \sin y = 13.$$

(b)* $x\sec^3 y + 3x\sec y \csc^2 y = 36$
$$x\csc^3 y + 3x\sec^2 y \csc y = 28$$

(c)* $\sec \theta - \csc \theta = \dfrac{4}{3}$

(Roorkee 1994)

37. If $\sin A = \sin B$ and $\cos A = \cos B$, find the values of A in terms of B.

38. (a) If $\tan(A - B) = 1$, $\sec(A + B) = 2/\sqrt{3}$, find the smallest + ive values of A and B and also their most general values.

(b) If $\cos(A-B) = \dfrac{1}{2}$ and $\sin(A+B) = \dfrac{1}{2}$, find the smallest positive values of A and B and also their most general values.

39. (a) $\cos(2\theta + 3\phi) = \dfrac{1}{2}$ and $\cos(3\theta + 2\phi) = \sqrt{3}/2$

(b) $\sin(\theta + \phi) = 1/\sqrt{2}$ and $\cos(\theta - \phi) = 1/\sqrt{2}$.

40. (a) The number of pairs (x, y) satisfying the equations
$\sin x + \sin y = \sin(x+y)$ and $|x| + |y| = 1$ is

(a) 2   (b) 4

(c) 6   (d) infinite.

(b) If $1 + \sin\theta + \sin^2\theta + \ldots \text{ to } \infty = 4 + 2\sqrt{3}$
$0 < \theta < \pi, \theta \neq \pi/2$, then

(a) $\theta = \pi/6$ (b) $\theta = \pi/3$

(c) $\theta = \pi/3$ or $\pi/6$ (d) $\theta = \pi/3$ or $2\pi/3$

41. (a) The smallest $+$ive x such that
$\tan(x + 20°) = \tan(x - 10°)\tan x \tan(x + 10°)$ is

(a) $30°$ (b) $45°$

(c) $60°$ (d) $75°$

(b) The solutions of the equation
$$9\cos^{12} x + \cos^2 2x + 1 = 6\cos^6 x \cos 2x$$
$$+ 6\cos^6 x - 2\cos 2x \text{ are given by } x =$$

(a) $n\pi + \dfrac{\pi}{2}$ (b) $n\pi + \cos^{-1}\sqrt{\dfrac{2}{3}}$

(c) $n\pi - \cos^{-1}\sqrt{\dfrac{2}{3}}$ (d) none

Solutions to Problem Set (1)

1. The equation can be written as
$$\sin^2 x = \sin^2(\pi/8)\,[(1 - \cos x)^2 + \sin^2 x]$$
$$= \sin^2(\pi/8)\,(2 - 2\cos x)$$

or $\quad 1 - \cos^2 x = (1 - \cos \pi/4)(1 - \cos x)$
$$[\because 2\sin^2(\pi/8) = 1 - \cos(\pi/4)]$$

$(1 - \cos x)\,[(1 + \cos x) - (1 - \cos\pi/4)] = 0$

or $\quad (1 - \cos x)(\cos x + \cos\pi/4) = 0$

$\therefore \quad \cos x = 1 \quad$ or $\quad \cos x = -\dfrac{1}{\sqrt{2}} = -\cos\dfrac{\pi}{4}$
$$= \cos\left(\pi - \dfrac{\pi}{4}\right) = \cos\dfrac{3\pi}{4}$$

Hence the solution sets are given by
$x = 2n\pi, \; x = 2m\pi \pm 3\pi/4, \; m, n \in \mathbf{I}$.

$x = 2n\pi$ gives no solution between $\dfrac{5}{2}\pi$ and $\dfrac{7}{2}\pi$.

And it is easy to check that
$$x = 2m\pi \pm \dfrac{3\pi}{4} = (8m \pm 3)\dfrac{\pi}{4}$$

gives the solutions $2\pi + 3\pi/4$ and $4\pi - 3\pi/4$ *i.e.*
$11\pi/4$ and $13\pi/4$ in the interval $5\pi/2$ and $7\pi/2$ *i.e.* $10\pi/4$
and $14\pi/4$. But $x = 11\pi/4$ does not satisfy the given equation.

Hence the only solution in the given interval is $x = 13\pi/4$.

$\because \quad \sin(11\pi/4) = +$ive and $(+) + (+) \neq 0$
and $\sin(13\pi/4) = -$ive and $(-) + (+) = 0$

2. (a) We write the given equation
$$(\sin^2 x + \cos^2 x)^2 - 2\sin^2 x \cos^2 x + \sin 2x + \alpha = 0$$

or $\quad 1 - \dfrac{1}{2}\sin^2 2x + \sin 2x + \alpha = 0$

or $\quad \sin^2 2x - 2\sin 2x - 2(1 + \alpha) = 0$.

If $\sin 2x = s$, then
$$s^2 - 2s = 2 + 2\alpha \quad \text{or} \quad s^2 - 2s + 1 = 3 + 2\alpha$$

or $\quad (s - 1)^2 = 3 + 2\alpha$

Since $\sin\theta$ lies between -1 and 1, $(s-1)^2$ lies between 0 and 4.

$\therefore \quad 0 < 3 + 2\alpha \leq 4 \quad$ or $\quad -\dfrac{3}{2} \leq \alpha \leq \dfrac{1}{2}$

and $(s - 1) = \pm\sqrt{3 + 2\alpha}$

or $\quad s = 1 \pm \sqrt{3 + 2\alpha}$

or $\quad s = 1 - \sqrt{3 + 2\alpha} \quad$ only as $s \leq 1$

Under this condition, let
$$1 - \sqrt{3 + 2\alpha} = \sin\beta \qquad \ldots(1)$$

Thus $\quad \sin 2x = \sin\beta$.
and so the general solution is given by
$$2x = n\pi + (-1)^n \beta, \quad n \in \mathbf{I}$$

or $\quad x = \dfrac{1}{2}n\pi + \dfrac{1}{2}(-1)^n \beta, \quad n \in \mathbf{I}$,

where β is given by (1).

(b) $1 - \dfrac{1}{2}s^2 = a \quad \therefore \quad s^2 = 2(1 - a) \geq 0 \quad \therefore \quad a \leq 1$

Again $s^2 \leq 1 \quad \therefore \quad 2(1 - a) \leq 1 \quad \therefore \quad \dfrac{1}{2} \leq a$

Hence $\dfrac{1}{2} \leq \alpha \leq 1$

(c) L.H.S. $= 1 - 3\sin^2 x \cos^2 x = 1 - \dfrac{3}{4}\sin^2 2x$
$$= 1 - \dfrac{3}{8}(1 - \cos 4x) = \dfrac{5 + 3\cos 4x}{8} = \lambda$$

$\therefore \quad \cos 4x = \dfrac{8\lambda - 5}{3}$

$\therefore \quad -1 \leq \dfrac{8\lambda - 5}{3} \leq 1 \quad$ or $\quad -3 \leq 8\lambda - 5 \leq 3$

$2 \leq 8\lambda \leq 8 \quad$ or $\quad \dfrac{1}{4} \leq \lambda \leq 1$

$\therefore \quad \lambda$ lies in $\left[\dfrac{1}{4}, 1\right]$.

3. (a) **Refer Q. 2 (a).**
$$1 - \dfrac{1}{2}s^2 = \dfrac{7}{4}s, \text{ where } s = \sin 2x$$

$\therefore \quad s = \dfrac{1}{2}, -4 \text{ (rejected)}$

$\therefore \quad 2x = n\pi + (-1)^n \dfrac{\pi}{6}$ etc.

(b) **As in Q. 2 (a)**, $1 - \dfrac{1}{2}\sin^2 2x - \dfrac{1}{2}\sin 2x = 0$

or $\quad s^2 + s - 2 = 0$

or $\quad (s+2)(s-1) = 0$

$\therefore \quad \sin 2x = 1 = \sin \dfrac{\pi}{2}$ or $\sin\left(2\pi + \dfrac{\pi}{2}\right)$ only

$\because \quad 0 \le x \le 2\pi \ \Rightarrow \ 0 \le 2x \le 4\pi$

$\therefore \quad 2x = \dfrac{\pi}{2} \quad$ or $\quad \dfrac{5\pi}{2} \quad$ or $\quad x = \dfrac{\pi}{4} \quad$ or $\quad \dfrac{5\pi}{4}$

in given interval.

4. (a) $1 - \dfrac{1}{2}\sin^2 2x = \cos 4x + \cos \dfrac{\pi}{3}$

or $\quad 1 - \dfrac{1}{4}(1 - \cos 4x) = \cos 4x + \dfrac{1}{2}$

or $\quad \cos 4x = \dfrac{1}{3} \ \therefore \ x = \dfrac{n\pi}{2} \pm \cos^{-1}\left(\dfrac{1}{3}\right)$

(b) As in last part, we have

$1 - \dfrac{1}{2}\sin^2 2\left(\dfrac{x}{3}\right) > \dfrac{1}{2} \quad$ or $\quad 1 > \sin^2 \dfrac{2x}{3}$

$\Rightarrow \quad \sin^2 \dfrac{2x}{3} < 1$ but not $= 1$.

Above is true for all real values of x except when

$\sin^2 \dfrac{2x}{3} = 1$ *i.e.*, when $\dfrac{2x}{3} = n\pi \pm \dfrac{\pi}{2}$

or $\quad x = \dfrac{3n\pi}{2} \pm \dfrac{3\pi}{4}$

$\therefore \quad$ Solution set is $R - \left\{ x : x = \dfrac{3n\pi}{2} \pm \dfrac{3\pi}{4} \right\}$

5. $2\sin^2 \theta = 1 - \cos 2\theta, \quad$ and $\quad \cos\left(2x + \dfrac{\pi}{2}\right) = -\sin 2x$

$\therefore \quad$ The given equation is

$(1 - \cos 2x)^2 + (1 + \sin 2x)^2 = 1$

$2 + 1 - 2(\cos 2x - \sin 2x) = 1$

$\therefore \quad \cos 2x - \sin 2x = 1$

or $\quad \cos\left(2x + \dfrac{\pi}{4}\right) = \dfrac{1}{\sqrt{2}}$

$\therefore \quad 2x + \dfrac{\pi}{4} = 2n\pi \pm \dfrac{\pi}{4}$

$\therefore \quad x = n\pi, n\pi - \dfrac{\pi}{4}$

6. For real roots, we have

$\cos^2 p - 4(\cos p - 1)\sin p \ge 0 \qquad [B^2 - 4AC \ge 0]$

or $\quad (\cos p - 2\sin p)^2 - 4\sin^2 p + 4\sin p \ge 0$

or $\quad (\cos p - 2\sin p)^2 + 4\sin p (1 - \sin p) \ge 0 \qquad \ldots(1)$

The first term is + ive and $(1 - \sin p) \ge 0$ for all real p.
Hence we must have $\sin p > 0$ for (1) to hold good.
Now $\sin p > 0$ if $0 < p < \pi$

7. (a) $\cos^2 x = \dfrac{(a+2) \pm \sqrt{(a+2)^2 + 4(a+3)}}{2}$

or $\quad \cos^2 x = \dfrac{1}{2}[(a+2) \pm (a+4)] = a + 3, -1$

$\therefore \quad \cos x = \pm\sqrt{a+3} = \cos\alpha, \cos^2 x \ne -1$

$\therefore \quad x = n\pi \pm \alpha$, where $\alpha = \cos^{-1}\sqrt{a+3}$

(b) The given equation is $\dfrac{3}{2}\cos x - \dfrac{\sqrt{3}}{2}\sin x = a$

$\sqrt{p^2 + q^2} = \sqrt{\dfrac{9}{4} + \dfrac{3}{4}} = \sqrt{3}$

$\therefore \quad \dfrac{\sqrt{3}}{2}\cos x - \dfrac{1}{2}\sin x = \dfrac{a}{\sqrt{3}}.$

$\cos\left(x + \dfrac{\pi}{6}\right) = \dfrac{a}{\sqrt{3}}.$

where $-1 \le \dfrac{a}{\sqrt{3}} \le 1 \quad \therefore \quad -\sqrt{3} \le a \le \sqrt{3}$

when $a = 1$, then $\cos\left(x + \dfrac{\pi}{6}\right) = \dfrac{1}{\sqrt{3}} = \cos\alpha$

$\therefore \quad x = 2n\pi \pm \alpha - \dfrac{\pi}{6}$

We have to find the solution in $(0, 2\pi)$

For $n = 0$, $x = \alpha - \dfrac{\pi}{6}\left(\alpha > \dfrac{\pi}{6}\right)$

$\cos\alpha = \dfrac{1}{\sqrt{3}} = \dfrac{\sqrt{3}}{3}, \ \cos\dfrac{\pi}{6} = \dfrac{\sqrt{3}}{2}$

$\therefore \quad \cos\alpha < \cos\dfrac{\pi}{6} \quad \therefore \quad \alpha > \dfrac{\pi}{6}$

For $n = 1$, $x = 2\pi - \alpha - \dfrac{\pi}{6} = \dfrac{11\pi}{6} - \alpha$

$\because \quad 2\pi + \left(\alpha - \dfrac{\pi}{6}\right) > 2\pi$

Hence the only two solutions are

$\alpha - \dfrac{\pi}{6}$ and $\dfrac{11\pi}{6} - \alpha$, where $\alpha = \cos^{-1}\dfrac{1}{\sqrt{3}}$

(c) Ans. (b).
We write the given equation as

$a\sin x + 1 - 2\sin^2 x = 2a - 7$

or $\quad 2\sin^2 x - a\sin x + 2a - 8 = 0$

$\therefore \quad \sin x = \dfrac{a \pm \sqrt{a^2 - 8(2a - 8)}}{4} = \dfrac{a \pm (a - 8)}{4}$

Hence $\sin x = (a - 4)/2, 2$.
But $\sin x = 2$ is ruled out.
and $\sin x = (a - 4)/2$ only if

$-1 \le (a - 4)/2 \le 1$ or $-2 \le (a - 4) \le 2$

or $\quad 2 \le a \le 6$.

8. (a) We have $2\cos x \cos 6x = -2$

or $\quad \cos 7x + \cos 5x + 2 = 0$

or $\quad 2\cos^2 (7x/2) + 2\cos^2 (5x/2) = 0.$

Hence we have to find those values of x which satisfy both the equations

$\cos (7x/2) = 0 \qquad \ldots(1)$

and $\cos (5x/2) = 0 \qquad \ldots(2)$

The general solution of (1) is

$$7x/2 = n\pi + \pi/2$$

or $\quad x = (2n+1)\,\pi/7 \qquad\qquad ...(3)$

and the general solution of (2) is

$$(5x/2) = m\pi + \pi/2.$$

or $\quad x = (2m+1)\,\pi/5 \qquad\qquad ...(4)$

where $m, n = 0, \pm 1, \pm 2, \pm 3, ...$ To find the values of x common to the solutions (3) and (4), we first find that value of x in the interval $[0, 2\pi]$ which is common (if any) to (3) and (4). For this purpose, we put $n = 0, 1, 2, 3, 4, 5, 6$. (Note that for $n = 7$, we go beyond 2π). Then (3) gives

$$x = \pi/7, 3\pi/7, 5\pi/7, \pi, 9\pi/7, 11\pi/7, 13\pi/7$$

Again, we put $m = 0, 1, 2, 3, 4$ (since for $m = 5$, we go beyond 2π).

Then (4) gives $x = \pi/5, 3\pi/5, \pi, 7\pi/5, 9\pi/5$.

Then the value common to the two solutions (3) and (4) in the interval $[0, 2\pi]$ is π.

Hence the required solution is

$$x = 2k\pi + \pi = (2k+1)\,\pi, \quad k \in \mathbf{I}.$$

Alternative : The equation can be written as

$$\cos 7x + \cos 5x = -2. \qquad\qquad ...(1)$$

Now we know that $\cos 7x \le -1$ and $\cos 5x \le -1$ so that $\cos 7x + \cos 5x \le -2$. Hence the equation (1) is satisfied if and only if we simultaneously have

$$\cos 7x = -1. \qquad\qquad ...(2)$$

and $\cos 5x = -1. \qquad\qquad ...(3)$

The solution set of (2) is given by

$$7x = 2n\pi + \pi \quad \text{or} \quad x = (2n+1)\,\pi/7$$

and the solution set of (3) is given by

$$5x = 2m\pi + \pi \quad \text{or} \quad x = (2m+1)\,\pi/5.$$

Now proceed as in the first solution.

(b) **Refer alt. method of part (a).** The given equation will hold good when both $\sin 3x = -1$ and $\cos 2x = -1$ are true simultaneously

$$\sin 3x = -1 = \sin(3\pi/2) \quad \therefore \quad x = \pi/2$$

$$\cos 2x = -1 = \cos \pi \qquad \therefore \quad x = \pi/2$$

$$\therefore \quad x = 2n\pi + \pi/2$$

9. (a) The given equation is

$$\sin\left(\theta + \frac{\theta}{4}\right) + \cos\theta = 2(\cos^2\theta + \sin^2\theta)$$

or $\quad \sin\dfrac{5\theta}{4} + \cos\theta = 2$

Since both terms in L.H.S. are ≤ 1, the above will hold only when $\sin\dfrac{5\theta}{4} = 1$ and $\cos\theta = 1$.

$$\frac{5\theta}{4} = 2n\pi + \frac{\pi}{2}, \theta = 2m\pi$$

$$\theta = (8n+2)\frac{\pi}{5} = 2m\pi \quad \forall \quad m, n \in I \qquad ...(1)$$

or $\quad \dfrac{4n+1}{5} = m \quad$ or $\quad (4n+1) = 5m$

Now both n and m are integers. Above will hold when $n = 1, 6, 11, ...$ or $-14, -9, -4, ...$

All these values of n are covered if we choose $n = 5k + 1$.

Putting the value of n in (1)

$$\theta = \frac{2(4n+1)\pi}{5} = \frac{2}{5}\{4(5k+1)+1\}\pi$$

or $\quad \theta = 2(4k+1)\pi$

Above is the most general solution of the given equations.

(b) $\cos 4\theta = 1, \sin 5\theta = 1$

$$4\theta = 2n\pi \qquad 5\theta = 2m\pi + \frac{\pi}{2}$$

$$\therefore \quad \theta = \frac{n\pi}{2} \qquad \theta = (4m+1)\frac{\pi}{10}$$

Common value between 0 and 2π is $\pi/2$.

$$\therefore \quad \text{G.V. is } 2r\pi + \frac{\pi}{2}.$$

10. (a) $\tan(x+y) = \dfrac{\tan x + \tan y}{1 - \tan x \tan y}$

or $\quad 1 = \dfrac{1}{1 - \tan x \tan y} \quad$ by given equations.

$$\therefore \quad \tan x \tan y = 0$$

Either $\tan x = 0 \quad \therefore \quad x = n\pi, y = \dfrac{\pi}{4} - x = \dfrac{\pi}{4} - n\pi$

or $\quad \tan y = 0 \quad \therefore \quad y = n\pi$

and $x = \dfrac{\pi}{4} - y = \dfrac{\pi}{4} - n\pi$

(b) **Ans. ϕ.** We write the second equation as

$$2\cos\frac{1}{2}(x+y)\cos\frac{1}{2}(x-y) = \frac{3}{2}$$

or $\quad 2\cos\left(\dfrac{1}{3}\pi\right)\cos\dfrac{1}{2}(x-y) = \dfrac{3}{2}$

$$[\because \ x+y = 2\pi/3 \text{ from the first equation}]$$

or $\quad 2 \times \dfrac{1}{2}\cos\dfrac{1}{2}(x-y) = \dfrac{3}{2}$

or $\quad \cos\dfrac{1}{2}(x-y) = \dfrac{3}{2}$, which is impossible.

$\therefore \quad$ The solution set of the given system of equation is the empty set ϕ.

11. (a) $2^{\sin x + \cos y} = 1 = 2^0$ gives

$$\sin x + \cos y = 0. \qquad\qquad ...(1)$$

and $16^{\sin^2 x + \cos^2 y} = 4 = 16^{1/2}$ gives

$$\sin^2 x + \cos^2 y = 1/2. \qquad\qquad ...(2)$$

Eliminating $\cos y$ from (1) and (2), we get

$$2\sin^2 x = \frac{1}{2}, \text{or} \quad \sin x = \pm\frac{1}{2}$$

Two cases arise :

(i) $\sin x = \dfrac{1}{2}$,

$$\cos y = -\frac{1}{2} = -\cos\frac{\pi}{3} = \cos\left(\pi - \frac{\pi}{3}\right)$$

$$\therefore \quad x = n\pi + (-1)^n (\pi/6), \ y = 2n\pi \pm (2\pi/3)$$

(ii) $\sin x = -\dfrac{1}{2}, \quad \cos x = \dfrac{1}{2}$

$$x = n\pi - (-1)^n (\pi/6)$$

and $y = 2n\pi \pm (\pi/3)$

(b) $3^{\sin 2x + 1 + \cos 2x} + 3^{1 - \sin 2x + 1 - \cos 2x} = 28$

or $\quad 3^1 . 3^y + 3^2 . 3^{-y} = 28,$

where $\quad y = \sin 2x + \cos 2x$

$$3t + \frac{9}{t} = 28$$

or $\quad 3t^2 - 28t + 9 = 0$ where $t = 3^y$

$$(3t - 1)(t - 9) = 0$$

$\therefore \quad t = 1/3, 9$ or $3^y = 3^{-1}$ or 3^2

$\therefore \quad \sin 2x + \cos 2x = -1$

or $\quad 2\sin x \cos x + 2\cos^2 x = 0$

or $\quad 2\cos x(\sin x + \cos x) = 0$

$\therefore \quad \cos x = 0, \sin x = -\cos x$

or $\quad \cos x = 0, \tan x = -1 \quad \therefore \quad x = \left(n + \dfrac{1}{2}\right)\pi$

or $\quad x = n\pi - (\pi/4).$

Again $\sin 2x + \cos 2x = 2$

or $\quad \sin(2x + \pi/4) = \dfrac{2}{\sqrt 2} = \sqrt 2 > 1.$

This is not possible.

12. (a) From Ist, $\sin x + \cos y = 0$

$\therefore \quad \cos y = -\sin x$ ...(1)

From IInd, $\sin^2 x + \cos^2 y = 1/2$

or $\quad 2\sin^2 x = 1/2,$ by (1)

$\therefore \quad \sin x = 1/2 \quad \therefore \quad \cos y = -1/2$

or $\quad \sin x = -1/2, \qquad \cos y = 1/2$

$\therefore \quad x = \pi/6, \pi - (\pi/6) = 5\pi/6,$

$\quad y = 2\pi/3, 2\pi - (2\pi/3) = 4\pi/3$

$\therefore \quad (\pi/6, 2\pi/3), (\pi/6, 4\pi/3), (5\pi/6, 2\pi/3),$

$\quad (5\pi/6, 4\pi/3).$

Similarly from 2nd set, we get

$\quad x = \pi + (\pi/6), 2\pi - (\pi/6)$ or $7\pi/6, 11\pi/6$

$\quad y = \pi/3, 2\pi - (\pi/3)$ or $\pi/3, 5\pi/3$

$\therefore \quad \left(\dfrac{7\pi}{6}, \dfrac{\pi}{3}\right)\left(\dfrac{7\pi}{6}, \dfrac{5\pi}{3}\right)\left(\dfrac{11\pi}{6}, \dfrac{\pi}{3}\right)\left(\dfrac{11\pi}{6}, \dfrac{5\pi}{3}\right).$

(b) $1 = 5^0$ and $64 = 2^6$

$\therefore \quad \csc^2 x - 3\sec^2 y = 0$ ...(1)

and $2\csc x + \sqrt 3 |\sec y| = 6$ ...(2)

$\therefore \quad \sqrt 3 |\sec y| = 2(3 - \csc x)$

or $\quad 3\sec^2 y = (6 - 2\csc x)^2$

$\therefore \quad \csc^2 x - (6 - 2\csc x)^2$ by (1)

or $\quad (3\csc x - 6)(6 - \csc x) = 0$

$\therefore \quad \csc x = 6 \ \text{ or } \ 2$ putting in (2)

$\therefore \quad 12 + \sqrt 3 |\sec y| = 6$ when $\csc x = 6$

or $\quad |\sec y| = -\dfrac{6}{\sqrt 3} = -2\sqrt 3$ is rejected

or $\quad 4 + \sqrt 3 |\sec y| = 6$ when $\csc x = 2$

or $\quad |\sec y| = \dfrac{2}{\sqrt 3}$

$\therefore \quad \sec y = \pm\dfrac{2}{\sqrt 3} \ \text{ or } \ \cos y = \pm\dfrac{\sqrt 3}{2}$

$\therefore \quad y = 30 \text{ or } 150$

when $\csc x = 2$ then $\sin x = \dfrac{1}{2}$

$\therefore \quad x = 30° \text{ or } 150°.$

13. (a) Adding and subtracting the given equations, we get

$$\cos(x - y) = \frac{\sqrt 3}{2} \text{ and } \cos(x + y) = 0$$

$\therefore \quad x - y = 2n\pi \pm \dfrac{\pi}{3}$

and $x + y = \left(m + \dfrac{1}{2}\right)\pi$

Take + and then take − with the first set and solve with second by adding and subtracting.

(b) From 1st, we have $2\cos^2\theta - 1 = 0$

$\therefore \quad \cos\theta = \pm\dfrac{1}{\sqrt 2}.$

(i) If $\cos\theta = \dfrac{1}{\sqrt 2}$ then from 2nd equation

$$4s - 6 = 5 + 4 - 4s^2$$

or $\quad 4s^2 + 4s - 15 = 0$

or $\quad (2s + 5)(2s - 3) = 0$

$\therefore \quad \sin\phi = -5/2$ or $3/2$ both are ruled out.

Thus in this case there is no solution.

(ii) If $\cos\theta = -\dfrac{1}{\sqrt 2}$ then as above we will have

$$4s^2 + 4s - 3 = 0$$

or $\quad (2s + 3)(2s - 1) = 0 \quad \therefore \quad s = \dfrac{1}{2}$ only.

$\therefore \quad \cos\theta = -\dfrac{1}{\sqrt 2} = -\cos\dfrac{\pi}{4} = \cos\dfrac{3\pi}{4}$

$\therefore \quad \theta = 2n\pi \pm \dfrac{3\pi}{4}$

$\quad \sin\phi = 1/2 = \sin\pi/6$

$\therefore \quad \phi = n\pi + (-1)^n \dfrac{\pi}{6}.$

14. (a) L.H.S. of the given equations are numerically less than or equal to 1. Hence the equations will be valid when

$$-1 \le (k^2 - 1)^2 + 1 \le 1$$ ...(1)

$\therefore \quad (k^2 - 1)^2 \le 0$

and $-1 \le k+1 \le 1$ or $-2 \le k \le 0$ ...(2)

Now $(k^2-1)^2 \le 0 \Rightarrow k^2-1=0$ ∴ $k=1,-1$

But $k=1$ does not satisfy the 2nd and hence $k=-1$ is the only value for which the equations are valid

∴ $\sin x \cos 2y = 1$

and $\cos x \sin 2y = 0$

Adding and subtracting, we get

$\sin(x+2y) = 1$ and $\sin(x-2y) = 1$

∴ $x+2y = 2n\pi + \dfrac{\pi}{2}$ and $x-2y = 2m\pi + \dfrac{\pi}{2}$

∴ $x = (n+m)\pi + \dfrac{\pi}{2}$

and $y = \dfrac{1}{2}(n-m)\pi$; $n, m \in I$.

Note : The second possibility of $(k^2-1)^2 + 2 \ge 0$ is true for all real values of k but all real values of k do not satisfy the second.

(b) $\sin x \cos y = \dfrac{1}{5}$ ...(1)

$\dfrac{\tan x}{\tan y} = \dfrac{1}{4} \Rightarrow \dfrac{\sin x \cos y}{\cos x \sin y} = \dfrac{1}{4}$

∴ $\cos x \sin y = \dfrac{4}{5}$ ...(2)

From (1) and (2) on adding and subtracting, we have $\sin(x+y) = 1$

and $\sin(x-y) = -3/5 = \sin \alpha$

∴ $x+y = n\pi + (-1)^n \pi/2$

$x-y = m\pi + (-1)^m \alpha$

Adding and subtracting, we get the values of x and y.

15. (a) Write $\cos 2x = 1 - 2\sin^2 x$ and put $2^{-\sin^2 x} = t$

$2^{\cos 2x} = 2^{1-2\sin^2 x} = 2 \cdot (2^{-\sin^2 x})^2 = 2t^2$

∴ $2t^2 - 3t + 1 = 0 \Rightarrow t = 1, 1/2$

$2^{-\sin^2 x} = 1 = 2^0 \Rightarrow \sin^2 x = 0$ ∴ $x = n\pi$

$2^{-\sin^2 x} = \dfrac{1}{2} = 2^{-1} \Rightarrow \sin^2 x = 1$ ∴ $x = n\pi \pm \dfrac{\pi}{2}$

(b) It is a general case of above question for $n=2$,

$x = \tan^{-1} \dfrac{1}{n}$, $y = 2r\pi + \dfrac{\pi}{2} - \tan^{-1} \dfrac{1}{n}$.

16. (a) $\dfrac{3+2i\sin\theta}{1-2i\sin\theta} = \dfrac{3+2i\sin\theta}{1-2i\sin\theta} \times \dfrac{1+2i\sin\theta}{1+2i\sin\theta}$

$= \dfrac{(3-4\sin^2\theta) + i(8\sin\theta)}{1+4\sin^2\theta}$

It will be purely real if I.P. = 0, i.e. $\sin\theta = 0$

∴ $\theta = n\pi$.

It will be purely imaginary if R.P. = 0, i.e.

$3 - 4\sin^2\theta = 0$

∴ $\sin\theta = \pm\sqrt{3}/2 = \pm\sin(\pi/3) = \sin(\pm\pi/3)$

∴ $\theta = n\pi \pm \pi/3$.

(b) We know that both $\cos^2(x/2)$ and $\sin^2 x$ numerically cannot exceed 1.

Also the product $\cos^2(x/2) \sin^2 x$ can never be 1.

∴ $2\cos^2(x/2) \cdot \sin^2 x < 2$. ...(1)

$x^2 + \dfrac{1}{x^2} \ge 2$. ∵ A.M. ≥ G.M. ...(2)

∴ The equation $2\cos^2 \dfrac{x}{2} \sin^2 x = x^2 + \dfrac{1}{x^2}$

in which L.H.S. < 2 and R.H.S. ≥ 2 by (1) and (2) has no real solution.

(c) The given expression $1 - \cos x + \sin^2 ax = 0$

or $2\sin^2 \dfrac{x}{2} + \sin^2 ax = 0$

$\sin \dfrac{x}{2} = 0$ and $\sin ax = 0$.

∴ $\dfrac{x}{2} = n\pi$ and $ax = m\pi$

or $x = 2n\pi$ and $x = \dfrac{m\pi}{a}$

∴ $2n\pi = m\pi/a$ ∴ $m = 2an$

or $a = m/(2n)$ ...(1)

Now m and n are integers so that a is rational, but a is irrational, hence the result (1) will hold good if $m = 0$ and $n = 0$ and in that case $x = 0$ is the only solution.

17. (a) Ans. (c). $(s-2)(3s-1) = 0$

$\Rightarrow s = 1/3 = \sin\alpha$, say

$x = n\pi + (-1)^n \alpha$, $n = 0, 1, 2, 3, 4, 5$ in $(0, 5\pi)$.

(b) Ans. (c).

The given equation can be written as

$\cos 4x \cdot \cos x - \sin 4x \cdot \sin x = 0$

∴ $\cos 5x = 0 \Rightarrow 5x = \left(n + \dfrac{1}{2}\right)\pi$

$x = \dfrac{(2n+1)}{10}\pi$ $0 < x < \pi$

Give n such values so that $2n+1$ is less than 10.

∴ $x = \dfrac{(1,3,5,7,9)}{10}\pi$ for $n = 0,1,2,3,4$

Thus there are only five solutions in given range.

18. (a) Choose $a = r\cos\alpha, b = r\sin\alpha$

∴ $r = \sqrt{(a^2+b^2)}$

Hence the given equation becomes

$\sin x \cos\alpha + \cos x \sin\alpha = c/r$

or $\sin(x+\alpha) = c/\sqrt{a^2+b^2}$.

But since $|c| > \sqrt{a^2+b^2}$, we have

$|\sin(x+\alpha)| > 1$, which is not possible.

Hence the given equation has no solution.

(b) As in last part $c/r = 2/\sqrt{2} = \sqrt{2} > 1$

19. (a) Ans. (c).

$$\frac{1+\sin x}{\cos x} = 2\cos x \quad (\cos x \neq 0)$$

$\therefore \quad 1 + \sin x = 2(1 + \sin x)(1 - \sin x)$

or $\quad 1 = 2(1 - \sin x)$

$\therefore \quad \sin x = \frac{1}{2} \quad \therefore \quad x = \frac{\pi}{6}$ or $\pi - \frac{\pi}{6} = \frac{5\pi}{6}$

$1 + \sin x \neq 0$ because if $1 + \sin x = 0$, *i.e.*
$\sin x = -1$, then $\cos x = 0$ which is not true.

(b) Ans. 5.

$$\sin 8x + \sin 2x = \sin 8x + \sin 4x$$

$\therefore \quad \sin 4x - \sin 2x = 0$ or $2\sin x \cos 3x = 0$

$\therefore \quad \sin x = 0 \implies x = 0, \pi$

$\cos 3x = 0 \implies x = \left(n + \frac{1}{2}\right)\frac{\pi}{3}$

$\therefore \quad \frac{\pi}{6}, \frac{\pi}{2}, \frac{5\pi}{6}$. Thus only 5 solutions.

20. (a) Ans. True. Multiply the 1st term by 1 *i.e.*,
$\sin^2\theta + \cos^2\theta$ and simplify

$\therefore \quad (\sin\theta + \cos\theta)^3 = 8$

or $\quad \sin\theta + \cos\theta = 2$

or $\quad \sin\left(\theta + \frac{\pi}{4}\right) = \frac{2}{\sqrt{2}} = \sqrt{2} > 1$

This is not possible.

(b) $\sin x \cos x (\sin^2 x + \cos^2 x + \sin x \cos x) = 1$

Multiplying both sides by 4, we have
$$\sin 2x (\sin 2x + 2) = 4$$
Above cannot hold for any value of x as
$-1 \leq \sin 2x \leq 1$ otherwise also solving as a
quadratic in $\sin 2x$
$$\sin 2x = -1 \pm \sqrt{5}$$
Both the values are numerically greater than 1.

21. (a) The given equation can be re-written as
$$\sin x + 4\sin x \cos x - (3\sin x - 4\sin^3 x) - 3 = 0$$
$$\sin x (1 + 4\cos x - 3 + 4 - 4\cos^2 x) - 3 = 0$$
Cancel – sign.
$$\sin x [4\cos^2 x - 4\cos x - 2] + 3 = 0$$
or $\quad \sin x (2\cos x - 1)^2 - 3\sin x + 3 = 0$

or $\quad \sin x (2\cos x - 1)^2 + 3(1 - \sin x) = 0$

In the given interval $\sin x$ is +ive and $1 - \sin x$ is
also +ive. Above will hold if $2\cos x - 1 = 0$ and
$1 - \sin x = 0$ simultaneously.
i.e., $\cos x = 1/2$ and $\sin x = 1$ at the same time.
This is not possible. Hence the given equation has
no solution.

(b) Ans. $n\pi$; $n\pi + (-1)^n (\pi/6)$, $n \in \mathbf{I}$

Hint : Write the equation as
$$\sin^2 x - \sin x \sin^2 3x + \frac{1}{4}\sin^2 3x = 0$$

or $\quad \left(\sin x - \frac{1}{2}\sin^2 3x\right)^2 + \frac{1}{4}\sin^2 3x(1 - \sin^2 3x) = 0$

or $\quad \left(\sin x - \frac{1}{2}\sin^2 3x\right)^2 + \frac{1}{16}\sin^2 6x = 0$

The equation is evidently equivalent to the system of
equations $\quad 2\sin x = \sin^2 3x$, $\sin 6x = 0$.

From second of these equations, we have
$$2\sin 3x \cos 3x = 0,$$
i.e. $\sin 3x = 0$ or $\cos 3x = 0$
When $\sin 3x = 0$, first equation gives $\sin x = 0$, from
which $x = n\pi$, $n \in \mathbf{I}$, and when $\cos 3x = 0$, then
$\sin^2 3x = 1$, and then from the first equation we get
$\sin x = \frac{1}{2}$, whose solution is $n\pi + (-1)^n (\pi/6)$, $n \in \mathbf{I}$

22. (a) R.H.S. $= \tan^2(x+y) + \cot^2(x+y) \geq 2$

$\qquad\qquad\qquad\qquad (\because \text{A.M.} \geq \text{G.M.})$

$\therefore \quad$ L.H.S. $= 1 - 2x - x^2 \geq 2$

or $\quad 0 > x^2 + 2x + 1$ or $(x+1)^2 \leq 0$

$\therefore \quad x + 1 = 0 \qquad\qquad\qquad \dots(1)$

$\because \quad (x+1)^2$ cannot be less than zero

$\therefore \quad x = -1$. Putting $x = -1$, we get

$$t^2 + \frac{1}{t^2} = 2, \quad \text{where } t = \tan(x+y)$$

or $\quad (t^2 - 1)^2 = 0$

$\therefore \quad t^2 = 1$ or $\tan^2(x+y) = \tan^2\frac{\pi}{4}$

$\therefore \quad x + y = n\pi \pm \frac{\pi}{4} \quad \therefore \quad y = n\pi \pm \frac{\pi}{4} - x$

or $\quad y = n\pi \pm \frac{\pi}{4} + 1$ by (1)

(b) $\sqrt{y^2 - 2y + 2} = \sqrt{(y-1)^2 + 1} \geq 1$

Since $\sin^2 x \leq 1$ $\therefore \frac{1}{\sin^2 x} \geq 1$ $\therefore 2^{\frac{1}{\sin^2 x}} \geq 2^1$

Hence L.H.S. is always ≥ 2.
But according to the question we have L.H.S. ≤ 2.
Hence the only possibility is that we have the sign
of equality throughout.

Hence we must have $(y-1)^2 + 1 = 1$ $\therefore$ $y = 1$

$\qquad 2^{1/\sin^2 x} = 2$ $\therefore$ $\sin^2 x = 1$ $\therefore$ $\sin x = \pm 1$

$\therefore \quad x = \frac{\pi}{2}, \frac{3\pi}{2}$. $\therefore \left(\frac{\pi}{2}, 1\right)$ and $\left(\frac{3\pi}{2}, 1\right)$ are the

required solutions.

23. (a) $|\tan x| = \pm\tan x$

for + ive, $\tan x = \tan x + \frac{1}{\cos x} \implies \frac{1}{\cos x} = 0$

or $\quad \cos x = \infty$ (not possible)

for – ive, $-\tan x = \tan x + \frac{1}{\cos x}$

$\therefore \quad -2\tan x = \dfrac{1}{\cos x} \quad (\cos x \neq 0)$

$\therefore \quad \sin x = -\dfrac{1}{2} = -\sin \dfrac{\pi}{6}$

or $\quad \sin x = \sin\left(\pi + \dfrac{\pi}{6}\right)$ or $\left(2\pi - \dfrac{\pi}{6}\right)$

$\therefore \quad x = \dfrac{7\pi}{6}$ or $\dfrac{11\pi}{6}$ in given interval.

(b) **Ans. (b).**

Because of $|\cot x|$ we will consider two cases when $\cot x = +$ ive and $\cot x = -$ ive

1st Case : $\cot x = +$ ive

$\cot x = \cot x + \dfrac{1}{\sin x} \Rightarrow \dfrac{1}{\sin x} = 0$

or $\quad \sin x = \infty$

This is not possible.

2nd Case : $\cot x$ is $-$ ive

$\therefore \quad -\cot x = \cot x + \dfrac{1}{\sin x}$

or $\quad 2\cot x + \dfrac{1}{\sin x} = 0$

or $\quad 2\cos x + 1 = 0, \quad \sin x \neq 0$

$\therefore \quad \cos x = -\dfrac{1}{2} = -\cos\dfrac{\pi}{3} = \cos\left(\pi + \dfrac{\pi}{3}\right)$

or $\quad \cos\left(\pi - \dfrac{\pi}{3}\right)$

$\therefore \quad x = \dfrac{2\pi}{3}, \dfrac{4\pi}{3} \quad \therefore \quad n = 2$

(c) **Ans. (b).**

From the given relation, $\quad 2\sin x |\cos x| = \dfrac{1}{\sqrt{2}}$

or $\quad 2\sin x \cos x = \dfrac{1}{\sqrt{2}}$ when $\cos x = +$ ive

$\qquad\qquad = -\dfrac{1}{\sqrt{2}}$ when $\cos x = -$ ive

or $\quad \sin 2x = \sin\dfrac{\pi}{4} = \sin\left(\pi - \dfrac{\pi}{4}\right)$

$\therefore \quad 2x = \dfrac{\pi}{4}, \dfrac{3\pi}{4} \quad \therefore \quad x = \dfrac{\pi}{8}, \dfrac{3\pi}{8}$

Again, $\sin 2x = -\dfrac{1}{\sqrt{2}} = \sin\left(\pi + \dfrac{\pi}{4}\right) = \sin\left(2\pi - \dfrac{\pi}{4}\right)$

$\therefore \quad 2x = \dfrac{5\pi}{4}, \dfrac{7\pi}{4} \quad \therefore \quad x = \dfrac{5\pi}{8}, \dfrac{7\pi}{8}$

$\therefore \quad x = \dfrac{\pi}{8}, \dfrac{3\pi}{8}, \dfrac{5\pi}{8}, \dfrac{7\pi}{8}$

i.e., they are in A.P. of common difference $\dfrac{\pi}{4}$.

24. (a) The given equation may be written as

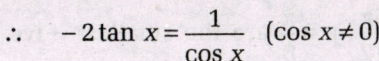

$1 + |\cos x| + \cos^2 x + \cos^3 x| + \ldots\ldots \text{to } \infty = 2$

$\qquad\qquad\qquad\qquad\qquad\qquad\qquad ....(1)$

To sum the G.P., we must observe that for $-\pi < x < \pi, x \neq 0$, we have $|\cos x| < 1$.

Hence $\dfrac{1}{1 - |\cos x|} = 2$ or $1 - |\cos x| = \dfrac{1}{2}$

by S_∞ for G.P.

or $\quad |\cos x| = 1/2$, that is, $\cos x = \pm 1/2$

The values of x in the interval $(-\pi, \pi)$ for which $\cos x = \pm 1/2$ are $\pm \pi/3, \pm 2\pi/3$.

(b) $|2\sin 2x (\sin x - 1)| = 2\sin x (\sin x - 1)$

or $\quad 2|\sin x||\cos x||\sin x - 1| = \sin x (\sin x - 1)$

Since $\sin x < 1 \quad \therefore \quad \sin x - 1 = -$ ive

$\therefore \quad |\sin x - 1| = -(\sin x - 1) = 1 - \sin x$

$\therefore \quad (1 - \sin x)[2|\sin x||\cos x| + \sin x] = 0$

$\therefore \quad 1 - \sin x = 0 \quad \therefore \quad x = 2n\pi + \dfrac{\pi}{2} \qquad ...(1)$

Now consider $2|\sin x||\cos x| + \sin x = 0$

If $\sin x \geq 0$, then $|\sin x| = \sin x$

$\therefore \quad \sin x [2|\cos x| + 1] = 0$

$\therefore \quad \sin x = 0 \quad$ or $\quad x = n\pi \qquad ...(2)$

Also $2|\cos x| + 1$ cannot be zero as sum of two $+$ ive quantities cannot be zero.

If $\sin x < 0$, then $|\sin x| = -\sin x$

Then from (2), we have

$\qquad\qquad \sin x (1 - 2|\cos x|) = 0$

Above implies $1 - 2|\cos x| = 0$

$\therefore \quad |\cos x| = \dfrac{1}{2}$

or $\quad \cos x = \pm\dfrac{1}{2} \quad \therefore \quad x = n\pi \pm \dfrac{\pi}{3} \qquad ...(3)$

$\therefore \quad x = 2n\pi + \dfrac{\pi}{2}, n\pi, n\pi \pm \dfrac{\pi}{3}.$

(c) Take log of both sides.

$\therefore \quad \dfrac{1}{2}(2s^2 - 3s + 1)\log|\cos x| = \log 1 = 0$

If $2s^2 - 3s + 1 = 0$ then $(2s - 1)(s - 1) = 0$

$\therefore \quad s = \dfrac{1}{2}, 1$

$\therefore \quad$ when $\sin x = \dfrac{1}{2}, x = n\pi + (-1)^n \dfrac{\pi}{6}$

But if $\sin x = 1$ then $\cos x = 0$ and by definition of log, $\cos x \neq 0$

If $\log|\cos x| = 0$, then $|\cos x| = 1$ then

$\qquad \cos x = 1, -1 \quad \therefore \quad x = 2n\pi, 2n\pi \pm \pi.$

25. (a) For the equation to hold we must have

$6 - \cos x - 7(1 - \cos^2 x) = +$ ive

$7c^2 - c - 1 = +$ ive

$c = \dfrac{1 - \sqrt{29}}{14}, \dfrac{1 + \sqrt{29}}{14} = \alpha, \beta; \alpha < \beta$

$\therefore \quad c < \alpha \quad$ or $\quad c > \beta \qquad\qquad ...(1)$

Further for the equation to hold good, $\cos x$ must be $-$ ive as $(+$ ive$) + (+$ ive$) \neq 0 \qquad ...(2)$

Transpose $\cos x$ on the other side and squaring,

we have $6c^2 - c - 1 = 0$

or $(2c-1)(3c+1) = 0$

$c = \dfrac{1}{2}$ is not possible as c has to be $-$ive by (2)

$\therefore \quad c = -\dfrac{1}{3}$ where $c < \alpha$ or $c > \beta$

Now c being $-1/3$ cannot be $> \beta$

$\therefore$ We ensure that $c < \alpha$ or $-\dfrac{1}{3} < \dfrac{1 - \sqrt{29}}{14}$

or $-14 < 3 - 3\sqrt{29}$

or $-17 < -3\sqrt{29}$ which is true.

$\therefore \quad \cos x = -\dfrac{1}{3} = -\cos z = \cos(\pi - z)$

$\therefore \quad x = 2n\pi \pm (\pi - z) = (2n \pm 1)\pi \pm \cos^{-1}\dfrac{1}{3}$.

(b) The given equation can be written as

$[x + \sin(xy)]^2 + [1 - \sin^2 xy] = 0$

or $[x + \sin(xy)]^2 + \cos^2(xy) = 0$

$\Rightarrow x + \sin xy = 0$ and $\cos xy = 0$

Now when $\cos xy = 0$ then $\sin xy = 1, -1$

then $x + 1 = 0$ or $x - 1 = 0$

$\therefore \quad x = -1, \sin xy = 1 \quad \therefore \quad \sin y = -1$

$x = 1, \sin xy = -1 \quad \therefore \quad \sin y = -1$

$\therefore \quad y = 2n\pi + \dfrac{3\pi}{2}$

$\therefore \quad (x, y) = \left(\pm 1, 2n\pi + \dfrac{3\pi}{2}\right)$

(c) From the given relation.

$2\cos\alpha \cos\beta \cos(\alpha + \beta) = -\dfrac{1}{4}$

or $[\cos(\alpha + \beta) + \cos(\alpha - \beta)]\cos(\alpha + \beta) = -1/4$

or $4t^2 + 4\cos(\alpha - \beta).t + 1 = 0 \qquad \ldots(1)$

The roots will be real if $\Delta \ge 0$

$16\cos^2(\alpha - \beta) - 16 \ge 0$ or $-\sin^2(\alpha - \beta) \ge 0$

Above is possible only when $\alpha - \beta = 0$, i.e. $\alpha = \beta$.

Then (1) reduces to

$4t^2 + 4t + 1 = 0$ or $(2t + 1)^2 = 0$

$t = -\dfrac{1}{2}$ or $\cos(\alpha + \beta) = \cos\dfrac{2\pi}{3}$

$\therefore \quad \alpha + \beta = \dfrac{2\pi}{3}$ and $\alpha = \beta \quad \therefore \quad \alpha = \beta = \dfrac{\pi}{3}$.

26. (a) $\sin(x + y) = 2\sin x \sin y = \cos(x - y) - \cos(x + y)$

$\therefore \quad \sin(x + y) + \cos(x + y) = \cos(x - y)$

$= \cos\dfrac{\pi}{4} = \dfrac{1}{\sqrt{2}}$

$\therefore \quad \sin\left(x + y + \dfrac{\pi}{4}\right) = \dfrac{1}{\sqrt{2}} \cdot \dfrac{1}{\sqrt{2}} = \dfrac{1}{2} = \sin\dfrac{\pi}{6}, \sin\dfrac{5\pi}{6}$

$\therefore \quad x + y + \dfrac{\pi}{4} = \dfrac{5\pi}{6}$ only as $\dfrac{\pi}{6}$ is rejected

or $x + y = \dfrac{7\pi}{12}$ and $x - y = \dfrac{\pi}{4} = \dfrac{3\pi}{12}$

$\therefore \quad x = \dfrac{5\pi}{12}, y = \dfrac{\pi}{6}$ are the smallest $+$ive values of x and y.

(b) $2 . 2\sin\dfrac{x+y}{2}\cos\dfrac{x-y}{2} - 2\left\{2\cos^2\dfrac{x-y}{2} - 1\right\} = 3$

or $4\cos\dfrac{x-y}{2}\left\{\sin\dfrac{x+y}{2} - \cos\dfrac{x-y}{2}\right\} = 1$

or $4\cos\dfrac{x-y}{2}\left\{\sin\dfrac{x+y}{2} - \sin\left(\dfrac{\pi}{2} - \dfrac{x-y}{2}\right)\right\} = 1$

or $4\cos\dfrac{x-y}{2}\left\{2\sin\left(\dfrac{x}{2} - \dfrac{\pi}{4}\right)\cos\left(\dfrac{y}{2} + \dfrac{\pi}{4}\right)\right\} = 1$

$\cos\left(\dfrac{x-y}{2}\right)\sin\left(\dfrac{x}{2} - \dfrac{\pi}{4}\right)\cos\left(\dfrac{y}{2} + \dfrac{\pi}{4}\right) = \left(\dfrac{1}{2}\right)\left(\dfrac{1}{2}\right)\left(\dfrac{1}{2}\right)$

It is given that x and y are $+$ive and smallest we must have

$\cos\dfrac{x-y}{2} = \dfrac{1}{2}, \sin\left(\dfrac{x}{2} - \dfrac{\pi}{4}\right) = \dfrac{1}{2}, \cos\left(\dfrac{y}{2} + \dfrac{\pi}{4}\right) = \dfrac{1}{2}$

$\therefore \quad \dfrac{x}{2} - \dfrac{\pi}{4} = \dfrac{\pi}{6}, \dfrac{y}{2} + \dfrac{\pi}{4} = \dfrac{\pi}{3} \quad \therefore \quad x = \dfrac{5\pi}{6}, y = \dfrac{\pi}{6}$

These values of x and y satisfy the third relation

$\cos\dfrac{x-y}{2} = \dfrac{1}{2}$.

27. (a) $\cos 2x + 2\sin x \cos x - \dfrac{\cos x}{\sin x} = 0$

or $\cos 2x - \cos x\left(\dfrac{1 - 2\sin^2 x}{\sin x}\right) = 0$

or $\cos 2x[1 - \cot x] = 0$

From 2nd equation $(2\cos^2 x - 1) + \cos^2 2x = 0$

or $\cos 2x[1 + \cos 2x] = 0$

$\therefore \quad \cos 2x = 0$ gives the common root.

$\therefore \quad 2x = \left(n + \dfrac{1}{2}\right)\pi$ or $x = \left(n + \dfrac{1}{2}\right)\dfrac{\pi}{2}$

(b) Here also $\cos 2x = 0$ is the common factor and hence $2x = \left(n + \dfrac{1}{2}\right)\pi$ or $x = (2n + 1)\dfrac{\pi}{4}$.

(c) We write the first equation as

$\sin^2 2x = 2 - 2\sin^2 x$

or $4\sin^2 x \cos^2 x = 2\cos^2 x$

or $\cos^2 x(2\sin^2 x - 1) = 0$

or $\cos^2 x \cos 2x = 0 \qquad \ldots(1)$

The second equation is

$\sin 2x + \cos 2x = \tan x$

or $2\sin x \cos x - \tan x + \cos 2x = 0$

or $\tan x(2\cos^2 x - 1) + \cos 2x = 0$

or $\cos 2x(\tan x + 1) = 0 \qquad \ldots(2)$

From (1) and (2), we get that the common roots of the two given equations are given by $\cos 2x = 0$, hence

$$2x = \left(n + \frac{1}{2}\right)\pi \quad \text{or} \quad x = \left(n + \frac{1}{2}\right)\frac{\pi}{2}$$

28. (a) From 1st either $\sin x = 0$ or $\cos y = 0$

But if $\sin x = 0$ then from 2nd, $\cos 2y = -2$

which is not possible. Therefore, $\sin x \neq 0$

Let $\cos y = 0$

i.e., $y = \left(n + \frac{1}{2}\right)\pi$ then from 2nd

$$2\sin^2 x - (2\cos^2 y - 1) - 2 = 0$$

$$\therefore \quad \sin x = \pm \frac{1}{\sqrt{2}}$$

But $\sin x$ must be +ive because of the factor $\sqrt{\sin x}$.

$$\therefore \quad \sin x = \frac{1}{\sqrt{2}} \text{ only.}$$

$$\therefore \quad x = n\pi + (-1)^n \frac{\pi}{4}.$$

(b) $S_\infty = \dfrac{\sin^2 x}{1 - \sin^2 x} = \dfrac{\sin^2 x}{\cos^2 x} = \tan^2 x$

$\text{L.H.S.} = e^{\tan^2 x \log 2} = e^{\log 2^{\tan^2 x}} = 2^{\tan^2 x} \quad \ldots(1)$

and the roots of $x^2 - 9x + 8 = 0$ are 1 and 8

$\therefore \quad 2^{\tan^2 x} = 1 = 2^0, \, 2^{\tan^2 x} = 8 = 2^3$

$\therefore \quad \tan^2 x = 0, \, \tan^2 x = 3$

or $\quad \tan x = 0, \, \tan x = \pm\sqrt{3}.$

$\therefore \quad x = \pi/3$ is the only value of x s.t. $0 < x < \pi/2$

$$\therefore \quad \frac{\cos x}{\cos x + \sin x} = \frac{1}{1 + \tan x} = \frac{1}{1 + \sqrt{3}}$$

$$= \frac{\sqrt{3} - 1}{3 - 1} = \frac{1}{2}(\sqrt{3} - 1)$$

(c) $|\cos x + \sin x| = -(\cos x + \sin x)$

$= -\sqrt{2}\cos(x - \pi/4)$ in given interval

$\therefore \quad \text{L.H.S.} \Rightarrow \cos 3x + \cos(x - \pi/4)$

or $\cos 3x = -\cos(x - \pi/4) = \cos[\pi - (x - \pi/4)]$

$\therefore \quad 3x = 2n\pi \pm (5\pi/4 - x)$

or $3x = (8n + 5)\dfrac{\pi}{4} - x$ or $(8n - 5)\dfrac{\pi}{4} + x$

$\therefore \quad x = (8n + 5)\dfrac{\pi}{16}$ or $(8n - 5)\dfrac{\pi}{8}$

But $\pi \leq x \leq \dfrac{3\pi}{2}$ or $\dfrac{16\pi}{16} \leq x \leq \dfrac{24\pi}{16} \quad \ldots(1)$

or $\dfrac{8\pi}{8} \leq x \leq \dfrac{12\pi}{8} \quad \ldots(2)$

$\therefore \quad x = \dfrac{21\pi}{16}$ by (1) and $\dfrac{11\pi}{8}$ by (2).

29. (a) Put $e^{\sin x} = t \quad \therefore \quad t^2 - 4t - 1 = 0$

$\therefore \quad t = e^{\sin x} = 2 \pm \sqrt{5}$

$\therefore \quad \sin x = \log_e(2 + \sqrt{5}), \log_e(2 - \sqrt{5})$

$2 + \sqrt{5} > e \Rightarrow \sin x > 1$ which is not possible and $2 - \sqrt{5} = -$ive and $\log_e x$ is defined only when x is +ive. Hence there does not exist any solution.

(b) $\text{R.H.S.} = \sin^2 x + \cos^2 x = 1$

$\therefore \quad \text{L.H.S.} = 1 \Rightarrow \tan x + \tan 3x = 0$

$\Rightarrow \quad \sin 4x = 0$

$\therefore \quad 4x = n\pi$ or $x = \dfrac{n\pi}{4}$ provided

$n \neq 2k$ as in that case $\tan x + \tan 3x \neq 0$ but ∞.

Note : If the L.H.S. $= (\sin 10°)^{\cot x + \cot 3x}$ then

also $x = \dfrac{n\pi}{4}$ but here $n \neq 4k$ as in this case

$\cot x + \cot 3x \neq 0$ but $= \infty$.

(c) $\left(\dfrac{1}{2}\right)^{\cot 3x + \cot x} = 2^{\cot x \cdot 1} = \left(\dfrac{1}{2}\right)^{-\cot x}$

$\therefore \quad \cot 3x + \cot x = -\cot x$

$\dfrac{1 - 3t^2}{3t - t^3} + \dfrac{2}{t} = 0$ where $t = \tan x$

or $t - 3t^3 + 6t - 2t^3 = 0$

$7t = 5t^3 \quad \therefore \quad t^2 = \dfrac{7}{5}$

as for $t = 0$ the equation is not defined

$\therefore \quad \tan x = \pm\sqrt{\dfrac{7}{3}}$

$\therefore \quad x = n\pi \pm \alpha = n\pi \pm \tan^{-1}\sqrt{\dfrac{7}{5}}.$

30. (a) $\log_4 \tan\theta = \log_4 3\sin\theta$

$\because \quad \log_b a = \log_x a \div \log_x b$

$\therefore \quad \tan\theta = 3\sin\theta$

$\therefore \quad \sin\theta = 0$ or $\cos\theta = \dfrac{1}{3}$

$\sin\theta = 0$ is rejected by definition of $\log_a x, x > 0,$ $x \neq 0$

$\therefore \quad \theta = 2n\pi \pm \cos^{-1}\dfrac{1}{3}$

Again $\theta = 2n\pi - \cos^{-1}\dfrac{1}{3}$ is rejected as

$\sin\theta = -$ive

$\therefore \quad \theta = 2n\pi + \cos^{-1}\dfrac{1}{3}$

(b) $\cos\theta = \sin\phi$

Above is possible when both $\theta = \phi = \pi/4$

or $\theta = \phi = 5\pi/4$

$\therefore \quad p\sin x = \pi/4$ or $p\sin x = 5\pi/4$

$p\cos x = \pi/4$ or $p\cos x = 5\pi/4$

Squaring and adding, $p^2 = \dfrac{\pi^2}{16} \cdot 2$ or $\dfrac{25\pi^2}{16} \cdot 2$

$\therefore \quad p = \dfrac{\pi}{4}\sqrt{2}$ only for least positive value or $\quad p = \dfrac{\pi}{2\sqrt{2}}$

(c) Ans. True.

We write the given relation as

$$a_1 + a_2 \cos 2x + a_3 \cdot \dfrac{1}{2}(1 - \cos 2x) = 0$$

or $\quad \left(a_1 + \dfrac{1}{2}a_3\right) + \left(a_2 - \dfrac{1}{2}a_3\right)\cos 2x = 0$

The above relation will hold for all x if

$$a_1 + \dfrac{1}{2}a_3 = 0 \text{ and } a_2 - \dfrac{1}{2}a_3 = 0$$

Choosing $a_3 = k$, $k \in R$, we get $a_1 = -k/2$, $a_2 = k/2$.

Hence the solution set is $(-k/2, k/2, k)$, where k is any real number. Thus the number of solutions is infinite.

31. (a) $\dfrac{\cos 3x \sin 5x}{\cos 5x} = \sin 7x$

or $\quad 2\cos 3x \sin 5x = 2\sin 7x \cos 5x$

or $\quad \sin 8x + \sin 2x = \sin 12x + \sin 2x$

$\therefore \quad 12x = n\pi + (-1)^n 8x$

n even $= 2k$: $4x = 2k\pi$ $\therefore$ $x = \dfrac{k\pi}{2}$

But if k is odd, then it will not satisfy the given equation because L.H.S. $= 0 \times \infty$ and R.H.S. $= \pm 1$

$\therefore \quad k = 2r$, say $\therefore$ $x = r\pi$, $r \in I$

or $\quad x = 0$ only in the given range $\left(0, \dfrac{\pi}{2}\right)$ ...(1)

n odd : $20x = (2k+1)\pi$

$\therefore \quad x = (2k+1)\dfrac{\pi}{20}$

$\therefore \quad x = \dfrac{\pi}{20}, \dfrac{3\pi}{20}, \dfrac{5\pi}{20}, \dfrac{7\pi}{20}, \dfrac{9\pi}{20}$ ...(2)

as we have to find the solution in the given range
Thus there are in all six solutions from (1) and (2).

(b) $\sin\left(x + \dfrac{\pi}{4}\right) = \sin 5x$

$\therefore \quad 5x = n\pi + (-1)^n\left(x + \dfrac{\pi}{4}\right)$

n even : $4x = 2r\pi + \dfrac{\pi}{4}$

$\therefore \quad x = (8r+1)\dfrac{\pi}{4}$, $r = 0, 1$ for $0 \le x \le \pi$

$\therefore \quad x = \dfrac{\pi}{16}, \dfrac{9\pi}{16}$

n odd : $6x = (2r+1)\pi - \dfrac{\pi}{4} = \dfrac{(8r+3)}{4}$

$\therefore \quad x = \dfrac{8r+3}{24}\pi$, $r = 0, 1, 2$ only

$\therefore \quad x = \dfrac{3\pi}{24}, \dfrac{11\pi}{24}, \dfrac{19\pi}{24}$ for $0 \le x \le \pi$.

Thus we have only 5 solutions listed above.

32. (a) We have $A + B + C = 180°$.

Also $2B = A + C$, since A, B, C are in A.P.

$\therefore \quad 3B = 180°$ or $B = 60°$ and $A + C = 120°$

Now from $\sin(2A + B) = 1/2$, we get

$$2A + B = 150° \text{ or } 390°$$

[The other values of $2A + B$ are ruled out, why?]

$\therefore \quad 2A + 60° = 150°$, that is, $A = 45°$

or $2A + 60° = 390°$ which gives $A = 165°$

Hence $C = 120° - A = 75°$

or $C = 120° - 165° = -45°$ (rejected)

$\therefore$ The only set of values of A, B, C is

$$A = 45°, \quad B = 60°, \quad \text{and} \quad C = 75°$$

and this set of values satisfies the other relations

$$\sin(C - A) = -\sin(B + 2C) = 1/2.$$

(b) The given equation can be written as

$$\sin 3x = k, 0 < k < 1$$

Since k lies between 0 and 1, the two values of $3x$ will be in the interval $(0, \pi)$ and will be supplementary angles. It follows that

$$3A + 3B = \pi \text{ or } A + B = \pi/3.$$

Hence $C = \pi - (A + B) = \pi - \pi/3 = 2\pi/3$.

(c) $\lambda = \dfrac{2\tan x}{1 + \tan^2 x} = \sin 2x < 1$.

The values of x are B and C. The value of $2x$ are $2B$ and $2C$ which will be supplementary.

$\therefore \quad 2x = 2B$ or $180° - 2B = 2C$

$\therefore \quad 2B + 2C = 180°$ or $B + C = 90°$

$\therefore \quad A = 90°$

33. (a) Ans. False. We solve the given equation as a quadratic in $\sin^2\theta$. We then get

$$\sin^2\theta = \dfrac{2 \pm \sqrt{4 + 4}}{2} = 1 \pm \sqrt{2}.$$

We reject $\sin^2\theta = 1 + \sqrt{2} > 1$. We also reject the value $1 - \sqrt{2}$ which is negative because $\sin^2\theta$ is certainly positive.

(b) Ans. $[0, \pi/6] \cup [5\pi/6, \pi] \cup \{\pi/2\}$

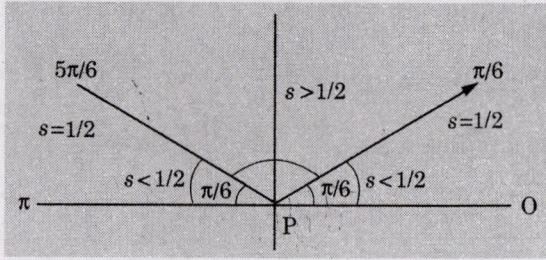

Fig. 2

$2\sin^2 x - 3\sin x + 1 = (2\sin x - 1)(\sin x - 1) \ge 0$

$\Rightarrow \quad \sin x \le 1/2$ or $\sin x \ge 1$.

Hence in the interval $[0, \pi]$, $\sin x \le 1/2$ gives

$0 \le x \le \pi/6$ or $5\pi/6 \le x \le \pi$

and $\sin x = 1$ gives $x = \pi/2$ only

[∵ $\sin x > 1$ is impossible]

Hence required solution set is

$[0, \pi/6] \cup [5\pi/6, \pi] \cup \{\pi/2\}$

(c) As above $2\sin\theta\left(\sin\theta - \dfrac{1}{2}\right) \ge 0$

∴ $\sin\theta \le 0$ or $\sin\theta \ge \dfrac{1}{2}$

∴ $\pi \le \theta \le 2\pi$ or $\dfrac{\pi}{6} \le \theta \le \dfrac{5\pi}{6}$

Given interval is $\left[\dfrac{\pi}{2}, \dfrac{3\pi}{2}\right]$.

∴ $\dfrac{\pi}{2} \le \theta \le \dfrac{5\pi}{6}$ or $\pi \le \theta \le \dfrac{3\pi}{2}$

34. $t(1-t) > 0 \Rightarrow t(t-1) < 0$

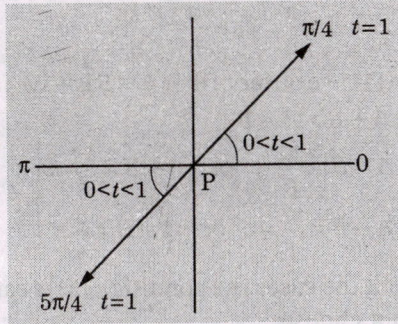

Fig. 3

∴ $0 < t < 1$

∴ $A = 0 < \theta < \dfrac{\pi}{4}$ (1st) or $\pi < \theta < \dfrac{5\pi}{4}$ (4th)

$B = |\sin\theta| < \dfrac{1}{2} \Rightarrow -\dfrac{1}{2} < \sin\theta < \dfrac{1}{2}$

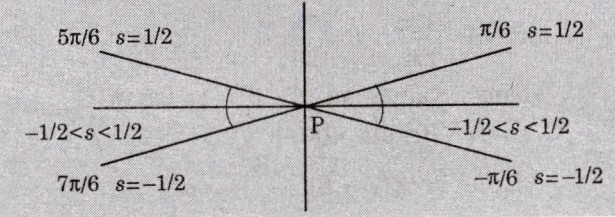

Fig. 4

∴ $B = -\dfrac{\pi}{6} < \theta < \dfrac{\pi}{6}$ or $\dfrac{5\pi}{6} < \theta < \dfrac{7\pi}{6}$

∴ $A \cap B = \begin{cases} 0 < \theta < \pi/6 \\ \text{or } \pi < \theta < 7\pi/6 \end{cases}$

35. Ans. (a) → (iii),   (b) → (i),

For A, $\dfrac{13\pi}{16} < 3\alpha < \dfrac{14\pi}{16}$ and $\dfrac{13\pi}{24} < 2\alpha < \dfrac{14\pi}{24}$

Both 3α and 2α are in 2nd quadrant so that $\sin 3\alpha$ is +ive and $\cos 2\alpha$ is –ive.

∴ $\dfrac{\sin 3\alpha}{\cos 2\alpha} = -$ive ∴ (b) → (i).

For C, $\dfrac{18\pi}{16} < 3\alpha < \dfrac{23\pi}{16}$ and $\dfrac{18\pi}{24} < 2\alpha < \dfrac{23\pi}{24}$

i.e., 3α is in 3rd quadrant,   ∴ $\sin 3\alpha$ is –ive,

2α is in 2nd,   ∴ $\cos 2\alpha$ is –ive.

Hence $\dfrac{\sin 3\alpha}{\cos 2\alpha} = +$ive   ∴   (a) → (iii)

36. (a) First note that $x \ne 0$. Dividing the given equations we get

$\dfrac{\cos^3 y + 3\cos y \sin^2 y}{\sin^3 y + 3\cos^2 y \sin y} = \dfrac{14}{13}$.

Applying componendo and dividendo, we get

$\left(\dfrac{\cos y + \sin y}{\cos y - \sin y}\right)^3 = \dfrac{14+13}{14-13} = 27 = (3)^3$

∴ $\dfrac{\cos y + \sin y}{\cos y - \sin y}$ or $\dfrac{1 + \tan y}{1 - \tan y} = \dfrac{3}{1}$

or $4\tan y = 2$

∴ $\tan y = \dfrac{1}{2}$ so that $\sin y = \dfrac{1}{\sqrt 5}$, $\cos y = \dfrac{2}{\sqrt 5}$.

∴ $y = \tan^{-1}\dfrac{1}{2}$ where $2n\pi < y < 2n\pi + \dfrac{\pi}{2}$

(1st Quad.)   ...(1)

or $\sin y = -1/\sqrt 5$ and $\cos y = -2/\sqrt 5$.

∴ $y = \tan^{-1}\dfrac{1}{2}$ where $2n\pi + \pi < y < 2n\pi + \dfrac{3\pi}{2}$

(3rd Quad.)   ...(2)

In the first case $x\left(\dfrac{8}{5\sqrt{(5)}} + 3 \cdot \dfrac{2}{5} \cdot \dfrac{1}{\sqrt{(5)}}\right) = 14$

∴ $x = 5\sqrt 5$ ...(3)

In the 2nd case $x = -5\sqrt 5$ as above.   ...(4)

(1) and (3); (2) and (4) give the required solutions.

(b) **Refer part (a) $x \ne 0$**

Divide and apply Comp. and Divi.

$\left(\dfrac{\sec y + \operatorname{cosec} y}{\sec y - \operatorname{cosec} y}\right)^3 = \dfrac{36+28}{36-28} = 8 = 2^3$

∴ $\dfrac{\sin y + \cos y}{\sin y - \cos y} = \dfrac{2}{1}$ Again C and D

or $\dfrac{2\sin y}{2\cos y} = \dfrac{2+1}{2-1}$

or $\tan y = 3$ ∴ $y = n\pi + \alpha$

where $\alpha = \tan^{-1} 3$, and from any $x = \pm\dfrac{27}{10\sqrt{10}}$,

corresponding to 1st and 3rd quadrants.

(c) The given equation can be written as

$3(\sin\theta - \cos\theta) = 4\sin\theta\cos\theta = 2\sin 2\theta$.

Square $9(1-s) = 4s^2$, where $s = \sin 2\theta$

or $4s^2 + 9s - 9 = 0$

or $(s+3)(4s-3) = 0$ ∴ $s = -3$ rejected)

or $\sin 2\theta = 3/4$

or $\dfrac{2t}{1+t^2} = \dfrac{3}{4}$, where $t = \tan\theta$.

or $3t^2 - 8t + 3 = 0$

∴ $\tan\theta = \dfrac{4+\sqrt{7}}{3}, \dfrac{4-\sqrt{7}}{3}$

If $\tan\theta = \dfrac{4+\sqrt{7}}{3}$, $\sec^2\theta = 1 + \dfrac{23+8\sqrt{7}}{9}$

$= \dfrac{4}{9}(8+2\sqrt{7}) = \left[\dfrac{2}{3}(\sqrt{7}+1)\right]^2$

∴ $\sec\theta = \dfrac{2}{3}(\sqrt{7}+1)$, $\operatorname{cosec}\theta = \dfrac{2}{3}(\sqrt{7}-1)$,

provided θ belongs to 1st quadrant   ...(1)

or $\sec\theta = -\dfrac{2}{3}(\sqrt{7}+1)$,

$\operatorname{cosec}\theta = -\dfrac{2}{3}(\sqrt{7}-1)$

provided θ belongs to 3rd quadrant   ...(2)

Now $\sec\theta - \operatorname{cosec}\theta = 4/3$

The above is satisfied by θ in 1st quadrant

∴ $\tan\theta = \dfrac{4+\sqrt{7}}{3} = \tan\alpha$

∴ $\theta = 2n\pi + \alpha$

If $\tan\theta = \dfrac{4-\sqrt{7}}{3}$, then $\sec\theta = \dfrac{2}{3}(\sqrt{7}-1)$,

$\operatorname{cosec}\theta = \dfrac{2}{3}(\sqrt{7}+1)$ provided θ lies in 1st quadrant.

        ...(3)

or $\sec\theta = -\dfrac{2}{3}(\sqrt{7}-1)$

and $\operatorname{cosec}\theta = -\dfrac{2}{3}(\sqrt{7}+1)$

provided θ lies in 3rd quadrant   ...(4)

Now $\sec\theta - \operatorname{cosec}\theta = 4/3$

The above is satisfied by θ in 3rd quadrant.

∴ $\tan\theta = \tan\beta$

∴ $\theta = 2n\pi + (\pi + \tan^{-1}\beta)$

where $\tan\beta = \dfrac{1}{3}(4-\sqrt{7})$.

37. $\sin A - \sin B = 0$, $\cos A - \cos B = 0$

$2\sin\dfrac{A-B}{2}\cos\dfrac{A+B}{2} = 0$,

and $2\sin\dfrac{A+B}{2}\sin\dfrac{B-A}{2} = 0$

or $-2\sin\dfrac{A+B}{2}\sin\dfrac{A-B}{2} = 0$.

From the two we observe that the common factor gives

$\sin\dfrac{A-B}{2} = 0$ ∴ $\dfrac{A-B}{2} = n\pi$

$A - B = 2n\pi$ ∴ $A = 2n\pi + B$.

38. (a) Let us consider the + ive values between 0 and 2π.

$\tan(A-B) = 1 = \tan\dfrac{\pi}{4}$.

∴ $A - B = n\pi + \dfrac{\pi}{4}$,

$A - B = \dfrac{\pi}{4}, \dfrac{5\pi}{4}$ ...(1)

$\sec(A+B) = \dfrac{2}{\sqrt{3}}$

∴ $\cos(A+B) = \dfrac{\sqrt{3}}{2} = \cos\dfrac{\pi}{6}$.

∴ $A + B = 2n\pi \pm \dfrac{\pi}{6}$,

∴ $A + B = \dfrac{\pi}{6}, 2\pi - \dfrac{\pi}{6} = \dfrac{11\pi}{6}$.   ...(2)

From (1), we observe that $A - B$ is + ive i.e. $A > B$.

∴ $A + B > A - B$ ...(3)

$\left\{\begin{array}{l} \therefore \ A + B = \dfrac{11}{6}\pi \ \text{ or } \ A + B = \dfrac{11}{6}\pi \\[2mm] \therefore \ A - B = \dfrac{\pi}{4} \quad\ \text{ or } \ A - B = \dfrac{5}{4}\pi \end{array}\right\}$ ...(4)

In both the cases the condition (3) is satisfied. We cannot choose

$A + B = \dfrac{\pi}{6}$ and $A - B = \dfrac{\pi}{4}$ or $\dfrac{5\pi}{4}$

because these equations will not satisfy the condition (3).

Solving the equations in (4), we get

$A = \dfrac{25}{24}\pi, \ B = \dfrac{19\pi}{24}$,

or $A = \dfrac{37\pi}{24}, \ B = \dfrac{7\pi}{24}$

General values $\tan(A-B) = 1 = \tan(\pi/4)$

∴ $A - B = m\pi + (\pi/4)$ ...(1)

Also $\cos(A+B) = \dfrac{\sqrt{3}}{2} = \cos\dfrac{\pi}{6}$

∴ $A + B = 2n\pi + \dfrac{\pi}{6}$ or $2n\pi - \dfrac{\pi}{6}$

Solving both with (1), we get

$A = (2n+m)\dfrac{\pi}{2} + \dfrac{5\pi}{24}, \ B = (2n-m)\dfrac{\pi}{2} - \dfrac{\pi}{24}$

or $A = (2n+m)\dfrac{\pi}{2} + \dfrac{\pi}{24}, \ B = (2n-m)\dfrac{\pi}{2} - \dfrac{5\pi}{24}$.

(b) Proceed as in part (a).

$A = \dfrac{7\pi}{12}, \ B = \dfrac{\pi}{4}$

$A = (2n+m)\dfrac{\pi}{2} + \dfrac{\pi}{6} + (-1)^m\dfrac{\pi}{12}$,

and $B = (m-2n)\dfrac{\pi}{2} - \dfrac{\pi}{6} + (-1)^m\dfrac{\pi}{12}$

or $A = (2n + m)\dfrac{\pi}{2} - \dfrac{\pi}{6} + (-1)^m \dfrac{\pi}{12}$

and $B = (m - 2n)\dfrac{\pi}{2} - \dfrac{\pi}{6} + (-1)^m \dfrac{\pi}{12}$.

39. (a) $\cos(2\theta + 3\phi) = \dfrac{1}{2} = \cos(\pi/3)$

∴ $2\theta + 3\phi = 2n\pi \pm \pi/3$. ...(1)

and $\cos(3\theta + 2\phi) = \sqrt{3}/2 = \cos(\pi/6)$.

∴ $3\theta + 2\phi = 2p\pi \pm \pi/6$. ...(2)

Multiply (1) by 3 and (2) by 2 and subtract

$\phi = (6n - 4p)\dfrac{\pi}{5} \pm \dfrac{\pi}{5} \mp \dfrac{\pi}{15}$.

Similarly, multiply (1) by 2 and (2) by 3 and subtract

$\theta = (6p - 4n)\dfrac{\pi}{5} \pm \dfrac{\pi}{10} \mp \dfrac{2\pi}{15}$.

(b) $\theta = (2n + p)\dfrac{\pi}{2} + (-1)^p \dfrac{\pi}{8} \pm \dfrac{\pi}{8}$

$\phi = (p - 2n)\dfrac{\pi}{8} + (-1)^p \dfrac{\pi}{8} \mp \dfrac{\pi}{8}$.

40. (a) Ans. (c).

The first equation can be written as

$2\sin\dfrac{1}{2}(x + y)\cos\dfrac{1}{2}(x - y)$

$= 2\sin\dfrac{1}{2}(x + y)\cos\dfrac{1}{2}(x + y)$.

or $2\sin\dfrac{1}{2}(x + y)\left\{\cos\dfrac{1}{2}(x - y)\right.$

$\left. - \cos\dfrac{1}{2}(x + y)\right\} = 0$

or $2\sin\dfrac{1}{2}(x + y) \cdot 2\sin\dfrac{1}{2}x\sin\dfrac{1}{2}y = 0$

∴ either $\sin\dfrac{1}{2}(x + y) = 0$,

or $\sin\dfrac{1}{2}x = 0$ or $\sin\dfrac{1}{2}y = 0$ ...(1)

∴ $x + y = 0$, $x = 0$, $y = 0$.

$|x| + |y| = 1$ i.e. $x + y = 1$, $x - y = 1$

$x + y = -1$, $x - y = -1$

When $x + y = 0$, we have to reject $x + y = 1$, or -1 and solve it with $x - y = 1$ or $x - y = -1$ which give $(1/2, -1/2)$ or $(-1/2, 1/2)$ as the possible solutions. Again solving with $x = 0$ we get $(0, \pm1)$ and solving with $y = 0$ we get $(\pm1, 0)$ as the other solutions. Thus we have six sets of solutions for x and y.

(b) Ans. (d).

The left hand side of the given equation is an infinite G.P. with common ratio $\sin\theta$. Since $0 < \theta < \pi, \theta \neq \pi/2$, we have $0 < \sin\theta < 1$. We now

sum up the infinite G.P. so that the given equation becomes $1/(1 - \sin\theta) = 4 + 2\sqrt{3}$

or $1 - \sin\theta = 1/(4 + 2\sqrt{3}) = \dfrac{4 - 2\sqrt{3}}{16 - 12} = \dfrac{4 - 2\sqrt{3}}{4}$

or $1 - \sin\theta = 1 - \dfrac{\sqrt{3}}{2}$ ∴ $\sin\theta = \dfrac{\sqrt{3}}{2} = \sin\dfrac{\pi}{3}$.

∴ $\theta = \pi/3$ or $2\pi/3$ in the interval $0 < \theta < \pi$.

41. (a) Ans. (c).

$\dfrac{\tan(x + 20°)}{\tan x} = \tan(x - 10°)\tan(x + 10°)$

or $\dfrac{\sin(x + 20°)\cos x}{\cos(x + 20°)\sin x} = \dfrac{\sin(x - 10°)\sin(x + 10°)}{\cos(x - 10°)\cos(x + 10°)}$

Apply componendo and dividendo,

$\dfrac{\sin(x + 20° + x)}{\sin(x + 20° - x)} = \dfrac{\cos(\overline{x + 10°} - \overline{x - 10°})}{-\cos(\overline{x + 10°} + \overline{x - 10°})}$

or $\sin(2x + 20°)\cos 2x = -\sin 20° \cos 20°$

$= -\dfrac{1}{2}\sin 40°$

Multiply both sides by 2.

∴ $\sin(4x + 20°) + \sin 20° = -\sin 40°$

∴ $\sin(4x + 20°) = -(\sin 40° + \sin 20°)$

or $\sin(4x + 20°) = -2\sin 30° \cos 10° = -\cos 10°$

or $\sin(4x + 20°) = -\sin 80° = \sin(-80°)$

∴ $4x + 20° = n\pi + (-1)^n(-80°)$ ∀ $n \in I$

We have to find smallest +ive value of x and we choose $n = 1$.

∴ $4x + 20° = \pi - (-80°) = 260°$

∴ $4x = 240°$ ∴ $x = 60°$

(b) Ans. (a), (b), (c).

The given equation can be written as

$9\cos^{12} x - 6\cos^6 x(1 + \cos 2x)$

$+ (1 + \cos^2 2x + 2\cos 2x) = 0$

or $(9\cos^{12} x - 6\cos^6 x \cdot 2\cos^2 x)$

$+ (1 + \cos 2x)^2 = 0$

or $9\cos^{12} x - 12\cos^8 x + (2\cos^2 x)^2 = 0$

or $\cos^4 x(9\cos^8 x - 12\cos^4 x + 4) = 0$

or $\cos^4 x(3\cos^4 x - 2)^2 = 0$

∴ $\cos x = 0 \Rightarrow x = n\pi + \dfrac{\pi}{2} \Rightarrow$ (a)

$\cos^2 x = \sqrt{2/3} = \cos^2 \alpha$, say

∴ $x = n\pi \pm \alpha = n\pi \pm \cos^{-1}\sqrt{2/3} \Rightarrow$ (b), (c).

Problem Set (3)

▶ **Multiple Choice Questions**

1. If $\sin \theta = \sin \alpha$, then the angles θ and α are related by
   (a) $\theta = n\pi \pm \alpha$
   (b) $\theta = 2n\pi + (-1)^n \alpha$
   (c) $\theta = n\pi + (-1)^n \alpha$
   (d) $\theta = (2n+1)\pi + \alpha$.

2. The general solution of the trigonometrical equation $\sin x + \cos x = 1$, for $n = 0, \pm 1, \pm 2, \ldots$ is given by
   (a) $x = 2n\pi$
   (b) $x = 2n\pi + \dfrac{1}{2}\pi$
   (c) $x = n\pi + (-1)^n (\pi/4) - \pi/4$
   (d) None of these

3. The general solution of equation
   $\sin^2 \theta \sec \theta + \sqrt{3} \tan \theta = 0$ is
   (a) $\theta = n\pi + (-1)^{n+1} \dfrac{\pi}{3}$
   (b) $\theta = n\pi$
   (c) $\theta = n\pi + (-1)^{n+1} \dfrac{\pi}{6}$
   (c) $\theta = \dfrac{n\pi}{2}$

4. The solution set of $(2\cos x - 1)(3 + 2\cos x) = 0$ in the interval $0 \le x \le 2\pi$ is
   (a) $\{\pi/3\}$
   (b) $\{\pi/3, 5\pi/3\}$
   (c) $\{\pi/3, 5\pi/3, \cos^{-1}(-3/2)\}$
   (d) None of these.

5. (i) If $\tan a\theta - \tan b\theta = 0$, then the values of θ form a series in
   (a) A.P.
   (b) G.P.
   (c) H.P.
   (d) None of these.

   (ii) The solutions of the equations $\cos a\theta + \cos b\theta = 0$ form an A.P. whose common difference is $\dfrac{2\pi}{a-b}$ or $\dfrac{2\pi}{a+b}$ where a and b are distinct real numbers. Is this statement true ?

6. If $\sin 5x + \sin 3x + \sin x = 0$, then the value of x other than zero, lying between $0 \le x \le \pi/2$ is
   (a) $\pi/6$
   (b) $\pi/12$
   (c) $\pi/3$
   (d) $\pi/4$

7. (i) The maximum value of $\sin\left(x + \dfrac{\pi}{6}\right) + \cos\left(x + \dfrac{\pi}{6}\right)$ in the interval $\left(0, \dfrac{\pi}{2}\right)$ is attained when $x =$
   (a) $\pi/12$
   (b) $\pi/6$
   (c) $\pi/3$
   (d) $\pi/2$

   (ii) If $x = X\cos\theta - Y\sin\theta$, and $y = X\sin\theta + Y\cos\theta$ and $x^2 + 4xy + y^2 = AX^2 + BY^2, 0 \le \theta \le \pi/2$, then
   (a) $\theta = \pi/6$
   (b) $\theta = \pi/4$
   (c) $A = 3$
   (d) $B = 1$

8. The general solution of the equation $\tan^2 \alpha + 2\sqrt{3}\tan \alpha = 1$ is given by
   (a) $\theta = \dfrac{\pi}{2}$
   (b) $\left(n + \dfrac{1}{2}\right)\pi$
   (c) $(6n+1)\dfrac{\pi}{12}$
   (d) $\dfrac{n\pi}{12}$

9. Let $P = \{\theta : \sin\theta - \cos\theta = \sqrt{2}\cos\theta\}$ and $\theta = \{\theta : \sin\theta + \cos\theta = \sqrt{2}\sin\theta]$ be two sets, then
   (a) $P \subset Q$ and $Q - P \ne \phi$
   (b) $Q \subset P$
   (c) $P \not\subset Q$
   (d) $P = Q$ **(IIT-JEE 2011)**

10. For $0 < \theta < \dfrac{\pi}{2}$ the solutions of
    $\displaystyle\sum_{m=1}^{6} \text{cosec}\left(\theta + \dfrac{(m-1)\pi}{4}\right)\text{cosec}\left(\theta + \dfrac{m\pi}{4}\right) = 4\sqrt{2}$ is
    (a) $\dfrac{\pi}{4}$
    (b) $\dfrac{\pi}{6}$
    (c) $\dfrac{\pi}{12}$
    (d) $\dfrac{5\pi}{12}$
    (IIT-JEE 2009)

11. The positive integer value of $n > 3$ satisfying the equation $\dfrac{1}{\sin\left(\dfrac{\pi}{n}\right)} = \dfrac{1}{\sin\left(\dfrac{2\pi}{n}\right)} + \dfrac{1}{\sin\left(\dfrac{3\pi}{n}\right)}$ is
    (a) 17
    (b) 3
    (c) $\dfrac{1}{7}$
    (d) $\dfrac{1}{3}$
    (IIT-JEE 2011)

12. The number of all possible values of 8, where $0 < \theta < \pi$ for which the system of equations
    $$(y + z)\cos 3\theta = (xyz)\sin 3\theta$$
    $$x\sin 3\theta = \dfrac{2\cos 3\theta}{y} + \dfrac{2\sin 3\theta}{z}$$
    and $(xyz)\sin 3\theta = (y + 2z)\cos 3\theta + y\sin 3\theta$
    have a solution (x_0, y_0, z_0) with $y_0 z_0 \ne 0$ is
    (a) 3
    (b) 2
    (c) 1
    (d) 4
    (IIT-JEE 2010)

13. The number of values of θ in the interval $\left(-\dfrac{\pi}{2}, \dfrac{\pi}{2}\right)$ such that $\theta \ne \dfrac{n\pi}{5}$ for $n = 0, \pm 1 \pm 2$ and $\tan\theta = \cot 5\theta$ as well as $\sin 2\theta = \cos 4\theta$ is
    (a) 3
    (b) 4
    (c) $\dfrac{1}{4}$
    (d) 0
    (IIT-JEE 2010)

▶ **True and False Type Questions :**

14. If $\sin x = \sin \lambda$, then the values of $\sin(x/3)$ are $\sin(\lambda/3), \sin[(\pi - \lambda)/3]$ and $-\sin[(\pi + \lambda)/3]$

15. (i) The solution set of the equation $\sin 2x + \cos 2x = -1$ is given by
    $[(-1)^{n+1} - 1]\dfrac{\pi}{8} + \dfrac{1}{2}n\pi, n \in I.$

(ii) $\theta + \frac{\pi}{4} = n\pi + (-1)^n \frac{\pi}{6}$ and $\theta - \frac{\pi}{4} = 2n\pi \pm \frac{\pi}{3}$. The two series of angle θ given by above are same.

Fill in the blanks :

16. $A = \{\theta : 2\cos^2\theta + \sin\theta \le 2\}$

$B = \left\{\theta : \frac{\pi}{2} \le \frac{3\pi}{2}\right\}$, then $A \cap B = \ldots\ldots$

Hints/Solutions and Answers to Problem Set (3)

1. Ans. (c).

2. Ans. (c).
We write the given equation as
$$\frac{1}{\sqrt{(2)}}\sin x + \frac{1}{\sqrt{(2)}}\cos x = \frac{1}{\sqrt{(2)}}$$
or $\cos(\pi/4)\sin x + \sin(\pi/4)\cos x = \sin(\pi/4)$
or $\sin(x + \pi/4) = \sin(\pi/4)$
$\therefore\ x + \pi/4 = n\pi + (-1)^n (\pi/4)$
or $x = n\pi + (-1)^n (\pi/4) - (\pi/4)$.
where $n = 0, \pm 1, \pm 2, \ldots\ldots$

3. Ans. (b). $\sin\theta(\sin\theta + \sqrt{3}) = 0$
$\therefore\ \sin\theta = 0$ as $\cos\theta \ne 0, \sin\theta \ne -\sqrt{3}$

4. Ans. (b).
We have $2\cos x - 1 = 0$ or $3 + 2\cos x = 0$
But $3 + 2\cos x = 0$ gives $\cos x = -3/2$ which is not possible. From $2\cos x - 1 = 0$, we get $\cos x = 1/2$ whence $x = \pi/3, 2\pi - \pi/3$, i.e., $5\pi/3$ in the interval $0 \le x \le 2\pi$. Thus the solution set in the given interval is $\{\pi/3, 5\pi/3\}$.

5. (i) Ans. (a). We have
$$\tan a\theta = \tan b\theta \Rightarrow a\theta = n\pi + b\theta, n \in I$$
$$\Rightarrow (a-b)\theta = n\pi \Rightarrow \theta = n\pi/(a-b), n \in I.$$
Putting $n = \ldots -3, -2, -1, 0, 1, 2, 3, \ldots$ we get
$$\theta = \ldots -3\pi/(a-b), -2\pi/(a-b), -\pi/(a-b)$$
$$0, \pi/(a-b), 2\pi/(a-b), 3\pi/(a-b), \ldots$$
Thus the values of θ form an A.P. with common difference $\pi/(a-b)$.

(ii) Ans. True.
$$2\cos\frac{a+b}{2}\theta\cos\frac{a-b}{2}\theta = 0 \text{ etc.}$$

6. Ans. (c). We have
$$\sin 5x + \sin 3x + \sin x = 0$$
$$\Rightarrow (\sin 5x + \sin x) + \sin 3x = 0$$
$$\Rightarrow 2\sin 3x\cos 2x + \sin 3x = 0$$
$$\Rightarrow \sin 3x(2\cos 2x + 1) = 0$$
$$\therefore\ \sin 3x = 0 \quad \text{or} \quad 2\cos 2x + 1 = 0$$
Now $\sin 3x = 0$ gives $3x = n\pi$ or $x = n\pi/3$.
and $2\cos 2x + 1 = 0 \Rightarrow \cos 2x = -\frac{1}{2}$
$$\Rightarrow 2x = 2n\pi \pm (2\pi/3) \Rightarrow x = n\pi \pm (\pi/3).$$
Hence in the interval
$0 \le x \le \pi/2$, $x = n\pi/3$ gives $x = 0, \pi/3$.

and $x = n\pi \pm (\pi/3)$ gives $x = \pi/3$.
Hence $\pi/3$ is the only value other than 0 satisfying the given equation .

7. (i) Ans. (a).
$$\sqrt{2}\cos\left(x + \frac{\pi}{6} - \frac{\pi}{4}\right) = \sqrt{2}\cos\left(x - \frac{\pi}{12}\right) \text{ etc.}$$
It is max., when $x - \pi/12 = 0$ i.e. $x = \pi/12$

(ii) Ans. (b) and (c).
On putting for x and y in the given relation, we get
$$(1 + 2\sin 2\theta)X^2 + 4\cos 2\theta\, XY$$
$$+ (1 - 2\sin 2\theta)Y^2 = AX^2 + BY^2.$$
Comparing, we get $4\cos 2\theta = 0$.
$\therefore\ 2\theta = \pi/2$ or $\theta = \pi/4$
$\therefore\ 1 + 2\sin 2\theta = A$ or $1 + 2.1 = A = 3$
$\because\ 2\theta = \pi/2$
$1 - 2\sin 2\theta$
or $1 - 2.1 = B$ $\therefore\ B = -1$
$\therefore$ (d) is not corrrect.

8. Ans. (c).
$$(\tan\alpha + \sqrt{3})^2 = 4$$
$\therefore\ \tan\alpha = 2 - \sqrt{3}, -2 - \sqrt{3}$
or $\tan\alpha = \tan 15°, -\tan 75° = \tan\frac{\pi}{12}, \tan\left(-\frac{5\pi}{12}\right)$
$\therefore\ \alpha = n\pi + \frac{\pi}{12} = 2n.\frac{\pi}{2} + \frac{\pi}{12} = \text{Even } \frac{\pi}{2} + \frac{\pi}{12}$ ...(1)
$\alpha = n\pi + \left(-\frac{5\pi}{12}\right) = n\pi - \frac{6\pi}{12} + \frac{\pi}{12}$
$= (2n-1)\frac{\pi}{2} + \frac{\pi}{12} = \text{odd } \frac{\pi}{2} + \frac{\pi}{12}$ ...(2)
From (1) and (2),
$$\alpha = k\frac{\pi}{2} + \frac{\pi}{12} = (6k+1)\frac{\pi}{12}.$$

9. Ans. (d).
$$P = [\theta : \sin\theta - \cos\theta = \sqrt{2}\cos\theta]$$
$$\Rightarrow \sin\theta = (\sqrt{2} + 1)\cos\theta \Rightarrow \theta = n\pi + \frac{3\pi}{8}, n \in I$$
and $Q = \{\theta : \sin\theta + \cos\theta = \sqrt{2}\sin\theta)$
$\therefore\ \cos\theta = (\sqrt{2} - 1)\sin\theta$
$$\Rightarrow \tan\theta = \frac{1}{\sqrt{2} - 1} = \sqrt{2} + 1 \Rightarrow \theta = n\pi + \frac{3\pi}{8}, n \in I$$
$$\Rightarrow P = Q$$

10. Ans. (c) and (d).
$$0 < \theta < \frac{\pi}{2}$$
$$\sum_{m=1}^{6} \csc\left(\theta + \frac{(m-1)\pi}{4}\right)\csc\left(\theta + \frac{m\pi}{4}\right) = 4\sqrt{2}$$
$$\Rightarrow \sum_{m=1}^{6} \frac{1}{\sin\left(\theta + \frac{(m-1)\pi}{4}\right).\sin\left(\theta + \frac{m\pi}{4}\right)} = 4\sqrt{2}$$

$\Rightarrow \displaystyle\sum_{m=1}^{6} \frac{\sin\left[\theta + \frac{m\pi}{4} - \left(\theta + \frac{(m-1)\pi}{4}\right)\right]}{\sin\frac{\pi}{4}\left\{\sin\left(\theta + \frac{(m-1)\pi}{4}\right)\sin\left(\theta + \frac{m\pi}{4}\right)\right\}} = 4\sqrt{2}$

$\Rightarrow \displaystyle\sum_{m=1}^{6} \frac{\cot\left(\theta + \frac{(m-1)\pi}{4}\right) - \cot\left(\theta + \frac{m\pi}{4}\right)}{1/\sqrt{2}} = 4\sqrt{2}$

$\Rightarrow \cot\theta - \cot\left(\theta + \frac{\pi}{4}\right) + \cot\left(\theta + \frac{\pi}{4}\right) - \cot\left(\theta + \frac{2\pi}{4}\right)$

$\qquad + \dots + \cot\left(\theta + \frac{5\pi}{4}\right) - \cot\left(\theta + \frac{6\pi}{4}\right) = 4$

$\Rightarrow \cot\theta - \cot\left(\frac{3\pi}{2} + \theta\right) = 4$

$\Rightarrow \cot\theta + \tan\theta = 4$

$\Rightarrow \tan^2\theta - 4\tan\theta + 1 = 0 \Rightarrow \theta = \frac{\pi}{12}, \frac{5\pi}{12}$

11. **Ans. (a)** $\dfrac{1}{\sin\frac{\pi}{n}} = \dfrac{1}{\sin\frac{3\pi}{n}} = \dfrac{1}{\sin\frac{2\pi}{n}}$

$\Rightarrow \dfrac{2\cos\frac{2\pi}{n}\sin\frac{\pi}{n}}{\sin\frac{\pi}{n}\sin\frac{3\pi}{n}} = \dfrac{1}{\sin\frac{2\pi}{n}}$

$\Rightarrow \sin\frac{4\pi}{n} = \sin\frac{3\pi}{n} \Rightarrow \frac{4\pi}{n} = (-1)^k \frac{3\pi}{n} + k\pi, k \in \mathbf{I}$

It $k = 2m \Rightarrow \frac{\pi}{n} = 2m\pi$

$\Rightarrow \frac{1}{n} = 2m$, not possible

If $k = 2m+1 \Rightarrow \frac{7\pi}{n} = (2m+1)\pi$

$\Rightarrow n = 7, m = 0$

12. **Ans. (a).**

Let $xyz = t$

$t\sin 3\theta - y\cos 3\theta - z\cos 3\theta = 0$ ...(1)

$t\sin 3\theta - 2y\sin 3\theta - 2z\cos 3\theta = 0$ ...(2)

$t\sin 3\theta - y(\cos 3\theta + \sin 3\theta) - 2z\cos 3\theta = 0$ ...(3)

Since $y_0 . z_0 \neq 0$, therefore, homogeneous equation has non-trivial solution

$D = \begin{vmatrix} \sin 3\theta & -\cos 3\theta & -\cos 3\theta \\ \sin 3\theta & -2\sin 3\theta & -2\cos 3\theta \\ \sin 3\theta & -(\cos 3\theta + \sin 3\theta) & -2\cos 3\theta \end{vmatrix} = 0$

$\Rightarrow \sin 3\theta \cos 3\theta (\sin 3\theta - \cos 3\theta) = 0$

$\Rightarrow \sin 3\theta = 0$ or $\cos 3\theta = 0$ or $\tan 3\theta = 0$

If $\sin 3\theta = 0$, then from (2) $z = 0$ not possible. If $\cos 3\theta = 0$, $\sin 3\theta \neq 0 \Rightarrow t\sin 3\theta = 0 \Rightarrow t = 0 \Rightarrow x = 0$

Then from (2), $y = 0$ not possible

Now if $\tan 3\theta = 1$

$\Rightarrow 3\theta = n\pi + \frac{\pi}{4}, \quad n \in \mathbf{I}$

$\Rightarrow xyz \sin 3\theta = 0 \Rightarrow \theta = \frac{n\pi}{3} + \frac{\pi}{12}, n \in \mathbf{I}$

$\Rightarrow x = 0, \sin 3\theta \neq 0 \quad \Rightarrow \quad \theta = \frac{5}{12}, \frac{5\pi}{12}, \frac{9\pi}{12}$.

Hence total 3 solutions.

13. **Ans. (a).**

$\tan\theta = \cot 5\theta$

$\Rightarrow \frac{\sin\theta}{\cos\theta} = \frac{\cos 5\theta}{\sin 5\theta} \quad \Rightarrow \quad \theta = (2n+1)\frac{\pi}{12}, n \in \mathbf{I}$

$\theta = -\frac{5\pi}{12}, -\frac{\pi}{4}, -\frac{\pi}{12}, \frac{\pi}{12}, \frac{\pi}{4}, \frac{5\pi}{12}$ ...(1)

$\sin 2\theta = \cos 4\theta \Rightarrow \sin 2\theta = 1 - 2\sin^2 2\theta$

$\Rightarrow 2\sin^2 2\theta + \sin 2\theta - 1 = 0$

$\Rightarrow \sin 2\theta = -1, \frac{1}{2}$

$\Rightarrow 2\theta = (4m-1)\frac{\pi}{2}, p\pi + (-1)^p \frac{\pi}{6}$

$\Rightarrow \theta = (4m-1)\frac{\pi}{4}, \frac{p\pi}{12} + (-1)^p \frac{\pi}{12}, m, p \in \mathbf{I}$

$\Rightarrow \theta = -\frac{\pi}{4}, \frac{\pi}{12}, \frac{5\pi}{12}$ ...(2)

From (1) and (2) $\theta \in \left\{-\frac{\pi}{4}, \frac{\pi}{12}, \frac{5\pi}{12}\right\}$

Hence, number of solutions is 3.

14. **Ans. True.** We have $\sin x = \sin\lambda$

$\Rightarrow x = n\pi + (-1)^n \lambda, n \in \mathbf{I}$

$\therefore \sin(x/3) = \sin[n\pi/3 + (-1)^n (\lambda/3)]$

Hence for $n = 0, 3$, we have

$\sin(x/3) = \sin(\lambda/3)$

and for $n = 1, 2$, we have

$\sin(x/3) = \sin(\pi/3 - \lambda/3)$

[Note that for $n = 2, \sin(x/3)$

$= \sin(2\pi/3 + \lambda/3) = \sin[\pi - (\pi/3 - \lambda/3)]$

$= \sin(\pi/3 - \lambda/3)$

and for $n = 4, 5$, we get

$\sin(x/3) = -\sin(\pi/3 + \lambda/3)$.

It is easy to see that all other values of n repeat only these values of $\sin(x/3)$.

15. **(i)** **Ans. True .**

We write the given equation as

$\frac{1}{\sqrt{2}}\sin 2x + \frac{1}{\sqrt{2}}\cos 2x = -\frac{1}{\sqrt{2}}$

or $\cos(\pi/4)\sin 2x + \sin(\pi/4)\cos 2x = \sin(-\pi/4)$

or $\sin(2x + \pi/4) = \sin(-\pi/4)$

$\therefore 2x + \pi/4 = n\pi + (-1)^n (-\pi/4)$

or $x = n\pi/2 + (-1)^{n+1} (\pi/8) - \pi/8$

$= [(-1)^{n+1} - 1](\pi/8) + \frac{1}{2}n\pi$.

(ii) **Ans. True.**

$\sin(\theta + \pi/4) = 1/2, \cos(\theta - \pi/4) = 1/2$

$\therefore \sin(\theta + \pi/4) = \cos(\theta - \pi/4)$

$= \sin\{\pi/2 + (\theta - \pi/4)\}$

or $\sin(\theta + \pi/4) = \sin(\theta + \pi/4)$.

Hence true. You can also say

$$\sin(\theta + \pi/4) = \cos\{\pi/2 - (\theta + \pi/4)\}$$
$$= \cos(\pi/4 - \theta) = \cos(\theta - \pi/4)$$

16. $2\cos^2\theta + \sin\theta - 2 \leq 0$

$\Rightarrow$ $2 - 2\sin^2\theta + \sin\theta - 2 \leq 0$

or $2\sin\theta(\sin\theta - 1/2) \geq 0$

or $2(\sin\theta - 0)(\sin\theta - 1/2) \geq 0$

∴ $\sin\theta \leq 0$ or $\sin\theta \geq 1/2$.

Now $\sin\theta \leq 0 \Rightarrow \theta$ lies in 3rd or 4th quadrant for A, but in B, θ lies in 2nd and 3rd quadrant.

∴ $A \cap B = \{\theta : \pi \leq \theta \leq 3\pi/2\}$, 3rd Q.   ...(1)

Again, $\sin\theta = 1/2$

∴ $\theta = \pi/6$ or $5\pi/6$

∴ $\sin\theta \geq 1/2$ if $\pi/6 \leq \theta \leq 5\pi/6$ for A but in B, θ lies in 2nd and 3rd quadrant

∴ $A \cap B = \{\theta : \pi/2 \leq \theta \leq 5\pi/6\}$, 2nd Q.   ...(2)

∴ $A \cap B$ is given by (1) and (2).

MISCELLANEOUS EXERCISE

Matching Entries

♦ *Match the entries of Column-I and Column-II.*

1.   **Column-I**

(a) If $3\cos^2\theta - 2\sqrt{3}\sin\theta\cos\theta - 3\sin^2\theta = 0$, then $\theta = ...$

(b) If $r\sin\theta = 3, r = 4(1 + \sin\theta)$ where $0 \leq \theta \leq 2\pi$, then $\theta = ...$

(c) If $\sin\theta = -\dfrac{1}{2}$ and $\tan\theta = \dfrac{1}{\sqrt{3}}$, then the general value of θ which satisfies both the equations is ...

(d) If $0 \leq x \leq \pi$ and $81^{\sin^2 x} + 81^{\cos^2 x} = 30$, then x is ...

Column-II

1. $\dfrac{\pi}{6}, \dfrac{5\pi}{6}$

2. $2n\pi + \dfrac{7\pi}{6}$

3. $\dfrac{\pi}{6}, \dfrac{\pi}{3}, \dfrac{5\pi}{6}, \dfrac{2\pi}{3}$

4. $\dfrac{n\pi}{2} + \dfrac{\pi}{6}$

2. A root of the equation on L.H.S. satisfies the ralation in R.H.S. Match the entries on L.H.S. and R.H.S.

Column-I

(a) $2\cos 2x - \sin 2x = 2\sin^2 x$

(b) $2\sin^2\left(\dfrac{\pi}{2}\cos^2 x\right) = 1 - \cos(\pi\sin 2x)$

(c) $6\sec^2 x - 11\tan x - 2 = 0$

(d) $7\cos^2 x + \sin x\cos x - 3 = 0$

Column-II

(p) $\tan x = -1$

(q) $\tan x = \dfrac{1}{2}$

(r) $\tan x = 4/3$

(s) $\cos 2x = 3/5$

3. A root of the equation $(0 < \theta < \pi)$ is given by

Column-I

(a) $2\sin\theta|\cos\theta| = \dfrac{1}{\sqrt{2}}$

(b) $2\cos 2\theta\cos 4\theta + 2\cos^2 2\theta - 1 = 0$

(c) $8\cos^2\theta\sin\theta - 4\cos^2\theta - 2\sin\theta + 1 = 0$

(d) $\sin 4\theta = \pm 1$

Column-II

(p) $\theta = \dfrac{3\pi}{8}$

(q) $\theta = \dfrac{7\pi}{8}$

(r) $\theta = \dfrac{2\pi}{3}$

(s) $\theta = \dfrac{\pi}{6}$

Answers

1.   (a)→ (p, q, s), (b) → (q, s), (c)→ (q, r, s),(d)→ (p, r)

2.   (a)→ (p, q), (b)→ (p, q, r), (c)→ (r, s),(d)→ (p, q)

Solutions

1. (a) → 4. See Q. 4 (b) P. 582-84

    (b) → 1. See Q. 23 (b) P. 582-89

    (c) → 2. See Q. 50 (a) P. 584-596

    (d) → 3. See Q. 10 (a) P. 583-587

2. (a) $2(1 - 2\sin^2 x) - 2\sin x \cos x - 2\sin^2 x = 0$

$3\sin^2 x + \sin x \cos x - 1 = 0$

Divide by $\cos^2 x$

∴ $3\tan^2 x + \tan x - (1 + \tan^2 x) = 0$

or $2\tan^2 x + \tan x - 1 = 0$

or $(\tan x + 1)(2\tan x - 1) = 0$

∴ $\tan x = -1, \dfrac{1}{2}$ ∴ $\cos 2x = \dfrac{1 - t^2}{1 + t^2} = 0, \dfrac{3}{5}$

∴ (a) → (p, q, s)

(b) $2\sin^2\left(\dfrac{\pi}{2}\cos^2 x\right) = 2\sin^2\left(\dfrac{\pi \sin 2x}{2}\right)$

∴ $\cos^2 x = \sin 2x = 2\sin x \cos x$

or $\cos x(\cos x - 2\sin x) = 0$

∴ $\cos x = 0$ or $\tan x = \dfrac{1}{2}$

$\cos 2x = \dfrac{1 - t^2}{1 + t^2} = \dfrac{1 - (1/4)}{1 + (1/4)} = \dfrac{3}{5}$

∴ (b) → (q, s)

(c) $6(1 + t^2) - 11t - 2 = 0$ or $6t^2 - 11t + 4 = 0$

∴ $(2t - 1)(3t - 4) = 0$

∴ $t = \dfrac{1}{2}, \dfrac{4}{3} \Rightarrow$ (q, r)

Also when $\tan x = \dfrac{1}{2}, \cos 2x = \dfrac{3}{5}$ as in (b)

∴ (c) → (s)

∴ (c) → (q, r, s)

(d) Divide by $\cos^2 x$

∴ $3\sec^2 x - \tan x - 7 = 0$

$3(1 + t^2) - t - 7 = 0$ or $3t^2 - t - 4 = 0$

or $(3t - 4)(t + 1) = 0$ ∴ $t = \tan x = -1, \dfrac{4}{3}$

∴ (d) → (p, r)

3. (a) $2\sin\theta\cos\theta = \dfrac{1}{\sqrt{2}}$ if $\cos\theta > 0$

$\sin 2\theta = \sin\dfrac{\pi}{4}$ ∴ $2\theta = \dfrac{\pi}{4}, \pi - \dfrac{\pi}{4}$ ∴ $\theta = \dfrac{\pi}{8}, \dfrac{3\pi}{8}$

or $2\sin\theta(-\cos\theta) = \dfrac{1}{\sqrt{2}}$ if $\cos\theta < 0$

$\sin 2\theta = -\dfrac{1}{\sqrt{2}} = \sin\left(\pi + \dfrac{\pi}{4}\right)$

or $\sin\left(2\pi - \dfrac{\pi}{4}\right)$

∴ $2\theta = \dfrac{5\pi}{4}, \dfrac{7\pi}{4}$ or $\theta = \dfrac{5\pi}{8}, \dfrac{7\pi}{8}$

∴ (a) → (p, q)

(b) $2\cos 2\theta\cos 4\theta + \cos 4\theta = 0$

∴ $\cos 4\theta(1 + 2\cos 2\theta) = 0$

∴ $\cos 4\theta = 0$ ∴ $4\theta = \dfrac{\pi}{2}, \dfrac{3\pi}{2}, \dfrac{5\pi}{2}, \dfrac{7\pi}{2}$

∴ $\theta = \dfrac{\pi}{8}, \dfrac{3\pi}{8}, \dfrac{5\pi}{8}, \dfrac{7\pi}{8}$ ∴ (b) → (p, q)

or $\cos 2\theta = -\dfrac{1}{2} = -\cos\dfrac{\pi}{3} = \cos\dfrac{2\pi}{3}, \cos\dfrac{4\pi}{3}$

∴ $2\theta = \dfrac{2\pi}{3}, \dfrac{4\pi}{3}$ ∴ $\theta = \dfrac{\pi}{3}, \dfrac{2\pi}{3}$

∴ (b) → (r)

(c) $(4\cos^2\theta - 1)(2\sin\theta - 1) = 0$

∴ $\sin\theta = \dfrac{1}{2}, \cos\theta = \pm\dfrac{1}{2}$

$\sin\theta = \sin\dfrac{\pi}{6}, \sin\dfrac{5\pi}{6}, \cos\theta = \cos\dfrac{\pi}{3}, \cos\dfrac{2\pi}{3}$

∴ $\theta = \dfrac{\pi}{6}, \dfrac{5\pi}{6}, \dfrac{\pi}{3}, \dfrac{2\pi}{3}$

∴ (c) → (r, s)

(d) $\sin 4\theta = \pm 1 = \sin\dfrac{\pi}{2}, \sin\dfrac{3\pi}{2}, \sin\dfrac{5\pi}{2}, \sin\dfrac{7\pi}{2}$

∴ $\theta = \dfrac{\pi}{8}, \dfrac{3\pi}{8}, \dfrac{5\pi}{8}, \dfrac{7\pi}{8}$

∴ (d) → (p, q)

❑

CHAPTER

14

Inverse Circular Functions

§ 1. Introduction

The reader is familiar with the definition of inverse of a function. However, for his convenience, we reproduce the definition here as follows :

$$f : A \to B$$

A function f is said to be **inversible** if f is bijective and then inverse function $f^{-1} : B \to A$ is defined by

$$f^{-1}(y) = x \text{ if } f(x) = y, \; x \in A, \; y \in B.$$

More generally, let A be the domain of definition of an injective function f, and B the set of its values. By definition, from $y = f(x)$, $x \in A$, it follows that $x = f^{-1}(y)$, $y \in B$. If $x_1 \neq x_2$, then $y_1 \neq y_2$, and conversely [here $y_1 = f(x_1)$, $y_2 = f(x_2)$]. It is evident that the domain of definition of f^{-1} is the set of values of f, and the set of values of f^{-1} is the domain of definition of the function f.

§2. General and Principal Values of Inverse Circular Functions.

Notation and Meaning : From the properties of the function $a = \sin x$, for $-1 \leq a \leq 1$ there are infinitely many angles x which satisfy the equation $\sin x = a$. This infinite number of angles is symbolically denoted by $\mathrm{Sin}^{-1} \, a$, that is , we use capital S to denote this infinite set of values of the angles . There is one value among these values , which lies in the interval $[-\pi/2, \pi/2]$. This value is sometimes called the **principal value** of the angle and is denoted by $\sin^{-1} x$ (note that we use small s here); $\sin^{-1} x$ is the angle whose sine is equal to a and which lies in the interval $[-\pi/2, \pi/2]$. In compact form, we may write this definition as follows :

$$\alpha = \sin^{-1} a \text{ if }$$

(1) $\sin \alpha = a$ and

(2) $-\pi/2 \leq \alpha \leq \pi/2$.

and $\mathrm{Sin}^{-1} a = n\pi + (-1)^n \alpha$. where $\alpha = \sin^{-1} a$.

Similarly, the definitions of the other inverse trigonometrical functions can be given. We tabulate these definitions as follows :

(1) $-\dfrac{\pi}{2} \leq \sin^{-1} a \leq \dfrac{\pi}{2}$	(1) $0 \leq \cos^{-1} a \leq \pi$
(2) $\mathrm{Sin}^{-1} a = n\pi + (-1)^n \alpha$ where $-\dfrac{\pi}{2} \leq \alpha \leq \dfrac{\pi}{2}$	(2) $\mathrm{Cos}^{-1} a = 2n\pi \pm \alpha$ where $0 \leq \alpha \leq \pi$
(1) $-\dfrac{\pi}{2} < \tan^{-1} a < \dfrac{\pi}{2}$	(1) $0 < \cot^{-1} a < \pi$
(2) $\mathrm{Tan}^{-1} a = n\pi + \alpha$ where $-\dfrac{\pi}{2} < \alpha < \dfrac{\pi}{2}$	(2) $\mathrm{Cot}^{-1} a = n\pi + \alpha$ where $0 < \alpha < \pi$.

§3. The graph of Inverse Circular Functions.

(A) The Function $\sin^{-1} x$ and its graph. As discussed in §1, inverse of the function $y = \sin x$, $x \in \left[-\dfrac{1}{2}\pi, \dfrac{1}{2}\pi\right]$ is denoted by $\sin^{-1} x$ and read as sine inverse x. According to the definition of inverse function $\sin^{-1} x$, the domain of $\sin^{-1} x$ is the closed interval $[-1, 1]$ and the set of its values is the closed interval $\left[-\dfrac{1}{2}\pi, \dfrac{1}{2}\pi\right]$.

The graph of the function $y = \sin^{-1} x$, $x \in [-1, 1]$ is symmetric to the graph of the function $y = \sin x$, $x \in \left[\dfrac{1}{2}\pi, \dfrac{1}{2}\pi\right]$ about the line $y = x$.

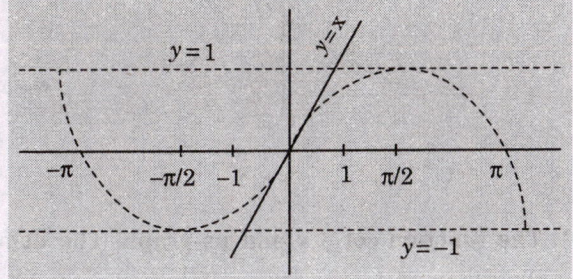

Fig. 1

(B) The function $\cos^{-1} x$ and its graph. For the function $\cos^{-1} x$, the domain of definition is the closed interval $[-1, 1]$ and the set of its values is the closed interval $[0, \pi]$. Note that the graph of the function

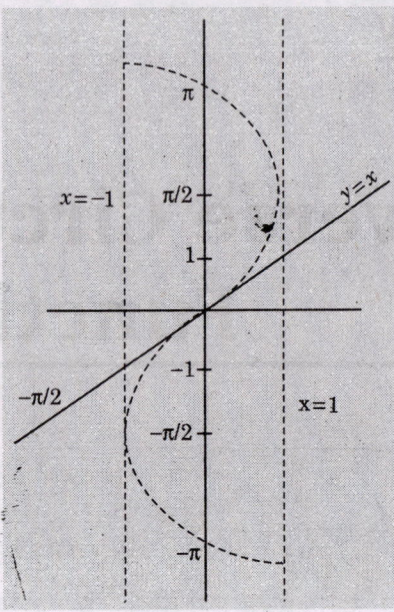

Fig. 2

$y = \cos^{-1} x$, $x \in [-1, 1]$ is symmetric to the graph of the function $y = \cos x$, $x \in [0, \pi]$ about the line $y = x$.

[Draw the graphs yourself]

(C) The function $\tan^{-1} x$ and its graph. The domain of definition of the function $\tan^{-1} x$ is the whole set R of real numbers and set of its values is the open interval $\left] -\frac{1}{2}\pi, \frac{1}{2}\pi \right[$. The graph of $y = \tan^{-1} x$, $x \in R$ is symmetric to the graph of the function $y = \tan x$, $x \in \left[-\frac{1}{2}\pi, \frac{1}{2}\pi \right]$ about the line $y = x$.

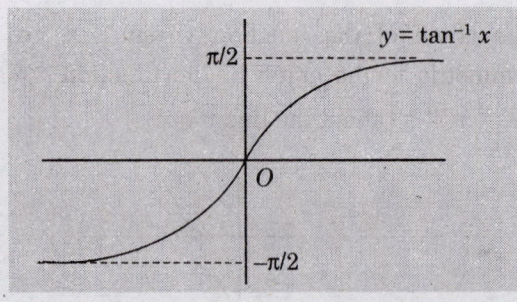

Fig. 3

(D) The function $\cot^{-1} x$ and its graph. The domain of definition of the function $\cot^{-1} x$ is the whole set R of real numbers and the open interval $]0, \pi[$ the set of its values. As in previous cases, the graph of $y = \cot^{-1} x$, $x \in R$ is symmetric to the graph of the function $y = \cot x$, $x \in]0, \pi[$ about the line $y = x$.

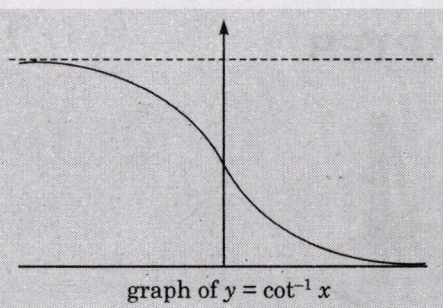

graph of $y = \cot^{-1} x$

Fig. 4

Similarly, domain of definition of the function $y = \mathrm{cosec}^{-1} x$ is the set of values of x given by $x \le -1$ or $x \ge 1$ and the set of its values is given by $-\frac{\pi}{2} < y < \frac{\pi}{2}$, $y \ne 0$.

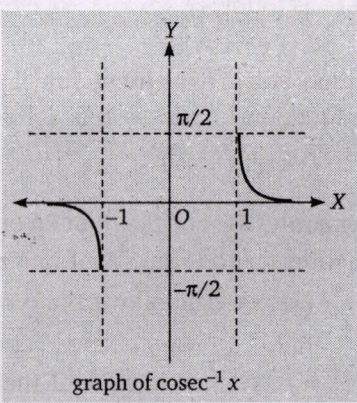

graph of $\mathrm{cosec}^{-1} x$

Fig. 5

For the function $y = \sec^{-1} x$ the domain of definition is given by $x \le -1$ or $x \ge 1$ and the set of its values by $0 \le y \le \pi$, $y \ne \frac{\pi}{2}$.

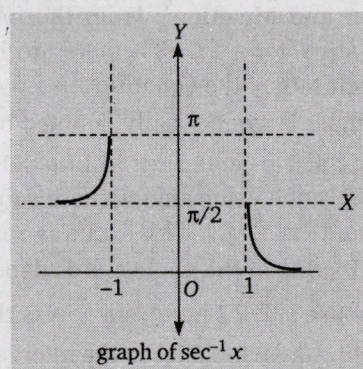

graph of $\sec^{-1} x$

Fig. 6

It may be observed from above that

1.	1st quadrant is common to all the inverse functions.
2.	3rd quadrant is not at all used in inverse functions.
3.	4th quadrant is used in clock-wise direction.

§ 4. Properties of inverse circular functions.

1. $\sin^{-1}(\sin \theta) = \theta$ and $\sin(\sin^{-1} x) = x$.

   If $x = \sin \theta$, then $\theta = \sin^{-1} x = \sin^{-1}(\sin \theta)$ and
   $\sin(\sin^{-1} x) = \sin(\theta) = x$

   Since $\sin^{-1} a$ means the principal value of the angle whose sine is a, the formula $\sin^{-1}(\sin \theta) = \theta$ is valid only when $-\dfrac{\pi}{2} \le \theta \le \dfrac{\pi}{2}$ and the formula $\sin(\sin^{-1} x) = x$ is meaningful only when $-1 \le x \le 1$.

   Similarly we can say that
   $$\cos^{-1}(\cos \theta) = \theta, \cos(\cos^{-1} x) = x,$$
   $$0 \le \theta \le \pi, -1 \le x \le 1,$$
   $$\tan^{-1}(\tan \theta) = \theta, \tan(\tan^{-1} x) = x$$
   $$-\frac{\pi}{2} \le \theta \le \frac{\pi}{2}, x \in \mathbf{R}.$$
   $$\cot^{-1}(\cot \theta) = \theta, (0 < \theta < \pi).$$

2. $\sin^{-1} x = \text{cosec}^{-1} \dfrac{1}{x}$ or $\text{cosec}^{-1} x = \sin^{-1} \dfrac{1}{x}$.

   If $x = \sin \theta$, then $\theta = \sin^{-1} x$ ...(1)

   $\therefore \quad \dfrac{1}{x} = \dfrac{1}{\sin \theta}$

   or $\text{cosec } \theta = \dfrac{1}{x} \therefore \theta = \text{cosec}^{-1} \dfrac{1}{x}$ ...(2)

   Hence from (1) and (2) on equating the value of θ,
   $$\sin^{-1} x = \text{cosec}^{-1}(1/x).$$

   Again if $x = \text{cosec } \theta$,

   then $\theta = \text{cosec}^{-1} x$ ...(3)

   $\therefore$ Also $\dfrac{1}{x} = \dfrac{1}{\text{cosec } \theta} = \sin \theta,$

   $\therefore \quad \theta = \sin^{-1} \dfrac{1}{x}.$ ...(4)

   Hence from (3) and (4) on equating the value of θ, we get
   $$\text{cosec}^{-1} x = \sin^{-1}(1/x).$$

   Similarly we can say that
   $$\cos^{-1} x = \sec^{-1}(1/x) \text{ and } \sec^{-1} x = \cos^{-1}(1/x)$$
   $$\tan^{-1} x = \cot^{-1}(1/x) \text{ and } \cot^{-1} x = \tan^{-1}(1/x)$$

§ 5. To find the value of one inverse function in terms of another inverse function.

   If $\sin \theta = x$, then
   $$\theta = \sin^{-1} x = \text{cosec}^{-1}(1/x) \quad ...(1)$$
   $$\cos \theta = \sqrt{1 - \sin^2 \theta} = \sqrt{1 - x^2}.$$
   $$\therefore \quad \theta = \cos^{-1} \sqrt{1 - x^2} = \sec^{-1} \frac{1}{\sqrt{(1 - x^2)}} \quad ...(2)$$

$$\tan \theta = \frac{\sin \theta}{\cos \theta} = \frac{x}{\sqrt{(1 - x^2)}}.$$

$$\therefore \quad \theta = \tan^{-1} \frac{x}{\sqrt{(1 - x^2)}} = \cot^{-1} \frac{\sqrt{1 - x^2}}{x} \quad ...(3)$$

Equating the values of θ from (1), (2) and (3), we get

$$\sin^{-1} x = \cos^{-1} \sqrt{1 - x^2}$$

$$= \tan^{-1} \frac{x}{\sqrt{(1 - x^2)}} = \cot^{-1} \frac{\sqrt{1 - x^2}}{x}$$

$$= \sec^{-1} \frac{1}{\sqrt{(1 - x^2)}} = \text{cosec}^{-1} \frac{1}{x} \quad ...(4)$$

Similarly we can say that

$$\cos^{-1} x = \sin^{-1} \sqrt{1 - x^2}$$

$$= \tan^{-1} \frac{\sqrt{1 - x^2}}{x} = \cot^{-1} \frac{x}{\sqrt{(1 - x^2)}}$$

$$= \sec^{-1} \frac{1}{x} = \text{cosec}^{-1} \frac{1}{\sqrt{(1 - x^2)}} \quad ...(5)$$

$$\tan^{-1} x = \sin^{-1} \frac{x}{\sqrt{(1 + x^2)}}$$

$$= \cos^{-1} \frac{1}{\sqrt{(1 + x^2)}} = \cot^{-1} \frac{1}{x}.$$

$$= \sec^{-1} \sqrt{1 + x^2} = \text{cosec}^{-1} \frac{\sqrt{1 + x^2}}{x}. \quad ...(6)$$

Note that the equations in (4) and (5) are valid only when $0 \le x \le 1$ and the equations in (6) hold when $x \ge 0$

§ 6.* $\sin^{-1} x + \cos^{-1} x = \pi/2, (-1 \le x \le 1)$
$\tan^{-1} x + \cot^{-1} x = \pi/2, x \in \mathbf{R}.$
$\sec^{-1} x + \text{cosec}^{-1} x = \pi/2, x \le -1$ or $x \ge 1.$

First Method : Let $\sin^{-1} x = \theta$ and $\cos^{-1} x = \phi$ so that
$$-\frac{\pi}{2} \le \theta \le \frac{\pi}{2} \quad \text{and} \quad 0 \le \phi \le \pi.$$

Hence $-\dfrac{\pi}{2} \le \theta + \phi \le \dfrac{3\pi}{2}.$

Now $\sin(\theta + \phi) = \sin \theta \cos \phi + \cos \theta \sin \phi,$
$$= x^2 + \sqrt{1 - x^2} \sqrt{1 - x^2} = x^2 + 1 - x^2 = 1.$$

But there is only one angle between $-\pi/2$ and $3\pi/2$ whose sine is 1, namely $\pi/2$. Hence $\sin^{-1} x + \cos^{-1} x = \pi/2.$

Second Method. We have to prove
$$\sin^{-1} x = \pi/2 - \cos^{-1} x.$$

But $\sin(\pi/2 - \cos^{-1} x) = \cos \cos^{-1} x = x.$ ...(1)

And since $0 \le \cos^{-1} x \le \pi$, we have
$$-\pi/2 \le \pi/2 - \cos^{-1} x \le \pi/2.$$

Hence (1) implies that
$$\pi/2 - \cos^{-1} x = \sin^{-1} x.$$

Prove the other results yourself.

§7. (a) $\tan^{-1} x + \tan^{-1} y = \tan^{-1} \dfrac{x+y}{1-xy}$, if $xy < 1$

(b)* $\tan^{-1} x + \tan^{-1} y = \pi + \tan^{-1} \dfrac{x+y}{1-xy}$,

if $xy > 1$.

(c) $\tan^{-1} x - \tan^{-1} y = \tan^{-1} \dfrac{x-y}{1+xy}$.

(d) $\tan^{-1} x + \tan^{-1} y + \tan^{-1} z$
$= \tan^{-1} \dfrac{p_1 - p_3}{1 - p_2}$

where $p_1 = \Sigma x$, $p_2 = \Sigma xy$, $p_3 = xyz$,

Put $x = \tan \theta$, $y = \tan \phi$

$\therefore \quad \theta = \tan^{-1} x$, $\phi = \tan^{-1} y$.

$\therefore \quad$ L.H.S. $= \theta + \phi$.

Now $\tan(\theta + \phi) = \dfrac{\tan \theta + \tan \phi}{1 - \tan \theta \tan \phi} = \dfrac{x+y}{1-xy}$.

$\therefore \quad \theta + \phi = \tan^{-1} \dfrac{x+y}{1-xy} =$ R.H.S.

Again putting $y = x$, we get

$2 \tan^{-1} x = \tan^{-1} \dfrac{2x}{1-x^2}$.

The second part may be proved similarly.

§8. $\sin^{-1}(-x) = -\sin^{-1}(x)$
$*\cos^{-1}(-x) = \pi - \cos^{-1}(x)$ **(Note)**
$\tan^{-1}(-x) = -\tan^{-1}(x)$
$\cot^{-1}(-x) = \pi - \cot^{-1}(x)$

Put $-x = \sin \theta$ $\therefore$ $\theta = \sin^{-1}(-x)$ ...(1)

$\therefore \quad x = -\sin \theta = \sin(-\theta)$

$\therefore \quad -\theta = \sin^{-1} x$ or $\theta = -\sin^{-1} x$ ...(2)

Hence from (1) and (2), we get

$\sin^{-1}(-x) = -\sin^{-1} x$.

Similarly, $\tan^{-1}(-x) = -\tan^{-1}(x)$.

Again put $-x = \cos \theta$ $\therefore$ $\theta = \cos^{-1}(-x)$.

$\therefore \quad x = -\cos \theta = \cos(\pi - \theta)$. ...(3)

$\therefore \quad \pi - \theta = \cos^{-1} x$ or $\theta = \pi - \cos^{-1} x$ ...(4)

Hence from (3) and (4), we get

$\cos^{-1}(-x) = \pi - \cos^{-1}(x)$.

§9. $2 \sin^{-1} x = \sin^{-1} 2x\sqrt{1-x^2}$
$2 \cos^{-1} x = \cos^{-1}(2x^2 - 1)$
$2 \tan^{-1} x = \tan^{-1} \dfrac{2x}{1-x^2}$.

Put $x = \sin \theta$ $\therefore$ $\theta = \sin^{-1} x$.

Now $\sin 2\theta = 2 \sin \theta \cos \theta$

$= 2 \sin \theta \sqrt{1 - \sin^2 \theta} = 2x\sqrt{1-x^2}$.

$\therefore \quad 2\theta = \sin^{-1} 2x\sqrt{1-x^2}$

or $2 \sin^{-1} x = \sin^{-1} 2x\sqrt{1-x^2}$

The other relations may be similarly proved.

§10. $2 \tan^{-1} x = \sin^{-1} \dfrac{2x}{1+x^2}$

$= \cos^{-1} \dfrac{1-x^2}{1+x^2} = \tan^{-1} \dfrac{2x}{1-x^2}$.

Put $x = \tan \theta$ $\therefore$ $\tan^{-1} x = \theta$.

$2\theta = \sin^{-1} \dfrac{2 \tan \theta}{1 + \tan^2 \theta}$

$= \cos^{-1} \dfrac{1 - \tan^2 \theta}{1 + \tan^2 \theta} = \tan^{-1} \dfrac{2 \tan \theta}{1 - \tan^2 \theta}$

or $2\theta = \sin^{-1} \sin 2\theta$

$= \cos^{-1} \cos 2\theta = \tan^{-1} \tan 2\theta$

or $2\theta = 2\theta = 2\theta = 2\theta$.

§11. $3 \sin^{-1} x = \sin^{-1}(3x - 4x^3)$,
$3 \cos^{-1} x = \cos^{-1}(4x^3 - 3x)$
$3 \tan^{-1} x = \tan^{-1} \dfrac{3x - x^3}{1 - 3x^2}$.

§12. $\sin^{-1} x \pm \sin^{-1} y$
$= \sin^{-1}\{x\sqrt{1-y^2} \pm y\sqrt{1-x^2}\}$
$\cos^{-1} x \pm \cos^{-1} y$
$= \cos^{-1}\{xy \mp \sqrt{1-x^2}\sqrt{1-y^2}\}$

Put $x = \sin \theta$, $y = \sin \phi$

$\therefore \quad \sin^{-1} x = \theta$, $\sin^{-1} y = \phi$.

$\therefore \quad$ L.H.S. $= \theta \pm \phi$.

R.H.S. $= \sin^{-1}\{\sin \theta \sqrt{1 - \sin^2 \phi} \pm \sin \phi \sqrt{1 - \sin^2 \theta}\}$

$= \sin^{-1}\{\sin \theta \cos \phi \pm \cos \theta \sin \phi\}$.

$= \sin^{-1} \sin(\theta \pm \phi) = \theta \pm \phi$.

Domain and range of some inverse circular functions

S.No.	Function	Domain	Range (Principal value)
1	$y = \sin^{-1} x$	$-1 \le x \le 1$	$-\dfrac{\pi}{2} \le y \le \dfrac{\pi}{2}$
2	$y = \cos^{-1} x$	$-1 \le x \le 1$	$0 \le y \le \pi$
3	$y = \tan^{-1} x$	$x \in \mathbf{R}$	$-\dfrac{\pi}{2} < y < \dfrac{\pi}{2}$
4	$y = \cot^{-1} x$	$x \in \mathbf{R}$	$0 < y < \pi$
5	$y = \operatorname{cosec}^{-1} x$	$|x| \ge 1$	$-\dfrac{\pi}{2} \le y \le \dfrac{\pi}{2}, y \ne 0$
6	$y = \sec^{-1} x$	$|x| \ge 1$	$0 \le y \le \pi, y \ne \dfrac{\pi}{2}$

Problem Set (1)

Inverse circular functions, Principal values of $\sin^{-1} x$, $\cos^{-1} x$, $\tan^{-1} x$.

$$\tan^{-1} x + \tan^{-1} y = \tan^{-1}\frac{x+y}{1-xy}, \qquad xy < 1$$

$$= \pi + \tan^{-1}\frac{x+y}{1-xy}, \qquad xy > 1.$$

1. Evaluate the following :

   (a) $\sin\left[\frac{\pi}{3} - \sin^{-1}\left(-\frac{1}{2}\right)\right]$

   (b) $\sin\left[\frac{\pi}{2} - \sin^{-1}\left(-\frac{\sqrt{3}}{2}\right)\right]$

2. (a) Principal value of $\sin^{-1}[\sin(2\pi/3)]$ is $\pi/3$.

   (b) $\sin^{-1}\left(\sin\frac{33\pi}{7}\right)$

3. (a) $\cos^{-1}\left(\cos\frac{7\pi}{6}\right)$

   (b)* $\cos^{-1}\left(\cos\frac{4\pi}{3}\right)$

4. (a) $\tan^{-1}\left(\tan\frac{3\pi}{4}\right)$

   (b)* $\tan^{-1}\left(\tan\frac{2\pi}{3}\right)$

   (c) $\cos\left[\cos^{-1}\left(\frac{-\sqrt{3}}{2}\right) + \frac{\pi}{6}\right]$

   (d) If $a \le \tan^{-1}\left(\frac{1-x}{1+x}\right) \le b$ where $0 \le x \le 1$

      then prove that $(a, b) = (0, \pi/4)$.

5. (a)* Prove that
   $$\sin^{-1}\sin\left(\frac{33\pi}{7}\right) + \cos^{-1}\left(\cos\frac{46\pi}{7}\right)$$
   $$+ \tan^{-1}\left(-\tan\frac{13\pi}{8}\right) + \cot^{-1}\left[\cot\left(-\frac{19\pi}{8}\right)\right] = \frac{13\pi}{7}$$

   (b) If $a\sin^{-1} x - b\cos^{-1} x = c$, then
      $$a\sin^{-1} x + b\cos^{-1} x =$$
      (a) 0   (b) π
      (c) $\dfrac{\pi ab + c(a-b)}{a+b}$ (d) $\dfrac{\pi ab - c(a-b)}{a+b}$

6. (a) $\sin\left(\cos^{-1}\frac{3}{5}\right)$

   (b) $\cos\left(\tan^{-1}\frac{3}{4}\right)$ and $\cos(\tan^{-1} x)$

   (c) If $\sin(\cot^{-1}(1+x)) = \cos(\tan^{-1} x)$ then x is
      (a) 1/2   (b) 1
      (c) 0   (d) $-1/2$ **(Screening 2004)**

   (d) $\sin(\cot^{-1} x)$

   (e) $\sin(2\sin^{-1} 0\cdot 8)$

7. (a)* $\tan\left[\frac{1}{2}\cos^{-1}\left(\frac{\sqrt{5}}{3}\right)\right]$

   (b)* $\tan\left[2\tan^{-1}\left(\frac{1}{5}\right) - \frac{\pi}{4}\right]$

8. Prove

   (a) $\sin^{-1}\frac{4}{5} + \sin^{-1}\frac{5}{13} + \sin^{-1}\frac{16}{65} = \frac{\pi}{2}$

   (b) $\sin^{-1}\frac{3}{5} + \sin^{-1}\frac{8}{17} = \cos^{-1}\frac{36}{85}$

   (c) $\sin^{-1}\frac{3}{5} + \cos^{-1}\frac{12}{13} = \cos^{-1}\frac{33}{65}$

9. (a)* $\sin^{-1}\frac{12}{13} + \cos^{-1}\frac{4}{5} + \tan^{-1}\frac{63}{16} = \pi$

   (b) $2\cos^{-1}\frac{3}{\sqrt{13}} + \cot^{-1}\frac{16}{63} + \frac{1}{2}\cos^{-1}\frac{7}{25} = \pi$

10. (a) $\cot^{-1} 9 + \operatorname{cosec}^{-1}\frac{\sqrt{41}}{4} = \frac{\pi}{4}$

    (b) $\tan^{-1}\frac{1}{7} + \tan^{-1}\frac{1}{13} = \tan^{-1}\frac{2}{9}$

    (c) $\tan^{-1} 2 + \tan^{-1} 3 = 3\pi/4$

11. (a) $\tan^{-1}\frac{1}{2} + \tan^{-1}\frac{1}{3} = \frac{\pi}{4}$.   **(M.N.R. 1990)**

    (b) $\tan^{-1}\frac{1}{2} + \tan^{-1}\frac{1}{5} + \tan^{-1}\frac{1}{8} = \frac{\pi}{4}$

    (c) $\tan^{-1}\frac{3}{4} + \tan^{-1}\frac{3}{5} - \tan^{-1}\frac{8}{19} = \frac{\pi}{4}$

12. (a) $\sin^{-1}\frac{4}{5} + 2\tan^{-1}\frac{1}{3} = \frac{\pi}{2}$

    (b) $\tan^{-1}\frac{1}{7} + 2\tan^{-1}\frac{1}{3} = \frac{\pi}{4}$

    (c)* $\tan^{-1}\frac{1}{5} + \tan^{-1}\frac{1}{7} + \tan^{-1}\frac{1}{3} + \tan^{-1}\frac{1}{8} = \frac{\pi}{4}$

13. (a) $\tan^{-1}\frac{1}{21} + \tan^{-1}\frac{1}{13} + \tan^{-1}\left(-\frac{1}{8}\right) = 0$

    (b) $\tan^{-1}\frac{2}{3} = \frac{1}{2}\tan^{-1}\frac{12}{5}$.

    (c) $\tan^{-1}\frac{1}{4} + \tan^{-1}\frac{2}{9} = \frac{1}{2}\cos^{-1}\frac{3}{5}$.

14. (a) The value of
    $$\tan[\cos^{-1}(4/5) + \tan^{-1}(2/3)]$$

    Other form : $\tan[\sin^{-1}(3/5) + \cot^{-1}(3/2)]$ is
    (a) 6/17   (b) 7/16

(c) $17/6$ (d) none of these

(M.N.R. 1992)

(b) If the sum of the acute angles $\tan^{-1} x$ and $\tan^{-1} \frac{1}{2}$ is $45°$, then the value of x is $\frac{1}{3}$.

(c) If $A = \tan^{-1} \frac{x\sqrt{3}}{2\lambda - x}$ and $B = \tan^{-1}\left(\frac{2x-\lambda}{\lambda\sqrt{3}}\right)$

then show that the value of $A - B$ is $30°$.

15. * $4\tan^{-1}\frac{1}{5} - \tan^{-1}\frac{1}{70} + \tan^{-1}\frac{1}{99} = \frac{\pi}{4}$

(M.N.R. 1995)

16. Prove that

(a) $2\tan^{-1}\frac{1}{5} + \sec^{-1}\frac{5\sqrt{2}}{7} + 2\tan^{-1}\frac{1}{8} = \frac{\pi}{4}$.

(b)* $\cos^{-1}\frac{12}{13} + 2\cos^{-1}\sqrt{\left(\frac{64}{65}\right)}$

$+ \cos^{-1}\sqrt{\left(\frac{49}{50}\right)} = \cos^{-1}\frac{1}{\sqrt{(2)}}$

17. (a) $\sin\left(2\tan^{-1}\frac{1}{3}\right) + \cos(\tan^{-1}2\sqrt{2}) = \frac{14}{15}$

(b) Prove that

$\sin^{-1}\left\{\cot\left(\sin^{-1}\sqrt{\left(\frac{2-\sqrt{3}}{4}\right)} + \cos^{-1}\frac{\sqrt{12}}{4}\right.\right.$

$\left.\left. + \sec^{-1}\sqrt{2}\right)\right\} = 0$

18. Using the principal values, express the following as a single angle :

$3\tan^{-1}\left(\frac{1}{2}\right) + 2\tan^{-1}\left(\frac{1}{5}\right) + \sin^{-1}\frac{142}{65\sqrt{5}}$.

(Roorkee 1999)

19. (a) Given $0 \le x \le \frac{1}{2}$ then the value of

$\tan\left[\sin^{-1}\left\{\frac{x}{\sqrt{2}} + \frac{\sqrt{1-x^2}}{\sqrt{2}}\right\} - \sin^{-1}x\right]$ is

(a) -1 (b) 1

(c) $\frac{1}{\sqrt{3}}$ (d) $\sqrt{3}$

(b) If $\alpha = \sin^{-1}\frac{4}{5} + \sin^{-1}\frac{1}{3}$

and $\beta = \cos^{-1}\frac{4}{5} + \cos^{-1}\frac{1}{3}$, then

(a) $\alpha < \beta$ (b) $\alpha = \beta$

(c) $\alpha > \beta$ (d) None of these

20. (a)* If $\cos^{-1}p + \cos^{-1}q + \cos^{-1}r = \pi$, then prove that

$p^2 + q^2 + r^2 + 2pqr = 1$

(Roorkee 1994)

(b)* If $\sin^{-1}x + \sin^{-1}y + \sin^{-1}z = \pi$, then prove that

$x^4 + y^4 + z^4 + 4x^2y^2z^2 = 2(x^2y^2 + y^2z^2 + z^2x^2)$

(M.N.R. 1997)

(c) If $\tan^{-1}x + \tan^{-1}y + \tan^{-1}z = \pi$ or $\pi/2$ show that $x + y + z = xyz$ or $xy + yz + zx = 1$.

21. (a)* If $\sin^{-1}x + \sin^{-1}y + \sin^{-1}z = 3\pi/2$, then the value of

$x^{100} + y^{100} + z^{100} - \dfrac{9}{x^{101} + y^{101} + z^{101}}$ is

(a) 0 (b) 1

(c) 2 (d) 3

(b) Solve :

$\sin^{-1}\frac{ax}{c} + \sin^{-1}\frac{bx}{c} = \sin^{-1}x$

where $a^2 + b^2 = c^2$, $c \ne 0$. (Roorkee 2000)

22. (a) If $\sin^{-1}\frac{2p}{1+p^2} - \cos^{-1}\frac{1-q^2}{1+q^2} = \tan^{-1}\frac{2x}{1-x^2}$,

then prove that $x = \dfrac{p-q}{1+pq}$.

(b) Solve for x

$\sin^{-1}\frac{2a}{1+a^2} + \sin^{-1}\frac{2b}{1+b^2} = 2\tan^{-1}x$

(c) Prove that

$\tan\left[\frac{1}{2}\sin^{-1}\frac{2a}{1+a^2} + \frac{1}{2}\cos^{-1}\frac{1-a^2}{1+a^2}\right] = \frac{2a}{1-a^2}$.

23. * Prove that

$\tan^{-1}\frac{1-x}{1+x} - \tan^{-1}\frac{1-y}{1+y} = \sin^{-1}\frac{y-x}{\sqrt{1+x^2}\sqrt{1+y^2}}$

24. (a)* $\tan^{-1}\frac{2mn}{m^2-n^2} + \tan^{-1}\frac{2pq}{p^2-q^2} = \tan^{-1}\frac{2MN}{M^2-N^2}$

where $M = mp - nq$, $N = np + mq$

(b) $\frac{2}{3}\tan^{-1}\frac{3mn^2 - m^3}{n^3 - 3m^2n} + \frac{2}{3}\tan^{-1}\frac{3pq^2 - p^3}{q^3 - 3p^2q}$

$= \tan^{-1}\frac{2MN}{M^2 - N^2}$

where $M = -mp + nq$, $N = np + mq$ and all the letters are +ive quantities.

25. (a) Prove that $\sin\left[\tan^{-1}\frac{1-x^2}{2x} + \cos^{-1}\frac{1-x^2}{1+x^2}\right] = 1$.

(b) If $\sin^{-1}\left(x - \frac{x^2}{2} + \frac{x^3}{4} - \ldots\right)$

$+ \cos^{-1}\left(x^2 - \frac{x^4}{2} + \frac{x^6}{4} - \ldots\right) = \frac{\pi}{2}$

for $0 < |x| < \sqrt{2}$, then x equals

(a) $\frac{1}{2}$ (b) 1

(c) $-\frac{1}{2}$ (d) -1

(I.I.T. Sc. 2001)

26. (a)* If $\cos^{-1}(p/a) + \cos^{-1}(q/b) = \alpha$, then

$$\frac{p^2}{a^2} - \frac{2pq}{ab}\cos\alpha + \frac{q^2}{b^2} = \sin^2\alpha.$$

(b) If $\cos^{-1}\frac{x}{2} + \cos^{-1}\frac{y}{3} = \theta$, then prove that

$$9x^2 - 12xy\cos\theta + 4y^2 = 36\sin^2\theta.$$

27.* If $u = \cot^{-1}[\sqrt{\cos 2\theta}] - \tan^{-1}[\sqrt{\cos 2\theta}]$, then prove that

$\sin u = \tan^2\theta$.

28.* Prove that

$$\tan\left(\frac{\pi}{4} + \frac{1}{2}\cos^{-1}\frac{a}{b}\right) + \tan\left(\frac{\pi}{4} - \frac{1}{2}\cos^{-1}\frac{a}{b}\right) = \frac{2b}{a}.$$

29. Evaluate

(a) $\cos^{-1}x + \cos^{-1}\left[\frac{x}{2} + \frac{\sqrt{(3-3x^2)}}{2}\right]$ $\qquad \left(\frac{1}{2} \le x \le 1\right)$

(b) $\cos(2\cos^{-1}x + \sin^{-1}x)$ at $x = 1/5$,

where $\quad 0 \le \cos^{-1}x \le \pi$

and $\quad -\pi/2 \le \sin^{-1}x \le \pi/2$

30. (a) If $\tan^{-1}\dfrac{\sqrt{1+x^2} - \sqrt{1-x^2}}{\sqrt{(1+x^2)} + \sqrt{(1-x^2)}} = \alpha$, then prove

that $x^2 = \sin 2\alpha$.

(b)* If $\dfrac{m\tan(\alpha - \theta)}{\cos^2\theta} = \dfrac{n\tan\theta}{\cos^2(\alpha - \theta)}$, then prove that

$$\theta = \frac{1}{2}\left[\alpha - \tan^{-1}\left(\frac{n-m}{n+m}\tan\alpha\right)\right].$$

(c) $\cos^{-1}\dfrac{\cos\alpha + \cos\beta}{1 + \cos\alpha\cos\beta} = 2\tan^{-1}\left(\tan\dfrac{\alpha}{2}\tan\dfrac{\beta}{2}\right)$

31.* $2\tan^{-1}\left(\sqrt{\left(\dfrac{a-b}{a+b}\right)}\tan\dfrac{\theta}{2}\right) = \cos^{-1}\dfrac{a\cos\theta + b}{a + b\cos\theta}$.

32. Solve for x the following :

(a) $\tan^{-1}\dfrac{x-1}{x-2} + \tan^{-1}\dfrac{x+1}{x+2} = \dfrac{\pi}{4}$

(b)* $\tan^{-1}\dfrac{x-1}{x+1} + \tan^{-1}\dfrac{2x-1}{2x+1} = \tan^{-1}\dfrac{23}{36}$

33. (a) $\tan^{-1}\dfrac{1}{4} + 2\tan^{-1}\dfrac{1}{5} + \tan^{-1}\dfrac{1}{6} + \tan^{-1}\dfrac{1}{x} = \dfrac{\pi}{4}$

(b) $\tan^{-1}(x-1) + \tan^{-1}x + \tan^{-1}(x+1) = \tan^{-1}3x$

34. (a) $\tan^{-1}2x + \tan^{-1}3x = \pi/4$

(b)* $\tan^{-1}\dfrac{1}{2x+1} + \tan^{-1}\dfrac{1}{4x+1} = \tan^{-1}\dfrac{2}{x^2}$

(c)* $3\tan^{-1}\dfrac{1}{2+\sqrt{(3)}} - \tan^{-1}\dfrac{1}{x} = \tan^{-1}\dfrac{1}{3}$

35. (a)* Solve the equation

$\tan^{-1}2x + \tan^{-1}3x = n\pi + (3\pi/4).$

(b)* Find all the positive integral solutions of

$$\tan^{-1}x + \cos^{-1}\left(\frac{y}{\sqrt{1+y^2}}\right) = \sin^{-1}\left(\frac{3}{\sqrt{10}}\right)$$

(Roorkee 1993)

36. Solve for x the following equations :

(a) $\cot^{-1}x + \sin^{-1}\dfrac{1}{\sqrt{(5)}} = \dfrac{\pi}{4}.$

(b) $2\tan^{-1}(\cos x) = \tan^{-1}(2\csc x).$

(c) $\tan(\cos^{-1}x) = \sin\left(\cot^{-1}\dfrac{1}{2}\right).$

37. (a)* If $\tan^{-1}\left(x + \dfrac{2}{x}\right) - \tan^{-1}\dfrac{4}{x} - \tan^{-1}\left(x - \dfrac{2}{x}\right) = 0$

then $\quad x = \ldots\ldots\ldots$ or $x = \ldots\ldots\ldots (x \in R)$

(b) If $\sin^{-1}x + \sin^{-1}y = 2\pi/3$

$\cos^{-1}x - \cos^{-1}y = \pi/3$

then $\quad x = \ldots\ldots\ldots, \quad y = \ldots\ldots\ldots$

(c) It $\tan^{-1}y = 4\tan^{-1}x, \left(|x| < \tan\dfrac{\pi}{8}\right)$, then

express y as an algebraic function of x. Also

deduce that $\tan(\pi/8)$ is a root of $x^4 - 6x^2 + 1 = 0.$

38. (a) $3\sin^{-1}\dfrac{2x}{1+x^2} - 4\cos^{-1}\dfrac{1-x^2}{1+x^2}$

$$+ 2\tan^{-1}\frac{2x}{1-x^2} = \frac{\pi}{3}$$

(b)* $\sin[(1/5)\cos^{-1}x] = 1$

(c) $\tan^{-1}\sqrt{x^2 + x} + \sin^{-1}\sqrt{x^2 + x + 1} = \dfrac{\pi}{2}$ **(I.I.T. 1999)**

39. (a) Solve the equation :

$\cos^{-1}(\sqrt{6}x) + \cos^{-1}(3\sqrt{3}x^2) = \dfrac{\pi}{2}.$ **(Roorkee 2001)**

(b) If $\sin^{-1}6x + \sin^{-1}6\sqrt{3}x = -\pi/2$, then $x = \ldots$

(c)* $\sin^{-1}x + \sin^{-1}2x = \pi/3$

40. (a)* Find whether $x = 2$ satisfies the equation

$$\tan^{-1}\frac{x+1}{x-1} + \tan^{-1}\frac{x-1}{x} = \tan^{-1}(-7).$$

If not, then how should the equation be re-written ?

(b) $\tan^{-1}\dfrac{4}{3} + \tan^{-1}\dfrac{5}{6} + \tan^{-1}\dfrac{39}{2} - \pi = \ldots\ldots$

(c) If x_1, x_2, x_3, x_4 are roots of equation

$x^4 - x^3\sin 2\beta + x^2\cos 2\beta - x\cos\beta - \sin\beta = 0,$

then prove that $\sum\limits_{i=1}^{4}\tan^{-1}x_i = \dfrac{\pi}{2} - \beta$

41. (a)* Solve for $x, \sin[2\cos^{-1}\cot(2\tan^{-1}x)] = 0.$ **(Roorkee 1992, 95)**

(b)* Evaluate $\sin\cot^{-1}\cos(\tan^{-1}x)$ **(M.N.R. 1993)**

(c) Prove that $\cos\tan^{-1}\sin\cot^{-1}x = \sqrt{\dfrac{x^2+1}{x^2+2}}.$ **(I.I.T. 2002)**

42. Solve :

(a)* $\cos(2\sin^{-1}x) = 1/9$

(b) $\cos^{-1}(3/5) - \sin^{-1}(4/5) = \cos^{-1}x$

(c)* If $\sin\left(\sin^{-1}\dfrac{1}{5}+\cos^{-1}x\right)=1$, then prove that x is equal to 1/5. **(M.N.R. 1994)**

43. (a) $\sin^{-1}(1-x)-2\sin^{-1}x=\pi/2$.

   (b) If $\sin^{-1}x+\sin^{-1}(1-x)=\cos^{-1}x$, then prove that x is equal to 0, 1/2.

44. (a) $\sin^{-1}(3x/5)+\sin^{-1}(4x/5)=\sin^{-1}x$.

   (b)* $\cos^{-1}x+\sin^{-1}\left(\dfrac{1}{2}x\right)=\dfrac{\pi}{6}$

   (c) If $a\leq\tan^{-1}\left(\dfrac{1-x}{1+x}\right)\leq b$ where $0\leq x\leq 1$ then

   $(a,b)=$
   (a) $(0,\pi)$ (b) $(0,\pi/4)$
   (c) $(-\pi/4,\pi/4)$ (d) $(\pi/4,\pi/2)$

   (d) If $a\leq(\sin^{-1}x)^3+(\cos^{-1}x)^3\leq b$, then (a,b) is equal to $\left(\dfrac{\pi^3}{32},\dfrac{7\pi^3}{8}\right)$.

45. (a)* Prove that $2\tan^{-1}\left\{\tan\dfrac{\alpha}{2}\tan\left(\dfrac{\pi}{4}-\dfrac{\beta}{2}\right)\right\}$

   $$=\tan^{-1}\left[\dfrac{\sin\alpha\cos\beta}{\sin\beta+\cos\alpha}\right].$$

   (b) Prove that
   $$\cos^{-1}\left(\dfrac{2+3\cos x}{3+2\cos x}\right)=2\tan^{-1}\left(\dfrac{1}{\sqrt{5}}\tan\dfrac{x}{2}\right).$$

46.* Prove that
   $$\tan^{-1}\left(\dfrac{1}{2}\tan 2A\right)+\tan^{-1}(\cot A)+\tan^{-1}(\cot^3 A)$$
   $$=0\text{ if }\pi/4<A<\pi/2$$
   and $=\pi$ if $0<A<\pi/4$.

47. (a) Evaluate $\tan^{-1}\dfrac{3\sin 2\alpha}{5+3\cos 2\alpha}+\tan^{-1}\dfrac{\tan\alpha}{4}$

   where $-\dfrac{\pi}{2}<\alpha<\dfrac{\pi}{2}$

   (b)* If $\theta=\tan^{-1}(2\tan^2\theta)-\dfrac{1}{2}\sin^{-1}\left(\dfrac{3\sin 2\theta}{5+4\cos 2\theta}\right)$

   then find the general value of θ.
   (Roorkee 1997; J.E.E.B.W. 2000)

   (c) If $\theta=\tan^{-1}\left[\dfrac{2\tan^2\theta-\dfrac{1}{3}\tan\theta}{1+\dfrac{2}{3}\tan^3\theta}\right]$, then $\tan\theta=$
   (a) -2 (b) 1
   (c) $\dfrac{2}{3}$ (d) 2

   (d) If $\tan^{-1}x=\dfrac{1}{2}\sin^{-1}\left(\dfrac{3\sin 2\theta}{5+4\cos 2\theta}\right)$, then $x=$
   (a) $\tan 3\theta$ (b) $2\tan\theta$
   (c) $\dfrac{1}{3}\tan\theta$ (d) $3\cot\theta$

48. (a)* Prove that
   $$\tan^{-1}\dfrac{c_1x-y}{c_1y+x}+\tan^{-1}\dfrac{c_2-c_1}{1+c_2c_1}+\tan^{-1}\dfrac{c_3-c_2}{1+c_3c_2}$$
   $$+\ldots+\tan^{-1}\dfrac{1}{c_n}=\tan^{-1}\dfrac{x}{y}.$$

   (b) $\cot^{-1}\dfrac{pq+1}{p-q}+\cot^{-1}\dfrac{qr+1}{q-r}+\cot^{-1}\dfrac{rp+1}{r-p}=0$

49. (a)* $\tan^{-1}\sqrt{\left\{\dfrac{x(x+y+z)}{yz}\right\}}+\tan^{-1}\sqrt{\left\{\dfrac{y(x+y+z)}{zx}\right\}}$

   $$+\tan^{-1}\sqrt{\left\{\dfrac{z(x+y+z)}{xy}\right\}}=\pi.$$

   (b) $\tan^{-1}\dfrac{yz}{xr}+\tan^{-1}\dfrac{zx}{yr}+\tan^{-1}\dfrac{xy}{zr}=\dfrac{\pi}{2}$,

   where $r^2=x^2+y^2+z^2$.

50. Solve for x the following equations :

   (a) $\sec^{-1}\dfrac{x}{a}-\sec^{-1}\dfrac{x}{b}=\sec^{-1}b-\sec^{-1}a$.

   (b) $\tan^{-1}\dfrac{a}{x}+\tan^{-1}\dfrac{b}{x}+\tan^{-1}\dfrac{c}{x}+\tan^{-1}\dfrac{d}{x}=\dfrac{\pi}{2}$.

   (c)* $\tan^{-1}\dfrac{1}{a-1}=\tan^{-1}\dfrac{1}{x}+\tan^{-1}\dfrac{1}{a^2-x+1}$.

   Another Form :
   $$\cot^{-1}x+\cot^{-1}(n^2-x+1)=\cot^{-1}(n-1).$$

51. Sum the following series :

   (a)* $\tan^{-1}\dfrac{1}{3}+\tan^{-1}\dfrac{1}{7}+\tan^{-1}\dfrac{1}{13}+\ldots n$ terms and ∞

   or $\tan^{-1}\dfrac{1}{1+1+1^2}+\tan^{-1}\dfrac{1}{1+2+2^2}$

   $$+\tan^{-1}\dfrac{1}{1+3+3^2}+\ldots$$

   (b)* $\tan^{-1}\dfrac{1}{2.1^2}+\tan^{-1}\dfrac{1}{2.2^2}$

   $$+\tan^{-1}\dfrac{1}{2.3^2}+\ldots n\text{ terms and }\infty$$

   or $\cot^{-1}(2.1^2)+\cot^{-1}(2.2^2)$

   $$+\cot^{-1}(2.3^2)+\ldots$$

   (c) Prove that $\displaystyle\sum_{\lambda=1}^{n}\tan^{-1}\left[\dfrac{2\lambda}{2+\lambda^2+\lambda^4}\right]$

   $$=\tan^{-1}(n^2+n+1)-\dfrac{\pi}{4}.$$

52. (a) $\cot^{-1}\left(2^2+\dfrac{1}{2}\right)+\cot^{-1}\left(2^3+\dfrac{1}{2^2}\right)$

   $$+\cot^{-1}\left(2^4+\dfrac{1}{2^3}\right)+\ldots\infty$$

   (b)* $\tan^{-1}\dfrac{1}{3}+\tan^{-1}\dfrac{2}{9}+\ldots+\tan^{-1}\dfrac{2^{n-1}}{1+2^{2n-1}}$

53. (a) $\cot^{-1}\left(1+\dfrac{3}{4}\right)+\cot^{-1}\left(2^2+\dfrac{3}{4}\right)$

$$+\cot^{-1}\left(3^2+\dfrac{3}{4}\right)+\ldots\infty$$

(b) Find the sum of the series

$$\sin^{-1}\left(\dfrac{1}{\sqrt{2}}\right)+\sin^{-1}\left(\dfrac{\sqrt{2}-1}{\sqrt{6}}\right)+\ldots$$

$$+\sin^{-1}\left[\dfrac{\sqrt{n}-\sqrt{n-1}}{\sqrt{\{n(n+1)\}}}\right]+\ldots\infty$$

54. If $0 < x < 1,$ then

$$\sqrt{1+x^2}\ [\{x\cos(\cot^{-1}x)+\sin(\cot^{-1}x)\}^2-1]^{1/2}$$

is equal to

(a) $\dfrac{x}{\sqrt{1+x^2}}$ (b) x

(c) $x\sqrt{1+x^2}$ (d) $\sqrt{1+x^2}$

(I.I.T. 2008)

Solutions to Problem Set (1)

1. (a) $\sin\left[\dfrac{\pi}{3}-\sin^{-1}\left(-\dfrac{1}{2}\right)\right]$

$$=\sin\left(\dfrac{\pi}{3}+\sin^{-1}\dfrac{1}{2}\right)=\sin\left(\dfrac{\pi}{3}+\dfrac{\pi}{6}\right)=\sin\dfrac{\pi}{2}=1$$

$$\because\quad \sin^{-1}(-x)=-\sin^{-1}x.$$

(b) Just as part (a).

$$\sin\left(\dfrac{\pi}{2}+\dfrac{\pi}{3}\right)=\cos\dfrac{\pi}{3}=\dfrac{1}{2}.$$

2. (a) $\sin^{-1}\left[\left(\sin\dfrac{2\pi}{3}\right)\right]=\dfrac{2\pi}{3}$ will be wrong as it is

greater than $\pi/2.$ Hence we say

$$\sin^{-1}\left(\sin\dfrac{2\pi}{3}\right)=\sin^{-1}\left[\sin\left(\pi-\dfrac{\pi}{3}\right)\right]$$

$$=\sin^{-1}\left(\sin\dfrac{\pi}{3}\right)=\dfrac{\pi}{3}.$$

(b) $\sin\dfrac{33\pi}{7}=\sin\left(4\pi+\dfrac{5\pi}{7}\right)=\sin\dfrac{5\pi}{7}$

$$=\sin\left(\pi-\dfrac{2\pi}{7}\right)=\sin\dfrac{2\pi}{7}$$

$$\therefore\quad \sin^{-1}\left(\sin\dfrac{33\pi}{7}\right)=\dfrac{2\pi}{7}.$$

3. (a) $\cos^{-1}\cos\left(\dfrac{7\pi}{6}\right)=\dfrac{7\pi}{6}$ is wrong, as $7\pi/6$ is greater

than $\pi.$

Here $\dfrac{7\pi}{6}=2\pi-\dfrac{5\pi}{6}$ so that $\dfrac{5\pi}{6}$ lies between 0 and π

$$\therefore\quad \cos^{-1}\cos\left(\dfrac{7\pi}{6}\right)=\cos^{-1}\cos\left(2\pi-\dfrac{5\pi}{6}\right)$$

$$=\cos^{-1}\cos\left(\dfrac{5\pi}{6}\right)=\dfrac{5\pi}{6}.$$

(b) $\cos^{-1}\cos\dfrac{4\pi}{3}=\cos^{-1}\cos\left(2\pi-\dfrac{2\pi}{3}\right)$

$$=\cos^{-1}\cos\dfrac{2\pi}{3}=\dfrac{2\pi}{3}.$$

4. (a) Let $x=\tan^{-1}\tan\left(\dfrac{3\pi}{4}\right),$ so that x must lie

between $-\dfrac{\pi}{2}$ and $\dfrac{\pi}{2}.$

Hence $x=\tan^{-1}\tan\left(\pi-\dfrac{\pi}{4}\right)$

$$=\tan^{-1}\tan\left(-\dfrac{\pi}{4}\right)=-\dfrac{\pi}{4}.$$

(b) Ans. $-\dfrac{\pi}{3}.$

(c) $\cos\left[\cos^{-1}\left(-\dfrac{\sqrt{3}}{2}\right)+\dfrac{\pi}{6}\right].$

Now $\cos^{-1}(-x)=\pi-\cos^{-1}x$

$$=\cos\left[\pi-\cos^{-1}\left(\dfrac{\sqrt{3}}{2}\right)+\dfrac{\pi}{6}\right]$$

$$=\cos\left[\pi-\dfrac{\pi}{6}+\dfrac{\pi}{6}\right]=\cos\pi=-1.$$

Alternative : Since $0\le\cos^{-1}x\le\pi,$ we have

$$\cos^{-1}\left(-\dfrac{\sqrt{3}}{2}\right)=\dfrac{5\pi}{6}\text{ etc.}$$

(d) $E=\tan^{-1}\dfrac{1-x}{1+x}=\tan^{-1}1-\tan^{-1}x=\dfrac{\pi}{4}-\tan^{-1}x$

Now $0\le x\le 1$ $\therefore$ $0\le\tan^{-1}x\le\dfrac{\pi}{4}$

Multiplying by minus sign and reversing the inequality,

$$-\dfrac{\pi}{4}\le-\tan^{-1}x\le 0$$

Add $\dfrac{\pi}{4}$ to both sides

$$\therefore\quad 0\le\dfrac{\pi}{4}-\tan^{-1}x\le\dfrac{\pi}{4}\text{ or }0\le E\le\dfrac{\pi}{4}$$

5. (a) **Refer § 1 (A, B, C, D) P. 619-620.**

$$T_1=\sin^{-1}\sin\left(5\pi-\dfrac{2\pi}{7}\right)=\sin^{-1}\sin\dfrac{2\pi}{7}=\dfrac{2\pi}{7}$$

$$T_2=\cos^{-1}\cos\left(6\pi+\dfrac{4\pi}{7}\right)=\cos^{-1}\cos\dfrac{4\pi}{7}=\dfrac{4\pi}{7}$$

$$T_3=\tan^{-1}\left\{-\tan\left(2\pi-\dfrac{3\pi}{8}\right)\right\}=\tan^{-1}\tan\dfrac{3\pi}{8}=\dfrac{3\pi}{8}$$

$$T_4=\pi-\cot^{-1}\left(\dfrac{19\pi}{8}\right)=\pi-\cot^{-1}\left(2\pi+\dfrac{3\pi}{8}\right)$$

$$=\pi-\dfrac{3\pi}{8}=\dfrac{5\pi}{8}$$

$$\therefore\quad S=\dfrac{2\pi}{7}+\dfrac{4\pi}{7}+\dfrac{3\pi}{8}+\dfrac{5\pi}{8}=\dfrac{6\pi}{7}+\pi=\dfrac{13\pi}{7}$$

(b) Ans. (c). $a\sin^{-1}x-b\cos^{-1}x=c$

Also $b\ [\sin^{-1}x+\cos^{-1}x]=b\cdot\pi/2$

Adding, $(a+b)\sin^{-1}x=\dfrac{\pi b}{2}+c$

$\therefore \quad \sin^{-1} x = \dfrac{1}{a+b}\left[\dfrac{\pi b}{2} + c\right]$

$\cos^{-1} x = \dfrac{\pi}{2} - \sin^{-1} x = \dfrac{\pi}{2} - \dfrac{b}{a+b} \cdot \dfrac{\pi}{2} - \dfrac{c}{a+b}$

$\qquad = \dfrac{1}{a+b}\left[\dfrac{\pi a}{2} - c\right]$

$\therefore \quad a\sin^{-1} x + b\cos^{-1} x = $ etc. as in (c).

6. (a) $\sin\cos^{-1}(3/5) = \sin\sin^{-1}\sqrt{1 - 9/25}$

$\qquad\qquad = \sin\sin^{-1}(4/5) = 4/5.$

[Here we have used the formula

$\qquad\qquad \cos^{-1} x = \sin^{-1}\sqrt{1 - x^2}$].

(b) We have $\tan^{-1} x = \cos^{-1}\dfrac{1}{\sqrt{(1 + x^2)}}$ ...(1)

$\therefore \quad \cos\left(\tan^{-1}\dfrac{3}{4}\right) = \cos\left(\cos^{-1}\dfrac{1}{\sqrt{(1 + 9/16)}}\right)$

$\qquad\qquad = \cos\left(\cos^{-1}\dfrac{4}{5}\right) = \dfrac{4}{5}, \quad$ by (1)

For the second part, we have

$\cos\tan^{-1} x = \cos\cos^{-1}\dfrac{1}{\sqrt{(1 + x^2)}} = \dfrac{1}{\sqrt{(1 + x^2)}}.$

(c) Ans. (d).

We know that $\cot^{-1} t = \sin^{-1}\dfrac{1}{\sqrt{1 + t^2}}, t = x + 1$

and $\tan^{-1} p = \cos^{-1}\dfrac{1}{\sqrt{1 + p^2}}, p = x$

Hence from the given relation we get

$\dfrac{1}{\sqrt{1 + (x + 1)^2}} = \dfrac{1}{\sqrt{1 + x^2}}$

or $\quad x^2 + 2x + 2 = x^2 + 1$

or $\quad 2x = -1 \quad \therefore x = -\dfrac{1}{2} \Rightarrow$ (d)

(d) By § 3, $\cot^{-1} x = \sin^{-1}\dfrac{1}{\sqrt{(1 + x^2)}}$

$\sin(\cot^{-1} x) = \dfrac{1}{\sqrt{(1 + x^2)}}.$

(e) $2\sin^{-1} x = \sin^{-1} 2x\sqrt{1 - x^2}.$

$\therefore \quad \sin(2\sin^{-1} 0\cdot 8) = 2\cdot\dfrac{8}{10}\sqrt{\left(1 - \dfrac{64}{100}\right)} = 0\cdot 96.$

7. (a) If $\cos^{-1}(\sqrt{5}/3) = \theta, \; 0 < \theta < \pi/2$, then

$\cos\theta = \sqrt{5}/3$

and $\sin\theta = \sqrt{1 - \cos^2\theta} = \sqrt{1 - 5/9}$

$\qquad\qquad = \sqrt{4/9} = 2/3.$

$\therefore \quad \tan\left[\dfrac{1}{2}\cos^{-1}\dfrac{\sqrt{5}}{3}\right] = \tan\dfrac{\theta}{2}$

$\qquad = \dfrac{1 - \cos\theta}{\sin\theta} = \dfrac{[1 - (\sqrt{5}/3)]}{(2/3)} = \dfrac{3 - \sqrt{5}}{2}.$

(b) $\because \quad 2\tan^{-1}\left(\dfrac{1}{5}\right) = \tan^{-1}\dfrac{2\cdot(1/5)}{1 - (1/5)^2} = \tan^{-1}\dfrac{5}{12},$

and $\pi/4 = \tan^{-1} 1$, we have

$\qquad\qquad \tan[2\tan^{-1}(1/5) - \pi/4]$

$\qquad = \tan[\tan^{-1}(5/12) - \tan^{-1} 1]$

$\qquad = \tan\tan^{-1}\dfrac{(5/12) - 1}{1 + (5/12)\cdot 1}$

$\qquad = \tan\tan^{-1}\left(-\dfrac{7}{17}\right) = -\dfrac{7}{17}.$

8. (a) To prove $\sin^{-1}(4/5) + \sin^{-1}(5/13)$

$\qquad = \dfrac{\pi}{2} - \sin^{-1}\dfrac{16}{65} = \cos^{-1}\left(\dfrac{16}{65}\right).$

Now $\sin^{-1} x \pm \sin^{-1} y$

$\qquad = \sin^{-1}[x\sqrt{1 - y^2} \pm y\sqrt{1 - x^2}].$

L.H.S. $= \sin^{-1}\left[\dfrac{4}{5}\sqrt{\left(1 - \dfrac{25}{169}\right)} + \dfrac{5}{13}\sqrt{\left(1 - \dfrac{16}{25}\right)}\right]$

$\qquad = \sin^{-1}\left(\dfrac{4}{5}\cdot\dfrac{12}{13} + \dfrac{5}{13}\cdot\dfrac{3}{5}\right) = \sin^{-1}\left(\dfrac{48}{65} + \dfrac{15}{65}\right)$

$\qquad = \sin^{-1}\dfrac{63}{65}$

and R.H.S. $= \cos^{-1}(16/65) = \sin^{-1}(63/65).$

(b) Do yourself, as in part (a).

(c) Do yourself, as in part (a).

9. (a) Since $\sin^{-1}\dfrac{12}{13} = \tan^{-1}\dfrac{12}{5}$

and $\cos^{-1}\dfrac{4}{5} = \tan^{-1}\dfrac{3}{4}$, we have

L.H.S. $= \tan^{-1}\dfrac{12}{5} + \tan^{-1}\dfrac{3}{4} + \tan^{-1}\dfrac{63}{16}$

and since $\dfrac{12}{5}\times\dfrac{3}{4} > 1$, we have

$\tan^{-1}\dfrac{12}{5} + \tan^{-1}\dfrac{3}{4} = \pi + \tan^{-1}\dfrac{(12/5) + (3/4)}{1 - (12/5)\cdot(3/4)}$

$\qquad = \pi + \tan^{-1}\left\{-\dfrac{63}{16}\right\} \qquad\qquad \textbf{(§ 5 P. 622)}$

$\qquad = \pi - \tan^{-1}\dfrac{63}{16} \quad [\because \tan^{-1}(-x) = -\tan^{-1} x]$

Hence

L.H.S. $= \pi - \tan^{-1}\dfrac{63}{16} + \tan^{-1}\dfrac{63}{16} = \pi = $ R.H.S.

(b) As in part (a), we will change each term to $\tan^{-1}$.

$2\cos^{-1}\dfrac{3}{\sqrt{13}} = \cos^{-1}(2x^2 - 1)$

$\qquad = \cos^{-1}\dfrac{5}{13} = \tan^{-1}\dfrac{12}{13}$

$\cot^{-1}\dfrac{16}{63} = \tan^{-1}\dfrac{63}{16}$

$\frac{1}{2}\cos^{-1}\frac{7}{25} = \theta, \text{say}. \quad \therefore \quad \cos 2\theta = \frac{7}{25}$

or $\frac{1-t^2}{1+t^2} = \frac{7}{25} \quad \therefore \quad t^2 = \frac{9}{16}$ or $t = \frac{3}{4}, -\frac{3}{4}$

Since $\cos 2\theta = +$ ive $\quad \therefore \quad 0 \le 2\theta < \pi$

$\therefore \quad 0 \le \theta < \pi/2$

and hence $t = \tan\theta = +$ ive $\quad \therefore \quad \tan\theta = 3/4$

$\therefore \quad$ L.H.S. $= \tan^{-1}\frac{12}{13} + \tan^{-1}\frac{63}{16} + \tan^{-1}\frac{3}{4}$

Rest as in part (a).

10. (a) $\operatorname{cosec}^{-1} x = \cot^{-1}\sqrt{x^2-1}$

L.H.S. $= \cot^{-1} 9 + \cot^{-1}\sqrt{(41/16)-1}$

$= \cot^{-1} 9 + \cot^{-1}(5/4)$

$= \tan^{-1}\frac{1}{9} + \tan^{-1}\frac{4}{5}$

$= \tan^{-1}\frac{(1/9)+(4/5)}{1-(1/9)\cdot(4/5)} = \tan^{-1}\frac{41}{41}$

$= \tan^{-1} 1 = \pi/4.$

(b) Do yourself.

(c) $\tan^{-1} 2 + \tan^{-1} 3 = \pi + \tan^{-1}\frac{2+3}{1-2.3},$

$\qquad \because xy = 2.3 = 6 > 1$

$= \pi + \tan^{-1}\{5/(-5)\}$

$= \pi + \tan^{-1}(-1) = \pi - \tan^{-1} 1$

$= \pi - \pi/4 = 3\pi/4.$

11. (a) $\tan^{-1}\frac{1/2+1/3}{1-1/2.1/3}$

$= \tan^{-1}\frac{5/6}{5/6} = \tan^{-1} 1 = \frac{\pi}{4}.$

(b) L.H.S. $= \tan^{-1}\frac{1/2+1/5}{1-(1/2)(1/5)} + \tan^{-1}\frac{1}{8}$

$= \tan^{-1}\frac{7}{9} + \tan^{-1}\frac{1}{8}$

$= \tan^{-1}\frac{7/9+1/8}{1-(7/9)(1/8)}$

$= \tan^{-1}\frac{65}{65} = \tan^{-1} 1 = \frac{\pi}{4}.$

(c) Do yourself.

12. (a) We have $2\tan^{-1}\frac{1}{3} = \tan^{-1}\frac{2/3}{1-(1/9)} = \tan^{-1}\frac{3}{4}$

and $\sin^{-1}(4/5) = \tan^{-1}(4/3)$

Hence L.H.S. $= \tan^{-1}(4/3) + \tan^{-1}(3/4).$

$= \tan^{-1}(4/3) + \cot^{-1}(4/3) = \pi/2.$

(b) Do yourself.

(c) Write the L.H.S. as

$[\tan^{-1}(1/3) + \tan^{-1}(1/5)] + [\tan^{-1}(1/7)$

$\qquad\qquad\qquad\qquad + \tan^{-1}(1/8)]$

and then use the formula

$\tan^{-1} x + \tan^{-1} y = \tan^{-1}\frac{x+y}{1-xy}.$

13. (a) $21 = 1+5.4, \quad 13 = 1+4.3,$

$-1/8 = -2/16 \quad$ and $\quad 16 = 1+5.3.$

$T_1 = \tan^{-1}\frac{5-4}{1+5.4} = \tan^{-1} 5 - \tan^{-1} 4$

$T_2 = \tan^{-1} 4 - \tan^{-1} 3$

$T_3 = \tan^{-1}\frac{-2}{1+15} = \tan^{-1} 3 - \tan^{-1} 5$

$\therefore \quad$ Sum $= 0.$

Note : You may combine first two terms to get

$\tan^{-1}\left(\frac{34}{272}\right) = \tan^{-1}\left(\frac{1}{8}\right)$

(b) We have to prove $\tan^{-1}\frac{12}{5} = 2\tan^{-1}\frac{2}{3}.$

Now R.H.S. $= \tan^{-1}\frac{2(2/3)}{1-(4/9)} = \tan^{-1}\frac{(4/3)}{(5/9)}$

$= \tan^{-1}(12/5) = $ L.H.S.

(c) L.H.S. $= \tan^{-1}\frac{1}{4} + \tan^{-1}\frac{2}{9} = \tan^{-1}\frac{1/4+2/9}{1-(1/4)(2/9)}$

$= \tan^{-1}\frac{1}{2} = \frac{1}{2}.2\tan^{-1}\frac{1}{2}$

$= \frac{1}{2}\tan^{-1}\frac{2(1/2)}{1-(1/4)} = \frac{1}{2}\tan^{-1}\frac{4}{3} = \frac{1}{2}\cos^{-1}\frac{3}{5}.$

14. (a) Ans. (c).

We have $\tan[\cos^{-1}(4/5) + \tan^{-1}(2/3)]$

$= \tan[\tan^{-1}(3/4) + \tan^{-1}(2/3)]$

$= \tan\tan^{-1}\left[\frac{(3/4)+(2/3)}{1-(3/4).(2/3)}\right]$

$= \tan\tan^{-1}\left[\frac{17/12}{1/2}\right]$

$= \tan\tan^{-1}\left(\frac{17}{6}\right) = \frac{17}{6}.$

Other forms :

Also $\cos^{-1}(4/5) = \sin^{-1}(3/5)$

and $\tan^{-1}(2/3) = \cot^{-1}(3/2)$

(b) Ans. True.

We have $\tan^{-1} x + \tan^{-1}(1/2) = 45°.$

$\therefore \quad \tan^{-1} x = 45° - \tan^{-1}(1/2)$

$= \tan^{-1} 1 - \tan^{-1}(1/2)$

$= \tan^{-1}\frac{1-(1/2)}{1+1.(1/2)} = \tan^{-1}\frac{1}{3}$

Hence $x = 1/3.$

(c) $\tan(A-B) = \frac{\tan A - \tan B}{1+\tan A\tan B} = \frac{\dfrac{x\sqrt{3}}{2\lambda-x} - \dfrac{2x-\lambda}{\lambda\sqrt{3}}}{1+\dfrac{x\sqrt{3}}{2\lambda-x}\cdot\dfrac{2x-\lambda}{\lambda\sqrt{3}}}$

$$= \frac{3x\lambda + (2x - \lambda)(x - 2\lambda)}{\sqrt{3}[\lambda(2\lambda - x) + x(2x - \lambda)]}$$

$$= \frac{1}{\sqrt{3}}\left[\frac{2x^2 - 2\lambda x + 2\lambda^2}{2x^2 - 2\lambda x + 2\lambda^2}\right] = \frac{1}{\sqrt{3}} = \tan 30°$$

$$\therefore \quad A - B = 30°$$

15. $2\tan^{-1}\dfrac{1}{5} = \tan^{-1}\dfrac{2/5}{1 - (1/25)} = \tan^{-1}\dfrac{5}{12}$.

$$\therefore \quad 4\tan^{-1}\frac{1}{5} = 2\tan^{-1}\frac{5}{12}$$

$$= \tan^{-1}\frac{2(5/12)}{1 - (25/144)} = \tan^{-1}\frac{120}{119}.$$

$$\therefore \quad \text{L.H.S.} = \tan^{-1}\frac{120}{119} - \left(\tan^{-1}\frac{1}{70} - \tan^{-1}\frac{1}{99}\right)$$

$$= \tan^{-1}\frac{120}{119} - \tan^{-1}\frac{1/70 - 1/99}{1 + (1/99)(1/70)}$$

$$= \tan^{-1}\frac{120}{119} - \tan^{-1}\frac{29}{6931}$$

$$= \tan^{-1}\frac{120}{119} - \tan^{-1}\frac{1}{239}$$

$$= \tan^{-1}\frac{120/119 - 1/239}{1 + (120/119) \cdot (1/239)}$$

$$= \tan^{-1}\frac{120 \cdot 239 - 119}{119 \cdot 239 + 120}$$

$$= \tan^{-1}\frac{119 \cdot 239 + (239 - 119)}{119 \cdot 239 + 120},$$

$$= \tan^{-1} 1 = \pi/4$$

writing $120x = (119 + 1)x$

16. (a) L.H.S.

$$= 2\left(\tan^{-1}\frac{1}{5} + \tan^{-1}\frac{1}{8}\right) + \tan^{-1}\sqrt{\left[\left(\frac{5\sqrt{2}}{7}\right)^2 - 1\right]}$$

$$= 2\tan^{-1}\frac{1/5 + 1/8}{1 - (1/5) \cdot (1/8)} + \tan^{-1}\frac{1}{7},$$

$$\because \sec^{-1} x = \tan^{-1}\sqrt{x^2 - 1}$$

$$= 2\tan^{-1}\frac{13}{39} + \tan^{-1}\frac{1}{7} = 2\tan^{-1}\frac{1}{3} + \tan^{-1}\frac{1}{7}$$

$$= \tan^{-1}\frac{2 \cdot 1/3}{1 - 1/9} + \tan^{-1}\frac{1}{7} = \tan^{-1}\frac{3}{4} + \tan^{-1}\frac{1}{7}$$

$$= \tan^{-1}\frac{3/4 + 1/7}{1 - (3/4) \cdot (1/7)} = \tan^{-1}\frac{25}{25}$$

$$= \tan^{-1} 1 = \frac{\pi}{4}.$$

(b) $\cos^{-1} x = \tan^{-1}\dfrac{\sqrt{1 - x^2}}{x}$.

$$\therefore \quad \cos^{-1}\frac{12}{13} = \tan^{-1}\frac{\sqrt{1 - 144/169}}{12/13} = \tan^{-1}\frac{5}{12}$$

$$\cos^{-1}\sqrt{\left(\frac{49}{50}\right)} = \tan^{-1}\frac{\sqrt{1 - 49/50}}{\sqrt{(49/50)}} = \tan^{-1}\frac{1}{7}.$$

Similarly $\cos^{-1}\sqrt{64/65} = \tan^{-1}(1/8)$,

$$\cos^{-1}(1/\sqrt{2}) = \tan^{-1} 1 = \pi/4$$

Thus we have to prove that

$$\tan^{-1}(5/12) + 2\tan^{-1}(1/8)$$
$$+ \tan^{-1}(1/7) = \tan^{-1} 1$$

or $\tan^{-1}\dfrac{5/12 + 1/7}{1 - (5/12) \cdot (1/7)}$

$$= \tan^{-1} 1 - \tan^{-1}\frac{2 \cdot 1/8}{1 - 1/64}$$

or $\tan^{-1}(47/79) = \tan^{-1} 1 - \tan^{-1}(16/63)$

or $\tan^{-1}\dfrac{47}{79} = \tan^{-1}\dfrac{1 - (16/63)}{1 + (16/63)} = \tan^{-1}\dfrac{47}{79}$.

17. (a) $2\tan^{-1} x = \sin^{-1}\dfrac{2x}{1 + x^2}$ § 8, P. 622

$$\tan^{-1} y = \cos^{-1}\frac{1}{\sqrt{(1 + y^2)}} \qquad \text{§ 3, P. 621}$$

L.H.S. $= \dfrac{2x}{1 + x^2} + \dfrac{1}{\sqrt{(1 + y^2)}}$, $x = \dfrac{1}{3}$, $y = 2\sqrt{2}$

$$= \frac{3}{5} + \frac{1}{3} = \frac{14}{15}$$

(b) $\sec^{-1}\sqrt{2} = \cos^{-1}\dfrac{1}{\sqrt{2}} = \dfrac{\pi}{4} = 45°$

$$\cos^{-1}\frac{\sqrt{12}}{4} = \cos^{-1}\frac{\sqrt{3}}{2} = \frac{\pi}{6} = 30°$$

$$\sin^{-1}\sqrt{\frac{2 - \sqrt{3}}{4}} = \sin^{-1}\sqrt{\frac{4 - 2\sqrt{3}}{8}}$$

$$= \sin^{-1}\frac{\sqrt{3} - 1}{2\sqrt{2}} = 15°$$

$$\therefore \quad \text{L.H.S.} = \sin^{-1}[\cot(45° + 30° + 15°)]$$
$$= \sin^{-1}(\cot 90°) = \sin^{-1} 0 = 0$$

$$\therefore \quad \text{L.H.S.} = 0.$$

18. $\sin^{-1}\dfrac{x}{a} = \tan^{-1}\dfrac{x}{\sqrt{(a^2 - x^2)}}$

$$\therefore \quad T_3 = \tan^{-1}\frac{142}{31}$$

$$2\tan^{-1} x = \tan^{-1}\frac{2x}{1 - x^2}$$

$$\therefore \quad T_2 = \tan^{-1}\frac{5}{12}$$

$$3\tan^{-1} x = \tan^{-1}\frac{3x - x^3}{1 - 3x^2}$$

$$\therefore \quad T_1 = \tan^{-1}\frac{11}{2}$$

$$\therefore \quad E = \tan^{-1}\frac{11}{2} + \tan^{-1}\frac{5}{12} + \tan^{-1}\frac{142}{31}$$

$$= \pi + \tan^{-1}\frac{\dfrac{11}{2} + \dfrac{5}{12}}{1 - \dfrac{55}{24}} + \tan^{-1}\frac{142}{31}$$

Here $ab > 1$ and hence $\pi + \tan^{-1}(\ )$

$$= \pi - \tan^{-1}\frac{142}{31} + \tan^{-1}\frac{142}{31} = \pi.$$

19. (a) Ans. (b). Put $x = \sin\theta$

$$\sin^{-1}\left(\frac{1}{\sqrt{2}}\sin\theta + \frac{1}{\sqrt{2}}\cos\theta\right) = \sin^{-1}\sin\left(\theta + \frac{\pi}{4}\right)$$

$$= \theta + \frac{\pi}{4}$$

$$\therefore \quad E = \tan\left[\theta + \frac{\pi}{4} - \theta\right] = \tan\frac{\pi}{4} = 1$$

(b) Ans. (a).

$$\alpha = \sin^{-1}\left[\frac{4}{5}\sqrt{1 - \frac{1}{9}} + \frac{1}{3}\sqrt{1 - \frac{16}{25}}\right]$$

$$= \sin^{-1}\left[\frac{8\sqrt{2}}{15} + \frac{3}{15}\right] = \sin^{-1}\left(\frac{8\sqrt{2} + 3}{15}\right)$$

Since $\dfrac{8\sqrt{2} + 3}{15} < 1 \quad \therefore \quad \alpha < \dfrac{\pi}{2}$ ...(I)

$$\beta = \left(\frac{\pi}{2} - \sin^{-1}\frac{4}{5} + \frac{\pi}{2} - \sin^{-1}\frac{1}{3}\right) = \pi - \alpha > \frac{\pi}{2}\ \text{by (I)}$$

$$\therefore \quad \alpha < \beta \Rightarrow (a)$$

20. (a) $\cos^{-1}p + \cos^{-1}q + \cos^{-1}r = \pi$

$$\Rightarrow \quad \cos^{-1}[pq - \sqrt{1 - p^2}\cdot\sqrt{1 - q^2}\,]$$

$$= \pi - \cos^{-1}r = \cos^{-1}(-r).$$

$$\therefore \quad pq - \sqrt{(1 - p^2)(1 - q^2)} = -r$$

or $(pq + r)^2 = (1 - p^2)(1 - q^2)$

or $p^2q^2 + r^2 + 2pqr = 1 - p^2 - q^2 + p^2q^2$

or $p^2 + q^2 + r^2 + 2pqr = 1$.

(b) $\sin^{-1}x + \sin^{-1}y = \pi - \sin^{-1}z$

Take cos of both sides and not sine for easy simplification.

$$\cos(\sin^{-1}t) = \cos(\cos^{-1}\sqrt{1 - t^2}\,) = \sqrt{(1 - t^2)}$$

$$\sqrt{1 - x^2}\sqrt{1 - y^2} - xy = -\sqrt{1 - z^2}$$

$$\therefore \quad (1 - x^2)(1 - y^2) = x^2y^2 + (1 - z^2)$$

$$- 2xy\sqrt{1 - z^2}$$

$$1 - x^2 - y^2 = 1 - z^2 - 2xy\sqrt{1 - z^2}$$

$$\therefore \quad x^2 + y^2 - z^2 = 2xy\sqrt{1 - z^2}.\ \text{Square again.}$$

(c) L.H.S. $= \tan^{-1}\dfrac{(x + y)}{1 - xy} + \tan^{-1}z$

$$= \tan^{-1}\frac{[(x + y)/(1 - xy)] + z}{1 - [(x + y)/(1 - xy)]\cdot z}$$

$$= \tan^{-1}\frac{x + y + z - xyz}{1 - xy - yz - zx} = \pi \quad\text{or}\quad \frac{\pi}{2}$$

$$\therefore \quad \frac{x + y + z - xyz}{1 - xy - yz - zx} = \tan\pi \ \text{or}\ \tan\frac{\pi}{2}$$

or $\qquad = 0$ or ∞

Hence $x + y + z - xyz = 0$ i.e. $N^r = 0$

i.e. $x + y + z = xyz$

or $1 - xy - yz - zx = 0$ i.e. $D^r = 0$

i.e. $xy + yz + zx = 1$

21. (a) Ans. (a). We know that $|\sin^{-1}x| \le \pi/2$

Hence from the given relation we observe that each of $\sin^{-1}x, \sin^{-1}y$ and $\sin^{-1}z$ will be $\pi/2$ so that $x = y = z = \sin(\pi/2) = 1 \quad \therefore \quad 3 - \dfrac{9}{3} = 0$

(b) $\sin^{-1}\left[\dfrac{ax}{c}\sqrt{1 - \dfrac{b^2x^2}{c^2}} + \dfrac{bx}{c}\sqrt{1 - \dfrac{a^2x^2}{c^2}}\right] = \sin^{-1}x$

$$\therefore \quad x[a\sqrt{c^2 - b^2x^2} + b\sqrt{c^2 - a^2x^2} - c^2] = 0$$

$\therefore \quad x = 0$ is one solution which satisfies the given equation.

Again $a\sqrt{c^2 - b^2x^2} + b\sqrt{c^2 - a^2x^2} = c^2$

Squaring both sides,

$$a^2(c^2 - b^2x^2) + b^2(c^2 - a^2x^2) + 2ab\sqrt{\ }\sqrt{\ } = c^4$$

$$c^2(a^2 + b^2) - 2a^2b^2x^2 + 2ab\sqrt{\ }\sqrt{\ } = c^4$$

Put $a^2 + b^2 = c^2$ and cancel c^4 from both sides

$$\therefore \quad abx^2 = \sqrt{c^2 - b^2x^2}\sqrt{c^2 - a^2x^2}$$

Square again

$$a^2b^2x^4 = c^4 - c^2(a^2 + b^2)x^2 + a^2b^2x^4$$

or $0 = c^4(1 - x^2) \quad \therefore x = \pm 1$

22. (a) By **§ 8 P. 622**, the given equation is

$$2\tan^{-1}p - 2\tan^{-1}q = 2\tan^{-1}x$$

or $\tan^{-1}p - \tan^{-1}q = \tan^{-1}x$

or $\tan^{-1}\dfrac{p - q}{1 + pq} = \tan^{-1}x,$

$$\therefore \quad x = \frac{p - q}{1 + pq}.$$

(b) $x = \dfrac{a + b}{1 - ab}$ As in part (a).

(c) L.H.S. $= \tan\left[\dfrac{1}{2}\cdot 2\tan^{-1}a + \dfrac{1}{2}\cdot 2\cdot\tan^{-1}a\right]$

$$= \tan[2\tan^{-1}a]$$

$$= \tan\tan^{-1}\frac{2a}{1 - a^2} = \frac{2a}{1 - a^2}.$$

23. Put $x = \tan\theta, y = \tan\phi$

$$\therefore \quad \text{L.H.S.} = \left(\frac{\pi}{4} - \theta\right) - \left(\frac{\pi}{4} - \phi\right) = \phi - \theta$$

$$= \tan^{-1}y - \tan^{-1}x = \tan^{-1}\frac{y - x}{1 + xy}$$

$$= \sin^{-1}\frac{y - x}{\{(y - x)^2 + (1 + xy)^2\}^{1/2}}$$

$$= \sin^{-1}\frac{y - x}{\sqrt{\{(1 + x^2)(1 + y^2)\}}}$$

24. (a) Dividing T_1, T_2 and T_3 by m^2, p^2 and M^2 respectively, $2\tan^{-1} x = \tan^{-1} \frac{2x}{1-x^2}$

L.H.S. $= 2\tan^{-1}\frac{n}{m} + 2\tan^{-1}\frac{q}{p}$

$= 2\tan^{-1}\frac{pn+mq}{pm-nq} = 2\tan^{-1}\frac{N}{M} =$ R.H.S.

(b) Dividing above and below by n^3 in T_1 and q^3 in T_2 and M^2 in T_3, we get

$\frac{2}{3}.3\tan^{-1}\frac{m}{n} + \frac{2}{3}.3\tan^{-1}\frac{p}{q} = 2\tan^{-1}\frac{N}{M}$

L.H.S. $= 2\left[\tan^{-1}\frac{(m/n)+(p/q)}{1-(m/n)(p/q)}\right]$

$= 2\tan^{-1}\frac{np+mq}{nq-mp} = 2\tan^{-1}\frac{N}{M} =$ R.H.S.

25. (a) $\sin\left[\tan^{-1}\frac{1-x^2}{2x} + \cos^{-1}\frac{1-x^2}{1+x^2}\right] = 1$

Put $x = \tan\theta$

L.H.S.

$= \sin\left[\tan^{-1}\frac{1-\tan^2\theta}{2\tan\theta} + \cos^{-1}\frac{1-\tan^2\theta}{1+\tan^2\theta}\right]$

$= \sin[\tan^{-1}\cot 2\theta + \cos^{-1}\cos 2\theta]$

$= \sin[\tan^{-1}\tan(\pi/2 - 2\theta) + 2\theta]$

$= \sin[\pi/2 - 2\theta + 2\theta] = \sin(\pi/2) = 1$.

(b) Ans. (b).

Given $\sin^{-1} A + \cos^{-1} B = \frac{\pi}{2}$ ...(1)

But $\sin^{-1} A + \cos^{-1} A = \frac{\pi}{2}$ ...(2)

From (1) and (2), we conclude that $A = B$

$\therefore x - \frac{x^2}{2} + \frac{x^3}{4}... = x^2 - \frac{x^4}{2} + \frac{x^6}{4}...$

or $\frac{x}{1-\left(-\frac{x}{2}\right)} = \frac{x^2}{1-\left(-\frac{x^2}{2}\right)}$ by S_∞ of a G.P.

or $x(2+x^2) = x^2(2+x)$

or $2x(x-1) = 0$ $\therefore x = 1$ as $x \neq 0$

26. (a) We have

$\cos^{-1}\left[\frac{p}{a}.\frac{q}{b} - \sqrt{\left(1-\frac{p^2}{a^2}\right)}\sqrt{\left(1-\frac{q^2}{b^2}\right)}\right] = \alpha$.

or $\frac{pq}{ab} - \sqrt{\left(1-\frac{p^2}{a^2}\right)}\sqrt{\left(1-\frac{q^2}{b^2}\right)} = \cos\alpha$

$\therefore \left(\frac{pq}{ab} - \cos\alpha\right)^2 = 1 - \frac{p^2}{a^2} - \frac{q^2}{b^2} + \frac{p^2q^2}{a^2b^2}$

or $\frac{p^2q^2}{a^2b^2} + \cos^2\alpha - \frac{2pq}{ab}\cos\alpha$

$= 1 - \frac{p^2}{a^2} - \frac{q^2}{b^2} + \frac{p^2q^2}{a^2b^2}$

or $\frac{p^2}{a^2} - \frac{2pq}{ab}\cos\alpha + \frac{q^2}{b^2} = 1 - \cos^2\alpha = \sin^2\alpha$.

(b) Proceed as above.

27. We have $u = \cot^{-1}\sqrt{\cos 2\theta} - \tan^{-1}\sqrt{\cos 2\theta}$

$= \tan^{-1}(1/\sqrt{\cos 2\theta}) - \tan^{-1}\sqrt{\cos 2\theta}$

$= \tan^{-1}\frac{1/(\sqrt{\cos 2\theta}) - \sqrt{\cos 2\theta}}{1+[1/\sqrt{(\cos 2\theta)}]\sqrt{(\cos 2\theta)}}$

$= \tan^{-1}\frac{1-\cos 2\theta}{2\sqrt{(\cos 2\theta)}}$

$\therefore \tan u = \frac{1-\cos 2\theta}{2\sqrt{(\cos 2\theta)}}$

or $\cot u = \frac{2\sqrt{\cos 2\theta}}{1-\cos 2\theta}$

Hence $\text{cosec}^2 u = 1 + \cot^2 u$

$= 1 + \frac{4\cos 2\theta}{(1-\cos 2\theta)^2} = \frac{(1+\cos 2\theta)^2}{(1-\cos 2\theta)^2}$

or $\text{cosec } u = \frac{1+\cos 2\theta}{1-\cos 2\theta} = \frac{2\cos^2\theta}{2\sin^2\theta} = \cot^2\theta$

or $\sin u = \tan^2\theta$.

28. Let $\cos^{-1}(a/b) = \theta$ so that $\cos\theta = a/b$.

$\therefore$ L.H.S. $= \tan(\pi/4 + \theta/2) + \tan(\pi/4 - \theta/2)$.

$= \frac{1+\tan(\theta/2)}{1-\tan(\theta/2)} + \frac{1-\tan(\theta/2)}{1+\tan(\theta/2)}$

$= \frac{[1+\tan(\theta/2)]^2 + [1-\tan(\theta/2)]^2}{1-\tan^2(\theta/2)}$

$= 2.\frac{1+\tan^2(\theta/2)}{1-\tan^2(\theta/2)}$

$= 2\frac{\cos^2(\theta/2) + \sin^2(\theta/2)}{\cos^2(\theta/2) - \sin^2(\theta/2)} = 2.\frac{1}{\cos\theta}$

$= 2.\frac{1}{a/b} = \frac{2b}{a}$.

29. (a) If $\cos^{-1} x = y$, then $x = \cos y$.

we have $\frac{1}{2} \leq x \leq 1$

$\Rightarrow \cos^{-1} 1 \leq \cos^{-1} x \leq \cos^{-1}\frac{1}{2}$ **(Note this)**

$\Rightarrow 0 \leq y \leq \pi/3$.

$\therefore \frac{x}{2} + \frac{\sqrt{3-3x^2}}{2} = \frac{1}{2}\cos y + \frac{\sqrt{3}}{2}\sin y$

$= \cos(\pi/3)\cos y + \sin(\pi/3)\sin y$

$= \cos(\pi/3 - y)$

It follows that

$$\cos^{-1}\left[\frac{x}{2}+\frac{1}{2}\sqrt{3-3x^2}\right]=\frac{1}{3}\pi-y$$

$$\left[\because \cos^{-1}\cos\theta=\theta \text{ for } 0\le\theta\le\pi\right.$$

$$\left.\text{and here } 0\le\frac{\pi}{3}-y\le\frac{\pi}{3}\right]$$

∴ The given expression $=y+\frac{\pi}{3}-y=\frac{\pi}{3}$.

(b) We have $\cos[2\cos^{-1}(1/5)+\sin^{-1}(1/5)]$

$$=\cos[\{\cos^{-1}(1/5)+\sin^{-1}(1/5)\}+\cos^{-1}(1/5)]$$

$$=\cos[\pi/2+\cos^{-1}(1/5)]=-\sin\cos^{-1}(1/5)$$

$$=-\sin\sin^{-1}[\sqrt{24}/5]=-\sqrt{24}/5=-2\sqrt{6}/5.$$

30. (a) From the given question

$$\frac{\sqrt{1+x^2}-\sqrt{1-x^2}}{\sqrt{(1+x^2)}+\sqrt{(1-x^2)}}=\tan\alpha=\frac{\sin\alpha}{\cos\alpha}.$$

Apply componendo and dividendo

$$\frac{2\sqrt{1+x^2}}{2\sqrt{(1-x^2)}}=\frac{\cos\alpha+\sin\alpha}{\cos\alpha-\sin\alpha}. \text{ Square}$$

$$\frac{1+x^2}{1-x^2}=\frac{1+\sin 2\alpha}{1-\sin 2\alpha}, \qquad \because \cos^2\alpha+\sin^2\alpha=1$$

and $2\sin\alpha\cos\alpha=\sin 2\alpha.$

Hence $x^2=\sin 2\alpha$ from above.

Alternative : Put $x^2=\cos\theta$. Rest do yourself or put $x^2=\sin 2\alpha$

∴ $\sqrt{1+x^2}=\sqrt{1+\sin 2\alpha}=\cos\alpha+\sin\alpha$ etc.

(b) From the given relation , we get

$$\frac{m}{n}=\frac{\cos^2\theta\tan\theta}{\tan(\alpha-\theta)\cos^2(\alpha-\theta)}$$

$$=\frac{2\sin\theta\cos\theta}{2\sin(\alpha-\theta)\cos(\alpha-\theta)}=\frac{\sin 2\theta}{\sin(2\alpha-2\theta)}$$

Now applying componendo and dividendo, we get

$$\frac{n+m}{n-m}=\frac{\sin(2\alpha-2\theta)+\sin 2\theta}{\sin(2\alpha-2\theta)-\sin 2\theta}=\frac{2\sin\alpha\cos(\alpha-2\theta)}{2\cos\alpha\sin(\alpha-2\theta)}$$

or $\tan(\alpha-2\theta)=\dfrac{n-m}{n+m}\tan\alpha$

∴ $\alpha-2\theta=\tan^{-1}\left(\dfrac{n-m}{n+m}\tan\alpha\right)$

or $\theta=\dfrac{1}{2}\left[\alpha-\tan^{-1}\left(\dfrac{n-m}{n+m}\tan\alpha\right)\right].$

(c) Let $\cos^{-1}\dfrac{\cos\alpha+\cos\beta}{1+\cos\alpha\cos\beta}=\theta$

∴ $\dfrac{\cos\theta}{1}=\dfrac{\cos\alpha+\cos\beta}{1+\cos\alpha\cos\beta}$

Apply componendo and dividendo

$$\frac{1-\cos\theta}{1+\cos\theta}=\frac{(1-\cos\alpha)(1-\cos\beta)}{(1+\cos\alpha)(1+\cos\beta)}$$

or $\tan^2\dfrac{\theta}{2}=\tan^2\dfrac{\alpha}{2}\tan^2\dfrac{\beta}{2}$

∴ $\tan\dfrac{\theta}{2}=\tan\dfrac{\alpha}{2}\tan\dfrac{\beta}{2}$

∴ $\theta=2\tan^{-1}\left(\tan\dfrac{\alpha}{2}\tan\dfrac{\beta}{2}\right)$

31. We know that $2\tan^{-1}x=\cos^{-1}\dfrac{1-x^2}{1+x^2}.$

Choose $x=\sqrt{\left(\dfrac{a-b}{a+b}\right)}\tan\dfrac{\theta}{2}$

∴ $2\tan^{-1}\left[\sqrt{\left(\dfrac{a-b}{a+b}\right)}\tan\dfrac{\theta}{2}\right]$

$$=\cos^{-1}\frac{1-[(a-b)/(a+b)]\tan^2(\theta/2)}{1+[(a-b)/(a+b)]\tan^2(\theta/2)}$$

$$=\cos^{-1}\frac{a[1-\tan^2(\theta/2)]+b[1+\tan^2(\theta/2)]}{a[1+\tan^2(\theta/2)]+b[1-\tan^2(\theta/2)]}$$

$$=\cos^{-1}\frac{\begin{array}{c}a[\cos^2(\theta/2)-\sin^2(\theta/2)]\\+b[\cos^2(\theta/2)+\sin^2(\theta/2)]\end{array}}{\begin{array}{c}a[\cos^2(\theta/2)+\sin^2(\theta/2)]\\+b[\cos^2(\theta/2)-\sin^2(\theta/2)]\end{array}}$$

$$=\cos^{-1}\frac{a\cos\theta+b}{a+b\cos\theta}.$$

32. (a) $\tan^{-1}\dfrac{x-1}{x-2}=\tan^{-1}1-\tan^{-1}\dfrac{x+1}{x+2}$

or $\tan^{-1}\dfrac{x-1}{x-2}=\tan^{-1}\dfrac{1-\dfrac{x+1}{x+2}}{1+\dfrac{x+1}{x+2}}$

or $\tan^{-1}\dfrac{x-1}{x-2}=\tan^{-1}\dfrac{1}{2x+3}$

∴ $\dfrac{x-1}{x-2}=\dfrac{1}{2x+3}$

or $(x-1)(2x+3)=x-2.$

or $2x^2+x-3=x-2$ or $2x^2=1$

or $x=\pm 1/\sqrt{2}.$

(b) Ans. $x=\dfrac{4}{3},\ -\dfrac{3}{8}.$

33. (a) The given question can be written as

$$\left(\tan^{-1}\frac{1}{4}+\tan^{-1}\frac{1}{6}\right)+2\tan^{-1}\frac{1}{5}$$

$$=\tan^{-1}1-\tan^{-1}\frac{1}{x}$$

∴ $\tan^{-1}\dfrac{(1/4)+(1/6)}{1-(1/4).(1/6)}+\tan^{-1}\dfrac{2.(1/5)}{1-(1/25)}$

$$=\tan^{-1}\frac{1-(1/x)}{1+(1/x)}.$$

or $\tan^{-1}\dfrac{10}{23}+\tan^{-1}\dfrac{5}{12}=\tan^{-1}\dfrac{x-1}{x+1}$

or $\tan^{-1}\dfrac{(10/23)+(5/12)}{1-(10/23).(5/12)}=\tan^{-1}\dfrac{x-1}{x+1}$

or $\dfrac{235}{226}=\dfrac{x-1}{x+1}$

Hence $(235-226)\,x=-235-226.$

or $9x=-461\quad\therefore\quad x=-(461/9).$

(b) $\tan^{-1}(x-1)+\tan^{-1}(x+1)$

$\qquad =\tan^{-1}3x-\tan^{-1}x$

or $\tan^{-1}\dfrac{(x-1)+(x+1)}{1-(x^2-1)}=\tan^{-1}\dfrac{3x-x}{1+3x.x}$

or $\dfrac{2x}{2-x^2}=\dfrac{2x}{1+3x^2}$

or $x+3x^3=2x-x^3$ or $4x^3-x=0$

or $x(4x^2-1)=0\quad\therefore\quad x=0,\ \pm\dfrac{1}{2}.$

34. (a) $\tan^{-1}\dfrac{2x+3x}{1-2x.3x}=\dfrac{\pi}{4}=\tan^{-1}1$

$\therefore\quad \dfrac{5x}{1-6x^2}=1\quad$ or $\quad 5x=1-6x^2$

$\therefore\quad 6x^2-5x-1=0\quad$ or $\quad(6x-1)(x+1)=0$

$\therefore\quad x=1/6,\ -1.$

We will reject the value $x=-1$ (Why ?) and hence $x=1/6$.

(b) $\tan^{-1}\dfrac{\dfrac{1}{2x+1}+\dfrac{1}{4x+1}}{1-\dfrac{1}{2x+1}.\dfrac{1}{4x+1}}=\tan^{-1}\dfrac{2}{x^2}$

$\therefore\quad \dfrac{6x+2}{(2x+1)(4x+1)-1}=\dfrac{2}{x^2}$

or $x^2(3x+1)=8x^2+6x.$

$\therefore\quad x=0,$

or $3x^2+x=8x+6$

or $3x^2-7x-6=0$

or $(3x+2)(x-3)=0$

$\therefore\quad x=3,-2/3.$

The value $x=-2/3$ is rejected as it makes L.H.S. – ive and R.H.S. + ive.

(c) The given equation can be written as

$\tan^{-1}\dfrac{1}{2+\sqrt{(3)}}=\tan^{-1}\dfrac{2-\sqrt{3}}{4-3}$

$\qquad\qquad =\tan^{-1}(2-\sqrt{3})=15°$

$\therefore\quad 3\tan^{-1}\dfrac{1}{2+\sqrt{(3)}}=3(15°)=45°=\tan^{-1}1$

Hence the given equation can be written as

$\tan^{-1}1-\tan^{-1}\dfrac{1}{3}=\tan^{-1}\dfrac{1}{x}$

or $\tan^{-1}\dfrac{1-1/3}{1+1/3}=\tan^{-1}\dfrac{1}{x}$

or $\tan^{-1}\dfrac{2}{4}=\tan^{-1}\dfrac{1}{x}$

$\therefore\quad \dfrac{1}{x}=\dfrac{1}{2}\qquad\qquad\therefore\quad x=2.$

35. (a) L.H.S. $=\tan^{-1}\dfrac{2x+3x}{1-2x.3x}=n\pi+\dfrac{3\pi}{4}$

or $\dfrac{5x}{1-6x^2}=\tan\dfrac{3\pi}{4}=-1$

or $6x^2-5x-1=0$

or $(x-1)(6x+1)=0\quad\therefore\quad x=1,\,-1/6$

(b) The given equation can be written as

$\tan^{-1}x+\tan^{-1}\dfrac{1}{y}=\tan^{-1}3$

or $\tan^{-1}\dfrac{x+1/y}{1-x.1/y}=\tan^{-1}3$

$\therefore\quad xy+1=3(y-x).\qquad\therefore\quad y=\dfrac{3x+1}{3-x}.$

There is only one equation in two variables, so we choose $x=k$

$\therefore\quad y=\dfrac{3k+1}{3-k}$. Further, we have to find only +ive and integral solutions. This is possible only when $k=1$ or 2 and for no other value.

Hence (1, 2), (2, 7) are the only two +ive integral solutions.

36. (a) $\sin^{-1}\dfrac{1}{\sqrt{(5)}}=\tan^{-1}\dfrac{1}{2}$ and $\tan\dfrac{\pi}{4}=1$

Ans. $x=3.$

(b) The given equation is equivalent to the equation

$\tan^{-1}\dfrac{2\cos x}{1-\cos^2 x}=\tan^{-1}(2\,\mathrm{cosec}\,x)$

or $2\cos x.\mathrm{cosec}^2 x=2\,\mathrm{cosec}\,x$

or $\mathrm{cosec}\,x(\cot x-1)=0$

$\therefore\quad \cot x-1=0\quad$ or $\quad\cot x=1\quad[\because\ \mathrm{cosec}\,x\neq0]$

$\therefore\quad x=n\pi+\pi/4,\quad n\in\mathbf{I}.$

(c) We write the given equation as

$\tan\left[\tan^{-1}\left(\dfrac{\sqrt{1-x^2}}{x}\right)\right]=\sin\left(\sin^{-1}\dfrac{2}{\sqrt{(5)}}\right)$

or $\dfrac{\sqrt{1-x^2}}{x}=\dfrac{2}{\sqrt{(5)}}$

or $5(1-x^2)=4x^2$

or $9x^2=5,\ \therefore\ x=\pm(\sqrt{5}/3)$

37. (a) Ans. $\pm\sqrt{2}$. Combine 1st and 3rd.

$x^4=4\quad\therefore\quad x^2=2$ only as -2 is rejected.

(b) Ans. $x=1/2,\,y=1$. Second relation can be written as

$$\left(\frac{\pi}{2} - \sin^{-1} x\right) - \left(\frac{\pi}{2} - \sin^{-1} y\right) = \frac{\pi}{3}$$

or $\sin^{-1} y - \sin^{-1} x = \pi/3$

Adding and subtracting, we get

$\sin^{-1} y = \pi/2$, $\sin^{-1} x = \pi/6$ etc.

(c) $2\tan^{-1} x = \tan^{-1} \dfrac{2x}{1 - x^2}$

$\therefore \quad 4\tan^{-1} x = 2\tan^{-1} \dfrac{2x}{1 - x^2}$

$$4\tan^{-1} x = \tan^{-1} \frac{2 \cdot \dfrac{2x}{1 - x^2}}{1 - \left(\dfrac{2x}{1 - x^2}\right)^2}$$

or $\tan^{-1} y = \tan^{-1} \dfrac{4x(1 - x^2)}{x^4 - 6x^2 + 1}$

$\therefore \quad y = \dfrac{4x(1 - x^2)}{x^4 - 6x^2 + 1}$

Now if $x = \tan \dfrac{\pi}{8}$, then

$\tan^{-1} x = \dfrac{\pi}{8}$ or $4\tan^{-1} x = \dfrac{\pi}{2} = \tan^{-1} y$

$\therefore \quad y = \tan \dfrac{\pi}{2} = \infty$

$\therefore \quad D^r$ of $y = 0$ or $x^4 - 6x^2 + 1 = 0$

where $x = \tan \dfrac{\pi}{8}$ is a root of above.

38. (a) We have

$3(2\tan^{-1} x) - 4(2\tan^{-1} x) + 2(2\tan^{-1} x) = \pi/3$.

or $2\tan^{-1} x = \pi/3$ $\therefore \tan^{-1} x = \pi/6$

or $x = \tan(\pi/6) = 1/\sqrt{3}$.

(b) Let $\dfrac{1}{5}\cos^{-1} x = \alpha$.

Since $0 \le \cos^{-1} x \le \pi$,

we have $0 \le \alpha \le \pi/5$.

Hence $\sin \alpha \ne 1$, that is, $\sin\left(\dfrac{1}{5}\cos^{-1} x\right) = 1$ has no

solution.

(c) Above equation is defined if $x^2 + x \ge 0$

and $x^2 + x + 1 \ge 0$ but ≤ 1

i.e., $0 \le x^2 + x + 1 \le 1$

Above is possible only when $x^2 + x = 0$

or $x(x + 1) = 0$ $\therefore x = 0, -1$.

39. (a) $\cos^{-1} 3\sqrt{3} x^2 = \dfrac{\pi}{2} - \cos^{-1}(\sqrt{6} x) = \sin^{-1}(\sqrt{6} x)$

$$= \cos^{-1}(1 - 6x^2)$$

$\therefore \quad 3\sqrt{3} x^2 = 1 - 6x^2$

or $x^2(6 + 3\sqrt{3}) = 1$

$\therefore \quad x^2 = \dfrac{1}{6 + 3\sqrt{3}} = \dfrac{6 - 3\sqrt{3}}{9} = \dfrac{2 - \sqrt{3}}{3} = \dfrac{4 - 2\sqrt{3}}{6}$.

or $x^2 = \dfrac{(2 - \sqrt{3})^2}{6}$ $\therefore x = \dfrac{2 - \sqrt{3}}{\sqrt{6}}$

(b) Ans. $-\dfrac{1}{12}$.

$\dfrac{\pi}{2} + \sin^{-1} 6\sqrt{3} x = -\sin^{-1} 6x$. Take sine.

$\cos(\sin^{-1} 6\sqrt{3} x) = -6x$

or $\sqrt{1 - 108 x^2} = -6x$. Square.

$1 - 108 x^2 = 36x^2$ or $x^2 = 1/144$

$\therefore \quad x = \dfrac{1}{12}, -\dfrac{1}{12}$

Since we have squared we must check the roots.

Clearly $x = -\dfrac{1}{12}$ satisfies and $x = \dfrac{1}{12}$ does not

satisfy.

(c) $\sin^{-1} x + \sin^{-1} 2x = \pi/3 = \sin^{-1}(\sqrt{3}/2)$

$\therefore \quad \sin^{-1} x - \sin^{-1}(\sqrt{3}/2) = -\sin^{-1} 2x$

$\therefore \quad \sin^{-1}\left[x\sqrt{\left(1 - \dfrac{3}{4}\right)} - \dfrac{\sqrt{3}}{2}\sqrt{1 - x^2}\right] = -\sin^{-1} 2x$

or $\dfrac{x}{2} - \dfrac{\sqrt{3}}{2}\sqrt{1 - x^2} = -2x$.

or $5x = \sqrt{3}\sqrt{1 - x^2}$. Square

$25 x^2 = 3 - 3x^2$ or $28x^2 = 3$,

$\therefore \quad x = \pm \sqrt{3}/(2\sqrt{7})$

Clearly from the given equation the value of x

must be + ive

$\therefore \quad x = \dfrac{1}{2}\sqrt{\dfrac{3}{7}}$

40. (a) $\tan^{-1} \dfrac{\dfrac{x+1}{x-1} + \dfrac{x-1}{x}}{1 - \dfrac{x+1}{x-1} \cdot \dfrac{x-1}{x}} = \tan^{-1}(-7)$

$\therefore \quad \dfrac{2x^2 - x + 1}{1 - x} = -7$ or $2x^2 - x + 1 = -7 + 7x$

or $2x^2 - 8x + 8 = 0$ or $x^2 - 4x + 4 = 0$

or $(x - 2)^2 = 0$, $\therefore x = 2$.

But if we put $x = 2$ in the given equation the L.H.S.

is + ive and R.H.S. is − ive. Hence $x = 2$ does not

satisfy. We will have to write the equation as

$\tan^{-1} \dfrac{x+1}{x-1} + \tan^{-1} \dfrac{x-1}{x} = \pi + \tan^{-1}(-7)$.

Now $x = 2$ will make both sides + ive.

Note : Here $xy = \dfrac{x+1}{x-1} \cdot \dfrac{x-1}{x} = \dfrac{x+1}{x} > 1$

Refer § 5 (b) P. 622.

$\therefore \quad$ R.H.S. $= \pi + \tan^{-1}(-7)$

(b) Since $ab > 1$, combine first two terms

$\therefore \quad$ L.H.S. $= \pi + \tan^{-1}\left(-\dfrac{39}{2}\right)$

$\qquad\qquad + \tan^{-1}\left(\dfrac{39}{2}\right) - \pi = 0$

(c) $p_1 = \Sigma\, x_1 = \sin 2\beta$

$p_2 = \Sigma\, x_1 x_2 = \cos 2\beta$

$p_3 = \Sigma\, x_1 x_2 x_3 = \cos \beta$

$p_4 = x_1 x_2 x_3 x_4 = -\sin \beta$

$\tan^{-1} x_1 + \tan^{-1} x_2 + \tan^{-1} x_3 + \tan^{-1} x_4$

$\qquad = \tan^{-1}\dfrac{p_1 - p_3}{1 - p_2 + p_4} \qquad \ldots(1)$

$p_1 - p_3 = \sin 2\beta - \cos \beta = \cos \beta\,(2\sin\beta - 1)$

$1 - p_2 + p_4 = 1 - \cos 2\beta - \sin \beta$

$\qquad = 2\sin^2\beta - \sin\beta = \sin\beta\,(2\sin\beta - 1)$

$\therefore \quad \tan^{-1}\dfrac{p_1 - p_3}{1 - p_2 + p_4} = \tan^{-1}\left(\dfrac{\cos\beta}{\sin\beta}\right)$

$\qquad = \tan^{-1}(\cot\beta) = \tan^{-1}\left[\tan\left(\dfrac{\pi}{2} - \beta\right)\right] = \dfrac{\pi}{2} - \beta$

41. (a) $2\tan^{-1} x = \tan^{-1}\dfrac{2x}{1 - x^2} = \cot^{-1}\dfrac{1 - x^2}{2x}$

$\therefore \quad \cot(2\tan^{-1} x) = \dfrac{1 - x^2}{2x}$

$\therefore \quad$ L.H.S. $= \sin\left[2\cos^{-1}\dfrac{1 - x^2}{2x}\right] = 0$

Now $\quad 2\cos^{-1} z = \cos^{-1}(2z^2 - 1)$

$\therefore \quad 2\cos^{-1}\dfrac{1 - x^2}{2x} = \cos^{-1}\left[2\cdot\dfrac{(1 - x^2)^2}{4x^2} - 1\right]$

$\qquad = \cos^{-1}\left[\dfrac{x^4 - 4x^2 + 1}{2x^2}\right]$

$\therefore \quad$ L.H.S. $= \sin\left[\cos^{-1}\dfrac{x^4 - 4x^2 + 1}{2x^2}\right] = 0. \quad \ldots(1)$

Again $\sin\cos^{-1} t = \sin\sin^{-1}\sqrt{1 - t^2} = 0,$

$\therefore \quad 1 - t^2 = 0.$

Hence from (1), we have

$\qquad (x^4 - 4x^2 + 1)^2 - (2x^2)^2 = 0$

or $\quad (x^4 - 4x^2 + 1 - 2x^2)(x^4 - 4x^2 + 1 + 2x^2) = 0$

or $\quad (x^4 - 2x^2 + 1)(x^4 - 6x^2 + 1) = 0$

From 1st factor $\quad (x^2 - 1)^2 = 0, \quad x = \pm 1$

From 2nd factor $\quad x^4 - 6x^2 + 9 = -1 + 9$

or $\quad (x^2 - 3)^2 = 8.$

$\qquad x^2 = 3 \pm 2\sqrt{2} = (1 \pm \sqrt{2})^2$

$\therefore \quad x = \pm(1 \pm \sqrt{2}).$

(b) $\sqrt{\left(\dfrac{1 + x^2}{2 + x^2}\right)}$. Let $x = \tan\theta$

$\therefore \quad \cos\theta = \dfrac{1}{\sqrt{(1 + x^2)}}$

$\therefore \quad \cos\tan^{-1} x = \dfrac{1}{\sqrt{(1 + x^2)}}$

$\therefore \quad \cot^{-1}\dfrac{1}{\sqrt{(1 + x^2)}} = \cot^{-1} z \;\text{(say)}$

$\qquad = \sin^{-1}\dfrac{1}{\sqrt{1 + z^2}} = \sin^{-1}\sqrt{\left(\dfrac{1 + x^2}{2 + x^2}\right)}$

and $\sin\sin^{-1} t = t.$

(c) It is exactly as part (b).

42. (a) Put $\sin^{-1} x = \theta$ so that $\sin\theta = x$.

Then the equation $\cos(2\sin^{-1} x) = 1/9$ takes the

form $\cos 2\theta = 1/9$

or $\quad 1 - 2\sin^2\theta = 1/9$ or $\sin^2\theta = 4/9$.

or $\quad x^2 = 4/9$, giving $x = \pm 2/3$.

(b) $\because \quad \sin^{-1}(4/5) = \cos^{-1}(3/5),$

the given equation can be written as

$\qquad \sin^{-1}(4/5) - \sin^{-1}(4/5) = \cos^{-1} x$

or $\quad \cos^{-1} x = 0 \Rightarrow x = \cos 0 = 1$

$\therefore \quad x = 1.$

(c) $\sin^{-1}\dfrac{1}{5} + \cos^{-1} x = \dfrac{\pi}{2}$

$\therefore \quad \sin^{-1}\dfrac{1}{5} = \dfrac{\pi}{2} - \cos^{-1} x = \sin^{-1} x$

$\therefore \quad x = 1/5.$

43. (a) The given equation can be written as

$\qquad \sin^{-1}(1 - x) = \pi/2 + 2\sin^{-1} x.$

Taking sine, we get

$\qquad 1 - x = \cos(2\sin^{-1} x) = 1 - 2(\sin\sin^{-1} x)^2$

or $\quad 1 - x = 1 - 2x^2 \qquad$ or $\qquad x = 2x^2.$

$\therefore \quad x = 0$ or $1/2.$

A check shows that $x = 1/2$ is not a root.

Hence $x = 0$ is the only root.

(b) $\sin^{-1}\left[x\sqrt{1 - (1 - x)^2} + (1 - x)\sqrt{(1 - x^2)}\right]$

$\qquad = \sin^{-1}\sqrt{1 - x^2}$

$\therefore \quad x\sqrt{2x - x^2} = \sqrt{1 - x^2}\,[1 - (1 - x)] = x\sqrt{1 - x^2}$

$\therefore \quad x = 0$ or $2x - x^2 = 1 - x^2$ or $x = 1/2$

44. (a) Let $\sin^{-1}\dfrac{3x}{5} = \theta, \sin^{-1}\dfrac{4x}{5} = \phi, \sin^{-1} x = \psi$

$\therefore \quad \sin\theta = \dfrac{3x}{5}, \; \sin\phi = \dfrac{4x}{5}, \; \sin\psi = x.$

Now the given equation can be written as

$\theta + \phi = \psi$ whence $\sin(\theta + \phi) = \sin \psi$.

or $\quad \sin \theta \cos \phi + \cos \theta \sin \phi = \sin \psi$

or $\quad \dfrac{3x}{5}\sqrt{\left(1 - \dfrac{16}{25}x^2\right)} + \dfrac{4x}{5}\sqrt{\left(1 - \dfrac{9x^2}{25}\right)} = x$

or $\quad x[3\sqrt{25 - 16x^2} + 4\sqrt{25 - 9x^2}] = 25x$

One root is $x = 0$ and the other roots are given by

$$4\sqrt{25 - 9x^2} = 25 - 3\sqrt{25 - 16x^2}$$

Squaring,

$16(25 - 9x^2) = 625 - 150\sqrt{25 - 16x^2} + 9(25 - 16x^2)$

or $\quad 150\sqrt{25 - 16x^2} = 450$

whence $25 - 16x^2 = 9$ or $x^2 = 1$

∴ $\quad x = \pm 1$.

A check shows that $x = 0, 1, -1$ are all roots of the given equation.

(b) The given equation is

$$\cos^{-1} x + \sin^{-1}(x/2) = \pi/6$$

Since $\sin^{-1}(x/2) = \pi/2 - \cos^{-1}(x/2)$, the given equation is equivalent to the equation

$\cos^{-1} x + \pi/2 - \cos^{-1}(\pi/2) = \pi/6$.

or $\quad \cos^{-1} x - \cos^{-1}(\pi/2) = \pi/6 - \pi/2 = -\pi/3$

or $\quad \cos^{-1} x = \cos^{-1}(x/2) - \pi/3$

$\qquad = \cos^{-1}(x/2) - \cos^{-1}(1/2)$

$\qquad = \cos^{-1}\left[\dfrac{x}{2} \cdot \dfrac{1}{2} + \sqrt{1 - \dfrac{x^2}{4}} \cdot \sqrt{1 - \dfrac{1}{4}}\right]$

∴ $\quad x = \dfrac{x}{4} + \sqrt{\left(1 - \dfrac{x^2}{4}\right)} \cdot \dfrac{\sqrt{3}}{2}$

∴ $\quad \dfrac{3}{4}x = \dfrac{\sqrt{3}}{4}\sqrt{4 - x^2}$

or $\quad 3x^2 = 4 - x^2$ or $4x^2 = 4$

∴ $\quad x = \pm 1$. But the value $x = -1$ does not satisfy the given equation.

Hence $x = 1$ is the only root of the given equation.

(c) Ans. (b).

$E = \tan^{-1}\dfrac{1 - x}{1 + x} = \tan^{-1} 1 - \tan^{-1} x = \dfrac{\pi}{4} - \tan^{-1} x$

Now $0 \le x \le 1$ ∴ $0 \le \tan^{-1} x \le \dfrac{\pi}{4}$

Multiplying by minus sign and reversing the inequality, $0 \ge -\tan^{-1} x \ge -\pi/4$

∴ $\quad -\dfrac{\pi}{4} \le -\tan^{-1} x \le 0$

Add $\dfrac{\pi}{4}$ to both sides

∴ $\quad 0 \le \dfrac{\pi}{4} - \tan^{-1} x \le \dfrac{\pi}{4}$ or $0 \le E \le \dfrac{\pi}{4}$

(d) $E = (\sin^{-1} x + \cos^{-1} x)^3 - 3(\sin^{-1} x \cos^{-1} x)$

$\qquad \times (\sin^{-1} x + \cos^{-1} x)$

$E = \dfrac{\pi^3}{8} - \dfrac{3\pi}{2}(\sin^{-1} x \cos^{-1} x)$ ...(1)

Now let $\sin^{-1} = t$ ∴ $\cos^{-1} x = \dfrac{\pi}{2} - t$

$E = \dfrac{\pi^3}{8} - \dfrac{3\pi}{2}\left[t\left(\dfrac{\pi}{2} - t\right)\right]$

$\quad = \dfrac{\pi^3}{8} + \dfrac{3\pi}{2}\left[t^2 - \dfrac{\pi}{2}t + \left(\dfrac{\pi}{4}\right)^2 - \left(\dfrac{\pi}{4}\right)^2\right]$

$\quad = \dfrac{\pi^3}{8} + \dfrac{3\pi}{2}\left[\left(t - \dfrac{\pi}{4}\right)^2 - \dfrac{\pi^2}{16}\right]$

$\quad = \dfrac{\pi^3}{8} - \dfrac{3\pi^3}{32} + \dfrac{3\pi}{2}\left(t - \dfrac{\pi}{4}\right)^2$

$\quad = \dfrac{\pi^3}{32} + \dfrac{3\pi}{2}\left(t - \dfrac{\pi}{4}\right)^2$ ...(2)

From above, least value is $\dfrac{\pi^3}{32}$. ...(3)

Again $-\dfrac{\pi}{2} \le \sin^{-1} x \le \dfrac{\pi}{2}$ or $-\dfrac{\pi}{2} \le t \le \dfrac{\pi}{2}$

∴ $\quad -\dfrac{\pi}{2} - \dfrac{\pi}{4} \le t - \dfrac{\pi}{4} \le \dfrac{\pi}{2} - \dfrac{\pi}{4}$

or $\quad -\dfrac{3\pi}{4} \le \left(t - \dfrac{\pi}{4}\right) \le \dfrac{\pi}{4}$

Above is a part of the double inequality

$\left(\dfrac{\pi}{4}\right)^2 \le \left(t - \dfrac{\pi}{4}\right)^2 \le \dfrac{9\pi^2}{16}$

Hence the greatest value by (2) is

$\dfrac{\pi^3}{32} + \dfrac{3\pi}{2}\dfrac{9\pi^2}{16} = \dfrac{28\pi^3}{32} = \dfrac{7\pi^3}{8}$ ...(4)

∴ $\quad (a, b) = \left(\dfrac{\pi^3}{32}, \dfrac{7\pi^3}{8}\right)$ by (3) and (4)

45. (a) We know that $2\tan^{-1} x = \tan^{-1}\dfrac{2x}{1 - x^2}$

∴ L.H.S. $= \tan^{-1}\dfrac{2\tan(\alpha/2)\tan(\pi/4 - \beta/2)}{1 - \tan^2(\alpha/2)\tan^2(\pi/4 - \beta/2)}$

Now change in terms of sine and cos

$= \tan^{-1}\dfrac{2\sin(\alpha/2)\cos(\alpha/2)}{\sin(\pi/4 - \beta/2)\cos(\pi/4 - \beta/2)}{\cos^2(\alpha/2)\cos^2(\pi/4 - \beta/2)}{-\sin^2(\alpha/2)\sin^2(\pi/4 - \beta/2)}$

$= \tan^{-1}\dfrac{\sin\alpha \cdot \sin(\pi/2 - \beta)}{2[\cos(\alpha/2 - \beta/2 + \pi/4)}{\cos(\alpha/2 + \beta/2 - \pi/4)]}$

$= \tan^{-1}\dfrac{\sin\alpha\cos\beta}{\cos\alpha + \cos(\pi/2 - \beta)}$

$= \tan^{-1}\dfrac{\sin\alpha\cos\beta}{\cos\alpha + \sin\beta}$

(b) Let $\theta = \cos^{-1}\dfrac{2+3\cos x}{3+2\cos x}$

$\therefore \quad \dfrac{\cos\theta}{1} = \dfrac{2+3\cos x}{3+2\cos x}$ [Apply Compo. & Divi.]

$\dfrac{1-\cos\theta}{1+\cos\theta} = \dfrac{1-\cos x}{5(1+\cos x)}$

$\therefore \quad \tan^2\dfrac{\theta}{2} = \dfrac{1}{5}\tan^2\dfrac{x}{2}$

$\therefore \quad \theta = 2\tan^{-1}\left[\dfrac{1}{\sqrt{5}}\tan\dfrac{x}{2}\right] = \text{R.H.S.}$

46. First note that $\cot A > 1$ if $0 < A < \pi/4$
and $\cot A < 1$ if $\pi/4 < A < \pi/2$. Hence

$\therefore \quad \tan^{-1}(\cot A) + \tan^{-1}(\cot^3 A)$

$= \pi + \tan^{-1}\dfrac{\cot A + \cot^3 A}{1 - \cot^4 A}$ if $0 < A < \dfrac{\pi}{4}$

and $= \tan^{-1}\dfrac{\cot A + \cot^3 A}{1 - \cot^4 A}$ if $\dfrac{\pi}{4} < A < \dfrac{\pi}{2}$.

Also $\dfrac{\cot A + \cot^3 A}{1 - \cot^4 A} = \dfrac{\cot A}{1 - \cot^2 A}$

$= \dfrac{\cos A \sin A}{(\sin^2 A - \cos^2 A)}$

$= -\dfrac{\sin 2A}{2\cos 2A} = -\dfrac{1}{2}\tan 2A$.

Hence $\tan^{-1}\left(\dfrac{1}{2}\tan 2A\right) + \tan^{-1}(\cot A)$

$+ \tan^{-1}(\cot^3 A)$.

$= \pi$ in the first case,
$= 0$ in the 2nd case because
$\tan^{-1}(-x) = -\tan^{-1}x$

47. (a) $\sin 2\alpha = \dfrac{2t}{1+t^2}, \cos 2\alpha = \dfrac{1-t^2}{1+t^2}$, where $t = \tan\alpha$

L.H.S. $= \tan^{-1}\dfrac{3t}{4+t^2} + \tan^{-1}\dfrac{t}{4}$

$= \tan^{-1}t\dfrac{(16+t^2)}{(16+t^2)} = \tan^{-1}(\tan\alpha) = \alpha$

(b) Let us put $\tan\theta = t$,

$\sin 2\theta = \dfrac{2t}{1+t^2}, \cos 2\theta = \dfrac{1-t^2}{1+t^2}$.

The 2nd term is

$\dfrac{1}{2}\sin^{-1}\dfrac{3 \cdot 2t}{5(1+t^2)+4(1-t^2)} = \dfrac{1}{2}\sin^{-1}\dfrac{6t}{9+t^2}$

$= \dfrac{1}{2}\sin^{-1}\dfrac{2 \cdot t/3}{1+(t/3)^2} = \dfrac{1}{2}\sin^{-1}\dfrac{2T}{1+T^2}$

$= \dfrac{1}{2} \cdot 2\tan^{-1}T = \tan^{-1}(t/3)$

$\therefore \quad \theta = \tan^{-1}2t^2 - \tan^{-1}\dfrac{t}{3} = \tan^{-1}\dfrac{2t^2 - t/3}{1+2t^2 \cdot t/3}$

or $\tan\theta = \dfrac{t(6t-1)}{3+2t^3}$ or $t(3+2t^3) = t(6t-1)$

$\therefore \quad t = 0$ or $2t^3 - 6t + 4 = 0$

or $t^3 - 3t + 2 = 0$

$\therefore \quad t = 0$ or $(t-1)(t^2+t-2) = 0$

or $t = 0$ or $(t-1)(t-1)(t+2) = 0$

$\therefore \quad t = 0, 1, -2$

$\therefore \quad \theta = n\pi, n\pi + \pi/4, n\pi + \alpha$ where $\tan\alpha = -2$.

(c) Ans. (a), (b).
From given relation, if $\tan\theta = t$

$\tan\theta = t = \dfrac{2t^2 - \dfrac{1}{3}t}{1 + \dfrac{2}{3}t^3}$

$\therefore \quad t = 0$ or $1 \cdot \left(1 + \dfrac{2}{3}t^3\right) = 2t - \dfrac{1}{3}$

or $2t^3 - 6t + 4 = 0$ or $t^3 - 3t + 2 = 0$

or $(t+2)(t^2 - 2t + 1) = 0$

or $(t+2)(t-1)^2 = 0$

$\therefore \quad t = \tan\theta = -2, 1 \Rightarrow$ (a), (b).

(d) If $t = \tan\theta$, then $\sin 2\theta = \dfrac{2t}{1+t^2}, \cos 2\theta = \dfrac{1-t^2}{1+t^2}$

$\therefore \quad \dfrac{3\sin 2\theta}{5+4\cos 2\theta} = \dfrac{3 \cdot 2t}{5(1+t^2)+4(1-t^2)} = \dfrac{6t}{9+t^2}$

$= \dfrac{2 \cdot t/2}{1+(t/3)^2} = \dfrac{2\tan\alpha}{1+\tan^2\alpha} = \sin 2\alpha$

where $\dfrac{t}{3} = \tan\alpha$

$\dfrac{1}{2}\sin^{-1}\left\{\dfrac{3\sin 2\theta}{5+4\cos 2\theta}\right\} = \alpha = \tan^{-1}\left(\dfrac{t}{3}\right)$

$= \tan^{-1}\left(\dfrac{1}{3}\tan\theta\right)$

$\Rightarrow \tan^{-1}x = \tan^{-1}\left(\dfrac{1}{3}\tan\theta\right) \quad \therefore \quad x = \dfrac{1}{3}\tan\theta$

48. (a) $T_1 = \tan^{-1}\dfrac{x/y - 1/c_1}{1+(x/y) \cdot (1/c_1)}$

$= \tan^{-1}\dfrac{x}{y} - \tan^{-1}\dfrac{1}{c_1}$ etc.

$\therefore \quad$ L.H.S.

$= \left(\tan^{-1}\dfrac{x}{y} - \tan^{-1}\dfrac{1}{c_1}\right) + \left(\tan^{-1}\dfrac{1}{c_1} - \tan^{-1}\dfrac{1}{c_2}\right)$

$+ \ldots - \tan^{-1}\dfrac{1}{c_n}$

$= \tan^{-1}\dfrac{x}{y}$

(b) $\cot^{-1} x = \tan^{-1} \dfrac{1}{x}$

∴ $T_1 = \tan^{-1} p - \tan^{-1} q$ etc.

49. (a) Put $x + y + z = r$

∴ $\tan^{-1} \sqrt{\left(\dfrac{rx}{yz}\right)} + \tan^{-1} \sqrt{\left(\dfrac{ry}{zx}\right)}$

$= \tan^{-1} \dfrac{\sqrt{r/xyz} \cdot (x+y)}{(1 - r/z)}$

$= \tan^{-1} \dfrac{\sqrt{(rz)/(xy)}\,(x+y)}{-(x+y)}$

$= \pi + \tan^{-1} \left\{ -\sqrt{\left(\dfrac{rz}{xy}\right)} \right\}$ § 5 (b) P. 622

$= \pi - \tan^{-1} \sqrt{\left(\dfrac{rz}{xy}\right)}$

∴ $\tan^{-1} \left(\dfrac{rx}{yz}\right) + \tan^{-1} \sqrt{\left(\dfrac{ry}{zx}\right)} + \tan^{-1} \sqrt{\left(\dfrac{rz}{xy}\right)} = \pi.$

(b) We have to prove that

$\tan^{-1} \dfrac{yz}{xr} + \tan^{-1} \dfrac{zx}{yr} + \tan^{-1} \dfrac{xy}{zr} = \dfrac{\pi}{2}$

or $\tan^{-1} \dfrac{(z/r)\,[(x^2 + y^2)/(xy)]}{1 - (z^2/r^2)} = \dfrac{\pi}{2} - \tan^{-1} \dfrac{xy}{zr}$

or $\tan^{-1} \dfrac{(zr/xy)\,(x^2 + y^2)}{x^2 + y^2} = \cot^{-1} \dfrac{xy}{zr}$

or $\tan^{-1} \dfrac{zr}{xy} = \tan^{-1} \dfrac{zr}{xy}$, which is true .

50. (a) From the given equation, we have

$\cos^{-1} \dfrac{a}{x} + \cos^{-1} \dfrac{1}{a} = \cos^{-1} \dfrac{1}{b} + \cos^{-1} \dfrac{b}{x}$

or $\cos^{-1} \left[\dfrac{a}{x} \cdot \dfrac{1}{a} - \left\{ \sqrt{\left(1 - \dfrac{a^2}{x^2}\right)\left(1 - \dfrac{1}{a^2}\right)} \right\} \right]$

$= \cos^{-1} \left[\dfrac{1}{b} \cdot \dfrac{b}{x} - \sqrt{\left(1 - \dfrac{1}{b^2}\right)\left(1 - \dfrac{b^2}{x^2}\right)} \right]$

or $\dfrac{1}{x} - \dfrac{\sqrt{x^2 - a^2}\,\sqrt{a^2 - 1}}{ax}$

$= \dfrac{1}{x} - \dfrac{\sqrt{b^2 - 1}\,\sqrt{x^2 - b^2}}{bx}$

or $b^2\,(a^2 - 1)\,(x^2 - a^2) = a^2\,(b^2 - 1)\,(x^2 - b^2)$

or $x^2\,(a^2 b^2 - b^2 - a^2 b^2 + a^2)$

$\qquad = a^2 b^2\,(a^2 - 1 - b^2 + 1)$

or $x^2\,(a^2 - b^2) = a^2 b^2\,(a^2 - b^2)$

∴ $x = ab.$

(b) $\tan^{-1} \dfrac{(a+b)\,x}{x^2 - ab} = \dfrac{\pi}{2} - \tan^{-1} \dfrac{(c+d)\,x}{x^2 - cd}$

or $\tan^{-1} \dfrac{(a+b)\,x}{x^2 - ab} = \cot^{-1} \dfrac{(c+d)\,x}{x^2 - cd}$

$= \tan^{-1} \dfrac{x^2 - cd}{(c+d)\,x}$

∴ $(x^2 - ab)\,(x^2 - cd) = (a+b)\,(c+d)\,x^2$

or $x^4 - x^2 \, \Sigma\, ab + abcd = 0$ ...(1)

where $\Sigma\, ab = ab + ac + ad + bc + bd + cd$.
x is given by equation (1).

(c) $\tan^{-1} \dfrac{1}{a-1} = \tan^{-1} \dfrac{(1/x) + 1/(a^2 - x + 1)}{1 - 1/[x\,(a^2 - x + 1)]}$

∴ $\dfrac{1}{a-1} = \dfrac{a^2 + 1}{(a^2 + 1) \cdot x - x^2 - 1}$

∴ $x^2 - x\,(a^2 + 1) + 1 + (a-1)\,(a^2 + 1) = 0$.

or $(x^2 - a^2) - (a^2 + 1)\,(x - a) = 0$

or $(x - a)\,(x + a - a^2 - 1) = 0$

∴ $x = a$ or $a^2 - a + 1.$

Another form :

We know that $\tan^{-1} x = \cot^{-1}\,(1/x)$ and hence it becomes part (c).

51. (a) $T_n = \tan^{-1} \dfrac{1}{1 + n + n^2} = \tan^{-1} \dfrac{(n+1) - n}{1 + (n+1)\,n}$

$\qquad\qquad = \tan^{-1}\,(n+1) - \tan^{-1} n$

Putting $n = 1, 2, 3, \ldots, n$ and adding, we get

$S_n = \tan^{-1}\,(n+1) - \tan^{-1} 1$

∴ $S_\infty = \tan^{-1}\,(\infty) - \dfrac{\pi}{4} = \dfrac{\pi}{2} - \dfrac{\pi}{4} = \dfrac{\pi}{4}$

(b) $T_n = \tan^{-1} \dfrac{1}{2 \cdot n^2} = \tan^{-1} \dfrac{2}{4n^2}$

$= \tan^{-1} \dfrac{2}{1 + (4n^2 - 1)}$

$= \tan^{-1} \dfrac{(2n+1) - (2n-1)}{1 + (2n+1)\,(2n-1)}$

$= \tan^{-1}\,(2n+1) - \tan^{-1}\,(2n-1)$

Putting $n = 1, 2, 3, \ldots n$ and adding, we get

$S_n = \tan^{-1}\,(2n+1) - \tan^{-1} 1$

∴ $S_\infty = \tan^{-1}\,(\infty) - \dfrac{\pi}{4} = \dfrac{\pi}{2} - \dfrac{\pi}{4} = \dfrac{\pi}{4}$

$\cot^{-1} x = \tan^{-1} \dfrac{1}{x}.$

(c) $2 + \lambda^2 + \lambda^4 = 1 + (\lambda^4 + \lambda^2 + 1)$

$= 1 + [(\lambda^2 + \lambda + 1)\,(\lambda^2 - \lambda + 1)]$

and $2\lambda = (\lambda^2 + \lambda + 1) - (\lambda^2 - \lambda + 1)$ etc.

$\therefore \quad T_n = \tan^{-1}(\lambda^2 + \lambda + 1) - \tan^{-1}(\lambda^2 - \lambda + 1)$

Now put $\lambda = 1, 2, 3, ..., n$ and add.

$\therefore \quad S_n = \tan^{-1}(n^2 + n + 1) - \tan^{-1} 1$

$\qquad = \tan^{-1}(n^2 + n + 1) - \dfrac{\pi}{4}$

Another form :

$S_n = \tan^{-1} \dfrac{(n^2 + n + 1) - 1}{1 + (n^2 + n + 1)} = \tan^{-1} \dfrac{n(n+1)}{n^2 + n + 2}$

52. (a) $\quad T_n = \cot^{-1}\left(2^{n+1} + \dfrac{1}{2^n}\right) = \cot^{-1} \dfrac{2^{n+1} \cdot 2^n + 1}{2^n}$

$\qquad = \tan^{-1} \dfrac{2^n(2-1)}{1 + 2^{n+1} \cdot 2^n}$ **(Note)**

$\qquad = \tan^{-1} \dfrac{2^{n+1} - 2^n}{1 + 2^{n+1} \cdot 2^n}$

$\qquad = \tan^{-1} 2^{n+1} - \tan^{-1} 2^n.$

Putting $n = 1, 2, 3, ..., n$ and adding, we get

$\qquad S_n = \tan^{-1} 2^{n+1} - \tan^{-1} 2$

$\therefore \quad S_\infty = \tan^{-1} \infty - \tan^{-1} 2$

$\qquad = \dfrac{\pi}{2} - \tan^{-1} 2 = \cot^{-1} 2 = \tan^{-1} \dfrac{1}{2}$

(b) $\quad T_n = \tan^{-1} \dfrac{2^{n-1}(2-1)}{1 + 2^n \cdot 2^{n-1}} = \tan^{-1} 2^n - \tan^{-1} 2^{n-1}$

Now put $n = 1, 2, 3, ..., n$ and add.

$\qquad S_n = \tan^{-1} 2^n - \tan^{-1} 1.$

$\qquad S_\infty = \dfrac{\pi}{2} - \dfrac{\pi}{4} = \dfrac{\pi}{4}.$

53. (a) $\quad T_n = \cot^{-1}\left(n^2 + \dfrac{3}{4}\right) = \cot^{-1} \dfrac{4n^2 + 3}{4}$

$\qquad = \tan^{-1} \dfrac{4}{4\left(n^2 + \dfrac{3}{4}\right)} = \tan^{-1} \dfrac{1}{1 + \left(n^2 - \dfrac{1}{4}\right)}$

$\qquad = \tan^{-1} \dfrac{\left(n + \dfrac{1}{2}\right) - \left(n - \dfrac{1}{2}\right)}{1 + \left(n + \dfrac{1}{2}\right)\left(n - \dfrac{1}{2}\right)}$

$\qquad = \tan^{-1}\left(n + \dfrac{1}{2}\right) - \tan^{-1}\left(n - \dfrac{1}{2}\right)$

Putting $n = 1, 2, 3, ..., n$ and adding

$\qquad S_n = \tan^{-1}\left(n + \dfrac{1}{2}\right) - \tan^{-1} \dfrac{1}{2}$

$\therefore \quad S_\infty = \dfrac{\pi}{2} - \tan^{-1} \dfrac{1}{2} = \cot^{-1} \dfrac{1}{2} = \tan^{-1} 2$

(b) $\quad T_n = \sin^{-1}\left[\dfrac{1}{\sqrt{n}} \cdot \sqrt{\left(\dfrac{n}{n+1}\right)} - \sqrt{\left(\dfrac{n-1}{n}\right)} \cdot \dfrac{1}{\sqrt{n+1}}\right]$

$\qquad = \sin^{-1}\left[\dfrac{1}{\sqrt{n}} \cdot \sqrt{\left(1 - \dfrac{1}{n+1}\right)} - \sqrt{\left(1 - \dfrac{1}{n}\right)} \cdot \dfrac{1}{\sqrt{n+1}}\right]$

If $\sin\theta = \dfrac{1}{\sqrt{n}}, \cos\theta = \sqrt{\left(1 - \dfrac{1}{n}\right)}$

If $\sin\phi = \dfrac{1}{\sqrt{n+1}}, \cos\phi = \sqrt{\left(1 - \dfrac{1}{n+1}\right)}$

L.H.S. $= \sin^{-1}(\sin\theta \cos\phi - \cos\theta \sin\phi)$

$\qquad = \sin^{-1} \sin(\theta - \phi)$

$\qquad = \theta - \phi = \sin^{-1} \dfrac{1}{\sqrt{n}} - \sin^{-1} \dfrac{1}{\sqrt{n+1}}$

Now put $n = 1, 2, 3, ...$ and add.

$\qquad S_n = \sin^{-1} 1 - \sin^{-1} \dfrac{1}{\sqrt{n+1}}$

$\therefore \quad S_\infty = \sin^{-1} 1 = \dfrac{\pi}{2}.$

54. Ans. (c). Let $\cot^{-1} x = \theta \quad \therefore \quad \cot\theta = x$

$\Rightarrow \quad \operatorname{cosec}\theta = \sqrt{1 + x^2}$ or $\sin\theta = \dfrac{1}{\sqrt{1 + x^2}}$

and $\cos\theta = \dfrac{x}{\sqrt{1 + x^2}}$

$\therefore \quad f(x) = \sqrt{1 + x^2} [\{x\cos\theta + \sin\theta\}^2 - 1]^{1/2}$

$\qquad = \sqrt{1 + x^2} \left[\left\{x \cdot \dfrac{x}{\sqrt{1 + x^2}} + \dfrac{1}{\sqrt{1 + x^2}}\right\}^2 - 1\right]^{1/2}$

$\qquad = \sqrt{1 + x^2} [1 + x^2 - 1]^{1/2} = x\sqrt{1 + x^2} \Rightarrow (c)$

Problem Set (2)

▶ **Multiple Choice Questions**

1. If $\cos^{-1}(1/x) = \theta$, then $\tan\theta$ will be

(a) $1/\sqrt{x^2 - 1}$ (b) $\sqrt{x^2 - 1}$

(c) $\sqrt{1 - x^2}$ (d) $\sqrt{x^2 + 1}$

2. If $A = \tan^{-1} x$, then the value of $\sin 2A$ is

(a) $2x/(1 - x^2)$ (b) $2x/(x^2 - 1)$

(c) $2x/(1 + x^2)$ (d) none of these

3. The value of $\sin\cot^{-1} x$ is

(a) $\sqrt{1 + x^2}$ (b) x

(c) $(1 + x^2)^{-3/2}$ (d) $(1 + x^2)^{-1/2}$

4. The value of $\cot^{-1}\left[\dfrac{\sqrt{1-\sin x}+\sqrt{1+\sin x}}{\sqrt{(1-\sin x)}-\sqrt{(1+\sin x)}}\right]$ is

(a) $\pi - x$ (b) $2\pi - x$

(c) $x/2$ (d) $\pi - \dfrac{1}{2}x$

5. The value of $\sin^{-1} x + \cos^{-1} x$ $(|x| \le 1)$ is

(a) 1   (b) π

(c) $\pi/2$ (d) $-\pi/2$

6. If $\sin\left(\sin^{-1}\dfrac{1}{5} + \cos^{-1} x\right) = 1$, then x is equal to

(a) 1   (b) 0   (c) $\dfrac{4}{5}$ (d) $\dfrac{1}{5}$

(M.N.R. 1994)

7. The value of $\cos^{-1}(-1) - \sin^{-1}(1)$ is

(a) π (b) $\dfrac{\pi}{2}$ (c) $\dfrac{3\pi}{2}$ (d) $-\dfrac{3\pi}{2}$

(AIEEE 2002)

8. If $\sin^{-1}\sqrt{x^2+2x+1} + \sec^{-1}\sqrt{x^2+2x+1}$
$= \dfrac{\pi}{2}, x \ne 0$ then the value of $2\sec^{-1}\dfrac{x}{2} + \sin^{-1}\dfrac{x}{2} =$

(a) $-\dfrac{\pi}{2}$ (b) $-\dfrac{3\pi}{2}, \dfrac{\pi}{2}$

(c) $\dfrac{3\pi}{2}$ (d) $-\dfrac{3\pi}{2}$

9. $\tan^{-1}\dfrac{1}{3} + \tan^{-1}\dfrac{2}{9} + \tan^{-1}\dfrac{4}{33} + \dots \infty$ is equal to

(a) $\dfrac{\pi}{4}$ (b) $\dfrac{\pi}{3}$ (c) $\dfrac{\pi}{2}$ (d) none

10. The equation $(\sin^{-1} x)^3 + (\cos^{-1} x)^3 = k\pi^3$ has no solution for

(a) $k > \dfrac{1}{32}$ (b) $k = \dfrac{1}{32}$

(c) $k < \dfrac{1}{32}$ (d) $k = 1$

True and False Type Question :

11. $\sin^{-1}\sqrt{2-x} = \cos^{-1}\sqrt{x-1}$ holds for all real x.

Hints/Answers to Problem Set (2)

1. Ans. (b).

2. Ans. (c).

3. Ans. (d).

We have

$\sin \cot^{-1} x = \sin \sin^{-1}\left[1/\sqrt{1+x^2}\right] = 1/\sqrt{1+x^2}$

4. Ans. (d).

We have $\cot\left[\dfrac{\sqrt{1-\sin x}+\sqrt{1+\sin x}}{\sqrt{(1-\sin x)}-\sqrt{(1+\sin x)}}\right]$

$= \cot^{-1}\left[\dfrac{\left(\cos\frac{1}{2}x - \sin\frac{1}{2}x\right) + \left(\cos\frac{1}{2}x + \sin\frac{1}{2}x\right)}{\left(\cos\frac{1}{2}x - \sin\frac{1}{2}x\right) - \left(\cos\frac{1}{2}x + \sin\frac{1}{2}x\right)}\right]$

$= \cot^{-1}\left(-\cot\dfrac{1}{2}x\right) = \cot^{-1}\cot\left(\pi - \dfrac{1}{2}x\right) = \pi - \dfrac{1}{2}x.$

5. Ans. (c).

6. Ans. (d).

(See Q. 42 (c) P. 626-636)

7. Ans. (b).

$E = \pi - \cos^{-1}(1) - \sin^{-1}(1) = \pi - \dfrac{\pi}{2} = \dfrac{\pi}{2}$

$\because \quad \cos^{-1}(-x) = \pi - \cos^{-1} x$

and $\cos^{-1} x + \sin^{-1} x = \dfrac{\pi}{2}$

8. Ans. (c).

$\sec^{-1} t = \cos^{-1}\dfrac{1}{t}$ and $\sin^{-1} z + \cos^{-1} z = \dfrac{\pi}{2}$

$\therefore \quad \sin^{-1}\sqrt{x^2+2x+1} + \cos^{-1}\dfrac{1}{\sqrt{x^2+2x+1}} = \dfrac{\pi}{2}$

Above implies that $\sqrt{x^2+2x+1} = \dfrac{1}{\sqrt{x^2+2x+1}}$

or $x^2 + 2x + 1 = 1$ or $x(x+2) = 0$

$\therefore \quad x = 0, -2 \therefore \quad x = -2$ as $x \ne 0$

$2\sec^{-1}\dfrac{x}{2} + \sin^{-1}\dfrac{x}{2}$

$= 2\sec^{-1}(-1) + \sin^{-1}(-1)$

$= 2\cos^{-1}(-1) + \sin^{-1}(-1)$

$= \cos^{-1}(-1) + \cos^{-1}(-1) + \sin^{-1}(-1)$

$= \pi + \dfrac{\pi}{2} = \dfrac{3\pi}{2}$

9. Ans. (a).

The given series can be rewritten as

$\tan^{-1}\dfrac{2^0}{1+2^1} + \tan^{-1}\dfrac{2^1}{1+2^3} + \tan^{-1}\dfrac{2^2}{1+2^5} + \dots$

$\therefore \quad T_n = \tan^{-1}\dfrac{2^{n-1}}{1+2^{2n-1}} = \tan^{-1}\dfrac{2^n - 2^{n-1}}{1+2^n \cdot 2^{n-1}}$

or $T_n = \tan^{-1} 2^n - \tan^{-1} 2^{n-1}$

Now put $n = 1, 2, 3, \dots$, and add. The terms cancel diagonally

$\therefore \quad S_n = \tan^{-1} 2^n - \tan^{-1} 1$

$\therefore \quad S_\infty = \tan^{-1}(\infty) - \tan^{-1} 1 = \dfrac{\pi}{2} - \dfrac{\pi}{4} = \dfrac{\pi}{4} \to (a)$

10. Ans. (c).

$(\sin^{-1} x + \cos^{-1} x)$

$\{(\sin^{-1} x)^2 + (\cos^{-1} x)^2 - \sin^{-1} x \cos^{-1} x\} = k\pi^3$

or $(\sin^{-1} x + \cos^{-1} x)^2 - 3 \sin^{-1} x \cos^{-1} x$

$$= k\pi^3 \cdot \frac{2}{\pi} = 2k\pi^2$$

or $\dfrac{\pi^2}{4} - 3 \sin^{-1} x \left(\dfrac{\pi}{2} - \sin^{-1} x \right) = 2k\pi^2$

or $3 (\sin^{-1} x)^2 - \dfrac{3\pi}{2} \sin^{-1} x + \pi^2 \left(\dfrac{1}{4} - 2k \right) = 0$

Above is a quadratic equation and will have solution if
$$\Delta \geq 0 \qquad \text{or} \qquad B^2 - 4AC \geq 0$$

or $\dfrac{9\pi^2}{4} - 4 \cdot 3 \cdot \pi^2 \left(\dfrac{1}{4} - 2k \right) \geq 0$

or $3 - 16 \left(\dfrac{1}{4} - 2k \right) \geq 0$ or $-1 + 32k \geq 0$

or $k \geq \dfrac{1}{32}$. In this case it will have a solution.

Therefore if $k < \dfrac{1}{32}$ it will have no solution.

11. Ans. False. The equality will hold only for those values of x for which
$$0 \leq 2 - x \leq 1 \text{ and } 0 \leq x - 1 \leq 1,$$
that is, for $1 \leq x \leq 2$ and not for all real values of x.

MISCELLANEOUS EXERCISE

Matching Entries

▶ *Match the entries of Column-I and Column-II.*

1. **Column-I**

(a) If $4 \sin^{-1} x + \cos^{-1} x = \pi$, then x equals

(b) If $\angle C = 90°$, then the value of $\tan^{-1} \dfrac{a}{b+c} + \tan^{-1} \dfrac{b}{c+a}$ is

(c) $\tan^{-1} 1 + \tan^{-1} 2 + \tan^{-1} 3$ is

(d) If $\sec^{-1} \dfrac{x}{a} - \sec^{-1} \dfrac{x}{b} = \sec^{-1} b - \sec^{-1} a$, then x equals

Column-II

1. ab

2. π

3. $\pi/4$

4. $1/2$

2. Let (x, y) be such that $\sin^{-1} (ax) + \cos^{-1} (y) + \cos^{-1} (bxy) = \dfrac{\pi}{2}$

Column-I

(a) If $a = 1$ and $b = 0$, then (x, y)

(b) If $a = 1$ and $b = 1$, then (x, y)

(c) If $a = 1$ and $b = 2$, then (x, y)

(d) If $a = 2$ and $b = 2$, then (x, y)

Column-II

(p) lies on the circle $x^2 + y^2 = 1$

(q) lies on $(x^2 - 1)(y^2 - 1) = 0$

(r) lies on $y = x$

(s) lies on $(4x^2 - 1)(y^2 - 1) = 0$

(I.I.T. 2007)

3. Number of real solutions of

Column-I

(a) $\tan\left(\dfrac{\pi}{4} + \dfrac{1}{2} \cos^{-1} x \right) + \tan\left(\dfrac{\pi}{4} - \dfrac{1}{2} \cos^{-1} x \right) = 1$

(b) $\tan^{-1} \dfrac{1}{2x+1} + \tan^{-1} \dfrac{1}{4x+1} = \tan^{-1} \dfrac{2}{x^2}$

(c) $\tan^{-1} \left(x + \dfrac{2}{x} \right) - \tan^{-1} \left(x - \dfrac{2}{x} \right) - \tan^{-1} \dfrac{4}{x} = 0$

(d) $\tan^{-1} (1 - x) + \tan^{-1} (1 + x) = \tan^{-1} 2x$

Column-II

(p) 0

(q) 2

(r) 3

(s) 1

4. **Column-I**

(a) $x = \operatorname{cosec}^2 (\cot^{-1} 3) - \sec^2 (\tan^{-1} 2)$

(b) $\tan^{-1} x + \tan^{-1} \dfrac{1}{y} = \tan^{-1} 3$ and $y^2 + y - 56 = 0$

(c) $\cos^{-1} x = \tan^{-1} y$ and $y^2 = 3$

Column-II

(p) $x = 2$

(q) $x = 5$

(r) $x = \dfrac{1}{2}$

(d) $\sin^{-1}\left(\tan\dfrac{\pi}{4}\right)-\sin^{-1}\sqrt{\dfrac{3}{y}}=\dfrac{\pi}{6}$ and $x^2=y$

(s) $x=-\dfrac{1}{2}$

Answers

1. (a) → (4), (b) → (3), (c) → (2), (d) → (1)
2. (a) → (p), (b) → (q), (c) → (p), (d) → (s)
3. (a) → (p), (b) → (r), (c) → (q), (d) → (s)
4. (a) → (q), (b) → (p, q), (c) → (r, s), (d) → (p)

Solutions

1. (a) → (4).

$$4\sin^{-1}x+\left(\dfrac{\pi}{2}-\sin^{-1}x\right)=\pi$$

$\therefore\quad 3\sin^{-1}x=\dfrac{\pi}{2}$ or $x=\sin\dfrac{\pi}{6}=\dfrac{1}{2}$

(b) → (3).

Use Rule 5 and $a^2+b^2=c^2$, $\tan^{-1}1=\pi/4$

See Q. 10 (c) P. 623-629

(c) → (2).

$$\tan^{-1}2+\tan^{-1}3=\pi+\tan^{-1}\dfrac{2+3}{1-2.3}$$

$$=\pi-\tan^{-1}1$$

$\therefore$ L.H.S. $=\tan^{-1}1+\tan^{-1}2+\tan^{-1}3=\pi$

(d) → (1). **See Q. 50 (a) P. 626-639**

2. (a) → (p).

$a=1, b=0$

$\Rightarrow\quad \sin^{-1}x+\cos^{-1}y+\cos^{-1}(0)=\pi/2$

$\therefore\quad \sin^{-1}x+\cos^{-1}y=0$ as $\cos^{-1}(0)=\pi/2$

or $\quad -\sin^{-1}x=\sin^{-1}\sqrt{1-y^2}$

or $\quad \sin^{-1}(-x)=\sin^{-1}\sqrt{1-y^2}$

$\therefore\quad \sqrt{1-y^2}=-x$ or $x^2+y^2=1$ $\therefore$ (a) → (p)

(b) → (q).

$a=1, b=1$

$\Rightarrow\quad \sin^{-1}x+\cos^{-1}y+\cos^{-1}(xy)=\dfrac{\pi}{2}$

$$=\sin^{-1}x+\cos^{-1}x$$

$\therefore\quad \cos^{-1}xy=\cos^{-1}x-\cos^{-1}y$

$$=\cos^{-1}[xy+\sqrt{1-x^2}\sqrt{1-y^2}]$$

$\therefore\quad \sqrt{1-x^2}\sqrt{1-y^2}=0$

or $\quad (x^2-1)(y^2-1)=0$ $\therefore$ (b) → (q)

(c) → (r).

$a=1, b=2$, then

$$\sin^{-1}x+\cos^{-1}y+\cos^{-1}(2xy)=\dfrac{\pi}{2}$$

$\therefore\quad \sin^{-1}x+\cos^{-1}y=\sin^{-1}(2xy)$

$\because\quad \dfrac{\pi}{2}-\cos^{-1}z=\sin^{-1}z$

$\therefore\quad \sin[\sin^{-1}x+\cos^{-1}y]=2xy$

or $\quad xy+\sqrt{1-x^2}\sqrt{1-y^2}=2xy$

or $\quad (1-x^2)(1-y^2)=x^2y^2$

$\therefore\quad x^2+y^2=1$ $\therefore$ (c) → (p)

(d) → (s).

$a=2, b=2$, then

$$\sin^{-1}2x+\cos^{-1}y+\cos^{-1}(2xy)=\dfrac{\pi}{2}$$

$\therefore\quad \sin^{-1}2x+\cos^{-1}y=\sin^{-1}(2xy)$

$$\sin[\sin^{-1}2x+\cos^{-1}y]=2xy$$

$$2x(y)+\sqrt{(1-4x^2)}\sqrt{1-y^2}=2xy$$

$\therefore\quad (4x^2-1)(y^2-1)=0$ $\therefore$ (d) → (s)

3. Ans. (a) → (p), (b) → (r), (c) → (q), (d) → (s)

Let $\dfrac{1}{2}\cos^{-1}x=\theta$ $\therefore$ $x=\cos 2\theta$

(a) $\dfrac{1+\tan\theta}{1-\tan\theta}+\dfrac{1-\tan\theta}{1+\tan\theta}=\dfrac{2(1+\tan^2\theta)}{(1-\tan^2\theta)}$

L.H.S. $=\dfrac{2}{\cos 2\theta}=\dfrac{2}{x}=1$ $\therefore$ $x=2=\cos 2\theta$

Since $\cos 2\theta\le 1$ $\therefore$ there does not exist any solution.

(b) $\tan^{-1}\dfrac{\dfrac{1}{2x+1}+\dfrac{1}{4x+1}}{1-\dfrac{1}{(2x+1)(4x+1)}}$

$$=\tan^{-1}\dfrac{6x+2}{8x^2+6x}=\tan^{-1}\dfrac{2}{x^2}$$

$\therefore\quad x^2(3x+1)=8x^2+6x$

or $\quad x(3x^2-7x+2)=0$ or $x(x-2)(3x-1)=0$

$\therefore\quad x=0,\dfrac{1}{3},2$ $\therefore$ (b) → (r)

(c) $\dfrac{\left(x+\dfrac{2}{x}\right)-\left(x-\dfrac{2}{x}\right)}{1+\left(x^2-\dfrac{4}{x^2}\right)}=\dfrac{4}{x}$

$$\dfrac{4}{x}=\dfrac{4}{x}\left(1+x^2-\dfrac{4}{x^2}\right)$$

$1 = 1 + x^2 - \dfrac{4}{x^2}$ ∴ $x^4 = 4$ or $x^2 = 2$ or $x = \pm\sqrt{2}$

∴ (c) → (q)

(d) $\dfrac{(1-x)+(1+x)}{1-(1-x^2)} = 2x$ or $\dfrac{2}{x^2} = 2x$ or $x^3 = 1$

∴ $x = 1$ only ∴ (d) → (s)

4. Ans. (a) → (q), (b) → (p, q), (c) → (r, s), (d) → (p)

(a) R.H.S. $= [1 + \cot^2(\cot^{-1} 3)] - [1 + \tan^2(\tan^{-1} 2)]$

$= 3^2 - 2^2 = 5$ ∴ $x = 5$

(b) $\dfrac{x + \dfrac{1}{y}}{1 - \dfrac{x}{y}} = 3$ provided $\dfrac{x}{y} < 1$, *i.e.*, $x < y$

$xy + 1 = 3(y - x)$ or $x = \dfrac{3y - 1}{y + 3}$

Also $y^2 + y - 56 = 0 \implies (y + 8)(y - 7) = 0$

∴ $y = -8, 7$

When $y = -8, x = \dfrac{-25}{-5} = 5$ ∴ $\dfrac{x}{y} = \dfrac{-5}{8} < 1$

When $y = 7, x = \dfrac{20}{10} = 2$ ∴ $\dfrac{x}{y} = \dfrac{2}{7} < 1$

∴ (b) → (p, q)

(c) $\tan^{-1} y = \theta$ ∴ $y = \tan\theta$ ∴ $1 + \tan^2\theta = 1 + y^2$

$\sec^2\theta = 1 + y^2$ ∴ $\cos\theta = \dfrac{1}{\sqrt{1 + y^2}}$

∴ $\theta = \cos^{-1}\dfrac{1}{\sqrt{1 + y^2}} = \cos^{-1} x$

∴ $x = \dfrac{1}{\sqrt{1 + y^2}} = \dfrac{1}{\sqrt{1 + 3}} = \dfrac{1}{\sqrt{4}} = \pm\dfrac{1}{2}$

∴ (c) → (r, s)

(d) $\sin^{-1}(1) - \dfrac{\pi}{6} = \sin^{-1}\sqrt{\dfrac{3}{y}}$ and $x^2 = y$

∴ $\dfrac{\pi}{2} - \dfrac{\pi}{6} = \sin^{-1}\sqrt{\dfrac{3}{y}}$ or $\sqrt{\dfrac{3}{y}} = \sin 60° = \dfrac{\sqrt{3}}{2}$

∴ $\sqrt{y} = 2$ or $y = 4 = x^2 \implies x = \pm 2$

∴ (d) → (p)

Fascinating Facts

(i) $\sin(\sin^{-1} x) = x$ if $1 \le x \le 1$ and $\sin^{-1}(\sin\theta) = \theta$ if $-\dfrac{\pi}{2} \le \theta \le \dfrac{\pi}{2}$

(ii) $\cos(\cos^{-1} x) = x$ if $1 \le x \le 1$ and $\cos^{-1}(\cos\theta) = \theta$ if $0 \le \theta \le \pi$

(iii) $\tan(\tan^{-1} x) = x$ if $-\infty < x < \infty$ and $\tan^{-1}(\tan\theta) = \theta$ if $-\dfrac{\pi}{2} < \theta < \dfrac{\pi}{2}$

(iv) $\cot(\cot^{-1} x) = x$ if $-\infty < x < \infty$ and $\cot^{-1}(\cot\theta) = \theta$ if $0 < \theta < \pi$

(v) $\sec(\sec^{-1} x) = x$ if $|x| \ge 1$ and $\sec(\sec^{-1}\theta) = \theta$ if $0 < \theta < \pi, \theta \ne \dfrac{\pi}{2}$

(vi) $\mathrm{cosec}(\mathrm{cosec}^{-1} x) = x$ if $|x| \ge 1$ and $\mathrm{cosec}^{-1}(\mathrm{cosec}\,\theta) = \theta$ if $-\dfrac{\pi}{2} < \theta < \dfrac{\pi}{2}, \theta \ne 0$

(vii) $\sin^{-1} x + \cos^{-1} x = \dfrac{\pi}{2}, -1 \le x \le 1$

(viii) $\tan^{-1} x + \cot^{-1} x = \dfrac{\pi}{2}, -\infty \le x \le \infty$

(ix) $\sec^{-1} x + \mathrm{cosec}^{-1} x = \dfrac{\pi}{2}, -\infty \le x \le \infty$

❏

Properties of Triangles

§1. Relations between the Sides and Trigonometrical Ratios of the Angles of any Triangle.

Basic Formulae : We shall denote by a, b, c the lengths of sides BC, CA and AB of a triangle ABC. Semi-perimeter of the triangle will be denoted by s and its area by S or Δ.

1. $\dfrac{\sin A}{a} = \dfrac{\sin B}{\cdot b} = \dfrac{\sin C}{c}$. **(Sine rule)**

2. $\cos A = \dfrac{b^2 + c^2 - a^2}{2bc}$, $\cos B = \dfrac{c^2 + a^2 - b^2}{2ca}$,

   $\cos C = \dfrac{a^2 + b^2 - c^2}{2ab}$. **(Cosine rule)**

3. $\sin \dfrac{A}{2} = \sqrt{\left\{\dfrac{(s-b)(s-c)}{bc}\right\}}$, $\sin \dfrac{B}{2} = \sqrt{\left\{\dfrac{(s-c)(s-a)}{ca}\right\}}$,

   $\sin \dfrac{C}{2} = \sqrt{\left\{\dfrac{(s-a)(s-b)}{ab}\right\}}$.

4. $\cos \dfrac{A}{2} = \sqrt{\left\{\dfrac{s(s-a)}{bc}\right\}}$, $\cos \dfrac{B}{2} = \sqrt{\left\{\dfrac{s(s-b)}{ca}\right\}}$,

   $\cos \dfrac{C}{2} = \sqrt{\left\{\dfrac{s(s-c)}{ab}\right\}}$.

5. $\tan \dfrac{A}{2} = \sqrt{\left\{\dfrac{(s-b)(s-c)}{s(s-a)}\right\}}$, $\tan \dfrac{B}{2} = \sqrt{\left\{\dfrac{(s-c)(s-a)}{s(s-b)}\right\}}$,

   $\tan \dfrac{C}{2} = \sqrt{\left\{\dfrac{(s-a)(s-b)}{s(s-c)}\right\}}$.

6. $\cot \dfrac{A}{2} = \sqrt{\left\{\dfrac{s(s-a)}{(s-b)(s-c)}\right\}}$, $\cot \dfrac{B}{2} = \sqrt{\left\{\dfrac{s(s-b)}{(s-c)(s-a)}\right\}}$,

   $\cot \dfrac{C}{2} = \sqrt{\left\{\dfrac{s(s-c)}{(s-a)(s-b)}\right\}}$.

7. $\sin A = \dfrac{2}{bc}\sqrt{s(s-a)(s-b)(s-c)} = \dfrac{2S}{bc}$

   with similar expressions for $\sin B$ and $\sin C$.

8. $a = b\cos C + c\cos B$, $b = c\cos A + a\cos C$,

   $c = a\cos B + b\cos A$. **(Projection rule)**

9. $\tan \dfrac{B-C}{2} = \dfrac{b-c}{b+c}\cot \dfrac{A}{2}$ **(Napier's Analogy)** .

10. $S = \dfrac{1}{2}bc\sin A = \dfrac{1}{2}ca\sin B = \dfrac{1}{2}ab\sin C$.

Another form :

$$S = \dfrac{b^2 \sin C \sin A}{2\sin B} = \dfrac{c^2 \sin A \sin B}{2\sin C} = \dfrac{a^2 \sin B \sin C}{2\sin A}$$

$S = \dfrac{1}{2}bc\sin A$, $\quad \dfrac{a}{\sin A} = k$ ...(1)

$\therefore \quad S = \dfrac{1}{2}\dfrac{k\sin B \cdot k\sin C \sin^2 A}{\sin A} = \dfrac{a^2 \sin B \sin C}{2\sin A}$

by (1), $k\sin A = a$

Few Important Results :

11. (i)* $\tan \dfrac{A}{2}\tan \dfrac{B}{2}$

   $= \left\{\dfrac{(s-b)(s-c)}{s(s-a)} \cdot \dfrac{(s-c)(s-a)}{s(s-b)}\right\}^{1/2} = \dfrac{s-c}{s}$

   $\therefore \quad \cot \dfrac{A}{2}\cot \dfrac{B}{2} = \dfrac{s}{s-c}$

   (ii)* $\tan \dfrac{A}{2} + \tan \dfrac{B}{2} = \sqrt{\left(\dfrac{s-c}{s}\right)}\left[\sqrt{\left(\dfrac{s-b}{s-a}\right)} + \sqrt{\left(\dfrac{s-a}{s-b}\right)}\right]$

   $= \sqrt{\left(\dfrac{s-c}{s}\right)}\left[\dfrac{s-b+s-a}{\sqrt{(s-a)(s-b)}}\right]$

   $= \dfrac{c}{s}\left[\dfrac{s(s-c)}{(s-a)(s-b)}\right]^{1/2} = \dfrac{c}{s}\cot \dfrac{C}{2}$

   Another form :

   $\dfrac{c \cdot (s-c)}{\{s(s-a)(s-b)(s-c)\}^{1/2}} = \dfrac{c}{S}(s-c)$

   (iii)* $\tan \dfrac{A}{2} - \tan \dfrac{B}{2} = \dfrac{a-b}{S}(s-c)$

   (iv) $\cot \dfrac{A}{2} + \cot \dfrac{B}{2} = \dfrac{\tan \dfrac{A}{2} + \tan \dfrac{B}{2}}{\tan \dfrac{A}{2}\tan \dfrac{B}{2}}$

   $= \dfrac{c}{s-c}\cot \dfrac{C}{2}$ by 11 (i), (ii)

12. Also note the following identities :

   (i) $\Sigma(p-q) = (p-q) + (q-r) + (r-p) = 0$

   (ii) $\Sigma\ p(q-r) = p(q-r) + q(r-p) + r(p-q) = 0$

   (iii) $\Sigma(p+a)(q-r) = \Sigma\ p(q-r)$

   $+ a\Sigma(q-r) = 0$, by (i) and (ii).

Note : Reference of these 12 results will be given in the solutions.

Problem Set (1)

$$\text{Sine rule } \frac{\sin A}{a} = \frac{\sin B}{b} = \frac{\sin C}{c} = k,$$

$$\text{Cosine rule } \cos A = (b^2 + c^2 - a^2)/2bc \quad \text{or} \quad a^2 = b^2 + c^2 - 2bc \cos A.$$

In any $\triangle ABC$, prove the following :

1. (a) $(b+c) \cos A + (c+a) \cos B + (a+b) \cos C$
    $$= a+b+c.$$

    (b) $a^2 \cos 2B + b^2 \cos 2A + 2ab \cos (A-B) = c^2$

    Is this statement true or false ?

2. (a)* $(a+b+c)(\cos A + \cos B + \cos C)$
    $$= 2\left(a \cos^2 \frac{1}{2} A + b \cos^2 \frac{1}{2} B + c \cos^2 \frac{1}{2} C\right).$$

    (b)* If $\angle A = 45°, \angle B = 75°$, prove that $a + c\sqrt{2} = 2b$.

3. (a)* $a(b \cos C - c \cos B) = b^2 - c^2$.

    (b) The sides of a triangle are 7 cm, $4\sqrt{3}$ cm, and $\sqrt{13}$ cm. Then the smallest angle is $30°$.

    (c) $c^2 = (a-b)^2 \cos^2 \frac{1}{2} C + (a+b)^2 \sin^2 \frac{1}{2} C$.

4. In a triangle ABC, $\quad 2ac \sin \frac{1}{2}(A-B+C) =$

    (a) $a^2 + b^2 - c^2$ (b) $c^2 + a^2 - b^2$

    (c) $b^2 - c^2 - a^2$ (d) $c^2 - a^2 - b^2$

    (I.I.T. Sc. 2000)

5. (a) $(b^2 - c^2) \cot A + (c^2 - a^2) \cot B$
    $$+ (a^2 - b^2) \cot C = 0.$$

    (b) $\dfrac{b^2 - c^2}{a^2} \sin 2A + \dfrac{c^2 - a^2}{b^2} \sin 2B$
    $$+ \dfrac{a^2 - b^2}{c^2} \sin 2C = 0.$$

6. If in a triangle $ABC, \angle A = 60°$, then

    (a) $\left(1 + \dfrac{a}{c} + \dfrac{b}{c}\right)\left(1 + \dfrac{c}{b} - \dfrac{a}{b}\right)$ is …..

    (b) If in a triangle $(a+b+c)(b+c-a) = k bc$, then k lies in $]0, 4[$.

7. (a) The sides of a triangle are $a, b, \sqrt{a^2 + ab + b^2}$, prove that the greatest angle is $120°$.

    (b) The sides of a triangle are in the ratio $2 : \sqrt{6} : (\sqrt{3} + 1)$, prove that its angles are $45°, 60°, 75°$.

    (c) In a triangle ABC, the side c has two values. Prove that both the values satisfy the equation
    $$\frac{(a+b)^2}{1 + \cos C} + \frac{(b-a)^2}{1 - \cos C} = \frac{2a^2}{\sin^2 A}$$

    (d) The sides of a triangle are 2, 3, $\sqrt{19}$, then the greatest angle of the triangle is ……

(e) The sides of a triangle are in A.P. and the greatest angle is double of smallest angle. Prove that the ratio of its sides is $4 : 5 : 6$.

(f) Sides of a $\triangle$ are in ratio $1 : \sqrt{3} : 2$, the angles of $\triangle$ are in ratio

     (a) $1 : 3 : 5$ (b) $2 : 3 : 4$

     (c) $3 : 2 : 1$ (d) $1 : 2 : 3$ **(Screening 2004)**

8. (a) If $\cos A = \sin B/(2 \sin C)$, prove that $\triangle ABC$ is isosceles.

    (b)* If $\dfrac{\cos A + 2 \cos C}{\cos A + 2 \cos B} = \dfrac{\sin B}{\sin C}$ then the triangle ABC is either isosceles or right angled.

    (c)* If in a triangle ABC
    $$\frac{2 \cos A}{a} + \frac{\cos B}{b} + \frac{2 \cos C}{c} = \frac{a}{bc} + \frac{b}{ca},$$
    then the value of the angle A is ….. degrees.

    (I.I.T. 1993)

9. If $\tan A$, $\tan B$ are the roots of the quadratic $ab x^2 - c^2 x + ab = 0$, where a, b, c are the sides of a triangle, then prove the following

    (a) $\tan A = \dfrac{a}{b}$ (b) $\tan B = \dfrac{b}{a}$

    (c) $\cos C = 0$ (d) $\tan A + \tan B = \dfrac{c^2}{ab}$

    (e) $\sin^2 A + \sin^2 B + \sin^2 C = 2$

10. If in a triangle $\sin^4 A + \sin^4 B + \sin^4 C$
    $$= \sin^2 B \sin^2 C + 2 \sin^2 C \sin^2 A + 2 \sin^2 A \sin^2 B$$
    then its angle A is equal to

    (a) $45°, 135°$ (b) $30°, 150°$

    (c) $60°, 120°$ (d) none of these

11. (a) In a triangle the angles A, B, C are in A.P., show that $2 \cos \dfrac{A-C}{2} = \dfrac{a+c}{\sqrt{(a^2 - ac + c^2)}}$

    (b) If the angles A, B, C of $\triangle ABC$ are in A.P., then

         (a) $c^2 = a^2 + b^2 - ab$ (b) $b^2 = a^2 + c^2 - ac$

         (c) $c^2 = a^2 + b^2$ (d) none of these

    (c) In a triangle, the lengths of the two larger sides are 10 and 9 respectively. If the angles are in A.P., then the length of the third side can be

         (a) $5 - \sqrt{6}$ (b) $3\sqrt{3}$

         (c) 5 (d) $5 + \sqrt{6}$

         (e) none of these   **(P.E.T. 1990)**

(d) If the angles of a triangle are in A.P. and sides a, b, c be in G.P. then a^2, b^2, c^2 are in

(a) A.P. (b) G.P.
(c) H.P. (d) none

(e) In a triangle ABC, the angles are in A.P., then $\underset{A \to C}{Lt} \dfrac{\sqrt{3 - 4 \sin A \sin C}}{|A - C|}$ is

(a) 1 (b) 2
(c) 3 (d) 4

12. In $\triangle ABC$, prove that $a^2 = (b - c)^2 + 4bc \sin^2 (A/2)$ and hence show that $a = (b - c) \sec \phi$ where $\tan \phi = \dfrac{2 \sqrt{bc} \sin (A/2)}{b - c}$.

13. (a) $a \sin \{(A/2) + B\} = (b + c) \sin (A/2)$.

(b) $a \cos \dfrac{1}{2} (B - C) = (b + c) \sin \dfrac{1}{2} A$.

14. (a) $\dfrac{b^2 - c^2}{a^2} = \dfrac{\sin (B - C)}{\sin (B + C)}$.

(b) In any triangle ABC, $\Pi \left[\dfrac{\sin^2 A + \sin A + 1}{\sin A} \right]$ is always greater than

(a) 9 (b) 3
(c) 27 (d) 10

15. (a) $\dfrac{1 + \cos (A - B) \cos C}{1 + \cos (A - C) \cos B} = \dfrac{a^2 + b^2}{a^2 + c^2}$.

(b) $a (\cos B \cos C + \cos A)$
$= b (\cos C \cos A + \cos B)$
$= c (\cos A \cos B + \cos C)$.

(c) $(b^2 + c^2 - a^2) \tan A = (c^2 + a^2 - b^2) \tan B$
$= (a^2 + b^2 - c^2) \tan C$.

16. (a)* $\dfrac{c}{a - b} = \dfrac{\tan \dfrac{1}{2} A + \tan \dfrac{1}{2} B}{\tan \dfrac{1}{2} A - \tan \dfrac{1}{2} B}$

(b) $\dfrac{c}{a + b} = \dfrac{1 - \tan \dfrac{1}{2} A \tan \dfrac{1}{2} B}{1 + \tan \dfrac{1}{2} A \tan \dfrac{1}{2} B}$.

(c) $\dfrac{a - b}{a + b} = \cot \dfrac{A + B}{2} \tan \dfrac{A - B}{2}$.

Also prove that the area of the triangle is $\dfrac{1}{2} a^2 \dfrac{\sin B \sin C}{\sin A}$

17. $\dfrac{\cos^2 \left\{ \dfrac{1}{2} (B - C) \right\}}{(b + c)^2} + \dfrac{\sin^2 \left\{ \dfrac{1}{2} (B - C) \right\}}{(b - c)^2} = \dfrac{1}{a^2}$

18. (a) $\dfrac{a^2 \sin (B - C)}{\sin B + \sin C} + \dfrac{b^2 \sin (C - A)}{\sin C + \sin A} + \dfrac{c^2 \sin (A - B)}{\sin A + \sin B} = 0$

(b) $a \sin (B - C) + b \sin (C - A) + c \sin (A - B) = 0$.

19. (a) $a \sin \dfrac{1}{2} A \sin \dfrac{1}{2} (B - C) + b \sin \dfrac{1}{2} B \sin \dfrac{1}{2} (C - A)$
$+ c \sin \dfrac{1}{2} C \sin \dfrac{1}{2} (A - B) = 0.$

(b) $a^2 (\cos^2 B - \cos^2 C) + b^2 (\cos^2 C - \cos^2 A)$
$+ c^2 (\cos^2 A - \cos^2 B) = 0.$

(c) $(b - c) \cot \dfrac{1}{2} A + (c - a) \cot \dfrac{1}{2} B + (a - b) \cot \dfrac{1}{2} C = 0.$

20. (a) $\dfrac{a \sin (B - C)}{b^2 - c^2} = \dfrac{b \sin (C - A)}{c^2 - a^2} = \dfrac{c \sin (A - B)}{a^2 - b^2}.$

(b) $a^2 - 2ab \cos (60° + C) = c^2 - 2bc \cos (60° + A).$

21. (a) $a^3 \sin (B - C) + b^3 \sin (C - A) + c^3 \sin (A - B) = 0.$

(b) $\dfrac{b^2 - c^2}{\cos B + \cos C} + \dfrac{c^2 - a^2}{\cos C + \cos A} + \dfrac{a^2 - b^2}{\cos A + \cos B} = 0.$

22. (a) If in any triangle the angles be to one another as $1 : 2 : 3$, prove that the corresponding sides are as $1 : \sqrt{3} : 2$. **(Bihar C.E.E. 1999)**

(b) If the angles of a triangle are in the ratio $1 : 2 : 4$, then prove that $a^2 b^2 c^2 = (b^2 - a^2)(c^2 - b^2)(a^2 - c^2).$

(c) The angles of a triangle are in the ratio $4 : 1 : 1$, then the ratio of the largest side to the perimeter

(a) $1 : 1 + \sqrt{3}$ (b) $2 : 3$
(c) $\sqrt{3} : 2 + \sqrt{3}$ (d) $1 : 2 + \sqrt{3}$
(Screening 2003)

23. (a) If $a \cos A = b \cos B$, prove that $\triangle ABC$ is either isosceles, or right angled.

(b)* If in a triangle $\dfrac{a^2 - b^2}{a^2 + b^2} = \dfrac{\sin (A - B)}{\sin (A + B)}$, prove that it is either a right angled or an isosceles triangle.

24. (a) In a triangle ABC, if $a = 3, b = 4$ and $\sin A = 3/4$, then $\angle B =$
(a) 60° (b) 90°
(c) 45° (d) 30°

(b) The angles of a triangle are as $1 : 2 : 7$, then the ratio of the greatest side to the least side is $\sqrt{5} + 1 : \sqrt{5} - 1$.

25. (a)* In a triangle ABC, AD is the altitude from A. Given $b > c, \angle C = 23°$ and $AD = \dfrac{abc}{b^2 - c^2}$, then $\angle B = \ldots\ldots\ldots$ **(I.I.T. 1994)**

(b) If $A = 30°$ and area of $\triangle ABC$ is $\dfrac{\sqrt{3} a^2}{4}$ then the triangle is right angled. Is this statement true?

26. Prove that the expression $\dfrac{(a + b + c)(b + c - a)(c + a - b)(a + b - c)}{4 b^2 c^2}$ is equal to $\sin^2 A$.

27. (a) In $\triangle ABC$ prove that if θ be any angle, then
$b\cos\theta = c\cos(A-\theta) + a\cos(C+\theta)$.

(b) If in a triangle ABC
$\cos A\cos B + \sin A\sin B\sin C = 1$
show that $a:b:c = 1:1:\sqrt{2}$.

28. (a) If the sides a,b,c of any triangle be in G.P., then prove that x,y,z are also in G.P. where
$$x = (b^2 - c^2)\frac{\tan B + \tan C}{\tan B - \tan C},$$
$$y = (c^2 - a^2)\frac{\tan C + \tan A}{\tan C - \tan A}$$
and $z = (a^2 - b^2)\dfrac{\tan A + \tan B}{\tan A - \tan B}$.

(b) If in a triangle PQR, $\sin P, \sin Q, \sin R$ are in A.P., then prove that the altitudes are in H.P.
(I.I.T. 1998)

29. (a) If in $\triangle ABC$, $\cos A + 2\cos B + \cos C = 2$, prove that the sides of the triangle are in A.P.

(b) If $\cos A + \cos C = 4\sin^2\dfrac{1}{2}B$, then the sides a,b,c of the triangle are in G.P. T or F.

(c) In a triangle ABC with fixed base BC, the vertex A moves such that $\cos B + \cos C = 4\sin^2\dfrac{A}{2}$. If a,b and c denote the lengths of the sides of the triangle opposite to the angles A, B and C respectively, then
(a) $b + c = 4a$
(b) $b + c = 2a$
(c) locus of point A is an ellipse
(d) locus of point A is a pair of straight lines
(I.I.T. 2009)

30. If the sides a,b,c of $\triangle ABC$ are in A.P., prove that
(a) $\cot\dfrac{1}{2}A, \cot\dfrac{1}{2}B, \cot\dfrac{1}{2}C$ are in A.P.

(b)* $\cos A\cot\dfrac{1}{2}A, \cos B\cot\dfrac{1}{2}B, \cos C\cot\dfrac{1}{2}C$ are in A.P.

(c)* $a\cos^2\dfrac{C}{2} + c\cos^2\dfrac{A}{2} = \dfrac{3b}{2}$

(d)* $\tan\dfrac{A}{2} + \tan\dfrac{C}{2} = \dfrac{2}{3}\cot\dfrac{B}{2}$.
(Roorkee 1993)

31. (a) If a^2, b^2, c^2 are in A.P., prove that $\cot A, \cot B$ and $\cot C$ are also in A.P.

(b) If in $\triangle ABC$, $\dfrac{\sin A}{\sin C} = \dfrac{\sin(A-B)}{\sin(B-C)}$, prove that a^2, b^2, c^2 are in A.P.

32.* If a,b,c are in H.P., prove that
$\sin^2\dfrac{1}{2}A, \sin^2\dfrac{1}{2}B, \sin^2\dfrac{1}{2}C$ are also in H.P.

33.* Prove that :
(a) $(b+c-a)\{\cot(B/2) + \cot(C/2)\} = 2a\cot(A/2)$.

(b) $(a+b+c)\{\tan(A/2) + \tan(B/2)\} = 2c\cot(C/2)$.

34. (a) $\{\cot(A/2) + \cot(B/2)\}\{a\sin^2(B/2) + b\sin^2(A/2)\} = c\cot(C/2)$.

(b) $1 - \tan\dfrac{1}{2}A\tan\dfrac{1}{2}B = \dfrac{2c}{(a+b+c)}$.

35. (a) $2abc\cos\dfrac{1}{2}A\cos\dfrac{1}{2}B\cos\dfrac{1}{2}C = (a+b+c)S$.

(b) $bc\cos^2\dfrac{1}{2}A + ca\cos^2\dfrac{1}{2}B + ab\cos^2\dfrac{1}{2}C = s^2$.

(c) $\dfrac{b-c}{a}\cos^2\dfrac{1}{2}A + \dfrac{c-a}{b}\cos^2\dfrac{1}{2}B$
$+ \dfrac{a-b}{c}\cos^2\dfrac{1}{2}C = 0$.

36.* $\dfrac{\tan\frac{1}{2}A}{(a-b)(a-c)} + \dfrac{\tan\frac{1}{2}B}{(b-c)(b-a)} + \dfrac{\tan\frac{1}{2}C}{(c-a)(c-b)} = \dfrac{1}{S}$.

37. (a) Given $S = a^2 - (b-c)^2$ in a triangle ABC whose area is S, then the value of $\tan\dfrac{A}{2}$ is ......

(b)* If $b + c = 3a$, prove that $\cot\dfrac{1}{2}B\cot\dfrac{1}{2}C = 2$.

(c) If $c + a = 2b$, prove that $\cot\dfrac{1}{2}A\cot\dfrac{1}{2}C = 3$.

Solutions to Problem Set (1)

1. (a) Re-writing the lefhand side, we get
L.H.S. $= (b\cos C + c\cos B)$
$\qquad + (c\cos A + a\cos C) + (a\cos B + b\cos A)$
$\qquad = a + b + c.$

(b) True.
$a^2(\cos^2 B - \sin^2 B) + b^2(\cos^2 A - \sin^2 A)$
$\qquad + 2ab(\cos A\cos B + \sin A\sin B)$
$= (a^2\cos^2 B + b^2\cos^2 A + 2ab\cos A\cos B)$
$\qquad - (a^2\sin^2 B + b^2\sin^2 A - 2ab\sin A\sin B)$
$= (a\cos B + b\cos A)^2 - (a\sin B - b\sin A)^2 = c^2 + 0$
by projection formula and sine rule.

2. (a) $(a+b+c)(\cos A + \cos B + \cos C)$
There will be nine terms :
$= a\cos A + b\cos B + c\cos C$
$\qquad + (b\cos C + c\cos B) + (c\cos A + a\cos C)$
$\qquad\qquad + (a\cos B + b\cos A)$
$= a(1 + \cos A) + b(1 + \cos B) + c(1 + \cos C)$
$\because \quad b\cos C + c\cos B = a$ etc.
$= 2(a\cos^2 A/2 + b\cos^2 B/2 + c\cos^2 C/2).$

(b) As $\angle A = 45°$, $\angle B = 75°$, we have
$\angle C = 180° - (45° + 75°) = 60°.$
$2b = 2(a\cos C + c\cos A)$ by Proj. Formula
$= 2(a\cos 60° + c\cos 45°)$
$= a + c\sqrt{2} = $ L.H.S.

3. (a) L.H.S. $= a(b\cos C - c\cos B)$

$$= a\left\{b \cdot \frac{a^2+b^2-c^2}{2ab} - c \cdot \frac{c^2+a^2-b^2}{2ca}\right\}$$

$$= \frac{1}{2}(a^2+b^2-c^2-c^2-a^2+b^2) = b^2-c^2.$$

Alt. On putting $a = b\cos C + c\cos B$,

L.H.S. $= b^2\cos^2 C - c^2\cos^2 B$

$$= b^2(1-\sin^2 C) - c^2(1-\sin^2 B) = b^2-c^2.$$

$$\because b\sin C = c\sin B$$

by sine formula.

(b) Clearly $c = \sqrt{13}$ is smallest side and hence c is the smallest angle

$$\therefore \cos C = \frac{a^2+b^2-c^2}{2ab} = \frac{\sqrt{3}}{2} \quad \therefore \quad C = 30°$$

(c) R.H.S. $= (a^2+b^2)\left(\cos^2\frac{C}{2} + \sin^2\frac{C}{2}\right)$

$$-2ab\left(\cos^2\frac{C}{2} - \sin^2\frac{C}{2}\right)$$

$$= a^2+b^2-2ab\cos C = c^2$$

4. Ans. (b).

$$A + C - B = A + B + C - 2B = 2\left(\frac{\pi}{2} - B\right)$$

$$\therefore \quad 2ac\sin\frac{1}{2}(A+C-B) = 2ac\cos B$$

$$= c^2+a^2-b^2.$$

5. (a) $(b^2-c^2)\cot A = (b^2-c^2)\frac{\cos A}{\sin A}$

$$= (b^2-c^2) \cdot \frac{b^2+c^2-a^2}{2bc \cdot ka}$$

$$= \frac{1}{2k \cdot abc}[(b^4-c^4) - a^2(b^2-c^2)].$$

$$\therefore \quad \text{L.H.S.}$$

$$= \frac{1}{2k \cdot abc}[(b^4-c^4) + (c^4-a^4) + (a^4-b^4)$$

$$- \{a^2(b^2-c^2) + b^2(c^2-a^2) + c^2(a^2-b^2)\}] = 0.$$

(b) Do yourself.

$$\sin 2A = 2\sin A\cos A.$$

$$\therefore \quad \frac{b^2-c^2}{a^2} \cdot 2\sin A\cos A$$

$$= 2k\frac{(b^2-c^2)(b^2+c^2-a^2)}{2abc}$$

L.H.S. $= \frac{k}{abc}[\Sigma(b^4-c^4) - \Sigma a^2(b^2-c^2)] = 0$

6. (a) Ans. 3.

$$\text{L.H.S.} = \frac{b^2+c^2-a^2+2bc}{bc} = 2\cos A + 2 = 3$$

$$[\because \angle A = 60°]$$

(b) L.H.S. $= 2bc\cos A + 2bc = kbc$

$$\therefore \quad \cos A = \frac{k-2}{2} \quad \therefore \quad -1 < \frac{k-2}{2} < 1$$

or $-2 < k-2 < 2$ or $0 < k < 4$ etc.

7. (a) The sides are a, b, c where $c = \sqrt{(a^2+b^2+ab)}$ is greatest side.
Hence $\angle C$ is greatest.

$$\therefore \quad \cos C = \frac{a^2+b^2-c^2}{2ab} = -\frac{ab}{2ab} = -\frac{1}{2}$$

$$\therefore \quad C = 120°.$$

(b) If the sides be a, b, c then

$$\cos A = \frac{b^2+c^2-a^2}{2bc} = \frac{6+(4+2\sqrt{3})-4}{2\sqrt{6}(\sqrt{3}+1)}$$

$$\cos A = \frac{6+2\sqrt{3}}{\sqrt{2}(\sqrt{36}+\sqrt{12})} = \frac{1}{\sqrt{2}} \quad \therefore \quad A = 45°$$

$$\cos B = \frac{c^2+a^2-b^2}{2ca} = \frac{(4+2\sqrt{3})+4-6}{2 \cdot 2(\sqrt{3}+1)}$$

$$= \frac{2(\sqrt{3}+1)}{4(\sqrt{3}+1)} = \frac{1}{2} \quad \therefore \quad B = 60°$$

Hence $C = 180° - (A+B) = 75°$

(c) L.H.S. $= \dfrac{(a+b)^2 + (b-a)^2 - \cos C \cdot 4ab}{1 - \cos^2 C}$

$$= \frac{2[a^2+b^2-2ab\cos C]}{\sin^2 C} = 2\left(\frac{c}{\sin C}\right)^2$$

$$= 2\left(\frac{a}{\sin A}\right)^2$$

(d) Ans. 120°.
If we set $a = 2, b = 3$ and $c = \sqrt{19}$, then C is the greatest angle given by

$$\cos C = \frac{a^2+b^2-c^2}{2ab} = \frac{4+9-19}{2 \cdot 2 \cdot 3} = -\frac{1}{2}$$

$$\therefore \quad \angle C = 120°.$$

(e) Let the sides be $a-d, a, a+d$
It is understood that $a > d > 0$ and from the figure $\angle C$ is greatest and $\angle A$ is smallest.

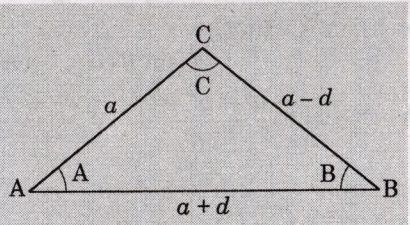

Fig. 1

By given condition $C = 2A$
and hence $B = \pi - (A+C) = \pi - 3A$
Hence by sine rule we have

$$\frac{a+d}{\sin C} = \frac{a-d}{\sin A} = \frac{a}{\sin B}$$

or $\dfrac{a+d}{\sin 2A} = \dfrac{a-d}{\sin A} = \dfrac{a}{\sin (\pi - 3A)}$

∴ $2 \cos A = \dfrac{a+d}{a-d}$ and $\dfrac{a}{a-d} = \dfrac{\sin 3A}{\sin A}$

∴ $\dfrac{a}{a-d} = 3 - 4 \sin^2 A = 3 - 4 + (2 \cos A)^2$

∴ $\dfrac{a}{a-d} = -1 + \left(\dfrac{a+d}{a-d}\right)^2 = \dfrac{4ad}{(a-d)^2}$

$a \neq 0$ ∴ $a - d = 4d$ or $a = 5d$

∴ sides are $a-d, a, a+d$

or $4d, 5d, 6d$

Hence the required ratio is $4 : 5 : 6$.

(f) **Ans. (d)** Let the sides a, b, c be $1\lambda, \sqrt{3}\lambda$ and 2λ respectively

Clearly $c^2 = a^2 + b^2$ ∴ $C = 90° = \dfrac{\pi}{2}$

$\cos A = \dfrac{b^2 + c^2 - a^2}{2bc} = \dfrac{\lambda^2 (3 + 4 - 1)}{\lambda^2 \, 4\sqrt{3}} = \dfrac{\sqrt{3}}{2}$

∴ $A = \pi/6$

and hence $B = \dfrac{\pi}{2} - A = \dfrac{\pi}{3}$ ∴ $A : B : C = 1 : 2 : 3$

Alt : By sine rule we can say that

$\sin A : \sin B : \sin C = \dfrac{1}{2} : \dfrac{\sqrt{3}}{2} : 1$

∴ $A = \dfrac{\pi}{6}, B = \dfrac{\pi}{3}$ and $C = \dfrac{\pi}{2}$

or $A : B : C = 1 : 2 : 3$

8. (a) Since $\cos A = \dfrac{\sin B}{2 \sin C}$, we have

$\dfrac{b^2 + c^2 - a^2}{2bc} = \dfrac{b}{2c}$

or $b^2 + c^2 - a^2 = b^2$ or $c^2 = a^2$.

Hence $c = a$ and so the ΔABC is isosceles.

(b) $\cos A (\sin B - \sin C) + (\sin 2B - \sin 2C) = 0$

or $\cos A (\sin B - \sin C)$
$\qquad\qquad + 2 \sin (B - C) \cos (B + C) = 0$

or $\cos A (\sin B - \sin C) - 2 \cos A \sin (B - C) = 0$

∴ either $\cos A = 0 \Rightarrow A = 90°$

or $(\sin B - \sin C)$
$\qquad\qquad - 2 (\sin B \cos C - \cos B \sin C) = 0$

∴ $(b - c) - 2\left(b \cdot \dfrac{a^2 + b^2 - c^2}{2ab} - c \cdot \dfrac{c^2 + a^2 - b^2}{2ca}\right) = 0$

or $a(b - c) - 2(b^2 - c^2) = 0$

$\Rightarrow (b - c)[a - 2(b + c)] = 0$

∴ $b - c = 0$ or $b = c$ ∴ Isosceles

(c) Combine first and third and put the value of $\cos B$

∴ $\dfrac{2}{ac} \cdot (b) + \dfrac{1}{b} \dfrac{c^2 + a^2 - b^2}{2ca} = \dfrac{a^2 + b^2}{abc}$

or $4b^2 + c^2 + a^2 - b^2 = 2a^2 + 2b^2$

∴ $b^2 + c^2 = a^2$ ∴ $\angle A = 90°$

9. $S = \tan A + \tan B = \dfrac{c^2}{ab}, P = \tan A \tan B = 1$

Now $\tan A \tan B = 1$

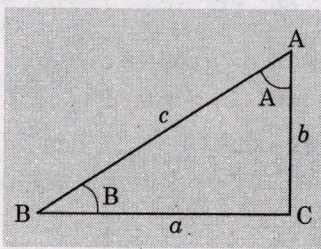

Fig. 2

$\Rightarrow \tan A = \cot B = \tan (90° - B)$

∴ $A = 90° - B$ or $A + B = 90°$

∴ $C = 90°$ ∴ $\cos C = 0$

Hence ΔABC is a rt. angled triangle.

∴ $\sin A = \dfrac{a}{c}, \sin B = \dfrac{b}{c}, a^2 + b^2 = c^2$ ...(1)

$\tan A = \dfrac{a}{b}, \tan B = \dfrac{b}{a}$

∴ $\tan A + \tan B = \dfrac{a^2 + b^2}{ab} = \dfrac{c^2}{ab}$

Again by (1) and $C = 90°$

$\sin^2 A + \sin^2 B + \sin^2 C = \dfrac{a^2}{c^2} + \dfrac{b^2}{c^2} + 1 = 1 + 1 = 2$

10. **Ans. (b).**

Use sin Rule. Add $2 \sin^2 B \sin^2 C$ to both sides to make perfect square.

$a^4 + b^4 + c^4 + 2b^2 c^2 - 2c^2 a^2 - 2a^2 b^2 = 3b^2 c^2$

or $(b^2 + c^2 - a^2)^2 = (\sqrt{3} bc)^2$

or $(2bc \cos A)^2 = 3b^2 c^2$ or $4 \cos^2 A = 3$

$\cos A = \pm \dfrac{\sqrt{3}}{2}$ ∴ $A = 30°$ or $150°$

11. (a) Since A, B, C are in A.P., we have $2B = A + C$

But $A + B + C = 180°$.

Hence $3B = 180°$ or $B = 60°$ and $A + C = 120°$

Now $b^2 = c^2 + a^2 - 2ca \cos B$
$= c^2 + a^2 - 2ca \cos 60°$
$= c^2 + a^2 - ca$ ...(1)

Hence $\dfrac{a+c}{\sqrt{(a^2 - ac + c^2)}} = \dfrac{a+c}{b}$ from (1)

$= \dfrac{k (\sin A + \sin C)}{k \sin B}$

$= \dfrac{2 \sin [(A + C)/2] \cos [(A - C)/2]}{\sin B}$

$= \dfrac{2 \sin 60° \cos \dfrac{A - C}{2}}{\sin 60°} = 2 \cos \left(\dfrac{A - C}{2}\right)$

(b) Ans. (b). We have $A + B + C = 180°$.
Also A, B, C are in A. P. $\Rightarrow 2B = A + C$.

$\therefore \quad 3B = 180°$ or $B = 60°$.

Now $b^2 = a^2 + c^2 - 2ac \cos B$

$\qquad = a^2 + c^2 - 2ac \cos 60°$

or $b^2 = a^2 + c^2 - ac$

(c) Ans. (a) and (d).
As in part (b), $\angle B = 60°$. Also $a = 10, b = 9$.

$\therefore \quad \cos B = (a^2 + c^2 - b^2)/2ac$

$\Rightarrow \quad \cos 60° = (100 + c^2 - 81)/(2.10 \, c)$

$\Rightarrow \quad 1/2 = (19 + c^2)/(20c) \Rightarrow 10c = 19 + c^2$

or $c^2 - 10c + 19 = 0$

$\therefore \quad c = \dfrac{10 \pm \sqrt{(100 - 76)}}{2} = 5 \pm \sqrt{6}$.

Since both the values of c are positive and less than both a and b, we have the answers (a).

(d) Ans. (a).
Angles in A.P. $\Rightarrow B = 60° \Rightarrow a^2 + c^2 - b^2 = ac$

Again $b^2 = ac$ given

$\therefore \quad a^2 + c^2 = 2b^2 \Rightarrow a^2, b^2, c^2$ are in A.P.

(e) Ans. (a). A, B, C in A.P. $\Rightarrow B = 60°$

$\qquad a^2 + c^2 - ac = b^2$ or $(a - c)^2 = b^2 - ac$

or $\quad |\sin A - \sin C| = \sqrt{\sin^2 B - \sin A \sin C}$

or $\quad \left| 2 \sin \dfrac{A - C}{2} \cos \dfrac{A + C}{2} \right| = \sqrt{\dfrac{3}{4} - \sin A \sin C}$

$\qquad\qquad\qquad\qquad\qquad\qquad (\because B = 60°)$

$\qquad \dfrac{\left| \sin \dfrac{A - C}{2} \right|}{\left| \dfrac{A - C}{2} \right|} = \dfrac{\sqrt{3 - 4 \sin A \sin C}}{|A - C|}$

Take limit of both sides when $A \to C$.

L.H. limit by $\underset{\theta \to 0}{\text{Lt}} \dfrac{\sin \theta}{\theta} = 1$

12. R.H.S. $= (b - c)^2 + 4bc \sin^2 (A/2)$

$\qquad = (b - c)^2 + 2bc (1 - \cos A)$

$\qquad = b^2 + c^2 - 2bc \cos A = a^2 \qquad \qquad ...(1)$

Now squaring the second relation,

$\qquad (b - c) \tan \phi = 2 \sqrt{bc} \sin (A/2)$

we get $(b - c)^2 \tan^2 \phi = 4bc \sin^2 (A/2) \qquad ...(2)$

Putting the value of $4bc \sin^2 (A/2)$ from (2) in (1), we get

$\qquad a^2 = (b - c)^2 + (b - c)^2 \tan^2 \phi$

$\qquad = (b - c)^2 \sec^2 \phi$

or $\quad a = (b - c) \sec \phi$.

13. (a) We have $\dfrac{b + c}{a} = \dfrac{k \sin B + k \sin C}{k \sin A}$

$\qquad = \dfrac{2 \sin [(B + C)/2] \cos [(B - C)/2]}{2 \sin (A/2) \cos (A/2)}$

$\qquad = \dfrac{\cos (A/2) \cos [(B - C)/2]}{\sin (A/2) \cos (A/2)}$

$\qquad = \dfrac{\cos [(B - C)/2]}{\sin (A/2)} = \dfrac{\sin [(A/2) + B]}{\sin (A/2)}$.

$\because \quad \sin [(B + C)/2] = \sin (\pi/2 - A/2) = \cos (A/2)$

and $\dfrac{(B - C)}{2} = \dfrac{1}{2}[B - (\pi - A - B)] = \dfrac{1}{2}[A + 2B - \pi]$

$\therefore \quad \cos [(B - C)/2] = \sin [(A/2) + B]$

(b) Do yourself.

14. (a) Do yourself. Use sine rule.

(b) Ans. (c).

$\qquad \sin A + \dfrac{1}{\sin A} + 1 > 2 + 1 = 3$ by A.M. $\geq$ G.M.

Each term is > 3

$\therefore \quad E > 3.3.3 = 27$

15. (a) $\dfrac{1 + \cos (A - B) \cos C}{1 + \cos (A - C) \cos B}$

$\qquad = \dfrac{1 - \cos (A - B) \cos (A + B)}{1 - \cos (A - C) \cos (A + C)}$.

$\qquad [\because A + B + C = \pi$ so that $\cos C = - \cos (A + B)]$.

$\qquad = \dfrac{1 - (\cos^2 A - \sin^2 B)}{1 - (\cos^2 A - \sin^2 C)}$

$\qquad = \dfrac{\sin^2 A + \sin^2 B}{\sin^2 A + \sin^2 C} = \dfrac{a^2 + b^2}{a^2 + c^2}$.

(b) $a (\cos B \cos C + \cos A)$

$\qquad = a \{\cos B \cos C - \cos (B + C)\}$

$\qquad = a \{\cos B \cos C - \cos B \cos C + \sin B \sin C\}$

$\qquad = a \sin B \sin C = k \sin A \sin B \sin C$

Similarly $b (\cos C \cos A + \cos B)$

$\qquad = c (\cos A \cos B + \cos C)$

$\qquad = k \sin A \sin B \sin C$.

(c) Do yourself. $\tan A = \sin A / \cos A$. Now sides.

16. (a) $\dfrac{c}{a - b} = \dfrac{k \sin C}{k \sin A - k \sin B}$

$\qquad = \dfrac{2 \sin (C/2) \cos (C/2)}{2 \cos [(A + B)/2] \sin [(A - B)/2]}$

$\qquad = \dfrac{\sin (C/2) \sin [(A + B)/2]}{\sin (C/2) \sin [(A - B)/2]}$

$\qquad\qquad [\because \cos \{(A + B)/2\} = \sin (C/2)$

and $\cos (C/2) = \sin \{(A + B)/2\}$

$\qquad = \dfrac{\sin \dfrac{A}{2} \cos \dfrac{B}{2} + \cos \dfrac{A}{2} \sin \dfrac{B}{2}}{\sin \dfrac{A}{2} \cos \dfrac{B}{2} - \cos \dfrac{A}{2} \sin \dfrac{B}{2}} = \dfrac{\tan \dfrac{A}{2} + \tan \dfrac{B}{2}}{\tan \dfrac{A}{2} - \tan \dfrac{B}{2}}$.

[Dividing both N^r and D^r by $\cos (A/2) \cos (B/2)$].

(b) Do yourself.

(c) Do yourself.
You could use results of **11 P. 645**.

$\qquad$ Area $= \dfrac{1}{2} ab \sin C = \dfrac{1}{2} a^2 \cdot \dfrac{b}{a} \sin C$

$$= \frac{1}{2} a^2 \frac{\sin B \sin C}{\sin A}$$

17. L.H.S. $= \cos^2\left(\frac{B-C}{2}\right) \Big/ k^2 (\sin B + \sin C)^2$

$$+ \sin^2\left(\frac{B-C}{2}\right) \Big/ k^2 (\sin B - \sin C)^2$$

$$= 1/4\, k^2 \sin^2\left(\frac{B+C}{2}\right) + 1/4\, k^2 \cos^2\left(\frac{B+C}{2}\right)$$

$$= \left\{ \cos^2\left(\frac{B+C}{2}\right) + \sin^2\left(\frac{B+C}{2}\right) \right\}$$

$$\div k^2 \left(2 \sin \frac{B+C}{2} \cos \frac{B+C}{2} \right)^2$$

$$= 1/k^2 \sin^2(B+C) = 1/k^2 \sin^2 A = 1/a^2.$$

18. (a) $\dfrac{a^2 \sin(B-C)}{\sin B + \sin C} = \dfrac{k^2 \sin^2 A \sin(B-C)}{\sin B + \sin C}$

$$= \frac{k^2 \sin A \sin(B+C) \sin(B-C)}{\sin B + \sin C}$$

$$= \frac{k^2 \sin A (\sin^2 B - \sin^2 C)}{\sin B + \sin C}$$

$$= k^2 \sin A (\sin B - \sin C).$$

$\therefore$ L.H.S. $= k^2 [\sin A (\sin B - \sin C)$

$$+ \sin B (\sin C - \sin A) + \sin C (\sin A - \sin B)] = 0$$

(b) Do yourself.

$a = k \sin A = k \sin(B+C)$ etc.

19. (a) $a \sin \dfrac{1}{2} A \sin \dfrac{1}{2}(B-C)$

$$= a \cos \frac{B+C}{2} \sin \frac{B-C}{2}$$

$$= \frac{a}{2} 2 \sin \frac{B-C}{2} \cos \frac{B+C}{2}$$

$$= \frac{a}{2}(\sin B - \sin C)$$

$$= \frac{k}{2} \sin A (\sin B - \sin C).$$

Hence L.H.S. $= \dfrac{k}{2} \Sigma \sin A (\sin B - \sin C) = 0.$

(b) Do yourself.

Change $\cos^2$ to $\sin^2$, $\Sigma a^2 (b^2 - c^2) = 0$

(c) $(b-c) \cot \dfrac{A}{2} = (b-c) \sqrt{\dfrac{s(s-a)}{(s-b)(s-c)}}$

$$= \frac{(b-c)\, s(s-a)}{S}$$

$\therefore$ $\Sigma (b-c) \cot \dfrac{A}{2} = \Sigma \dfrac{s}{S}(b-c)(s-a)$

$$= \frac{s}{S}[s\,\Sigma(b-c) - \Sigma a(b-c)] = 0$$

Alt. $(b-c) \cot \dfrac{A}{2} = k(\sin B - \sin C) \cot \dfrac{A}{2}$

$$= 2k \sin \frac{B-C}{2} \cos \frac{B+C}{2} \cdot \frac{\cos(A/2)}{\sin(A/2)}$$

$$= k \cdot 2 \sin \frac{B-C}{2} \sin \frac{B+C}{2}$$

$$= -k (\cos B - \cos C) \text{ etc.}$$

20. (a) $\dfrac{a \sin(B-C)}{b^2 - c^2} = \dfrac{k \sin A \sin(B-C)}{k^2 (\sin^2 B - \sin^2 C)}$

$$= \frac{1}{k} \cdot \frac{\sin(B+C) \sin(B-C)}{\sin^2 B - \sin^2 C} = \frac{1}{k}$$

$$[\because \sin(B+C) \sin(B-C) = \sin^2 B - \sin^2 C]$$

Similarly $\dfrac{b \sin(C-A)}{c^2 - a^2} = \dfrac{c \sin(A-B)}{a^2 - b^2} = \dfrac{1}{k}.$

(b) $a^2 - 2ab \cos(60° + C)$

$$= a^2 - 2ab (\cos 60° \cos C - \sin 60° \sin C)$$

$$= a^2 - 2ab \cdot \left(\frac{1}{2} \cos C - \frac{\sqrt{3}}{2} \sin C \right)$$

$$= a^2 - ab \cdot \frac{a^2 + b^2 - c^2}{2ab} + \sqrt{3}\, ab \sin C$$

$$= \frac{a^2 - b^2 + c^2}{2} + \sqrt{3} k\, abc.$$

Similarly we can prove that

$$c^2 - 2bc \cos(60° + A) = \frac{c^2 - b^2 + a^2}{2} + \sqrt{3} k\, abc.$$

21. (a) $a^3 \sin(B-C) = k^3 \sin^3 A \sin(B-C)$

$$= k^3 \sin^2 A \sin(B+C) \sin(B-C)$$

$$[\because \sin A = \sin(B+C)]$$

$$= k^3 \sin^2 A (\sin^2 B - \sin^2 C)$$

Hence L.H.S. $= k^3 [\sin^2 A (\sin^2 B - \sin^2 C)$

$$+ \sin^2 B (\sin^2 C - \sin^2 A)$$

$$+ \sin^2 C (\sin^2 A - \sin^2 B)] = 0$$

(b) $\dfrac{b^2 - c^2}{\cos B + \cos C} = \dfrac{k^2 (\sin^2 B - \sin^2 C)}{\cos B + \cos C}$

$$= -k^2 \frac{(\cos^2 B - \cos^2 C)}{\cos B + \cos C}$$

$\therefore$ L.H.S. $= -k^2 \Sigma (\cos B - \cos C) = 0.$

22. (a) Let $A, 2A, 3A$ be the angles.

Then $A + 2A + 3A = 180°$ or $A = 30°$.

The angles are $30°, 60°$ and $90°$.

If a, b, c denote the sides opposite to these angles, then

$$\frac{a}{\sin 30°} = \frac{b}{\sin 60°} = \frac{c}{\sin 90°}$$

$\therefore$ $a : b : c = \sin 30° : \sin 60° : \sin 90°$

$$= 1/2 : \sqrt{3}/2 : 1 = 1 : \sqrt{3} : 2$$

(b) $A + B + C = A + 2A + 4A = 7A = \pi$

$\therefore$ $A = \dfrac{\pi}{7}$

Hence the angles are $A = \dfrac{\pi}{7}, B = \dfrac{2\pi}{7}, C = \dfrac{4\pi}{7}$

Now by sine Rule $\dfrac{a}{\sin A} = \lambda$ (say) ...(1)

R.H.S. $= \lambda^6 (\sin^2 B - \sin^2 A)(\sin^2 C - \sin^2 B)$

$$(\sin^2 A - \sin^2 C)$$

$$= \lambda^6 [\sin (B+A).\sin (B-A)]$$

$$[\sin (C+B).\sin (C-B)]$$

$$[\sin (A+C) \sin (A-C)]$$

$$= \lambda^6 \left(\sin \dfrac{3\pi}{7} \cdot \sin \dfrac{\pi}{7} \right)\left(\sin \dfrac{6\pi}{7} \cdot \sin \dfrac{2\pi}{7} \right)$$

$$\left(\sin \dfrac{5\pi}{7} \cdot \sin \dfrac{3\pi}{7} \right)$$

$$\sin \dfrac{6\pi}{7} = \sin \left(\pi - \dfrac{\pi}{7} \right) = \sin \dfrac{\pi}{7}$$

$$\sin \dfrac{5\pi}{7} = \sin \left(\pi - \dfrac{2\pi}{7} \right) = \sin \dfrac{2\pi}{7}$$

$$\sin \dfrac{3\pi}{7} = \sin \left(\pi - \dfrac{4\pi}{7} \right) = \sin \dfrac{4\pi}{7}$$

$\therefore$ R.H.S. $= \lambda^6 \left(\sin^2 \dfrac{\pi}{7} \cdot \sin^2 \dfrac{2\pi}{7} \cdot \sin^2 \dfrac{4\pi}{7} \right)$

$$= (\lambda^2 \sin^2 A)(\lambda^2 \sin^2 B)(\lambda^2 \sin^2 C)$$

$$= a^2 b^2 c^2 = \text{L.H.S.} \qquad \text{by (1)}$$

(c) Ans. (c). $4A + A + A = 180° \Rightarrow A = 30°$

$\therefore$ Angles are $120°, 30°, 30°$

$\therefore \quad \dfrac{\sin 120°}{a} = \dfrac{\sin 30°}{b} = \dfrac{\sin 30°}{c} = k$, say

$\therefore \quad \dfrac{a}{a+b+c} = \dfrac{k}{k} \dfrac{\sin 120°}{\sin 120° + \sin 30° + \sin 30°}$

$$= \dfrac{\sqrt{3}}{2 + \sqrt{3}}.$$

23. (a) Since $a \cos A = b \cos B$, we have

$\qquad k \sin A \cos A = k \sin B \cos B$

or $\quad \sin 2A = \sin 2B$.

$\therefore \quad 2A = 2B$ or $\pi - 2B$

$\therefore \quad A = B$, i.e. the $\Delta\ ABC$ is isosceles

or $\quad A + B = \pi/2$ so that $C = \pi/2$, i.e. $\Delta\ ABC$ is right angled at C.

(b) $\dfrac{\sin (A-B)}{\sin (A+B)} = \dfrac{k^2 (\sin^2 A - \sin^2 B)}{k^2 (\sin^2 A + \sin^2 B)}$

$\qquad\qquad\qquad$ by sine formula

or $\quad \dfrac{\sin (A-B)}{\sin C} = \dfrac{\sin (A-B) \sin (A+B)}{\sin^2 A + \sin^2 B}$

or $\quad \sin (A-B)\left[\dfrac{1}{\sin C} - \dfrac{\sin C}{\sin^2 A + \sin^2 B} \right] = 0$

$\therefore$ Either $\sin (A-B) = 0$ $\therefore A = B$ i.e. Δ is isosceles

or $\quad \sin^2 A + \sin^2 B = \sin^2 C$ or $a^2 + b^2 = c^2$

$\therefore \quad \Delta$ is rt. angled.

24. (a) Ans. (b). We have

$$\dfrac{\sin A}{a} = \dfrac{\sin B}{b} \Rightarrow \sin B = \dfrac{b}{a} \sin A$$

since $a = 3, b = 4, \sin A = \dfrac{3}{4}$,

we get $\sin B = \dfrac{4}{3} \times \dfrac{3}{4} = 1$ $\therefore$ $B = 90°$.

(b) Ans. True. Let the angles of triangle be $\alpha, 2\alpha$ and 7α so that $\alpha + 2\alpha + 7\alpha = 180°$, giving $\alpha = 18°$.

$\therefore$ Angles of the triangle are $A = 18°$, $B = 36°$, and $C = 126°$. Then a is least and c, the greatest side. Hence

$\dfrac{a}{\sin A} = \dfrac{c}{\sin C} \Rightarrow \dfrac{a}{\sin 18°} = \dfrac{c}{\sin 126°}$

$\Rightarrow \dfrac{c}{a} = \dfrac{\sin 126°}{\sin 18°} = \dfrac{\cos 36°}{\sin 18°} = \dfrac{(\sqrt{5}+1)/4}{(\sqrt{5}-1)/4} = \dfrac{\sqrt{5}+1}{\sqrt{5}-1}.$

25. (a) Ans. $90° + 23° = 113°$, By sine rule

$$AD = c \sin B = \dfrac{\sin A \sin B . c}{\sin^2 B - \sin^2 C} \qquad \text{(given)}$$

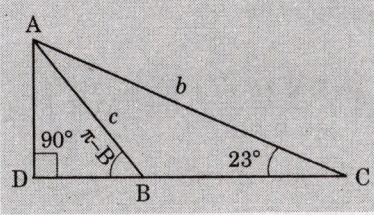

Fig. 3

$\therefore \quad \sin (B+C) \sin (B-C) = \sin A$

or $\quad \sin (B-C) = 1 = \sin 90°$

$\therefore \quad B = 90° + C$

(b) False. $A = 30° \Rightarrow B + C = 150°$

$\quad \Delta = \dfrac{\sqrt{3}\ a^2}{4} = \dfrac{1}{2} ab \sin C$ $\therefore$ $\dfrac{\sqrt{3}}{2} a = b \sin C$

or $\quad \sin B \sin C = \dfrac{\sqrt{3}}{2} \sin A = \dfrac{\sqrt{3}}{2} \cdot \dfrac{1}{2} = \dfrac{\sqrt{3}}{4}$ ...(1)

$\cos (B+C) = \cos 150° = -\cos 30° = -\dfrac{\sqrt{3}}{2}$

$\therefore \quad \cos B \cos C - \sin B \sin C = -\dfrac{\sqrt{3}}{2}$

or $\quad \cos B \cos C = \dfrac{\sqrt{3}}{4} - \dfrac{\sqrt{3}}{2} = -\dfrac{\sqrt{3}}{4}$ ...(2)

$\therefore \quad \tan B \tan C = -1$ by (1) and (2)

$\therefore \quad \tan B = -\cot C = \tan (90° + C)$

$\therefore \quad B - C = 90°$

Also $B + C = 150°$ $\therefore B = 120°$ and $C = 30°$

26. $E = \dfrac{2s . 2(s-a) . 2(s-b) . 2(s-c)}{4b^2 c^2}$

$$= \dfrac{4}{b^2 c^2} . S^2 = \dfrac{4}{b^2 c^2} \cdot \left(\dfrac{1}{2} bc \sin A \right)^2 = \sin^2 A$$

27. (a) R.H.S. $= k \sin C \cos (A - \theta) + k \sin A \cos (C + \theta)$

$\qquad = k [\sin C \cos A \cos \theta + \sin C \sin A \sin \theta$

$\qquad\qquad + \sin A \cos C \cos \theta - \sin A \sin C \sin \theta]$

$= k \cos\theta (\sin A \cos C + \cos A \sin C)$
$= k \cos\theta \sin(A+C) = k \sin B \cos\theta = b \cos\theta.$

(b) From the given relation

$$\sin C = \frac{1 - \cos A \cos B}{\sin A \sin B} \le 1 \qquad \dots(1)$$

$\Rightarrow \quad 1 \le \cos A \cos B + \sin A \sin B$

or $\quad 1 \le \cos(A-B)$ or $\cos(A-B) \ge 1$

$\Rightarrow \quad \cos(A-B) = 1 \Rightarrow A - B = 0$

$\therefore \quad A = B \qquad \because \cos(A-B) \ngtr 1 \qquad \dots(2)$

Hence from (1)

$$\sin C = \frac{1 - \cos^2 A}{\sin^2 A} = \frac{\sin^2 A}{\sin^2 A} = 1$$

$\therefore \quad C = 90° \quad \therefore \quad A + B = 90°$

or $\quad A = B = 45°$, by (2)

$a : b : c = \sin A : \sin B : \sin C$

$$= \frac{1}{\sqrt 2} : \frac{1}{\sqrt 2} : 1 = 1 : 1 : \sqrt 2$$

28. (a) $x = (b^2 - c^2)\dfrac{\sin(B+C)}{\sin(B-C)}$

$$= \frac{\sin^2(B+C)}{\sin^2 B - \sin^2 C} \cdot k^2 (\sin^2 B - \sin^2 C)$$

$$= k^2 \sin^2 A = a^2$$

Similarly $y = b^2$ and $z = c^2$

Obviously a^2, b^2, c^2 are also in G.P. as a, b, c are in G.P.

(b) Altitudes PD, QE and RF are $q \sin R, r \sin P, p \sin Q$ where p, q, r are the sides

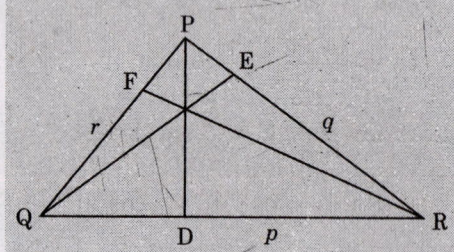

Fig. 4

Apply sine rule.

or $\quad k \sin Q \sin R, k \sin R \sin P, k \sin P \sin Q$

or $\quad \dfrac{k \sin P \sin Q \sin R}{\sin P}, \dfrac{k \sin P \sin Q \sin R}{\sin Q},$

$$\frac{k \sin P \sin Q \sin R}{\sin R}$$

But $\sin P, \sin Q, \sin R$ are in A.P.

$\therefore \quad$ Altitudes are in H.P.

29. (a) We have $\cos A + 2\cos B + \cos C = 2$

or $\quad \cos A + \cos C = 2(1 - \cos B)$

or $\quad 2\cos\dfrac{A+C}{2}\cos\dfrac{A-C}{2} = 2 \cdot 2\sin^2\dfrac{B}{2}$

or $\quad \cos\dfrac{A-C}{2} = 2\sin\dfrac{B}{2} \quad \left[\because \cos\dfrac{A+C}{2} = \sin\dfrac{B}{2}\right]$

Multiplying both sides by $2\cos\dfrac{B}{2}$, we get

$$2\cos\frac{B}{2}\cos\frac{A-C}{2} = 2\left(2\sin\frac{B}{2}\cos\frac{B}{2}\right)$$

or $\quad 2\sin\dfrac{A+C}{2}\cos\dfrac{A-C}{2} = 2\sin B,$

or $\quad \sin A + \sin C = 2\sin B$ or $a + c = 2b$

$\therefore \quad a, b, c$ are in A.P.

(b) Ans. False. Correct is A.P.

(c) Ans. (b), (c).

$$2\cos\frac{B+C}{2}\cos\frac{B-C}{2} = 4\sin^2\frac{A}{2}$$

or $\quad \sin\dfrac{A}{2}\cos\dfrac{B-C}{2} = 2\sin^2\dfrac{A}{2}$ Cancel $\sin\dfrac{A}{2} \ne 0$

or $\quad \cos\dfrac{B-C}{2} = 2\sin\dfrac{A}{2} = 2\cos\dfrac{B+C}{2}$

$\therefore \quad \dfrac{\cos\dfrac{B-C}{2}}{\cos\dfrac{B+C}{2}} = \dfrac{2}{1}$ Apply Compo. & Divi.

$$\frac{2\sin(B/2)\sin(C/2)}{2\cos(B/2)\cos(C/2)} = \frac{1}{3}$$

or $\quad \tan\dfrac{B}{2}\tan\dfrac{C}{2} = \dfrac{1}{3}$

or $\quad \dfrac{s-a}{s} = \dfrac{1}{3}$ **(See page 645)**

or $\quad 2s = 3a$ or $b + c = 2a \Rightarrow$ (b)

Also $AC + AB > BC$

Hence locus of point A is an ellipse.

30. (a) $\cot\dfrac{1}{2}A, \cot\dfrac{1}{2}B, \cot\dfrac{1}{2}C$ are in A.P.

if $\quad 2\cot\dfrac{1}{2}B = \cot\dfrac{1}{2}A + \cot\dfrac{1}{2}C$

i.e. if $2\sqrt{\left\{\dfrac{s(s-b)}{(s-c)(s-a)}\right\}} = \sqrt{\left\{\dfrac{s(s-a)}{(s-b)(s-c)}\right\}}$

$$+ \sqrt{\left\{\frac{s(s-c)}{(s-a)(s-b)}\right\}}$$

i.e., if $\quad 2(s-b) = (s-a) + (s-c)$

i.e., if $\quad 2b = a + c$

i.e., if $\quad a, b, c$ are in A.P.

(b) We have $\cos A \cot\dfrac{1}{2}A = \left(1 - 2\sin^2\dfrac{1}{2}A\right) \cdot \dfrac{\cos\dfrac{1}{2}A}{\sin\dfrac{1}{2}A}$

$$= \cot\frac{1}{2}A - \sin A.$$

Now a, b, c are in A.P.

$\therefore \quad \sin A, \sin B, \sin C$ are also in A.P.

Also we have proved in part (i) that $\cot(A/2)$, $\cot(B/2), \cot(C/2)$ are in A.P. Hence their differences are also in A.P.

(c) L.H.S. $= \dfrac{1}{2}\{a(1+\cos C) + c(1+\cos A)\}$

$\qquad = \dfrac{1}{2}(a+c) + \dfrac{1}{2}\{a\cos C + c\cos A\}$

$\qquad = b + \dfrac{1}{2}b = \dfrac{3}{2}b.$

(d) By result **11 P. 645** we have

$$\tan\frac{A}{2} + \tan\frac{C}{2} = \frac{b}{s}\cot\frac{B}{2} = \frac{2b}{2s}\cot\frac{B}{2}$$

where $2s = a + b + c = b + 2b = 3b$

$\therefore \quad \tan\dfrac{A}{2} + \tan\dfrac{C}{2} = \dfrac{2}{3}\cot\dfrac{B}{2}$

Note : In the examination you should prove the result **11 as on P. 645.**

31. (a) $b^2 - a^2 = c^2 - b^2$

$\qquad \sin^2 B - \sin^2 A = \sin^2 C - \sin^2 B$

or $\quad \sin(B+A)\sin(B-A)$
$\qquad\qquad = \sin(C+B)\sin(C-B)$

or $\quad \sin C(\sin B\cos A - \cos B\sin A)$
$\qquad\qquad = \sin A(\sin C\cos B - \cos C\sin B)$

Divide each term by $\sin A\sin B\sin C$

$\therefore \quad \cot A - \cot B = \cot B - \cot C$

$\therefore \quad \cot A, \cot B, \cot C$ are in A.P.

(b) $\sin A = \sin(B+C)$

$\therefore \quad \sin^2 B - \sin^2 C = \sin^2 A - \sin^2 B$

or $\quad 2b^2 = a^2 + c^2$ by sine rule

$\therefore \quad a^2, b^2, c^2$ are in A.P.

32. $\dfrac{1}{b} - \dfrac{1}{a} = \dfrac{1}{c} - \dfrac{1}{b}$

$\Rightarrow \quad \dfrac{(\sin A - \sin B)}{\sin A\sin B} = \dfrac{\sin B - \sin C}{\sin B\sin C}.$

or $\quad \dfrac{2\sin\dfrac{A-B}{2}\cos\dfrac{A+B}{2}}{2\sin(A/2)\cos(A/2)}$

$\quad = \dfrac{2\sin\dfrac{B-C}{2}\cos\dfrac{B+C}{2}}{2\sin(C/2)\cos(C/2)}$

or $\quad \sin^2\dfrac{C}{2}\cos\dfrac{C}{2}\sin\dfrac{A-B}{2}$

$\quad = \sin^2\dfrac{A}{2}\cos\dfrac{A}{2}\sin\dfrac{B-C}{2}$

or $\quad \sin^2\dfrac{C}{2}\sin\dfrac{A+B}{2}\sin\dfrac{A-B}{2}$

$\quad = \sin^2\dfrac{A}{2}\sin\dfrac{B+C}{2}\sin\dfrac{B-C}{2}$

or $\quad \sin^2\dfrac{C}{2}\left(\sin^2\dfrac{A}{2} - \sin^2\dfrac{B}{2}\right)$

$\qquad = \sin^2\dfrac{A}{2}\left(\sin^2\dfrac{B}{2} - \sin^2\dfrac{C}{2}\right)$

Divide by $\sin^2(A/2)\sin^2(B/2)\sin^2(C/2)$

$\therefore \quad \dfrac{1}{\sin^2(B/2)} - \dfrac{1}{\sin^2(A/2)}$

$\quad = \dfrac{1}{\sin^2(C/2)} - \dfrac{1}{\sin^2(B/2)}$

$\therefore \quad \dfrac{1}{\sin^2(A/2)}, \dfrac{1}{\sin^2(B/2)}, \dfrac{1}{\sin^2(C/2)}$ are in A.P.

or $\quad \sin^2(A/2), \sin^2(B/2), \sin^2(C/2)$ are in H.P.

33. (a) L.H.S. $= 2(s-a)\dfrac{\sin\dfrac{B+C}{2}}{\sin\dfrac{B}{2}\sin\dfrac{C}{2}}$

$\quad = \dfrac{2(s-a)\cdot\cos(A/2)}{\left[\dfrac{(s-c)(s-a)}{ca}\cdot\dfrac{(s-a)(s-b)}{ab}\right]^{1/2}}$

$\quad = \dfrac{2a\cos(A/2)}{\left[\dfrac{(s-b)(s-c)}{bc}\right]^{1/2}}$

$\quad = 2a\dfrac{\cos(A/2)}{\sin(A/2)} = 2a\cot\dfrac{A}{2}$

(b) $2s\cdot\dfrac{c}{s}\cot\dfrac{C}{2} = 2c\cot\dfrac{C}{2}$

as proved in **Q. 11 (ii) P. 645.**

34. (a) L.H.S. $= \dfrac{\sin[(A+B)/2]}{\sin(A/2)\sin(B/2)} \times$

$\qquad k\{\sin A\sin^2(B/2) + \sin B\sin^2(A/2)\}$

$\because \quad a/(\sin A) = k$, etc.

Cancel $\sin A/2\sin B/2$ from N^r and D^r

$\therefore \quad$ L.H.S. $= \cos(C/2)\cdot k\{2\cos(A/2)\sin(B/2)$
$\qquad\qquad\qquad\qquad + 2\cos(B/2)\sin(A/2)\}$

$\quad = \cos\dfrac{C}{2}\cdot\dfrac{c}{\sin C}\cdot 2\sin\left(\dfrac{A+B}{2}\right)$

$\quad = c\cdot\dfrac{2\cos^2(C/2)}{2\sin(C/2)\cos(C/2)} = c\cot\dfrac{C}{2}.$

Note : You may also use the values of $\cot(A/2)$, $\sin(A/2)$ in terms of s.

(b) $1 - \tan\dfrac{1}{2}A\tan\dfrac{1}{2}B$ \hfill **(Use R. 11 P. 645)**

$\quad = 1 - \sqrt{\left(\dfrac{(s-b)(s-c)}{s(s-a)}\right)}\cdot\sqrt{\left(\dfrac{(s-c)(s-a)}{s(s-b)}\right)}$

$\quad = 1 - \dfrac{s-c}{s} = \dfrac{c}{s} = \dfrac{2c}{2s} = \dfrac{2c}{a+b+c}.$

35. (a) $2abc\cos\dfrac{1}{2}A\cos\dfrac{1}{2}B\cos\dfrac{1}{2}C$

$\quad = 2abc\sqrt{\left(\dfrac{s(s-a)}{bc}\right)}\cdot\sqrt{\left(\dfrac{s(s-b)}{ca}\right)}\cdot\sqrt{\left(\dfrac{s(s-c)}{ab}\right)}$

$= 2s\sqrt{s(s-a)(s-b)(s-c)} = (a+b+c)\,S.$

(b) $bc\cos^2\dfrac{1}{2}A = bc\cdot\dfrac{s(s-a)}{bc} = s(s-a).$

$\therefore$ L.H.S. $= s[(s-a)+(s-b)+(s-c)]$

$= s[3s - s(a+b+c)] = 3s^2 - s\cdot2s$

$= 3s^2 - 2s^2 = s^2.$

(c) $\dfrac{b-c}{a}\cos^2\dfrac{A}{2} = \dfrac{b-c}{a}\cdot\dfrac{s(s-a)}{bc} = \dfrac{s(s-a)(b-c)}{abc}$

$\therefore$ L.H.S. $= \dfrac{s}{abc}[(s-a)(b-c)$

$+ (s-b)(c-a) + (s-c)(a-b)]$

$= \dfrac{s}{abc}[s\{b-c+c-a+a-b\}$

$-\{a(b-c)+b(c-a)+c(a-b)\}]$

$= \dfrac{s}{abc}\times 0 = 0.$

36. Putting $\tan\dfrac{1}{2}A = \sqrt{\left(\dfrac{(s-b)(s-c)}{s(s-a)}\right)}$ etc.,

we have, L.H.S.

$= \left[\dfrac{\sqrt{\left\{\dfrac{(s-b)(s-c)}{s(s-a)}\right\}}}{(a-b)(a-c)} + \dfrac{\sqrt{\left\{\dfrac{(s-c)(s-a)}{s(s-b)}\right\}}}{(b-c)(b-a)}\right.$

$\left. + \dfrac{\sqrt{\left\{\dfrac{(s-a)(s-b)}{s(s-c)}\right\}}}{(c-a)(c-b)}\right].$

$= \dfrac{(c-b)(s-b)(s-c)+(a-c)(s-c)(s-a)}{+(b-a)(s-a)(s-b)}{(a-b)(b-c)(c-a)\sqrt{[s(s-a)(s-b)(s-c)]}}.$ ...(1)

$N^r = -\Sigma\{(b-c)\{s^2 - s(b+c)+bc\}$

$= -s^2\,\Sigma(b-c) + s\Sigma(b^2-c^2) - \Sigma bc(b-c)$

$= 0 + 0 + (b-c)(c-a)(a-b)$

Note that on simplification,

$bc(b-c) + ca(c-a) + ab(a-b)$

$= -(b-c)(c-a)(a-b)].$

Substituting in (1), we get

L.H.S. $= \dfrac{N^r}{D^r} = \dfrac{1}{\sqrt{[s(s-a)(s-b)(s-c)]}} = \dfrac{1}{S}.$

37. (a) Ans. $\dfrac{1}{4}$.

$S = \dfrac{1}{2}bc\sin A = (a+b-c)(a-b+c)$

or $\sin\dfrac{A}{2}\cos\dfrac{A}{2} = \dfrac{2(s-b)\cdot2(s-c)}{bc} = 4\sin^2\dfrac{A}{2}$

$\therefore$ $\tan\dfrac{A}{2} = \dfrac{1}{4}.$

(b) Since $b+c=3a$, we have $\sin B + \sin C = 3\sin A$

or $2\sin\dfrac{B+C}{2}\cos\dfrac{B-C}{2} = 6\sin\dfrac{A}{2}\cos\dfrac{A}{2}$

or $\cos\dfrac{B-C}{2} = 3\sin\dfrac{A}{2}$ $\left[\because \sin\dfrac{B+C}{2} = \cos\dfrac{A}{2}\right]$

or $\cos\dfrac{B-C}{2} = 3\cos\dfrac{B+C}{2}$

or $\left\{\cos\dfrac{B-C}{2}\right\}\Big/\left\{\cos\dfrac{B+C}{2}\right\} = \dfrac{3}{1}$

Apply C and D $\therefore$ $\cot(B/2)\cot(C/2) = 2$

Converse Method :

On putting the values of $\cot(B/2)$ and $\cot(C/2)$ in R.H.S., you will get

$s/(s-a) = 2$ or $s = 2a$

or $a+b+c = 4a$ $\therefore$ $b+c = 3a.$

This proves the converse.

(c) Do yourself.

Problem Set (2)

Formulae for $\sin\dfrac{A}{2}$ and $\tan\dfrac{A}{2}$, Area of a triangle and quadrilateral. Miscellaneous type.

1. (a)* $a^3\cos(B-C) + b^3\cos(C-A)$

$+ c^3\cos(A-B) = 3abc.$

(b) $\sin^3 A\cos(B-C) + \sin^3 B\cos(C-A)$

$+ \sin^3 C\cos(A-B)$

$= 3\sin A\sin B\sin C.$

2. $a^3\cos B\cos C + b^3\cos C\cos A + c^3\cos A\cos B$

$= abc(1 - 2\cos A\cos B\cos C).$

3. (a)* In a triangle ABC, if

$\tan\dfrac{1}{2}A = \dfrac{5}{6}$ and $\tan\dfrac{1}{2}B = \dfrac{20}{37}$

find $\tan\dfrac{1}{2}C$, and prove that in this triangle

$a+c = 2b.$

(b) In a triangle ABC, if

$\dfrac{\cot(A/2)}{1} = \dfrac{\cot(B/2)}{4} = \dfrac{\cot(C/2)}{15}$ then $a:b:c$ is

(a) $5:16:19$ (b) $19:16:5$

(c) $16:19:5$ (d) $9:6:5$

4. In an isosceles right angled triangle a straight line is drawn from the middle point of one of the equal sides to the opposite angle. Show that it divides the angle into two parts whose cotangents are 2 and 3.

5.* The sides of a triangle are in A.P. and the greatest angle exceeds the least by $90°$, prove that the sides are proportional to $\sqrt{7}+1, \sqrt{7}$ and $\sqrt{7}-1$.

6. The sides of a triangle are in A.P. and its area is $\frac{3}{5}$th of an equilateral triangle of same perimeter. Prove that its sides are in the ratio $3:5:7$.

7.* The sides of a triangle are three consecutive natural numbers and its largest angle is twice the smallest one. Determine the sides of the triangle. **(I.I.T. 1991)**

8.* If the sides of a triangle are in A.P. , and if its greatest angle exceeds the least angle by α, show that the sides are in the ratio $1-x:1:1+x$ where $x=\sqrt{\left(\frac{1-\cos\alpha}{7-\cos\alpha}\right)}$.

9. If in a triangle ABC, we define

$$x=\tan\frac{B-C}{2}\tan\frac{A}{2},$$

$$y=\tan\frac{C-A}{2}\tan\frac{B}{2}, z=\tan\frac{A-B}{2}\tan\frac{C}{2},$$

then show that $x+y+z=-xyz$. **(EAMCET 1993)**

10. (a)* If in a triangle ABC, $\angle C=60°$, then prove that

$$\frac{1}{a+c}+\frac{1}{b+c}=\frac{3}{a+b+c}.$$

(J.E.E.B.W. 2000)

(b) Find the greatest angle of the triangle whose sides are $x^2+x+1, 2x+1$ and x^2-1.

11. Can there exist triangles ABC satisfying the following relations ? Write yes or no giving reasons :

(i) $\tan A+\tan B+\tan C=0$

(ii)* $\frac{\sin A}{2}=\frac{\sin B}{3}=\frac{\sin C}{7}$

(iii) $(a+b)^2=c^2+ab$ and $\sqrt{2}(\sin A+\cos A)=\sqrt{3}$.

(iv) $\sin A+\sin B=\frac{\sqrt{3}+1}{2}$,

$\cos A\cos B=\frac{\sqrt{3}}{4}=\sin A\sin B$.

12. If a, b, c the sides of a triangle ABC be 5, 4, 3 respectively and D, E are the points of trisection of side BC, then prove that $\tan\angle CAE=3/8$.

13. If the angles of a triangle are $30°$ and $45°$ and the included side is $(\sqrt{3}+1)$ cm, the area of the triangle is $\frac{1}{2}(\sqrt{3}+1)$ sq. cm.

14. (a) If in a triangle $a=5, b=4$, and $\cos(A-B)=\frac{31}{32}$, prove that the third side c will be 6.

(b) If in a triangle ABC, $a=6$, $b=3$ and $\cos(A-B)=4/5$, then find its area. **(Roorkee 1997)**

15. If in a triangle ABC, $a=(1+\sqrt{3})$ cm, $b=2$ cm, and $\angle C=60°$, then find the other two angles and the third side.

16. (a) The base angles of a triangle are $22\frac{1}{2}°$ and $112\frac{1}{2}°$. Show that the base is equal to twice the height.

(b) In a right angled triangle ABC, the bisector of the right angle C divides AB into segments p and q, and $\tan\frac{A-B}{2}=t$, then show that $p:q=(1-t):(1+t)$.

17. (a)* In a triangle $\angle B=45°$, side $BC=2(\sqrt{3}+1)$ units and area $=6+2\sqrt{3}$ sq. units. Determine the side b.

(b)* In a triangle ABC, $\angle C=60°$ and $\angle A=75°$. If D is a point on AC such that the area of the $\Delta\,BAD$ is $\sqrt{3}$ times the area of the $\Delta\,BCD$, find the $\angle ABD$.

(Roorkee 1996)

18. (a)* If in $\Delta\,ABC$,

$$a\tan A+b\tan B=(a+b)\tan\frac{1}{2}(A+B),$$

prove that $A=B$.

(b)* If in $\Delta\,ABC, \cos^2 A+\cos^2 B+\cos^2 C=1$, prove that the triangle is right angled .

19.* If in $\Delta\,ABC$, $c(a+b)\cos\frac{1}{2}B=b(a+c)\cos\frac{1}{2}C$, prove that the triangle is isosceles .

20. (a)* If $a^2+c^2=2b^2$ where a, b, c are the sides of a triangle, then prove that $\frac{\sin 3B}{\sin B}=\left[\frac{a^2-c^2}{2ac}\right]^2$.

(b) In $\Delta\,ABC$, if $B=3C$, prove that

$$\cos C=\sqrt{\left(\frac{b+c}{4c}\right)}, \sin C=\sqrt{\left(\frac{3c-b}{4c}\right)}$$

and $\sin\frac{A}{2}=\frac{b-c}{2c}$.

21.* Let $1<m<3$. In a triangle ABC if $2b=(m+1)a$ and $\cos A=\frac{1}{2}\sqrt{\frac{(m-1)(m+3)}{m}}$, prove that there are two values of the third side one of which is m times the other.

22.* If the median of $\Delta\,ABC$ through A is perpendicular to AB prove that $\tan A+2\tan B=0$.

23.* In a triangle ABC if D be any point of the base BC, such that $BD:DC::m:n$,

if $\angle BAD=\alpha$, $\angle DAC=\beta$.

$\angle CDA=\theta$, and $AD=x$, prove that

(a) $(m+n)\cot\theta=m\cot\alpha-n\cot\beta$

$=n\cot B-m\cot C$ and

(b) $(m+n)^2\,x^2=(m+n)(mb^2+nc^2)-mna^2$.

24. In a triangle ABC, the median to the side BC is of length $\frac{1}{\sqrt{(11-6\sqrt{3})}}$ and it divides angle A into angles of $30°$ and $45°$. Prove that side BC is of length 2 units.

25.* If p and q be perpendiculars from the angular points A and B on any line passing through the vertex C of the $\Delta\,ABC$, prove that

$$a^2 p^2+b^2 q^2-2abpq\cos C=a^2 b^2\sin^2 C.$$

26.* ABC is a triangle and D is the middle point of BC. If AD is perpendicular to AC, prove that

$$\cos A \cos C = \frac{2(c^2 - a^2)}{3ac}.$$

27. CF is the internal bisector of angle C of $\Delta\, ABC$ then CF is equal to

(a) $\dfrac{2ab}{a+b} \cos \dfrac{C}{2}$

(b) $\dfrac{a+b}{2ab} \cos \dfrac{C}{2}$

(c) $\dfrac{b \sin A}{\sin\left(B + \dfrac{C}{2}\right)}$

(d) none of these

28. (a)* If p_1, p_2, p_3 are the altitudes of a triangle from the vertices A, B, C and Δ, the area of the triangle, prove that $\dfrac{1}{p_1} + \dfrac{1}{p_2} - \dfrac{1}{p_3} = \dfrac{2ab}{(a+b+c)\Delta} \cos^2 \dfrac{C}{2}$.

(b) If D be the mid-point of side BC of triangle ABC and if Δ is the area of the triangle ABC, prove that
$$\cot ADB = \frac{b^2 - c^2}{4\Delta}$$

29. * $\dfrac{(a+b+c)^2}{a^2 + b^2 + c^2} = \dfrac{\cot \dfrac{1}{2} A + \cot \dfrac{1}{2} B + \cot \dfrac{1}{2} C}{\cot A + \cot B + \cot C}$.

30. * If α, β, γ are lengths of the altitudes of a triangle ABC, prove that
$$\alpha^{-2} + \beta^{-2} + \gamma^{-2} = (\cot A + \cot B + \cot C)/\Delta$$
where Δ is the area of the triangle.   (Roorkee 1990)

31. If α, β, γ are the lengths of internal bisectors of the angles of a triangle ABC, then prove that
$$\frac{1}{\alpha}\cos\frac{A}{2} + \frac{1}{\beta}\cos\frac{B}{2} + \frac{1}{\gamma}\cos\frac{C}{2} = \frac{1}{a} + \frac{1}{b} + \frac{1}{c}$$
Determine the lengths of medians also.

32. * Let O be a point inside a triangle ABC such that
$$\angle OAB = \angle OBC = \angle OCA = \omega,$$
then show that
(a) $\cot \omega = \cot A + \cot B + \cot C$.
(b) $\csc^2 \omega = \csc^2 A + \csc^2 B + \csc^2 C$.

33. * $ABCD$ is a trapezium such that AB is parallel to CD and CB is perpendicular to them. If $\angle ADB = \theta, BC = p$ and $CD = q$, show that
$$AB = \frac{(p^2 + q^2)\sin\theta}{p\cos\theta + q\sin\theta}.$$

34. With usual notations, if in a triangle, ABC
$$\frac{b+c}{11} = \frac{c+a}{12} = \frac{a+b}{13}$$
then prove that $\dfrac{\cos A}{7} = \dfrac{\cos B}{19} = \dfrac{\cos C}{25}$.

35. * The sides of a triangle are such that
$$\frac{a}{1 + m^2 n^2} = \frac{b}{m^2 + n^2} = \frac{c}{(1 - m^2)(1 + n^2)}$$
Prove that $A = 2\tan^{-1}\dfrac{m}{n}$, $B = 2\tan^{-1}(mn)$ and
$$\Delta = \frac{mn\, bc}{m^2 + n^2}$$

36. * The sides a, b, c of the triangle ABC are the roots of the equation $x^3 - px^2 + qx - r = 0$.
Prove that its area is $\dfrac{1}{4}\{p(4pq - p^3 - 8r)\}^{1/2}$.

37. * For a triangle ABC, prove that
$$\cos A + \cos B + \cos C \le 3/2.$$
In case of equality, triangle will be equilateral.

38. If the tangents of the angles of a triangle are in A.P., prove that the squares of the sides are in the ratio $x^2(x^2 + 9) : (3 + x^2)^2 : 9(1 + x^2)$, where x is tangent of the least or greatest angle.

39. (a)* The two adjacent sides of a cyclic quadrilateral are 2 and 5 and the angle between them is $60°$. If the area of the quadrilateral is $4\sqrt{3}$, find the remaining two sides.   (Roorkee 1991)

(b)* The two adjacent sides of a cyclic quadrilateral are 2 and 5 and the angle between them is $60°$. If the third side is 3, the remaining fourth side is
(i) 2
(ii) 3
(iii) 4
(iv) 5   (M.N.R.1994)

(c)* A cyclic quadrilateral $ABCD$ of area $3\sqrt{3}/4$ is inscribed in a unit circle. If one of its sides $AB = 1$ and the diagonal $BD = \sqrt{3}$, find lengths of the other sides.   (Roorkee 1995)

40. In a triangle of base a, the ratio of the other sides is $r\,(<1)$. Show that the altitude of the triangle is less than or equal to $\dfrac{ar}{1 - r^2}$.   (I.I.T. 1991)

41. Consider the following statements concerning a triangle ABC.
(i) The sides a, b, c and area Δ are rational
(ii) $a, \tan\dfrac{B}{2}, \tan\dfrac{C}{2}$ are rational
(iii) $a, \sin A, \sin B, \sin C$ are rational
Prove that (i) $\to$ (ii) $\to$ (iii) $\to$ (i).   (I.I.T. 1994)

42. There exists a triangle ABC satisfying the conditions
(a) $b\sin A = a$, $A < \pi/2$
(b) $b\sin A > a$, $A > \pi/2$
(c) $b\sin A > a$, $A < \pi/2$
(d) $b\sin A < a$, $A < \pi/2$, $b > a$
(e) $b\sin A < a$, $A > \pi/2$, $b = a$.

43. (a) In a ΔABC, $A = 45°$ and c_1, c_2 are the two values of side c in the ambiguous case, show that
$$\cos B_1 CB_2 = \frac{2c_1 c_2}{c_1^2 + c_2^2}.$$

(b) In the ambiguous case, given a, b and A, prove that the difference between the two values of c is
$$2\sqrt{a^2 - b^2 \sin^2 A}.$$

44. In the ambiguous case, if b and A are given and c_1, c_2 are the two values of third side, prove that
(i) $c_1 + c_2 = 2b\cos A$ and $c_1 c_2 = b^2 - a^2$.

(ii) $c_1^2 - 2c_1 c_2 \cos 2A + c_2^2 = 4a^2 \cos^2 A.$

(iii) $(c_1 - c_2)^2 + (c_1 + c_2)^2 \tan^2 A = 4a^2.$

45. (a) In a $\Delta ABC, a, c, A$ are given and $b_2 = 2b_1$ where b_1, b_2 are two values of the third side, then prove that $3a = c\sqrt{(1 + 8\sin^2 A)}$.

(b) In the ambiguous case, if the remaining angles of the triangles formed with a, b and A be B_1, C_1 and B_2, C_2, then prove that $\dfrac{\sin C_1}{\sin B_1} + \dfrac{\sin C_2}{\sin B_2} = 2\cos A.$

(c) In the ambiguous case, if two triangles are formed with a, b and A, then prove that the sum of the areas of these triangles is $\dfrac{1}{2} b^2 \sin 2A.$

46. (a) If $2b = 3a$ and $\tan^2 A = 3/5$, prove that there are two values of third side, one of which is double the other.

(b)* Two sides of a triangle are of lengths $\sqrt{6}$ and 4 and the angle opposite to smaller side is 30°. How many such triangles are possible ? Find the length of their third side and area. **(Roorkee 1998)**

Solutions to Problem Set (2)

1. (a) $a^3 \cos(B - C) + b^3 \cos(C - A) + c^3 \cos(A - B)$

$= k^3 \sin^3 A \cos(B - C) + k^3 \sin^3 B \cos(C - A)$
$\qquad\qquad + k^3 \sin^3 C \cos(A - B)$

$= k^3 [\sin^2 A \sin(B + C) \cos(B - C)$
$\qquad + \sin^2 B \sin(C + A) \cos(C - A)$
$\qquad\qquad + \sin^2 C \sin(A + B) \cos(A - B)]$

$= \dfrac{1}{2} k^3 [\sin^2 A (\sin 2B + \sin 2C)$

$\qquad\qquad + \sin^2 B (\sin 2C + \sin 2A)$

$\qquad\qquad + \sin^2 C (\sin 2A + \sin 2B)]$ **(Note)**

$= k^3 [\sin^2 A \sin B \cos B + \sin^2 A \sin C \cos C$
$\qquad + \sin^2 B \sin C \cos C + \sin^2 B \sin A \cos A$
$\qquad + \sin^2 C \sin A \cos A + \sin^2 C \sin B \cos B]$

$= k^3 [\sin A \sin B (\sin A \cos B + \cos A \sin B)$
$\qquad + \sin B \sin C (\sin B \cos C + \cos B \sin C)$
$\qquad + \sin C \sin A (\sin C \cos A + \cos C \sin A)]$

$= k^3 [\sin A \sin B \sin(A + B)$
$\qquad + \sin B \sin C \sin(B + C)$
$\qquad\qquad + \sin C \sin A \sin(C + A)]$

$= k^3 [\sin A \sin B \sin C + \sin B \sin C \sin A$
$\qquad\qquad + \sin C \sin A \sin B]$

$= 3k \sin A. k \sin B. k \sin C = 3 abc.$

(b) It is same as part (a) by sine formula.

2. L.H.S. $= k^3 [\sin^3 A \cos B \cos C$
$\qquad + \sin^3 B \cos C \cos A + \sin^3 C \cos A \cos B]$

$= k^3 [\sin^3 A \cos B \cos C + \sin B (1 - \cos^2 B) \cos C \cos A$
$\qquad\qquad + \sin C (1 - \cos^2 C) \cos A \cos B]$

$= k^3 [\sin^3 A \cos B \cos C + \cos A (\sin B \cos C$
$\qquad + \sin C \cos B) - \dfrac{1}{2} \cos A \cos B \cos C$
$\qquad\qquad\qquad\qquad (\sin 2B + \sin 2C)]$

$= k^3 [\sin^3 A \cos B \cos C + \cos A \sin(B + C)$
$\qquad - \cos A \cos B \cos C \sin(B + C) \cos(B - C)]$

$= k^3 [\sin A (1 - \cos^2 A) \cos B \cos C + \cos A \sin A$
$\qquad - \cos A \cos B \cos C \sin A \cos(B - C)]$

$= k^3 \sin A [\cos B \cos C (1 - \cos^2 A) + \cos A$
$\qquad - \cos A \cos B \cos C \cos(B - C)]$

$= k^3 \sin A [\cos A + \cos B \cos C$
$\qquad - \cos A \cos B \cos C \{\cos A + \cos(B - C)\}]$

$= k^3 \sin A [-\cos(B + C) + \cos B \cos C$
$\qquad - \cos A \cos B \cos C \{-\cos(B + C) + \cos(B - C)\}]$

$= k^3 \sin A [\sin B \sin C - \cos A \cos B \cos C.$
$\qquad\qquad\qquad\qquad 2 \sin B \sin C]$

$= k^3 \sin A \sin B \sin C (1 - 2\cos A \cos B \cos C)$

$= abc (1 - 2\cos A \cos B \cos C).$

3. (a) We have $\tan \dfrac{C}{2} = \tan\left(90° - \dfrac{A + B}{2}\right) = \cot\left(\dfrac{A}{2} + \dfrac{B}{2}\right)$

$= \dfrac{\cot \dfrac{A}{2} \cot \dfrac{B}{2} - 1}{\cot \dfrac{B}{2} + \cot \dfrac{A}{2}} = \dfrac{\dfrac{6}{5}.\dfrac{37}{20} - 1}{\dfrac{37}{20} + \dfrac{6}{5}}$

$= \dfrac{222 - 100}{5 \times 61} = \dfrac{122}{5 \times 61} = \dfrac{2 \times 61}{5 \times 61} = \dfrac{2}{5}.$

Again $\tan \dfrac{A}{2}.\tan \dfrac{C}{2} = \sqrt{\left\{\dfrac{(s - b)(s - c)}{s(s - a)}\right\}}$

$\sqrt{\left\{\dfrac{(s - a)(s - b)}{s(s - c)}\right\}}$

Hence $\dfrac{5}{6}.\dfrac{2}{5} = \dfrac{s - b}{s}$ **(R. 11 P. 645)**

$\therefore \quad 3s - 3b = s \quad$ or $\quad 2s = 3b$

or $\quad a + b + c = 3b \quad$ or $\quad a + c = 2b.$

(b) Ans. (b).

$\cot \dfrac{A}{2} = \sqrt{\dfrac{s(s - a)}{(s - b)(s - c)}} = \dfrac{s(s - a)}{S}$

$\therefore \quad \cot \dfrac{A}{2} : \cot \dfrac{B}{2} : \cot \dfrac{C}{2}$

$\therefore \quad s - a : s - b : s - c = 1 : 4 : 15$

$\qquad a = (s - b) + (s - c) = 19k,$

$\qquad b = (s - c) + (s - a) = 16k,$

$\qquad c = (s - a) + (s - b) = 5k$

$\therefore \quad a : b : c = 19 : 16 : 5.$

4. Let ABC be the triangle, right angled at C, and D be the mid-point of AC. Join DB.

Since $AC = BC = x$, we have
$$DC = \frac{1}{2} AC = \frac{1}{2} BC = \frac{x}{2}$$

Also $\quad \angle CAB = \angle CBA = 45°.$

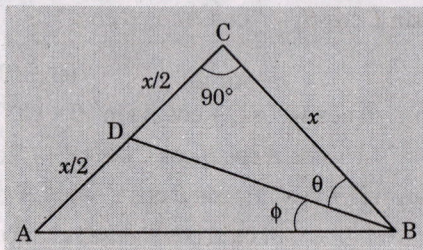

Fig. 5

If $\quad \angle DBC = \theta$ and $\angle DBA = \phi,$

$$\tan \theta = \frac{DC}{BC} = \frac{x/2}{x} = \frac{1}{2}$$

$$\tan \phi = \tan(45° - \theta) = \frac{1 - \tan \theta}{1 + \tan \theta}$$

or $\quad \tan \phi = \frac{1 - 1/2}{1 + 1/2} = \frac{1}{3}$

$\therefore \quad \cot \theta = 2, \cot \phi = 3.$

5. Let A be the greatest and C the least angle of $\triangle ABC$. It is given that a, b, c are in A.P. so that
$$a + c = 2b \qquad \qquad \ldots(1)$$
Also $\quad A - C = 90°$
From (1), $\quad \sin A + \sin C = 2 \sin B = 2 \sin(A + C) \quad \ldots(2)$

$\therefore \quad 2 \sin \frac{A+C}{2} \cos \frac{A-C}{2} = 4 \sin \frac{A+C}{2} \cos \frac{A+C}{2}$

or $\quad \cos \frac{A-C}{2} = 2 \cos \frac{A+C}{2} = 2 \sin \frac{B}{2}$

$\therefore \quad 2 \sin(B/2) = \cos(90°/2) = \cos 45° = 1/\sqrt{2}, \quad$ by (2)

Hence $\quad \sin \frac{B}{2} = \frac{1}{2\sqrt{2}}$

and $\cos \frac{B}{2} = \sqrt{\left(1 - \frac{1}{8}\right)} = \frac{\sqrt{7}}{2\sqrt{2}}$

$\therefore \quad \sin B = 2 \sin \frac{B}{2} \cos \frac{B}{2}$

$$= 2 \cdot \frac{1}{2\sqrt{2}} \cdot \frac{\sqrt{7}}{2\sqrt{2}} = \frac{\sqrt{7}}{4}$$

$\therefore \quad \sin A + \sin C = 2 \sin B = \sqrt{7}/2. \qquad \ldots(3)$

Also $\quad \sin A - \sin C = 2 \cos[(A+C)/2] \cdot \sin[(A-C)/2]$

$$= 2 \sin(B/2) \sin 45° = 2 \cdot \frac{1}{2\sqrt{2}} \cdot \frac{1}{\sqrt{2}} = \frac{1}{2} \quad \ldots(4)$$

Adding and subtracting (3) and (4), we get
$$2 \sin A = (\sqrt{7} + 1)/2$$
i.e. $\quad \sin A = (\sqrt{7} + 1)/4$
and $2 \sin C = (\sqrt{7} - 1)/2.$
i.e. $\quad \sin C = (\sqrt{7} - 1)/4$

Hence $\quad a : b : c = \sin A : \sin B : \sin C$
$$= \sqrt{7} + 1 : \sqrt{7} : \sqrt{7} - 1.$$

6. Let the sides be $k - d, k, k + d$ *i.e.*, a, b, c
$\therefore \quad 2s = 3k \quad \therefore \quad$ side of equilateral $\triangle$ is also $k.$

$S = \frac{3}{5}$ area of equilateral $\triangle$ of same perimeter $3a$

$$S^2 = \frac{9}{25} \left(\frac{\sqrt{3}}{4} k^2\right)^2$$

$$s(s-a)(s-b)(s-c) = \frac{9 \times 3 k^4}{25 \times 16}$$

$$\frac{3k}{2} \left(\frac{3k}{2} - k + d\right) \left(\frac{3k}{2} - k\right) \left(\frac{3k}{2} - k - d\right) = \frac{27}{400} k^4$$

$$\frac{3k^2}{4} \frac{(k + 2d)(k - 2d)}{4} = \frac{27}{400} k^4$$

or $\quad k^2 - 4d^2 = \frac{9}{25} k^2 \quad$ or $\quad 16k^2 = 100 d^2$

$\therefore \quad \frac{d}{k} = \sqrt{\left\{\frac{4}{25}\right\}} = \frac{2}{5}.$

Hence the sides $k - d, k, k + d$ are in the ratio
$$1 - \frac{d}{k}, 1, 1 + \frac{d}{k}$$
or $\quad 1 - \frac{2}{5}, 1, 1 + \frac{2}{5} \quad$ or $\quad 3 : 5 : 7.$

7. Let the sides of the $\triangle ABC$ be $a = n, b = n + 1, c = n + 2,$ where n is a natural number. Then C is the greatest and A the least angle.

As given $C = 2A$
$\therefore \quad \sin C = \sin 2A = 2 \sin A \cos A$

$\therefore \quad kc = 2ka \cdot \frac{b^2 + c^2 - a^2}{2bc}$

or $\quad bc^2 = a(b^2 + c^2 - a^2).$

Substituting the values of $a, b, c,$ we get
$$(n+1)(n+2)^2 = n[(n+1)^2 + (n+2)^2 - n^2]$$
or $\quad (n+1)(n+2)^2 = n(n^2 + 6n + 5) = n(n+1)(n+5)$

Since $n \neq -1,$ we can cancel $n + 1.$

Thus $\quad (n+2)^2 = n(n+5)$
or $\quad n^2 + 4n + 4 = n^2 + 5n.$

This gives $n = 4$
Hence the sides are 4, 5 and 6.

8. We are given that $A - C = \alpha$ and $2b = a + c$

$\therefore \quad 2 \sin B = \sin A + \sin C \qquad \ldots(1)$

$$= 2 \sin \frac{A+C}{2} \cos \frac{A-C}{2}$$

or $\quad 4 \sin \frac{B}{2} \cos \frac{B}{2} = 2 \cos \frac{B}{2} \cos \frac{\alpha}{2}$

$\therefore \quad \sin \frac{B}{2} = \frac{1}{2} \cos \frac{\alpha}{2}$

or $\quad \cos^2 \frac{B}{2} = 1 - \sin^2 \frac{B}{2} = 1 - \frac{1}{4} \cos^2 \frac{\alpha}{2} = 1 - \frac{1 + \cos \alpha}{8}$

or $\cos \dfrac{B}{2} = \dfrac{\sqrt{7 - \cos \alpha}}{2\sqrt{2}}$ ...(2)

Again $\dfrac{a}{c} = \dfrac{\sin A}{\sin C}$. Apply Compo. & Divi.

$\dfrac{a+c}{a-c} = \dfrac{\sin A + \sin C}{\sin A - \sin C} = \dfrac{2 \sin B}{2 \sin \dfrac{A-C}{2} \cos \dfrac{A+C}{2}}$ by (1)

$= \dfrac{4 \sin (B/2) \cos (B/2)}{2 \sin (B/2) \sin (\alpha/2)}$, by given relation

$= \dfrac{2\sqrt{2} \cos (B/2)}{\sqrt{(1 - \cos \alpha)}} = \sqrt{\dfrac{7 - \cos \alpha}{1 - \cos \alpha}}$, by (2)

$\therefore \quad \dfrac{a-c}{a+c} = \dfrac{x}{1}$, by given relation

Again apply Compo. & Divi.

$\dfrac{2a}{2c} = \dfrac{1+x}{1-x}$

or $\dfrac{a}{1+x} = \dfrac{c}{1-x} = \dfrac{a+c}{2}$ or $\dfrac{2b}{2} = \dfrac{b}{1}$

or $\dfrac{a}{1+x} = \dfrac{b}{1} = \dfrac{c}{1-x}$

Hence the sides are in the ratio

$1 + x : 1 : 1 - x.$

9. $\tan \dfrac{B-C}{2} = \dfrac{b-c}{b+c} \cot \dfrac{A}{2}$

$\therefore \quad \dfrac{x}{1} = \tan \dfrac{B-C}{2} \tan \dfrac{A}{2} = \dfrac{b-c}{b+c}$

$\therefore \quad \dfrac{1+x}{1-x} = \dfrac{2b}{2c}$. Similarly

$\dfrac{1+y}{1-y} = \dfrac{2c}{2a}, \dfrac{1+z}{1-z} = \dfrac{2a}{2b}$

$\therefore \quad \dfrac{(1+x)(1+y)(1+z)}{(1-x)(1-y)(1-z)} = 1$

or $1 + \Sigma x + \Sigma xy + xyz = 1 - \Sigma x + \Sigma xy - xyz$

or $2\Sigma x = -2 xyz$ or $\Sigma x = - xyz$

10. (a) Since $C = 60°$, we have

$c^2 = a^2 + b^2 - 2ab \cos C$

$= a^2 + b^2 - 2ab \cos 60°$

or $c^2 = a^2 + b^2 - ab$ ...(1)

Also $\dfrac{1}{a+c} + \dfrac{1}{b+c} = \dfrac{3}{a+b+c}$

if $\dfrac{a+b+2c}{(a+c)(b+c)} = \dfrac{3}{a+b+c}$

i.e. if $(a+b+2c)(a+b+c) = 3(a+c)(b+c)$

i.e. if $(a+b)^2 + 2c^2 + 3c(a+b)$

$= 3(ab + ac + bc + c^2)$

i.e. if $a^2 + b^2 + 2ab + 2c^2 + 3ca + 3cb$

$= 3ab + 3ac + 3bc + 3c^2$

i.e. if $a^2 + b^2 - ab = c^2$,

which is the same as (1).

(b) Since the sides are +ive

$\therefore \quad x^2 - 1$ or $(x+1)(x-1) > 0$

$\therefore \quad x < -1$ or $x > 1$

$\therefore \quad x > 1$ only

$\therefore \quad x < -1$ will make $b = 2x + 1$ –ive

$a = x^2 + x + 1 > x + x + 1 = 2x + 1 = b$

$\therefore \quad a > b$

Also $a > c \quad \because a - c = x + 2 = +$ ive or > 0.

Hence a is the greatest side so A is the greatest angle.

$\therefore \quad \cos A = \dfrac{b^2 + c^2 - a^2}{2bc} = -\dfrac{1}{2}$

$\therefore \quad A = 120°$

11. (i) No. Since $A + B + C = \pi$

$\therefore \quad \Sigma \tan A = \tan A \tan B \tan C = 0$

$\Rightarrow$ Either $A = 0$ or $B = 0$ or $C = 0$

which is not possible in a triangle.

(ii) No. By sine rule, $\dfrac{a}{2} = \dfrac{b}{3} = \dfrac{c}{7} = \dfrac{a+b}{5}$

$\therefore \quad a + b = \dfrac{5}{7} c < c$ .Not possible as sum of two sides

is always greater than the third.

(iii) Yes.

$a^2 + b^2 - c^2 + ab = 0 \quad \Rightarrow 2ab \cos C + ab = 0$

$\cos C = -\dfrac{1}{2} \quad \Rightarrow \quad C = 120°.$

Also from 2nd relation

We have $\sin \left(A + \dfrac{\pi}{4} \right) = \dfrac{\sqrt{3}}{2} = \sin \dfrac{\pi}{3} \quad \therefore \quad A = 15°$

and hence $B = 45°$. Such a Δ is possible.

(iv) Yes. Adding and subtracting the relation in 2nd

$\cos (A - B) = \dfrac{\sqrt{3}}{4} + \dfrac{\sqrt{3}}{4} = \dfrac{\sqrt{3}}{2} \quad \therefore \quad A - B = 30°$

$\cos (A + B) = 0 \quad \therefore \quad A + B = 90°$

$\therefore \quad A = 60°, B = 30°$

$\therefore \quad C = 180° - (A + B) = 90°$

These values also satisfy the first given relation.

12. $5^2 = 4^2 + 3^2 \quad \therefore \quad \angle A = 90°,$

$\therefore \quad \cos C = 4/5$

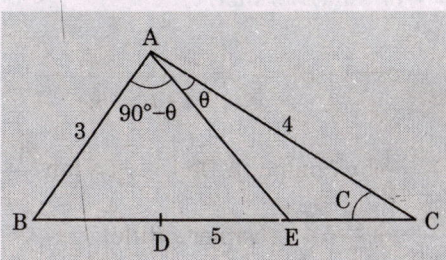

Fig. 6

Also $CE = \frac{1}{3}CB = \frac{5}{3}$

Hence by cosine formula on $\triangle AEC$

$$AE^2 = 4^2 + \left(\frac{5}{3}\right)^2 - 2.4.\frac{5}{3}\cos C$$

$$= \frac{169}{9} - \frac{40}{3}.\frac{4}{5} = \frac{73}{9}$$

Now we know all the sides of $\triangle ACE$

∴ By cosine rule, $\cos\theta = \frac{8}{\sqrt{73}}$ ∴ $\tan\theta = \frac{3}{8}$.

13. Let $\angle A = 30°, \angle B = 45°$ so that $AB = c = (\sqrt{3}+1)$ ...(1)

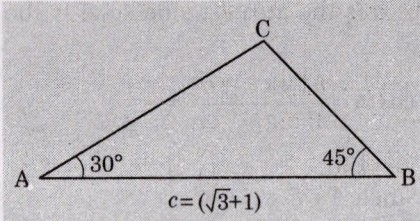

Fig. 7

Also $\angle C = 180° - (30° + 45°) = 105°$

∴ $\sin C = \sin(90° + 15°) = \cos 15°$

or $\sin C = \cos(45° - 30°)$

$$= \frac{1}{2\sqrt{2}}(\sqrt{3}+1) = \frac{1}{2\sqrt{2}}.c \text{ by (1)}. \qquad ...(2)$$

By sine formula $\frac{b}{\sin B} = \frac{c}{\sin C} = 2\sqrt{2}$, by (2).

∴ $b = \sin B.2\sqrt{2} = 2$ ∵ $B = 45°$

∴ $\Delta = \frac{1}{2}bc \sin A = \frac{1}{2}.2.(\sqrt{3}+1).\frac{1}{2} = \frac{1}{2}(\sqrt{3}+1)$.

14. (a) $\tan\frac{\alpha}{2} = \left(\frac{1-\cos\alpha}{1+\cos\alpha}\right)^{1/2} = \left\{\frac{1-(31/32)}{1+(31/32)}\right\}^{1/2}$

$$= \frac{1}{\sqrt{63}} = \frac{1}{3\sqrt{7}} \text{ where } \alpha = A - B$$

Now $\tan\frac{A-B}{2} = \frac{a-b}{a+b}\cot\frac{C}{2}$ (Nap. Analogy)

Put $a = 5, b = 4$ ∴ $\frac{1}{3\sqrt{7}} = \frac{1}{9}\cot\frac{C}{2}$ or $\tan\frac{C}{2} = \frac{\sqrt{7}}{3}$

Now $\cos C = \frac{1-\tan^2(C/2)}{1+\tan^2(C/2)} = \frac{1-7/9}{1+7/9} = \frac{1}{8}$

But $c^2 = a^2 + b^2 - 2ab\cos C = 36$ ∴ $c = 6$

(b) $\Delta = \frac{1}{2}ab\sin C = 9\sin C$ ...(1)

$$\cos(A-B) = \frac{4}{5} \Rightarrow \frac{1-t^2}{1+t^2} = \frac{4}{5}$$

∴ $\frac{2t^2}{2} = \frac{1}{9}$ by Compo. & Divi. ∴ $t = \tan\frac{A-B}{2} = \frac{1}{3}$

∴ $\frac{a-b}{a+b}\cot\frac{C}{2} = \frac{1}{3}$ (Napier's Rule)

∴ $\frac{3}{9}\cot\frac{C}{2} = \frac{1}{3}$ ∴ $\cot\frac{C}{2} = 1$ ∴ $\frac{C}{2} = 45°$

$\Rightarrow C = 90°$ ∴ $\Delta = 9$ sq. units, from (1)

15. $c^2 = a^2 + b^2 - 2ab\cos C = 6$ ∴ $c = \sqrt{6}$.

$$\frac{b}{\sin B} = \frac{c}{\sin C} = \frac{\sqrt{6}}{\sin 60°} = \frac{2\sqrt{6}}{\sqrt{3}} = 2\sqrt{2}.$$

∴ $\sin B = \frac{b}{2\sqrt{2}} = \frac{2}{2\sqrt{2}} = \frac{1}{\sqrt{2}}$

∴ $B = 45°$ (135° is ruled out.)

Hence $A = 180° - (B + C) = 75°$.

16. (a) $\frac{a}{\sin A} = \frac{c}{\sin 112\frac{1}{2}°} = \frac{c}{\cos 22\frac{1}{2}°}$ ...(1)

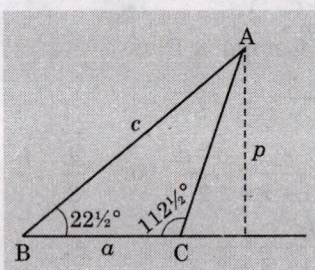

Fig. 8

Also $p = c\sin 22\frac{1}{2}°$, ...(2)

$$A = 180° - \left(22\frac{1}{2}° + 112\frac{1}{2}°\right) = 45° \qquad ...(3)$$

Putting for A and c from (2) and (3) in (1)

$$\frac{a}{\sin 45°} = \frac{p}{\sin 22\frac{1}{2}° \cos 22\frac{1}{2}°} = \frac{2p}{\sin 45°}$$

∴ $a = 2p$

(b) Let $CD = x$, then by sine rule

$$\frac{x}{\sin A} = \frac{p}{\sin 45°} = p\sqrt{2}.$$

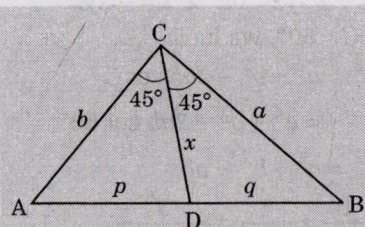

Fig. 9

Similarly, $\frac{x}{\sin B} = q\sqrt{2}$

∴ $\frac{p}{q} = \frac{\sin B}{\sin A}$. Apply Compo. & Divi.

∴ $\frac{q-p}{q+p} = \frac{\sin A - \sin B}{\sin A + \sin B} = \tan\frac{A-B}{2} = \frac{t}{1}$

Again apply Compo. & Divi. and you get the result.

17. (a) $\Delta = \dfrac{1}{2} p \cdot BC = 2\sqrt{3}(1 + \sqrt{3})$

or $p = \dfrac{4\sqrt{3}(1 + \sqrt{3})}{2(\sqrt{3} + 1)} = 2\sqrt{3}$

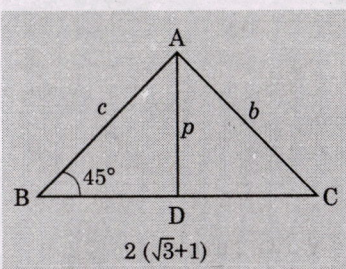

Fig. 10

or $b \sin C = 2\sqrt{3} = c \sin B$ by sine rule ...(1)

∴ But $\angle B = 45°$

∴ $c \cos B = c \sin B = 2\sqrt{3}$

Again $b \cos C + c \cos B = a$

∴ $b \cos C = 2(\sqrt{3} + 1) - 2\sqrt{3} = 2$, by (1) ...(2)

Squaring and adding (1) and (2),

$b^2 = 4 + 12 = 16$ ∴ $b = 4$.

(b) Let $\angle ABD = \theta$, $\angle B = 45°$, $\Delta_1 = \sqrt{3} \cdot \Delta_2$

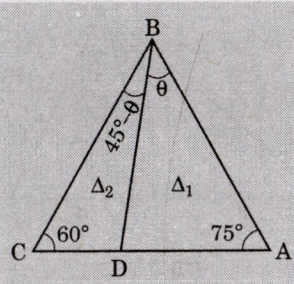

Fig. 11

$\dfrac{1}{2} BD \cdot BA \sin \theta = \sqrt{3} \cdot \dfrac{1}{2} BD \cdot BC \sin(B - \theta)$

∴ $\dfrac{BA}{BC} \sin \theta = \sqrt{3} \sin(45° - \theta)$

$\dfrac{1}{\sqrt{3}} \dfrac{\sin 60°}{\sin 75°} = \dfrac{\sin(45° - \theta)}{\sin \theta}$

or $\dfrac{1}{\sqrt{3}} \cdot \dfrac{\sqrt{3}}{2} \cdot \dfrac{2\sqrt{2}}{\sqrt{3} + 1} = \dfrac{1}{\sqrt{2}} \dfrac{\cos \theta - \sin \theta}{\sin \theta}$

or $\dfrac{2}{\sqrt{3} + 1} = \cot \theta - 1$

∴ $\cot \theta = \dfrac{3 + \sqrt{3}}{\sqrt{3} + 1} = \sqrt{3}$

or $\tan \theta = \dfrac{1}{\sqrt{3}}$ ∴ $\theta = 30°$.

18. (a) We have $a \tan A + b \tan B = (a + b) \tan \dfrac{1}{2}(A + B)$

or $a \left[\tan A - \tan \dfrac{1}{2}(A + B) \right]$

$= b \left[\tan \dfrac{1}{2}(A + B) - \tan B \right]$ ...(1)

or $a \left[\dfrac{\sin A \cos \dfrac{1}{2}(A + B) - \cos A \sin \dfrac{1}{2}(A + B)}{\cos A \cos \dfrac{1}{2}(A + B)} \right]$

$= b \left[\dfrac{\sin \dfrac{1}{2}(A + B) \cos B - \cos \dfrac{1}{2}(A + B) \sin B}{\cos \dfrac{1}{2}(A + B) \cos B} \right]$

or $\dfrac{k \sin A \sin \dfrac{1}{2}(A - B)}{\cos A} = \dfrac{k \sin B \sin \dfrac{1}{2}(A - B)}{\cos B}$

or $\sin \dfrac{1}{2}(A - B) \left(\dfrac{\sin A}{\cos A} - \dfrac{\sin B}{\cos B} \right) = 0$.

or $\sin \dfrac{1}{2}(A - B)(\tan A - \tan B) = 0$.

From this equation, we conclude that $A = B$.

(b) From the given relation, we have

$\cos^2 A + \cos^2 B - (1 - \cos^2 C) = 0$

or $\cos^2 A + (\cos^2 B - \sin^2 C) = 0$

or $\cos^2 A + \cos(B + C)\cos(B - C) = 0$

or $\cos A[-\cos(B + C) - \cos(B - C)] = 0$

or $2 \cos A \cos B \cos C = 0$ **(See Q. 17 (a) P. 368)**

Hence either $\cos A = 0$, $\cos B = 0$ or $\cos C = 0$

i.e., either $A = \pi/2$ or $B = \pi/2$ or $C = \pi/2$.

It follows that the ΔABC is righangled.

19. We have $c(a + b) \cos \dfrac{1}{2} B = b(a + c) \cos \dfrac{1}{2} C$

∴ $c(a + b) \sqrt{\left\{ \dfrac{s(s - b)}{ca} \right\}} = b(a + c) \sqrt{\left\{ \dfrac{s(s - c)}{ab} \right\}}$

or $(a + b)\sqrt{c(s - b)} = (a + c)\sqrt{b(s - c)}$

Squaring, $(a + b)^2 c(s - b) = (a + c)^2 b(s - c)$

or $s\{c(a + b)^2 - b(a + c)^2\} - bc\{(a + b)^2$

$- (a + c)^2\} = 0$

or $s\{ca^2 + 2abc + cb^2 - ba^2 - 2abc - bc^2\}$

$- bc(2a + b + c)(b - c) = 0$

or $s\{bc(b - c) - a^2(b - c)\} - bc(b - c)(2a + b + c) = 0$

or $(b - c)\{s(bc - a^2) - bc(2a + b + c)\} = 0$

or $(b - c)\{s(bc - a^2) - bc(2s + a)\} = 0$

or $-(b - c)\{s(bc + a^2) + abc\} = 0$

Since a, b, c are all positive and so

$s(bc + a^2) + abc \neq 0$

It follows that $b - c = 0$ or $b = c$

Hence ΔABC is isosceles.

20. (a) L.H.S. $= 3 - 4\sin^2 B = -1 + 4\cos^2 B$ ...(1)

From the given relation, we have

$a^2 + c^2 - b^2 = b^2$ or $2ac \cos B = b^2$

$$\therefore \quad 4\cos^2 B = \left(\frac{b^2}{ac}\right)^2 = \left(\frac{a^2+c^2}{2ac}\right)^2 \quad \text{Put in (1) etc.}$$

$$\therefore \quad \text{L.H.S.} = \frac{(a^2+c^2)^2 - 4a^2c^2}{4a^2c^2} = \left[\frac{a^2-c^2}{2ac}\right]^2$$

(b) $\dfrac{b+c}{4c} = \dfrac{\sin B + \sin C}{4\sin C}$

$$= \frac{\sin 3C + \sin C}{4\sin C} = \frac{2\sin 2C \cos C}{4\sin C}$$

$$= \frac{4\sin C \cos C \cos C}{4\sin C} = \cos^2 C.$$

$$\therefore \quad \cos C = \sqrt{(b+c)/4c}$$

$$\therefore \quad \sin C = \sqrt{(1-\cos^2 C)} \text{ etc.}$$

Again $\dfrac{b-c}{2c} = \dfrac{\sin B - \sin C}{2\sin C}$

$$= \frac{\sin 3C - \sin C}{2\sin C} = \frac{2\cos 2C \sin C}{2\sin C} = \cos 2C.$$

But $A + B + C = 180°$ and $B = 3C$

$$\Rightarrow \quad A + 4C = 180° \Rightarrow 4C = 180° - A$$

or $\quad 2C = 90° - \dfrac{1}{2}A.$

Hence $\dfrac{b-c}{2c} = \cos\left(90° - \dfrac{A}{2}\right) = \sin\dfrac{A}{2}.$

Alt. $\dfrac{\sin B}{\sin C} = \dfrac{b}{c}$ or $\dfrac{\sin 3C}{\sin C} = \dfrac{b}{c}$

or $3 - 4\sin^2 C = \dfrac{b}{c}$ $\therefore$ $\sin C = \sqrt{\dfrac{3c-b}{4c}}$

Again $A = 180° - (B+C) = 180° - 4C.$

$$\therefore \quad A/2 = 90° - 2C,$$

$$\therefore \quad \sin(A/2) = \cos 2C = 1 - 2\sin^2 C \text{ etc.}$$

21. Given $\quad 2b = (m+1)a$ ...(1)

and $4m\cos^2 A = (m-1)(m+3)$ ...(2)

$$2bc\cos A = b^2 + c^2 - a^2$$

$$(m+1)ac\cos A = (m+1)^2\frac{a^2}{4} - a^2 + c^2, \quad \text{by (1)}$$

$$= [(m+1)^2 - 2^2]\frac{a^2}{4} + c^2$$

$$\therefore \quad mac\cos A + ac\cos A = (m-1)(m+3)\frac{a^2}{4} + c^2$$

$$= a^2 m\cos^2 A + c^2, \quad \text{by (2)}$$

$$\therefore \quad mac\cos A + ac\cos A - a^2 m\cos^2 A - c^2 = 0$$

Factorizing, we get

$$mac\cos A(c - a\cos A) - c(c - a\cos A) = 0$$

$$(c - a\cos A)(mac\cos A - c) = 0$$

$$\therefore \quad c = a\cos A \qquad \text{or} \qquad c = mac\cos A$$

Hence one value of c is m times the other.

22. We are given

$$BD = DC \text{ and } \angle DAB = 90°.$$

Draw $CN \perp$ to BA produced

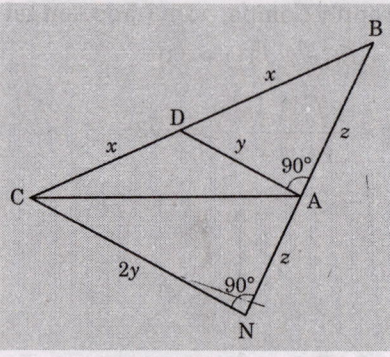

Fig. 12

Then in $\triangle BCN$, we have

$$DA = \frac{1}{2}CN = y \text{ and } AB = AN = z.$$

$$\therefore \quad \tan A = \tan(\pi - \angle CAN)$$

$$= -\tan(\angle CAN) = -\frac{CN}{AN} = -\frac{2y}{z}$$

or $\quad \tan A = -(2AD/AB) = -2\tan B$

or $\quad \tan A + 2\tan B = 0.$

23. (a) We are given

$$\frac{m}{n} = \frac{BD}{DC} \qquad \text{or} \qquad m.DC = n.BD \qquad \text{...(1)}$$

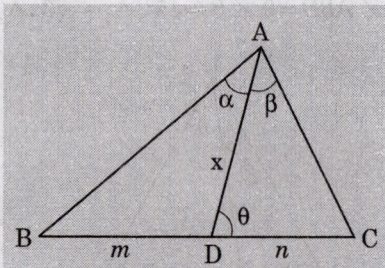

Fig. 13

Now $\dfrac{m}{n} = \dfrac{BD}{DC} = \dfrac{BD}{AD} \cdot \dfrac{AD}{DC}$ (Note)

$$= \frac{\sin\alpha}{\sin(\theta-\alpha)} \cdot \frac{\sin[\pi-(\theta+\beta)]}{\sin\beta}$$

or $\quad m\sin\beta\sin(\theta-\alpha) = n\sin\alpha\sin(\theta+\beta)$

or $\quad m\sin\beta\sin\theta\cos\alpha - m\sin\beta\cos\theta\sin\alpha$

$$= n\sin\alpha\sin\theta\cos\beta + n\sin\alpha\cos\theta\sin\beta$$

Dividing by $\sin\alpha\sin\beta\sin\theta$, we get

$$m\cot\alpha - m\cot\theta = n\cot\beta + n\cot\theta$$

or $\quad m\cot\alpha - n\cot\beta = (m+n)\cot\theta$

Similarly second result can be proved.

(b) From (1), we have

$$\frac{BD}{m} = \frac{DC}{n} = \frac{BD+DC}{m+n} = \frac{BC}{m+n} = \frac{a}{m+n}.$$

$$\therefore \quad BD = \frac{am}{m+n}, DC = \frac{an}{m+n} \qquad \text{...(1)}$$

Now $AC^2 = AD^2 + DC^2 - 2AD.DC\cos\theta$

or $\quad b^2 = x^2 + DC^2 - 2x\,DC\cos\theta$ ...(2)

Similarly, $\quad c^2 = x^2 + BD^2 - 2x\,BD\cos(\pi-\theta)$

or $c^2 = x^2 + BD^2 + 2x \cdot BD \cos\theta$ ...(3)

Multiplying (2) by m and (3) by n and adding, we get

$$mb^2 + nc^2 = (m+n)\, x^2 + m \cdot DC^2 + n \cdot BD^2$$
$$+ 2x \cos\theta \cdot (m \cdot DC - n \cdot BD)$$
$$= (m+n)\, x^2 + m \cdot DC^2 + n \cdot BD^2 \qquad \text{from (1)}$$

Hence substituting the values of BD and DC, we get

$$mb^2 + nc^2$$
$$= (m+n)\, x^2 + m \cdot \frac{a^2 n^2}{(m+n)^2} + n \cdot \frac{a^2 m^2}{(m+n)^2}$$
$$= (m+n)\, x^2 + \frac{a^2 mn}{m+n}$$

or $(m+n)(mb^2 + nc^2) = (m+n)^2\, x^2 + a^2 mn$

or $(m+n)^2\, x^2 = (m+n)(mb^2 + nc^2) - a^2 mn$

24. By m-n theorem, $\cot\theta = \dfrac{\sqrt{3}-1}{2}$

or $\tan\theta = \dfrac{2}{\sqrt{3}-1}$

∴ $\sin\theta = \dfrac{2}{\sqrt{(8-2\sqrt{3})}}$, $\cos\theta = \dfrac{\sqrt{3}-1}{\sqrt{(8-2\sqrt{3})}}$

Now by sine rule on $\Delta\, ADC$ in which
$AD = \dfrac{1}{\sqrt{(11-6\sqrt{3})}}$ and $DC = \dfrac{a}{2}$, we have

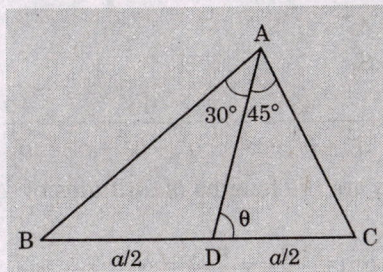

Fig. 14

$\dfrac{a/2}{\sin 45°} = \dfrac{AD}{\sin\{\pi - (\theta + 45°)\}} = \dfrac{AD}{\dfrac{1}{\sqrt{2}}(\sin\theta + \cos\theta)}$

$\dfrac{a}{2} = \dfrac{AD}{\sin\theta + \cos\theta} = \dfrac{\sqrt{8-2\sqrt{3}}}{\sqrt{3}+1} \cdot \dfrac{1}{\sqrt{(11-6\sqrt{3})}}$

$= \dfrac{\sqrt{8-2\sqrt{3}}}{\sqrt{(4+2\sqrt{3})}\,\sqrt{(11-6\sqrt{3})}} = \dfrac{\sqrt{8-2\sqrt{3}}}{\sqrt{(8-2\sqrt{3})}} = 1.$

∴ $a = 2$ ∵ $(\sqrt{3}+1)^2 = 4 + 2\sqrt{3}$

25. We are given $AM = p$, $BN = q$.
Let $\angle ACM = \theta$ and $\angle BCN = \phi$.
Then $\sin\theta = p/b$ and $\cos\theta = \sqrt{1 - p^2/b^2}$;
$\sin\phi = q/a$ and $\cos\phi = \sqrt{1 - q^2/a^2}$
Now $C = \pi - (\theta + \phi)$
∴ $\cos C = \cos[\pi - (\theta + \phi)] = -\cos(\theta + \phi)$

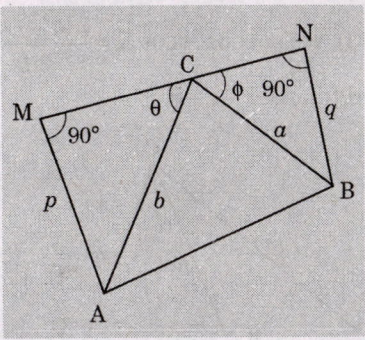

Fig. 315

or $\cos C = -\cos\theta\cos\phi + \sin\theta\sin\phi$

Hence $\cos C = -\sqrt{\left(1 - \dfrac{p^2}{b^2}\right)}\sqrt{\left(1 - \dfrac{q^2}{a^2}\right)} + \dfrac{p}{b} \cdot \dfrac{q}{a}$

or $\sqrt{\left(1 - \dfrac{p^2}{b^2}\right)}\sqrt{\left(1 - \dfrac{q^2}{a^2}\right)} = \dfrac{pq}{ab} - \cos C.$

Squaring,

$1 - \dfrac{p^2}{b^2} - \dfrac{q^2}{a^2} + \dfrac{p^2 q^2}{a^2 b^2} = \dfrac{p^2 q^2}{a^2 b^2} - \dfrac{2pq}{ab}\cos C + \cos^2 C.$

or $a^2 p^2 + b^2 q^2 - 2abpq \cos C$
$= a^2 b^2 (1 - \cos^2 C) = a^2 b^2 \sin^2 C.$

26. Median AD is perpendicular to AC. From B, draw BE perpendicular to CA produced. Then by geometry, we know that A is the mid-point of CE, so that $CA = AE = b$ and if $AD = y$ then $BE = 2y$.

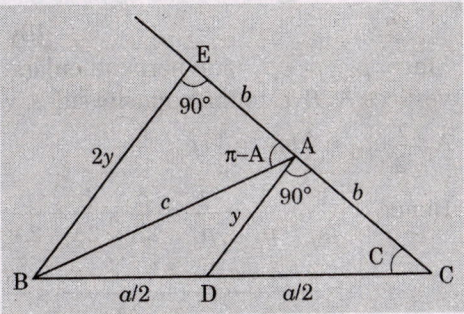

Fig. 16

$\cos C = \dfrac{b}{a/2} = \dfrac{2b}{a}$ ...(1)

$\cos(\pi - A) = b/c$

∴ $\cos A = -b/c$ ...(2)

∴ $\cos A \cos C = -2b^2/ac$ ...(3)

Now we have to eliminate b^2 from (3). Apply Pythagoras theorem on Δ^s BEA and DAC.

$4y^2 + b^2 = c^2$ (In $\Delta\, BEA$)

and $y^2 + b^2 = a^2/4$ (In $\Delta\, DAC$)

or $4y^2 + 4b^2 = a^2.$

Subtracting, we get $3b^2 = a^2 - c^2$

∴ $-b^2 = (c^2 - a^2)/3$

Putting in (3), we get $\cos A \cos C = \dfrac{2(c^2 - a^2)}{3ac}$.

27. Ans. (a) and (c).

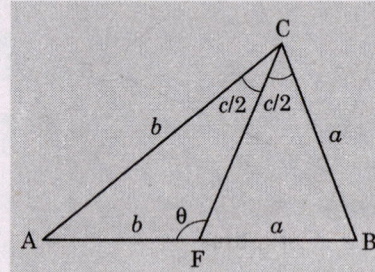

Fig, 17

$\Delta = \Delta_1 + \Delta_2$

$\dfrac{1}{2} ab \sin C = \dfrac{1}{2} b\,(CF) \sin \dfrac{C}{2} + \dfrac{1}{2} a\,(CF) \sin \dfrac{C}{2}$

or $\quad CF = \dfrac{ab \sin C}{(a+b) \sin \dfrac{C}{2}} = \dfrac{2ab \cos \dfrac{C}{2}}{a+b} \Rightarrow$ (a)

Again in $\Delta\,CFB$ by sine rule,

$\dfrac{CF}{\sin B} = \dfrac{a}{\sin(\pi - \theta)} = \dfrac{a}{\sin \theta} = \dfrac{a}{\sin\left(B + \dfrac{C}{2}\right)}$

$\because \quad \theta + B + \dfrac{C}{2} = \pi$

$\therefore \quad CF = \dfrac{a \sin B}{\sin\left(B + \dfrac{C}{2}\right)} = \dfrac{b \sin A}{\sin\left(B + \dfrac{C}{2}\right)} \Rightarrow$ (c)

(By sine rule)

28. (a) Since p_1, p_2, p_3 are perpendiculars from the vertices A, B, C to the opposite sides, we have

$\Delta = \dfrac{1}{2} a p_1 = \dfrac{1}{2} b p_2 = \dfrac{1}{2} c p_3$

Hence $\quad \dfrac{1}{p_1} + \dfrac{1}{p_2} - \dfrac{1}{p_3} = \dfrac{a}{2\Delta} + \dfrac{b}{2\Delta} - \dfrac{c}{2\Delta}$

$= \dfrac{a+b-c}{2\Delta} = \dfrac{a+b+c-2c}{2\Delta} = \dfrac{2s-2c}{2\Delta}$

$= \dfrac{s-c}{\Delta} = \dfrac{ab}{\Delta s} \cdot \dfrac{s(s-c)}{ab}$

$= \dfrac{ab}{\Delta s} \cos^2 \dfrac{1}{2} C = \dfrac{2ab}{(a+b+c)\Delta} \cos^2 \dfrac{1}{2} C.$

(b) Apply m-n theorem and use sine and cosine rule.

$(1 + 1) \cot \theta = 1 . \cot C - 1 . \cot B$

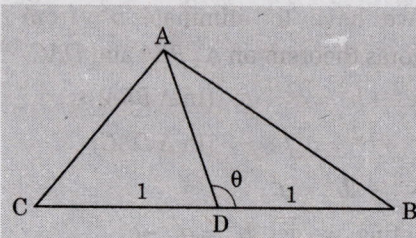

Fig. 18

or $\quad \cot \theta = \dfrac{1}{2}\left\{\dfrac{a^2 + b^2 - c^2}{2ab \sin C} - \dfrac{c^2 + a^2 - b^2}{2ca \sin B}\right\}$

$2\Delta = ab \sin C = ca \sin B$ etc.

29. $\cot \dfrac{1}{2} A + \cot \dfrac{1}{2} B + \cot \dfrac{1}{2} C$

$= \sqrt{\left\{\dfrac{s(s-a)}{(s-b)(s-c)}\right\}} + \sqrt{\left\{\dfrac{s(s-b)}{(s-c)(s-a)}\right\}}$

$\qquad\qquad + \sqrt{\left\{\dfrac{s(s-c)}{(s-a)(s-b)}\right\}}$

$= \dfrac{\sqrt{s}\,[(s-a) + (s-b) + (s-c)]}{\sqrt{[(s-a)(s-b)(s-c)]}}$

$= \dfrac{\sqrt{s}\,\sqrt{s}\,(3s - 2s)}{\sqrt{[s(s-a)(s-b)(s-c)]}} = \dfrac{s^2}{S}$

and $\cot A + \cot B + \cot C$

$= \dfrac{\cos A}{\sin A} + \dfrac{\cos B}{\sin B} + \dfrac{\cos C}{\sin C}$

$= \dfrac{(b^2 + c^2 - a^2)/2bc}{2S/bc} + \dfrac{(c^2 + a^2 - b^2)/2ca}{2S/ca}$

$\qquad\qquad + \dfrac{(a^2 + b^2 - c^2)/2ab}{2S/ab}$

$= (1/4S)\,[b^2 + c^2 - a^2 + c^2 \div a^2 - b^2$

$\qquad\qquad\qquad + a^2 + b^2 - c^2]$

$= \dfrac{a^2 + b^2 + c^2}{4S}. \qquad\qquad\qquad \dots(I)$

Hence R.H.S.

$= \dfrac{s^2}{S} \times \dfrac{4S}{a^2 + b^2 + c^2} = \dfrac{4 s^2}{a^2 + b^2 + c^2} = \dfrac{(a+b+c)^2}{a^2 + b^2 + c^2}.$

30. Since α, β, γ are the lengths of altitudes of $\Delta\,ABC$, we have

$\dfrac{1}{2} \alpha a = \dfrac{1}{2} \beta b = \dfrac{1}{2} \gamma c = \Delta \qquad\qquad \dots(1)$

Also $\quad \dfrac{1}{2} ab \sin C = \dfrac{1}{2} bc \sin A$

$\qquad\qquad = \dfrac{1}{2} ca \sin B = \Delta \qquad\qquad \dots(2)$

Hence from (1), we have

$\dfrac{1}{\alpha^2} + \dfrac{1}{\beta^2} + \dfrac{1}{\gamma^2} = \dfrac{a^2}{4\Delta^2} + \dfrac{b^2}{4\Delta^2} + \dfrac{c^2}{4\Delta^2} = \dfrac{a^2 + b^2 + c^2}{4\Delta^2}$

$\qquad\qquad\qquad\qquad\qquad\qquad \dots(3)$

And $\dfrac{1}{\Delta}(\cot A + \cot B + \cot C) = \dfrac{1}{\Delta}\dfrac{a^2 + b^2 + c^2}{4\Delta}$

$= \dfrac{a^2 + b^2 + c^2}{4\Delta^2}$ as in (I) of Q. 29.

$\alpha^{-2} + \beta^{-2} + \gamma^{-2} = (\cot A + \cot B + \cot C)/\Delta.$

31. $\Delta\,ABC = \Delta\,ABD + \Delta\,ADC$

$\dfrac{1}{2} bc \sin A = \dfrac{1}{2} c \alpha \sin \dfrac{A}{2} + \dfrac{1}{2} b \alpha \sin \dfrac{A}{2}$

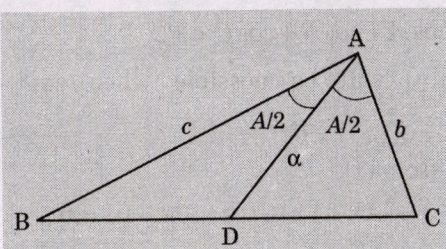

Fig. 19

Divide by $\alpha bc \sin (A/2)$

$$\frac{1}{\alpha} \cos \frac{A}{2} = \frac{1}{2} \left(\frac{1}{b} + \frac{1}{c} \right) \quad \text{or} \quad \alpha = \frac{2bc}{b+c} \cos \frac{A}{2}$$

Write similar expressions and add.

Lengths of medians :

If D be the mid-point, then we know that

$$b^2 + c^2 = 2(BD^2 + AD^2) = 2 \left(\frac{a^2}{4} + AD^2 \right)$$

$$\frac{2b^2 + 2c^2 - a^2}{4} = AD^2$$

or $\quad AD^2 = \dfrac{b^2 + c^2 + 2bc \cos A}{4}$

$\therefore \quad AD = \dfrac{1}{2} \sqrt{b^2 + c^2 + 2bc \cos A}$ etc.,

similar expressions for medians BE and CF.

32. $\angle OCB = C - \omega$ and

$$\angle BOC = 180° - \omega - (C - \omega) = 180° - C.$$

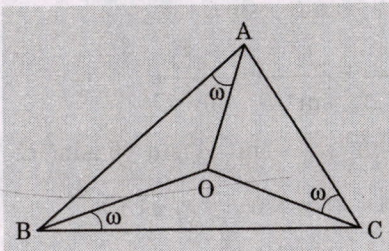

Fig. 20

Similarly $\angle AOB = 180° - B$.

Now from $\triangle OAB$, we have

$$\frac{OB}{\sin \omega} = \frac{AB}{\sin (180° - B)} = \frac{c}{\sin B}$$

so that $\quad OB = \dfrac{c \sin \omega}{\sin B} \quad \dots (1)$

Again from $\triangle OBC$, we get

$$\frac{OB}{\sin (C - \omega)} = \frac{BC}{\sin (180° - C)} = \frac{a}{\sin C}$$

$\therefore \quad OB = \dfrac{a \sin (C - \omega)}{\sin C} \quad \dots (2)$

From (1) and (2), we get

$$\frac{c \sin \omega}{\sin B} = \frac{a \sin (C - \omega)}{\sin C}$$

or $\quad k \sin C \sin \omega \sin C = k \sin A \sin B \sin (C - \omega)$

or $\quad \sin C \sin \omega \sin (A + B) = \sin A \sin B \sin (C - \omega)$

or $\quad \sin C \sin \omega \sin A \cos B + \sin C \sin \omega \cos A \sin B$
$\qquad = \sin A \sin B \sin C \cos \omega - \sin A \sin B \cos C \sin \omega$

Dividing by $\sin A \sin B \sin C \sin \omega$, we get

$$\cot B + \cot A = \cot \omega - \cot C$$

or $\quad \cot \omega = \cot A + \cot B + \cot C$

Squaring,

$$\cot^2 \omega = \cot^2 A + \cot^2 B + \cot^2 C + 2 \cot A \cot B$$
$$+ 2 \cot B \cot C + 2 \cot C \cot A$$

or $\quad \text{cosec}^2 \omega - 1 = \text{cosec}^2 A - 1 + \text{cosec}^2 B$
$$- 1 + \text{cosec}^2 C - 1 + 2$$

$[\because$ In a $\triangle, \cot A \cot B + \cot B \cot C + \cot C \cot A = 1]$

Q. 26 (b) P. 369-74

or $\quad \text{cosec}^2 \omega = \text{cosec}^2 A + \text{cosec}^2 B + \text{cosec}^2 C.$

33. From righangled $\triangle BCD$, we get

$$BD = \sqrt{p^2 + q^2}$$

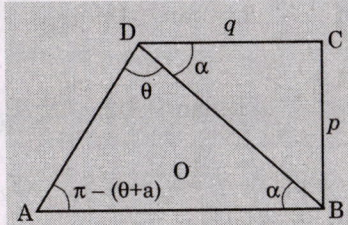

Fig. 21

Let $\angle ABD = \angle BDC = \alpha$

then $\qquad \angle DAB = \pi - (\alpha + \theta)$

and $\tan \alpha = p/q$.

Now from $\triangle ABD$, we have

$$\frac{AB}{\sin \theta} = \frac{BD}{\sin [\pi - (\theta + \alpha)]} = \frac{BD}{\sin (\theta + \alpha)}$$

$\therefore \quad AB = \dfrac{BD \sin \theta}{\sin (\theta + \alpha)} = \dfrac{BD^2 \sin \theta}{BD \sin (\theta + \alpha)}$

$$= \frac{BD^2 \sin \theta}{BD \sin \theta \cos \alpha + BD \cos \theta \sin \alpha}$$

$$= \frac{(p^2 + q^2) \sin \theta}{q \sin \theta + p \cos \theta}.$$

$[\because BD^2 = p^2 + q^2$ and $BD \cos \alpha = q$

$\qquad\qquad\qquad$ and $BD \sin \alpha = p]$.

34. If each ratio be k, then we have

$$b + c = 11k, \quad c + a = 12k, \quad a + b = 13k$$

so that $2(a + b + c) = 36k$ or $a + b + c = 18k$

$\therefore \quad a = 7k, b = 6k, c = 5k$

Now $\cos A = \dfrac{b^2 + c^2 - a^2}{2bc}$

$$= \frac{36 + 25 - 49}{2 \cdot 6 \cdot 5} = \frac{12}{60} = \frac{1}{5}$$

Similarly, $\cos B = 19/35$ and $\cos C = 5/7$

$\therefore \quad \cos A : \cos B : \cos C = \dfrac{1}{5} : \dfrac{19}{35} : \dfrac{5}{7} = 7 : 19 : 25.$

35. From the given ratios, we have

$$\frac{a+b}{(1+m^2)(1+n^2)} = \frac{a-b}{(1-m^2)(1-n^2)} = \frac{c}{(1-m^2)(1+n^2)}$$

$$\frac{a+b}{c} = \frac{1+m^2}{1-m^2}, \frac{a-b}{c} = \frac{1-n^2}{1+n^2}$$

Now as in **Q. 16 (c) P. 647-651** by sine rule we get

$$\frac{\cos\dfrac{A-B}{2}}{\cos\dfrac{A+B}{2}} = \frac{1+m^2}{1-m^2}, \frac{\sin\dfrac{A-B}{2}}{\sin\dfrac{A+B}{2}} = \frac{1-n^2}{1+n^2}$$

Apply Compo. & Divi. on both.

$$\tan\frac{A}{2}\tan\frac{B}{2} = m^2, \cot\frac{A}{2}\tan\frac{B}{2} = n^2$$

Multiplying and dividing them, we get

$$\therefore \quad \tan^2\frac{A}{2} = \frac{m^2}{n^2}, \tan^2\frac{B}{2} = m^2 n^2$$

$$\therefore \quad A = 2\tan^{-1}\frac{m}{n}, B = 2\tan^{-1}(mn)$$

$$\Delta = \frac{1}{2}bc\sin A = \frac{1}{2}bc \cdot \frac{2\tan(A/2)}{1+\tan^2(A/2)} \text{ etc.}$$

36. Remember

$$(x-\alpha)(x-\beta)(x-\gamma) = x^3 - x^2 S_1 + x S_2 - S_3$$

Since a, b, c are the roots of

$$x^3 - px^2 + qx - r = 0$$

$$s_1 = a+b+c = p = 2s \text{ or } s = p/2$$
$$s_2 = \Sigma ab = q, s_3 = abc = r$$
$$\Delta^2 = s(s-a)(s-b)(s-c)$$

$$= \frac{p}{2}\left(\frac{p}{2}-a\right)\left(\frac{p}{2}-b\right)\left(\frac{p}{2}-c\right)$$

$$= \frac{p}{2}\left\{\left(\frac{p}{2}\right)^3 - \left(\frac{p}{2}\right)^2 s_1 + \frac{p}{2}s_2 - s_3\right\}$$

$$= \frac{p}{2}\left\{\left(\frac{p}{2}\right)^3 - \frac{p^2}{4}p + \frac{p}{2}q - r\right\}$$

$$= \frac{p}{2}\left\{\frac{-p^3 + 4pq - 8r}{8}\right\}$$

$$\therefore \quad \Delta = \frac{1}{4}\left\{p(4pq - p^3 - 8r)\right\}^{1/2}$$

37. $E = 2\cos\dfrac{A+B}{2}\cos\dfrac{A-B}{2} + 1 - 2\sin^2\dfrac{C}{2} - \dfrac{3}{2}$

$$= -2\sin^2\frac{C}{2} + 2\cos\frac{A-B}{2}\sin\frac{C}{2} - \frac{1}{2}$$

$$= -2x^2 + 2x\cos\frac{A-B}{2} - \frac{1}{2}, x = \sin\frac{C}{2} \quad ...(1)$$

Now we know that sign of a quadratic is the same as that of the first term provided $\Delta < 0$.

Here $\Delta = 4\cos^2\dfrac{A-B}{2} - 4$, which is clearly –ive as

$\cos^2\dfrac{A-B}{2} < 1 \, (A \neq B).$

Hence the sign of E is same as of -2 i.e. –ive. $\therefore E < 0.$

$\therefore \quad \cos A + \cos B + \cos C < 3/2$

Equality will be possible when $\cos^2\dfrac{A-B}{2} = 1$

$(i.e. \Delta = 0)$ or $A = B$.

Then from (1),

$$4x^2 - 4x + 1 = 0 \quad \text{or} \quad (2x-1)^2 = 0$$

$$\therefore \quad x = \sin\frac{C}{2} = \frac{1}{2} \quad \therefore \quad C = 60° \quad \therefore \quad A = B = C = 60°$$

Hence the triangle is equilateral.

38. Since $\tan A$, $\tan B$, $\tan C$ are in A.P., we have

$$\tan A + \tan C = 2\tan B \quad ...(1)$$
$$\text{or} \quad x + \tan C = 2\tan B \quad ...(2)$$

where $x = \tan A$.

[Observe that if $\tan A$, $\tan B$, $\tan C$ are in A.P., then $\tan A$ is either the greatest or the least amongst $\tan A$, $\tan B$ and $\tan C$].

Now in a triangle ABC, we always have

$$\tan A\tan B\tan C = \tan A + \tan B + \tan C \quad ....(3)$$

$\therefore$ From (1), (2) and (3), we obtain

$$x\tan B(2\tan B - x) = 2\tan B + \tan B$$

$$\text{or} \quad x(2\tan B - x) = 3 \quad [\because \tan B \neq 0]$$

$$\therefore \quad \tan B = (3 + x^2)/2x.$$

and $\tan C = 2\tan B - x = (3 + x^2)/x - x = 3/x.$

Now in a ΔABC, we have

$$\frac{a}{\sin A} = \frac{b}{\sin B} = \frac{c}{\sin C}$$

$$\Rightarrow \quad \frac{a^2}{\sin^2 A} = \frac{b^2}{\sin^2 B} = \frac{c^2}{\sin^2 C}$$

Hence $a^2 : b^2 : c^2 = \sin^2 A : \sin^2 B : \sin^2 C$

But $\tan A = x \Rightarrow \sin A = x/\sqrt{1+x^2}$

$$\Rightarrow \quad \sin^2 A = x^2/(1+x^2)$$

and $\tan B = (3 + x^2)/2x$

$$\Rightarrow \quad \sin^2 B = (3+x^2)^2/[(3+x^2)^2 + 4x^2]$$

$$= (3+x^2)^2/(1+x^2)(9+x^2)$$

and $\tan C = 3/x \Rightarrow \sin C = 3/\sqrt{9+x^2}$

$$\Rightarrow \quad \sin^2 C = 9/(9+x^2)$$

$$\therefore \quad a^2 : b^2 : c^2 :: \frac{x^2}{1+x^2} : \frac{(3+x^2)^2}{(1+x^2)(9+x^2)}$$

$$: \frac{9}{x^2+9} :: x^2(9+x^2) : (3+x^2)^2 : 9(1+x^2).$$

Ambiguous case : When two sides say a and b are given and one angle opposite to these sides say A is given, then by sine rule $\dfrac{a}{\sin A} = \dfrac{b}{\sin B}$

$$\therefore \quad \sin B = \frac{b}{a}\sin A = k, \text{ say.}$$

There will be two values of angle B say B_1 and B_2 which will satisfy the equation $\sin B = k$.

Evidently these two values are supplementary i.e., if $B_1 = \alpha$ then $B_2 = \pi - \alpha$ i.e., $B_1 + B_2 = \pi$

39. (a) Let $AB = 2$ and $BC = 5$. $\angle ABC = 60°$ (given).

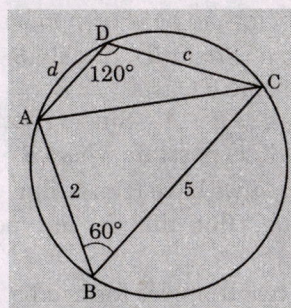

Fig. 22

Since the quadrilateral is cyclic,

$$\angle CDA = 180° - 60° = 120°$$

Let $CD = c$ and $DA = d$.

Area of quadrilateral $ABCD$

$$= \text{Area of } \Delta ABC + \text{Area of } \Delta ACD$$

$$= \frac{1}{2} AB.BC \sin 60° + \frac{1}{2} CD.DA \sin 120°$$

$$= \frac{1}{2}.2.5.\frac{\sqrt{3}}{2} + \frac{1}{2} c.d.\frac{\sqrt{3}}{2} = 4\sqrt{3} \qquad \text{(given)}$$

$$\therefore \quad \frac{\sqrt{3}}{4} cd = 4\sqrt{3} - \frac{5\sqrt{3}}{2} = \frac{3\sqrt{3}}{2}$$

or $\quad cd = 6$ ...(1)

Also $AB^2 + BC^2 - 2AB.BC \cos 60° = AC^2$

$$= CD^2 + DA^2 - 2CD.DA \cos 120°$$

by cosine rule.

or $\quad 4 + 25 - 2.2.5.\frac{1}{2} = c^2 + d^2 + cd$

or $\quad c^2 + d^2 + cd = 19$ or $c^2 + d^2 = 13$,

by (1) ...(2)

Now from (1) and (2), we have

$$c^2 + d^2 = 13, \quad c^2 d^2 = 36$$

$\therefore \quad c^2$ and d^2 are the roots of

$$t^2 - 13t + 36 = 0 \quad \therefore \quad t = 9, 4.$$

or $\quad c^2 = 9, d^2 = 4$ or $c^2 = 4, d^2 = 9$

$\therefore \quad c = 3, d = 2$ or $c = 2, d = 3$.

Hence the other two sides are 2 and 3.

(b) Ans. (i). Refer result (2) of part (a).

$$19 = c^2 + d^2 + cd = 9 + d^2 + 3d$$

$\therefore \quad d^2 + 3d - 10 = 0$

or $\quad (d + 5)(d - 2) = 0 \quad \therefore \quad d = 2$

(c) $AB = 1, BD = \sqrt{3}, OA = OB = OD = 1$

The given circle of radius 1 is also circum-circle of ΔABD.

$\therefore \quad R = 1$ for $\Delta ABD \quad \therefore \quad \frac{a}{\sin A} = 2R$

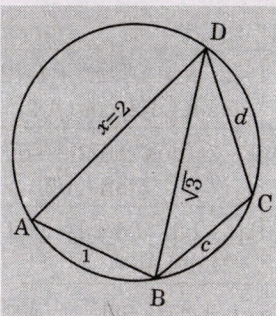

Fig. 23

$$\therefore \quad \frac{\sqrt{3}}{\sin A} = 2R = 2 \quad \therefore \quad \sin A = \frac{\sqrt{3}}{2} \quad \therefore \quad A = 60°$$

and hence $C = 120°$.

Also by cosine rule on ΔABD

$$(\sqrt{3})^2 = 1^2 + x^2 - 2x \cos 60°$$

or $\quad x^2 - x - 2 = 0$

$\therefore \quad (x - 2)(x + 1) = 0 \quad \therefore \quad x = 2$

Now the question reduces to **part (a) above.**

$$\Delta = \Delta_1 + \Delta_2$$

$$\Rightarrow \quad \frac{3\sqrt{3}}{4} = \frac{1}{2}(1.2.\sin 60°) + \frac{1}{2}(c.d \sin 120°)$$

or $\quad \frac{3\sqrt{3}}{4} = \frac{\sqrt{3}}{2} + \frac{\sqrt{3}}{4} cd$

$\therefore \quad cd = 1$ or $c^2 d^2 = 1$

Also by cosine rule on ΔBCD, we have

$$(\sqrt{3})^2 = c^2 + d^2 - 2cd \cos 120° = c^2 + d^2 + cd$$

$\therefore \quad c^2 + d^2 = 2$ as $cd = 1$

$\therefore \quad c^2$ and d^2 are the roots of $t^2 - 2t + 1 = 0$

$\therefore \quad c^2 = d^2 = 1$

$\therefore \quad BC = 1 = CD$ and $AD = x = 2$.

40. $\quad \frac{b}{c} = r\,(<1) \quad \Rightarrow \quad b = rc$ ...(1)

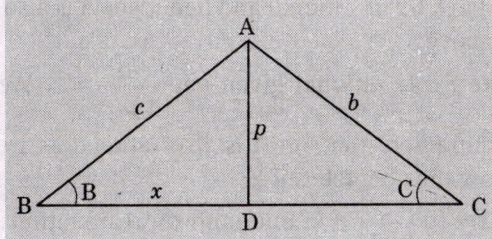

Fig. 24

Then $\quad a^2 = b^2 + c^2 - 2bc \cos A$

$$= r^2 c^2 + c^2 - 2rc^2 \cos A \qquad ...(2)$$

or $\quad a^2 = c^2 (r^2 + 1 - 2r \cos A)$

$\therefore \quad p = b \sin C = \frac{bc}{a} \sin A \qquad \left[\because \frac{\sin C}{c} = \frac{\sin A}{a} \right]$

$$= \frac{a r c^2 \sin A}{a^2}, \text{ by (1)}$$

$$= \frac{a\,r\,c^2 \sin A}{c^2\,(r^2 + 1 - 2r\cos A)} = \frac{ar\sin A}{r^2 + 1 - 2r\cos A}, \text{ by (2)}$$

$$\therefore \quad \frac{p}{ar} = \frac{2\sin(A/2)\cos(A/2)}{(r^2 + 1) - 2r[\cos^2(A/2) - \sin^2(A/2)]}$$

$$= \frac{2\tan(A/2)}{(r^2 + 1)[1 + \tan^2(A/2)] - 2r[1 - \tan^2(A/2)]}$$

$$= \frac{2\tan(A/2)}{(1 - r)^2 + (1 + r)^2 \tan^2(A/2)}$$

$$\therefore \quad (1+r)^2 \tan^2 \frac{A}{2} - \frac{2ra}{p}\tan\frac{A}{2} + (1-r)^2 = 0 \quad \dots(3)$$

Since $\tan(A/2)$ must be real, we have

$$\left(\frac{2ra}{p}\right)^2 - 4(1+r)^2 (1-r)^2 \geq 0$$

or $\quad \dfrac{2ra}{p} \geq 2(1+r)(1-r) \qquad [\because r < 1]$

or $\quad p\,\dfrac{r\alpha}{1 - r^2}.$

41. (i) $\Rightarrow$ (ii) a, b, c and Δ are rational (given)

$\therefore \quad s, s-a, s-b, s-c$ are also rational

Now $\tan \dfrac{B}{2} = \sqrt{\left\{\dfrac{(s-c)(s-a)}{s(s-b)}\right\}}$

$$= \frac{\sqrt{[s(s-a)(s-b)(s-c)]}}{s(s-b)}$$

$$= \frac{\Delta}{s(s-b)} = \text{Rational etc. by (i)}$$

(ii) $\Rightarrow$ (iii) $\sin B = \dfrac{2\tan(B/2)}{1 + \tan^2(B/2)} = \text{rational by (ii)}$

Similarly $\sin C$ is also rational

$$\tan\left(\frac{A}{2}\right) = \cot\left(\frac{B+C}{2}\right) \text{ by Comp. Rule.}$$

$$= \frac{1 - \tan(B/2)\tan(C/2)}{\tan(B/2) + \tan(C/2)} = \text{rational by (ii)}$$

$\therefore \quad \tan(A/2)$ is rational and hence $\sin A$ is also rational as above.

Note : a is rational given and $\dfrac{a}{\sin A} = k$. We cannot

assume here that $\sin A$ is also rational as we do not know the character of k.

(iii) $\Rightarrow$ (i) $\dfrac{a}{\sin A} = k$. But a and $\sin A$ are rational by (iii)

$\therefore \quad k$ is rational. Hence by sine rule $\dfrac{b}{\sin B} = \dfrac{c}{\sin C} = k$

implies that b and c are also rational as $\sin B, \sin C$ and k are rational.

Also $\Delta = \dfrac{1}{2} bc\sin A$ is also rational.

42. Ans. (a) and (d).

We have $\dfrac{\sin A}{a} = \dfrac{\sin B}{b} \Rightarrow a\sin B = b\sin A$

(a) $b\sin A = a \Rightarrow a\sin B = a$

$\Rightarrow \quad \sin B = 1 \Rightarrow B = \pi/2.$

Since $A < \pi/2$, the ΔABC is possible.

(b) $b\sin A > a \Rightarrow a\sin B > a \Rightarrow \sin B > 1,$

which is impossible. Hence the possibility (b) is ruled out.

Similarly (c) can be shown to be impossible.

(d) $b\sin A < a \Rightarrow a\sin B < a \Rightarrow \sin B < 1.$

so value of $\angle B$ exists.

Now $b > a \Rightarrow B > A$. Since $A < \pi/2.$

The ΔABC is possible where $B > $ or $< \pi/2.$

(e) Since $b = a$, we have $B = A$. But $A > \pi/2$

$\therefore \quad B > \pi/2$. But this is not possible for any triangle.

43. (a) Let the two triangles formed be AB_1C and AB_2C. Draw $CN \perp$ to AB_1. Then since ΔB_1CB_2 is isosceles, we have $\angle B_1CN = \angle B_2CN = \theta$, say.

Since $\quad \angle A = 45°,$

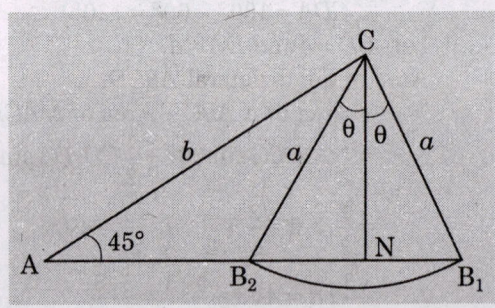

Fig. 25

we have $CN = b\sin 45° = b/\sqrt{2}.$

Now $a^2 = b^2 + c^2 - 2bc\cos A$

$$= b^2 + c^2 - 2bc\cos 45° = b^2 + c^2 - \sqrt{2}\,bc$$

or $\quad c^2 - \sqrt{2}\,bc + b^2 - a^2 = 0$

If c_1, c_2 are the two values of c, then

$$c_1 + c_2 = \sqrt{2}\,b \text{ and } c_1 c_2 = b^2 - a^2. \qquad \dots(1)$$

$\therefore \quad c_1^2 + c_2^2 = (c_1 + c_2)^2 - 2c_1 c_2$

$$= 2b^2 - 2(b^2 - a^2) = 2a^2 \qquad \dots(2)$$

Now $\cos B_1CB_2 = \cos 2\theta = 2\cos^2\theta - 1.$

$$= 2\cdot\left(\frac{CN}{a}\right)^2 - 1 = 2\cdot\frac{b^2}{2a^2} - 1 \quad (\because CN = b/\sqrt{2})$$

$$\frac{b^2 - a^2}{a^2} = \frac{c_1 c_2}{\frac{1}{2}(c_1^2 + c_2^2)} = \frac{2c_1 c_2}{c_1^2 + c_2^2} \text{ by (1) and (2)}$$

(b) We have $a^2 = b^2 + c^2 - 2bc\cos A$

or $\quad c^2 - 2bc\cos A + b^2 - a^2 = 0$

Let the two values of c be c_1 and c_2. Then

$$c_1 + c_2 = 2b\cos A \text{ and } c_1 c_2 = b^2 - a^2.$$

Hence $(c_1 - c_2)^2 = (c_1 + c_2)^2 - 4c_1 c_2$

$$= 4b^2\cos^2 A - 4(b^2 - a^2)$$

$$= 4[a^2 - b^2(1 - \cos^2 A)]$$
$$= 4[a^2 - b^2 \sin^2 A]$$
$$\therefore \quad c_1 \sim c_2 = 2\sqrt{a^2 - b^2 \sin^2 A}.$$

44. As in Q 43 (a), the quadratic giving the two values c_1, c_2 of c is $c^2 - 2bc \cos A + (b^2 - a^2) = 0$.

Then we have

(i) $\qquad c_1 + c_2 = 2b \cos A$ ...(1)

and $c_1 c_2 = b^2 - a^2$ ...(2)

(ii) From (1) and (2),

$$(c_1 + c_2)^2 = 4b^2 \cos^2 A = 4(c_1 c_2 + a^2)\cos^2 A$$

or $c_1^2 + 2c_1 c_2 + c_2^2 - 4c_1 c_2 \cos^2 A = 4a^2 \cos^2 A$

or $c_1^2 - 2c_1 c_2 (2\cos^2 A - 1) + c_2^2 = 4a^2 \cos^2 A$

or $c_1^2 - 2c_1 c_2 \cos 2A + c_2^2 = 4a^2 \cos^2 A$

45. (a) Here the quadratic for third side b is given by

$$b^2 - 2bc \cos A + (c^2 - a^2) = 0$$

$\therefore \quad b_1 + b_2 = 2c \cos A$ ...(1)

and $b_1 b_2 = c^2 - a^2$ ...(2)

Also it is given that

$$b_2 = 2b_1 \qquad ...(3)$$

Hence from (1) and (3),

$$3b_1 = 2c \cos A \qquad ...(4)$$

and from (2) and (3),

$$2b_1^2 = c^2 - a^2 \qquad ...(5)$$

Finally from (4) and (5), we have

$$2 \cdot \frac{4c^2 \cos^2 A}{9} = c^2 - a^2$$

or $8c^2(1 - \sin^2 A) = 9c^2 - 9a^2$

or $9a^2 = c^2(1 + 8\sin^2 A)$

Hence $3a = c\sqrt{1 + 8\sin^2 A}$.

(b) c_1, c_2 are two values of c, we have

$$c_1 + c_2 = 2b \cos A. \quad \text{[Part (b)]} \qquad ...(1)$$

Also B_1, B_2 are supplementary angles, that is

$B_2 = 180° - B_1$ so that $\sin B_2 = \sin B_1$

Hence $\dfrac{\sin C_1}{\sin B_1} + \dfrac{\sin C_2}{\sin B_2} = \dfrac{\sin C_1}{\sin B_1} + \dfrac{\sin C_2}{\sin B_1}$

$$= \frac{\sin C_1 + \sin C_2}{\sin B_1}$$

$$= \frac{kc_1 + kc_2}{kb} = \frac{c_1 + c_2}{b} = 2\cos A, \text{ from (1)}$$

(c) Sum of the areas of the two triangles

$$= \frac{1}{2} ab \sin C_1 + \frac{1}{2} ab \sin C_2$$

$$= \frac{1}{2} ab (\sin C_1 + \sin C_2) \qquad ...(1)$$

Now from part (b), we have

$$c_1 + c_2 = 2b \cos A$$

or $k(\sin C_1 + \sin C_2) = 2k \sin B \cos A$

or $\sin C_1 + \sin C_2 = 2 \sin B \cos A$

Hence from (1),

sum of the areas of the two triangles

$$= \frac{1}{2} ab \cdot 2 \sin B \cos A$$

$$= b^2 \left(\frac{a \sin B}{b}\right) \cos A = b^2 \sin A \cos A$$

$$= \frac{1}{2} b^2 \cdot 2 \sin A \cos A = \frac{1}{2} b^2 \sin 2A.$$

46. (a) $\sec^2 A = 1 + \tan^2 A = \dfrac{8}{5}$ $\therefore \cos A = \sqrt{\left(\dfrac{5}{8}\right)}$

or $b^2 + c^2 - a^2 = 2bc \cdot \dfrac{\sqrt{5}}{2\sqrt{2}}$. Put $a = \dfrac{2b}{3}$

$\therefore \quad b^2 + c^2 - \dfrac{4b^2}{9} = bc \dfrac{\sqrt{5}}{\sqrt{2}}$

$$c^2 - cb\sqrt{\left(\frac{5}{2}\right)} + \frac{5b^2}{9} = 0$$

$\therefore \quad c_1 + c_2 = b\sqrt{\left(\dfrac{5}{2}\right)}, c_1 c_2 = \dfrac{5b^2}{9}$

$\therefore \quad (c_1 - c_2)^2 = (c_1 + c_2)^2 - 4c_1 c_2$

$$= \frac{5b^2}{2} - \frac{20}{9} b^2 = \frac{5}{18} b^2$$

$\therefore \quad c_1 - c_2 = \dfrac{b}{3}\sqrt{\left(\dfrac{5}{2}\right)}$

$\therefore \quad c_1 = \dfrac{2b}{3}\sqrt{\left(\dfrac{5}{2}\right)}, c_2 = \dfrac{b}{3}\sqrt{\left(\dfrac{5}{2}\right)}$

$\therefore \quad c_1 = 2c_2.$

(b) $\dfrac{4}{\sin C} = \dfrac{\sqrt{6}}{\sin 30°}$ $\therefore \sin C = \dfrac{2}{\sqrt{6}} = \sqrt{\dfrac{2}{3}}$

There will be two values of C which will be supplementary. Hence there will be two such triangles.

Again by cosine rule,

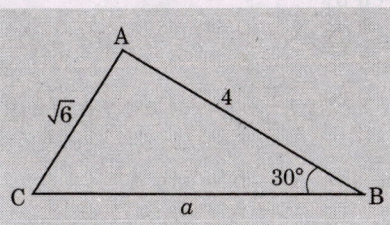

Fig. 26

$$(\sqrt{6})^2 = a^2 + 16 - 2a \cdot 4 \cos 30°$$

or $a^2 - 4\sqrt{3} a + 10 = 0$

$\therefore \quad a = \dfrac{4\sqrt{3} \pm \sqrt{48 - 40}}{2} = 2\sqrt{3} \pm \sqrt{2}$

Above gives the values of two sides.

Problems Set (3)

1. If in a triangle ABC, the altitudes from the vertices upon the opposite sides are in H.P. then $\sin A, \sin B, \sin C$ are in

(a) A.P.　　(b) G.P.　　(c) H.P.　　(d) A.G.S.

(AIEEE 2005)

Sol. Ans. (a). **Refer Q. 29 (b) P. 648-654**, the three altitudes AD, BE and CF are $c \sin B, a \sin C, b \sin A$ which are in H.P. or $\sin B \sin C, \sin C \sin A, \sin A \sin B$ are in H.P.

or $\dfrac{1}{\sin B \sin C}, \dfrac{1}{\sin C \sin A}, \dfrac{1}{\sin A \sin B}$ are in A.P.

or $\sin A, \sin B, \sin C$ are in A.P.
We have multiplied each term by $\sin A \sin B \sin C$.

2. The sides of a triangle are $\sin \alpha$, $\cos \alpha$ and $\sqrt{1 + \sin \alpha \cos \alpha}$ for some $\alpha : 0 < \alpha < \dfrac{\pi}{2}$, then greatest angle of the triangle is :

(a) 60°　　(b) 90°　　(c) 120°　　(d) 150°

(AIEEE 2003)

Sol. Ans. (c). Apply cosine rule. Angle opposite to $\sqrt{1 + \sin \alpha \cos \alpha}$ is greatest.

$\therefore \quad \cos \theta = \dfrac{\sin^2 \alpha + \cos^2 \alpha - (1 + \sin \alpha \cos \alpha)}{2 \sin \alpha \cos \alpha} = -\dfrac{1}{2}$

$\therefore \quad \theta = 120°$

3. In a triangle $\Sigma (b + c) \cos A = 3\sqrt[3]{abc}$, then the triangle is

(a) rt. angled　　　　(b) isosceles

(c) equilateral　　　　(d) none

Sol. Ans. (c). By **Q. 1 (a) P. 646**, we have $a + b + c = 3\sqrt[3]{abc}$

But $(a + b + c) \geq 3\sqrt[3]{abc}$ as A.M.>G.M.

Equality is possible only when $a = b = c$, i.e., Δ is equilateral.

4. The sides of a triangle are $\sqrt{(b^2 + c^2)}, \sqrt{(c^2 + a^2)}, \sqrt{(a^2 + b^2)}$ where $a, b, c > 0$. The area of the triangle is given by

(a) $\dfrac{1}{2}\sqrt{\Sigma b^2 c^2}$　　　　(b) $\dfrac{1}{2}\sqrt{\Sigma a^4}$

(c) $\dfrac{\sqrt{3}}{2}\sqrt{\Sigma b^2 c^2}$　　　　(d) $\dfrac{\sqrt{3}}{2}(\Sigma bc)$

Sol. Ans. (a). $\Delta = \dfrac{1}{2} b'c' \sin A'$

$\cos A' = \dfrac{b'^2 + c'^2 - a'^2}{2b'c'}$

or $\cos A' = \dfrac{(c^2 + a^2) + (a^2 + b^2) - (b^2 + c^2)}{2\sqrt{\{(c^2 + a^2)(a^2 + b^2)\}}}$

$= \dfrac{2a^2}{2\sqrt{\{(c^2 + a^2)(a^2 + b^2)\}}}$

$\therefore \quad \sin^2 A' = 1 - \cos^2 A'$

$= 1 - \dfrac{a^4}{c^2 b^2 + c^2 a^2 + a^2 b^2 + a^4} = \dfrac{\Sigma (b^2 c^2)}{b'^2 c'^2}$ ...(I)

$\therefore \quad$ Area $= \dfrac{1}{2} b'c' \sin A' = \dfrac{1}{2}\sqrt{\Sigma b^2 c^2}$ by (I)

5. The sides of a triangle ABC are 6, 7, 8, the smallest angle being C, then

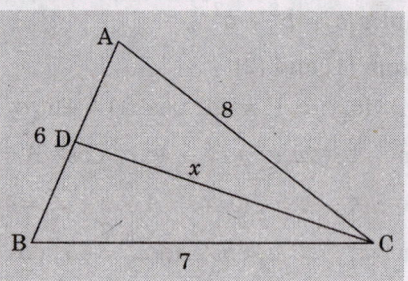

Fig. 27

(a) the length of altitude from C is

(a) $\dfrac{7}{2}\sqrt{15}$　　　　(b) $\dfrac{7}{3}\sqrt{15}$

(c) $\dfrac{7}{4}\sqrt{15}$　　　　(d) none

Sol. Ans. (c).

$2s = 21 \quad \therefore \quad s = \dfrac{21}{2}, s - a = \dfrac{7}{2}, s - b = \dfrac{5}{2}, s - c = \dfrac{9}{2}$

$\therefore$ If Δ be the area, then

$2\Delta = [s(s - a)(s - b)(s - c)]^{1/2} = \dfrac{21}{2}\sqrt{15}$

If x be the altitude from C to AB, then

$\dfrac{1}{2} x \times AB = \Delta \quad$ or $\quad 3x = \dfrac{21}{4}\sqrt{15}$

$\therefore \quad x = \dfrac{7}{4}\sqrt{15}$

(b) the length of the median from C is

(a) $\sqrt{\dfrac{95}{1}}$　　　　(b) $\sqrt{\dfrac{95}{2}}$

(c) $\sqrt{\dfrac{95}{3}}$　　　　(d) none

Sol. Ans. (b).

If x be the length of the median then applying cosine rule on Δ^s ACD and BCD, we get

$8^2 = x^2 + 3^2 - 2.x.3 \cos \theta$

$7^2 = x^2 + 3^2 - 2x.3 \cos (\pi - \theta)$

$113 = 2(x^2 + 9) \quad \therefore \quad 2x^2 = 95 \quad \Rightarrow \quad x = \sqrt{\dfrac{95}{2}}$

(c) the length of internal bisector of angle C is ...

Sol. Ans. $\dfrac{14}{5}\sqrt{6}$.

If x be the length of internal bisector of $\angle C$, then it divides the opposite side in the ratio of arms of the angle.

$\therefore \quad \dfrac{AD}{8} = \dfrac{BD}{7} = \dfrac{AD+BD}{8+7} = \dfrac{6}{15} = \dfrac{2}{5} \quad \therefore \quad AD = \dfrac{16}{5}$

Applying cosine formula on $\triangle ADC$,

$AD^2 = x^2 + 8^2 - 2 \cdot x \cdot 8 \cos \dfrac{C}{2}$

$\left(\dfrac{16}{5}\right)^2 = x^2 + 64 - 16x \cdot \cos \dfrac{C}{2}$ ...(1)

where $\cos \dfrac{C}{2} = \sqrt{\dfrac{s(s-c)}{ab}} = \dfrac{3}{4}\sqrt{\dfrac{3}{2}}$

Hence from (1) on putting for $\cos \dfrac{C}{2}$, we get $x = \dfrac{14}{5}\sqrt{6}$.

6. In a triangle ABC we define

$x = \tan \dfrac{B-C}{2} \tan \dfrac{A}{2}$,

$y = \tan \dfrac{C-A}{2} \tan \dfrac{B}{2}$ and $z = \tan \dfrac{A-B}{2} \tan \dfrac{C}{2}$

then the value of $x + y + z$ (in terms of x, y, z) is

(a) xyz (b) $-xyz$ (c) $2xyz$ (d) none

Sol. Ans. (b).

$\tan \dfrac{B-C}{2} = \dfrac{b-c}{b+c} \cot \dfrac{A}{2}$, Napier's analogy

$\therefore \quad \dfrac{x}{1} = \tan \dfrac{B-C}{2} \tan \dfrac{A}{2} = \dfrac{b-c}{b+c} \quad \therefore \quad \dfrac{1+x}{1-x} = \dfrac{2b}{2c} = \dfrac{b}{c}$

Similarly $\dfrac{1+y}{1-y} = \dfrac{c}{a}$ and $\dfrac{1+z}{1-z} = \dfrac{a}{b}$

$\therefore \quad \dfrac{(1+x)(1+y)(1+z)}{(1-x)(1-y)(1-z)} = \dfrac{b}{c} \cdot \dfrac{c}{a} \cdot \dfrac{a}{b} = 1$

or $1 + \Sigma x + \Sigma xy + xyz = 1 - \Sigma x + \Sigma xy - xyz$

$\therefore \quad 2\Sigma x = -2xyz \quad \therefore \quad \Sigma x - xyz \Rightarrow (b)$

7. Can there exist triangles ABC satisfying the following relations ? Write yes or no giving reasons :

(i) $\tan A + \tan B + \tan C = 0$

(ii) $\dfrac{\sin A}{2} = \dfrac{\sin B}{3} = \dfrac{\sin C}{7}$

(iii) $(a+b)^2 = c^2 + ab$ and $\sqrt{2}(\sin A + \cos A) = \sqrt{3}$.

(iv) $\sin A + \sin B = \dfrac{\sqrt{3}+1}{2}$,

$\cos A \cos B = \dfrac{\sqrt{3}}{4} = \sin A \sin B$.

Note : This question be done.

Sol. (i) No. Since $A + B + C = \pi$

$\therefore \quad \Sigma \tan A = \tan A \tan B \tan C = 0$

$\Rightarrow$ Either $A = 0$ or $B = 0$ or $C = 0$ which is not possible in a triangle.

(ii) No. By sine rule, $\dfrac{a}{2} = \dfrac{b}{3} = \dfrac{c}{7} = \dfrac{a+b}{5}$

$\therefore \quad a+b = \dfrac{5}{7}c < c$. Not possible as sum of two sides is always greater than the third.

(iii) Yes.

$a^2 + b^2 - c^2 + ab = 0 \Rightarrow 2ab \cos C + ab = 0$

$\cos C = -\dfrac{1}{2} \Rightarrow C = 120°$.

Also from 2nd relation

We have $\sin\left(A + \dfrac{\pi}{4}\right) = \dfrac{\sqrt{3}}{2} = \sin \dfrac{\pi}{3} \quad \therefore \quad A = 15°$

and hence $B = 45°$. Such a $\triangle$ is possible.

(iv) Yes. Adding and subtracting the relation in 2nd,

$\cos(A-B) = \dfrac{\sqrt{3}}{4} + \dfrac{\sqrt{3}}{4} = \dfrac{\sqrt{3}}{2} \quad \therefore \quad A - B = 30°$

$\cos(A+B) = 0 \quad \therefore \quad A + B = 90°$

$\therefore \quad A = 60°, B = 30°$

$\therefore \quad C = 180° - (A+B) = 90°$

These values also satisfy the first given relation.

8. In a triangle ABC with fixed base BC, the vertex A moves such that $\cos B + \cos C = 4 \sin^2 \dfrac{A}{2}$. If a, b and c denote the lengths of the sides of the triangle opposite to the angles A, B and C respectively, then

(a) $b + c = 4a$

(b) $b + c = 2a$

(c) locus of point A is an ellipse

(d) locus of point A is a pair of straight lines

                 (IIT JEE 2009)

Sol. Ans. (b) and (c).

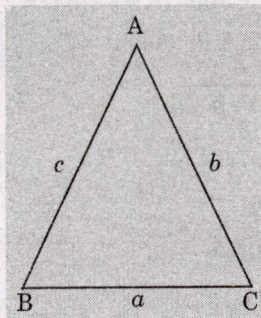

Fig. 28

$\cos B + \cos C = 4 \sin^2 \dfrac{A}{2}$

$\Rightarrow \quad 2 \cos \dfrac{B+C}{2} \cos \dfrac{B-C}{2} = 4 \sin^2 \dfrac{A}{2}$

$\Rightarrow \quad 2 \sin \dfrac{A}{2} \left[\cos \dfrac{B-C}{2} - 2 \sin \dfrac{A}{2}\right] = 0$

$\Rightarrow \quad \cos\left(\dfrac{B-C}{2}\right) - 2 \cos\left(\dfrac{B+C}{2}\right) = 0$ as $\sin \dfrac{A}{2} \neq 0$

$\Rightarrow \quad -\cos \dfrac{B}{2} \cos \dfrac{C}{2} + 3 \sin \dfrac{B}{2} \sin \dfrac{C}{2} = 0$

$\Rightarrow \quad \tan \dfrac{B}{2} + \tan \dfrac{C}{2} = \dfrac{1}{3}$

$\Rightarrow \quad \sqrt{\dfrac{(s-a)(s-c)}{s(s-b)} \cdot \dfrac{(s-b)(s-a)}{s(s-c)}} = \dfrac{1}{3}$

$\Rightarrow \quad \dfrac{s-a}{s} = \dfrac{1}{3} \Rightarrow 2s = 3a \Rightarrow b+c = 2a$

$\Rightarrow$ locus of point A is an ellipse.

MISCELLANEOUS EXERCISE

Matching Entries

♦ *Match the entries of Column-I and Column-II.*

1.   **Column-I**   **Column-II**

(a)   If $\dfrac{\cos A}{a} = \dfrac{\cos B}{b} = \dfrac{\cos C}{c}$ then the area of the triangle when side $a = 2$ is   1. $\pi/2$

(b)   In a triangle ABC, $\dfrac{1 + \cos(A - B)\cos C}{1 + \cos(A - C)\cos B} =$ 2. $\sqrt{3}$

(c)   In a triangle ABC, if $\dfrac{2\cos A}{a} + \dfrac{\cos B}{b} + \dfrac{2\cos C}{c} = \dfrac{a}{bc} + \dfrac{b}{ca}$, then $\angle A$ is   3. $8/15$

(d)   In a triangle ABC, if $S = a^2 - (b - c)^2$, then the value of $\tan A$ is   4. $\dfrac{a^2 + b^2}{a^2 + c^2}$

2.   If a, b, c are the sides of the triangle ABC and a^2, b^2, c^2 are the roots of the equation $x^3 - px^2 + qx - \lambda = 0$, then match the entries of col. I with those of col. II.

   Column-I   **Column-II**

(a) $\dfrac{\cos A}{a} + \dfrac{\cos B}{b} + \dfrac{\cos C}{c} = \dfrac{1}{2}$ (p) $p = 2, q = 1, \lambda = 4$

(b) $a\cos A + b\cos B + c\cos C = 0$ (q) $p = 1, q = 1/4, \lambda = 1$

(c) $\sin 2A + \sin 2B + \sin 2C = 0$ (r) $p = 3, q = 9/4, \lambda = 9$

(d) $a\sin A + b\sin B + c\sin C = 2\Delta$ (s) $p = 4, q = 4, \lambda = 2$

3.   In a triangle ABC,

   Column-I   **Column-II**

(a) $(c - a)^2 = b^2 - ac$ and $\cos B + \sin C = 3/2$ (p) $A = 30°$

(b) A, B and C are in A.P. and $3A = C$ (q) $B = 60°$

(c) $\dfrac{1}{a+b} + \dfrac{1}{b+c} = \dfrac{3}{a+b+c}$ (r) $C = 90°$

4.   In a triangle ABC,

   Column-I   **Column-II**

(a) $b\cos C + c\cos B$ (p) a

(b) $b^2 + c^2 - 2bc\cos A$ (q) $(a + b + c)\,a$

(c) $bc\sin A$ (r) a^2

(d) $b\sin A - a\sin B$ (s) 0

Answers

1.   (a) → 2, (b) → 4, (c) → 1, (d) → 3   2.   (a), (d) → (p, q, r); (b), (c) → (p, q, r, s)

3.   (a, b) → (p, q, r), (c) → (q)   4.   (a) → (p), (b) → (r), (c) → (q), (d) → (s)

Solutions

1.   (a)   → (2).   By sine rule $\cot A = \cot B = \cot C$

   ∴ Δ is equilateral   ∴ $\Delta = \dfrac{1}{2} a \cdot a \sin 60°$

$= \sqrt{3}$, as $a = 2$

(b)   → (4). **See Q. 15 (a) P. 647-651**

(c)   → (1). **See Q. 8 (c) P. 646-650**

(d)   → (3). **See Q. 37 (a) P. 648-656**

   ∴ $\tan A = \dfrac{2\tan(A/2)}{1 - \tan^2(A/2)} = \dfrac{8}{15}$

2.   Ans. (a), (d) → (p, q, r); (b), (c) → (p, q, r, s)

   Given $\sum a^2 = p, \sum a^2 b^2 = q, a^2 b^2 c^2 = \lambda$

(a) $\dfrac{\cos A}{a} = \dfrac{1}{a} \dfrac{b^2 + c^2 - a^2}{2bc}$

∴ $\sum\left(\dfrac{\cos A}{a}\right) = \dfrac{a^2 + b^2 + c^2}{2abc} = \dfrac{p}{2\sqrt{\lambda}} = \dfrac{1}{2}$ (given)

$\Rightarrow$ $p^2 = \lambda$ which is true in (p), (q) and (r).

(b) $a\cos A = a \cdot \dfrac{(b^2 + c^2 - a^2)}{2bc} = a^2 \cdot \dfrac{b^2 + c^2 - a^2}{2abc}$

∴ $\sum a\cos A = \dfrac{1}{2abc}[\sum a^2(b^2 + c^2) - \sum a^4]$

$= \dfrac{1}{2abc}[2\sum a^2 b^2 - \{(\sum a^2)^2 - 2\sum a^2 b^2\}]$

$= \dfrac{1}{2abc}[4\sum a^2 b^2 - (\sum a^2)^2]$

$= \dfrac{1}{2abc}[4q - p^2] = 0$ (given)   ∴ $p^2 = 4q$

The above relation is satisfied by all (p), (q), (r), (s).

(c) It follows from (b). ∴ (c) → (p, q, r, s)

(d) $\frac{1}{2} bc \sin A = \Delta$ ∴ $\sin A = \frac{2\Delta}{bc}$

∴ $a \sin A = 2\Delta \cdot \frac{a}{bc} = \frac{2\Delta a^2}{abc}$

$\sum a \sin A = \frac{2\Delta}{abc}(a^2 + b^2 + c^2) = \frac{2\Delta p}{\sqrt{\lambda}} = 2\Delta.$ (given)

∴ $p^2 = \lambda$

This is satisfied by all (p), (q), (r), (s).

3. **Ans.** (a, b) → (p, q, r), (c) → (q)

(a) Given $c^2 + a^2 - b^2 = ac$ or $\frac{c^2 + a^2 - b^2}{2ac} = \frac{1}{2}$

∴ $\cos B = \frac{1}{2} \Rightarrow B = 60°$

∴ $\sin C = \frac{3}{2} - \cos B = \frac{3}{2} - \frac{1}{2} = 1$ ∴ $C = 90°$

and hence, $A = 180° - (90° + 60°) = 30°$

∴ (a) → (p, q, r)

(b) Given $2B = A + C = 180° - B$

∴ $3B = 180°$ or $B = 60°$

∴ $A + C = 120°$ or $A + 3A = 120°$ ∴ $A = 30°$

∴ $C = 90°$ ∴ (b) → (p, q, r)

(c) $(a + b + c)(a + b + c + b) = 3(a + b)(b + c)$

or $(a + b + c)^2 + b(a + b + c) = 3(b^2 + ab + bc + ca)$

$\sum a^2 + 2 \sum ab = 3 \sum ab + 2b^2 - b(c + a)$

$a^2 + c^2 - b^2 = \sum ab - b(c + a) = ca$

∴ $\frac{c^2 + a^2 - b^2}{2ca} = \frac{1}{2}$ or $\cos B = \frac{1}{2}$ ∴ $B = 60°$

∴ (c) → (q)

4. **Ans.** (a) → (p), (b) → (r), (c) → (q), (d) → (s)

These follow from definitions.

§ 2. Circumcircle and Incircle

(i) **Circumcircle :** The circle which passes through the angular points of a ΔABC is called circumscribing circle or, more briefly, its **circumcircle**. We shall denote its radius by R.

(ii) **Incircle :** The circle which can be inscribed within the triangle so as to touch each of the sides is called inscribed circle or, more briefly, its **incircle**. We denote its radius by r.

(iii) **Escribed circles :** The circle which touches BC and the two sides AB and AC produced is called the **escribed** circle opposite the angle A. We denote its radius by r_1. Similarly we denote by r_2 and r_3 the radii of the escribed circles opposite the angles B and C respectively.

Students should commit to memory the following formulae. **For proofs see Q. 1, 2, 3 P. 678-681**

* $2R = \frac{a}{\sin A} = \frac{b}{\sin B} = \frac{c}{\sin C}$ ...(1)

Note : In a right angled triangle $R = \frac{c}{2}, \angle C = 90°$

* $R = \frac{abc}{4S}$ ...(2)

* $r = \frac{S}{s}$ ...(3)

* $r = (s - a) \tan \frac{A}{2} = (s - b) \tan \frac{B}{2} = (s - c) \tan \frac{C}{2}$ ...(4)

* $r = 4R \sin \frac{A}{2} \sin \frac{B}{2} \sin \frac{C}{2}$ ...(5)

* $r_1 = \frac{S}{s - a}, r_2 = \frac{S}{s - b}, r_3 = \frac{S}{s - c}$ ...(6)

* $r_1 = s \tan \frac{A}{2}, r_2 = s \tan \frac{B}{2}, r_3 = s \tan \frac{C}{2}$ ...(7)

* $r_1 = a \frac{\cos(B/2) \cos(C/2)}{\cos(A/2)} = 4R \sin \frac{A}{2} \cos \frac{B}{2} \cos \frac{C}{2}$ ...(8)

* $r_2 = b \frac{\cos(C/2) \cos(A/2)}{\cos(B/2)} = 4R \cos \frac{A}{2} \sin \frac{B}{2} \cos \frac{C}{2}$ ...(9)

* $r_3 = c \frac{\cos(A/2) \cos(B/2)}{\cos(C/2)} = 4R \cos \frac{A}{2} \cos \frac{B}{2} \sin \frac{C}{2}$ ...(10)

§ 3. Orthocentre

Let AL, BM and CN be the perpendiculars from A, B, C on opposite sides in a ΔABC. Then from geometry, we know that these perpendiculars are concurrent. Their point of intersection P is called the orthocentre of the triangle ABC. The ΔLMN is called the pedal triangle of ΔABC.

The distance of the orthocentre from the vertices.

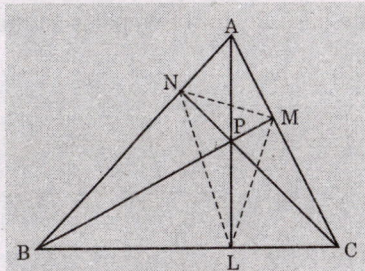

Fig. 29

From ΔAPM, we have

$AP = AM \sec PAM = AM \sec LAC$

$= AM \sec(90° - C) = AM \operatorname{cosec} C$

$= AB \cos A \operatorname{cosec} C = c \cos A / \sin C$

$= \frac{2R \sin C \cos A}{\sin C}$ [∵ $c = 2R \sin C$]

$= 2R \cos A$

*Thus $AP = 2R \cos A$

Similarly, $BP = 2R \cos B$ and $CP = 2R \cos C$.

Again $PL = BL \tan LBP = BL \tan(90° - C)$

$= AB \cos B \cot C = c \cos B \cot C$

$= 2R \sin C \cos B (\cos C / \sin C)$

$= 2R \cos B \cos C$

Similarly, $PM = 2R \cos C \cos A$

and $PN = 2R \cos A \cos B$

§ 4. Circumcentre, Centroid and Orthocentre are collinear.

Let O be the circumcentre and P the orthocentre in a $\triangle ABC$. If OD is perpendicular to BC, then D will be its mid-point. Let the median AD meet OP in G. Then it is clear that $\triangle OGD$ and $\triangle PGA$ are similar.

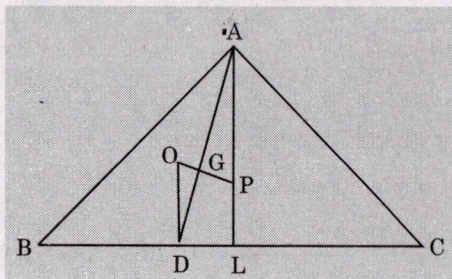

Fig. 30

$$\therefore \quad \frac{DG}{AG} = \frac{OG}{PG} = \frac{OD}{PA}$$

But $\quad OD = R\cos A$ and $PA = 2R\cos A$

Hence $\quad \dfrac{OD}{PA} = \dfrac{R\cos A}{2R\cos A} = \dfrac{1}{2}$

Thus $\quad \dfrac{DG}{AG} = \dfrac{OG}{PG} = \dfrac{OD}{PA} = \dfrac{1}{2}$.

It follows that G is the centroid of the $\triangle ABC$ and is situated on the line OP and divides it in the ratio $1:2$

§ 5. Bisectors of the angles.

Let AD be the bisector of angle A and suppose AD divides the base BC into two parts x and y. Then by geometry,

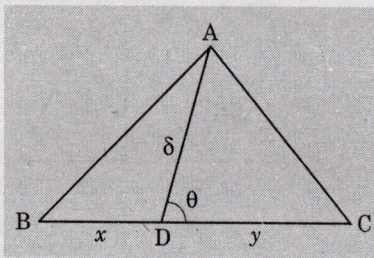

Fig. 31

$$\frac{x}{y} = \frac{AB}{AC} = \frac{c}{b} \qquad \ldots(1)$$

$$\therefore \quad \frac{x}{c} = \frac{y}{b} = \frac{x+y}{c+b} = \frac{a}{b+c}$$

Again if δ be the length of AD and θ the angle it makes with BC, then

$$\triangle ABD + \triangle ACD = \triangle ABC$$

or $\quad \dfrac{1}{2}c\delta\sin\dfrac{A}{2} + \dfrac{1}{2}b\delta\sin\dfrac{A}{2} = \dfrac{1}{2}bc\sin A$

or $\quad \delta = \dfrac{bc}{b+c} \cdot \dfrac{\sin A}{\sin(A/2)} = \dfrac{2bc}{b+c}\cos\dfrac{A}{2}$ $\qquad \ldots(2)$

Also $\theta = \angle DAB + \angle B = (A/2) + B$ $\qquad \ldots(3)$

§ 6 . Area of Cyclic Quadrilateral.

Let $ABCD$ be a cyclic quadrilateral whose sides AB, BC, CD and DA are respectively a, b, c and d.

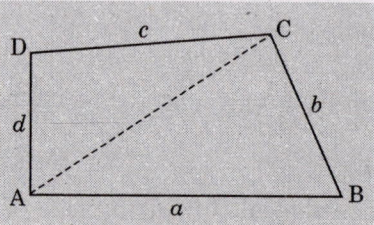

Fig. 32

Then the area of quadrilateral

$= \text{Area of } \triangle ABC + \text{Area of } \triangle ACD$

$= \dfrac{1}{2}ab\sin B + \dfrac{1}{2}cd\sin D$

$= \dfrac{1}{2}ab\sin B + \dfrac{1}{2}cd\sin(180° - B)$

$\qquad\qquad [\because \ \angle B + \angle D = 180°]$

$= \dfrac{1}{2}(ab + cd)\sin B \qquad\qquad \ldots(1)$

But $a^2 + b^2 - 2ab\cos B = AC^2 = c^2 + d^2 - 2cd\cos D$

$\qquad\qquad = c^2 + d^2 + 2cd\cos B \quad \because \ D = \pi - B$

or $\quad a^2 + b^2 - c^2 - d^2 = 2(ab + cd)\cos B$

Hence $(a^2 + b^2 - c^2 - d^2)^2 = 4(ab + cd)^2 \cos^2 B$

$\qquad\qquad = 4(ab + cd)^2 (1 - \sin^2 B)$

or $\quad 4(ab + cd)^2 \sin^2 B = 4(ab + cd)^2$

$$\qquad\qquad\qquad - (a^2 + b^2 - c^2 - d^2)^2$$

$= (2ab + 2cd + a^2 + b^2 - c^2 - d^2)$

$\qquad\qquad \times (2ab + 2cd - a^2 - b^2 + c^2 + d^2)$

$= [(a+b)^2 - (c-d)^2][(c+d)^2 - (a-b)^2]$

$= (a + b + c - d)(a + b - c + d)$

$\qquad\qquad \times (c + d + a - b)(c + d - a + b)$

$= (2s - 2d)(2s - 2c)(2s - 2b)(2s - 2a)$

where $\quad a + b + c + d = 2s$

$\therefore \quad (ab + cd)\sin B = 2\{(s-a)(s-b)(s-c)(s-d)\}^{1/2}$

Hence from (1) and (2), we get the area of quadrilateral

$= \sqrt{[(s-a)(s-b)(s-c)(s-d)]} \qquad \ldots(2)$

Note. Remember : $\cos B = \dfrac{a^2 + b^2 - c^2 - d^2}{2(ab + cd)}$

§ 7. Ptolemy's Theorem.

If $ABCD$ is a cyclic quadrilateral, then

$$AC . BD = AB . CD + BC . AD$$

Proof. We have

$AC^2 = a^2 + b^2 - 2ab\cos B$ $\qquad$ [See fig. of § 6]

But $\quad \cos B = \dfrac{(a^2 + b^2 - c^2 - d^2)}{2(ab + cd)}$ $\qquad$ [See § 6]

$\therefore \quad AC^2 = (a^2 + b^2) - \dfrac{ab(a^2 + b^2 - c^2 - d^2)}{(ab + cd)}$

$$= \left\{ \frac{(a^2+b^2)\,cd + ab\,(c^2+d^2)}{(ab+cd)} \right\} = \frac{(ac+bd)\,(ad+bc)}{(ab+cd)}$$

Similarly, $BD^2 = \dfrac{(ab+cd)\,(ac+bd)}{(ad+bc)}$

Hence $AC^2 \cdot BD^2 = (ac+bd)^2$ or $AC \cdot BD = ac+bd$.

Thus $AC \cdot BD = AB \cdot CD + BC \cdot AD$

Cor. Since circumcircle of quadrilateral $ABCD$ is also the circumcircle of $\triangle ABC$, the circumradius of $ABCD$

$$= \frac{AC}{2\sin B} = \frac{(ab+cd)}{4\Delta} \cdot AC$$

where Δ is the area of quadrilateral

$$= \frac{ab+cd}{4\Delta} \cdot \sqrt{\left[\frac{(ac+bd)\,(ad+bc)}{(ab+cd)} \right]}$$

$$= \frac{1}{4} \cdot \sqrt{\left[\frac{(ab+cd)\,(ac+bd)\,(ad+bc)}{(s-a)\,(s-b)\,(s-c)(s-d)} \right]}$$

§ 8. Radii of the inscribed and circumscribing circles of a regular polygon.

Let AB, BC and CD be three successive sides of the polygon and let n be the number of its sides. Let the angles ABC and BCD be bisected by the lines BO and CO meeting at O. Draw ON perpendicular to BC. Then it is clear that O is the centre of both the incircles and the circumcircle of the polygon.

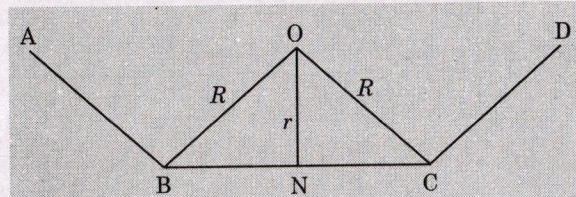

Fig. 33

Also $BN = CN$.

Hence $OB = OC = R$, the radius of the circumcircle and $ON = r$, the radius of in-circle.

Now $\angle BOC = (2\pi/n)$ radians.

Hence $\angle BON = \angle CON = \frac{1}{2} \angle BOC = \frac{\pi}{n}$.

If a be the length of a side of the polygon, then

$a = BC = 2BN = 2R \sin BON = 2R \sin(\pi/n)$

or $R = \dfrac{a}{2}\operatorname{cosec}\dfrac{\pi}{n}$

Again $a = 2BN = 2ON \tan BON = 2r \tan(\pi/n)$

$\therefore \quad r = \dfrac{a}{2}\cot\dfrac{\pi}{n}$

§ 9. Area of a regular polygon.

Area of the polygon is n times the area of the $\triangle BOC$. Hence the area of the polygon

$$= n \times \frac{1}{2} ON \cdot BC = n \cdot ON \cdot BN$$

$$= n \cdot BN \cot\frac{\pi}{n} \cdot BN = n \cdot \left(\frac{a}{2}\right)^2 \cot\frac{\pi}{n} \quad \left[\because BN = \frac{1}{2}\right]$$

$$= \frac{1}{4} na^2 \cot\frac{\pi}{n}.$$

Above is an expression for the area in terms of the sides.

Also the area $= n \cdot ON \cdot BN = n \cdot OB \cos\dfrac{\pi}{n} \cdot OB \sin\dfrac{\pi}{n}$

$$= n \cdot R^2 \sin\frac{\pi}{n}\cos\frac{\pi}{n}$$

$$= \frac{1}{2} \cdot nR^2 \sin\frac{2\pi}{n} \qquad \dots(2)$$

Again, the area $= n \cdot ON \cdot BN = n \cdot ON \cdot ON \tan(\pi/n)$

$$= nr^2 \tan(\pi/n) \qquad \dots(3)$$

The formulae (2) and (3) give the area in terms of the radius of the circumscribed and inscribed circles.

(V. Imp.)

If I_n represents area of n-sided regular polygon inscribed in a unit circle O_n the area of the n-sided regular polygon circumscribing it, prove that

$$I_n = \frac{O_n}{2}\left[1 + \sqrt{1 - \left(\frac{2I_n}{n}\right)^2} \right]$$

(IIT 2003)

The given circle is unit circle.

I_n = area of the polygon inscribed in a unit circle.

$\therefore \quad I_n = \dfrac{1}{2} n \sin\dfrac{2\pi}{n}$

or $\dfrac{2I_n}{n} = \sin\dfrac{2\pi}{n}$, by (2) $\qquad \dots(a)$

O_n = area of the polygon circumscribed to a unit circle

$O_n = n \tan\dfrac{\pi}{n}$, by (3) $\qquad \dots(b)$

$\text{R.H.S.} = \dfrac{1}{2} O_n\left[1 + \sqrt{1 - \left(\dfrac{2I_n}{n}\right)^2} \right]$ use (a), (b)

$$= \frac{1}{2} n \tan\frac{\pi}{n}\left[1 + \cos\frac{2\pi}{n} \right]$$

$$= \frac{1}{2} n \tan\frac{\pi}{n} 2\cos^2\frac{\pi}{n}$$

$$= \frac{1}{2} n\, 2\sin\frac{\pi}{n}\cdot\cos\frac{\pi}{n}$$

$$= \frac{1}{2} n \sin\frac{2\pi}{n} = I_n = \text{L.H.S.}$$

Before proceeding to do the questions the following identities be remembered. For proof see the references given. **If A, B, C be the angle of a triangle, then**

(a) $\sin 2A + \sin 2B + \sin 2C$

$\qquad = 4\sin A \sin B \sin C$

(b) $\sin A + \sin B + \sin C$

$\qquad = 4\cos\dfrac{A}{2}\cos\dfrac{B}{2}\cos\dfrac{C}{2}$

(c) $\cos A + \cos B + \cos C$

$$= 1 + 4 \sin \frac{A}{2} \sin \frac{B}{2} \sin \frac{C}{2}$$

(d) $\tan A + \tan B + \tan C = \tan A \tan B \tan C$

Problem Set (4)

Incircle, Circumcircle and Excircle.

1. If R is the radius of circumcircle of $\triangle ABC$, prove the following formulae :

   (a) $\dfrac{a}{\sin A} = \dfrac{b}{\sin B} = \dfrac{c}{\sin C} = 2R$

   (b) $R = \dfrac{abc}{4S}$

2. If r is the radius of incircle of $\triangle ABC$, prove the following formulae :

   (a) $r = S/s$

   (b) $r = 4R \sin (A/2) \sin (B/2) \sin (C/2)$

   (c) $r = (s - a) \tan (A/2) = (s - b) \tan (B/2)$
   $$= (s - c) \tan (C/2)$$

3. Prove the formulae :

   (a) $r_1 = S/(s - a), r_2 = S/(s - b), r_3 = S/(s - c)$

   (b) $r_1 = s \tan (A/2), r_2 = s \tan (B/2), r_3 = s \tan (C/2)$

   (c) $r_1 = 4R \sin (A/2) \cos (B/2) \cos (C/2)$
   and similar expressions for r_2 and r_3
   $$r_2 = 4R \cos (A/2) \sin (B/2) \cos (C/2)$$
   $$r_3 = 4R \cos (A/2) \cos (B/2) \sin (C/2)$$
   where r_1, r_2, r_3 have their usual meanings .

4. Prove the following :

   (a) $\sqrt{r r_1 r_2 r_3} = S = r^2 \cot (A/2) \cot (B/2) \cot (C/2)$

   (b) $r_1 r_2 r_3 = r^3 \cot^2 (A/2) \cot^2 (B/2) \cot^2 (C/2)$

   (c) $r_1 = r \cot (B/2) \cot (C/2)$

5. (a)* If the area of a triangle is 81 square cm and its perimeter is 27 cm, then its in-radius is
   (a) 6 cm   (b) 3 cm
   (c) 1·5 cm   (d) none of these

   (b) If the sides be 18, 24, 30 cms, then radius of incircle is
   (i) 2   (ii) 4
   (iii) 6   (iv) 9   **(M.N.R. 1993)**

   (c)* If in any triangle the sides a, b, c are respectively 13, 14, 15, then $r_1 = ..., r_2 = ..., r_3 = ...$

6. (a)* In a triangle the sides are 3, 4, 5 units then R (cricumradius) = ...   **(M.N.R. 1990)**

   (b) In a triangle ABC, $a : b : c = 4 : 5 : 6$. The ratio of the radius of the circumcircle to that of the incircle is ....   **(I.I.T. 1996)**

   (c) If $r_1 = 2r_2 = 3r_3$ then prove that $a : b$ is 5 : 4.

   (d) Which of the following pieces of data does **NOT** uniquely determine as acute-angled triangle ABC (R being the radius of the circumcircle) ?
   (a) $a, \sin A, \sin B$ (b) A, b, c
   (c) $a, \sin B, R$ (d) $a, \sin A, R$
   (I.I.T. Sc. 2002)

7. (a) $rr_1 \cot (A/2) = S$.

   (b) $r_1 \cot (A/2) = r_2 \cot (B/2) = r_3 \cot (C/2) = s$.

8. (c) $r_2 r_3 = S \cot (A/2)$.

   (a) $r_2 r_3 + r_3 r_1 + r_1 r_2 = s^2 = S^2/r^2$.

   (b) $r_1 r_2 r_3 = rs^2$.

   (c) $r r_1 r_2 r_3 = $
   (a) R^2 (b) S^2
   (c) s^2 (d) None

9. (a)* $1/r_1 + 1/r_2 + 1/r_3 = 1/r$.

   (b) $(r_1 + r_2) \tan (C/2) = (r_3 - r) \cot (C/2) = c$.

   (c) $(r_1 - r)/a + (r_2 - r)/b = c/r_3$.

10. (a)* $a(rr_1 + r_2 r_3) = b(rr_2 + r_3 r_1) = c(rr_3 + r_1 r_2)$.

    (b) $r_1 (r_2 + r_3)/a = r_2 (r_3 + r_1)/b = r_3 (r_1 + r_2)/c$.

    (c) $(ab - r_1 r_2)/r_3 = (bc - r_2 r_3)/r_1 = (ca - r_3 r_1)/r_2 = r$.

11. (a) $r_1 + r_2 + r_3 - r = 4R$.

    (b)* $r_1 + r_2 - r_3 + r = 4R \cos C$.

    (c) Prove that the cubic equation whose roots are the radii r_1, r_2, r_3 of escribed circles of a triangle is
    $$t^3 - (r + 4R) t + s^2 t - s^2 r = 0$$

12. (a)* $(r_1 - r)(r_2 - r)(r_3 - r) = 4r^2 R$.

    (b) $(r_1 - r)(r_2 + r_3) = a^2$.

13. (a)* $\left(\dfrac{1}{r} - \dfrac{1}{r_1}\right)\left(\dfrac{1}{r} - \dfrac{1}{r_2}\right)\left(\dfrac{1}{r} - \dfrac{1}{r_3}\right) = \dfrac{16 R}{r^2 (a + b + c)^2}$.

    (b) $\dfrac{1}{r_1^2} + \dfrac{1}{r_2^2} + \dfrac{1}{r_3^2} + \dfrac{1}{r^2} = \dfrac{a^2 + b^2 + c^2}{S^2}$.

14. (a)* $\left(\dfrac{1}{r_1} + \dfrac{1}{r_2}\right)\left(\dfrac{1}{r_2} + \dfrac{1}{r_3}\right)\left(\dfrac{1}{r_3} + \dfrac{1}{r_1}\right) = \dfrac{64R^3}{(a^2 b^2 c^2)}$.

    (b) $(r_1 + r_2)(r_2 + r_3)(r_3 + r_1) = 4Rs^2$.

    (c) $R = \dfrac{(r_1 + r_2)(r_2 + r_3)(r_3 + r_1)}{4(r_1 r_2 + r_2 r_3 + r_3 r_1)}$

15. (a)* $\dfrac{r_1}{(s - b)(s - c)} + \dfrac{r_2}{(s - c)(s - a)} + \dfrac{r_3}{(s - a)(s - b)} = \dfrac{3}{r}$.

    (b) $\dfrac{1}{2Rr} = \dfrac{1}{bc} + \dfrac{1}{ca} + \dfrac{1}{ab}$.

16. In an acute angled triangle which one of the following is true ?

    (a) $\dfrac{a \sec A + b \sec B + c \sec C}{\tan A . \tan B . \tan C} = 2R$

    (b) $b^2 = a^2 \cos^2 C + c^2 \cos^2 A + 2ac \cos A . \cos C$

17. (a) $\dfrac{\cos A}{\sqrt{4R^2 - a^2}} = \dfrac{\cos B}{\sqrt{4R^2 - b^2}} = \dfrac{\cos C}{\sqrt{4R^2 - c^2}}$

    (b) $r \cot \dfrac{A}{2} + a = r \cot \dfrac{B}{2} + b = r \cot \dfrac{C}{2} + c$

18. Two sides of a triangle are 2 and $\sqrt{3}$ and the included angle is 30° then the in-radius r of the triangle is equal to

 (a) $\frac{1}{4}(\sqrt{3}-1)$ (b) $\frac{1}{2}(\sqrt{3}+1)$

 (c) $\frac{1}{2}(\sqrt{3}-1)$ (d) $\frac{1}{4}(\sqrt{3}+1)$

19. (a) In a triangle ABC if $r_1 = R$, then

 (a) $\cos A + \cos B = \cos C$

 (b) $\cos B + \cos C = \cos A$

 (c) $\cos C + \cos A = \cos B$

 (d) $\cos A + \cos B + \cos C = 1$

 (b) If twice the square on the diameter of a circle is equal to sum of the squares on the sides of the inscribed triangle ABC, then $\sin^2 A + \sin^2 B + \sin^2 C$ is equal to

 (a) 2   (b) 3

 (c) 4   (d) 1

Prove the following :

20. (a) $S/Rr = (\sin A + \sin B + \sin C) = s/R$.

 (b)* $(a\cos A + b\cos B + c\cos C)$
 $= (a+b+c)(r/R) = 4R\sin A \sin B \sin C$.

21. $S = \{2abc/(a+b+c)\}\cos(A/2)\cos(B/2)\cos(C/2)$
 $= 4Rr\cos\frac{1}{2}A\cos\frac{1}{2}B\cos\frac{1}{2}C$.

22. (a)* $S = 4Rr\cos(A/2)\cos(B/2)\cos(C/2)$.

 (b) $s = 4R\cos(A/2)\cos(B/2)\cos(C/2)$.

23. (a)* $\cos A + \cos B + \cos C = 1 + r/R$.

 Another form :

 If $b\cot B + c\cot C = 2(r+R)$ then prove that $\triangle ABC$ is right angled.

 (b) $a\cot A + b\cot B + c\cot C = 2(R+r)$.

 (c) In a triangle $ABC, R = 8$ and $r = 3$, then the value of $a\cot A + b\cot B + c\cot C$ is ....

24. (a) $(b+c)\tan(A/2) + (c+a)\tan(B/2)$
 $+ (a+b)\tan(C/2)$
 $= 4R(\cos A + \cos B + \cos C) = 4(R+r)$.

 (b)* $\cos^2(A/2) + \cos^2(B/2) + \cos^2(C/2) = 2 + r/2R$.

25. (a) If A, A_1, A_2 and A_3 are respectively the areas of the inscribed and escribed circles, prove that
 $$\frac{1}{\sqrt{(A)}} = \frac{1}{\sqrt{(A_1)}} + \frac{1}{\sqrt{(A_2)}} + \frac{1}{\sqrt{(A_3)}}.$$

 (b) If s be the semi-perimeter of the triangle, then prove that
 $$\frac{s}{\cos\frac{A}{2}\cos\frac{B}{2}\cos\frac{C}{2}} = 2\sqrt[3]{\frac{abc}{\sin A \sin B \sin C}}$$

26. (a) In triangle ABC, prove that
 $$\sum \frac{\cos^2 A + \cos^2 B}{\cos A + \cos B} \geq 1 + \frac{r}{R}$$

 (b) $8Rr\left(\cos^2\frac{A}{2} + \cos^2\frac{B}{2} + \cos^2\frac{C}{2}\right) = 2\Sigma bc - \Sigma a^2$

27. (a) $(r+r_1)\tan[(B-C)/2] + (r+r_2)\tan[(C-A)/2]$
 $+ (r+r_3)\tan[(A-B)/2] = 0$.

 (b) $\frac{b-c}{r_1} + \frac{c-a}{r_2} + \frac{a-b}{r_3} = 0$.

28. $(r_2 + r_3)/(1 + \cos A) = (r_3 + r_1)/(1 + \cos B)$
 $= (r_1 + r_2)/(1 + \cos C)$.

29.* If p_1, p_2, p_3 are respectively the perpendiculars from the vertices of a triangle to the opposite sides, prove that

 (a) $\frac{1}{p_1} + \frac{1}{p_2} + \frac{1}{p_3} = \frac{1}{r}$.

 (b) $p_1 p_2 p_3 = \frac{a^2 b^2 c^2}{8R^3}$.

 (c) $\frac{\cos A}{p_1} + \frac{\cos B}{p_2} + \frac{\cos C}{p_3} = \frac{1}{R}$.

 (d) $\frac{bp_1}{c} + \frac{cp_2}{a} + \frac{ap_3}{b} = \frac{a^2 + b^2 + c^2}{2R}$.

30. (a) If α, β, γ are the distances of the vertices of a triangle from the corresponding points of contact with the incircle, prove that $r^2 = \alpha\beta\gamma/(\alpha + \beta + \gamma)$.

 (b)* If x, y, z are respectively perpendiculars from the circumcentre to the sides of the $\triangle ABC$, prove that
 $$\frac{a}{x} + \frac{b}{y} + \frac{c}{z} = \frac{abc}{4xyz}.$$

31. (a) Prove that the distances of the orthocentre of $\triangle ABC$ from its vertex A and side BC are respectively.
 $$2R\cos A \text{ and } 2R\cos B\cos C.$$

 (b)* If x, y, z are respectively the distances of the vertices of the $\triangle ABC$ from its orthocentre, prove that

 (i) $\frac{a}{x} + \frac{b}{y} + \frac{c}{z} = \frac{abc}{xyz}$.

 (ii) $x + y + z = 2(R+r)$.

32. (a) If in a triangle $r_1 = r_2 + r_3 + r$, prove that the triangle is right angled.

 (b)* If in triangle $8R^2 = a^2 + b^2 + c^2$, prove that the triangle is right angled.

33. (a) If in a triangle $(1 - r_1/r_2)(1 - r_1/r_3) = 2$, prove that the triangle is righangled.

 (b) In a $\triangle ABC$, if $C = 90°$ prove that

 (i) $R + r = \frac{1}{2}(a+b)$ **(I.I.T. Sc. 2000)**

 (ii) $c/r = (c+a)/b + (c+b)/a$.

34. (a)* If in a triangle ABC, $(a-b)(s-c) = (b-c)(s-a)$, prove that r_1, r_2, r_3 are in A.P.

 (b)* The ex-radii r_1, r_2, r_3 of $\triangle ABC$ are in H.P. Show that its sides a, b, c are in A.P.

 (c) The radii r_1, r_2, r_3 of escribed circles of a triangle ABC are in harmonic progression. If its area is 24 sq. cm. and its perimeter is 24 cm., find the lengths of its sides.   **(Roorkee 1999)**

Prove the following :

35. (a)* $\dfrac{r_1}{bc} + \dfrac{r_2}{ca} + \dfrac{r_3}{ab} = \dfrac{1}{r} - \dfrac{1}{2R}$.

    (b)* $\dfrac{bc}{r_1} + \dfrac{ca}{r_2} + \dfrac{ab}{r_3}$

    $$= 2R\left\{\left(\dfrac{a}{b}+\dfrac{b}{a}\right)+\left(\dfrac{b}{c}+\dfrac{c}{b}\right)+\left(\dfrac{c}{a}+\dfrac{a}{c}\right)-3\right\}$$

36. (a) $r^2 + r_1^2 + r_2^2 + r_3^2 = 16R^2 - a^2 - b^2 - c^2$.

    (b) Prove that $\dfrac{a+b+c}{r_1+r_2+r_3} \cdot \left(\dfrac{a}{r_1}+\dfrac{b}{r_2}+\dfrac{c}{r_3}\right) = 4$

37. (a)* Prove that the distance of the incentre of $\triangle ABC$ from A is $4R\sin(B/2)\sin(C/2)$.

    (b) If I be the centre of $\triangle ABC$, then prove that
    $IA . IB . IC = abc \tan\dfrac{1}{2}A \tan\dfrac{1}{2}B \tan\dfrac{1}{2}C$.

38. Let ABC be a triangle having O and I as its circumcentre and incentre, respectively. If R and r are the circumradius and the inradius respectively, then prove that $(IO)^2 = R^2 - 2Rr$. Further show that the triangle BIO is rightangled triangle if and only if b is the arithmetic mean of a and c. **(I.I.T. 1999)**

39. (a) O is the circumcentre of $\triangle ABC$ and R_1, R_2 and R_3 are respectively the radii of the circumcentre of the $\triangle^s\ OBC, OCA$ and OAB, prove that

    $$\dfrac{a}{R_1} + \dfrac{b}{R_2} + \dfrac{c}{R_3} = \dfrac{abc}{R^3}.$$

    (b) I is the incentre of $\triangle ABC$ and P_1, P_2 and P_3 are respectively the radii of the circumcircles of the $\triangle^s\ IBC, ICA$ and IAB. Prove that $P_1P_2P_3 = 2R^2r$.

40. (a) Tangents are drawn to the incircle of triangle ABC which are parallel to its sides. If x, y, z be the lengths of the tangents and a, b, c be the sides of triangle, then $\dfrac{x}{a}+\dfrac{y}{b}+\dfrac{z}{c}=1$

    (b) If t_1, t_2, t_3 be the lengths of tangents from the centres of escribed circles to the circumcircle, prove that $\dfrac{1}{t_1^2}+\dfrac{1}{t_2^2}+\dfrac{1}{t_3^2}=\dfrac{2s}{abc}$.

    (c) Let ABC be a triangle with incentre I and inradius r. Let D, E, F be the feet of the perpendiculars from I to the sides BC, CA and AB respectively. If r_1, r_2 and r_3 are the radii of circles inscribed in the quadrilaterals $AFIE, BDIF$ and $CEID$ respectively, prove that

    $$\dfrac{r_1}{r-r_1}+\dfrac{r_2}{r-r_2}+\dfrac{r_3}{r-r_3}=\dfrac{r_1r_2r_3}{(r-r_1)(r-r_2)(r-r_3)}$$

    (I.I.T. 2000)

41.* In a right angled triangle $\triangle ABC$ with C as a righangle, a perpendicular CD is drawn to AB. The radii of the circles inscribed into the triangles ACD and BCD are

equal to x and y respectively. Find the radius of the circle inscribed into the $\triangle ABC$.

42. (a) In triangle ABC, prove that the area of the in-circle is to the area of the triangle itself as $\pi : \cot(A/2)\cot(B/2)\cot(C/2)$.

    (b) At the points A, B, C tangents are drawn to the circumcircle of triangle ABC. These tangents enclose a triangle PQR. Prove that its angles and sides are respectively $180° - 2A, 180° - 2B, 180° - 2C$ and

    $$\dfrac{a}{2\cos B\cos C}, \dfrac{b}{2\cos C\cos A}, \dfrac{c}{2\cos A\cos B}.$$

43. In a cyclic quadrilateral $ABCD$, prove that
    $$\tan^2\dfrac{B}{2} = \dfrac{(s-a)(s-b)}{(s-c)(s-d)}.$$

44. Prove that the sum of the radii of the circles, which are respectively inscribed and circumscribed about a regular polygon of n sides, is $(a/2)\cot(\pi/2n)$, where a is the side of the polygon.

45. Prove that the area of a regular polygon of $2n$ sides inscribed in a circle is a mean proportional between the areas of the regular inscribed and circumscribed polygons of n sides.

46. If the number of sides of two regular polygons having the same perimeter be n and $2n$ respectively, prove that their areas are in the ratio
    $$2\cos(\pi/n):[1+\cos(\pi/n)].$$

47. (a)* Three circles touch one-another externally. The tangents at their points of contact meet at a point whose distance from any point of contact is 4. Find the ratio of the product of the radii to the sum of the radii of circles. **(I.I.T. 1992)**

    (b) Three circles of radius 3, 4, 5 touch each other externally. Tangents are drawn at the point of contact, which meet at P. Find the distance between point of contact and P. **(I.I.T. 2005)**

    (c)* Three circles, whose radii are a, b, c touch one another externally, and the tangents at their points of contact meet in a point, prove that the distance of this point from either of their points of contact is $\left(\dfrac{abc}{a+b+c}\right)^{1/2}$.

Paragraph for question No. 48 :

Consider the circle $x^2 + y^2 = 9$ and the parabola $y^2 = 8x$. They intersect at P and Q in the first and the fourth quadrants respectively. Tangents to the circle at P and Q intersect the x-axis at R and tangents to the parabola at P and Q intersect the x-axis at S. **(I.I.T. 2007)**

48. (a) The ratio of the area of the triangles PQS and PQR is

    (a) $1:\sqrt{2}$ (b) $1:2$

    (c) $1:4$ (d) $1:8$

    (b) The radius of the circumcircle of the triangle PRS is

(a) 5   (b) $3\sqrt{3}$

(c) $3\sqrt{2}$ (d) $2\sqrt{3}$

(c) The radius of the incircle of the triangle PQR is

(a) 4   (b) 3

(c) 8/3   (d) 2

Solutions to Problem Set (4)

1. (a) Describe a circle with centre O and passing through the vertices of the $\Delta\ ABC$. Clearly $\Delta\ BOD = \Delta\ COD$, we know that the angle subtended at the centre is double the angle subtended on the circumference, *i.e.*

$$\angle BOC = 2A$$

$$\therefore \quad \angle BOD = \angle COD = A.$$

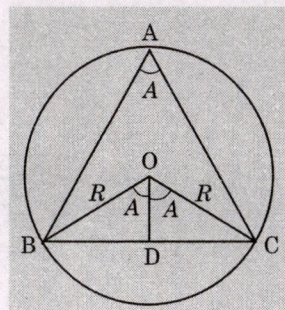

Fig. 34

Now if OD is perp. to side BC, then

$$BD = DC = \frac{a}{2} \quad \text{and} \quad \frac{BD}{OB} = \sin A$$

or $\dfrac{a}{2R} = \sin A$; $\quad \therefore \quad \dfrac{a}{\sin A} = 2R.$

Hence by sine formula,

$$\frac{a}{\sin A} = \frac{b}{\sin B} = \frac{c}{\sin C} = 2R.$$

(b) We have proved in (i) that

$$a = 2R\sin A = 2R.2\sin(A/2)\cos(A/2)$$

or $\quad a = 2R \cdot \dfrac{2}{bc}\sqrt{s(s-a)(s-b)(s-c)} = \dfrac{4RS}{bc}$

$$\therefore \quad R = \frac{abc}{4S}.$$

2. The bisectors of the angles of $\Delta\ ABC$ meet in I. Draw ID, IE, IF perpendicular to the sides from I.

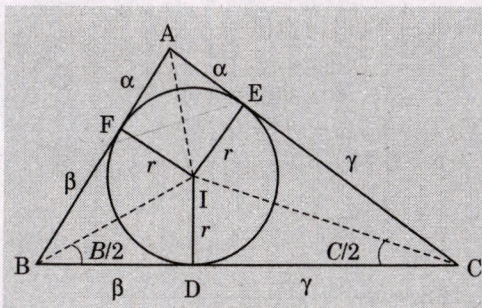

Fig. 35

By Geometry, $ID = IE = IF = r$

(a) $\Delta\ ABC = \Delta\ IBC + \Delta\ ICA + \Delta\ IAB$

or $\quad S = \dfrac{1}{2}ar + \dfrac{1}{2}br + \dfrac{1}{2}cr$

or $\quad S = \dfrac{1}{2}r(a+b+c) = \dfrac{1}{2}r \cdot 2s = r \cdot s$

$$\therefore \quad r = S/s$$

(b) $a = BC = BD + DC = r\cot(B/2) + r\cot(C/2)$

or $\quad 2R\sin A$

$$= r\left(\frac{\cos(B/2)\sin(C/2) + \cos(C/2)\sin(B/2)}{\sin(B/2)\sin(C/2)}\right)$$

[from 1 (i)]

or $\quad 2R.2\sin(A/2)\cos(A/2)\sin(B/2)\sin(C/2)$

$$= r \cdot \sin(B+C)/2 = r\cos(A/2)$$

$$\therefore \quad 4R\sin(A/2)\sin(B/2)\sin(C/2) = r,$$

$$\because \quad (B+C)/2 = 90° - A/2$$

(c) We know by Geometry that

$$BD = BF = \beta\ (\text{say}), CD = CF = \gamma, AE = AF = \alpha$$

$$\therefore \quad 2\alpha + 2\beta + 2\gamma = a + b + c = 2s$$

or $\quad \alpha + \beta + \gamma = s,$

$$\therefore \quad AF = \alpha = s - (\beta + \gamma) = s - BC = s - a$$

or $\quad BD = \beta = s - (\gamma + \alpha) = s - AC = s - b,$

$$CD = \gamma = s - (\alpha + \beta) = s - AB = s - c.$$

Now $\quad \dfrac{ID}{BD} = \tan\dfrac{B}{2}$,

$$\therefore \quad r = \beta\tan\frac{B}{2} = (s-b)\tan\frac{B}{2}$$

Similarly, $\quad \dfrac{ID}{CD} = \tan\dfrac{C}{2}$

$$\therefore \quad r = \gamma\tan\frac{C}{2} = (s-c)\tan\frac{C}{2} \text{ and } \frac{IF}{AF} = \tan\frac{A}{2},$$

$$\therefore \quad r = \alpha\tan\frac{A}{2} = (s-a)\tan\frac{A}{2}$$

3. Produce the sides AB, AC of $\Delta\ ABC$ and let the bisectors of the exterior angles B and C meet in I_1. From I_1 draw perpendiculars to the sides.

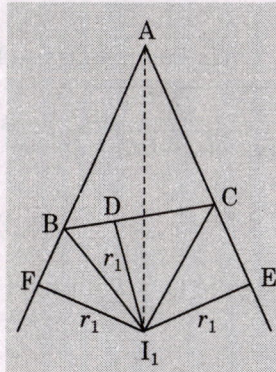

Fig. 36

By Geometry, $ID = IE = IF = r_1$

(a) $\Delta\ ABC = \Delta\ I_1 AF + \Delta\ I_1 AE - \Delta\ I_1 AC$

or $\quad S = \dfrac{1}{2}r_1 c + \dfrac{1}{2}r_1 b - \dfrac{1}{2}r_1 a$

or $S = \frac{1}{2} r_1 (b + c - a) = \frac{1}{2} r_1 \cdot 2(s - a)$

$\therefore \quad r_1 = \dfrac{S}{s - a}$.

Similarly, $r_2 = \dfrac{S}{s - b}, r_3 = \dfrac{S}{s - c}$.

(b) $AF = AB + BF = AB + BD$,

$\quad AE = AC + CE = AC + CD$

$\therefore \quad AF + AE = AB + AC + (BD + CD)$

or $\quad AB + AC + BC$

$\quad = a + b + c = 2s$

or $\quad 2 AF = 2s$ or $AF = s$ $\because$ $AF = AE$

$\dfrac{I_1 F}{AF} = \tan \dfrac{A}{2}$ or $r_1 = s \tan \dfrac{A}{2}$.

Similarly, $r_2 = s \tan \dfrac{B}{2}$ and $r_3 = s \tan \dfrac{C}{2}$

(c) $a = BD + DC = r_1 \cot \left(\dfrac{180° - B}{2} \right)$

$\qquad\qquad\qquad\qquad + r_1 \cot \left(\dfrac{180° - C}{2} \right)$

or $\quad a = r_1 [\tan (B/2) + \tan (C/2)]$

$2R \sin A = r_1 \cdot \dfrac{[\sin (B/2) \cos (C/2) + \cos (B/2) \sin (C/2)]}{\cos (B/2) \cos (C/2)}$

$\therefore \quad 2R \cdot 2 \sin \dfrac{A}{2} \cos \dfrac{A}{2} \cos \dfrac{B}{2} \cos \dfrac{C}{2}$

$\qquad = r_1 \sin \dfrac{B + C}{2} = r_1 \cos \dfrac{A}{2}$

or $\quad 4R \sin (A/2) \cos (B/2) \cos (C/2) = r_1$

Similarly,

$\quad 4R \sin (B/2) \cos (C/2) \cos (A/2) = r_2$

and $\quad 4R \sin (C/2) \cos (A/2) \cos (B/2) = r_3$

4. (a) L.H.S. $= \sqrt{\left(\dfrac{S}{s} \cdot \dfrac{S}{s-a} \cdot \dfrac{S}{s-b} \cdot \dfrac{S}{s-c} \right)} = \sqrt{\left(\dfrac{S^4}{S^2} \right)} = S$

R.H.S.

$= \dfrac{S^2}{s^2} \sqrt{\left[\dfrac{s(s-a)}{(s-b)(s-c)} \cdot \dfrac{s(s-b)}{(s-c)(s-a)} \cdot \dfrac{s(s-c)}{(s-a)(s-b)} \right]}$

$= \dfrac{S^2}{s^2} \sqrt{\left[\dfrac{s^4}{s(s-a)(s-b)(s-c)} \right]}$

$= \dfrac{S^2}{s^2} \cdot \dfrac{s^2}{S} = S = \text{L.H.S.}$

(b), (c). Proceed as in Q. 4. Put for $\cot \dfrac{A}{2}$ etc.

5. (a). Ans. (a).

Here as $S = 81, s = 27/2$

$\therefore \quad r = \dfrac{S}{s} = \dfrac{81 \times 2}{27} = 6$ cm

(b) Ans. (iii). $2s = 72$, $\therefore$ $s = 36$

$r = \dfrac{S}{s} = \dfrac{\{s(s-a)(s-b)(s-c)\}^{1/2}}{s}$

$r = \dfrac{(36 . 18 . 12 . 6)^{1/2}}{36} = \dfrac{36 . 6}{36} = 6$

(c) Ans. 10·5, 12, 14,

$2s = 42$ $\therefore$ $s = 21$

$s - a = 8, s - b = 7, s - c = 6$ and

$S^2 = 21 \times 8 \times 7 \times 6 = 7^2 \times 3^2 \times 4^2$

$\therefore \quad S = 84$

Now $\quad r_1 = \dfrac{S}{s - a}$ etc. for r_2 and r_3

6. (a) Ans. (2.5). Triangle is right angled $\angle C = 90°$

$\therefore \quad \dfrac{c}{\sin C} = 2R$ $\therefore$ $R = \dfrac{5}{2} = 2 \cdot 5$

Otherwise also in a right angled triangle hypotenuse c is diameter.

$\therefore \quad R = \dfrac{1}{2} c = 2 \cdot 5$

(b) Ans. $\dfrac{16}{7}$.

$a = 4k, b = 5k, c = 6k$

$s = \dfrac{15}{2} k, s - a = \dfrac{7}{2} k, s - b = \dfrac{5}{2} k, s - c = \dfrac{3}{2} k$

$S^2 = 15 \times 7 \times 5 \times 3 \left(\dfrac{k}{2} \right)^4$ $\therefore$ $S = 15 \sqrt{7} \left(\dfrac{k}{2} \right)^2$

$r = \dfrac{S}{s} = 15 \sqrt{7} \left(\dfrac{k}{2} \right)^2 \div \dfrac{15}{2} k = \sqrt{7} \dfrac{k}{2}$

$R = \dfrac{abc}{4S} = \dfrac{4 . 5 . 6 \, k^3}{4 . 15 \sqrt{7} \, k^2 / 4} = \dfrac{8}{\sqrt{7}} k$.

$\therefore \quad \dfrac{R}{r} = \dfrac{8}{\sqrt{7}} \div \dfrac{\sqrt{7}}{2} = \dfrac{16}{7}$

(c) $\dfrac{S}{s-a} = 2 . \dfrac{S}{s-b} = 3 . \dfrac{S}{s-c}$

$\therefore \quad \dfrac{s-a}{1} = \dfrac{s-b}{2} = \dfrac{s-c}{3} = \dfrac{3s-2s}{6} = \dfrac{s}{6}$

$\therefore \quad a = \dfrac{5s}{6}, b = \dfrac{4s}{6}$ $\therefore$ $a : b = 5 : 4$

(d) Ans. (d). $\dfrac{a}{\sin A} = 2R$.

7. (a), (b). $r_1 = s \tan (A/2)$ $\therefore$ $r_1 \cot (A/2) = s$ etc.

$\therefore \quad r r_1 \cot (A/2) = rs = S$

(c) $r_2 r_3 = \dfrac{S}{s-b} \cdot \dfrac{S}{s-c} = s(s-a)$

$S \cot \dfrac{A}{2} = \sqrt{()()()()} \sqrt{\dfrac{s(s-a)}{(s-b)(s-c)}}$

$\qquad = s(s-a)$ on putting for S.

8. (a) $\Sigma r_2 r_3 = \Sigma s(s-a)$ by Q. 7 (c).

$\qquad = s [s - a + s - b + s - c] = s(3s - 2s)$

$\qquad = s^2 = S^2 \cdot \dfrac{s^2}{S^2} = S^2 \cdot \dfrac{1}{r^2}$

(b) L.H.S. $= \dfrac{S^3}{(s-a)(s-b)(s-c)} = S . s$

$\qquad = \dfrac{S}{s} \cdot s^2 = r s^2 = \text{R.H.S.}$

(c) L.H.S. $= r(S \cdot s) = \dfrac{S}{s}(S \cdot s) = S^2$ by (b)

9. (a) L.H.S. $= \dfrac{1}{S}[(s-a)+(s-b)+(s-c)]$

$= \dfrac{1}{S}(3s-2s) = \dfrac{s}{S} = \dfrac{1}{r}$

(b) $(r_1 + r_2)\tan\dfrac{C}{2} = \left(\dfrac{S}{s-a} + \dfrac{S}{s-b}\right)\tan\dfrac{C}{2}$

$= \dfrac{S(2s-a-b)}{(s-a)(s-b)} \cdot \sqrt{\dfrac{(s-a)(s-b)}{s(s-c)}}$

$= S \cdot c \cdot \dfrac{1}{S} = c.$

(c) L.H.S. $= \dfrac{1}{a}\left[\dfrac{S}{s-a} - \dfrac{S}{s}\right] + \dfrac{1}{b}\left[\dfrac{S}{s-b} - \dfrac{S}{s}\right]$

$= \dfrac{S}{a} \cdot \dfrac{s-s+a}{s(s-a)} + \dfrac{S}{b} \cdot \dfrac{s-s+b}{s(s-b)}$

$= \dfrac{S}{s}\left[\dfrac{1}{s-a} + \dfrac{1}{s-b}\right] = \dfrac{S}{s} \cdot \dfrac{2s-a-b}{(s-a)(s-b)}$

$= \dfrac{S \cdot c}{s(s-a)(s-b)} \cdot \dfrac{s-c}{s-c} = \dfrac{S \cdot c \cdot (s-c)}{S^2}$

$= \dfrac{c(s-c)}{S} = \dfrac{c}{r_3}.$

10. (a) $a(rr_1 + r_2 r_3)$

$= aS^2\left[\dfrac{1}{s(s-a)} + \dfrac{1}{(s-b)(s-c)}\right]$

$= aS^2\left[\dfrac{2s^2 - s(a+b+c) + bc}{S^2}\right]$

$= a(2s^2 - 2s^2 + bc) = abc$

By symmetry each is abc.

(b) $\dfrac{r_1(r_2 + r_3)}{a} = \dfrac{S}{a(s-a)}\left[\dfrac{S}{s-b} + \dfrac{S}{s-c}\right]$

$= \dfrac{S^2(2s-b-c)}{a(s-a)(s-b)(s-c)} = s.$

By symmetry each is s.

(c) $\dfrac{ab - r_1 r_2}{r_3} = \dfrac{1}{r_3}\left(ab - \dfrac{S}{s-a} \cdot \dfrac{S}{s-b}\right)$

$= \dfrac{ab}{r_3}\left\{1 - \dfrac{s(s-c)}{ab}\right\} \quad [\because\ S^2 = s(s-a)(s-b)(s-c)]$

$= \dfrac{ab}{r_3}\left(1 - \cos^2\dfrac{C}{2}\right) = \dfrac{ab}{r_3} \cdot \sin^2\dfrac{C}{2}$

$= ab \cdot \dfrac{s-c}{S} \cdot \dfrac{(s-a)(s-b)}{ab}$

$= \dfrac{(s-a)(s-b)(s-c)}{S}.$

Similarly each other term is equal to above.

11. (a) L.H.S. $= \left[\dfrac{S}{s-a} + \dfrac{S}{s-b}\right] + \left[\dfrac{S}{s-c} - \dfrac{S}{s}\right]$

$= S \cdot \dfrac{[2s-b-a]}{(s-a)(s-b)} + S \cdot \dfrac{[s-s+c]}{s(s-c)}$

$= S \cdot c \cdot \dfrac{[s^2 - cs + s^2 - s(a+b) + ab]}{s(s-a)(s-b)(s-c)}$

$= S \cdot c \cdot \dfrac{[2s^2 - s(a+b+c) + ab]}{S^2}$

$= \dfrac{c}{S}[2s^2 - s \cdot 2s + ab]$

$= \dfrac{abc}{S} = 4 \cdot \dfrac{abc}{4S} = 4R.$

(b) As above, L.H.S.

$= S \cdot c \cdot \left[\dfrac{1}{(s-a)(s-b)} - \dfrac{1}{s(s-c)}\right]$

$= S \cdot c \cdot \left[\dfrac{s(s-c) - (s-a)(s-b)}{S^2}\right]$

$= (c/S)[s(a+b-c) - ab]$

$= (c/2S)[(a+b+c)(a+b-c) - 2ab]$

$= \dfrac{abc}{2S}\left[\dfrac{(a+b)^2 - c^2 - 2ab}{ab}\right]$

$= \dfrac{abc}{S} \cdot \dfrac{a^2 + b^2 - c^2}{2ab} = 4R\cos C.$

(c) The required equation is

$t^3 - t^2 S_1 + t S_2 - S_3 = 0$

where $S_1 = r_1 + r_2 + r_3 = r + 4R$

by Q. 11 (a) P. 678

$S_2 = \Sigma\, r_1 r_2 = s^2$

$S_3 = r_1 r_2 r_3 = rs^2$, **by Q. 8 (b), 678.**

12. (a) L.H.S. $= \left(\dfrac{S}{s-a} - \dfrac{S}{s}\right)\left(\dfrac{S}{s-b} - \dfrac{S}{s}\right)\left(\dfrac{S}{s-c} - \dfrac{S}{s}\right)$

$= S^3 \cdot \dfrac{abc}{s^2 \cdot s(s-a)(s-b)(s-c)} = \dfrac{S^3 \cdot abc}{s^2 \cdot S^2}$

$= \dfrac{S}{s^2} \cdot abc = 4 \cdot \dfrac{S^2}{s^2}\left(\dfrac{abc}{4S}\right) = 4r^2 \cdot R.$

(b) As in part (a), we have

L.H.S. $= \left(\dfrac{S}{s-a} - \dfrac{S}{s}\right)\left(\dfrac{S}{s-b} + \dfrac{S}{s-c}\right)$

$= \dfrac{S \cdot a \cdot Sa}{s(s-a)(s-b)(s-c)} = a^2.$

13. (a) L.H.S. $= \dfrac{s-(s-a)}{S} \cdot \dfrac{s-(s-b)}{S} \cdot \dfrac{s-(s-c)}{S} = \dfrac{abc}{S^3}.$

R.H.S. $= 16 \cdot \dfrac{abc}{4S} \cdot \dfrac{s^2}{S^2(2s)^2} = \dfrac{abc}{S^3} = $ L.H.S.

(b) L.H.S. $= \dfrac{(s-a)^2 + (s-b)^2 + (s-c)^2 + s^2}{S^2}$

$= \dfrac{4s^2 - 2s(a+b+c) + (a^2+b^2+c^2)}{S^2}.$

$= \dfrac{(a^2+b^2+c^2)}{S^2}$

14. (a) L.H.S. $= \dfrac{(s-a)+(s-b)}{S} \cdot \dfrac{(s-b)+(s-c)}{S}$

$$\cdot \dfrac{(s-c)+(s-a)}{S}$$

$$= \dfrac{abc}{S^3}, \qquad \because 2s = (a+b+c) \text{ etc.}$$

R.H.S. $= \dfrac{64}{(a^2 b^2 c^2)} \cdot \left(\dfrac{abc}{4S}\right)^3 = \dfrac{abc}{S^3} = \text{L.H.S.}$

(b) L.H.S.

$$= \left(\dfrac{S}{s-a}+\dfrac{S}{s-b}\right)\left(\dfrac{S}{s-b}+\dfrac{S}{s-c}\right)\left(\dfrac{S}{s-c}+\dfrac{S}{s-a}\right)$$

$$= S^3 \left[\dfrac{2s-(a+b)}{(s-a)(s-b)}\right]\left[\dfrac{2s-(b+c)}{(s-b)(s-c)}\right]\left[\dfrac{2s-(c+a)}{(s-c)(s-a)}\right]$$

$$= S^3 \cdot \dfrac{abc}{[(s-a)(s-b)(s-c)]^2}$$

$$= S^3 \cdot \dfrac{abc s^2}{[s(s-a)(s-b)(s-c)]^2}$$

$$= S^3 \cdot \dfrac{s^2 \, abc}{S^4} = \dfrac{abc}{4S} \cdot 4s^2 = 4Rs^2.$$

(c) $\dfrac{N^r}{D^r} = \dfrac{4Rs^2}{4s^2} = R$ by **Q. 8 (a) P. 678-82 and part (b).**

15. (a) $\dfrac{r_1}{(s-b)(s-c)} = \dfrac{S}{(s-a)(s-b)(s-c)} = \dfrac{s \cdot S}{S^2} = \dfrac{s}{S} = \dfrac{1}{r}.$

Similarly each term is equal to $1/r$ etc.

(b) R.H.S. $= \dfrac{a+b+c}{abc} = \dfrac{2s}{4SR} = \dfrac{1}{2r \cdot R}.$

16. Ans. (a), (b), (c), (d) all hold good.

$$\dfrac{a}{\sin A} = 2R \quad \therefore \quad a = 2R \sin A$$

(a) $\Rightarrow \dfrac{2R\,[\tan A + \tan B + \tan C]}{\tan A \tan B \tan C} = 2R$ as $S_1 = S_3$

(b) $\Rightarrow b = a\cos C + c\cos A$. Square both sides

17. (a) $\Rightarrow \dfrac{\cos A}{2R\sqrt{1-\sin^2 A}} = \dfrac{1}{2R}$ etc.

(b) $\Rightarrow r = (s-a)\tan\dfrac{A}{2}$

$$\therefore \quad r\cot\dfrac{A}{2} + a = s \text{ etc.}$$

18. Ans. (c).

We know that $r = (s-a)\tan(A/2)$ etc.

If the given sides be b and c and $A = 30°$, then

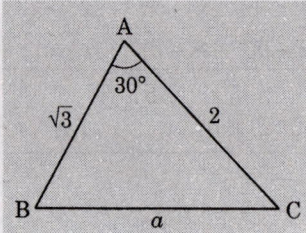

Fig. 37

$$a^2 = b^2 + c^2 - 2bc\cos A$$

$$= 4 + 3 - 4\sqrt{3}\cos 30°$$

$$a^2 = 7 - 4\sqrt{3}\times\dfrac{\sqrt{3}}{2} = 7 - 6 = 1$$

$\therefore \quad a^2 = 1 \Rightarrow a = 1$ by cosine rule.

$\therefore \quad 2s = a + b + c = 1 + 2 + \sqrt{3} = 3 + \sqrt{3}$

$\therefore \quad 2s - 2a = 3 + \sqrt{3} - 2$

$\Rightarrow \quad (s-a) = \dfrac{\sqrt{3}+1}{2}$

$A = 30° \quad \therefore \dfrac{A}{2} = 15°$

$\therefore \quad \tan\dfrac{A}{2} = \tan 15° = \dfrac{\sqrt{3}-1}{\sqrt{3}+1}$

$\therefore \quad r = (s-a)\tan\dfrac{A}{2} = \dfrac{\sqrt{3}+1}{2}\cdot\dfrac{\sqrt{3}-1}{\sqrt{3}+1}$

$$= \dfrac{1}{2}(\sqrt{3}-1) \Rightarrow \text{(c)}$$

19. (a) Ans. (b). $r_1 = R$

$\Rightarrow 4R\sin\dfrac{A}{2}\cdot\cos\dfrac{B}{2}\cdot\cos\dfrac{C}{2} = R$ **Rule 9 P. 677**

$\Rightarrow 2\left[\cos\dfrac{B+C}{2}+\cos\dfrac{B-C}{2}\right]\sin\dfrac{A}{2} = 1$

or Replace $\sin\dfrac{A}{2}$ by $\cos\dfrac{B+C}{2}$

$\therefore \quad 2\cos^2\dfrac{B+C}{2}+2\cos\dfrac{B+C}{2}\cdot\cos\dfrac{B-C}{2} = 1$

$\Rightarrow \quad 1 + \cos(B+C) + \cos B + \cos C = 1$

$\therefore \quad \cos B + \cos C = -\cos(B+C) = \cos A$

(b) Ans. (a).

If R be the circumradius of the circumcircle of the ΔABC, then $2(d)^2 = a^2 + b^2 + c^2$ (given)

where $d = 2R$ and $\dfrac{a}{\sin A} = 2R$

$\therefore \quad 8R^2 = 4R^2(\sin^2 A + \sin^2 B + \sin^2 C)$

$\therefore \quad \sin^2 A + \sin^2 B + \sin^2 C = 2$

20. (a) Mid-term $= \left(\dfrac{a}{2R}+\dfrac{b}{2R}+\dfrac{c}{2R}\right) = \dfrac{2s}{2R} = \dfrac{s}{R} = \dfrac{S}{rR} = \text{L.H.S.}$

(b) $T_1 = R(2\sin A\cos A + 2\sin B\cos B$

$$+ 2\sin C\cos C)$$

$$= R(\sin 2A + \sin 2B + \sin 2C)$$

$$= R \cdot 4\sin A\sin B\sin C = T_3 \qquad \text{(why ?)}$$

$a + b + c = 2R(\sin A + \sin B + \sin C)$

$$= 8R\cos\dfrac{1}{2}A\cos\dfrac{1}{2}B\cos\dfrac{1}{2}C \qquad \dots(1)$$

$\therefore \quad T_2 = (a+b+c)(r/R)$

$= 8R \cos \frac{1}{2} A \cos \frac{1}{2} B \cos \frac{1}{2} C$, by (1)

$$\times \left(\frac{4R \sin \frac{1}{2} A \sin \frac{1}{2} B \sin \frac{1}{2} C}{R} \right)$$

$= 4R \sin A \sin B \sin C = T_3$

$\because \quad 2 \sin \frac{A}{2} \cos \frac{A}{2} = \sin A$

21. R.H.S. $T_2 = \frac{2abc}{2s} \cdot \sqrt{\left\{ \frac{s(s-a)}{bc} \cdot \frac{s(s-b)}{ca} \cdot \frac{s(s-c)}{ab} \right\}}$

$= \sqrt{s(s-a)(s-b)(s-c)} = S =$ L.H.S.

Again $T_3 = 4Rr \cos \frac{A}{2} \cos \frac{B}{2} \cos \frac{C}{2}$

$= rR (\sin A + \sin B + \sin C)$

$= \frac{r}{2}(a+b+c) = r \cdot s = S$

22. (a) R.H.S. $= Rr (\sin A + \sin B + \sin C)$

$R \cdot \frac{S}{s} \left(\frac{a+b+c}{2R} \right) = S$

(b) R.H.S. $= R \cdot \frac{2s}{2R} = s$.

23. (a) $\cos A + \cos B + \cos C$

$= 1 + 4 \sin (A/2) \sin (B/2) \sin (C/2)$ (prove) ...(1)

$= 1 + \frac{4R \sin (A/2) \sin(B/2) \sin (C/2)}{R} = 1 + \frac{r}{R}$

(Remember the result)

Another form :

L.H.S. $= \frac{b \cos B}{\sin B} + \frac{c \cos C}{\sin C} = 2R (\cos B + \cos C)$

by sine rule

$\cos B + \cos C = \frac{2(r+R)}{2R} = 1 + \frac{r}{R}$

But $\cos A + \cos B + \cos C = 1 + \frac{r}{R} = \cos B + \cos C$

$\therefore \cos A = 0$ i.e., $A = 90°$ so that triangle is rt. angled and hence the circumcentre lies on the hypotenuse which is diameter.

(b) L.H.S. $= \left(2R \sin A \cdot \frac{\cos A}{\sin A} + ... + ... \right)$

$= 2R (\cos A + \cos B + \cos C)$

$= 2R [1 + 4 \sin (A/2) \sin (B/2) \sin (C/2)]$ (prove)

$= 2R (1 + r/R) = 2(R + r)$

(c) Ans. 22. By part (b),

$E = 2(R + r) = 2(11) = 22$.

24. (a) $(b + c) \tan (A/2)$

$= 2R (\sin B + \sin C) \tan (A/2)$

$= 2R \cdot 2 \sin \frac{B+C}{2} \cdot \cos \frac{B-C}{2} \cdot \frac{\sin (A/2)}{\cos (A/2)}$

$= 2R \cdot 2 \cos \frac{B-C}{2} \cdot \cos \frac{B+C}{2}$

$= 2R (\cos B + \cos C)$

$\therefore$ L.H.S. $= 4R (\cos A + \cos B + \cos C)$

$= 4R \left(1 + \frac{r}{R} \right) = 4(R + r)$ as in Q. 23.

(b) L.H.S. $= \frac{1}{2}[1 + \cos A + 1 + \cos B + 1 + \cos C]$

$= \frac{1}{2}[3 + 1 + (r/R)]$

$= 2 + \frac{r}{2R}$.

25. (a) Area of a circle $= \pi \,(\text{radius})^2 = \pi r^2$.

Thus we have to prove that

or $\frac{1}{\sqrt{(\pi r^2)}} = \frac{1}{\sqrt{(\pi r_1^2)}} + \frac{1}{\sqrt{(\pi r_2^2)}} + \frac{1}{\sqrt{(\pi r_3^2)}}$

$\frac{1}{r} = \frac{1}{r_1} + \frac{1}{r_2} + \frac{1}{r_3}$.

This is **Q. 9. P. 678-683.**

(b) R.H.S. $= 2 \cdot \sqrt[3]{\frac{2R \sin A \cdot 2R \sin B \cdot 2R \sin C}{\sin A \sin B \sin C}} = 4R$

L.H.S. $= \frac{4s}{4 \cos \dfrac{A}{2} \cos \dfrac{B}{2} \cos \dfrac{C}{2}}$

$= \frac{2(a+b+c)}{\sin A + \sin B + \sin C}$

$= \frac{2 \cdot 2R (\sin A + \sin B + \sin C)}{\sin A + \sin B + \sin C} = 4R$.

26. (a) Let $\cos A = x, \cos B = y, \cos C = z$, then

$x + y = 2 \cos \frac{A+B}{2} \cos \frac{A-B}{2} > 0$

$x^2 + y^2 \geq 2xy$. Add $x^2 + y^2$ to both sides

$\therefore 2(x^2 + y^2) > (x + y)^2$

Since $x + y$ is + ive so we can divide by it

$\therefore \frac{2(x^2 + y^2)}{x + y} > x + y$

Similarly write other inequalities and add

$\therefore 2\Sigma \frac{x^2 + y^2}{x + y} > 2(x + y + z)$

or $\Sigma \frac{\cos^2 A + \cos^2 B}{\cos A + \cos B} > \cos A + \cos B + \cos C$

$> 1 + \frac{r}{R}$ by part (a)

(b) Here we need the result in terms of sides and hence we put the values in terms of sides.

L.H.S. $= 8 \cdot \frac{abc}{4S} \cdot \frac{S}{s} \Sigma \frac{s(s-a)}{bc}$

$= 2 \cdot \frac{abc}{s} \cdot \frac{s}{abc} \Sigma a(s-a)$

$= 2 [s \Sigma a - \Sigma a^2]$

$= 2s \cdot 2s - 2 \Sigma a^2 = (\Sigma a)^2 - 2 \Sigma a^2$

$= 2 \Sigma bc - \Sigma a^2$

27. (a) We know that

$$\tan \frac{B-C}{2} = \frac{b-c}{b+c} \cot \frac{A}{2}$$

$$\therefore \quad (r+r_1) \tan \frac{B-C}{2} = \left(\frac{S}{s} + \frac{S}{s-a}\right) \cdot \frac{b-c}{b+c} \cdot$$

$$\sqrt{\left\{\frac{s(s-a)}{(s-b)(s-c)}\right\}}$$

$$= \frac{S(2s-a)}{s(s-a)} \cdot \frac{b-c}{b+c} \cdot \frac{\sqrt{s(s-a)}}{\sqrt{[(s-b)(s-c)]}}$$

$$= \frac{S(b+c)}{\sqrt{[s(s-a)(s-b)(s-c)]}} \cdot \frac{b-c}{b+c}$$

$$= \frac{S}{S}(b-c) = b-c.$$

$$\therefore \quad \text{L.H.S.} = b-c+c-a+a-b = 0$$

(b) L.H.S. $(b-c) \cdot \dfrac{(s-a)}{S} + (c-a) \cdot \dfrac{(s-b)}{S}$

$$+ (a-b) \cdot \frac{(s-c)}{S}$$

$$= \frac{s}{S}[b-c+c-a+a-b]$$

$$- \frac{1}{S}[a(b-c) + b(c-a) + c(a-b)] = 0$$

28. $1 + \cos A = 2\cos^2 \dfrac{A}{2} = 2 \cdot \dfrac{s(s-a)}{bc} = D^r$

$$r_2 + r_3 = \frac{S}{s-b} + \frac{S}{s-c} = \frac{S \cdot a}{(s-b)(s-c)} = N^r$$

$$\therefore \quad T_1 = \frac{N^r}{D^r} = \frac{S}{S^2} \frac{a(bc)}{2} = \frac{abc}{2S}$$

Hence $T_1 = T_2 = T_3 = \dfrac{abc}{2S}$, by symmetry.

29. (a) Clearly, $S = \triangle ABC = \dfrac{1}{2}ap_1 = \dfrac{1}{2}bp_2 = \dfrac{1}{2}cp_3$

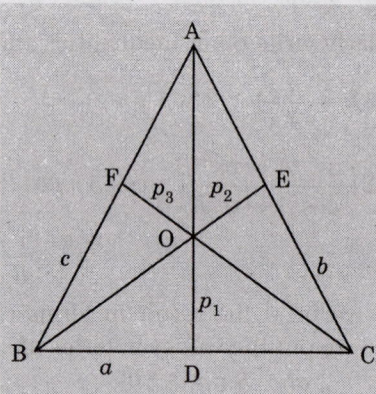

Fig. 38

$$\therefore \quad p_1 = \frac{2S}{a}, p_2 = \frac{2S}{b}, p_3 = \frac{2S}{c}$$

$$\frac{1}{p_1} + \frac{1}{p_2} + \frac{1}{p_3} = \frac{a+b+c}{2S} = \frac{2s}{2S} = \frac{s}{S} = \frac{1}{r}$$

(b) $p_1 p_2 p_3 = \dfrac{8S^3}{abc} = \dfrac{64S^3}{a^3 b^3 c^3} \times \dfrac{a^2 b^2 c^2}{8} = \dfrac{a^2 b^2 c^2}{8R^3}$

(c) Putting for p_1, p_2, p_3 we get L.H.S.

$$= \frac{1}{2S}(a\cos A + b\cos B + c\cos C)$$

$$= \frac{1}{2S} \cdot 2R(\sin A \cos A + \sin B \cos B + \sin C \cos C)$$

$$= \frac{R}{2S}[\sin 2A + \sin 2B + \sin 2C]$$

$$= \frac{R}{2S} \cdot 4\sin A \sin B \sin C$$

$$= \frac{4R}{2S} \cdot \frac{a}{2R} \cdot \frac{b}{2R} \cdot \sin C$$

$$= \frac{1}{RS}\left[\frac{1}{2}ab\sin C\right]$$

$$= \frac{1}{RS} \cdot S = \frac{1}{R}.$$

(d) Putting $p_1 = \dfrac{2S}{a}$ etc.

$$\text{L.H.S.} = 2S\left[\frac{b}{ac} + \frac{c}{ab} + \frac{a}{bc}\right] = \frac{4S}{abc} \frac{(a^2+b^2+c^2)}{2}$$

$$= \frac{a^2+b^2+c^2}{2R}.$$

30. (a) It is easy to prove as **Q. 2 (c), P, 678-81** that

$$2\alpha + 2\beta + 2\gamma = 2s \qquad \dots(1)$$

and $\alpha = s-a, \beta = s-b, \gamma = s-c \qquad \dots(2)$

$$\therefore \quad r^2 = \frac{S^2}{s^2} = \frac{s(s-a)(s-b)(s-c)}{s^2}$$

$$= \frac{\alpha \cdot \beta \cdot \gamma}{\alpha + \beta + \gamma}, \text{ by (1), (2)}.$$

(b) See fig. of **Q. 1 (a) P. 681**.

$$x = OD = R\cos A = \frac{a}{2\sin A} \cdot \cos A,$$

$$\therefore \quad \frac{a}{x} = 2\tan A.$$

Hence we have to show that

$$2\tan A + 2\tan B + 2\tan C$$

$$= \frac{1}{4} \cdot 2\tan A \cdot 2\tan B \cdot 2\tan C$$

or $\tan A + \tan B + \tan C = \tan A \tan B \tan C$

Now prove yourself.

31. (a) **See § 3, P. 675.**

(b) (i) From figure of **Q. 38 P. 688**, since angle between two st. lines is equal to the angle between perpendiculars on them hence $\angle AOE = \angle C$.

$$x = OA, y = OB, z = OC \qquad \text{(given)}$$

$$x = OA = AE \text{ cosec } AOE$$

$$= AB \cos A \text{ cosec } C$$

or $x = c\cos A \text{ cosec } C$

$$= 2R\sin C \cos A \text{ cosec } C = 2R\cos A$$

Similarly, $y = 2R \cos B$, $z = 2R \cos C$ [§ 3 P. 675]

$\therefore \quad \dfrac{a}{x} = \dfrac{2r \sin A}{2R \cos A} = \tan A,$

$\dfrac{b}{y} = \tan B, \dfrac{c}{z} = \tan C$

Hence we have to prove that

$\tan A + \tan B + \tan C = \tan A \tan B \tan C$

You prove it yourself.

(ii) $x + y + z = 2R(\cos A + \cos B + \cos C)$

$= 2R\left[1 + 4 \sin \dfrac{1}{2}A \sin \dfrac{1}{2}B \sin \dfrac{1}{2}C\right]$

$= 2R + 2r = 2(R + r)$. **Q. 23 (a) P. 679-685**

32. (a) From the given relation $r_1 - r = r_2 + r_3$

or $\dfrac{S}{s-a} - \dfrac{S}{s} = \dfrac{S}{s-b} + \dfrac{S}{s-c}$

or $\dfrac{a}{s(s-a)} = \dfrac{a}{(s-b)(s-c)}$

or $\dfrac{(s-b)(s-c)}{s(s-a)} = 1$ or $\tan^2 \dfrac{A}{2} = 1$

or $\tan(A/2) = 1$ $\therefore$ $(A/2) = 45°$ or $A = 90°$

$\therefore$ The triangle is righangled.

(b) We know that $a = 2R \sin A$ etc.

We are given that

$8R^2 = 4R^2(\sin^2 A + \sin^2 B + \sin^2 C)$

or $\sin^2 A + \sin^2 B + \sin^2 C = 2$

or $1 - \cos^2 A + 1 - \cos^2 B + \sin^2 C = 2$

or $(\cos^2 A - \sin^2 C) + \cos^2 B = 0$

or $\cos(A + C)\cos(A - C) + \cos^2 B = 0$

or $- \cos B[\cos(A - C) - \cos B] = 0$

          $[\because \cos B = -\cos(A + C)]$

or $\cos B[\cos(A - C) + \cos(A + C)] = 0$

or $\cos B . 2\cos A \cos C = 0$

$\therefore$ $\cos A = 0$ or $\cos B = 0$ or $\cos C = 0$

or $A = \pi/2$ or $B = \pi/2$ or $C = \pi/2$

33. (a) We have $\left(1 - \dfrac{s-b}{s-a}\right)\left(1 - \dfrac{s-c}{s-a}\right) = 2$, $\because r_1 = \dfrac{s}{s-a}$

or $\dfrac{b-a}{s-a} . \dfrac{c-a}{s-a} = 2$

or $2(b-a)(c-a) = 4(s-a)^2 = (2s-2a)^2$

or $2(bc - ac - ab + a^2) = (b + c - a)^2$

or $2bc - 2ac - 2ab + 2a^2 = (b^2 + c^2 + a^2)$

                $+ 2bc - 2ac - 2ab)$

or $a^2 = b^2 + c^2$

$\therefore$ The triangle is righangled.

(b) We have $R = \dfrac{c}{2 \sin C} = \dfrac{c}{2 \sin 90°} = \dfrac{c}{2}$ ...(1)

Also $r = \dfrac{S}{s} = \dfrac{2S}{2s} = \dfrac{ab}{a+b+c}$ ...(2)

$\left[\because C = 90°, S = \dfrac{1}{2}ab \sin C = \dfrac{1}{2}ab\right]$

(i) Ans. (a).

$\dfrac{c}{\sin C} = 2R$ $\therefore$ $c = 2R \sin 90° = 2R$ ...(1)

Also $r = (s-c)\tan(C/2) = s - c$ $\because \tan 45° = 1$

$2r = 2s - 2c = a + b - c = a + b - 2R$ by (1)

$\therefore$ $2(r + R) = a + b$.

(ii) By (1), $\dfrac{c}{r} = \dfrac{c(a+b+c)}{ab} = \dfrac{ca + cb + c^2}{ab}$

$= \dfrac{ca + cb + a^2 + b^2}{ab} = \dfrac{a(c+a) + b(c+b)}{ab}$

$= \dfrac{a(c+a)}{ab} + \dfrac{b(c+b)}{ab} = \dfrac{c+a}{b} + \dfrac{c+b}{a}$.

34. (a) r_1, r_2, r_3 are in A.P., if $r_2 - r_1 = r_3 - r_2$

or $\dfrac{S}{s-b} - \dfrac{S}{s-a} = \dfrac{S}{s-c} - \dfrac{S}{s-b}$

or $\dfrac{b-a}{s-a} = \dfrac{c-b}{s-c}$

or $(a-b)(s-c) = (b-c)(s-a)$

which is given.

(b) Since r_1, r_2, r_3 are in H.P., it follows that

or $\dfrac{s-a}{S}, \dfrac{s-b}{S}, \dfrac{s-c}{S}$ are in A.P.

Hence $\dfrac{2(s-b)}{S} = \dfrac{s-a}{S} + \dfrac{s-c}{S}$

or $-2b = -a - c$ or $b = \dfrac{1}{2}(a + c)$

Hence a, b, c are in A.P.

(c) r_1, r_2, r_3 in H.P. $\Rightarrow a, b, c$ are in A.P. as in (b)

or $2b = a + c$ ...(1)

$2s = a + b + c = 24$

$\therefore$ $3b = 24 \Rightarrow b = 8$ ..(2)

Hence $a + c = 16$, by (1) and (2)

Again we are given that $S = 24$

or $s(s-a)(s-b)(s-c) = 24^2$

or $12(12 - a)(12 - 8)(12 - c) = 576$

or $(12 - a)(12 - c) = 12$

or $144 - 12(a + c) + ac = 12$

Put $a + c = 16$ $\therefore$ $ac = 60$

Thus a, c are the roots of $t^2 - 16t + 60 = 0$

$t = 10, 6$ $\therefore$ $a = 10, c = 6, b = 8$, $a = 6, c = 10, b = 8$

Hence sides are 6, 8, 10, or 10, 8, 6.

35. (a) $\dfrac{r_1}{bc} = \dfrac{4R \sin(A/2)\cos(B/2)\cos(C/2)}{2R \sin B . 2R \sin C}$

$= \dfrac{\sin(A/2)}{4R \sin(B/2)\sin(C/2)}$ $\because \sin\theta = 2\sin\dfrac{\theta}{2}\cos\dfrac{\theta}{2}$

$$= \frac{\sin^2 (A/2)}{4R \sin (A/2) \sin (B/2) \sin (C/2)}$$

$$= \frac{\sin^2 (A/2)}{r}$$

L.H.S. $= \frac{1}{r} [\sin^2 (A/2) + \sin^2 (B/2) + \sin^2 (C/2)]$

$$= \frac{1}{2r} [1 - \cos A + 1 - \cos B + 1 - \cos C]$$

$$= \frac{1}{2r} [3 - \Sigma \cos A]$$

$$= \frac{1}{2r} \left[3 - \left(1 + \frac{r}{R} \right) \right] \quad \textbf{by Q. 23 P. 679-85}$$

$$= \frac{1}{2r} \left[2 - \frac{r}{R} \right] = \frac{1}{r} - \frac{1}{2R}.$$

(b) L.H.S. $= abc \left[\frac{1}{ar_1} + \frac{1}{br_2} + \frac{1}{cr_3} \right]$

Put $r_1 = \frac{S}{s-a}$ and $R = \frac{abc}{4S}$

L.H.S. $= 4RS \cdot \frac{1}{S} \left[\frac{s-a}{a} + \frac{s-b}{b} + \frac{s-c}{c} \right]$

$$= 2R \left[\frac{2(s-a)}{a} + \frac{2(s-b)}{b} + \frac{2(s-c)}{c} \right]$$

$$= 2R \left[\frac{b+c-a}{a} + \frac{c+a-b}{b} + \frac{a+b-c}{c} \right]$$

$$= 2R \left[\frac{b}{a} + \frac{c}{a} - 1 + \frac{c}{b} + \frac{a}{b} - 1 + \frac{a}{c} + \frac{b}{c} - 1 \right]$$

$$= \text{R.H.S.}$$

36. (a) $(r_1 + r_2 + r_3 - r)^2 = r_1^2 + r_2^2 + r_3^2 + r^2$

$$- 2r (r_1 + r_2 + r_3) + 2 (r_1 r_2 + r_2 r_3 + r_3 r_1).$$

Now from Q. 11, $r_1 + r_2 + r_3 - r = 4R$

and from Q. 8 (a), $(r_1 r_2 + r_2 r_3 + r_3 r_1) = s^2$.

$$\therefore \quad (4R)^2 = r_1^2 + r_2^2 + r_3^2 + r^2$$

$$- 2r (r_1 + r_2 + r_3) + 2s^2$$

$$\therefore \quad r_1^2 + r_2^2 + r_3^2 + r^2 = 16 R^2$$

$$+ 2 (rr_1 + rr_2 + rr_3) - 2s^2 \quad ....(1)$$

Now $2 (rr_1 + rr_2 + rr_3)$

$$= 2 \left[\frac{S^2}{s(s-a)} + \frac{S^2}{s(s-b)} + \frac{S^2}{s(s-c)} \right]$$

$$= 2S^2 \cdot \frac{(s-b)(s-c) + (s-c)(s-a) + (s-a)(s-b)}{S^2}$$

$$= 2 [3s^2 - s(b+c+c+a+a+b) + bc + ca + ab]$$

$$= 2 [3s^2 - s \cdot 4s + bc + ca + ab]$$

$$= -2s^2 + 2 (ab + bc + ca).$$

Hence from (1)

$$r_1^2 + r_2^2 + r_3^2 + r^2 = 16 R^2 - 2s^2$$

$$+ 2 (ab + bc + ca) - 2s^2$$

$$= 16 R^2 - [(a+b+c)^2 - 2 (ab + bc + ca)]$$

$$= 16 R^2 - (a^2 + b^2 + c^2).$$

(b) Putting the values of r_1, r_2, r_3, we have

$$T_1 = \frac{2s}{S \left[\frac{1}{s-a} + \frac{1}{s-b} + \frac{1}{s-c} \right]} = \frac{2S^2}{S [\Sigma (s-b)(s-c)]}$$

$$= \frac{2S}{3s^2 - 2s(a+b+c) + \Sigma bc} = \frac{2S}{\Sigma bc - s^2}$$

$$T_2 = \frac{1}{S} [a(s-a) + b(s-b) + c(s-c)]$$

$$= \frac{1}{S} [s(a+b+c) - \Sigma a^2]$$

$$= \frac{1}{2S} [2s \cdot 2s - 2 \{(\Sigma a)^2 - 2 \Sigma bc\}]$$

$$= \frac{1}{2S} [4s^2 - 8s^2 + 4 \Sigma bc]$$

$$= \frac{1}{2S} [\Sigma bc - s^2] \cdot 4 = \frac{4}{T_1}$$

$$\therefore \quad T_1 T_2 = 4$$

37. (a) See figure of **Q. 2, P. 681**

We have $\frac{IF}{IA} = \sin \frac{A}{2}$ or $r = IA \sin (A/2)$ ...(I)

or $4R \sin (A/2) \sin (B/2) \sin (C/2) = IA \sin (A/2)$

(R. 6, P. 676)

$$\therefore \quad IA = 4R \sin (B/2) \sin (C/2)$$

(b) L.H.S. $= IA \cdot IB \cdot IC$ from (I) of (a)

$$= \frac{r^3}{\sin \frac{A}{2} \sin \frac{B}{2} \sin \frac{C}{2}} = \frac{r^3 \cdot 4R}{4 R \sin \frac{A}{2} \sin \frac{B}{2} \sin \frac{C}{2}}$$

$$= \frac{r^3 \cdot 4R}{r} = 4r^2 R = 4 \cdot \frac{S^2}{s^2} \cdot \frac{abc}{4S} = \frac{abc}{s^2} \cdot S$$

R.H.S. $= abc \cdot \frac{S}{s^2}$ on putting for

$$\tan \frac{A}{2}, \tan \frac{B}{2} \text{ and } \tan \frac{C}{2}$$

38. We know the following results from Trigonometry

$$IO = R \sqrt{1 - 8 \sin \frac{A}{2} \sin \frac{B}{2} \sin \frac{C}{2}} \quad ...(1)$$

and $r = 4R \sin \frac{A}{2} \sin \frac{B}{2} \sin \frac{C}{2}$ ...(2)

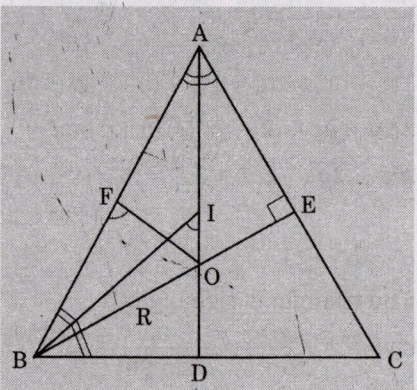

Fig. 38(a)

$(IO)^2 = R^2 - 8R^2 \sin\dfrac{A}{2}\sin\dfrac{B}{2}\sin\dfrac{C}{2}$

$\qquad = R^2 - 2R(r) = R^2 - 2Rr$, by (1) and (2).

2nd Part : For $\Delta\, BIO$ to be right angled, we have

$\qquad BI^2 + IO^2 = BO^2$

From part (i) above

$\qquad BI = 4R\sin\dfrac{A}{2}\sin\dfrac{C}{2}$ and $(IO)^2 = R^2 - 2Rr$

$\therefore \quad 16R^2\sin^2(A/2)\sin^2(C/2) + R^2 - 2R.$

$\qquad\qquad (4R\sin(A/2)\sin(B/2)\sin(C/2)) = R^2$

or $\quad 2\sin(A/2)\sin(C/2) = \sin(B/2)$

Now putting the values of $\sin(A/2)$ etc. in terms of sides, we get

$\qquad \dfrac{2(s-b)}{b} = 1$ or $2s = 3b$ or $a + c = 2b$

i.e. b is A.M. of a and c.

39. (a) We know that $R = \dfrac{abc}{4S}$. ...(1)

Let $\Delta\, OBC = S_1$, $\Delta\, OCA = S_2$, $\Delta\, OAB = S_3$.

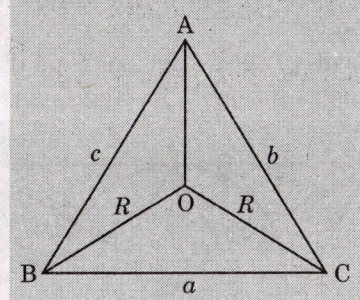

Fig. 39

$\therefore \quad R_1 = \dfrac{OB \cdot OC \cdot BC}{4\,\Delta\, OBC} = \dfrac{R \cdot R \cdot a}{4S_1}$

$\therefore \quad \dfrac{a}{R_1} = \dfrac{4S_1}{R^2}.$

$\therefore \quad \dfrac{a}{R_1} + \dfrac{b}{R_2} + \dfrac{c}{R_3} = \dfrac{4}{R^2}(S_1 + S_2 + S_3)$

$\qquad = \dfrac{4}{R^2}\Delta\, ABC = \dfrac{4S}{R^2} = \dfrac{1}{R^2}\cdot\dfrac{abc}{R} = \dfrac{abc}{R^3}$ [from (1)]

(b) $\angle BIC = 180° - \left(\dfrac{B+C}{2}\right)$

$\qquad = 180° - (90° - A/2) = 90° + A/2$

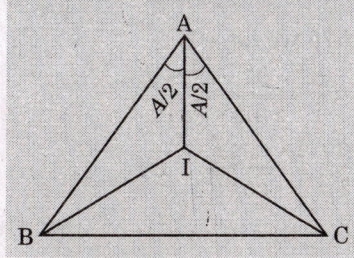

Fig. 40

We know that $R = \dfrac{a}{2\sin A}$

$\therefore \quad P_1 = \dfrac{BC}{2\sin BIC} = \dfrac{a}{2\sin(90° + A/2)} = \dfrac{a}{2\cos(A/2)}$

$\therefore \quad P_1 = \dfrac{2R\sin A}{2\cos(A/2)} = 2R\sin\dfrac{A}{2}$ $\quad(\because\ a = 2R\sin A)$

$\therefore \quad P_1 P_2 P_3 = 8R^3 \sin(A/2)\sin(B/2)\sin(C/2)$

$\qquad = 2R^2 \cdot 4R\sin(A/2)\sin(B/2)\sin(C/2)$

$\qquad = 2R^2 \cdot r.$

40. (a) In $\Delta\, ALM$ by sine rule

$\qquad \dfrac{x}{\sin A} = \dfrac{AM}{\sin B} = \dfrac{AL}{\sin C}$ $\therefore\ AL = x\dfrac{\sin C}{\sin A} = \dfrac{cx}{a}$

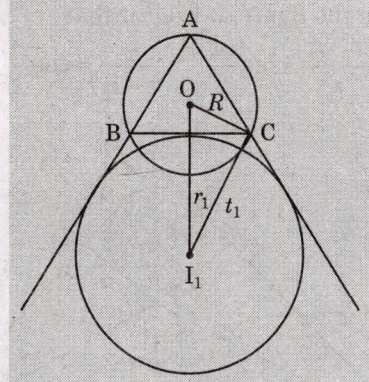

Fig. 41

$\qquad AM = x\dfrac{\sin B}{\sin A} = \dfrac{bx}{a}$

From the figure r (the radius of the incircle of $\Delta\, ABC$) = exradius of $\Delta\, ALM$

$\qquad r = \text{exradius} \left(r_1 = s\tan\dfrac{A}{2}\right)$

$\qquad r = \dfrac{x + AL + AM}{2}\cdot\tan\dfrac{A}{2} = \left(\dfrac{x + \dfrac{cx}{a} + \dfrac{bx}{a}}{2}\right)\tan\dfrac{A}{2}$

$\qquad r = \dfrac{a+b+c}{2a}\cdot x\tan\dfrac{A}{2} = s\cdot\dfrac{x}{a}\tan\dfrac{A}{2}$

But we know that

$\qquad r = (s-a)\tan\dfrac{A}{2} = (s-b)\tan\dfrac{B}{2} = (s-c)\tan\dfrac{C}{2}$

$\therefore \quad (s-a)\tan\dfrac{A}{2} = s\cdot\dfrac{x}{a}\tan\dfrac{A}{2}$

$\qquad s - a = \dfrac{sx}{a}$

Similarly, $\quad s - b = s\dfrac{y}{b}, s - c = s\dfrac{z}{c}$

Adding, $\quad s\Sigma(x/a) = 3s - \Sigma a = 3s - 2s = s$

$\therefore \quad \dfrac{x}{a} + \dfrac{y}{b} + \dfrac{z}{c} = 1.$

(b) $t_1^2 = OI_1^2 - R^2 = (R^2 + 2Rr_1) - R^2 = 2Rr_1$

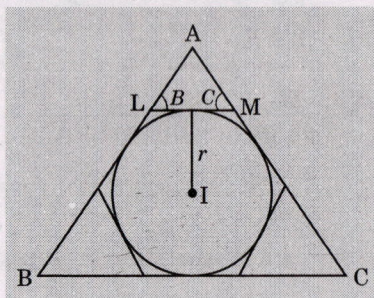

Fig. 42

L.H.S. $= \dfrac{1}{2R}\left[\dfrac{1}{r_1}+\dfrac{1}{r_2}+\dfrac{1}{r_3}\right] = \dfrac{2S}{abc}\cdot\dfrac{1}{r}$ by Q. 9

$= \dfrac{2S}{abc}\cdot\dfrac{s}{S} = \dfrac{2s}{abc}$

(c) From the figure, it is clear that

$\dfrac{r-r_1}{r_1} = \tan\dfrac{A}{2}$ $\therefore$ $\dfrac{r_1}{r-r_1} = \cot\dfrac{A}{2}$

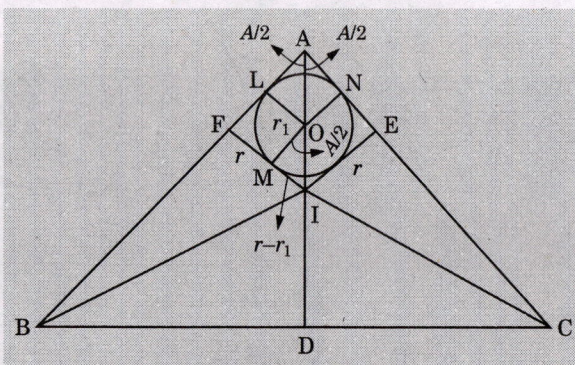

Fig. 43

Hence we have to prove that

$\Sigma \cot\dfrac{A}{2} = \cot\dfrac{A}{2}\cot\dfrac{B}{2}\cot\dfrac{C}{2}$

41. Let x, y and r be radii of the circles inscribed into the Δ^s ACD, BCD ABC and respectively. Then from similar Δ^s ABC and ACD, we get

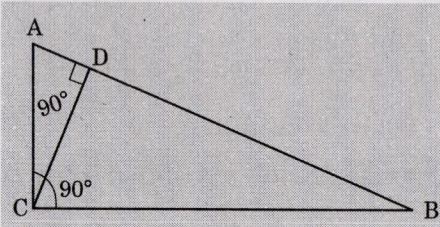

Fig. 44

$\dfrac{r}{x} = \dfrac{AB}{AC} = \dfrac{c}{b}$, where $b = \dfrac{cx}{r}$.

Similarly from similar

Δ^s ABC and BCD, we get

$\dfrac{r}{y} = \dfrac{AB}{BC} = \dfrac{c}{a}$, where $a = \dfrac{cy}{r}$.

Now $c^2 = AB^2 = a^2 + b^2 = \dfrac{c^2 y^2}{r^2} + \dfrac{c^2 x^2}{r^2} = \dfrac{c^2 (x^2+y^2)}{r^2}$

This gives $r = \sqrt{x^2+y^2}$

[Note that in similar triangles, radii of inscribed circles are proportional to corresponding sides].

42. (a) $\dfrac{\text{area of circle}}{\text{area of triangle}} = \dfrac{\pi r^2}{S} = \dfrac{\pi}{S}\cdot\dfrac{S^2}{s^2} = \pi\cdot\dfrac{S}{s^2}$ ...(1)

Now $\cot(A/2)\cdot\cot(B/2)\cdot\cot(C/2)$

$= \left[\dfrac{s(s-a)}{(s-b)(s-c)}\cdot\dfrac{s(s-b)}{(s-c)(s-a)}\cdot\dfrac{s(s-c)}{(s-a)(s-b)}\right]^{1/2}$

$= \left[\dfrac{s^3}{(s-a)(s-b)(s-c)}\right]^{1/2}$

$= \left[\dfrac{s^4}{s(s-a)(s-b)(s-c)}\right]^{1/2} = \dfrac{s^2}{S}.$

Now

$\dfrac{\pi}{\cot(A/2)\cot(B/2)\cot(C/2)} = \dfrac{\pi}{s^2/S} = \dfrac{\pi S}{s^2}.$ ...(2)

Hence from (1) and (2), we prove the required relation.

(b) Angles of ΔPQR are obvious from the figure as $\angle P = 90° - A + 90° - A = 180° - 2A$

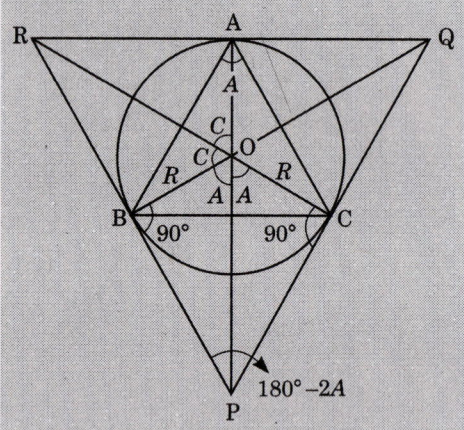

Fig. 45

Side opposite vertex Q is

$RP = BP + BR = R(\tan A + \tan C)$

$= R\dfrac{\sin(A+C)}{\cos A\cos C} = \dfrac{R\sin B}{\cos A\cos C}$

$= \dfrac{b}{2\cos A\cos C}$ etc. $\left[\because \dfrac{a}{\sin A} = 2R\text{ etc.}\right]$

43. By § 6, P. 676 we have

$\cos B = \dfrac{a^2+b^2-c^2-d^2}{2(ab+cd)}$

$\therefore$ $\tan^2\dfrac{B}{2} = \dfrac{1-\cos B}{1+\cos B}$

$= \dfrac{2(ab+cd)-(a^2+b^2-c^2-d^2)}{2(ab+cd)+(a^2+b^2-c^2-d^2)}$

$$= \frac{(c+d)^2 - (a-b)^2}{(a+b)^2 - (c-d)^2} = \frac{(c+d+a-b)(c+d-a+b)}{(a+b+c-d)(a+b-c+d)}$$

$$= \frac{(2s-2b)(2s-2a)}{(2s-2d)(2s-2c)} = \frac{(s-a)(s-b)}{(s-c)(s-d)}$$

44. We have $r + R = \frac{a}{2} \cot \frac{\pi}{n} + \frac{a}{2} \operatorname{cosec} \frac{\pi}{n}$ (§ 8. P. 677)

$$= \frac{a}{2}\left[\frac{\cos(\pi/n)+1}{\sin(\pi/n)}\right] = \frac{a}{2} \cdot \frac{2\cos^2(\pi/2n)}{2\sin(\pi/2n)\cos(\pi/2n)}$$

$$= \frac{a}{2} \cot \frac{\pi}{2n}.$$

45. Let ρ be the radius of the circle . If A_1, A_2, A_3 denote the areas of the three polygons (*i.e.* an inscribed polygon of $2n$ sides, inscribed polygon of n sides and circumscribed polygon of n sides), then **by § 9. P. 677**

$$A_1 = n\rho^2 \sin\frac{\pi}{n}, A_2 = \frac{n}{2}\rho^2 \sin\frac{2\pi}{n},$$

and $A_3 = n\rho^2 \tan\frac{\pi}{n}$, respectively.

[by eq. (2) and (3) P. 677]

Now $A_1^2 = n^2 \rho^4 \sin^2\frac{\pi}{n}$

$$= n\rho^2 \tan\frac{\pi}{n} \cdot n\rho^2 \sin\frac{\pi}{n}\cos\frac{\pi}{n}$$

$$= n\rho^2 \tan\frac{\pi}{n} \cdot \frac{n}{2}\rho^2 \sin\frac{2\pi}{n} = A_3 A_2$$

$$\therefore \qquad A_1 = \sqrt{A_2 A_3},$$

that is, A_1 is mean proportional between A_2 and A_3.

46. Let p be the perimeter of both the polygons . Then each side of first polygon is of length (p/n) and that of the second polygon is $(p/2n)$. If A_1, A_2 denote their areas , then **by § 9 P. 677**

$$A_1 = \frac{1}{4} n \cdot \frac{p^2}{n^2} \cot\frac{\pi}{n}$$

and $A_2 = \frac{1}{4} \cdot 2n \cdot \frac{p^2}{4n^2} \cdot \cot\frac{\pi}{2n}$

$$\therefore \quad \frac{A_1}{A_2} = \frac{2\cot\frac{\pi}{n}}{\cot\frac{\pi}{2n}} = \frac{2\cos\frac{\pi}{n}\sin\frac{\pi}{2n}}{\sin\frac{\pi}{n}\cos\frac{\pi}{2n}}$$

$$= \frac{2\cos\frac{\pi}{n}\sin\frac{\pi}{2n}}{2\sin\frac{\pi}{2n}\cos\frac{\pi}{2n}\cos\frac{\pi}{2n}}$$

$$= \frac{2\cos\frac{\pi}{n}}{2\cos^2\frac{\pi}{2n}} = \frac{2\cos\frac{\pi}{n}}{1+\cos\frac{\pi}{n}}.$$

47. (a) C_1, C_2, C_3 are the centres of three circles whose radii are r_1, r_2 and r_3 respectively which touch each other externally. The tangents to these meeting at O where

$$OP = OQ = OR = 4 \qquad \qquad ...(1)$$

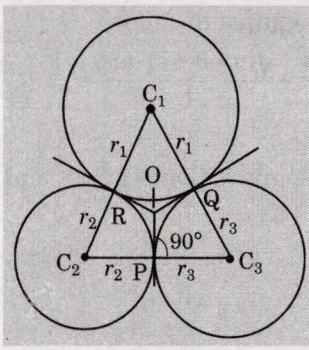

Fig. 46

Hence O is the radical centre and clearly OP is perpendicular to $C_2 C_3$ etc. By virtue of condition (i) we can say that the circle with centre O is the incircle of triangle $C_1 C_2 C_3$

where $\quad r = \frac{S}{s} = 4$ ...(2)

and S represents the area of triangle $C_1 C_2 C_3$ and s the semi-perimeter

$$a = r_2 + r_3, b = r_3 + r_1, c = r_1 + r_2$$

$\therefore \quad 2s = a + b + c = 2(r_1 + r_2 + r_3)$

or $\quad s = r_1 + r_2 + r_3$ ..(3)

$$S^2 = \text{area} = s(s-a)(s-b)(s-c)$$

$$= (r_1 + r_2 + r_3) r_1 r_2 r_3 \qquad ...(4)$$

Now $\quad r^2 = \frac{S^2}{s^2} = 16,$ by (2)

or $\quad \frac{(r_1 + r_2 + r_3) r_1 r_2 r_3}{(r_1 + r_2 + r_3)^2} = 16,$ by (3) and (4)

$\therefore \qquad \frac{r_1 r_2 r_3}{r_1 + r_2 + r_3} = \frac{16}{1}$

$\therefore \quad$ Reqd. ratio = 16 : 1

(b) $PD = PE = PF = r = \frac{S}{s}$

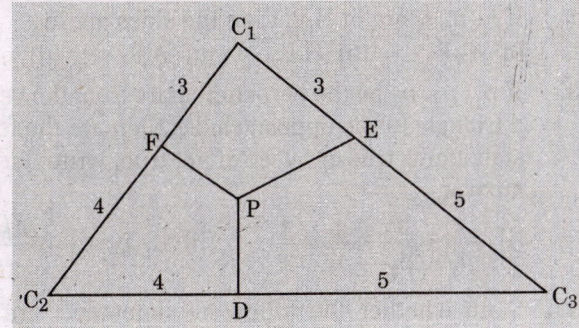

Fig. 47

where $2s = 2(3+4+5)$ or $s = 12$

$$S^2 = s(s-a)(s-b)(s-c)$$

$$= 12(12-7)(12-9)(12-8)$$

$$= 12 \cdot 5 \cdot 3 \cdot 4 = 12 \cdot 12 \cdot 5$$

$\therefore \quad S = 12\sqrt{5}$

$\therefore \quad r = \frac{S}{s} = \sqrt{5} = PD = PE = PF.$

(c) The required distance

$$= r = \frac{S}{s} = \frac{\sqrt{(a+b+c)\,abc}}{(a+b+c)} = \sqrt{\left(\frac{abc}{a+b+c}\right)} \text{ by part (a)}$$

48. (a) Ans. (c).

The points P, Q are $(1, 2\sqrt{2})$ and $(1, -2\sqrt{2})$ so that $PQ = 4\sqrt{2}$

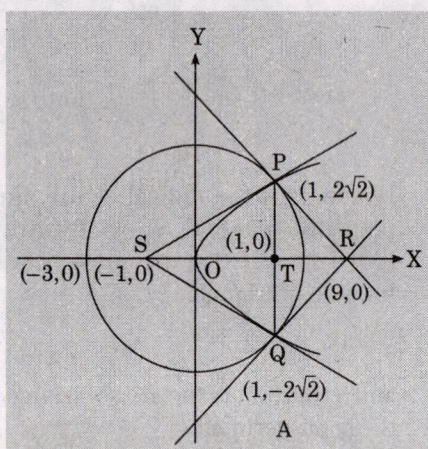

Fig. 48

·For circle.

T_P is $x.1 + y.2\sqrt{2} = 9$,

T_Q is $x.1 - y.2\sqrt{2} = 9$.

Solving we get the point as R as $(9,0)$.

For parabola.

T_P is $y.2\sqrt{2} = 4(x+1)$,

T_Q is $y(-2\sqrt{2}) = 4(x+1)$.

Solving we get the point S as $(-1, 0)$.

Also $PQ = 4\sqrt{2}$

∴ $\Delta PQR = \frac{1}{2} PQ.RT = \frac{1}{2} 4\sqrt{2}.8 = 16\sqrt{2}$

$\Delta PQS = \frac{1}{2} PQ.ST = \frac{1}{2} 4\sqrt{2}.2 = 4\sqrt{2}$

∴ $\Delta PQS : \Delta PQR = 4\sqrt{2} : 16\sqrt{2} = 1 : 4$

(b) Ans. (b).

We know that cicumradius $R = \dfrac{abc}{4S}$

For triangle PRS, $PA = \sqrt{(4+8)} = 2\sqrt{3}$,

$PR = \sqrt{(64+8)} = 6\sqrt{2}$, $RS = 10$

and $S = $ area $= \frac{1}{2}.10.2\sqrt{2} = 10\sqrt{2}$

∴ $R = \dfrac{2\sqrt{3}.6\sqrt{2}.10}{4.10\sqrt{2}} = 3\sqrt{3} \Rightarrow$ (b).

(c) Ans. (d).

Radius of incircle of ΔPQR is $r = \dfrac{S}{s}$

$2s = PQ + QR + RP$

$= 4\sqrt{2} + \sqrt{72} + \sqrt{72} = 16\sqrt{2}$ ∴ $s = 8\sqrt{2}$

Also $S = \frac{1}{2} PQ.TR = \frac{1}{2} 4\sqrt{2}.8 = 16\sqrt{2}$

$r = \dfrac{16\sqrt{2}}{8\sqrt{2}} = 2 \Rightarrow$ (d).

Problem Set (5)

▶ **Multiple Choice Questions**

1. If in a triangle ABC, $(a-b)(s-c) = (b-c)(s-a)$ then the statement r_1, r_2, r_3 are in A.P. is true or false.

2. If r_1, r_2, r_3 are in H.P. then the sides are in
   (a) G.P.   (b) H.P.   (c) A.P.   (d) none.

3. If p_1, p_2, p_3 be the perpendiculars from the vertices of a triangle to the opposite sides then are the following statements true or false ? If not true, write the corrrect answer.

   (i) $\dfrac{1}{p_1} + \dfrac{1}{p_2} + \dfrac{1}{p_3} = \dfrac{1}{R}$ (ii) $p_1 p_2 p_3 = \dfrac{a^2 b^2 c^2}{8R^3}$

4. State whether the following statements are true or false :

   $a\cos A + b\cos B + c\cos C = 4R\sin A \sin B \sin C$

   $= (a+b+c)\dfrac{r}{R}$

5. $r_2 r_3 + r_3 r_1 + r_1 r_2 = S^2/r^2$, true or false ?

6. If a triangle of maximum area is inscribed within a circle of radius R, then

   (a) $S = 2R^2$ (b) $\dfrac{1}{r_1} + \dfrac{1}{r_2} + \dfrac{1}{r_3} = \dfrac{\sqrt{2}+1}{R}$

   (c) $r = (\sqrt{2} - 1)R$ (d) $s = (1 + \sqrt{2}).2R$

7. If the sides of a triangle are in A.P. as well as in G.P., then the value of $\dfrac{r_1}{r_2} - \dfrac{r_2}{r_3}$ is

   (a) 1   (b) 0   (c) $2r$ (d) none

8. Two sides of a triangle are the roots of the equation $x^2 - 5x + 3 = 0$. If the angle between the sides is $\dfrac{\pi}{3}$, then $r.R =$

   (a) $\dfrac{4}{3}$ (b) $\dfrac{2}{3}$ (c) $\dfrac{2\sqrt{2}}{3}$ (d) $\dfrac{4\sqrt{2}}{3}$

9. If $r_1 < r_2 < r_3$ are the ex-radii of a right angled triangle and $r_1 = 1, r_2 = 2$, then $r_3 = \ldots$

10. In an isosceles triangle of which one angle $120°$, circle of radius $\sqrt{3}$ is inscribed, then the area of the triangle is :
    (a) 4π sq. units   (b) $(12 - 7\sqrt{3})$ sq. units
    (c) $(12 + 7\sqrt{3})$ sq. units   (d) $(7 + 12\sqrt{3})$ sq. units

    (I.I.T. 2006)

11. AD is internal angle bisector of ΔABC at $\angle A$ and DE perpendicular to AD which intersects AC at E and meets AB in F, then :

(a) $AF = \dfrac{4bc}{b+c}\sin\dfrac{A}{2}$ (b) $AD = \dfrac{2bc}{b+c}\cos\dfrac{A}{2}$

(c) AE is harmonic mean of b and c

(d) $\Delta\,AEF$ is an isosceles triangle (I.I.T. 2006)

12. Consider a triangle ABC and let a, b and c denote the lengths of the sides opposite to vertices A, B and C respectively. Suppose $a = 6, b = 10$ and the area of the triangle is $15\sqrt{3}$. If $\angle ACB$ is obtuse and if r denotes the radius of the incircle of the triangle, then r^2 equals to

(a) 3 (b) 4 (c) 5 (d) 1

(IIT JEE 2010)

Solutions to Problem Set (5)

1. Ans. True.
$$\frac{r_2 - r_1 = r_3 - r_2}{\dfrac{S}{s-b} - \dfrac{S}{s-c} = \dfrac{S}{s-c} - \dfrac{S}{s-b}}$$
or $(b-a)(s-c) = (c-b)(s-a)$
which is given.

2. Ans. (c).

3. (i) Ans. False. Correct is $\dfrac{1}{r}$.
$$\tfrac{1}{2}ap_1 = S \quad \therefore \quad \frac{1}{p_1} = \frac{a}{2S}$$
$$\therefore \ \Sigma\frac{1}{p_1} = \frac{a+b+c}{2S} = \frac{2s}{2S} = \frac{1}{r}$$

(ii) True. $8p_1p_2p_3 = \dfrac{8S^3}{abc} = a^2b^2c^2 \cdot \dfrac{8S^3}{a^3b^3c^3}$
$$= a^2b^2c^2 \cdot 8\left(\frac{S}{abc}\right)^3 = \frac{8a^2b^2c^2}{(4R)^3} = \frac{a^2b^2c^2}{8R^3}$$

4. True. $a = 2R\sin A$
$\therefore$ L.H.S. $= R(\sin 2A + \sin 2B + \sin 2C)$
$= 4R\sin A\sin B\sin C = $ Middle term.
Again $(a+b+c)\dfrac{r}{R}$
$$= 2R(\sin A + \sin B + \sin C)$$
$$\times \frac{4R\sin(A/2)\sin(B/2)\sin(C/2)}{R}$$
$= 8R[4\cos(A/2)\cos(B/2)\cos(C/2)]$
$\qquad [\sin(A/2)\sin(B/2)\sin(C/2)]$
$= 4R\sin A\sin B\sin C$
$\because \ \sin A = 2\sin\dfrac{A}{2}\cos\dfrac{A}{2}$

5. True. **See Q. 8 (a), P. 678**

6. Ans. (b).
Let ABC be the right angled triangle inscribed in a circle of radius R.
$\therefore \quad BC = 2R = $ diameter
$\Delta = \tfrac{1}{2}AB.AC\sin 90°$. It will be maximum if $AB = AC$
$\therefore \quad AB^2 + AC^2 = BC^2 \Rightarrow 2(AB)^2 = 4R^2$
$\therefore \quad S = \tfrac{1}{2}AB.AC = \tfrac{1}{2}(AB)^2 = R^2$

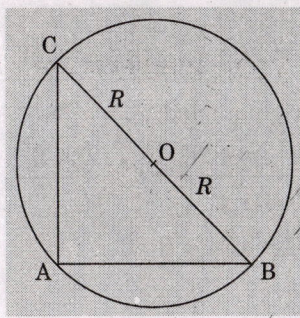

Fig. 49

$\therefore$ (a) is not correct,
$2s = AB + BC + CA = 2R + R\sqrt2 + R\sqrt2$
$\qquad = 2R(1+\sqrt2)$
$\therefore \quad s = R(1+\sqrt2) \qquad \therefore$ (d) is not correct.
$$r = \frac{S}{s} = \frac{2R^2}{R(\sqrt2+1)} = 2(\sqrt2-1)R$$
$\therefore$ (c) is not correct.
Hence (a), (c), (d) are not correct.
Also we know that
$$\frac{1}{r_1} + \frac{1}{r_2} + \frac{1}{r_3} = \frac{1}{r} = \frac{s}{S} = \frac{R(\sqrt2+1)}{R^2}$$
$$\therefore \ \frac{1}{r_1} + \frac{1}{r_2} + \frac{1}{r_3} = \frac{\sqrt2+1}{R} \Rightarrow \text{(b) is correct.}$$

7. Ans. (b).
$$2b = a+c, b^2 = ac$$
$$\therefore \ \left(\frac{a+c}{2}\right)^2 = ac \Rightarrow \tfrac{1}{4}(a-c)^2 = 0 \quad \therefore \quad a=c$$
$$\therefore \ 2b = 2a \quad \therefore \quad a=b=c$$
$$r_1 = \frac{S}{s-a}, r_2 = \frac{S}{s-b}, r_3 = \frac{S}{s-c}$$
$\therefore \ r_1 = r_2 = r_3$ as $a=b=c$
$$\therefore \ \frac{r_1}{r_2} - \frac{r_2}{r_3} = 1-1 = 0 \Rightarrow \text{(b)}.$$

8. Ans. (b).
If a, b be the sides then $a+b=5, ab=3$.
Also $\cos C = \dfrac{a^2+b^2-c^2}{2ab}$
or $\dfrac{1}{2} = \dfrac{(a+b)^2 - 2ab - c^2}{2ab}$
$\therefore \ 3 = 25 - 6 - c^2$ or $c^2 = 16 \quad \therefore \quad c = 4$
$$\therefore \ r.R = \frac{S}{s}.\frac{abc}{4S} = \frac{abc}{2(a+b+c)} = \frac{3.4}{2(5+4)} = \frac{2}{3}$$

9. Ans. $r_3 = \dfrac{3+\sqrt{17}}{2}$
$$r_1 = \frac{S}{s-a} = 1, r_2 = \frac{S}{s-b} = 2, r_3 = \frac{S}{s-c} = ?$$
$$s-a = k.1, \quad s-b = k.\frac{1}{2}, \quad s-c = k.\frac{1}{r_3}$$
Adding pairwise and putting $2s = a+b+c$,

$c = k\left(1 + \dfrac{1}{2}\right), a = k\left(\dfrac{1}{2} + \dfrac{1}{r_3}\right), b = k\left(1 + \dfrac{1}{r_3}\right)$

Since triangle is right angled, $c^2 = a^2 + b^2$

$\therefore \quad k^2 \cdot \left(\dfrac{3}{2}\right)^2 = \dfrac{k^2(r_3 + 2)^2}{4(r_3)^2} + k^2 \dfrac{(r_3 + 1)^2}{(r_3)^2}$

$\therefore \quad 9r_3^2 = (r_3 + 2)^2 + 4(r_3 + 1)^2$

or $\quad 4r_3^2 - 12r_3 - 8 = 0$

or $\quad r_3^2 - 3r_3 - 2 = 0$

$\therefore \quad r_3 = \dfrac{3 \pm \sqrt{17}}{2} = \dfrac{3 + \sqrt{17}}{2}$ as r_3 is + ive.

10. Ans. (c).

Δ being isosceles the base angles are $30°$ each as $\angle A = 120°$.

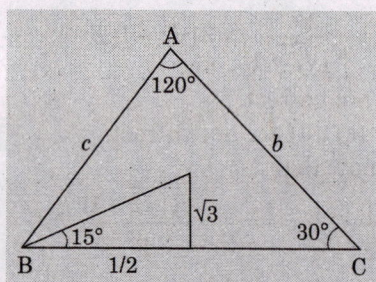

Fig. 50

By sine rule $\dfrac{a}{\sin 120°} = \dfrac{b}{\sin 30°}$ ...(1)

$\dfrac{a}{\sqrt{3}} = \dfrac{b}{1}$ or $a = b\sqrt{3}$

Also from the figure, $r = \sqrt{3}$

$\therefore \quad \dfrac{\sqrt{3}}{a/2} = \tan 15° = 2 - \sqrt{3}$

or $\dfrac{2\sqrt{3}}{2 - \sqrt{3}} = a, \; b = a \dfrac{\sin 30°}{\cos 30°} = \dfrac{a}{\sqrt{3}}$

$\therefore \quad$ Area $= \dfrac{1}{2}ab \sin 30°$

$= \dfrac{1}{2} \cdot \dfrac{1}{2} \cdot \dfrac{2\sqrt{3}}{2 - \sqrt{3}} \cdot \dfrac{2}{2 - \sqrt{3}} = \dfrac{\sqrt{3}(2 + \sqrt{3})^2}{(4 - 3)^2}$

$= \sqrt{3}(7 + 4\sqrt{3}) = 12 + 7\sqrt{3}$

11. Ans. (a), (b), (c), (d).

$\Delta ABC = \Delta ABD + \Delta ACD$

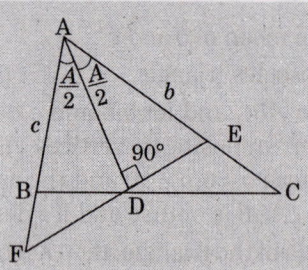

Fig. 51

$\dfrac{1}{2}bc \sin A = \dfrac{1}{2}AD \cdot c \sin \dfrac{A}{2} + \dfrac{1}{2}AD \cdot b \sin \dfrac{A}{2}$

or $\quad bc\left(2 \cos \dfrac{A}{2}\right) = AD(b + c)$

$\therefore \quad AD = \dfrac{2bc}{b + c}\cos \dfrac{A}{2}$ ...(1)

Again $AD = AE \cos \dfrac{A}{2}$ from ΔAED

$\therefore \quad AE = \dfrac{AD}{\cos A/2} = \dfrac{2bc}{b + c}$, by (1)

i.e., AE is H.M. of b and c.

Again $EF = ED + DF = 2ED = 2AD \tan \dfrac{A}{2}$

$= 2 \cdot \dfrac{2bc}{b + c}\cos \dfrac{A}{2}\tan \dfrac{A}{2} = \dfrac{4bc}{b + c}\sin \dfrac{A}{2}$

$\Delta AED = \Delta AFD \Rightarrow AE = AF \Rightarrow \Delta AEF$ is isosceles.

12. Ans. (a).

Area of triangle $= \dfrac{1}{2}ab \sin C = 15\sqrt{3}$

$\Rightarrow \dfrac{1}{2} \cdot 6 \cdot 1 \cdot \sin C = 15\sqrt{3} \Rightarrow \sin C = \dfrac{\sqrt{3}}{2}$

$\Rightarrow C = \dfrac{2\pi}{3}$ ($\because C$ is obtuse)

Now $\cos C = \dfrac{a^2 + b^2 - c^2}{2ab}$

$\Rightarrow -\dfrac{1}{2} = \dfrac{36 + 100 - c^2}{2 \times 6 \times 10} \Rightarrow C = 14$

$\therefore \quad r = \dfrac{\Delta}{s} = \dfrac{15\sqrt{3}}{\dfrac{6 + 10 + 14}{2}} = \sqrt{3} \Rightarrow r^2 = 3$

MISCELLANEOUS EXERCISE

Matching Entries

▶ *Match the entries of Column-I and Column-II.*

1. **Column-I**

(a) $r_2 r_3 + r_3 r_1 + r_1 r_2 = \ldots$

(b) $\dfrac{1}{r_1} + \dfrac{1}{r_2} + \dfrac{1}{r_3} = \ldots$

(c) If $(a - b)(s - c) = (b - c)(s - a)$ then r_1, r_2, r_3 are in which series ?

Column-II

1. $1/r$

2. c/r

3. s^2 or $\dfrac{S^2}{r^2}$

(d) If $\angle C = 90°$, then $\dfrac{c+a}{b} + \dfrac{c+b}{a} = \ldots$ 4.   A.P.

2. If R, r denote respectively the radii of the circumcircle and incircle of a triangle ABC, then

Column-I	Column-II
(a) $a\cos A + b\cos B + c\cos C$	(p) r
(b) $a\cot A + b\cot B + c\cot C$	(q) $2(R+r)$
(c) $4R\sin\dfrac{A}{2}\sin\dfrac{B}{2}\sin\dfrac{C}{2}$	(r) $4R\sin A\sin B\sin C$
(d) $\dfrac{a}{\sin A} + \dfrac{b}{\sin B} + \dfrac{c}{\sin C}$	(s) $6R$

3. The area of a triangle ABC is $400\sqrt{3}$, then match the entries of col. I with those of col. II

Column-I	Column-II
(a) $s = 20(2+\sqrt{3})$	(p) $R = 40$
(b) $s - a = 20\sqrt{3}$	(q) $r = 20(2\sqrt{3}-3)$
(c) $a + b - c = 40(2-\sqrt{3})$	(r) $r_3 = 20(2+\sqrt{3})\sqrt{3}$
(d) $abc = 64000\sqrt{3}$	(s) $r_1 = 20$

Hints / Solutions

1. (a) → 3. **See Q. 8 (a) P. 678-25**
   (b) → 1. **See Q. 34 P. 679-83**
   (c) → 4. **See Q. 9 (a) P. 678-83**
   (d) → 2. **See Q. 31 P. 769-86**

2. **Ans.** (a) → (r), (b) → (p), (c) → (q), (d) → (s)

   (a) $\dfrac{a}{\sin A} = 2R$

   $\therefore \quad \sum a\cos A = \sum 2R\sin A\cos A = R\sum \sin 2A$
   $\qquad = R(4\sin A\sin B\sin C)$

   $\therefore \quad$ (a) → (r)

   (b) $a = 2R\sin A$

   $\sum a\cot A = 2R\sum \cos A = 2R\left(1+\dfrac{r}{R}\right)$

   $\qquad = 2(R+r)$

   (c) $4R\sin\dfrac{A}{2}\sin\dfrac{B}{2}\sin\dfrac{C}{2} = r$ **(See R 6, P. 676)**

(d) $\sum \dfrac{a}{\sin A} = 2R + 2R + 2R = 6R$

3. **Ans.** (a) → (q), (b) → (s), (c) → (r), (d) → (p)

   (a) $S = 400\sqrt{3}, s = 20(2+\sqrt{3})$

   $\therefore \quad r = \dfrac{S}{s} = \dfrac{400\sqrt{3}}{20(2+\sqrt{3})} = 20\sqrt{3}(2-\sqrt{3}) = 20(2\sqrt{3}-3)$

   $\therefore \quad$ (a) → (q)

   (b) $\dfrac{S}{s-a} = r_1 \quad \therefore \quad \dfrac{400\sqrt{3}}{20\sqrt{3}}\, r_1$ or $r_1 = 20$

   $\therefore \quad$ (b) → (s)

   (c) $2(s-c) = 40(2-\sqrt{3}) \quad \therefore \quad s-c = 20(2-\sqrt{3})$

   $\therefore \quad \dfrac{S}{s-c} = r_3 \quad$ or $\quad \dfrac{400\sqrt{3}}{20(2-\sqrt{3})} = 20\sqrt{3}(2+\sqrt{3})$

   $\therefore \quad$ (c) → (r)

   (d) $R = \dfrac{abc}{4S} = \dfrac{64000\sqrt{3}}{4(400\sqrt{3})} = 40$

   $\therefore \quad$ (d) → (p)

Fascinating Facts

- The mid-point of the hypotenuse of a right angled triangle is equidistant from the three vertices of the triangle.
- The mid-point of the hypotenuse of a right angled triangle is the circumcentre of the triangle.
- The circumcentre, centroid and orthocentre are always collinear
- In any right angled triangle, the orthocentre coincides with the vertex containing the right angle.

- $\sin A + \sin B + \sin C$ is maximum when $A = B = C$
- $\cos A + \cos B + \cos C$ is maximum when $A = B = C$
- $\tan A + \tan B + \tan C$ is minimum when $A = B = C$
- If $\cos^2 A + \cos^2 B + \cos^2 C = 1$, then triangle is right angled.
- If $\cot A + \cot B + \cot C = \sqrt{3}$ or $\tan A + \tan B + \tan C = 3\sqrt{3}$, then triangle is equilateral.

❑

Heights and Distances

§1. (a) Angle of elevation and depression of a point.

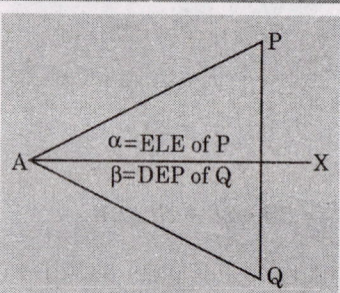

Fig. 1

Suppose a straight line *AX* is drawn in the horizontal direction. Then the angle *XAP* where *P* is a point above *AX* is called the angle of elevation of *P* as seen from *A*. Similarly the angle *XAQ* where *Q* is below *AX*, is called the angle of depression of some point *Q*.

(b) **Any line perpendicular to a plane is perpendicular to every line lying in the plane.**

Place your pen *PQ* upright on your note book, so that its lower end *Q* is on the note book. Through the point *Q* draw lines *QA*, *QB*, *QC*, ..., in your note book in different directions and you will observe that each of the angles *PQA*, *PQB*, *PQC*,..., is a right angle. In other words *PA* is perpendicular to each of the lines *QA*, *QB*, *QC*, lying in the plane.

(c) **To express one side of a right angled triangle in terms of the other side.**

Let ∠ *ABC* = θ, where *ABC* is a right angled triangle in which ∠ *C* = 90°.   (*AB* = *H* is hypotenuse)

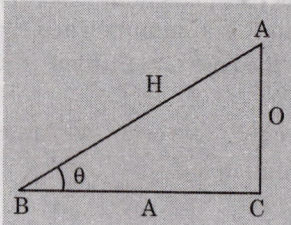

Fig. 2

The side opposite to right angle *C* will be denoted by *H* (hypotenuse), the side opposite to angle θ will be denoted by *O* (opposite) and the side containing the

angle θ (other than *H*) will be denoted by *A* i.e. adjacent side.

Then from the figure it is clear that

O = A (tan θ) or **A = O (cot θ)** *i.e.* opposite
   = adj (tan θ) or **adj = opposite (cot θ)**

Also *O* = *H* (sin θ) or *A* = *H* (cos θ)

or   **opposite = hyp. (sin θ)**

or   **adj = hyp. (cos θ)**

The above results will be used very frequently.

(d)   Geometrical properties.

(i)   In a triangle the internal bisector of an angle divides the opposite side in the ratio of the arms of the angle.

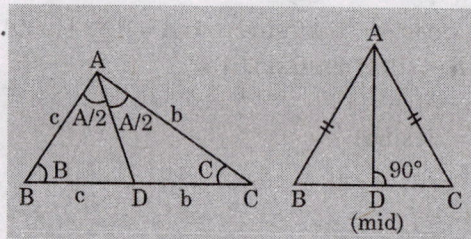

Fig. 3

(ii)   In an isosceles triangle the median is perpendicular to the base.

(iii)   In similar triangles the corresponding sides are proportional.

(iv)   The exterior angle is equal to sum of interior opposite angles.

(v)   **Sine Rule**

$$\frac{a}{\sin A} = \frac{b}{\sin B} = \frac{c}{\sin C} = 2R,$$

where *R* is the circumradius of triangle *ABC*.

$$R = \frac{abc}{4\Delta},$$

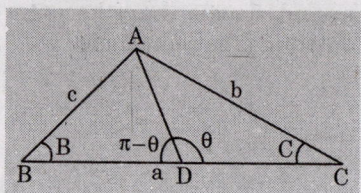

Fig. 4

where Δ is the area of $\Delta\,ABC$.

(vi) Cosine Rule

$$a^2 = b^2 + c^2 - 2bc\cos A$$

$$\text{or} \quad \cos A = \frac{b^2 + c^2 - a^2}{2bc}$$

(vii) Projection Formula

$$a = b\cos C + c\cos B$$

(viii) If D be the mid-point of side BC of any triangle, then $AB^2 + AC^2 = 2(AD^2 + DB^2)$ by use of cosine rule.

If Δ be right angled, then mid-point of hypotenuse is equidistant from the three vertices so that

$$DA = DB = DC.$$

$$\therefore \quad AB^2 + AC^2 = 2.2\,DB^2 = (2.DB)^2 = BC^2,$$

which is Pythagoras theorem.

(e) Trigonometrical results.

$$\tan A \pm \tan B = \frac{\sin(A \pm B)}{\cos A \cos B}$$

$$\cot A \pm \cot B = \frac{\sin(B \pm A)}{\sin A \sin B}$$

$$\therefore \quad \sin(\alpha + \beta)\sin(\alpha - \beta) = \sin^2\alpha - \sin^2\beta$$

$$= \cos^2\beta - \cos^2\alpha$$

$$\cos(\alpha + \beta)\cos(\alpha - \beta) = \cos^2\alpha - \sin^2\beta$$

(f) (a) _mn_ theorem of trigonometry to be remembered.

$$(m + n)\cot\theta = m\cot\alpha - n\cot\beta$$

$$= n\cot A - m\cot B \quad \text{(See the figure)}$$

In the application of mn theorem, angle θ is on the right.

Note : If θ is on the left then angle in the right is

$$\pi - \theta \quad \text{and} \quad \cot(\pi - \theta) = -\cot\theta$$

Hence in this case m–n theorem becomes

$$-(m + n)\cot\theta = m\cot\alpha - n\cot\beta = n\cot A - m\cot B$$

(θ on the left)

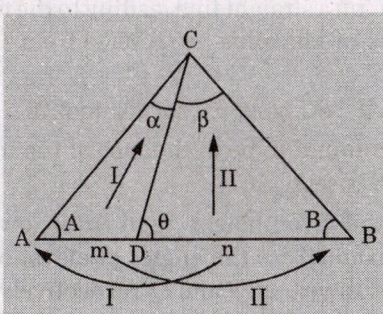

Fig. 5

(b) Sine formula and cosine formula

$$\frac{\sin A}{a} = \frac{\sin B}{b} = \frac{\sin C}{c}, \quad \cos A = \frac{b^2 + c^2 - a^2}{2bc}$$

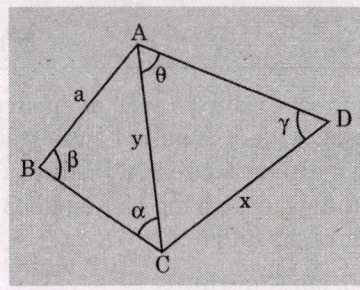

Fig. 6

In the application of sine rule the following point be noted. We are given one side a and some other side x is to be found. Both these are in different triangles. We choose a common side y of these triangles. Then apply sine rule for a and y in one triangle and for x and y for the other triangle and eliminate y. Thus you will know unknown side x in terms of a. In the adjoining figure a is a known side of $\Delta\,ABC$ and x unknown is a side of triangle ACD. The common side of these triangles is $AC = y$ say. Now apply sine rule.

$$\therefore \quad \frac{a}{\sin\alpha} = \frac{y}{\sin\beta} \quad \text{and} \quad \frac{x}{\sin\theta} = \frac{y}{\sin\gamma}$$

Dividing thereby eliminating y, we get

$$\frac{x\sin\alpha}{a\sin\theta} = \frac{\sin\beta}{\sin\gamma} \quad \therefore \quad x = \frac{a\sin\beta\sin\theta}{\sin\alpha\sin\gamma}$$

(g) Angles in the same segment of a circle are equal. The angle subtended by arc AB at P, Q or R is the same θ.

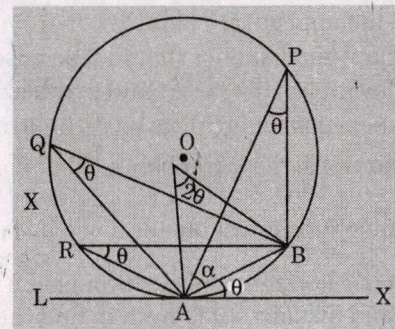

Fig. 7

(h) General Rule. Know thyself and know thy enemies. You should know fully about your ammunition in stock with which you have to annihilate your enemies. By ammunition in stock we mean what is given to you *i.e.* α, β, a, b etc. By your enemies we mean which are unknown say x or y. By annihilation, we mean to eliminate. If you have to find x, then eliminate y and get the value of x in terms of known quantities α, β, a, b etc.

Problem Set (1)

*1. (a) A ladder rests against a wall at an angle α to the horizontal. Its foot is pulled away from the wall through a distance a, so that it slides a distance b down the wall making an angle β with the horizontal, show that

$$a = b \tan \frac{1}{2}(\alpha + \beta).$$

(M.N.R. 1992; I.I.T. 1985)

(b) A ladder leaning against a vertical wall is inclined at an angle α to the horizontal. The top of the ladder touches the parapet. On moving its foot a feet away from the wall, the ladder now stands inclined at an angle β to the horizon, and its top now touching a window. Prove that the distance of the parapet from the window is

$$a \cot[(\alpha + \beta)/2].$$

(c) A ladder 20 ft. long reaches a point 20 ft. below the top of a flag. The angle of elevation of the top of the flag at the foot of the ladder is 60°. Find the height of the flag.

*(d) The angle of elevation of the top and bottom of a flag staff fixed at the top of a tower at a point distance a ft. from the foot of a tower are α and β. Prove that the height of the flag staff is $a(\tan \alpha - \tan \beta)$.

*2. (a) the angle of elevation of the top of a tower (which is yet incomplete) at a point 120 ft. from its base is 45°. How much higher should it be raised, so that the elevation at the same point may become 60°?

*(b) A vertical pole (more than 100 ft. high) consists of two portions, the lower being $\frac{1}{3}$rd of the whole. If the upper portion subtends an angle $\tan^{-1}\frac{1}{2}$ at a point in a horizontal plane through the foot of the pole and distance 40 ft. from it, find the height of the pole. **(Aligarh Engg. 1981)**

(c) On the bank of a river there is a column 200 ft. high supporting a statue of 30 ft. height, the statue to an observer on the opposite bank subtends an equal angle which a man 6 ft. high standing on the base of the column subtends. Find the breadth of the river neglecting the height of the observer's eye from the ground.

*(d) AB is a vertical pole. The end A is on the level ground, C is the middle point of AB and P is a point on the level ground. The portion CB subtends an angle β at P. If $AP = n AB$; then show that

$$\tan \beta = n/(2n^2 + 1).$$

(M.N.R. 1989; I.I.T. 1980)

(e) A vertical tower stands on a horizontal plane and is surmounted by a vertical flag staff of height h.

At a point P on the plane, the angle of elevation of the bottom of the flag staff is β and that of the top is α, prove that the height of the tower is

$$\frac{h \tan \beta}{\tan \alpha - \tan \beta}$$

(Aligarh Engg. 1983)

*3. (a) The angles of elevation of the top of a tower standing on a horizontal plane from two points on a line passing through the foot of the tower at distance a and b respectively are complementary angles. Prove that the height of the tower is $\sqrt{ab}$. If the line joining the two points subtends and angle θ at the top of the tower, show that $\sin \theta = \frac{(a-b)}{(a+b)}$.

(Aligarh Engg. 1980)

(b) A tower is observed from two stations A and B where B is East of A at a distance 100 metres. The tower is due North of A and due North-West of B. The angles of elevation of the tower from A and B are complementary. Find the height of the tower.

*4. (a) The distances of three points on a pole from its foot are in A.P. If the angles of elevation of these points from a point on the ground are θ, ϕ, ψ respectively, then

$$\cot \phi \; \cot \psi, \cot \psi \cot \theta, \cot \theta \cot \phi \text{ are in G.P.,}$$
True or False ?

*(b) from a point on the ground, the angles of elevation of a bird flying with a constant speed in a horizontal direction at equal intervals of time are α, β, γ and δ. Prove that $\cot^2 \alpha - \cot^2 \delta = 3 (\cot^2 \beta - \cot^2 \gamma)$.

*(c) The top of a tower is observed from three points A, B, C on a straight line leading to the tower. If the angles of elevation are $\theta, 2\theta, 3\theta$ from them prove that

$$AB : BC :: (\cot \theta - \cot 2\theta) : (\cot 2\theta - \cot 3\theta).$$

If C is found to be at the foot of the tower prove that B trisects AC.

5. PQ is post of given height a and AB is tower at some distance; α and β are the angles of elevation of B, the top of the tower, at P and Q respectively. Find the height of the tower and its distance from the post.

*6. (a) The angle of elevation of a cloud at a height h above the level of wager in a lake is α and the angle of depression of its image in the lake is β. Prove that the height of the cloud above the surface of the lake is

$$\frac{h (\tan \beta + \tan \alpha)}{\tan \beta - \tan \alpha} \text{ or } \frac{h \sin (\alpha + \beta)}{\sin (\beta - \alpha)}$$

or $\dfrac{h (\cot \alpha + \cot \beta)}{\cot \alpha - \cot \beta}$

(C.E.E. 1983)

*(b) The angle of elevation of a cloud from a point x feet above a lake is θ and the angle of depression of its reflection in the lake is ϕ, prove that its height is $\dfrac{x\sin(\phi+\theta)}{\sin(\phi-\theta)}$ **(C.E.E. 1985, 93; Roorkee 1983)**

(c) The angle of elevation of a stationary cloud from a point 2500 cm above a lake is 15° and the angle of depression of its reflection in the lake is 45°. What is the height of the cloud above the lake level ?

(d) If the angle of elevation of a cloud from a point h metres above a lake be θ and the angle of depression of its reflection in the lake be ϕ, prove that the distance of the cloud from the point of observation is $\dfrac{2h\cos\phi}{\sin(\phi-\theta)}$

Also find the horizontal distance of the cloud from the place of observation.

*(c) A vertical tower 50 ft. high stands on a sloping ground. The foot of the tower is at the same level as the middle point of a vertical flag pole. From the top of the tower the angle of depression of the top and the bottom of the pole are 15° and 45° respectively. Find the length of the pole.

7. (a) From the top of cliff 200 ft. high, the angles of depression of the top and bottom of a tower are observed to be 30° and 60° respectively. Find the height of the tower.

*(b) From the top of a spire, the angles of depression of the top and bottom of a tower of height h are θ and ϕ. show that the height of the spire and its horizontal distance from the tower are respectively

$$h\cdot\frac{\cos\theta\sin\phi}{\sin(\phi-\theta)}\text{ and }\frac{h\cos\theta\cos\phi}{\sin(\phi-\theta)}$$

(c) A tower of height 60 metres stands on the top of a cliff. An observer in a boat finds that the elevation of the top of the tower is 30° and that of the top of the cliff is 23°. Find the height of the cliff, and the distance of the boat from the foot of the cliff. **(Roorkee 1982)**

*8. (a) The angular depressions of the top and the foot of a chimney as seen from the top of a second chimney which is 150 metres high and standing on the same level as the first are θ and ϕ respectively. Find the distance between their tops when

$$\tan\theta=\frac{4}{3}\text{ and }\tan\phi=\frac{5}{2}.$$

*(b) From the bottom of a pole of height h, the angle of elevation of the top of the tower is α. The pole subtends angle β at the top of the tower. Obtain the height of the tower. **(Roorkee 1988)**

(c) The height of a house subtends a right angle at the opposite window. The angle of elevation of the window from the base of the house is 60°. If the width of the road be 6 metres, find the height of the house.

9. (a) A tower subtends an angle α at a point A in the plane of its base and the angle of depression of the foot of the tower at a point b ft. just above A is β. Prove that the height of the tower is $b\tan\alpha\cot\beta$. **(P.E.T. 1990)**

*(b) The width of a road is b feet., on one side of which there is a window h feet height. A building in front of it subtends an angle θ at it. Prove that the height of the building is $\dfrac{(b^2+h^2)\sin\theta}{b\cos\theta+h\sin\theta}$.

*10. (a) The angle of elevation of the top of a pillar at any point A on the ground is 15°. On walking 100 ft. towards the pillar, the angle becomes 30°. Find the height of the pillar and its distance from A.

*(b) A person standing on the bank of a river observes that the angle subtended by a tree on the opposite bank is 60°, when he retires 40 feet from the bank he finds the angle to be 30°. Find the height of the tree and the breadth of the river.

(c) The angle of elevation of the top of a tower from a point on the same level as the foot of the tower is 30°. On advancing 150 metres towards the foot of the tower the angle of elevation increases to 60°. Find the height of the tower.

(d) The angle of elevation of the top of a tower at a point A on the ground is 30°. On walking 20 metres towards the tower, the angle of elevation is 60°. Find the height of the tower and its distance from A.

(e) On level ground the angle of elevation of the top of a tower is 30°. On moving 20 m nearer, the angle of elevation is 60°. What is the height of the tower. **(C.E.E., 1984)**

11. (a) Find the height of a chimney when it is found that on walking towards it 100 ft. in a horizontal line through its base the angular elevation of its top changes from 30° to 45°.

(b) The shadow of a tower standing on a level ground is found to be 60 metres longer then the sun's altitude is 30° than when it is 45°. Find the height of the tower.

*(c) A man in a boat rowed away from a cliff 150 metres high takes 2 minutes to change the angle of elevation of the top of the cliff from 60° to 45°. Find the speed of the boat.

(c) A man on a cliff observes a boat at an angle of depression 30° which is sailing towards the shore to the point immediately beneath him. three minutes later the angle of depression of the boat is found to be 60°.

Assuming that the boat sails at a uniform speed, determine how much more time it will take to reach the shore.

(e) The length of the shadow of a rod inclined at 10° to the vertical towards the sun is 2.05 metres when the elevation of the sun is 38°. Find the length of the rod.

12. (a) From an aeroplane vertically over a straight horizontal road, the angles of depression of two consecutive milestones on opposite sides of the aeroplane are observed to be α and β. Show that the height in miles of aeroplane above the road is given by

$$\frac{\tan \alpha \tan \beta}{\tan \alpha + \tan \beta}.$$

(b) From a light house the angle of depression of two ships on opposite sides of the light house are observed to be 30° and 45°. If the height of the light house be 100 metres, find the distance between the ships if the line joining them passes through the foot of the light house.

(c) An aeroplane flying horizontally 1 km. above the ground is observed at an elevation of 60°. If after 10 seconds the elevation is observed to be 30°, find the uniform speed per hour of the aeroplane.

*13. (a) A man observes that when he moves up a distance c metres on a slope, the angle of depression of a point on the horizontal plane from the base of the slope is 30°; and when he moves up further a distance c metres the angle of depression of that point is 45°. Obtain the angle of inclination of the slope with the horizontal.

(Roorkee 1986)

*(b) A man observes that when he has walked c metres up an incline, the angular depression of an object in a horizontal plane through the foot of the slope is α, and that when he has walked a further distance of c metres the depression is β. Prove that the inclination of the slope to the horizon is the angle whose cotangent is

$$(2 \cot \beta - \cot \alpha). \quad \textbf{(Roorkee 1981)}$$

*(c) A man observes when he has climbed up 1/3 of the length of an inclined plane placed against a wall, the angular depression of an object on the floor is α and that after he has climbed the plane fully, the depression is β. Find the inclination of the plane to the floor. **(Roorkee 1994)**

*14. (a) Due south of a tower which is leaning towards north, there are two stations at distance x, y

x, y respectively from its foot. If α, β respectively be the angles of elevation of the top of the tower at these stations, show that the inclination of the tower to the horizon is

$$\cot^{-1} \frac{y \cot \alpha - x \cot \beta}{y - x}$$

(b) A tree standing on a horizontal plane is leaning towards east. At two points situated at distances a and b exactly due West of it, the angles of elevation of the top are respectively α and β. Prove that the height of the top from the ground is

$$\frac{(b - a) \tan \alpha \tan \beta}{\tan \alpha - \tan \beta}.$$

*15. (a) A chimney leans towards North. At equal distances due North and South of it in a horizontal plane, the elevations of the top are α, β. Show that the inclination of the chimney to the vertical is

$$\tan^{-1} \left[\frac{\sin (\alpha - \beta)}{2 \sin \alpha \sin \beta} \right].$$

*(b) A tower AB leans towards west making an angle α with the vertical. The angular elevation of B, the topmost point of the tower, is β as observed from a point C due east of A at a distance d from A. If the angular elevation of B from a point due east of C at a distance $2d$ from C is γ, then prove that $2 \tan \alpha = 3 \cot \beta - \cot \gamma$ **(I.I.T. 1994)**

(c) A flag leaning towards east is inclined at an angle θ to the level ground. A man walks a distance l from the foot of the flag towards West and observes the angle of elevation of the top of the flag to be α. On walking further a distance l_1, in the same direction, the angle of elevation decreases by β, Show that

$$\tan \theta = \frac{l_1}{(l + l_1) \cot \alpha - l \cot (\alpha - \beta)}.$$

*(d) A train is moving at a constant speed at an angle θ East of north. Observations of the train are made from a fixed point. It is due north at some instant. Ten minutes earlier it bearing was α_1 west of north, whereas ten minutes afterwards its bearing is α_2 east of north. Find $\tan \theta$. **(Roorkee 1990)**

*16. (a) A balloon moving in a straight line passes vertically above two points A and B on a horizontal plane 1000 ft. apart. When above A it has an altitude of 60° as seen from B and when above B it has an altitude of 45° as seen from A. Find the distance from A of the point at which it will touch the plane.

(b) A balloon moving in a straight line passes vertically above two points A and B on a horizontal plane 1000 ft. apart. When above A it has an altitude of 60° as seen from B and when above B, 30° as seen from A. Find the distance from A at which it will strike the plane.

*17. (a) A vertical pole stands at a point O on a horizontal ground. A and B are points on the ground d metres apart. The pole subtends angles α and β at A and B respectively. AB subtends an angle γ at O. Find the height of the pole.   **(I.I.T. 1982)**

(b) A and B are two points on the same level. The distance AB is c. The angles of elevation of the top P of a vertical tower PQ from A and B are α and β. If Q the foot of tower is on the same level as A and B, then $\angle QAB = \gamma$ and $\angle QBA = \delta$. Find an expression for the height of the tower in terms of c, γ, δ and α. Also prove that

$$\sin \delta \tan \alpha = \sin \gamma \tan \beta. \quad \textbf{(Dhanbad 1992)}$$

(c) Two pillars of height a and b subtend the same angle α at a point on the line joining their feet. If the pillars subtend angles β and γ at another point in the horizontal plane at which the line joining their feet subtends a right angle, prove that

$$(a+b)^2 \cot^2 \alpha = a^2 \cot^2 \beta + b^2 \cot^2 \gamma.$$

(Dhanbad 1989)

*18. (a) The elevation of a tower due North of a station A is α or (at a place due South of it is α) and at another station B due West of A it is β. Prove that the height of the tower is

$$\frac{AB}{\sqrt{(\cot^2 \beta - \cot^2 \alpha)}} \text{ or } \frac{AB \sin \alpha \sin \beta}{\sqrt{(\sin^2 \alpha - \sin^2 \beta)}}$$

or

$$\frac{AB \sin \alpha \sin \beta}{[\sin (\alpha + \beta) \sin (\alpha - \beta)]^{1/2}}$$

or

$$\frac{AB \tan \alpha \tan \beta}{\sqrt{(\tan^2 \alpha - \tan^2 \beta)}}$$

(b) The angle of elevation of a tower at a place A due south it is θ and at a place due west of A and at a distance a from it, the elevation is ϕ. find the height of tower.   **(M.N.R. 1986)**

* 19. (a) The angle of elevation of a tower at a point A due North of it is 30° and at another point due East of A is 18°. If $AB = a$, show that the height of the tower is $\dfrac{a}{\sqrt{(2 + 2\sqrt{5})}}$.

(b) The angle of elevation of the top of a tower from a point A on the ground is θ and that from B is ϕ. If $AB = 100$ metres and AB is perpendicular to the line joining A with the foot of the tower, then find the height of the tower.

Given $\cot \theta = 3/10$ and $\cot \phi = 1/2$.

20. (a) PQ is a tower standing on a horizontal plane, Q being its foot. Two points A and B are taken on the plane such that $AB = 32$ and $\angle QAB$ is a right

angle. It is found that $\cot PAQ = 2/5$ and $\cot PBQ = 3/5$, find the height of the tower.

(b) A flastaff PN stands up right on level ground. A base AB is measured at right angles to AN such that points A, B, N lie in the same horizontal plane. If $\angle PAN = \alpha$ and $\angle PBN = \beta$, prove that the height of the flag staff is

$$\frac{AB \sin \alpha \sin \beta}{\sqrt{[\sin (\alpha + \beta) \sin (\alpha - \beta)]}}$$

Solutions to Problem Set (1)

1. (a) $b = BC = AB - AC = l \sin \alpha - l \sin \beta$

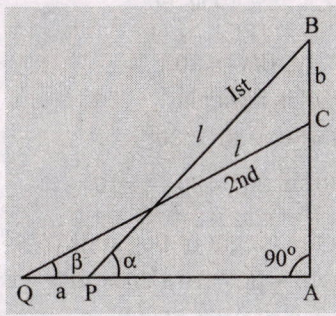

Fig. 8

$a = PQ = AQ - AP = l \cos \beta - l \cos \alpha$

$\therefore \dfrac{a}{b} = \dfrac{\cos \alpha - \cos \beta}{\sin \beta - \sin \alpha} = \tan \dfrac{\alpha + \beta}{2}$ etc.

(b) Let the length of the ladder be
$x = PB = QC.$
$PA = x \cos \alpha \quad QA = x \cos \beta$
$AC = x \sin \beta, \quad AB = x \sin \alpha.$
$CB = AB - AC = x (\sin \alpha - \sin \beta)$

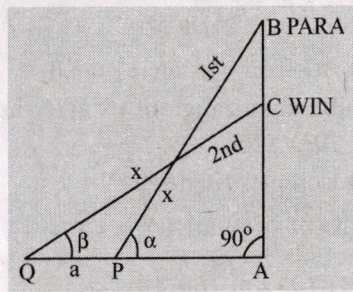

Fig. 9

$QP = a = QA - PA = x (\cos \beta - \cos \alpha)$

$\therefore \dfrac{CB}{a} = \dfrac{\sin \alpha - \sin \beta}{\cos \beta - \cos \alpha}$

$= \dfrac{2 \sin [(\alpha - \beta)/2] . \cos [(\alpha + \beta)/2]}{2 \sin [(\alpha + \beta)/2 . \sin [(\alpha - \beta)/2]},$

$\therefore \quad CB = a \cot \dfrac{\alpha + \beta}{2}.$

(c) $PB = \text{ladder} = BC = 20$ given.
Also $\angle CPA = 60° \quad \therefore \quad \angle ACP = 30°$

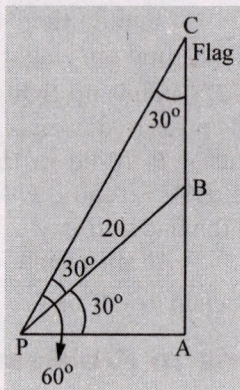

Fig. 10

$\therefore$ $\angle BCP = \angle BPC = 30°$
as ΔBCP is isosceles.

$\therefore$ $\angle BPA = 60° - 30° = 30°$

$\therefore$ $AB = 30 \sin 30° = 20 \cdot \dfrac{1}{2} = 10$

Hence the height of flag staff
  $= AB + BC = 10 + 20 = 30$ ft.

(d) $AC = a \tan \alpha$, $AB = a \tan \beta$

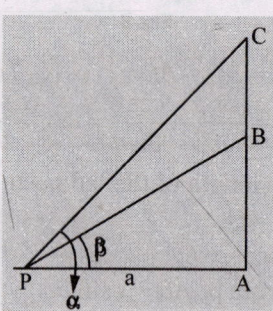

Fig. 11

$\therefore$ $BC = AC - AB = a(\tan \alpha - \tan \beta)$

2. (a) AB subtends an angle of $45°$ at P where $AP = 120$.

$\therefore$ $AB = AP = 120$

from isosceles tingle ABP

Again $\dfrac{120 + h}{120} = \tan 60° = \sqrt{3}$

$\therefore$ $h = 120 (\sqrt{3} - 1)$. (fig. 151)

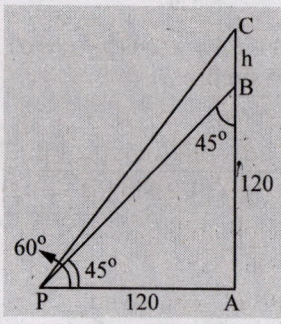

Fig. 12

(b) We are given that $\tan \theta = \dfrac{1}{2}$

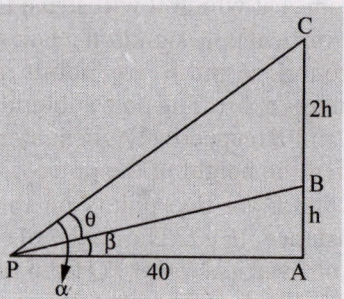

Fig. 13

where θ is the angle subtended by the upper portion.

Also $\tan \alpha = \dfrac{3h}{40}$, $\tan \beta = \dfrac{h}{40}$

and $\theta = \alpha - \beta$, $\therefore$ $\tan \theta = \dfrac{\tan \alpha - \tan \beta}{1 + \tan \alpha \tan \beta}$

or $\dfrac{1}{2} = \dfrac{(3h/40) - (h/40)}{1 + (3h^2/40^2)} = \dfrac{80h}{1600 + 3h^2}$

or $3h^2 + 1600 = 160h$

or $3h^2 - 160h + 1600 = 0.$

or $3h^2 - 120h - 40h + 1600 = 0.$

or $(h + 40)(3h - 40) = 0.$

$\therefore$ $h = 40$ and hence $3h = 120$ is the required length of the pole. $3h \neq 40$ as the pole of given to be the more than 100 ft.

(c) BC (statue) $= 30$,

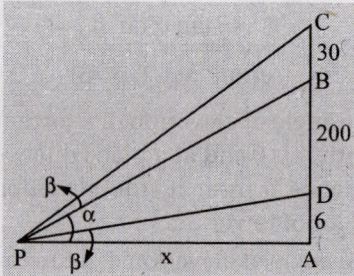

Fig. 14

AB (column) $= 200$, AD (man) $= 6$

$AP = x =$ breadth of river.

$\angle CPB = \beta = \angle DPA$.

Let $\angle BPA = \alpha$, $\tan \beta = \dfrac{6}{x}$

$\tan \alpha = \dfrac{200}{x}$. $\tan (\alpha + \beta) = \dfrac{230}{x}$.

$\therefore$ $\tan (\alpha + \beta) = \dfrac{\tan \alpha + \tan \beta}{1 - \tan \alpha \tan \beta}$

$$= \frac{230}{x} = \frac{(200/x) + (6/x)}{1 - (200/x)(6/x)} = \frac{206x}{x^2 - 1200}$$

$$230(x^2 - 1200) = 206x^2$$

or $\quad 24x^2 = 230 \times 1200.$

$$x^2 = 230 \times 50 = 11500$$

∴ $\quad x = 10\sqrt{115}$ ft.

(d) Let $AB = 2x$ so that $AC = CB = x$

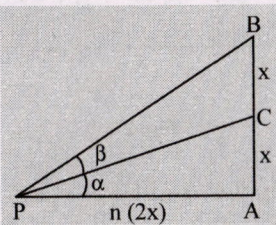

Fig. 15

By given condition

$AP = n. \ AB = n.2x,$

and let $\quad \angle CPA = \alpha$

then $\tan \alpha = \dfrac{x}{2nx} = \dfrac{1}{2n}$.(1)

$\tan(\alpha + \beta) = \dfrac{2x}{2nx} = \dfrac{1}{n}.$

∴ $\quad \tan \beta = \tan\{(\alpha + \beta) - \alpha\}$

$$= \frac{\tan(\alpha + \beta) - \tan \alpha}{1 + \tan(\alpha + \beta)\tan \alpha}$$

$$= \frac{\dfrac{1}{n} - \dfrac{1}{2n}}{1 + \dfrac{1}{n} \cdot \dfrac{1}{2n}} = \frac{n}{2n^2 + 1}.$$

(e) $H = x \tan \beta$

$H + h = x \tan \alpha$

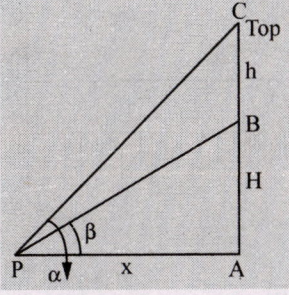

Fig. 16

∴ $\quad \dfrac{H + h}{H} = \dfrac{\tan \alpha}{\tan \beta} \quad$ or $\quad 1 + \dfrac{h}{H} = \dfrac{\tan \alpha}{\tan \beta}$

∴ $\quad \dfrac{h}{H} = \dfrac{\tan \alpha}{\tan \beta} - 1 = \dfrac{\tan \alpha - \tan \beta}{\tan \beta}$

∴ $\quad H = \dfrac{h \tan \beta}{\tan \alpha - \tan \beta}$

3. (a) $h = a \tan \alpha, \quad h = b \tan(90° - \alpha) = b \cot \alpha.$

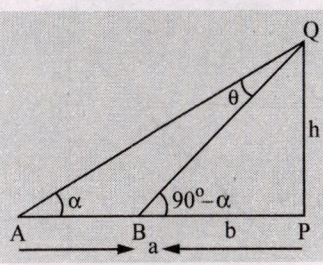

Fig. 17

Multiply $h^2 = ab \tan \alpha \cot \alpha = ab.$

∴ $\quad h = \sqrt{ab}$

Also $\tan \alpha = \dfrac{h}{a} = \dfrac{\sqrt{ab}}{a} = \sqrt{\left(\dfrac{b}{a}\right)} \qquad \dots(1)$

If AB subtends an angle θ at Q then

$$90° - \alpha = \theta + \alpha$$

or $\quad \theta = 90° - 2\alpha$

∴ $\quad \sin \theta = \cos 2\alpha = \dfrac{1 - \tan^2 \alpha}{1 + \tan^2 \alpha}$

or $\quad \sin \theta = \dfrac{1 - b/a}{1 + b/a} = \dfrac{a - b}{a + b}$, by (1)

(b) $h = AP \tan \theta, \quad h = BP \tan(90° - \theta).$

∴ $\quad h^2 = AP \cdot BP \qquad \dots(1)$

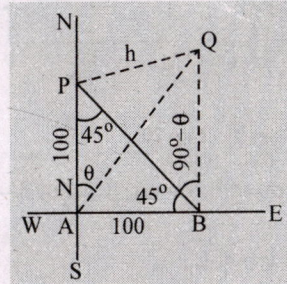

Fig. 18

Clearly $AP = AB = 100.$

∴ $\quad BP = \sqrt{100^2 + 100^2} = 100\sqrt{2}.$

Putting the values of AP and BP in (1), we get

$$h^2 = 100 \times 100\sqrt{2}$$

∴ $\quad h = 100(2)^{1/4}.$

▶ **General Rule for Q. 28 and its parts :**

All the questions are based upon sine rule. Two length are given and they come in different triangles. Choose a common side of the two triangles and apply sine rule on both the triangles and eliminate the common side.

4. (a) Ans. False

$$OP = a \cot \theta = (a + d) \cot \phi$$

$$= (a + 2d) \cot \psi$$

or $\quad ac_1 = (a + d)c_2 = (a + 2d)c_3$

Dividing by $c_1 c_2 c_3$, we get

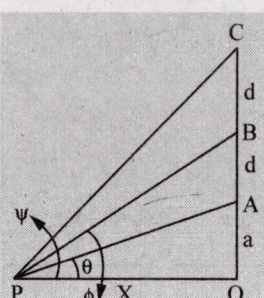

Fig. 19

$$\frac{a}{c_2 c_3} = \frac{a+d}{c_3 c_1} = \frac{a+2d}{c_1 c_2} = \lambda \text{ say}$$

Since N^r s are in A.P., hence D^r s are also in A.P.

or $\cot \phi \cot \psi, \cot \psi \cot \theta, \cot \theta \cot \phi$ are also in A.P.

(b) If h be the height of the bird

$$OL = h \cot \alpha, OM = h \cot \beta,$$
$$ON = h \cot \gamma, \quad OP = h \cot \delta. \qquad \text{Also}$$
$$AB = BC = CD \text{ or } LM = MN = NP$$

or $OM - OL = ON - OM = OP - ON$

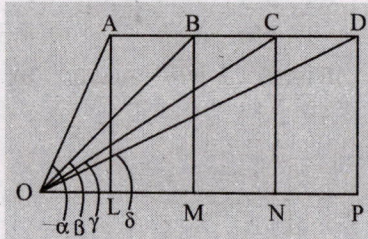

Fig. 20

$$\cot \beta - \cot \alpha = \cot \gamma - \cot \beta = \cot \delta - \cot \gamma = k \text{ say} \qquad ...(1)$$

Adding all we get

$$\cot \delta - \cot \alpha = 3k = 3 (\cot \gamma - \cot \beta) \qquad ...(2)$$

Again from 1st and 3rd of (1), we get

$$\cot \delta + \cot \alpha = \cot \beta + \cot \gamma \qquad ...(3)$$

Multiplying (2) and (3), we get

$$\cot^2 \delta - \cot^2 \alpha = 3 (\cot^2 \gamma - \cot^2 \beta)$$

or $\cot^2 \alpha - \cot^2 \delta = 3 (\cot^2 \beta - \cot^2 \gamma)$

(c) From the figure of Q. 14 (a), we get

$$\frac{AB}{BC} = \frac{AD - BD}{BD - CD} = \frac{h (\cot \theta - \cot 2\theta)}{h (\cot 2\theta - \cot 3\theta)} \qquad ...(1)$$

or $$\frac{AB}{BC} = \frac{\cot \theta - \cot 2\theta}{\cot 2\theta - \cot 3\theta}$$

Note. In case C is the root, then $3\theta = 90°$

∴ $\theta = 30$, and $\cot 30° = \sqrt{3}, \cot 90° = 0$

$$\frac{AB}{BC} = \frac{\sqrt{3} - \frac{1}{\sqrt{(3)}}}{\frac{1}{\sqrt{(3)}} - 0} = \frac{2}{1}$$

or $AB = 2 BC$.

Hence B trisects AC.

5. Let $AB = h$ be the height of tower at a distance x from the post $PQ = a$.

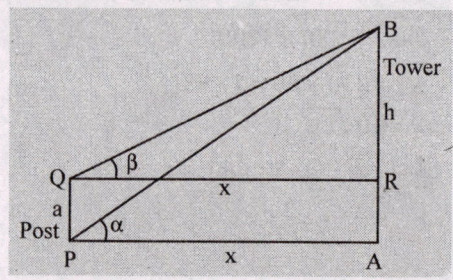

Fig. 21

AB subtends angles α and β at P and Q respectively. We have to determine h and x in terms of known quantities α, β and a.

$$AB = x \tan \alpha; BR = x \tan \beta.$$

∴ $PQ = AR = AB - BR$
$$= x (\tan \alpha - \tan \beta)$$

∴ $$x = \frac{PQ}{\tan \alpha - \tan \beta} = \frac{a}{\tan \alpha - \tan \beta}$$
$$= \frac{a \cos \alpha \cos \beta}{\sin (\alpha - \beta)}$$

∴ $$h = AB = x \tan \alpha = \frac{a \cos \alpha \cos \beta}{\sin (\alpha - \beta)} \cdot \frac{\sin \alpha}{\cos \alpha}$$
$$= \frac{a \sin \alpha \cos \beta}{\sin (\alpha - \beta)}$$

6. (a) M is the image of L in the water so that $BL = BM. P$ is a point at heigh h above level of water at which the angle of elevation of L is α and the angle of depression of M is β. We have to find $BL = x$, say.

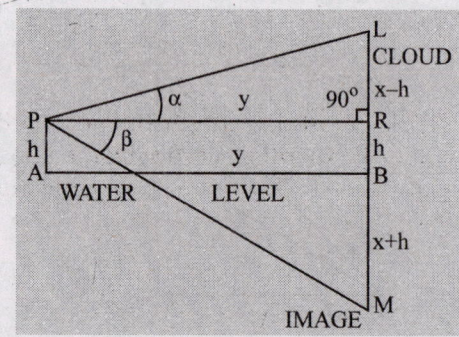

Fig. 22

Let $AB = PR = y$.

$$LR = y \tan \alpha, MR = y \tan \beta$$

∴ $$\frac{x + h}{x - h} = \frac{y \tan \beta}{y \tan \alpha} = \frac{\tan \beta}{\tan \alpha}.$$

Apply comp. and divi.

$$\frac{2x}{2h} = \frac{\tan \beta + \tan \alpha}{\tan \beta - \tan \alpha}$$

$$\therefore \qquad x = h\frac{\tan \beta + \tan \alpha}{\tan \beta - \tan \alpha} \qquad \ldots(1)$$

Another form. If we divide above and below of (1) by $\tan \alpha \tan \beta$, then

$$x = h\frac{\cot \alpha + \cot \beta}{\cot \alpha - \cot \beta}$$

If we change in terms of sin and cos, then from (1)

$$x = h\frac{\sin (\beta - \alpha)}{\sin (\beta - \alpha)}$$

Note : You can do it by $m - n$ theorem with $\theta = 90°, m = MR = x + h, n = RL = x - h$.

(b) Proceed as above.

(c) Proceed as above, $h = 2500$, $\beta = 45°$, $\alpha = 15°$.

$$\therefore \quad x = 2500 \times \frac{\sin (45° - 15°)}{\sin (45° - 15°)} = 2500 \times \frac{\sin 60°}{\sin 30°}$$

$$= 2500 \, (\sqrt{3}) \text{ metres.}$$

(d) With the same figure as of Q. 2, we have to find PL. Replacing α by θ and β by ϕ, we have

$$x + h = y \tan \phi$$
$$x - h = y \tan \theta$$

Subtract $2h = y \, (\tan \phi - \tan \theta) = \dfrac{y \sin (\phi - \theta)}{\cos \phi \cos \theta}$

$$\therefore \qquad y = \frac{2h \cos \theta \cos \phi}{\sin (\phi - \theta)} \qquad \ldots(1)$$

Above gives, the horizontal distance of the cloud from the point of observation.

Again $y = PL = \cos \theta$

$$\therefore \qquad PL = \frac{2h \cos \phi}{\sin (\phi - \theta)}, \quad \text{from (1).}$$

(e) $OC = 50$ is the tower standing on a sloping ground OB.

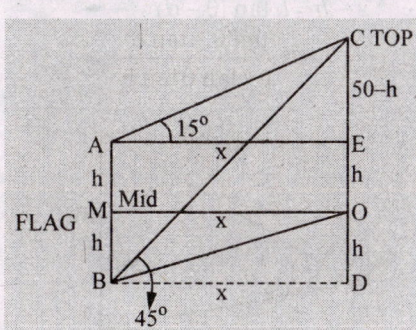

Fig. 23

$BA = 2h$ is the flag pole whose mid-point M is in level with O.

The angles of depression of A and B as seen from C, the top of the tower, are 15° and 45° respectively.

Let $BD = x = OM = AE$

$$50 - h = x \tan 15°, \Delta \, CAE$$
$$50 + h = x \tan 45°, \Delta \, CBD$$

Dividing in order to eliminate x, we get

$$\frac{50 + h}{50 - h} = \frac{\tan 45°}{\tan 15°}$$

Applying componendo and dividendo, we get

$$\frac{2h}{100} = \frac{\sin (45° - 15°)}{\sin (45° + 15°)} = \frac{\sin 30°}{\sin 60°} = \frac{1}{\sqrt{(3)}}.$$

$$\therefore \quad 2h = \frac{100}{\sqrt{(3)}} = \frac{100\sqrt{3}}{3}$$

7. (a) Let $PQ = h$ be the height of tower where angles of depression of Q and P are 30° and 60° as seen from top B of cliff AB of height 200 ft.

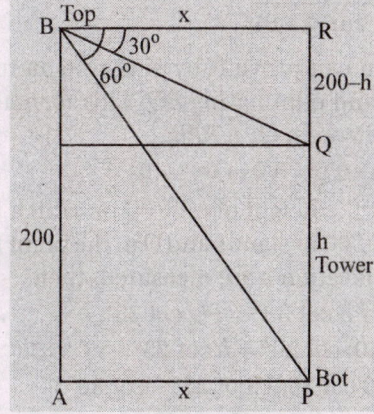

Fig. 24

Let $AP = x$.

$$200 - h = x \tan 30° = x/\sqrt{3}; \, \Delta \, BQR.$$
$$200 = x \tan 60° = \sqrt{3} \, x; \Delta \, BPR.$$

Dividing, we get $\dfrac{200 - h}{200} = \dfrac{1}{3}$

or $\quad 3 \, (200 - h) = 200$

or $\quad 400 \, 3h \therefore \, h = \dfrac{400}{3} \text{ ft.}$

(b) As in part (a),

$y - h = x \tan \theta$, form $\Delta \, BQR$.

$y = x \tan \phi$, from $\Delta \, BPA$.

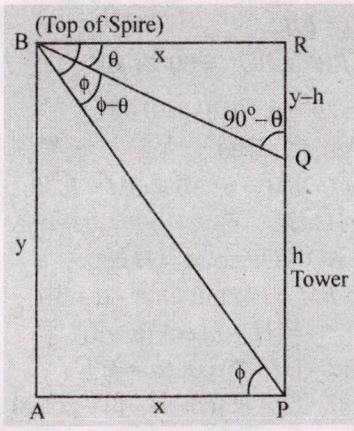

Fig. 25

$\therefore \quad \dfrac{y-h}{y} = \dfrac{\tan\theta}{\tan\phi} = \dfrac{\sin\theta\cos\phi}{\cos\theta\sin\phi}$

$\therefore \quad 1 - \dfrac{h}{y} = \dfrac{\sin\theta\cos\phi}{\cos\theta\sin\phi}$

or $\quad \dfrac{\sin\phi\cos\theta - \cos\phi\sin\theta}{\sin\phi\cos\theta} = \dfrac{h}{y}$

$\therefore \quad y = \dfrac{h\sin\phi\cos\theta}{\sin(\phi-\theta)} \qquad \qquad \dots(1)$

Again $y = x\tan\phi$

or $\quad \dfrac{h\sin\phi\cos\theta}{\sin(\phi-\theta)} = x\dfrac{\sin\phi}{\cos\phi} \quad$ by (1)

$\therefore \quad x = h\dfrac{\cos\theta\cos\phi}{\sin(\phi-\theta)}$

Note : You can prove it by sine rule on triangle BQR and BQP and eliminating BQ. This man also be done by $m - n$ theorem on Δ BPR.

$\alpha = \phi - \theta, \beta = \theta, \theta \to 90° - \theta.$

(c) If h is the height of cliff PQ on which tower QR of height 60 m stands and O in the point from which the elevation s are measured, then
$OP = PR\cot 30° = PQ\cot 23°$

or $\quad (h + 60)\cot 30° = h\cot 23°$

or $\quad h = 60\cot 30°/(\cot 23° - \cot 30°)$
$= 60\sqrt{3}/(\cot 23° - \sqrt{3})$

and distance of the boat from the cliff
$= h\cdot\cot 23°$

8. (a) As in Q 7. (b),
$\dfrac{y-h}{y} = \dfrac{\tan\theta}{\tan\phi} = \dfrac{4}{3}\cdot\dfrac{2}{3} = \dfrac{8}{15}$

or $\quad 1 - \dfrac{h}{y} = \dfrac{8}{15}$

or $\quad 1 - \dfrac{8}{15} = \dfrac{h}{150} \qquad \because y = 150$

or $\quad \dfrac{7}{15} = \dfrac{h}{150} \quad \therefore h = 70 = PQ$

$\therefore \quad QR = 150 - 70 = 80.$

Also $PR = x\tan\phi$ or $150 = x\cdot 5/2$

$\therefore \quad x = 60 = BR$

$\therefore \quad BQ = BR^2 + RQ^2 = 60^2 + 80^2$
$= 20^2(9 + 16) = 20^2\cdot 5^2$

$\therefore \quad BQ = 20 \times 5 = 100$

(b) Let $AO = BM = a, AB = OM = h$

$\therefore \quad PM = H - h.$
$BM = AO = OP\cot\alpha = H\cot\alpha.$
Again $BM = PM\tan(90° - \alpha + \beta)$
$= (H - h)\cot(\alpha - \beta)$

$\therefore \quad H\cot\alpha = (H - h)\cot(\alpha - \beta)$
$h\cot(\alpha - \beta) = H[\cot(\alpha - \beta) - \cot\alpha]$

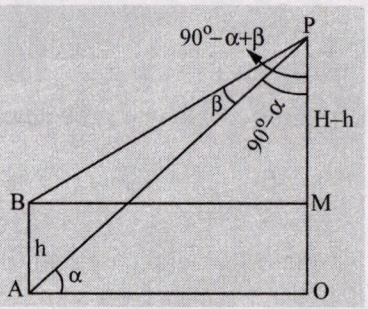

Fig. 26

$\therefore \quad H = \dfrac{h\sin\alpha\cos(\alpha - \beta)}{\sin\beta},$

on changing to sin and cos.

(c) Ans. $8\sqrt{3}$ m.

9. (a) From the figure

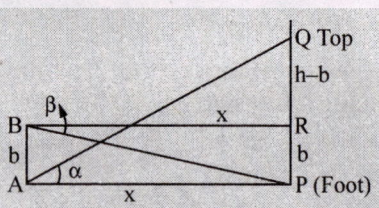

Fig. 27

$h = x\tan\alpha,$
$b = x\tan\beta$
$h = \dfrac{b}{\tan\beta}\cdot\tan\alpha$
$b = \tan\alpha\cot\beta$

(b) We have to find the value of $BC = x$ in terms of known quantities b, h and θ.

Let us suppose that $\angle BDE = \alpha$.

$\therefore \quad h = b\tan\alpha \qquad \qquad \dots(1)$
$x - h = b\tan(\theta - \alpha)$
$= b\dfrac{\tan\theta - \tan\alpha}{1 + \tan\theta\tan\alpha}$

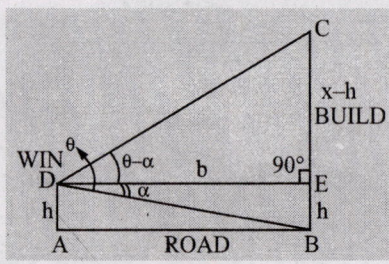

Fig. 28

Put for $\tan\alpha$ from (1)

$\therefore \quad x = h + b\dfrac{\tan\theta - h/b}{1 + \tan\theta\cdot h/b}$

$= h + b\cdot\dfrac{(b\sin\theta - h\cos\theta)}{b\cos\theta + h\sin\theta}$

or $\quad x = \dfrac{bh\cos\theta + h^2\sin\theta + b^2\sin\theta - bh\cos\theta}{b\cos\theta + h\sin\theta}$

$\qquad = \dfrac{(b^2 + h^2)\sin\theta}{b\cos\theta + h\sin\theta}$

Note : You can do it by $m-n$ theorem with $\theta = 90°, m = ME = h, n = EC = x - h.$

10. (a) PQ subtends an angle of 15° at A and an angle of 30° at B where $AB = 100$ ft. From the figure it is clear that $AB = BP = 100$, and $\dfrac{h}{BP} = \sin 30°$

$\therefore \qquad h = 100 \times \dfrac{1}{2} = 50$ ft.

Also $h/BQ = \tan 30° = 1/\sqrt{3}$,

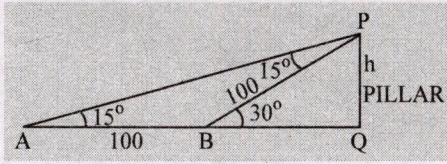

Fig. 29

$\therefore \qquad BQ = h\sqrt{3} = 50\sqrt{3}$ ft.

Hence $AQ = AB + BQ = 100 + 50\sqrt{3}$

$\qquad = 50(2 + \sqrt{3})$ ft.

(b) Exactly as above $\dfrac{h}{40} = \sin 60°$

$\therefore \qquad h = 20\sqrt{3}$ ft.

$\dfrac{h}{BQ} = \tan 60° = \sqrt{3}, BQ = \dfrac{h}{\sqrt{(3)}} = 20$ ft.

$\qquad$ = breadth of the river.

(c) $AB = BP = 150.$ $\quad$ Also $h/BP = \sin 60°$

$\therefore \qquad h = 150\sqrt{3}/2 = 75\sqrt{3}.$

(d) Ans. $PQ = 10\sqrt{3}$ m, $AQ = 30$ m.

(e) Proceed as in Q. 10 (a) Ans. $10\sqrt{3}$ m.

11. Parts (a), (b) and (c) are left for the reader.

(d) Refer figure Q. 10 (a). If

$AB = x, BQ = y$ then $BP = x$

$\therefore \quad BQ = BP\cos 60° = x/2.$ Hence the time taken for $x/2$ is half the time taken for $AB = x$ i.e., half of 3 minutes $= 1\dfrac{1}{2}$ minutes.

(e) In the figure, OB represents the rod inclined at 10° to the vertical towards the sum and $OA = 2.05$ m represents the shadow where the elevation of the sun is

$\qquad \angle OAB = 38°$ and so we have

$\qquad \angle OBA = 180° - (38° + 100°) = 42°.$

From $\triangle OAB$, we have

$\qquad \dfrac{OB}{\sin 38°} = \dfrac{OA}{\sin 42°} = \dfrac{2.05}{\sin 42°}$

$\therefore \qquad OB = \dfrac{2.05\sin 38°}{\sin 42°}$

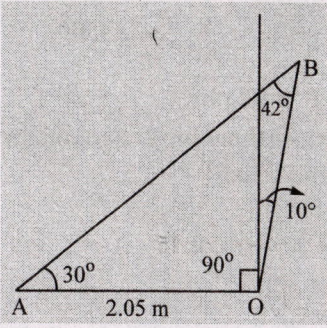

Fig. 30

$\therefore \quad \log OB = \log 2.05 + \log\sin 38° - \log\sin 42°$

$\qquad = .31175 + \overline{1}.78934 - \overline{1}.82551$ (from the tables)

$\qquad = .31175 + .03617 = .27458$

Hence $OB = 1.88$ metres (From anilog tables)

12. (a) $h = BD\tan\alpha = DC\tan\beta$

But $BD + DC = 1$ mile

$\qquad h\left(\dfrac{1}{\tan\alpha} + \dfrac{1}{\tan\beta}\right) = 1$

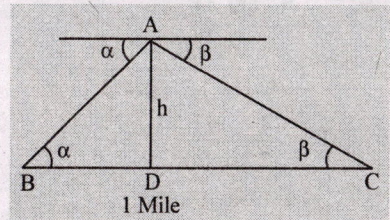

Fig. 31

$\therefore \qquad h = \dfrac{\tan\alpha\tan\beta}{\tan\alpha + \tan\beta}$

(b) The required distance

$\qquad = 100\cot 30° + 100\cot 45°$

$\qquad = 100(\sqrt{3} + 1)$ metres.

(c) $PQ = MN = LN - LM$

$\qquad = (1.\cot 30° - 1.\cot 60°)$

$\qquad = \left(\sqrt{3} - \dfrac{1}{\sqrt{(3)}}\right) = \dfrac{2}{\sqrt{(3)}}$

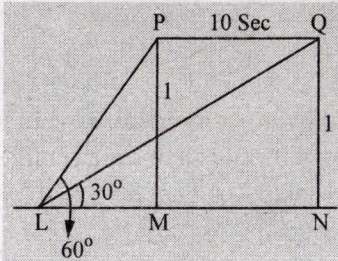

Fig. 32

PQ is covered in 10 seconds

$\qquad = \dfrac{100}{3600}$ hours $= \dfrac{1}{360}$ hours.

∴   speed $= \dfrac{s}{t} = \dfrac{2}{\sqrt{(3)}} \div \dfrac{1}{360} = \dfrac{2}{\sqrt{(3)}} (360)$

$= 240\sqrt{3}$ km/hour.

13. (a) Applying $m - n$ theorem of trigonometry, we get
[$(\theta - 30°)$ **on the left**]

$- (c + c) \cot (\theta - 30°)$

$= c \cot 30° - c \cot 15°$

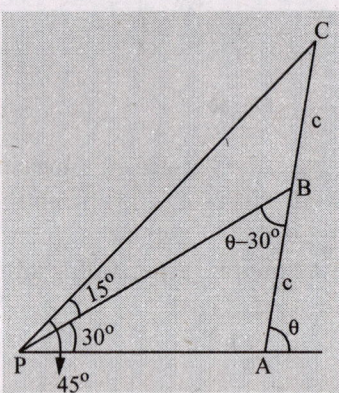

Fig. 33

or $\cot (\theta - 30°) = \dfrac{1}{2} \dfrac{\sin (30° - 15°)}{\sin 15° \sin 30°}$

or $\cot (\theta - 30°) = \dfrac{1}{2} \dfrac{1}{\sin 30°}$

$= 1 = \cot 45°$

∴ $\theta = 30° = 45°$ or $\theta = 75°$

(b) Figure is self-explanatory.
Here $AB = BC = c$.

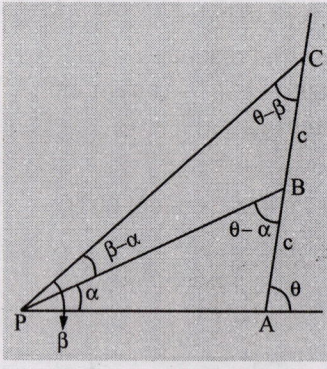

Fig. 34

As in part (b) by $m - n$ theorem, $\theta - \alpha$ **in left.**

$- (c + c) \cot \theta - \alpha) = c \cot \alpha - c \cot (\beta - \alpha)$

or $2 \cot (\theta - \alpha) = \cot (\beta - \alpha) - \cot \alpha$

or $\cot (\theta - \alpha) + \cot \alpha$

$= \cot (\beta - \alpha) - \cot (\theta - \alpha)$

or $\dfrac{\sin (\alpha + \theta - \alpha)}{\sin (\theta - \alpha) \sin \alpha} = \dfrac{\sin (\overline{\theta - \alpha} - \overline{\beta - \alpha})}{\sin (\beta - \alpha) \sin (\theta - \alpha)}$

∴ $\sin \theta \sin (\beta - \alpha) = \sin \alpha \sin (\theta - \beta)$ ...(1)

Expand $\sin (\beta - \alpha)$ and $\sin (\theta - \beta)$
and divide by $\sin \alpha \sin \beta \sin \theta$

∴ $\cot \alpha - \cot \beta = \cot \beta - \cot \theta$

∴ $\cot \theta = 2 \cot \beta - \cot \alpha$

Note : The result (1) could also be obtained by using sine formula and equating the value of PB from $\Delta^s APB$ and BPC.

(c) Ans. $2 \cot \theta = 3 \cot \beta - \cot \alpha$. Here $AB = c$ and $BC = 2c$. Rest as in (a) and (b) exactly.

4. (a) $AQ = x$, $BQ = y$ and PQ is a tower leaning towards North at an angle θ. Apply $m - n$ theorem on ΔPBQ.

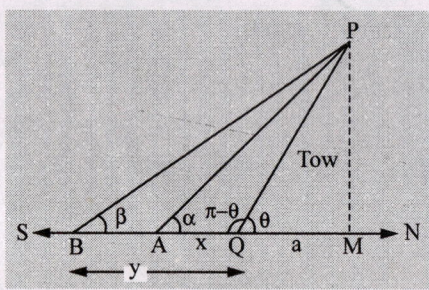

Fig. 35

$(y - x + x) \cot \alpha = x \cot \beta - (y - x) \cot (\pi - \theta)$

or $y \cot \alpha - x \cot \beta = (y - x) \cot \theta$

∴ $\theta =$ etc.

(b) Proceed as in part (a)

5. (a) Applying $(m - n)$ theorem of trigonometry on ΔAPB in which angle

$$\angle PQA = 90° - \theta$$

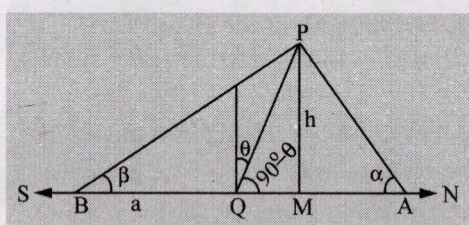

Fig. 36

$(a + a) \cot (90° - \theta) = a \cot \beta - a \cot \alpha$ ...(1)

∴ $2 \tan \theta = \dfrac{\sin (\alpha - \beta)}{\sin \alpha \sin \beta}$

∴ $\theta = \tan^{-1} \left(\dfrac{\sin (\alpha - \beta)}{2 \sin \alpha \sin \beta} \right)$

From (1) we can also say that

$$\theta = \tan^{-1} \dfrac{1}{2} (\cot \beta - \cot \alpha)$$

(b) Proceed exactly as in part (a).

(c) Apply $(m - n)$ theorem on ΔPBQ

$(l + l_1) \cot \alpha = l \cot (\alpha - \beta) - l_1 \cot (\pi - \theta)$

$(l + l_1) \cot \alpha - l \cot (\alpha - \beta) = l_1 \cot \theta$

∴ $\tan \theta =$ etc.

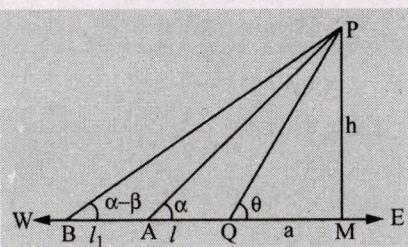

Fig. 37

(d) Let the train be moving along PQ and A be the point of observation. The train is at O at some instant so it is due north of A then. Ten minutes earlier, it was at P whose bearing from A is α_1 west of north so that the $- PAQ = \alpha_1$. Ten minutes afterwards,

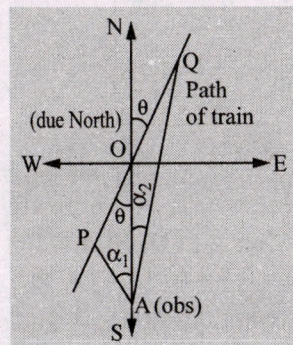

Fig. 38

it is at Q whose bearing is α_2 east of north so that
$$\angle\, OAQ = = \alpha_2.$$
Since PO and OQ are covered in equal times, we have $OP = OQ = a$, say.

Now applying trigonometrical theorem in $\Delta\, PAQ$, we get
$$(a+a)\cot\theta = a\cot\alpha_2 - a\cot\alpha_1$$

or $\cot\theta = \dfrac{1}{2}(\cot\alpha_2 - \cot\alpha_1)$

∴ $\tan\theta = \dfrac{2}{\cot\alpha_2 - \cot\alpha_1} = \dfrac{2\sin\alpha_1\sin\alpha_2}{\sin(\alpha_1 - \alpha_2)}$

16. (a) Let the balloon touch the horizontal plane through A in R. We have to determine AR.

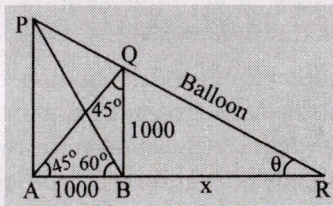

Fig. 39

$AB = 1000$ and let $BR = x$.
$$PA = AB\tan 60° = 1000\sqrt{3} \qquad\qquad …(1)$$

Also $AB = QB = 1000 \qquad\qquad …(2)$
as $\Delta\, ABQ$ is isosceles.

Now from similar triangles, APR and BQR, we have

$$\tan\theta = \frac{AP}{AR} = \frac{BQ}{BR} \text{ or } \frac{1000\sqrt{3}}{1000 + x} = \frac{1000}{x}$$

∴ $x\sqrt{3} = 1000 + x$ or $x(\sqrt{3} - 1) = 1000$

∴ $x = \dfrac{1000}{\sqrt{(3)} - 1} = \dfrac{1000(\sqrt{3} + 1)}{3 - 1}$
$$= 500(\sqrt{3} + 1)$$

∴ $AR = 1000 + x = 1000 + 500(\sqrt{3} + 1)$
$$= 500(2 + \sqrt{3} + 1) = 500\sqrt{3}(\sqrt{3} + 1) \text{ ft.}$$

(b) Proceed exactly as above.
Here $BQ = AB\tan 30° = \dfrac{1000}{\sqrt{(3)}}$

∴ $\dfrac{AP}{AR} = \dfrac{BQ}{BR}$ or $\dfrac{1000\sqrt{3}}{1000 + x} = \dfrac{1000}{\sqrt{(3)}\, x}$

or $3x = 1000 + x$ ∴ $x = 500$
Hence $AR = 1000 + x = 1000 + 500 = 1500$.

17. (a) $OA = h\cot\alpha$, $OB = h\cot\beta$

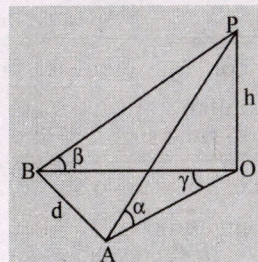

Fig. 40

Now from $\Delta\, OAB$ by cosine formula
$$d^2 = OA^2 + OB^2 - 2\,OA \cdot OB\cos\gamma$$
$$= h^2[\cot^2\alpha + \cot^2\beta - 2\cot\alpha\cot\beta\cos\gamma]$$

∴ $h = \dfrac{d}{[\cot^2\alpha + \cot^2\beta - 2\cot\alpha\cot\beta\cos\gamma]^{1/2}}$

(b) Ans. $h = \dfrac{c\tan\alpha\sin\delta}{\sin(\gamma + \delta)}$.

Use sine rule

(c) Use Pythagoras theorem in which hypotenuse

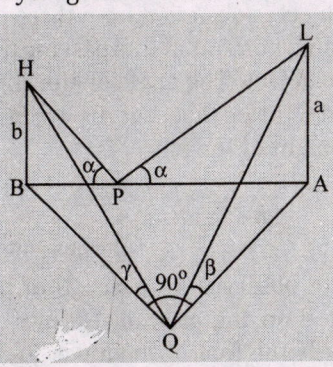

Fig. 41

$AB = AP + PB = a \cot \alpha + b \cot \alpha$

and sides are $QA = a \cot \beta$ and $QB = b \cot \gamma$.

18. (a) $h = PA \tan \alpha$ ∴ $PA = h \cot \alpha$

and $h = PB \tan \beta$ ∴ $PB = h \cot \beta$.

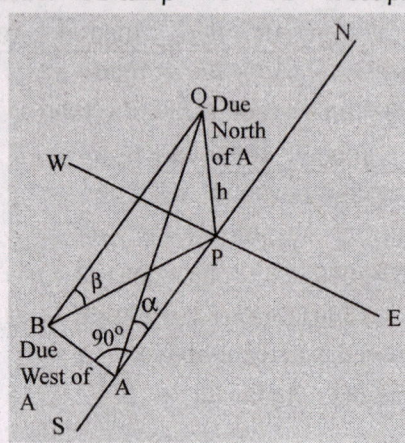

Fig. 42

Also from right angled triangle PAB, we get

$$PB^2 = PA^2 + AB^2$$

∴ $AB^2 = PB^2 - PA^2 = h^2 (\cot^2 \beta - \cot^2 \alpha),$

∴ $h = \dfrac{AB}{\sqrt{\cot^2 \beta - \cot^2 \alpha}} = \dfrac{AB \tan \alpha \tan \beta}{\sqrt{\tan^2 \alpha - \tan^2 \beta}}$

on changing on tan.

or $h = \dfrac{AB \sin \alpha \sin \beta}{\sqrt{(\sin^2 \alpha \cos^2 \beta - \cos^2 \alpha \sin^2 \beta)}}$

changing on sin and cos.

$= \dfrac{AB \sin \alpha \sin \beta}{\sqrt{[\sin^2 \alpha (1 - \sin^2 \beta) - \sin^2 \beta (1 - \sin^2 \alpha)]}}$

$= \dfrac{AB \sin \alpha \sin \beta}{\sqrt{(\sin^2 \alpha - \sin^2 \beta)}} = \dfrac{AB \sin \alpha \sin \beta}{\sqrt{[\sin (\alpha + \beta) \sin (\alpha - \beta)]}}$

∵ $\sin^2 \alpha - \sin^2 \beta = \sin (\alpha + \beta) \sin (\alpha - \beta)$

(b) Same as part (a). Replace α by θ and β by ϕ.

19. (a) It is same question as $Q. 18$ where

$AB = a$, α $30°$ and $\beta = 18°$.

∴ $h = \dfrac{AB \sin \alpha \sin \beta}{\sqrt{(\sin^2 \alpha - \sin^2 \beta)}}$

$\sin \alpha = \sin 30° = \dfrac{1}{2},$

$\sin \beta = \sin 18° = \dfrac{\sqrt{5} - 1}{4}$

∴ $\sin^2 \alpha - \sin^2 \beta = \dfrac{1}{4} - \dfrac{6 - 2\sqrt{5}}{16} = \dfrac{\sqrt{5} - 1}{8}$

and $\sin \alpha \sin \beta = \dfrac{\sqrt{5} - 1}{8}$

∴ $h = a \dfrac{\sqrt{5} - 1}{8} \cdot \sqrt{\left(\dfrac{8}{\sqrt{(5)} - 1}\right)} = a \sqrt{\left(\dfrac{\sqrt{5} - 1}{8}\right)}$

$= a \sqrt{\left(\dfrac{\sqrt{5} - 1}{8} \cdot \dfrac{\sqrt{5} + 1}{\sqrt{(5)} + 1}\right)}$

$= a \sqrt{\left(\dfrac{4}{8 [\sqrt{(5)} + 1]}\right)}$

$= a \sqrt{\left(\dfrac{1}{2\sqrt{(5)} + 2}\right)} = \dfrac{a}{\sqrt{[2 + 2\sqrt{(5)}]}}$

(b) In the figure of **Q. 18, P. 710** take

$\alpha = \theta$, $\beta = \phi$, $AB = 100$ m.

It is given that $\cot \theta = \dfrac{3}{10}$ and $\cot \phi = 1/2$.

∴ $h = \dfrac{AB}{\sqrt{(\cot^2 \phi - \cot^2 \theta)}} = \dfrac{100}{\sqrt{\left(\dfrac{1}{4} - \dfrac{9}{100}\right)}}$

$= \dfrac{1000}{\sqrt{(25 - 9)}} = \dfrac{1000}{4} = 250$ m.

20. (a) Proceed as in Q. 18.

$h = \dfrac{AB}{\sqrt{(\cot^2 \beta - \cot^2 \alpha)}} = \dfrac{32}{\sqrt{\left(\dfrac{9}{25} - \dfrac{4}{25}\right)}} = 32\sqrt{5}$

(b) Proceed as in Q. 18.

Problem Set (2)

*1. (a) An object is observed from three points A, B, C in the same horizontal line passing through the base of the object. The angle of elevation at B is twice and at C thrice that A. If $AB = a$, $BC = b$, prove that the height of the object is

$$\dfrac{a}{2b} \sqrt{(a+b)(3b-a)}$$

(Dhanbad 1988; Roorkee 1980)

(b) A man observes a tower AB of height h from a point P on the ground. He moves a distance d towards the foot of the tower and finds that the angle of elevation is doubled. He further moves a

distance $3d/4$ in the same direction and finds that the angle of elevation is three times that of P. Prove that $36h^2 = 35d^2$. **(I.I.T. 1986)**

(c) A balloon is observed simultaneously from three points A, B and C on a straight road directly under it. The angular-elevation at B is twice that at A and the angular elevation at C is thrice that at A. If the distance between A and B is 200 metres and the distance between B and C is 100 metres, find the height of the balloon. **(Roorkee 1989)**

(d) DE is a tower standing on a horizontal plane and $ABCD$ is a straight line in the plane. The height of the tower subtends an angle θ at A, 2θ at B and 3θ at C. If AB and BC be respectively 50 and 20 metres, find the height of the tower and the distance CD.

(Roorkee 1980)

*(e) Segments AB, BC, CD of a horizontal line subtend equal angles at a point O vertically above A. If the length of OA is a and that of AB is b, prove that

$$CD = \frac{b(b^2 + a^2)^2}{(a^2 - 3b^2)(a^2 - b^2)}$$

*2. (a) A chimney 20 metres high, standing on the top of a building subtends an angle whose tangent is 1/6 at a distance 70 metres from the foot of the building. Find the height of the building.

*(b) A statue 20 m. High standing at the top of a column 150 m. high on the bank of a river, subtends at a point on the opposite bank directly facing the column, the same angle as subtended at the same point by a man 2 m high standing at the base of the column. Find the breadth of the river.

*(c) A tower 51 m. high has a mark at a height of 25 m. from the ground. Find at what distance the two parts subtend equal angles to an eye at the height of 5 m. from the ground.

(d) A flag-staff a metre high placed on the top of a tower b metre high subtends the same angle as the tower to an observer h metre high standing on a horizontal plane at a distance d metres from the foot of the tower. Prove that

$$(a-b)d^2 = (a+b)b^2 - 2b^2h - (a-b)h^2$$

3. (a) At the foot of the mountain the angle of elevation of its summit is found to be α. After ascending a ft. towards the mountain up a slope of inclination β, the angle of elevation is found to be γ. Show that the height of the mountain is

$$\frac{a\sin\alpha\sin(\gamma-\beta)}{\sin(\gamma-\alpha)} \text{ feet.}$$

* (b) From a point on a hill side of a constant inclination the angle of elevation of the top of a flag-stafff on its summit is observed to be α and a metre nearer the top of the hill it is β. If h is the height of the flag staff then the inclination of the hill to the horizon is

$$\cos^{-1}\left[\frac{a\sin\alpha\sin\beta}{h\sin(\beta-\alpha)}\right]$$

Another form :

Three points A, B, C are in a line inclined at an angle θ to the horizon. Of these points, A is the lowest and C is the highest; D is a point vertically above C. If $AB = p$, $CD = q$ the angle $DAB = \alpha$ and the angle $DBC = \beta$, prove that

$$\cot\theta = \frac{p\sin\alpha\sin\beta}{q\sin(\beta-\alpha)}.$$

(c) A vertical tree stands on a hill side that makes an angle α with the horizontal. From a point directly up the hill from the tree, the angle of elevation of three top is β. From a point m cm., further up the hill, the angle of depression of the tree top is γ. If the tree is H cm. tall, express H in terms of α, β, γ.

*(d) A man on a hill observes that three towers on a horizontal plane subtend equal angles on his eye and that the angles of depression of their bases are θ, ϕ and ψ. Prove that if a, b and c are their heights, then

$$\frac{\sin(\theta-\phi)}{c\sin\psi} + \frac{\sin(\phi-\psi)}{a\sin\theta} + \frac{\sin(\psi-\theta)}{b\sin\phi} = 0$$

(e) A and B are two points on one bank of a straight river, C and D are two points on the other bank. The direction from C to D is the same as from A to B. If $AB = a$, $\angle CAD = \alpha$, $\angle DAB = \beta$,

$$\angle CBA = \gamma \text{ prove that}$$

$$CD = \frac{a\sin\alpha\sin\gamma}{\sin\beta . \sin(\alpha+\beta+\gamma)}.$$

*(f) There is a vertical tower of height H with its lowest point C on the ground and its height point D at a height of H above the ground. From two points A and B distance c apart on the ground, the following angles are measured.

$$\angle BAC = \alpha, \angle ABC = \beta, \angle CAD = \theta$$

and $\angle CBD = \phi$. Find H in terms of $c, \alpha \beta, \theta$ and ϕ.

(M.NR. 1995)

(g) The summit of a church spire is observed from two different stations at a distance a from each other in a horizontal plane to have the same altitude α. The line joining the summit to one of the stations is observed to subtend an angle β at the other station. Prove that the height of the spire is $\dfrac{a\sin\alpha}{2\cos\beta}$.

*(h) A mast stands at P on a square field $ABCD$ of side a. It is observed that

$\angle PAB = \alpha$ and $\angle PBA = \beta$. If the mast subtends an angle θ at A, prove that the height of the mast is

$$\frac{(a\sin\beta\tan\theta)}{\sin(\alpha+\beta)}.$$

(Dhanbad 1987)

* (i) If top P of a mountain is observed from A and B at the sea level. If N is the point vertically below P and $\angle NAB = \alpha$,

$\angle NBA = \beta$, $\angle NAP = \theta$, $\angle NBP = \phi$ then show that $\cot\phi\sin\beta = \cot\theta\sin\alpha$. **(M.N.R. 1990)**

4. (a) A vertical tower stands on a declivity which is inclined at 15° to the horizon. From the foot of the tower a man ascends the declivity for 80 feet and then finds that the tower subtends an angle of 30°. Prove that the height of the tower is

$$40(\sqrt{6} - \sqrt{2}) \text{ feet.}$$

*(b) A person observes the top P of a vertical tower OP of height h from a station S_1 and finds that β_1 is the angle of elevation. He moves in a horizontal plane to second station S_2 and finds that $\angle PS_2S_1$ is γ_1 and the angle subtended by S_2S_1 at P is δ_1 and the angle of elevation is β_2. He moves again to a third station S_3 such that $S_3S_2 = S_2S_1$, $\angle PS_3S_2 = \gamma_2$ and the angle subtended by S_3S_2 at P is δ_2. Show that

$$\frac{\sin \gamma_1 \sin \beta_1}{\sin \delta_1} = \frac{\sin \gamma_2 \sin \beta_2}{\sin \delta_2} = \frac{h}{S_1S_2}$$

(Roorkee 1985)

*(c) An observer at O notices that the angle of elevation of the top of a tower is 30°. The line joining O to the base of the tower makes an angle of $\tan^{-1}(1/\sqrt{2})$ with the North and is inclined Eastwards. The observer travels a distance of 300 metres towards the North to a point A and finds the tower to his East. The angle of elevation of the top of the tower at A is ϕ. Find ϕ and the height of the tower. **(I.I.T. 1993)**

*5. (a) A straight pillar PQ stands at a point P. the points A and B are situated due south and east of P respectively. M is the mid-point of AB. PAM is an equilateral triangle and N is the foot of the perpendicular from P on AB. Suppose $AN = 20$ metre and the angle of elevation of the top of the pillar at N is $\tan^{-1} 2$. Find the height of the pillar and the angles of elevation of its top at A and B. **(I.I.T. 1990)**

*(b) A tower stands vertically in a field. The field is in the shape of an equilateral triangle of side 100 metres. The tower subtends angles of 45°, 60°, and 60° at the vertices of the triangle. Find the height of tower. **(Roorkee 1998)**

*6. (a) A tower is b ft. high having a flag staff at its top. The tower and the flag staff subtend equal angles at a point distant a feet from the foot of the tower.

Show that the length of the flag staff is $\dfrac{b(a^2 + b^2)}{a^2 - b^2}$.

(b) A wireless pole 25 metres high is fixed on the top of a verandah of a house which is 15 metres high. At a point R on the ground directly opposite the wireless pole and verandah subtend equal angles. Find the distance of R from the verandah.

*7. (a) A tower has flag staff at its top which subtends equal angles α at a points distance 9 yds and 11 yds from the foot of the tower. If $\tan \alpha = \dfrac{1}{10}$, find the height of the tower and the flag staff.

*(b) A flag staff on the top of a house subtends the same angle α at two points distant a and b from the house and on the same side of it. Prove that the length of flag-staff is $(a + b)\tan \alpha$. **(M.N.R. 1996)**

(c) A statue standing on a column subtends equal angles α at two points which are at a distance of 18 m. and 22 m. from the column. If $\tan \alpha = \dfrac{1}{10}$, find the height of the column and the statue.

(M.N.R. 1985)

(d) A flag-staff is on the top of a tower standing on a level plane. At certain point in the plane the tower subtends an angle α and the flastaff an angle β. At another point a ft. nearer the base of the tower, the flag-staff again subtends an angle β. Prove that the height of the tower is

$$\frac{a \tan \alpha}{1 - \tan \alpha \tan (\alpha + \beta)}$$ and the length of the flag-staff

is $\dfrac{a \sin \beta}{\cos (2\alpha + \beta)}$.

*(e) A flag staff on the top of a tower is observed to subtend the same angle α at two points on a horizontal plane, which lie on a line passing through the centre of the base of the tower and whose distance from one another is $2a$ and an angle β at a point half-way between them. Prove that the height of the flag-staff is

$$a \sin \alpha \sqrt{\left(\frac{2 \sin \beta}{\cos \alpha \sin (\beta - \alpha)}\right)}$$

(M.N.R. 1982)

*8. A flag staff is on the top of tower which stands on a horizontal plane. A person observes the angles, α and β, subtended at a point on the horizontal plane by the flag staff and the tower; he then walks a known distance a towards the tower and finds that the flag staff subtends the same angle as before; prove that the height of the tower and the length of the flag staff are respectively

$$\frac{a \sin \beta \cos (\alpha + \beta)}{\cos (\alpha + 2\beta)} \text{ and } \frac{a \sin \alpha}{\cos (\alpha + 2\beta)}.$$

*9. (a) A person stands at a point A due South of a tower and observes its elevation is 60°. He then walks westward towards B where the elevation is 45°. At a point C on AB produced he finds it to be 30°. Prove that $AB = BC$.

(b) A man walking due North, observes that the elevation of a balloon, which is due East of him and is sailing towards the North-West is then 60°; after he has walked 400 yards the balloon is vertically over his head. Find its height, supposing it is have always remained the same.

*10. (a) The angle of elevation of a certain peak when observed from each end of a horizontal base line of length $2a$ is found to be θ. When observed from the mid-point of the base the angle of elevation is ϕ. Prove that the height of the peak is

$$\frac{a \sin \theta \sin \phi}{\sqrt{[\sin(\phi + \theta) \sin(\phi - \theta)]}}$$

*(b) A man moves along the bank of a canal and observes a tower on the other bank. He finds that the angle of elevation of the top of tower from each of the two points A and B, at a distance $6d$ apart, is α. From a third point C, between A and B at a distance $2d$ from A, the angle elevation is found to be β. Find the length of the tower and the width of the canal. **(Roorkee 1987)**

(c) A tower HP standing vertically at the orthocentre H of a triangle ABC subtends an angle A at the vertex A of the triangle. The height of the tower is....

11. (a) The angle of elevation of the top of a tower from a point A due South of the tower is α and from B due East of the tower is β. If $AB = d$, show that the height of the tower is

$$\frac{d}{\sqrt{(\cot^2 \alpha + \cot^2 \beta)}}$$

(b) The elevation of the top of a tower at a point E due east of the tower is α and at a point S due south of tower is β. Prove that the elevation θ at a point mid-way between E and S is given by

$$\tan \theta = \frac{2 \tan \alpha \tan \beta}{\sqrt{(\tan^2 \alpha + \tan^2 \beta)}}.$$

(c) From three collinear points A, B, C on a straight level road, the angles of elevation of a hill top are α, α, β. If $AB = BC = a$, then the height of the hill is

$$\frac{a\sqrt{2} \sin \alpha \sin \beta}{\sqrt{\{\sin(\alpha + \beta) \sin(\alpha - \beta)\}}}$$

*(d) An observer at an anti-aircraft post A identifies an enemy aircraft due East of his post at an angle of elevation of 60°. At the same instant a detection post D situated 4 kms South of A reports the aircraft at an elevation of 30°. Calculate the altitue at which the plane is flying.

*12. (a) A man standing South of a lamp post observes his shadow on the horizontal plane to be 24 feet long. On walking Eastwards 300 feet, he finds his shadow as 30 feet. If his height is 6 ft., obtain the height of the lamp above the plane.

*(b) A circular plate of radius a touches a vertical wall. The plate is fixed horizontally at a height b above the ground. A lighted candle of length c stands vertically at the centree of the plate. Prove that the breadth of the shadow thrown on the wall

where it meets the horizontal ground is $\frac{2a}{c}\sqrt{b^2 + 2bc}$.

*13. A 2 metre long object is fired vertically upwards from the mid-point of two locations A and B, 8 metres apart. The speed of the object after t seconds is given by $\frac{ds}{dt} = 2t + 1$ metres per second. Let α and β be the angles subtended by the object at A and B, respectively after one and two seconds. Find the value of $\cos(\alpha - \beta)$. **(I.I.T. 1987)**

*14. (a) A man observes two objects in a straight line in the West. On walking a distance c to the North, the objects subtend an angle α, in front of him and on walking a further distance c to the North, they subtend an angle β. Prove that the distance between the objects is

$$\frac{3c}{2 \cot \beta - \cot \alpha}.$$

(b) A man notices two objects in a straight line due west. After walking a distance c due north he observes that the objects subtend and angle α at his eye; and, after walking a further distance $2c$ due north they subtend an angle β. Show that the distance between the objects is $\frac{8c}{3 \cot \beta - \cot \alpha}$; the height of the man is being ignored. **(I.I.T. 1991)**

15. A round balloon of radius r subtends an angle α at the eye of the observer, while the angle of elevation of its centre is β. Find the height of the centre of balloon.

*16. (a) PQ is a vertical tower. P is the foot, Q the top of the tower, A, B, C are three points in the horizontal plane through P. The angles of elevation of Q from A, B, C are equal and each is equal to θ. The sides of the triangle ABC are a, b, c and the area of the triangle ABC is Δ. Show that the height of the tower is $\frac{(abc \tan \theta)}{4\Delta}$. **(I.I.T. 1980)**

(b) Three poles standing at the points A, B and C subtend angles α, β, γ respectively at the circumcentre of the triangle ABC. If the lengths of these poles are in A.P., then $\cot \alpha, \cot \beta, \cot \gamma$ are also in A.P. Is it true?

*(c) A stationary balloon is observed from three points $A, B,$ and C on the plane ground and is found that its angle of elevation from each of these points is α, If $\angle ABC = \beta$ and $AC = b$, find the height of the balloon. **(Roorkee 1996)**

*(d) A vertical tower stands at a point P within the horizontal triangle ABC and makes angles α, β, γ at A, B and C respectively. If the sides of the triangle makes equal angles at P, then prove that

$$\Sigma \sin^2 A (\cot \beta - \cot \gamma) = 0$$

*(c) ABC is a triangular park with $AB = AC = 100$ m. A television tower stands at the mid-point of BC. The angles of elevation of the top of the tower at A, B, C are $45°, 60°, 60°$ respectively. Find the height of the tower. **(I.I.T. 1989)**

(f) A person on the summit of mountain observes that the angles of depression of a car moving on a straight road at three consecutive kilometre stones are α, β and γ respectively. Prove that the height of the mountain is]

$$\left[\frac{2}{\cot^2 \alpha - 2\cot^2 \beta + \cot^2 \gamma} \right]^{1/2}$$

*17. (a) On the top of a hemispherical dome of radius r, there stands a flag of height h. From a point on the ground the elevation of the top of the flag is $30°$. After moving a distance d towards the dome, when the flag is just visible, the elevation si $45°$. find r and h in terms of d. **(M.N.R. 1990)**

*(b) A semicircular arch AB of length $2L$ and a vertical tower PQ are situated in the same vertical plane. The feet A and B of the arch and the base Q of the tower are at the same horizontal level, with B between A and Q. A man at A finds the tower hidden from his view due to the arch. He starts crawling up the arch and just sees the topmost point P of the tower after covering a distance $\frac{L}{2}$ along the arch. He crawls further to the topmost point of the arch and notes the angle of elevation of P to be θ. Compute the height of the tower in terms of L and θ. **(I.I.T. 1997)**

*(c) A pole stands at the bank of a circular pond. A man walking along the bank finds that the angle of elevation of the top of the pole from the two points A and B is $30°$ each and from the third point C, it is $45°$. If the distances from A to B and from B to C measured along the bank are 40 m and 20 m respectively; find the radius of the pond and the height of the pole. **(Roorkee 1991)**

*18. A ten mete high tower is standing at the centre of an equilateral triangle and each side of the triangle subtends an angle of $60°$ at the top of the tower. Prove that the length of each side of the triangle is $5\sqrt{6}$ metres. **(M.N.R. 1987)**

*19. (a) A person standing by the side of a road observes a row of equidistant telephone poles of equal height. Neglecting the height of the person's eye, the tenth and seventeenth poles subtend the same angles that they would do if they were in the position of the first pole and were respectively 1/2 and 1/3 of their height. Find, correct to one place

of decimal, the secant of the angle between the base line of the poles and the line drawn from the person's eye to the base of the first pole. **(Roorkee 1993)**

*(b) A man walks in a horizontal circle round the foot of a pole which is inclined to the vertical. The foot of the pole is at the centre of the circle. The greatest and least angles which the pole subtends at his eye are $\tan^{-1}\left(\frac{9}{5}\right)$ and $\tan^{-1}\left(\frac{6}{5}\right)$ respectively and when he is midway between the corresponding positions, the angle is θ. If the man's height be neglected, find the length of the pole. **(Roorkee 1997)**

*(c) A bird flies in a circle on a horizontal plane. An observer stands at a point on the ground. Suppose $60°$ and $30°$ are the maximum and the minimum angles of elevation of the bird and that they occur when the bird is at the points P and Q respectively on its path. Let θ be the angle of elevation of the bird when it is a point on the are of the circle exactly midway between P and Q. Find the numerical value of $\tan^2 \theta$. (Assume that the observer is not inside the vertical projection of the path of the bird). **(I.I.T. 1998)**

*20. (a) A person moving towards a house observes that a flag-staff on the top of the house subtends the greatest angle θ when his distance from the house is d. Prove the heights of the flag staff and the house are $2d \tan \theta$ and $d \tan\left(45° - \frac{\theta}{2}\right)$ respectively.

*(b) A person walks along a straight road and observes that the greatest angle subtended by two objects is α; from the point where this greatest angle is subtended he walks distance c along the road, and finds that the two objects are now in a straight line which makes an angle β with the road; prove that the distance between the objects is

$$c \sin \alpha \sin \beta \sec \frac{\alpha + \beta}{2} \sec \frac{\alpha - \beta}{2}$$

or $\frac{2c \sin \alpha \sin \beta}{\cos \alpha + \cos \beta}$.

*(c) A person walking on a straight road towards a tower observes that the angle of elevation of the top of a flag staff on the tower is α; after going a distance a towards the tower he finds that the flag staff subtends the greatest angle β. Prove that the length of the flag staff is $\frac{2a \sin \alpha \sin \beta}{\cos \alpha - \cos (\alpha - \beta)}$.

*21. A curve in the shape of a quadrant of a circle, has n posts, at its ends and at equal distances along the curve. A man stationed at a point on one of the extreme radii produced sees the pth and qth post from the end nearest to him in a straight line.

Show that the radius of the curve is

$$\frac{b}{2}\cos(p+q)\cos\phi\operatorname{cosec}p\phi\operatorname{cosec}q\phi,$$

where $\phi = \dfrac{\pi}{4(n-1)}$ and b is the distance of the man from the nearest end of the curve. **(Roorkee 1992)**

*22. A wheel with diameter AB touches the horizontal ground at the point A. There is a rod BC fixed at B such that ABC is vertical. A man from a point P on the ground, in the same plane as that of wheel and at a distance d from A, is watching C and finds that its angle of elevation is α. The wheel is then rotated about its fixed centre O such that C moves away from the man. The angle of elevation of C when it is just about to disappear is β. Find the radius of the wheel and the length of the rod. Also find distance PC when C is just to disappear. **(Roorkee 1995)**

*23. A circle passes through three points A, B and C with the line segment AC as its diameter. A line through A intersects the chord BC at a point D inside the circle. If angles DAB and CAB are α and β respectively and the distance between the point A and the mid-point of the line segment DC is d, prove that the area of the circle is

$$\frac{\pi d^2 \cos^2\alpha}{\cos^2\alpha + \cos^2\beta + 2\cos\alpha\cos\beta\cos(\beta-\alpha)}$$

(I.I.T. 1996)

24. A, B, C are three consecutive milestones on a straight road from each of which a distant spire is visible. The spire is observed to bear North-East at A, East at B and 60° East of South at C. Prove that the shortest distance of th spire from the road is

$$\frac{7+5\sqrt{3}}{13}\text{ miles.}$$

25. A tower stands on the edge of the circular lake $ABCD$. the foot of the tower is at D and the angles of elevation of its top at A, B, C are respectively α, β and γ. If the angles BAC, BCA are each θ, show that

$$2\cos\theta\cot\beta = \cot\alpha + \cot\gamma.$$

26. A flag staff stands in the middle of a square tower. A man on the ground, opposite the middle of one face and distant 100 metre just sees the flag; on his receding another 100 metre, the tangents of elevation of the top of the tower and top of flag staff are fond to be $\dfrac{1}{2}$ and $\dfrac{5}{9}$.

Find the dimensions of the tower and the height of the flag staff, the ground being horizontal.

27. The extremity of the shadow of a flag staff, which is h metres high and stands on the top of a pyramid on a square base just reaches the side of the base, and is distant x metre and y metre respectively from the ends of the side, prove that the height of the pyramid is

$$\sqrt{\left(\frac{x^2+y^2}{2}\right)}\tan\alpha - h,$$

where α is the elevation of the sun.

*28. (a) A right circular cylindrical tower of height h and radius r stands on a horizontal plane. Let A be a point in the horizontal plane and PQR be the semi-circular edge of the top of the tower such that Q is the point in it nearest to A. the angles of elevation of the points P and Q from A are 45° and 60° respectively. Show that

$$\frac{h}{r} = \frac{\sqrt{3}(1+\sqrt{5})}{2}.$$

(b) A sign-post in the form of an isoceles triangle ABC is mounted on a pole of height h fixed to the ground. the base BC of the triangle is parallel to the ground. A man standing on the ground at a distance d from the sign-post finds that the top vertex A of the triangle subtends an angle β and eighter of the other two vertices subtends the same angle α at his feet. Find the area of the triangle. **(I.I.T. 1988)**

29. A square tower stands upon a horizontal plane. From a point in this plane from which three of its upper corners are visible, their angular elevations are 45°, 60° and 45°. If h is the height of the tower and a the breadth of one of its sides then show that

$$\frac{h}{a} = \frac{\sqrt{6}(\sqrt{5}+1)}{4}$$

*30. A person wishing to ascertain the height of a tower stations himself on a horizontal plane through its foot at a point at which the elevation of the top is 30°. On walking a distance a in a certain direction he finds that the elevation of the top is the same as before, and on walking a distance $\dfrac{5}{3}a$ at right angles to his former direction, he finds the elevation of the top to be 60°. Prove that the height of the tower is either.

$$\sqrt{\left(\frac{5}{6}\right)}a \quad \text{or} \quad \sqrt{\left(\frac{85}{48}\right)}a.$$

31. Four ships A, B, C and D are at sea in the following relative positions : B is on the straight line segment AC, B is due north of D, and D is due west of C. The distance between B and D is 2 km, $\angle BDA = 40°$, $\angle BCD = 25°$. What is the distance between A and D?

(Take $\sin 25° = 0.423$). **(I.I.T. 1983)**

32. A tower on a hill subtends the same angle at two points A and B on the level ground and the angles of elevation of the top of the tower from these points are respectively α and β. If the tower and the two points of

observation are in the same vertical plane, prove that the height of the tower is

$$AB \frac{|\cos(\alpha + \beta)|}{\sin(\alpha - \beta)}.$$

Solutions to Problem Set (2)

1. (a) Let $PD = h$ and θ be the angle subtended at A where θ is unknown. Clearly
$AB = PB = a$ from isosceles $\triangle ABP$.
$h = a \sin 2\theta = 2a \sin \theta \cos \theta$
from $\triangle PBD$ ...(1)

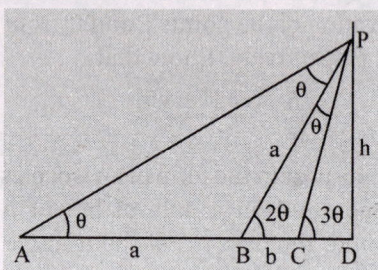

Fig. 43

Again from $\triangle PBC$

$$\frac{PB}{\sin(\pi - 3\theta)} = \frac{BC}{\sin \theta}$$

or $\quad \dfrac{a}{b} = \dfrac{\sin 3\theta}{\sin \theta} = \dfrac{3 \sin \theta - 4 \sin^3 \theta}{\sin \theta}$

or $\quad \dfrac{a}{b} = 3 - 4 \sin^2 \theta.$ $\quad \therefore \quad \sin^2 \theta = \dfrac{3b - a}{4b}$

$\therefore \quad \cos^2 \theta = 1 - \sin^2 \theta = 1 - \dfrac{3b - a}{4b} = \dfrac{a + b}{4b}.$

Now putting for $\sin \theta$ and $\cos \theta$ from above in (1), we get

$$h = 2a \sqrt{\left(\frac{3b - a}{4b}\right)} \sqrt{\left(\frac{a + b}{4b}\right)}$$

$$= \frac{a}{2b} \sqrt{(a + b)(3b - a)}$$

(b) Put $a = d, b = \dfrac{3d}{4}$ in part (a) and you get the result.

(c) Put $a = 200$ and $b = 100$ in part (a)
Then $h = \dfrac{100}{2 \times 50} \sqrt{(100 + 50)(150 - 100)}$
$= 50\sqrt{3}$ m.

(d) Put $a = 50, b = 20$ so that
$$h = \frac{50}{2 \times 20} \sqrt{(50 + 20)(60 - 50)}$$
$$= \frac{5}{4} \times 10\sqrt{7} = 33.07 \text{ m}.$$
and $CD = 17.5$ m.

(e) $\tan \theta = \dfrac{b}{a}, \tan 2\theta = \dfrac{b + x}{a},$

$\tan 3\theta = \dfrac{b + x + y}{a}$

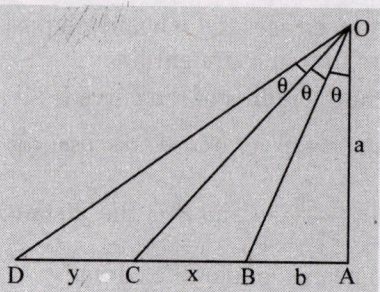

Fig. 44

5We have to find the value of y and hence we should eliminate x.

$$\frac{3t - t^3}{1 - 3t^2} = \frac{b + x + y}{a}. \text{Put } t = \frac{b}{a}$$

$$\therefore \quad y = \frac{b(3a^2 - b^2)}{a^2 - 3b^2} - (b + x) \qquad \text{...(1)}$$

Also $\dfrac{2t}{1 - t^2} = \dfrac{b + x}{a}$

$\therefore \quad b + x = \dfrac{2at}{1 - t^2} = \dfrac{2a^2 b}{a^2 - b^2}$ Put in (1) etc.

2. (a) $\tan \theta = \dfrac{1}{6},$

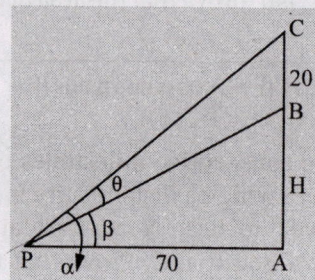

Fig. 45

$\tan \beta = \dfrac{H}{70}, \tan \alpha = \dfrac{H + 20}{70}$

$\alpha = \theta + \beta$

$\therefore \quad \tan \alpha = \dfrac{\tan \theta + \tan \beta}{1 - \tan \theta \tan \beta}$

or $\quad \dfrac{H + 20}{70} = \dfrac{\dfrac{1}{6} + \dfrac{H}{70}}{1 - \dfrac{1}{6} \cdot \dfrac{H}{70}} = \dfrac{70 + 6H}{420 - H}$

or $\quad (20 + h)(420 - H) = 70(70 + 6H)$

or $\quad 8400 + 400H - H^2 = 4900 + 420H$

or $\quad H^2 + 20H - 3500 = 0$

or $\quad (H + 70)(H - 50) = 0 \quad \therefore \quad H = 50$

(b) $AD = 2, AB = 150, BC = 20$

Let $PA = x$

$\qquad 2 = x \tan \beta; \triangle PDA$

$\qquad 150 = x \tan \alpha; \triangle PBA$

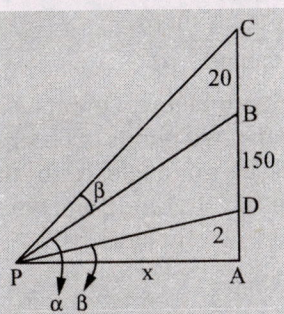

Fig. 46

$$170 = x \tan(\alpha + \beta)$$

$$\tan(\alpha + \beta) = \frac{\tan\alpha + \tan\beta}{1 - \tan\alpha \tan\beta}$$

$$\therefore \quad \frac{170}{x} = \frac{\left(\frac{150}{x}\right) + \left(\frac{2}{x}\right)}{1 - \left(\frac{150}{x}\right)\left(\frac{2}{x}\right)} = \frac{152\,x}{x^2 - 300}$$

or $\quad 152x^2 = 170x^2 - 51000$

or $\quad 18x^2 = 51000$

or $\quad x^2 = \dfrac{25500}{9}$

$\therefore \quad x = \dfrac{1}{3}\sqrt{25500} = \dfrac{10}{3}\sqrt{255}$

$\quad\quad = \dfrac{10}{3}\cdot 16 = \dfrac{160}{3}$

$\quad\quad = 53$ metres approx.

(c) $\quad \angle CQB = \angle AQB$ given.

$\therefore \quad$ QB is bisector of angle AQC and as such it divides the base AC in the ratio of the arms of the angle

$$\frac{AB}{BC} = \frac{QA}{QC}$$

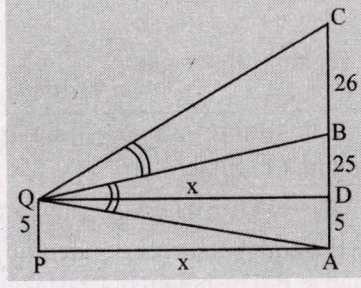

Fig. 47

or $\quad \dfrac{25}{26} = \dfrac{\sqrt{QD^2 + DA^2}}{\sqrt{(QD^2 + DC^2)}}$

or $\quad \dfrac{25}{26} = \dfrac{\sqrt{x^2 + 5^2}}{\sqrt{(x^2 + 46^2)}}$. Square

$$625(x^2 + 46^2) = 676(x^2 + 25)$$

$$51x^2 = (625 \times 46^2 - 676 \times 25)$$

$$= 25[25 \times 2116 - 676]$$

$$= 25 \times 4[25 \times 529 - 169]$$

or $\quad x^2 = \dfrac{100[13225 - 169]}{51}$

or $\quad x^2 = 100 \times \dfrac{13056}{51} = 100 \times \dfrac{4352}{17} = 100 \times 256$

$\therefore \quad x = 10 \times 16 = 160$ m.

(d) $\quad BM$ is bisector of $\angle AMC$ and hence it divides the apposite side in the ratio of the arms of the angle.

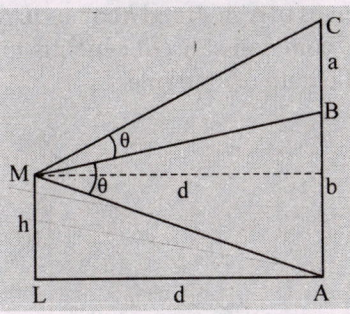

Fig. 48

$\dfrac{b}{a} = \dfrac{AM}{CM}$ $\quad\quad$ or $\quad \dfrac{b^2}{a^2} = \dfrac{d^2 + h^2}{d^2 + (a+b-h)^2}$

$\therefore \quad a^2(d^2 + h^2) = b^2[d^2 + (a+b)^2 + h^2 - 2h(a+b)]$

or $\quad d^2(a^2 - b^2) = -h^2(a^2 - b^2) + b^2(a+b)^2$
$$\quad\quad\quad\quad\quad\quad\quad\quad\quad\quad\quad - 2hb^2(a+b)$$

Cancel $a + b$ etc. and you get the result.

3. (a) The angle of elevation of summit A at C is α, and at D is γ where $CD = a$ and $\angle DCB = \beta$.

From ΔEAD, $\gamma = \angle DAE + \alpha$.

$\therefore \quad \angle DAE = \gamma - \alpha$.

Also from ΔCAD,

$\quad\quad \alpha - \beta + \gamma - \alpha + \angle CDA = 180°$

$\therefore \quad \angle CDA = 180° - (\gamma - \beta)$.

$\therefore \quad \sin CDA = \sin(\gamma - \beta)$.

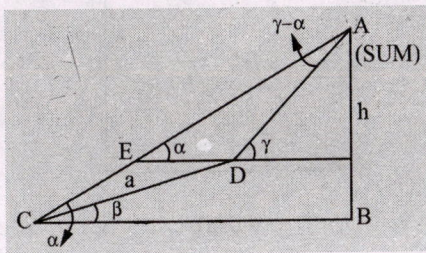

Fig. 49

Now two sides $h = AC$ and $a = CD$ are given. They come in triangles ACB and ACD respectively and both have side AC common.

Applying sine rule on both and eliminate common side AC

$$\frac{h}{\sin \alpha} = \frac{AC}{\sin 90°} \quad \Delta\, ACB \quad \therefore \quad AC = \frac{h}{\sin \alpha} \qquad …(1)$$

$$\frac{AC}{\sin CDA} = \frac{CD}{\sin CAD} \quad \Delta\, ACD$$

or $$AC = \frac{a \sin \alpha \sin (\gamma - \beta)}{\sin (\gamma - \alpha)} \qquad …(2)$$

Hence from (1) by the help of (2).

$$h = \frac{a \sin \alpha \sin (\gamma - \beta)}{\sin (\gamma - \alpha)}$$

(b) A comes in $\Delta\, AQR$ and h comes in $\Delta\, PQR$ and both have common side QR which is to be eliminated by the help of sine rule.

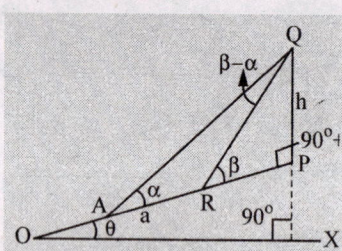

Fig. 50

By sine rule,

$$\frac{a}{\sin (\beta - \alpha)} = \frac{QR}{\sin \alpha} \quad \Delta\, AQR$$

$$\frac{h}{\sin \beta} = \frac{QR}{\sin (90° + \theta)} \quad \Delta\, PQR$$

Eliminate QR etc.

Another form :

Given $AB = p$ and $CD = q$.
From $\Delta\, BCD$,

$$\frac{BD}{\cos \theta} = \frac{1}{\sin \beta} \qquad …(1)$$

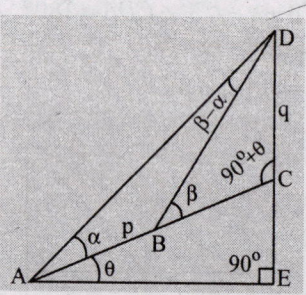

Fig. 51

From $\Delta\, ABD$,

$$\frac{BD}{\sin \alpha} = \frac{p}{\sin (\beta - \alpha)} \qquad …(2)$$

From (1) and (2) on equating the value of BD, we get

$$\frac{q \cos \theta}{\sin \beta} = \frac{p \sin \alpha}{\sin (\beta - \alpha)},$$

or $$\cos \theta = \frac{p \sin \alpha \sin \beta}{1 \sin (\beta - \alpha)}$$

(c) In the figure below, OP represents the tree and A and B the two points of observations in the hill inclined at an angle α to the horizon. The elevation of P at A and β and the depression of P at B is γ. We clearly have

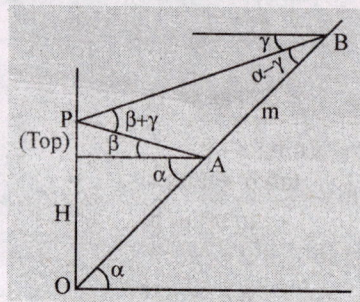

Fig. 52

$$\angle POA = 90° - \alpha, \quad \angle OAP = \alpha + \beta,$$
$$\angle ABP = \alpha - \gamma$$
and $\angle APB = (\alpha + \beta) - (\alpha - \gamma) = \beta + \gamma$.
Also $OP = H$ cm and $AB = m$ cm.

H comes in $\Delta\, OPA$ and m comes in ΔBPA and both have side PA common, which is to be eliminated.
Now from $\Delta\, OAP$,

$$\frac{PA}{\sin (90° - \alpha)} = \frac{OP}{\sin (\alpha + \beta)}$$

or $$\frac{PA}{\cos \alpha} = \frac{H}{\sin (\alpha + \beta)} \qquad …(1)$$

and from $\Delta\, PAB$,

$$\frac{AB}{\sin (\beta + \gamma)} = \frac{PA}{\sin (\alpha - \gamma)}$$

or $$\frac{m}{\sin (\beta + \gamma)} = \frac{PA}{\sin (\alpha - \gamma)} \qquad …(2)$$

Multiplying (1) and (2), we get

$$\frac{m \cdot PA}{\cos \alpha \sin (\beta + \gamma)} = \frac{H \cdot PA}{\sin (\alpha + \beta) \sin (\alpha - \gamma)}$$

or $$H = \frac{m \sin (\alpha + \beta) \sin (\alpha - \gamma)}{\cos \alpha \sin (\beta + \gamma)}$$

(d) Let α be the equal angle subtended by the towers at the man at P. The height of P be taken as x. Both x and α are unknown and they have to be eliminated. a comes in $\Delta\, APB$ and x comes in

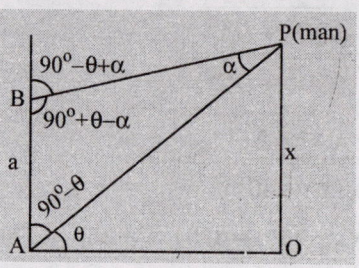

Fig. 53

Δ *APO* and both have side *AP* common which is to be eliminated. By sine in Δ *ABP*.

$$\frac{a}{\sin \alpha} = \frac{AP}{\cos(\theta - \alpha)} \qquad \ldots(1)$$

Now $\dfrac{x}{\sin \theta} = \dfrac{AP}{\sin 90°}$ $\quad \therefore \quad AP = \dfrac{x}{\sin \theta}, \Delta \, OAP$

Putting in (1) we get

$$\frac{a}{\sin \alpha} = \frac{x}{\sin \theta \cos (\theta - \alpha)}$$

$$\therefore \quad \frac{x \sin \alpha}{a \sin \theta} = \cos (\theta - \alpha)$$

$$\frac{x \sin \alpha}{b \sin \phi} = \cos (\phi - \alpha),$$

$$\frac{x \sin \alpha}{c \sin \psi} = \cos (\psi - \alpha)$$

$$T_1 = \frac{\sin (\theta - \phi)}{c \sin \psi} = \frac{\sin [(\theta - \alpha) - (\phi - \alpha)]}{c \sin \psi}$$

$$= \frac{\sin (\theta - \alpha) \cos (\phi - \alpha) - \cos (\theta - \alpha) \sin (\phi - \alpha)}{c \sin \psi}$$

$$= \frac{1}{c \sin \psi} \left[\sin (\theta - \alpha) \frac{x \sin \alpha}{b \sin \phi} - \sin (\phi - \alpha) \frac{x \sin \alpha}{a \sin \theta} \right]$$

$$= \frac{x \sin \alpha}{abc \sin \theta \sin \phi \sin \psi}$$

$$[\sin \theta \sin (\theta - \alpha) - \sin \phi \sin (\phi - \alpha)]$$

$$T_1 = k \, [\sin \theta \sin (\theta - a) - \sin \phi \sin (\phi - a)]$$

Similarly write T_2 and T_3 by symmetry and then add. $T_1 + T_2 + T_3 = 0$ as $\Sigma \, (a - b) = 0$.

(e) We have marked the angles as given

$$\angle ACB = 180° - (\alpha + \beta) - \gamma = 180° - (\alpha + \beta + \gamma)$$

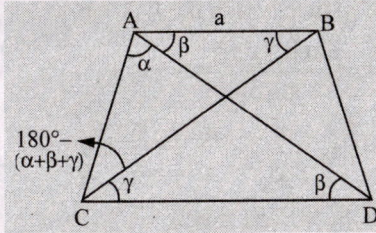

Fig. 54

$$\sin ACB = \sin (\alpha + \beta + \gamma) \qquad \ldots(1)$$

Using sine formula on Δ *ABC*

$$\frac{AB}{\sin ACB} = \frac{AC}{\sin \gamma}$$

$$\therefore \quad AC = \frac{a \sin \gamma}{\sin (\alpha + \beta + \gamma)}, \qquad \text{by (1)} \qquad \ldots(2)$$

Again from Δ *ACD* by sine formula we have

$$\frac{CD}{\sin \alpha} = \frac{AC}{\sin \beta}$$

$$\therefore \quad CD = \frac{\sin \alpha}{\sin \beta} \cdot \frac{a \sin \gamma}{\sin (\alpha + \beta + \gamma)} \qquad \text{by (2)}$$

$$= \frac{a \sin \alpha \sin \gamma}{\sin \beta \sin (\alpha + \beta + \gamma)}$$

(f) The angles have been marked. the two distances are $H = CD$ and $AB = c$,

$AC = H \cot \theta, BC = h \cot \phi$

By projection formula on Δ *ABC* i.e.,

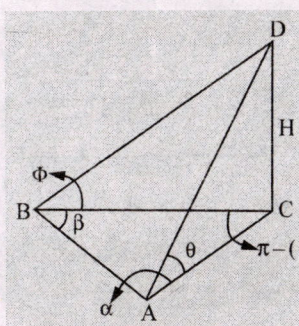

Fig. 55

$c = a \cos B + b \cos A$ we have

$AB = AC \cos \alpha + BC \cos \beta$

or $\quad c = H \cot \theta \cos \alpha + H \cot \phi \cos \beta,$ $\qquad$ by (1)

$$\therefore \quad H = \frac{c}{\cot \theta \cos \alpha + \cot \phi \cos \beta}$$

(g) h comes in Δ *AQP* and a comes in Δ *AQB* and both have side *AQ* as common which has to be eliminated by sine rule.

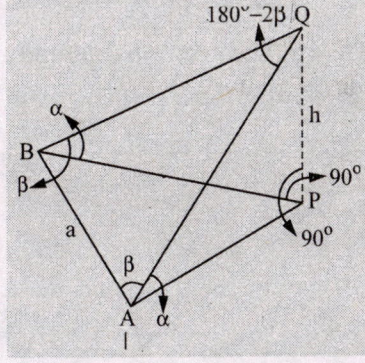

Fig. 56

Now from Δ *AQB* $\dfrac{AQ}{\sin \beta} = \dfrac{a}{\sin (180° - 2\beta)} = \dfrac{a}{\sin 2\beta}$

$$\therefore \quad AQ = \frac{a \sin \beta}{2 \sin \beta \cos \beta} = \frac{a}{2 \cos \beta} \qquad \ldots(1)$$

Also $\dfrac{AQ}{\sin 90°} = \dfrac{h}{\sin \alpha}$ $\quad$ from Δ *AQP* $\qquad \ldots(2)$

$$\therefore \quad \frac{a}{2 \cos \beta} = \frac{h}{\sin \alpha} = AQ \qquad \text{from (1) and (2)}$$

$$\therefore \quad h = \frac{a \sin \alpha}{2 \cos \beta}$$

(h)   Let PQ be the mast which stands at a point P of a square field $ABCD$ of side a. the mast subtends an angle θ at A so that
$$\angle QAP = \theta$$
Also $\angle PAB = \alpha$ and $\angle PBA = \beta$.
We have $PA = PQ \cot \theta = h \cot \theta$,

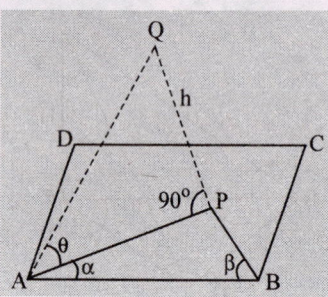

Fig. 57

where $PQ = h$
Now from ΔPAB, we have
$$\frac{PA}{\sin \beta} = \frac{AB}{\{\sin 180° - (\alpha + \beta)\}} = \frac{a}{\sin (\alpha + \beta)}$$

$$\therefore \quad PA = \frac{a \sin \beta}{\sin (\alpha + \beta)}$$

or $h \cot \theta = \dfrac{a \sin \beta}{\sin (\alpha + \beta)}$

Hence $h = \dfrac{a \sin \beta \tan \theta}{\sin (\alpha + \beta)}$

(i)   Let $PN = h$. Then $AN = h \cot \theta$ and
$$BN = h \cot \phi.$$

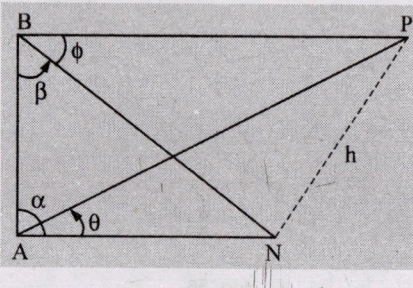

Fig. 58

Now from ΔABN, we get
$$\frac{AN}{\sin \beta} = \frac{BN}{\sin \alpha}$$

or $AN \sin \alpha = BN \sin \beta$
or $h \cot \theta \sin \alpha = h \cot \phi \sin \beta$.
or $\cot \theta \sin \alpha = \cot \phi \sin \beta$.

4.   (a)   From triangle ABC by since formula
$$\frac{BC}{\sin 75°} = \frac{AB}{\sin 30°}.$$

$$h = 80 \frac{\sin 30°}{\sin (45° + 30°)} = \frac{40 \times 2\sqrt{2}}{[\sqrt{(3)} + 1]}$$

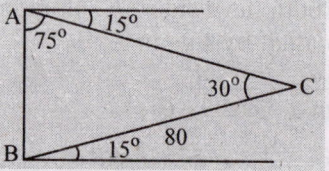

Fig. 59

$$= \frac{40. 2\sqrt{2} \, (\sqrt{3} - 1)}{3 - 1}$$
$$= 40\sqrt{2} \, (\sqrt{3} - 1) = 40 \, (\sqrt{6} - \sqrt{2}).$$

(b) $h = PS_1 \sin \beta_1$ or $PS_1 = h \operatorname{cosec} \beta_1.$

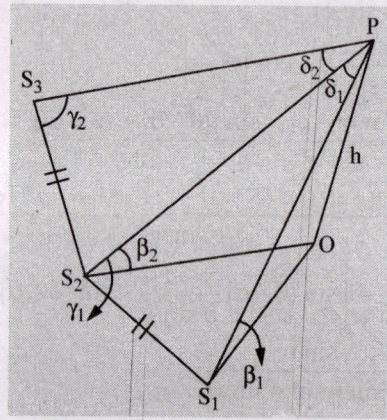

Fig. 60

From $\Delta PS_1 S_2$ by sine formula
$$\frac{PS_1}{\sin \gamma_1} = \frac{S_1 S_2}{\sin \delta_1}$$

or $\dfrac{h}{\sin \beta_1 \sin \gamma_1} = \dfrac{S_1 S_2}{\sin \delta_1}$ by (1)

or $\dfrac{h}{S_1 S_2} = \dfrac{\sin \beta_1 \sin \gamma_2}{\sin \delta_1}.$

Similarly $\dfrac{h}{S_2 S_3} = \dfrac{\sin \beta_2 \sin \gamma_2}{\sin \delta_2}$

But $S_2 S_3 = S_1 S_3$ given
$$\therefore \quad \frac{\sin \beta_1 \sin \gamma_1}{\sin \delta_1} = \frac{\sin \beta_2 \sin \gamma_2}{\sin \delta_2} = \frac{h}{S_1 S_2}$$

(c) $AQ = h \cot \phi, PQ = h \cot 30°$ ...(1)

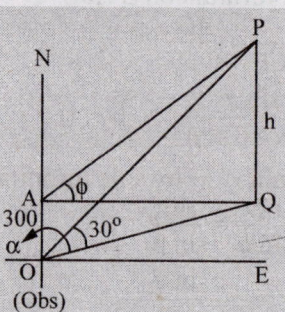

Fig. 61

Also $\tan \alpha = \dfrac{1}{\sqrt{2}}$ $\therefore$ $\sin \alpha = \dfrac{1}{\sqrt{3}}$

or $\dfrac{AQ}{OQ} = \sin \alpha = \dfrac{1}{\sqrt{3}}$ from ΔOAQ

or $\dfrac{h \cot \phi}{h \cot 30°} = \dfrac{1}{\sqrt{3}}$

$\therefore$ $\cot \phi = 1$ or $\phi = 45°$

$h = AQ \tan 45° = AQ.$

or $h = OA \tan \alpha = 300 . \dfrac{1}{\sqrt{2}} = 150\sqrt{2}$

from ground ΔOAQ.

5. (a) PQ is a vertical pillar. The points A and B are respectively due south and due east of the point P so that $\angle APB = 90°$, M is the mid-point of AB and N is the foot of perpendicular from P on AB where $AN = 20$ metres.

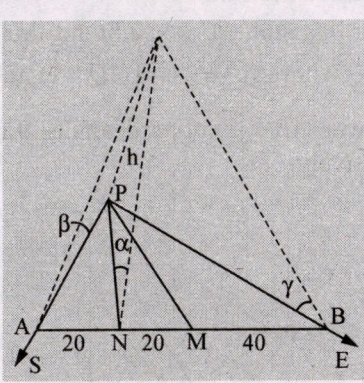

Fig. 62

N is mid-point of AM as ΔPAM is equilateral

$\therefore$ $AM = 2AN = 40$ ...(1)

$AB = 2AM = 80$ ...(2)

Also $\angle PAM = \angle MPA = 60°$, since the ΔPAM is equilateral. Elevation of Q as seen from N is α where $\tan \alpha = 2$.

If $PQ = h$, then

$PN = h \cot \alpha = AN \tan 60° = 20\sqrt{3}$

$\therefore$ $h . \left(\dfrac{1}{2}\right) = 20\sqrt{3}$ so that $h = 40\sqrt{3}$.

To find the elevations of A and B, we first find PA and PB. We have

$PA = AM = 40$ by (1) as ΔPAM is equilateral

$\therefore$ $PB = \sqrt{AB^2 - PA^2} = \sqrt{80^2 - 40^2}$

$= 40\sqrt{3}$ metre. by (1) and (2)

$\therefore$ $\tan \beta = \dfrac{PQ}{PA} = \dfrac{40\sqrt{3}}{40} = \sqrt{3}$ so that $\beta = 60°$

and $\tan \gamma = \dfrac{PQ}{PB} = \dfrac{40\sqrt{3}}{40\sqrt{(3)}} = 1$ and so $\gamma = 45°$.

(b) Let the tower stand at O and its height $OP = h$ which subtends an angle of $45°$, $60°$, $60°$ at A, B, C respectively.

$\therefore$ $OA = h \cot 45° = h;$

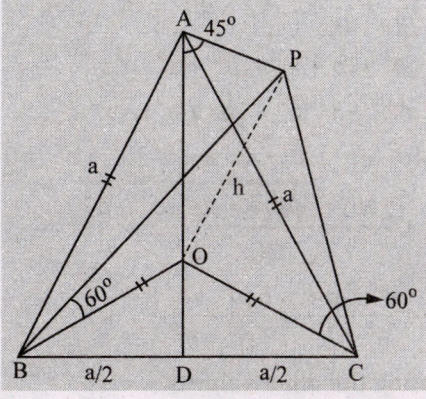

Fig. 63

$OB = h \cot 60° = \dfrac{h}{\sqrt{3}} = OC$

$\therefore$ $OB = OC$

Also $AB = AC = BC = a$ say.

If D be the mid-point of BC then OD and AD both are perpendicular to base BC.

$\therefore$ AD is median as well as altitude. In an isosceles or equilateral Δ, both centroid and orthocentre coincide, then

$OA = \dfrac{2}{3} AD = \dfrac{2}{3} \sqrt{a^2 + \dfrac{a^2}{4}}$

or $h = OA = \dfrac{2}{3} . \dfrac{1}{2} \sqrt{5} a$

$= \dfrac{100\sqrt{5}}{3}$ $\because$ $a = 100$, given.

6. (a) $\dfrac{b}{a} = \tan \theta$, $\dfrac{b + x}{a} = \tan 2\theta$

or $\dfrac{b + x}{a} = \dfrac{2 \tan \theta}{1 - \tan^2 \theta} = \dfrac{2 . \dfrac{b}{a}}{1 - \dfrac{b^2}{a^2}}$

$\dfrac{b + x}{a} = \dfrac{2ab}{a^2 - b^2}$ $\therefore$ $x = \dfrac{2a^2 b}{a^2 - b^2} - b$

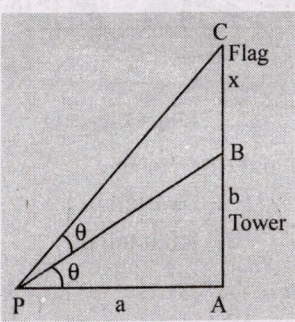

Fig. 64

or $x = \dfrac{a^2 b + b^3}{a^2 - b^2} = \dfrac{b(a^2 + b^2)}{a^2 - b^2}$

Alt. Since PB is the bisector of $\angle APC$ we have

$\dfrac{BA}{BC} = \dfrac{PA}{PC}$ or $PC^2 . BA^2 = BC^2 . PA^2$

or $\{a^2 + (b + x)^2\} . b^2 = x^2 . a^2$

or $a^2 b^2 + b^2(b^2 + 2bx + x^2) = x^2 a^2$

or $(a^2 - b^2) x^2 - 2b^3 x - b^2 (a^2 + b^2) = 0$

or $x = \dfrac{2b^3 \pm \sqrt{4b^6 + 4b^2 (a^4 - b^4)}}{2(a^2 - b^2)}$

$= \dfrac{b^3 \pm a^2 b}{a^2 - b^2} = \dfrac{b(a^2 + b^2)}{a^2 - b^2}$

rejecting the other value of $x = -b$.

3rd Method. Use $m - n$ theorem.

$\angle PBC = 90° + \theta$

(b) Proceed as above $\tan 2\theta = \dfrac{40}{a}$,

$\tan \theta = \dfrac{15}{a}$ $\therefore$ $a = 30$.

where $AB = 15$, $BC = 25$, $AP = a$ etc.

7. (a) $AB = y$, tower, $BC = x$, flag staff, $AP = 9$, $AQ = 11$. BC subtends equal angles α at P and Q s.t. $\tan \alpha = \dfrac{1}{10}$. Hence the circle through C and B must also pass through P and Q as angles in the same segment are equal. From the figure it is clear that segment BP subtends equal angles say β at C and Q.

$y = 11 \tan \beta$ ...(1)

and $x + y = 11 \tan (\alpha + \beta)$. ...(2)

$AP = 9 = (x + y) \tan \beta$ ...(2)

$\therefore$ $9 = 11 \tan (\alpha + \beta) \tan \beta$,

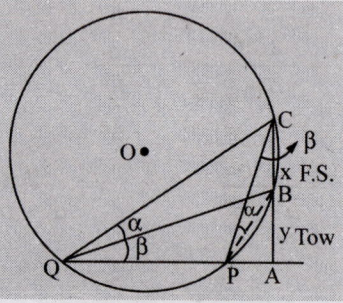

Fig. 65

from (2) and (3).

or $9 = 11 \tan \beta \left(\dfrac{\tan \alpha + \tan \beta}{1 - \tan \alpha \tan \beta} \right)$.

Put $\tan \alpha = \dfrac{1}{10}$.

$\therefore$ $9 \left[1 - \left(-\dfrac{1}{10} \right) \tan \beta \right] = 11 \tan \beta \left(\dfrac{1}{10} + \tan \beta \right)$.

$9 (10 - \tan \beta) = 11 \tan \beta (1 + 10 \tan \beta)$.

$110 \tan^2 \beta + 20 \tan \beta - 90 = 0$

or $11 \tan^2 \beta + 2 \tan \beta - 9 = 0$.

$(11 \tan \beta - 9) (\tan \beta + 1) = 0$.

$\therefore$ $\tan \beta = \dfrac{9}{11}$ (β acute)

Hence from (1),

$y = 11 \tan \beta = 11 . \dfrac{9}{11} = 9$.

From (3),

$9 = (x + y) \tan \beta = (x + 9) . \dfrac{9}{11}$.

$\therefore$ $x + 9 = 11$ or $x = 2$.

Alternative Method :

Let the flag staff $BC = x$ subtend the same angle α at P and Q where $AP = 9$ and $AQ = 11$ and $\tan \alpha = \dfrac{1}{10}$. Let the tower $AB = y$ subtend angles θ and φ at P and Q respectively.

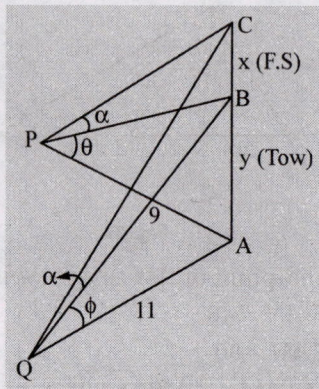

Fig. 66

$\therefore$ $\tan \theta = \dfrac{y}{9}$, $\tan \varphi = \dfrac{y}{11}$, $\tan (\alpha + \theta) = \dfrac{x + y}{9}$

Now $\alpha (\alpha + \theta) - \theta$

$\therefore$ $\tan \alpha = \dfrac{\tan (\alpha + \theta) - \tan \theta}{1 + \tan (\alpha + \theta) \tan \theta}$

or $\dfrac{1}{10} = \dfrac{\dfrac{x + y}{9} - \dfrac{y}{9}}{1 + \dfrac{(x + y) y}{81}} = \dfrac{9x}{81 + (x + y) y}$

$81 + (x + y) y = 90x$ ...(1)

Similarly writing $\alpha = (\alpha + \varphi) - \varphi$, we have as above

$121 + (x + y) y = 110 x$ ...(2)

Subtracting (1) from (2), we get

$40 = 20x$ $\therefore$ $x = 2$

Putting in (1), we get

$81 + 2y + y^2 = 180$ or $(y + 1)^2 = 10^2$

∴ $y = -1 \pm 10 = 9,$ -11 (rej.)

(b) Let BC represent the flag staff on the house AB such that $\angle PBC = \angle BQC = \alpha$ where $AP = a$, $AQ = b$. Let M be the mid-point of PQ and L that of BC. If O be the centre of the circle then angle at centre O is 2α. As in last part te circle through B and C will pass through P and Q.

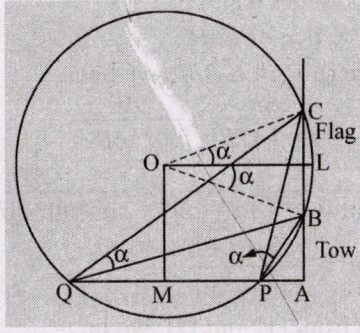

Fig. 67

$$BC = 2LC = 2OL \tan \alpha$$
or $BC = 2[AM]\tan \alpha = 2[AP + PM]\tan \alpha$
$$= 2\left[a + \frac{1}{2}(b - a)\right]\tan \alpha$$
$$= (a + b)\tan \alpha$$

In the last part $a = 9, b = 11, \tan \alpha = \dfrac{1}{10}$.

∴ $BC = x = (9 + 11) \cdot \dfrac{1}{10} = 2.$

(c) **Ans.** The height of column = 18 metres and height of the statue = 4 metres.

(d) $\angle BQC = \angle BPC = \beta$. Hence a circle will pass through B, C, P, Q. Angle subtended by PB and Q and hence at C is also is α

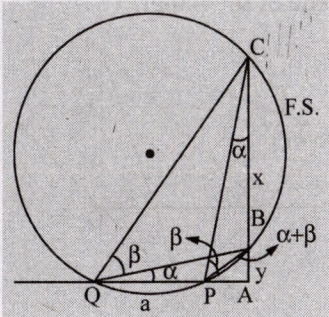

Fig. 68

∴ $\angle ABP = \alpha + \beta$ (sum of interior opposite angles)
We have to find the vlaues of x and y in the given form, where $AB = y$ and $BC = x$
We have the following relations :
$$y = QA \tan \alpha \qquad \qquad ...(1)$$
$$x + y = QA \tan(\alpha + \beta) \qquad ...(2)$$
$$PA = y \tan(\alpha + \beta) = (x + y)\tan \alpha \qquad ...(2)$$

$$PA = y \tan(\alpha + \beta) = (x + y)\tan \alpha \qquad ...(3)$$
$$QA = QP + PA = a + PA$$
or $QA = a + y \tan(\alpha + \beta)$,   by (3)
∴ $y = [a + y \tan(\alpha + \beta)]\tan \alpha$ by (1)
∴ $y[1 - \tan \alpha \tan(\alpha + \beta)] = a \tan \alpha$
∴ $y = $ etc.
∴ $y = \dfrac{a \tan \alpha}{1 - \tan \alpha \tan(\alpha + \beta)}$

Again from (3),
$x \tan \alpha = y[\tan(\alpha + \beta) - \tan \alpha]$. Put for y
∴ $x \tan \alpha = \dfrac{a \tan \alpha [\tan(\alpha + \beta) - \tan \alpha]}{1 - \tan \alpha \tan(\alpha + \beta)}$
∴ $x = \dfrac{a \sin(\alpha + \beta - \alpha)}{\cos(\alpha + \alpha + \beta)} = \dfrac{a \sin \beta}{\cos(2\alpha + \beta)}$

(e) Let OP represent the tower and $PQ = 2h$ the flag staff. Let R, S and M be the points of observation where $RS = 2a$, so that
$$\angle QRP = \alpha = \angle QSP,$$
$$\angle QMP = \beta, \text{ and } RM = a = MS.$$
Since $\angle QRP = \angle QSP$, a circle will pass through the four points P, Q, R and S. Let C be the centre of this circle, and from C draw CL and CM perpendiculars to PQ and RS, bisecting them in L and M respectively so that $LP = LQ = h$. Join CQ, CP and CR.

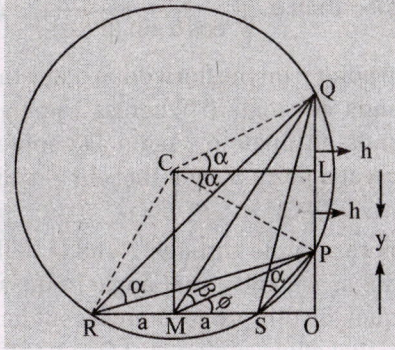

Fig. 69

Let he $\angle PMO = \phi$. We then have
Angle at the centre = Twice the angle at the circumference
$$\angle PCQ = 2\alpha, \text{ so that}$$
$$\angle PCL = \alpha = \angle LCQ$$
Let $OL = CM = y$ then, $OQ = y + h, OP = y - h$
If $OM = x = Cl = h \cot \alpha$ [In ΔCLQ]
∴ $x = h \cot \alpha \qquad ...(1)$
Also $CQ = h \operatorname{cosec} \alpha = CR \qquad ...(2)$
[From ΔCLQ]

Now from rt. angled ΔCRM
$$CR^2 = RM^2 + CM^2$$
or $h^2 \operatorname{cosec}^2 \alpha - a^2 = y^2 \qquad ...(3)$

We have to find the height $PQ = 2h$ of the flag-staff in terms of known quantities a, α and β by eliminating unknown quantities x and y.

Now $\tan(\beta + \phi) = \dfrac{OQ}{OM} = \dfrac{y+h}{x}$

and $\tan \phi = \dfrac{OP}{OM} = \dfrac{y-h}{x}$

∴ $\beta = (\beta + \phi) - \phi = \tan^{-1}\dfrac{y+h}{x} - \tan^{-1}\dfrac{y-h}{x}$

or $\beta = \tan^{-1}\dfrac{\dfrac{y+h}{x} - \dfrac{y-h}{x}}{1 + \dfrac{y^2 - h^2}{x^2}}$

or $\tan \beta = \dfrac{2hx}{x^2 + y^2 - h^2}$

Now put the values of x and y from (1) and (3).

∴ $\tan \beta (h^2 \cot^2 \alpha + h^2 \operatorname{cosec}^2 \alpha - a^2 - h^2)$
$\qquad = 2h^2 (\cot \alpha)$

or $\tan \beta (2h^2 \cot^2 \alpha - a^2) = 2h^2 \cot \alpha$

or $a^2 \tan \beta = h^2 (2 \tan \beta \cot^2 \alpha - 2\cot \alpha)$
$\qquad = 2h^2 \cot \alpha (\tan \beta \cot \alpha - 1)$

∴ $a^2 \dfrac{\sin \beta}{\cos \beta} = 2h^2 \dfrac{\cos \alpha \sin(\beta - \alpha)}{\sin \alpha \cos \beta \sin \alpha}$

or $2h = a \sin \alpha . \sqrt{\left(\dfrac{2\sin \beta}{\cos \alpha \sin(\beta - \alpha)}\right)}$

8. At the point A on the horizontal plane the tower $OP = d$ subtends an angle β whereas the flag staff $PQ = h$ subtends an angle α. Again PQ subtends the same angle α at a point B such that $AB = a$. Since
$$\angle PQA = \angle PQB = \alpha,$$
therefore a circle through P and Q will pass through A and B as we know that angle in the same segments are equal. By this property angles subtended by PB at A is β so that angle subtends at Q is also β. Now we shall try to have angle as are required in the solution i.e, $\alpha + 2\beta$ and $\alpha + \beta$. ΔAOQ is a right angles triangle with one angle as $\alpha + \beta$ at A so that other angle at Q is $90° - (\alpha + \beta) = \angle AQP$,

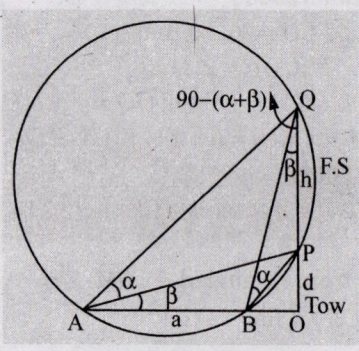

Fig. 70

∴ $\angle AQB = 90° - (\alpha + \beta) - \beta$
$\qquad = 90° - (\alpha 2\beta) = \angle APB$

(Same segment AB)

∴ $\angle ABP = 180° - \beta - \angle APB$
$\qquad = 180 - \beta - \{90° - (\alpha + 2\beta)\}$
$\qquad = 90° - (\alpha + \beta)$

We have to find the values of d and h in terms of a and known angles α and β.

Now $\qquad d = AP \sin \beta$ ...(1)

By sine rule on ΔABP, we have
$$\dfrac{AB}{\sin(APB)} = \dfrac{AP}{\sin(ABP)}$$

or $\dfrac{a}{\sin\{90° - (\alpha + 2\beta)\}} = \dfrac{AP}{\sin\{90° - (\alpha - \beta)\}}$

∴ $AP = \dfrac{a\cos(\alpha + \beta)}{\cos(\alpha 2\beta)}$ ...(2)

Hence from (1) and (2), we have
$$d = AP \sin \beta$$
$$\dfrac{a\cos(\alpha + \beta)\sin \beta}{\cos(\alpha + 2\beta)} = \text{height of tower}$$

Now we have to find the height of flag staff PQ. We know the value of AP and hence by sine rule on ΔAPQ, we have
$$\dfrac{h}{\sin PAQ} = \dfrac{AP}{si\ PQA}$$

or $h = AP . \dfrac{\sin \alpha}{\sin\{90° - (\alpha + \beta)\}} = \dfrac{AP \sin \alpha}{\cos(\alpha + \beta)}$

Putting the value of AP from (2) in the above, we get
$$h = \dfrac{a\sin \alpha}{\cos(\alpha + 2\beta)}.$$

9. (a) PQ is tower standing on the plane of the paper, and as such PQ is perpendicular to every line in the plane of the paper.

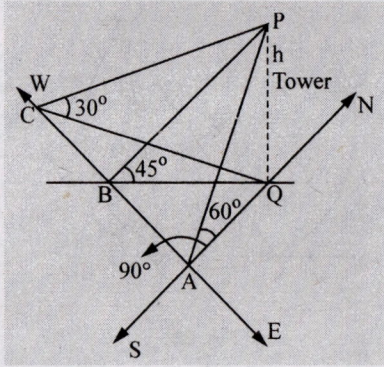

Fig. 71

∴ PQ is perpendicular to all the lines AQ, BQ and CQ.

Also angles at A, B, C are $60°$, $45°$ and $30°$ respectively.

Also $\angle QAB = \angle QAC = 90°$ and $PQ = h$.

$AQ = h \cot 60°$, $BQ = h \cot 45°$
and $CQ = h \cot 30°$

or $\qquad AQ = \dfrac{h}{\sqrt{3}}$, $BQ = h$ and $CQ = h\sqrt{3}$.

From right angled $\triangle QAB$, we have

$$AB = \sqrt{BQ^2 - AQ^2}$$

$$= \sqrt{\left(h^2 - \dfrac{h^2}{3}\right)} = \sqrt{\left(\dfrac{2}{3}\right)}h \qquad \ldots(1)$$

Again from right angled triangle QAC

$$AC = \sqrt{CQ^2 - AQ^2} = \sqrt{\left(3h^2 - \dfrac{h^2}{3}\right)}$$

$$= 2\sqrt{\left(\dfrac{2}{3}\right)}h = 2AB, \text{ by}(1)$$

or $AB + BC = 2AB$ $\qquad \therefore \ AB = BC$

(b) $AQ = h \cot 60°$ $\qquad \therefore \ AQ = \dfrac{h}{\sqrt{3}}$.

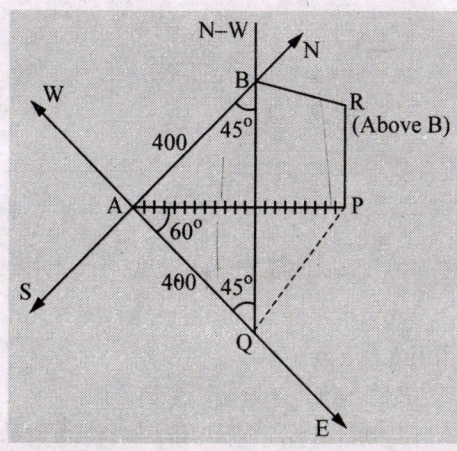

Fig. 72

As the man walks $AB = 400$ towards North the balloon sailing towards the North-West comes to position R above B, as it is seen vertically over his head. From the figure

$$\angle AQB = \angle ABQ = 45°$$

$$\therefore \quad AB = AQ = \dfrac{h}{\sqrt{(3)}}$$

or $\quad 400 = \dfrac{h}{\sqrt{(3)}}$ $\qquad \therefore \quad h = 400\sqrt{3}$

10. (a) PQ is perpendicular to each of the lines QA, QC and QB

$h = QB \tan \theta = QA \tan \theta$.

$\therefore \quad QB = QA = h \cot \theta$ $\qquad \ldots(1)$

Also $h = QC \tan \phi$ $\qquad \therefore \ QC = h \cot \phi$ $\quad \ldots(2)$

$\triangle QAB$ is isosceles triangle in which C is mid-point of AB. Therefore QC is perpendicular to AB.

$\therefore \quad BQ^2 = CB^2 + CQ^2$.

or $\quad h^2 (\cot^2 \theta - \cot^2 \phi) = a^2$, $\qquad$ by (1) and (2)

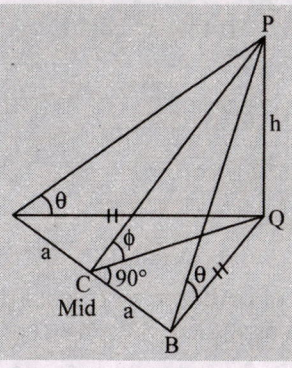

Fig. 73

$$\therefore \quad h = \dfrac{a}{\sqrt{(\cot^2 \theta - \cot^2 \phi)}}$$

$$= \dfrac{a \sin \theta \sin \phi}{\sqrt{[\sin(\phi + \theta) \sin(\phi - \theta)]}} \text{ as in Q. 38}$$

(b) Let PQ represent the tower on one bank and A, C, B be the points on the other bank such that $AB = 6d$ and $AC = 2d$. If h be the height of the tower then by the given condition

$$PA = PB = h \cot \alpha, PC = h \cot \beta \qquad \ldots(1)$$

Since triangle PAB is isosceles therefore if D be

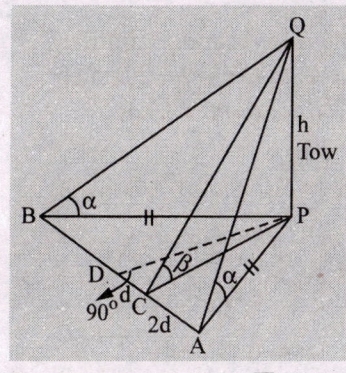

Fig. 74

the mid-point of AB then median PD will be perpendicular to AB and hence it will represent the width of the river.

Also $CD = AD - AC = 3d - 2d = d$.

$\therefore \quad PA^2 = PD^2 + DA^2$ from rt. angled $\triangle PDA$ $\quad \ldots(2)$

$PC^2 = PD^2 + CD^2$ from rt. angled $\triangle PDC$ $\quad \ldots(3)$

Subtracting we get

$$PA^2 - PC^2 = DA^2 - CD^2$$

or $\quad h^2 (\cot^2 \alpha - \cot^2 \beta) = 9d^2 - d^2 = 8d^2 \qquad$ by (1)

$\therefore \quad h = \dfrac{2\sqrt{2}d}{\sqrt{\cos^2 \alpha - \cos^2 \beta)}} = $ height of the tower.

Again from (2) the width PD of the canal is given by

$$PD^2 = PA^2 - DA^2 = h^2 \cot^2 \alpha - 9d^2$$

$$= \frac{8d^2 \cot^2 \alpha}{\cot^2 \alpha - \cot^2 \beta} - 9d^2$$

$$PD = d \sqrt{\left(\frac{9 \cot^2 \beta - \cot^2 \alpha}{\cot^2 \alpha - \cot^2 \beta} \right)}$$

(c) **Ans.** a

The distance of **orthocentre** H from the vertices A, B, C are $2R \cos A, 2R \cos B$ and $2R \cos C$ where R is circum-radius of the triangle and $\frac{a}{\sin A} = 2R$

$$AH = HP \cot A \qquad \text{or} \qquad 2R \cos A = h \cot A$$

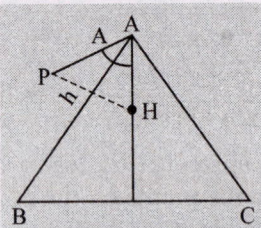

Fig. 75

or $\qquad \frac{a}{\sin A} \cos A = h \cot A \quad \therefore \quad h = a$

11. (a) PQ is $\perp$ to PA and PB both
$h - PA \tan \alpha$ and $h = PB \tan \beta$

$\therefore \quad PA = h \cot \alpha, PB = h \cot \beta$

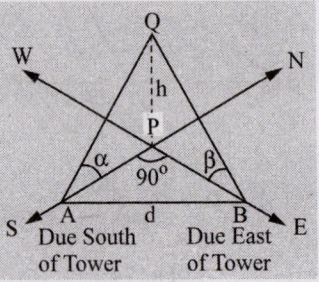

Fig. 76

Also $AB^2 = PA^2 + PB^2$.

or $\quad d^2 = h^2 (\cot^2 \alpha + \cot^2 \beta)$.

$\therefore \quad h = \dfrac{d}{\sqrt{\cot^2 \alpha + \cot^2 \beta)}}$.

(b) $PE = h \cot \alpha, PS = h \cot \beta, PM = h \cot \theta \,\Delta\, SPE$ is rt. angled and M is mid-point of hypotenuse which is equidistant from the vertices

$$PM = SM = ME = \frac{SE}{2}$$

$$SE^2 = SP^2 + PE^2$$

$$4PM^2 = PS^2 + PE^2$$

$\therefore \quad 4h^2 (\cot^2 \theta) = h^2 [\cot^2 \alpha + \cot^2 \beta]$

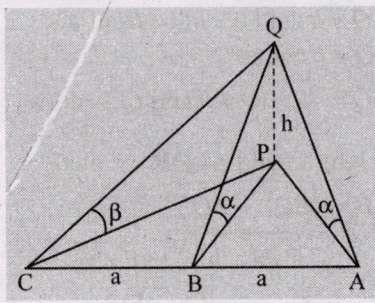

Fig. 77

Change in terms of tan etc.

(c) As in last question

$$PA = PB = h \cot \alpha$$

$$PC = h \cot \beta$$

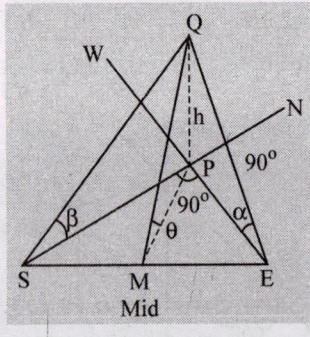

Fig. 78

Applying cosine formula on Δ^s PCB and PAB and adding, we get

$$PA^2 + PC^2 = 2(PB^2 + BC^2)$$

$$= 2PB^2 + 2a^2 \quad \because \quad BC = BA = a$$

or $\quad PC^2 - PB^2 = 2a^2 \quad \because \quad PA = PB.$

or $\quad h^2 (\cot^2 \beta - \cot^2 \alpha) = 2a^2$

Now changing in terms of sin and cos etc.

(d) PQ is $\perp$ to AP and DP where

$$AP = h \cot 60°, Dp = h \cot 30°$$

$\therefore \quad AP = \dfrac{h}{\sqrt{3}}, DP = h\sqrt{3}.$

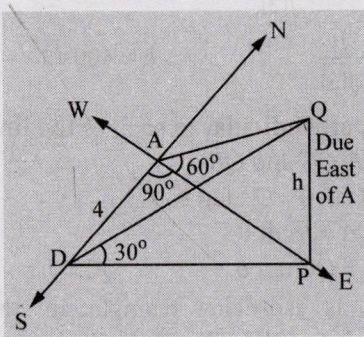

Fig. 79

Now from rt. angled triangle DAP we have

$$DP^2 = AD^2 + AP^2$$

$$\therefore \quad (h\sqrt{3})^2 = 4^2 + \left(\frac{h}{\sqrt{3}}\right)^2$$

or $\quad h^2\left(3 - \frac{1}{3}\right) = 16$

or $\quad h^2 = 6$ or $h = \sqrt{6}$ km.

12. (a) $PQ = h$ is the lamp post; AL the man due South of it and of height 6 ft. and $AC = 24$ ft. is the length of the shadow. After walking 300 ft. Eastwards he comes to B and now the length of shadow is $BD = 30$ ft.

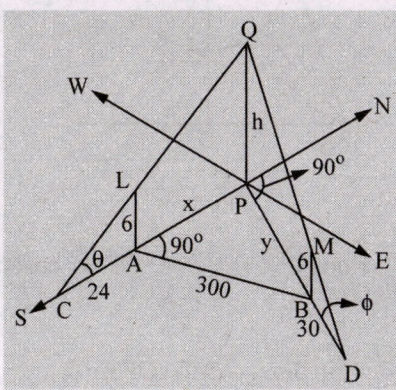

Fig. 80

Now let $AP = x$ and $BP = y$, $AC = 24$, $BD = 30$.
From Δ's QPC and LAC
We have $\dfrac{h}{6} = \dfrac{24 + x}{24}$ $\quad \therefore \quad x = 4(h - 6)$ $\quad$ ...(1)

Similarly from Δ^s QPD and MBD

$\dfrac{h}{6} = \dfrac{y + 30}{30}$ $\quad \therefore \quad y = 5(h - 6)$. $\quad$ ...(2)

From (1) and (2), we get

$h = \dfrac{24 + x}{4} = \dfrac{y + 30}{5} \therefore \quad y = \dfrac{5}{4}x.$

Again from rt. angled traingle PAB in which
$\angle PAB = 90°$
$PB^2 = PA^2 + AB^2$ or $y^2 - x^2 = (300)^2$

Putting for y and x from (1) and (2) in (3), we get
$(h - 6)^2[25 - 16] = 300^2 = 9.100^2$

$\therefore \quad h - 6 = 100$ $\quad$ or $\quad h = 6 + 100 = 106$ ft.

(b) Let C denote the centre of the plate touching the wall at R. Let $CD = c$ be the height of candle at the centre C of the plate. Also $OC = b$ is the height of the plate above the ground. If r be the radius of the shadow on the ground then $OM = OQ = r$. From the figure the breadth of the shadow

$= LM = 2MN = 2\sqrt{r^2 - a^2}$ $\quad$ ...(1)

Now from similar triangles CPD and OQD we have

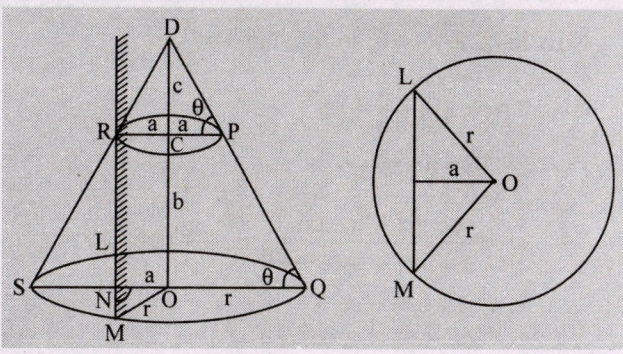

Fig. 81

$$\frac{c}{a} = \frac{c + b}{r} = \tan\theta$$

$\therefore \quad r = \dfrac{a}{c}(b + c)$. Putting in (1), we get

$$LM = 2\sqrt{\left[\frac{a^2}{c^2}(b + c)^2 - a^2\right]} = 2\frac{a}{c}\sqrt{(b^2 + 2bc)}$$

13. Let O be the mid-point of $AB = 8$
$\therefore \quad OA = OB = 4$
Also $OP = 2$ is the initial position of the object which is two metres long.

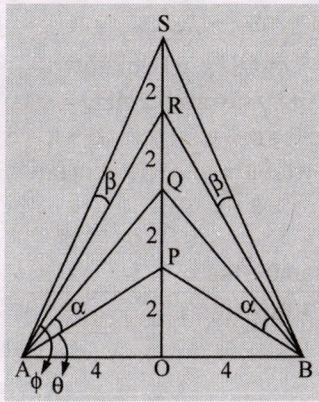

Fig. 82

$\dfrac{ds}{dt} = 2t + 1.$ $\quad$ Integrating we get

$s = t^2 + t + k$

when $t = 0$, $s = OP = 2$, $\quad \therefore \quad k = 2$

$\therefore \quad s = r^2 + t + 2.$ $\quad$ ...(1)

For $t = 0$, $s = 2 = OP$

For $t = 1$, $s = 4 = OQ$ $\quad \therefore \quad PQ = 2$ where PQ is the position of object after 1 second. For $t = 2$, $s = 8 = OS$ but $RS = 2$ where RS is the position of the object after 2 seconds.

$\therefore \quad OR = OS - RS = 6$. Also $OQ = 4$

$\therefore \quad QR = OR - OQ = 6 - 4 = 2$

$\therefore \quad OP = PQ = QR = RS = 2$

As per the condition of the question PQ and RS the positions of the object at $t = 1$ and $t = 2$ subtend angles α and β at A and B respectively.

Now let $\angle PAO = \theta$, so that $\tan \theta = \dfrac{2}{4} = \dfrac{1}{2}$

Also $\tan (\alpha + \theta) = \dfrac{4}{4} = 1$

$\alpha = (\alpha + \theta - \theta)$

$\tan \alpha \dfrac{\tan (\alpha + \theta) - \tan \theta}{1 + \tan (\alpha + \theta) \tan \theta} = \dfrac{1 - \dfrac{1}{2}}{1 + \dfrac{1}{2}} = \dfrac{1}{3}$.

$\therefore \qquad \sin \alpha = \dfrac{1}{\sqrt{10}}, \cos \alpha = \dfrac{3}{\sqrt{10}} \qquad \ldots(A)$

similarly taking $\angle RAQ = \varphi$ so that

$\tan \varphi = \dfrac{6}{4} = \dfrac{3}{2}$ and $\tan (\beta + \varphi) = \dfrac{8}{4} = 2$.

$\beta = \beta + \phi - \phi$

$\therefore \quad \tan \beta = \dfrac{\tan (\beta - \phi) - \tan \phi}{1 + \tan (\beta + \phi) \tan \phi} = \dfrac{2 - \dfrac{3}{2}}{1 + 2 \cdot \left(\dfrac{3}{2}\right)} = \dfrac{1}{8}$.

$\therefore \quad \sin \beta = \dfrac{1}{\sqrt{65}}$ and $\cos \beta = \dfrac{8}{\sqrt{65}} \qquad \ldots(B)$

$\therefore \quad \cos (\alpha - \beta) = \cos \alpha \cos \beta + \sin \alpha \sin \beta$

$= \dfrac{25}{\sqrt{10}\sqrt{65}} = \dfrac{5}{\sqrt{2}\sqrt{13}} = \dfrac{5}{\sqrt{26}}$

14. (a) Let $PQ = x$ or $QO = y$ (Unknown)

$\angle AQO$ θ say and $\angle APO = \phi$ say,

then $\theta = \alpha + \phi$ $\qquad \therefore \quad \alpha = \theta - \phi$.

Now $c = y \tan \theta$ and $c = (x + y) \tan \phi$.

$\alpha = \theta - \phi$

$\therefore \quad \tan \alpha = \dfrac{\tan \theta - \tan \phi}{1 + \tan \theta \tan \phi} \dfrac{\dfrac{c}{y} - \dfrac{c}{x + y}}{1 + \dfrac{c^2}{y(x + y)}}$

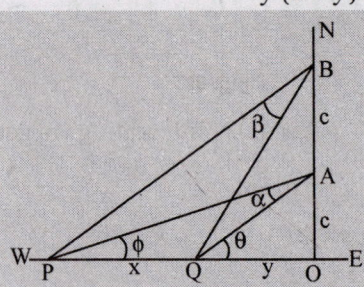

Fig. 83

or $\tan \alpha = \dfrac{cx}{xy + y^2 + c^2}$

$\therefore \quad xy + y^2 + c^2 = cx \cot \alpha \qquad \ldots(1)$

Now replacing c by $2c$ and α by $\beta \qquad \ldots(2)$

in (1) we get $\quad xy + y^2 + (2c^2) = (2c) x \cot \beta$

Subtracting (1) from (2), we get

$3c^2 = cx (2 \cot \beta - \cot \alpha)$.

$\therefore \quad PQ = x = \dfrac{3c}{2 \cot \beta - \cot \alpha}$

(b) Proceed as in part (a).

15. If the observer is at P and PA, PB are tangents drawn from P to the balloon, then $\angle APB = \alpha$.

$\therefore \qquad \angle APO = \angle BPO = \alpha / 2$.

Further we are given that the angle of elevation of the centre, *i.e.*, $\angle OPQ = \beta$. We have to find the height OQ of the centre O.

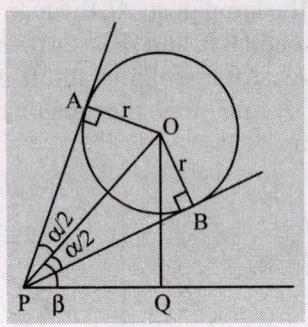

Fig. 84

$\dfrac{OA}{OP} = \sin \dfrac{\alpha}{2}$. $\qquad \therefore \quad OP = r \operatorname{cosec} \left(\dfrac{\alpha}{2}\right) \quad \ldots(1)$

Also $\dfrac{OQ}{OP} = \sin \beta$. $\therefore \quad OQ = OP \sin \beta$

$= r \operatorname{cosec} (\alpha / 2) \sin \beta$, by (1)

16. (a) Let the height PQ of the tower be h. Since the angles of elevation of Q from each of the points A, B, C is θ, we have

$PA = PB = PC = h \cot \theta \qquad \ldots(1)$

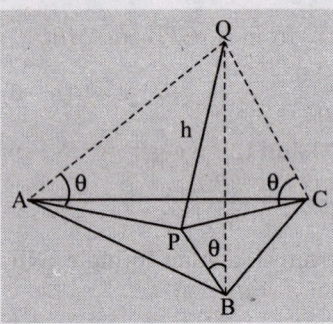

Fig. 85

Since P is equidistant from A, B and C it is the circuim-centre of the $\triangle ABC$.

$\therefore \quad PA = PB = PC$

$= $ circumradius of $\triangle ABC = \dfrac{abc}{4 \Delta} \qquad \ldots(2)$

Hence from (1) and (2), we obtain

$h \cot \theta = \dfrac{abc}{4 \Delta}$ or $h = \dfrac{abc \tan \theta}{4 \Delta}$

(b) False. $\quad h_1 = OA \tan \alpha = R \tan \alpha$

$\therefore \quad h_1 \cot \alpha = h_2 \cot \beta = h_3 \cot \gamma = R$

Since h_1, h_2, h_3 are in A.P., it follows that $\cot \alpha$, $\cot \beta$, $\cot \gamma$ are in H.P. as $h_1 = R / \cot \alpha$ etc.

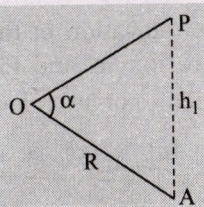

Fig. 86

(c) $PA = PB = PC = h \cot \alpha = R$,

where R is the circuim-radius of $\triangle ABC$.

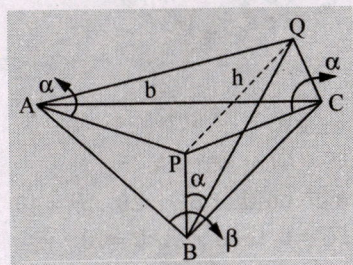

Fig. 87

$\therefore \quad 2R = \dfrac{b}{\sin B} = \dfrac{b}{\sin \beta} \quad$ or $\quad 2h \cot \alpha = \dfrac{b}{\sin \beta}$

$\therefore \quad h = \dfrac{b}{2 \sin \beta \cot \alpha}$

(d) Sides subtend equal angles at P which is 120° each.

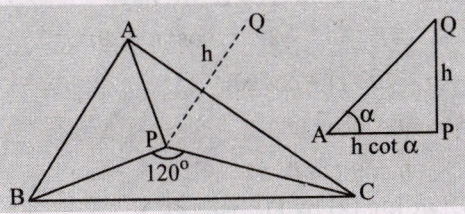

Fig. 88

$PA = h \cot \alpha, PB = h \cot \beta, PC = h \cot \gamma$

From $\triangle PBC$ by cosine rule.

$\dfrac{BP^2 + CP^2 - BC^2}{2BP.CP} = \cos \angle BP$

$= \cos 120° = -\dfrac{1}{2}$

$h^2 \cot^2 \beta + h^2 \cot^2 \gamma = a^2 = -h^2 \cot \beta \cot \gamma$

or $\quad h^2 (\cot^2 \beta + \cot^2 \gamma + \cot \beta \cot \gamma) = a^2$

Multiply both sides by $\cot \beta - \cot \gamma$, weget

$h^2 (\cot^3 \beta - \cot^3 \gamma) = a^2 (\cot \beta - \cot \gamma)$

Write similar expressions and add

$h^2 . (0) = \Sigma a^2 (\cot \beta - \cot \gamma)$

or $\quad \Sigma \sin^2 A (\cot \beta - \cot \gamma) = 0$

(e) Ans. $50\sqrt{3}$.

[**Hint :** If O is the mid-point of BC and h the height of tower, then $OA = h \cot 45° = h$

and $\quad OB = OC = h \cot 60° = \dfrac{h}{\sqrt{3}}$

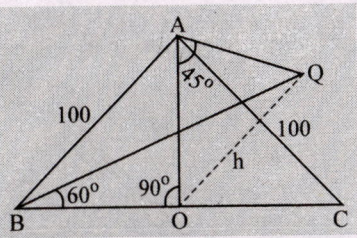

Fig. 89

Also $AB = AC = 100$. Therefore median AO is perpendicular to base. Hence from right angled $\triangle AOB, OA^2 + OB^2 = AB^2$

or $\quad h^2 + \dfrac{h^2}{3} = 100^2 \quad$ or $h^2 = \dfrac{100^2 \times 3}{4}$

which gives $h = 50\sqrt{3}$ m]

(f) Do yourself.

17. (a) $PQ = h$ is a pole standing on the top of hemispherical dome of radius r. the elevation of top Q as seen from A is 30°.

$\therefore \quad r + h = OA \tan 30° \qquad \qquad \text{...(1)}$

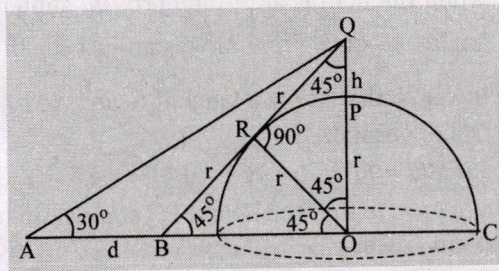

Fig. 90

On walking $AB = d$, the top is just visible from B which means that BQ is a tangent touching at R say, $\therefore OR$ is normal. Also $\angle OBQ = 45°$ (given) $= \angle OQB$. $\therefore OB = OQ = r + h$ and $OA = r + h + d$. The angle which are clearly 45° have been marked.

$\therefore \quad r = OR = RQ = RB \quad$ and $BQ = BR + RQ = 2r$

Hence from right angled $\triangle OBQ$ we have

$(2r)^2 = (r + h)^2 + (r + h)^2$

or $\quad 4r^2 = 2(r + h)^2 \quad \therefore \quad r + h = r\sqrt{2}$

or $\quad h = r(\sqrt{2} - 1) \qquad \qquad \text{...(2)}$

From (1) $r + h = (r + h + d) . \dfrac{1}{\sqrt{3}}$

or $\quad (\sqrt{3} - 1)(r + h) = d$ or $(\sqrt{3} - 1) r\sqrt{2} = d.$ by (2)

$\therefore \quad r = \dfrac{d}{\sqrt{2}} \dfrac{1}{(\sqrt{3} - 1)} = \dfrac{d(\sqrt{3} + 1)}{2\sqrt{2}} \qquad \text{...(3)}$

$$\therefore \quad h = r(\sqrt{2}-1) = \frac{d(\sqrt{3}-1)}{2\sqrt{2}}(\sqrt{2}-1),$$

by (2) and (3)

(b) $2L = \pi r$ (semi circumference)

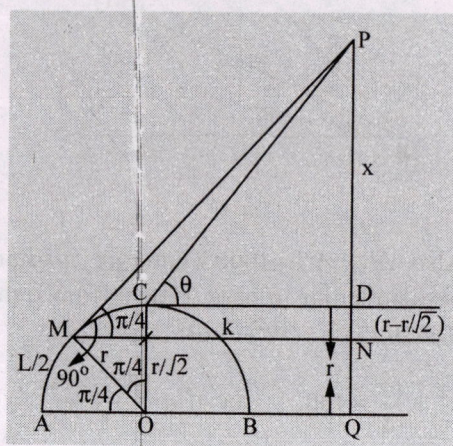

Fig. 91

$$\therefore \quad \frac{L}{2} = \frac{\pi r}{4}$$

Since $\dfrac{l}{r} = \theta$ $\quad \therefore \quad \dfrac{L/2}{r} = \dfrac{\pi}{4}$

i.e., when the man is at M then arc AM subtend and angle of $\dfrac{\pi}{4}$ at O. From M we can just see th top of tower so that MP is a tangent to arc at M

$\therefore$ OM is normal.

$\therefore$ $\angle PMO = 90°$ or $\angle PMN = 45° = \angle CMO$

We have to find the height PQ of tower in term of θ and L, were

$$2L = \pi r \text{ or } r = \frac{2L}{\pi} \qquad \ldots(1)$$

Let $PD = x$ so that $PQ = x + r$ $\qquad \ldots(2)$

No $CD = x \cot \theta$w in ΔFCD.

$$MN = PN \cot 45° = PN$$

$$MK + KN = PD + DN$$

$$\frac{r}{\sqrt{2}} + CD = x + (DQ - NQ)$$

$$\frac{r}{\sqrt{2}} + x \cot \theta = x + \left(r - \frac{r}{\sqrt{2}}\right)$$

$\therefore \quad r(\sqrt{2}-1) = x(1 - \cot \theta)$

$\therefore \quad x = \dfrac{r(\sqrt{2}-1)}{1 - \cot \theta}$

$\therefore \quad PQ = x + r = \dfrac{r(\sqrt{2}-1)}{1-\cot\theta} + r$

or $\quad PQ = \dfrac{\sqrt{2} - \cot\theta}{1 - \cot\theta} = \dfrac{2L}{\pi}\left(\dfrac{\sqrt{2} - \cot\theta}{1 - \cot\theta}\right)$ by (1)

(c) Let P be the centre and r the radius of the circular pond. If h is the height of the pole at O, then since

the angles of elevation of the top of th pole at A, B and C are 30°, 30° and 45°, we have

$$OA = OB = h \cot 30° = h\sqrt{3}$$

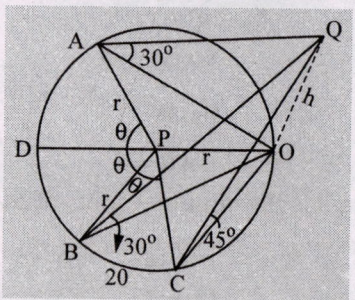

Fig. 92

and $OC = h \cot 45° = h$.

We are given that $BC = 20, AB = 40$.

If $\angle BPC = \theta$ then $\angle APB = 2\theta$

or $\angle APD = \angle BPD = \angle CPB = \theta$

By cosine formula on ΔOPA, we have

$$OA^2 = r^2 + r^2 - 2r \cdot r \cdot \cos(\pi - \theta)$$

$$2r^2(1 + \cos\theta)$$

or $(h\sqrt{3})^2 = 4r^2 \cos^2 \dfrac{\theta}{2}$

or $h\sqrt{3} = 2r \cos\dfrac{\theta}{2}$ $\qquad \ldots(1)$

Similarly from ΔOPC, we have

$$OC^2 = r^2 + r^2 - 2r \cdot r \cdot \cos(\pi - 2\theta)$$

$$= 2r^2(1 + \cos 2\theta)$$

$\therefore \quad h^2 = 4r^2 \cos^2 \theta$

$\therefore \quad h = 2r \cos\theta$ $\qquad \ldots(2)$

Dividing (2) by (1), we get

$$\frac{1}{\sqrt{(3)}} = \frac{\cos\theta}{\cos\left(\dfrac{\theta}{2}\right)}$$

or $\sqrt{3}\left[2\cos^2\left(\dfrac{\theta}{2}\right) - 1\right] = \cos\left(\dfrac{\theta}{2}\right)$

or $2\sqrt{3}\cos^2\left(\dfrac{\theta}{2}\right) - \cos\left(\dfrac{\theta}{2}\right) - \sqrt{3} = 0$

or $2\sqrt{3}\cos^2\left(\dfrac{\theta}{2}\right) - 3\cos\left(\dfrac{\theta}{2}\right) + 2\cos\left(\dfrac{\theta}{2}\right) - \sqrt{3} = 0$

or $\left[2\cos\left(\dfrac{\theta}{2}\right) - \sqrt{3}\right]\left[\sqrt{3}\cos\left(\dfrac{\theta}{2}\right) + 1\right] = 0$

Since θ is an acute angle, $\sqrt{3}\cos\left(\dfrac{\theta}{2}\right) + 1 \neq 0$.

Hence we must have

$2\cos\dfrac{\theta}{2} - \sqrt{3} = 0$ or $\cos\dfrac{\theta}{2} = \dfrac{\sqrt{3}}{2}$

$\therefore \quad \dfrac{\theta}{2} = \dfrac{\pi}{6}$ or $\theta = \dfrac{\pi}{3}$

Now from (1) or (2), we have $h = r$

Since arc $AD = 20$, we have

$$\frac{20}{r} = \theta \text{ (in radians)}$$

$$\therefore \quad \frac{20}{r} = \frac{\pi}{3} \text{ or } r = \frac{60}{\pi}$$

Hence $h = r = \dfrac{60}{\pi}$

18. Let ABC be the equilateral triangle and PQ, the tower standing at the centre P of the triangle, where $PQ = 10$ m.

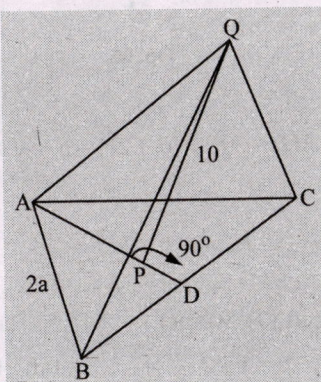

Fig. 93

Since each side of the triangle subtends an angle of $60°$ at Q, the top of the tower, we have

$$\angle BQC = \angle CQA = \angle AQB = 60°$$

Now $AQ = QB$ and since $\angle AQB = 60°$

$\therefore \quad \Delta AQB$ is equilateral.

Hence $QA = QB = AB = 2a$ (ΔABC being equilateral whose side is $2a$). similarly

$$QB = QC = 2a$$

$\therefore \quad QA = QB = QC = 2a$

Now $AP = \dfrac{2}{3} . AD$

$$= \frac{2}{3} . 2a \sin 60° = \frac{2a}{\sqrt{(3)}}.$$

$\therefore \quad$ From ΔAPQ, we have

$$AQ^2 = AP^2 = PQ^2$$

or $\quad 4a^2 - \dfrac{4a^2}{3} = 10^2$ or $\dfrac{8a^2}{3} = 100$

or $\quad a^2 = \dfrac{75}{2}$ or $a = 5\sqrt{\dfrac{3}{2}}$

$\therefore \quad$ Length of side of $\Delta = 2a = 2 \times 5\sqrt{\dfrac{3}{2}} = 5\sqrt{6}$ m.

19. (a) Subject to correction if any. This is a difficult question as it is not simple to understand its language. A is a person on one side of road and Q, R, S are respectively the 1st, 10th, and 17th poles of height h standing on other side of the road each pole being at equal distances of d so

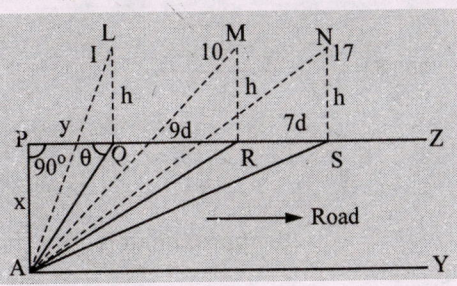

Fig. 94

that $QR = 9d$ and $QS = 16d$. Let α, β be the angles subtended by the 10 th and 17th pole at A. θ is the angle between the base line $PQRS$ of the poles and the line AQ drawn from the person's eye to the base of the first pole. Now from ground right angled triangles APQ, APR and APS, we have

$$AQ^2 = (x^2 + y^2) , AR^2 = \{x^2 + (y + 9d)^2\},$$

$$AS^2 = x^2 + (y + 16d)^2 \qquad \ldots(1)$$

10th Pole $AR = h \cot \alpha \qquad \ldots(2)$

Now consider 10th pole placed at 1st pole's position but of height $\dfrac{h}{2}$.

$\therefore \quad AQ = \dfrac{h}{2} \cot \alpha$

$\therefore \quad 2AQ = h \cot \alpha = Ar$, by (2)

Similarly consider 17th pole

$$AS = h \cot \beta \qquad \ldots(3)$$

Now consider 17th pole placed at 1st position but of height $\dfrac{h}{3}$.

$$AQ = \frac{h}{3} \cot \beta$$

$\therefore \quad 3AQ = h \cot \beta = AS, \qquad$ by (3) $\qquad \ldots(4)$

From (2) and (3), on squaring

$$4AQ^2 = AR^2 \text{ and } 9AQ^2 = AS^2$$

Putting the values from (1), we have the equations

$$4(x^2 + y^2) = x^2 + y^2 + 18yd + 81d^2$$

$$9(x^2 + y^2) = x^2 + y^2 + 32yd + 256d^2$$

These two equations on simplification reduce to

$$x^2 + y^2 = 6yd + 27d^2$$

and $\quad x^2 + y^2 = 4yd + 32d^2$

Subtracting these, we get

$$5d^2 - 2yd = 0 \text{ or } d(5d - 2y) = 0$$

$\therefore \quad d = \dfrac{2y}{5} \qquad \ldots(1)$

Putting $d = \dfrac{2y}{5}$ in any, we get

$$x^2 = \frac{143}{25} y^2 \qquad \ldots(2)$$

Hence from ground triangle APQ.

$$\sec\theta = \frac{AQ}{PQ} = \frac{\sqrt{x^2 + y^2}}{y}$$

$$= \sqrt{\frac{x^2 + y^2}{y^2}} = \sqrt{\frac{x^2}{y^2} + 1} = \sqrt{\left(\frac{168}{25}\right)}$$

$$= \frac{13}{5} = 2.6 \text{ approximately,} \qquad \text{by (2)}$$

(b) $OA = OB = OC = r$ the radius of the horizontal circle where C is a poinmid way between the points A and B. OP is pole which is inclined to the vertical. It ill subtend least angle say α at A and greatest angle β at B. From P draw PM perpendicular to AB and let $PM = y$ and $OM = x$

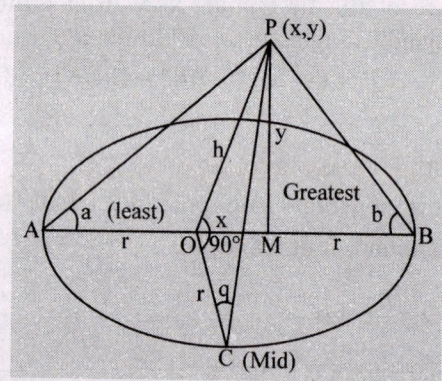

Fig. 95

$$\tan\alpha = \frac{y}{x+r} = \frac{6}{5} \text{ given}$$

$$\tan\beta = \frac{y}{r-x} = \frac{9}{5} \text{ given}$$

$$\therefore \quad 5y - 6x = 6r \text{ and } 5y + 9x = 9r$$

$$\therefore \quad x = \frac{r}{5}, \ y = \frac{36}{25}r$$

Also as given angle subtended at C is θ

$$\therefore \quad \tan\theta = \frac{h}{r} = \frac{\sqrt{x^2 + y^2}}{r} = \frac{\frac{r}{5}\sqrt{1 + \left(\frac{36}{5}\right)^2}}{r}$$

$$\therefore \quad h = \frac{1}{25}\sqrt{1321}$$

(c) $\quad \tan 60° \frac{PP'}{AP'} = \frac{h}{d} = \sqrt{3}$ ...(1)

$$\tan 30° = \frac{QQ'}{AQ} = \frac{h}{d+2r} = \frac{1}{\sqrt{3}}$$ ...(2)

$$\tan\theta = \frac{RR'}{AR'} = \frac{h}{\{\sqrt{(d+r)^2 + r^2}\}}$$

or $\quad \cot^2\theta = \frac{d^2 + 2dr + 2r^2}{h^2}$

$$= \frac{d}{h} \cdot \frac{d+2r}{h} + \frac{2r^2}{h^2} = \frac{1}{\sqrt{3}} \cdot \sqrt{3} + 2\left(\frac{r}{h}\right)^2$$ ...(3)

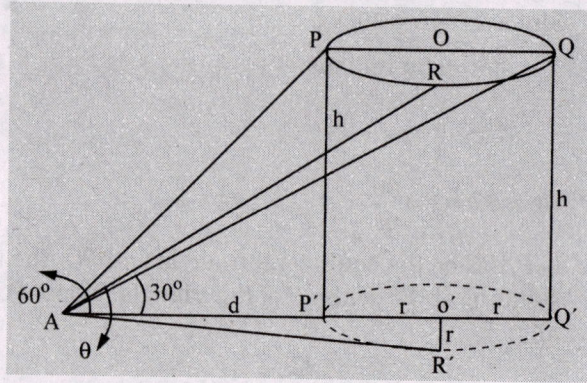

Fig. 96

Now,

$$P'Q' = AQ' - AP' = (d + 2r) - d = \sqrt{3}h - \frac{h}{\sqrt{3}} = \frac{2h}{\sqrt{3}}$$

by (1) and (2)

or $\quad 2r = \frac{2h}{\sqrt{3}} \qquad \therefore \quad \frac{r^2}{h^2} = \frac{1}{3}.$

Putting in (3), we get

$$\cot^2\theta = 1 + 2 \cdot \frac{1}{3} = \frac{5}{3} \quad \therefore \quad \tan^2\theta = \frac{3}{5}$$

20. (a) Let $OP = y$ and $PQ = x$ represent the height of the house and the flag staff and the direction of the person is from D to O. Clearly the flag staff PQ subtends the greatest angle at a point A at which a circle through P, Q touches DO.

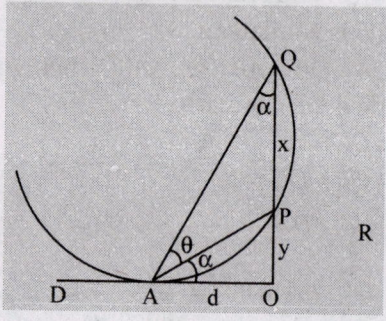

Fig. 97

Hence $\angle PAQ = \theta$ and $AO = d$.

Let $\angle OAP = \alpha$. Then in the alternate segment, $\angle AQP = \alpha$ so that

$2\alpha + \theta = 90°.$ $\quad \therefore \quad \theta + \alpha = 90° - \alpha$ ...(1)

As angle between chord AP and tangent at A is the same as the angle subtended by segment AP at any point Q on the circumference. Now,

$$PQ = OQ - OP = d \{\tan(\alpha + \theta) - \tan\alpha\}$$
$$= d\{\cot\alpha - \tan\alpha\} \qquad \text{by (1)}$$
$$= 2d\frac{(\cos^2\alpha - \sin^2\alpha)}{2\sin\alpha\cos\alpha}$$
$$= 2d\cot 2\alpha = 2d\cot(90° - \theta) \qquad \text{by (1)}$$
$$= 2d\tan\theta$$

and $\quad OP = d\tan\alpha = d\tan(45° - \theta/2)$ $\quad$ by (1)

(b) *RS* is a road on which there is a point *A* at which two objects *P* and *Q* subtend the greatest angle α. then by geometry, we know that the circle through *P, Q* and *A* will touch the road *RS* at the point *A*. If the line joining the objects *PQ* cuts the road at *B*, then *AB = c* and ∠ *ABP* = β as given now suppose ∠ *QAB* = θ so that ∠ *QPA* = θ as explained in Q. 55. We have to find *PQ* whereas we are given *AB = c*. We will apply sine rule on Δ^s in which these two sides occur and eliminate the common side. Consider Δ^s *PQA* and *BQA* with common side *QA* which is to be eliminated.

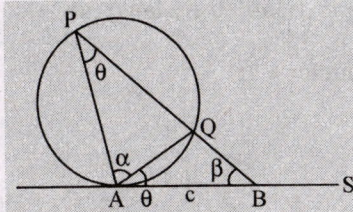

Fig. 98

From Δ *PAB*, $(θ + α) + β + θ = 180°$

∴ $θ = 90° - \dfrac{α + β}{2}$ ...(A)

From Δ *PQA* $\dfrac{PQ}{\sin α} = \dfrac{AQ}{\sin θ}$ ...(1)

From Δ *BQA*

$\dfrac{AB}{\sin \{180° - (β + θ)\}} = \dfrac{AQ}{\sin β}$ ...(2)

Eliminating *AQ* from (1) and (2), we get

$\dfrac{PQ}{c} \dfrac{\sin (β + θ)}{\sin α} = \dfrac{\sin β}{\sin θ}$, by dividing

$PQ = \dfrac{c \sin α \sin β}{\sin θ \sin (β + θ)}$.

Now put for unknown θ from (A)

$PQ = \dfrac{c \sin α \sin β}{\cos \left(\dfrac{α + β}{2}\right) \cos \left(\dfrac{α - β}{2}\right)} = \dfrac{2c \sin α \sin β}{\cos α + \cos β}$

(c) Let *OP* and *PQ* represent the tower and flag staff respectively and let the circle through *P, Q* touch the road *AO* at *B* where *A* is the initial position of

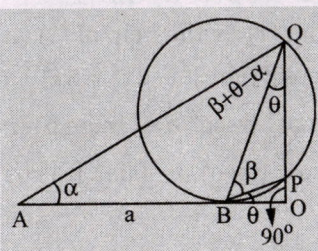

Fig. 99

the person where the elevation of *Q* is α. Then *B* is the point at which the flag staff subtends the greatest angle β. Now if ∠ *PBO* = θ, then by geometry, ∠ *PQB* = θ also.

Hence from Δ *OBQ*, $β + θ + θ = 90°$ ...(1)
so that $2θ = 90° - β$. Also ∠ *AQB* = β + θ - α.

As in part (a) we shall apply sine rule on Δ *BQP* and Δ *BQA* and eliminate the common side *BQ* to get *PQ* in terms of α.

Note from Δ *ABQ*,

$\dfrac{BQ}{\sin α} = \dfrac{1}{\sin (β + θ - α)}$ ...(2)

and from ∠ *BPQ*,

$\dfrac{BQ}{\sin \{π (β + θ)\}} = \dfrac{PQ}{\sin β}$ ...(3)

Hence from (2) and (3), on equating the value of *BQ*, we get

$BQ = \dfrac{a \sin α}{\sin (β + θ - α)} = \dfrac{\sin (β + θ)}{\sin β} PQ$

or $PQ = \dfrac{a \sin α \sin β}{\sin (β + θ - α) \sin (β + θ)}$

$= \dfrac{2a \sin α \sin β}{2 \sin (β + θ - α) \sin (β + θ)}$

$= \dfrac{2a \sin α \sin β}{\cos α - \cos (2β + 2θ - α)}$

$= \dfrac{2a \sin α \sin β}{\cos α - \sin (α - β)}$ by (1)

21. *OAB* is a quadrant of a circle, ∠ *AOB* = $\dfrac{π}{2}$ and radius *r*. There are *n* posts, one at *A*, the other at *B* and

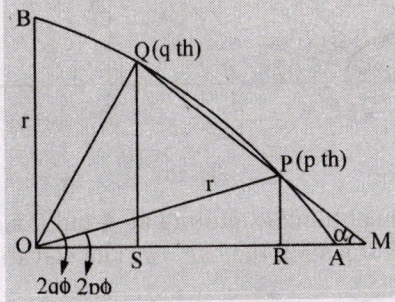

Fig. 100

remaining $(n - 2)$ posts along the arc at equal distances. There is a man *M* standing whose distance from the nearest post is *b = AM*. This man sees the *p*th and *q*th posts in a straight line. In between any two consecutive posts there will be eqal angle each equal to $\dfrac{1}{n - 1} . \dfrac{π}{2} = 2φ$ by given condition. Hence the angle at the centre subtended by *p*th and *q*th posts are $2p φ$ and $2q φ$ as shown in the figure. From *P* and *Q* draw perpendiculars PR and QS on OM. Hence from similar Δ's MQS and MPR, we have

$$\frac{QS}{SM} = \frac{PR}{RM} = \tan\alpha$$

$$\frac{QS}{PR} = \frac{SM}{RM} \quad \text{or} \quad \frac{r\sin 2q\,\phi}{r\sin 2p\,\phi} = \frac{SA+b}{RA+b}$$

or $\quad \dfrac{\sin 2q\,\phi}{\sin 2p\,\phi} = \dfrac{OA-OS+b}{OA-OR+b}$

or $\quad \dfrac{\sin 2q\,\phi}{\sin 2p\,\phi} = \dfrac{r - r\cos 2q\,\phi + b}{r - r\cos 2p\,\phi + b}$

or $\quad \dfrac{\sin 2q\,\phi}{\sin 2p\,\phi} = \dfrac{r.2\sin^2 q\,\phi + b}{r.2\sin^2 p\,\phi + b}$

$\therefore \quad 2r[\sin^2 p\,\phi\,(2\sin q\,\phi\cos q\,\phi)$
$$\qquad\qquad - \sin^2 q\,\phi\,(2\sin p\,\phi\cos p\,\phi)]$$
$$= b\,(\sin 2p\,\phi - \sin 2q\,\phi)$$

or $\quad 4r\sin p\,\phi\sin q\,\phi[\sin p\,\phi\cos q\,\phi - \cos p\,\phi\sin q\,\phi]$
$$= b.2\sin(p-q)\,\phi.\cos(p+q)\,\phi$$

or $\quad 4r\sin p\,\phi\sin q\,\phi\sin(p-q)\,\phi$
$$= b.2\,\text{sn}\,(p-q)\,\phi\cos(p+q)\,\phi$$

$\therefore \quad r = \dfrac{1}{2}b\cos(p+q)\,\phi\,\text{cosec}\,p\,\phi\,\text{cosec}\,q\,\phi$

22. Know quantities are d, α, β. Required quantities are radius a, road $BC = x$ and PC

$$BC = \text{rod} = x \qquad \therefore \qquad AC = 2a + x$$

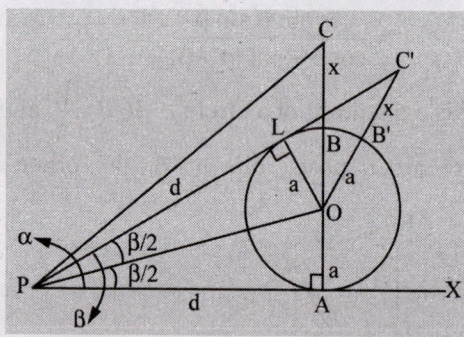

Fig. 101

The wheel touches ground at A and P is the point of observation such that $AP = d$. The elevation of C from P is α

$\therefore \qquad \tan\alpha = \dfrac{2a+x}{d}$

$\therefore \qquad x = d\tan\alpha - 2a \qquad\qquad\qquad …(1)$

Now the wheel is rotated so that rod BC becomes $B'C'$ and C' is just on the point of disappearing as seen from P so that PC' is a tangent to wheel at L. The angle of elevation of C' from P is given to be β. Now $PL = PA$ as tangent from P are equal and $OA = OL = a$.

$\therefore \qquad \Delta POL = \Delta POA$

and OP bisects and angle β.

$\therefore \qquad \tan\dfrac{\beta}{2} = \dfrac{a}{d}$

$\therefore \qquad a = d\tan\dfrac{\beta}{2} \qquad\qquad\qquad …(2)$

$\therefore \qquad x = d\left(\tan\alpha - 2\tan\dfrac{b}{2}\right)$ by (1) and (2) $\quad …(3)$

above gives the radius of wheel and length x of rod in terms of known quantities d, α, β.

$PC' = PL + LC'$
$$= d + \sqrt{\{(x+a)^2 - a^2\}} = d + \sqrt{(x^2 + 2ax)}$$
$$= d + \sqrt{[x(x+2a)]}$$
$$= d + \sqrt{\left\{d\tan\alpha.d\left(\tan\alpha - 2\tan\dfrac{\beta}{2}\right)\right\}}$$
$$= d + d\sqrt{\left\{\tan^2\alpha - 2\tan\alpha\tan\dfrac{\beta}{2}\right\}} \quad \text{by (2) and (3)}$$

23. $AC = \text{diameter} = 2r$

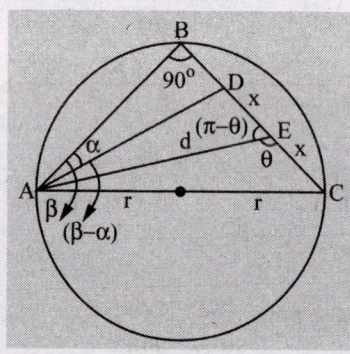

Fig. 102

$\therefore \qquad AB = 2r\cos\beta$ and $BC = 2r\sin\beta$

$AE = d$ given and we have to find the radius r order to find the area.

$$AC^2 = d^2 + x^2 + 2dx\cos\theta$$
$$AD^2 = d^2 + x^2 + 2dx\cos(\pi - \theta)$$

$\therefore \qquad 4r^2 + AD^2 = 2(d^2 + x^2) \qquad\qquad …(1)$

Now we have to find the values of AD and x.

$$BD = AB\tan\alpha = 2r\cos\beta\tan\alpha$$

$\therefore \qquad 2x = DC = BC - BD$
$$= 2r\sin\beta - 2r\cos\beta\tan\alpha$$

$\therefore \qquad x = r\sin\beta - r\cos\beta\tan\alpha \qquad\qquad …(2)$

Now $AB = AD\cos\alpha$

or $\qquad 2r\cos\beta\sec\alpha = AD \qquad\qquad …(3)$

Hence from (1) by the help of (2) and (3)

$$4r^2 + (2r\cos\beta\sec\alpha)^2 - 2x^2 = 2d^2$$
$$2r^2 + 2r^2\cos^2\beta\sec^2\alpha - \{r\sin\beta - r\cos\beta\tan\alpha\}^2 = \alpha$$
$$r^2\{2 + 2\cos^2\beta\sec^2\alpha - (\sin^2\beta + \cos^2\beta\tan^2$$
$$\qquad\qquad - 2\sin\beta\cos\beta\tan\alpha) = \alpha$$
$$r^2\{2 + \cos^2\beta(\sec^2\alpha - \tan^2\alpha) + \cos^2\beta\sec^2\alpha$$
$$\qquad\qquad - \sin^2\beta + 2\sin\beta\cos\beta\tan\alpha\} = \alpha$$

∴   Multiply both sides by $\cos^2 \alpha$ as suggested the answers or change $\sec^2 \alpha$ to $\dfrac{1}{\cos^2 \alpha}$

$$r^2 \{2 \cos^2 \alpha + \cos^2 \beta + \cos^2 \beta \cos^2 \alpha$$
$$- \sin^2 \beta \cos^2 \alpha + 2 \sin \beta \cos \beta \sin \alpha \cos \theta$$
$$= d^2 \cos^2 \alpha\, r^2 \{\cos^2 \alpha + \cos^2 \beta + \cos^2 \alpha (1 - \sin^2 \beta)$$
$$+ \cos^2 \beta \cos^2 \alpha + 2 \sin \beta \cos \beta \sin \alpha \cos \theta$$
$$= d^2 \cos^2 \alpha\, r^2 \{\cos^2 \alpha + \cos^2 \beta + 2 \cos^2 \alpha \cos^2 \beta$$
$$+ 2 \cos \alpha \cos \beta \sin \alpha \sin \beta\} = d^2 \cos^2$$
$$r^2 \{\cos^2 + \cos^2 \beta + 2 \cos \alpha \cos \beta \cos (\alpha - \beta) = d^2 \cos^2 \alpha$$

∴   Area $= pr^2$ etc.

Let P denote the position of spire and A, B, C the positions of consecutive mile stones so that
$$AB = BC = 1 \text{ mile}.$$

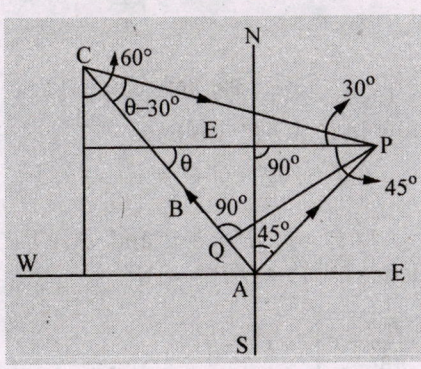

Fig. 103

[**Note :** The total angle at $C = 60°$ in figure].

Let $\angle PBA = \theta$. then by trigonometrical theorem, we have
$$(1 + 1) \cot \theta = 1 \cot 30° - 1 \cot 45°$$
or $\cot \theta = \dfrac{(\sqrt{3} - 1)}{2}$.   ...(1)

If PQ is perpendicular to the road ABC, then PQ is the shortest distance of P from the road.

Now from $\triangle CBP$, we have
$$\frac{PB}{\sin(\theta - 30°)} = \frac{BC}{\sin 30°} = \frac{1}{\sin 30°} = 2$$
or $BP = 2 \sin(\theta - 30°)$
$$= 2 [\sin \theta \cos 30° - \cos \theta \sin 30°]$$
$$= 2 \left[\frac{\sqrt{3}}{2} \sin \theta - \frac{1}{2} \cos \theta\right] = \sqrt{3} \sin \theta - \cos \theta.$$

Then $PQ = PB \sin \theta = (\sqrt{3} \sin \theta - \cos \theta) \sin \theta$
$$= (\sqrt{3} - \cot \theta) \sin^2 \theta = \frac{\sqrt{3} - \cot \theta}{1 + \cot^2 \theta}$$
$$= \frac{\{\sqrt{3} - (\sqrt{3} - 1)/2\}}{1 + \{[\sqrt{(3)} - 1]/2\}^2} = \frac{(\sqrt{3} + 1)/2}{[4 - \sqrt{(3)}]/2}$$

$$= \frac{(\sqrt{3} + 1)(\sqrt{3} + 4)}{16 - 3} = \frac{7 + 5\sqrt{3}}{13}$$

Let h be the height of the tower. Then $DA = h \cot \alpha$, $DB = h \cot \beta$, and $DC = h \cot \gamma$.

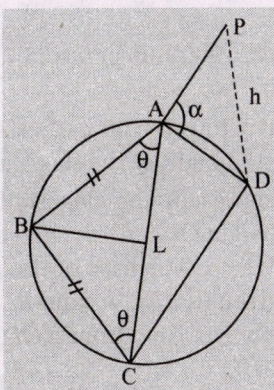

Fig. 104

Also it is given that $\angle BAC = \angle BCA = \theta$ so that $BA = BC$ and hence
$$AC = LA + LC = AB \cos \theta + BC \cos \theta$$
or $AC = 2AB \cos \theta$ ...(1)

Again $ABCD$ is a cyclic quadrilateral and hence by Ptolemy's theorem, we get
$$AB.CD + AD.BC = AC.BD$$
∴ $AB.h \cot \gamma + h \cot \alpha\, AB = h \cot \beta.2\,AB \cos \theta$
or $\cot \alpha + \cot \gamma = 2 \cos \theta \cot \beta$.

26. Let $ABCD$ represent the vertical cross-section of the tower through the middle so that side of the square is of length $AB = a$, say and height of the tower is $OP = h$, say. Let height of flag staff $PQ = b$. The two points of observation are N and M where $AN = NM = 100$ metre. It is given that $\tan \alpha = \dfrac{5}{9}$ and $\tan \beta = \dfrac{1}{2}$. Also since at N, the man sees the flag, the points N, D, Q are in a straight line.

Now $\dfrac{1}{2} = \tan \beta = \dfrac{AD}{AM} = \dfrac{AD}{200}$

or $AD = 100 = OP$ ∴ $h = OP = 100$.   ...(1)

∴ $AD = AN = 100$
so that $\angle AND = \angle NDA = 45°$
Hence also $\angle QDP = 45°$ so that $\angle DQP = 45°$

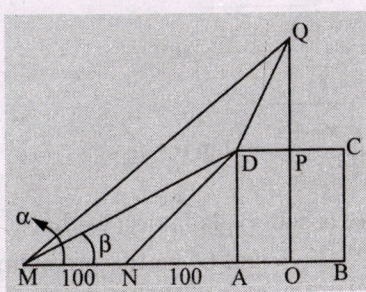

Fig. 105

Therefore $PD = PQ$ or $\dfrac{a}{2} = b$.

Again $\dfrac{5}{9} = \tan\alpha = \dfrac{OQ}{OM} = \dfrac{h+b}{200+\dfrac{a}{2}} = \dfrac{100+b}{200+b}$

by (1) and (2)

or $1000 + 5b = 900 + 9b$ or $b = 25$

and so $a = 2b = 50$.

Hence height of tower = 100 metres, side of square base = 50 metrs and height of the flag staff = 25 metres.

27. Let $PQ = h$ represent the flag staff on the top of a pyramid of height $OP = p$, say. Elevation of the sum is the angle $QLO = \alpha$. The base of the pyramid is square $ABCD$. It is given that $CL = x$ and $BL = y$ so that side of the square is $x + y$. Now from $\Delta\,OLQ$.

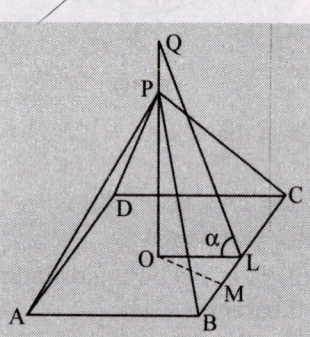

Fig. 106

$OL = OQ\cot\alpha$

or $OL = (OP + PQ)\cot\alpha$

$= (p + h)\cot\alpha$ ...(1)

If OM is perpendicular on BC, then

$\angle OML = 90°$

and $OM = MC = \dfrac{x+y}{2}$ so that $LM = MC - CL$

or $LM = \dfrac{x+y}{2} - x = \dfrac{y-x}{2}$.

Finally from $\Delta\,OML$,

$OL^2 = OM^2 + ML^2$

or $OL^2 \left(\dfrac{x+y}{2}\right)^2 + \left(\dfrac{y-x}{2}\right)^2 = \dfrac{x^2+y^2}{2}$

$\therefore$ $(p+h)^2 \cot^2\alpha = \dfrac{x^2+y^2}{2}$

or $p + h = \sqrt{\left(\dfrac{x^2+y^2}{2}\right)}\tan\alpha$

or $p = \sqrt{\left(\dfrac{x^2+y^2}{2}\right)}\tan\alpha - h$

28. (a) Figure is self-explanatory; we have,

Let P', Q', R' and O' be the projections of P, Q, R and O in the base of the tower.

$AP' = AR' = h\cot 45° = h$

and $AQ' = h\cot 60° = \dfrac{h}{\sqrt{3}}$.

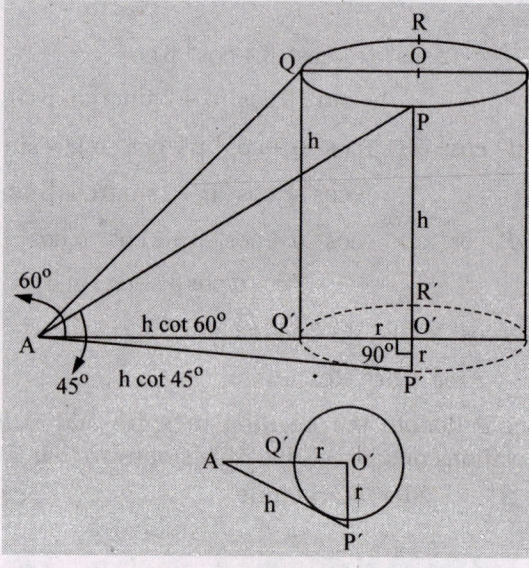

Fig. 107

Now in $\angle\,AO'P'$, we have

$AO' = AQ' + Q'O' = \dfrac{h}{\sqrt{(3)}} + r$,

$O'P' = r$, $AP' = h$ and $\angle\,AO'P' = 90°$

Hence $O'A^2 + O'P'^2 = AP'^2$

$\therefore$ $\left(\dfrac{h}{\sqrt{(3)}} + r\right)^2 + r^2 = h^2$

or $h^2 - \sqrt{3}\,hr - 3r^2 = 0$.

$\therefore$ $h = \dfrac{\sqrt{3}\,r \pm \sqrt{3r^2 + 12r^2}}{2}$

or $\dfrac{h}{2} = \dfrac{\sqrt{3} + \sqrt{15}}{2} = \dfrac{\sqrt{3}\,(\sqrt{5}+1)}{2}$.

[**Note** : that here, we rejected – ive sign since h and r are positive quantities].

(b) Let ABC be isosceles triangle mounted on the pole PD and O be the position of the man on the

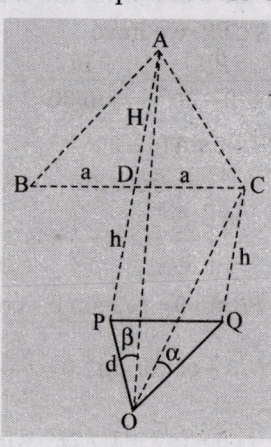

Fig. 108

ground so that $OP = d$. Let $BC = 2a$ and the height $AD = H$. Angles α and β are the angles subtended by the vertex C and A at O respectively. (see that figure). CO is parallel to DP so that $CQ = h$ and then $PQ = a$.

Now $d = PO = (h + H) \cot \beta$.

or $\quad H = d \tan \beta - h$.

Also $OQ = h \cot \alpha$. Also from right angled $\triangle OPQ$, we have

$$A = PQ = \sqrt{OQ^2 - OP^2} = \sqrt{h^2 \cot^2 \alpha - d^2}$$

Hence are of $\triangle ABC = \dfrac{1}{2} BC \cdot AD = aH$

$$= (d \tan \beta - h) \sqrt{h^2 \cot^2 \alpha - d^2}$$

29. Let $ABCD$, $A'B'C'D'$ represent the tower on square base $ABCD$. since the elevations of B' and D' at O are the same each equal to $45°$, it follows that the position O of the observer must be on the diagonal CA of the base produced. The elevation of A' at O is $60°$. Then from the figure it is clear that

$$OA = h \cot 60° = \dfrac{h}{\sqrt{3}}$$

and $\quad OB = OD = h \cot 45° = h$.

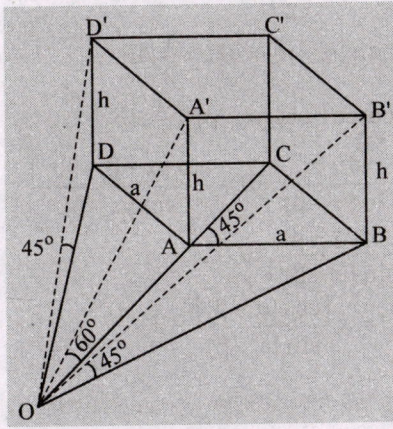

Fig. 109

Also $\angle OAB = 135°$

Hence from $\triangle OAB$, we have

$$OB^2 = OA^2 + AB^2 - 2 \cdot OA \cdot AB \cos 135°$$

or $\quad h^2 = \dfrac{h^2}{3} + a^2 - 2 \left(\dfrac{h}{\sqrt{3}} \right) \cdot a \left(\dfrac{-1}{\sqrt{2}} \right)$

or $\quad 2h^2 - \sqrt{6} ah - 3a^2 = 0$.

$\therefore \quad h = \dfrac{\sqrt{6}a \pm \sqrt{6a^2 + 24a^2}}{4}$ or $\dfrac{h}{a} = \dfrac{\sqrt{6}(\sqrt{5} + 1)}{4}$.

rejecting the negative sign.

30. PQ is a tower of height h subtending an angle of $30°$ both at A and B where $AB = a$ and an angle of $60°$ at C where $BC = \dfrac{5a}{3}$ and BC is at right angles to AB

$h = AQ \tan 30°$ and also

$h = BQ \tan 30°$.

$\therefore \quad AQ = BQ = h\sqrt{3}$ i.e., $\triangle ABQ$ is isosceles.

Also $h = CQ \tan 60°$ $\quad \therefore \quad CQ = \dfrac{h}{\sqrt{(3)}}$

Also $AM = MB = \dfrac{a}{2} = CL$

and $BC = LM = \dfrac{5a}{3}$.

Now $QM^2 = BQ^2 - BM^2 = 3h^2 - \dfrac{a^2}{4}$

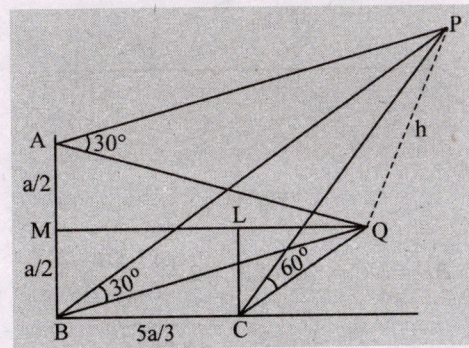

Fig. 110

from right angled $\triangle MBQ$.

$$QL^2 = CQ^2 - LC^2 = \dfrac{h^2}{3} - \dfrac{a^2}{4}$$

from right angled $\triangle LCQ$.

$$QM = QL + LM$$

$\therefore \quad \sqrt{\left(3h^2 - \dfrac{a^2}{4} \right)} - \sqrt{\left(\dfrac{h^2}{3} - \dfrac{a^2}{4} \right)} = \dfrac{5a}{3}$. ...(1)

Apply $L - M$ method.

$$\left(3h^2 - \dfrac{a^2}{4} \right) - \left(\dfrac{h^2}{3} - \dfrac{a^2}{4} \right) = \dfrac{8h^2}{3}$$ ...(2)

Dividing (1) and (2), we get

$$\sqrt{\left(3h^2 - \dfrac{a^2}{4} \right)} + \sqrt{\left(\dfrac{h^2}{3} - \dfrac{a^2}{4} \right)} = \dfrac{8h^2}{5a}$$ ...(3)

Subtracting (3) and (1), we get

$$2 \sqrt{\left(\dfrac{h^2}{4} - \dfrac{a^2}{4} \right)} = \dfrac{8h^2}{5a} - \dfrac{5a}{3}.$$

Squaring $4 \cdot \dfrac{(4h^2 - 3a^2)}{12} = \dfrac{(24h^2 - 25a^2)^2}{225 \, a^2}$

$75(4h^2 - 3a^2) = 576 \, h^4 - 1200 \, a^2h^2 + 625 \, a^4$

or $\quad 576 \, h^4 - 1500 \, a^2h^2 + 850 \, a^2 = 0$. Cancel 2

or $\quad 288 \, h^4 - 750 \, a^2h^2 + 425 \, a^4 = 0$

or $\quad 288 \, h^4 - 510 \, a^2h^2 - 240 \, a^2h^2 + 425 \, a^4 = 0$

or $\quad 6h^2(48h^2 - 85a^2) - 5a^2(48h^2 - 85a^2) = 0$

or $(48h^2 - 85a^2)(6h^2 - 5a^2) = 0$.

∴ $h = \sqrt{\left(\dfrac{85}{48}\right)} a$ or $\sqrt{\left(\dfrac{5}{6}\right)} a$

31. The figure is self-explanatory. In $\triangle ADC$, we have

$\angle ADC = 40° + 90° = 130°$

and $\angle DCA = 25°$

∴ $\angle DAC = 180° - (130° + 25°) = 25°$

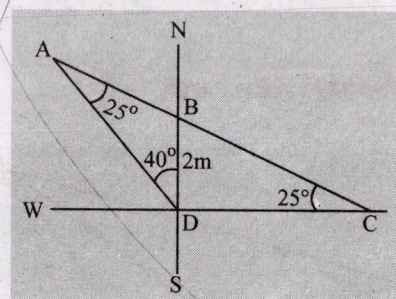

Fig. 111

Hence $AD = DC = 2 \cot 25° = 2 \cdot \dfrac{\sqrt{1 - \sin^2 25°}}{\sin 25°}$

$= 2 \cdot \dfrac{\sqrt{1 - 0.423^2}}{0.423} = \dfrac{2\sqrt{.82171}}{0.423}$

$= \dfrac{2 \times .906}{0.423} = \dfrac{1.812}{0.423} = 4.283$ km.

32. Let PQ represent the tower in a hill OP and A, B the points of observation on the ground. Since PQ subtends the same angle at A and B, the four point Q, P, A and B are concyclic. Since angle of elevation of Q at A and B are respectively α and β, we have

$\angle QAO = \alpha$ and $\angle QBO = \beta$ so that

$\angle BQA = (\alpha - \beta)$

Let C be the centre of circle.

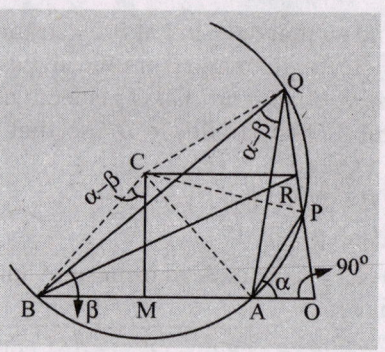

Fig. 112

Now draw CM and CR perpendiculars to the chords AN and PQ so that $AM = BM = \dfrac{1}{2} AB$

and $PR = QR = \dfrac{1}{2} PQ$. Join CA, CB, CP and CQ.

Now $\angle ACB = 2 \angle AQB = 2(\alpha - \beta)$.

Hence $\angle ACM = \angle BCM = \alpha - \beta$.

If $\angle PBQ = \theta$, then $\angle PCQ = 2\theta$

so that $\angle PCR = \angle QCR = \theta$.

We have $\beta = 90° - \alpha + \theta$

so that $\theta = \alpha + \beta - 90°$

Now $BC = CQ = \left(\dfrac{x}{2}\right) \operatorname{cosec} \theta$ where $PQ = x$.

Then $BC \sin(\alpha - \beta) = BM = \dfrac{1}{2} AB$.

or $\left(\dfrac{x}{2}\right) \operatorname{cosec} \theta \sin(\alpha - \beta) = \dfrac{1}{2} AB$

or $x = \dfrac{\sin \theta}{\sin(\alpha - \beta)} AB = \dfrac{\sin(\alpha + \beta - 90°)}{\sin(\alpha - \beta)} AB$

$= -\dfrac{\cos(\alpha + \beta)}{\sin(\alpha - \beta)} AB$.

Hence $PQ = x \dfrac{|\cos(\alpha - \beta)|}{\sin(\alpha - \beta)} AB$.

Problem Set (3)

MULTIPLE CHOICE QUESTIONS

1. The angle of elevation of the top of a tower from a point 20 metres away from its base is $45°$. The height of the tower is

(a) 10 m (b) 20 m (c) 40 m (d) $20\sqrt{3}$

2. At a point 15 metres away from the base of a 15 metres high house, the angle of elevation of the top is

(a) $45°$ (b) $30°$ (c) $60°$ (d) $90°$

3. From the top of a light house 60 m high with its base at sea level the angle of depression of a boat is $15°$. The distance of the boat from the light house is

(a) $\left(\dfrac{\sqrt{3}-1}{\sqrt{3}+1}\right) 60$ m (b) $\left(\dfrac{\sqrt{3}+1}{\sqrt{3}-1}\right) 60$ m

(c) $\left(\dfrac{\sqrt{3}-1}{\sqrt{3}+1}\right)^2$ m (d) None

4. The angle of elevation of the sun when the length of the shadow of a pole is $\sqrt{3}$ times the height of the pole is

(a) $30°$ (b) $45°$ (c) $60°$ (d) $15°$

5. The angle of elevation of the top of an incomplete vertical pillar at horizontal distance 100 m from its base is $45 ⊃$. If the angle of elevation of the top of the complete pillar at the same point is to be $60°$, then the height of the incomplete pillar is to be increased by

(a) $50\sqrt{2}$ m (b) 100 m

(c) $100(\sqrt{3}-1)$ m (d) $100(\sqrt{3}+1)$ m

6. The angle of elevation of the top of a T.V. tower from three points A, B, C in a straight line in the horizontal plane through the foot of the tower are α, 2α, 3α respectively. If $AB = a$, the height of the tower is
   (a) $a \tan \alpha$
   (b) $a \sin \alpha$
   (c) $a \sin 2\alpha$
   (d) $a \sin 3\alpha$

7. The angle of elevation of the top of a certain tower from a point A on the ground is α, at B is 2α and at C is 3α. If $AB = \frac{4}{3} BC$ then which of the following is true
   (a) $\sin \alpha = \sqrt{\frac{5}{12}}$
   (b) $\cos \alpha = \sqrt{\frac{5}{12}}$
   (c) $\sin \alpha = \frac{3}{4}$
   (d) $\cos \alpha = \frac{3}{8}$

8. The angles of depression of two points A and B on a horizontal plane such that $AB = 200$ from the top P of a tower PQ of height 100 are $45° - \theta$ and $45° + \theta$. If the line AB passess through Q the foot of the tower, then angle θ is equal to
   (a) $45°$
   (b) $30°$
   (c) $22 \cdot 5°$
   (d) $15°$

9. An aeroplane flying at a height 300 metres above the ground passes vertically above another plane at an instant when the angles of elevation of the two planes from the same point on the ground are $60°$ and $45°$ respectively. Then the height of the lower plane from the ground in metres is
   (a) $100\sqrt{3}$
   (b) $100 / \sqrt{3}$
   (c) 50
   (d) $150 (\sqrt{3} + 1)$

   (B.I.T. Ranchi 1993)

10. $ABCD$ is a square plot. The angle of elevation of the top of a pole standing at D from A or C is $30 \supset$ and that from B is θ, then $\tan \theta$ is equal to
    (a) $\sqrt{6}$
    (b) $1 / \sqrt{6}$
    (c) $\sqrt{3} / 2$
    (d) $\sqrt{2} / 3$

11. A tree is broken by wind, its upper part touches the ground at a point 10 metres from the foot of the tree and makes an angle of $45°$ with the ground. The entire length of the tree is
    (a) 15 m
    (b) 20 m
    (c) $10 (1 + \sqrt{2})$ m
    (d) $10 (1 + \sqrt{3} / 2)$ m

    (B.I.T. Ranchi 1992)

12. **(A)** The angle of elevation of the top of a tower standing on a horizontal plane from a point A is α. After walking a distance d towards the foot of the tower, the angle of elevation is found to be β. The height of the tower is
    (a) $\dfrac{d \sin \alpha \sin \beta}{\sin (\beta - \alpha)}$
    (b) $\dfrac{d \sin \alpha \sin \beta}{\sin (\alpha - \beta)}$
    (c) $\dfrac{d \sin (\beta - \alpha)}{\sin \alpha \sin \beta}$
    (d) $\dfrac{d \sin (\alpha - \beta)}{\sin \alpha \sin \beta}$

(B) AB is a vertical pole with B at the ground level and A at the top. A man finds that the angle of elevation of the point A from a certain point C on the ground is $60°$. He moves away from the pole along the line BC to a point D such that $CD = 7$ m. From D the angle of elevation of the point A is $45°$. Then the height of the pole is :
(a) $\dfrac{7\sqrt{3}}{2} \cdot \dfrac{1}{\sqrt{3} - 1}$ m
(b) $\dfrac{7\sqrt{3}}{2} \cdot (\sqrt{3} + 1)$ m
(c) $\dfrac{7\sqrt{3}}{2} \cdot (\sqrt{3} - 1)$ m
(d) $\dfrac{7\sqrt{3}}{2} \cdot \dfrac{1}{\sqrt{3} + 1}$ m

(AIEEE 2008)

13. A man from the top of a 100 metre high tower sees a car moving towards the tower at an angle of depression of $30°$. After some time, the angle of depression becomes $60°$. The distance (in metre) travelled by the car during this time is
    (a) $100\sqrt{3}$
    (b) $\dfrac{200\sqrt{3}}{3}$
    (c) $\dfrac{100\sqrt{3}}{3}$
    (d) $200\sqrt{3}$

    (I.I.T. Sc. 2001)

14. At a point on a level plane a tower subtends an angle θ and a flag staff a ft. in length at the top of the tower subtends an angle ϕ. The height of the tower is
    (a) $\dfrac{a \sin \theta \cos \phi}{\cos (\theta + \phi)}$
    (b) $\dfrac{a \sin \phi \cos (\theta + \phi)}{\sin \theta}$
    (c) $\dfrac{a \cos (\theta + \phi)}{\sin \theta \sin \phi}$
    (d) None

15. A vertical pole PS has two marks at Q and R such that the portions PQ, PR and PS subtend angles α, β, γ at a point on the ground distant x from the pole. If $PQ = a$, $PR = b$, $PS = c$ and $\alpha + \beta + \gamma = 180°$, then $x^2 =$
    (a) $\dfrac{a}{a + b + c}$
    (b) $\dfrac{b}{a + b + c}$
    (c) $\dfrac{c}{a + b + c}$
    (d) $\dfrac{abc}{a + b + c}$

16. The shadow of a tower is found to be 60 ft. longer when the sun's altitude has become $60°$ from $30°$. The height of the tower from the ground is
    (a) 350 ft. app.
    (b) 400 ft. app.
    (c) 51 ft. app.
    (d) None

17. An observer standing on a 300 m high tower observes two boats in the same direction; their angle of depression are $60°$ and $30°$ respectively. The distance between the boats is
    (a) $173 \cdot 2$ m
    (b) $346 \cdot 4$ m
    (c) 25 m
    (d) 72 m

18. The angle of elevation of the top of two vertical towers as seen from the middle point of the line joining the

foot of the towers are $60°$ and $30°$ respectively. The ratio of the heights of the tower is

(a) $2:1$ (b) $\sqrt{3}:1$ (c) $3:2$ (d) $3:1$

19. Two towers stand on a horizontal plane. P and Q where $PQ = 30$ m, are two points on the line joining their feet. As seen from P the angle of elevation of the tops of the towers are $30°$ and $60°$ but as seen from Q are $60°$ and $45°$. The distance between the towers is equal to

(a) $15(4+\sqrt{3})$ m   (b) $15(4-\sqrt{3})$ m

(c) $15(3+\sqrt{3})$ m   (d) $15(2+\sqrt{3})$ m

20. Two vertical poles AP and BQ of heights h and H subtend the same angle $45°$ at a point C on the line AB joining their feet. Then the square of the distance between their tops i.e. PQ^2 is given by

(a) $(h+H)^2$ (b) $2(h^2+H^2)$

(c) h^2+H^2 (d) $\dfrac{1}{2}(h^2+H^2)$

21. Two verticals AL and BM of heights 20 m and 80 m respectively and stand apart on a horizontal plane. If A, B be the feet of the poles and AM and BL intersect at P, then the height of P is equal to

(a) 50 m   (b) 18 m   (c) 16 m   (d) 15 m

22. Angle of depression from the top of a light house of two boats are $45°$ and $30°$ due east which are 60 m apart. The height of the light house is

(a) $60\sqrt{3}$ (b) $30(\sqrt{3}+1)$

(c) $30(\sqrt{3}-1)$ (d) None

23. PQ is a part of a given height a and AB is a tower at some distance, α and β are the angles of elevation of B, the top of the tower at P and Q respectively. The height of the tower is

(a) $\dfrac{a \sin\alpha \sin\beta}{\sin(\alpha-\beta)}$ (b) $\dfrac{a \cos\alpha \cos\beta}{\sin(\alpha-\beta)}$

(c) $\dfrac{a \sin\alpha \cos\beta}{\sin(\alpha-\beta)}$ (d) None

24. A ladder rests against a wall at an angle α to the horizontal. Its foot is pulled away from the wall through a distance a so that it slides a distance b down the wall making an angle β with the horizontal, then

(a) $a=b \tan\dfrac{\alpha+\beta}{2}$ (b) $a=b \cot\dfrac{\alpha+\beta}{2}$

(c) $a \tan\dfrac{\alpha-\beta}{2}$ (d) None

25. A man on a cliff observes a boat at an angle of depression $30°$ which is sailing towards the shore to the point immediately beneath him. Three minutes later the angle of depression of the boat is found to be

$60°$. Assuming that the boat sails at a uniform speed, it will now reach the shore in

(a) 2 minutes   (b) $1\dfrac{1}{2}$ minutes

(c) 1 minute   (d) None

26. A chimney 20 metres high standing on the top of a building subtends an angle whose tangent is 1/6 at a distance 70 metres from the foot of the building. The height of the building is

(a) 50 m   (b) 40 m   (c) 60 m   (d) None

27. If a flag-staff subtends the same angle at the points A, B, C, D on the horizontal plane through the foot of the flag-staff, then A, B, C, D are the vertices of a

(a) square   (b) cyclic quadrilateral

(c) rectangle   (d) none of these

28. PQ is a vertical tower. P is the foot, Q the top of the tower, A, B, C are three points in the horizontal plane through P. The angles of elevation of Q from A, B, C are equal and each is equal to θ. The sides of the triangle ABC are a, b, c and the area of the triangle ABC is Δ. The height of the tower is

(a) $(abc) \tan\theta / 4\Delta$ (b) $(abc) \cot\theta / 4\Delta$

(c) $(abc) \sin\theta / 4\Delta$ (d) None

29. A pole stands at the centre of a rectangular field and it subtends angles of $15°$ and $45°$ at the mid- points of the sides of the field. If the length of its diagonal is 1200 m, then the height of the flag staff is

(a) 400 m   (b) 200 m

(c) $300\sqrt{2+\sqrt{3}}$ m   (d) $300\sqrt{2-\sqrt{3}}$ m

30. A pole stands vertically inside a triangular park $\Delta\,ABC$. If the angle of elevation of the top of the pole from each corner of the park is same, then in $\Delta\,ABC$ the foot of the pole is at the

(a) centroid   (b) circumcentre

(c) incentre   (d) orthocentre

(I.I.T. Sc. 2000)

31. **(A)** A and B are two points in the horizontal plane through O, the foot of a pillar OP of height h such that $\angle AOB = \theta$. If the elevation of the top of the pillar from A and B are also equal to θ, then AB is equal to

(a) $h \cot\theta$ (b) $h \cos\theta \sec\dfrac{\theta}{2}$

(c) $h \cot\theta \sin\dfrac{\theta}{2}$ (d) $h \cos\theta \operatorname{cosec}\dfrac{\theta}{2}$

(B) A tower stands at the centre of a circular park. A and B are two points on the boundary of the park such that $AB\,(=a)$ subtends an angle $60°$ at the foot of the tower, and the angle of elevation of the top of the tower from A or B is $30°$. The height of the tower is :

(a) $\dfrac{2a}{\sqrt{3}}$ (b) $2a\sqrt{3}$

(c) $\dfrac{a}{\sqrt{3}}$ (d) $a\sqrt{3}$

(AIEEE 2007)

32. A flag-staff 20 m long standing on a wall 10 m high subtends an angle whose tangent is 0·5 at a point on the ground. If θ is the angle subtended by the wall at this point, then

(a) $\tan\theta = 1$ (b) $\tan\theta = 1/3$

(c) $\tan\theta = 3$ (d) $\tan\theta = 1/2$

33. A tower subtends an angle of 30° at a point on the same level as the foot of the tower. At a second point h metre above the first, the depression of the foot of the tower is 60°. The horizontal distance of the tower from the point is

(a) $h\cot 60^\circ$ (b) $\dfrac{1}{3}h\cot 30^\circ$

(c) $\dfrac{h}{3}\cot 60^\circ$ (d) $h\cot 30^\circ$

34. The angle of elevation of the top of the tower observed from each of the three points A, B, C on the ground, forming a triangle is the same angle α. If R is the circum-radius of the $\Delta\,ABC$, then the height of the tower is

(a) $R\sin\alpha$ (b) $R\cos\alpha$ (c) $R\cot\alpha$ (d) $R\tan\alpha$

35. A flag-staff 5 m high stands on a building 25 m high. To an observer at a height of 30 m the flag-staff and the building subtend equal angles. The distance of the observer from the top of the flag-staff is

(a) $\dfrac{5\sqrt{3}}{2}$ (b) $5\sqrt{\dfrac{3}{2}}$

(c) $5\sqrt{\dfrac{2}{3}}$ (d) none of these

(EAMCET 1993)

36. From the top of a cliff of height a the angle of depression of the foot of a certain tower is found to be double the angle of elevation of the top of the tower of height h. If θ be the angle of elevation then its value is

(a) $\cos^{-1}\sqrt{\dfrac{2h}{a}}$ (b) $\sin^{-1}\sqrt{\dfrac{2h}{a}}$

(c) $\sin^{-1}\sqrt{\dfrac{a}{2-h}}$ (d) $\tan^{-1}\sqrt{3-\dfrac{2h}{a}}$

37. If a flag-staff 6 metres high placed on the top of a tower throws a shadow of $2\sqrt{3}$ m along the ground, then the angle (in degrees) that the sun makes with the ground is

(a) 60° (b) 30°

(c) 45° (d) none of these

(EAMCET 1990)

38. The top of a hill observed from the top and bottom of a building of height h is at angles of elevation α and β respectively. The height of the hill is

(a) $\dfrac{h\cot\beta}{\cot\beta - \cot\alpha}$ (b) $\dfrac{h\cot\alpha}{\cot\alpha - \cot\beta}$

(c) $\dfrac{h\tan\alpha}{\tan\alpha - \tan\beta}$ (d) none of these

39. The angles of elevation of a cliff at a point A on the ground and a point B, 100 m vertically above A are α and β respectively. The height of the cliff is

(a) $\dfrac{100\cot\alpha}{\cot\alpha - \cot\beta}$ (b) $\dfrac{100\cot\beta}{\cot\alpha - \cot\beta}$

(c) $\dfrac{100\cot\beta}{\cot\beta - \cot\alpha}$ (d) $\dfrac{100\cot\beta}{\cot\beta + \cot\alpha}$

40. The angle of elevation of a cloud from a point h m above the level of water in a lake is α and the angle of depression of its reflection in the lake is β. Then the height of the cloud above the water level is

(a) $\dfrac{h\sin(\beta-\alpha)}{\sin(\beta+\alpha)}$ (b) $\dfrac{h\sin(\beta+\alpha)}{\sin(\beta-\alpha)}$

(c) $\dfrac{h\sin(\alpha+\beta)}{\sin(\alpha-\beta)}$ (d) none of these

41. On the level ground the angle of elevation of the top of a tower is 30°. On moving 20 m nearer the tower, the angle of elevation is found to be 60°. The height of the tower is

(a) 10 m   (b) 20 m

(c) $10\sqrt{3}$ m   (d) none of these

(C.E.E. Andhra 1984)

42. A person standing on the bank of a river observes that the angle subtended by a tree on the opposite bank is 60°; when he retires 40 metres from the bank he finds the angle to be 30°. Then the breadth of the river is

(a) 40 m   (b) 60 m   (c) 20 m   (d) 30 m

(AIEEE 2004)

43. A tower subtends an angle α at a point in the plane of its base and the angle of depression of the foot the tower at a point b metres just above A is β. The height of the tower is

(a) $b\tan\alpha\cot\beta$ (b) $b\cot\alpha\tan\beta$

(c) $b\tan\alpha\tan\beta$ (d) $b\cot\alpha\cot\beta$

(P.E.T. Raj. 1990)

44. From an aeroplane vertically over a straight horizontal road, the angles of depression of two consecutive milestones on opposite sides of the aeroplane are observed to be α and β. The height of the aeroplane above the road is

(a) $\dfrac{\tan\alpha + \tan\beta}{\tan\alpha\tan\beta}$ (b) $\dfrac{\tan\alpha\tan\beta}{\tan\alpha + \tan\beta}$

(c) $\dfrac{\cot\alpha\cot\beta}{\cot\alpha+\cot\beta}$　　　(d) none of these

45. ABC is an equilateral triangle of side a with centre at O. OP is a tower of height h and each side of the triangle subtends an angle of $60°$ at P the top of the tower, then
   (a) $3a^2 = h^2$ 　　　　(b) $a^2 = 3h^2$
   (c) $2a^2 = 3h^2$ 　　　(d) $3a^2 = 2h^2$

46. ABC is a triangular park in the form of an equilateral triangle. A pillar at A subtends an angle of $45°$. If θ be the angle of elevation of the pillar at D, the middle point of BC, then $\tan\theta =$
   (a) $\dfrac{\sqrt{3}}{2}$ 　　　　(b) $\dfrac{2}{\sqrt{3}}$
   (c) $\sqrt{3}$ 　　　　　(d) $\dfrac{1}{\sqrt{3}}$

47. Each side of a square $ABCD$ subtends an angle of $60°$ at the top of a tower of height h standing at the centre of a square. If a be the length of the side of the square, then
   (a) $3a^2 = 2h^2$ 　　　　(b) $2a^2 = 3h^2$
   (c) $2h^2 = a^2$ 　　　　(d) $h^2 = 2a^2$

48. AB is a vertical pole. The end A is on the level ground. C is middle point of AB and P is a point on the level ground. The portion CB subtends an angle β at P. If $AP = n\,AB$, then $\tan\beta =$
   (a) $\dfrac{n}{n^2 - 1}$ 　　　　(b) $\dfrac{n}{n^2 + 1}$
   (c) $\dfrac{n}{2n^2 + 1}$ 　　　(d) none

TRUE AND FALSE

1. The angle of elevation of a stationary cloud from a point 2500 m above a lake is $15°$ and the angle of depression of its reflection in the lake is $45°$. The height of the cloud above lake level is $2500\sqrt{3}$ metres.

2. From a light house the angle of depression of two ships on opposite sides of the light house are observed to be $30°$ and $45°$. If the height of the light house be 100 metres, then the distance between the ships of the line joining them passes through the foot of the light house is $100(\sqrt{3} - 1)$.

3. From the top of a spire the angle of depression of the top and bottom of a tower of height h are θ and ϕ respectively. Then the height of the spire and its horizontal distance from the tower are respectively $\dfrac{h\cos\theta\sin\phi}{\sin(\theta+\phi)}$ and $\dfrac{h\cos\theta\cos\phi}{\sin(\theta+\phi)}$

4. The angular depression of the top and foot of a chimney as seen from the top of a second chimney which is 150 metres high and standing on the same level as the first are θ and ϕ respectively. If $\tan\theta = 4/3$ and $\tan\phi = 5/2$, then the distance between tops is 50 metres.

5. The height of a house subtends a right angle at the opposite window. The angle of elevation of the window from the base of the house is $60°$. If the width of the road be 6 metres, then the height of the house is $8\sqrt{3}$ m.

6. A vertical tower stands on a horizontal plane and is surmounted by a vertical flag staff of height h. At a point P on the plane, the angle of elevation of the bottom of the flag staff is β and that of the top is α, then the height of the tower is
   $$\dfrac{h\tan\beta}{\tan\alpha\tan\beta}.$$

7. A ladder 20 ft. long reaches a point 20 ft. below the top of a flag. The angle of elevation of the top of the flag at the foot of the ladder is $60°$. The height of the flag is 30 ft.

8. The angle of elevation of the top of a tower which is incomplete at a point 120 ft. from its base is $45°$. If the elevation at the same point of the top is desired to be $60°$ then the tower should be raised by $120(\sqrt{3} - 1)$ ft.

9. A ladder leaning against a vertical wall is inclined at an angle α to the horizontal. The top of the ladder touches the parapet. On moving its foot a feet away from the wall, the ladder now stands inclined at an angle β to the horizon and its top now touching a window. Then the distance of the parapet from the window is
   $$a\cot\dfrac{\alpha+\beta}{2}$$

10. A vertical tower 50 ft. high stands on a sloping ground. The foot of the tower is at the same level as the middle part of a vertical flag pole. From the top of the tower the angle of depression of the top and bottom of the pole are $15°$ and $45°$ respectively. Then the length of the pole is $100\sqrt{3}$.

11. Two pillars of height a and b subtend the same angle α at a point on the line joining their feet. If the pillars subtend angles β and γ at another point in the horizontal plane at which the line joining their feet subtends a right angle then
   $$(a+b)\cot^2\alpha = a^2\cot^2\beta + b^2\cot^2\gamma$$

FILL IN THE BLANKS

1. The angle of elevation of a cloud from a point x feet above a lake is θ and the angle of depression of its reflection in the lake is ϕ then its height is ....

2. The width of a road is b feet. On one side of which there is a window h feet high. A building in front of it subtends an angle θ at it, then the height of the building is ....

3. The angle of elevation of the top of a pillar at any point A on the ground is 15°. On walking 100 ft. towards the pillar, the angle becomes 30°. Height of the pillar and its distance from A are .... and .... respectively.

4. The angle of elevation of the top of a tower from a point on the same level as the foot of the tower is 30°. On advancing 150 metres towards the foot of the tower the angle of elevation increases to 60°. The height of the tower is ....

5. The angle of elevation of the top of a tower at a point A on the ground is 30°. On walking 20 metres towards the tower, the angle of elevation is 60°. The height of the tower and its distance from A are .... and ....

6. The height of a chimney when it is found that on walking towards it 100 ft. in a horizontal line through its base the angular elevation of its top changes from 30° to 45° is ....

7. The shadow of a tower standing on a level ground is found to be 60 metres longer when the sun's altitude is 30° than when it is 45°. The height of the tower is ....

8. A man in a boat rowed away from a cliff 150 metres high takes 2 minutes to change the angle from 60° to 45°. The speed of the boat is ....

9. An aeroplane is flying horizontally 1 km above the ground is observed at an elevation of 60°. If after 10 seconds the elevation is observed to be 30°, the uniform speed of the aeroplane is ....

10. The angle of elevation of the top and bottom of a flag staff fixed at the top of a tower at a point distant a ft. from the foot of the tower are α and β. The height of the tower is ....

11. From the top of a cliff 200 ft. high, the angles of depression of the top and bottom of a tower are observed to be 30° and 60° respectively. The height of the tower is ....

12. A balloon moving in a straight line passes vertically above two points A and B on a horizontal plane 1000 ft. apart; when above A it has an altitude of 60° as seen from B when above B it has an altitude of 45° as seen from A. The distance of A from the point at which it will touch the plane is ....

13. A balloon moving in a straight line passes vertically above two points A and B on a horizontal plane 1000 ft. apart. When above A it has an altitude of 60° as seen from B and when above B 30° as seen from A. The distance from A of the point at which it will touch the plane is ....

14. A vertical pole (more than 100 ft. high) consists of two portions the lower being $\frac{1}{3}$rd of the whole. If the upper portion subtends an angle $\tan^{-1}\frac{1}{2}$ at a point in a horizontal plane through the foot of the pole and distance 40 ft. from it, then the height of the pole is ....

15. The angles of elevation of the top of a tower standing on a horizontal plane from two points on a line passing through the foot of the tower at distances a and b respectively are complementry angles. If the line joining the two points subtend an angle θ at the top of the tower then $h = $ .... and $\sin \theta = $ ....

16. A tower is b ft. high having a flag staff at its top. The tower and the flag staff subtend equal angles at a point distant a feet from the foot of the tower. Then the length of flag staff is ....

17. A wireless pole 25 metres high is fixed on a top of a verandah of a house which is 15 metres high. At a point R on the ground, directly opposite, the wireless pole and verandah subtend equal angles. The distance of R from the verandah is ....

18. A round balloon of radius r subtends an angle α at the eye of the observer, while the angle of elevation of its centre is β. The height of the centre of the balloon is ....

19. A stationary balloon is observed from three points A, B and C on the plane ground and is found that its angle of elevation from each of these points is α. If $\angle ABC = \beta$ and $AC = b$, the height of the balloon is ....
   (Roorkee 1996)

20. From the top of a pole of height h, the angle of elevation of the top of the tower is α. The pole subtends an angle β at the top of the tower. The height of the tower is ....

21. A tower subtends an angle α at a point A in the plane of its base and the angle of depression of the foot of the tower at a point b ft. just above A is β. The height of the tower is ....
   (P.E.T. 1990)

Answers to Problem Set (3)

▶ **MULTIPLE CHOICE QUESTIONS**

1. (b)	**2.** (a)	**3.** (b)	**4.** (a)	**5.** (c)	**6.** (c)	**7.** (a)	**8.** (c)	**9.** (a)	**10.** (c)
11. (c)	**12. (A)** (a)	**(B)** (b)	**13.** (b)	**14.** (b)	**15.** (d)	**16.** (c)	**17.** (b)	**18.** (d)	**19.** (a)
20. (b)	**21.** (c)	**22.** (c)	**23.** (c)	**24.** (a)	**25.** (b)	**26.** (a)	**27.** (b)	**28.** (a)	**29.** (b)
30. (d)	**31. (A)** (b)	**(B)** (c)	**32.** (a, b)	**33.** (a, b)	**34.** (d)	**35.** (b)	**36.** (d)	**37.** (a)	**38.** (b)
39. (c)	**40.** (b)	**41.** (c)	**42.** (c)	**43.** (a)	**44.** (b)	**45.** (c)	**46** (b)	**47.** (c)	**48.** (c)

▶ **TRUE AND FALSE**

1. T	**2.** F	**3.** F	**4.** F	**5.** T	**6.** F	**7.** T	**8.** T	**9.** T	**10.** F
11. T	**12.** T								

▶ **FILL IN THE BLANKS**

1. $\dfrac{x \sin (\phi + \theta)}{\sin (\phi - \theta)}$ **2.** $\dfrac{(b^2 + h^2) \sin \theta}{b \cos \theta + h \sin \theta}$ **3.** $h = 50, d = 50 (2 + \sqrt{3})$ **4.** $75\sqrt{3}$ **5.** $10\sqrt{3}$

6. $50 (\sqrt{3} + 1)$ **7.** $30 (\sqrt{3} + 1)$ **8.** $\dfrac{150 (\cot 45^\circ - \cot 60^\circ)}{2}$ **9.** $240\sqrt{3}$ km/ h

10. $h = a (\tan \beta - \tan \alpha)$ **11.** $h \dfrac{400}{\sqrt{3}}$ **12.** $500\sqrt{3} (\sqrt{3} + 1)$ **13.** 500 ft   **14.** $h = 40$ ft

15. $h = \sqrt{ab}$ **16.** $\dfrac{b (a^2 + b^2)}{a^2 - b^2}$ **17.** 30 m   **18.** $r \operatorname{cosec} \dfrac{\alpha}{2} \sin \beta$ **19.** $\dfrac{b}{2 \sin \beta \cot \alpha}$

20. $\dfrac{h \sin \alpha \cos (\alpha - \beta)}{\sin \beta}$ **21.** $b \tan \alpha \cot \beta$

Hints/Solutions to Problem Set (3)

MULTIPLE CHOICE QUESTIONS

1. Ans. (b).

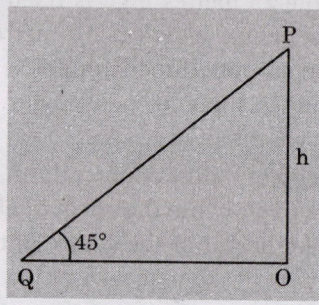

Fig. 113

$h = OQ \tan 45^\circ = 20$

2. Ans. (a).

$\tan \theta = \dfrac{15}{15} = 1 \quad \therefore \ \theta = 45^\circ$

3. Ans. (b).

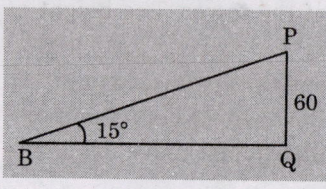

Fig. 114

$BQ = 60 \cot 15^\circ = 60 \tan 75^\circ$

$\qquad = 60 \tan (45^\circ + 30^\circ)$ etc.

4. Ans. (a).

$\tan \theta = \dfrac{h}{h\sqrt{3}} = \dfrac{1}{\sqrt{3}}$

$\therefore \quad \theta = 30^\circ$

5. Ans. (c).

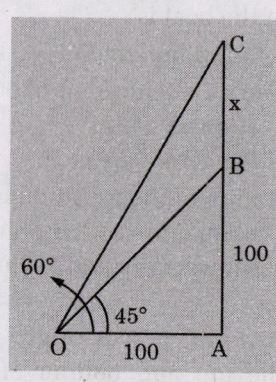

Fig. 115

$AB = 100 \tan 45^\circ = 100$

$\therefore \quad AC = (100 + x) = 100 \tan 60^\circ = 100\sqrt{3}$

$\therefore \quad x = 100 (\sqrt{3} - 1)$

6. Ans. (c).

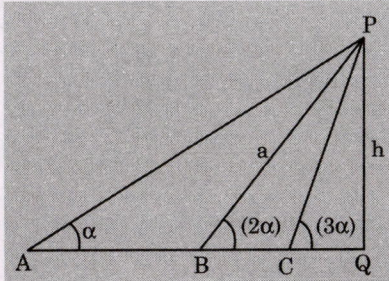

Fig. 116

$AB = a$

∴ $BP = a$ from isosceles △ ABP

∴ $h = BP \sin 2\alpha = a \sin 2\alpha$

7. Ans. (a).

From the figure it is clear that PB is bisector of ⊚APC and hence it divides the opposite side BC in the ratio of arms of the angle

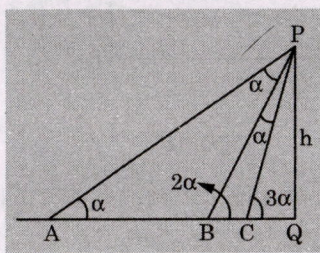

Fig. 117

$$\frac{AB}{BC} = \frac{AP}{PC} \quad \text{or} \quad \frac{4}{3} = \frac{h/\sin\alpha}{h/\sin 3\alpha} = \frac{\sin 3\alpha}{\sin \alpha}$$

or $\dfrac{4}{3} = \dfrac{3\sin\alpha - 4\sin^3\alpha}{\sin\alpha} = 3 - 4\sin^2\alpha$

or $4\sin^2\alpha = 3 - \dfrac{4}{3} = \dfrac{5}{3}$

∴ $\sin^2\alpha = \dfrac{5}{12} \Rightarrow \sin\alpha = \sqrt{\dfrac{5}{12}} \Rightarrow$ (a).

8. Ans. (c).

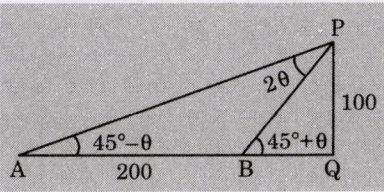

Fig. 118

$AB = 200 = AQ - BQ$

$200 = 100 \cot(45° - \theta) - 100\cot(45° + \theta)$

$200 = 100\left[\dfrac{1 + \tan\theta}{1 - \tan\theta} - \dfrac{1 - \tan\theta}{1 + \tan\theta}\right]$

$2 = \dfrac{4\tan\theta}{1 - \tan^2\theta} = 2\tan 2\theta$

∴ $\tan 2\theta = 1 = \tan 45°$

⇒ $2\theta = 45° \Rightarrow \theta = 22 \cdot 5° \Rightarrow$ (c).

9. Ans. (a).

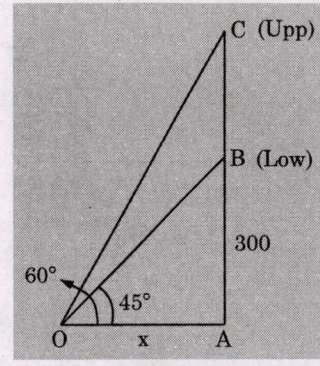

Fig. 119

B and C represent lower and upper planes such that $AC = 300$. At O the elevations of B and C are $45°$ and $60°$ respectively.

∴ $AB = OA \tan 45° = OA = x$, say

$AC = OA \tan 60°$

or $300 = x\sqrt{3} \qquad$ ∴ $x = 100\sqrt{3}$

10. Ans. (c).

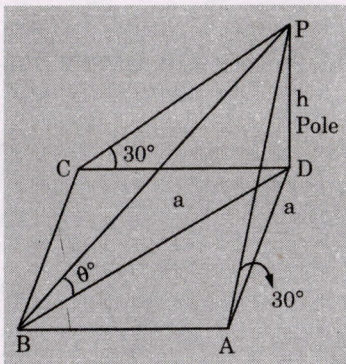

Fig. 120

$h = a \tan 30° = a/\sqrt{3}$ from △ PAD or △ PCD

$h = BD\tan\theta$

$\quad = \sqrt{(a^2 + a^2)}\tan\theta \qquad$ from △ PBD and

diagonal $BD = a\sqrt{2}$

or $\dfrac{a}{\sqrt{3}} = a\sqrt{2}\tan\theta \quad$ ∴ $\tan\theta = \dfrac{1}{\sqrt{6}}$

11. Ans. (c).

$AC = 10 = AB$

$BC = BC' = \sqrt{(10^2 + 10^2)} = 10\sqrt{2}$

∴ $AC = AB + BC = 10(\sqrt{2} + 1)$

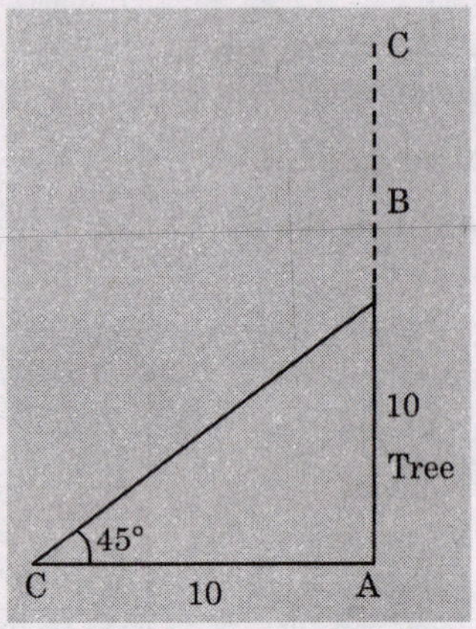

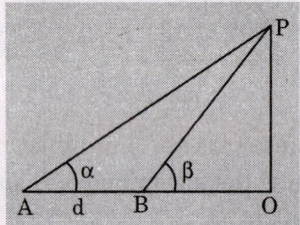

Fig. 121

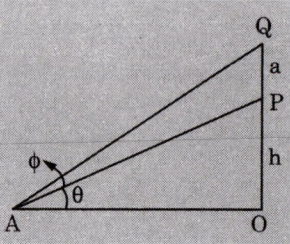

Fig. 124

$$\therefore \quad \frac{a}{h} = \frac{\tan(\theta + \phi) - \tan\phi}{\tan\phi}$$

$$\text{or} \quad \frac{a}{h} = \frac{\sin(\theta + \phi - \phi)}{\cos(\theta + \phi)\sin\phi} = \frac{\sin\theta}{\cos(\theta + \phi)\sin\phi}$$

12. (A) Ans. (a).

15. Ans. (d).

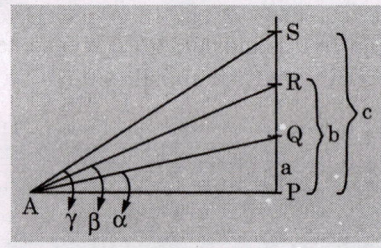

Fig. 122

$$d = AB = OA - OB$$
$$= h(\cot\alpha - \cot\beta) = \frac{h\sin(\beta - \alpha)}{\sin\alpha \sin\beta}$$

$\therefore \quad h = $ etc. as in (a)

(B) Ans. (b). Proceed as in **Q. 12 P. 722-29.**

13. Ans. (b).

Fig. 125

$$PQ = a = x\tan\alpha, \quad PR = b = x\tan\beta$$
$$PS = c = x\tan\gamma$$
$$\therefore \quad a + b + c = x(\tan\alpha + \tan\beta + \tan\gamma)$$
$$abc = x^3 \cdot \tan\alpha \cdot \tan\beta \cdot \tan\gamma$$

Dividing $\dfrac{abc}{a+b+c} = x^2 \cdot 1 \implies$ (d)

$\because \quad$ when $\alpha + \beta + \gamma = 180°$ then

$$\tan\alpha + \tan\beta + \tan\gamma = \tan\alpha \cdot \tan\beta \cdot \tan\gamma$$

i.e. $S_1 = S_3$.

16. Ans. (c).

Refer Q. 12; $d = 60, \beta = 60°, \alpha = 30°$

17. Ans. (b).

Refer Q. 12, $h = 300, d = ?$

18. Ans. (d).

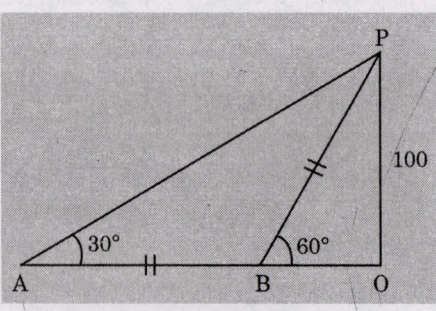

Fig. 123

$$d = AB = OA - OB = 100(\cot 30° - \cot 60°)$$
$$= 100\left(\sqrt{3} - \frac{1}{\sqrt{3}}\right) = \frac{200}{\sqrt{3}} = \frac{200\sqrt{3}}{3}$$

14. Ans. (b).

$$h = x\tan\theta \qquad\qquad \dots(1)$$
$$\text{and } (h + a) = x\tan(\theta + \phi) \qquad \dots(2)$$
$$\text{Divide } 1 + \frac{a}{h} = \frac{\tan(\theta + \phi)}{\tan\phi}$$

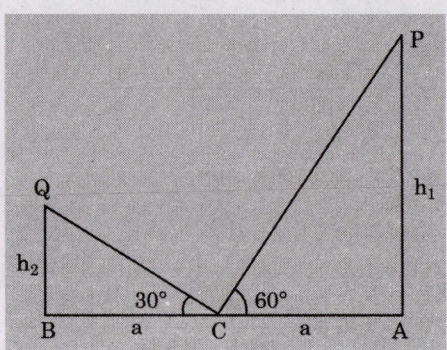

Fig. 126

$$\frac{h_1}{h_2} = \frac{a\tan 60^\circ}{a\tan 30^\circ} = \frac{3}{1}$$

19. Ans. (a).

Figure is drawn as per given data.

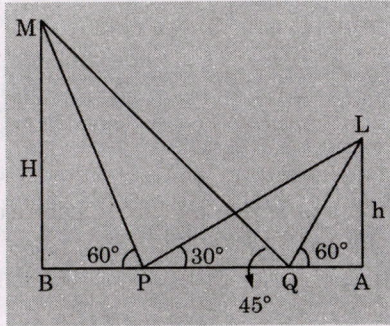

Fig. 127

Also $PQ = 30$ m

If h and H be the heights of the towers

$$PQ = 30 = AP - AQ = h\cot 30^\circ - h\cot 60^\circ$$

$$30 = h\left[\sqrt{3} - \frac{1}{\sqrt{3}}\right] \quad \therefore h = 15\sqrt{3}$$

Also $PQ = 30 = BQ - BP$

$$= H\cot 45^\circ - H\cot 60^\circ = H\frac{(\sqrt{3}-1)}{\sqrt{3}}$$

$$\therefore \quad H = \frac{30\sqrt{3}}{\sqrt{3}-1} = \frac{30\sqrt{3}(\sqrt{3}+1)}{2} = 15(3+\sqrt{3})$$

Hence the distance between the towers is

$$AB = AQ + BQ = h\cot 60^\circ + H\cot 45^\circ$$

$$= \frac{h}{\sqrt{3}} + H = \frac{15\sqrt{3}}{\sqrt{3}} + 15(3+\sqrt{3})$$

$$AB = 15 + 45 + 15\sqrt{3} = 60 + 15\sqrt{3}$$

$$= 15(4+\sqrt{3}) \Rightarrow \text{(a).}$$

20. Ans. (b).

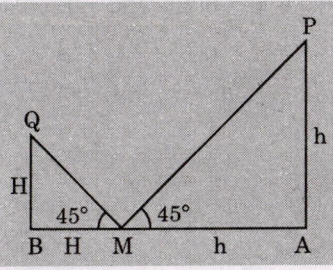

Fig. 128

Both the poles subtend an angle of 45° at M.

$$\therefore \quad BM = H, \ AM = h$$

$$\therefore \quad \frac{BM}{QM} = \cos 45^\circ, \frac{AM}{PM} = \cos 45^\circ$$

$$\therefore \quad QM = \sqrt{2}H, PM = \sqrt{2}h$$

$$\therefore \quad PQ^2 = QM^2 + PM^2 = 2(h^2 + H^2) \Rightarrow \text{(b).}$$

21. Ans. (c).

From the figure

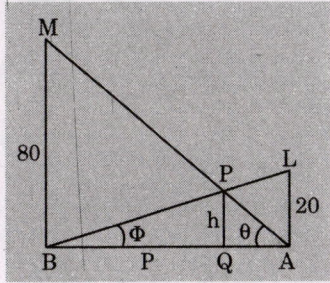

Fig. 129

$$\tan\theta = \frac{80}{AB} = \frac{h}{QA} \quad \therefore AQ = h\cdot\frac{AB}{80}$$

$$\tan\phi = \frac{20}{AB} = \frac{h}{BQ} \quad \therefore BQ = h\cdot\frac{AB}{20}$$

Now $AB = AQ + BQ = h\cdot AB\left(\frac{1}{80} + \frac{1}{20}\right)$

or $\quad 1 = h\left(\frac{1+4}{80}\right)$

or $\quad h = \frac{80}{5} = 16 \Rightarrow h = 16$ m $\Rightarrow$ (c).

22. Ans. (c).

23. Ans. (c).

24. Ans. (a).

See Fig. 130 below in Q. 25.

$$BC = AB - AC = b = l(\sin\alpha - \sin\beta)$$

$$PQ = AQ - AP = a = l(\cos\beta - \cos\alpha)$$

Divide $\quad \therefore \quad \frac{a}{b} = \tan\frac{\alpha + \beta}{2}$

25. Ans. (b).

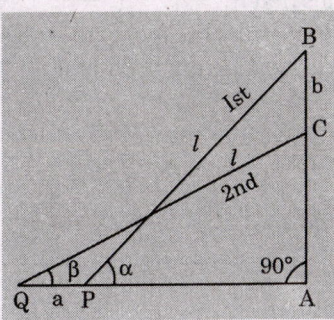

Fig. 130

Refer Fig. Q. 41 on page **733**

If $AB = x, BQ = y$, then $BP = x$

$$\therefore \quad BQ = BP\cos 60^\circ = x/2.$$

Hence the time taken for $x/2$ is half the time taken for

$AB = x$, i.e. half of 3 minutes $= 1\frac{1}{2}$ minutes.

26. Ans. (a).

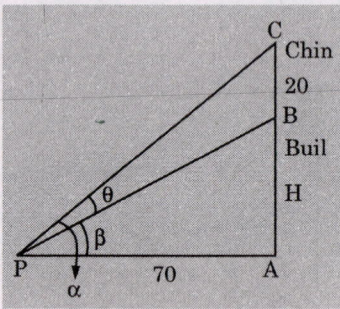

Fig. 131

$\alpha = \theta + \beta$

$\tan \theta = \dfrac{1}{6}, \tan \alpha = \dfrac{H+20}{70}, \tan \beta = \dfrac{H}{70}$

∴ $\tan \alpha = \dfrac{\tan \alpha + \tan \beta}{1 - \tan \theta \tan \beta}$

∴ $H^2 + 20H - 3500 = 0$

or $(h-50)(H+70) = 0$

27. Ans. (b).

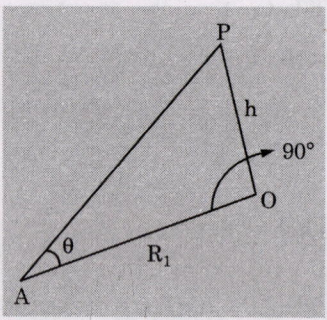

Fig. 132

$h = R_1 \tan \theta = R_2 \tan \theta = R_3 \tan \theta = R_4 \tan \theta$

Above implies that $R_1 = R_2 = R_3 = R_4$ *i.e.* the distances of the four points from the foot of the tower O are equal. Thus $ABCD$ is a cyclic quadrilateral.

28. Ans. (a).

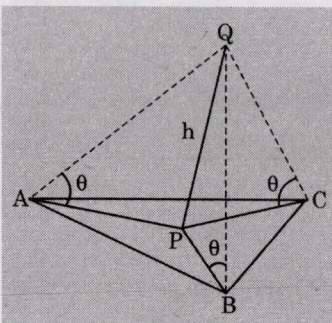

Fig. 133

Let the height PQ of the tower be h. Since the angles of elevation of Q from each of the points A, B, C is θ, we have

$PA = PB = PC = h \cot \theta$ ...(1)

Since P is equidistant from A, B and C it is the circum-centre of the $\triangle ABC$.

∴ $PA = PB = PC$ = circumradius of $\triangle ABC = \dfrac{abc}{4\Delta}$ ...(2)

Hence from (1) and (2), we obtain

$h \cot \theta = \dfrac{abc}{4\Delta}$ or $h = \dfrac{abc \tan \theta}{4\Delta}$.

29. Ans. (b).

See last question.

P, the foot of pole is at the circumcentre of the triangle as $PA = PB = PC = h \cot \theta$.

30. Ans. (d).

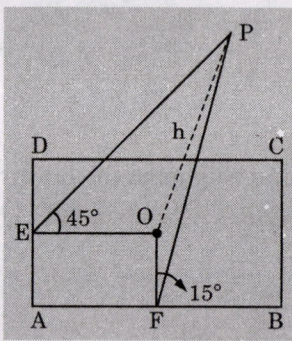

Fig. 134

$OP = h$ is a vertical pole subtending an angle of $45°$ and $15°$ respectively at E and F the mid-points.

Also $AC = BD = 1200$ m = length of diagonal

∴ $EF = \dfrac{1}{2} BD = 600$ m

$OE = h \cot 45° = h$

$OF = h \cot 15° = h(2+\sqrt{3})$

∴ $EF^2 = OE^2 + OF^2 = h^2[1 + (2+\sqrt{3})^2]$

$EF^2 = h^2[8 + 4\sqrt{3}]$

or $600 \times 600 = h^2 \cdot 4(2+\sqrt{3})$

∴ $h^2 = \dfrac{600 \times 600}{4(2+\sqrt{3})} = \dfrac{600 \times 150}{(2+\sqrt{3})} = \dfrac{(300)^2}{(2+\sqrt{3})}$

or $h = 300\sqrt{2-\sqrt{3}}$ m $\Rightarrow$ (d).

31. **(A)** Ans. (b).

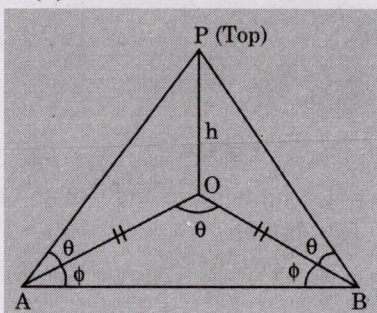

Fig. 135

$OA = OB = h \cot \theta$

Also $\theta + 2\phi = \pi$ $\therefore$ $\phi = \left(\dfrac{\pi}{2} - \dfrac{\theta}{2}\right)$

By sine rule $\dfrac{AB}{\sin \theta} = \dfrac{OA}{\sin \phi}$

$\therefore$ $AB = \dfrac{h \cot \theta \cdot \sin \theta}{\cos (\theta / 2)} = h \cos \theta \sec \dfrac{\theta}{2}$

(B) Ans. (c).

Clearly, $h = AC \tan 30° = BC \tan 30°$ ...(1)

$\therefore$ $AC = BC$

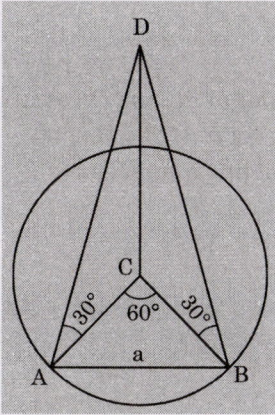

Fig. 136

i.e., $\triangle ABC$ is isosceles triangle.

But $\angle ACB = 60°$

Hence it is an equilateral triangle.

$\therefore$ $AB = BC = CA = a$

Hence from (1),

$h = a \tan 30° = \dfrac{a}{\sqrt{3}}$

32. Ans. (a), (b).

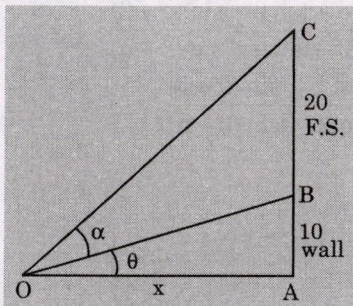

Fig. 137

$\tan \alpha = \dfrac{1}{2}, \tan \theta = \dfrac{10}{x}$ $\therefore$ $\tan (\alpha + \theta) = \dfrac{30}{x}$

$\dfrac{\tan \alpha + \tan \theta}{1 - \tan \alpha \tan \theta} = \dfrac{30}{x}$ $\therefore$ $x^2 - 40x + 300 = 0$

$\therefore$ $x = 30$ or 10

$\therefore$ $\tan \theta = 1$ or $1/3$

33. Ans. (a), (b).

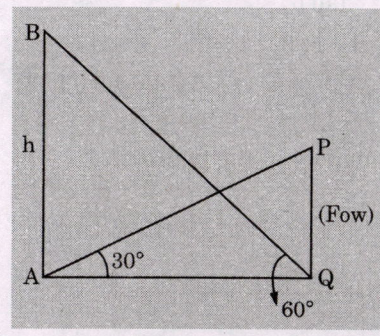

Fig. 138

$x = h \cot 60° = h \tan 30°$

$= h \cdot \dfrac{1}{\sqrt{3}} = \dfrac{1}{3} \cdot h \cdot \sqrt{3} = \dfrac{1}{3} h \cot 30°$

34. Ans. (d).

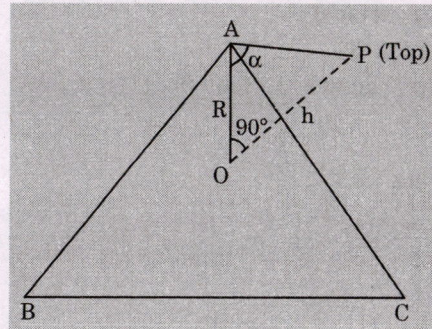

Fig. 139

OP subtends same angle at A, B, C

$\dfrac{OP}{OA} = \tan \alpha$ $\therefore$ $h = R \tan \alpha.$

35. Ans. (b).

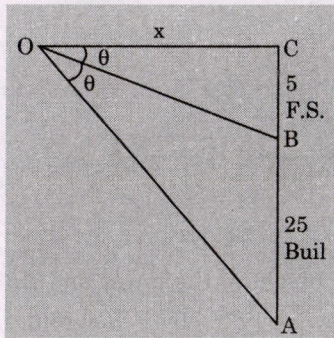

Fig. 140

$AB = 25$ m is building, $BC = 5$ m is flag-staff. O is observer at a height of 30 m. $OC = x$ is the distance of observer from the top of flag-staff. AB and BC subtend same angle at O.

$\therefore$ $\tan \theta = \dfrac{5}{x}, \tan 2\theta = \dfrac{30}{x}$

Eliminate x. $\dfrac{\tan 2\theta}{\tan \theta} = 6$

$1 - \tan^2 \theta = 1/3$

∴ $\tan \theta = \sqrt{2/3}$ ∴ $x = 5 \cot \theta = 5\sqrt{3/2}$

36. Ans. (d).

The data is marked in the figure

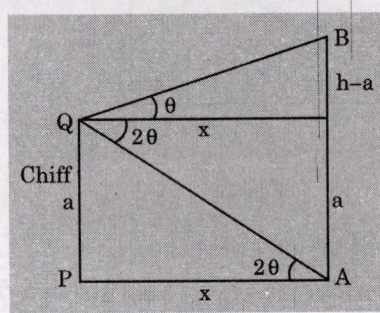

Fig. 141

$h - a = x \tan \theta$

$a = x \tan 2\theta$

∴ $\dfrac{h - a}{a} = \dfrac{\tan \theta}{\tan 2\theta} = \dfrac{1 - \tan^2 \theta}{2}$

$\dfrac{h}{a} - 1 = \dfrac{1 - \tan^2 \theta}{2}$

∴ $\dfrac{h}{a} - 1 - \dfrac{1}{2} = -\dfrac{\tan^2 \theta}{2}$, ∴ $\tan^2 \theta = 3 - \dfrac{2h}{a}$

∴ $\tan \theta = \sqrt{3 - \dfrac{2h}{a}}$ ⇒ (d).

37. Ans. (a).

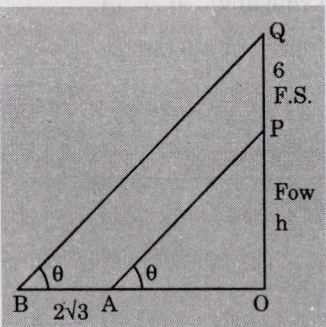

Fig. 142

Let h be the height of the tower and $AB = 2\sqrt{3}$ be the shadow thrown by $PQ = 6$ on the ground.

If $OA = x$, then

$\dfrac{h}{x} = \dfrac{h + 6}{x + 2\sqrt{3}} = \tan \theta$

∴ $2\sqrt{3}\, h = 6x$

∴ $\dfrac{h}{x} = \dfrac{6}{2\sqrt{3}} = \sqrt{3} = \tan \theta$ ∴ $\theta = 60°$

38. Ans. (b).

Let $OP = H$ be the height of the hill.

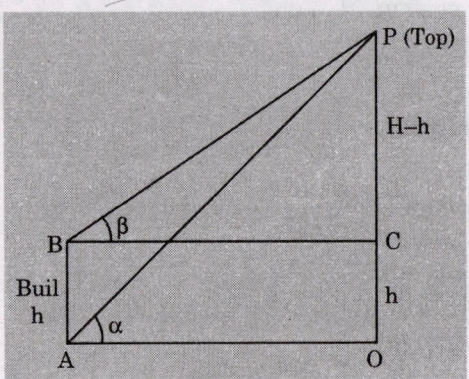

Fig. 143

Equating the values of BC and OA as in last question,

$BC = (H - h) \cot \alpha = OA = H \cot \beta$

∵ $H (\cot \alpha - \cot \beta) = h \cot \alpha$ etc.

39. Ans (c).

Proceed as in last Q. 38.

40. Ans. (b).

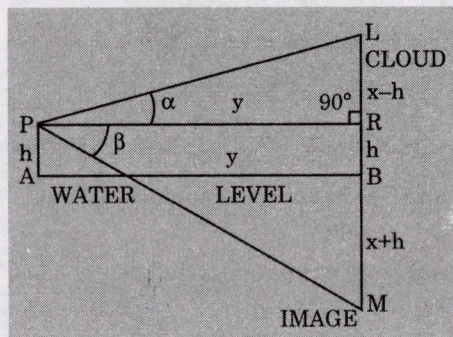

Fig. 144

$\dfrac{x - h}{x + h} = \dfrac{y \tan \alpha}{y \tan \beta}$ Comp. and divi.

$\dfrac{2x}{2h} = \dfrac{\tan \alpha + \tan \beta}{\tan \beta - \tan \alpha} = \dfrac{\sin(\alpha + \beta)}{\sin(\beta - \alpha)}$

or $\dfrac{\cot \alpha + \cot \beta}{\cot \alpha - \cot \beta} = \dfrac{\sin(\alpha + \beta)}{\sin(\beta - \alpha)}$

or $x = $ etc.

41. Ans. (c).

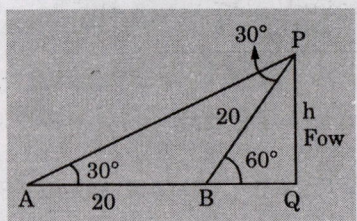

Fig. 145

$AB = BC = 20$ ∴ $h = 20 \sin 60° = 10\sqrt{3}$.

42. Ans. (c).

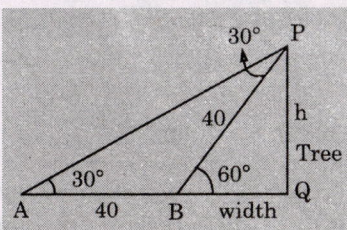

Fig. 146

$$\frac{h}{40} = \sin 60^\circ \quad \therefore \quad h = 20\sqrt{3}$$

Now $BQ = h \cot 60^\circ = 20\sqrt{3} \cdot \frac{1}{\sqrt{3}} = 20$

43. Ans. (a).

$$h = x \tan \alpha, b = x \tan \beta$$

Divide $\dfrac{h}{b} = \tan \alpha \cdot \cot \beta$

44. Ans. (b).

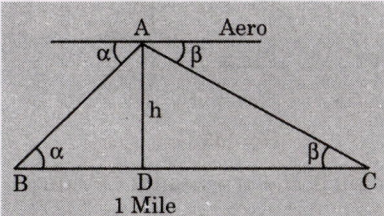

Fig. 147

$$BD + DC = 1$$
$$\Rightarrow \quad h \left(\cot \alpha + \cot \beta \right) = 1$$

45. Ans. (c).

From the figure

$$PA = PB = PC$$

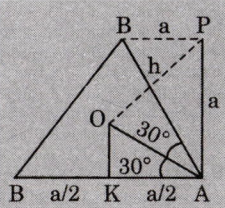

Fig. 148

Consider triangle PAB whcih is isosceles triangle and since AB subtends an angle 60° at P, this triangle becomes equilateral. Hence triangles PAB, PBC, PCA each are equilateral. Again with side a Δ ABC is equilateral with centre (centroid, incentre, orthocentre and circum centre all coincident) at O.

OA is bisector of angle A

$$\therefore \quad \frac{a/2}{OA} = \cos 30^\circ = \frac{\sqrt{3}}{2} \quad \therefore \quad OA = \frac{a}{\sqrt{3}} \cdot$$

Now from right angled Δ OPA, we have

$$PA^2 = OP^2 + OA^2 \quad \text{or} \quad a^2 = h^2 + \frac{a^2}{3}$$

or $\dfrac{2a^2}{3} = h^2$ or $2a^2 = 3h^2 \Rightarrow$ (c).

46. Ans. (b).

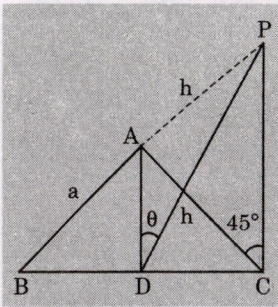

Fig. 149

AP is the pillar of height h subtending an angle of 45° at C so that $AC = AP \cot 45^\circ$ or $a = h$

Also $\tan \theta = \dfrac{AP}{AD} = \dfrac{h}{\sqrt{a^2 - \dfrac{a^2}{4}}}$

$$= \frac{a}{a \cdot \sqrt{3}/2} = \frac{2}{\sqrt{3}} \Rightarrow \text{(b)}.$$

47. Ans. (c).

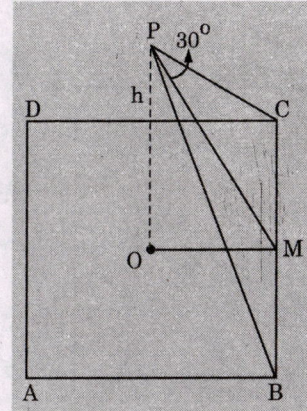

Fig. 150

$PB = PC$ and since BC subtends an angle of 60° at P therefore isosceles triangle PBC become equilateral triangle. If M be the mid-point of BC then PM is bisector of angle at P and also perpendicular to BC. Now in right angled triangle PBM

$$\frac{CM}{PM} = \tan 30^\circ = \frac{1}{\sqrt{3}}$$

$$\therefore \quad PM = \sqrt{3} \cdot CM = \sqrt{3} \cdot \frac{a}{2}$$

Again from right angled triangle OPM, we have

$$PM^2 = OP^2 + OM^2 \quad \text{or} \quad \frac{3}{4} a^2 = h^2 + \frac{a^2}{4}$$

or $\dfrac{a^2}{2} = h^2$ or $a^2 = 2h^2 \Rightarrow$ (c).

48. Ans. (c).

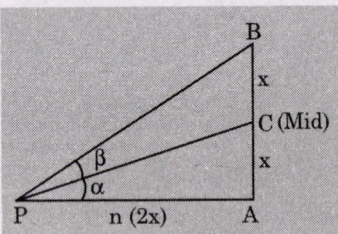

Fig. 115

$$\tan \alpha = \dfrac{x}{2nx} = \dfrac{1}{2n}, \tan (\alpha + \beta) = \dfrac{2x}{2nx} = \dfrac{1}{n}$$

$$\tan \beta = \tan (\alpha + \beta - \alpha) = \dfrac{\tan (\alpha + \beta) - \tan \alpha}{1 + \tan (\alpha + \beta) \tan \alpha}$$

TRUE AND FALSE

1. Ans. True.

$$2500 \dfrac{\sin (45^\circ + 15^\circ)}{\sin (45^\circ - 15^\circ)} = 2500\sqrt{3}. \qquad \text{Refer Q. 40}$$

2. Ans. False.
Correct is

$$100 (\cot 30^\circ + \cot 45^\circ) = 100 (\sqrt{3} + 1)$$

3. Ans. False.

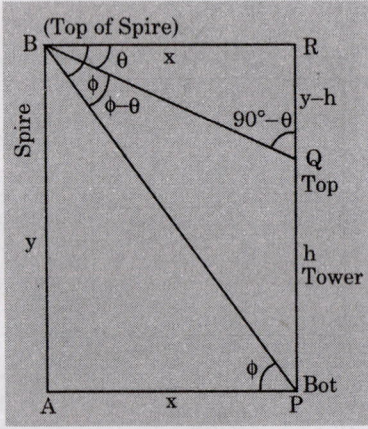

Fig. 169

Correct is $\phi - \theta$ in place of $\phi + \theta$

$$y - h = x \tan \theta, y = x \tan \phi$$

Divide $\dfrac{y - h}{y} = \dfrac{\tan \theta}{\tan \phi}$

$$1 - \dfrac{\tan \theta}{\tan \phi} = \dfrac{h}{y}$$

$$\therefore \quad y = \dfrac{h \tan \phi}{\tan \phi \tan \theta} = \dfrac{h \sin \phi \cos \theta}{\sin (\phi - \theta)}$$

$x = y \cot \phi$ etc.

4. Ans. False.
Correct is 100.

$$y = 150, \tan \theta = \dfrac{4}{3}, \tan \phi = \dfrac{5}{2}$$

$$\therefore \quad h = 70, QR = 150 - 70 = 80, y = x \tan \theta$$

$$\Rightarrow \quad x = 60 \quad \therefore \quad \text{By Pythagoras theorem}$$

$$BQ^2 = BR^2 + RQ^2 = 60^2 + 80^2$$

$$\therefore \quad BQ = 20 \times 5 = 100$$

5. Ans. True.

6. Ans. False.   Corret is $\dfrac{h \tan \beta}{\tan \alpha - \tan \beta}$

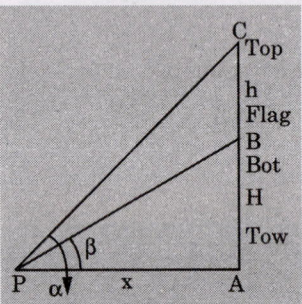

Fig. 153

$H = x \tan \beta, H + h = x \tan \alpha$. Divide

7. Ans. True.

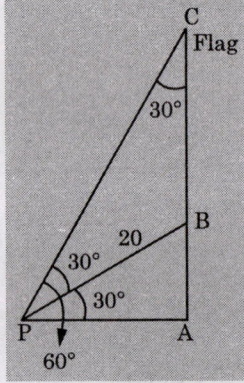

Fig. 154

$AB = 20 \sin 30^\circ = 10 \quad \therefore \quad AC = 20 + 10 = 30$

8. Ans. True.

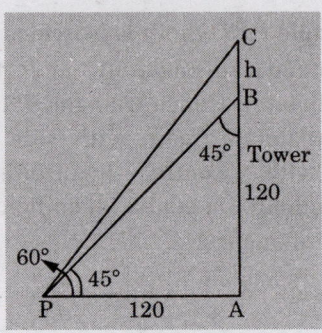

Fig. 155

$$120 + h = 120 \tan 60^{\circ}$$

9. Ans. True.

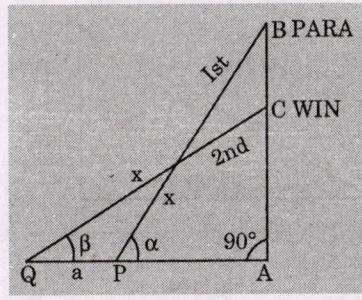

Fig. 156

$$a = PQ = AQ - AP$$
$$a = x \cos \beta - x \cos \alpha$$
$$BC = AB - AC = x \sin \alpha - x \sin \beta$$

Divide and eliminate x.

10. Ans. False.

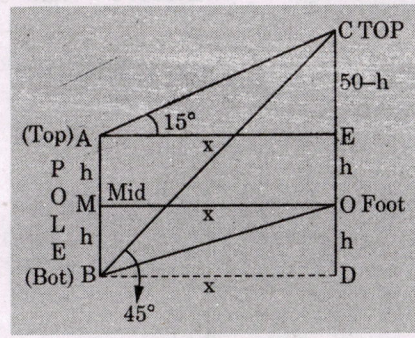

Fig. 157

Correct is $100 / \sqrt{3}$

$$50 - h = x \tan 15^{\circ}, 50 + h = x \tan 45^{\circ}$$

Divide and apply comp. and divi.

$$2h = \frac{100}{\sqrt{3}}.$$

11. Ans. True.

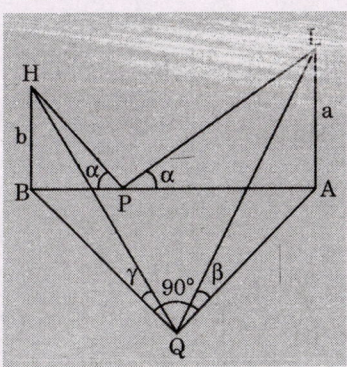

Fig. 158

$$AB = AP + PB = (a + b) \cot \alpha$$
$$AQ = a \cot \beta, BQ = b \cot \gamma$$

Apply Pythagoras theorem on Δ ABQ.

FILL IN THE BLANKS

1. Ans. $\dfrac{x \sin(\phi + \theta)}{\sin(\phi - \theta)}$

2. Ans. $\dfrac{(b^2 + h^2) \sin \theta}{b \cos \theta + h \sin \theta}$

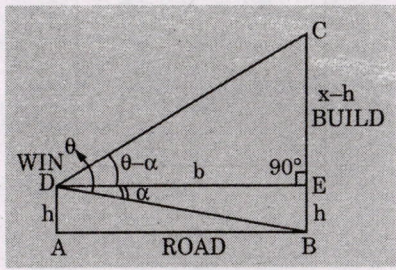

Fig. 159

$$h = b \tan \alpha, \ x - h = b \tan(\theta - \alpha)$$

Eliminating α by putting the value of $\tan \alpha$ and change to sin and cos

3. Ans. $h = 50, d = 50(2 + \sqrt{3})$

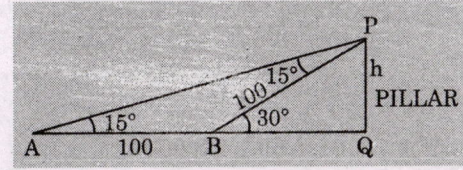

Fig. 160

$$h = 100 \sin 30^{\circ} = 50,$$
$$BQ = h \cot 30^{\circ} = 50\sqrt{3}$$

4. Ans. $75\sqrt{3}$.

Proceed as in Q. 3.

5. Ans. $10\sqrt{3}, d = 30$

6. Ans. $h = 50(\sqrt{3} + 1)$

$$100 = h(\cot 30^{\circ} - \cot 45^{\circ})$$

7. Ans. $h = 30(\sqrt{3} + 1)$

8. $v = \dfrac{\text{distance}}{\text{time}} = \dfrac{150(\cot 45^{\circ} - \cot 60^{\circ})}{2}$

9. Ans. $240\sqrt{3}$ km/h

$$v = \frac{s}{t} = \frac{(1. \cot 30^{\circ} - 1. \cot 60^{\circ})}{10 / 3600}$$

$$= \frac{2}{\sqrt{3}}(360) = 240\sqrt{3} \text{ km}/h$$

10. Ans. $h = a(\tan \beta - \tan \alpha)$

11. Ans. $h = 400 / 3$ ft.

$$200 = x \tan 60^{\circ},$$

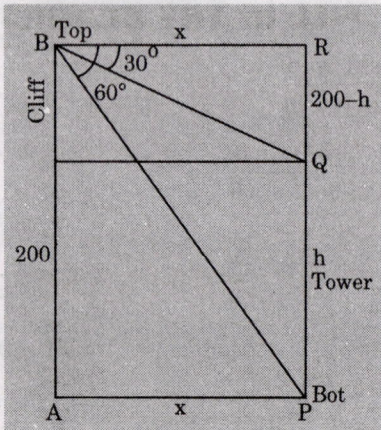

Fig. 161

$200 - h = x \tan 30^\circ$ Divide

12. Ans. $500\sqrt{3}(\sqrt{3}+1)$ ft.

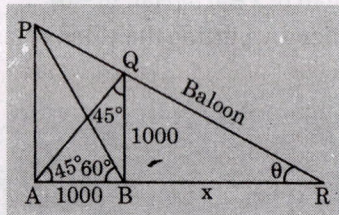

Fig. 162

$AP = 1000 \tan 60^\circ = 1000\sqrt{3}$,

$BQ = 1000 \tan 45^\circ = 1000$

$\dfrac{AP}{BQ} = \dfrac{100+x}{x} = \sqrt{3}$

∴ x is etc.

13. Ans. 500 ft.

14. Ans. $h = 40, \tan\theta = \dfrac{1}{2}$ where $\theta = \alpha - \beta$

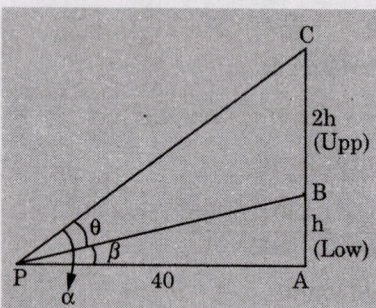

Fig. 163

$\tan\theta = \tan(\alpha-\beta) = \dfrac{\tan\alpha - \tan\beta}{1 + \tan\alpha\tan\beta}$

$\tan\alpha = \dfrac{3h}{40}, \quad \tan\beta = \dfrac{h}{40}$

$(h-40)(3h-40) = 0$

15. Ans. $h = \sqrt{(ab)}, \sin\theta = \dfrac{a-b}{a+b}$

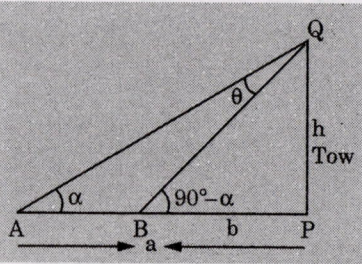

Fig. 164

$h = a\tan\alpha = b\cot\alpha$

∴ $h^2 = ab$

Also $\tan^2\alpha = b/a, \quad 90^\circ - \alpha = \theta + \alpha$

∴ $\theta = 90^\circ - 2\alpha$ ∴ $\sin\theta = \cos 2\alpha$

or $\sin\theta = \dfrac{1-t^2}{1+t^2}$ where $t^2 = \tan^2\alpha = b/a$

16. Ans. $\dfrac{b(a^2+b^2)}{(a^2-b^2)}$

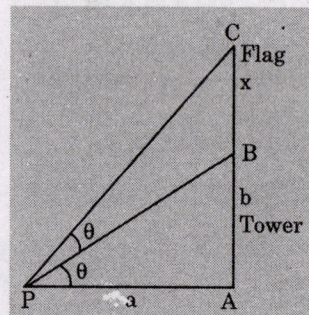

Fig. 165

$t = \tan\theta = \dfrac{b}{a}, \tan 2\theta = \dfrac{b+x}{a} = \dfrac{2t}{1+t^2}$

∴ $x =$ etc.

17. Ans. 30.

$\tan\theta = \dfrac{15}{a}, \tan 2\theta = \dfrac{40}{a}$ etc.

18. Ans. $r \operatorname{cosec}\dfrac{\alpha}{2}\sin\beta$

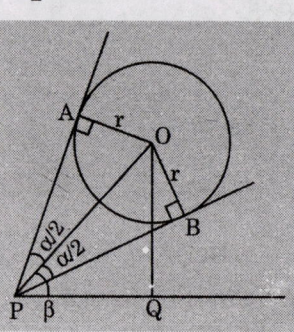

Fig. 166

$h = OP \sin \beta$, $\dfrac{r}{OP} = \sin \dfrac{\alpha}{2}$ etc.

19. Ans. $\dfrac{b}{2 \sin \beta \cot \alpha}$.

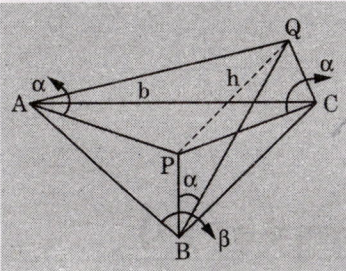

Fig. 167

$PA = PB = PC = h \cot \alpha = R$,

where R is the circum-radius of Δ ABC.

$\therefore$ $2R = \dfrac{b}{\sin B} = \dfrac{b}{\sin \beta}$ or $2h \cot \alpha = \dfrac{b}{\sin \beta}$

$\therefore$ $h = \dfrac{b}{2 \sin \beta \cot \alpha}$

20. Ans. $H = \dfrac{h \sin \alpha \cos (\alpha - \beta)}{\sin \beta}$

$OA = H \cot \alpha$, $BM = (H - h) \tan (90° - \alpha + \beta)$

$\therefore$ $H \cot \alpha = (H - h) \cot (\alpha - \beta)$

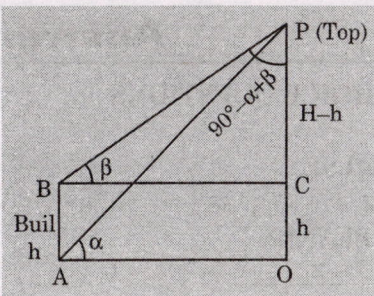

Fig. 168

$\therefore$ $H [\cot (\alpha - \beta) - \cot \alpha] = h \cot (\alpha - \beta)$.
Change to sin and cos.

21. Ans. $b \tan \alpha \cot \beta$

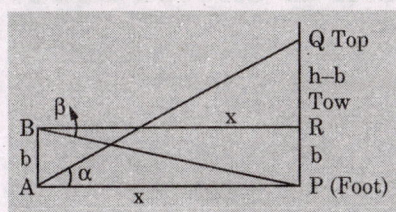

Fig. 169

$h = x \tan \alpha$, $b = x \tan \beta$. Divide.

Problem Set (4)

MULTIPLE CHOICE QUESTIONS

1. A man observes that when he moves up a distance c metres on a slope, the angle of depression of a point on the horizontal plane from the base of the slope is $30°$ and when he moves up further distance c metres the angle of depression of that point is $45°$. The angle of inclination of the slope with the horizontal is

(a) $60°$ (b) $75°$ (c) $70°$ (d) None

TRUE AND FALSE

1. Due south of a tower which is leaning towards north there are two stations at distances x and y respectively from its foot. If α, β respectively be the angles of elevation of the top of the tower at these stations and θ be the inclination of the tower to the horizon, then

$\cot \theta = \dfrac{y \cot \alpha - x \cot \beta}{y - x}$.

2. A tree standing on a horizontal plane is leaning towards East. At two points situated at distances a and b exactly due West of it, the angle of elevation of the top are respectively α and β. Height of the top from the ground is

$\dfrac{(b - a) \tan \alpha \tan \beta}{\tan \alpha + \tan \beta}$

3. A chimney leans towards North. At equal distances due North and South of it in a horizontal plane the elevation of the top are α, β. The inclination of the chimney to the vertical is

$\tan^{-1} \dfrac{\sin (\alpha - \beta)}{2 \sin \alpha \sin \beta}$

or $\tan^{-1} \dfrac{1}{2} (\cot \beta - \cot \alpha)$

4. A flag leaning towards East is inclined at an angle θ to the level ground. A man walks a distance l from the foot of the flag towards West and observes the angle of elevation of the top of the flag to be α. On walking further distance l_1 in the same direction, the angle of elevation is decreased by β, then

$\tan \theta = \dfrac{l_1}{(l + l_1) \cot \alpha - l \cot (\alpha - \beta)}$

FILL IN THE BLANKS

1. A train is moving at a constant rate at an angle θ East of North. Observations of the train are made from a fixed point. It is due north at some instant. Ten minutes earlier its bearing was α_1 West of North whereas ten minutes afterwards its bearing α_2 East of North, then $\tan \theta = \ldots\ldots\ldots$ **(Roorkee 1990)**

Answers to Problem Set (4)

MULTIPLE CHOICE QUESTIONS
    1. (b)

TRUE AND FALSE
    1. T   **2.** F   **3.** T   **4.** T

FILL IN THE BLANKS
    1. $\tan \theta = \dfrac{2}{\cot \alpha_2 - \cot \alpha_1}$

Hints / Solutions to Problem Set (4)

MULTIPLE CHOICE QUESTIONS

1. Ans. (b).

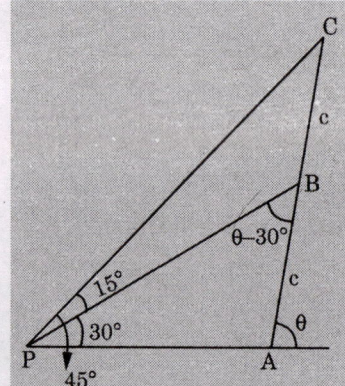

Fig. 170

Apply mn theorem of trigonometry

$(c + c)\cot(\theta - 30^\circ) = c\cot 15^\circ - \cot 30^\circ$

$\therefore \quad \cot(\theta - 30^\circ) = \dfrac{1}{2}\dfrac{\sin(30^\circ - 15^\circ)}{\sin 15^\circ \sin 30^\circ}$

$\qquad\qquad\qquad = 1 = \cot 45^\circ$

$\therefore \quad \theta = 75^\circ$

If $AB = x$, then $BP = x$ from isosceles Δ

$\therefore \quad BQ = BD \cos 60^\circ = x/2.$

TRUE AND FALSE

1. Ans. True. mn theorem of trigonometry

$(x + y - x)\cot \alpha = x \cot \beta - (y - x)\cot(\pi - \theta)$

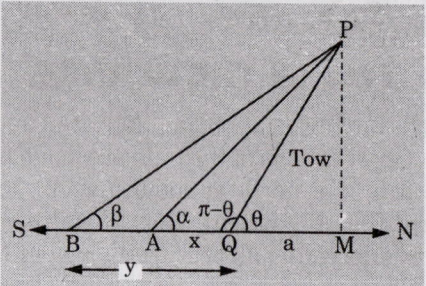

Fig. 171

2. Ans. False.

Correct is $\dfrac{(b - a)\tan \alpha \tan \beta}{\tan \alpha - \tan \beta}$ as in Q. 1.

3. Ans. True.

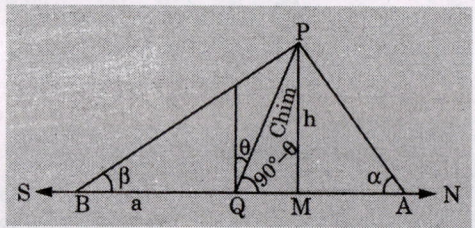

Fig. 172

Apply mn theorem on $\Delta\,PAB$ in **Fig. 55.**

4. Ans. True. **See Fig. 54.**
Apply mn theorem on $\Delta\,PBQ$.

FILL IN THE BLANKS

1. Ans. $\tan \theta = \dfrac{2}{\cot \alpha_2 - \cot \alpha_1} = \dfrac{2 \sin \alpha_1 \sin \alpha_2}{\sin(\alpha_1 - \alpha_2)}$

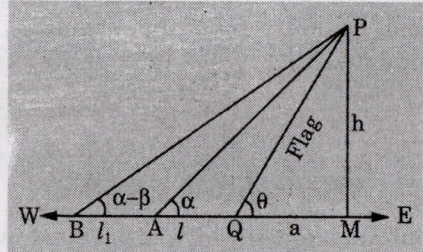

Fig. 173

Since the speed is uniform $OP = OQ = a$, say

$(a + a)\cot \theta = a \cot \alpha_2 - a \cot \alpha_1$

$\tan \theta = \dfrac{2}{\cot \alpha_2 - \cot \alpha_1}$ etc.

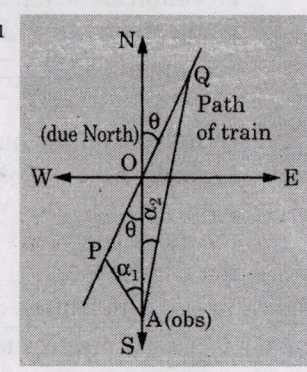

Fig. 74

Problem Set (5)

MULTIPLE CHOICE QUESTIONS

1. *ABC* is a triangular park with $AB = AC = 100$ m. A clock tower is situated at the mid-point of *BC*. The angles of elevation of the top of the tower at *A* and *B* are $\cot^{-1} 3 \cdot 2$ and $\csc^{-1} 2 \cdot 6$ respectively. The height of the tower is

(a) 16 m   (b) 25 m

(c) 50 m   (d) none of these

(EAMCET 1992)

2. A vertical tower stands on a declivity which is inclined at 15° to the horizon. From the foot of the tower a man ascends the declivity for 80 m and then finds that the tower subtends an angle of 30°. The height of the tower is

(a) $20(\sqrt{6} - \sqrt{2})$ (b) $40(\sqrt{6} - \sqrt{2})$

(c) $40(\sqrt{6} + \sqrt{2})$ (d) none of these

3. A tower *PQ* of height h subtends an angle of 45° at a point *A* on the horizontal plane. At another point *B* on *AB* inclined to horizontal at angle of 30°, the elevation of top of the tower is found to be 60°. If $AB = a$, then

(a) $a = h(\sqrt{3} + 1)$ (b) $a = h(\sqrt{3} - 1)$

(c) $h = a(\sqrt{3} + 1)$ (d) $h = a(\sqrt{3} - 1)$

4. From a point on a horizontal plane, the elevation of the top of a hill is 45°. The elevation becomes 75° after walking a distance of 500 m up a slope of inclined at an angle of 15° to the horizon. The height of the hill is

(a) $500\sqrt{6}$ (b) $500\sqrt{3}$

(c) $250\sqrt{6}$ (d) $250\sqrt{3}$

5. At each end of a horizontal base *AB* of length $2a$ the angular height of a certain peak is 15° and that at the mid-point *C* of base *AB* it is 45°. The height of the peak is

(a) $\dfrac{\sqrt{3} - 1}{6} a$ (b) $\dfrac{\sqrt{3} - 1}{6} 3^{3/4} a$

(c) $\dfrac{3 - \sqrt{3}}{2} a$ (d) $\dfrac{\sqrt{3} - 1}{2\sqrt{3}} a$

6. The angle of elevation of a certain peak when observed from each end of a horizontal base line of length $2a$ is found to be θ. When observed from the mid-point of the base the angle of elevation is φ. The height of the peak is

(a) $\dfrac{a}{\sqrt{(\cos\theta - \cos\psi)}}$ (b) $\dfrac{a}{\sqrt{(\cot^2\theta - \cot^2\psi)}}$

(c) $\dfrac{a}{\sqrt{(\cos^2\theta - \cos^2\psi)}}$ (d) none

TRUE AND FALSE

1. A person stands at a point *A* due south of a tower and observes his elevation is 60°. He then walks westwards towards *B* where the elevation is 45°. At a point *C* on *AB* produced he finds it to be 30°, then $AB = 2BC$.

2. An object is observed from three points *A, B, C* in the same horizontal plane passing through the base of the object. The angle of elevation at *B* is twice and at *C* is thrice that at *A*. If $AB = a$, $BC = b$, then the height of the object is $\dfrac{a}{2b}\sqrt{(a+b)(3b-a)}$.

3. A man observes a tower *AB* of height h from a point *P* on the ground. He moves a distance d towards the foot of the tower and finds that the angle of elevation is doubled. He further moves a distance $3d/4$ in the same direction and finds that the angle of elevation is three times that at *P* then $36h^2 = 35d^2$.

4. A balloon is observed simultaneously from three points *A, B* and *C* on a straight road directly under it. The angular elevation at *B* is twice that at *A* and the angular elevation at *C* is thrice that at *A*. If the distance between *A* and *B* is 200 metres and the distance between *B* and *C* is 100 metres, then the height of balloon is 50 metres.

5. *DE* is a tower standing on a horizontal plane and *ABCD* is a straight line in the plane. The height of the tower substends an angle θ at *A*, 2θ at *B* and 3θ at *C*. If *AB* and *BC* be respectively 50 metres and 20 metres then the height of the tower and the distance *CD* are $\dfrac{25}{2}\sqrt{7}$ m and 17.5 m.

6. The top of a tower is observed from three points *A, B, C* on a straight line leading to the tower. If the angles of elevation are θ, 2θ, 3θ from them, then
$$\frac{AB}{BC} = \frac{\cot\theta - \cot 2\theta}{\cot 2\theta - \cot 3\theta}$$

7. The angle of elevation of the top of a tower from a point *A* due South of the tower is α and from *B* due East of tower is β. If $AB = d$, then the height of the tower is
$$\frac{d}{\sqrt{(\cot^2\alpha + \cot^2\beta)}}$$

8. Three points *A, B, C* are in a line inclined at an angle θ to the horizon of three points. *A* is the lowest and *C* is highest. *D* is a point vertically above *C*. If $AB = p$, $CD = q$, $\angle DAB = \alpha$ and $\angle DBC = \beta$, then
$$\cos\theta = \frac{p\sin\alpha\cos\beta}{q\sin(\beta-\alpha)}.$$

9. Top of a mountain is observed from A and B at the sea level. If N is the point vertically below P and $\angle NAB = \alpha$, $\angle NBA = \beta$, $\angle NAP = \theta$, $\angle NBP = \phi$, then

$$\tan \phi \sin \beta = \tan \theta \sin \alpha$$ **(M.N.R. 1990)**

10. A man observes two objects in a straight line in the West. On walking a distance c to the North, the objects subtend an angle α in front of him and on walking a further distance c to the North, they subtend an angle β. Then the distance between the objects is

$$\frac{3c}{2 \cot \beta - \cot \alpha}.$$

11. A man notices two objects in a staraight line due West after walking a distance c due North he observes that the objects subtend an angle α at his eye and after walking a further distance $2c$ due North, they subtend an angle β. Then the distance between the objects is

$$\frac{8c}{3 \cot \beta - \cot \alpha}.$$

FILL IN THE BLANKS

1. A man observes that when he has walked c metres up an incline, the angular depression of an object in a horizontal plane through the foot of the slope in α, and when he has walked a further distance of c metres the depression is β. The inclination of the slope to the horizon is ....

2. A tower is observed from two stations A and B where B is East of A at a distance 100 metres. The tower is due North of A and due North-West of B. The angles

of elevation of the tower from A and B are complementary, the height of the tower is ....

3. The elevation of a tower due North of a station A is α and at another station B due West of A it is β. The height of the tower is ....

4. The angle of elevation of a tower at a place due south of it is θ and at a place due west of A and at a distance a from it, the elevation ϕ. The height of the tower is ....

5. PQ is a tower standing on a horizontal plane, Q being its foot. Two points A and B are taken on the plane such that $AB = 32$ and © QAB is a right angle. It is found that $\cot PAQ = 2/5$ and $\cot PBQ = 3/5$, then the height of tower is ....

6. A flag staff PN stands upright on a level ground. A base AB is measured at right. angle to AN such that points A, B, N lie in the same horizontal plane. If $\angle PAN = \alpha$ and $\angle PBN = \beta$, then height of flag staff is ....

7. The angle of elevation of the top of a tower from a point A on the ground is θ and that from B is ϕ. If $AB = 100$ metres and AB is perpendicular to the line joining A with the foot of the tower, then the height of the tower is ....

   (given $\cot \theta = 3/10, \cot \phi = 1/2$)

8. The angle of elevation of a tower at a point A due North of it is $30°$ and at another point due East of A is $18°$. If $AB = a$, then the height of the tower is ....

9. A vertical pole stands at a point O on a horizontal ground. A and B are points on the ground d metres apart. The pole subtends angles α and β at A and B respectively. AB subtends an angle at O. The height of the pole is ....

Answers to Problem Set (5)

MULTIPLE CHOICE QUESTIONS

   1. (b)   2. (b)   3. (b)   4. (c)   5. (b)   6. (b)

TRUE AND FALSE

   1. T   2. T   3. T   4. F   5. T   6. T   7. T
   8. F   9. F   10. T   11. T

FILL IN THE BLANKS

1. $\cot^{-1}(2 \cot \beta - \cot \alpha)$

2. $100\,(2)^{1/4}$

3. $\dfrac{AB \sin \alpha \sin \beta}{\sqrt{(\sin^2 \alpha - \sin^2 \beta)}}$ or $\dfrac{AB \sin \alpha \sin \beta}{\sqrt{[\sin (\alpha + \beta) \sin (\alpha - \beta)]}}$ or $\dfrac{AB \tan \alpha \tan \beta}{\sqrt{(\tan^2 \alpha - \tan^2 \beta)}}$

4. Same as of Q. 3.

5. $32\sqrt{5}$,

6. Same as of Q. 3

7. 250

8. $\dfrac{a}{\sqrt{(2 + 2\sqrt{5})}}$

9. $\dfrac{d}{[\cot^2 \alpha + \cot^2 \beta - 2 \cot \alpha \cot \beta \cot \gamma]^{1/2}}$

Hints/Solutions to Problem Set (5)

MULTIPLE CHOICE QUESTIONS

1. Ans. (b).

    $\cot \alpha = 3 \cdot 2, \cot \beta = 2 \cdot 6$

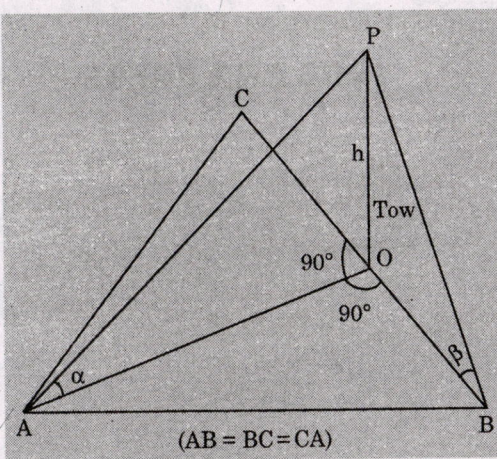

    Fig. 175

    The triangle being isosceles, $AB = AC$ the median AO is perpendicular to base BC

    $OA = h \cot \alpha = 3 \cdot 2 h$

    $OB = h \cot \beta = h \sqrt{(\csc^2 \beta - 1)} = (2 \cdot 4) h$

    $100^2 = OA^2 + OB^2 = h^2 \left[\dfrac{32^2 + 24^2}{100} \right]$

    $100 \times 10 = h \cdot 4 \sqrt{8^2 + 6^2} = h \cdot 4 \cdot 10$

    $\therefore \quad h = 25 \, \text{m}.$

2. Ans. (b).

    From triangle ABC by sine formula

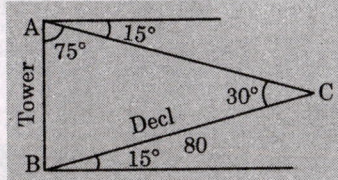

    Fig. 176

    $\dfrac{BC}{\sin 75^\circ} = \dfrac{AB}{\sin 30^\circ}.$

    $h = 80 \, \dfrac{\sin 30^\circ}{\sin (45^\circ + 30^\circ)} = \dfrac{40 \times 2\sqrt{2}}{[\sqrt{(3)} + 1]}$

    $= \dfrac{40 \cdot 2\sqrt{2} \, (\sqrt{3} - 1)}{3 - 1} = 40\sqrt{2} \, (\sqrt{3} - 1) = 40 \, (\sqrt{6} - \sqrt{2}).$

3. Ans. (b).

    If $PQ = h$, then

    $AQ = h \cot 45^\circ = h$

    $\therefore \quad \angle APQ$ is isosceles

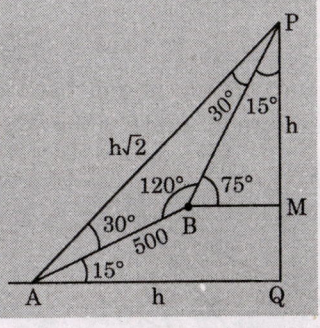

    Fig. 177

    $\therefore \quad \angle APQ = 45^\circ$

    Also $\angle BPM = 30^\circ$

    $\therefore \quad \angle APB = 15^\circ$

    $\therefore \quad \angle ABP = 180^\circ - (15^\circ + 15^\circ)$

    $\angle ABP = 150^\circ$

    Also $AP = \sqrt{AQ^2 + PQ^2} = \sqrt{h^2 + h^2} = h\sqrt{2}$

    Now by sine rule on $\Delta \, ABP$ we have

    $\dfrac{AP}{\sin 150^\circ} = \dfrac{AB}{\sin 15^\circ}$

    or $\quad h\sqrt{2} = \dfrac{a \cdot 1/2}{\dfrac{\sqrt{3} - 1}{2\sqrt{2}}} \qquad$ or $\quad h\sqrt{2} = \dfrac{a\sqrt{2}}{\sqrt{3} - 1}$

    $\Rightarrow \quad a = h \, (\sqrt{3} - 1) \Rightarrow$ (b).

4. Ans. (c).

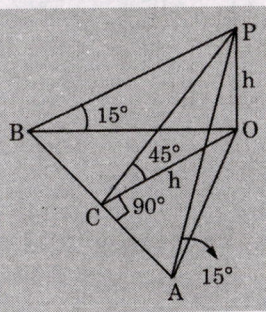

    Fig. 178

    $PQ = AQ = h \quad \therefore \quad AP = h\sqrt{2}$

    $\angle BPM = 90^\circ - 75^\circ = 15^\circ$

    $\therefore \quad \angle APB = 45^\circ - 15^\circ = 30^\circ$

    By sine rule on $\Delta \, ABP$ we have

    $\dfrac{h\sqrt{2}}{\sin 120^\circ} = \dfrac{500}{\sin 30^\circ}$

    $\therefore \quad h\sqrt{2} = \dfrac{\sin 120^\circ \times 500}{\sin 30^\circ} \quad \therefore \quad h\sqrt{2} = \dfrac{\sqrt{3}}{2} \times 500 \times 2$

$\Rightarrow \quad h\sqrt{2} = 500\sqrt{3}$

$h = \dfrac{500\sqrt{6}}{2} = 250\sqrt{6} \Rightarrow$ (c).

5. Ans. (b).

$OP = h$ is peak and $AB = 2a$ is any base. Angles of elevation at A and B are $15°$ and C at the mid point it is $45°$.

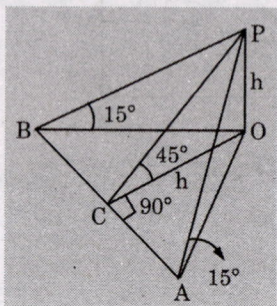

Fig. 179

$OA = OB = h \cot 15°$

$OC = h \cot 45° = h$

$\therefore \Delta OAB$ is isosceles and OC being its median is perpendicular to base

$\therefore \quad OA^2 = OC^2 + CA^2$

or $\quad h^2 \cot^2 15° = h^2 + a^2$

or $\quad h^2 [\cot^2 15° - 1] = a^2$ ...(1)

Now $\tan 15° = \dfrac{\sqrt{3}-1}{\sqrt{3}+1} \quad \therefore \cot 15° = \dfrac{\sqrt{3}+1}{\sqrt{3}-1}$

Putting in (1), we get

$h^2 \left[\dfrac{(\sqrt{3}+1)^2 - (\sqrt{3}-1)^2}{(\sqrt{3}-1)^2} \right] = a^2$

$\Rightarrow \quad h^2 \, 4\sqrt{3} = a^2 (\sqrt{3}-1)^2$

$\Rightarrow \quad h^2 = \dfrac{a^2 (\sqrt{3}-1)^2}{4\sqrt{3}}$

$\therefore \quad h = \dfrac{a(\sqrt{3}-1)}{2 \cdot 3^{1/4}} = \dfrac{a}{6} \cdot (\sqrt{3}-1) \cdot 3^{3/4} \Rightarrow$ (b).

6. Ans. (b).

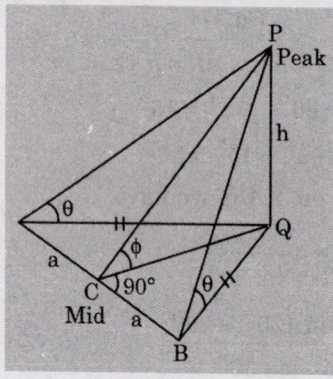

Fig. 180

$= \dfrac{a \sin\theta \sin\phi}{\sqrt{[\sin(\phi+\theta)\sin(\phi-\theta)]}}$

$AQ = BQ = h\cot\theta, CQ = h\cot\phi$

CQ is perpendicular to base AB of isosceles triangle $\therefore$

$BQ = a^2 + CQ^2$

$h^2 (\cot^2 \theta - \cot^2 \phi) = a^2$

TRUE AND FALSE

1. Ans. True.

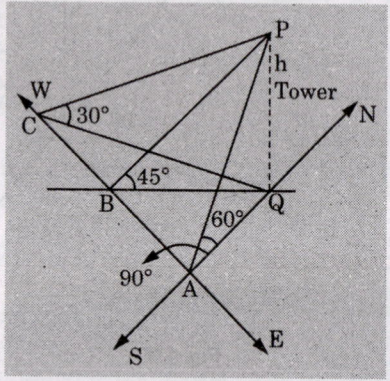

Fig. 181

Correct is $AB = BC$

$AQ = h \cot 60° = h/\sqrt{3}, BQ = h$

$CQ = h\sqrt{3}$

From rt. angled $\angle ABQ, \angle A = 90°$, we have

$AB^2 = BQ^2 - AQ^2 = \dfrac{2}{3} h^2$

$AC^2 = CQ^2 - AQ^2 = \dfrac{8}{3} h^2$

$\therefore \quad \dfrac{AC}{AB} = \sqrt{4}$

or $\quad AC = 2AB \qquad$ or $\quad AB + BC = 2AB$

$\therefore \quad AB = BC$

2. Ans. True.

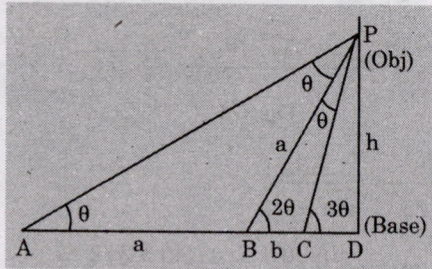

Fig. 182

$h = a \sin 2\theta = 2a \sin\theta \cos\theta$

(Also by sine rule on ΔPBC)

$\dfrac{a}{\sin(\pi - 3\theta)} = \dfrac{b}{\sin\theta}$

$\therefore \quad \dfrac{a}{b} = \dfrac{3\sin\theta - 4\sin^3\theta}{\sin\theta} \qquad \therefore \sin^2\theta = \dfrac{3b-a}{4b}$

∴ $\cos^2 \theta = \dfrac{a+b}{4b}$ put in the above.

3. Ans. True.

$a = d, b = 3d/4$. from Q. 2.

4. Ans. False.

Correct is $50\sqrt{3}, a = 200, b = 100$ in Q. 2.

5. Ans. True. Put $a = 50, b = 20$ in Q. 2.

$h = AD \tan \theta, \qquad AD = CD + b + a$

6. Ans. True.

Refer figure Q. 2.

$\dfrac{AB}{BC} = \dfrac{AD - BD}{BD - CD} = \dfrac{h(\cot \theta - \cot 2\theta)}{h(\cot 2\theta - \cot 3\theta)}$

7. Ans. True.

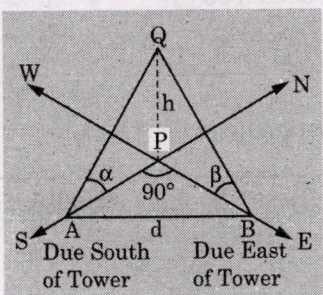

Fig. 183

$AP = h \cot \alpha, BP = h \cot \beta$

Apply Pythagoras theorem on ΔPAB.

8. Ans. False.

Correct is $\dfrac{p \sin \alpha \sin \beta}{q \sin (\beta - \alpha)}$

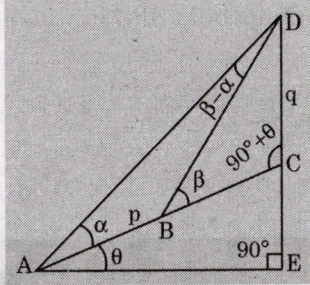

Fig. 184

Use sine formula on $\Delta^s\ ABD$ and DBC and equate the values of common side BD.

9. Ans. False.

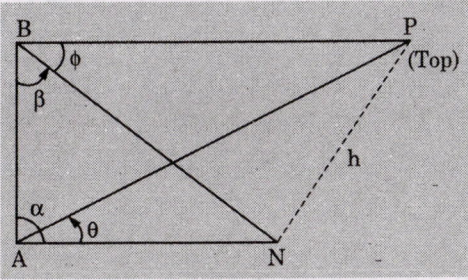

Fig. 185

Correct is $\cot \phi \sin \beta = \cot \theta \sin \alpha$

$AN = h \cot \theta, BN = h \cot \phi$

Now apply sin rule on $\Delta\ ABN$.

10. Ans. True.

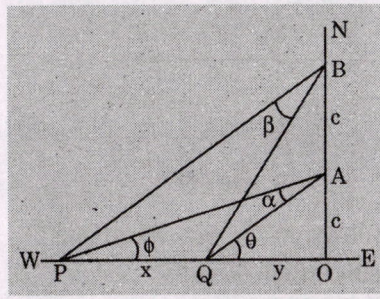

Fig. 186

$PQ = x, \angle PAQ = \alpha$ given $OA = c$

If $\quad OQ = y$ (unknown), $\angle AQO = \theta$, then

$c = y \tan \theta, c = (x + y) \tan \phi$

$\theta = \alpha + \phi \qquad\qquad \therefore \quad \alpha = \theta - \phi$

or $\quad \tan \alpha = \dfrac{\tan \theta - \tan \phi}{1 + \tan \theta \tan \phi}$

$x^2 + y^2 + c^2 = cx \tan \alpha$ on putting for $\tan \theta$ and $\tan \phi$.

Replacing c by $2c$ and α by β, we get

$xy + y^2 + (2c)^2 = 2cx \tan \beta$. Subtract etc.

11. Ans. True.

Proceed as in Q. 10.

FILL IN THE BLANKS

1. Ans. $\cot^{-1} (2 \cot \beta - \cot \alpha)$

$\dfrac{c}{\sin \alpha} = \dfrac{PB}{\sin (\pi - \theta)}, \dfrac{c}{\sin (\beta - \alpha)} = \dfrac{PB}{\sin (\theta - \beta)}$

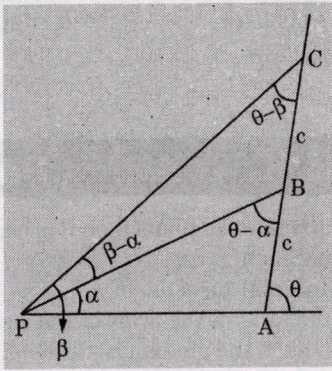

Fig. 187

Equate the values of PB

$\sin \theta \sin (\beta - \alpha) = \sin \alpha \sin (\theta - \beta)$

Open and divide by $\sin \alpha \sin \beta \sin \theta$ and find $\cot \theta$.

2. Ans. $100 (2)^{1/4}$

$h = AP \tan \theta = BP \cot \theta$

∴ $\quad h^2 = AP . BP, \quad BP = 100\sqrt{2}$ by Phythagoras

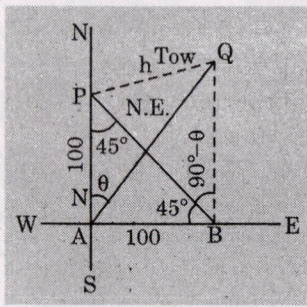

Fig. 188

$$\therefore \quad h^2 = 100 \times 100\sqrt{2} \quad \text{or} \quad h = 100\,(2)^{1/4}$$

3. Ans. $\dfrac{AB \sin \alpha \sin \beta}{\sqrt{\sin^2 \alpha - \sin^2 \beta}}$

or $\dfrac{AB \sin \alpha \sin \beta}{\sqrt{[\sin(\alpha + \beta)\sin(\alpha - \beta)]}}$

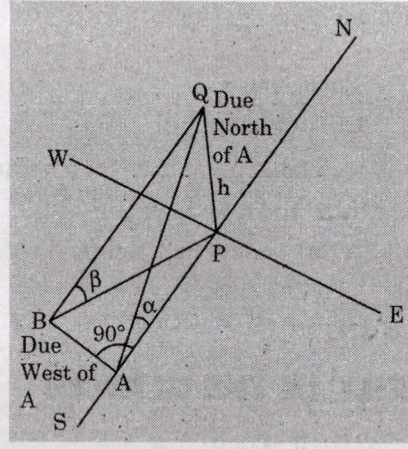

Fig. 189

or $\dfrac{AB}{\sqrt{(\cot^2 \beta - \cot^2 \alpha)}}$ or $\dfrac{AB \tan \alpha \tan \beta}{\sqrt{(\tan^2 \alpha - \tan^2 \beta)}}$

$AP = h \cot \alpha,\ BP = h \cot \beta$

$$BP^2 = AB^2 + AP^2$$

$$h^2 (\cot^2 \beta - \cot^2 \alpha) = AB^2$$

Now change to tan or sin and cosine etc.

4. Same as of Q. 3.

5. Ans. $32\sqrt{5}$, $AB = 32$, $\cot \alpha = 2/5$,

$\cot \beta = 3/5$. See Q. 3.

6. Same as of Q. 3.

7. Ans. 250, $AB = 100$, $\cot \theta = 3/10$,

$\cot \phi = 1/2$. See Q. 2.

8. Ans. $\dfrac{a}{\sqrt{(2 + 2\sqrt{5})}}$.

$AB = a$, $\sin \alpha = \sin 30^\circ = \dfrac{1}{2}$

$\sin \beta = \sin 18^\circ = \dfrac{\sqrt{5} - 1}{4}$.

Simplify and Rationalize. See Q. 3.

9. Ans. $h = \dfrac{d}{[\cot^2 \alpha + \cot^2 \beta - 2 \cot \alpha \cot \beta \cos \gamma]^{1/2}}$

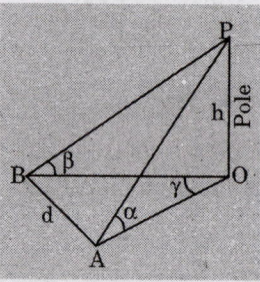

Fig. 190

Apply cosine formula on $\triangle ABO$ in which

$AB = d$,

$OA = h \cot \alpha$,

$OB = h \cot \beta$,

$\angle AOB = \gamma$

Fascinating Facts

- If a line is perpendicular to a plane then it is perpendicular to every line in that plane.
- If a triangle the internal bisector of an angle divides the opposite side in the ratio of the arms of the angle.
- In an isoscales triangle, the median is perpendicular to the base.
- Angles in the segment of a circle are equal.

- Angle of alternate segment of a circle are equal.
- The angle subtended by any chord on centre is twice the angle subtended by the same chord on any point on the circumference of the circle.
- The exterior angle is equal to the sum of interior opposite angles.

❑

Co-ordinate Geometry
(2D & 3D)

Vector algebra

CHAPTER 17

Rectangular Cartesian Co-ordinate System and Straight Line

Rectangular Cartesian Coordinates

Two perpendicular lines $X'OX$, and $Y'OY$ divides the plane into four quadrants i.e., XOY, YOX', $X'OY'$ & $Y'OX$ which are respectively called the first, second, third and fourth quadrants.

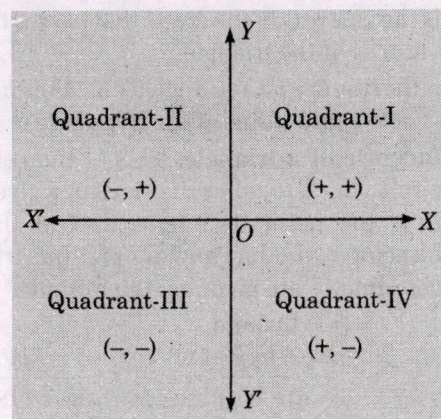

Here, the line $X'OX$ is called X-axis.

The line $Y'OY$ is called Y-axis.

The two axes intersect at O(origin). Any point P in the plane associated with a pair of real numbers (x, y) where x is called abscissa and y is called ordinate.

▶ Some Points

- x-axis and y-axis together are called axes of coordinates or axes of reference.
- The coordinate of the origin is $(0, 0)$
- The x-coordinate of every point on y-axis is zero and vice versa.
- The direction of OX and OY is positive while the directions of OX', OY' is negative.
- If (x, y) are the cartesian coordinates of a point P, then $x = r\cos\theta$, $y = r\sin\theta \Rightarrow r = \sqrt{x^2 + y^2}$ and $\theta = \tan^{-1}\dfrac{y}{x}$

§2. Area of some Geometrical Figures

(i) **Area of a triangle :** The area of a triangle ABC with vertices $A(x_1, y_1)$, $B(x_2, y_2)$ and $C(x_3, y_3)$ is given by

$$\Delta = \frac{1}{2}\begin{vmatrix} x_1 & y_1 & 1 \\ x_2 & y_2 & 1 \\ x_3 & x_3 & 1 \end{vmatrix}$$

$$= \frac{1}{2}[|x_1(y_2 - y_3) + x_2(y_3 - y_1) + x_3(y_1 - y_2)|]$$

(ii) **Area of Qudrilateral :** The area of a quadrilateral with vertices $(x_1, y_1), (x_2, y_2), (x_3, y_3)$ and (x_4, y_4) is

$$= \frac{1}{2}[(x_1 y_2 - x_2 y_1) + (x_2 y_3 - x_3 y_2)$$
$$+ (x_3 y_4 - x_4 y_3) + (x_4 y_1 - x_1 y_4)]$$

(iii) **Area of a Polygon :** The area of a polygon whose vertices $(x_1, y_1), (x_2, y_2), \ldots (x_n, y_n)$ is

$$= \frac{1}{2}\big|[(x_1 y_2 - x_2 y_1) + (x_2 y_3 - x_3 y_2)$$
$$+ \ldots + (x_n y_1 - x_1 y_n)]\big|$$

$$= \frac{1}{2}\begin{Vmatrix} x_1 & y_1 \\ x_2 & y_2 \\ x_3 & y_3 \\ \vdots & \vdots \\ x_n & y_n \\ x_1 & y_1 \end{Vmatrix}$$

§3. Important Formulae

1. **Distance between two points**

    (x_1, y_1) and $(x_2, y_2) = \sqrt{(x_2 - x_1)^2 + (y_2 - y_1)^2}$

    $= \sqrt{(\text{Diff. of abscissas})^2 + (\text{Diff. of ordinates})^2}$

    Distance of (x_1, y_1) from origin $= \sqrt{x_1^2 + y_1^2}$.

2. (a) **Point (x, y) which divides the join of two given points (x_1, y_1) and (x_2, y_2) in a given ratio $m_1 : m_2$ (Internally and Externally)**

    $x = \dfrac{m_1 x_2 + m_2 x_1}{m_1 + m_2}$, $\quad y = \dfrac{m_1 y_2 + m_2 y_1}{m_1 + m_2}$ **(Internally)**

    $x = \dfrac{m_1 x_2 - m_2 x_1}{m_1 - m_2}$, $\quad y = \dfrac{m_1 y_2 - m_2 y_1}{m_1 - m_2}$ **(Externally)**

    Co-ordinates of any point on the join of (x_1, y_1) and (x_2, y_2) can be taken as

    $$\left(\frac{\lambda x_2 + x_1}{\lambda + 1}, \frac{\lambda y_2 + y_1}{\lambda + 1}\right).$$

    This point divides the given line in the ratio $\lambda : 1$.

(b) Mid-point $\left(\dfrac{x_1 + x_2}{2}, \dfrac{y_1 + y_2}{2}\right)$.

3. **Area of a triangle whose vertices are $(x_1, y_1), (x_2, y_2)$ and (x_3, y_3)**

$$= \frac{1}{2}\{x_1(y_2 - y_3) + x_2(y_3 - y_1) + x_3(y_1 - y_2)\}$$

$$= \frac{1}{2}\begin{vmatrix} x_1 & y_1 & 1 \\ x_2 & y_2 & 1 \\ x_3 & y_3 & 1 \end{vmatrix}$$

Note that if one vertex (x_3, y_3) is at the origin $(0, 0)$, then

$$\text{Area} = \frac{1}{2}(x_1 y_2 - x_2 y_1) \qquad \because x_3 = 0, \ y_3 = 0.$$

Another form :

$$\frac{1}{2}\begin{vmatrix} x_1 & x_2 & x_3 & x_1 \\ y_1 & y_2 & y_3 & y_1 \end{vmatrix} = \frac{1}{2}\left|\underset{\text{Three terms}}{\Sigma(x_1 y_2 - x_2 y_1)}\right|$$

4. **Also area of a quadrilateral $ABCD$ whose vertices are $(x_r, y_r), r = 1, 2, 3, 4 = \Delta_1 + \Delta_2 = \Delta\,ABC + \Delta\,BCD$**

Another form :

$$\text{Area} = \frac{1}{2}\begin{vmatrix} x_1 & x_2 & x_3 & x_4 & x_1 \\ y_1 & y_2 & y_3 & y_4 & y_1 \end{vmatrix}$$
$$\underset{\text{Four terms}}{}$$

$$= \frac{1}{2}\left|\Sigma(x_1 y_2 - x_2 y_1)\right|$$

Particular Case :

(a)* If the two vertices be on x-axis say $(a, 0), (b, 0)$ and third vertex is (h, k) then area
$$= \frac{1}{2}\,\text{base} \times \text{height} = \frac{1}{2}(a - b)\,k$$

(b) Similarly if the two vertices be on y-axis say $(0, c)$, $(0, d)$ and third vertex is (h, k) then area
$$= \frac{1}{2}(c - d).h \text{ as above.}$$

(c) $\Delta\,OAB$ where O is $(0, 0)$, A is $(a, 0)$ on x-axis and B is $(0, b)$ on y-axis then $\Delta = \dfrac{1}{2}ab$.

(d)* $\Delta\,PAB = 10$ units $\Rightarrow |\Delta| = 10 \ \therefore \Delta = \pm 10$

§4. Condition for three points to be collinear :

If the area of the triangle be zero then the three points will be collinear.

§5. Properties of geometrical figures :

(i) **Equilateral triangle :** All sides equal.

(ii) **Isosceles triangle :** Two sides equal.

(iii) **Rhombus :** All sides equal and no angle a right angle, but diagonals are at right angles and unequal.

(iv) **Square :** All sides equal and each angle is right angle. The diagonals are also equal.

(v) **Parallelogram :** Opposite sides parallel and equal, diagonals bisect each other.

(vi) **Rectangle :** Opposite sides equal and each angle a right angle. Diagonals equal.

(vii) The line joining the mid-points of the two sides of a triangle is parallel to the third side and half its length.

§6. Co-ordinates of standard point :

(i) **Centroid of a triangle.** The point is the intersection of the medians (i.e. line joining a vertex to the mid-point of the opposite side). This point divides each median in the ratio $2:1$. Its coordinates are
$$G\left(\frac{x_1 + x_2 + x_3}{3}, \frac{y_1 + y_2 + y_3}{3}\right).$$

(ii) **Circum-centre of triangle.** This is a point which is equidistant from the three vertices of the triangle. It is also the point of intersection of right bisectors of the sides of the triangle (i.e. the lines through the mid-point of a side and perpendicular to it). It is the centre O of the circle that passes through the vertices of the triangle.

(iii) If the triangle be a rt. angled one, the circumcentre is at the **mid-point of the hypotenuse.**

(iv) **Incentre of a triangle.** This is the centre of the circle which touches the sides of a given triangle. It is the point of intersection of the internal bisectors of the angles of the triangle. Its coordinates are given by the formula
$$I = (x, y) \text{ where}$$
$$x = \frac{ax_1 + bx_2 + cx_3}{a + b + c}, \ y = \frac{ay_1 + by_2 + cy_3}{a + b + c}$$
where a, b, c are the lengths of the sides of the triangle.

(v) **The centre of the escribed circle** which is opposite to vertex A is
$$\left(\frac{-ax_1 + bx_2 + cx_3}{-a + b + c}, \frac{-ay_1 + by_2 + cy_3}{-a + b + c}\right)$$
Similarly taking $-b$ and $-c$, we will get centres of escribed circles drawn opposite to vertex B and vertex C respectively.

(vi)* **Orthocentre of a triangle.** This point H is the intersection of the altitudes, (i.e. the lines through the vertices and perpendicular to opposite sides). **In a right angled $\Delta\,ABC, \angle\,C = 90°$, the orthocentre H is the vertex C of the triangle.**

(vii)* The points O, G, H are collinear and G divides OH in the ratio $1:2$.

(viii)* In an equilateral triangle the points G, H and I coincide.

(ix) The internal bisector of the angle of a triangle divides the opposite side in the ratio of the arms of the angle.

(x) The mid-point of hypotenuse of a right angled triangle is equidistant from the three vertices.

[See Q. 8 P. 775-777]

(xi) If the triangle be isosceles, then perpendicular from vertex to base bisects it.

[See. Q. 13. P. 775-778]

§7. Various forms of equation of straight line (First Degree)

(i) $Ax + By + C = 0$. General form
(ii) $x = 0$. y-axis.
(iii) $y = 0$. x-axis.
(iv) $x = a$. Parallel to y-axis.
(v) $y = b$. Parallel to x-axis.
(vi) The distance of a point (x, y) from x-axis is $|y|$ and from y-axis $|x|$.
(vii) $y = mx + c$. Line which cuts off an intercept c on y-axis and makes an angle θ with the +ive direction (anticlockwise) of x-axis and $\tan \theta = m$ is called its slope or gradient.
(viii) $y = mx$. Any line through the origin.
(ix) $\dfrac{x}{a} + \dfrac{y}{b} = 1$. **Intercept form** : Here a and b are the intercepts on the axis of x and y respectively.

In this case the portion AB of the line intercepted between the axes is of length $\sqrt{(a^2 + b^2)}$ by Pythagoras rule.

(x) $y - y_1 = m(x - x_1)$. Equation of a line through a given point (x_1, y_1) and having slope m i.e., $\tan \theta = m$.

*Note : $\dfrac{y - y_1}{x - x_1} = m$. If $m = 0$, i.e. the line is parallel to x-axis, then its equation will be $N^r = 0$ or $y - y_1 = 0$. If $m = \infty$, i.e. the line is perpendicular to x-axis, then its equation will be $D^r = 0$ or $x - x_1 = 0$.

(xi) $y - y_1 = \dfrac{y_2 - y_1}{x_2 - x_1}(x - x_1)$.

Equation of a line passing through two given points (x_1, y_1) and (x_2, y_2).

or $\dfrac{x - x_1}{x_2 - x_1} = \dfrac{y - y_1}{y_2 - y_1}$

Its slope $= m = \dfrac{y_2 - y_1}{x_2 - x_1} = \dfrac{\text{Diff. of ordinates}}{\text{Diff. of abscissas}}$.

The difference being taken in the same order.

Another form : $\begin{vmatrix} x & y & 1 \\ x_1 & y_1 & 1 \\ x_2 & y_2 & 1 \end{vmatrix} = 0$

(xii) $x \cos \alpha + y \sin \alpha = p$. Equation of a line on which the length of perpendicular from origin is p and α is the angle which this perpendicular makes with the +ive direction of x-axis.

(xiii)* **Parametric Form :**

V. Imp. $\dfrac{x - x_1}{\cos \theta} = \dfrac{y - y_1}{\sin \theta} = r$.

This is another form of the equation given in (x), $0 < \theta < \pi,\ \theta \neq \pi/2$

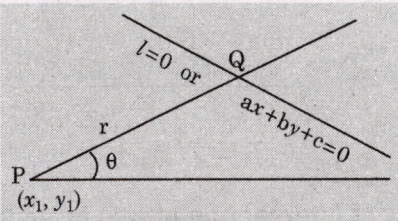

Fig. 2

i.e. $y - y_1 = m(x - x_1)$. Any point Q on this line is $(x_1 + r \cos \theta,\ y_1 + r \sin \theta)$.

Its distance from the given point $P(x_1, y_1)$ is

$= \sqrt{(x_1 + r \cos \theta - x_1)^2 + (y_1 + r \sin \theta - y_1)^2}$

$= \sqrt{r^2 (\cos^2 \theta + \sin^2 \theta)} = r = PQ$

This form is very useful when we are concerned with the distance of any point on the line from the given point (x_1, y_1).

Cor. Distance of given point P from the point of intersection Q of given line with another line $ax + by + c = 0$ i.e., $l = 0$.

Any point $Q(x_1 + r \cos \theta, y_1 + r \sin \theta)$ lies on $ax + by + c = 0$ i.e., $l = 0$

$*\quad a(x_1 + r \cos \theta) + b(y_1 + r \sin \theta) + c = 0$

$\therefore^* \quad r = -\dfrac{ax_1 + by_1 + c}{a \cos \theta + b \sin \theta} = -\dfrac{l}{a \cos \theta + b \sin \theta}$

or$^* \quad \dfrac{1}{r} = -\dfrac{a \cos \theta + b \sin \theta}{ax_1 + by_1 + c} = -\dfrac{a \cos \theta + b \sin \theta}{l}$

Use the above results directly and remember them.

§8. (a) Slope and intercepts on axes by the line $Ax + By + C = 0$

Slope $= m = \dfrac{-A}{B} = -\dfrac{\text{coeff. of } x}{\text{coeff. of } y}$

Intercepts : Put $y = 0$ in the given equation and find $x = \dfrac{-C}{A}$ and then put $x = 0$ and find $y = \dfrac{-C}{B}$ which are respectively the intercepts on the axes of x and y.

§8. (b) The equation $Ax + By + C = 0$ represents a line

(1)* **parallel to x-axis** $\Leftrightarrow A = 0$ i.e. coeff. of x is 0.
(2)* **parallel to y-axis** $\Leftrightarrow B = 0$ i.e. coeff. of y is 0.
(3)* **passing through origin** $\Leftrightarrow C = 0$ i.e. constant term is 0.
(4)* **Equally inclined to axes**

$m = \tan(\pm 45°) = \pm 1$

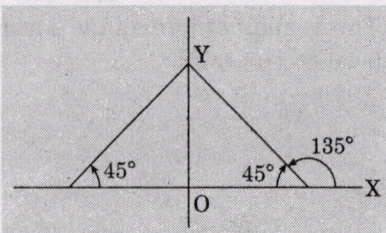

Fig. 3

§9. Point of intersection of two given lines

Solve their equations for x and y by the method of cross multiplication or by any other method.

§10. Three points collinear

Find the equation of the line joining any two points by [7 (xi)], and show that the coordinates of the third point satisfy it (see also 4)

or, if the three points be A, B, C then show that slope of AB = slope of BC [7 (xi)].

§11. Angle between two given lines

$$\tan \theta = \left| \frac{m_1 \sim m_2}{1 + m_1 m_2} \right| = \left| \frac{A_1 B_2 \sim A_2 B_1}{A_1 A_2 + B_1 B_2} \right|$$

$$\tan \theta = \left| \frac{\Delta}{\text{Tim Tim}} \right|$$

By Δ we mean $\begin{vmatrix} A_1 & B_1 \\ A_2 & B_2 \end{vmatrix} = A_1 B_2 - A_2 B_1$

By 'Tim Tim' we mean $A_1 A_2 + B_1 B_2$
where $A_1 x + B_1 y + C_1 = 0$
and $A_2 x + B_2 y + C_2 = 0$
Also m_1 and m_2 are the slopes of the given lines, $m_1 \sim m_2$ means the difference between m_1 and m_2 i.e. it stands for both $m_1 - m_2$ if $m_1 > m_2$ and for $m_2 - m_1$ if $m_2 > m_1$. If α is the angle between two given lines then $\pi - \alpha$ is also the angle between them and
$$\tan (\pi - \alpha) = -\tan \alpha.$$
It may be taken from the value of $\tan \theta$ given above that

$$\cos \theta = \left| \frac{A_1 A_2 + B_1 B_2}{\sqrt{(A_1^2 + B_1^2)} \sqrt{(A_2^2 + B_2^2)}} \right|$$

and $\sin \theta = \left| \dfrac{A_1 B_2 - A_2 B_1}{\sqrt{(A_1^2 + B_1^2)} \sqrt{(A_2^2 + B_2^2)}} \right|$

The above two results may be taken for granted. Both $\sin \theta$ and $\cos \theta$ have same denominator $\sqrt{} \cdot \sqrt{}$ and

N^r of $\sin \theta$ is $\begin{vmatrix} A_1 & B_1 \\ A_2 & B_2 \end{vmatrix} = \Delta$ and N^r of

$\cos \theta = A_1 A_2 + B_1 B_2 = \text{Tim Tim}$.

§12. Condition for two given lines to be parallel.

In this case $\theta = 0$ or $180°$,
$\therefore \quad \tan \theta = 0$; hence from 11,

$m_1 \sim m_2 = 0$ or $m_1 = m_2$
i.e., their slopes are equal.
or $-\dfrac{A_1}{B_1} = -\dfrac{A_2}{B_2}$ $\therefore$ $\dfrac{A_1}{A_2} = \dfrac{B_1}{B_2}$

i.e. coefficients of x and y are proportional in their equations.

Identical lines $\dfrac{A_1}{A_2} = \dfrac{B_1}{B_2} = \dfrac{C_1}{C_2}$

§13. Method to write a line parallel to a given line.

Change only the constant term in the given equation, the terms of x and y remaining unchanged. The changed constant will be found by an additional given condition.
For example, a line parallel to
$$2x - 3y - 5 = 0 \text{ is}$$
$$2x - 3y + \lambda = 0.$$
*Alt. A line through (h, k) and parallel to $ax + by + c = 0$ is $a(x - h) + b(y - k) = 0$. This is another straight method to write a line parallel to a given line and passing through a given point.

§14.(a) Condition for two lines to be perpendicular.

In this case, $\theta = 90°$ and $\tan \theta = \tan 90° = \infty$; hence from 11,
$$m_1 m_2 = -1$$
or **Product of their slopes = −1**
or $m_2 = -1/m_1$
*i.e., slope of one is negative reciprocal of the slope of the other
or $\left(-\dfrac{A_1}{B_1} \right)\left(-\dfrac{A_2}{B_2} \right) = -1$ or $A_1 A_2 + B_1 B_2 = 0$

*i.e. Product of the coeff. of x + Product of the coeff. of $y = 0$

(b) Condition for the lines to be equally inclined to axes.

In this case $m_1 = -m_2$ $\therefore$ $-\dfrac{A_1}{B_1} = \dfrac{A_2}{B_2}$

$\therefore \quad \tan (\pi - \theta) = -\tan \theta$
or $\dfrac{A_1}{A_2} = -\dfrac{B_1}{B_2}$

Hence $2x + 3y + 7 = 0$ and $2x - 3y + 9 = 0$ are equally inclined to the axes of co-ordinates.

§15. Rule to write a line perpendicular to a given line.

Interchange the coefficients of x and y in the given equation and change the sign in between them. Also change the constant term. The value of the new constant is to be found by an additional given condition.
For example, a line perpendicular to
$$2x - 3y + 5 = 0 \text{ is}$$

$$3x + 2y + \lambda = 0.$$

***Alt.** A line through (h, k) perpendicular to a given line $ax + by + c = 0$ is

$$b(x - h) - a(y - k) = 0$$

§16. The general equation of a line through the intersection of two given lines $P = 0$ and $Q = 0$ is $P + \lambda Q = 0$.

The value of λ is to be found by an additional given condition.

Deduction : Very Important Result

The line through the intersection of
$l_1 \equiv a_1 x + b_1 y + c_1 = 0$ and $l_2 \equiv a_2 x + b_2 y + c_2 = 0$
and perpendicular or parallel to

$$l_3 \equiv a_3 x + b_3 y + c_3 = 0$$
$$P + \lambda Q = 0 \qquad \ldots (1)$$

Condition of perpendicularity with third line gives

$$(a_1 + \lambda a_2) a_3 + (b_1 + \lambda b_2) b_3 = 0$$

$$\therefore \quad \lambda = -\frac{a_1 a_3 + b_1 b_3}{a_2 a_3 + b_2 b_3}$$

Putting in (1) the required line is

$$\frac{a_1 x + b_1 y + c_1}{a_1 a_3 + b_1 b_3} = \frac{a_2 x + b_2 y + c_2}{a_2 a_3 + b_2 b_3} \qquad \ldots (2)$$

$(D^r = \text{Trin-Trin of } 1, 3 \text{ and of } 2, 3)$

Trin Trin of 1, 3 means sum of products of the coefficients of x and y in the lines (1) and (3) *i.e.*, $a_1 a_3 + b_1 b_3$.

Note the form, you need not find the point of intersection. You can use it as a formula.

Condition of parallelism gives

$$\frac{a_1 - \lambda a_2}{a_3} = \frac{b_1 - \lambda b_2}{b_3}$$

or $\quad a_1 b_3 - b_1 a_3 = \lambda (a_2 b_3 - a_3 b_2)$
Putting for λ in (1), required line is

$$\frac{a_1 x + b_1 y + c_1}{a_1 b_3 - a_3 b_1} = \frac{a_2 x + b_2 y + c_2}{a_2 b_3 - a_3 b_2}$$

$$D^r = \text{det. of } (1, 3) \text{ and det. of } (2, 3).$$

det of 1, 3 ⇒ determinant formed by the coefficients of x and y is the equation of the lines (1) and (3)

i.e., $\quad \begin{vmatrix} a_1 & b_1 \\ a_3 & b_3 \end{vmatrix} = a_1 b_3 - a_3 b_1$

Above results are given in question form in **Q. 9 (a, b), P. 822 Problem Set (5).**

§17. (a) Length of perpendicular from a given point (x_1, y_1) to a given line $ax + by + c = 0$ is

$$\frac{|ax_1 + by_1 + c|}{\sqrt{(a^2 + b^2)}}$$

i.e. Substitute the co-ordinates of the point and divide by square root of the sum of the squares of the coefficients of x and y.

(b) Position of two points $L(x_1, y_1)$ and $M(x_2, y_2)$ with respect to a given line AB, $ax + by + c = 0$.

Rule : Put the co-ordinates of the given points in the equation of the line and if the results are of the same sign *i.e.*, either both $+$ or both $-$, then the two points L and M lie on the same side of line AB as in Fig. (a).

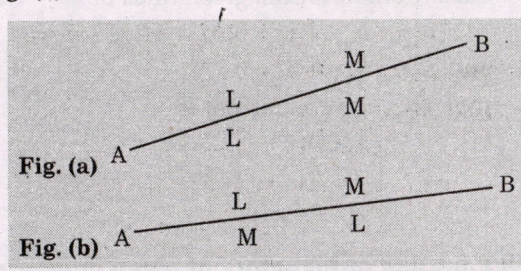

Fig. (a)

Fig. (b)

Fig. 4

In case the results are of opposite signs then the two points are on opposite sides of the line as in Fig. (b).

$\left[\begin{array}{l} ax_1 + by_1 + c_1 \text{ and } ax_2 + by_2 + c_2 \text{ i.e. } l_1 \text{ and } l_2 \\ \text{If of the same sign then } L, M \text{ on same side of } l = 0. \\ \text{If of opposite signs then } L, M \text{ on opposite sides.} \end{array}\right.$

(c) Origin side and non-origin side

Choosing (x_2, y_2) as $(0, 0)$ we say that (x_1, y_1) and $(0, 0)$ lie on the same side (**origin side**) if $ax_1 + by_1 + c_1$ and c_1 have the same sign. But if they have opposite signs, then we say that the points (x_1, y_1) and $(0, 0)$ lie on the opposite sides (**non-origin side**).

Consider the line $4x + 5y - 7 = 0$. The points $(2, 1)$ and $(0, 1)$ when put in the equation of the line, gives $+6, -2$ *i.e.* of the opposite sign and hence they lie on the opposite sides.

The point $(2, 1)$ lies on **non-origin side** as $+6$ and -7 are of opposite signs. But $(0, 1)$ lies on origin side as -2 and -7 are of same sign.

Ex. If the points $(3, 5)$ and $(\cos \theta, \sin \theta)$ $(0 < \theta < \pi)$ lie on the same side of the line $x + y - 1 = 0$, then prove that θ must lie in the first quadrant.

Both the points when put must give results of the same sign, $(3, 5)$ gives $+7$ *i.e.* $+$ive.

$\therefore \quad \cos \theta + \sin \theta - 1 > 0$

or $\quad \dfrac{1}{\sqrt{2}} \cos \theta + \dfrac{1}{\sqrt{2}} \sin \theta > \dfrac{1}{\sqrt{2}}$

$\therefore \quad \sin\left(\theta + \dfrac{\pi}{4}\right) > \dfrac{1}{\sqrt{2}} = \sin \dfrac{\pi}{4}$ or $\sin \dfrac{3\pi}{4}$

or $\quad \dfrac{\pi}{4} < \theta + \dfrac{\pi}{4} < \dfrac{3\pi}{4}$

$\therefore \quad 0 < \theta < \dfrac{\pi}{2}$ *i.e.* θ lies in 1st quadrant.

§18. Method to prove three lines to be concurrent

1st Method : Find the point of intersection of any two lines and show that it satisfies the third also.

2nd Method : If $P = 0, Q = 0$, and $R = 0$ be the equations of the given lines and if

$$lP + mQ + nR = 0 \text{ takes the form}$$
$$0x + 0y + 0 = 0$$

where l, m and n are any three constants to be found by inspection then the three given lines are concurrent.

*3rd Method : If the given lines be

$$a_1 x + b_1 y + c_1 = 0, \quad a_2 x + b_2 y + c_2 = 0$$

and $a_3 x + b_3 y + c_3 = 0$

then they are concurrent if

$$\begin{vmatrix} a_1 & b_1 & c_1 \\ a_2 & b_2 & c_2 \\ a_3 & b_3 & c_3 \end{vmatrix} = 0.$$

§19. Equation of bisectors of given lines are

$$\frac{a_1 x + b_1 y + c_1}{\sqrt{(a_1^2 + b_1^2)}} = \pm \frac{a_2 x + b_2 y + c_2}{\sqrt{(a_2^2 + b_2^2)}} \qquad ...(1)$$

Any point on the bisector is equidistant from the given lines.

§20. Some special cases :

(a) **To find the equation of the bisector in which the origin lies :** First make the constants c_1 and c_2 either both +ive or both −ive in the two equations and then take only + sign in (1) of (19) out of ± .
If the given lines be $3x + 4y + 5 = 0$ and $5x - 12y - 7 = 0$ then write the 2nd equation as $-5x + 12y + 7 = 0$ so that the constant terms in both are of the same sign.

(b)* **Bisector of acute or obtuse angle :** By (a) find the bisector of the angle in which origin lies by choosing + sign only out of ± signs after making the constants c_1 and c_2 of the same sign. Now evaluate $a_1 a_2 + b_1 b_2$ and if **+ ive then origin lies in obtuse angle and if $a_1 a_2 + b_1 b_2$ is − ive then origin lies in acute angle.** **(Remember)**

Alternative method is given below :

(c) **To find the bisector of acute or obtuse angle :** If θ be the angle between one of the given lines and any one bisector, then find $\tan \theta$. If $|\tan \theta| < 1$, it is the bisector of the acute angle and if $|\tan \theta| > 1$, then it is the bisector of the obtuse angle.

Ex. 1. If the given lines be $3x + 4y - 11 = 0$ and $12x - 5y - 2 = 0$, then find the bisectors of the angles between them and discriminate which bisects the acute angle or which bisects the obtuse angle.

Sol. The constants in both the equations are of the same sign.

Also $a_1 a_2 + b_1 b_2 = 36 - 20 = 16$, + ive therefore origin lies in obtuse angle by **20 (b)**. The two bisectors are

$$\frac{3x + 4y - 11}{5} = \pm \frac{12x - 5y - 2}{13}$$

+ive sign will give the bisector of the angle in which origin lies and it lies in obtuse angle

$$(39 - 60) x + (52 + 25) y + (-11.13 + 5.2) = 0$$
or $\quad -21x + 77y - 133 = 0$
or $\quad 3x - 11y + 19 = 0$

Verification by Alternative Method :

Find the angle which this bisector makes with any line, say $3x + 4y - 11 = 0$

$$\tan \theta = \left| \frac{3.4 + 11.3}{3.3 - 11.4} \right| = \frac{45}{35} > 1 \qquad \textbf{(by § 11 P. 768)}$$

$\therefore \quad \theta > 45° \quad$ or $\quad 2\theta > 90°$

Hence this bisector is bisector of obtuse angle.

Ex. 2. Find the equation of the bisector of acute angle between the lines $5y - 12x = 20$ and $3x - 4y = 8$.

Sol. Rewrite the given equations so that the constant terms in both the equations are of the same sign.

$\therefore \quad 12x - 5y + 20 = 0$
$\quad\quad -3x + 4y + 8 = 0$

Also $a_1 a_2 + b_1 b_2 = -36 - 20 = -56 = -$ive

Origin lies in acute angle.

$\therefore$ Choose + sign only out of ± from the equation of bisectors

$$\frac{12x - 5y + 20}{13} = + \frac{-3x + 4y + 8}{5}$$

or $\quad (60 + 39) x - (25 + 52) y + (100 + 104) = 0$
or $\quad 99x - 77y - 4 = 0$

is the bisector of acute angle.

Verification by Alternate Method.

Choose any one line and any bisector, say

$l \quad\quad 3x - 4y - 8 = 0$
$B \quad\quad 99x - 77y - 4 = 0$

$$\tan \theta = \frac{3(-77) + 4(99)}{3(99) + 4(77)} \qquad \textbf{(by § 11 P. 768)}$$

$$= \frac{-21 + 36}{27 + 28} = \frac{15}{55} = \frac{3}{11} < 1$$

$\therefore \quad \theta < 45° \quad$ or $\quad 2\theta < 90°$

Hence this is a bisector of acute angle between the given lines.

(d)* **Internal bisector :** Find the two bisectors. Let B_1 be one of them. Now if the points B and C are on opposite sides of B_1, then it is internal and other B_2 is external. **[17 (b)]**

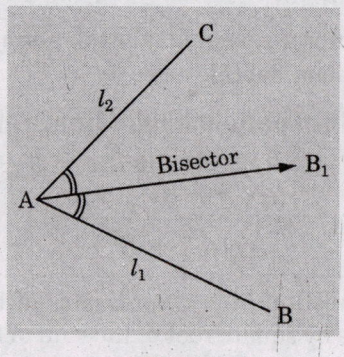

Fig. 5

§21. Distance between parallel lines

First Method : Find the distance of each from the origin and **retain their signs**. If these be p_1 and p_2 respectively, the required distance between parallel lines is $p_1 \sim p_2$.

*Second Method : Choose a point on any of the lines (Put $x = 0$ and find the value of y or put $y = 0$ and find the value of x). Now find the perpendicular distance of this point from the other line which will be the required distance between the given parallel lines.

§22. Area of a parallelogram

Area of $\|^m = 2$. Area of $\Delta\, ABD$

$= 2 \cdot (1/2)\, AB \cdot AD \cdot \sin\theta$.

But if p_1 and p_2 be the distances between the parallel sides, then from the figure

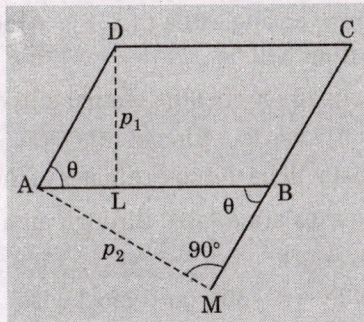

Fig. 6

$\dfrac{p_1}{AD} = \sin\theta, \dfrac{p_2}{AB} = \sin\theta$

$\therefore$ Area $= \dfrac{p_2}{\sin\theta} \cdot \dfrac{p_1}{\sin\theta} \cdot \sin\theta = \dfrac{p_1 p_2}{\sin\theta}$

*Area $= \dfrac{p_1 p_2}{\sin\theta}$ where p_1 and p_2 are the distances between parallel sides and θ is the angle between two adjacent sides. In case of a rhombus $p_1 = p_2$. Also area of rhombus $= \dfrac{1}{2} d_1 d_2$ where d_1, d_2 are the lengths of two perpendicular diagonals of a rhombus.

Illustration : If the sides of a parallelogram be

$a_1 x + b_1 y + c_1 = 0 \quad a_1 x + b_1 y + d_1 = 0$

$a_2 x + b_2 y + c_2 = 0 \quad a_2 x + b_2 y + d_2 = 0 \quad$ then

Area $= \dfrac{p_1 p_2}{\sin\theta} = \dfrac{(c_1 - d_1)(c_2 - d_2)}{\sqrt{} \cdot \sqrt{}} \div \dfrac{a_1 b_2 - a_2 b_1}{\sqrt{} \cdot \sqrt{}}$

i.e., $\sin\theta$

$= \dfrac{\left|(c_1 - d_1)(c_2 - d_2)\right|}{\begin{vmatrix} a_1 & b_1 \\ a_2 & b_2 \end{vmatrix}}$

Formula by **Rule 11 P. 768.**

Numerical :

$2x - 3y + a = 0 \qquad 3x - 2y - 2a = 0$

$2x - 3y + 3a = 0 \qquad 3x - 2y - a = 0$

Area of $\|^m = \left| \dfrac{(3a - a)(-a + 2a)}{\begin{vmatrix} 2 & -3 \\ 3 & -2 \end{vmatrix}} \right| = \dfrac{2a^2}{5}$.

§23. The locus and how to find its equation

Definition : The locus of a moving point is the path traced out by that point when it moves under certain given condition or conditions.

To find the locus of a point P, we proceed as follows : Take co-ordinates of P as (h, k). Then find a relation between h, k by eliminating the parameter or parameters for different values of which the locus of (h, k) is to be obtained. Now generalize (h, k) by replacing h by x and k by y to get the required equation of the locus.

Important : To find the locus of the point of intersection of two straight lines, eliminate the parameter or parameters from the given lines.

If there are more than one parameter, then additional condition or conditions will also be given.

Locus in Special Cases

(a) Locus of the point represented by the equation $x^2 + y^2 = 0$ is the point origin $(0, 0)$ only. The above equation is satisfied only when both $x = 0$ and $y = 0$. **(See Q. 18 P. 776-780)**

(b) Similarly if the point satisfies the relation

$\{p(x, y)\}^2 + \{q(x, y)\}^2 = 0$

The locus of the point is the intersection of the loci of the equations $p(x, y) = 0$ and $q(x, y) = 0$

(c) Locus of points satisfying the relation $xy = 0$ Locus is given by $x = 0$ or $y = 0$ or both are zero) is set of all points on the axes of co-ordinates.

(d) If A and B be two fixed points then the locus of moving point P which is equidistant from both A and B is **the right bisector** of the line AB.

(e) Similarly if $l_1 = 0$ and $l_2 = 0$ be two intersecting lines then the locus of a point P which is equidistant from the given two lines is the pair of bisectors (internal and external bisectors) of angle between the given lines. **(See Q. 31 P. 825-836)**

(f) Locus of $xy > 0$ (*i.e.,* both x, y are either + ive or both − ive) is the set of all points either in Ist or in 3rd quadrant excluding the points on the co-ordinate axes because neither $x = 0$ nor $y = 0$. Similarly $xy < 0$ represents the points either in 2nd or in 4th quadrants excluding the points on the co-ordinate axes.

§24. Certain important rules

(a)* Any two points A and B may be taken along the axis of x and their middle point be chosen as origin. If the length $AB = 2a$ then $OA = OB = a$ so that A is $(a, 0)$ and B is $(-a, 0)$. Choosing the points as such will make the problems simple.

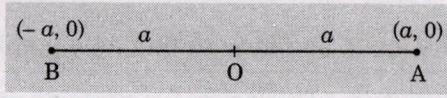

Fig. 7

(b)* Any two perpendicular lines may be chosen as axes of co-ordinates i.e. x-axis and y-axis.

(c) Shifting of origin $O(0, 0)$ to $P(h, k)$.
For this replace x by $x + h$ and y by $y + k$ in the given equation.
If the old co-ordinates (x, y) become (X, Y) with the shifting of origin, then

Old New Pt.
$x = X + h$
$y = Y + k$

After substitution change X, Y to x, y.
∴ Original equation $f(x, y) = 0$ becomes new equation

$$f(X + h, Y + k) = 0 \qquad ...(1)$$

Converse. If the new equation by shifting the origin to (h, k) is $f(X, Y)$, then the original will be

$$f(x - h, y - k) = 0 \qquad ...(2)$$

(h, k) of (1) go to $(-h, -k)$.

Illustrations :

Ex. 1. The origin is shifted to $(-2, 3)$ then what are the co-ordinates of the point $(3, -5)$ in the new position ?
$(x, y) \Rightarrow (X + h, Y + k) = (X - 2, Y + 3)$
$(3, -5) \Rightarrow (X - 2, Y + 3)$ ∴ $(X, Y) = (5, -8)$

Ex. 2. If the origin is shifted to $(1, -2)$, the co-ordinates of A become $(2, 3)$. What are the original co-ordinates of A ?

Old New Pt.
$x = X + h = 2 + 1 = 3$
$y = Y + k = 3 - 2 = 1$ ∴ $(3, 1)$

Ex. 3. Determine as to what point the axes of the co-ordinates be shifted so as to remove the first degree terms from the equation

$$f(x, y) = 2x^2 + 3y^2 - 12x + 12y + 24 = 0$$

Let the origin be shifted to (h, k).
Old New Pt.
$x = X + h$
$y = Y + k$
$2(X + h)^2 + 3(Y + k)^2 - 12(X + h) + 12(Y + k) + 24 = 0$
$2X^2 + 3Y^2 + X(4h - 12) + Y(6k + 12)$
$\qquad + (2h^2 + 3k^2 - 12h + 12k) = 0$

Since the equation is to be free of first degree terms, therefore coefficients of X and Y is each separately zero.
∴ $4h - 12 = 0$ and $6k + 12 = 0$
∴ $(h, k) = (3, -2)$

(d) Rotation of axes through an angle θ
Replace x by $\qquad x \cos\theta - y \sin\theta$
and y by $\qquad x \sin\theta + y \cos\theta$
Old New Pt.
$x = X \cos\theta - Y \sin\theta$
$y = X \sin\theta + Y \cos\theta$
After substitution change X, Y to x, y.
Original equation $f(x, y) = 0$ becomes new equation

$$f(X \cos\theta - Y \sin\theta, X \sin\theta + Y \cos\theta) = 0 \qquad ...(1)$$

Converse. If new equation by rotating the axes through an angle θ be $f(X, Y) = 0$ then the original equation will be

$$f[(x \cos\theta + y \sin\theta), (-x \sin\theta + y \cos\theta)] = 0 \qquad ...(2)$$

θ of (1) goes to $-\theta$ to get (2).

Ex. 4. What will be the co-ordinates of the point $(4, 2\sqrt{3})$ when the axes are rotated through an angle of $30°$ in clockwise sense ?

Old New Pt. $\theta = -30°$ (anti-clockwise)
$x = X \cos\theta - Y \sin\theta$
$y = X \sin\theta + Y \cos\theta$
$4 = X \dfrac{\sqrt{3}}{2} + \dfrac{Y}{2}$ or $X\sqrt{3} + Y = 8$
$2\sqrt{3} = -\dfrac{X}{2} + Y \dfrac{\sqrt{3}}{2}$ or $-X + Y\sqrt{3} = 4\sqrt{3}$

Solving, we get $X = \sqrt{3}, Y = 5$

Hence co-ordinates in new position are $(\sqrt{3}, 5)$.

Ex. 5. What will be the co-ordinates of the point in original position if its co-ordinates after rotation of axes through an angle $60°$ be $(2, -\sqrt{3})$?

Old New
$x = X \cos\theta - Y \sin\theta$ $\qquad \theta = 60°$
$y = X \sin\theta + Y \cos\theta$ $\qquad (X, Y) = (2, -\sqrt{3})$
$x = 2 \cdot \dfrac{1}{2} + \sqrt{3} \cdot \dfrac{\sqrt{3}}{2} = \dfrac{5}{2}$
$y = 2 \cdot \dfrac{\sqrt{3}}{2} - \sqrt{3} \cdot \dfrac{1}{2} = \dfrac{\sqrt{3}}{2}$ ∴ $\left(\dfrac{5}{2}, \dfrac{\sqrt{3}}{2}\right)$

(e)* Foot of perpendicular from a point (α, β) to a given line $l \equiv ax + by + c = 0$
If (h, k) be the foot, then

$$ah + bk + c = 0 \qquad ...(1)$$

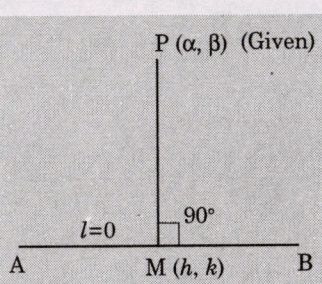

Fig. 8

Also $\dfrac{k-\beta}{h-\alpha} \times \left(-\dfrac{a}{b}\right) = -1$ by $m_1 m_2 = -1$

or $\dfrac{h-\alpha}{a} = \dfrac{k-\beta}{b} = \dfrac{a(h-\alpha)+b(k-\beta)}{a.a+b.b}$

$= -\dfrac{(a\alpha+b\beta+c)}{a^2+b^2} = -\dfrac{l'}{a^2+b^2}$ by (1)

The above relations will give the foot of perpendicular straight way.

Alt. Write the equation of a line through the given point (α, β) and perpendicular to $ax+by+c=0$ as $b(x-\alpha)-a(y-\beta)=0$.

Solving these two, we get the foot of perpendicular.

Illustration :

Foot of perpendicular from $C(1,2)$ on line AB i.e. $l \equiv 2x+3y+5=0$

1st Method : Equation of CD through $C(1,2)$ and $\perp$ to $AB : 2x+3y+5=0$. is

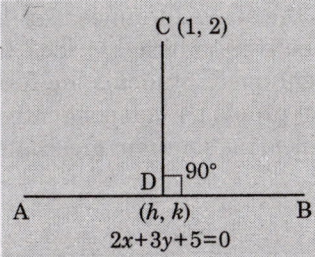

Fig. 9

$3(x-1)-2(y-2)=0$

or $3x-2y+1=0$

Solving this with AB $2x+3y+5=0$, we get the point D as $(-1,-1)$.

2nd Method : We can straight way write as under

$\dfrac{h-1}{2} = \dfrac{k-2}{3} = -\dfrac{(2.1+3.2+5)}{2^2+3^2} = -1$

i.e. $-\dfrac{l'}{a^2+b^2} = -1$

$\therefore h=-1, k=-1$. i.e. $(-1,-1)$ is the foot of perpendicular as found above.

(e₁)* Reflection (Image) of a point P about a line

Reflection of P about a line l will be the point Q such that the mid-point of PQ lies on the line l and PQ is perpendicular to l.

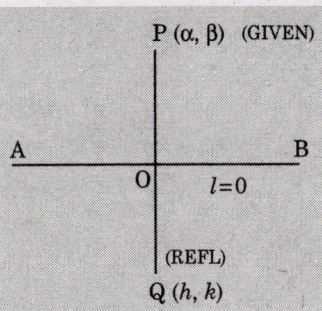

Fig. 10

The mid-point of PQ lies on $l = 0$.

$a\left(\dfrac{h+\alpha}{2}\right) + b\left(\dfrac{k+\beta}{2}\right) + c = 0$

or $ah+bk = -a\alpha-b\beta-2c$ ...(1)

Again PQ is $\perp$ to AB

$\left(\dfrac{k-\beta}{h-\alpha}\right)\left(-\dfrac{a}{b}\right) = -1$

$\dfrac{h-\alpha}{a} = \dfrac{k-\beta}{b} = \dfrac{a(h-\alpha)+b(k-\beta)}{a^2+b^2}$

$= -\dfrac{2(a\alpha+b\beta+c)}{a^2+b^2} = -\dfrac{2l'}{a^2+b^2}$ by (1)

Note that the formulae for the foot of $\perp$ as in (e) and image as written above in (e₁) are almost identical except that there is -2 instead of -1. (α, β) is known point and (h,k) is either foot of $\perp$ or image.

Particular Case

The image of the point $P(x,y)$ about

(a) x-axis is the point $(x,-y)$

(b) y-axis is the point $(-x, y)$

(c) line $y=x$ is the point (y, x)

(d) line $y=x\tan\theta$ is the point $(x\cos 2\theta + y\sin 2\theta, x\sin 2\theta - y\cos 2\theta)$

Ex. Let $0 < \alpha < \pi/2$ be a fixed angle. If $P = (\cos\theta, \sin\theta)$ and $Q = (\cos(\alpha-\theta), \sin(\alpha-\theta))$, then Q is obtained from P by

(a) clockwise rotation around origin through an angle α

(b) Anticlockwise rotation around orgin through an angle α

(c) reflection in the line through origin with slope $\tan\alpha$

(d) reflection in the line through origin with slope $\tan(\alpha/2)$ **(I.I.T. Sc. 2002)**

Ans. (d). Clearly $OP=OQ=1$

and $\angle QOP = \alpha-\theta-\theta = (\alpha-2\theta)$

The bisector of $\angle QOP$ will a perpendicular to PQ and also bisect it. Hence Q is reflection of P in the line OM which makes an angle $\angle MOP + \angle POX$ with x-axis i.e. $\dfrac{1}{2}(\alpha-2\theta)+\theta = \dfrac{\alpha}{2}$ so that slope of OM is $\tan\dfrac{\alpha}{2}$.

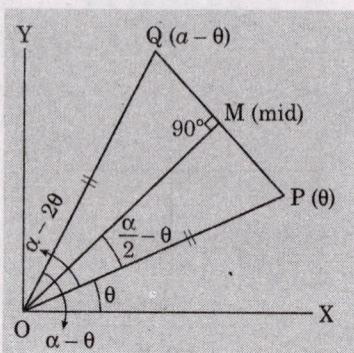

Fig. 11

Converse : If a point P and its image Q are given, then to find the line.

Write a line through mid-point of PQ and perpendicular to PQ whose slope is known.

(f)   Ratio in which a line $L \equiv ax + by + c = 0$ is divided by the line joining the points (x_1, y_1) and (x_2, y_2)

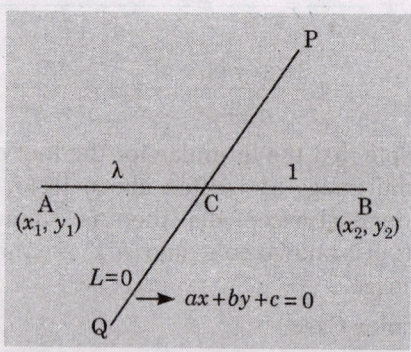

Fig. 12

The point $C \left(\dfrac{\lambda x_2 + x_1}{\lambda + 1}, \dfrac{\lambda y_2 + y_1}{\lambda + 1} \right)$ lies on

$ax + by + c = 0$.

$$a \left(\frac{\lambda x_2 + x_1}{\lambda + 1} \right) + b \left(\frac{\lambda y_2 + y_1}{\lambda + 1} \right) + c = 0$$

or $\lambda (ax_2 + by_2 + c) + (ax_1 + by_1 + c) = 0$

$$\frac{\lambda}{1} = - \frac{ax_1 + by_1 + c}{ax_2 + by_2 + c} = - \frac{L_1}{L_2} \quad \text{(Formula)}$$

Example : PQ $x + y - 4 = 0$ divides AB joining $(-1, 1)$ and $(5, 7)$ in the ratio

$$= - \frac{ax_1 + by_1 + c}{ax_2 + by_2 + c} = - \frac{L_1}{L_2}$$

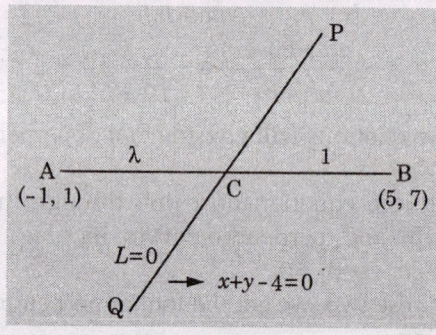

Fig. 13

$$= - \frac{-1 + 1 - 4}{5 + 7 - 4} = \frac{4}{8} = \frac{1}{2} = 1 : 2$$

Note : In all the questions to follow we shall give reference to the above formulae. For the proofs of the above, students are advised to look to the reference books as mentioned. Students are further advised to work out the problems independently and in case of difficulty look to the solutions given after the exercise.

Problem Set (1)

Distance between two points, Nature of triangles, centroid etc.

1. (a) The vertices A, B, C of a triangle are $(2, 1)$, $(5, 2)$ and $(3, 4)$ respectively. Find the coordinates of the circumcentre and also the radius of the circum-circle.

   (b)* The co-ordinates of base BC of an isosceles triangle ABC are given by $B(1, 3)$ and $C(-2, 7)$. Which of the following points can be the possible co-ordinates of the vertex A :

   (i) $\left(-7, \dfrac{1}{8} \right)$ (ii) $(1, 6)$

   (iii) $\left(-\dfrac{1}{2}, 5 \right)$ (iv) $\left(\dfrac{5}{6}, 6 \right)$

2. (a) Prove that the points $(0, -1), (2, 1), (0, 3)$ and $(-2, 1)$ are the vertices of a square.

   (b) Show that the points $A(-4, -1)$, $B(-2, -4), C(4, 0)$ and $D(2, 3)$

are the vertices of rectangle.

   (c) P and Q are points on the line joining $A(-2, 5)$ and $B(3, 1)$ such that $AP = PQ = QB$. Prove that the mid-point of PQ is $(1/2, 3)$.

3. (a) Show that the points $(2a, 4a), (2a, 6a)$ $(2a + \sqrt{3}a, 5a)$ are the vertices of an equilateral triangle.

   (b) Find a if the distance between $(a, 2)$ and $(3, 4)$ is 8.

4. (a) Show that the points $(12, 8), (-2, 6)$ and $(6, 0)$, are the vertices of a right angled triangle.

   (b) Discuss the nature of the triangle formed by the lines :

   (i) $x + y = 0$, $3x + y - 4 = 0$, $x + 3y - 4 = 0$

   (ii) $x + y - 4 = 0$, $3x + y - 4 = 0$, $x + 3y - 4 = 0$

5. (i) Find the co-ordinates of the incentre and centroid of the triangle whose vertices are $(-36, 7)$, $(20, 7), (0, -8)$.

(ii) The incentre of the triangle with vertices $(1, \sqrt{3})$, $(0, 0)$ and $(2, 0)$ is

(a) $\left(1, \dfrac{\sqrt{3}}{2}\right)$ (b) $\left(\dfrac{2}{3}, \dfrac{1}{\sqrt{3}}\right)$

(c) $\left(\dfrac{2}{3}, \dfrac{\sqrt{3}}{2}\right)$ (d) $\left(1, \dfrac{1}{\sqrt{3}}\right)$ **(I.I.T. Sc. 2000)**

(iii) If a vertex of a triangle is $(1, 1)$ and the mid-point of two sides through the vertex are $(-1, 2)$ and $(3, 2)$, then the centroid of the triangle is

(a) $(1, 7/3)$ (b) $(1/3, 7/3)$

(c) $(-1, 7/3)$ (d) $(-1/3, 7/3)$ **(AIEEE 2005)**

6. (a)* If the point $P(x, y)$ be equidistant from the points $A(a+b, b-a)$ and $B(a-b, a+b)$ then prove that $bx = ay$.

(b) If the equation of the locus of a point equidistant from the points (a_1, b_1) and (a_2, b_2) is
$$(a_1 - a_2)x + (b_1 - b_2)y + c = 0,$$
then the value of c is :

(a) $\dfrac{1}{2}(a_2^2 + b_2^2 - a_1^2 - b_1^2)$

(b) $(a_1^2 - a_2^2 + b_1^2 - b_2^2)$

(c) $\dfrac{1}{2}(a_1^2 + a_2^2 + b_1^2 + b_2^2)$

(d) $\sqrt{(a_1^2 + b_1^2 - a_2^2 - b_2^2)}$ **(AIEEE 2003)**

7.* If G be the centroid of a triangle ABC and O be any other point, then prove that
(i) $AB^2 + BC^2 + CA^2 = 3(GA^2 + GB^2 + GC^2)$
(ii) $OA^2 + OB^2 + OC^2 = GA^2 + GB^2 + GC^2 + 3GO^2$.

8. Prove analytically that in a right angled triangle the mid-point of the hypotenuse is equidistant from the three angular points.

9. Prove analytically the line joining the mid-points of two sides of a triangle is half the third side.

10. In any triangle ABC, prove that
$$AB^2 + AC^2 = 2(AO^2 + OC^2)$$
where O is mid-point of BC.

11. (a) If O be the origin and if co-ordinates of any two points Q_1 and Q_2 be (x_1, y_1) and (x_2, y_2) respectively, prove that
$$OQ_1 \cdot OQ_2 \cos Q_1 O Q_2 = x_1 x_2 + y_1 y_2$$

(b) The vertices of a triangle ABC are $A(0, 0)$, $B(2, -1)$, and $C(9, 2)$. Evaluate $\cos B$.

12. (a) The extremities of the diagonal of a parallelogram are the points $(3, -4)$ and $(-6, 5)$. Third vertex is the point $(5, 4)$. Find the co-ordinates of the fourth vertex.

(b) Show that the points $(-2, -1)$, $(1, 0)$, $(4, 3)$ and $(1, 2)$ are the vertices of a parallelogram.

13. (a) Prove that perpendicular from origin to the line joining the points $(c \cos \alpha,\ c \sin \alpha)$ and $(c \cos \beta,\ c \sin \beta)$ bisects it as well.

(b) The triangle OAB is right angled where points O, A, B are $(0, 0)$, $(\cos \theta, \sin \theta)$ and $(\cos \phi,\ \sin \phi)$ respectively, then θ and ϕ are connected by the relations
$$\sin\left(\frac{\theta - \phi}{2}\right) = \pm \frac{1}{\sqrt{2}} \text{ and } \cos\left(\frac{\theta - \phi}{2}\right) = \pm \frac{1}{\sqrt{2}}$$

(c) The line joining the points $A(b \cos \theta, b \sin \theta)$ and $B(a \cos \phi,\ b \cos \phi)$ is produced to the point $L(x, y)$ so that $AL : LB = b : a$, then
$$x \cos \frac{\theta + \phi}{2} + y \sin \frac{\theta + \phi}{2} =$$
(a) 1   (b) -1
(c) 0   (d) $a^2 + b^2$

14. (a)* A point moves such that the sum of its distances from two fixed points $(ae, 0)$, and $(-ae, 0)$ is always $2a$. Prove that the equation of the locus is
$$\frac{x^2}{a^2} + \frac{y^2}{a^2(1 - e^2)} = 1.$$
     (B.I.T.S. 1999)

(b) A and B are two points in a plane so that
(i) $PA + PB = $ constant, or (ii) $PA - PB = $ constant, or (iii) $PA^2 + PB^2 = $ constant. Show that the locus of P is an ellipse in case (i), is a hyperbola in case (ii), and is a circle in case (iii).

(c)* The equation $\sqrt{(x-2)^2 + y^2} + \sqrt{(x+2)^2 + y^2} = 4$ represents a pair of coincident lines. T or F.

15. The ends of a rod of length l move on two mutually perpendicular lines. Find the locus of the point on the rod which divides it in the ratio $1 : 2$.

16.* A circle is inscribed in an equilateral triangle of side a. The area of any square inscribed in the circle is .....   **(I.I.T. 1994)**

17.* (a) If $(\alpha, \beta), (\bar{x}, \bar{y})$ and (p, q) are the co-ordinates of the circumcentre, centroid and orthocentre of a triangle, prove that $3\bar{x} = 2\alpha + p$ and $3\bar{y} = 2\beta + q$

(b) Find the co-ordinates of the centroid and circumcentre of the triangle whose vertices are $(2, 3)$, $(3, 4)$ and $(6, 8)$ and hence find the coordinates of its orthocentre.

(c) Find the co-ordinates of the centroid, circumcentre and orthocentre of the triangle formed by the lines $3x - 2y - 6 = 0$, $3x + 4y + 12 = 0$ and $3x - 8y + 12 = 0$.

(d) The line $Ax + By + C = 0$ cuts the x-axis at P and y-axis at Q. Find the co-ordinates of the ortho-centre, centroid and circum-centre of the $\triangle OPQ$.

(e) The vertices of a triangle are the points $A(-36, 7), B(20, 7)$ and $C(0, -8)$. If G and I be the centroid and incentre of the triangle, then GI is equal to

(a) $\frac{1}{3}\sqrt{397}$ (b) $\frac{1}{3}\sqrt{173}$

(c) $\frac{1}{3}\sqrt{205}$ (d) none

(f) The co-ordinates of the base BC of an isosceles triangle are $B(1,3)$ and $C(-2,7)$ then the co-ordinates of its vertex A are

(a) $\left(\frac{5}{6},6\right)$ (b) $\left(-7,\frac{1}{8}\right)$

(c) $(1,6)$ (d) $\left(-\frac{1}{2},5\right)$

18. (a) What is the nature of the locus represented by the equation $(x-y+c)^2+(x+y-c)^2=0$

(b) If a,b,c are related by $4a^2+9b^2-9c^2+12ab=0$ then the greatest distance between any two lines of the family of lines $ax+by+c=0$ is :

(a) $\frac{4}{3}$ (b) $\frac{2}{3}\sqrt{13}$

(c) $3\sqrt{3}$ (d) 0

19. If two medians of a triangle be equal then the triangle must be isosceles.

20.* The co-ordinates of four points on axis of x are $A(p,0)$, $B(q,0)$, $C(r,0)$, $D(s,0)$ such that p,q are the roots of $ax^2+2hx+b=0$ and r,s are the roots of $a'x^2+2h'x+b'=0$. If $\frac{AC}{CB}=\lambda$ and $\frac{AD}{DB}=\mu$ then $\lambda+\mu=0$ if $ab'+a'b=2hh'$.

21.* P,Q,R divide the sides of a triangle ABC in the same ratio. Prove that centroids of the triangles ABC and PQR coincide.

22. $A_r=(x_r,y_r)$, $r=1,2,3,\ldots,n$ is a set of n points. P_1 divides $A_1 A_2$ in the ratio $1:1$, P_2 divides $P_1 A_3$ in the ratio $1:2$, P_3 divides $P_2 A_4$ in the ratio $1:3$ and so on. P_{n-1} divides $P_{n-2} A_n$ in the ratio $1:n-1$. Find the co-ordinates of P_{n-1}.

23.* If $P(1,2),Q(4,6),R(5,7)$ and $S(a,b)$ are the vertices of a parallelogram $PQRS$, then

(A) $a=2,b=4$ (B) $a=3,b=4$

(C) $a=2,b=3$ (D) $a=3,b=5$ **(I.I.T. 1998)**

24.* If the vertices P,Q,R of a triangle PQR are rational points, which of the following points of the triangle PQR is (are) always rational point(s) ?

(A) centroid (B) incentre

(C) circumcentre (D) orthocentre **(I.I.T. 1998)**

25. If the line $y=x\sqrt{3}$ cuts the curve $x^3+y^3+3xy+5x^2+3y^2+4x+5y+1=0$ at the points A,B,C then prove that the value of $OA.OB.OC$ is equal to $\frac{4}{13}(3\sqrt{3}-1)$.

Solutions to Problem Set (1)

1. (a) Let $P(x,y)$ be the co-ordinates of the centre of the circumcircle.

$\therefore$ $PA^2=PB^2$ and $PB^2=PC^2$ **[Result 1, P. 765]**

$\therefore$ $3x+y=12$ and $x+3y=10$.

Solving these two we get the centre as $(13/4,9/4)$.

Having found P we can now say that $PA^2=r^2=50/16$ $\therefore$ $r=5\sqrt{2}/4$.

(b) Ans. (i), (iv). If A be (x,y) then $AB=AC$ as Δ ABC is isosceles

$\therefore$ $AB^2=AC^2 \Rightarrow 6x-8y+43=0$

Clearly the points given by (i), (iii) and (iv) satisfy the above relation. The point $\left(-\frac{1}{2},5\right)$ being the mid-point of BC cannot be the point A. Hence (i), (iv).

2. (a) Show that $AB=BC=CD=DA$ and $AC^2=AB^2+BC^2$ i.e. $\angle B=\pi/2$.

(b) Do yourself.

(c) Mid-point of PQ is the same as that of AB in view of the given conditions, i.e. $\left(\frac{1}{2},3\right)$.

3. (a) Show that $AB=BC=CA=2a$.

(b) Ans. $3\pm\sqrt{60}$.

4. (a) Determine the lengths of sides and show that sum of the squares of two is equal to square of the third.

(b) (i) Solving the given equations in pairs, we get the vertices as $A(1,1)$, $B(2,-2)$, $C(-2,2)$. Here $AB=AC=\sqrt{10}$ and $BC=\sqrt{32}$. It follows that the triangle is isosceles.

(ii) Proceed as in (i) $A(0,4)$, $B(1,1)$, $C(4,0)$, $AB=BC=\sqrt{10}$ $\therefore$ Isosceles

5. (i) Determine the sides

$BC=a=25$, $CA=b=39$, $AB=c=56$.

where A,B,C are the vertices as given. Then the incentre by the formula **(6) (iv) P. 766** given by

$x=\frac{\Sigma\,ax_1}{\Sigma\,a}$, $y=\frac{\Sigma\,ay_1}{\Sigma\,a}$ is $(-1,0)$.

Centroid by **6 (i) P. 4** i.e.

$x=(\Sigma\,x_1)/3$, $y=(\Sigma\,y_1)/3$ is $(-16/3,2)$

(ii) Ans. (d).

If the points be A,B,C, then $AB=BC=CA=2$

$\therefore$ Δ is equilateral.

Hence the incentre will coincide with the centroid.

$\left(\frac{\Sigma\,x_1}{3},\frac{\Sigma\,y_1}{3}\right)=\left(1,\frac{1}{\sqrt{3}}\right)$.

(iii) Ans. (a).

E and F are mid-points of AC and AB respectively which pass through vertex A. Hence by mid-point

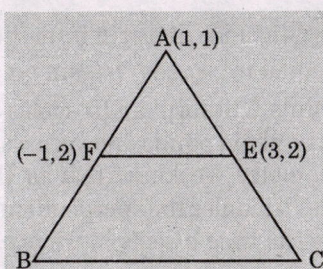

Fig. 14

formula the points C and B are $(5,3)$ and $(-3,3)$ respectively. Hence centroid of $\triangle ABC$ by $\left(\dfrac{\Sigma x_1}{3}, \dfrac{\Sigma y_1}{3}\right)$ is $\left(1, \dfrac{7}{3}\right)$.

6. (a) $PA = PB$, $\therefore$ $PA^2 = PB^2$

or $[x - (a + b)]^2 + [y - (b - a)]^2$

$= [x - (a - b)]^2 + [y - (a + b)]^2$

or $[(x - a) - b]^2 - [(x - a) + b]^2$

$= [(y - b) - a]^2 - [(y - b) + a]^2$

or $-4(x - a)b = -4(y - b)a$

$\qquad [\because (L - M)^2 - (L + M)^2 = -4LM]$

or $bx - ab = ay - ab$ or $\qquad bx = ay$.

Alt. $PA = PB \Rightarrow P$ lies on the right bisector of AB.

Slope of AB is $-\dfrac{a}{b}$. Hence slope of right bisector is

$\dfrac{b}{a}$ and it passes through the mid-point of AB

i.e. (a, b). Its equation is

$y - b = \dfrac{b}{a}(x - a)$ or $bx = ay$.

(b) Ans. (a).

If A, B be the given points then the locus represents the right bisector of AB. Hence it will pass through mid-point of $AB, i.e.,$ $\left(\dfrac{a_1 + a_2}{2}, \dfrac{b_1 + b_2}{2}\right)$. Hence c is as given in (a).

Note : You may use $PA^2 = PB^2$ also.

7. For the sake of convenience let us choose G as origin and the points A, B, C as $(x_1, y_1), (x_2, y_2)$ and (x_3, y_3) respectively and the other point O be taken as (h, k).

Co-ordinates of G are $(\Sigma x_1 / 3, \Sigma y_1 / 3)$

But we have chosen G as origin

$\therefore$ $(\Sigma x_1)/3 = 0$, $(\Sigma y_1)/3 = 0$

or $x_1 + x_2 + x_3 = 0$ and $y_1 + y_2 + y_3 = 0$ ...(1)

(i) $AB^2 + BC^2 + CA^2 = (x_1 - x_2)^2$

$\qquad\qquad\qquad + (y_1 - y_2)^2 + ... + ...$

$= 2(\Sigma x_1^2 + \Sigma y_1^2) - 2(\Sigma x_1 x_2 + \Sigma y_1 y_2)$

$= 3(\Sigma x_1^2 + \Sigma y_1^2) - \Sigma x_1^2 - \Sigma y_1^2$

$\qquad\qquad\qquad - 2\Sigma x_1 x_2 - 2\Sigma y_1 y_2$

[By adding and subtracting $\Sigma x_1^2 + \Sigma y_1^2$]

$= 3(GA^2 + GB^2 + GC^2) - (x_1 + x_2 + x_3)^2$

$\qquad\qquad\qquad - (y_1 + y_2 + y_3)^2$

$= 3(GA^2 + GB^2 + GC^2)$

$\qquad [\because \Sigma x_1 = 0, \Sigma y_1 = 0, \text{by (1)}]$

and $GA^2 = (x_1 - 0)^2 + (y_1 - 0)^2 = x_1^2 + y_1^2$ etc.

(ii) $OA^2 + OB^2 + OC^2 = (h - x_1)^2 + (k - y_1)^2 + ... + ...$

$(x_1^2 + y_1^2) + (x_2^2 + y_2^2) + (x_3^2 + y_3^2)$

$\qquad + (h^2 + k^2) + (h^2 + k^2) + (h^2 + k^2)$

$\qquad - 2h(x_1 + x_2 + x_3) - 2k(y_1 + y_2 + y_3)$

$= GA^2 + GB^2 + GC^2 + GO^2 + GO^2 + GO^2 - 0 - 0,$

$\qquad\qquad\qquad\qquad\qquad\qquad\qquad \text{by (1)}$

$= GA^2 + GB^2 + GC^2 + 3GO^2$

$\qquad [\because GO^2 = (h - 0)^2 + (k - 0)^2 = h^2 + k^2].$

8. Choose the vertices of the right angled triangle as $O(0,0), A(a,0), B(0,b)$. Since the triangle is right angled

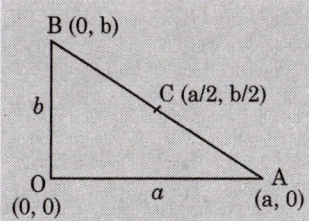

Fig. 15

$\therefore$ $AB^2 = a^2 + b^2$ or $AB = \sqrt{a^2 + b^2}$

If C be the mid-point of AB, then

$CA = CB = \dfrac{1}{2} AB = \dfrac{1}{2}\sqrt{a^2 + b^2}$

Also $CO^2 = (a/2 - 0)^2 + (b/2 - 0)^2$

$\qquad\qquad = \dfrac{1}{4}(a^2 + b^2)$ so that

$CO = \dfrac{1}{2}\sqrt{a^2 + b^2}$.

Hence $CA = CB = CO$.

9. **(V. Imp. Rule)** Let the base $BC = 2a$ be chosen along **x-axis** and its mid-point be taken as origin so that the co-ordinates of the point B are $(-a, 0)$ and of C are $(a, 0)$. Let A be the point (h, k)

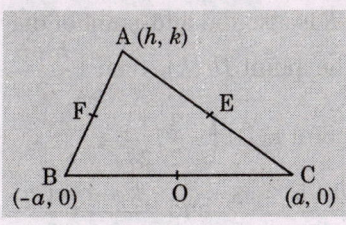

Fig. 16

The mid-point of AB is

$F\left(\dfrac{h-a}{2}, \dfrac{k}{2}\right)$ and of AC is $E\left(\dfrac{h+a}{2}, \dfrac{k}{2}\right)$

$$FE^2 = \left(\dfrac{h-a}{2} - \dfrac{h+a}{2}\right)^2 + \left(\dfrac{k}{2} - \dfrac{k}{2}\right)^2 = a^2 + 0 = a^2$$

$\therefore \quad FE = a = \dfrac{1}{2}(2a) = \dfrac{1}{2} BC$.

10. Refer figure **Q. 9 above** and prove.

11. (a) From triangle OQ_1Q_2 by applying cosine formula, we get

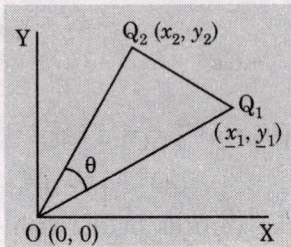

Fig. 17

$Q_1Q_2^2 = OQ_1^2 + OQ_2^2 - 2OQ_1 \cdot OQ_2 \cos Q_1OQ_2$

or $(x_1 - x_2)^2 + (y_1 - y_2)^2$

$\qquad = x_1^2 + y_1^2 + x_2^2 + y_2^2 - 2OQ_1 . OQ_2 . \cos\theta$

or $x_1^2 + x_2^2 - 2x_1 x_2 + y_1^2 + y_2^2 - 2y_1 y_2$

$\qquad = x_1^2 + y_1^2 + x_2^2 + y_2^2 - 2OQ_1 . OQ_2 \cos\theta$

or $x_1 x_2 + y_1 y_2 = OQ_1 . OQ_2 \cos Q_1OQ_2$.

(b) Ans. $\cos B = -11/\sqrt{(290)}$.

Hint : Use the formula $\cos B = \dfrac{c^2 + a^2 - b^2}{2ca}$.

12. (a) We know that in a parallelogram the diagonals bisect each other. Mid-point E of diagonal AC is
$\left(\dfrac{3-6}{2}, \dfrac{-4+5}{2}\right)$ or $\left(-\dfrac{3}{2}, \dfrac{1}{2}\right)$

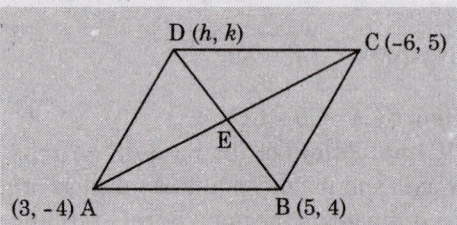

Fig. 18

Then E is also the mid-point of diagonal BD. If D be the point (h,k), then $\left(\dfrac{h+5}{2}, \dfrac{k+4}{2}\right)$ is the mid-point E, i.e. $\left(-\dfrac{3}{2}, \dfrac{1}{2}\right)$

$\therefore \quad \dfrac{h+5}{2} = -\dfrac{3}{2}$ and $\dfrac{k+4}{2} = \dfrac{1}{2}$

$\therefore \quad h = -8, k = -3$.

Hence the fourth vertex D is the point $(-8, -3)$.

(b) Prove yourself.

13. (a) Since the distance of origin from the given points is each equal to c as $\cos^2 \alpha + \sin^2 \alpha = 1$. Hence the three points will form an isosceles triangle with base as the given points and vertex as origin. Now from geometry we know that in the case of an isosceles triangle the perpendicular from the vertex to the base bisects it. Hence proved.

(b) Clearly $OA = OB = 1$ as $\cos^2 x + \sin^2 x = 1$

$\therefore \quad AB^2 = OA^2 + OB^2 = 2$

or $(\cos\theta - \cos\phi)^2 + (\sin\theta - \sin\phi)^2 = 2$

or $1 + 1 + 2(\cos\theta . \cos\phi + \sin\theta . \sin\phi) = 2$

or $\cos(\theta - \phi) = 0$ or $2\cos^2 \dfrac{\theta - \phi}{2} - 1 = 0$

or $1 - 2\sin^2 \dfrac{\theta - \phi}{2} = 0$

All the four relations follow from above.

(c) Ans. (c).

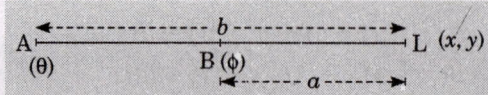

Fig. 19

$L(x, y)$ divides AB externally in the ratio $b : a$. Hence,

$\therefore \quad x = \dfrac{b(a\cos\phi) - a(b\cos\theta)}{b - a}$

$\qquad y = \dfrac{b(a\sin\phi) - a(b\sin\theta)}{b - a}$

$\therefore \quad \dfrac{x}{y} = \dfrac{\cos\phi - \cos\theta}{\sin\phi - \sin\theta} = \dfrac{2\sin\dfrac{\phi+\theta}{2}\sin\dfrac{\theta-\phi}{2}}{2\sin\dfrac{\phi-\theta}{2}\cos\dfrac{\theta+\phi}{2}}$

$\therefore \quad \dfrac{x}{y} = -\dfrac{\sin\dfrac{\theta+\phi}{2}}{\cos\dfrac{\theta+\phi}{2}}$

$\therefore \quad x\cos\dfrac{\theta+\phi}{2} + y\sin\dfrac{\theta+\phi}{2} = 0 \Rightarrow$ (c)

14. (a) Suppose that the co-ordinates of the point are (x, y), then by the given condition

$\sqrt{[(x - ae)^2 + y^2]} + \sqrt{[(x + ae)^2 + y^2]} = 2a \quad ...(1)$

Now

$[(x - ae)^2 + y^2] - [(x + ae)^2 + y^2] = -4aex \quad ...(2)$

$[\because (a-b)^2 - (a+b)^2 = -4ab]$

On dividing (2) by (1), we get

$\sqrt{[(x - ae)^2 + y^2]} - \sqrt{[(x + ae)^2 + y^2]} = -2ex \quad ...(3)$

$\left[\because \dfrac{L - M}{\sqrt{(L)} + \sqrt{(M)}} = \sqrt{(L)} - \sqrt{(M)}.\right]$

Adding (1) and (3), we get

$2\sqrt{[(x-ae)^2 + y^2]} = 2(a - ex)$. Square

$x^2 - 2aex + a^2e^2 + y^2 = a^2 - 2aex + e^2x^2$

or $x^2(1 - e^2) + y^2 = a^2(1 - e^2)$

or $\dfrac{x^2}{a^2} + \dfrac{y^2}{a^2(1 - e^2)} = 1$.

Note : The above method will be referred to as **L-M** method throughout this book.

(b) Choose $AB = 2a$ along x-axis and mid-point as origin so that A is $(-a, 0)$ and B is $(a, 0)$ as in **Q. 9 P. 12**. Hence we have

(i) $\sqrt{\{(x + a)^2 + y^2\}} + \sqrt{\{(x - a)^2 + y^2\}} = 2k$ say.

Proceeding as in 14 (a) above, the locus is

$2\sqrt{\{(x + a)^2 + y^2\}} = 2k + \dfrac{2ax}{k}$

$\therefore \quad (x + a)^2 + y^2 = \left(\dfrac{k^2 + ax}{k}\right)^2$

$x^2(k^2 - a^2) + 2x(ak^2 - ak^2) + y^2k^2$
$= k^2(k^2 - a^2)$

or $\dfrac{x^2}{k^2} + \dfrac{y^2}{k^2 - a^2} = 1$

Above represents an ellipse if $k^2 - a^2 > 0$.

(ii) In this case the locus will be

$\dfrac{x^2}{k^2} - \dfrac{y^2}{a^2 - k^2} = 1$

which is a hyperbola if $a^2 - k^2 > 0$

(iii) $2(x^2 + y^2 + a^2) = 2k$ or $x^2 + y^2 = k - a^2$

Above represents a circle provided $k > a^2$.

(c) Ans. True. $L + M = 4$ ....(1)
$L^2 - M^2 = -8x$ (Actual calculation)

Dividing, $L - M = -2x$ ...(2)
Adding (1) and (2), we get $2L = -2(x - 2)$
Squaring, $L^2 = (x - 2)^2$
or $(x - 2)^2 + y^2 = (x - 2)^2$ $\therefore$ $y^2 = 0$
Thus the equation represents a pair of coincident lines.

Note : Actually the given equation represents the line segment
$y = 0, -2 \leq x \leq 2$, since the other points on $y = 0$ do not satisfy the given equation.

15. Let the equation of the rod be $\dfrac{x}{a} + \dfrac{y}{b} = 1$ where

$a^2 + b^2 = l^2$ ...(1)

The point $A(a, 0)$ is on x-axis and $B(0, b)$ is on y-axis. Let (h, k) divide AB in the ratio $2 : 1$.

$\therefore$ $h = \dfrac{2 \cdot 0 + 1 \cdot a}{2 + 1} = \dfrac{a}{3}$ $\therefore$ $a = 3h$

$k = \dfrac{2 \cdot b + 1 \cdot 0}{2 + 1} = \dfrac{2b}{3}$ $\therefore$ $b = \dfrac{3k}{2}$

Putting for a and b in (1), we get
$9h^2 + 9\dfrac{k^2}{4} = l^2$.

Generalizing the required locus is $\dfrac{x^2}{1} + \dfrac{y^2}{4} = \dfrac{l^2}{9}$.

16. If $p = AD$ be the altitude, then
$p = AB \sin 60° = a \sin 60° = \dfrac{a}{2}\sqrt{3}$.

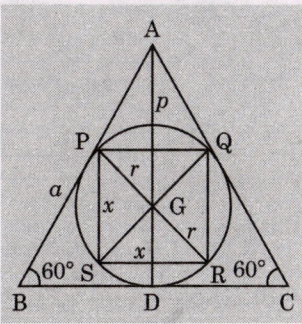

Fig. 20

Since the triangle is equilateral, G, H, I all coincide. Hence r the radius of the inscribed circle is
$GD = r = \dfrac{1}{3}p = \dfrac{1}{3}a \sin 60° = \dfrac{a}{2\sqrt{3}}$ or diameter $= 2r = \dfrac{a}{\sqrt{3}}$.

Now if x be the side of the square inscribed then angle in a semi-circle being a right angle

$x^2 + x^2 = d^2 = 4r^2$ or $2x^2 = \dfrac{a^2}{3}$

$\therefore$ Area $= x^2 = \dfrac{a^2}{6}$.

17. (a) We must remember that the three points O, G, H are collinear and $OG : GH = 1 : 2$ i.e. G divides OH in the ratio $1 : 2$.

(b) G is $\left(\dfrac{\Sigma x_1}{3}, \dfrac{\Sigma y_1}{3}\right) = \left(\dfrac{11}{3}, 5\right)$ and if O be the circumcentre, then $OA = OB = OC$ and as in **Q. 1 (a) P. 774-76** we find that O is $\left(-\dfrac{27}{2}, \dfrac{39}{2}\right)$. If $H(h, k)$ be orthocentre then G divides OH in the ratio $1 : 2$

$\therefore$ H is $(38, -24)$.

(c) Solving in pairs the co-ordinates of the vertices of the triangle are $A(0, -3), B(4, 3), C(-4, 0)$.
If G be the centroid, then

$G = \left(\dfrac{\Sigma x}{3}, \dfrac{\Sigma y}{3}\right) = (0, 0)$ ...(1)

If O be the circumcentre, then $OA = OB = OC$ gives
$2x + 3y - 4 = 0$ and $8x - 6y + 7 = 0$.
Solving the above, point O is $\left(\dfrac{1}{12}, \dfrac{23}{18}\right)$.

If $H\,(\alpha, \beta)$ be the orthocentre, then G divides OH in the ratio $1:2$.

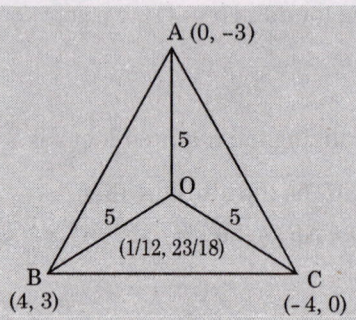

Fig. 21

$$0 = \frac{\alpha + 2 \cdot (1/12)}{1+2} \text{ and } 0 = \frac{\beta + 2 \cdot (23/18)}{1+2}$$

$\therefore \quad (\alpha, \beta)$ is $\left(-\dfrac{1}{6}, -\dfrac{23}{9}\right)$.

(d) Ans. $H\,(0,0), G\left(-\dfrac{C}{3A}, -\dfrac{C}{3B}\right), O\left(-\dfrac{C}{2A}, -\dfrac{C}{2B}\right)$

The vertices are $O\,(0,0), P\left(-\dfrac{C}{A}, 0\right), Q\left(0, -\dfrac{C}{B}\right)$

and $\Delta\,OPQ$ is right angled $\therefore$ H is at $O\,(0,0)$.

[See 6. (vi) P. 4]

(e) Ans. (c).

The co-ordinates of G are $\left(\dfrac{-16}{3}, 2\right)$. For incentre

we have to calculate the lengths of sides a, b, c which are $25, 39, 56$ respectively. Hence, the incentre is

$$\left(\frac{\sum a x_i}{a+b+c}, \frac{\sum a y_i}{a+b+c}\right) = (-1, 0)$$

$\therefore \quad GI = \left[\left(-1 + \dfrac{16}{3}\right)^2 + (0-2)^2\right]^{1/2} = \dfrac{1}{3}\sqrt{205} \Rightarrow (c)$

(f) Ans. (a), (b).

If $A\,(x, y)$ be the vertex, then $AB = AC$ implies $6x - 8y + 43 = 0$. All (a), (b), (c) satisfy this relation. Since $C\left(-\dfrac{1}{2}, 5\right)$ is middle point of base BC, it cannot be vertex.

Hence, (a), (b) are correct.

18. (a) Ans. Point $(0, c)$. The given equation is possible only when $x - y + c = 0$ and $x + y - c = 0$ together. On solving these, we get the point $(0, c)$.

(b) Ans. (b).

Given relation implies $(2a + 3b)^2 - (3c)^2 = 0$

$\therefore \quad (2a + 3b + 3c)(2a + 3b - 3c) = 0$

or $\left(\dfrac{2}{3} a + b + c\right)\left(-\dfrac{2}{3} a - b + c\right) = 0$

Above shows that the given line $ax + by + c = 0$ passes through the points $\left(\dfrac{2}{3}, 1\right)$ and $\left(-\dfrac{2}{3}, -1\right)$ and distance between them is $\dfrac{2}{3}\sqrt{13}$.

19. Take the base $BC = 2a$ along x-axis and its mid-point as origin so that $B\,(-a, 0)$ and $C\,(a, 0)$ and let A be (h, k). We have to prove that

$AB^2 = AC^2$ where

$AB^2 = (h+a)^2 + k^2$ and $AC^2 = (h-a)^2 + k^2$ ...(1)

Given $BE^2 = CF^2$

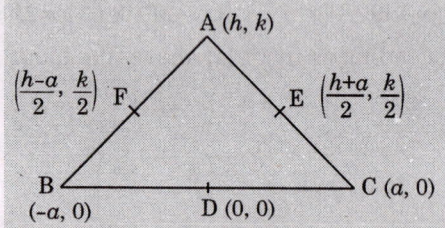

Fig. 22

$\therefore \quad \left(\dfrac{h+a}{2} + a\right)^2 + \dfrac{k^2}{4} = \left(\dfrac{h-a}{2} - a\right)^2 + \dfrac{k^2}{4}$

or $(h + 3a)^2 - (h - 3a)^2 = 0$

or $12ah = 0$ $\therefore$ $h = 0$ $\therefore$ A is $(0, k)$

In this case $AB^2 = AC^2 = a^2 + k^2$ by (1)

Hence Δ is isosceles.

20. $p + q = -\dfrac{2h}{a}, pq = \dfrac{b}{a}, r + s = -\dfrac{2h'}{d}, rs = \dfrac{b'}{d}$

C divides AB in the ratio $\lambda : 1$

$\therefore \quad r = \dfrac{p \cdot 1 + \lambda \cdot q}{\lambda + 1}$

$\therefore \quad \lambda = -\dfrac{p-r}{q-r}$. Similarly $\mu = -\dfrac{p-s}{q-s}$

Since $\lambda + \mu = 0$

$\therefore \quad (p-r)(q-s) + (p-s)(q-r) = 0$

or $2(pq + rs) - (p+q)(r+s) = 0$

or $2\left(\dfrac{b}{a} + \dfrac{b'}{d}\right) - \dfrac{4hh'}{ad} = 0$

or $ab' + d'b = 2hh'$

21. Choose $BC = 2a$ along x-axis and its mid-point as origin. $G_1 = $ centroid of $\Delta\,ABC = (h/3, k/3)$

$$P\left(\frac{\lambda a - a}{\lambda + 1}, 0\right), Q\left(\frac{\lambda h + a}{\lambda + 1}, \frac{\lambda k}{\lambda + 1}\right), R\left(\frac{\lambda(-a) + h}{\lambda + 1}, \frac{k}{\lambda + 1}\right)$$

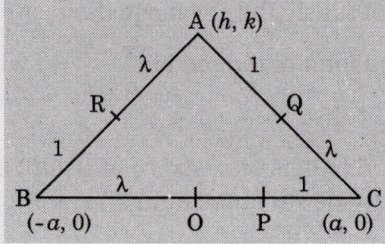

Fig. C-23

Clearly C.G. of ΔPQR is $(h/3, k/3)$.

22. $P_1 = \left(\dfrac{x_1 + x_2}{2}, \dfrac{y_1 + y_2}{2} \right)$

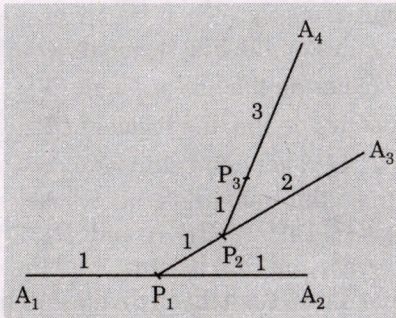

Fig. 24

$$P_2 = \left(\dfrac{2 \cdot \dfrac{x_1 + x_2}{2} + 1 \cdot x_3}{2 + 1}, \dfrac{2 \cdot \dfrac{y_1 + y_2}{2} + 1 \cdot y_3}{2 + 1} \right)$$

$$= \left(\dfrac{\Sigma x_1}{3}, \dfrac{\Sigma y_1}{3} \right)$$

Continuing like this $P_{n-1} = \left(\dfrac{\Sigma x_1}{n}, \dfrac{\Sigma y_1}{n} \right)$.

23. Ans. (C).

Refer Q. 12 P. 774-78. Diagonals bisect each other.

24. Refer Q. 5. P. 775-76.

Ans. (A), (C), (D). Sides a, b, c may not be rational and we know that $I = \dfrac{\Sigma a x_1}{\Sigma a}$

25. Putting $y = x\sqrt{3}$ in the given equation, we get a cubic in x as

$$x^3 (3\sqrt{3} + 1) + x^2 (3\sqrt{3} + 5) + (4 + 5\sqrt{3}) x - 1 = 0$$

If its roots be x_1, x_2, x_3, then

$$x_1 x_2 x_3 = \dfrac{1}{3\sqrt{3} + 1} = \dfrac{3\sqrt{3} - 1}{27 - 1} = \dfrac{3\sqrt{3} - 1}{26} \qquad \dots(1)$$

Also A is $(x_1, x_1 \sqrt{3})$ so that OA where O is origin is

$$\sqrt{x_1^2 + 3x_1^2} = 2x_1$$

$$\therefore \quad OA \cdot OB \cdot OC = 8 x_1 x_2 x_3 = \dfrac{8}{26} (3\sqrt{3} - 1)$$

$$= \dfrac{4}{13} (3\sqrt{3} - 1).$$

Problem Set (2)

Area of a triangle and collinear points

1. (a) The co-ordinates of two points A and B are $(3, 4)$ and $(5, -2)$ respectively. Find the co-ordinates of any point P if $PA = PB$ and $\Delta PAB = 10$.

(b) The area of a triangle is 5. Two of its vertices are $(2, 1)$ and $(3, -2)$. The third vertex lies on $y = x + 3$. Find the third vertex.

(c) The area of a triangle is 3/2 sq. units. Two of its vertices are the points $A (2, -3)$ and $B (3, -2)$, the centroid of the triangle lies on the line $3x - y - 8 = 0$. Find the third vertex C.

2.* (a) If the vertices of a triangle have integral co-ordinates, prove that the triangle cannot be equilateral.

(b) Triangle is formed by the co-ordinates $(0, 0)$, $(0, 21)$ and $(21, 0)$. Find the numbers of integral co-ordinate strictly inside the triangle (integral co-ordinates of both x and y)

    (a) 190   (b) 105

    (c) 231   (d) 205   **(Screening 2003)**

3. The point A divides the join of $P(-5, 1)$ and $Q(3, 5)$ in the ratio $k : 1$. Find the two values of k for which the area of ΔABC where B is $(1, 5)$ and $C(7, -2)$ is equal to 2 units.

4. (a) The co-ordinates of three points O, A, B are $(0, 0), (0, 4)$ and $(6, 0)$ respectively. A point P moves so that area of ΔPOA is always twice the area of ΔPOB. Find the equation to both parts of the locus of P.

(b) Find the locus of a point whose sum of the distances from the origin and the line $x = 2$ is 4 units. Sketch the path.   **(M.N.R. 1993)**

5. (a) Prove that the area of a triangle is four times the area of a triangle formed by joining the mid-points of its sides.

(b) Show that area of the triangle with vertices $(a, b), (x_1, y_1)$ and (x_2, y_2) where a, x_1, x_2 are in G.P. with common ratio r and b, y_1, y_2 are in G.P. with common ratio s, is $\dfrac{1}{2} ab (r - 1) (s - 1) (s - r)$

(c) If x_1, x_2, x_3 as well as y_1, y_2, y_3 are in G.P. with the same common ratio, then the points (x_1, y_1), (x_2, y_2) and (x_3, y_3)

    (a) lie on a straight line

    (b) lie on an ellipse

    (c) lie on a circle

    (d) are vertices of a triangle   **(I.I.T. 1999)**

6. (a)* The equations of the sides of a triangle are

$$y = m_1 x + c_1,$$

$$y = m_2 x + c_2 \text{ and } x = 0 ;$$

prove that its area is $\dfrac{1}{2} \dfrac{(c_1 - c_2)^2}{m_1 - m_2}$.

(b) If the coordinates of points A, B, C, D are $(6, 3)$, $(-3, 5), (4, -2)$ and $(x, 3x)$ respectively and if $\dfrac{\Delta DBC}{\Delta ABC} = \dfrac{1}{2}$ then prove that the value of x is 11/8.

7. (a) A line passes through $P(h, k)$ and is parallel to the x-axis, such that area enclosed by the line, $y = x$ and $x + y = 2$ is $4h^2$, then find the locus of point P.

(I.I.T. 2005)

(b) Let $O(0, 0), P(3, 4), Q(6, 0)$ be the vertices of the triangle OPQ. The point R inside the triangle OPQ is such that the triangles OPR, PQR, OQR are of equal area. The co-ordinates of R are

(a) $\left(\dfrac{4}{3}, 3\right)$ (b) $\left(3, \dfrac{2}{3}\right)$

(c) $\left(3, \dfrac{4}{3}\right)$ (d) $\left(\dfrac{4}{3}, \dfrac{2}{3}\right)$

(I.I.T. 2007)

8. The co-ordinates of A, B, C are $(6, 3), (-3, 5)$ and $(4, -2)$ respectively and P is any point (x, y). Show that the ratio of the areas of the triangles PBC and ABC is $\left|\dfrac{x + y - 2}{7}\right|$.

9. If $\begin{vmatrix} x_1 & y_1 & 1 \\ x_2 & y_2 & 1 \\ x_3 & y_3 & 1 \end{vmatrix} = \begin{vmatrix} a_1 & b_1 & 1 \\ a_2 & b_2 & 1 \\ a_3 & b_3 & 1 \end{vmatrix}$

then the two triangles with vertices $(x_1, y_1), (x_2, y_2)$, (x_3, y_3) and $(a_1, b_1), (a_2, b_2), (a_3, b_3)$ must be congruent. Is this true ?

10. (a) Prove that the points $(a, b + c), (b, c + a)$, and $(c, a + b)$ are collinear.

(b) Prove that the points $(a, 0), (0, b)$ and $(1, 1)$ will be collinear if $1/a + 1/b = 1$.

(c) If a, b, c are all unequal and different from 1 and the points $\left(\dfrac{t^3}{t - 1}, \dfrac{t^2 - 3}{t - 1}\right), t = a, b, c$ are collinear then

$ab + bc + ca =$

(a) abc (b) $-abc$

(c) $abc + 3\Sigma a$ (d) none

11. (a) For what value of k are the points $(k, 2 - 2k)$, $(-k + 1, 2k), (-4 - k, 6 - 2k)$ collinear ?

(b) A, B, C are the points $(a, p), (b, q)$ and (c, r) respectively such that a, b, c are in A.P. and p, q, r are in G.P. If the points are collinear, then prove that $p = q = r$.

12. (A) (i) Show that the points $A(2, 5), B(4, 6)$ and $R(8, 8)$ are collinear.

(ii) Find whether the following points are collinear or not :

$(-2, 1), (0, 5), (-1, 2)$.

(iii)* Find if the points $(0, 8/3), (1, 3)$ and $(82, 30)$ are the vertices of a Δ or are collinear ?

(iv)* Are the points $(-a, -b), (0, 0), (a, b)$ and (a^2, ab) vertices of a rectangle or collinear ?

(B) Consider three points $P = (-\sin(\beta - \alpha), -\cos\beta)$, $Q = (\cos(\beta - \alpha), \sin\beta)$ and $R = (\cos(\beta - \alpha + \theta), \sin(\beta - \theta))$, where $0 < \alpha, \beta, \theta < \dfrac{\pi}{4}$. Then

(a) P lies on the line segment RQ

(b) Q lies on the line segment PR

(c) R lies on the line segment QP

(d) P, Q, R are non-collinear   (I.I.T. 2008)

13. Prove that the quadrilateral whose vertices are $A(-2, 5), B(4, -1), \quad C(9, 1)$ and $D(3, 7)$ is a parallelogram and find its area. Find the co-ordinates of a point E in AC such that it divides AC in the ratio 2 : 1. Prove that D, E and F, the mid-point of BC, are collinear.

14. Show that the straight lines

$7x - 2y + 10 = 0$

$7x + 2y - 10 = 0$

and $y + 2 = 0$

form an isosceles triangle and find its area.

15. Find the equation of the locus of the point whose distance from x-axis is twice that from y-axis.

16. Find the locus of the moving point P such that $2PA = 3PB$, where A is $(0, 0)$ and B is $(4, -3)$.

17.* The set of all real numbers x such that $x^2 + 2x, 2x + 3$ and $x^2 + 3x + 8$ are the sides of a triangle is ....

18. If $p, x_1, x_2, \dots x_i \dots$ and $q, y_1, y_2, \dots, y_i, \dots$ are in A.P. with common differences a and b respectively then the centre of mean position of the points $A_i(x_i, y_i), i = 1, 2, \dots n$ lies on the line

(a) $ax - by = aq - bp$ (b) $ax - by = bq - ap$

(c) $bx - ay = ap - bq$ (d) $bx - ay = bp - aq$

Solutions to Problem Set (2)

1. (a) Let the point P be (x, y)

As $PA = PB \therefore PA^2 = PB^2$

$\therefore \quad x - 3y - 1 = 0$ ...(1)

$\Delta PAB = 10 \Rightarrow \Delta = \pm 10$ **(Ref. 4 (d), P. 726)**

$\therefore \quad 3x + y - 23 = 0$ ...(2)

or $3x + y - 3 = 0$ ...(3)

Solving (1), (2) and (1), (3),

we get point P as $(7, 2)$ or $(1, 0)$.

(b) Let the third vertex be (p, q) which lies on

$y = x + 3 \qquad \therefore \qquad q = p + 3$ ...(1)

$\Delta = 5 \Rightarrow q + 3p - 7 = \pm 10$

or $3p + q - 17 = 0$ ...(2)

and $3p + q + 3 = 0$ ...(3)

Solving (1) with (2) and with (3), we get the 3rd vertex as $(-3/2, 3/2)$ or $(7/2, 13/2)$.

(c) Ans. $(1, -1)$ or $(-2, -10)$.

2. (a) Let the vertex be $(x_r, y_r), r = 1, 2, 3$ where both x_r and y_r are integers. Hence its area

$$= \frac{1}{2} \Sigma x_1 (y_2 - y_3) = \text{rational number} \quad ...(1)$$

Also if a be its side, then

$$a^2 = (x_1 - x_2)^2 + (y_1 - y_2)^2$$
$$= \text{a positive integer.}$$

But the area of an equilateral triangle $= \frac{\sqrt{3}}{4} a^2$.

∴ Area $= (\sqrt{3}/4) a^2$, which is irrational, since a^2 is a positive integer. ...(2)

Thus the two statements (1) and (2) for area are contradictory. Therefore if the vertices are integers, then that triangle cannot be an equilateral triangle.

(b) The three points form a right angled triangle whose hypotenuse by intercepts form is $\frac{x}{21} + \frac{y}{21} = 1$ or $x + y = 21$. We have to find the number of points having integral co-ordinates and lying within the triangle. In other words we have to find the number of points having integral solution of the inequality $x + y < 21$ or $x < 21 - y$, where $0 < x, y < 21$.

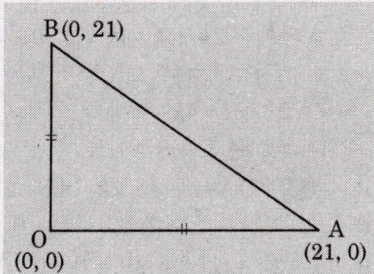

Fig. 25

For $x = 1$, $y = 20$ but the point $(1, 20)$ lies on the line AB and hence excluded. So for $x = 1$ we can have $y = 1, 2, ..., 19$ (20 is excluded). Similarly, for $x = 2$, we can have $y = 1, 2, ..., 18$ and so on. Hence the total is

$$19 + 18 + 17 + ... + 1 = \Sigma n = \frac{n(n+1)}{2}$$
$$= \frac{19.20}{2} = 190.$$

3. By **Rule 2, P. 726** the co-ordinates of point A which divides the join of $P(-5, 1)$ and $Q(3, 5)$ in the ratio $k : 1$ is

$$\left(\frac{3k - 5}{k + 1}, \frac{5k + 1}{k + 1} \right)$$

Also B is $(1, 5)$ and C is $(7, -2)$.
Area of $\Delta ABC = \frac{1}{2} \{ x_1 (y_2 - y_3) + x_2 (y_3 - y_1)$

$$+ x_3 (y_1 - y_2) \} = \pm 2 \text{ (given)}$$

or $\frac{1}{2} \left\{ \frac{3k - 5}{k + 1} (5 + 2) + \left(-2 - \frac{5k + 1}{k + 1} \right) \right\} + 7 \left(\frac{5k + 1}{k + 1} - 5 \right)$

$$= \pm 2$$

or $21k - 35 - 7k - 3 - 28 = \pm 4(k + 1)$

∴ $14k - 66 = 4k + 4$ or $14k - 66 = -4k - 4$

∴ $10k = 70$ or $18k = 62$

∴ $k = 7$ or $31/9$.

4. (a) The three given points are origin, one on x-axis the other on y-axis. Let P be (x, y). We know that area of a triangle

$$= \frac{1}{2} \text{ base} \times \text{height} \qquad \text{by 3(a), P. 726}$$

$\Delta POA = 2 \Delta POB$ ∴ $\frac{1}{2} .4x = \pm 2 . \frac{1}{2} .6 . y$

or $2x = \pm 6y$ or $x = \pm 3y$

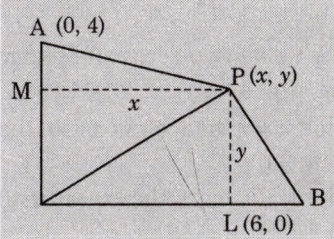

Fig. 26

Hence the required locus of both the parts is $(x - 3y)(x + 3y) = 0$.

(b) $OP + PM = 4$

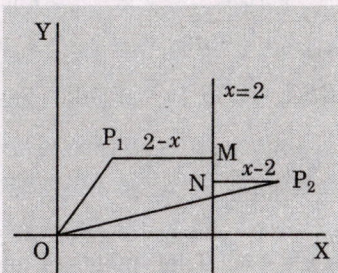

Fig. 27

∴ $\sqrt{(x^2 + y^2)} + (2 - x) = 4$

or $\sqrt{(x^2 + y^2)} + (x - 2) = 4$

according as P is on the left or right of the line $x = 2$

∴ $(x^2 + y^2) = (2 + x)^2$ or $(6 - x)^2$

∴ $y^2 = 4(x + 1)$ or $y^2 = -12(x - 3)$

5. (a) Refer to figure C-15 **Q. 9, P. 777.**

Area of $\Delta ABC = \frac{1}{2} \text{ base} \times \text{height}$

$$= \frac{1}{2} (2a) k = ak.$$

Area of ΔODE where $O, D,$ and E are the mid-points of the sides and O is $(0, 0)$, D is

$\left(\dfrac{h-a}{2}, \dfrac{k}{2}\right)$, E is $\left(\dfrac{h+a}{2}, \dfrac{k}{2}\right)$

Hence by the formula $\Delta = \dfrac{1}{2}(x_1 y_2 - x_2 y_1)$ as one

vertex is origin (**Refer 3. P. 3**).

$\Delta ODE = \dfrac{1}{2}\left\{\dfrac{h-a}{2} \cdot \dfrac{k}{2} - \dfrac{h+a}{2} \cdot \dfrac{k}{2}\right\}$

$= \dfrac{1}{8}(-2ak)$

$= -\dfrac{1}{4}ak = \dfrac{1}{4}ak.$

(b) a, x_1, x_2 are in G.P. of common ratio r

∴ a, ar, ar^2. Similarly b, bs, bs^2

$\Delta = \dfrac{1}{2}\begin{vmatrix} a & b & 1 \\ ar & bs & 1 \\ ar^2 & bs^2 & 1 \end{vmatrix} = \dfrac{1}{2}ab\begin{vmatrix} 1 & 1 & 1 \\ r & s & 1 \\ r^2 & s^2 & 1 \end{vmatrix}$

Now make two zeros and expand.

(c) Ans. (c).

Since $r = s$ hence $\Delta = 0$ so that the points are collinear.

6. (a) Solving in pairs the co-ordinates of the vertices are

$\left(\dfrac{c_1 - c_2}{m_2 - m_1}, \dfrac{m_2 c_1 - m_1 c_2}{m_2 - m_1}\right)$, $(0, c_1)$ and $(0, c_2)$

Area $= \dfrac{1}{2}(c - d)h$ **By 3 (b), P. 726**

$= \dfrac{1}{2}\dfrac{c_1 - c_2}{m_2 - m_1} \cdot (c_1 - c_2) = \dfrac{1}{2}\dfrac{(c_1 - c_2)^2}{m_2 - m_1}.$

(b) $2\Delta DBC = \Delta ABC$ ∴ $2(14x - 7) = \dfrac{49}{2}$

∴ $x = \dfrac{77}{58} = \dfrac{11}{8}.$

7. (a) The three lines are $AB \equiv y = k, BC \equiv y = x,$
$CA \equiv x + y = 2$. Their points of intersection P, Q, R are $(k, k), (1, 1)$ and $(2 - k, k)$.

$\Delta PQR = \dfrac{1}{2}\{k(1 - k) + 1(k - k) + (2 - k)(k - 1)\} = 4h^2$

or $(1 - k)^2 = 4h^2$

∴ Locus is $4x^2 = (1 - y)^2.$

(b) Ans. (c).

Since $\Delta_1 = \Delta_2 = \Delta_3$ therefore R is the centroid of the triangle OPQ i.e. $(3, 4/3)$.

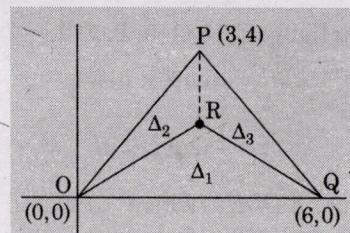

Fig. 28

8. Do yourself.

9. If Δ_1 and Δ_2 be the areas of the two triangles, then the given equality implies $2\Delta_1 = 2\Delta_2$.
Areas are equal and this does not necessarily implies that they are congruent as well.

10. (a) $\Delta = \dfrac{1}{2}\begin{vmatrix} a & b+c & 1 \\ b & c+a & 1 \\ c & a+b & 1 \end{vmatrix}$

Apply $C_2 + C_1$ and take out $a + b + c$ and then two columns become indentical so that $\Delta = 0$.
Since $\Delta = 0$, ∴ the points are collinear.
Note : You may use

$\Delta = \dfrac{1}{2}\Sigma x_1 (y_2 - y_3) = \dfrac{1}{2}\Sigma a(c - b) = 0$

(b) Proceed as in Q. 9 or the line through $(a, 0)$ and $(0, b)$ is $\dfrac{x}{a} + \dfrac{y}{b} = 1.$

The point $(1, 1)$ lies on it.   **7 (ix), P. 727**

11. (a) $\Delta = \dfrac{1}{2}\begin{vmatrix} k & 2-2k & 1 \\ -k+1 & 2k & 1 \\ -4-k & 6-2k & 1 \end{vmatrix} = 0$

Apply $R_2 - R_1$ and $R_3 - R_1$

$\Delta = \dfrac{1}{2}\begin{vmatrix} k & 2-2k & 1 \\ -2k+1 & 4k-2 & 0 \\ -4-2k & 4 & 0 \end{vmatrix} = 0$

or $\begin{vmatrix} -2k+1 & 4k-2 \\ -4-2k & 4 \end{vmatrix} = 0.$

or $4(1 - 2k) - (-4 - 2k)(4k - 2) = 0$

or $(1 - 2k) + (k + 2)(2k - 1) = 0$

or $1 - 2k + (2k^2 + 3k - 2) = 0$

or $2k^2 + k - 1 = 0]$

or $(k + 1)(2k - 1) = 0$

∴ $k = \dfrac{1}{2}, -1.$

(b) Since the points are collinear we must have $\Delta = 0$

∴ $\begin{vmatrix} a & p & 1 \\ b & q & 1 \\ c & r & 1 \end{vmatrix} = 0$

Since a, b, c are in A.P., apply $R_1 + R_3 - 2R_2$

$\begin{vmatrix} 0 & p+r-2q & 0 \\ b & q & 1 \\ c & r & 1 \end{vmatrix} = 0$

∴ $(p + r - 2q)(b - c) = 0$ ∴ $2q = p + r$

but $q^2 = pr$ or $\left(\dfrac{p+r}{2}\right)^2 = pr$

or $(p - r)^2 = 0$ ∴ $p = r$

∴ $2q = 2p$ or $p = q$ ∴ $p = q = r.$

(c) Ans. (c).

Let the given points lie on the line
$px + qy + r = 0$, then
$pt^3 + q(t^2 - 3) + r(t - 1) = 0$

or $pt^3 + qt^2 + rt - (3q + r) = 0$ has roots a, b, c

$\therefore \quad \sum a = -\dfrac{q}{p}, \sum ab = \dfrac{r}{p}, abc = \dfrac{3q + r}{p}$

Let us eliminate p, q, r from above

$$abc = 3\frac{q}{p} + \frac{r}{p} = -3 \sum a + \sum ab$$

$\therefore \quad \sum ab = abc + 3 \sum a \Rightarrow$ (c)

12. (A) (i) Do yourself.

(ii) No. Show that the area of the triangle formed by the three points is not zero.

(iii) Ans. collinear. If the points are $P(0, 8/3), Q(1, 3)$, $R(82, 30)$, then

$$m_1 = \text{slope of } PQ = \frac{3 - (8/3)}{1 - 0} = \frac{1}{3},$$

$$m_2 = \text{slope of } QR = \frac{30 - 3}{82 - 1} = \frac{1}{3}.$$

Since slope of PQ is the same as the slope of QR, the three points P, Q, R are collinear.

(iv) The slopes of OA, OB, OC are b/a each and hence the four points O, A, B, C are collinear.

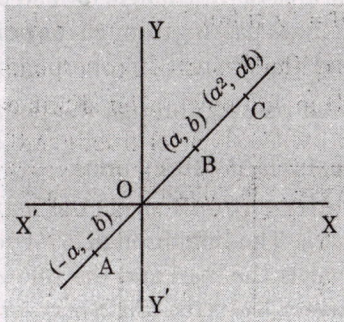

Fig. 29

(B) Ans. (d).

$P = \{-\sin(\beta - \alpha), -\cos\beta\} = (x_1, y_1)$

$Q = \{\cos(\beta - \alpha), \sin\beta\} = (x_2, y_2)$

$R = \{\cos(\beta - \alpha)\cos\theta - \sin(\beta - \alpha)\sin\theta,$
$\qquad\qquad\qquad \sin\beta\cos\theta - \cos\beta\sin\theta\}$

or $R = \{x_2 \cos\theta + x_1 \sin\theta, y_2 \cos\theta + y_1 \sin\theta\}$

But if T be the point which divides PQ in the ratio $\cos\theta : \sin\theta$ then

$$T = \left\{\frac{x_2 \cos\theta + x_1 \sin\theta}{\cos\theta + \sin\theta}, \frac{y_2 \cos\theta + y_1 \sin\theta}{\cos\theta + \sin\theta}\right\}$$

From above it is clear R does not lie on PQ and hence P, Q and R are non-collinear.

13. $AB = CD = \sqrt{72}$

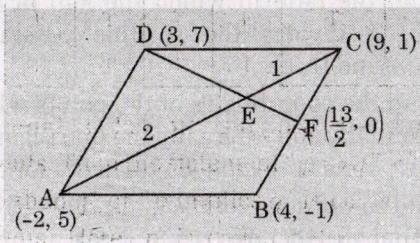

Fig. 30

$BC = AD = \sqrt{29}$

Area $= 2 \triangle ABC = 42$.

E is $(16/3, 7/3), F$ is $(13/2, 0)$.

Now show as usual that D, E, F are collinear.

14. Solving in pairs, the vertices are

$A(0, 5), \ B(-2, -2), \ C(2, -2)$

Clearly $AB = AC = \sqrt{53}$. Hence isosceles and area $= 14$ units.

15. Let the co-ordinates of the point P be (h, k).

Then distances of P from x-axis is k and from y-axis is h. From given condition we have $k = 2h$.

$\therefore$ The locus of P is $y = \pm 2x$ as the point P could be in any of the four quadrants.

16. Let the co-ordinates of P be (h, k).

Then by given condition

$2 PA = 3 PB$ or $4 PA^2 = 9 PB^2$

$\therefore \quad 4[(h - 0)^2 + (k - 0)^2] = 9[(h - 4)^2 + (k + 3)^2]$

or $5h^2 + 5k^2 - 72h + 54k + 225 = 0$

$\therefore$ The required locus is

$5x^2 + 5y^2 - 72x + 54y + 225 = 0$.

17. In any triangle sum of any two sides $\geq$ third side

$\therefore \quad x \geq 5, x \geq -11/3, 2x^2 + 3x + 5 \geq 0$ ...(I)

Sign of a quadratic expression

Note : For all real values of x, the sign of a quadratic expression is same as that of its first term provided its $\Delta = -$ ive. Here $\Delta = 9 - 40 = -31 = -$ ive. Hence its sign is same as that of its first term 2 $i.e. +$ ive.

Alt. $2\left\{x^2 + \dfrac{3}{2}x + \dfrac{5}{2}\right\} = +$ ive

or $2\left\{\left(x + \dfrac{3}{4}\right)^2 + \dfrac{5}{2} - \dfrac{9}{16}\right\} = +$ ive

or $2\left\{\left(x + \dfrac{3}{4}\right)^2 + \dfrac{31}{16}\right\} = +$ ive for all real values of x.

Hence $x \geq 5$ will satisfy all the three conditions given in (I).

18. Ans. (d).

If (x, y) be the centre of mean position of the given points, then $x = \dfrac{\sum x_i}{n}, y = \dfrac{\sum y_i}{n}$

$x_i = T_{i+1} = p + ia$

$\therefore \quad \sum_{i=1}^{n} x_i = np + a(1 + 2 + 3 + \dots n)$

$\sum x_i = np + \dfrac{n(n+1)}{2}a$

$\therefore \quad x = \dfrac{\sum x_i}{n} = p + \dfrac{n+1}{2}a$ or $x - p = \dfrac{n+1}{2}a$

Similarly, $y - q = \dfrac{n+1}{2}b$

$\therefore \quad \dfrac{x - p}{y - q} = \dfrac{a}{b}$ or $bx - ay = bp - aq \Rightarrow$ (d)

Problem Set (3)

**Equation of a line, Line through a given point equally inclined to a line,
Two lines through a given point equally inclined to two given lines.**

Find the equations of lines which satisfy the conditions given in Q. 1 to 5.

1. Which makes an angle α with x-axis and cuts an intercept of length a on it.

2. (a) Whose slope is 3 and bisects the join of the points $(-2, 5)$ and $(3, 4)$.

   (b) Any line of slope 2 is intercepted by the lines $4x + y - 9 = 0$, $x - 2y + 3 = 0$, $5x - y - 6 = 0$. Prove that the portions intercepted are equal.

   (c) Find the equations to the straight lines which pass through origin and are inclined at $75°$ to the straight line $(x + y) + \sqrt{3}(y - x) = a$.

3. (a) The portion of which intercepted between the axes is divided by the point $(-5, 4)$ in the ratio $1 : 2$.

   (b) Whose intercept by the axes is bisected at the point (x_1, y_1).

4. Which passes through the points $(3, 3)$ and $(7, 6)$ and find the length of the intercept cut off by the axes.

5. (a) Which cuts off equal intercepts from the axes and passes through $(1, -2)$.

   (b) Which passes through the point $(-3, 8)$ and cuts off +ive intercepts on the axes whose sum is 7.

6. Show that the points $(1, 3), (3, -2), (-1, -4)$ and $(-4, 1)$ lie in four different compartments of xy plane made by the lines $L_1 \equiv x - 2y - 2 = 0, L_2 \equiv 3x + 2y + 6 = 0$

7. On which the perpendicular from the origin makes an angle of $30°$ with x-axis and which forms a triangle of area $50/\sqrt{3}$ with the axes.

8. (a)* Prove that the points $(a, b), (c, d)$ and $(a - c, b - d)$ are collinear if $ad = bc$. Also show that the straight line passing through these points passes through origin.

   (b)* If the equations
   $$(q - r)x + (r - p)y + (p - q) = 0 \text{ and}$$
   $$(q^3 - r^3)x + (r^3 - p^3)y + (p^3 - q^3) = 0$$
   represent the same line, then prove that either
   $p = q$ or $q = r$ or $r = p$ or $p + q + r = 0$.

   (c) The lines $p(p^2 + 1)x - y + q = 0$ and $(p^2 + 1)^2 x + (p^2 + 1)y + 2q = 0$ are perpendicular to a common line for :
   (a) more than two values of p
   (b) no value of p
   (c) exactly one value of p
   (d) exactly two values of p **(AIEEE 2009)**

9. If (x_r, y_r) where $r = 1, 2, 3$ be the co-ordinates of the points A, B, C respectively, then prove the following :
   (a) The equation of median through A is

$$\begin{vmatrix} x & y & 1 \\ x_1 & y_1 & 1 \\ x_2 & y_2 & 1 \end{vmatrix} + \begin{vmatrix} x & y & 1 \\ x_1 & y_1 & 1 \\ x_3 & y_3 & 1 \end{vmatrix} = 0$$

   (b)* The equation of internal bisector of angle A is

$$b\begin{vmatrix} x & y & 1 \\ x_1 & y_1 & 1 \\ x_2 & y_2 & 1 \end{vmatrix} + c\begin{vmatrix} x & y & 1 \\ x_1 & y_1 & 1 \\ x_3 & y_3 & 1 \end{vmatrix} = 0$$

   where $b = AC$ and $c = AB$.

10.* The vertices of a triangle are $A(-1, -7), B(5, 1)$ and $C(1, 4)$. The equation of the bisector of the angle $\angle ABC$ is ....   **(I.I.T. 1993)**

11. (a) Straight line L is perpendicular to the line $5x - y = 1$. The area of the triangle formed by the line L and co-ordinate axes is 5. Find the equation of the line.

    (b) Find the area of the triangle formed by y-axis, the straight line L passing through the points $(1, 1)$ and $(2, 0)$ and the straight line perpendicular to the line L and passing through the point $\left(\frac{1}{2}, 0\right)$ and show that it is $25/16$ sq. units.

    (c) The line $2x + 3y = 12$ meets the x-axis at A and y-axis at B. The line through $(5, 5)$ perpendicular to AB meets the axes and the line AB at C, D, E respectively. If O is the origin of co-ordinates, find the area of figure $OCEB$.

12.* The line $x \cos\theta + y \sin\theta = p$ meets the axes of co-ordinates at A and B respectively. Through A and B lines are drawn parallel to axes so as to meet the perpendicular drawn from origin to given line in P and Q respectively; then show that $|PQ| = \dfrac{4p|\cos 2\theta|}{\sin^2 2\theta}$

13. (a) Prove that the line $y - x + 2 = 0$ divides the join of points $(3, -1)$ and $(8, 9)$ in the ratio $2 : 3$.

    (b) In what ratio the line $x + y = 4$ divides the line joining the points $(-1, 1)$ and $(5, 7)$?

14. (a) Prove that perpendicular drawn from the point $(4, 1)$ on the join of $(2, -1)$ and $(6, 5)$ divides it in the ratio $5 : 8$.

    (b) Find the ratio in which the join of $(-5, 1)$ and $(1, -3)$ divides the st. line passing through $(3, 4)$ and $(7, 8)$.

    (c) Find the co-ordinates of the points which divide internally and externally the line segment joining the points $(1, 7)$ and $(6, -3)$ in the ratio $2 : 3$.

15. (a) The co-ordinates of the mid-points of the sides of a triangle ABC are $D(2, 1), E(5, 3)$ and $F(3, 7)$. Find the lengths and equations of its sides.

(b) Find the co-ordinates of the vertices of a triangle if the mid-points of its sides be the points $(6, -1)$, $(-1, -2)$ and $(1, -4)$.

16. The number of integer values of m, for which the x-co-ordinate of the point of intersection of the lines $3x + 4y = 9$ and $y = mx + 1$ is also an integer, is
(a) 2   (b) 0   (c) 4   (d) 1
(I.I.T. Sc. 2001)

17. The equation $y - k = m(x - h)$ in which only m and h are fixed represents what ?

18. (a) Find the equation of the straight line which passes through $(4, 5)$ and is (a) parallel (b) perpendicular to the straight line $3x - 2y + 5 = 0$.
(b) Find the equation of the straight line which passes through $(1, 2)$ and is perpendicular to the line $x + y + 4 = 0$.

19. Let PS be the median of the triangle with vertices $P(2, 2), Q(6, -1)$ and $R(7, 3)$. The equation of the line passing through $(1, -1)$ and parallel to PS is
(a) $2x - 9y - 7 = 0$ (b) $2x - 9y - 11 = 0$
(c) $2x + 9y - 11 = 0$ (d) $2x + 9y + 7 = 0$
(I.I.T. Sc. 2000)

20.* The vertices of a triangle OBC are $O(0,0)$, $B(-3, -1), C(-1, -3)$. Find the equation of the line parallel to BC and intersecting the sides OB and OC and whose perpendicular distance from the point $(0, 0)$ is $1/2$.

21. (a) Prove that the equation to the straight line passing through the point $(a\cos^3\theta, a\sin^3\theta)$ and perpendicular to the line $x\sec\theta + y\cosec\theta = a$ is $x\cos\theta - y\sin\theta = a\cos 2\theta$.
(b)* One side of a square makes an angle α with x-axis and one vertex of the square is at the origin. Prove that the equations of its diagonals are
$$y(\cos\alpha - \sin\alpha) = x(\sin\alpha + \cos\alpha)$$
and $y(\sin\alpha + \cos\alpha) + x(\cos\alpha - \sin\alpha) = a$
where a is the length of the side of the square.
(AIEEE 2003)

22. (a) Find the equation to the straight line which divides the join of the points $(2, 3)$ and $(-5, 8)$ in the ratio $3 : 4$ and is also perpendicular to it.
(b) Find the equation of the right bisector of the line segment joining the points $(7, 4)$ and $(-1, -2)$.
(c) Find the co-ordinates of the foot of the perpendicular drawn from the point $(2, 3)$ to the line $y = 3x + 4$.

23. (i) Find the equation to the straight line which passes through the point $(3, -2)$ and inclined at $60°$ to the line $\sqrt{3}x + y = 1$.
(ii) If the line $y = 3x + 1$ and $2y = x + 3$ are equally inclined to the line $y = mx + 4$, then evaluate m.
(iii) Let PQR be a right angled isosceles triangle, right angled at $P(2, 1)$. If the equation of the line QR is

$2x + y = 3$, then the equation representing the pair of lines PQ and PR is
(a) $3x^2 - 3y^2 + 8xy + 20x + 10y + 25 = 0$
(b) $3x^2 - 3y^2 + 8xy - 20x - 10y + 25 = 0$
(c) $3x^2 - 3y^2 + 8xy + 10x + 15y + 20 = 0$
(d) $3x^2 - 3y^2 - 8xy - 10x - 15y - 20 = 0$
(I.I.T. 1999)

24. (a) A vertex of an equilateral triangle is $(2, 3)$ and the equation of the opposite side is $x + y = 2$. Find the equations of the other sides of the triangle.
(b)* The straight lines $3x + 4y = 5$ and $4x - 3y = 15$ intersect at the point A. On these lines, the points B and C are chosen so that $AB = AC$. Find possible equation of the line BC passing through the point $(1, 2)$.
(I.I.T. 1990)

25. Show that the point $(3, -5)$ lies between the parallel lines $2x + 3y = 7$ and $2x + 3y + 12 = 0$ and find the equation of lines through $(3, -5)$ cutting the above lines at an angle of $45°$.

26. (i) Find the equations to the straight lines passing through the point $(2, 3)$ and inclined at an angle of $45°$ to the line $3x + y - 5 = 0$.
(ii) Find the equation of the straight lines passing through the point $(3, 2)$ and making an angle of $45°$ with the line $x - 2y = 3$.

27. (a) Find the equation to the sides of an isosceles right angled triangle the equation of whose hypotenuse is $3x + 4y = 4$ and the opposite vertex is the point $(2, 2)$.
(b)* A pair of straight lines drawn through the origin form with the line $2x + 3y = 6$ an isosceles right-angled triangle. Find the equation of the pair of straight lines and the area of the triangle correct to two places of decimals. (Roorkee 1993)

28. (a)* The opposite angular points of a square are $(3, 4)$ and $(1, -1)$. Find the co-ordinates of the other two vertices.
(b)* The extremities of the diagonal of a square are $(1, 1), (-2, -1)$. Obtain the other two vertices and the equation of the other diagonal.
(c)* The points $(1, 3)$ and $(5, 1)$ are two opposite vertices of a rectangle. The other two vertices lie on the line $y = 2x + c$. Find c and the remaining vertices.

29. (a) The diagonal of a square lies along the line $8x - 15y = 0$ and one vertex of the square is $(1, 2)$. Find the equations to the sides of the square passing through this vertex.
(b) $(1, 2), (3, 8)$ are a pair of opposite vertices of a square. Find the equation of the sides and the diagonal of the square passing through $(1, 2)$.

(c)* A rectangle has two opposite vertices at the points $(1, 2)$ and $(5, 5)$. If the other vertices lie on the line $x = 3$, determine their co-ordinates and the equations of the sides.

30. One side of a rectangle lies along the line $4x + 7y + 5 = 0$. Two of its vertices are $(-3, 1)$ and $(1, 1)$. Find the equations of the other three sides.

31. (a) Two consecutive sides of a parallelogram are $4x + 5y = 0$ and $7x + 2y = 0$. If the equation to one diagonal is $11x + 7y = 9$, find the equation of other diagonal.

   (b) The equation
   $$8x^2 - 14xy + 3y^2 + 10x + 10y - 25 = 0$$
   represents two adjacent sides of a parallelogram whose diagonals intersect at the point $(3, 2)$. Determine the equation of other two sides.

32. (a) One diagonal of a square is the portion of the line $\frac{x}{a} + \frac{y}{b} = 1$ which is intercepted between the axes. Find the co-ordinates of other two vertices of the square. Also prove that if two opposite vertices of a square move on two perpendicular lines, the other two vertices also move on two perpendicular lines.

   (b)* Show that the diagonal of the parallelogram whose sides are $u = p, u = q, v = r, v = s$ where $u = ax + by + c = 0$ and $v = d'x + b'y + c' = 0$ which passes through the points of intersection of $u = p$, $v = r$ and $u = q, v = s$ is given by
   $$\begin{vmatrix} u & v & 1 \\ p & r & 1 \\ q & s & 1 \end{vmatrix} = 0.$$

33. (a)* The extremities of the diagonal of a square are the points $(1, 5)$ and $(8, 8)$. Find the equation to its sides and the co-ordinates of the other vertices.

   (b)* The extremities of the base of an isosceles triangle are the points $(2a, 0)$ and $(0, a)$ and the equations of one of the equal sides is $x = 2a$. Find the equation of the other equal side.

34. (a) Find the equations to the straight lines passing through the point $(4, 5)$ and equally inclined to the lines $3x = 4y + 7$ and $5y = 12x + 6$.

   (b) A ray of light is sent along the line $x - 2y + 5 = 0$; upon reaching the line $3x - 2y + 7 = 0$, the ray is reflected from it. Find the equation of the line containing the reflected ray.

35. (a)* A ray of light is sent along the line $x - 2y - 3 = 0$. Upon reaching the line $3x - 2y - 5 = 0$, the ray is reflected from it. Find the equation of the line containing the reflected ray. **(Roorkee 1990)**

   (b) From a point $(-2, 3)$ a ray of light is sent at an angle α ($\tan \alpha = 3$) to the axis of x. Upon reaching the x-axis the ray is reflected from it. Find the

equation of the straight line which contains the reflected ray.

36. (a) A line $4x + y = 1$ through the point $A(2, -7)$ meets the line BC whose equation is $3x - 4y + 1 = 0$ at the point B. Find the equation to the line AC so that $AB = AC$.

   (b) The equations of two equal sides AB and AC of an isosceles triangle ABC are $x + y = 5$ and $7x - y = 3$ respectively. Find the equations of the side BC if the area of the triangle ABC is 5 units.
   (Roorkee 1999)

   (c) Two sides of an isosceles triangle are given by the equation $7x - y + 3 = 0$ and $x + y - 3 = 0$ and its third side passes through the point $(1, -10)$. Determine the equation of the third side.

37. (a)* The sides AB, BC, CD, DA of a quadrilateral have the equations $x + 2y = 3$, $x = 1, x - 3y = 4$, $5x + y + 12 = 0$ respectively. Find the angle between the diagonals AC and BD. **(Roorkee 1993)**

   (b)* Two parallel lines are at a distance 1 apart and a point P between them is at a distance p from one of them. Q and R are chosen on these two parallel lines such that $\triangle PQR$ is an equilateral triangle. Prove that the length of the side of this equilateral triangle is $2\sqrt{\dfrac{p^2 - p + 1}{3}}$.

38. (a) Find the co-ordinates of the reflection of the point (a, b) about the line $x \cos\theta + y \sin\theta = p$.

   (b) Find the position of point $(4, 1)$ after it undergoes the following transformations successively:
   (i) Reflection about the line $y = x - 1$.
   (ii) Translation by one unit along x-axis in the positive direction.
   (iii) Rotation through an angle $\pi/4$ about the origin in the anti-clockwise direction.
   (Roorkee 2000)

   (c) The point $(2, 1)$ is shifted through a distance $3\sqrt{2}$ units measured parallel to the line $x + y = 1$ in the direction of decreasing ordinates to reach Q. The image of Q w.r.t. given line is :
   (a) $(3, -4)$ (b) $(-3, 2)$
   (c) $(0, -1)$ (d) none

39. $(x_r, y_r), r = 1, 2, 3$ respectively. The order of description of the boundary of triangle is anti-clockwise. Show that the angle A is acute or obtuse according as
   $$(x_1 - x_2)(x_1 - x_3) + (y_1 - y_2)(y_1 - y_3)$$
   is +ive or −ive.

40. (a)* The equation of perpendicular bisectors of the sides AB and AC of a triangle ABC are $x - y + 5 = 0$ and $x + 2y = 0$ respectively. If the point A is $(1, -2)$, find the equation of the line BC.

   (b)* The base of a triangle passes through a fixed point (f, g) and its sides are respectively bisected at right angles by the lines $y^2 - 8xy - 9x^2 = 0$.

Determine the locus of its vertex.

(c) The base of a triangle passes through a fixed point (a, b) and its sides are respectively bisected at right angles by the lines $y^2 - 4xy - 5x^2 = 0$. Find the locus of its vertex. **(M.N.R. 1997)**

41.* Let ABC be a triangle with $AB = AC$. If D is the mid-point of BC, E foot of the perpendicular drawn from D to AC and F the mid-point of DE, prove that AF is perpendicular to BE.

Solutions to Problem Set (3)

1. A is $(a, 0)$, $m = \tan \alpha$
   $\therefore \quad y - 0 = \tan \alpha (x - a)$
   $\therefore \quad y = x \tan \alpha - a \tan \alpha$

2. (a) Mid-point is $(1/2, 9/2)$, $m = 3$.
   $$y - y_1 = m(x - x_1)$$
   or $\quad y - 9/2 = 3(x - 1/2)$ or $3x - y + 3 = 0$

   (b) Any line whose slope is 2 is $y = 2x + c$. Let it meet the given lines in A, B and C respectively. Solving with given lines, we get

   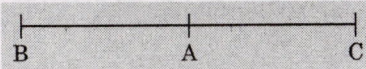

   Fig. 31

   $A\left(\dfrac{9-c}{6}, \dfrac{9+2c}{3}\right)$, $B\left(\dfrac{3-2c}{3}, \dfrac{6-c}{3}\right)$ and

   $C\left(\dfrac{6+c}{3}, \dfrac{12+5c}{3}\right)$.

   Clearly A is mid-point of BC so that $BA = AC$. Hence the portions intercepted are equal.

   (c) The slope of the given line
   $$x(1 - \sqrt{3}) + y(\sqrt{3} + 1) = 0 \text{ is}$$
   $$-\frac{1 - \sqrt{3}}{\sqrt{3} + 1} = \frac{\sqrt{3} - 1}{\sqrt{3} + 1} = 2 - \sqrt{3} = \tan 15°.$$

   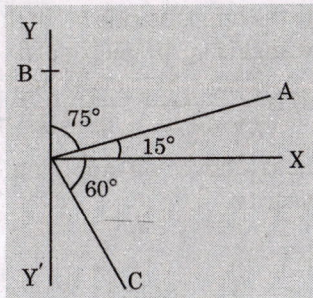

   Fig. 32

   Hence it makes an angle of $15°$ with x-axis. Hence the lines OB and OC inclined at $75°$ to it will make angle of $90°$ or $-60°$ respectively.

   $\therefore \quad x = 0$ or $y = \tan(-60°)x$ or $y + \sqrt{3}x = 0$.

3. (a) $\dfrac{x}{a} + \dfrac{y}{b} = 1$ $A(a, 0)$, $B(0, b)$

Now $(-5, 4)$ divides AB in the ratio $1 : 2$.
$\therefore \quad -5 = \dfrac{1 \cdot 0 + 2 \cdot a}{2 + 1}$, $4 = \dfrac{1 \cdot b + 2 \cdot 0}{2 + 1}$

$\therefore \quad a = -\dfrac{15}{2}$, $b = 12$

Hence the line is $5y - 8x = 60$.

(b) $A(a, 0)$, $B(0, b)$, mid-point of AB is $(a/2, b/2) = (x_1, y_1)$ given
$\therefore \quad a = 2x_1, b = 2y_1$ $\therefore$ Line is $\dfrac{x}{a} + \dfrac{y}{b} = 1$

or $\quad \dfrac{x}{2x_1} + \dfrac{y}{2y_1} = 1$ or $xy_1 + yx_1 = 2x_1 y_1$.

4. Slope $= \dfrac{y_2 - y_1}{x_2 - x_1} = \dfrac{6 - 3}{7 - 3} = \dfrac{3}{4}$

$\therefore \quad y - 3 = \dfrac{3}{4}(x - 3)$ or $3x - 4y + 3 = 0$.

Intercept on x-axis put $y = 0$. $\therefore a = -1$.
Intercept on y-axis put $x = 0$. $\therefore b = 3/4$.
$\therefore$ Length of the portion intercepted between the axes
$$= \sqrt{a^2 + b^2} = 5/4. \qquad \text{[7 (ix) P. 727]}$$

5. (a) Let the intercepts be equal to a numerically so that the equations of the lines are $x + y = a$ or $x - y = a$. Making these pass through the given point $(1, -2)$, we get the required lines as $x + y = -1$ and $x - y = 3$.

   (b) Here $a + b = 7$ and $-3/a + 8/b = 1$ as $x/a + y/b = 1$ passes through $(-3, 8)$.
   $\therefore \quad -3b + 8a = ab$ but $b = 7 - a$;
   $\therefore \quad -3(7 - a) + 8a = a(7 - a)$
   or $\quad a^2 + 4a - 21 = 0$
   $\therefore \quad (a + 7)(a - 3) = 0$; $\therefore a = 3, -7$
   Since the intercepts are +ive;
   $\therefore \quad a = 3$, hence $b = 7 - a = 4$.
   Hence its equation is
   $$\frac{x}{3} + \frac{y}{4} = 1 \qquad \text{or} \qquad 4x + 3y = 12.$$

6. Two points $L(x_1, y_1)$ and $M(x_2, y_2)$ lie on the same side or opposite sides of line AB according as $ax_1 + by_1 + c_1$ and $ax_2 + by_2 + c_2$ are of same sign or of opposite signs.

   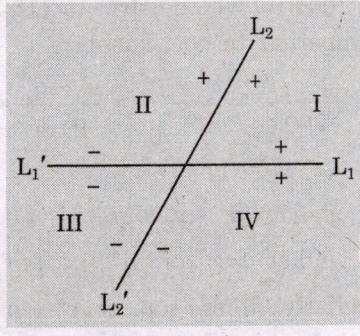

   Fig. 33

All points which make L_1 + ive lie above L_1L_1' and those which make L_1 – ive will lie below L_1L_1'. Similarly all points which make L_2 + ive will lie on right of L_2L_2' and those which make L_2' – ive will lie on left of L_2L_2'.

Now $L_1 = x - 2y - 2 = 0, L_2 = 3x + 2y + 6 = 0$

P_1 is $(1, 3)$. It makes $(L_1, L_2) = (-7, 15)$ or $(-, +)$. Hence P_1 lies below the line L_1L_1' and to the left of line L_2L_2'. Thus it lies in 4th quadrant made by the two lines.

Similarly $(3, -2)$ makes $(L_1, L_2) = (5, 11)$ or $(+, +)$. Hence it lies above the line L_1L_1' and to the right of line L_2L_2'. Thus it lies in 1st quadrant made by the lines.

Similarly $(-1, -4)$ makes $(L_1, L_2) = (5, -5)$ or $(+, -)$. It lies above the line L_1L_1' and to the left of line L_2L_2'. Thus it lies in the 3rd quadrant made by the lines.

Lastly the point $(-4, 1)$ makes $(L_1, L_2) = (-8, -4)$ or $(-, -)$, which lies in the 3rd quadrant. Hence all the four points lie in different quadrants made by the given two lines.

7. $\alpha = 30°$. Line is $x \cos 30° + y \sin 30° = p$

or $x \cdot \dfrac{\sqrt{3}}{2} + y \cdot \dfrac{1}{2} = p$

a = Intercept on x-axis, $y = 0$;

∴ $a = \dfrac{2p}{\sqrt{3}} = OA$

b = Intercept on y-axis, $x = 0$;

∴ $b = 2p = OB$.

Area of right angled $\triangle OBA = \dfrac{1}{2} ab$

$= \dfrac{1}{2}(2p/\sqrt{3}) \cdot 2p = 50/\sqrt{3}$, given.

∴ $p^2 = 25$ ∴ $p = \pm 5$.

Hence the lines are $x\sqrt{3} + y = \pm 10$.

8. (a) If the given points be A, B, C then as they are collinear therefore slopes of AC and BC are same.

∴ $\dfrac{d}{c} = \dfrac{b}{a}$ or $ad = bc$ ...(1)

Since AC is $y - b = \dfrac{d}{c}(x - a)$.

It will pass through $(0, 0)$ if $-b = \dfrac{d}{c}(-a)$

or $bc = ad$ which is true by (1).

(b) Comparing the coefficients

$\dfrac{q^3 - r^3}{q - r} = \dfrac{r^3 - p^3}{r - p} = \dfrac{p^3 - q^3}{p - q} = \lambda$, say

∴ $q^3 - r^3 = (q - r)\lambda$

or $(q - r)\{(q^2 + r^2 + qr - \lambda)\} = 0$

∴ either $q = r$ or $q^2 + r^2 + qr = \lambda$ ...(1)

Similarly either $r = p$ or $r^2 + p^2 + rp = \lambda$ ...(2)

and $p = q$ or $p^2 + q^2 + pq = \lambda$ ...(3)

Hence either $p = q$ or $q = r$ or $r = p$

Again eliminating λ from (2), (3), we get

$q^2 - r^2 + p(q - r) = 0$

or $(q - r)(q + r + p) = 0$

∴ $q = r$ or $p + q + r = 0$

Hence either $p = q$ or $q = r$ or $r = p$

or $p + q + r = 0$.

(c) Ans. (c).

The given lines being perpendicular to a common line implies that they are parallel and hence the coefficients of x and y are proportional.

∴ $\dfrac{p(p^2 + 1)}{(p^2 + 1)^2} = -\dfrac{1}{(p^2 + 1)} \Rightarrow p = -1$

9. (a) If $P(x, y)$ be any point on the median AD then A, P, D points are collinear where D is mid-point of BC. Apply the condition of collinearity.

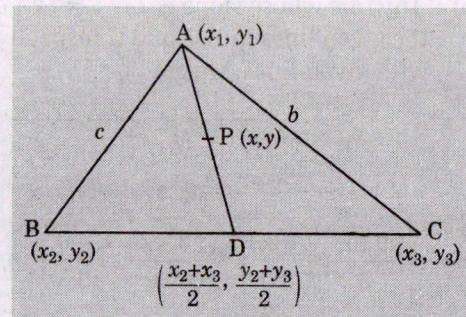

Fig. 34

$\begin{vmatrix} x & y & 1 \\ x_1 & y_1 & 1 \\ \dfrac{x_2 + x_3}{2} & \dfrac{y_2 + y_3}{2} & 1 \end{vmatrix} = 0$

Cancel $\dfrac{1}{2}$ and split into two determinants.

(b) In this case if AD be the internal bisector it will divide the opposite side BC in the ratio of the arms of the angle i.e. $AB : AC$ or $c : b$

∴ D is $\left(\dfrac{cx_3 + bx_2}{c + b}, \dfrac{cy_3 + by_2}{c + b} \right)$.

Then, as above, on applying the condition of collinearity

$\begin{vmatrix} x & y & 1 \\ x_1 & y_1 & 1 \\ \dfrac{cx_3 + bx_2}{c + b} & \dfrac{cy_3 + by_2}{c + b} & 1 \end{vmatrix}$

Multiply R_3 by $c + b$ and split into two determinants.

10. Ans. $x - 7y + 2 = 0$. $AB = 10, BC = 5$. The bisector of $\angle ABC$ will divide the opposite side AC in the ratio of arms of the angle.

i.e., $5 : 10$. Point D by ratio formula is $(1/3, 1/3)$.

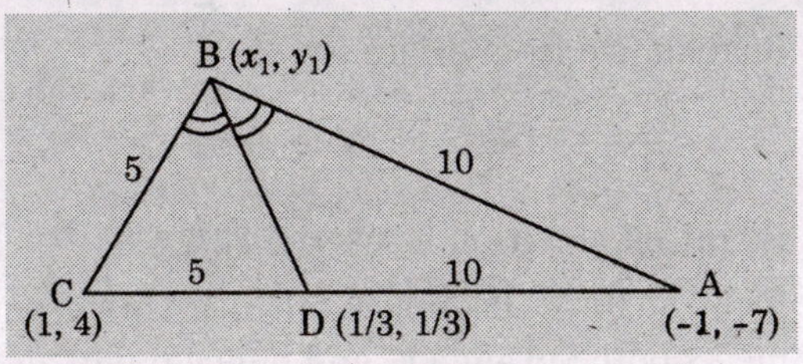

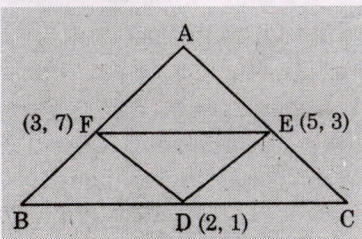

Fig. 35

∴ Equation of BD by two point formula is

$x - 7y + 2 = 0$.

11. (a) Any line L perpendicular to $5x - y = 1$ is $x + 5y = k$.

Its intercepts on the axes are $a = k$ (as $y = 0$).

$b = \dfrac{k}{5}$ (as $x = 0$). $\Delta = \dfrac{1}{2} ab = 5$.

∴ $\dfrac{k^2}{10} = 5$ or $k^2 = 50$; ∴ $k = \pm 5\sqrt{2}$.

Hence the line L is $x + 5y = \pm 5\sqrt{2}$.

(b) The line L is $x + y = 2$ ...(1)

Line $\perp$ to L passing through $(1/2, 0)$ is

$x - y = \lambda$

or $x - y = 1/2$ ...(2)

y-axis $x = 0$ ...(3)

Solving them in pairs, we get the points

$(0, 2), \left(0, -\dfrac{1}{2}\right)$ and $\left(\dfrac{5}{4}, \dfrac{3}{4}\right)$

Its area $= \dfrac{1}{2} \cdot \dfrac{5}{4}\left(2 + \dfrac{1}{2}\right) = \dfrac{25}{16}$ **(3 (b), P. 726)**

(c) $O(0, 0), B(0, 4), C(5/3, 0), E(3, 2)$.

Area of $OCEB = \Delta_1 + \Delta_2$.

12. $A\left(\dfrac{p}{\cos\theta}, 0\right), B = \left(0, \dfrac{p}{\sin\theta}\right)$

Lines through A, B parallel to axes are

$x = \dfrac{p}{\cos\theta}, y = \dfrac{p}{\sin\theta}$

These meet the line through origin and $\perp$ to given line

i.e., $x \sin\theta - y \cos\theta = 0$ in P and Q.

∴ $P\left(\dfrac{p}{\cos\theta}, \dfrac{p\sin\theta}{\cos^2\theta}\right), Q\left(\dfrac{p\cos\theta}{\sin^2\theta}, \dfrac{p}{\sin\theta}\right)$

∴ $PQ^2 =$ by distance formula

$= p^2 \cos^2 2\theta \cdot \left[\dfrac{1}{\sin^4\theta\cos^2\theta} + \dfrac{1}{\cos^4\theta\sin^2\theta}\right]$

$= 16\, p^2 \cos^2 2\theta \cdot \dfrac{1}{(2\sin\theta\cos\theta)^4}$

∴ $PQ = \dfrac{4p\,|\cos 2\theta|}{\sin^2 2\theta}$.

13. (a) Any point on the line joining $(3, -1)$ and $(8, 9)$

dividing it in the ratio $\lambda : 1$ is $\left(\dfrac{8\lambda + 3}{\lambda + 1}, \dfrac{9\lambda - 1}{\lambda + 1}\right)$.

If it lies on $y - x + 2 = 0$, then

$(9\lambda - 1) - (8\lambda + 3) + 2(\lambda + 1) = 0$,

$3\lambda - 2 = 0$, $\lambda = 2/3$.

Hence the required ratio is $2 : 3$.

(b) Ans. $1 : 2$. **See result 24 (f) P. 774**

14. (a) The line joining given points $(2, -1)$ and $(6, 5)$ is

$3x - 2y = 8$ **[7 (xi), P. 727]** ...(1)

Any line perpendicular to it is $2x + 3y = k$. If it

passes through $(4, 1)$, then $k = 11$. Hence the line is

$2x + 3y = 11$. ...(2)

Now prove as in **Q. 13** that line (2) divides the join

of the given points in the ratio $5 : 8$.

(b) Equation of 1st line is $2x + 3y + 7 = 0$ and it divides

the line externally in the ratio $5 : 9$.

(c) Ans. $(3, 3)$ and $(-9, 27)$.

15. (a) We know that the lines joining the mid-points of

the sides of a triangle is parallel to opposite side

and half its length.

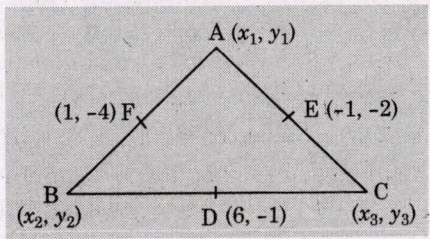

Fig. 36

Slope of BC = Slope of $EF = -2$ and it passes

through mid-point $D(2, 1)$. Also $BC = 2FE$.

$BC : 2x + y - 5 = 0$, $4\sqrt{5}$

$CA : 6x - y - 27 = 0, 2\sqrt{37}$

$AB : 2x - 3y + 15 = 0, 2\sqrt{13}$.

(b) $\dfrac{x_2 + x_3}{2} = 6, \dfrac{y_2 + y_3}{2} = -1$

Fig. 37

∴ $x_2 + x_3 = 12, x_3 + x_1 = -2, x_1 + x_2 = 2$

∴ $2(x_1 + x_2 + x_3) = 12$

or $x_1 + x_2 + x_3 = 6$

∴ $x_1 = -6, x_2 = 8, x_3 = 4$

Similarly $y_1 = -5, y_2 = -3, y_3 = 1$. Hence the

vertices are $(-6, -5), (8, -3)$ and $(4, 1)$.

16. Ans. (a).

Eliminating y, the x-co-ordinate of point of

intersection is given by

$x = \dfrac{5}{3 + 4m} = \dfrac{5}{1}$ or $\dfrac{5}{-1}$ or $\dfrac{5}{5}$ or $\dfrac{5}{-5}$

because x is also an integer

$\therefore \quad 3 + 4m = 1, -1, 5$ or -5

or $\quad 4m = -2, -4, 2, -8$

$\therefore \quad m = -\dfrac{1}{2}, -1, \dfrac{1}{2}, -2$ in all four values but

integral values of m are only two *i.e.*, -1 and -2.

17. Since m is fixed it represents a family of parallel lines. Again as h is fixed, all of them intersect the line $x = h$.

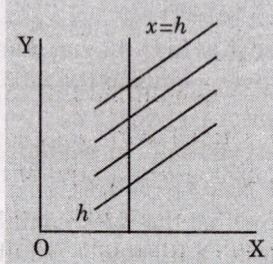

Fig. 38

18. **Refer Rule 13, 14 P. 728.**

(a) Ans. $3x - 2y = 2$, $2x + 3y = 23$.

(b) Ans. $x - y + 1 = 0$.

19. Ans. (d).

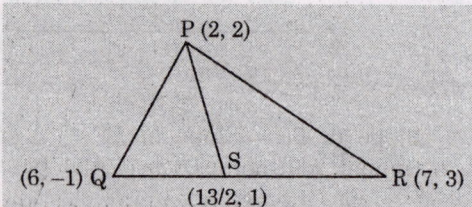

Fig. 39

Slope of PS is $\dfrac{1-2}{(13/2)-2} = -\dfrac{2}{9}$

Hence the required line through $(1, -1)$ parallel to PS is

$$y + 1 = -\dfrac{2}{9}(x - 1) \quad \text{or} \quad 2x + 9y + 7 = 0.$$

20. $B(-3, -1)$ and C is $(-1, -3)$.

Slope of $BC = \dfrac{-3 - (-1)}{-1 - (-3)} = -1.$

Hence any line parallel to BC will have its slope $= -1$. Hence its equation is

$$y = -x + c \quad \text{or} \quad x + y - c = 0.$$

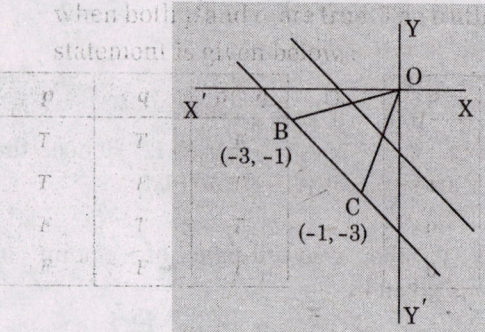

Fig. 40

Its distance from origin is $1/2$.

$$\dfrac{(-c)}{(\sqrt{1+1})} = \pm\dfrac{1}{2} \quad \therefore \quad c = \pm\dfrac{\sqrt{2}}{2}$$

Required equation is $x + y \pm \sqrt{2}/2 = 0$

Now the lines OB and OC are in 3rd quadrant. This line meets both OB and OC and hence it will also be in 3rd quadrant, so that the intercepts on the axes will be –ive. Therefore we should choose + sign out of $\pm$. Hence the required line is

$$x + y + \sqrt{2}/2 = 0 \quad \text{or} \quad 2x + 2y + \sqrt{2} = 0.$$

21. (a) Slope of given line $= -\dfrac{\sec\theta}{\text{cosec}\,\theta} = -\dfrac{\sin\theta}{\cos\theta}$

Rule 8, P. 5.

$\therefore \quad$ Slope of a line perpendicular to it will be

$\dfrac{\cos\theta}{\sin\theta}.$ **Rule 14, P. 6.**

The line passes through the point $(a\cos^3\theta, a\sin^3\theta)$ and hence its equation is

$$(y - a\sin^3\theta) = (\cos\theta/\sin\theta)(x - a\cos^3\theta)$$

or $\quad x\cos\theta - y\sin\theta = a(\cos^4\theta - \sin^4\theta)$

$$= a\cos 2\theta.$$

$\because \quad \cos^4\theta - \sin^4\theta = (\cos^2\theta - \sin^2\theta)$

$(\cos^2\theta + \sin^2\theta) = (\cos 2\theta) \cdot 1 = \cos 2\theta.$

Note : You may use **Rule 15, P. 728** alternative method also.

(b) Let the side OA make an angle α with x-axis and since the side of the square $OABC$ is a, therefore coordinates of point A are $(a\cos\alpha, a\sin\alpha)$. Now the diagonal OB will make an angle of $45° + \alpha$ with x-axis and pass through origin O. Hence its equation is

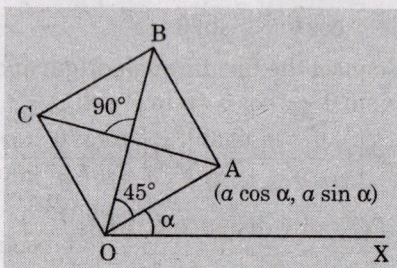

Fig. 41

$$y = \tan(45° + \alpha)x \quad \text{or} \quad y = \dfrac{1 + \tan\alpha}{1 - \tan\alpha}x$$

or $\quad y(\cos\alpha - \sin\alpha) - x(\cos\alpha + \sin\alpha) = 0 \quad \dots(1)$

The other diagonal AC will be perpendicular to (1) and pass through the point A and hence its equation is

$$y(\cos\alpha + \sin\alpha) + x(\cos\alpha - \sin\alpha) = k$$

where, $k = a$.

22. **(a)** By two point formula **7 (xi) P. 727**, the equation of given line is $35x + 49y - 217 = 0$ and the point C on it dividing AB in the ratio $3:4$ is $\left(-1, \dfrac{36}{7}\right)$

Rule 2, P. 726. Hence the line through C and perpendicular to AB by **Rule 15 (alt.) P. 729** is

$$49(x+1) - 35\left(y - \frac{36}{7}\right) = 0$$

or $\quad 49x - 35y + 229 = 0$

(b) As above given line AB is $3x - 4y - 5 = 0$ and its mid-point C is $(3, 1)$. Hence the right bisector will be a line perpendicular to AB and passing through mid-point $C(3,1)$.

$\therefore \quad 4(x-3) + 3(y-1) = 0$ or $4x + 3y - 15 = 0$

(c) The given line is $l \equiv 3x - y + 4 = 0$ ...(1)

Any line through $(2, 3)$ and perpendicular to above is $1(x-2) + 3(y-3) = 0$

or $\quad x + 3y - 11 = 0$ ...(2)

Both intersect at foot of perpendicular which on solving (1) and (2) is $\left(\dfrac{1}{10}, \dfrac{37}{10}\right)$.

Alt. direct method by Cor. 15 P. 728 :

If (h, k) be the foot of perpendicular from $(2, 3)$ to the line (1), then its co-ordinates are given by

$$\frac{h-2}{3} = \frac{k-3}{-1} = \frac{-l'}{a^2 + b^2} = -\frac{6-3+4}{9+1} = -\frac{7}{10}$$

$\therefore \quad (h, k)$ is $\left(\dfrac{1}{10}, \dfrac{37}{10}\right)$.

Working Rule for finding the equation of a line under given conditions : **(V. Imp.)**

(a) **Two lines through a given point equally inclined to a given line.**

Let the given line be LM whose slope is given to be say m.

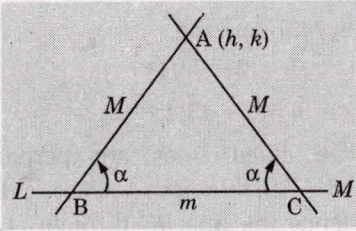

Fig. 42

Any line through $A(h, k)$ is say

$$y - k = M(x - h), \quad \text{where } M \text{ is unknown,}$$

which is equally inclined to given line of slope m. Now angle between m and M is $\alpha, -\alpha$ i.e., $\pm \alpha$, as one is clockwise and other is anti-clockwise.

$\therefore \quad \tan(\pm\alpha) = \dfrac{M-m}{1+Mm}$

(m and α known, M unknown)

or $\quad \pm\tan\alpha = \dfrac{M-m}{1+Mm}$

Above will give two values of M and hence we get the equations of two lines AB and AC through (h, k) equally inclined to given line LM. **[See Q. 23 (i) below]**

Another direct method :

Let the slope of given line AP be $m = \tan\theta$ and slopes of lines AL and AM equally inclined to this be m_1 and m_2. Their equations are

$$y - k = m_1(x - h)$$
$$y - k = m_2(x - h)$$

From the figure AL makes an angle $\theta - \alpha$ and AM makes an angle $\theta + \alpha$ with x-axis.

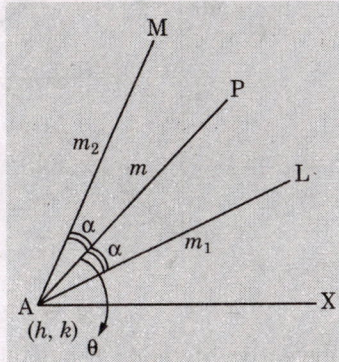

Fig. 43

$$m_1 = \tan(\theta - \alpha) = \frac{\tan\theta - \tan\alpha}{1 + \tan\theta.\tan\alpha} = \frac{m-t}{1+m.t} \quad ...(1)$$

$$m_2 = \tan(\theta + \alpha) = \frac{\tan\theta + \tan\alpha}{1 - \tan\theta.\tan\alpha} = \frac{m+t}{1-m.t} \quad ...(2)$$

Since $m = \tan\theta$ **is given**, being the slope of the given line and since α **is known**, $\tan\alpha = t$ is also known, hence we know the values of m_1 and m_2. **The results (1) and (2) giving the values of m_1 and m_2 may be used as formulae and note their forms.**

Note : Particular case.

If $\alpha = 45°$ then the angle at $A = 90°$ so that the two lines through A will be perpendicular and hence their slopes will be such that $m_1 m_2 = -1$.

In this case find only one value say m_1 and the other will be obtained by taking negative reciprocal of m_1 as $m_1 m_2 = -1$. In case $m_1 = -3/7$, then m_2 will be $7/3$.

See Q. 28 (iii) P. 796 or Q. 34 (a, b) P. 798

(b) **Two lines through a given point equally inclined to two given lines**

Let the slopes of the given lines AB and AC be m_1 and m_2. Let any line through given point $L(h, k)$ be

$$y - k = M(x - h), \quad \text{where } M \text{ is to be found.}$$

This line is equally inclined to given lines of slopes m_1 and m_2. We write

$$\tan \theta = \frac{M - m_1}{1 + M m_1} = -\frac{M - m_2}{1 + M m_2}$$

(Note '−' sign and that M is kept first on both sides)

Above when simplified will give a quadratic in M. It will be found that the two values of M will be such that their product is − 1. In other words these two lines will be perpendicular to each other.

[See Q. 23 (ii) below]

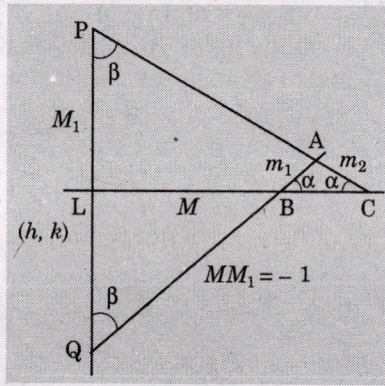

Fig. 44

Alternative Method : The two lines LBC and LPQ are parallel to the two bisectors external and internal respectively of angle A and we know that these two bisectors are perpendicular to each other.

23. (i) Any line through $(3, -2)$ is

$$y + 2 = m(x - 3) \qquad \ldots(1)$$

Slope of $\sqrt{3}x + y = 1$ is $-\sqrt{3}$ **Rule 8, P. 5.**

Angle between the two lines is 60°.

$$\therefore \quad \tan(\pm 60^\circ) = \frac{m - (-\sqrt{3})}{1 + m(-\sqrt{3})}$$

or $\pm \sqrt{3}(1 - m\sqrt{3}) = m + \sqrt{3}$

+ ive sign,

$$\sqrt{3} - 3m = m + \sqrt{3} \quad \text{or} \quad 4m = 0$$

$$\therefore \quad m = 0$$

− ive sign,

$$-\sqrt{3} + 3m = m + \sqrt{3} \quad \text{or} \quad 2m = 2\sqrt{3}$$

$$\therefore \quad m = \sqrt{3}.$$

Putting in (1), the required lines are

$$y + 2 = 0 \quad \text{and} \quad \sqrt{3}x - y = 2 + 3\sqrt{3}.$$

Alternative direct method :

Slope of given line is $-\sqrt{3} = m$, say

$$t = \tan \alpha = \tan 60^\circ = \sqrt{3}$$

$$\therefore \quad m_1 = \frac{m - t}{1 + mt}, m_2 = \frac{m + t}{1 - m.t}$$

$$\therefore \quad m_1 = \frac{-2\sqrt{3}}{1 - 3} = \sqrt{3} \quad \text{and} \quad m_2 = 0$$

Hence the lines on putting $m = m_1$ or m_2 in (1) are as found above.

(ii) Slopes of the given lines are 3 and 1/2. Since these lines are equally inclined to line $y = mx + 4$, we have

$$\frac{m - 3}{1 + m.3} = -\frac{m - 1/2}{1 + m(1/2)} \qquad \textbf{(Note −ive sign)}$$

or $(m - 3)(m + 2) = (1 + 3m)(1 - 2m)$

or $7m^2 - 2m - 7 = 0.$

$$\therefore \quad m = [2 \pm \sqrt{200}]/14 = (1 \pm 5\sqrt{2})/7.$$

It may be noted that product of the two values of m is $\frac{1}{49}(1 - 50) = -1.$

(iii) Ans. (b).

Here $m = -2$, $\alpha = 45^\circ$ $\therefore$ $t = \tan \alpha = 1.$

$$m_1 = \frac{m - t}{1 + mt} = 3$$

$$m_2 = \frac{m + t}{1 - mt} = -\frac{1}{3}$$

$$\therefore \quad (y - 1) = 3(x - 2)$$

and $(y - 1) = -\frac{1}{3}(x - 2)$

or $(y - 3x + 5)(3y + x - 5) = 0 \Rightarrow$ (b).

after multiplication.

24. (a) Here $m = -1, t = \tan \alpha = \tan 60^\circ = \sqrt{3}$

$$m_1 = \frac{m - t}{1 + m.t}, \qquad m_2 = \frac{m + t}{1 - mt}$$

$$= \frac{\sqrt{3} + 1}{\sqrt{3} - 1} \qquad = \frac{\sqrt{3} - 1}{\sqrt{3} + 1}$$

$$\therefore \quad m_1 = 2 + \sqrt{3}, \quad m_2 = 2 - \sqrt{3}$$

on rationalizing.

Ans. $(y - 3) = (2 - \sqrt{3})(x - 2),$

$(y - 3) = (2 + \sqrt{3})(x - 2).$

(b) The given lines are perpendicular and as $AB = AC$, therefore $\triangle ABC$ is a rt. angled isosceles. Hence the line BC through $(1, 2)$ will make an

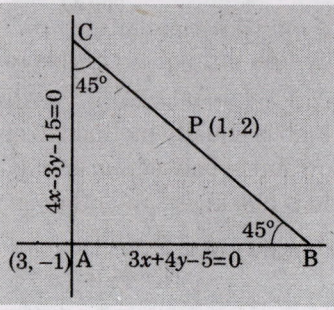

Fig. 45

angle of $\pm 45°$ with the given lines. Its equation is $y - 2 = m(x - 1)$ where $m = 1/7$ and -7, as in **Q. 23 or 25.** Hence the possible equations are $7x + y - 9 = 0$ and $x - 7y + 13 = 0$.

Alt : The two lines will be parallel to bisectors of angle between given lines and they pass through $(1, 2)$.   **(see alt. method rule P. 31)**

$\therefore \quad y - 2 = m(x - 1)$ ...(1)

where m is slope of any of bisectors given by

$$\frac{3x + 4y - 5}{5} = \pm \frac{4x - 3y - 15}{5}$$

or $x - 7y + 10 = 0$ or $7x + y - 20 = 0$

$\therefore \quad m = 1/7$ or -7.

Putting in (1), the required lines are $7x + y - 9 = 0$ and $x - 7y + 13 = 0$ as found above.

25. Ans. $x - 5y - 28 = 0$ or $5x + y - 10 = 0$.

26. (i) $\tan(\pm 45°) = \dfrac{m - (-3)}{1 + m(-3)}$,

$\therefore \quad m = 2, -1/2$ and the lines are :

$x + 2y - 8 = 0$ and $2x - y - 1 = 0$.

(ii) Ans. $3x - y - 7 = 0$ and $x + 3y - 9 = 0$.

27. (a)   Isosceles right angled triangle will have base angles $\pm 45°$.

$7x + y = 16$, $x - 7y + 12 = 0$.

(b)   Any line through the origin making an angle of $45°$ with the given line $2x + 3y = 6$ is of the form $y = mx$, where

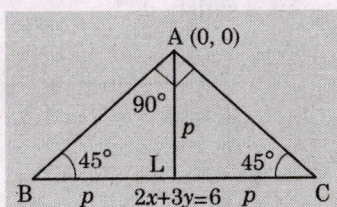

Fig. 46

$\tan(\pm 45°) = \dfrac{m - (-2/3)}{1 + m(-2/3)} = \pm 1.$

$\therefore \quad 3m + 2 = \pm(3 - 2m) \quad \therefore m = \dfrac{1}{5}, -5$

Hence the sides are $x - 5y = 0$, $5x + y = 0$ and $2x + 3y = 6$.

If p be perpendicular from vertex $A(0, 0)$ to base, then $p = \dfrac{6}{\sqrt{13}}$. Hence its area

$$= \frac{1}{2} AL . BC = \frac{1}{2} p(2p) = p^2 = \frac{36}{13} \text{ sq. units}$$

(Δ being isosceles)

Note : The working rule of **Q. 28 (a)** below is very important and will be helpful for other parts.

28. (a)   Slope of AC is $5/2$ and slopes of two lines inclined at an angle of $\pm 45°$ are easily found to be $3/7$ and $-7/3$.

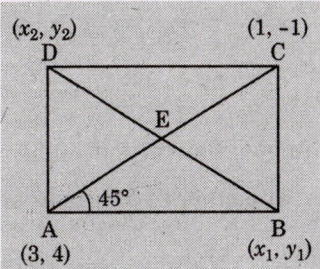

Fig. 47

Using $m = 5/2$, $t = \tan \alpha = \tan 45° = 1$.

$$m_1 = \frac{m - t}{1 + m.t} = \frac{5/2 - 1}{1 + (5/2).1} = \frac{3}{7}$$

$$m_2 = \frac{m + t}{1 - mt} = -\frac{7}{3}$$

Hence AB is $y - 4 = (3/7)(x - 3)$

or $3x - 7y + 19 = 0$.

Also CB is

$y + 1 = -(7/3)(x - 1)$ ...(1)

or $7x + 3y - 4 = 0$ ...(2)

Solving (1) and (2), we get the point B as $(-1/2, 5/2)$ i.e., (x_1, y_1).

If the point D be (x_2, y_2), then mid-points of AC and BD are same.

$$\frac{3 + 1}{2} = \frac{x_1 + x_2}{2}$$

or $x_2 = 4 - x_1 = 4 + \dfrac{1}{2} = \dfrac{9}{2}$

$$\frac{4 - 1}{2} = \frac{y_1 + y_2}{2}$$

or $y_2 = 3 - y_1 = 3 - \dfrac{5}{2} = \dfrac{1}{2}$

$\therefore$ Point D is $(9/2, 1/2)$.

Note : We could directly find the point D by writing the equations of AD and CD as above whose slopes are known and then solving them.

Another method by the parametric form :

Slope of $AC = \dfrac{5}{2}$

Slope of $BD = -\dfrac{2}{5} = \tan \theta$

$\therefore \quad \cos \theta = -\dfrac{5}{\sqrt{29}}, \sin \theta = \dfrac{2}{\sqrt{29}}$

Length of $AC = \sqrt{29} = BD$ and mid-point E of AC is $\left(2, \dfrac{3}{2}\right)$. Any line through E is

$$\frac{x-2}{\cos\theta} = \frac{y-3/2}{\sin\theta} = \underset{B}{r}, \underset{D}{-r} \qquad \text{where } r = \frac{1}{2}\sqrt{29}$$

$x = r\cos\theta + 2, \; y = r\sin\theta + 3/2$

$x = \frac{1}{2}\sqrt{29}\left(-\frac{5}{\sqrt{29}}\right) + 2, \; y = \frac{1}{2}\sqrt{29}\cdot\frac{2}{\sqrt{29}} + \frac{3}{2}$

$B = (x, y) = \left(-\frac{1}{2}, \frac{5}{2}\right).$

Writing $-r$ for r in above, the point D is $(9/2, 1/2)$.

(b) Ans. The other two vertices are $\left(\dfrac{1}{2}, -\dfrac{3}{2}\right)$

and $\left(-\dfrac{3}{2}, \dfrac{3}{2}\right)$ and the equation of the other

diagonal is $6x + 4y + 3 = 0$.

(c) Let $A(1, 3)$ and C be $(5, 1)$ whose mid-point $(3, 2)$ will be on the line joining other vertices as the diagonals bisect

$$2 = 2.3 + c \quad \therefore \; c = -4.$$

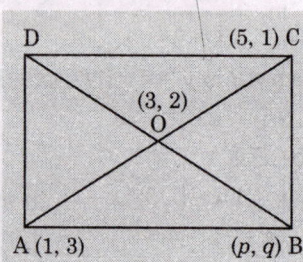

Fig. 48

Hence the other diagonal is

$$y = 2x - 4. \qquad \ldots(1)$$

Now let (p, q) be the vertex B, then since $BC \perp BA$ we have

$$\frac{q-1}{p-5} \times \frac{q-3}{p-1} = -1$$

or $\quad p^2 + q^2 - 6p - 4q + 8 = 0 \qquad \ldots(2)$

But (p, q) lies on (1).

$\therefore \quad q = 2p - 4. \qquad \ldots(3)$

From (2) and (3) eliminating q, we get

$$p^2 - 6p + 8 = 0 \quad \text{or} \quad (p - 4)(p - 2) = 0.$$

$\therefore \quad p = 4$ and hence $q = 4$

or $\quad p = 2$ and hence $q = 0$.

Hence the other vertices are $(4, 4)$ and $(2, 0)$.

Here the figure is a rectangle, not a square and hence we have followed a different method. Had it been a square we would have followed the method of part (a).

29. (a) **Hint :** The sides of the square through given vertex $(1, 2)$ will be inclined at $\pm 45°$ to the given diagonal $8x - 15y = 0$

Ans. $23x - 7y = 9, \; 7x + 23y = 53.$

(b) $x - 2y + 3 = 0, \; 2x + y - 4 = 0$ and diagonal is $3x - y - 1 = 0$.

(c) The vertices A and C are given and the vertices B and D are on the line $x = 3$ and hence the figure is drawn with B as $(3, k_1)$ and D as $(3, k_2)$

$$AC = BD \quad \Rightarrow \quad 5 = k_2 - k_1 \qquad \ldots(1)$$

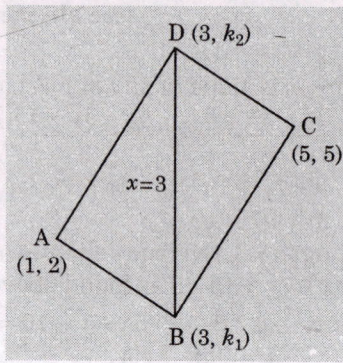

Fig. 49

Diagonals bisect $\dfrac{k_1 + k_2}{2} = \dfrac{7}{2}$

or $\quad k_2 + k_1 = 7 \qquad \ldots(2)$

Solving (1) and (2), we get $k_1 = 1, \; k_2 = 6$.

$\therefore \quad B$ is $(3, 1)$ and D is $(3, 6)$. Since all the vertices are known the sides can easily be found to be

$$x + 2y = 5, \; x + 2y = 15$$

and $2x - y = 5, \; 2x - y = 0$.

30. AB is $4x + 7y + 5 = 0$ and the co-ordinates $(-3, 1)$ of the point A satisfy it.

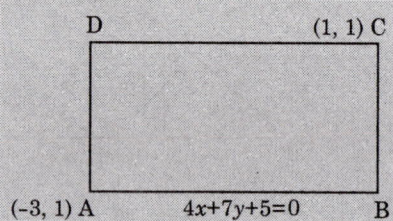

Fig. 50

In writing lines parallel or perpendicular to a given line we shall use **Rule 15 (alt.) P. 729.**

AD is $\perp$ to $4x + 7y - 5 = 0$ and passes through $A(-3, 1)$.

$$7(x + 3) - 4(y - 1) = 0$$

or $\quad 7x - 4y + 25 = 0$

DC is $\parallel$ to $4x + 7y - 5 = 0$ and passes through $C(1, 1)$.

$$4(x - 1) + 7(y - 1) = 0$$

or $\quad 4x + 7y - 11 = 0$

CB is $\parallel$ to AD and passes through $C(1, 1)$.

$$7(x - 1) - 4(y - 1) = 0$$

or $\quad 7x - 4y - 3 = 0.$

Note : The point D cannot be taken as $(1, 1)$ as in that case slope of AD will be $0/4 = 0$ but its slope is $7/4$.

31. (a) AB is $4x + 5y = 0$.

AD is $7x + 2y = 0$.

Both of them intersect at $A(0,0)$. Then diagonal $11x + 7y = 9$ does not pass through A i.e., $(0,0)$ and hence it cannot be the equation of AC. Therefore it represents diagonal BD.

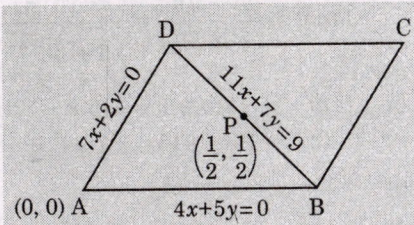

Fig. 51

Solving the diagonal BD with AB and AD respectively, we get the points B and D as $(5/3, -4/3), (-2/3, 7/3)$.

The mid-point P of diagonal BD is $(1/2, 1/2)$.

Since the diagonals of a parallelogram bisect each other therefore diagonal AC will pass through A and P, i.e. $(0,0)$ and $\left(\dfrac{1}{2}, \dfrac{1}{2}\right)$.

Its equation is clearly $y = x$ or $x - y = 0$.

(b) $8x^2 - 14xy + 3y^2 = (2x - 3y)(4x - y)$

Hence the factors of given expression are

$(2x - 3y + p)(4x - y + q)$

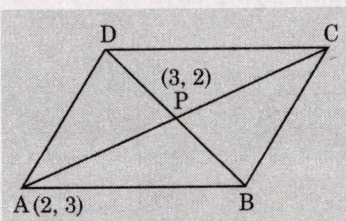

Fig. 52

Comparing coefficients, we get $p = 5, q = -5$

∴ AB and AD are

$2x - 3y + 5 = 0$ and $4x - y - 5 = 0$

and their point of intersection A is $(2, 3)$.

Again C is found, as $P(3, 2)$ is mid-point of diagonal AC

∴ C is $(4, 1)$. Now CD is parallel to AB and passes through C,

∴ CD is $2x - 3y - 5 = 0$. Similarly CB is $4x - y - 15 = 0$.

32. (a) The slope of the given line is $-b/a$ and the two vertices are clearly on the diagonal BD of the square $ABCD$. If m be the slope of the line inclined at an angle of $45°$ to BD, then

$$\tan(\pm 45°) = \frac{m + \dfrac{b}{a}}{1 - m \cdot \dfrac{b}{a}} = \pm 1$$

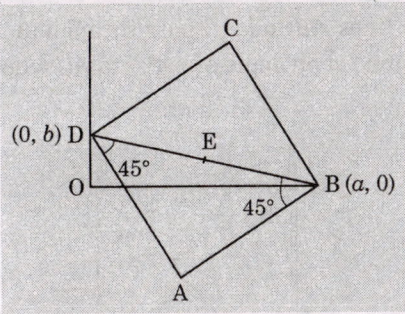

Fig. 53

∴ $m = \dfrac{a - b}{a + b}$ or $-\dfrac{(a + b)}{(a - b)}$

∴ AB is $y - 0 = \dfrac{a - b}{a + b}(x - a)$

AD is $y - b = -\dfrac{a + b}{a - b}(x - 0)$

Solving these by subtracting etc. the point A is $\left(\dfrac{a - b}{2}, -\dfrac{a - b}{2}\right)$. C is obtained by using the fact that mid-point of AC and BD is same.

∴ C is $\left(\dfrac{a + b}{2}, \dfrac{a + b}{2}\right)$.

2nd part :

The opposite vertices BD move on two perpendicular lines x-axis and y-axis. Now the point $A\left(\dfrac{a - b}{2}, -\dfrac{a - b}{2}\right)$ lies on $y = -x$ and point $C\left(\dfrac{a + b}{2}, \dfrac{a + b}{2}\right)$ lies on $y = x$. Both these lines are also perpendicular.

(b) The given determinant when expanded gives an equation of first degree in x and y, therefore it represents a straight line. Further it is satisfied by $u = p$ and $v = r$ [two rows identical]. Hence this

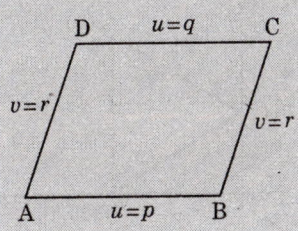

Fig. 54

line passes through the vertex A given by $u = p$ and $v = r$. Similarly it passes through the vertex C given by $u = q$ and $v = s$ which is opposite vertex and as such it is the equation of the diagonal AC.

33. (a) Slope of $AC = \dfrac{8 - 5}{8 - 1} = \dfrac{3}{7}$.

The lines AB and AD pass through $(8,8)$ and are inclined at an angle of $\pm 45°$ to AC whose slope is $3/7$.

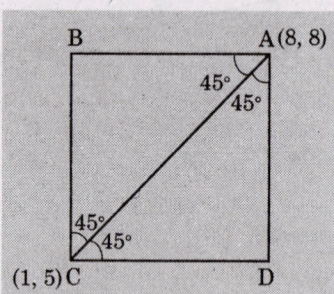

Fig. 55

Hence proceeding as in **Ex. 18** their equations are
$$AB \equiv 5x - 2y - 24 = 0.$$
$$AD \equiv 2x + 5y - 56 = 0.$$
CD is parallel to AB and passes through $(1,5)$;
$$\therefore \quad CD \text{ is } 5x - 2y + 5 = 0.$$
CB is parallel to AD and passes through $(1,5)$;
$$\therefore \quad CB \text{ is } 2x + 5y - 27 = 0.$$
Solving AB and CB, we get point B as
$$\frac{x}{54 + 120} = \frac{y}{48 + 135} = \frac{1}{25 + 4};$$
$$\therefore \quad B \text{ is } \left(\frac{174}{29}, \frac{87}{29}\right) \text{ or } (6, 3).$$

Solving AD and CD, we get the point D as
$$\frac{x}{112 - 25} = \frac{y}{10 + 280} = \frac{1}{25 + 4};$$
$$\therefore \quad D \text{ is } \left(\frac{87}{29}, \frac{290}{29}\right) \text{ or } (3, 10).$$

(b) Figure is drawn in accordance with given data.
$x = 2a$ is the line BA passing through $B(2a, 0)$. Choose the point A on it as $(2a, k)$

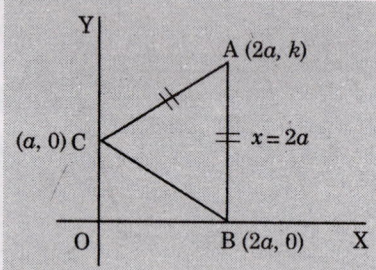

Fig. 56

Now $AC = AB \Rightarrow 4a^2 + (k - a)^2 = k^2$
$$\therefore \quad 5a^2 - 2ak = 0 \quad \therefore \quad a(5a - 2k) = 0$$
$$\therefore \quad k = \frac{5a}{2} \text{ as } a \neq 0 \quad \therefore \quad A \text{ is } \left(2a, \frac{5a}{2}\right).$$

Hence by two point formula the equation of side AC is $3x - 4y + 4a = 0$

34. (a) The slopes of the given lines are $3/4$ and $12/5$ respectively. If m be the slope of the required line and since it passes through $(4,5)$ its equation is
$$y - 5 = m(x - 4) \quad \text{...(1)}$$
By the given condition we have
$$\tan\theta = \frac{m - 3/4}{1 + m.3/4} = -\frac{m - \dfrac{12}{5}}{1 + m.\dfrac{12}{5}} \quad \text{(Note)}$$
or $(4m - 3)(12m + 5) = -(5m - 12)(3m + 4)$
or $48m^2 - 16m - 15 = -15m^2 + 16m + 48$
or $63m^2 - 32m - 63 = 0$
or $63m^2 - 81m + 49m - 63 = 0$
or $(7m - 9)(9m + 7) = 0$;
$$\therefore \quad m = 9/7 \text{ or } -7/9$$
On putting the values of m in (1) the required lines are
$$9x - 7y = 1$$
and $\quad 7x + 9y = 73$ respectively.

Alt. The two lines will be parallel to bisectors of given lines i.e. $\dfrac{3x - 4y - 7}{5} = \pm \dfrac{12x - 5y + 6}{13}$

Their slopes are $9/7$ and $-7/9$.

(b) Students of Physics know that the incident ray and reflected ray are equally inclined to the normal to the surface. Here incident ray is along the line $x - 2y + 5 = 0$.

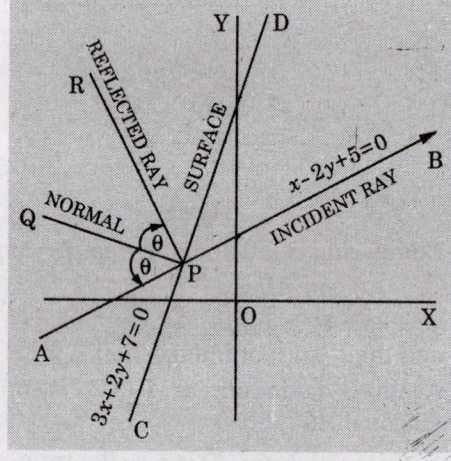

Fig. 57

$\left(\text{slope } m_1 = \dfrac{1}{2}\right)$. Surface is given by the line $3x - 2y + 7 = 0 \left(\text{slope} = \dfrac{3}{2}\right)$ and the incident ray meets it at P whose co-ordinates are easily found to be $(-1, 2)$. Normal to the surface (i.e. perpendicular) will have slope $-2/3 = m$. If the slope of reflected ray be m_2, then it passes through $P(-1, 2)$ and hence its equation is
$$y - 2 = m_2 (x + 1) \quad \text{...(1)}$$

Now normal $(m = -2/3)$ is equally inclined to incident ray $(m_1 = 1/2)$ and reflected ray m_2.

$$\frac{(-2/3) - m_1}{1 + (-2/3) m_1} = -\frac{(-2/3) - m_2}{1 + (-2/3) m_2}$$

or $\quad \dfrac{7}{4} = \dfrac{3m_2 + 2}{2m_2 - 3} \quad$ on putting $m_1 = \dfrac{1}{2}$.

or $\quad (14 - 12) m_2 = 8 + 21 \quad$ or $\quad m_2 = 29/2$

Putting in (1) the reflected ray is

$$y - 2 = (29/2)(x + 1)$$

or $\quad 29x - 2y + 33 = 0$. **(See figure)**

35. **(a)** Proceed as above in **34 (b)**.

Ans. $29x - 2y - 31 = 0$

(b) Proceed as above and draw the line. Incident ray $y - 3 = 3(x + 2)$, $\tan \alpha = 3$. Surface is x-axis *i.e.* $y = 0$, point P is $(-3, 0)$. Normal to surface is y-axis. Incident ray makes an angle $90° - \alpha$ with normal y-axis and so will the reflected ray but in opposite sense. Hence it will make an angle $-\alpha$ with x-axis where $\tan(-\alpha) = -\tan \alpha = -3$.

Hence its equation is $y - 0 = -3(x + 3)$

or $\quad y + 3x + 9 = 0$

36. **(a)** AB is $4x + y = 1$ $\qquad$ Its slope is -4.

BC is $3x - 4y + 1 = 0$ $\qquad$ Its slope is $3/4$.

If m be the slope of AC, then AB and AC are equally inclined to BC.

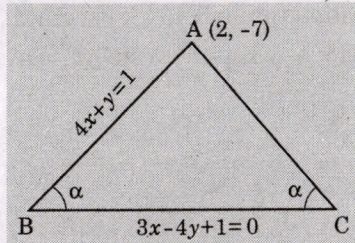

Fig. 58

$$\therefore \quad \frac{3/4 - (-4)}{1 + (3/4)(-4)} = -\frac{3/4 - m}{1 + (3/4) m}$$

(note '−' sign on right)

or $\quad \dfrac{19}{-8} = \dfrac{4m - 3}{3m + 4}$

or $\quad 19(3m + 4) = -8(4m - 3)$

$\therefore \quad m = -52/89$

$\therefore$ Equation of AC through $A(2, -7)$ is

$$y + 7 = \frac{-52}{89}(x - 2)$$

or $\quad 89y + 623 = -52x + 104$

or $\quad 52x + 89y + 519 = 0$.

(b) **Refer rule (b) P. 793 and part (a) above.** If m be the slope of BC, then it is equally inclined to the given lines

$$\therefore \quad \frac{m - 7}{1 + m.7} = -\frac{m - (-1)}{1 + m(-1)} \qquad \textbf{(Note – sign)}$$

or $\quad 3m^2 + 8m - 3 = 0 \quad$ or $\quad (m + 3)(3m - 1) = 0$

$\therefore \quad m = -3, 1/3$

We may also say that BC will be parallel to bisectors of the given lines whose slopes are as found above. Hence the possible equations of BC are

$$y + 3x = \lambda \text{ and } 3y - x = \mu \qquad \dots(1)$$

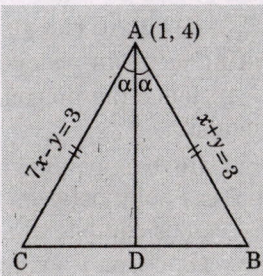

Fig. 59

In order to find λ, μ we need a point C or B. We have to make use of the fact that area of $\Delta = 5$. If 2α be the angle between the lines, then

$$\tan 2\alpha = \frac{7 - (-1)}{1 + 7(-1)} = -\frac{4}{3}$$

$\therefore \quad \sin 2\alpha = \dfrac{4}{5}$

If l be the length of each side AB or AC, then

$$\Delta = \frac{1}{2} l.l \sin 2\alpha = 5 \quad \text{or} \quad \frac{1}{2} l^2 . \frac{4}{5} = 5$$

$\therefore \quad l = \pm \dfrac{5}{\sqrt{2}}$

Now let us find the point C on the line $7x - y = 3$ whose distance from the point of intersection $(1, 4)$ is $l = \pm \dfrac{5}{\sqrt{2}}$

$$\frac{x - 1}{\cos \phi} = \frac{y - 4}{\sin \phi} = \pm \frac{5}{\sqrt{2}} \quad \text{where } \tan \phi = \frac{7}{1}$$

so that $\sin \phi = \dfrac{7}{5\sqrt{2}}, \cos \phi = \dfrac{1}{5\sqrt{2}}$.

Point C is $1 \pm \dfrac{5}{\sqrt{2}} \cdot \dfrac{1}{5\sqrt{2}}, 4 \pm \dfrac{5}{\sqrt{2}} \cdot \dfrac{7}{5\sqrt{2}}$

$\therefore \quad C$ is $\left(\dfrac{3}{2}, \dfrac{15}{2}\right) \quad$ or $\quad \left(\dfrac{1}{2}, \dfrac{1}{2}\right)$

$\qquad\qquad$ for (+) $\qquad\qquad$ for (−)

Making the lines pass through C, the equations of BC are $y + 3x = 2$, $y + 3x = 12$ and $3y - x = 21$, $3y - x = 1$

(c) Any line through $(1, -10)$ is $(y + 10) = m(x - 1)$

Since it makes equal angles, say θ, with the given lines, we have

$$\tan \theta = \frac{m-7}{1+7m} = -\frac{m-(-1)}{1+m(-1)} \qquad \textbf{(Note)}$$

This gives $m = \dfrac{1}{3}$ or -3.

Hence the equation of third side is

$$y + 10 = \frac{1}{3}(x-1) \quad \text{or} \quad y + 10 = -3(x-1)$$

i.e. $x - 3y - 31 = 0$ or $3x + y + 7 = 0$.

37. (a) Ans. $90°$. Solving the equations in pairs we get the co-ordinates of the vertices as

$$A(-3,3), \quad B(1,1), \quad C(1,-1), \quad D(-2,-2).$$

m_1 = slope of $AC = -1$, m_2 = slope of $BD = 1$

∴ $m_1 m_2 = -1$. Hence the diagonals AC and BD are perpendicular.

(b) $y = 0$ and $y = 1$ are two parallel lines, distance $QL = 1$ apart. P is a point between them such that $PM = p$ and $\triangle PQR$ is equilateral.

Let Q lie on $y = 1$ and R on $y = 0$ may be chosen as origin $(0,0)$ if RP be inclined at θ, then

$$p = a \sin \theta \qquad \qquad \dots (1)$$

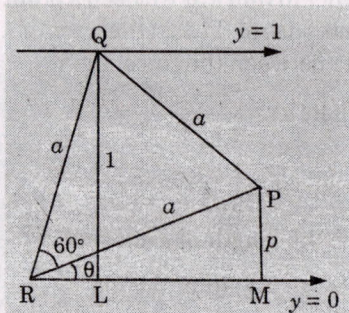

Fig. 60

$QL = 1 = QR \sin(\theta + 60°) = a \sin(\theta + 60°)$

or $\quad 1 = a(\sin\theta \cos 60° + \cos\theta \sin 60°) \qquad \dots(2)$

We have to eliminate θ between (1) and (2) and then find the length of side a in terms of known quantity p.

$$\left(1 - \frac{a \sin\theta}{2}\right)^2 = \frac{3a^2 \cos^2\theta}{4} = \frac{3a^2}{4}(1 - \sin^2\theta)$$

Now put $\sin\theta = p/a$ from (1).

$$\left(1 - \frac{p}{2}\right)^2 = \frac{3a^2}{4}\left[1 - \frac{p^2}{a^2}\right] = \frac{3a^2}{4} - \frac{3p^2}{4}$$

or $\quad 4 - 4p + p^2 + 3p^2 = 3a^2$

or $\quad a = 2\sqrt{\dfrac{p^2 - p + 1}{3}}$.

38. (a) If $P(l, m)$ be the reflection then its mid-point will lie on the line $x \cos\theta + y \sin\theta = p$

∴ $\quad \dfrac{a+l}{2} \cos\theta + \dfrac{b+m}{2} \sin\theta = p$

$l \cos\theta + m \sin\theta = 2p - a\cos\theta - b\sin\theta \qquad \dots(1)$

Again AP is ⊥ to the given line

∴ $\quad \dfrac{m-b}{l-a}\left(-\dfrac{\cos\theta}{\sin\theta}\right) = -1$

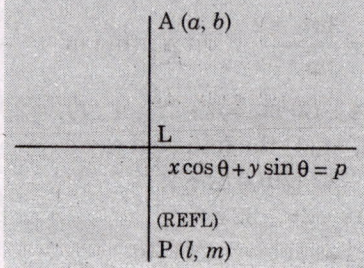

Fig. 61

∴ $\quad l\sin\theta - m\cos\theta = a\sin\theta - b\cos\theta \qquad \dots(2)$

In order to find l, m we have to solve (1) and (2) by cross-multiplication or by eliminating m and finding l etc. Hence point $P(l, m)$ is

$(2p\cos\theta - a\cos 2\theta - b\sin 2\theta,$
$\qquad\qquad 2p\sin\theta - a\sin 2\theta + b\cos 2\theta)$

(b) If (h, k) be reflection of $(4,1)$ about the line $x - y - 1 = 0 = l$ then

$$\frac{h-4}{1} = \frac{k-1}{1} = -2 \cdot \frac{4-1-1}{1^2 + 1^2} \quad \textbf{See 24 (e), P. 773}$$

∴ $\quad (h, k)$ is $(2, 3)$.

By translation it becomes $(2+1, 3)$ *i.e.* $(3, 3)$.

By rotation through $45°$ it becomes

$(x\cos 45° - y\sin 45°, x\sin 45° + y\cos 45°)$
$$= (0, 3\sqrt{2})$$

(c) Ans. (a).

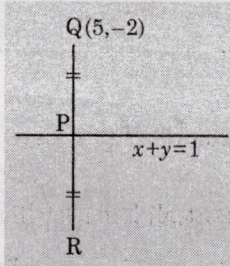

Fig. 62

$\tan\theta = -1 \Rightarrow \theta = 135°$

∴ $\quad \cos\theta = -\dfrac{1}{\sqrt{2}}, \sin\theta = \dfrac{1}{\sqrt{2}}$

$$\frac{x-2}{\cos\theta} = \frac{y-1}{\sin\theta} = -3\sqrt{2} \quad \text{(decreasing)}$$

∴ $\quad Q$ is $(5, -2)$.

If (h, k) be the image of $Q(5, -2)$ in the line $x + y - 1 = 0$, then

$$\frac{h-5}{2} = \frac{k+2}{1} = \frac{-2l}{a^2+b^2} = -2\frac{5-2-1}{1^2+1^2} = -2$$

by 24 (e) P. 773

∴ $\quad (h, k)$ is $(3, -4)$.

39. $m_1 = $ slope of $AB = \dfrac{y_2 - y_1}{x_2 - x_1}$

$m_2 = $ slope of $AC = \dfrac{y_3 - y_1}{x_3 - x_1}$

$\therefore \quad \tan A = \dfrac{m_1 - m_2}{1 + m_1 m_2}$.

Now put the values of m_1 and m_2 the denominator will be $(x_2 - x_1)(x_3 - x_1) + (y_2 - y_1)(y_3 - y_1)$ whereas numerator will consist of eight terms, two of which shall cancel and rest will be $2\Delta = +$ive, $\tan A = \dfrac{+\text{ive}}{E}$.

Where $E = (x_1 - x_2)(x_1 - x_3) + (y_1 - y_2)(y_1 - y_3)$

$= +$ive $(E +$ive$)$

$= -$ive $(E -$ive$)$

Hence A is acute or obtuse according as E is $+$ive or $-$ive.

40. (a) Let the co-ordinates of B and C be (x_1, y_1) and (x_2, y_2). Perpendicular bisector of AB is

$x - y + 5 = 0$ whose slope is 1. ...(1)

Mid-point $F\left(\dfrac{x_1 + 1}{2}, \dfrac{y_1 - 2}{2}\right)$ of AB lies on (1)

$\therefore \quad x_1 - y_1 + 13 = 0$. ...(2)

Also AB is perpendicular to HF i.e. $m_1 m_2 = -1$

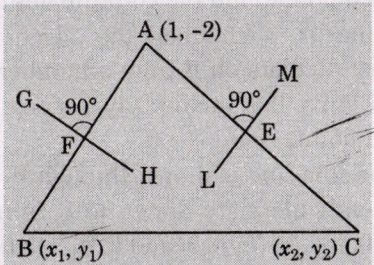

Fig. 63

or $\dfrac{y_1 + 2}{x_1 - 1} \times 1 = -1$ or $x_1 + y_1 + 1 = 0$.

Solving (2) and (3), we get $x_1 = -7, y_1 = 6$

$\therefore \quad B$ is $(-7, 6)$.

Similarly C is $\left(\dfrac{11}{5}, \dfrac{2}{5}\right)$.

$\therefore \quad$ Equation of BC is $y - 6 = \dfrac{2/5 - 6}{11/5 + 7}(x + 7)$

or $-23(y - 6) = 14(x + 7)$

or $14x + 23y - 40 = 0$

(b) Let the base be BC which passes through a fixed point $L(f, g)$. The three points L, B, C are collinear.

$\therefore \quad \begin{vmatrix} f & g & 1 \\ x_1 & y_1 & 1 \\ x_2 & y_2 & 1 \end{vmatrix} = 0$

or $f(y_1 - y_2) - g(x_1 - x_2) + (x_1 y_2 - x_2 y_1) = 0$ ...(1)

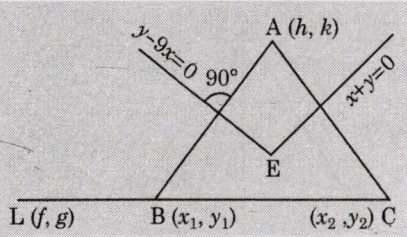

Fig. 64

Let the vertex A be (h, k) whose locus we are to find.

Lines $y^2 - 8xy - 9x^2 = 0$

or $(y - 9x)(y + x) = 0$

are the right bisectors of sides.

AB is perpendicular to $y - 9x = 0$

$\therefore \quad \dfrac{k - y_1}{h - x_1} \times 9 = -1,$

$\therefore \quad x_1 + 9y_1 = h + 9k.$ ...(2)

Mid-point $D = \left(\dfrac{h + x_1}{2}, \dfrac{k + y_1}{2}\right)$ of AB lies on

$y - 9x = 0.$

$\therefore \quad (k + y_1) - 9(h + x_1) = 0$

or $9x_1 - y_1 = k - 9h$ ...(3)

Solving (2) and (3) for x_1 and y_1, we get

$x_1 = \dfrac{9k - 40h}{41}, \quad y_1 = \dfrac{40k + 9h}{41}.$

Proceeding exactly as above we get the values of x_2, y_2 as

$x_2 = -k$ and $y_2 = -h$

$\therefore \quad x_1 - x_2 = \dfrac{50k - 40h}{41}, y_1 - y_2 = \dfrac{40k + 50h}{41}$

and $x_1 y_2 - x_2 y_1 = -(1/41)[h(9k - 40h)$

$- k(40k + 9h)]$

$= (40/41)[h^2 + k^2]$

Putting the above values in (1), we get

$f \cdot \dfrac{40k + 50h}{41} - g \cdot \dfrac{50k - 40h}{41} + \dfrac{40}{41} \cdot (h^2 + k^2) = 0$

Hence the locus of the vertex (h, k) is

$4(x^2 + y^2) + (4g + 5f)x + (4f - 5g)y = 0.$

Above equation represents a circle.

(c) See part (b).

Ans. $2(x^2 + y^2) + (3a + 2b)x + (2a - 3b)y = 0.$

41. Let the side BC be chosen along x-axis, its length be $2a$ and mid-point D be origin so that the points B and C are $(-a, 0)$ and $(a, 0)$. Since the triangle is isosceles therefore median AD will be perpendicular to base BC so that AD is along y-axis and as such let A be $(0, h)$.

Equation to AC by intercepts form is $x/a + y/h = 1$

$\therefore \quad$ Equation to $DE \perp$ to AC is $x/h - y/a = 0$

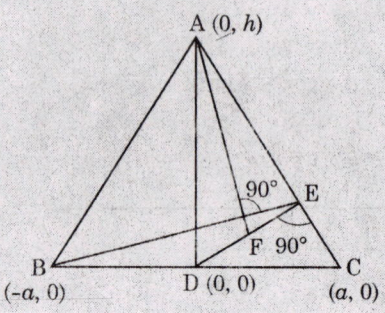

Fig. 65

Solving these, we get the point E as

$$\left(\frac{ah^2}{a^2+h^2}, \frac{a^2h}{a^2+h^2}\right)$$

∴ F the mid-point of DE is

$$\left(\frac{ah^2}{2(a^2+h^2)}, \frac{a^2h}{2(a^2+h^2)}\right).$$

Now find m_1 the slope of BE and m_2 the slope of AF and show that $m_1 m_2 = -1$.

Problem Set (4)

Equation of a line through the intersection of two given lines $P + \lambda Q = 0$.

Area of Parallelogram and square. Parametric Equation of a line $\dfrac{x - x_1}{\cos\theta} = \dfrac{y - y_1}{\sin\theta} = r.$

1. (a) Find the equations to the straight lines that pass through the intersection of the lines $2x - 3y = 0$ and $4x - 5y = 2$ and
    (i)   Passes through the point $(2, 1)$.
    (ii) Is perpendicular to the line $x + 2y + 1 = 0$.
    (iii) Is parallel to the line $3x - 4y + 5 = 0$.

    (b) Find the equations of the lines which pass through the point of intersection of the lines $4x - 3y - 1 = 0, 2x - 5y + 3 = 0$ and are equally inclined to the axes.

2. Find the value of λ such that the straight line $(2x + 3y + 4) + \lambda(6x - y + 12) = 0$.
    (a)* Is parallel to y-axis.
    (b) Is perpendicular to the line $7x + 5y = 4$.

3. Show that the straight lines given by
    (a) $x(a + 2b) + y(a + 3b) = a + b$.
        For different values of a and b pass through a fixed point.
    (b) $(2 + k)x + (1 + k)y = 5 + 7k$.
        For different values of k pass through a fixed point.
    (c)* The set of lines
        $ax + by + c = 0$ where $3a + 2b + 4c = 0$
        is concurrent at the point ....
    (d)* If a, b, c are in A.P., then the straight lines $ax + by + c = 0$ will always pass through the point ....
    (e) Given the family of lines
        $a(2x + y + 4) + b(x - 2y - 3) = 0$. The number of lines belonging to the family at a distance $\sqrt{10}$ from any point $(2, -3)$ is :
        (a) 0   (b) 1
        (c) 2   (d) 4

4. (a) Let the algebraic sum of the perpendicular distances from the points $(2, 0), (0, 2), (1, 1)$ to a variable straight line be zero, then prove that the line passes through a fixed point whose coordinates are $(1, 1)$.   **(I.I.T. 1991)**

    (b)* Prove that the family of straight lines $lx + my + n = 0$ where l, m, n are connected by the relation $4l^2 + 9m^2 - n^2 + 12lm = 0$ are concurrent. Find the point of concurrency.

    (c) If the sum of the lengths of perpendiculars from the points $(3, 4)$ and $(7, 2)$ on a variable line is thrice the length of perpendicular from $(1, 3)$ on that line, show that the line always passes through a fixed point. Find the co-ordinates of that point.

    (d)* A line is such that the algebraic sum of perpendiculars on it from a number of points is zero. Prove that the line always passes through a fixed point.

5. (a) A variable line is drawn through the point $(2, 1)$. Perpendiculars are drawn to it from the points $(a_1, 4), (a_2, 5), (a_3, -3)$ and $(2, b_1), (3, b_2)$ and $(7, b_3)$ such that their sum is zero. If all the a_i^s and b_i^s are non-negative real numbers determine their values.

    (b) If $u = a_1 x + b_1 y + c_1 = 0$ and
            $v = a_2 x + b_2 y + c_2 = 0$
        and $\dfrac{a_1}{a_2} = \dfrac{b_1}{b_2} = \dfrac{c_1}{c_2}$ prove that the curve $u + kv = 0$ is nothing but any of the given straight lines $u = 0$ or $v = 0$

6. (a) Find the equations of the lines through the point of intersection of the lines
            $x - 3y + 1 = 0$ and $2x + 5y - 9 = 0$
        and whose distance from the origin is $\sqrt{5}$.

    (b) Given the pencil of lines
            $a(2x + y + 4) + b(x - 2y - 3) = 0$.
        Prove that among the lines of the pencil there exists only one line whose distance from the point $(2, -3)$ is $\sqrt{10}$. Write the equation of this line.

(c)* Prove that for all values of α the lines

$(2\cos\alpha + 3\sin\alpha)\,x + (3\cos\alpha - 5\sin\alpha)\,y$
$$= (5\cos\alpha - 2\sin\alpha)$$

pass through a fixed point. What are the co-ordinates of this point ? What is the reflection of this point in the line $x + y = \sqrt{2}$?

7. (a)* Find the equation of the straight line joining the point (a, b) to the point of intersection of the lines

$$\frac{x}{a} + \frac{y}{b} = 1 \quad \text{and} \quad \frac{x}{b} + \frac{y}{a} = 1.$$

Also prove that sum of intercepts made by this line on co-ordinate axes is $\dfrac{(b - a)(a^2 - b^2)}{ab}$.

(b) The equal sides AB and AC of an isosceles triangle ABC are produced to points P and Q respectively such that $BP \cdot CQ = AB^2$. Prove that the line PQ always passes through a fixed point.

8.* (a) A variable straight line drawn through the point of intersection of the straight lines

$$\frac{x}{a} + \frac{y}{b} = 1 \quad \text{and} \quad \frac{x}{b} + \frac{y}{a} = 1$$

meets the co-ordinate axes in A and B. Show that the locus of the mid-point of AB is the curve

$$2xy\,(a + b) = ab\,(x + y). \quad \text{(J.E.E. W.B. 1995)}$$

(b) A straight line L through the origin meets the lines $x + y = 1$ and $x + y = 3$, at P and Q respectively. Through P and Q two straight lines L_1 and L_2 are drawn, parallel to $2x - y = 5$ and $3x + y = 5$ respectively. Lines L_1 and L_2 intersect at R. Show that the locus of R, as L varies, is a straight line.

(I.I.T. 2002)

(c) Two sides of a triangle are along the co-ordinate axes and its hypotenuse passes through the point of intersection of the lines $px + qy + r = 0$ and $lx + my + n = 0$. Prove that the locus of the circum-centre of the triangle is

$2xy\,(mp - lq) + x\,(pn - lr) + y\,(mr - qn) = 0$

9. (a) Two parallel straight lines inclined at an angle of $135°$ to the axis of x meet the x-axis at the points A, B and y-axis at the points C and D respectively. Find the equation of the locus of point of intersection of AD and BC.

(b) Find the equation of the diagonal through the origin of the quadrilateral formed by $x = 0$, $y = 0$, $x + y = 1$ and $6x + y = 3$.

(c) The mid-point of the base BC of a triangle ABC is the point (h, k) and the equations of its sides AB and AC are $hx + ky = 1$ and $kx + hy = 1$. Find the equation of the median through A.

10.* The following four lines $ax + by + c = 0$ and $ax + by + d = 0$, $d'x + b'y + c' = 0$, $d'x + b'y + d' = 0$ represent in pairs the sets of parallel lines of a parallelogram. Write the equations of its diagonals.

11. (a) Show that the lines
$$3x - 4y + 5 = 0, \ 7x - 8y + 5 = 0$$
and $4x + 5y = 45$ are concurrent.

(b) Given four lines with equations
$$x + 2y - 3 = 0, \quad 3x + 4y - 7 = 0,$$
$$2x + 3y - 4 = 0, \quad 4x + 5y - 6 = 0, \text{ then}$$
(a) they are all concurrent
(b) they are the sides of a quadrilateral
(c) none of these.

12. (a) For what value of a will the lines
$$3x + 4y + 1 = 0, \ ax + 2y - 3 = 0$$
and $2x - y - 3 = 0$ be concurrent ?

(b) For what value of k will the following lines be concurrent ?
$$3x - 4y + 5 = 0, 7x - 8y + 5 = 0,$$
$$4x + 5y + k = 0.$$

(c) Prove that the straight line $5x + 4y = 0$ passes through the point of intersection of the straight lines $x + 2y - 10 = 0$ and $2x + y + 5 = 0$.

13. (a)* The lines $2x + 3y - 8 = 0$, $5x - 6y + 7 = 0$ and $px + qy - 1 = 0$ are concurrent; then prove that the line $x + 2y - 1 = 0$ passes through a fixed point.

(b) The three straight lines $2x + 11y - 5 = 0$, $24x + 7y = 20$ and $4x - 3y - 2 = 0$ are such that
(a) they form a triangle
(b) they are concurrent
(c) one of them is a bisector of the other two.
(d) none

(c)* Determine whether the triangle formed by the lines $x - 7y + 12 = 0$, $7x + y - 16 = 0$ and $3x + 4y - 4 = 0$ is
(a) equilateral   (b) right-angled
(c) isosceles   (d) none.

14. (a)* Prove that the lines
$$ax + by + c = 0, \ bx + cy + a = 0$$
and $cx + ay + b = 0$ are concurrent
if $a^3 + b^3 + c^3 = 3abc$
or if $a + b + c = 0$. (D.C.E. 1998)

(b) The lines $ax + 2y + 1 = 0$, $bx + 3y + 1 = 0$ and $cx + 4y + 1 = 0$ are concurrent, show that a, b, c are in A. P.

15. (a) If the lines
$$p_1x + q_1y = 1, \ p_2x + q_2y = 1, \ p_3x + q_3y = 1$$
are concurrent then prove that the points (p_1, q_1), (p_2, q_2) and (p_3, q_3) are collinear.

(b) Find the condition of concurrency of the lines $y = m_1x + c_1, y = m_2x + c_2$, and $y = m_3x + c_3$.

16. (a) Prove that the lines
$(p - q)\,x + (q - r)\,y + (r - p) = 0$
$(q - r)\,x + (r - p)\,y + (p - q) = 0$
$(r - p)\,x + (p - q)\,y + (q - r) = 0$
are concurrent.

(b)* Prove that the lines

$$(b+c)\,x - bcy = a\,(b^2 + c^2 + bc),$$

$$(c+a)\,x - cay = b\,(c^2 + a^2 + ca),$$

$$(a+b)\,x - aby = c\,(a^2 + b^2 + ab),$$

are concurrent at the point $(\Sigma\,ab, \Sigma\,a)$ where a, b, c are distinct real numbers.

(c) Prove that the lines

$$(p+q)\,x + (p+q)\,y - (p-q) = 0,$$

$$(p-q)\,x - (p-q)\,y - (p+q) = 0,$$

$$px + qy - p = 0,\ qx + py + q = 0\ \text{are all concurrent.}$$

17. (a)* Using co-ordinate geometry, prove that the three altitudes of any triangle are concurrent.

(I.I.T. 1998)

(b) If the lines

$$(a - b - c)\,x + 2ay + 2a = 0,$$

$$2bx + (b - c - a)\,y + 2b = 0$$

and $(2c + 1)\,x + 2cy + (c - a - b) = 0$

are concurrent, then prove that either

$$a + b + c \quad \text{or} \quad (a + b + c)^2 + 2a = 0$$

18. The base of an isosceles triangle is of length $2a$ and if p be its altitude then what is the distance of the mid-point of the base from either of equal sides ?

19. (a) Find the co-ordinates of the points on the line $x + 5y = 13$ at a distance of 2 units from the line $12x - 5y + 26 = 0$.

(b) Find all the points on the line $x + y = 4$ that lie at a unit distance from the line $4x + 3y = 10$.

(c) A point moves so that square of its distance from the point $(3, -2)$ is numerically equal to its distance from the line $5x - 12y = 13$. Find the equation of its locus.

20. p_1 and p_2 are the distances of a variable point from the two lines $2x + y - 1 = 0$ and $x + 2y + 1 = 0$ satisfying the condition that $p_1^2 = p_2^2 + 3$. Prove that the product of the distances of the same point from the lines $x + y + 2 = 0$ and $x - y - 3 = 0$ varies as its distance from the line $x - 3y - 1 = 0$.

21. Find the equation of the line joining the point $(3, 5)$ to the point of intersection of the lines

$$4x + y - 1 = 0 \quad \text{and} \quad 7x - 3y - 35 = 0$$

and prove that the line is equidistant from the origin and the point $(8, 34)$.

22. (a) If p and p' be the lengths of perpendiculars from origin to the lines $x \sec\theta - y\,\text{cosec}\,\theta = a$ and $x \cos\theta - y \sin\theta = a \cos 2\theta$ respectively, then prove that $4p^2 + p'^2 = a^2$.

(b) Prove that the product of the perpendiculars from the points $[\pm\sqrt{(a^2 - b^2)}, 0]$ to the line

$$\frac{x}{a}\cos\theta + \frac{y}{b}\sin\theta = 1 \text{ is } b^2.$$

(c) Are the points $(3, 4)$ and $(2, -6)$ on the same or opposite sides of the line $3x - 4y = 8$?

23. (a) Find the equations of two lines each parallel to $3x + 4y + 7 = 0$ one of which passes through $(1, 1)$ and other through $(-2, -1)$. Also find the perpendicular distance between them.

(b)* Determine the equation of the line parallel to $x + 2y = 5$ and is at the same distance from the point $(3, 2)$ as the given line.

(c) Prove that the lines $2x + 3y = 19$ and $2x + 3y = -7$ are equidistant from the line $2x + 3y = 6$.

(d)* The following lines are the sides of two squares

(1) $2x - y - 4 = 0$ (2) $x + 2y - 7 = 0$

(3) $x + 2y + 3 = 0$

What will be the equations of the fourth side of the squares ?

24. (a) Show that the area of the parallelogram formed by the lines $3y - 2x = a$, $2y - 3x + a = 0$, $2x - 3y + 3a = 0$ and $3x - 2y = 2a$ is $2a^2/5$.

(b) Prove that the area of the parallelogram formed by the lines $4y - 3x - a = 0$, $3y - 4x + a = 0$, and $4y - 3x - 3a = 0$, $3y - 4x + 2a = 0$ is $\dfrac{2}{7}a^2$.

(c) Prove that the diagonals of the parallelogram formed by the four straight lines $\sqrt{3}x + y = 0$, $\sqrt{3}y + x = 0$, $\sqrt{3}x + y = 1$ and $\sqrt{3}y + x = 1$ are perpendicular to each other.

(d) Prove that the four straight lines

$$\frac{x}{a} + \frac{y}{b} = 1, \frac{x}{b} + \frac{y}{a} = 1,$$

$$\frac{x}{a} + \frac{y}{b} = 2 \text{ and } \frac{x}{b} + \frac{y}{a} = 2$$

form a rhombus. Find its area.

25. (a)* Show that the area of the parallelogram whose sides are

$$x \cos\alpha + y \sin\alpha = p,$$

$$x \cos\alpha + y \sin\alpha = q,$$

$$x \cos\beta + y \sin\beta = r,$$

$$x \cos\beta + y \sin\beta = s \text{ is}$$

$$\pm (p - q)(r - s)\,\text{cosec}\,(\alpha - \beta).$$

(b)* Prove that the area of the parallelogram, the equations of whose sides are

$$a_1 x + b_1 y + c_1 = 0,\ a_1 x + b_1 y + d_1 = 0$$

$$a_2 x + b_2 y + c_2 = 0,\ a_2 x + b_2 y + d_2 = 0$$

is $\dfrac{(d_1 - c_1)(d_2 - c_2)}{a_1 b_2 - a_2 b_1}$.

Deduce the condition for these lines to form a rhombus.

(c) Area of the parallelogram formed by the lines $y = mx$, $y = mx + 1$, $y = nx$ and $y = nx + 1$ equals

(a) $\dfrac{|m + n|}{(m - n)^2}$ (b) $\dfrac{2}{|m + n|}$

(c) $\dfrac{1}{|m+n|}$

(d) $\dfrac{1}{|m-n|}$ (I.I.T. Sc. 2001)

(d) The area bounded by the curves $y=|x|-1$ and $y=-|x|+1$ is

(a) 1   (b) 2

(c) $2\sqrt{2}$ (d) 4   (I.I.T. Sc. 2002)

26. (a)* Show that the four lines $ax \pm by \pm c = 0$ enclose a rhombus whose area is $\dfrac{2c^2}{ab}$.

(b) Show that the diagonals of the parallelogram whose sides are $lx+my+n=0$, $lx+my+n'=0$, $mx+ly+n=0$, $mx+ly+n'=0$ include an angle $\pi/2$.   (EAMCET 1994)

(c) The area enclosed within the curve $|x|+|y|=1$ is ....

27. If the sum of the distances of point from two perpendicular lines in a plane is 1, then prove that its locus is a square.   (I.I.T. 1992)

28. If one vertex of an equilateral triangle of side a lies at the origin and the other lies on the line $x-\sqrt{3}\,y=0$, the co-ordinates of the third vertex are

(a) $(0,a)$ (b) $(\sqrt{3}a/2,-a/2)$

(c) $(0,-a)$ (d) $(-\sqrt{3}a/2,a/2)$

29.* If $x\cos\alpha + y\sin\alpha = p$ where, $p = -\dfrac{\sin^2\alpha}{\cos\alpha}$ be a straight line, prove that perpendiculars p_1, p_2 and p_3 on this line from the points $(m^2, 2m), (mm', m+m')$ and $(m'^2, 2m')$ respectively are in geometrical progression.   (Bihar C.E.E. 1999)

Questions based on parametric form of the equation of a line $\dfrac{x-x_1}{\cos\theta} = \dfrac{y-y_1}{\sin\theta} = r$ **(See 7 xiii P. 727)**

30. (a) If the straight line through the point $P(3,4)$ makes an angle $\pi/6$ with the x-axis and meets the line $12x+5y+10=0$ at Q, find the length of PQ.

(b) A line making an angle θ with the + ive direction of x-axis passes through $P(5,6)$ to meet the line $x=6$ at Q and $y=9$ at R then QR is :

(a) $\dfrac{2(\cos\theta+3\sin\theta)}{\sin 2\theta}$ (b) $\dfrac{2(3\cos\theta+\sin\theta)}{\sin 2\theta}$

(c) $\dfrac{2(3\cos\theta-\sin\theta)}{\sin 2\theta}$ (d) $\dfrac{2(\cos\theta-3\sin\theta)}{\sin 2\theta}$

31. (a)* The line joining two points $A(2,0)$, $B(3,1)$ is rotated about A in anticlockwise direction through an angle of $15°$. Find the equation of the line in the new position. If B goes to C in the new position, what will be the co-ordinates of C?

(b) The point $P(1,1)$ is translated parallel to $2x=y$ in the first quadrant through a unit distance. Show that the co-ordinates of the new position of P are $\left(1\pm\dfrac{1}{\sqrt{5}}, 1\pm\dfrac{2}{\sqrt{5}}\right)$.

32. (a) Find the direction in which a straight line must be drawn through the point $(1,2)$ so that its point of intersection with the line $x+y=4$ may be at a distance $\sqrt{6}/3$ from this point.

(b)* Through the point $P(4,1)$ a line is drawn to meet the line $3x-y=0$ at Q where $PQ=11/(2\sqrt{2})$. Determine the equation of the line.

33. (a) A line is drawn through $P(3,4)$ inclined to x-axis at an angle $3\pi/4$. Find its equation and also the co-ordinates of two points on it on opposite sides of P at a distance $\sqrt{2}$ from it.

(b)* A line through $A(-5,-4)$ meets the lines $x+3y+2=0$, $2x+y+4=0$ and $x-y-5=0$ at the points B, C and D respectively. If $(15/AB)^2 + (10/AC)^2 = (6/AD)^2$, find the equation of the line.   (I.I.T. 1993)

(c)* Find the co-ordinates of the points on each line but at a unit distance from the other line. Their equations are $3x-4y+1=0$ and $8x+6y+1=0$.

34. (a)* Find the equation of the straight lines passing through $(-2,-7)$ and having an intercept of length 3 between the straight lines $4x+3y=12$, $4x+3y=3$.

(b) Find the equation of the line passing through the point $(2,3)$ and making intercept of length 2 units between the lines $y+2x=3$ and $y+2x=5$ (I.I.T. 1991)

(c) Find the equation of the straight line through the point $(-5,4)$ given that its segment intercepted by the lines $x+2y+1=0$ and $x+2y-1=0$ is of length $2/\sqrt{5}$.

35. (a)* P is the point $(-1,2)$, a variable line through P cuts the co-ordinate axes in A and B respectively. Q is a point on AB such that PA, PQ and PB are in H.P. Show that the locus of Q is the line $y=2x$.

(b) Find the equation of the line passing through the point $P(1,2)$ and cutting the lines $x+y-5=0$ and $2x-y=7$ at A and B respectively such that the harmonic mean of PA and PB is 10.

(c) The co-ordinates of base BC of a triangle ABC are $B(1,3), C=(-2,7)$. If ABC be an equilateral triangle, then find the co-ordinates of A.

(d)* A line is such that its segment between the straight lines $5x-y-4=0$ and $3x+4y-4=0$ is bisected at the point $(1,5)$. Obtain its equation.

36. (a)* Given n straight lines and a fixed point O. Through O is drawn a straight line meeting these lines in the points $A_1, A_2, ..., A_n$ and on it is taken point A such that $\dfrac{n}{OA} = \dfrac{1}{OA_1} + \dfrac{1}{OA_2} + \dfrac{1}{OA_3} + ... + \dfrac{1}{OA_n}$. Prove that the locus of the point A is a straight line.

(b) A variable straight line is drawn through O to cut two fixed straight lines L_1 and L_2 in A_1 and A_2. A

point A is taken on the variable line such that
$$\frac{m+n}{OA} = \frac{m}{OA_1} + \frac{n}{OA_2}.$$

Show that locus of P is a straight line passing through the point of intersection of L_1 and L_2.

37. (a) The sides of a triangle ABC are as under : $AB : 2x + 3y = 29$ and $AC : x + 2y = 16$. If the mid-point of BC is $(5, 6)$ then find the equation of BC.

(b) The base of a triangle ABC passes through the point $P(1, 5)$ which divides it in the ratio $2 : 1$. If the equation of the sides are $AC : 5x - y - 4 = 0$ and $BC : 3x - 4y - 4 = 0$, then the co-ordinates of vertex A are $\left(\frac{75}{17}, \frac{307}{17}\right)$.

(c) A straight line through the origin O meets the parallel lines $4x + 2y = 9$ and $2x + y + 6 = 0$ at points P and Q respectively. Then the point O divides the segment PQ in the ratio

(a) $1 : 2$ (b) $3 : 4$

(c) $2 : 1$ (d) $4 : 3$ **(I.I.T. Sc. 2002)**

38. (a)* A and B are two fixed points whose co-ordinates respectively are $(3, 2)$ and $(5, 1)$. ABP is an equilateral triangle on AB situated on the side opposite to that of origin. Find the co-ordinates of P and those of the orthocentre of triangle ABP.

(b)* The co-ordinates of base BC of an equilateral triangle ABC are given by $B(1, 3)$ and $C(-2, 7)$. What could be the possible co-ordinates of the vertex A ?

(c) The point $(1, 1)$ is translated parallel to $y = 2x$ in the first quadrant through unit distance. What will be its co-ordinates in the new position ?

39. (a) Prove that the co-ordinates of the third vertex of an equilateral triangle whose two vertices are at $(3, 4)$ and $(-2, 3)$ are

$$\left(\frac{1+\sqrt{3}}{2}, \frac{7-5\sqrt{3}}{2}\right) \text{ or } \left(\frac{1-\sqrt{3}}{2}, \frac{7+5\sqrt{3}}{2}\right).$$

(b) If $A(9, -9), B(1, -3)$ are the ends of the side AB a right angled isosceles triangle, then the third vertex is $(8, -2)$ and $(2, -10)$.

(c) If a and b are real numbers between 0 and 1 such that the points $(a, 1), (1, b)$ and $(0, 0)$ form an equilateral triangle, then $a = b = 2 - \sqrt{3}$.

40. (a)* Through a given point O a straight line is drawn to cut two given straight lines in L and M. Find the locus of a point N on the variable line such that ON is (a) A.M. (b) H.M. (c) G.M. of OL and OM.

(b)* A variable line L passing through the point $B(2, 5)$ intersects the lines $2x^2 - 5xy + 2y^2 = 0$ at P and Q. Find the locus of the point R on L such that distances BP, BR and BQ are in harmonic progression.   **(Roorkee 1998)**

41. A line is drawn through a variable point $A(t + 1, 2t)$ so as to meet the following lines in points indicated with them.

$7x + y - 16 = 0$ in B, $5x - y - 8 = 0$ in C,
$x - 5y + 8 = 0$ in D.

Show that AC, AB, AD are in H.P.

42. (a)* The sides of a square are parallel to co-ordinate axes and it is inscribed in the circle $x^2 + y^2 - 2x + 4y - 93 = 0$. Find the co-ordinates of the vertices of the square.

(b)* One diagonal of a square is the portion of the line $7x + 5y = 35$ intercepted by the axes, obtain the extremities of the other diagonal.   **(Roorkee 1997)**

43. A line is drawn through the point $A(3, 4)$ inclined at an acute angle θ with the +ive direction of x-axis. If it cuts the circle $x^2 + y^2 = 4$ in B and C then prove that the lengths AB and AC are the roots of

$$r^2 + 2(3\cos\theta + 4\sin\theta)r + 21 = 0.$$

44.* Through the origin O, a straight line is drawn to cut the line $y = mx + c$ at a point P. Prove that the locus of the point Q on this variable line satisfying $OP \cdot OQ = k^2$ is a circle passing through the origin.

45.* Consider a curve $ax^2 + 2hxy + by^2 = 1$ and a point P not on the curve. A line drawn from the point P intersects the curve at points Q and R. If the product $PQ \cdot PR$ is independent of the slope of the line, then show that the curve is a circle.   **(I.I.T. 1997)**

Solutions to Problem Set (4)

1. (a) Any line through the intersection of given lines is
$$P + \lambda Q = 0$$
or $2x - 3y + \lambda(4x - 5y - 2) = 0$
or $x(2 + 4\lambda) - y(3 + 5\lambda) - 2\lambda = 0$ ...(1)

(i) Pass through $(2, 1) \Rightarrow \lambda = -1$.

(ii) $\perp$ to $x + 2y + 1 = 0$
$\therefore \quad a_1 a_2 + b_1 b_2 = 0 \Rightarrow \lambda = -2/3$.

(iii) Parallel to $3x - 4y + 5 = 0$
$\therefore \quad \dfrac{a_1}{a_2} = \dfrac{b_1}{b_2} \Rightarrow \lambda = 1$

Putting the values of λ in (1), the required equations are

(i) $x - y - 1 = 0$ (ii) $2x - y - 4 = 0$

(iii) $3x - 4y - 1 = 0$.

(b) By **8 (4) P. 5**, the slope of the line equally inclined to axes is $\tan(\pm 45°) = \pm 1$. Hence by $P + \lambda Q = 0$,

$$\frac{2\lambda + 4}{5\lambda + 3} = \pm 1$$

$\Rightarrow \lambda = \dfrac{1}{3}, -1$. Putting for λ, the two lines are

$x - y = 0, x + y - 2 = 0$.

2. Slope of the given line $= -\dfrac{2 + 6\lambda}{3 - \lambda} = \infty \Rightarrow \lambda = 3$

(a) We may also say that since the line is parallel to y-axis, the coefficient of y in its equation $P + \lambda Q = 0$ must be zero. Therefore $3 - \lambda = 0$ or $\lambda = 3$. [**By 8 (b) (2) P. 727**]

(b) $a_1 a_2 + b_1 b_2 = 0$

or $m_1 m_2 = -1 \Rightarrow \lambda = -29/37$.

3. The given equation can be put in the form

(a) $a(x + y - 1) + b(2x + 3y - 1) = 0$

or $(x + y - 1) + \lambda(2x + 3y - 1) = 0$

where $\lambda = b/a$

Above is of the form $P + \lambda Q = 0$ and as such it represents a line through the intersection of the lines $P = 0$ and $Q = 0$

i.e. $x + y - 1 = 0$ and $2x + 3y - 1 = 0$.

Solving the above, we get the point $(2, -1)$ which is fixed.

(b) Proceed as above. $(-2, 9)$

(c) Dividing by 4, we get

$$\frac{3}{4}a + \frac{1}{2}b + c = 0.$$

Compare with $ax + by + c = 0$

Hence the set of lines pass through the point $(3/4, 1/2)$.

(d) Ans. $(1, -2)$

$a + c = 2b$ or $a - 2b + c = 0$

(e) Ans. (b).

Putting $\dfrac{b}{a} = \lambda$, the given family is

$(2 + \lambda)x + (1 - 2\lambda)y + (4 - 3\lambda) = 0$

Its distance from $(2, -3)$ is $\sqrt{10}$

$$\therefore \quad \frac{(2 + \lambda)2 - 3(1 - 2\lambda) + (4 - 3\lambda)}{\sqrt{(2 + \lambda)^2 + (1 - 2\lambda)^2}} = \sqrt{10}$$

or $\dfrac{5 + 5\lambda}{\sqrt{5\lambda^2 + 5}} = \sqrt{10}$

or $5(\lambda + 1)^2 = 10(\lambda^2 + 1)$

or $\lambda^2 - 2\lambda + 1 = 0$

or $(\lambda - 1)^2 = 0 \quad \therefore \quad \lambda = 1$ only.

4. (a) Let the variable line be $px + qy + 1 = 0$, then by given condition

$p_1 + p_2 + p_3 = 0 \Rightarrow 3p + 3q + 3 = 0$

or $p + q + 1 = 0$ ....(1)

condition (1) shows that the variable line passes through the point $(1, 1)$.

(b) The given relation is $(2l + 3m)^2 - n^2 = 0$

$\therefore \quad 2l + 3m + n = 0$ and $2l + 3m - n = 0$

or $-2l - 3m + n = 0$

$\therefore$ Passes through the points $(2, 3)$ and $(-2, -3)$.

(c) Let the line be $lx + my + 1 = 0$. By given condition,

$$\frac{(3l + 4m + 1) + (7l + 2m + 1)}{\sqrt{(l^2 + m^2)}} = \frac{3(l + 3m + 1)}{\sqrt{(l^2 + m^2)}}$$

$\therefore \quad 7l - 3m - 1 = 0$

or $-7l + 3m + 1 = 0$

Above shows that $lx + my + 1 = 0$ passes through the point $(-7, 3)$ which is fixed.

(d) $lx + my - 1 = 0$ s.t. $\displaystyle\sum_{i=1}^{n} \frac{(lx_i + my_i - 1)}{\sqrt{(l^2 + m^2)}} = 0$

$\therefore \quad l\Sigma x_i + m\Sigma y_i - n = 0.$

or $\dfrac{l\Sigma x_i}{n} + \dfrac{m\Sigma y_i}{n} - 1 = 0$

Above shows that the line $lx + my - 1 = 0$ passes through the centroid $\left(\dfrac{\Sigma x_i}{n}, \dfrac{\Sigma y_i}{n}\right)$ of the given points.

5. (a) Any line through $(2, 1)$ is $y - 1 = m(x - 2)$

or $m(x - 2) - (y - 1) = 0$

$\Sigma p_i = 0$. Substitute the co-ordinates of six points and divide by $\sqrt{a^2 + b^2}$

$$\therefore \quad \frac{m[\Sigma a_1 + 12 - 6 \cdot 2] - [\Sigma b_1 + 6 - 6]}{\sqrt{1 + m^2}} = 0$$

or $m(\Sigma a_1) - \Sigma b_1 = 0 \quad \forall \; m$

Hence we must have

$\Sigma a_1 = 0$ and $\Sigma b_1 = 0$

$\because \quad px + q = 0 \; \forall \; x$

$\Rightarrow \quad p = 0, q = 0$

$\therefore \quad a_1 + a_2 + a_3 = 0, \; b_1 + b_2 + b_3 = 0$

$\Rightarrow \quad a_i = 0 \; \forall \; i, b_i = 0 \; \forall \; i$

as a_i^s and b_i^s are non-negative real numbers.

(b) The equations of the given lines are :

$u = a_1 x + b_1 y + c_1 = 0, \quad v = a_2 x + b_2 y + c_2 = 0$

Also it is given that

$a_1/a_2 = b_1/b_2 = c_1/c_2 = \lambda$, say ...(1)

By using relation in (1), the family of lines $u + kv = 0$ becomes $\lambda v + kv = 0$

or $(\lambda + k)v = 0$ or $v = 0$ or $u + \dfrac{k}{\lambda}u = 0$

or $\left(1 + \dfrac{k}{\lambda}\right)u = 0$ or $u = 0$.

6. (a) The required line by $P + \lambda Q = 0$ is

$(x - 3y + 1) + \lambda(2x + 5y - 9) = 0$

or $x(1 + 2\lambda) + y(5\lambda - 3) + (1 - 9\lambda) = 0$ ...(1)

Its distance from origin is given to be $\sqrt{5}$.

$$\therefore \quad \frac{1 - 9\lambda}{[(1 + 2\lambda)^2 + (5\lambda - 3)^2]^{1/2}} = \sqrt{5}, \quad \text{Square}$$

$\therefore \quad (1 - 9\lambda)^2 = 5(1 + 4\lambda^2 + 4\lambda + 25\lambda^2 - 30\lambda + 9)$

or $64\lambda^2 - 112\lambda + 49 = 0$ or $(8\lambda - 7)^2 = 0$

$\therefore \quad \lambda = 7/8$.

Putting for λ in (1) and simplifying we get the required line as $2x + y - 5 = 0$

(b) Put $b/a = \lambda$ then $(\lambda - 1)^2 = 0$

$\therefore \quad \lambda = 1, \ 3x - y + 1 = 0$

Since there is only one value of λ hence there will be only one line.

(c) The given equation can be written as

$$P \cos \alpha + Q \sin \alpha = 0$$

or $\quad P + Q \tan \alpha = 0 \qquad \qquad \qquad ...(1)$

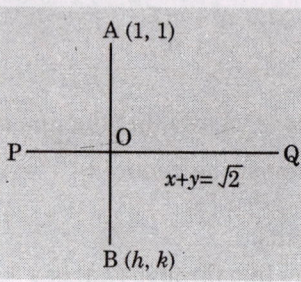

Fig. 66

where $P = 0, Q = 0$ are the equations of two lines. Clearly (1) is of the form $P + \lambda Q = 0$ which represents a family of lines passing through the intersection of $P = 2x + 3y - 5 = 0$

and $\qquad Q = 3x - 5y + 2 = 0$

i.e. the point $(1, 1)$ say A.

Reflection of $A (1, 1)$ in the line $x + y - \sqrt{2} = 0$ will be point $B (h, k)$ given by $\qquad \qquad \qquad$ **(e_1, P. 773)**

$$\frac{h - 1}{1} = \frac{k - 1}{1} = -2 \frac{l}{a^2 + b^2}$$

$$= -2 \frac{2 - \sqrt{2}}{2} = \sqrt{2} - 2$$

$\therefore \quad h = k = \sqrt{2} - 1$

Hence the reflection of A is $(\sqrt{2} - 1, \sqrt{2} - 1)$.

7. (a) Solving the equations by subtracting, we get $x = y$ and putting in any, the point of intersection is $\left(\frac{ab}{a + b}, \frac{ab}{a + b} \right)$. By two-point formula the equation of the line joining this point and (a, b) is

$$a^2 y - b^2 x = ab (a - b)$$

Sum of intercepts

$$= ab (a - b) \left[\frac{1}{a^2} - \frac{1}{b^2} \right] = \frac{a - b}{ab} (b^2 - a^2) \text{ etc.}$$

(b) Let the base BC be taken along axis of x and its mid-point be chosen as origin so that the points B and C are $(-a, 0)$ and $(a, 0)$ respectively. The third vertex A will lie on y-axis at $(0, b)$ say. By given condition

$$\frac{BP}{AB} = \frac{AB}{CQ} = \lambda \text{ say or } \frac{BP}{AB} = \frac{AC}{CQ} = \lambda \ \because \ AB = AC$$

B divides PA in the ratio $\lambda : 1$ and C divides AQ in the ratio $\lambda : 1$ as shown in the figure. Hence by

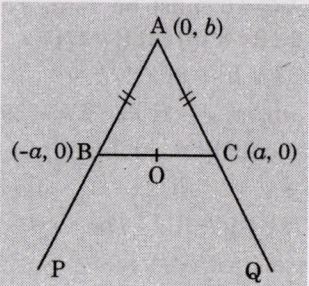

Fig. 67

ratio formula the co-ordinates of P are $[-a(\lambda + 1), -\lambda b]$ and Q is $\left[a \frac{(\lambda + 1)}{\lambda}, -\frac{b}{\lambda} \right]$.

Slope of PQ by $\frac{y_2 - y_1}{x_2 - x_1}$ is $\frac{b}{a} \frac{\lambda - 1}{\lambda + 1}$.

Hence equation of PQ is

$$y + \lambda b = \frac{b}{a} \frac{\lambda - 1}{\lambda + 1} [x + a(\lambda + 1)]$$

or $\quad a(\lambda + 1) y + ab\lambda (\lambda + 1)$

$$= b (\lambda - 1) x + ab (\lambda^2 - 1)$$

Cancel $ab\lambda^2$ and collect the terms of λ

$$(ay + bx + ab) + \lambda (bx - ay - ab) = 0$$

Above is of the form $u + \lambda v = 0$ which represents a family of straight lines passing through the intersection of $u = 0$ and $v = 0$, *i.e.* the point $(0, -b)$ which is a fixed point.

8. (a) As in **Q. 7 (a)** the point of intersection of given lines is $\left(\frac{ab}{a + b}, \frac{ab}{a + b} \right)$. Any line through this point is

$$\left(y - \frac{ab}{a + b} \right) = m \left(x - \frac{ab}{a + b} \right)$$

Putting $y = 0$ and then $x = 0$ the points where it meets the axes are

$$A \left(\frac{ab}{a + b} \frac{m - 1}{m}, 0 \right), \ B \left(0, -\frac{ab}{a + b} (m - 1) \right).$$

If (h, k) be the mid-point of AB, then

$$2h = \frac{ab}{a + b} \frac{m - 1}{m}, \ 2k = \frac{ab}{a + b} (1 - m)$$

In order to find the locus of (h, k) we have to eliminate the variable m.

$$\therefore \quad \frac{1}{2h} + \frac{1}{2k} = \frac{a + b}{ab} \left[\frac{m}{m - 1} - \frac{1}{m - 1} \right] = \frac{a + b}{ab}$$

Hence the locus is $ab (x + y) = 2xy (a + b)$.

(b) Any line through origin is $y = mx$ (m variable). It meets the given lines in points

$P\left(\dfrac{1}{m+1},\dfrac{m}{m+1}\right)$ and $Q\left(\dfrac{3}{m+1},\dfrac{3m}{m+1}\right)$.

Any line L_1 through P parallel to $2x-y=5$ is

$$2\left(x-\dfrac{1}{m+1}\right)-\left(y-\dfrac{m}{m+1}\right)=0 \quad \textbf{Rule 13 P. 6}$$

or $\quad 2x-y=\dfrac{2-m}{m+1}$ \hfill ...(1)

Any line through Q parallel to $3x+y=5$ is

$$3\left(x-\dfrac{3}{m+1}\right)+\left(y-\dfrac{3m}{m+1}\right)=0$$

or $\quad 3x+y=\dfrac{3(3+m)}{m+1}$ \hfill ...(2)

In order to find the locus of their point of intersection, we have to eliminate the variable m between their equations. We rewrite the equations of lines as

$$2x-y=\dfrac{-m-1+3}{m+1} \quad \text{or} \quad 2x-y+1=\dfrac{3}{m+1}$$

$$3x+y=\dfrac{3(2+m+1)}{m+1} \quad \text{or} \quad 3x+y-3=\dfrac{6}{m+1}$$

Dividing the above two thereby eliminating the variable m, the required locus is given by

$$\dfrac{2x-y+1}{3x+y-3}=\dfrac{1}{2}$$

or $\quad 4x-2y+2=3x+y-3$

or $\quad x-3y+5=0$

which being of first degree, represents the equation of a line.

(c) Any line through the intersection of given lines is

$$(px+qy+r)+\lambda(lx+my+n)=0$$

It meets the axes $y=0$ and $x=0$ at

$$A\left(-\dfrac{r+\lambda n}{p+\lambda l},0\right), \quad B\left(0,-\dfrac{r+\lambda n}{q+\lambda m}\right)$$

Since the triangle is right angled, the circum-centre will be at the mid-point of hypotenuse AB. If (x,y) be the circumcentre then

$$2x=-\dfrac{r+\lambda n}{p+\lambda l}, \quad 2y=-\dfrac{r+\lambda n}{q+\lambda m}$$

$\therefore \quad \lambda(2xl+n)+(2px+r)=0$

and $\lambda(2ym+n)+(2qy+r)=0$

Now eliminate λ from the above two

$$\dfrac{2xl+n}{2px+r}=\dfrac{2ym+n}{2qy+r}=\left(-\dfrac{1}{\lambda}\right)$$

Now cross multiply and cancel 2 to get the locus as given.

9. (a) $\tan 135°=-1=m$. Let the two lines be

$x+y=a, x+y=b$

They meet the axis of x in A,B, y-axis in C,D.

$\therefore \quad A(a,0), \ B(b,0), \ C(0,a), \ D(0,b)$

By intercepts form equations of AD and BC are

$AD, \dfrac{x}{a}+\dfrac{y}{b}=1; \ BC, \dfrac{x}{b}+\dfrac{y}{a}=1$

We have to eliminate the variables a,b in order to find the locus of their point of intersection. Subtracting we get

$$x\left(\dfrac{1}{a}-\dfrac{1}{b}\right)-y\left(\dfrac{1}{a}-\dfrac{1}{b}\right)=0 \quad \therefore \ x-y=0$$

is the required locus.

(b) Use $P+\lambda Q=0$ and find λ by passing through $(0,0)$.

Ans. $3x-2y=0$.

(c) Median AD is given by $P+\lambda Q=0$

$$(hx+ky-1)+\lambda(kx+hy-1)=0$$

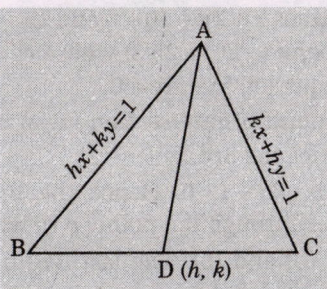

Fig. 68

Since it passes through (h,k)

$\therefore \quad \lambda=-(h^2+k^2-1)/(2hk-1)$ etc.

10. The diagonal AC can be written

$P+\lambda Q=0$ i.e. **(through A)**

$(a,b,c)+\lambda(d',b',d')=0$ \hfill ...(I)

It can also be written as **(through C)**

$(a,b,d)+\mu(d',b',c')=0$ \hfill ...(II)

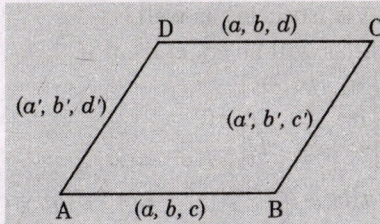

Fig. 69

Comparing the co-efficients of x,y and constant in (I) and (II) $\quad \lambda=\mu$ and $c+\lambda d'=d+\mu c'$

or $c-d=\lambda(c'-d')$ $\therefore \ \lambda=\dfrac{c-d}{c'-d'}=\mu$

$\therefore \quad AC$ is $(c'-d')(ax+by+c)$

$\qquad\qquad +(c-d)(d'x+b'y+d')=0$

Similarly BD can be written as

$(c'-d')(ax+by+d)-(c-d)(d'x+b'y+c')=0$.

11. (a) The first two lines meet at the point $(5,5)$ which clearly satisfies the equation $4x+5y-45=0$ of the third line. Hence the three lines are concurrent.

(b) Ans. (c).

The point of intersection of

$$x + 2y - 3 = 0 \text{ and } 2x + 3y - 4 = 0$$

is found to be $(-1, 2)$. The co-ordinates of this point satisfy the equation $4x + 5y - 6 = 0$ but not $3x + 4y - 7 = 0$. Hence all the four lines are not concurrent. Again since three of the lines meet at a point they cannot form a quadrilateral. Hence (c) is the correct answer.

12. (a) The first and third lines meet at $(1, -1)$ and putting in the equation of second line, we get $a = 5$.

(b) $k = -45$. $(5, 5)$ is point of intersection.

(c) The lines $x + 2y - 10 = 0$ and $2x + y + 5 = 0$ meet at the point $(-20/3, 25/3)$ whose co-ordinates satisfy the equation $5x + 4y = 0$.

13. (a) The point of intersection $(1, 2)$ of first two lines satisfies the 3rd.

∴ $p + 2q - 1 = 0$. Hence the line $x + 2y - 1 = 0$ passes through the point (p, q) which is fixed.

(b) Ans. (b) and (c). The last two lines meet at the point $\left(\dfrac{37}{50}, \dfrac{8}{25}\right)$ and these co-ordinates satisfy the 1st also. Hence they are concurrent. Again if you find the bisectors of last two then one of the bisectors is line given by (1).

(c) Ans. (b) and (c). The first two lines are clearly perpendicular. Also angle between 2nd and 3rd is

$$\tan \theta = \frac{7.4 - 3.1}{7.3 + 1.4} = 1 \quad \therefore \theta = 45°$$

Hence the 3rd angle is also $45°$.

∴ Δ is isosceles as well.

14. (a) The lines will be concurrent if

$$\begin{vmatrix} a & b & c \\ b & c & a \\ c & a & b \end{vmatrix} = 0$$

or $a(bc - a^2) - b(b^2 - ac) + c(ab - c^2) = 0$

or $a^3 + b^3 + c^3 - 3abc = 0$

or $(a + b + c)(a^2 + b^2 + c^2 - ab - bc - ca) = 0$

or $a + b + c = 0$

as the other factor is always $+ive = \dfrac{1}{2}\Sigma(a - b)^2$.

(b) As above $\begin{vmatrix} a & 2 & 1 \\ b & 3 & 1 \\ c & 4 & 1 \end{vmatrix} = 0$

Apply $R_1 + R_3 - 2R_2$

$$\therefore \begin{vmatrix} a + c - 2b & 0 & 0 \\ b & 3 & 1 \\ c & 4 & 1 \end{vmatrix} = 0$$

or $(a + c - 2b)(3 - 4) = 0$ ∴ $a + c - 2b = 0$

or $a + c = 2b$ ∴ a, b, c are in A.P.

15. (a) The lines will be concurrent if

$$\begin{vmatrix} p_1 & q_1 & -1 \\ p_2 & q_2 & -1 \\ p_3 & q_3 & -1 \end{vmatrix} = 0$$

or $\dfrac{1}{2}\begin{vmatrix} p_1 & q_1 & 1 \\ p_2 & q_2 & 1 \\ p_3 & q_3 & 1 \end{vmatrix} = 0$

or $\Delta = 0$

i.e., area of a triangle formed by the points (p_1, q_1), (p_2, q_2) and (p_3, q_3) is zero and as such the points are collinear.

(b) Required condition is $\Sigma m_1(c_2 - c_3) = 0$.

16. (a) The lines will be concurrent if

$$\begin{vmatrix} p - q & q - r & r - p \\ q - r & r - p & p - q \\ r - p & p - q & q - r \end{vmatrix} = 0$$

Adding column no. 2 and 3 to column no. 1, we get

$$\begin{vmatrix} 0 & q - r & r - p \\ 0 & r - p & p - q \\ 0 & p - q & q - r \end{vmatrix} = 0$$

(b) Multiplying the 1st equation by $a^2(b - c)$, 2nd by $b^2(c - a)$ and 3rd by $c^2(a - b)$, their equations become

$$a^2(b^2 - c^2)x - a^2bc(b - c)y - a^3(b^3 - c^3) = 0$$

and so on. They will be concurrent if $\Delta = 0$ as in part (a).

Point of intersection :

Subtract 1st two and cancel $(b - a)$.

∴ $x - cy = ab - c^2$

or $x = cy + (ab - c^2)$ ...(1)

Putting for x in any and simplifying, we get $y = a + b + c$ and hence $x = ab + bc + ca$, by (1).

(c) First three lines will be concurrent if

$$\begin{vmatrix} p + q & p + q & -(p - q) \\ p - q & -(p - q) & -(p + q) \\ p & q & -p \end{vmatrix} = 0$$

$R_1 + R_2$ will make R_1 and R_3 identical ∴ $\Delta = 0$ Hence concurrent. Similarly 1st, 2nd and 4th are also concurrent as $R_1 - R_2$ will make R_1 and R_3 identical. Hence the four lines are concurrent.

17. (a) Choose one side $BC = 2a$ along x-axis with its mid-point O as origin so that the points B and C are

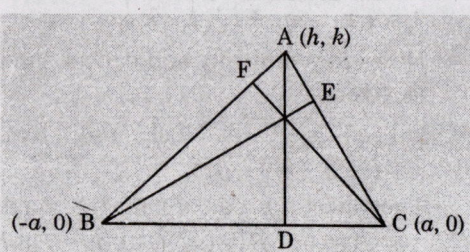

Fig. 70

$(-a, 0)$ and $(a, 0)$ respectively. Let the third vertex be the point (h, k).

AD, BE and CF are three altitudes whose equations are

$$AD \quad x = h \quad \text{or} \quad x + 0.y - h = 0 \qquad \text{...(1)}$$

$$BE \quad y - 0 = -\frac{(h-a)}{k}(x+a)$$

$$\text{or} \quad x(h-a) + ky + a(h-a) = 0 \qquad \text{...(2)}$$

CF Replace a by $-a$ in (2)

$$\text{or} \quad x(h+a) + ky - a(h+a) = 0 \qquad \text{...(3)}$$

The three lines will be concurrent if $\Delta = 0$.

$$\text{or} \quad \begin{vmatrix} 1 & 0 & -h \\ h-a & k & a(h-a) \\ h+a & k & -a(h+a) \end{vmatrix}$$

Apply $R_3 - R_2$ and two rows become identical.

$\therefore \quad \Delta = 0 \quad \therefore$ Concurrent.

(b) $\Delta = 0$ for concurrency

$$\Rightarrow \quad \begin{vmatrix} (a-b-c) & 2a & 2a \\ 2b & b-c-a & 2b \\ 2c+1 & 2c & c-a-b \end{vmatrix}$$

Split C_1 into two

$$= \begin{vmatrix} a-b-c & 2a & 2a \\ 2b & b-c-a & 2b \\ 2c & 2c & c-a-b \end{vmatrix}$$

$$+ \begin{vmatrix} 0 & 2a & 2a \\ 0 & b-c-a & 2b \\ 1 & 2c & c-a-b \end{vmatrix}$$

$$\Delta = \Delta_1 + \Delta_2$$

$\therefore \quad \Delta_2 = 2a[2b - (b-c-a)] = 2a(a+b+c)$

For Δ_1 Apply $R_1 + R_2 + R_3$ and take $a+b+c$

$$\therefore \quad \Delta_1 = (a+b+c)\begin{vmatrix} 1 & 1 & 1 \\ 2b & b-c-a & 2b \\ 2c & 2c & c-a-b \end{vmatrix}$$

Apply $C_1 - C_2, C_2 - C_3$

$$= (a+b+c)\begin{vmatrix} 0 & 0 & 1 \\ a+b+c & -(a+b+c) & 2b \\ 0 & a+b+c & c-a-b \end{vmatrix}$$

$\therefore \quad \Delta_1 = (a+b+c)^3$

$\therefore \quad \Delta = \Delta_1 + \Delta_2 = (a+b+c)[(a+b+c)^2 + 2a]$

18. Choosing the base along x-axis and its mid-point as origin so that B is $(-a, 0)$ and C $(a, 0)$.

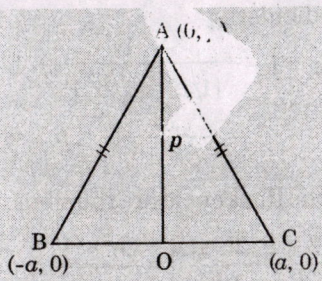

Fig. 71

Now the triangle being isosceles its altitude will be along the median $AO = p$ and will be along y-axis. Vertex A be $(0, p)$. By intercepts form the equations of AB and AC are

$$\frac{x}{-a} + \frac{y}{p} = 1 \quad \text{and} \quad \frac{x}{a} + \frac{y}{p} = 1$$

Distance of each from the mid-point $(0, 0)$ of base is

$$\frac{1}{\sqrt{\left(\frac{1}{a^2} + \frac{1}{p^2}\right)}} = \frac{ap}{\sqrt{a^2 + p^2}}$$

19. (a) Let the point be (p, q) so that

$$p + 5q = 13. \qquad \text{...(1)}$$

Its distance from the line $12x - 5y + 26 = 0$ is

$$\frac{12p - 5q + 26}{\sqrt{(144 + 25)}} = \pm 2, \quad \text{given.}$$

$$\text{or} \quad 12p - 5q + 26 = \pm 26.$$

+ive sign $12p - 5q = 0$ \qquad ...(2)

–ive sign $12p - 5q = -52$. \qquad ...(3)

Solving (1) and (2), we get the point (p, q) as $(1, 12/5)$.

Solving (1) and (3), we get the point (p, q) as $(-3, 16/5)$.

Alternative method

Any point on the line $x + 5y = 13$ be taken as $(13 - 5t, t)$, choosing $y = t$ \qquad ...(1)

Its distance from $12x - 5y + 26 = 0$ is 2

$$\therefore \quad \frac{12(13 - 5t) - 5t + 26}{\sqrt{144 + 25}} = \pm 2$$

$$\text{or} \quad 14 \times 13 - 13(5t) = \pm 2(13)$$

$$\text{or} \quad 14 - 5t = \pm 2 \quad \therefore 5t = 16 \quad \text{or} \quad 12$$

Putting for t in (1), the points are

$$\left(1, \frac{12}{5}\right) \quad \text{or} \quad \left(-3, \frac{16}{5}\right)$$

(b) Ans. $(3, 1), (-7, 11)$.

(c) Apply $d^2 = \pm p$.

$$\therefore \quad 13(x^2 + y^2 - 6x + 4y + 13)$$

$$= \pm (5x - 12y - 13).$$

20. $p_1^2 - p_2^2 = 3 \Rightarrow (h+k)(h-k-2) = 5$

$$\text{or} \quad h^2 - k^2 = 5 + 2h + 2k \qquad \text{...(1)}$$

Now product of perpendiculars from (h, k) to other two lines is $d_1 \cdot d_2 = \dfrac{h+k+2}{\sqrt{2}} \cdot \dfrac{h-k-3}{\sqrt{2}}$

$$\frac{1}{2}[(h^2 - k^2) + (2h - 2k) - 3(h+k) - 6]$$

$$= \frac{1}{2}[5 + 2h + 2k + 2h - 2k - 3h - 3k - 6]$$

$$= \frac{h - 3k - 1}{2} \quad \text{by (1)} \qquad \text{...(2)}$$

Again if p be distance of (h, k) from

$$x - 3y - 1 = 0$$

then $p = \dfrac{h - 3k - 1}{\sqrt{10}}$ ...(3)

$\therefore \quad \dfrac{d_1 \cdot d_2}{p} = \dfrac{\sqrt{10}}{2} = $ constant, by (2) and (3)

Hence $d_1 \cdot d_2$ varies as p.

21. By $P + \lambda Q = 0$ the line is $12x - y - 31 = 0$.
Its distance from $(0, 0)$ is
$$\dfrac{|-31|}{\sqrt{(145)}} = \dfrac{31}{\sqrt{(145)}}.$$
Its distance from $(8, 34)$ is
$$\dfrac{96 - 34 - 31}{\sqrt{(145)}} = \dfrac{31}{\sqrt{(145)}}.$$

22. (a) $p = \dfrac{-a}{\sqrt{(\sec^2 \theta + \mathrm{cosec}^2 \theta)}}$

$\therefore \quad 4p^2 = \dfrac{4a^2 \sin^2 \theta \cos^2 \theta}{\sin^2 \theta + \cos^2 \theta}$

or $\quad 4p^2 = a^2 (2 \sin \theta \cos \theta)^2 = a^2 \sin^2 2\theta$.

$p' = \dfrac{-a \cos 2\theta}{\sqrt{(\cos^2 \theta + \sin^2 \theta)}}$,

$\therefore \quad p'^2 = a^2 \cos^2 2\theta$

$\therefore \quad 4p^2 + p'^2 = a^2 (\sin^2 2\theta + \cos^2 2\theta) = a^2$.

(b) Equation of the given line is
$$x (b \cos \theta) + y (a \sin \theta) - ab = 0.$$

$\therefore \quad p_1 = \dfrac{\sqrt{(a^2 - b^2)} (b \cos \theta) - ab}{\sqrt{(b^2 \cos^2 \theta + a^2 \sin^2 \theta)}}$

$\therefore \quad p_2 = \dfrac{-\sqrt{(a^2 - b^2)} (b \cos \theta) - ab}{\sqrt{(b^2 \cos^2 \theta + a^2 \sin^2 \theta)}}$

$\therefore \quad p_1 p_2 = -\dfrac{(a^2 - b^2) b^2 \cos^2 \theta - a^2 b^2}{b^2 \cos^2 \theta + a^2 \sin^2 \theta}$

$\because \quad (L + M)(L - M) = L^2 - M^2$

$= b^2 \dfrac{[a^2 - a^2 \cos^2 \theta + b^2 \cos^2 \theta]}{b^2 \cos^2 \theta + a^2 \sin^2 \theta}$

$= b^2 \dfrac{[a^2 \sin^2 \theta + b^2 \cos^2 \theta]}{b^2 \cos^2 \theta + a^2 \sin^2 \theta} = b^2$.

(c) The equation of the line is $u = 3x - 4y - 8 = 0$.
Refer 17 (b) P. 6. Putting the co-ordinates of the two points in the equation of line, we get -15 and 22 which are of opposite signs. Hence the two points are on opposite sides of the given line.

23. (a) The required lines are
$$3x + 4y - 7 = 0 \text{ and } 3x + 4y + 10 = 0$$
$$p_1 = -7/5, \quad p_2 = 10/5$$
$\therefore \quad d = $ distance between parallel lines,
$$= p_1 \sim p_2 = -\dfrac{7}{5} - \dfrac{10}{5}$$

$= -\dfrac{17}{5} = \dfrac{17}{5}$, numerically.

Alt : Any point on $3x + 4y - 7 = 0$ is $(1, 1)$ by inspection. Required distance is its perpendicular distance from the other line $3x + 4y + 10 = 0$ and is
$$\dfrac{3.1 + 4.1 + 10}{5} = \dfrac{17}{5}.$$

(b) $p = \dfrac{2}{\sqrt{5}}$. Parallel line is $x + 2y + \lambda = 0$.
$$\left| \dfrac{7 + \lambda}{\sqrt{5}} \right| = \dfrac{2}{\sqrt{5}} \text{ by the given condition.}$$
$\therefore \quad 7 + \lambda = \pm 2 \quad \therefore \quad \lambda = -5 \text{ or } -9$
But $\lambda = -5$ gives the given line and hence the required line is $x + 2y - 9 = 0 \quad \because \lambda = -q$

(c) All the three lines are parallel. Any point on the third line on putting $x = 0$ is $(0, 2)$. Its distance from the other two lines are
$$\dfrac{0 + 6 - 19}{\sqrt{(13)}} = -\sqrt{13} \text{ and } \dfrac{0 + 6 + 7}{\sqrt{(13)}} = \sqrt{13}.$$
Above shows that these lines are equidistant from the third line and on opposite sides of it.

(d) Distance between parallel sides
$$= \dfrac{3 + 7}{\sqrt{5}} = \dfrac{10}{\sqrt{5}} = 2\sqrt{5}.$$
Let the fourth side parallel to $2x - y - 4 = 0$ be $2x - y + k = 0$
Distance between these two
$$= \dfrac{k + 4}{\sqrt{5}} = \pm 2\sqrt{5}$$
$\therefore \quad k = -4 \pm 10 = -14 \text{ or } 6$.
Hence the other two fourth sides are
$$2x - y - 14 = 0$$
or $\quad 2x - y + 6 = 0$.

24. (a) The sets of parallel sides are
$$3x - 2y - a = 0,$$
$$3x - 2y - 2a = 0$$
and $2x - 3y + a = 0$,
$$2x - 3y + 3a = 0.$$

$\therefore \quad$ Area $= \left| \dfrac{(2a - a)(3a - a)}{\begin{vmatrix} 3 & -2 \\ 2 & -3 \end{vmatrix}} \right| = \dfrac{2a^2}{5}$
Rule 22, P. 731.

(b) Do yourself.

(c) Here $p_1 = p_2$
$\therefore \quad$ Rhombus and hence diagonals are perpendicular.

(d) Here $p_1 = p_2 = \dfrac{1}{(1/a^2 + 1/b^2)^{1/2}}$
$$= \dfrac{ab}{\sqrt{(a^2 + b^2)}} = p, \text{ say.}$$
Hence the lines enclose a rhombus, whose area is
$$\left| \dfrac{(2 - 1)(2 - 1)}{\begin{vmatrix} 1/a & 1/b \\ 1/b & 1/a \end{vmatrix}} \right| = \dfrac{a^2 b^2}{a^2 - b^2}$$

25. (a) Use Area $= \dfrac{p_1 p_2}{\sin \theta} = p_1 p_2 \operatorname{cosec} \theta$ **Rule 22, P. 731.**

Here $p_1 = p - q$, $p_2 = r - s$
and $\tan \theta = \tan(\alpha - \beta)$
∴ $\theta = \alpha - \beta$.

(b) $p_1 = \dfrac{d_1 - c_1}{\sqrt{(a_1^2 + b_1^2)}}$, $\quad p_2 = \dfrac{d_2 - c_2}{\sqrt{(a_2^2 + b_2^2)}}$.

Also $\sin \theta = \dfrac{a_1 b_2 - a_2 b_1}{\sqrt{(a_1^2 + b_1^2)} \sqrt{(a_2^2 + b_2^2)}}$

Area of parallelogram

$= \dfrac{p_1 p_2}{\sin \theta} = \dfrac{(c_1 - d_1)(c_2 - d_2)}{a_1 b_2 - a_2 b_1}$

Note : If these lines enclose a rhombus, then $p_1 = p_2$.
∴ $(c_1 - d_1)(a_2^2 + b_2^2) = (c_2 - d_2)(a_1^2 + b_1^2)$.

(c) Ans (d).
Refer rule 22, P. 731

$\text{Area} = \dfrac{p_1 p_2}{\sin \theta} = \left| \dfrac{(c_1 - d_1)(c_2 - d_2)}{\begin{vmatrix} a_1 & b_1 \\ a_2 & b_2 \end{vmatrix}} \right|$

$\begin{array}{c} mx - y - 0 = 0 \\ mx - y + 1 = 0 \end{array}$ and $\begin{array}{c} nx - y - 0 = 0 \\ nx - y + 1 = 0 \end{array}$

∴ $\text{Area} = \left| \dfrac{(1-0)(1-0)}{\begin{vmatrix} m & -1 \\ n & -1 \end{vmatrix}} \right| = \dfrac{1}{|m - n|}$

(d) Ans. (b). The given lines are :
$y = x - 1$, $y = -x - 1$
and $y = x + 1$, $y = -x + 1$
according as $x > 0$ or $x < 0$
Above represent two sets of parallel lines which are perpendicular which enclose a quadrilateral whose area is $\dfrac{p_1 p_2}{\sin 90°} = p_1^2 = \left(\dfrac{2}{\sqrt{2}} \right)^2 = 2$.

26. (a) The four sides of the rhombus are
$ax + by + c = 0$ ...(1)
$ax + by - c = 0$ ...(2)
$ax - by + c = 0$ ...(3)
$ax - by - c = 0$ ...(4)

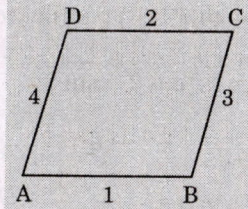

Fig. 72

Solving (1) with (3) and (2) with (4), we get the vertices $(-c/a, 0)$, $(c/a, 0)$.

Solving (2) with (3) and (1) with (4), we get the vertices as $(0, c/b)$, $(0, -c/b)$.

Above shows that one diagonal is of length $2c/a$ and is along x-axis whereas the other is along y-axis and is of length $2c/b$. Since the diagonals being along the axes, they are perpendicular and hence a rhombus.

The area is $\dfrac{1}{2}(d_1 \cdot d_2) = \dfrac{1}{2} \left(\dfrac{2c}{a} \cdot \dfrac{2c}{b} \right) = \dfrac{2c^2}{ab}$.

Note : You may do it as in **Q. 25.**

$\text{Area} = \dfrac{p_1 p_2}{\sin \theta} = \left| \dfrac{(c_1 - d_1)(c_2 - d_2)}{\begin{vmatrix} a_1 & b_1 \\ a_2 & b_2 \end{vmatrix}} \right|$

$= \left| \dfrac{(2c)(2c)}{\begin{vmatrix} a & b \\ a & -b \end{vmatrix}} \right| = \dfrac{4c^2}{2ab} = \dfrac{2c^2}{ab}$ · **(R. 22, P. 731)**

(b) The distances between two sets of parallel sides is each $\dfrac{n - n'}{\sqrt{(l^2 + m^2)}}$ i.e. $p_1 = p_2$ hence the parallelogram is rhombus whose diagonals we know intersect at right angles.

(c) Ans. Area $= 2$. Clearly the figure formed by the lines $|x| + |y| = 1$, that is, by the lines $x + y = 1$, $-x + y = 1$, $-x - y = 1$ and $x - y = 1$ is a square of side $\sqrt{2}$ so that its area $= (\sqrt{2})^2 = 2$.

27. Let the perpendicular lines be chosen along the axes and if (x, y) be the required point in the Ist quadrant then $x + y = 1$. Similarly if the points were in other three quadrants, then the result will be $x - y = 1$, $-x + y = 1$, $-x - y = 1$ or $x + y = \pm 1$, and $x - y = \pm 1$. These four lines clearly enclose a square.

28. Ans. (a), (b), (c), (d).
The two vertices are on $OP = a$ which makes an angle of $30°$ with x-axis. The third vertex will lie on OL or OM inclined at $60°$ each to OP where $OL = OM = a$.

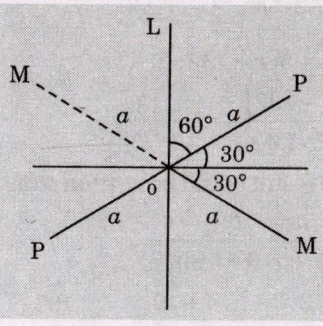

Fig. 73

OL makes an angle of $90°$ and OM makes an angle of $-30°$ with + ive direction of x-axis. Hence the vertices are given by

$$\frac{x-0}{\cos 90^\circ} = \frac{y-0}{\sin 90^\circ} = a, -a;$$

$$\frac{x-0}{\cos(-30^\circ)} = \frac{y-0}{\sin(-30^\circ)} = a, -a.$$

$+a\,(P)$ corresponds to vertices L and M,

$-a\,(P')$ corresponds to vertices L' and M'.

29. $p_1 = \dfrac{m^2 \cos\alpha + 2m\sin\alpha - (-\sin^2\alpha/\cos\alpha)}{\sqrt{(\cos^2\alpha + \sin^2\alpha)}}$

$$p_1 = \left(\frac{m\cos\alpha + \sin\alpha}{\sqrt{(\cos\alpha)}}\right)^2.$$

Similarly $p_3 = \left(\dfrac{m'\cos\alpha + \sin\alpha}{\sqrt{(\cos\alpha)}}\right)^2$

Also

$$p_2 = \frac{mm'\cos\alpha + (m+m')\sin\alpha - (-\sin^2\alpha/\cos\alpha)}{\sqrt{(\cos^2\alpha + \sin^2\alpha)}}$$

or $p_2 = \dfrac{1}{\cos\alpha}[mm'\cos^2\alpha + (m+m')$

$$\sin\alpha\cos\alpha + \sin^2\alpha]$$

or $p_2 = \dfrac{(m\cos\alpha + \sin\alpha)}{\sqrt{(\cos\alpha)}} \cdot \dfrac{m'\cos\alpha + \sin\alpha}{\sqrt{(\cos\alpha)}}$

or $p_2 = \sqrt{p_1 \cdot p_3}$ or $p_2{}^2 = p_1 p_3$

Hence p_1, p_2, p_3 are in G.P.

30. (a) Any line through $P\,(3,4)$ making an angle $\pi/6$ with x-axis is

$$\frac{x-3}{\cos 30^\circ} = \frac{y-4}{\sin 30^\circ} = r$$

where r represents the distance of any point on this line from the given point $P\,(3,4)$.

Any point Q on it is $[(r\sqrt{3}/2) + 3, (r/2) + 4]$ and Q lies on $12x + 5y + 10 = 0$

$$\therefore\quad 12\left[\left(\frac{r\sqrt{3}}{2}\right) + 3\right] + 5\left(\frac{r}{2} + 4\right) + 10 = 0$$

$$\therefore\quad (12\sqrt{3} + 5)\,r + 132 = 0$$

$$\therefore\quad r = \frac{|-132|}{12\sqrt{(3)} + 5} = \frac{132}{12\sqrt{(3)} + 5}.$$

The above result could be written straight way as

$$r = -\frac{ax_1 + by_1 + c}{a\cos\theta + b\sin\theta} \qquad \text{(e, P. 773)}$$

or $r = -\dfrac{12.3 + 5.4 + 10}{12 \cdot \dfrac{\sqrt{3}}{2} + 5 \cdot \dfrac{1}{2}} = -\dfrac{132}{12\sqrt{3} + 5} = \dfrac{132}{12\sqrt{3} + 5}.$

(b) Ans. (c).

$$\frac{x-5}{\cos\theta} = \frac{y-6}{\sin\theta} = r$$

Any point on the line is $(r\cos\theta + 5, r\sin\theta + 6)$ and Q lies on $x = 6$.

$$\therefore\quad r\cos\theta + 5 = 6 \quad \therefore\quad r = \frac{1}{\cos\theta}$$

$$\therefore\quad y = r\sin\theta + 6 = \tan\theta + 6$$

$$\therefore\quad Q \text{ is } (6, 6 + \tan\theta)$$

Similarly R on $y = 9$ is $(5 + 3\cot\theta, 9)$

$$\therefore\quad QR^2 = (1 - 3\cot\theta)^2 + (\tan\theta - 3)^2$$

$$= 10 - 6(\tan\theta + \cot\theta) + 9\cot^2\theta + \tan^2\theta$$

$$= 9\,\text{cosec}^2\theta + \sec^2\theta - 6 \cdot \frac{1}{\sin\theta\cos\theta}$$

$$= \frac{9\cos^2\theta + \sin^2\theta - 6\sin\theta\cos\theta}{\sin^2\theta\cos^2\theta}$$

$$= \frac{4(3\cos\theta - \sin\theta)^2}{\sin^2 2\theta}$$

$$\therefore\quad QR = \frac{2(3\cos\theta - \sin\theta)}{\sin 2\theta} \Rightarrow \text{(c)}$$

31. (a) A is $(2,0)$, B is $(3,1)$
Also $AB = \sqrt{2}$.

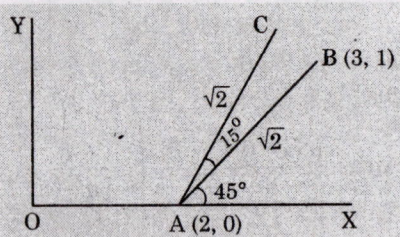

Fig. 74

Slope of $AB = (1 - 0)/(3 - 2) = 1 = \tan\theta$,

$$\therefore\quad \theta = 45^\circ$$

Now AB is rotated through 15° in anti-clockwise direction and hence it makes an angle of 60° with x-axis. Since it passes through $(2,0)$ its equation in new position is

$$\frac{x-2}{\cos 60^\circ} = \frac{y-0}{\sin 60^\circ} = r = AC = AB = \sqrt{2}.$$

Hence the co-ordinates of C are

$$2 + \sqrt{2}\cos 60^\circ, \ 0 + \sqrt{2}\sin 60^\circ$$

or $[(4 + \sqrt{2})/2, \sqrt{6}/2]$.

(b) Any line through $P\,(1,1)$ parallel to $2x = y$ whose slope $= 2 = \tan\theta$ is $\dfrac{x-1}{\cos\theta} = \dfrac{y-1}{\sin\theta} = r$

or $\dfrac{x-1}{1/\sqrt{5}} = \dfrac{y-1}{2/\sqrt{5}} = \pm 1$ as given.

$$\therefore\quad (x, y) \text{ is as given.}$$

32. (a) Let the line through $(1, 2)$ make an angle θ with x-axis so that its equation is

$$\frac{x-1}{\cos\theta} = \frac{y-2}{\sin\theta} = r$$

where r is the distance of any point on the line from the point $(1, 2)$.

Any point on it is $(r \cos \theta + 1, r \sin \theta + 2)$,

If it lies on $x + y = 4$, then

$$[[(r \cos \theta + 1) + (r \sin \theta + 2) = 4]$$

$$r(\cos \theta + \sin \theta) = 1 . \text{ But } r = \frac{1}{3}\sqrt{6} \text{ given}$$

$$\therefore \quad \frac{1}{3}\sqrt{6}(\cos \theta + \sin \theta) = 1$$

or $\cos \theta + \sin \theta = 3/\sqrt{6}$. ...(1)

Divide both sides by $\sqrt{2}$

$$\therefore \quad \frac{1}{\sqrt{(2)}}\cos \theta + \frac{1}{\sqrt{(2)}}\sin \theta = \frac{3}{\sqrt{(6)} . \sqrt{(2)}} = \frac{\sqrt{3}}{2}$$

or $\cos(\theta - 45°) = \cos 30°$

$\therefore \quad \theta - 45° = \pm 30°$

$\therefore \quad \theta = 75°$ or $15°$.

Note : The result (1) written above can be directly written by **Rule 7 (xiii) P. 767** as

$$r = -\frac{l}{a \cos \theta + b \sin \theta} = \frac{1}{3}\sqrt{6},$$

where $l = 1 + 2 - 4 = -1, a = 1, b = 1.$

(b) $\dfrac{x - 4}{\cos \theta} = \dfrac{y - 1}{\sin \theta} = r = \dfrac{11}{2\sqrt{2}}$

It meets the line $3x - y = 0$

$$\therefore \quad \frac{1}{r} = -\frac{3 \cos \theta - \sin \theta}{3.4 - 1} = \frac{2\sqrt{2}}{11}$$

(Refer Rule 7(xiii) P. 767)

$$\sin \theta = (2\sqrt{2} + 3 \cos \theta) \quad \text{Square} \qquad ...(1)$$

$$1 - \cos^2 \theta = 8 + 12\sqrt{2} \cos \theta + 9 \cos^2 \theta$$

or $10 \cos^2 \theta + 12\sqrt{2} \cos \theta + 7 = 0$

$$\therefore \quad \cos \theta = \frac{-12\sqrt{2} \pm \sqrt{(288 - 280)}}{20}$$

$$\cos \theta = -\frac{1}{\sqrt{2}} \quad \text{or} \quad -\frac{7\sqrt{2}}{10}, \text{ then from (1)}$$

$$\sin \theta = \frac{1}{\sqrt{2}} \quad \text{or} \quad -\frac{\sqrt{2}}{10}$$

$$\therefore \quad \tan \theta = -1, \frac{1}{7}$$

$\therefore$ Lines are $x + y = 5$ and $x - 7y + 3 = 0$

33. (a) Line is $\dfrac{x - 3}{\cos(3\pi/4)} = \dfrac{y - 4}{\sin(3\pi/4)} = r$, say.

or $\dfrac{x - 3}{-1/\sqrt{(2)}} = \dfrac{y - 4}{1/\sqrt{(2)}} = r$.

Its equation is $x - 3 = -(y - 4)$

or $x + y - 7 = 0$.

Any point on it is $(-r/\sqrt{2} + 3, r/\sqrt{2} + 4)$

Since the two points are at a distance $\sqrt{2}$ from P on opposite sides,

hence choosing $r = \pm\sqrt{2}$, we get the points as

$(-\sqrt{2} . 1/\sqrt{2} + 3, \sqrt{2} . 1/\sqrt{2} + 4)$

and $(\sqrt{2} . 1/\sqrt{2} + 3, -\sqrt{2} . 1/\sqrt{2} + 4)$

or $(2, 5)$ and $(4, 3)$.

(b) Any line through $A(-5, -4)$ is

$$y + 4 = \tan \theta(x + 5) \qquad ...(1)$$

or $\dfrac{x + 5}{\cos \theta} = \dfrac{y + 4}{\sin \theta} = r_1 = r_2 = r_3$

for $B \quad C \quad D$

B, C, D lie on the given lines respectively, where $r_1 = AB, r_2 = AC, r_3 = AD$.

$$r_1 = -\frac{a x_1 + b y_1 + c}{a \cos \theta + b \sin \theta} \qquad \text{[7 (xiii) P. 767]}$$

for B which lies on $x + 3y + 2 = 0$

$$AB = -\frac{1(-5) + 3(-4) + 2}{\cos \theta + 3 \sin \theta} = \frac{15}{\cos \theta + 3 \sin \theta}$$

or $\dfrac{15}{AB} = \cos \theta + 3 \sin \theta$.

Similarly $\dfrac{10}{AC} = 2 \cos \theta + \sin \theta$

and $\dfrac{6}{AD} = \cos \theta - \sin \theta$.

Hence from the given relation

$$(\cos \theta + 3 \sin \theta)^2 + (2 \cos \theta + \sin \theta)^2$$
$$= (\cos \theta - \sin \theta)^2$$

or $4 \cos^2 \theta + 12 \sin \theta \cos \theta + 9 \sin^2 \theta = 0$

or $(2 \cos \theta + 3 \sin \theta)^2 = 0 \quad \therefore \quad \tan \theta = -2/3$

Hence from (1), the equation of the line through A is

$$y + 4 = -\frac{2}{3}(x + 5)$$

or $2x + 3y + 22 = 0$.

(c) The two lines are perpendicular and meet at O $\left(-\dfrac{2}{10}, \dfrac{1}{10}\right)$ and $\tan \theta = \dfrac{3}{4}$ for AB.

$\therefore \quad \cos \theta = 4/5, \sin \theta = 3/5$

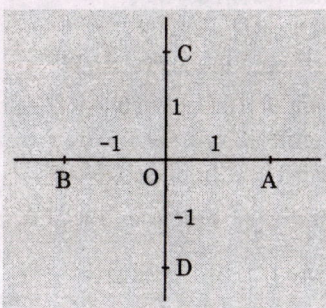

Fig. 75

$$\therefore \quad AB \text{ is } \frac{x + \dfrac{2}{10}}{4/5} = \frac{y - \dfrac{1}{10}}{3/5} = \frac{1}{\text{for } A}, \quad -\frac{1}{\text{for } B}$$

$$\therefore \quad A \text{ is } \left(\frac{4}{5} - \frac{2}{10}, \frac{3}{5} + \frac{1}{10}\right)$$

and B is $\left(-\dfrac{4}{5}-\dfrac{2}{10}, -\dfrac{3}{5}+\dfrac{1}{10}\right)$

or A is $\left(\dfrac{3}{5}, \dfrac{7}{10}\right)$ and B is $\left(-1, -\dfrac{1}{2}\right)$

It can be verified that distance of these two points from line CD $\quad 8x+6y+1=0$ is each unity.

Similarly C and D can be found on $8x+6y+1=0$, $\tan\theta = -4/3$

so that $\quad \cos\theta = -3/5, \quad \sin\theta = 4/5$.

CD is $\dfrac{x+\dfrac{2}{10}}{-3/5} = \dfrac{y-\dfrac{1}{10}}{4/5} = 1, \quad \underset{C}{-1}\ \underset{D}{}$

$\therefore \quad C$ is $\left(-\dfrac{8}{10}, \dfrac{9}{10}\right)$ and D is $\left(\dfrac{4}{10}, -\dfrac{7}{10}\right)$.

34. (a) The given parallel lines are

$\qquad 4x+3y=3 \qquad \qquad \qquad ...(1)$

$\qquad 4x+3y=12. \qquad \qquad \qquad ...(2)$

Any line through the point $(-2,-7)$ is

$\qquad \dfrac{x+2}{\cos\theta} = \dfrac{y+7}{\sin\theta} = r. \qquad \qquad ...(3)$

This line makes an intercept of length 3 between parallel lines (1) and (2). Hence we shall choose two values of r say r, and $r+3$ and the two corresponding points obtained will lie on lines (1) and (2). Thus

$\qquad r = -\dfrac{ax_1+by_1+c}{a\cos\theta+\sin\theta} \qquad$ **[7 (xiii) P. 767]**

where (x_1, y_1) is $(-2,-7)$ and $4x+3y-3=0$

$\qquad r = -\dfrac{4(-2)+3(-7)-3}{4\cos\theta+3\sin\theta} = \dfrac{32}{4\cos\theta+3\sin\theta}$

$\qquad r+3 = -\dfrac{4(-2)+3(-7)-12}{4\cos\theta+3\sin\theta} = \dfrac{41}{4\cos\theta+3\sin\theta}$

Eliminating r by subtracting, we get

$\qquad 3 = \dfrac{9}{4\cos\theta+3\sin\theta}$

or $\quad 4\cos\theta+3\sin\theta = 3$

or $\quad 4\cos\theta = 3(1-\sin\theta) \qquad \qquad ...(4)$

or $\quad 16(1-\sin^2\theta) = 9(1-\sin\theta)^2$

or $\quad (1-\sin\theta)[16(1+\sin\theta)-9(1-\sin\theta)] = 0$

or $\quad (1-\sin\theta)(25\sin\theta+7) = 0$

$\therefore \quad \sin\theta = 1$ and hence $\cos\theta = 0$

or $\quad \sin\theta = -\dfrac{7}{25}$ and $\cos\theta = \dfrac{24}{25}$ from (4)

Hence from (3), the lines are

$\qquad \dfrac{x+2}{24/25} = \dfrac{y+7}{-7/25}$

or $\quad 7x+24y+182=0$

and $\dfrac{x+2}{0} = \dfrac{y+7}{1}$

or $\quad \dfrac{y+7}{x+2} = \infty, \quad \therefore \quad x+2=0.$

Hence the two lines are

$\qquad 7x+24y+182=0$, and $\quad x+2=0$.

Alternative Method :

The slope of the given line is $-4/3$ and the distance PQ between these parallel lines is $9/5$. If $PB = P'C = 3$ then $QB = Q'C = 12/5$.

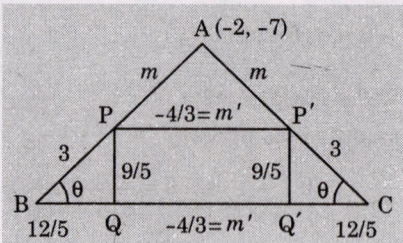

Fig. C-71

$\therefore \quad \tan\theta = \dfrac{9}{5} \div \dfrac{12}{5} = \dfrac{3}{4}$

Any line through $A(-2,-7)$ is

$\qquad y+7 = m(x+2) \qquad \qquad ...(1)$

It is equally inclined to parallel lines with slope $-4/3$.

$\therefore \quad \tan(\pm\theta) = \dfrac{m-(-4/3)}{1+m(-4/3)}$

or $\quad \pm\dfrac{3}{4} = \dfrac{3m+4}{3-4m}$

or $\quad 9-12m = 12m+16 \quad$ or $\ 9-12m = -12m-16$

$\therefore \quad m = -7/24$

or $\quad 0m+25=0 \quad \therefore \quad m=\infty$

Hence from (1) the required lines are

$\qquad 24(y+7)+7(x+2)=0$

or $\quad 7x+24y+182=0$

and $\dfrac{y+7}{x+2} = \infty \qquad$ or $\quad x+2=0$

(b) Proceed as in part (a).

Ans. $x-2=0, 3x+4y=18$.

(c) The given lines are parallel and distance between them is $2/\sqrt{5}$ which is perpendicular distance.

Hence the required line is one through the point $(-5,4)$ and perpendicular to $x+2y+1=0$

Its equation is $2(x+5)-(y-4)=0$

or $\quad 2x-y+14=0 \qquad \qquad$ **Rule 15, P. 768.**

35. (a) Any line through $P(-1,2)$ is

$\qquad \dfrac{x+1}{\cos\theta} = \dfrac{y-2}{\sin\theta} = r_1, r_2, r_3$

where r_1, r_2, r_3 are respectively the distances of the points A, Q and B from the given point $P(-1,2)$. Point A is $(r_1\cos\theta-1, r_1\sin\theta+2)$

where $\quad r_1\sin\theta+2=0 \qquad \qquad ...(1)$

as the point A lies on x-axis.

Point B is $(r_3\cos\theta-1, r_3\sin\theta+2)$

where $\quad r_3\cos\theta-1=0 \qquad \qquad ...(2)$

as the point B lies on y-axis.

Let the point Q be (h, k).

$\therefore \quad h = r_2 \cos \theta - 1$

and $k = r_2 \sin \theta + 2$ ...(3)

We have to find the locus of the point Q.

Also it is given that r_1, r_2, r_3 are in H.P.

$\therefore \quad \dfrac{2}{r_2} = \dfrac{1}{r_1} + \dfrac{1}{r_3} = -\dfrac{\sin \theta}{2} + \cos \theta$, by (1) and (2)

or $\quad \dfrac{2}{r_2} = -\dfrac{1}{2}\dfrac{(k-2)}{r_2} + \dfrac{(h+1)}{r_2}$, by (3)

or $\quad 2 = (-k/2) + 1 + h + 1$

or $\quad k = 2h$ or $y = 2x$

(b) Any line through $P(1, 2)$ is $\dfrac{x-1}{\cos \theta} = \dfrac{y-2}{\sin \theta} = r_1, r_2$

where r_1 and r_2 correspond to points A and B on given lines, i.e., $r_1 = PA, r_2 = PB$. $\therefore$ A is $(r_1 \cos \theta + 1, r_1 \sin \theta + 2)$ and it lies on $x + y - 5 = 0$

$\therefore \quad (r_1 \cos \theta + 1 + r_1 \sin \theta + 2) - 5 = 0$

or $\quad r_1 = \dfrac{2}{\cos \theta + \sin \theta}$

Similarly as B lies on $2x - y = 7$

$\therefore \quad r_2 = \dfrac{7}{2 \cos \theta - \sin \theta}$

Now given 10 is H.M. of r_1 and r_2

$\therefore \quad r_1, 10, r_2$ are in H.P. or $\dfrac{1}{r_1}, \dfrac{1}{10}, \dfrac{1}{r_2}$ are in A.P.

or $\quad \dfrac{2}{10} = \dfrac{1}{r_1} + \dfrac{1}{r_2}$

or $\quad \dfrac{1}{5} = \dfrac{\cos \theta + \sin \theta}{2} + \dfrac{2 \cos \theta - \sin \theta}{7}$

or $\quad 14 = 35 (\cos \theta + \sin \theta) + 10 (2 \cos \theta - \sin \theta)$

or $\quad 55 \cos \theta + 25 \sin \theta = 14$

Put $55 = R \cos \alpha, 25 = R \sin \alpha$

$\therefore \quad R \cos (\theta - \alpha) = 14$, where

$\quad R = \sqrt{(55^2 + 25^2)} = 5\sqrt{146}$

$\therefore \quad \theta - \alpha = \cos^{-1} \dfrac{14}{R} = \cos^{-1} \dfrac{11}{5\sqrt{146}}$

or $\quad \theta = \alpha + \cos^{-1} \dfrac{14}{5\sqrt{146}}$

and $\alpha = \cos^{-1} \dfrac{55}{R} = \cos^{-1} \dfrac{11}{\sqrt{146}}$

$\therefore \quad \theta = \cos^{-1} \dfrac{11}{\sqrt{146}} + \cos^{-1} \dfrac{14}{5\sqrt{146}}$ ...(A)

Hence the line is $y - 2 = \tan \theta (x - 1)$ where θ is given by (A).

(c) $\left(2\sqrt{3} - \dfrac{1}{2}, \dfrac{3\sqrt{3}}{2} + 5\right)$ and $\left(-2\sqrt{3} - \dfrac{1}{2}, -\dfrac{3\sqrt{3}}{2} + 5\right)$

Proceed exactly as in **35 (a) P. 816**. $BC = 5$, slope of $BC = -4/3$ and hence slope of perpendicular to BC is $3/4$. A will be at a distance of $p = a \sin 60° = \dfrac{5\sqrt{3}}{2}$

$\therefore \quad r = \pm \dfrac{5\sqrt{3}}{2}$ from the mid-point of BC.

(d) Any line through mid-point $(1, 5)$ of intercept AB may be taken as

$\dfrac{x-1}{\cos \theta} = \dfrac{y-5}{\sin \theta} = r, -r$ for A and B

respectively.

Point $A (r \cos \theta + 1, r \sin \theta + 5)$ lies on 1st line and point $B (-r \cos \theta + 1, -r \sin \theta + 5)$ lies on 2nd line.

$\therefore \quad r (5 \cos \theta - \sin \theta) = 4$

and $r (3 \cos \theta + 4 \sin \theta) = 19$

Eliminating r on dividing the two, we get

$\dfrac{5 \cos \theta - \sin \theta}{3 \cos \theta + 4 \sin \theta} = \dfrac{4}{19}$

or $83 \cos \theta = 35 \sin \theta$.

$\therefore \quad \dfrac{\cos \theta}{35} = \dfrac{\sin \theta}{83}$.

Hence the required line is $\dfrac{x-1}{35} = \dfrac{y-5}{83}$

or $83 x - 35 y + 92 = 0$

36. (a) Let the fixed point O be chosen as origin and any straight line through O be

$\dfrac{x-0}{\cos \theta} = \dfrac{y-0}{\sin \theta} = r_i, \quad r_{A_i}, \quad r_A$

$\therefore \quad OA_i = r_i, OA = r$

Again let the given n straight lines be

$\quad p_i x + q_i y = 1 (i = 1, 2, 3, \dots n)$

The point A_i is $(r_i \cos \theta, r_i \sin \theta)$ and it lies on the above line

$\therefore \quad (p_i \cos \theta + q_i \sin \theta) r_i = 1$

$\therefore \quad \dfrac{1}{OA_i} = \dfrac{1}{r_i} = p_i \cos \theta + q_i \sin \theta$

$\therefore \quad \sum_{i=1}^{n} \dfrac{1}{OA_i} = \sum_{i=1}^{n} p_i \cos \theta + \sum_{i=1}^{n} q_i \sin \theta = \dfrac{n}{r}$

$\therefore \quad \sum_{i=1}^{n} \dfrac{p_i}{n} (r \cos \theta) + \sum_{i=1}^{n} \dfrac{q_i}{n} (r \sin \theta) = 1$

Therefore locus of the point $A (r \cos \theta, r \sin \theta)$ is

$\dfrac{\Sigma p_i}{n} x + \dfrac{\Sigma q_i}{n} y = 1$

Above equation represents a straight line.

(b) Proceeding as above, we get

$\dfrac{m}{OA_1} + \dfrac{n}{OA_2} = m (p_1 \cos \theta + q_1 \sin \theta)$

$\qquad\qquad + n (p_2 \cos \theta + q_2 \sin \theta) = \dfrac{m+n}{r}$

$\therefore \quad m \{p_1 (r \cos \theta) + q_1 (r \sin \theta)\}$

$\qquad + n \{p_2 (r \cos \theta) + q_2 (r \sin \theta)\} = m + n$

Replace $r \cos \theta$ by $x, r \sin \theta$ by y. Hence the required locus is

$\quad m (p_1 x + q_1 y - 1) + n (p_2 x + q_2 y - 1) = 0$

or $mL_1 + nL_2 = 0$ or $L_1 + \lambda L_2 = 0$

Above represents a line through the intersection of given lines $L_1 = 0$ and $L_2 = 0$.

37. (a) The line BC is $(y-6) = m(x-5)$

$$\frac{x-5}{\cos\theta} = \frac{y-6}{\sin\theta} = \frac{r, -r}{C \quad B}$$

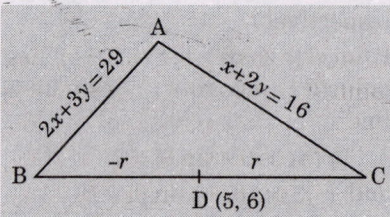

Fig. 77

∴ C $(r\cos\theta + 5, r\sin\theta + 6)$ lies on AC

B $(-r\cos\theta + 5, -r\sin\theta + 6)$ lies on AB

∴ $r(\cos\theta + 2\sin\theta) = -1$

and $r(2\cos\theta + 3\sin\theta) = -1$

Dividing, we get

$\cos\theta + 2\sin\theta = 2\cos\theta + 3\sin\theta$

∴ $\tan\theta = -1$ and hence the line BC is $x + y = 11$

(b) Any line through $P(1, 5)$ is

$$\frac{x-1}{\cos\theta} = \frac{y-5}{\sin\theta} = \frac{r}{\text{for } B} = -\frac{2r}{\text{for } A}$$

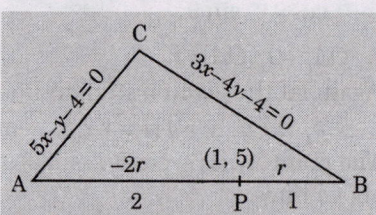

Fig. 78

A $(1 - 2r\cos\theta, 5 - 2r\sin\theta)$

B $(1 + r\cos\theta, 5 + r\sin\theta)$

A lies on $5x - y - 4 = 0$

$5(1 - 2r\cos\theta) - (5 - 2r\sin\theta) - 4 = 0$

or $r(\sin\theta - 5\cos\theta) = 2$ ...(1)

B lies on $3x - 4y - 4 = 0$

$3(1 + r\cos\theta) - 4(5 + r\sin\theta) - 4 = 0$

or $r(3\cos\theta - 4\sin\theta) = 21$ ...(2)

Dividing (1) by (2) to eliminate r

$$\frac{\sin\theta - 5\cos\theta}{3\cos\theta - 4\sin\theta} = \frac{2}{21}$$

∴ $29\sin\theta = 111\cos\theta$

∴ $\dfrac{\sin\theta}{111} = \dfrac{\cos\theta}{29} = k$ say

Hence from (1)

$r(111k - 145k) = 2$ or $rk = -\dfrac{1}{17}$

Same value will be found from (2).

If point A is (x, y) then

$x = 1 - 2r(29k) = 1 - 58\left(-\dfrac{1}{17}\right) = \dfrac{75}{17}$

$y = 5 - 2r(111k) = 5 - 222\left(-\dfrac{1}{17}\right) = \dfrac{307}{17}$

∴ A is $\left(\dfrac{75}{17}, \dfrac{307}{17}\right)$ which satisfies $5x - y - 4 = 0$

(c) Ans. **(b)**.

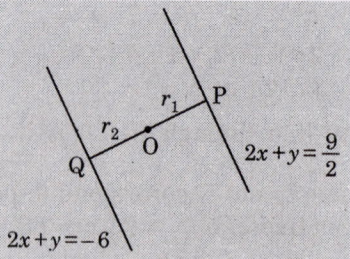

Fig. 79

Origin lies between the two lines. Any line through $O(0, 0)$ is

$$\frac{x}{\cos\theta} = \frac{y}{\sin\theta} = \frac{r_1, -r_2}{P \quad Q}$$

$r_1(2\cos\theta + \sin\theta) = 9/2$

$-r_2(2\cos\theta + \sin\theta) = -6$

Dividing $\dfrac{r_1}{r_2} = \dfrac{9}{12} = \dfrac{3}{4}$.

38. (a) Equation of AB is $x + 2y = 7$ and its length $a = \sqrt{5}$, and mid-point of AB is the point $L(4, 3/2)$. If P be the vertex of the equilateral triangle then its perpendicular distance p from AB is $a\sin 60°$

or $p = \sqrt{5} \cdot \left(\dfrac{\sqrt{3}}{2}\right) = \dfrac{1}{2}\sqrt{15}$

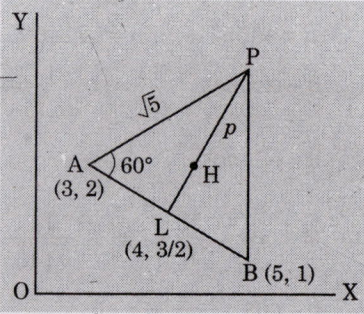

Fig. 80

Also distance of orthocentre H from AB is $\dfrac{1}{3}p$.

Now both H and P lie on a line perpendicular to AB whose slope will be 2 and passing through $L(4, 3/2)$,

∴ $\tan\theta = 2$ or $\sin\theta = 2/\sqrt{5}$

and $\cos\theta = 1/\sqrt{5}$

Hence H and P lie on

$$\frac{x-4}{\cos\theta} = \frac{y-3/2}{\sin\theta} = p \text{ for } P$$

and $$= \frac{1}{3}p \text{ for } H.$$

$$x = 4 + p\cos\theta, \quad y = 3/2 + p\sin\theta \qquad \text{for } P$$
$$x = 4 + (p/3)\cos\theta, \quad y = 3/2 + (p/3)\sin\theta \quad \text{for } H$$

Putting the values of $p, \cos\theta$ and $\sin\theta$ in the above, we get

Point $P(4 + \sqrt{3}/2, 3/2 + \sqrt{3})$

Point $H[5 + \sqrt{3}/6, 3/2 + (1/2)\sqrt{3}]$

(b) Since the triangle is equilateral, each side is $BC = 5$.

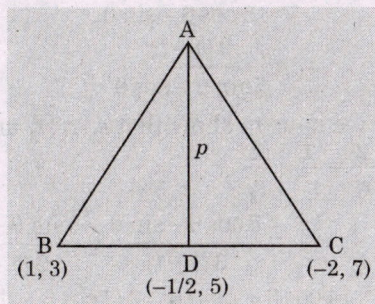

Fig. 81

$$\therefore \quad p = AD = 5\sin 60°$$

$$\therefore \quad p = \frac{\sqrt{3}}{2}5. \text{ Also slope of } BC \text{ is } -\frac{4}{3}.$$

$$\therefore \quad \text{Slope of } DA \text{ is } \frac{3}{4} = \tan\theta$$

$$\therefore \quad \cos\theta = \frac{4}{5}, \sin\theta = \frac{3}{5}.$$

Since DA can be written in parametric form as

$$\frac{x+\frac{1}{2}}{4/5} = \frac{y-5}{3/5} = r = \pm\ p = \pm\ \frac{\sqrt{3}}{2}.5.$$

We have chosen $r = \pm\ p$ as the point could be on either side of line BC. Hence co-ordinates of A are

$$\left(-\frac{1}{2} + 2\sqrt{3},\ 5 + 3\frac{\sqrt{3}}{2}\right) \text{ and } \left(-\frac{1}{2} - 2\sqrt{3},\ 5 - 3\frac{\sqrt{3}}{2}\right).$$

(c) Any line through $(1, 1)$ parallel to $y = 2x$ is

$$y - 1 = 2(x - 1)$$

$$\tan\theta = 2 \quad\therefore\quad \cos\theta = \frac{1}{\sqrt{5}},\ \sin\theta = \frac{2}{\sqrt{5}}.$$

Now we have to find a point on this line which is at a unit distance from $(1, 1)$.

$$\therefore \quad \frac{x-1}{\cos\theta} = \frac{y-1}{\sin\theta} = r = \pm 1$$

$$\therefore \quad x = \cos\theta + 1, y = \sin\theta + 1$$

or $(x = -\cos\theta + 1,\ y = -\sin\theta + 1)$

or $\left(1 + \frac{1}{\sqrt{5}}, 1 + \frac{2}{\sqrt{5}}\right)$ or $\left(1 - \frac{1}{\sqrt{5}}, 1 - \frac{2}{\sqrt{5}}\right)$

Both lie in Ist quadrant.

39. (a) $PA^2 = PB^2 = 26 = AB^2$

$PA^2 = PB^2$ imply $5h + k = 6$ ...(1)

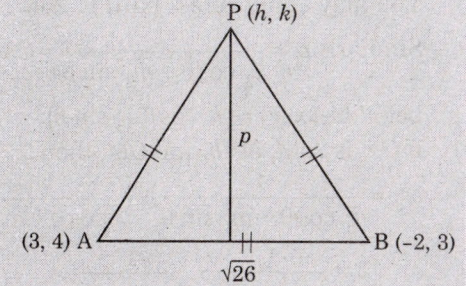

Fig. 82

$PA^2 = 26$ imply

$$(h-3)^2 + (k-4)^2 = 26 \qquad \text{...(2)}$$

Eliminate k between (1) and (2),

$$2h^2 - 2h - 1 = 0$$

$$\therefore \quad h = \frac{1+\sqrt{3}}{2} \text{ or } \frac{1-\sqrt{3}}{2}$$

$$\therefore \quad k = \frac{7-5\sqrt{3}}{2} \text{ or } \frac{7+5\sqrt{3}}{2}, \qquad \text{by (1)}$$

(b) Let the third vertex be P

$$PA = PB \quad\Rightarrow\quad 4h - 3k - 38 = 0 \qquad \text{...(1)}$$

$$PA \perp PB \quad\Rightarrow\quad \frac{k+9}{h-9}\cdot\frac{k+3}{h-1} = -1$$

$$h^2 + k^2 - 10h + 12k + 36 = 0 \qquad \text{...(2)}$$

Eliminate k between (1) and (2) you will have a quadratic in h giving $h = 2, 8 \quad\therefore\quad k = -10, -2$.

$$\therefore \quad \text{Points are } (2, -10) \text{ and } (8, -2).$$

(c) $(a-1)^2 + (1-b)^2 = a^2 + 1 = b^2 + 1 = (\text{side})^2$

The last two imply $a = b$ or $a = -b$

The first two imply $b^2 - 2b - 2a + 1 = 0$

If $a = -b$, then $b^2 + 1 = 0$ not possible

If $a = b$, then $b^2 - 4b + 1 = 0$

$$\therefore \quad b = 2 + \sqrt{3}, 2 - \sqrt{3}$$

Since $b < 1 \qquad\therefore\quad b = 2 - \sqrt{3} = a$

40. (a) Any line through $O(0, 0)$ is

$$\frac{x}{\cos\theta} = \frac{y}{\sin\theta} = \frac{r_1}{OL}, \frac{r_2}{OM}, \frac{r_3}{ON}.$$

Let the given lines be $l_1 x + m_1 y = 1$ ...(1)

and $l_2 x + m_2 y = 1$ ...(2)

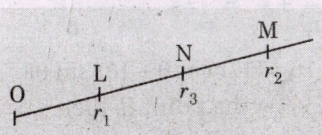

Fig. 83

L lies on (1)

$\therefore \quad l_1 r_1 \cos\theta + m_1 r_1 \sin\theta = 1$.

$\therefore \quad r_1 = \dfrac{1}{l_1 \cos\theta + m_1 \sin\theta} = OL$

You may apply **rule 7 (xiii) P. 766.**

Similarly $r_2 = \dfrac{1}{l_2 \cos\theta + m_2 \sin\theta} = OM$.

Let N be $(x, y) = (r_3 \cos\theta, r_3 \sin\theta)$ ...(3)

(i) If ON is A.M. of OL and OM, then $2r_3 = r_1 + r_2$

$2r_3 = \dfrac{1}{l_1 \cos\theta + m_1 \sin\theta} + \dfrac{1}{l_2 \cos\theta + m_2 \sin\theta}$

$\therefore \quad 2 = \dfrac{1}{l_1 x + m_1 y} + \dfrac{1}{l_2 x + m_2 y}$ by (3)

is the required locus.

(ii) If ON is H.M. of OL and OM, then

$\dfrac{2}{r_3} = \dfrac{1}{r_1} + \dfrac{1}{r_2}$

or $\quad \dfrac{2}{r_3} = (l_1 \cos\theta + m_1 \sin\theta)$

$+ (l_2 \cos\theta + m_2 \sin\theta)$

$\therefore \quad 2 = (l_1 x + m_1 y) + (l_2 x + m_2 y)$ by (3)

(iii) If ON is G.M. of OL and OM, then

$r_3^{\,2} = r_1 r_2$ or $\quad \dfrac{r_3}{r_1} \cdot \dfrac{r_3}{r_2} = 1$

or $\quad r_3 (l_1 \cos\theta + m_1 \sin\theta)$

$\cdot r_3 (l_2 \cos\theta + m_2 \sin\theta) = 1$

or $\quad (l_1 x + m_1 y)(l_2 x + m_2 y) = 1$ by (3)

(b) L is $\dfrac{x-2}{\cos\theta} = \dfrac{y-5}{\sin\theta} = \dfrac{r_1}{P} \quad \dfrac{r}{R} \quad \dfrac{r_2}{Q}$

where r_1, r, r_2 are in H.P.

or $\quad \dfrac{2}{r} = \dfrac{1}{r_1} + \dfrac{1}{r_2}$

$2x^2 - 5xy + 2y^2 = 0$

or $\quad (2x - y)(x - 2y) = 0$

P lies on $2x - y = 0, Q$ on $x - 2y = 0$

$2(r_1 \cos\theta + 2) - (r_1 \sin\theta + 5) = 0$

$r_1 (2\cos\theta - \sin\theta) = 1$

$\therefore \quad \dfrac{1}{r_1} = 2\cos\theta - \sin\theta$

Similarly $\dfrac{1}{r_2} = \dfrac{\cos\theta - 2\sin\theta}{8}$

$\therefore \quad \dfrac{1}{r_1} + \dfrac{1}{r_2} = \dfrac{17\cos\theta - 10\sin\theta}{8}$

But $\dfrac{1}{r_1} + \dfrac{1}{r_2} = \dfrac{2}{r} = \dfrac{2(17\cos\theta - 10\sin\theta)}{8}$

$\therefore \quad 16 = (17r\cos\theta - 10r\sin\theta)$ ...(1)

If (x, y) be the point R, then

$x = r\cos\theta + 2$,   or $\quad r\cos\theta = x - 2$

$y = r\sin\theta + 5$

$\therefore \quad r\sin\theta = y - 5$ ...(2)

Eliminating θ between (1) and (2), we get

$16 = [17(x-2) - 10(y-5)] = (17x - 10y + 16)$

or $\quad 17x - 10y = 0$ is the required locus.

41. Any line through $A(t+1, 2t)$ is

$\dfrac{x - (t+1)}{\cos\theta} = \dfrac{y - 2t}{\sin\theta} = \dfrac{r_1, \ r_2, \ r_3}{B \quad C \quad D}$

where $r_1 = AB$, $r_2 = AC$, $r_3 = AD$

$[r_1 \cos\theta + (t+1), r_1 \sin\theta + 2t]$ is point B which lies on

$7x + y - 16 = 0$

then, $\quad r_1 = \dfrac{9(1-t)}{7\cos\theta + \sin\theta}$ ...(1)

Similarly, $r_2 = \dfrac{3(1-t)}{5\cos\theta - \sin\theta}$ ...(2)

and $\quad r_3 = \dfrac{9(1-t)}{5\sin\theta - \cos\theta}$ ...(3)

Now we have to show that r_2, r_1, r_3 are in H.P.

or $\quad \dfrac{2}{r_1} = \dfrac{1}{r_2} + \dfrac{1}{r_3}$

Now $\dfrac{1}{r_2} + \dfrac{1}{r_3} = \dfrac{5\cos\theta - \sin\theta}{3(1-t)} + \dfrac{5\sin\theta - \cos\theta}{9(1-t)}$

$= \dfrac{14\cos\theta + 2\sin\theta}{9(1-t)} = \dfrac{2(7\cos\theta + \sin\theta)}{9(1-t)} = \dfrac{2}{r_1}$ by (1).

Hence in H.P.

42. (a) The given circle is $(1, -2)$ and $7\sqrt{2}$. The sides are parallel to axes. Diagonal AC will be making an angle of $45°$ and BD will make an angle $135°$ with x-axis.

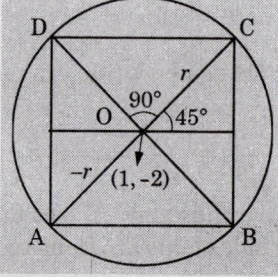

Fig. 84

A and C will lie on $\dfrac{x-1}{\cos\theta} = \dfrac{y+2}{\sin\theta} = \dfrac{7\sqrt{2}, \ -7\sqrt{2}}{C, \quad A}$

Put $\theta = 45°$ $\therefore$ C and A are $(8, 5)$ and $(-6, -9)$

B and D will lie on $\dfrac{x-1}{\cos\theta} = \dfrac{y+2}{\sin\theta} = \dfrac{7\sqrt{2}, \ -7\sqrt{2}}{B, \quad D}$

Put $\theta = 135°$ $\therefore$ B and D are $(-6, 5)$ and $(8, -9)$

(b) Slope of diagonal $AB = -7/5$ and hence slope of diagonal CD which is perpendicular to AB is $5/7$.

$\therefore \quad \tan\theta = \dfrac{5}{7} \quad \Rightarrow \quad \sin\theta = \dfrac{5}{\sqrt{74}}, \cos\theta = \dfrac{7}{\sqrt{74}}$

Also mid-point P of AB is $(5/2, 7/2)$.

Also $\quad AB = CD = \sqrt{25 + 49} = \sqrt{74}$

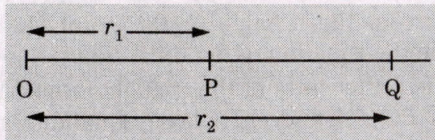

Fig. 85

The diagonal CD passes through P, its equation is

$$\frac{x - 5/2}{7/\sqrt{74}} = \frac{y - 7/2}{5/\sqrt{74}} = \frac{r}{C}, \frac{-r}{D}$$

where $r = \frac{1}{2} CD = \frac{1}{2} \sqrt{74}$

$\therefore \quad C = \left(\frac{5}{2} + \frac{7}{2}, \frac{7}{2} + \frac{5}{2}\right) = (6, 6)$

$\quad D = \left(\frac{5}{2} - \frac{7}{2}, \frac{7}{2} - \frac{5}{2}\right) = (-1, 1)$.

43. $\frac{x - 3}{\cos \theta} = \frac{y - 4}{\sin \theta} = r = AB$ or AC where A is $(3, 4)$

$(r \cos \theta + 3)^2 + (r \sin \theta + 4)^2 = 4$.

This is same as given quadratic in r which gives AB and AC the two values of r.

44. Any line through origin is $y = mx$

or $\quad \frac{x}{\cos \theta} = \frac{y}{\sin \theta} = \frac{r_1}{P}, \frac{r_2}{Q}$

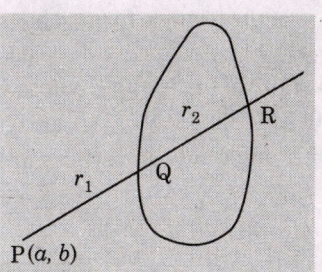

Fig. 86

Now $P(r_1 \cos \theta, r_1 \sin \theta)$ lies on $y = mx + c$

$r_1 \sin \theta = mr_1 \cos \theta + c$ ...(1)

$\therefore \quad r_1 = \frac{c}{\sin \theta - m \cos \theta}$

But $OP \cdot OQ = k^2$ or $r_1 r_2 = k^2$

$$r_2 \cdot \frac{c}{\sin \theta - m \cos \theta} = k^2$$

Multiplying both sides by r_2

$c \cdot r_2^2 = k^2 (r_2 \sin \theta - mr_2 \cos \theta)$

Hence the locus of $Q(x, y) = (r_2 \cos \theta, r_2 \sin \theta)$ is

$c (x^2 + y^2) = k^2 (y - mx)$

Above equation clearly represents a circle.

45. Any line through $P(\alpha, \beta)$ is

$$\frac{x - \alpha}{\cos \theta} = \frac{y - \beta}{\sin \theta} = r \text{ (say)}$$

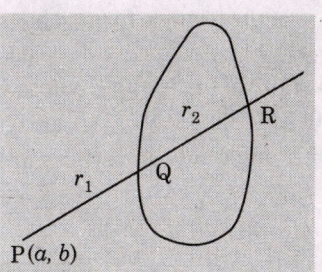

Fig. 87

It meets the given curve where

$(r \cos \theta + \alpha)^2 + 2h (r \cos \theta + \alpha) (r \sin \theta + \beta)$

$\qquad\qquad + b (r \sin \theta + \beta)^2 = 1$

$r^2 (a \cos^2 \theta + 2h \cos \theta \sin \theta + b \sin^2 \theta) + r(\ )$

$\qquad\qquad + (a\alpha^2 + 2h\alpha\beta + b\beta^2 - 1) = 0$

Above is a quadratic in r and gives two values of r say r_1 and r_2 which represent PQ and PR

$\therefore \quad PQ \cdot PR = r_1 \cdot r_2$

$$= \frac{a\alpha^2 + 2h\alpha\beta + b\beta^2 - 1}{a \cos^2 \theta + 2h \cos \theta \sin \theta + b \sin^2 \theta} \quad ...(1)$$

Above result will be independent of slope i.e., θ if $a = b$ and $h = 0$ $\because$ $\cos^2 \theta + \sin^2 \theta = 1$

Hence the given equation of curve becomes a circle as $a = b$ and $h = 0$.

Problem Set (5)

Incentre, Orthocentre, Bisectors of angle between two given lines, Locus

Note : Before attempting questions of this exercise, read and remember the **result 6 (all parts)** on **P. 766** and result 20 (a, b, c, d) **P. 770.**

1. The sides of a triangle are

$$y = x, \quad y = 2x \quad \text{and} \quad y = 3x + 4.$$

(a) Find the equation of the medians and hence the co-ordinates of its centroid.

(b) Find the equation of the right bisectors of the sides and hence the co-ordinates of its circumcentre.

(c) Find the equation of the perpendiculars drawn from the vertices to the opposite sides and hence the co-ordinates of its orthocentre.

(d) Find the area of the triangle.

2. (a) The line $3x + 2y = 24$ meets the y-axis at A and the x-axis at B. The perpendicular bisector of AB meets the line through $(0, -1)$ parallel to x-axis at C. Find the area of the triangle ABC.

(b)* In a triangle ABC, the equation of the perpendicular bisector of AC is $3x - 2y + 8 = 0$. If the co-ordinates of the points A and B are $(1, -1)$ and $(3, 1)$ respectively, find the equation of the line BC and the centre of the circum-circle of the triangle ABC. **(Roorkee 1995)**

3. Find the orthocentre of the triangle with sides

(a)* $x + y = 6$, $2x + y = 4$ and $x + 2y = 5$.

(b) Find the orthocentre of the triangle the equations of whose sides are

$x + y = 1$, $2x + 3y = 6$, $4x - y + 4 = 0$.

In which quadrant does it lie ?

4. (a) Prove that the co-ordinates of the orthocentre of the triangle whose vertices are $(0, 0), (2, -1)$ and $(1, 3)$ is $(-4/7, -1/7)$.

(b) The orthocentre of the triangle formed by the lines $xy = 0$ and $x + y = 1$ is .... **(I.I.T. 1995)**

(c) Find the orthocentre of the triangle whose vertices are $(0, 0)$, $(3, 0)$, $(0, 4)$.

(d) Orthocentre of triangle whose vertices are $(0, 0)$, $(3, 4)$, $(4, 0)$ is

(a) $(3, 7/3)$ (b) $(3, 5/4)$

(c) $(5, -2)$ (d) $(3, 3/4)$ **(Screening 2003)**

5. (a) Of the three lines $x + \sqrt{3}y = 0$, $x + y = 1$ and $x - \sqrt{3}y = 0$ two are equations of two altitudes of an equilateral triangle. Prove that the centroid of Δ is the point $(0, 0)$.

(b) Vertices of a triangle ABC are the points $(0, 0), (a, 0)$ and $\left(\dfrac{a}{2}, \dfrac{a\sqrt{3}}{2}\right)$. Prove that its incentre is the point $\left(\dfrac{a}{2}, \dfrac{a\sqrt{3}}{6}\right)$.

(c) The three lines $4x - 7y + 10 = 0$, $x + y = 5$ and $7x + 4y = 15$ form the sides of a triangle. The point $(1, 2)$ is its

(a) Centroid   (b) Incentre

(c) Orthocentre   (d) None of these

(d) The equations to the sides of a triangle are $x - 3y = 0$, $4x + 3y = 5$ and $3x + y = 0$. The line $3x - 4y = 0$ passes through

(a) the centre

(b) the centroid

(c) the circumcentre

(d) the orthocentre of the triangle **(EAMCET 1994)**

6. (a)* The vertices of a triangle are

$[at_1t_2, a(t_1 + t_2)], [at_2t_3, a(t_2 + t_3)],$

$[at_3t_1, a(t_3 + t_1)]$

Find the co-ordinates of its orthocentre.

(b) Prove that the orthocentre of the triangle formed by the three lines

$y = m_1x + a/m_1$, $y = m_2x + a/m_2$, and

$y = m_3x + a/m_3$ is

$$\left\{-a, a\left(\dfrac{1}{m_1} + \dfrac{1}{m_2} + \dfrac{1}{m_3} + \dfrac{1}{m_1m_2m_3}\right)\right\}$$

(c) The sides of a triangle are

$L_r \equiv x\cos\alpha_r + y\sin\alpha_r - p_r = 0, r = 1, 2, 3.$

Prove that the orthocentre is given by

$L_1\cos(\alpha_2 - \alpha_3) = L_2\cos(\alpha_3 - \alpha_1)$

$= L_3\cos(\alpha_1 - \alpha_2).$

7. (a)* Two vertices of a triangle are $(5, -1)$ and $(-2, 3)$. If orthocentre of the triangle is the origin, find the co-ordinates of the third vertex.

(b) Two vertices of a triangle are $(4, -3)$ and $(-2, 5)$. If the orthocentre of the triangle is at $(1, -2)$, prove that the third vertex is $\left(-\dfrac{55}{9}, -\dfrac{22}{3}\right)$.

8. (a)* AD, BE and CF are the altitudes of a triangle ABC whose vertex A is the point $(-4, 5)$. The co-ordinates of the points D, E, F are respectively $\left(\dfrac{16}{5}, -\dfrac{23}{5}\right)$, $(4, 1)$ and $(-1, -4)$. Find the equation of the sides of the triangle and the co-ordinates of the other two vertices of the triangle.

(b) The altitudes AD, BE, CF of a ΔABC are $x + y = 0$, $x - 4y = 0$ and $2x - y = 0$ respectively. Its vertex A is the point $(\alpha, -\alpha)$. Determine the co-ordinates of the other two vertices and hence prove that the locus of centroid of the triangle ABC is the line $x + 5y = 0$.

(c)* Two sides of a triangle are given by the equations $3x - 2y + 6 = 0$ and $4x + 5y - 20 = 0$. If the orthocentre of the triangle be the point $(1, 1)$, determine the equation of the third side.

9. (a) If P be the orthocentre of the triangle formed by the lines BC, CA and AB whose equations are $u_r = a_rx + b_ry + c_r = 0, r = 1, 2, 3$ then prove that the line $\dfrac{a_1x + b_1y + c_1}{a_1a_3 + b_1b_3} = \dfrac{a_2x + b_2y + c_2}{a_2a_3 + b_2b_3}$ will pass through the point P.

(b) The line through A and parallel to BC is

$$\dfrac{u_3}{a_1b_3 - a_3b_1} = \dfrac{u_2}{a_1b_2 - a_2b_1}$$

10. (a) The base of a triangle is axis of x and its other two sides are given by the equations

$y = \dfrac{1 + \alpha}{\alpha}x + (1 + \alpha)$ and $y = \dfrac{1 + \beta}{\beta}x + (1 + \beta)$.

Prove that locus of its orthocentre is the line $x + y = 0$.

(b) Two vertices of a triangle are the points $(1, 4), (7, 2)$ and centroid is the point $(5, 3)$. Find the co-ordinates of the third vertex.

11. (a) One vertex of the equilateral triangle with centroid at the origin and one side as $x + y - 2 = 0$ is

(a) $(-1,-1)$ (b) $(2,2)$

(c) $(-2,-2)$ (d) none of these

(b) A point equidistant from the lines $4x+3y+10=0$, $5x-12y+26=0$ and $7x+24y-50=0$ is

(a) $(1,-1)$ (b) $(1,1)$

(c) $(0,0)$ (d) $(0,1)$ **(EAMCET 1994)**

12. (a)* Find the co-ordinates of those points on the line $3x+2y=5$ which are equidistant from the lines
$$4x+3y=7 \quad \text{and} \quad 2y-5=0.$$

(b) Show that each point on the line $2x+11y=5$ is at equal distances from the lines $24x+7y=20$ and $4x-3y=2$.

(c) Prove that the lenghts of the perpendiculars from any point on the line $7x-9y+10=0$ to the line $3x+4y=5$ and $12x+5y=7$ are equal.

(d) Let $P=(-1,0)$, $Q=(0,0)$ and $R=(3,3\sqrt{3})$ be three points. Then the equation of the bisector of the angle PQR is

(a) $\dfrac{\sqrt{3}}{2}x+y=0$ (b) $x+\sqrt{3}\,y=0$

(c) $\sqrt{3}x+y=0$ (d) $x+\dfrac{\sqrt{3}}{2}y=0$

                       (IIT-Sc. 2002)

(e) Area of Δ formed by line $x+y=3$ and $\angle$ bisectors of pair of straight lines $x^2-y^2+2y=1$ is

(a) 2   (b) 4

(c) 6   (d) 8   **(IIT-Sc. 2004)**

13. (a) Find the equation of the lines bisecting the angles between the line $Ax+By+C=0$ and the line passing through the point (h,k) and perpendicular to this line.

(b)* $px+qy+r+\lambda\,(qx-py+r')=0$ and
$px+qy+r-\lambda\,(qx-py+r')=0$
are two given lines. Determine the equations of their bisectors.

(c) Find the equations of the bisectors B_1 and B_2 between the lines $3x-4y+5=0$ and $5x+12y-1=0$. If B_1 meets the axes of co-ordinates in A and B whereas B_2 meets in C and D then find the ratio $AC:DB$.

14. (a)* Find the equation of the bisector of the acute angle between the lines
$3x-4y+7=0$ and $12x+5y-2=0$

(b) Prove that the bisector of the acute angle between the lines $4x-3y-12=0$ and $3x-4y+16=0$ is $7x-7y+4=0$

(c) Find the equation of the line which bisects the obtuse angle between the lines
$x-2y+4=0$ and $4x-3y+2=0$

15. (a)* Two sides of a rhombus, lying in the first quadrant, are given by $3x-4y=0$ and $12x-5y=0$. If the length of the longer diagonal is 12, find the equations of the other two sides of the rhombus.   **(Roorkee 1996)**

(b)* Given vertices $A(1,1)$, $B(4,-2)$ and $C(5,5)$ of a triangle, find the equation of the perpendicular dropped from C to the interior bisector of the angle A.   **(Roorkee 1994)**

(c) In a triangle ABC, co-ordinates of A are $(1,2)$ and the equations of the medians through B and C are $x+y=5$ and $x=4$ respectively. Find the co-ordinates of B and C.

16. (a)* Find the co-ordinates of the incentre of the triangle, equations of whose sides are
$$x+1=0, \; -3x+4y+5=0, \; 5x+12y=27.$$

(b) Find the co-ordinates of the incentre of the triangle formed by the lines whose equations are
$$AB:3x-4y-17=0, BC:y-4=0,$$
$$CA:12x+5y-12=0.$$

(c) How many circles can be drawn each touching all the three lines $x+y=1$, $y=x+1$, $7x-y=6$? Find the centre and radius of one of them.

(d)* The equations of the sides of a triangle ABC are $BC:7x-y+3=0, CA:x+y+1=0$ and $AB:x-y+3=0$
Find the centre of the circle escribed to side BC.

17. (a) The sides of a triangle are
$$4x+3y+7=0, \; 5x+12y=27$$
and $3x+4y+8=0.$
Find the equations of the internal bisectors of the angles and show that they are concurrent.

(b)* Write the equation of the internal bisector of the angle between the lines
$$2x-3y-5=0, 6x-4y+7=0$$
which is the supplement of the angle containing the point $(2,-1)$.

(c) Find the co-ordinates of the points at unit distance from the lines $3x-4y+11=0$ and $5x-12y+7=0$

18. (a) Find the locus of the mid-point of the portion of the line $x\cos\alpha+y\sin\alpha=p$ which is intercepted between the axes.

(b) A line APB of constant length meets the x-axis at A and y-axis at B. If $AP=b$, $PB=a$ and the line slides with its extremities on the co-ordinate axes, show that equation of the locus of the point P is
$$\frac{x^2}{a^2}+\frac{y^2}{b^2}=1.$$

19. (a) A variable line through the point $(6/5,6/5)$ cuts the co-ordinate axes in the points A and B. If the point P divides AB internally in the ratio $2:1$, show that the equation to the locus of P is $5xy=2(2x+y)$.

(b) A straight line passing through the point $(1,1)$ is terminated by the axes of co-ordinates. Show that the locus of the mid-point of the line has the equation $2xy=x+y$.

(c)* A variable straight line passes through the points of intersection of the lines

$x + 2y = 1$ and $2x - y = 1$ and meets the co-ordinate axes in A and B. Find the locus of the middle point of AB.

20. (a) A line drawn through the origin intersects the lines $2x + y - 2 = 0$ and $x - 2y + 2 = 0$ in A and B. Show that locus of the mid-point of AB is $2x^2 - 3xy - 2y^2 + x + 3y = 0$.

(b)* A point moves so that square of its distance from the point $(3, -2)$ is numerically equal to its distance from the line $5x - 12y = 13$. Find the equation to its locus.

21. (a) If the line $\frac{x}{a} + \frac{y}{b} = 1$ moves in such a way that

$\frac{1}{a^2} + \frac{1}{b^2} = \frac{1}{c^2}$ where c is a constant, prove that the

foot of the perpendicular from the origin on the straight line describes the circle $x^2 + y^2 = c^2$.

(b)* The straight line $\frac{x}{a} + \frac{y}{b} = 1$ cuts the axes in A

and B and a line perpendicular to AB cuts the axes in P and Q. Find the locus of the point of intersection of AQ and BP.

(c) A line intersects x-axis at $(7, 0)$ and y-axis at $B(0, -5)$. A variable line PQ which is perpendicular to AB intersects x-axis at P and y-axis at Q. If AQ and BP intersect at R, then find the locus of R. **(I.I.T. 1990)**

(d)* The line $\frac{x}{a} + \frac{y}{b} = 1$ cuts the axes in A and B.

Another variable line cuts the axes in A' and B' such that $OA + OB = OA' + OB'$ then prove that the locus of the point of intersection of the lines AB' and $A'B$ is the line $x + y = a + b$.

22. (a)* The line L has intercepts a and b on the co-ordinate axes. When keeping the origin fixed, the co-ordinate axes are rotated through a fixed angle, then the same line has intercepts p and q on the rotated axes. Then prove that

$$\frac{1}{a^2} + \frac{1}{b^2} = \frac{1}{p^2} + \frac{1}{q^2}$$

(I.I.T. 1990)

(b) The point $(4, 1)$ undergoes the following three transformations successively :

(i) Reflection about the line $y = x$

(ii) Transformation through a distance 2 units along the positive direction of x-axis.

(iii) Rotation through an angle $\pi/4$ about the origin in the anti-clockwise direction. Prove that the final position of the point is given by the point $(-1/\sqrt{2}, 7/\sqrt{2})$.

23. (a) A straight line passes through a fixed point (h, k). Find the locus of feet of the perpendiculars on it drawn from the origin.

(b) Find the projection of the point $(1, 0)$ on the line joining the points, $P(-1, 2)$ and $Q(5, 4)$.

24.* Prove that the lines

$(a + b) x + (a - b) y - 2ab = 0$ ...(1)
$(a - b) x + (a + b) y - 2ab = 0$ ...(2)
and $x + y = 0$ ...(3)

form an isosceles triangle whose vertical angle is $2\tan^{-1} (a/b)$.

25. (a) Two points P and Q are given, R is a variable point on one side of the line PQ such that $\angle RPQ - \angle RQP$ is a positive constant 2α. Find the locus of the point R.

(b)* ABC is an isosceles triangle with vertex at A and P is any point inside the triangle. If the rectangle contained by perpendicular from P to sides AB and AC is equal to square of the perpendicular from P to base BC, then prove that the locus of P is a circle.

26. (a)* The ends A, B of a straight line segment of constant length c slide upon the fixed rectangular axes OX, OY respectively. If the rectangle $OAPB$ be completed, then show that the locus of the foot of the perpendicular drawn from P to AB is $x^{2/3} + y^{2/3} = c^{2/3}$

(b) A variable straight line passes through the point $P(\alpha, \beta)$ and cuts the axes of co-ordinates in points A and B respectively. If the parallelogram $OABC$ is completed then prove that the locus of vertex C is $\frac{\alpha}{x} + \frac{\beta}{y} = 1$.

27. (a)* A rectangle $PQRS$ has its side PQ parallel to the line $y = mx$ and vertices P, Q and S on the lines $y = a, x = b$ and $x = -b$, respectively. Find the locus of the vertex R. **(I.I.T. 1996)**

(b) The diagonals of a rhombus $ABCD$ intersect at the point $(1, 2)$ and its two sides are parallel to the lines $x - y + 2 = 0$ and $7x - y + 3 = 0$. If the vertex A be situated on y-axis, find the possible co-ordinates of A.

28. O is a fixed point and AP and BQ are two fixed parallel straight lines. BOA is perpendicular to both and $\angle POQ$ is a rt. angle. Prove that the locus of the foot of the perpendicular from O on PQ is a circle whose diameter is AB.

29.* Find the co-ordinates of the feet of the perpendiculars let fall from the point $(5, 0)$ upon the sides of the triangle formed by joining the three points $(4, 3), (-4, 3)$ and $(0, -5)$. Prove also that the points so determined lie on a straight line.

30.* The vertices of a triangle are $A(p, p \tan \alpha)$ $B(q, q \tan \beta), C(r, r \tan \gamma)$. If circumcentre O of triangle ABC is at the origin and $H(\bar{x}, \bar{y})$ be its orthocentre, then show that

$$\frac{\bar{x}}{\bar{y}} = \frac{\cos\alpha + \cos\beta + \cos\gamma}{\sin\alpha + \sin\beta + \sin\gamma}.$$

31. (a)* The line $lx + my + n = 0$ bisects the angle between a pair of straight lines of which one is $px + qy + r = 0$. Show that the equation to the other line is

$$(px + qy + r)(l^2 + m^2) - 2(lp + mq)$$
$$(lx + my + n) = 0.$$

(b)* Lines $\quad L_1 = ax + by + c = 0$ and
$$L_2 = lx + my + n = 0$$

intersect at the point P and makes an angle θ with each other. Find the equation of a line L different from L_2 which passes through P and makes the same angle θ with L_1.

(c) The straight line $2x + 3y + 1 = 0$ bisects the angle between two straight lines one of which is $3x + 2y + 4 = 0$. Determine the equation of the other line.

(d)* $3x^2 - 8xy - 3y^2 + 10x + 20y - 25 = 0$ are the bisectors of angle between two lines l_1 and l_2 one of which passes through origin. Determine the equation of the other line.

32. (a) OA and OB are equal sides of an isosceles triangle lying in the first quadrant, where O is the origin. OA and OB make angles ψ_1 and ψ_2 respectively with the +ive x-axis. Show that the slope of the bisector of the acute angle AOB is $\operatorname{cosec}\psi - \cot\psi$ where $\psi = \psi_1 + \psi_2$. **(Dhanbad 1992)**

(b) The angle between the straight lines $x\cos\alpha + y\sin\alpha = p$ and $ax + by + p = 0$ is $\pi/4$. They meet the straight line $x\sin\alpha - y\cos\alpha = 0$ in the same point; then prove that $a^2 + b^2 = 2$.

33. (a)* Find the equation of the bisectors of the angle between the lines

$$y - b = \frac{2m}{1 - m^2}(x - a) \text{ and } y - b = \frac{2M}{1 - M^2}(x - a).$$

(b) Two sides of a rhombus $ABCD$ are parallel to the lines $y = x + 2$ and $y = 7x + 3$. If the diagonals of the rhombus intersect at the point $P(1, 2)$ and if the vertex A is on y-axis find the possible co-ordinates of A.

34.* Derive the condition to be imposed on β so that $(0, \beta)$ should be on or inside the triangle having sides

$$y + 3x + 2 = 0, 3y - 2x - 5 = 0$$
and $\qquad 4y + x - 14 = 0.$ **(Roorkee 1990)**

35.* Determine all values of α for which the point (α, α^2) lies inside the triangle formed by the lines

$$2x + 3y - 1 = 0, \quad x + 2y - 3 = 0,$$
and $5x - 6y - 1 = 0.$ **(I.I.T. 1992)**

Solutions to Problem Set (5)

1. Solving the given equations in pairs the co-ordinates of the vertices of the triangle are
$$A(-4, -8), B(-2, -2), C(0, 0).$$

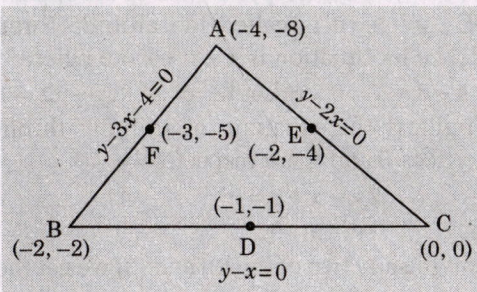

Fig. 88

The mid-points of the sides of the triangle are $D(-1, -1), E(-2, -4), F(-3, -5)$.
Equation to median AD joining $(-4, -8)$ and $(-1, -1)$ is

$$y + 8 = \frac{-1 - (-8)}{-1 - (-4)}(x + 4)$$

or $\quad 3(y + 8) = 7(x + 4)$
or $\quad 7x - 3y - 4 = 0.$ ...(1)
Similarly the equations to medians BE and CF are respectively

$$x + 2 = 0 \qquad \text{...(2)}$$
and $\qquad 5x - 3y = 0.$ ...(3)
Note : If $y - y_1 = m(x - x_1)$
or $\dfrac{y - y_1}{x - x_1} = m = \infty$, then $x - x_1 = 0.$

Solving any two of (1), (2) and (3), we get the point of intersection as $(-2, -10/3)$ which clearly satisfies the third. Hence the three medians are concurrent and the point of concurrency is called centroid of the triangle. We can, however, find the co-ordinates of the centroid by using the formula
$$\left(\frac{x_1 + x_2 + x_3}{3}, \frac{y_1 + y_2 + y_3}{3}\right) \text{ i.e. } \left(-2, \frac{-10}{3}\right).$$

(b) **Right Bisector :** Any line which passes through the middle point of any side and is perpendicular to it is called its right bisector.

Any line ⊥ to BC $\ y - x = 0$ is $\ x + y + k = 0.$
Since it passes through mid-point $D(-1, -1)$;
∴ $\quad -1 - 1 + k = 0$ or $k = 2.$
∴ Right bisector of BC is $x + y + 2 = 0.$ ...(1)
Similarly the right bisectors of sides CA and AB are respectively
$$2y + x + 10 = 0 \qquad \text{...(2)}$$
$$3y + x + 18 = 0 \qquad \text{...(3)}$$
Solving any two of (1), (2) and (3) we get the point $(6, -8)$ which satisfies the third also. Hence the right bisectors of the sides of a triangle are concurrent and the point of **concurrency** is called

(c) **Orthocentre :** Any line through the vertex $A(-4,-8)$ and perpendicular to the opposite side BC, $y - x = 0$ is called the altitude through A. Hence its equation is $x + y + k = 0$ where $-4 - 8 + k = 0$ or $k = 12$ or $x + y + 12 = 0$ ...(1) Similarly the equations of altitudes through the vertices B and C are respectively

$$2y + x + 6 = 0 \qquad ...(2)$$

and $\qquad 3y + x = 0.$ ...(3)

Solving any two of (1), (2) and (3) we get the point $(-18, 6)$ which satisfies the third also. Hence the altitudes of a triangle are concurrent and the point of concurrency is called the **orthocentre** of the triangle.

(d) **Area of triangle :** Since one vertex is at the origin the area of the triangle is

$$\frac{1}{2}(x_1 y_2 - x_2 y_1) = \frac{1}{2}[-4(-2) - (-2)(-8)]$$

$$= -4 = 4 \text{ sq. units.}$$

2. (a) $A(0, 12)$, $B(8, 0)$, mid-point P of AB is $(4, 6)$. Right bisector of AB, $3x + 2y - 24 = 0$ is

$2(x - 4) - 3(y - 6) = 0$ **Rule 15, P 768**

or $2x - 3y + 10 = 0$ ...(1)

Line through $(0, -1)$ parallel to y-axis is

$$y = -1 \qquad ...(2)$$

It meets (1) at $C(-13/2, -1)$

∴ $\Delta ABC = 91$ sq. units

(b) Take C to be (h, k). Mid-point $\left(\dfrac{h+1}{2}, \dfrac{k-1}{2}\right)$ of AC lies on the bisector

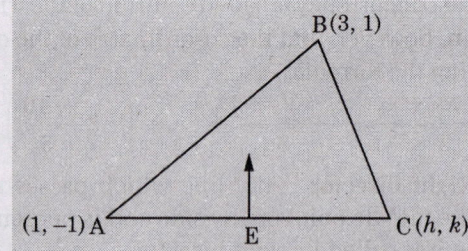

Fig. 89

$3x - 2y + 8 = 0$ ∴ $3h - 2k + 21 = 0$ ...(1)

AC is $\perp$ to $3x - 2y + 8 = 0$

∴ $m_1 m_2 = -1 \Rightarrow 2h + 3k + 1 = 0$ ...(2)

Solving (1) and (2), the point C is $(-5, 3)$

By two point formula, equation of BC is

$$x + 4y - 7 = 0$$

The centre of circumcircle be found as in **Q. 1 Page 774-75** by putting $OA = OB = OC$ where O is (α, β) is circumcentre or find the right bisector of BC or AB and solve it with given bisector.

Ans. $\left(-\dfrac{4}{5}, \dfrac{14}{5}\right)$.

3. (a) The three vertices are

$$A(7, -1), B(-2, 8), C(1, 2)$$

Altitudes through A and B are $x - 2y = 9$ and $x = -11$ respectively.

Solving these we get the orthocentre as $(-11, -10)$.

Alternative method : **(Note the method)**

The altitude AL is given by

$$\frac{x + 2y - 5}{1.1 + 2.1} = \frac{2x + y - 4}{2.1 + 1.1}$$

(Refer imp. result (2), P. 766)

or $\qquad x - y + 1 = 0$ ...(1)

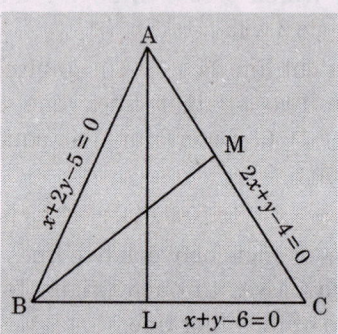

Fig. 91

Similarly altitude BM is

$$\frac{x + y - 6}{1.2 + 1.1} = \frac{x + 2y - 5}{1.2 + 2.1}$$

or $4(x + y - 6) = 3(x + 2y - 5)$

or $x - 2y - 9 = 0$ ...(2)

Solving (1) and (2), we get the orthocentre as $(-11, -10)$.

(b) Orthocentre is $(3/7, 22/7)$.

4. (a) Do yourself.

(b) **Ans.** $(0, 0)$. $x = 0$, $y = 0$ are two altitudes which intersect at $(0, 0)$.

(c) **Ans.** $(0, 0)$. **Refer 6 (iv), P. 766.**

(d) **Ans. (d).**

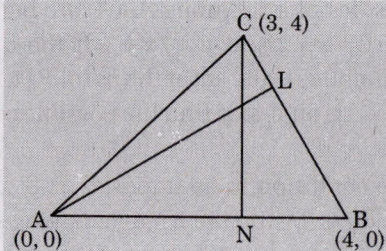

Fig. C-86

AB is x-axis and altitude CN is $x = 3$. Altitude AL is $y = \dfrac{1}{4}x$. Both intersect at $(3, 3/4)$.

5. (a) The two lines $x + \sqrt{3}y = 0$ and $x - \sqrt{3}y = 0$ are equally inclined to x-axis. Hence these will be the

two altitudes of equilateral triangle which intersect at $(0,0)$. Hence the orthocentre is $(0,0)$ which coincides with centroid.

(b) Here again $AB = BC = CA = a$ so that the triangle is equilateral. Hence all the points O, G, H, I coincide.

Its centroid is $\left(\dfrac{\Sigma x_1}{3}, \dfrac{\Sigma y_1}{3}\right)$ or $\left(\dfrac{a}{2}, \dfrac{a\sqrt{3}}{6}\right)$

which is also its incentre.

(c) Ans. (c). $(1, 2)$ is the intersection of two perpendicular lines $4x - 7y + 10 = 0$ and $7x + 4y - 15 = 0$. It is therefore its orthocentre.

(d) Ans. (d). The three equations of straight lines form a right-angled triangle whose orthocentre is at $(0, 0)$ where right angle is formed. The line $3x - 4y = 0$ passes through origin i.e., orthocentre.

6. (a) Let the given points be A, B and C respectively.

Slope of BC by $\dfrac{y_2 - y_1}{x_2 - x_1}$ is $\dfrac{1}{t_3}$.

Hence the line through A perpendicular to BC is
$$y - a(t_1 + t_2) = -t_3(x - at_1t_2) \qquad \ldots(1)$$
Similarly the line through $B \perp$ to CA is
$$y - a(t_2 + t_3) = -t_1(x - at_2t_3) \qquad \ldots(2)$$
Subtracting, we get $\quad x = -a$, and
hence $\quad y = a(t_1 + t_2 + t_3 + t_1t_2t_3)$.

(b) Proceed as above.

(c) Any line through the intersection of lines L_1 and L_2 and perpendicular to L_3 by **Result 16. (2) P. 769** is

$$\frac{L_1}{\cos\alpha_1\cos\alpha_3 + \sin\alpha_1\sin\alpha_3}$$
$$= \frac{L_2}{\cos\alpha_2\cos\alpha_3 + \sin\alpha_2\sin\alpha_3}$$

$$\therefore \quad L_1\cos(\alpha_2 - \alpha_3) = L_2\cos(\alpha_3 - \alpha_1)$$
$$= L_3\cos(\alpha_1 - \alpha_2)$$
$$\text{by symmetry}$$

7. (a) Let the vertex A be (p, q). O is orthocentre $(0, 0)$ which is intersection of altitudes through A and B.

Slope of $BC = \dfrac{3 - (-1)}{-2 - 5} = -\dfrac{4}{7}$

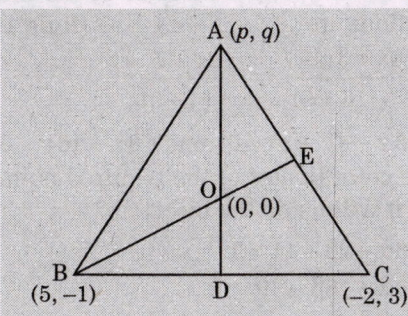

Fig. 92

Slope of AD = slope of $AO = q/p$.

But $\quad m_1 m_2 = -1$

$$\therefore \quad \left(-\frac{4}{7}\right)\frac{q}{p} = -1 \quad \text{or} \quad 7p = 4q. \qquad \ldots(1)$$

Slope of $CA = \dfrac{q - 3}{p + 2}$

Slope of BE = slope of $BO = -1/5$

But $m_1 m_2 = -1 \quad \therefore \quad \left(\dfrac{q-3}{p+2}\right)\left(\dfrac{-1}{5}\right) = -1$

or $\quad 5p - q + 13 = 0.$ $\qquad \ldots(2)$

Solving (1) and (2), we get $p = -4$, $q = -7$.
Hence the third vertex A is the point $(-4, -7)$.

(b) Do yourself.

8. (a) Slope of AD is $-\dfrac{4}{3}$ so that slope of BC is $\dfrac{3}{4}$

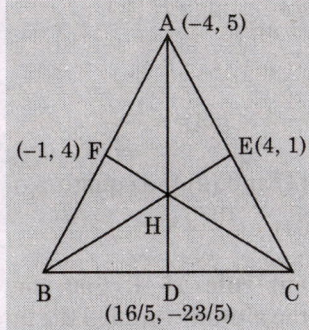

Fig. 93

and it passes through D so that its equation is
$$3x - 4y - 28 = 0 \qquad \ldots(1)$$
by $\quad y - y_1 = m(x - x_1)$
Equation of AB (AF) by two point formula is
$$3x + y + 7 = 0 \qquad \ldots(2)$$
and of AC is $\quad x + 2y - 6 = 0$ $\qquad \ldots(3)$
Solving [(1), (2)] and [(2), (3)] the co-ordinates of vertices B and C are found to be $(0, -7)$ and $(8, -1)$ respectively.

Note : Numerical calculations are to be done by yourself and not by me as I am not to appear in the examination. At the most I can render the services of my **Sewak/personal secretary 'Ramu'** for solving the equations and for other simple calculations.

(b) Proceed as in last question
$$B\left(-\frac{2}{3}\alpha, -\frac{1}{6}\alpha\right), C\left(\frac{1}{2}\alpha, \alpha\right)$$

If G be (x, y) then $x = \dfrac{\Sigma x_1}{3} = \dfrac{5\alpha}{18}$, $y = \dfrac{\Sigma y_1}{3} = -\dfrac{\alpha}{18}$

Eliminate α. $\quad x + 5y = 0$

(c) Altitude AD passes through the intersection of AB and AC. Its equation is $P + \lambda Q = 0$. It also passes through orthocentre $H(1, 1)$

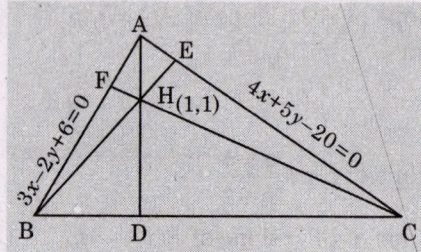

Fig. 94

$\therefore \quad \lambda = \dfrac{7}{11} \quad$ or $\quad AD$ is $61x + 13y - 74 = 0$

Hence BC being perpendicular to AD will have its
equation $\quad 13x - 61y + p = 0 \quad$ ...(1)
Altitude BE by **result 16 P. 769** is

$$\dfrac{3x - 2y + 6}{3.4 - 2.5} = \dfrac{13x - 61y + p}{13.4 - 61.5}$$

It also passes through $H(1, 1)$

$\therefore \quad \dfrac{7}{2} = \dfrac{p - 48}{52 - 305}$

$\therefore \quad p = 48 - \dfrac{7}{2} \times 253 = -\dfrac{1675}{2} \quad$ ...(2)

Now from (1) and (2) the equation of BC is

$$13x - 61y - \dfrac{1675}{2} = 0$$

9. (a) By important **rule 16 P. 769** the given line
represents the altitude through the intersection of
I and II.
Orthocentre P will lie on this altitude.

(b) **See rule 16 P. 769.**

10. (a) Let A be the vertex and given lines be AB and AC
so that the base BC is along x-axis, *i.e.* $y = 0$.
Solving with the given lines
B is $(-\alpha, 0)$ and C is $(-\beta, 0)$.

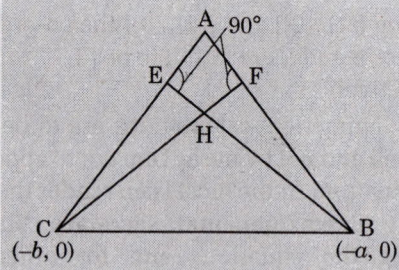

Fig. 95

Altitudes BE and CF are as below

$$BE \text{ is } y - 0 = \dfrac{-\beta}{1 + \beta}(x + \alpha)$$

$$CF \text{ is } y - 0 = \dfrac{-\alpha}{1 + \alpha}(x + \beta)$$

or $\quad y(1 + \beta) + x\beta + \alpha\beta = 0 \quad$ ...(1)

$\quad y(1 + \alpha) + x\alpha + \alpha\beta = 0 \quad$ ...(2)

They intersect at orthocentre whose locus is
obtained by eliminating α, β. Subtracting we get

$y(\beta - \alpha) + x(\beta - \alpha) = 0$

$\therefore \quad x + y = 0$

(b) If (h, k) be the third vertex then $\dfrac{\Sigma x}{3} = 5$,

$\dfrac{\Sigma y}{3} = 3 \quad \therefore \quad 8 + h = 15, \quad 6 + k = 9$

$\therefore \quad h = 7, k = 3 \quad \therefore \quad (7, 3)$ is the third vertex.

11. (a) Ans. (c). Since the triangle is equilateral the
centroid $G(0, 0)$ is also orthocentre or median AD
is also its altitude and G divides it in the ratio $2 : 1$.
The point $D(\alpha, \beta)$ lies on BC.

$\therefore \quad \alpha + \beta - 2 = 0 \quad$ ...(1)

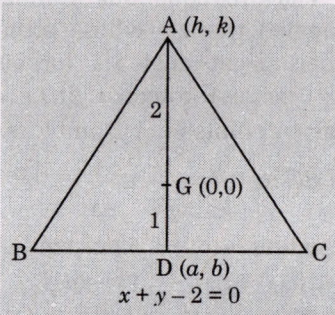

Fig. 96

If A be the point (h, k) then $\dfrac{2\alpha + h}{3} = 0, \dfrac{2\beta + k}{3} = 0$

$\therefore \quad h = -2\alpha, \quad k = -2\beta \quad$ ...(2)

AD is perpendicular to BC

$\therefore \quad \dfrac{h - \alpha}{k - \beta} \times (-1) = -1$

$\therefore \quad h - \alpha = k - \beta \quad$ or $\quad -3\alpha = -3\beta$, by (2)

or $\quad \alpha = \beta = 1$, by (1)

$\therefore \quad h = -2, k = -2$, by (2)

$\therefore \quad A$ is $(-2, -2)$.

(b) Ans. (c).

$$4^2 + 3^2 = 5^2, \quad 5^2 + 12^2 = 13^2, 7^2 + 24^2 = 25^2$$

Hence the distance of $(0, 0)$ from the three sides are
$\dfrac{10}{5}, \dfrac{26}{13}, \dfrac{50}{25} \quad$ *i.e.* each 2.

12. (a) Any point which is equidistant from the given
lines will lie on the bisector of the lines whose
equations are **(Rule 19, P. 770)**

$$\dfrac{4x + 3y - 7}{\sqrt{(16 + 9)}} = \pm \dfrac{2y - 5}{\sqrt{(4 + 0)}}$$

or $\quad 8x - 4y + 11 = 0$ and $8x + 16y - 39 = 0$.
If the co-ordinates of the required point be (α, β)
then it will lie on the bisectors.

$\therefore \quad 8\alpha - 4\beta + 11 = 0. \quad$ ...(1)

and $8\alpha + 16\beta - 39 = 0. \quad$ ...(2)

Since it lies on the line $3x + 2y = 5$

$\therefore \quad 3\alpha - 2\beta = 5. \quad$ ...(3)

Solving (1) and (3) and solving (2) and (3) we get the co-ordinates of the required points as

$$\left(\frac{-1}{14}, \frac{73}{28}\right) \text{ and } \left(\frac{1}{16}, \frac{77}{32}\right)$$

(b) Do yourself.

(c) The first line be shown to be one of the bisectors of the other two lines as the distance of any point on the bisector from the given lines are equal.

(Rule 19, P. 770)

(d) Ans. (c).

The bisector QM will divide the opposite side RP in the ratio of arms of the angle. Hence point M is

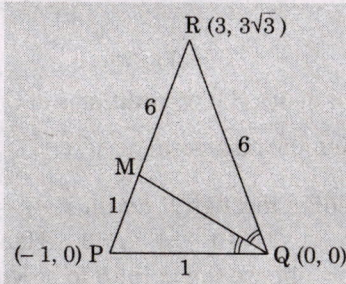

Fig. 97

$\left(-\dfrac{3}{7}, \dfrac{3\sqrt{3}}{7}\right)$. Slope of $OM = -\sqrt{3}$. Hence its

equation is $y = -\sqrt{3}\, x$ or $\sqrt{3}x + y = 0$.

(e) Ans. (a) The given lines are $x^2 - (y-1)^2 = 0$

or $x - y + 1 = 0$, $x + y - 1 = 0$

Their bisectors are $x = 0$ and $y = 1$. The sides of the triangle are $x = 0$, $y = 1$ and $x + y = 3$

Solving in pairs the vertices of $\triangle ABC$ are $(0, 1)$, $(0, 3)$ and $(2, 1)$. One side along y-axis.

∴ Area $= \dfrac{1}{2} b \times h = \dfrac{1}{2} \cdot 2 \cdot 2 = 2$

13. (a) The two lines are $Ax + By + C = 0$ and $B(x-h) - A(y-k) = 0$ as it is perp. to the above and passes through (h, k). **(R. 15 P. 768)**

Their bisectors are
$$\frac{B(x-h) - A(y-k)}{\sqrt{(B^2 + A^2)}} = \pm \frac{Ax + By + C}{\sqrt{(A^2 + B^2)}}$$

or $B(x-h) - A(y-k) = \pm(Ax + By + C)$

(b) The required bisectors are
$$\frac{P + \lambda Q}{\sqrt{\{(p + \lambda q)^2 + (q - p\lambda)^2\}}}$$
$$= \pm \frac{P - \lambda Q}{\sqrt{\{(p - \lambda q)^2 + (q + p\lambda)^2\}}}$$

The denominator on both sides cancel as each is $\sqrt{\{(p^2 + q^2)(1 + \lambda^2)\}}$

Hence the bisectors are $P + \lambda Q = \pm(P - \lambda Q)$.

or $P = 0$ or $Q = 0$

∴ $px + qy + r = 0$ or $qx - py + r' = 0$

Clearly these lines are perpendicular as we know that the bisectors of angles of two given lines are always perpendicular.

(c) The two bisectors as usual are

B_1, $16x + 2y + 15 = 0$

∴ $A\left(-\dfrac{15}{16}, 0\right), B\left(0, -\dfrac{15}{2}\right)$

B_2, $x - 8y + 5 = 0$

$C(-5, 0), D(0, 5/8)$

∴ $AC = 5 - \dfrac{15}{16} = \dfrac{65}{16}$,

$DB = \dfrac{5}{8} + \dfrac{15}{2} = \dfrac{65}{8}$

∴ $AC : DB = \dfrac{8}{16} = \dfrac{1}{2}$ or $1 : 2$

14. (a) The bisectors of given lines are given by
$$\frac{3x - 4y + 7}{\sqrt{(25)}} = \pm \frac{12x + 5y - 2}{\sqrt{(169)}}$$

The bisectors are

$21x + 77y - 101 = 0$ and $11x - 3y + 9 = 0$

Let θ be the angle between one of the lines say $3x - 4y + 7 = 0$ and one of the bisectors say $11x - 3y + 9 = 0$. Their slopes are

$m_1 = 3/4$, $m_2 = 11/3$

∴ $\tan\theta = \dfrac{(3/4) - (11/3)}{1 + (3/4)(11/3)} = -\dfrac{35}{45}$

and it is numerically less than 1.

Hence $\theta < 45°$ or $2\theta < 90°$. Therefore this is the bisector of the acute angle between the lines and hence the other bisects the obtuse angle.

Alternative Method : Write the equation of the lines so that constant term in both are $+$ ive *i.e.* $3x - 4y + 7 = 0$ and $-12x - 5y + 2 = 0$.

Their bisectors are
$$\frac{3x - 4y + 7}{5} = \pm \frac{-12x - 5y + 2}{13}$$

Taking +ive sign the bisector is $11x - 3y + 9 = 0$ and the other is $21x + 77y - 101 = 0$. Hence $11x - 3y + 9 = 0$ is the bisector of the angle in which origin lies. Again

$a_1 a_2 + b_1 b_2 = 3(-12) - 4(-5)$
$= -16 = -$ive

Hence origin lies in the acute angle therefore $11x - 3y + 9 = 0$ bisects the acute angle between the lines.

(b) Proceed as in part (a).

(c) $x - 2y + 4 = 0$, $4x - 3y + 2 = 0$

c_1 and c_2 are both $+$ ive and hence taking $+$ out of $\pm$ signs we shall get the bisector of the angle in which origin lies. Again

$a_1 a_2 + b_1 b_2 = 4 + 6 = 10$, +ive

Therefore origin lies in obtuse angle.

$$\frac{x - 2y + 4}{\sqrt{5}} = + \frac{4x - 3y + 2}{5} \qquad \ldots(1)$$

is the bisector of angle in which origin lies and it lies in obtuse angle. Its equation is

$$(4 - \sqrt{5}) x - (3 - 2\sqrt{5}) y + (2 - 4\sqrt{5}) = 0$$

Hence the other bisector of acute angle whose equation is

$$(4 + \sqrt{5}) x - (3 + 2\sqrt{5}) y + (2 + 5\sqrt{5}) = 0$$

15. (a) $AB = 3x - 4y = 0, AD = 12x - 5y = 0$

They intersect at $A(0, 0)$. AC is the longer diagonal.

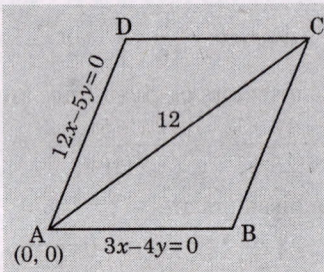

Fig. 98

AC is one of the bisectors of AB and AD.

$$\therefore \quad \frac{3x - 4y}{5} = \pm \frac{12x - 5y}{13}$$

$$\Rightarrow \quad 99x - 77y = 0 \quad \text{and} \quad 21x + 27y = 0$$

or $\quad \dfrac{x}{7} = \dfrac{y}{9}$. \qquad It lies in Ist quadrant.

$$\tan \theta = 9/7.$$

The other bisector does not lie in Ist quadrant, as it makes obtuse angle with x-axis,

$$\tan \theta = -21/27 = -7/9$$

or $\quad \dfrac{x}{7/\sqrt{130}} = \dfrac{y}{9/\sqrt{130}} = r = AC = 12.$

$$\therefore \quad C = \left(\frac{84}{\sqrt{(130)}}, \frac{108}{\sqrt{(130)}} \right) = (x_1, y_1)$$

Now write the equation of the lines through C which are parallel to given lines whose slopes are 3/4 and 12/5 by

$$y - y_1 = m(x - x_1)$$

Ans. $3x - 4y + \dfrac{180}{\sqrt{(130)}} = 0, 12x - 5y = \dfrac{468}{\sqrt{(130)}}$

(b) The internal bisector of the angle A will divide the opposite side BC at D in the ratio of arms of the angle *i.e.* $AB = 3\sqrt{2}$ and $AC = 4\sqrt{2}$. Hence by ratio formula the point D is $\left(\dfrac{31}{7}, 1 \right)$.

Slope of AD by $\dfrac{y_2 - y_1}{x_2 - x_1} = 0.$

$\therefore$ Slope of a line perpendicular to AD is ∞. Any line through C perpendicular to this bisector is

$$\frac{y - 5}{x - 5} = m = \infty \quad \therefore \quad x - 5 = 0$$

(c) Mark the point $A(1, 2)$ and trace the median $x + y = 5$ through B. $x = 4$ is the median through C

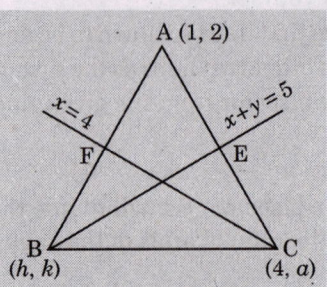

Fig. 99

and hence the co-ordinates of C be taken as $(4, a)$. Then the mid-point of AC *i.e.* $\left(\dfrac{5}{2}, \dfrac{a + 2}{2} \right)$ will lie on

median through B, *i.e.* on $x + y = 5$

$$a + 7 = 10 \quad \Rightarrow \quad a = 3. \quad \text{Hence } C \text{ is } (4, 3)$$

Now choose the point B to be (h, k) which lies on $x + y = 5$ $\therefore$ $h + k = 5$. Also the mid point of AB *i.e.* $\left(\dfrac{h + 1}{2}, \dfrac{k + 2}{2} \right)$ will lie on median through C *i.e.* $x = 4$

$$\therefore \quad \frac{h + 1}{2} = 4 \quad \Rightarrow \quad h = 7 \text{ and hence } k = -2$$

$$\therefore \quad B \text{ is } (7, -2).$$

16. (a) By solving the equations of given lines find the co-ordinates of the vertices as $A(3, 1)$, $B(-1, -2)$ and $C(-1, 8/3)$.

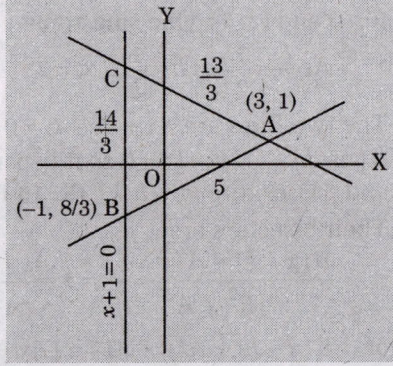

Fig. 100

The bisectors of $\angle A$ are given by

$$\frac{3x - 4y - 5}{5} = \pm \frac{5x + 12y - 27}{13}$$

or $\quad x - 8y + 5 = 0$ and $8x + y - 25 = 0$

Since we have to find the internal bisector of angle A, the points $B(-1, -2)$ and $C(-1, 8/3)$ must lie on the opposite sides of the internal bisector. Putting in any equation of the bisector say in $x - 8y + 5 = 0$, we get $20, -\dfrac{52}{3}$ *i.e.*, of opposite signs or $\quad p\left(\dfrac{13}{2}-p\right)=\dfrac{15}{2}\quad$ or $\quad 2p^2-13p+15=0$

$\therefore\quad (p-5)(2p-3)=0$

or $\quad p=5,\dfrac{3}{2};\quad \therefore\quad q=\dfrac{3}{2},5$

$\therefore\quad 2x+y+5=0,\quad 2x+y+\dfrac{3}{2}=0$

are the required lines.

If p_1 and p_2 be their distances from origin, then the distance between them is

$$p=p_1\sim p_2=\dfrac{5}{\sqrt{(4+1)}}\sim\dfrac{3/2}{\sqrt{(4+1)}}=\dfrac{7}{2\sqrt5}$$

(ii) As in part (a) the two parallel lines are
$$(x+\sqrt2 y+p)(x+\sqrt2 y+q)=0$$
where $p+q=4$ and $pq=1$

$\therefore\quad p-q=\sqrt{(16-4)}=2\sqrt3$

$\therefore\quad$ Req. distance $=\dfrac{p}{\sqrt3}-\dfrac{q}{\sqrt3}=\dfrac{1}{\sqrt3}(2\sqrt3)=2$

$\therefore\quad$ (c) is correct.

14. As on **P. 944** result **§ 1 (c)** we can show that the general equation of second degree will represent a pair of parallel straight lines if $h^2=ab$ or $h=\sqrt{(ab)}$. In order to find the second condition, put the value of h in the equation.

$\therefore\quad ax^2+2\sqrt{(ab)}\,xy+by^2+2gx+2fy+c=0$

or $\quad [\sqrt{(ax)}+\sqrt{(by)}]^2+2gx+2fy+c=0.$

Now suppose that above is equal to
$$[\sqrt{(ax)}+\sqrt{(by)}+p][\sqrt{(ax)}+\sqrt{(by)}+q]=0$$

Comparing the coefficients,

$p\sqrt a+q\sqrt a=2g\quad$ or $\quad (p+q)=\dfrac{2g}{\sqrt a}\qquad$ ...(1)

$p\sqrt b+q\sqrt b=2f\quad$ or $\quad p+q=\dfrac{2f}{\sqrt b}\qquad$ ...(2)

$pq=c\qquad$ ...(3)

Now from (1) and (2),

$\dfrac{2g}{\sqrt a}=\dfrac{2f}{\sqrt b}\quad$ or $\quad bg^2=af^2$

Distance between the lines as in **R. 21, P. 8.**

$$=\dfrac{0+0+p}{\sqrt{(a+b)}}-\dfrac{0+0+q}{\sqrt{(a+b)}}=\dfrac{p-q}{\sqrt{(a+b)}}$$

$$=\dfrac{\{(p+q)^2-4pq\}^{1/2}}{\sqrt{(a+b)}}=\left\{\dfrac{\dfrac{4g^2}{a}-4.c}{(a+b)}\right\}^{1/2}$$

[by (1) and (3)]

$$=2\sqrt{\left\{\dfrac{g^2-ac}{a(a+b)}\right\}}.$$

Now from above, we have $h^2=ab$ and $bg^2=af^2$.

$\dfrac{a}{h}=\dfrac{h}{b}=k$ say,

$\therefore\quad a=hk$ and $b=\dfrac{h}{k}$;

$\therefore\quad$ from the condition $bg^2=af^2$,
$$\dfrac{h}{k}g^2=hk.f^2\ ;$$

$\therefore\quad \dfrac{g^2}{f^2}=k^2\qquad$ or $\qquad \dfrac{g}{f}=k$;

$\therefore\quad \dfrac{a}{h}=\dfrac{h}{b}=\dfrac{g}{f}$ as each is equal to k.

15. (a) $3x-y-2=0\quad$ or $\quad \dfrac{3x-y}{2}=1.$

Making the equation of the curve homogeneous, we get
$$7x^2-4xy+8y^2+2(x-2y)\dfrac{(3x-y)}{2}$$
$$-8\cdot\left(\dfrac{3x-y}{2}\right)^2=0$$

or $\quad (7x^2-4xy+8y^2)+(3x^2-7xy+2y^2)$
$$-2(9x^2-6xy+y^2)=0$$

or $-8x^2+xy+8y^2=0$ is the required equation to the lines.

Since $a+b=-8+8=0$, and hence the lines are perpendicular.

(b) Proceed as in part (a).

(c) From the equation of the line we have $x-y=2$

or $\quad \dfrac{x-y}{2}=1.\qquad$ ...(1)

Equation of the curve
$$5x^2+12xy-8y^2+4(2x-y)+12=0$$
$$5x^2+12xy-8y^2+4(2x-y)\cdot1+12\cdot1^2=0$$

[Make it homogeneous]

Equation of the required lines is
$$5x^2+12xy-8y^2+4(2x-y)\left(\dfrac{x-y}{2}\right)$$
$$+12\left(\dfrac{x-y}{2}\right)^2=0\quad \text{[by (1)]}$$

or $\quad (5x^2+12xy-8y^2)+2(2x^2-3xy+y^2)$
$$+3(x^2-2xy+y^2)=0$$

or $\quad 12x^2+0xy-3y^2=0\quad$ or $\quad y=\pm2x.$

If $\tan\theta=2$, then $-2=-\tan\theta=\tan(\pi-\theta)$.

They are clearly equally inclined to axes.

Angle between them is $\pi-2\theta=\pi-2\tan^{-1}2$.

16. Making the equation of circle homogeneous,
$$x^2+y^2-2(hx+ky)\cdot\dfrac{1}{2}\left(\dfrac{x}{h}+\dfrac{y}{k}\right)$$
$$=(h^2+k^2-r^2)\cdot\dfrac{1}{4}\left(\dfrac{x}{h}+\dfrac{y}{k}\right)^2$$

$$A + B = 0 \quad \Rightarrow \quad \left(\frac{h^2 + k^2 - r^2}{4}\right)\left(\frac{1}{h^2} + \frac{1}{k^2}\right) = 0$$

$$\therefore \quad h^2 + k^2 - r^2 = 0, \text{ as } \frac{1}{h^2} + \frac{1}{k^2} \neq 0$$

$$\therefore \quad \text{Locus of } (h, k) \text{ is } x^2 + y^2 = r^2.$$

17. (a) From the equation $\dfrac{y - mx}{c} = 1$.

$$\therefore \quad x^2 + y^2 = a^2 . 1^2,$$

or $\quad x^2 + y^2 = a^2 \dfrac{(y - mx)^2}{c^2}$

Ans. $(c^2 - a^2 m^2) x^2 + 2am^2 xy + (c^2 - a^2) y^2 = 0.$

If it represents two perpendicular straight lines, then

coeff. of x^2 + coeff. of $y^2 = 0$.

$$c^2 - a^2 m^2 + c^2 - a^2 = 0$$

$$2c^2 = a^2 (1 + m^2) \text{ is the required condition.}$$

(b) The centre of the circle is origin. The equations of the lines joining origin to the points of intersection of the line and circle are

$$x^2 + y^2 = a^2 (lx + my)^2$$

or $\quad x^2 (a^2 l^2 - 1) + 2 lm\, a^2\, xy + y^2 (a^2 m^2 - 1) = 0$

$$Ax^2 + 2Hxy + By^2 = 0$$

$$\tan 45° = 1 = \frac{2\sqrt{H^2 - AB}}{A + B}$$

$$(A + B)^2 = 4 [H^2 - AB]$$

$$[a^2 (l^2 + m^2) - 2]^2 = 4 [a^2 (l^2 + m^2) - 1]$$

18. We know that the combined equation of the lines through the origin is homogeneous. Hence eliminating the first degree terms of x between the given equations we shall obtain homogeneous equation which will represent the required lines. Multiplying the first equation by g_1 and 2nd by g and subtracting, we get

$$g_1 (ax^2 + 2hxy + by^2 + 2gx)$$

$$- g (a_1 x^2 + 2h_1 xy + b_1 y^2 + 2g_1 x) = 0$$

or $\quad (g_1 a - a_1 g) x^2 + 2xy (hg_1 - h_1 g)$

$$+ (g_1 b - b_1 g) y^2 = 0$$

If the above equation represents two perpendicular lines, then

coeff. of x^2 + coeff. of $y^2 = 0$.

$$\therefore \quad g_1 a - a_1 g + g_1 b - b_1 g = 0$$

$$\therefore \quad (a + b) g_1 = (a_1 + b_1) g \text{ is the required condition.}$$

19. (i) Ans. [a].

(ii) Ans. $\dfrac{1}{5}$.

$$\tan\theta = \frac{2\sqrt{(h^2 - ab)}}{a + b} = \frac{1}{5} \quad \therefore \quad \theta = \tan^{-1}\frac{1}{5}.$$

20. Ans. (a).

21. Ans. (d).

Collecting the terms y^2 and y the given equation can be written as

$$y^2 (x^2 - 2x - 3) - 4y (x^2 - 2x - 3) = 0$$

or $\quad (x - 3)(x + 1)\, y\,(y - 4) = 0$

It represents four lines $x = -1$, $x = 3$, $y = 0$ and $y = 4$. These two sets of parallel lines form a square of side four.

22. Let the axes be rotated through an angle θ so that $\left.\begin{array}{l} x \to x\cos\theta - y\sin\theta \\ y \to x\sin\theta + y\cos\theta \end{array}\right\}$ by **(d) P. 17**

$$a (x\cos\theta - y\sin\theta)^2 + 2h (x\cos\theta - y\sin\theta)$$

$$(x\sin\theta + y\cos\theta) + b (x\sin\theta + y\cos\theta)^2$$

$$+ 2g (x\cos\theta - y\sin\theta)$$

$$+ 2f (x\sin\theta + y\cos\theta) + c = 0$$

Collect the coefficients of xy and put it equal to zero

$$(-a\sin 2\theta + b\sin 2\theta) + 2h (\cos^2\theta - \sin^2\theta) = 0$$

$$\frac{\sin 2\theta}{\cos 2\theta} = \frac{2h}{a - b} \Rightarrow \tan 2\theta = \frac{2h}{a - b}$$

23. (a) $AB \equiv x + 3y = 0$, $BC = 3x - y = 0$ represent two perpendicular lines passing through the point $B (0, 0)$. The other two lines are $(x + 3y + 1)(3x - y - 1) = 0$

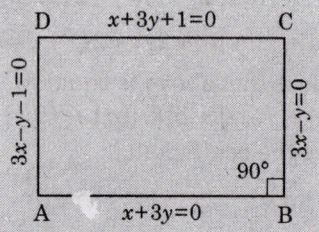

Fig. 6

$$\therefore \quad \text{These are parallel to } AB \text{ and } BC \text{ respectively.}$$

$$\therefore \quad \text{Equation of } CD \text{ is } x + 3y + 1 = 0.$$

(b) Since $a + b = 0$, the two pairs represent pair of perpendicular straight lines. Hence the quadrilateral is a square or a rectangle. But distance between parallel sides $= \dfrac{1}{\sqrt{10}}$ each and hence it is a square.

(c) Area $p^2 = \dfrac{1}{10}$.

(d) Solving CD and AD, the point D is $\left(\dfrac{1}{5}, -\dfrac{2}{5}\right)$.

24. Ans. (b).

$$x^2 - 5xy + 6y^2 = 0 \Rightarrow (x - 3y)(x - 2y) = 0$$

Above represents two straight lines through $(0, 0)$.

$$ax^2 + by^2 + c = 0 \Rightarrow x^2 + y^2 = -\frac{c}{a} \qquad \dots(1)$$

where, $c = 0$ and a and b are of same sign i.e., of the form $5x^2 + 9y^2 = 0$. This is not possible.

When $a=b$ and c is of sign opposite to that of a then from (1), 2nd factor is $x^2 + y^2 = +$ive $= k^2$. Hence a circle $\Rightarrow$ (b) is correct.

Both (c) and (d) are obviously incorrect.

MISCELLANEOUS EXERCISE

Matching Entries

◆ Match the entries of List-A and List-B.

1. **List-A**

(a) The lines joining the origin to the points of intersection of the line $4x - 3y = 10$ with the circle $x^2 + y^2 + 3x - 6y - 20 = 0$ include an angle

(b) The two lines given by $a^2x^2 + 2hxy + b^2y^2 = 0$ are such that slope of one is three times of the other, then h is equal to

(c) If the equation $12x^2 - 10xy + 2y^2 + 11x - 5y + \lambda = 0$ represents a pair of straight lines then $\lambda =$

(d) If $x^2 - 3xy + \lambda y^2 + 3x - 5y + 2 = 0$ represents a pair of lines which include an angle θ, then $\operatorname{cosec}^2 \theta =$

List-B

1. $h = \pm \frac{2}{3}\sqrt{ab}$

2. 2

3. 10

4. $\pi/2$

2. Match the entries of col. I with those of col. II.
The lines given by left hand side in col. I have the property mentioned in col. II.

Column I

(a) $6x^2 + 5xy - 6y^2 - x + 5y - 1 = 0$

(b) $30x^2 + 36xy + 6y^2 - 35x - 11y + 5 = 0$

(c) $30x^2 + 41xy + 6y^2 - 35x - 11y + 5 = 0$

(d) $6x^2 + 12xy + 6y^2 - 7x - 7y + 1 = 0$

Column II

(p) parallel

(q) perpendicular

(r) $I_x = 5/6$

(s) $I_y = 1/6$

Answers

1. (a) → (4), (b) → (1), (c) → (2), (d) → (3)
2. (a) → (q, r, s), (b) → (r, s), (c) → (r, s), (d) → (p, r)

Hints/Solutions

1. (a) $2x^2 - 3xy - 2y^2 = 0$, $\pi/2$

(b) $m + 3m = -\frac{2h}{b^2}$, $m \cdot 3m = \frac{a^2}{b^2}$

$\therefore 2m = -\frac{h}{b^2} \Rightarrow m = -\frac{h}{2b^2}$

$\therefore 3\left(-\frac{h}{2b^2}\right)^2 = \frac{a^2}{b^2} \therefore h^2 = \frac{4}{3}a^2b^2$

$\therefore h = \pm\frac{2}{\sqrt{3}}ab$

(c) See Q. 9, P. 952-95

(d) See Q. 11, P. 952-954

$m_1 = 2, m_2 = 1$

$\therefore \tan\theta = 1/3 \therefore \operatorname{cosec}^2\theta = 1 + \cot^2\theta = 10$

2. (a) → (q) as $a+b=0$. Its intersection with x-axis ($y=0$) is given by

$6x^2 - x - 1 = 0$ or $(3x+1)(2x-1)=0$ $\therefore x = \frac{1}{2}, -\frac{1}{3}$

$\therefore I_x = x_1 - x_2 = \frac{1}{2} + \frac{1}{3} = \frac{5}{6}$ $\therefore$ (a) → (r)

Its intersection with y-axis ($x=0$) is given by

$-6y^2 + 5y - 1 = 0$ or $6y^2 - 5y + 1 = 0$

or $(3y-1)(2y-1) = 0$ $\therefore y = \frac{1}{2}, \frac{1}{3}$.

$I_y = y_1 - y_2 = \frac{1}{2} - \frac{1}{3} = \frac{1}{6}$ $\therefore$ (a) → (s)

$\therefore$ (a) → (q, r, s)

(b) → (r, s), (c) → (r, s). Proceed as in (a).

(d) $6(x+y)^2 - 7(x+y) + 1 = 0$ or $6t^2 - 7t + 1 = 0$

$\therefore (t-1)(6t-1) = 0$

$\therefore x+y-1 = 0$ or $x+y-\frac{1}{6} = 0$

$\therefore$ Parallel lines (d) → (p)

$y=0, x=1, \frac{1}{6}$ $\therefore I_x = 1 - \frac{1}{6} = \frac{5}{6}$ $\therefore$ (d) → (r)

$x=0, y=1, \frac{1}{6}$ $\therefore I_y = 1 - \frac{1}{6} = \frac{5}{6}$ $\therefore$ (d) → (p, r)

Fascinating Facts

- Two points (x_1, y_1) and (x_2, y_2) not lying on the line $ax + by + c = 0$ lie on the same side or on opposite sides of $ax + by + c = 0$ according as $ax_1 + by_1 + c$ and $ax_2 + by_2 + c$ are of the same sign or of opposite sign.
- The point of concurrence of the altitudes of a triangle is called its orthocentre and the point of concurrence of the right bisectors of the sides of a triangle is called its circumcentre.
- If two linear equations represent the same line, then their corresponding coefficients are proportional.
- A system of two equations in which one equation can be obtained from the other by multiplying by an appropriate (non-zero) real number is called a system of dependent equations.
- The equation $ax + by + c = 0$, where k is a parameter, represents a family of straight lines parallel to the line $ax + by + c = 0$
- The equation $bx - ay + k = 0$, k is a parameter, represents a family of straight lines perpendicular to the line $ax + by + c = 0$.
- The equation $x = a, a \in \mathbf{R}$ represents the family of lines which are parallel to y-axis.
- The equation $y = b, b \in \mathbf{R}$ represents the family of lines which are parallel to x-axis.
- If the lines represented by the general equation $ax^2 + 2hxy + by^2 + 2gx + 2fy + c = 0$ are perpendicular, then the square of the distance between the points of intersection and origin is $\dfrac{f^2 + g^2}{h^2 + b^2}$ or $\dfrac{f^2 + g^2}{h^2 + a^2}$
- The two pairs of straight lines
  $$ax^2 + 2hxy + by^2 + 2gx + 2fy + c = 0 \text{ forms a}$$
  (i) square if $(a - b)fg + h(f^2 - g^2) = 0$, $a + b = 0$
  (ii) rectangle if $(a - b)fg + h(f^2 - g^2) \neq 0$, $a + b = 0$
  (iii) rhombus if $(a - b)fg + h(f^2 - g^2) = 0$, $a + b \neq 0$
  (iv) parallelogram if $(a - b)fg + h(f^2 - g^2) \neq 0$, $a + b \neq 0$
- The square of the distance between the points of intersection of the lines represented by the equation $ax^2 + 2hxy + by^2 + 2gx + 2fy + c = 0$ and origin is $\dfrac{c(a + b) - f^2 - g^2}{ab - h^2}$

❑

and hence this bisector is internal bisector of angle A. It may be verified that B and C when put in 2nd bisector will give results of the same sign. Similarly the internal bisector of angle C is found to be $9x + 6y - 7 = 0$. Solving these two internal bisectors, we get the co-ordinates of incentre as $\left(\frac{1}{3}, \frac{2}{3}\right)$.

Alternative Method :

The vertices and lengths of opposite sides are marked in the figure. Hence the incentre is the point $\left(\frac{\Sigma ax_1}{\Sigma a}, \frac{\Sigma ay_1}{\Sigma a}\right) = \left(\frac{1}{3}, \frac{2}{3}\right)$.

(b) Proceeding as in part (a), the vertices are found to be $A\left(\frac{19}{9}, -\frac{8}{3}\right)$, $B(11, 4)$, $C\left(-\frac{2}{3}, 4\right)$. Bisectors of $\angle A$ are $3x + 11y + 23 = 0$ and $99x - 27y - 281 = 0$. B, C when put in 1st, we get 100, 65 *i.e.*, of same sign and hence it cannot be internal.

∴ $99x - 27y - 281 = 0$ is the internal bisector. Similarly the internal bisector of $\angle B$ is found to be $x - 3y + 1 = 0$.

Solving the two internal bisectors, the incentre is the point $\left(\frac{29}{9}, \frac{38}{27}\right)$.

(c) The two internal bisectors are found to be $12x - 6y - 1 = 0$ and $12x + 4y - 11 = 0$ and the co-ordinates of incentre are $\left(\frac{7}{12}, 1\right)$.

(d) The internal bisector of angle A is found as above to be $y - 1 = 0$

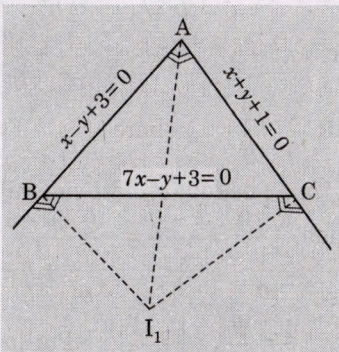

Fig. 101

The bisectors of $\angle C$ are $3x + y + 2 = 0$ and $x - 3y + 1 = 0$. The points A and B when put in 1st give results of opposite signs and hence it is internal. Therefore $x - 3y + 1 = 0$ is external. You may see that points A and B when put give −ive sign.

Similarly bisectors of $\angle B$ are $2x - y + 3 = 0$ and $x + 2y - 6 = 0$. Points A and C when put in 1st give both opposite signs and hence they are on the opposite sides. Therefore it is internal and as such

$x + 2y - 6 = 0$ is external. Hence one internal and two external bisectors are $y - 1 = 0$, $x - 3y + 1 = 0$ and $x + 2y - 6 = 0$. All these three are concurrent at the point $(2, 1)$.

17. (a) Prove as in **Q. 16 (a)**.

(b) Substitute the co-ordinates of the point $(2, -1)$ in the left hand side of the given equations, the results are 2 and 23 *i.e.*, both +ive. Hence the bisector of the angle in which $(2, -1)$ lies is obtained by taking +ive out of ±. Therefore the equation of bisector of the supplement of that angle is obtained by taking −ive sign. Hence the required equation is

$$\frac{2x - 3y - 5}{\sqrt{(4 + 9)}} = -\frac{6x - 4y + 7}{\sqrt{(36 + 16)}}$$

or $10x - 10y - 3 = 0$.

(c) Let the given lines be l_1 and l_2 which have two bisectors of angle as B_1 and B_2. Any point on the bisector is equidistant from the two lines.

Thus we will have four points like P_1, P_2, P_3 and P_4.

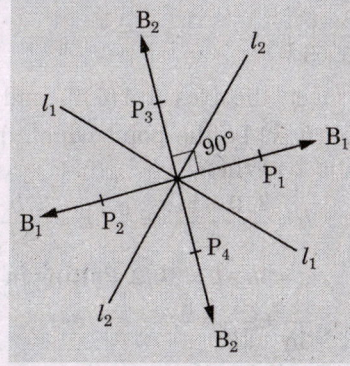

Fig. 102

Let $P(x, y)$ which is equidistant.

$$\frac{3x - 4y + 11}{\sqrt{(3^2 + 4^2)}} = 1 \text{ and } \frac{5x - 12y + 7}{\sqrt{(5^2 + 12^2)}} = 1$$

or $3x - 4y + 11 = \pm 5$, $5x - 12y + 7 = \pm 13$

or $3x - 4y + 16 = 0$ ...(1)

$3x - 4y + 6 = 0$ ...(2)

and $5x - 12y + 20 = 0$ ...(3)

$5x - 12y - 6 = 0$ ...(4)

Solving (1) with (3) and (4), and then (2) with (3) and (4), we get the points as $(-7, -5/4)$, $(-27/2, -49/8), (1/2, 15/8), (-6, -3)$.

See a similar **Q. 33 (c) on P. 805-815.**

18. (a) Let the line cut the axes in A and B and if (h, k) be the mid-point of AB, then

$$2h = \frac{p}{\cos\theta}, 2k = \frac{p}{\sin\theta}.$$

In order to find the locus, eliminate the variable θ by $\cos^2\theta + \sin^2\theta = 1$

$$\frac{1}{x^2} + \frac{1}{y^2} = \frac{4}{p^2}.$$

(b) If P be the point (h, k) on the line, then
$$h = OQ = RP = a\cos\theta, \quad k = PQ = b\sin\theta$$

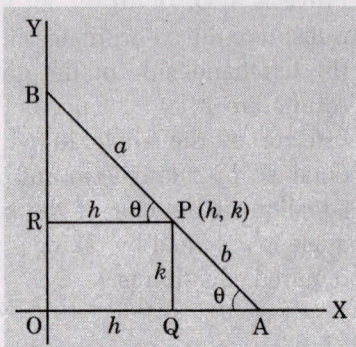

Fig. 103

Eliminating θ, we get
$$\frac{x^2}{a^2} + \frac{y^2}{b^2} = 1.$$

19. (a) Let the line be $x/a + y/b = 1$ and since it passes through the point
$$\left(\frac{6}{5}, \frac{6}{5}\right) \quad \therefore \quad \frac{1}{a} + \frac{1}{b} = \frac{5}{6} \qquad \dots(1)$$

It meets the axes at $A(a, 0)$, and $B(0, b)$.
Let (h, k) be the point which divides AB in the ratio $2 : 1$ then
$$h = \frac{2 \cdot 0 + 1 \cdot a}{3} = \frac{a}{3}, \quad k = \frac{2 \cdot b + 1 \cdot 0}{3} = \frac{2b}{3}.$$
$$\therefore \quad a = 3h, \, b = 3k/2. \text{ Putting in (1), we get}$$
$$\frac{1}{3h} + \frac{2}{3k} = \frac{5}{6}.$$

Generalising (h, k), the locus is
$$\frac{y + 2x}{3xy} = \frac{5}{6} \quad \text{or} \quad 2(y + 2x) = 5xy.$$

(b) As in part (a), $\frac{x}{a} + \frac{y}{b} = 1$, where $\frac{1}{a} + \frac{1}{b} = 1$

(c) The point of intersection of given lines is $\left(\frac{3}{5}, \frac{1}{5}\right)$

and line is $\frac{x}{a} + \frac{y}{b} = 1$, where $\frac{1}{5}\left(\frac{3}{a} + \frac{1}{b}\right) = 1.$

Ans. $10\, xy = x + 3y$

20. (a) Any line through origin is $y = mx$.
It meets the line $2x + y - 2 = 0$ in A
$$\left(\frac{2}{m+2}, \frac{2m}{m+2}\right)$$
It meets the line $x - 2y + 2 = 0$ in point
$$B\left(\frac{2}{2m+1}, \frac{2m}{2m-1}\right)$$
If (h, k) be the mid-point of AB, then
$$2h = \frac{2}{m+2} + \frac{2}{2m-1}$$

or $\quad h = \dfrac{3m+1}{(m+2)(2m-1)} \qquad \dots(1)$

$$2k = \frac{2m}{m+2} + \frac{2m}{2m-1}$$

or $\quad k = \dfrac{m(3m+1)}{(m+2)(2m-1)} \qquad \dots(2)$

In order to find the locus we have to eliminate the variable m.
Dividing (1) and (2), we get $(k/h) = m$. Putting in (1), we get
$$h\left(\frac{k}{h} + 2\right)\left(\frac{2k}{h} - 1\right) = 3 \cdot \frac{k}{h} + 1$$

or $\quad (k + 2h)(2k - h) = 3k + h$

or $\quad 2k^2 + 3hk - 2h^2 - 3k - h = 0.$

Hence the locus is
$$2y^2 + 3xy - 2x^2 - 3y - x = 0$$

or $\quad 2x^2 - 3xy - 2y^2 + x + 3y = 0.$

(b) $13(x^2 + y^2) - 83x + 64y + 182 = 0.$

21. (a) The given line is $\dfrac{x}{a} + \dfrac{y}{b} = 1.$ $\qquad \dots(1)$

Any line through origin and perpendicular to (1) is
$$\frac{x}{b} - \frac{y}{a} = 0. \qquad \dots(2)$$

Now foot of the perpendicular is the point of intersection of lines (1) and (2). In order to find its locus we have to eliminate the variables a and b. Squaring and adding (1) and (2), we get
$$x^2\left(\frac{1}{a^2} + \frac{1}{b^2}\right) + y^2\left(\frac{1}{b^2} + \frac{1}{a^2}\right) = 1$$

or $\quad x^2 + y^2 = c^2$ $\quad \because \dfrac{1}{a^2} + \dfrac{1}{b^2} = \dfrac{1}{c^2}$ (given)

Alt. $\dfrac{x}{a} + \dfrac{y}{b} = 1$, where $\dfrac{1}{a^2} + \dfrac{1}{b^2} = \dfrac{1}{c^2}$ $\quad \dots(1)$

If (h, k) be foot of perpendicular from $(0, 0)$ on it then
$$\frac{h - 0}{\frac{1}{a}} = \frac{k - 0}{\frac{1}{b}} = -\frac{0 + 0 - 1}{\frac{1}{a^2} + \frac{1}{b^2}} = \frac{1}{\frac{1}{c^2}} = c^2$$

$\therefore \quad \dfrac{1}{a} = \dfrac{h}{c^2}, \quad \dfrac{1}{b} = \dfrac{k}{c^2}.$ Put in (1)

$\therefore \quad x^2 + y^2 = c^2.$

(b) Any line $\perp$ to AB is $\dfrac{x}{b} - \dfrac{y}{a} = \lambda$ (variable)
$$\therefore \quad A(a, 0), B(0, b)$$
$$P(b\lambda, 0), Q(0, -a\lambda)$$
By intercepts form the equations of AQ and BP are
$$\frac{x}{a} + \frac{y}{-a\lambda} = 1 \quad \therefore \lambda = \frac{y}{x - a}$$
and $\dfrac{x}{b\lambda} + \dfrac{y}{b} = 1 \quad \therefore \lambda = -\dfrac{x}{y - b}$

In order to find the locus of the point of intersection of these lines, eliminate the variable λ

∴ $\quad \dfrac{y}{x-a} = -\dfrac{x}{y-b} = \lambda$

∴ $\quad x(x-a) + y(y-b) = 0$

or $\quad x^2 + y^2 - ax - by = 0$ is the required locus.

(c) Exactly as part (b), $a = -7, b = 5$

Ans. $x^2 + y^2 - 7x + 5y = 0$

(d) Let the other variable line be $\dfrac{x}{a'} + \dfrac{y}{b'} = 1$, where

$$a + b = a' + b' \qquad \ldots(1)$$

AB' is $\quad \dfrac{x}{a} + \dfrac{y}{b'} = 1 \qquad \ldots(2)$

$A'B$ is $\quad \dfrac{x}{a'} + \dfrac{y}{b} = 1 \qquad \ldots(3)$

Subtracting $x\left(\dfrac{1}{a} - \dfrac{1}{a'}\right) + y\left(\dfrac{1}{b'} - \dfrac{1}{b}\right) = 0$

or $\quad x\dfrac{(a'-a)}{aa'} + y\dfrac{(b-b')}{bb'} = 0$

or $\quad \dfrac{x}{aa'} + \dfrac{y}{bb'} = 0 \qquad$ by (1) $\qquad \ldots(4)$

In order to find the locus of their point of intersection, we have to eliminate the variables a', b' (a, b being fixed) from their equations.

∴ Putting for a' and b' from (2) and (3) in (4)

$$\dfrac{x}{a}\left(1 - \dfrac{y}{b}\right) \cdot \dfrac{1}{2} + \dfrac{y}{b}\left(1 - \dfrac{x}{a}\right) \cdot \dfrac{1}{y} = 0$$

or $\quad \dfrac{1}{a} - \dfrac{y}{ab} + \dfrac{1}{b} = \dfrac{1}{b} - \dfrac{x}{ab}$

or $\quad \dfrac{x+y}{ab} = \dfrac{1}{a} + \dfrac{1}{b} = \dfrac{a+b}{ab}$

∴ $\quad x + y = a + b$ is the required locus.

22. (a) Suppose the axes are rotated in the anti-clockwise direction through an angle α. The equation of the line L with respect to the old axes is given by $x/a + y/b = 1$. To find the equation of L with respect to the new axes, we replace x by $x\cos\alpha - y\sin\alpha$ and y by $x\sin\alpha + y\cos\alpha$, so that the equation of L with respect to the new axes is

$\dfrac{1}{a}(x\cos\alpha - y\sin\alpha) + \dfrac{1}{b}(x\sin\alpha + y\cos\alpha) = 1.$

Since p, q are the intercepts made by this line on the co-ordinate axes, we have on putting $(p, 0)$ and then $(0, q)$

$\quad 1/p = (1/a)\cos\alpha + (1/b)\sin\alpha$

and $\quad 1/q = -(1/a)\sin\alpha + (1/b)\cos\alpha.$

Eliminate α

Squaring and adding, we get

$\quad 1/p^2 + 1/q^2 = 1/a^2 + 1/b^2$

Alt. Solution :

$\dfrac{x}{a} + \dfrac{y}{b} = 1$ transforms to $\dfrac{x}{p} + \dfrac{y}{q} = 1$ after rotation of axes. Since origin and the lines are fixed and hence perpendicular from origin is same.

∴ $\quad \dfrac{1}{\sqrt{(1/a^2) + (1/b^2)}} = \dfrac{1}{\sqrt{(1/p^2) + (1/q^2)}}$

∴ $\quad \dfrac{1}{a^2} + \dfrac{1}{b^2} = \dfrac{1}{p^2} + \dfrac{1}{q^2}$

(b) $(4,1) \to (1,4)$ by (i)

$(1,4) \to (1+2,4)$ i.e., $(3,4)$ by (ii)

$(3,4) \to 3\cos 45° - 4\sin 45°$,

$\quad 3\sin 45° + 4\cos 45°$

or $\quad \left(-\dfrac{1}{\sqrt{2}}, \dfrac{7}{\sqrt{2}}\right)$

23. (a) $y - k = m(x - h)$ where m is parameter. $\ldots(1)$

Equation of the line through $(0, 0)$ perpendicular to (1) is

$\quad y = (-1/m)x. \qquad \ldots(2)$

Foot of perpendicular is intersection of (1) and (2) and its locus is obtained by eliminating m

$\quad y - k = -\dfrac{x}{y}(x - h)$

or $\quad x^2 + y^2 - hx - ky = 0.$

(b) Line PQ is $x - 3y + 7 = 0$ and the line through $(1, 0)$ perpendicular to it is $3x + y - 3 = 0$. Solving we get the foot of perpendicular as $(1/5, 12/5)$ which is the projection of $(1, 0)$ on the given line.

Alternative Method :

If (h, k) be foot of perp. from $(1, 0)$ to the line $x - 3y + 7 = 0$, then by **Rule 15, P. 6**

$\dfrac{h-1}{1} = \dfrac{k-0}{-3} = -\dfrac{l}{a^2 + b^2} = -\dfrac{8}{10} = -\dfrac{4}{5}$

∴ $\quad (h, k)$ is $\left(\dfrac{1}{5}, \dfrac{12}{5}\right).$

24. Slopes of the given lines are respectively

$\quad -\dfrac{a+b}{a-b}, -\dfrac{a-b}{a+b}, -1$

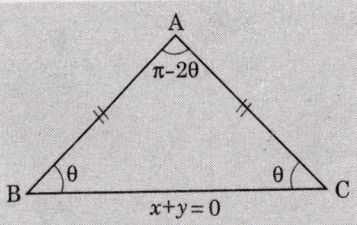

Fig. 104

The triangle will be isosceles if $x + y = 0$ is equally inclined to other two whose slopes are written above

$$\dfrac{-1 + \left(\dfrac{a+b}{a-b}\right)}{1 + \left(\dfrac{a+b}{a-b}\right)} = -\dfrac{-1 + \dfrac{a-b}{a+b}}{1 + \dfrac{a-b}{a+b}} = \tan\theta$$

∴ $\quad \tan\theta = b/a$

∴ Δ is isosceles whose vertical angle is

$$\pi - 2\theta = 2\left(\frac{\pi}{2} - \tan^{-1}\frac{b}{a}\right)$$

$$= 2\left(\cot^{-1}\frac{b}{a}\right) = 2\tan^{-1}\frac{a}{b}.$$

25. (a) Let QP be chosen along x-axis and its length $= 2a$ and mid-point as origin so that P is $(a, 0)$ and Q is $(-a, 0)$. Let R be (x, y) and $\angle RPQ = \theta$ and $\angle RQP = \phi$

∴ $\theta - \phi = 2\alpha$ given and RM be the perpendicular on x-axis

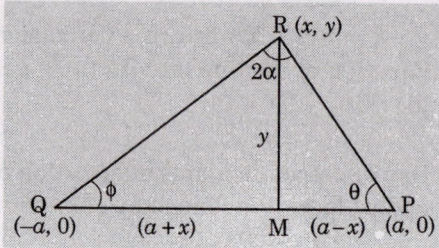

Fig. 105

∴ $$\frac{\tan\theta - \tan\phi}{1 + \tan\theta\tan\phi} = \tan 2\alpha \qquad \dots(1)$$

But $\tan\theta = \dfrac{RM}{MP} = \dfrac{y}{a - x}$,

$$\tan\phi = \frac{RM}{MQ} = \frac{y}{a + x}$$

Putting in (1), we get

$$\frac{y/(a-x) - y/(a-x)}{1 + [y/(a+x)] \cdot [y/(a-x)]} = \tan 2\alpha$$

or $2xy \cot 2\alpha = a^2 - x^2 + y^2$

or $y^2 - x^2 - 2xy \cot 2\alpha + a^2 = 0$

is the required locus.

(b) As in part (a) since the triangle is isosceles its median is also its right bisector. Hence the vertices are marked with

$$AB = AC = \sqrt{a^2 + b^2}.$$

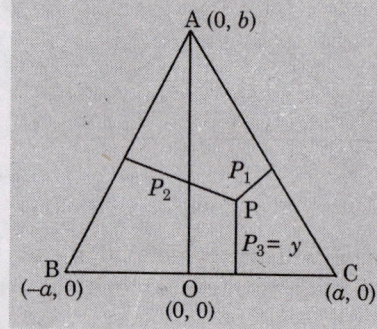

Fig. 106

The equations of the sides by intercepts form are

$$\frac{x}{a} + \frac{y}{b} - 1 = 0, \qquad \frac{x}{-a} + \frac{y}{b} - 1 = 0$$

or $bx + ay - ab = 0$, $-bx + ay - ab = 0$

and base BC is $y = 0$. The constant term in both the equations of sides is kept of same sign as the point P is inside.

If P be (x, y) then

$$\frac{bx + ay - ab}{\sqrt{a^2 + b^2}} \cdot \frac{-bx + ay - ab}{\sqrt{a^2 + b^2}} = y^2$$

or $(ay - ab)^2 - b^2 x^2 = (a^2 + b^2) y^2$

or $b^2(x^2 + y^2) + 2a^2 by - a^2 b^2 = 0$

or $x^2 + y^2 + \dfrac{2a^2}{b} y - a^2 = 0$

Above equation represents a circle whose centre is at $\left(0, -\dfrac{a^2}{b}\right)$.

26. (a) Let the co-ordinates of A and B be $(a, 0)$ and $(0, b)$ on the axes so that its equation is $x/a + y/b = 1$

or $bx + ay - ab = 0$ ...(1)

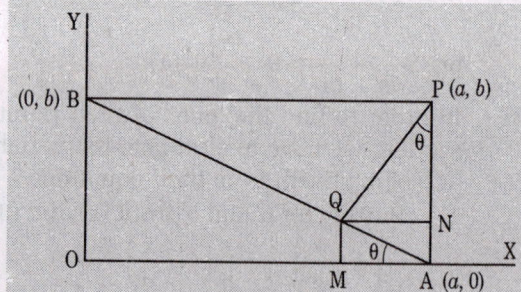

Fig. 107

By given condition, $AB = c$

or $a^2 + b^2 = c^2$ ...(2)

Again if P be the vertex of rectangle then point P is (a, b).

If (h, k) be the foot of perpendicular from $P(a, b)$ on AB, then by **cor. Rule 15, P. 6.**

$$\frac{h - a}{\frac{1}{a}} = \frac{k - b}{\frac{1}{b}} = -\frac{1 + 1 - 1}{\frac{1}{a^2} + \frac{1}{b^2}} = -\frac{a^2 b^2}{a^2 + b^2}$$

$$h = a - \frac{ab^2}{a^2 + b^2} = \frac{a^3}{c^2} \quad \text{or} \quad a = (c^2 h)^{1/3}$$

Similarly $b = (c^2 k)^{1/3}$. Putting in (2) and generalizing, we get

$$c^{4/3}(x^{2/3} + y^{2/3}) = c^2 \quad \text{or} \quad x^{2/3} + y^{2/3} = c^{2/3}$$

(b) $\dfrac{x}{a} + \dfrac{y}{b} = 1$ passes through (α, β)

∴ $$\frac{\alpha}{a} + \frac{\beta}{b} = 1 \qquad \dots(1)$$

Also C is (a, b) whose locus is $\dfrac{\alpha}{x} + \dfrac{\beta}{y} = 1$. Here $OACB$ will be a rectangle and you may call it a parallelogram.

27. (a) Given P on $y = a$ ∴ $P(x_1, a)$

Q on $x = b$ $\therefore$ $Q(b, y_1)$

S on $x = -b$ $\therefore$ $S(-b, y_2)$

Let R be (h, k). Also PQ is parallel to $y = mx$.

In a rectangle the diagonals bisect each other

$\therefore$ $h + x_1 = b - b = 0$ $\therefore$ $x_1 = -h$

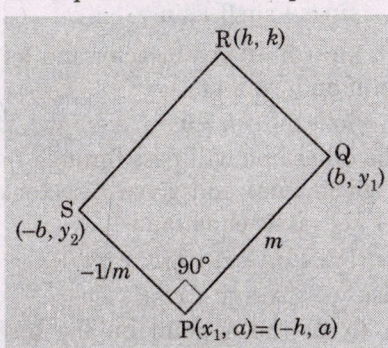

$R(h, k)$

$Q(b, y_1)$

$S(-b, y_2)$

m

$-1/m$ $90°$

$P(x_1, a) = (-h, a)$

Fig. 108

$\therefore$ P is $(-h, a)$.

Now we have only two variables y_1 and y_2 which are to be eliminated for which we need three relations.

$$y_1 + y_2 = k + a \qquad \ldots(1)$$

Slope of $PQ = m$

$\therefore$ $\dfrac{y_1 - a}{b + h} = m$

$\therefore$ $y_1 = m(b + h) + a \qquad \ldots(2)$

Slope of $PS = -\dfrac{1}{m}$

$\therefore$ $\dfrac{y_2 - a}{-b + h} = -\dfrac{1}{m}$

$\therefore$ $y_2 = \dfrac{1}{m}(b - h) + a \qquad \ldots(3)$

Putting the values of y_1 and y_2 in (1)

$\therefore$ $m(b + h) + a + \dfrac{1}{m}(b - h) + a = k + a$

$m^2(b + h) + am + (b - h) = km$

$\therefore$ $h(m^2 - 1) - km + (m^2 + 1)b + am = 0$

$\therefore$ Locus of (h, k) is

$x(m^2 - 1) - ym + (m^2 + 1)b + am = 0$

(b) Choose the vertex A to be $(0, k)$ as it is on y-axis. The sides through A being parallel to given lines and pass through $(0, k)$

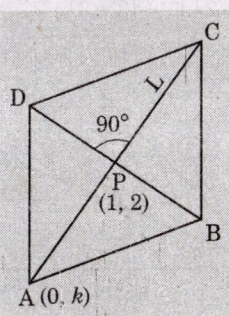

C

D

$90°$

P (1, 2)

B

A (0, k)

Fig. 109

AB, $x - y + k = 0$;

AD, $7x - y + k = 0$.

The point P which is intersection of diagonals will be on the bisectors of these sides.

$$\frac{x - y + k}{\sqrt{2}} = \pm \frac{7x - y + k}{5\sqrt{2}}.$$

They pass through $(1, 2)$

$\therefore$ $k = 0, 5/2$. Hence A is $(0, 0)$ or $(0, 5/2)$.

28. We take O as origin and x-axis along BOA. Let the co-ordinates of A and B be $(a, 0)$ and $(-b, 0)$. Let the fixed parallel lines AP and BQ be taken parallel to y-axis so that BOA is perpendicular to both.

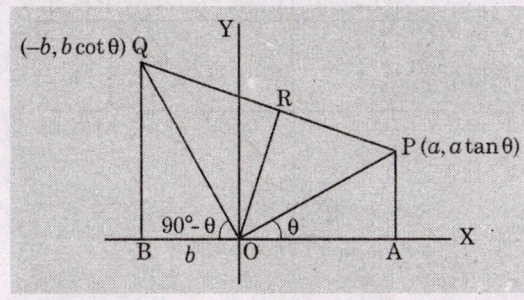

$(-b, b\cot\theta)\, Q$

Y

R

$P\,(a, a\tan\theta)$

$90° - \theta$ θ

B b O A X

Fig. 110

If $\angle POA = \theta$ then as $\angle POQ = 90°$

We have $\angle QOB = 90° - \theta$.

$\therefore$ Co-ordinates of P are $(a, a\tan\theta)$ and those of Q are $(-b, b\cot\theta)$.

Equation to line PQ is

$$y - a\tan\theta = \frac{b\cot\theta - a\tan\theta}{-(b + a)}(x - a)$$

or $x(b\cot\theta - a\tan\theta) + y(a + b) = ab(\cot\theta + \tan\theta)$

or changing into $\sin\theta$ and $\cos\theta$ it becomes

$x(b\cos^2\theta - a\sin^2\theta) + y(a + b)\sin\theta\cos\theta = ab$.

Multiplying by 2, it becomes

$x(2b\cos^2\theta - 2a\sin^2\theta) + y(a + b)\sin 2\theta = 2ab \qquad \ldots(1)$

Also equation to perpendicular OR on PQ is

$x(a + b)\sin 2\theta - y(2b\cos^2\theta - 2a\sin^2\theta) = 0 \qquad \ldots(2)$

But $2b\cos^2\theta - 2a\sin^2\theta$

$= b(1 + \cos 2\theta) - a(1 - \cos 2\theta)$

$= (a + b)\cos 2\theta - (a - b)$

Hence the two lines (1) and (2) can be written as

$x(a + b)\cos 2\theta + y(a + b)\sin 2\theta$

$= 2ab + (a - b)x \qquad \ldots(3)$

and $x(a + b)\sin 2\theta - y(a + b)\cos 2\theta$

$= -(a - b)y. \qquad \ldots(4)$

In order to find the locus of point of intersection R, we have to eliminate θ for which we square and add the equations (3) and (4).

$\therefore$ $x^2(a + b)^2 + y^2(a + b)^2$

$= 4a^2b^2 + 4ab(a - b)x + (a - b)^2(x^2 + y^2)$

or $(x^2 + y^2) [(a+b)^2 - (a-b)^2]$
$= 4ab [ab + (a-b) x]$

or $x^2 + y^2 = ab + (a-b) x$

or $x^2 - (a-b) x - ab + y^2 = 0$

or $(x-a)(x+b) + y^2 = 0$.

Above represents the equation of a circle on AB as diameter.

29. Let the points be denoted by A, B and C respectively as marked. The equation of the sides are found to be as $AB, y = 3, BC, 2x + y = -5$ and $CA, 2x - y = 5$.

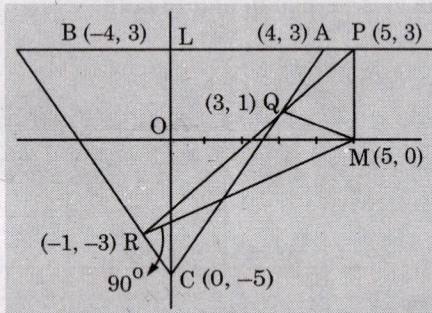

Fig. 111

Point P, the foot of perpendicular from M on AB is clearly $(5, 3)$. R is the foot of perpendicular from $(5,0)$ on BC whose equation is $2x + y + 5 = 0$. If R is (h, k), then by **R. (e), P. 10**

$$\frac{h-5}{2} = \frac{k-0}{1} = -\frac{2.5 + 0 + 5}{5} = -3.$$

∴ (h, k) is the point $R (-1, -3)$.

Similarly Q is foot of perpendicular from M on CA whose equation is $2x - y = 5$. As above the point Q is $(3, 1)$.

It can be easily shown that area of $\Delta PQR = 0$ so that these points are collinear. We may also say that slope of $PQ = $ slope of $PR = 1$ so that these points are collinear.

30. Let $x^2 + y^2 = R^2$ be the equation of the circle circumscribing the triangle ABC as its centre O is $(0, 0)$. The vertices lie on it

∴ $p^2 + p^2 \tan^2 \alpha = R^2$ or $p \sec \alpha = R$

∴ $p = R \cos \alpha$

Hence the point $A (p, p \tan \alpha)$ is $(R \cos \alpha, R \sin \alpha)$. Similarly B and C are

$(R \cos \beta, R \sin \beta)$ and $(R \cos \gamma, R \sin \gamma)$

If G be the centroid of triangle ABC, then

$$G = \left(\frac{R \Sigma \cos \alpha}{3}, \frac{R \Sigma \sin \alpha}{3} \right), O = (0, 0)$$

and $H = (\bar{x}, \bar{y})$

From geometry we know that O, G, H are collinear.
[Refer 6 (vi), P. 766]

Hence slope of $OG = $ slope of OH

∴ $\frac{\bar{y} - 0}{\bar{x} - 0} = \frac{\frac{\Sigma R \sin \alpha}{3} - 0}{\frac{\Sigma R \cos \alpha}{3} - 0}$

∴ $\frac{\bar{x}}{\bar{y}} = \frac{\cos \alpha + \cos \beta + \cos \gamma}{\sin \alpha + \sin \beta + \sin \gamma}$

31. (a) $lx + my + n = 0$ is a bisector and let (α, β) be any point on it so that

$$l\alpha + m\beta + n = 0. \qquad ...(1)$$

The other line will pass through the intersection of given lines and given bisector and hence by $P + \lambda Q = 0$ its equation is

$$(px + qy + r) + \lambda (lx + my + n) = 0. \qquad ...(2)$$

Also $px + qy + r = 0 \qquad ...(3)$

If (α, β) be a point on the bisector then its perpendicular distance from the lines (2) and (3) is same

∴ $\frac{(p\alpha + q\beta + r) + \lambda (l\alpha + m\beta + n)}{\sqrt{[(p + l\lambda)^2 + (q + m\lambda)^2]}} = \pm \frac{p\alpha + q\beta + r}{\sqrt{(p^2 + q^2)}}$

Putting $l\alpha + m\beta + n = 0$ by (1) in the above and cancelling $p\alpha + q\beta + r$ and then squaring both sides, we get

$$(p + l\lambda)^2 + (q + m\lambda)^2 = p^2 + q^2$$

or $2\lambda (pl + qm) + \lambda^2 (l^2 + m^2) = 0$

∴ $\lambda = -2 \cdot \frac{pl + qm}{l^2 + m^2}$

Putting for λ in (2), the required line is

$$(l^2 + m^2)(px + qy + r)$$
$$- 2 (lp + mq)(lx + my + n) = 0.$$

(b) Hint : Same as part (a) in a different form.

Ans. $(lx + my + n)(a^2 + b^2) - 2(al + bm)$
$$(ax + by + c) = 0$$

(c) Refer parts (a), (b) above. The line l_2 will pass through the intersection of $l_1 = 0$ and $B = 0$. Its equation is

$$3x + 2y + 4 + \lambda (2x + 3y + 1) = 0 \qquad ...(1)$$

Now choose a point (α, β) on the bisector so that $2\alpha + 3\beta + 1 = 0$. Apply the condition $p_1 = p_2$ for the two lines

$$\frac{3\alpha + 2\beta + 4 + \lambda (2\alpha + 3\beta + 1)}{(3 + 2\lambda)^2 + (2 + 3\lambda)^2} = \frac{3\alpha + 2\beta + 4}{\sqrt{9 + 4}}$$

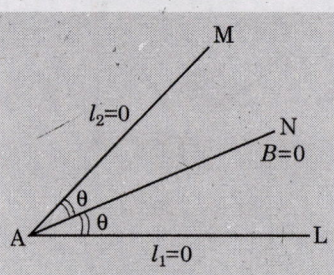

Fig. 112

Put $2\alpha + 3\beta + 1 = 0$. Cancel $3\alpha + 2\beta + 4$

$\therefore \quad 13 = 13\lambda^2 + 24\lambda + 13 = 0$

$\therefore \quad \lambda = 0, -\dfrac{24}{13}$

But $\lambda = 0$ corresponds to given line hence $\lambda = -\dfrac{24}{13}$

will give the other line whose equation from (1) is
$9x + 46y = 28$

(d) On factorizing **[See Q. 7 (a)]**, the equations of the bisectors are $x - 3y + 5 = 0$ and $3x + y - 5 = 0$ which intersect at $(1, 2)$. Both the lines will pass through $(1, 2)$ and one line passes through origin and hence its equation is $y = 2x$ or $2x - y = 0$. The other line through $(1, 2)$ may be taken as

$$y - 2 = m(x - 1)$$

or $\quad mx - y + (2 - m) = 0 \qquad \ldots(1)$

In order to find m, we choose a point on any bisector say $3x + y - 5 = 0$ say $(0, 5)$. Its distance from both the lines is same

$$\frac{0 - 5}{\sqrt{5}} = \pm \frac{+5 + 2 - m}{\sqrt{1 + m^2}}$$

$\therefore \qquad 5(1 + m^2) = (m + 3)^2$

or $\quad 2m^2 - 3m - 2 = 0$

or $\quad (m - 2)(2m + 1) = 0 \quad \therefore \quad m = 2, -1/2.$

But $m = 2$ corresponds to the line $2x - y = 0$. Hence $m = -1/2$ is the required value. Putting in (1), we have $x + 2y - 5 = 0$ is the other line.

32. (a) The bisector OC is perpendicular to AB as $\Delta\,OAB$ is isosceles. $\angle AOB = \psi_2 - \psi_1$

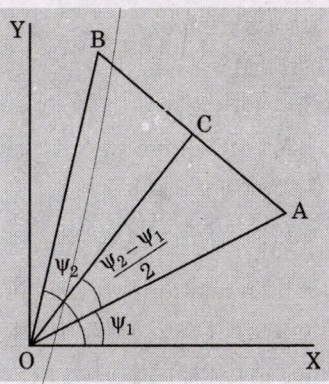

Fig. 113

$\therefore \quad \angle COX = \dfrac{1}{2}(\psi_2 - \psi_1) + \psi_1$

$$= \frac{(\psi_1 + \psi_2)}{2} = \frac{\psi}{2}$$

Hence slope of bisector is

$$\tan \frac{\psi}{2} = \frac{\sin(\psi/2)}{\cos(\psi/2)}$$

$$= \frac{2 \sin^2(\psi/2)}{2 \sin(\psi/2) \cos(\psi/2)} = \frac{1 - \cos \psi}{\sin \psi}$$

$$= \operatorname{cosec} \psi - \cot \psi.$$

(b) Two of the lines are evidently perpendicular and

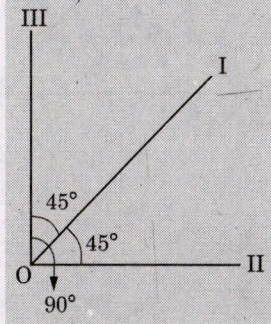

Fig. 114

the line $ax + by + p = 0$ makes an angle of $45°$ with one of them and hence it is bisector of the two lines.

$\therefore$ The bisectors of given lines are

$$\frac{x \cos \alpha + y \sin \alpha - p}{1} = \pm \frac{x \sin \alpha - y \cos \alpha}{1}$$

or $\quad x(\cos \alpha - \sin \alpha) + y(\sin \alpha + \cos \alpha) - p = 0.$

Compare with $ax + by + p = 0$.

$$\frac{\cos \alpha - \sin \alpha}{a} = \frac{\sin \alpha + \cos \alpha}{b} = -1.$$

$\therefore \quad -a = \cos \alpha - \sin \alpha, -b = \sin \alpha + \cos \alpha.$

$\therefore \quad a^2 + b^2 = 2$

33. (a) If $m = \tan \theta, M = \tan \phi$, then

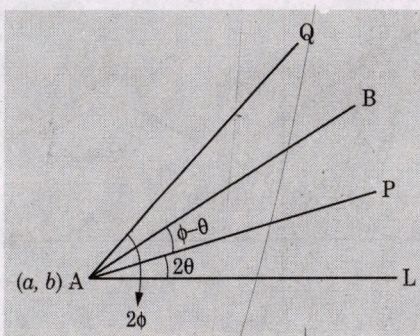

Fig. 115

$$\frac{2m}{1 - m^2} = \tan 2\theta.$$

Both the lines pass through (a, b) and are inclined to axis of x at an angle $2\theta, 2\phi$ respectively.

Hence the bisector of these lines will make an angle $\theta + \phi$ with x-axis so that its stope will be

$$\tan(\theta + \phi) = \frac{m + M}{1 - mM} = M_1.$$

The other bisector will be perpendicular to it whose slope will be $-\dfrac{1 - mM}{m + M} = M_2.$

Both these pass through (a,b). Hence their equations are $(y-b)=M_1(x-a)$ and

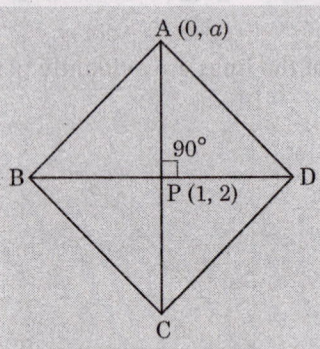

A (0, a)

90°

B — P (1, 2) — D

C

Fig. 116

$(y-b)=M_2(x-a)$.

(b) A being on y-axis may be chosen as $(0, a)$. The diagonals intersect at $P(1, 2)$. Again we know that diagonals will be parallel to the bisectors of the two sides

i.e., $\dfrac{x-y+2}{\sqrt{2}}=\pm\dfrac{7x-y+3}{5\sqrt{2}}$

∴ d_1 is parallel to $x+2y-\dfrac{7}{2}=0$ and d_2 is parallel

to $2x-y+\dfrac{13}{6}=0$. The vertex A could be on any of the two diagonals.

Hence slope of $AP=2$ or $-1/2$

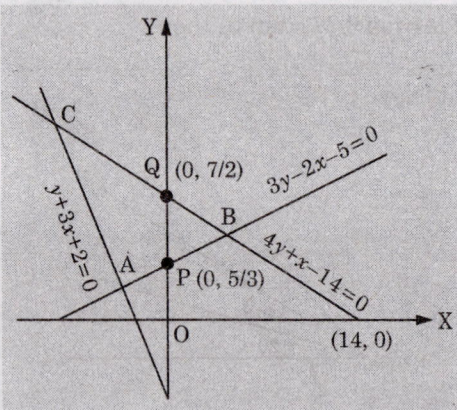

Y

C

Q (0, 7/2) $3y-2x-5=0$

$y+3x+2=0$ B

$4y+x-14=0$

A

P (0, 5/3)

O   (14, 0)   X

Fig. 117

∴ $\dfrac{2-a}{1-0}=2$ or $-\dfrac{1}{2}$ ∴ $a=0,\dfrac{5}{2}$

∴ A is $(0,0)$ or $(0, 5/2)$

34. The sides BC, CA and AB of the $\triangle ABC$ are represented by equations

$$4y+x-14=0,$$
$$y+3x+2=0,$$
$$3y-2x-5=0$$

respectively as shown in the figure. From the figure, it is clear that if the point $(0, \beta)$ lies on or inside the $\triangle ABC$, then the value of β varies from $P\left(0, \dfrac{5}{3}\right)$ to $Q\left(0, \dfrac{7}{2}\right)$, that is, $\dfrac{5}{3}\le\beta\le\dfrac{7}{2}$.

35. Solving the equations in pairs, we get the vertices of the triangle as $A(5/4, 7/8)$, $B(1/3, 1/9)$, $C(-7, 5)$ if the given lines be BC, CA and AB respectively. Putting the co-ordinates in the opposite sides, we get the results $+$, $-$, $-$ respectively. Hence we write the equations by multiplying by $-$ sign so that all the results are $+$, $+$, $+$.

∴ $BC: 2x+3y-1=0$, $CA: -x-2y+3=0$,

$AB: -5x+6y+1=0$.

Now the points A, B, C are on the positive sides of the triangle whose revised forms of equations are written above. If the point (α, α^2) lies inside the triangle then the results obtained by putting the co-ordinates in the revised form of equations will be all $+$ive.

∴ $2\alpha+3\alpha^2-1=+$ive,

or $(\alpha+1)(3\alpha-1)=+$ive   ...(1)

$-\alpha-2\alpha^2+3=+$ive,

$(2\alpha+3)(\alpha-1)=-$ive   ...(2)

$-5\alpha+6\alpha^2+1=+$ive,

$(3\alpha-1)(2\alpha-1)=+$ive   ...(3)

(1) $\Rightarrow\alpha<-1$ or $\alpha>1/3$

(2) $\Rightarrow -3/2<\alpha<1$

(3) $\Rightarrow\alpha<1/3$ or $\alpha>1/2$

From above three relations we conclude that

$-3/2<\alpha<-1$ and $1/2<\alpha<1$

∴ α belongs to $\left(-\dfrac{3}{2},-1\right)\cup\left(\dfrac{1}{2},1\right)$.

Problem Set (6)

▶ **Multiple Choice Questions**

1. (i) The triangle joining the points $A(2, 7)$, $B(4, -1)$, $C(-2, 6)$ is
   (a) Equilateral   (b) Right angled
   (c) Isosceles   (d) None of these

   (ii) The area of the triangle with vertices at $(-4, 1)$, $(1, 2)$, $(4, -3)$ is
   (a) 14   (b) 16

   (c) 15   (d) None of these

   (iii) The area of the triangle with vertices at the point $(a, b+c), (b, c+a), (c, a+b)$ is
   (a) 0   (b) $a+b+c$
   (c) $ab+bc+ca$ (d) None of these

   (iv) The equation of the straight line which passes through the point $(1, -2)$ and cuts off equal intercepts from the axes will be

(a) $x + y = 1$ (b) $x - y = 1$

(c) $x + y + 1 = 0$ (d) $x - y - 2 = 0$

(v) The equation of the straight line which is perpendicular to $y = x$ and passes through (3, 2) will be given by

(a) $x - y = 5$ (b) $x + y = 5$

(c) $x + y = 1$ (d) $x - y = 1$

(vi) The equation of the line passing through (1, 2) and perpendicular to $x + y + 1 = 0$ is

(a) $y - x + 1 = 0$ (b) $y - x - 1 = 0$

(c) $y - x + 2 = 0$ (d) $y - x - 2 = 0$

2. If $P = (1, 0)$, $Q = (-1, 0)$ and $R = (2, 0)$ are three given points, then the locus of point S satisfying the relation $SQ^2 + SR^2 = 2SP^2$ is

(a) a st. line parallel to x-axis

(b) circle through origin

(c) circle with centre at the origin

(d) a straight line parallel to y-axis.

3. If A and B are the points $(-3, 4)$ and $(2, 1)$, then the co-ordinates of point C on AB produced such that $AC = 2BC$ are

(a) $(2, 4)$ (b) $(3, 7)$

(c) $(7, -2)$ (d) $\left(-\dfrac{1}{2}, \dfrac{5}{2}\right)$.

4. P and Q are points on the line joining $A(-2, 5)$ and $B(3, 1)$ such that $AP = PQ = QB$. Then the mid-point of PQ is

(a) $\left(\dfrac{1}{2}, 3\right)$ (b) $\left(-\dfrac{1}{2}, 4\right)$

(c) $(2, 3)$ (d) $(1, 4)$

5. If the lines $3y + 4x = 1$, $y = x + 5$ and $5y + bx = 3$ are concurrent then the value of b is

(a) 1   (b) 3   (c) 6   (d) 0

6. The distance between the lines $3x + 4y = 9$ and $6x + 8y = 15$ is

(a) 3/2   (b) 3/10

(c) 6   (d) None of these

7. Let the vertices of a triangle be $(0, 0)$, $(3, 0)$ and $(0, 4)$. Its orthocentre is

(a) $(0, 0)$ (b) $(1, 4/3)$

(c) $(3/2, 2)$ (d) None of these

8. The line $3x + 4y - 24 = 0$ cuts the x-axis at A and y-axis at B. Then the incentre of the triangle OAB where O is the origin is

(a) $(1, 2)$ (b) $(2, 2)$

(c) $(12, 12)$ (d) $(2, 12)$

9.* The three lines $3x + 4y + 6 = 0$, $\sqrt{2}x + \sqrt{3}y + 2\sqrt{2} = 0$ and $4x + 7y + 8 = 0$ are

(a) sides of a triangle   (b) concurrent

(c) parallel   (d) none of these

10. The three lines $ax + by + c = 0$,

$bx + cy + a = 0$, $cx + ay + b = 0$

are concurrent only when

(a) $a + b + c = 0$

(b) $a^2 + b^2 + c^2 = ab + bc + ca$

(c) $a^3 + b^3 + c^3 = 3abc$

(b) None of these

11. The line $(p + 2q) x + (p - 3q) y = p - q$ for different values of p and q passes through the point

(a) $(3/2, 5/2)$ (c) $(2/5, 2/5)$

(c) $(3/5, 3/5)$ (d) $(2/5, 3/5)$

12. The equation $\sqrt{(x-2)^2 + y^2} + \sqrt{(x+2)^2 + y^2} = 4$ represents

(a) circle   (b) pair of a lines

(c) a parabola   (d) an ellipse

13. All points lying inside the triangle formed by the points $(1, 3)$, $(5, 0)$ and $(-1, 2)$ satisfy

(a) $3x + 2y \geq 0$ (b) $2x + y - 13 \geq 0$

(c) $2x - 3y - 12 \leq 0$ (d) $-2x + y \geq 0$

(e) None of these

14. The locus of the mid-point of the portion intercepted between the axes by the line $x \cos \alpha + y \sin \alpha = p$ where p is constant is

(a) $x^2 + y^2 = 4p^2$

(b) $(1/x^2) + (1/y^2) = 4/p^2$

(c) $x^2 + y^2 = 4/p^2$

(d) $(1/x^2) + (1/y^2) = 2/p^2$

15. The straight line passing through the point of intersection of the straight lines

$$x - 3y + 1 = 0 \text{ and } 2x + 5y - 9 = 0$$

and having infinite slope and at a distance 2 units from the origin has the equation

(a) $x = 2$ (b) $3x + y - 1 = 0$

(c) $y = 1$ (d) None of these

16. The points $(1, 1)$, $(-1, -1)$ and $(-\sqrt{3}, \sqrt{3})$ are the angular points of a triangle, then the triangle is

(a) right angled   (b) isosceles

(c) equilateral   (d) none of these

17. The points $(0, 8/3)$, $(1, 3)$ and $(82, 30)$ are the vertices of

(a) obtuse angled triangle (b) acute angled triangle

(c) right angled triangle (d) isosceles triangle

(e) none of these

18. (i) The straight lines $x + y = 0$, $3x + y - 4 = 0$, $x + 3y - 4 = 0$ form a triangle which is

(a) isosceles   (b) equilateral

(c) right angled   (d) none of these

(ii) The right lines $x + y - 4 = 0$, $3x + y - 4 = 0$, $x + 3y - 4 = 0$ form a triangle which is

(a) isosceles   (b) right angled

(c) equilateral   (d) none of these

(M.N.R. 1992)

(iii) The diagonals of parallelogram $PQRS$ are along the lines $x + 3y = 4$ and $6x - 2y = 7$. Then $PQRS$ must be a

(a) rectangle

(b) square

(c) cyclic quadrilateral

(d) rhombus   **(I.I.T. 1998)**

19. The points $(-a, -b), (0, 0), (a, b)$ and (a^2, ab) are

(a) collinear

(b) vertices of a rectangle

(c) vertices of a parallelogram

(d) none of these

20. The equation of a line through $(2, -3)$ parallel to y-axis is

(a) $y = -3$ (b) $y = 2$

(c) $x = 2$ (d) $x = -3$

21. The equations of the line, the reciprocal of whose intercepts on the axes are a and b is given by

(a) $x/a + y/b = 1$ (b) $ax + by = 1$

(c) $ax + by = ab$ (d) $ax - by = 1$

22. The line L has intercepts a and b on the co-ordinate axes. When keeping the origin fixed, the co-ordinate axes are rotated through a fixed angle, then the same line has intercepts p and q on the rotated axes. Then

(a) $a^2 + b^2 = p^2 + q^2$ (b) $\dfrac{1}{a^2} + \dfrac{1}{b^2} = \dfrac{1}{p^2} + \dfrac{1}{q^2}$

(c) $a^2 + p^2 = b^2 + q^2$ (d) $\dfrac{1}{a^2} + \dfrac{1}{p^2} = \dfrac{1}{b^2} + \dfrac{1}{q^2}$

                    (I.I.T. 1990)

23. The locus of the orthocentre of the triangle formed by the lines $(1 + p)x - py + p(1 + p) = 0$, $(1 + q)x - qy + q(1 + q) = 0$ and $y = 0$, where $p \ne q$ is

(a) a parabola   (b) a hyperbola

(c) an ellipse   (d) a straight line

                    (IIT JEE 2009)

24. Orthocentre of the triangle formed by the lines $x + y = 1$ and $xy = 0$ is

(a) $(0, 0)$ (b) $(0, 1)$

(c) $1, 0)$ (d) $(-1, +1)$

                    (IIT 1995, DCE 2009, Orissa JEE 2004, 08)

25. The incentre of the triangle with vertices $(1, \sqrt{3}), (0, 0)$ and $(2, 0)$ is

(a) $\left(1, \dfrac{\sqrt{3}}{2}\right)$ (b) $\left(\dfrac{2}{3}, \dfrac{1}{\sqrt{3}}\right)$

(c) $\left(\dfrac{2}{3}, \dfrac{\sqrt{3}}{2}\right)$ (d) $\left(1, \dfrac{1}{\sqrt{3}}\right)$

                    (IIT 2000)

26. The orthocentre of the triangle with vertices $\left(2, \dfrac{\sqrt{3} - 1}{2}\right), \left(\dfrac{1}{2}, \dfrac{-1}{2}\right)$ and $\left(2, -\dfrac{1}{2}\right)$ is

(a) $\left(\dfrac{3}{2}, \dfrac{\sqrt{3} - 3}{6}\right)$ (b) $\left(2, -\dfrac{1}{2}\right)$

(c) $\left(\dfrac{5}{4}, \dfrac{\sqrt{3} - 2}{4}\right)$ (d) $\left(\dfrac{1}{2}, -\dfrac{1}{2}\right)$

                    (IIT 1993)

27. Consider three points

$P = (-\sin(\beta - \alpha), -\cos\beta), Q = (\cos(\beta - \alpha), \sin\beta)$ and

$R = (\cos(\beta - \alpha + \theta), \sin(\beta - \theta))$, where $\theta < \alpha, \beta, \theta < \dfrac{\pi}{4}$

Then

(a) P lies on the line segment RQ

(b) Q lies on the line segment PR

(c) R lies on the line segment QP

(d) P, Q, R are collinear   **(IIT 2008)**

28. The locus of a point which moves so that its distance from x-axis is double of its distance from y-axis is

(a) $x = 2y$ (b) $y = 2x$

(c) $y = 2x + 3$ (d) $x = 5y + 1$

                    (Karnatka CET 2011)

29. Let P be the point $(1, 0), Q$ a point on the curve $y^2 = 8x$. The locus of mid point of PQ is

(a) $x^2 + 4y + 2 = 0$ (b) $x^2 - 4y + 6 = 0$

(c) $y^2 - 4x + 2 = 0$ (d) $y^2 + 4x + 2 = 0$

                    (AIEEE 2005)

30. Locus of the centroid of the triangle whose vertices are $(a\cos t, a\sin t), (b\sin t, -b\cos t)$ and $(1, 0)$, where t is a parameter; is

(a) $(3x - 1)^2 + (3y)^2 = a^2 - b^2$

(b) $(3x - 1)^2 + (3y)^2 = a^2 + b^2$

(c) $(3x + 1)^2 + (3y)^2 = a^2 + b^2$

(d) $(3x + 1)^2 + (3y)^2 = a^2 - b^2$ **(AIEEE 2003)**

31. The line $y = x$ meets $y = ke^x, k \le 0$ at

(a) no point   (b) one point

(c) two points   (d) none of these

                    (IIT JEE 2007)

32. Let $O(0, 0), P(3, 4), Q(6, 0)$ be the vertices of the triangle OPQ. The point R inside the triangle OPQ is such that the triangles OPR, PQR, OQR are of equal area. The coordinates of R are

(a) $\left(3, \dfrac{2}{3}\right)$ (b) $\left(\dfrac{4}{3}, 3\right)$

(c) $\left(3, \dfrac{4}{3}\right)$ (d) $\left(\dfrac{4}{3}, \dfrac{2}{3}\right)$

                    (IIT JEE 2007)

33. Let $A(2, -3)$ and $B(-2, 1)$ be vertices of a triangle ABC. If the centroid of this triangle moves on the line $2x + 3y = 1$, then the locus of the vertices C is the line

(a) $3x - 2y = 6$ (b) $2x - 3y = 7$

(c) $3x + 2y = 5$ (d) $2x + 3y = 9$ **(AIEEE 2004)**

34. If the vertices P, Q, R of a triangle PQR are rational points, which of the following points of the triangle PQR is (are) always rational

(a) centroid   (b) Incentric

(c) circumcentre   (d) orthocentre

(IIT JEE 1998)

35. A straight line through the vertex P of a triangle PQR intersect the side QR at a point S and the circumcentre of the triangle PQR at the point T. If S is not the centre of the circumcircle, then

(a) $\dfrac{1}{PS} + \dfrac{1}{PT} < \dfrac{2}{\sqrt{QS \times SR}}$ (b) $\dfrac{1}{PS} + \dfrac{1}{ST} > \dfrac{2}{\sqrt{QS \times SR}}$

(c) $\dfrac{1}{PS} + \dfrac{1}{ST} < \dfrac{4}{QR}$ (d) $\dfrac{1}{PS} + \dfrac{1}{ST} > \dfrac{4}{QR}$

(IIT JEE 2008)

True and False Type Questions

State whether the following statements are true or false.

36. The lines $3x + 4y + 7 = 0$ and $4x + 3y + 5 = 0$ are perpendicular.

37. The lines $ax + by + c = 0$ and $Ax + By + C = 0$ are perpendicular if $aA + bB = 0$.

38. The points $(1, 2)$ and $(3, 4)$ are on the same side of the line $2x - 3y + 5 = 0$

Fill in the blanks

39. If the points $(-2, -5), (2, -2), (8, a)$ are collinear, then the value of a is ....

40. A, B, C are the points $(-2, -1), (0, 3), (4, 0)$. Then the co-ordinates of the point D such that $ABCD$ is a parallelogram are ....

41.* If the sum of the distances of point from two perpendicular lines in a plane is 1, then its locus is

(a) square   (b) circle

(c) straight line   (d) two intersecting lines

(I.I.T. 1992)

Hints and Solutions to Problem Set (6)

1. (i) Ans. (b).

   (ii) Ans. (a).

   (iii) Ans. (a).

   (iv) Ans. (c). Line cutting equal intercepts on axes is of the form $x + y = c$ or $x - y = c$.

      It passes through $(1, -2)$

      $\therefore$ $x + y + 1 = 0$ or $x - y - 3 = 0$.

      Hence (c) is correct.

   (v) (b) is the correct answer.

   (vi) Ans. (b).

2. Ans. (d), $2x + 3 = 0$

3. Ans. (c).

4. Ans. (a). **See Q. 2 (c), P. 774-776.**

5. Ans. (c).

6. Ans. (b).

7. Ans. (a).

8. Ans. (b).

9. Ans. (b).

Solving the equations

$$3x + 4y + 6 = 0, \quad 4x + 7y + 8 = 0,$$

we get their point of intersection as $(-2, 0)$. Since the co-ordinates of this point satisfy the equation,

$$\sqrt{2}x + \sqrt{3}y + 2\sqrt{2} = 0.$$

It follows that the three lines are concurrent.

10. Ans. (a) and (c). Solve any two and put in 3rd,

$$\therefore \quad \Delta = \begin{vmatrix} a & b & c \\ b & c & a \\ c & a & b \end{vmatrix} = 0.$$

or $3abc - a^3 - b^3 - c^3 = 0$. This is (c)

i.e. $(a + b + c)(a^2 + b^2 + c^2 - ab - bc - ca) = 0$

$\therefore$ $a + b + c = 0$ This is (a)

or $a^2 + b^2 + c^2 = ab + bc + ca$

$\therefore$ $\dfrac{1}{2}[2a^2 + 2b^2 + 2c^2 - 2ab - 2bc - 2ca] = 0$

or $\dfrac{1}{2}[(a-b)^2 + (b-c)^2 + (c-a)^2] = 0$.

This will be possible only when $a - b = 0$, $b - c = 0$, $c - a = 0$ i.e., $a = b = c$. But this will not be possible because the three lines will reduce to only one line. Hence (a) and (c) are correct.

11. Ans. (d). $(x + y - 1) + q/p(2x - 3y + 1) = 0$

i.e., $P + \lambda Q = 0$ which passes through the intersection of $P = 0$ and $Q = 0$. On solving, the point is $(2/5, 3/5)$.

$\therefore$ (d) is correct.

12. Ans. (b). **See Q. 14 (c) P. 775.**

13. Ans. (a) and (c).

Substituting the co-ordinates of the points $(1, 3), (5, 0)$ and $(-1, 2)$ in $3x + 2y$, we obtain the values $8, 15$ and 1 which are all +ive. Therefore all the points lying inside the triangle formed by given points satisfy $3x + 2y \geq 0$. Hence (a) is the correct answer.

Substituting the co-ordinates of the points $(1, 3), (5, 0)$ and $(-1, 2)$ in $2x + y = 13$, we find the values $-8, -3$ and -13 which are all $-$ive. So (b) is not correct. Again substituting the co-ordinates of the points $(1, 3)$, $(5, 0)$ and $(-1, 2)$ in $2x - 3y - 12$ we get $-19, -2$ and -20 which are all $-$ive. It follows that all the points lying inside the triangle formed by given lines satisfy $2x - 3y - 12 \leq 0$. So (c) is correct.

Finally substituting the co-ordinates of the points $(1, 3), (5, 0)$ and $(-1, 2)$ in $-2x + y$, we get $1, -10$ and 4 which are not all +ive. Hence (d) is not correct.

14. Ans. (b). Let the line $x \cos \alpha + y \sin \alpha = p$ meet the x-axis and y-axis respectively in A and B. Then co-ordinates of A are $(p/\cos\alpha, 0)$ and those of B are $(0, p/\sin\alpha)$. If (h, k) is the mid-point of AB, then

$$h = p/2\cos\alpha \quad \text{and} \quad k = p/2\sin\alpha.$$

To find the locus of (h, k) we have to eliminate α. We have $\cos \alpha = p/2h$,

and $\qquad \sin \alpha = p/2k$

whence squaring and adding, we get

$\qquad 1 = p^2/4h^2 + p^2/4k^2$.

∴ The required locus of (h, k) is

$\qquad p^2/4x^2 + p^2/4y^2 = 1$

or $\quad 1/x^2 + 1/y^2 = 4/p^2$.

15. Ans. (a).

Any line through the intersection of given lines is

$\qquad P + \lambda Q = 0$

or $\quad (x - 3y + 1) + \lambda(2x + 5y - 9) = 0$

Its slope will be infinite if it is perpendicular to x-axis *i.e.* parallel to y-axis.

Hence the coefficient of y will be zero.

∴ $\qquad -3 + 5\lambda = 0$

or $\lambda = 3/5$. Putting for λ the line is $x - 2 = 0$. Clearly its distance from $(0, 0)$ is 2.

16. Ans. (c).

17. Ans. (e).

See Q. 12 (iii) P. 782-785.

18. (i) (ii) Ans. (a).

See Q. 4 (b) P. 774.

(iii) Ans. (d). d_1 and d_2 are perpendicular.

19. Ans. (a).

See Q. 12 (iv) P. 782-785.

20. Ans. (c).

21. (i) Ans. (b).

22. Ans. (b).

See 22 (a) P. 824-833.

23. Ans. (d).

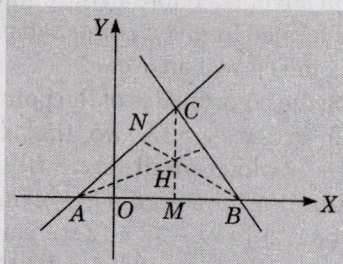

Fig. 118

On solving the given equation (i) and (ii) we get $c(pq, (1 + p)(1 + q))$,

Equation of altitude *CM* passing through *C* and perpendicular to *AB* is $x = pq$

Now, slope of line (ii) is $\dfrac{1+q}{q}$ ...(iii)

⇒ Slope of altitude *BN* is $= \dfrac{-q}{1+q}$

∴ Equation of *BN* is $y - 0 = \dfrac{-q}{1+q}(x + p)$

⇒ $\quad y = \dfrac{-q}{1+q}(x + p)$ ...(iv)

Let us suppose that orthocentre of triangle be $H(h, k)$ which is the point of intersection of (iii) & (iv). From (iii) and (iv) we get $x = pq, y = -pq$

⇒ $\quad h = pq, \quad k = -pq \qquad \Rightarrow \quad h + k = 0$

Hence required locus is $x + y = 0$

24. Ans. (a).

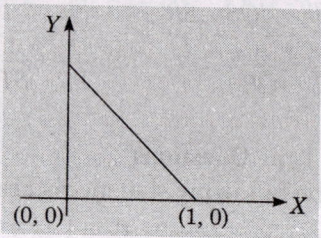

Fig. 119

Given $x + y = 1, \qquad xy = 0$

If $x = 0, y = 1$

If $x = 1$ then $y = 0$

∴ $(0, 1)$ and $(1, 0)$ are the vertices of the triangle. Clearly triangle is right angled isoscales. Orthocentre of right angled triangle is same as the vertex of right angle. Thus, the point of intersection of $x + y = 1$ and $xy = 0$ is $(0, 0)$

25. Ans. (d). Obviously triangle is equilateral

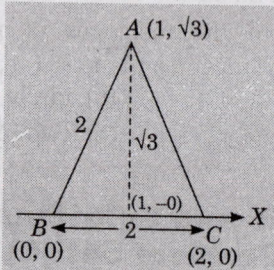

Fig. 120

∴ Required incentre $= \left(\dfrac{1+0+2}{3}, \dfrac{\sqrt{3}+0+0}{3}\right) = \left(1, \dfrac{1}{\sqrt{3}}\right)$

26. Ans. (b). The given triangle is a right angled triangle at the vertex $\left(2, -\dfrac{1}{2}\right)$.

∴ The orthocentre is at $\left(2, -\dfrac{1}{2}\right)$

27. Ans. (d). As per given

$X(R) = \cos(\beta - \alpha)\cos\theta - \sin(\beta - \alpha)\sin\theta$

$\qquad = X(Q)\cos\theta + X(P)\sin\theta$

$Y(R) = \sin\beta\cos\theta - \cos\beta\sin\theta$

$\qquad = Y(Q)\cos\theta + Y(P)\sin\theta$

For P, Q, R be collinear we have $\sin\theta + \cos\theta = 1$

$\Rightarrow$ $\sin\left(\theta+\dfrac{\pi}{4}\right)=\dfrac{1}{\sqrt{2}}$, which is not possible for the

given interval $\theta\in\left(0,\dfrac{\pi}{4}\right)$

Hence, P,Q,R are collinear.

28. Ans. (b).

29. Ans. (c).

30. Ans. (b).

Let the coordinates of centroid of the triangle whose vertices are

$(a\cos t,a\sin t),(b\sin t,-b\cos t)$ and $(1,0)$ is (x,y) then

$$x=\frac{a\cos t+b\sin t+1}{3}$$

$\Rightarrow$ $\quad 3x-1=a\cos t+b\sin t$ ...(1)

and $\quad y=\dfrac{a\sin t+b\sin t}{3}$

$\Rightarrow$ $\quad y=\dfrac{a\sin t+b\sin t}{3}$

$\Rightarrow$ $\quad 3y=a\sin t-b\cos t$ ...(2)

On squaring and adding (1) and (2) we get

$(3x-1)^2+(3y)^2=a^2+b^2$

31. Ans. (b). It is obvious

32. Ans. (c).

33. Ans. (d). Let the third vertex be $C(h,k)$

$\therefore$ Centroid of $\triangle ABC$ is

$$G\left(\frac{2-2+h}{3},\frac{-3+1+k}{3}\right)\equiv G\left(\frac{h}{3},\frac{k-2}{3}\right)$$

which lies on $2x+3y=1$

$\therefore$ $\quad \dfrac{2h}{3}+3\left(\dfrac{k-2}{3}\right)=1$

$\Rightarrow$ $\quad 2h+3k=9$

34. Ans. (a), (c) and (d)

Sides a,b,c may not be rational and we know that

$I=\dfrac{\Sigma ax_1}{\Sigma a}$.

35. Ans. (b) and (d).

36. Ans. False.

37. Ans. True.

38. Ans. False.

39. Ans. 5/2.

40. Ans. $(2,-4)$.

41. Ans. (a).

See Q. 27 P. 805-813.

MISCELLANEOUS EXERCISE

Matching Entries

♦ *Match the entries of Column I and Column II.*

1. **Column I**

(a) If the sum of the + ive intercepts on the axes made by a line passing through the point $(-3,8)$ be 7, then its eqn. is ...

(b) If $P(a,b)$ lies on $3x+2y-13=0$ and $Q(b,a)$ lies on $4x-y-5=0$ then the equation of line PQ is ...

(c) The line $x-y-2=0$ cuts x-axis at A. The equation of the line through A perpendicular to $ax+by+c=0$ is ...

(d) The incentre of triangle whose vertices are the points $(1,\sqrt{3}),(0,0)$ and $(2,0)$ is ...

(e) The segment of the line intercepted between the lines $5x-y-4=0$ and $3x+4y-4=0$ is bisected at the point $(1,5)$. Its equation is ...

Column II

1. $x+y=5$

2. $83x-35y+92=0$

3. $4x+3y=12$

4. $bx-ay-2b=0$

5. $(1,1/\sqrt{3})$

2. In the adjoining figure, the sides AB, BC and CA of the triangle ABC are $2x+y=0, x+py=q$ and $x-y=3$ respectively. The point P inside the triangle is $(2,3)$, then match the entries of column I and column II.

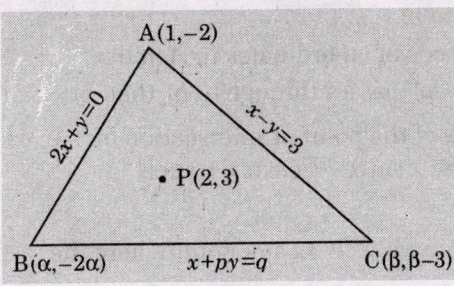

Fig. 121

Column I	Column II
$P(2, 3)$ is	Value of $p + q$
(a) Centroid	(i) 47
(b) Orthocentre	(ii) 50
(c) Circumcentre	(iii) 65
	(iv) 74

3. Consider the lines given by
$$L_1 : x + 3y - 5 = 0, \qquad L_2 : 3x - ky - 1 = 0, \qquad L_3 : 5x + 2y - 12 = 0$$

Column I	Column II
(a) L_1, L_2, L_3 are concurrent, if	(p) $k = -9$
(b) One of L_1, L_2, L_3 is parallel to at least one of the other two, if	(q) $k = -\dfrac{6}{5}$
(c) L_1, L_2, L_3 form a triangle, if	(r) $k = \dfrac{5}{6}$
(d) L_1, L_2, L_3 do not form a triangle, if	(s) $k = 5$

4. Match the entries of col. I with col. II in the following : The vertices of a triangle are $A(a, 0)$, $B(0, b)$ and $C(a, b)$.

Column I	Column II
(a) Centroid of Δ	(p) $(a/2, b/2)$
(b) Orthocentre	(q) (a, b)
(c) Circumcentre	(r) $(2a/3, 2a/3)$
(d) Foot of altitude from C	(s) $\left(\dfrac{a^3}{a^2 + b^2}, \dfrac{b^3}{a^2 + b^2} \right)$

5. The vertices of a triangle ABC are $A(1, -2)$, $B(-7, 6)$ and $C(11/5, 2/5)$.

Column I	Column II
(a) Eq. of right bisector of AB	(p) $26x + 17y + 8 = 0$
(b) Eq. of side BC	(q) $14x + 23y - 40 = 0$
(c) Eq. of altitude through C	(r) $x - y + 5 = 0$
(d) Eq. of median through A	(s) $5x - 5y - 9 = 0$

6. If $A(2a, 4a)$, $B(2a, 6a)$ be two vertices of a triangle ABC and C be the third vertex then match the entries of points in col I, with the nature of Δ in col II.

Column I	Column II
(a) $(4a, 5a)$	(p) equilateral
(b) $[(2 + \sqrt{3})a, 5a]$	(q) rt. angled
(c) $(6a, 4a)$	(r) obtuse angled
(d) $(a, 3a)$	(s) isosceles

7. Match the entries of col. I with col. II under the following conditions :

Column I	Column II
(a) The x-co-ordinate of the point of intersection of lines $3x + 4y = 9$ and $y = mx + 1$ is an integer. Then $m = \ldots\ldots$	(p) $m = -1$
(b) The line $2x - 3y - 6 = 0$ cuts the axis of co-ordinates in $A(a, 0)$ and $B(0, b)$ and the line $y = mx + m^2$ passes through (a, b), then $m = \ldots\ldots$	(q) $m = -2$
(c) If the point $(3, 4)$ lies on the locus of the point of intersection of the lines $x \cos\alpha + y \sin\alpha = m$ and $x \sin\alpha - y \cos\alpha = n$ such that $3m - 4n = 0$, then $m =$	(r) $m = 4$
(d) If the line $y = mx - \dfrac{8}{m}$ meets the curve $y^2 = 4x$ at a point where the curve meets the line $y = 2$, then $m =$	(s) $m = -4$

8. Normals are drawn at point P, Q and R lying on the parabola $y^2 = 4x$ which intersect at $(3, 0)$. Then match the conditions/expression in column I with statement in column II

Column I		Column II	
(a)	Area of ΔPQR	(p)	2
(b)	Radius of circumcircle of ΔPQR	(q)	5/2
(c)	Centroid of ΔPQR	(r)	$\left(\frac{5}{2}, 0\right)$
(d)	circumcentre of ΔPQR.	(s)	$\left(\frac{2}{3}, 0\right)$

(IIT JEE 2006)

Answers

1. (a) → (3), (b) → (1), (c) → (4), (d) → (5), (e) → (2)
2. (a) → (iv), (b) → (ii), (c) → (i)
3. (a) → (s), (b) → (p, q), (c) → (r), (d) → (p, q, s)
4. (a) → (r), (b) → (q), (c) → (p), (d) → (s)
5. (a) → (r), (b) → (q), (c) → (s), (d) → (p)
6. (a) → (s), (b) → (p), (c) → (q), (d) → (r)
7. (a) → (p,q), (b) → (p,q), (c) → (r, s), (d) → (q,r)
8. (a) → (p), (b) → (q), (c) → (s), (d) → (r)

Hints/Solutions

1. (a) **See Q. 5 (b) P. 774-776**
   (b) Put the points in respective equations and solve for a and b ∴ $a = 3, b = 2$. The equation of PQ is $y - b = -1(x - a)$ or $x + y = a + b = 5$.
   (c) A is $(2, 0)$. Slope of given line is $-\frac{a}{b}$ and hence slope of line through A perpendicular to given line is $\frac{b}{a}$. Its equation is
   $$y - 0 = \frac{b}{a}(x - 2) \quad \text{or} \quad bx - ay - 2b = 0$$
   (d) If the vertices be A, B, C, then $AB = BC = CA = 2$ ∴ Δ is equilateral.
   Hence the incentre will coincide with the centroid.
   $$\left(\frac{\Sigma x_1}{3}, \frac{\Sigma y_1}{3}\right) = \left(1, \frac{1}{\sqrt{3}}\right).$$
   (e) **See Q. 35 (d) P. 804-816**

2. Ans. (a) → (iv), (b) → (ii), (c) → (i)
   The point B on AB, $2x + y = 0$ may be chosen as $(\alpha, -2\alpha)$ and the point C on AC, $x - y = 3$ be taken as $(\beta, \beta - 3)$.
   If $P(2, 3)$ is centroid, i.e., $\left(\frac{1}{3}\Sigma x_1, \frac{1}{3}\Sigma y_1\right)$ then
   $$2 = \frac{1 + \alpha + \beta}{3}, 3 = \frac{-2 - 2\alpha + \beta - 3}{3}$$
   ∴ $\alpha + \beta = 5, -2\alpha + \beta = 14$
   ∴ $\alpha = -3, \beta = 8$
   ∴ B is $(-3, 6)$ and C is $(8, 5)$.
   Both these points lie on $BC, x + py = q$
   ∴ $-3 + 6p = q$ and $8 + 5p = q$
   Solving $p = 11, q = 63$.
   ∴ $p + q = 74$ ∴ (a) ⇒ (iv).
   If $P(2, 3)$ is orthocentre, then
   $CP \perp BC$ and $BP \perp CA$. Apply $m_1 m_2 = -1$
   ∴ $2\beta - 12 = \beta - 2 \Rightarrow \beta = 10, 2\alpha + 3 = \alpha - 2$
   ⇒ $\alpha = -5$

∴ B is $(-5, 10)$ and C is $(10, 7)$. Both these points lie on BC.
∴ $-5 + 10p = q$ and $10 + 7p = q$
∴ $p = 5, q = 45 \Rightarrow p + q = 50$ ∴ (b) → (ii)
If $P(2, 3)$ is circumcentre, then $PA = PB = PC$
$26 = (\alpha - 2)^2 + (2\alpha + 3)^2 = (\beta - 2)^2 + (\beta - 6)^2$
$(5\alpha + 13)(\alpha - 1) = 0 \Rightarrow \alpha = -\frac{13}{5}$ as $\alpha = 1$ will give $(1, -2)$
which is point A not B. Similarly $(\beta - 7)(\beta - 1) = 0 \Rightarrow$ $\beta = 7$ as $\beta = 1$ will give $(1, -2)$ which is point A not C.
∴ B is $\left(-\frac{13}{5}, \frac{26}{5}\right)$ and C is $(7, 4)$.
Both these points lie on $x + py = q$.
∴ $-\frac{13}{5} + \frac{26}{5}p = q$ and $7 + 4p = q$
Solving $p = 8, q = 39$ ∴ $p + q = 47$
∴ (c) → (i).

3. Ans. (a) → (s), (b) → (p, q), (c) → (r), (d) → (p, q, s)
   (a) L_1 and L_3 intersect at $(1, 2)$ and it will lie on L_2 if $k = 5$
   (b) Condition of parallelism gives
   $$\frac{3}{1} = -\frac{k}{3} = \frac{1}{5} \quad ∴ \quad k = -9 \quad ∴ \quad \text{(b)} → \text{(p)}$$
   Also $\frac{3}{5} = -\frac{k}{2} = \frac{1}{12}$ ∴ $k = -\frac{6}{5}$ ∴ (b) → (q)
   ∴ (b) → (p,q)
   (c) If $k \neq 5, -9, -\frac{6}{5}$ i.e., (a) and (b) are ruled out and hence they form a triangle.
   ∴ (c) → (r)
   (d) Exclude the cases of (a) and (b) i.e., $k = 5, -9, -6/5$, they will not form a triangle.
   ∴ (d) → (p,q,s)

4. Ans. (a) → (r), (b) → (q), (c) → (p), (d) → (s)

Centroid is $\left(\dfrac{a+a+0}{3},\dfrac{0+b+b}{3}\right)$, i.e., $\left(\dfrac{2a}{3},\dfrac{2b}{3}\right)$

Circumcentre is mid-point of diameter AB i.e., $(a/2, b/2)$ ∴ (c) → (p)

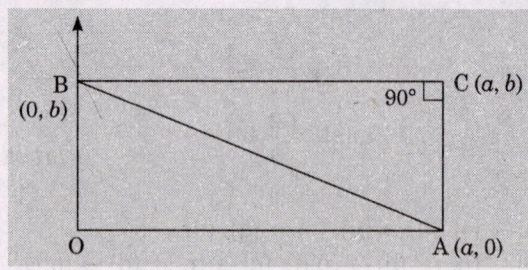

Fig. 122

Orthocentre is the intersection of altitudes AC and BC which intersect at $C(a,b)$. ∴ (b) → (q).

Equation of AB is $\dfrac{x}{a}+\dfrac{y}{b}=1$. Its slope is $\dfrac{-b}{a}$. Any line perpendicular to AB and passing through opposite vertex C is

$$y-b=\dfrac{a}{b}(x-a) \text{ or } ax-by-(a^2-b^2)=0$$

AB is $bx+ay-ab=0$

Solving the above two, we get the foot of perpendicular from C as

$$\dfrac{x}{ab^2+a(a^2-b^2)}=\dfrac{y}{-a^2b+b(a^2-b^2)}=\dfrac{1}{a^2+b^2}$$

$$\therefore \quad x=\dfrac{a^3}{a^2+b^2}, y=\dfrac{b^3}{a^2+b^2}$$

5. Ans. (a) → (r), (b) → (q), (c) → (s), (d) → (p)

(a) Mid-point of AB is $(-3, 2)$ and its slope is -1. ∴ Equation of right bisector is $(y-2)=1(x+3)$ or $x-y+5=0$ i.e., (r).

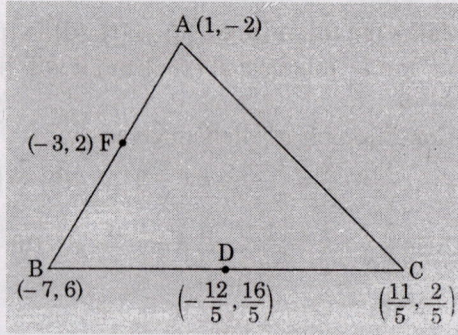

Fig. 123

(b) By two-point formula, equation of BC is

$$y-6=-\dfrac{14}{23}(x+7)$$

or $14x+23y-40=0 \to$ (q)

(c) Altitude through $C\left(\dfrac{11}{5},\dfrac{2}{5}\right)$ on $AB\,(m=-1)$ is

$$y-\dfrac{2}{5}=1\left(x-\dfrac{11}{5}\right) \text{ or } 5x-5y-9=0 \to \text{(s)}$$

(d) Mid-point of BC is $\left(\dfrac{-12}{5},\dfrac{16}{5}\right)$ and A is $(1,-2)$ and hence, by two-point formula, equation of median through A is

$$y+2=-\dfrac{26}{17}(x-1) \text{ or } 26x+17y+8=0 \to \text{(p)}$$

6. Ans. (a) → (s), (b) → (p), (c) → (q), (d) → (r)

(a) If C is $(4a, 5a)$ where A is $(2a, 4a)$ and B is $(2a, 6a)$, then $AB=2a, AC=a\sqrt5, BC=a\sqrt5$

∴ (a) → (s).

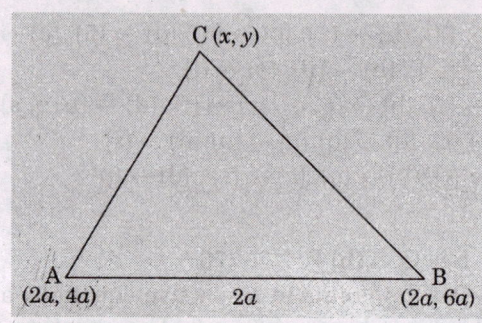

Fig. 124

(b) If C is $[(2+\sqrt3)\,a, 5a]$, then $AC=\sqrt{3a^2+a^2}=2a$,

$BC=\sqrt{3a^2+a^2}=2a, AB=2a$

∴ Δ is equilateral ∴ (b) → (p)

(c) If C is $(6a, 4a)$ then, $AC=4a$,

$BC=\sqrt{16a^2+4a^2}=2\sqrt5\,a, AB=2a$

$AC^2+AB^2=16a^2+4a^2=20a^2=(2\sqrt5a)^2=BC^2$

∴ Δ is rt. angled, $\angle A$ being $90°$ ∴ (c) → (q)

(d) If C is $(a, 3a)$, then $CA=\sqrt2a, CB=\sqrt{10}\,a, AB=2a$

The side BC is greatest and hence, angle A opposite to BC is greatest.

∴ $\cos A=\dfrac{b^2+c^2-a^2}{2bc}=\dfrac{2a^2+4a^2-10a^2}{2a\sqrt2\cdot a\cdot 2}=$ –ive

or $\cos A=<0$

∴ $\angle A$ is obtuse. ∴ Δ is obtuse angled.

7. Ans. (a) → (p,q), (b) → (p,q), (c) → (r, s), (d) → (q,r)

(a) Solving, $\dfrac{9-3x}{4}=mx+1$ ∴ $x=\dfrac{5}{3+4m}$

As x is an integer ∴ $3+4m=\pm1$ or ±5 or $4m=-3\pm1$ or -3 ± 5 or $-2, -4, 2, -8$.

Since m is an integer

∴ $4m=-4, -8$ or $m=-1, -2$

∴ (a) → (p, q)

(b) $A(3,0), B(0,-2)$ ∴ $(a,b)=(3,-2)$

The line $y=mx+m^2$ passes through $(3,-2)$

∴ $-2=3m+m^2$ or $m^2+3m+2=0$

or $(m+2)(m+1)=0$ ∴ $m=-1, -2$

∴ (b) → (p, q)

(c) Squaring and adding, we have $x^2 + y^2 = m^2 + n^2$

Point $(3, 4)$ lies on it. $\therefore$ $m^2 + n^2 = 25$

Also $3m - 4n = 0$

Solving, $m^2 + \left(\dfrac{3m}{4}\right)^2 = 25$ or $25m^2 = 25 \times 16$

$\therefore$ $m^2 = 16$ or $m = \pm 4$

$\therefore$ $(c) \to (r, s)$

(d) When $y = 2, 4x = 4$ $\therefore$ $x = 1$ $\therefore$ $(1, 2)$

$y = mx - \dfrac{8}{m}$ passes though $(1, 2)$.

$\therefore$ $2 = m - \dfrac{8}{m}$ or $m^2 - 2m - 8 = 0$ or $(m - 4)(m + 2) = 0$

$\therefore$ $m = 4, -2$ $\therefore$ $(d) \to (q, r)$

Assertion / Reason

1. Lines $L_1 : y - x = 0$ and $L_2 : 2x + y = 0$ intersect the line $L_3 : y + 2 = 0$ at P and Q, respectively. The bisector of the acute angle between L_1 and L_2 intersects L_3 at R.

STATEMENT-1 : The ratio $PR : RQ$ equals $2\sqrt{2} : \sqrt{5}$.

because

STATEMENT-2 : In any triangle, bisector of an angle divides the triangle into two similar triangles.

(I.I.T. 2007)

Sol. Ans. (c).

$AP = 2\sqrt{2}, AB = \sqrt{5}$

By definition bisector of $\angle A$ will divide PQ in the ratio of arms of the angle, $i.e.,$ $2\sqrt{2} : \sqrt{5}$

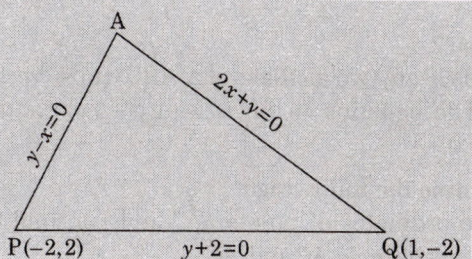

Fig. 125

$\therefore$ Statement (1) is true but statement-2 is false.

Comprehension

1. **Passage 1**

Shifting of origin $(0, 0)$ to (h, k)

$f(x, y) \Rightarrow f(x + h, y + k)$

Rotation of axes through an angle θ.

$f(x, y) \Rightarrow f(x\cos\theta - y\sin\theta, x\sin\theta + y\cos\theta)$

Now Answer the following Questions :

(i) By rotating the axes through an angle θ the equation $xy - y^2 - 3y + 4 = 0$ is transformed to the form which does not contain the term of xy then $\sin\theta = \ldots$

(ii) The equation $2xy = 9$ is transformed to $x^2 - y^2 = 9$ by rotating the axes through an angle $\pi/4$. Is this statement true or false ?

(iii) By rotating the axes through an angle θ in anti-clockwise direction the equation $f(x, y) = x^2 - 2xy + 3y^2 + 4x - 4y + 1 = 0$ transforms to the form which does not contain the term of y then $\theta = 135^\circ$.

(iv) Axes are rotated through a +ive obtuse angle θ so that the transformed equation of the curve $3x^2 - 6xy + 3y^2 + 7x - 3 = 0$ is free from the term of xy then the coefficient of x^2 in the transformed equation is $\ldots$

Sol. (i) Ans. $\sin\theta = \dfrac{1}{\sqrt{2}}$

The transformed equation is

$(x\cos\theta - y\sin\theta)(x\sin\theta + y\cos\theta) + \ldots = 0$

The coefficient of xy is $-\sin^2\theta + \cos^2\theta = \cos 2\theta = 0$

$\therefore$ $2\theta = \dfrac{\pi}{2}$ or $\theta = \dfrac{\pi}{4}$

$\therefore$ $\sin\theta = \dfrac{1}{\sqrt{2}}$

(ii) True. $2\left(x\cos\dfrac{\pi}{4} - y\sin\dfrac{\pi}{4}\right)\left(x\sin\dfrac{\pi}{4} + y\cos\dfrac{\pi}{4}\right) = 9$

or $2 \cdot \dfrac{x - y}{\sqrt{2}} \cdot \dfrac{x + y}{\sqrt{2}} = 9$ or $x^2 - y^2 = 9$

(iii) True. The transformed equation becomes

$(x\cos\theta - y\sin\theta)^2 - 2( )( ) + 3( )^2$

$+ 4(x\cos\theta - y\sin\theta) - 4(x\sin\theta + y\cos\theta) + 1 = 0$

The coefficient of y is $-4\sin\theta - 4\cos\theta = 0$

$\therefore$ $\tan\theta = -1$. Hence $\theta = 135^\circ$

(iv) Ans. 6.

$3(x\cos\theta - y\sin\theta)^2 - 6(x\cos\theta - y\sin\theta)$

$(x\sin\theta + y\cos\theta) + 3(x\sin\theta + y\cos\theta)^2$

$+ 7(x\cos\theta - y\sin\theta) - 3 = 0$

Coefficient of $xy = 0$

$\Rightarrow \quad -6 \sin \theta \cos \theta - 6 (\cos^2 \theta - \sin^2 \theta)$

$+ 6 \sin \theta \cos \theta = 0$

$\therefore \quad \cos 2\theta = 0 \quad \therefore \quad 2\theta = \dfrac{\pi}{2}, \dfrac{3\pi}{2} \quad \therefore \quad \theta = \dfrac{\pi}{4}, \dfrac{3\pi}{4}$

Since θ is obtuse we choose $\theta = \dfrac{3\pi}{4}$

$\therefore \quad$ Coefficient of x^2

$= 3 (\cos^2 \theta + \sin^2 \theta) - 6 \sin \theta \cos \theta$

$= 3 . 1 - 3 . \sin 2\theta = 3 + 3 = 6 \quad \because \quad \sin 2\theta = \sin \dfrac{3\pi}{2} = -1$

2. **Passage 2**

BE and CF are two medians of $\triangle ABC$ whose vertex A is $(1, 3)$. The equation to BE is $x - 2y + 1 = 0$ and CF is $y - 1 = 0$.

Determine the following :

The co-ordinates of points B, C and centroid G. The equations of lines AB and AC.

Sol. F lies on median CF, $y - 1 = 0$

$\therefore \quad F$ is $(\alpha, 1)$ say.

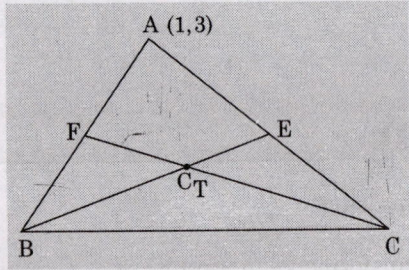

Fig. 126

This is mid-point of AB. If B be (h, k), then

$k + 1 = 2\alpha, k + 3 = 2 . 1$

$\therefore \quad k = -1.$

$\therefore \quad$ Point B is $(2\alpha - 1, -1)$.

It lies on median BE $x - 2y + 1 = 0$

$\therefore \quad (2\alpha - 1) + 2 + 1 = 0$

$\therefore \quad \alpha = -1.$

$\therefore \quad F$ is $(-1, 1)$ and B is $(-3, -1)$.

Now let C be $(\beta, 1)$ as it lies on median CF, $y = 1$ so that mid-point E of AC is $\left(\dfrac{\beta + 1}{2}, \dfrac{1 + 3}{2}\right)$ lies on median BE,

$x - 2y + 1 = 0$

$\therefore \quad \dfrac{\beta + 1}{2} - 2 \left(\dfrac{1 + 3}{2}\right) + 1 = 0$

$\therefore \quad \beta = 5 \quad$ and $\quad C$ is $(5, 1)$.

$\therefore \quad A = (1, 3), B = (-3, -1), C = (5, 1).$

$\therefore \quad$ Centroid G is $(1, 1)$.

The equation of AB and AC by two point formula are

$3x + 2y - 7 = 0$ and $x - y + 2 = 0$.

3. $A_1 (x_1, y_1), A_2 (x_2, y_2), A_3 (x_3, y_3), \ldots$ are n points in a plane such that

(a) $A_1 A_2$ is bisected at $G_1, G_1 A_3$ is divided in the ratio $1 : 2$ at $G_2, G_2 A_4$ is divided in the ratio $1 : 3$ at G_3. The process is continued until all n points are exhausted, then find the co-ordinates of the final point G_n.

Sol. **Ans.** $\left(\dfrac{\sum x_i}{n}, \dfrac{\sum y_i}{n}\right)$

G_1 bisects $A_1 A_2 \quad \therefore \quad G_1 = \left(\dfrac{x_1 + x_2}{2}, \dfrac{y_1 + y_2}{2}\right)$

G_2 divides $G_1 A_3$ in the ratio $1 : 2$

$\therefore \quad G_2 = \dfrac{1}{3}\left[2 . \dfrac{x_1 + x_2}{2} + 1 . x_3\right], \dfrac{1}{3}\left[2 . \dfrac{y_1 + y_2}{2} + 1 . y_3\right]$

$G_2 = \left(\dfrac{\sum x_i}{3}, \dfrac{\sum y_i}{3}\right)$

Continuing like this, $G_n = \left(\dfrac{\sum x_i}{n}, \dfrac{\sum y_i}{n}\right)$

(b) If $x_1 = a, y_1 = b$ and x_i's form an A.P. with common difference 2 and y_i's form an A.P. with common difference 4, then find the co-ordinates of G, the centroid.

Sol. $\sum x_i = x_1 + x_2 + x_3 + \ldots + x_n$

$= \dfrac{n}{2} [2a + (n - 1) 2]$

$\therefore \quad \dfrac{\sum x_i}{n} = a + (n - 1).$ Similarly, $\dfrac{\sum y_i}{n} = b + (n - 1) 2$

$\therefore \quad G$ is $[a + (n - 1), b + (n - 1) 2]$

(c) If $x_1 = 1, y_1 = 2$ and x_i's form a G.P. with common ratio 2 and y_i's form a G.P. with common ratio 3, then find the co-ordinates of G.

Sol. $\dfrac{\sum x_i}{n} = \dfrac{1}{n}\left[\dfrac{1 . (2^n - 1)}{2 - 1}\right] = \dfrac{1}{n} (2^n - 1)$

$\dfrac{\sum y_i}{n} = \dfrac{1}{n}\left[\dfrac{2 . (3^n - 1)}{3 - 1}\right] = \dfrac{1}{n} (3^n - 1)$

$\therefore \quad G$ is $\left[\dfrac{1}{n} (2^n - 1), \dfrac{1}{n} (3^n - 1)\right]$

(d) If a straight line be such that algebraic sum of the perpendiculars drawn from the points $A_1, A_2, \ldots, A_n$ is zero, then prove that the straight line passes through a fixed point whose co-ordinate is the centroid G of the given points.

Sol. Let the straight line be $ax + by + c = 0$ such that

$p_1 + p_2 + p_3 + \ldots + p_n = 0$

$\therefore \quad p_1 = \dfrac{ax_1 + by_1 + c}{\sqrt{(a^2 + b^2)}}, p_2 = \dfrac{ax_2 + by_2 + c}{\sqrt{(a^2 + b^2)}}$

$\therefore \quad p_1 + p_2 + p_3 + \ldots + p_n = 0$

$\Rightarrow \quad \dfrac{1}{\sqrt{a^2 + b^2}} [a \sum x_i + b \sum y_i + nc] = 0$

or $\quad a\dfrac{\sum x_i}{n}+b\dfrac{\sum y_i}{n}+c=0$

Above shows that the given line passes through the point $\left(\dfrac{\sum x_i}{n},\dfrac{\sum y_i}{n}\right)$, i.e., centroid of the given points.

4. $A(x_1,y_1), B(x_2,y_2), C(x_3,y_3)$ are the vertices of a triangle ABC and $ax+by+c=0$ is the equation of a line L, then answer the following questions :

(a) If the centroid of the triangle ABC is at the origin and algebraic sum of the lengths of perpendiculars from the vertices of the triangle on the line L is equal to 1, then prove that sum of the squares of the intercepts made by L on the co-ordinate axes is 9.

Sol. Given $\dfrac{\sum x_i}{3}=0,\dfrac{\sum y_i}{3}=0, i=1,2,3,$ ...(1)

and $p_1+p_2+p_3=0\Rightarrow\dfrac{a\sum x_i+b\sum y_i+3c}{\sqrt{a^2+b^2}}=1$

$\therefore\quad 9c^2=a^2+b^2$ by (1) ... (2)

Now sum of the squares of the intercepts made by the line on co-ordinate axes is

$$\left(-\dfrac{a}{c}\right)^2+\left(\dfrac{-b}{c}\right)^2=\dfrac{a^2+b^2}{c^2}=9 \text{ by (2)}$$

(b) If a line $ax+by+c=0$ cuts the sides BC, CA and AB of triangle ABC at points P,Q and R respectively, the prove that

$$\dfrac{BP}{PC}\cdot\dfrac{CQ}{QA}\cdot\dfrac{AR}{RB}=-1$$

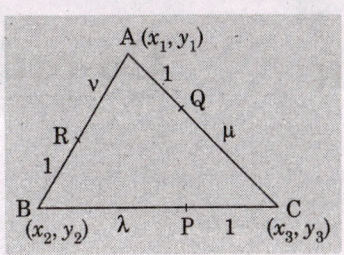

Fig. 127

Sol. P is $\left(\dfrac{\lambda\, x_3+x_2}{\lambda+1},\dfrac{\lambda\, y_3+y_2}{\lambda+1}\right)$ where $\lambda=\dfrac{BP}{PC}$

P lies on line $ax+by+c=0$

$a\dfrac{(\lambda\, x_3+x_2)}{\lambda+1}+b\dfrac{(\lambda\, y_3+y_2)}{\lambda+1}+c=0$

$\therefore\quad \lambda(a x_3+by_3+c)+(a x_2+by_2+c)=0$

$\therefore\quad \lambda=-\dfrac{(a x_2+by_2+c)}{(ax_3+by_3+c)}=-\dfrac{l_2}{l_3}$ where $\lambda=\dfrac{BP}{PC}$

Similarly, $\quad \mu=-\dfrac{l_3}{l_1}$ where $\mu=\dfrac{CQ}{QA}$

and $\quad v=-\dfrac{l_1}{l_2}$ where $v=\dfrac{AR}{RB}$

$\therefore\quad \lambda\mu v=\left(-\dfrac{l_2}{l_3}\right)\times\left(-\dfrac{l_3}{l_1}\right)\times\left(-\dfrac{l_1}{l_2}\right)=-1$

(c) If P divides BC in ratio $2:1$ and Q divides CA in ratio $1:3$ then R divides AB in the ratio $3:2$ externally.

Sol. Given $\lambda=2, \mu=\dfrac{1}{3}$ and let R divide AB in the ratio $v:1$.

Then by part (b) $\lambda\mu v=-1$. $\therefore\ 2\cdot\dfrac{1}{3}v=-1\ \therefore\ v=-\dfrac{3}{2}$

$\therefore\ R$ divides AB in the ratio $3:2$ externally, as $v=-\dfrac{3}{2}$.

Fascinating Facts

- Three points A,B,C are collinear if exactly one of the following three conditions is satisfied.
  (i) $|AB|+|BC|=|AC|$ (ii) $|AC|+|BC|=|AB|$
  (iii) $|AB|+|AC|=|BC|$
- Three points A, B and C are non-collinear if and only if
  $|AB|+|BC|>|AC|; |AC|+|BC|>|AB|$
  and $|AB|+|AC|>|BC|$
- A point P is the circumcentre of a triangle ABC if and only if $|PA|=|PB|=|PC|$
- Remember the following results :
  (i) A quadrilateral is a parallelogram iff opposite sides are equal.

- (ii) A quadrilateral is a rhombus iff all the four sides are equal.
- (iii) A quadrilateral is a rectangle iff opposite sides are equal and also the diagonals are equal.
- (iv) A quadrilateral is a square iff all the four sides are equal and also, diagonals are equal
- A translation of axes can not affect magnitude like the distance between two points, distance of a point to a line, area of the figure etc.

□

§ 1. Introduction

A circle is the locus of a point which moves in a plane in such a manner that its distance from a fixed point in the plane is constant. The fixed point is called the centre and the constant distance is called the radius of the circle.

§ 2. Equation of a Circle in different forms.

(a) Centre (h, k), radius a.

Then the equation of the circle is

$$(x - h)^2 + (y - k)^2 = a^2 \qquad ...(1)$$

$x^2 + y^2 = a^2$ with centre $(0, 0)$, radius a ...(2)

(b) Centre (h, k) and passes through origin.

Here $r = \sqrt{(h - 0)^2 + (k - 0)^2} = \sqrt{(h^2 + k^2)}$

$\therefore \quad (x - h)^2 + (y - k)^2 = h^2 + k^2$

$$x^2 + y^2 - 2hx - 2ky = 0. \qquad ...(3)$$

(c)* Centre (h, k) and touches the axis of x. From the figure it is clear that radius will be k.

$\therefore \quad (x - h)^2 + (y - k)^2 = k^2,$

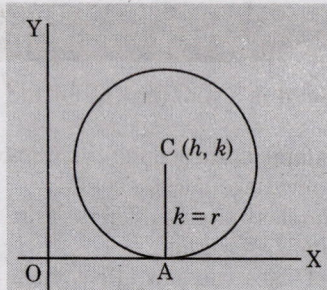

Fig. 1

or $\quad x^2 + y^2 - 2hx - 2ky + h^2 = 0 \qquad ...(4)$

Its intersection with x-axis *i.e.* $y = 0$, is

$x^2 - 2hx + h^2 = 0 \quad$ or $\quad (x - h)^2 = 0.$

i.e., it gives two equal values of x as x-axis is a tangent.

(d) Centre (h, k) and touching the axis of y

$$(x - h)^2 + (y - k)^2 = h^2$$

or $\quad x^2 + y^2 - 2hx - 2ky + k^2 = 0. \qquad ...(5)$

Its intersection with y-axis *i.e.* $x = 0$ is $y^2 - 2ky + y^2 = 0$ or $(y - k)^2 = 0$ *i.e.* it gives two equal values of y as y-axis is a tangent.

(e) Which touches both the axes. In this case the centre of the circle will be (h, h) and radius h. But since the centre could be in any of the four quadrants, its co-ordinates can be taken as $(\pm h, \pm h)$ and radius h

$\therefore \quad x^2 + y^2 \pm 2hx \pm 2hy + h^2 = 0. \qquad ...(6)$

(f) General equation of a circle

$$x^2 + y^2 + 2gx + 2fy + c = 0.$$

The coefficients of x^2 and y^2 are both unity and there is no term of xy.

$(x^2 + 2gx) + (y^2 + 2fy) = -c,$

Add $g^2 + f^2$ to both sides

$(x^2 + 2gx + g^2) + (y^2 + 2fy + f^2) = g^2 + f^2 - c$

or $\quad (x + g)^2 + (y + f)^2 = [\sqrt{g^2 + f^2 - c}]^2.$

Thus radius is

$\sqrt{g^2 + f^2 - c}$ provided $g^2 + f^2 - c > 0 \quad ...(7)$

and centre is $(-g, -f) \qquad ...(8)$

i.e., $\left(\dfrac{1}{2} \text{ coeff. of } x \text{ with sign changed,} \right.$

$\left. \dfrac{1}{2} \text{ coeff. of } y \text{ with sign changed} \right).$

The general equation of a circle passing through the origin is

$$x^2 + y^2 + 2gx + 2fy = 0.$$

Note that this equation does not contain the constant term.

*Note : In case the coefficients of x^2 and y^2 be each λ instead of unity then divide by λ first before finding the co-ordinates of the centre and radius.

The general equation of second degree in x and y i.e. $ax^2 + 2hxy + by^2 + 2gx + 2fy + c = 0$ will represent a circle if $a = b$ and $h = 0$ i.e. coefficient of x^2 and y^2 are same and there is no term of xy.

(g) Lengths of intercepts on the axes made by the circle
$$x^2 + y^2 + 2gx + 2fy + c = 0.$$

Let it cut the axis of x i.e. $y = 0$ in points $(x_1, 0)$ and $(x_2, 0)$.

∴ x_1, x_2 are the roots of $x^2 + 2gx + c = 0$.

∴ $x_1 + x_2 = -2g$, $x_1 x_2 = c$,

∴   Intercept $= x_2 - x_1$

$$= [(x_2 + x_1)^2 - 4x_1 x_2]^{1/2} = \sqrt{4g^2 - 4c}$$

*or **Intercept** $= 2\sqrt{g^2 - c} = I_x$ ...(9)

Similarly intercept on y-axis is

* $y_1 - y_2 = 2\sqrt{f^2 - c} = I_y$ ...(10)

*Note : In case the circle touches the axis of x at $(x_1, 0)$ then it will intersect the x-axis i.e. $y = 0$ in two coincident points.

∴ $x^2 + 2gx + c = (x - x_1)^2$ **(Note)**   ...(11)

Comparing coefficients, we find g and c.

Similarly if it touches the y-axis at $(0, y_1)$, then

$$y^2 + 2fy + c = (y - y_1)^2 \quad \textbf{(Note)} \quad ...(12)$$

Comparing coefficients, we find f and c.

In general the length of intercept made by the circle on any line is given by the formula $2\sqrt{r^2 - p^2}$) where r is the radius of the circle and p the perpendicular distance of centre $(-g, -f)$ from the line   **[See (m) P. 850]**

∴ $I_x = 2\sqrt{g^2 + f^2 - c - f^2} = 2\sqrt{g^2 - c}$

    $I_y = 2\sqrt{g^2 + f^2 - c - g^2} = 2\sqrt{f^2 - c}$

(h) Condition for a given line to be a tangent. In this case the perpendicular distance from the centre on the line should be equal to radius i.e. $p = r$.

(i) Circle whose diameter is the line joining two points $A(x_1, y_1)$ and $B(x_2, y_2)$

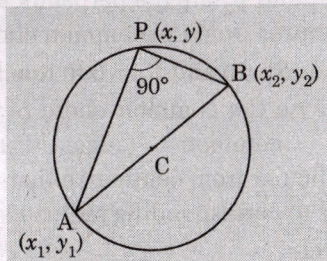

Fig. 2

Angle in a semi-circle is a right angle.

If $P(x, y)$ be any point on it, then PA is perpendicular to PB.

∴ $m_1 m_2 = -1$ or $\dfrac{y - y_1}{x - x_1} \cdot \dfrac{y - y_2}{x - x_2} = -1$

or $(x - x_1)(x - x_2) + (y - y_1)(y - y_2) = 0$ ...(13)

(j) Circle through three given points.

1st Method :

Let the equation of the circle be
$$x^2 + y^2 + 2gx + 2fy + c = 0.$$

The co-ordinates of the three points will satisfy it and thus we will have three equations in g, f and c and solving them we shall find their values.

2nd Method : (Note Carefully)

If the three points be A, B and C then write

    S = circle on AB as diameter

    P = line through A, B

The required circle will be $S + \lambda P = 0$ where λ is found by passing it through the point C.

         See Q. 26 P. 857-873.

3rd Method :

Circle circumscribing a triangle equation of whose sides are given by $P = 0$, $Q = 0$ and $R = 0$.

In case **the circle circumscribes a triangle the equations of whose sides are given**, then solving them in pairs we shall get the three vertices of the triangle.

Another Method : (Note Carefully)

Without solving the equations of lines in pairs to get the vertices, the following method be adopted :

Consider the equation

$$S \equiv QR + \lambda RP + \mu PQ = 0 \quad ...(1)$$

The above equation is satisfied whenever any two of P, Q, R is zero. In other words, it passes through the vertices of the triangle given by the three lines. In order to find λ, μ we need two equations in λ, μ. For this apply the condition that (1) represents the equation of a circle i.e. $a = b$ and $h = 0$. **(See Note (f) above)** For illustration see Q. 24 P. 856-871.

*Particular case : circle OAB where O is $(0, 0)$, A is $(a, 0)$ and B is $(0, b)$. The above circle is clearly on AB as diameter as we know that angle in a semicircle is a right angle. Its equation is

$$(x - 0)(x - a) + (y - 0)(y - b) = 0.$$

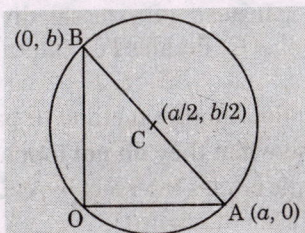

Fig. 3

or $x^2 + y^2 - ax - by = 0$

You may find its equation by the method given in (j). It passes through origin and intercepts on axes are a and b and its centre is $(a/2, b/2)$.

(a) **Centre of a circle.** Centre of a circle circumscribing a right-angled triangle **is at the mid-point of the hypotenuse.**

(b) If there be given any two intersecting tangents to a circle, then its **centre lies on the bisectors of the angle between the two tangents** as $p = r$ for both the tangents.

(k) **Parametric equations of the circle** (V. Imp.)

$$x^2 + y^2 = a^2$$

are $x = a\cos\theta,\ y = a\sin\theta,$

and for $(x-h)^2 + (y-k)^2 = r^2$

are $x - h = r\cos\theta,\ y - k = r\sin\theta$

or $x = h + r\cos\theta,\ y = k + r\sin\theta.$ ...(14)

(k₁) **Equation of chord joining two points A and B on the circle $x^2 + y^2 = a^2$ whose parameters are θ and ϕ is**

$$x\cos\left(\frac{\theta+\phi}{2}\right) + y\sin\left(\frac{\theta+\phi}{2}\right) = a\cos\left(\frac{\theta-\phi}{2}\right)$$

(See also § 2 P. 850)

(l) **Conditions for two circles to touch.**

In case the two circles touch then from the above figure it is clear that

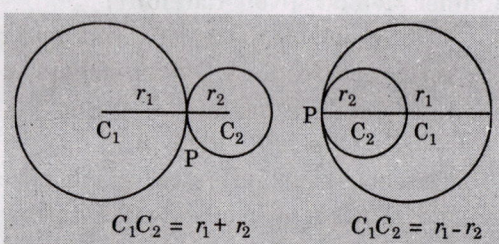

$$C_1C_2 = r_1 + r_2 \qquad C_1C_2 = r_1 - r_2$$

Fig. 4

The distance between their centres C_1C_2
= Sum of the radii (Externally) = $r_1 + r_2$
= Difference of the radii (Internally) = $r_1 - r_2$
...(15)

Also the point of contact P divides the join of centres in the ratio of the radii internally (for touching externally) and externally (for touching internally).

Note 1 : Instead of external division, we may assume that C_2 divides PC_1 internally in the ratio $r_2 : r_1 - r_2$ i.e., $PC_2 : C_2C_1$.

Note 2 : See another method in part (m).

The case when they do not touch

(a) In case the circles **intersect in real points**, then as is clear from the figure :

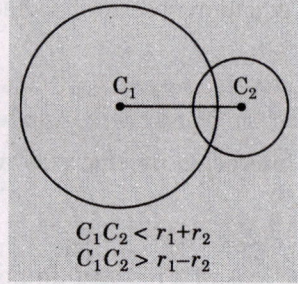

$$C_1C_2 < r_1 + r_2$$
$$C_1C_2 > r_1 - r_2$$

Fig. 5

$$C_1C_2 < r_1 + r_2 \quad \text{or} \quad > r_1 - r_2$$

(b) In case the circles **do not intersect in real points,** then as shown in figure :

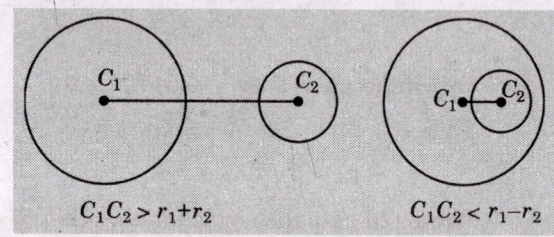

$$C_1C_2 > r_1 + r_2 \qquad C_1C_2 < r_1 - r_2$$

Fig. 6

$$C_1C_2 > r_1 + r_2 \quad \text{or} \quad C_1C_2 < r_1 - r_2$$

(m) **Length and Equation of the common chord of two circles $S_1 = 0$ and $S_2 = 0$.**

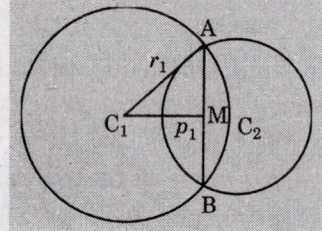

Fig. 7

Ensure that the coefficients of x^2 and y^2 in both the equations are each unity, then the equation of the common chord is given by

$$S_1 - S_2 = 0. \qquad ...(16)$$

Also its length

$$= 2AM = 2\sqrt{r_1^2 - p_1^2} = 2\sqrt{r_2^2 - p_2^2}$$

where p_1 and p_2 are the perpendicular distances of the centres from the common chord.

Conditions for $S_1 = 0$ and $S_2 = 0$ to touch. (V. Imp.)
In this case the common chord $S_1 - S_2 = 0$ will become common tangent and hence perpendicular from centre of either circle should be equal to corresponding radius i.e. $p = r$.

Line and Circle

(a) In case a line AB intersects a circle then its length
$$= AB = 2AM = 2\sqrt{r^2 - p^2} \text{ where } p < r$$

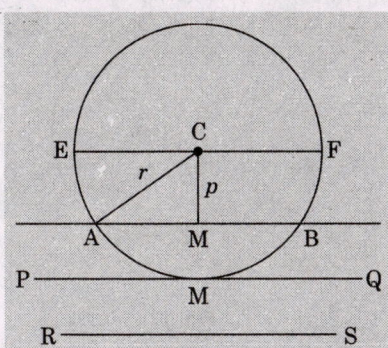

Fig. 8

(b) In case the line PQ touches the circle then length of chord is zero so that $p = r$ i.e. length of perpendicular from centre on tangent = radius.

(c) In case the line RS does not intersect the circle the their length of the chord is imaginary so that $p > r$.

(d) In case the line EF passes through centre C then $p = 0$, so that its length becomes $2r$ i.e., chord EF becomes a diameter.

(n) Equation of family of circles passing through the intersection of given circle $S = 0$ and given line $P = 0$ is

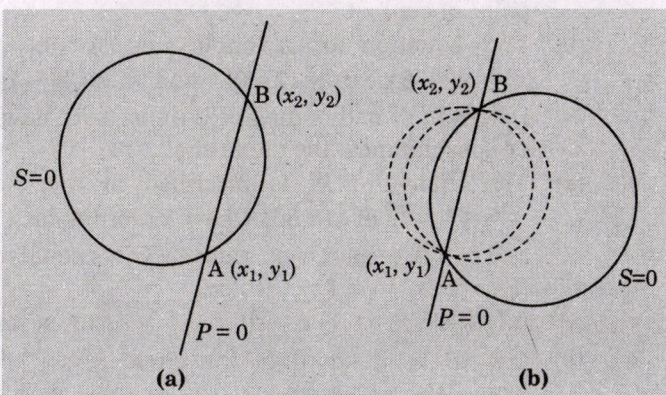

(a)　　　　　　　　(b)

Fig. 9

$$S + \lambda P = 0 \qquad \qquad ...(17)$$

where λ is found by an additional given condition.

Above represents a family of circles for different values of λ and they are shown by dotted circles. Each member of the family will pass through the points A and B. For a given value of λ, it will be only one circle. **See Q. 19 (b) P. 856–869.**

Another form : (V. Imp.)

The equation of family of circles passing through the points A and B. (See Fig. 9 (b).

$$(x - x_1)(x - x_2) + (y - y_1)(y - y_2) + \lambda P = 0$$

Circle on AB as diameter　　　line through A & B

(n₁) **The equation of a circle which touches a given circle at a given point (x_1, y_1):** (V. Imp.)

$$S + \lambda P = 0$$

In case $B \to A$ then chord AB tends to be a tangent at A and S becomes $(x - x_1)^2 + (y - y_1)^2$ when

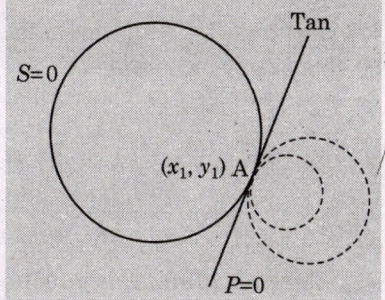

Fig. 10

$x_2 \to x_1$ and $y_2 \to y_1$ i.e. a **point circle of zero radius**. Required family of circles in this case is

* $$(x - x_1)^2 + (y - y_1)^2 + \lambda P = 0 \qquad \text{(V. Imp.)}$$

　Point circle　　　　　Tangent

where $P = 0$ is tangent at (x_1, y_1). λ is found by an additional given condition.

(o) **Equation of a circle passing through the intersection of given circles $S_1 = 0$ and $S_2 = 0$ (in standard form)**

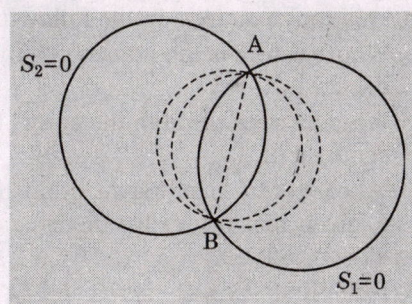

Fig. 11

is　　$S_1 + \lambda S_2 = 0$　$(\lambda \neq -1)$.

or　　$S + \lambda P = 0$

where S is either S_1 or S_2 and P is $S_1 - S_2$

The value of λ is found by an additional given condition.

(p) **Remember that the homogeneous equation of second degree in x and y, i.e.**

$$ax^2 + 2hxy + by^2 = 0$$

represents two straight lines passing through the origin. The angle θ between the lines is given by

$$\tan \theta = \frac{2\sqrt{h^2 - ab}}{a + b}.$$

The lines are coincident if $h^2 = ab$ and they are perpendicular if $a + b = 0$, i.e. if the sum of the coefficients of x^2 and y^2 is zero.

(q) **The position of a point $P(x_1, y_1)$ with respect to the circle**

$$x^2 + y^2 + 2gx + 2fy + c = 0.$$

The centre C of the circle is $(-g, -f)$ and the radius $r = \sqrt{g^2 + f^2 - c}$.

Now the point $P(x_1, y_1)$ lies outside, on, or inside the given circle according as

$$CP^2 >, =, \text{or} < r^2$$

i.e. $(x_1 + g)^2 + (y_1 + f)^2 >, =, \text{or} < g^2 + f^2 - c$

i.e. $x_1^2 + y_1^2 + 2gx_1 + 2fy_1 + c >, =, \text{or} < 0.$

i.e. $S = +$ ive (Point P is outside the circle),

$= 0$ (Point P is on the circle),

$= -$ ive (Point P is inside the circle)

(r) The greatest and least distance of a point $A(x_1, y_1)$ from a circle.

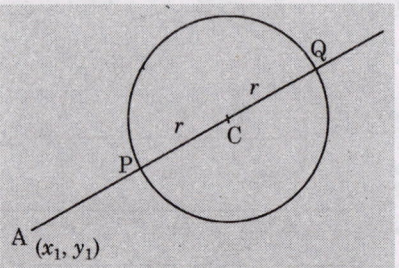

Fig. 12

Let the diameter of the circle through A cut the circle in points P and Q then

$AP = AC - r =$ Least distance

and $AQ = AC + r =$ Greatest distance

Problem Set (1)

Equation of a circle. Circle on given line as diameter. Length and equation of common chord. Circle touching axis of co-ordinates. Intercepts made by a circle on the axes. Family of circles of $S + \lambda P = 0$ or $S_1 + \lambda S_2 = 0$.

Find the equation of a circle in the following cases :

1. (a) Whose centre is the point $(1, -3)$ and touches the line $2x - y - 4 = 0$.

   (b) Which passes through the point $(4, 5)$ and has its centre at $(2, 2)$.

   (c) Whose centre is in first quadrant and radius being 4, given that it touches the x-axis and the line $4x - 3y = 0$.

   (d) If the lines $3x - 4y - 7 = 0$ and $2x - 3y - 5 = 0$ are two diameters of a circle of area 49π square units, then the equation of the circle is :

   (a) $x^2 + y^2 + 2x - 2y - 62 = 0$

   (b) $x^2 + y^2 - 2x + 2y - 62 = 0$

   (c) $x^2 + y^2 - 2x + 2y - 47 = 0$

   (d) $x^2 + y^2 + 2x - 2y - 47 = 0$ **(AIEEE 2006)**

2. (a)* Which touches the axis of y at $(0, 3)$ and cuts an intercept of 8 units on the axis of x.

   (b) Which touches the axis of y at $(0, \sqrt{3})$ and cuts the axis of x in the points $(-1, 0)$ and $(-3, 0)$.

   (c) Which passes through origin and cuts off intercepts a and b respectively from the axes.

   (d) A variable circle passes through a fixed point $A(p, q)$ and touches the x-axis. The locus of the other end of the diameter through A is :

   (a) $(x - p)^2 = 4qy$ (b) $(x - q)^2 = 4py$

   (c) $(y - p)^2 = 4qx$ (d) $(y - q)^2 = 4px$

   (AIEEE 2004)

   (e) A circle touches the x-axis and also touches the circle with centre $(0, 3)$ and radius 2. The locus of the centre of the circle is :

   (a) hyperbola   (b) parabola

   (c) an ellipse   (d) a circle

3. (a) If the circle $x^2 + y^2 - 4x - 6y + \lambda = 0$ touches the axis of x, then determine the value of λ and the point of contact.

   (b)* The equation of a circle and a line are $x^2 + y^2 - 8x + 2y + 12 = 0$ and $x - 2y - 1 = 0$. Determine whether the line is a chord or a tangent or does not meet the circle at all.

4. (a) The triangle PQR is inscribed in the circle $x^2 + y^2 = 25$. If Q and R have co-ordinates $(3, 4)$ and $(-4, 3)$ respectively, then $\angle QPR$ is equal to

   (a) $\pi/2$ (b) $\pi/3$

   (c) $\pi/4$ (d) $\pi/6$ **(I.I.T. Sc. 2000)**

   (b) Let AB be a chord of the circle $x^2 + y^2 = a^2$ subtending a right angle at the centre. Then the locus of the centroid of the triangle PAB as P moves on the circle is

   (a) a parabola

   (b) a circle

   (c) an ellipse

   (d) a pair of straight lines   **(I.I.T. Sc. 2001)**

   (c) The lines joining the origin to the points of intersection of the line $4x + 3y = 24$ with the circle $(x - 3)^2 + (y - 4)^2 = 25$ are

   (a) coincident

   (b) perpendicular

   (c) equally inclined to x-axis

   (d) none of these

   (d) Find the angle which the common chord of the circles $x^2 + y^2 - 4x - 4y = 0$ and $x^2 + y^2 - 16 = 0$ subtends at the origin.

   (e) If the circles $x^2 + y^2 + 2ax + cy + a = 0$ and $x^2 + y^2 - 3ax + dy - 1 = 0$ intersect in two distinct points P and Q then the line $5x + by - a = 0$ passes through P and Q for :

(a) infinitely many values of a

(b) exactly two values of a

(c) exactly one value of a

(d) no value of a **(AIEEE 2005)**

5. (a) If the point $(0, g)$ lies inside the circle $x^2 + y^2 + 2gx + c = 0$, then show that c cannot be + ive.

(b) How are the following points $(0, 1)$, $(3, 1)$ and $(1, 3)$ situated w.r.t. the circle $x^2 + y^2 - 2x - 4y + 3 = 0$?

(c)* A variable circle touches the x-axis and passes through the point $A(\alpha, \beta)$. Prove that the locus of the other end of the diameter through A is the parabola $(x - \alpha)^2 = 4\beta y$.

6. (a)* Find the equation of circle which passes through the point $(1, 1)$, $(2, 2)$ and whose radius is 1 and show that there are two such circles
$$(x - 2)^2 + (y - 1)^2 = 1$$
and $(x - 1)^2 + (y - 2)^2 = 1$.

(b) The intercept on the line $y = x$ by the circle $x^2 + y^2 - 2x = 0$ is AB. Equation of the circle on AB as diameter is :

(a) $x^2 + y^2 - x - y = 0$

(b) $x^2 + y^2 - x + y = 0$

(c) $x^2 + y^2 + x + y = 0$

(d) $x^2 + y^2 + x - y = 0$ **(AIEEE 2004)**

7. (a) The lines $2x - 3y = 5$ and $3x - 4y = 7$ are diameters of a circle of area 154 sq. units. Then the equation of this circle is $x^2 + y^2 - 2x + 2y = 47$.

(b) If the two straight lines $3x - 2y - 8 = 0$ and $2x - y - 5 = 0$ lie along two diameters of a circle which touches the x-axis then the equation of the circle is .... **(J.E.E. 1999)**

8. (a) Find the equation of circle which passes through the points $(0, 5)$ and $(6, 1)$ and whose centre lies on the line $12x + 5y = 25$.

(b) Which passes through the points $(1, -2)$ and $(4, -3)$ and whose centre lies on the line $3x + 4y = 7$.

9. (a)* Find the equation of circle which touches the lines $4x - 3y + 10 = 0$ and $4x - 3y - 30 = 0$ and whose centre lies on the line $2x + y = 0$.

(b) Determine the radius of the circle two of whose tangents are the lines $2x + 3y - 9 = 0$ and $4x + 6y + 19 = 0$.

10. (a)* Find the equation of circle which touches the x-axis and the line $4x - 3y + 4 = 0$. Its centre lying in the third quadrant and lies on the line $x - y - 1 = 0$. **(Dhanbad 1992)**

(b) Circles are drawn through the point $(2, 0)$ to cut intercept of 5 units on the axis of x. If their centres lie in the first quadrant, then prove that its equation is $x^2 + y^2 - 9x - 2ky + 14 = 0$

11. (a) A circle has radius 3 units and its centre lies on the line $y = x - 1$. Find the equation of the circle if it passes through $(7, 3)$.

(b)* Find the equation of the circle passing through the point $A(1, 2)$, $B(3, 4)$ and tangent to the straight line $3x + y - 3 = 0$.

12. (a) Find the equation of a circle which passes through the point $(2, 0)$ and whose centre is the limit of the point of intersection of the lines $3x + 5y = 1$, $(2 + c)x + 5c^2 y = 1$ as c tends to 1.

(b) The centre of a circle passing through the point $(0, 1)$ and touching the curve $y = x^2$ at $(2, 4)$ is $\left(\dfrac{-16}{5}, \dfrac{53}{10}\right)$.

13. (a) Find the equation of circle which passes through the point $(1, -2)$ and $(3, -4)$ and touches the axis of x.

(b)* Two circles are drawn through the points $(a, 5a)$ and $(4a, a)$ touching the axis of y. Prove that they intersect at an angle $\tan^{-1}(40/9)$.

(c) Find the equation of the circle passing through the points $A(4, 3)$ and $B(2, 5)$ and touching the axis of y. Also find the point P on the y-axis such that the angle APB has largest magnitude. **(Roorkee 1991)**

(d) On the line joining the points $A(3, 0)$ and $B(0, 4)$ a square $ABCD$ is constructed on the side of the line away from origin. Prove that equation of the circle having centre at C and touching the axis of x is
$$x^2 + y^2 - 14x - 6y + 49 = 0$$

14. (a) Find the equation of circle which touches both the axes and the line $x = c$.

(b) The equation of the circle which touches both the axes and also the straight line $4x + 3y = 6$ in the first quadrant and lies below it is $4x^2 + 4y^2 - 4x - 4y + 1 = 0$.

(c) Which touches the axes of co-ordinates at their positive sides and also touches the line $3x + 2y = 6$.

15. (a)* What is the peculiarity of the circle $x^2 + y^2 + 6x - 6y + 9 = 0$? Determine the equations of tangents which make equal intercepts on the axes.

(b) Find the equation of family of circles which touch the pair of lines $x^2 - y^2 + 2y - 1 = 0$.

(c)* A circle touches the sides AB and AD of a rectangle at P and Q respectively and passes through the vertex C. If the distance of C from PQ is 5 units, then prove that the area of the rectangle is 25 sq. units.

16. (a) Find the equation of circle whose diameter is the line joining the points $(-4,3)$ and $(12,-1)$. Find also the intercept made by it on y-axis.

(b) Whose diameter is the line joining the points $(0,-1)$ and $(2,3)$. Find also the intercept made by it on the axis of x.

(c) Prove that the circle circumscribing the rectangle whose sides in order are $x-3y-4=0$, $3x+y-22=0$, $x-3y-14=0$ and $3x+y-62=0$ is $x^2+y^2-27x-3y+142=0$

(d) A square is formed by following two pairs of straight lines $y^2-14y+45=0$ and $x^2-8x+12=0$. A circle is inscribed in it. The centre of the circle is

(a) $(7,4)$ (b) $(4,7)$

(c) $(3,7)$ (d) $(3/8,4)$ **(Screening 2003)**

17. (a) On the line segment joining the points $(1,0)$ and $(2,0)$ an equilateral triangle is constructed whose vertex lies in the positive quadrant. Find the equation of circles which are drawn on the sides of the triangle as diameter.

(b)* Two vertices of an equilateral triangle are $(-1,0)$ and $(1,0)$, and its third vertex lies above the x-axis. The equation of its circumcircle is .... **(I.I.T. 1997)**

(c) The equation of a circle with centre at origin and passing through the vertices of an equilateral triangle whose median is of length $3a$ is ....
(B.I.T.S. 1992)

(d) The equation of the circumcircle of triangle formed by the lines $y+\sqrt{3}x=6$, $y-\sqrt{3}x=6$ and $y=0$ is .... **(C.E.E. Andhra 1992)**

18. (a)* $A(x_1,y_1)$, $B(x_2,y_2)$ are two given points. Circles are drawn on OA and OB as diameters where O is origin. Prove that the length of the common chord is $\dfrac{x_1y_2-x_2y_1}{AB}$.

(b) Let PQ and RS be tangents at the extremities of the diameter PR of a circle of radius r. If PS and RQ intersect at a point X on the circumference of the circle, then $2r$ equals

(a) $\sqrt{PQ.RS}$ (b) $\dfrac{PQ+RS}{2}$

(c) $\dfrac{2PQ.RS}{PQ+RS}$ (d) $\sqrt{\dfrac{PQ^2+RS^2}{2}}$

(I.I.T. Sc. 2001)

(c) A diameter of $x^2+y^2-2x-6y+6=0$ is a chord to circle centre $(2,1)$, then radius of the circle is

(a) 1   (b) 2
(c) 3   (d) 4   **(Screening 2004)**

19. (a) Find the equation of circle which passes through the points $(3,0),(1,-6)$ and $(4,-1)$.

(b)* Determine the equation of family of circles passing through two given points $A(x_1,y_1)$ and $B(x_2,y_2)$. If a fixed circle S_1 cuts each member of the family in various chords then prove that all these chords pass through a fixed point.

20. (a) Find the equation of the circle passing through the point $(0,0)$ and the points where the straight line $3x+4y=12$ meets the axes of the co-ordinates.

(b) Which circumscribes a square of side a.
(J.E.E., W.B. 1992)

21. (a) A circle passes through a fixed point O and cuts two perpendicular straight lines through O in A and B. If the line AB passes through a fixed point (p,q), then the locus of the centre of the circle OAB is $\dfrac{p}{x}+\dfrac{q}{y}=2$.

(b) A circle of constant radius $3k$ passes through origin and meets the axes in points A and B. Prove that the locus of the centroid of the $\Delta\,OAB$ is the circle $x^2+y^2=4k^2$.

(c) Find the equation of circle which circumscribes the triangle formed by the lines $x=0$, $y=0$ and $lx+my=1$. Also find the locus of its centre if $l^2+m^2=4l^2m^2$. **(J.E.E., W.B. 1992)**

(d) A straight rod AB of fixed length c moves so that its extremities A,B lie on two fixed mutually perpendicular lines. Prove that the locus of the circumcentre of triangle OAB is a circle, where O is the point of intersection of mutually perpendicular straight lines.

22. (a) The line $x+3y=0$ is a diameter of the circle $x^2+y^2-6x+2y=0$.

Is this true or false ?

(b)* The lines $3x-4y+4=0$ and $6x-8y-7=0$ are tangents to the same circle. The radius of the circle is ....

23. (a)* Determine the equation of the circle passing through the points $(a,0)$ and $(0,a)$ and whose radius is as small as possible. Show that it will pass through the origin.

(b) The vertices of a triangle ABC are the points $(6,0)$, $(0,6)$ and $(7,7)$. Prove that the equation of the circle inscribed in the triangle is $x^2+y^2-9x-9y+36=0$.

24. (a) Find the equation of circle which passes through the vertices of the triangle formed by the lines $x+y+1=0$, $3x+y-5=0$, and $2x+y-5=0$.

(b)* Prove that the equation of the circle circumscribing the triangle formed by the sides whose equations are $2x+y-3=0$, $3x-y-7=0$ and $x-2y+1=0$ is $x^2+y^2-5x-y+4=0$.

(c) The sides of a triangle are given by the equations $x + y - 7 = 0$; $2x + y - 6 = 0$ and $2x - 3y - 6 = 0$. Find the equation of the circle circumscribing the triangle.

25. (a)* If $u_r = a_r x + b_r y + c_r = 0$ $(r = 1, 2, 3)$ be the three sides of a triangle then the equation of the circumcircle of this triangle is

$$\begin{vmatrix} \dfrac{1}{u_1} & \dfrac{1}{u_2} & \dfrac{1}{u_3} \\ a_2 a_3 - b_2 b_3 & a_3 a_1 - b_3 b_1 & a_1 a_2 - b_1 b_2 \\ a_2 b_3 + a_3 b_2 & a_3 b_1 + a_1 b_3 & a_1 b_2 + a_2 b_1 \end{vmatrix} = 0$$

Another form :

$$\begin{vmatrix} \dfrac{a_1^2 + b_1^2}{u_1} & \dfrac{a_2^2 + b_2^2}{u_2} & \dfrac{a_3^2 + b_3^2}{u_3} \\ a_1 & a_2 & a_3 \\ b_1 & b_2 & b_3 \end{vmatrix} = 0$$

(b)* If the circumcircle of the triangle formed by the lines $ax + by + c = 0$, $bx + cy + a = 0$, $cx + ay + b = 0$ passes through origin, prove that

$$\begin{vmatrix} b^2 & c^2 & a^2 \\ ab & bc & ca \\ ac & ab & bc \end{vmatrix} = \begin{vmatrix} b^2 & c^2 & a^2 \\ bc & ca & ab \\ ac & ab & bc \end{vmatrix}$$

Another form : $(b^2 + c^2)(c^2 + a^2)(a^2 + b^2)$
$$= abc(b + c)(c + a)(a + b)$$

(c)* The lines $L_r = x \cos \alpha_r + y \sin \alpha_r = p_r$ $(r = 1, 2, 3)$ are the sides of a triangle ABC. Find the equation of the circumcircle of triangle ABC. If the circle passes through origin, then prove that

$$\Sigma \, p_1 p_2 \sin(\alpha_1 - \alpha_2) = 0.$$

26. (a) Find the equation of circle which passes through the points $(9, 1)$, $(7, 9)$, $(-2, 12)$ and hence show that the four points $(9, 1)$, $(7, 9)$, $(-2, 12)$ and $(6, 10)$ lie on a circle.

(b) For what value of c are the points $(2, 0)$, $(0, 1)$, $(4, 5)$ and $(0, c)$ concyclic ?

(c)* Show that a cyclic quadrilateral is formed by the lines $5x + 3y = 9$, $x = 3y$, $2x = y$ and $x + 4y + 2 = 0$ taken in order. Find the equation of the circum-circle.

(d)* The equations of the sides of a quadrilateral are given by $L_r = A_r x + B_r y + C_r = 0$ where $r = 1, 2, 3, 4$. If the quadrilateral be cyclic then prove that $(A_1 B_2 - A_2 B_1)(A_3 A_4 - B_3 B_4)$
$$+ (A_1 A_2 + B_1 B_2)(A_3 B_4 - A_4 B_3) = 0$$

Another form : $\dfrac{A_1 A_3 - B_1 B_3}{A_1 B_3 + A_3 B_1} = \dfrac{A_2 A_4 - B_2 B_4}{A_2 B_4 - A_4 B_2}$.

(e) If $\alpha, \beta, \gamma, \delta$ be four angles of a cyclic quadrilateral taken in clockwise direction then the value of $(2 + \Sigma \cos \alpha \cos \beta)$ will be :

(a) $\sin^2 \alpha + \sin^2 \beta$ (b) $\cos^2 \gamma + \cos^2 \delta$

(c) $\sin^2 \alpha + \sin^2 \delta$ (d) $\cos^2 \beta + \cos^2 \gamma$

27. (a) Find the equation of circle which passes through the origin and cuts off chords of length b from lines $y = x$ and $y = -x$.

(b) Find the locus of mid-points of all chords of the circle $x^2 + y^2 - 2x = 0$ such that the pair of lines joining the origin and the extremities of the chord make equal angles with the x-axis.

28. (a) Find the equation of circle on which the co-ordinates of any point are $(2 + 4\cos\theta, -1 + 4\sin\theta)$, θ being the parameter.

(b) Find the parametric equation of the circle $x^2 + y^2 + x + \sqrt{3}y = 0$.

(c) Prove that the farthest point on the circle $x^2 + y^2 - 2x - 4y - 11 = 0$ from the origin is $\left(1 + \dfrac{4}{\sqrt{5}}, 2 + \dfrac{8}{\sqrt{5}}\right)$.

29. Find whether the point $\left(1, \dfrac{\sqrt{11} + 6}{6}\right)$ lies inside or outside the circle whose equation is
$$3x^2 + 3y^2 - 5x - 6y + 4 = 0.$$
Find its centre and radius.

30. (a)* The circle $x^2 + y^2 - 6x - 10y + k = 0$.
does not touch or intersect the co-ordinate axes and the point $(1, 4)$ is inside the circle. Find the ranges of the values of k.

(b) If the line $y = mx$ does not intersect the circle $(x + 10)^2 + (y + 10)^2 = (6\sqrt{5})^2$, then prove that $-2 < m < -1/2$.

(c) Find the condition for the line $px + qy + r = 0$ to touch the circle $x^2 + y^2 = a^2$.
Also find the co-ordinates of the point of contact.

31. (a)* If the lines
$a_1 x + b_1 y + c_1 = 0$ and $a_2 x + b_2 y + c_2 = 0$
cut the co-ordinate axes in concyclic points, prove $a_1 a_2 = b_1 b_2$ and also find the equation of that circle.

(b)* If a circle passes through the points of intersection of the co-ordinate axes with the lines $\lambda x - y + 1 = 0$ and $x - 2y + 3 = 0$, then the value of λ is ....

(I.I.T. 1991)

(c) P, Q, R and S are the points of intersection with the co-ordinate axes of the lines $ax + by = ab$ and $bx + ay = ab$, then P, Q, R, S are concyclic.

32.* Two rods of lengths a and b slide along the axes which are rectangular in such a manner that their ends are concyclic. Prove that the locus of the centre of circle passing through these ends is the curve $4(x^2 - y^2) = a^2 - b^2$.

33. (a) Prove that the locus of the point of intersection of the lines
$$x\cos\alpha + y\sin\alpha = a$$
and $x\sin\alpha - y\cos\alpha = b$,
is a circle whatever α may be.
(Another form is given in part (b))

(b) A tangent is drawn to each of the circles
$$x^2 + y^2 = a^2, \quad x^2 + y^2 = b^2.$$
Show that if the two tangents are mutually perpendicular, the locus of their point of intersection is a circle concentric with the given circles.

(c) Show that if two tangents are mutually perpendicular, the locus of their point of intersection is a circle concentric with the given circles.

(d) Find the radius of the circle
$$(x\cos\theta + y\sin\theta - a)^2$$
$$+ (x\sin\theta - y\cos\theta - b)^2 = k^2.$$
If θ bvaries then prove that locus of the centre of above circle is again a circle.

34. Show that the equation of the image of the circle
$$x^2 + y^2 + 16x - 24y + 183 = 0$$
by the line mirror $4x + 7y + 13 = 0$ is
$$x^2 + y^2 + 32x + 4y + 235 = 0$$

35. (a)* Show that the locus of a point such that the ratio of its distances from two given points is constant, is a circle. Hence show that the circle cannot pass through the given points.

(b) Given the base of a triangle and the ratio of the lengths of the other two unequal sides, prove that the vertex lies on a fixed circle.

36. (a)* A point moves so that the sum of the squares of the perpendiculars let fall from it on the sides of an equilateral triangle is constant, prove that its locus is a circle. **(M.N.R. 1996)**

(b) A point moves such that sum of the squares of its distances from the sides of a square of side unity is equal to 9. Show that the locus is a circle whose centre coincides with the centre of the square. Find also its radius.

(c) A point moves in such a manner that the sum of the squares of its distances from the vertices of a triangle is constant. Prove that the locus of the point is a circle whose centre is at the centroid of the triangle.

37. (a)* Two straight lines rotate about two fixed points. If they start from their position of coincidence such that one rotates at the rate double that of the other, prove that the locus of their point of intersection is a circle.

(b) A square is inscribed in the circle $x^2 + y^2 - 10x - 6y + 30 = 0$. One side of the square is parallel to $y = x + 3$, then determine the co-ordinates of its vertices.

38. (a) An isosceles triangle ABC with vertex at $A(a, 0)$ is inscribed in the circle $x^2 + y^2 = a^2$. If the base angles B and C be each $75°$, then the co-ordinates of B and C are

(a) $\left(\dfrac{a\sqrt{3}}{2}, \dfrac{a}{2}\right)$ (b) $\left(-\dfrac{a\sqrt{3}}{2}, \dfrac{a}{2}\right)$

(c) $\left(\dfrac{a\sqrt{3}}{2}, -\dfrac{a}{2}\right)$ (d) $\left(-\dfrac{a\sqrt{3}}{2}, -\dfrac{a}{2}\right)$

(b) A square is inscribed in the circle
$$x^2 + y^2 - 2x + 4y + 3 = 0.$$
Its sides are parallel to the co-ordinate axes. Then one vertex of the square is

(a) $(1 + \sqrt{2}, -2)$ (b) $(1 - \sqrt{2}, -2)$

(c) $(1, -2 + \sqrt{2})$ (d) None of these

39. (a) If a straight line through $C(-\sqrt{8}, \sqrt{8})$ making an angle of $135°$ with the x-axis cuts the circle $x = 5\cos\theta$, $y = 5\sin\theta$ in points A and B, find the length of segment AB. **(Bihar C.C.E. 1999)**

(b) Find the point on the straight line $y = 2x + 11$ which is nearest to the circle $16(x^2 + y^2) + 32x - 8y - 50 = 0$. **(Roorkee 2000)**

40. (a) The least and the greatest distances of the point $(10, 7)$ from the circle $x^2 + y^2 - 4x - 2y - 20 = 0$ are 5 and 15. Is this statement true or false ?

(b) Find the locus of a point whose shortest distance from the circle $x^2 + y^2 - 2x + 6y - 6 = 0$ is equal to its distance from the line $x - 3 = 0$.

41. (a) Find the equation of the circle whose radius is 5 and which touches externally the circle $x^2 + y^2 - 2x - 4y - 20 = 0$ at the point $(5, 5)$.

(b)* Two circles, each of radius 5 units, touch each other at $(1, 2)$. If the equation of their common tangent is $4x + 3y = 10$, find the equations of the circles. **(I.I.T. 1991)**

(c) A circle passes through the point $(-1, 7)$ and touches the line $y = x$ at $(1, 1)$. Its diameter is

(a) $4\sqrt{2}$ (b) 5
(c) $5\sqrt{2}$ (d) 6

(d)* Find the equation of the circle which touches the circle $x^2 + y^2 - 6x + 6y + 17 = 0$ externally and to which the lines $x^2 - 3xy - 3x + 9y = 0$ are normals. **(Roorkee 1994)**

42. (a) Find the equation of the circle whose radius is 3 and which touches internally the circle $x^2 + y^2 - 4x - 6y - 12 = 0$ at the point $(-1, -1)$.

(b) Prove that the circles $x^2 + y^2 + 2x + 2y + 1 = 0$ and $x^2 + y^2 - 4x - 6y - 3 = 0$ touch each other and find the co-ordinates of the point of contact.

(c) AB is a diameter of a circle; CD is a chord parallel to AB and $2CD = AB$. The tangent at B meets the line AC produced at E. Prove that $AE = 2AB$.

43. (a)* Find the co-ordinates of the point at which the circles
$$x^2 + y^2 - 4x - 2y = 4$$
and $x^2 + y^2 - 12x - 8y = 12$
touch each other. Also find equations of common tangents touching the circles in distinct points.
(I.I.T. 1993)

(b)* Prove that the locus of the centre of a circle which touches externally the circle $x^2 + y^2 - 6x - 6y + 14 = 0$ and also touches the y-axis is given by the equation $y^2 - 10x - 6y + 14 = 0$
(I.I.T. 1993)

(c) Find the equation of circles with radius 12 and touching the circle $x^2 + y^2 = 25$ at the point $(3, 4)$.

(d) Find the equation of circles with radius 15 and touching the circle $x^2 + y^2 = 100$ at the point $(6, -8)$.

44. (a)* Show that the circles
$$x^2 + y^2 - 10x + 4y - 20 = 0$$
and $x^2 + y^2 + 14x - 6y + 22 = 0$
touch each other. Find the co-ordinates of the point of contact and the equation of the common tangent at the point of contact.

(b)* Prove that the following circles are such that each of them touches the other two. Determine the points of contact. Show also that the three tangents concur at the point $(-3, -3)$.
$$S_1 \equiv x^2 + y^2 + 4y - 1 = 0,$$
$$S_2 \equiv x^2 + y^2 + 6x + y + 8 = 0,$$
$$S_3 \equiv x^2 + y^2 - 4x - 4y - 37 = 0$$

(c) Find the equation of the circle of minimum radius which contains the three circles
$$S_1 \equiv x^2 + y^2 - 4y - 5 = 0,$$
$$S_2 \equiv x^2 + y^2 + 12x + 4y + 31 = 0,$$
and $S_3 \equiv x^2 + y^2 + 6x + 12y + 36 = 0$

(d) If the circles $S_1 \equiv 0, S_2 \equiv 0$ i.e., g_1, f_1, c_1 and g_2, f_2, c_2 touch each other, then prove that $[2g_1g_2 + 2f_1f_2 - (c_1 + c_2)]^2 = 4r_1^2 r_2^2$, where r_1, r_2 are the radii of the two circles.

45. (a)* A circle of radius 2 lies in the first quadrant and touches both the axes of co-ordinates. Find the equation of the circle with centre at $(6, 5)$ and touching the above externally.

(b)* Determine the locus of the centres of the circles, which touch the two circles $x^2 + y^2 = a^2$ and $x^2 + y^2 = 4ax$ and are external to both.

46. (a) Show that the circles
$$x^2 + y^2 + 2ax + 4ay - 3a^2 = 0$$
and $x^2 + y^2 - 8ax - 6ay + 7a^2 = 0$
touch and determine the point of contact.

(b) Prove that the circles
$$x^2 + y^2 + 2ax + c = 0$$
and $x^2 + y^2 + 2by + c = 0$
will touch one another if $1/a^2 + 1/b^2 = 1/c$.

Another form :
$$\frac{1}{a^2}, \frac{1}{2c}, \frac{1}{b^2} \text{ are in A.P.}$$
or $a^2, 2c, b^2$ are in H.P.

(c) Prove that the two circles
$$x^2 + y^2 + 2ax + 2by + c = 0 \text{ and}$$
$x^2 + y^2 + 2bx + 2ay + c = 0$ will touch each other if $(a + b)^2 = 2c$.

47. (a) Given the equations of two circles
$$x^2 + y^2 = r^2 \text{ and } x^2 + y^2 - 10x + 16 = 0,$$
the value of r such that they intersect in real and distinct points is given by $2 < r < 8$.

(b)* If the two circles
$$(x - 1)^2 + (y - 3)^2 = r^2$$
and $x^2 + y^2 - 8x + 2y + 8 = 0$
intersect in two distinct points, then prove that $2 < r < 8$.

(c)* Prove that the two circles $x^2 + y^2 - 2x - 3 = 0$ and $x^2 + y^2 - 4x - 6y - 8 = 0$ are such that they intersect each other. **(M.N.R. 1995)**

48. (a)* The centres of the circle passing through the points $(0, 0), (1, 0)$ and touching the circle $x^2 + y^2 = 9$ are $(1/2, \pm\sqrt{2})$. **(I.I.T. 1992)**

(b)* Without drawing a diagram to scale, show that the circle $x^2 + (y - 1)^2 = 16$ lies completely inside the circle $x^2 + y^2 - x = 26$.

(c) Let C_1 and C_2 be two circles with C_2 lying inside C_1. A circle C lying inside C_1 touches C_1 internally and C_2 externally. Identify the locus of the centre of C. **(I.I.T. 2001)**

(d) Find the equation of the circle having the lines $x^2 + 2xy + 3x + 6y = 0$ as its normal and having size just sufficient to contain the circle $x(x - 4) + y(y - 3) = 0$. **(Roorkee 1990)**

49. (a) If the line $x \cos \alpha + y \sin \alpha = p$ cuts the circle $x^2 + y^2 = a^2$ in M and N, then show that the circle whose diameter is MN is
$$x^2 + y^2 - a^2 = 2p(x \cos \alpha + y \sin \alpha - p).$$

(b)* The intercept on the line $y = x$ by the circle $x^2 + y^2 - 2x = 0$ is AB. Equation of the circle with AB as a diameter is .... **(I.I.T. 1996)**

(c) Determine equation of the circle whose diameter is the chord $x + y = 1$ of the circle $x^2 + y^2 = 4$ **(M.N.R. 1993)**

50. (a)* $y = mx$ is a chord of the circle of radius a through the origin and whose diameter is along the axis of x. Find the equation of the circle whose diameter is the chord. Hence find the locus of its centre for all values of m.

(b) A circle of radius 4 is drawn whose diameter is along the axis of x. The line $y = 2x$ is a chord of the circle. Determine the equation of the circle whose diameter is this chord.

51. (a)* The equation of two circles are
$$(x - a)^2 + y^2 = a^2 \text{ and } x^2 + (y - b)^2 = b^2.$$
Prove that the equation of the circle whose diameter is their common chord is
$$(a^2 + b^2)(x^2 + y^2) = 2ab(bx + ay).$$

(b) The equation of the line passing through the intersection of the circles
$$3x^2 + 3y^2 - 2x + 12y - 9 = 0$$
and $x^2 + y^2 + 6x + 2y - 15 = 0$ is ....

(c) Show that the equation of the circle which has for its diameter, the chord cut off by the straight line $ax + by + c = 0$ by the circle
$$(a^2 + b^2)(x^2 + y^2) = 2c^2 \text{ is}$$
$$(a^2 + b^2)(x^2 + y^2) + 2c(ax + by) = 0$$

52. (a) Find the equation of the circle in which the chord joining the points (a, b) and $(b, -a)$ subtends an angle of $45°$ at any point on the circumference of the circle.

(b)* Find the equation of circle(s) at any point on which the line joining the points $(-1, 1)$ and $(5, 5)$ subtends an angle of $45°$.

53. (a) Find the equations of the circles passing through the points of intersection of the circles
$$x^2 + y^2 - 2x - 4y - 4 = 0$$
and $x^2 + y^2 - 10x - 12y + 40 = 0$
and whose radius is 4.

(b) Find the equation of the circle passing through the points of intersection of the circles
$$x^2 + y^2 - 6x + 2y + 4 = 0,$$
and $x^2 + y^2 + 2x - 4y - 6 = 0$
and with its centre on the line $y = x$.

(c)* The equation of the circle having its centre on the line $x + 2y - 3 = 0$ and passing through the points of intersection of the circles
$$x^2 + y^2 - 2x - 4y + 1 = 0$$
and $x^2 + y^2 - 4x - 2y + 4 = 0$ is

(a) $x^2 + y^2 - 6x + 7 = 0$

(b) $x^2 + y^2 - 3y + 4 = 0$

(c) $x^2 + y^2 - 2x - 2y + 1 = 0$

(d) $x^2 + y^2 - 2x - 4y + 4 = 0$ **(M.N.R. 1992)**

54. (a) Find the equations of circles which touch $2x - y + 3 = 0$ and pass through the points of intersection of the line $x + 2y - 1 = 0$ and the circle $x^2 + y^2 - 2x + 1 = 0$.

(b)* A circle passes through the point $(2, 1)$ and the line $x + 2y = 1$ is a tangent to it at the point $(3, -1)$. Determine its equation.

(c)* Find the equation of the circles passing through the intersection of the circles
$$x^2 + y^2 - 4 = 0$$
and $x^2 + y^2 - 2x - 4y + 4 = 0$
and touching the line $x + 2y = 0$.

(d) A fixed circle is cut by circles passing through two fixed points $A(x_1, y_1)$ and $B(x_2, y_2)$. Prove that the chord of intersection of the fixed circle with any of the circles passes through a fixed point.

55. (a) Two circles $x^2 + y^2 = 6$ and $x^2 + y^2 - 6x + 8 = 0$ are given. Find the equation of the circle through their points of intersection and the point $(1, 1)$.

(b) The equation of the circle passing through $(1, 1)$ and the points of intersection of the circle
$$x^2 + y^2 + 13x - 3y = 0$$
and $2x^2 + 2y^2 + 4x - 7y - 25 = 0$ is
$$4x^2 + 4y^2 + 30x - 13y - 25 = 0.$$

56. (a)* The circle $x^2 + y^2 + 2gx + 2fy + c = 0$ bisects the circumference of the circle
$$x^2 + y^2 + 2g'x + 2f'y + c' = 0.$$
Prove that $2g'(g - g') + 2f'(f - f') = (c - c')$.

(b) The circumference of the circle
$$x^2 + y^2 - 2x + 8y - q = 0$$
is bisected by the circle
$$x^2 + y^2 + 4x + 22y + p = 0.$$
Prove that $p + q = 50$.

(c) Determine the equation of the circle which touches the line $x - y = 0$ at the origin and bisects the circumference of the circle $x^2 + y^2 + 2y - 3 = 0$.

(d) Find the equation of the circle which cuts each of the circles

$x^2 + y^2 - 4 = 0$, $x^2 + y^2 - 6x - 8y + 10 = 0$,
$x^2 + y^2 + 2x - 4y - 2 = 0$
at the extremities of a diameter.

57. (a)* Prove that the length of the common chord of the circles $(x-a)^2 + (y-b)^2 = c^2$ and $(x-b)^2 + (y-a)^2 = c^2$ is $\sqrt{4c^2 - 2(a-b)^2}$. Hence find the condition that the two circles may touch each other.

(b) If the circle $c_1, x^2 + y^2 = 16$ intersects another circle c_2 of radius 5 in such a manner that the common chord is of maximum length and has a slope equal to $3/4$, then the co-ordinates of the centre of c_2 are ......

(c) Let L_1 be a straight line passing through the origin and L_2 be the straight line $x + y = 1$. If the intercepts made by the circle $x^2 + y^2 - x + 3y = 0$ on L_1 and L_2 are equal, then which of the following equations can represent L_1 ?
 (a) $x + y = 0$ (b) $x - y = 0$
 (c) $x + 7y = 0$ (d) $x - 7y = 0$ (I.I.T. 1999)

58. (a) Prove that the length of the common chord of the circles $x^2 + y^2 + ax + by + c = 0$
and $x^2 + y^2 + bx + ay + c = 0$
is $\sqrt{\dfrac{1}{2}(a+b)^2 - 4c}$.

(b) Prove that the length of the common chord of the two circles $x^2 + y^2 + 2hx + a^2 = 0$
and $x^2 + y^2 - 2ky - a^2 = 0$ is
$$2\sqrt{\left[\dfrac{(h^2 - a^2)(k^2 + a^2)}{h^2 + k^2}\right]}.$$

(c)* The circle $x^2 + y^2 - 2x + 2y - 14 = 0$ cuts chords of length $2\sqrt{3}$ from lines which belong to the family of lines $(x + 5y - 22) - \lambda(x - 8y + 30) = 0$. Determine the equations of the lines of the family.

(d) Find the equation of a circle whose centre is the point $(3, -1)$ and which cuts off a chord of length 6 on the line $2x + 5y + 18 = 0$.

(e) If a chord of the circle $x^2 + y^2 - 4x - 2y - c = 0$ is trisected at the points $P\left(\dfrac{1}{3}, \dfrac{1}{3}\right), Q\left(\dfrac{8}{3}, \dfrac{8}{3}\right)$, then prove the following :
 (a) length of chord $= 7\sqrt{2}$
 (b) radius of circle $= 5$
 (c) $c = 20$.

59.* Two chords of length 5 are drawn from any point $(3, 4)$ on the circle $4x^2 + 4y^2 - 24x - 7y = 0$. Prove that their equations are given by $y - 4 = \pm \dfrac{4}{3}(x - 3)$.

60. (a)* The points of intersection of the line $4x - 3y - 10 = 0$ and the circle $x^2 + y^2 - 2x + 4y - 20 = 0$ are .... and ....

(b) Find the range of λ if the line $3x - 4y = \lambda$ meets the circle $x^2 + y^2 - 4x - 8y - 5 = 0$ in real points.

61. (a) The abscissas of the two points A and B are the roots of the equation $x^2 + 2ax - b^2 = 0$ and their ordinates are the roots of the equation $x^2 + 2px - q^2 = 0$. Find the equation and the radius of the circle with AB as diameter.

(b)* The abscissas of the two points A and B are the roots of the equation $x^2 + 2x - a^2 = 0$ and the ordinates are the roots of the equation $y^2 + 4y - b^2 = 0$. Find the equation of the circle with AB as its diameter. Also find the co-ordinates of the centre and the length of the radius of the circle.

62.* Obtain the equation of the straight lines passing through the point $A(2, 0)$ and making an angle of $45°$ with the tangent at A to the circles $(x + 2)^2 + (y - 3)^2 = 25$. Find the equation of the circle each of radius 3, whose centres are on these straight lines at a distance of $5\sqrt{2}$ units from A.

63. If $(m_i, 1/m_i), m_i > 0, i = 1, 2, 3, 4$ are four distinct points on a circle, then show that $m_1 m_2 m_3 m_4 = 1$.

64. (a)* The extremities of a diagonal of rectangle are $(-4, 4)$ and $(6, -1)$. A circle circumscribes the rectangle and cuts an intercept AB on the y-axis. Find the area of the triangle formed by AB and tangents to the circle at A and B.   (Roorkee 1992)

(b) $2x - y + 4 = 0$ is a diameter of the circle which circumscribes a rectangle $ABCD$. If the co-ordinates of A, B are $(4, 6)$ and $(1, 9)$, find the area of $ABCD$, and show that it is a square.
     (J.E.E., W.B. 1992)

(c)* One of the diameters of the circle circumscribing the rectangle $ABCD$ is $4y = x + 7$. If A and B are the points $(-3, 4)$ and $(5, 4)$ respectively, then find the area of the rectangle.

65. (a)* Find the radius of the smallest circle which touches the straight line $3x - y = 6$ at $(1, -3)$ and also touches the line $y = x$. Compute upto one place of decimal only.   (I.I.T. 1991)

(b)* Find the equation of the circles which touch at the point $(1, 2)$, one of the two intersecting lines which are tangents to it and whose equations are $7x - y - 5 = 0$ and $x + y + 13 = 0$

66.* Find the equation of circles which touch the two lines $x - 2y + 4 = 0$ and $2x - y - 8 = 0$ and also pass through the point $(4, -1)$.

67. (a)* Consider a family of circles passing through two fixed points $A(3, 7)$ and $B(6, 5)$. Show that the

chords in which the circle $x^2 + y^2 - 4x - 6y - 3 = 0$ cuts the members of the family are concurrent at a point. Find the co-ordinates of this point. **(I.I.T. 1993)**

(b)* Find the equations of the circles which pass through the points $A(-1, 4)$ and $B(1, 2)$ and which touch the line $3x - y - 3 = 0$.

68.* Show that all chords of the curve $3x^2 - y^2 - 2x + 4y = 0$ which subtend a right angle at the origin are concurrent. Does this result hold for the curve $3x^2 + 3y^2 - 2x + 4y = 0$? If yes, what is the point of concurrency and if not, give reasons. **(Roorkee 1992)**

69. (a)* The two circles $x^2 + y^2 + 2ax - c^2 = 0$ and $x^2 + y^2 + 2bx - c^2 = 0$ meet in points P and Q. Parallel lines are drawn through P and Q to meet the circles in points R and S. Prove that the locus of mid-point of RS is the circle

$$x^2 + y^2 + (a+b)x = 0.$$

(b) Let $ABCD$ be a quadrilateral with area 18, with side AB parallel to the side CD and $AB = 2CD$. Let AD be perpendicular to AB and CD. If a circle is drawn inside the quadrilateral $ABCD$ touching all the sides, then its radius is

(a) 3 (b) 2
(c) 3/2 (d) 1 **(I.I.T. 2007)**

70.* Let C be any circle with centre $(0, \sqrt{2})$. Prove that at the most two rational points can be there on C. (A rational point is a point both of whose co-ordinates are rational numbers). **(I.I.T. Re-ex. 1997)**

Solutions to Problem Set (1)

1. (a) Since it touches $2x - y - 4 = 0$, hence perpendicular from centre $(1, -3)$ is equal to radius.

Thus $r = \dfrac{2 \cdot 1 - (-3) - 4}{\sqrt{(4+1)}} = \dfrac{1}{\sqrt{(5)}}$.

Equation is $(x-1)^2 + (y+3)^2 = 1/5$.

(b) Centre $C(2, 2)$ and $r = CP$ where P is any point $(4, 5)$. ∴ $r = CP = \sqrt{13}$ etc.

Ans. $x^2 + y^2 - 4x - 4y - 5 = 0$.

(c) Let the circle be (h, k), 4 and as it touches x-axis therefore $(h, 4)$, 4. But h is +ive as C is in 1st quadrant.
$4x - 3y = 0$ is a tangent and hence $p = r$ gives $4h - 12 = \pm 20$ ∴ $h = 8$ only being +ive
∴ Circle is $(8, 4)$, 4.

Ans. $x^2 + y^2 - 16x - 8y + 64 = 0$.

(d) Ans. (c).
Centre is $(1, -1)$ the point of intersection of diameters. Area ⇒ $r = 7$. Hence its equation is $(x-1)^2 + (y+1)^2 = 49$

2. (a) Let the circle be
$$x^2 + y^2 + 2gx + 2fy + c = 0.$$
It touches y-axis i.e. $x = 0$ at $(0, 3)$
∴ $y^2 + 2fy + c = (y-3)^2 = y^2 - 6y + 9$

Eq. (12) P. 850

Comparing $f = -3$, $c = 9$.
Intercept on x-axis is
$$I_x = 2\sqrt{g^2 - c} = 8 \quad ∴ \quad g^2 - 9 = 16$$
or $g^2 = 16 + 9 = 25$ or $g = \pm 5$.
Hence the required equation is
$$x^2 + y^2 \pm 10x - 6y + 9 = 0.$$

(b) Touches axis of y i.e. $x = 0$ at $(0, \sqrt{3})$
∴ $y^2 + 2fy + c = (y - \sqrt{3})^2 = y^2 - 2\sqrt{3}y + 3$

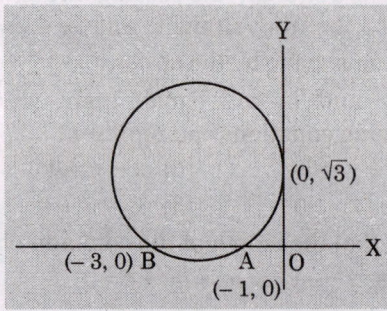

Fig. 13

∴ $f = -\sqrt{3}$, $c = 3$.
It intersects x-axis i.e. $y = 0$ at $(-1, 0)$ and $(-3, 0)$
∴ $x^2 + 2gx + c = (x+1)(x+3) = x^2 + 4x + 3$
∴ $g = 2$ and $c = 3$.
Hence the circle is
$$x^2 + y^2 + 4x - 2\sqrt{3}y + 3 = 0$$

Alt : Clearly $I_x = 2 = 2\sqrt{g^2 - c}$ ∴ $1 = g^2 - 3$
or $g^2 = 4$ ∴ $g = \pm 2$.
Centre $(-g, -f)$ lies in 2nd quadrant.
∴ $-g = -$ive, $-f = +$ive
∴ $g = 2$ so that $-g = -2$ etc.

(c) Since it passes through origin, ∴ $c = 0$ and its equation is
$$x^2 + y^2 + 2gx + 2fy = 0.$$
Intercept on x-axis
$$2\sqrt{g^2 - c} = a. \quad ∴ \quad g = \pm a/2, \because c = 0$$
Intercept on y-axis
$$2\sqrt{f^2 - c} = b. \quad ∴ \quad f = \pm b/2, \because c = 0.$$
Hence the circle is $x^2 + y^2 \pm ax \pm by = 0$.

(d) Ans. (a).
Let $B(\alpha, \beta)$ be the other end of diameter through $A(p, q)$. Centre is $\left(\dfrac{p+\alpha}{2}, \dfrac{q+\beta}{2}\right)$ and $AB = 2r$.

We know that if a circle touches the axis of x then it is of the form $(h, k), k$ i.e., ordinate of centre = radius

$\therefore \quad \dfrac{q+\beta}{2} = r$ or $(q+\beta)^2 = 4r^2 = (2r)^2 = AB^2$

or $\quad (q+\beta)^2 = (p-\alpha)^2 + (q-\beta)^2$

or $\quad 4q\beta = (p-\alpha)^2$

$\therefore \quad$ Locus of (α, β) is $(x-p)^2 = 4qy$.

(e) **Ans. (b).**

Let the circle be $(h, k), k$ as it touches the axis of x. Again it touches the circle $(0, 3), 2$ therefore distance between the centres is equal to $r_1 \pm r_2$

$\therefore \quad \sqrt{h^2 + (k-3)^2} = k \pm 2$

$\quad h^2 + k^2 - 6k + 9 = k^2 \pm 4k + 4$

$\therefore \quad$ Locus of (h, k) is $x^2 = 10y - 5$

or $\quad x^2 = 2y - 5$

In either case it is a parabola.

3. (a) Its intersection with x-axis will give equal roots.
$x^2 - 4x + \lambda = 0$ has equal roots.

$\therefore \quad \Delta = 0$ i.e. $16 - 4\lambda = 0$ or $\lambda = 4$

and it becomes $x^2 - 4x + 4 = 0$

or $\quad (x-2)^2 = 0$

$\therefore \quad$ Point of contact is $(2, 0)$.

(b) **$p < r$ chord; $p = r$ tangent; $p > r$ does not meet.**
Circle is $(4, -1), \sqrt{5}$ and $p = r$ and hence the line is a tangent.

Alt. Eliminate y and find a quadratic in x. If real roots–chord, equal roots–tangent, and if imaginary roots– it does not meet the circle. Here the line is a tangent as $p = r$ or as quadratic has equal roots given by $(x-3)^2 = 0$.

4. (a) **Ans. (c).**
Angle subtended by QR at centre O is $90°$ as
$$m_1 m_2 = \frac{4}{3} \cdot \frac{3}{-4} = -1.$$

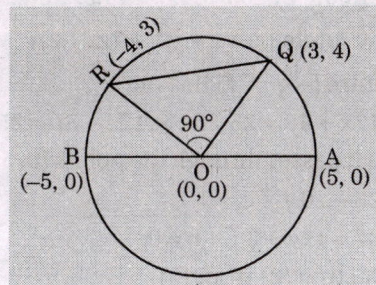

Fig. 14

Hence angle at circumference at P (anywhere) will be half of $\pi/2$. $\therefore$ Angle at P i.e. $\angle QPR = \pi/4$.

(b) **Ans. (b).**
Let AB be any chord subtending an angle of $90°$ at centre $O(0, 0)$, then

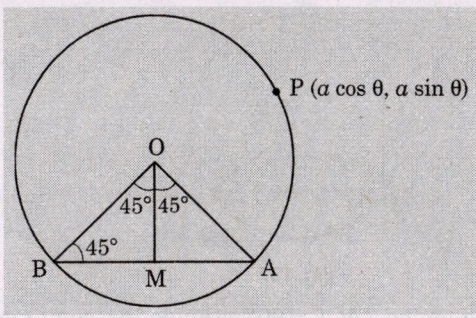

Fig. 15

$OM = AM = BM = a\cos 45° = \dfrac{a}{\sqrt{2}}$

$\therefore \quad A\left(\dfrac{a}{\sqrt{2}}, -\dfrac{a}{\sqrt{2}}\right), B = \left(-\dfrac{a}{\sqrt{2}}, -\dfrac{a}{\sqrt{2}}\right)$

If P be any point on the circle, then P is $(a\cos\theta, a\sin\theta)$

If (h, k) be the centroid, then

$$3h = a\cos\theta + 0, 3k = a\sin\theta - \frac{a}{\sqrt{2}} - \frac{a}{\sqrt{2}}$$

Eliminate θ

$(3h - 0)^2 + (3k + a\sqrt{2})^2 = a^2$

or $\quad x^2 + \left(y + \dfrac{a}{3}\sqrt{2}\right)^2 = \left(\dfrac{a}{3}\right)^2$

or $\quad$ Circle $\left(0, -\dfrac{a}{3}\sqrt{2}\right), \dfrac{a}{3}.$

(c) **Ans. (b).**
Make homogeneous
$$x^2 + y^2 - (6x + 8y)\frac{(4x + 3y)}{24} = 0$$

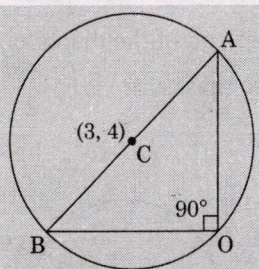

Fig. 16

or $\quad 50xy = 0 \quad \therefore \quad x = 0, y = 0$

These lines are clearly perpendicular.

2nd Method : The given line AB is a diameter as it passes through centre $(3, 4)$. $O(0, 0)$ is a point on the circle as $9 + 16 = 25$.

$\therefore \quad \angle AOB = \pi/2$ as angle in a semi-circle is $90°$.

$\therefore \quad OA$ is perpendicular to OB.

(d) The common chord is given by $S_1 - S_2 = 0$

or $\quad 4x + 4y = 16$ or $\quad x + y = 4$

which is a diameter of the first circle as it passes through centre $(2, 2)$. Also $(0, 0)$ lies on this circle

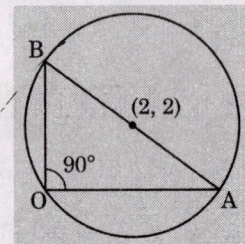

Fig. 137

and hence $\angle AOB = 90°$ as angle in a semi-circle is a right angle.

(e) Ans. (d).

PQ is the common chord of the two circles whose equation is given by $S_1 - S_2 = 0$ or $5ax + (c - d)y + (a + 1) = 0$.

Compare with given line PQ,

$$5x + by - a = 0$$

$$\therefore \quad \frac{a}{1} = \frac{c-d}{b} = \frac{a+1}{-a}$$

$$\therefore \quad -a^2 = a + 1 \text{ or } a^2 + a + 1 = 0$$

Above gives only imaginary values of a, i.e., no real values of a.

5. (a) **Refer (q) P. 853.**

Since $(0, g)$ lies inside

$$\therefore \quad S' = g^2 + c = - \text{ive}$$

If c is +ive, then $S' = + $ive always.

Hence c cannot be +ive.

(b) A point P is outside, on or inside a circle $S = 0$ according as $S' > = < 0$

$\therefore \quad (0, 1)$ is on the circle, $(3, 1)$ is outside and $(1, 3)$ inside.

(c) Let the other end of the diameter through $A(\alpha, \beta)$ be $B(p, q)$ so that centre is $\left(\dfrac{p+\alpha}{2}, \dfrac{q+\beta}{2}\right)$ and

$$(\text{diameter})^2 = 4r^2 = (p - \alpha)^2 + (q - \beta)^2 \quad ...(1)$$

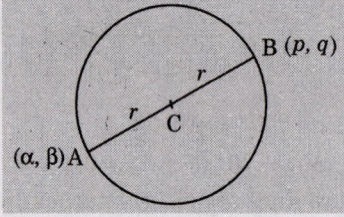

Fig. 18

Since the circle touches x-axis, its radius is ordinate of centre, i.e. $\dfrac{q+\beta}{2} = r$

or $(q + \beta)^2 = 4r^2$ ...(2)

$\therefore \quad (q + \beta)^2 - (q - \beta)^2 = (p - \alpha)^2$ by (1) and (2)

or $(p - \alpha)^2 = 4\beta q$

Hence locus of (p, q) is $(x - \alpha)^2 = 4\beta y$.

6. (a) Let the centre be (h, k).

$$(x - h)^2 + (y - k)^2 = 1$$

or $(1 - h)^2 + (1 - k)^2 = 1$

$(2 - h)^2 + (2 - k)^2 = 1$. Subtract.

$(3 - 2h).1 + (3 - 2k).1 = 0$

or $h + k = 3 \quad \therefore \quad k = 3 - h$

$(1 - h)^2 + (1 - 3 + h)^2 = 1$

or $(1 - h)^2 + (h - 2)^2 = 1$

$2h^2 - 6h + 4 = 0 \quad$ or $\quad h^2 - 3h + 2 = 0$

or $h = 1, 2 \quad \therefore \quad k = 2, 1$

Centres are $(1, 2)$ or $(2, 1)$ and radius $= 1$

Ans. $(x - 1)^2 + (y - 2)^2 = 1$,

$(x - 2)^2 + (y - 1)^2 = 1$

(b) Ans. (a).

$S + \lambda P = 0$ where P is line AB. **(n) P. 853**

$$x^2 + y^2 - 2x + \lambda(x - y) = 0 \quad ...(1)$$

Its centre $\left(\dfrac{2-\lambda}{2}, \dfrac{\lambda}{2}\right)$ lies on diameter AB, i.e.,

$y = x$.

$$\therefore \quad \frac{\lambda}{2} = \frac{2-\lambda}{2} \quad \therefore \quad 2\lambda = 2 \text{ or } \lambda = 1$$

$$\therefore \quad x^2 + y^2 - x - y = 0 \text{ by (1)}.$$

7. (a) If r is radius of the circle, then $\pi r^2 = 154$

or $r^2 = 154 \times \dfrac{7}{22} = 49 \quad \left[\text{Taking } \pi = \dfrac{22}{7}\right]$

$\therefore \quad r = 7$.

Also solving the equations of two given diameters we get the co-ordinates of the centre as $(1, -1)$. Hence the equation of the circle is as given.

(b) Ans. $(x - 2)^2 + (y + 1)^2 = 1$.

Centre is point of intersection of the diameters i.e. $(2, -1)$ and as it touches x-axis, radius is y co-ordinate of centre i.e. -1 i.e. 1 etc.

8. (a) Let the circle be $x^2 + y^2 + 2gx + 2fy + c = 0$.

Its centre $(-g, -f)$ lies on

$$12x + 5y = 25 \quad \therefore \quad -12g - 5f = 25. \quad ...(1)$$

Again it passes through the points $(0, 5)$ and $(6, 1)$

$\therefore \quad 25 + 10f + c = 0$ ...(2)

and $37 + 12g + 2f + c = 0$. ...(3)

Subtracting (2) from (3),

$$12g - 8f = -12. \quad ...(4)$$

Adding (1) and (4),

$-13f = 13, \quad \therefore \quad f = -1$.

$\therefore \quad g = -5/3$ and $c = -15$.

Hence the circle is $x^2 + y^2 - \dfrac{10}{3}x - 2y - 15 = 0$.

(b) Proceed as in part (a).

Ans.$15x^2 + 15y^2 - 94x + 18y + 55 = 0$.

9. (a) The given tangents are parallel and therefore the distance between them

$$= 2r = \frac{10 - (-30)}{5} = 8 \quad \therefore \quad r = 4$$

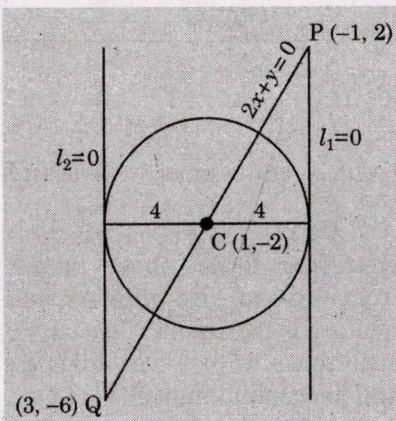

Fig. 19

Now the diameter $2x + y = 0$ cuts the given line in the points $P(-1, 2)$ and $Q(3, -6)$ whose middle point is therefore the centre $(1, -2)$.

Hence its equation is $(x - 1)^2 + (y + 2)^2 = 4^2$

(b) $x^2 + y^2 - 2x + 4y - 11 = 0$

The given tangents are parallel

$$\therefore \quad d = 2r = \frac{37}{2\sqrt{13}} \quad \therefore \quad r = \frac{37}{4\sqrt{3}}$$

10. (a) Let the circle be g, f, c so that its centre $(-g, -f)$ is in 3rd quadrant so that both g and f are to be + ive. Centre lies on $x - y - 1 = 0$

$$\therefore \quad -g + f - 1 = 0 \qquad \ldots(1)$$

Touches x-axis

$$\therefore \quad I_x = 2\sqrt{g^2 - c} = 0 \quad \therefore \quad g^2 = c \qquad \ldots(2)$$

Touches $4x - 3y + 4 = 0 \quad \therefore \quad p = r$

$$\Rightarrow \quad \frac{-4g + 3f + 4}{\pm 5} = \sqrt{g^2 + f^2 - c} = f, \text{ by (2)}$$

$$\therefore \quad -4g + 3f + 4 = 5f \quad \text{or} \quad -5f$$

$$\therefore \quad -g + 2f + 1 = 0 \qquad \ldots(3)$$

or $2g + f - 2 = 0 \qquad \ldots(4)$

Solving (1), (3) or (1), (4), we get

$g = -3, f = -2$ rejected

$g = \frac{1}{3}, f = \frac{4}{3}$ both + ive $\therefore \quad c = g^2 = \frac{1}{9}$

$$\therefore \quad x^2 + y^2 + \frac{2}{3}x + \frac{8}{3}f + \frac{1}{9} = 0$$

or $9(x^2 + y^2) + 6x + 24y + 1 = 0$.

(b) Let the circle be g, f, c.

It passes through $(2, 0) \quad \therefore \quad 4 + 4g + c = 0 \quad \ldots(1)$

Since it makes an intercept 5 on x-axis hence it must pass through $(5 + 2, 0)$ i.e. $(7, 0)$.

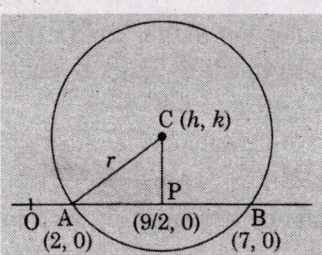

Fig. 20

$$\therefore \quad 49 + 14g + c = 0 \qquad \ldots(2)$$

Solving, $2g = -9, c = 14$

There is no other relation to give the value of f.

$$\therefore \quad x^2 + y^2 - 9x + 2fy + 14 = 0$$

where $2f$ is – ive as centre lies in 1st quadrant.

11. (a) If (h, k) be the centre then $k = h - 1$ as it lies on $y = x - 1$. Also $r = 3$.

$$\therefore \quad \text{Equation is } (x - h)^2 + (y - h + 1)^2 = 9 \quad \ldots(1)$$

It passes through the point $(7, 3)$

$$\therefore \quad h^2 - 11h + 28 = 0 \quad \therefore \quad h = 4, 7. \text{ Put in (1)}.$$

(b) Let $C(h, k)$ be the centre and A, B be the given points, then

$$CA^2 = CB^2 = r^2 = p^2$$

where p is perpendicular from centre to the tangent $3x + y - 3 = 0$

$$CA^2 = CB^2 \Rightarrow h + k = 5 \qquad \ldots(1)$$

$$CA^2 = p^2 \Rightarrow (h - 1)^2 + (k - 2)^2$$

$$= \left(\frac{3h + k - 3}{\sqrt{10}}\right)^2 \qquad \ldots(2)$$

Now eliminate k and you will find

$$2h^2 - 11h + 12 = 0$$

$$\therefore \quad h = 4, 3/2, \quad k = 1, 7/2 \text{ and } r^2 = 10, 10/4$$

Hence the circles are $(x - h)^2 + (y - k)^2 = r^2$

12. (a) Eliminating y, we get

$$(3c^2 - c - 2)x = c^2 - 1$$

$$\therefore \quad x = \frac{(c - 1)(c + 1)}{(c - 1)(3c + 2)} = \frac{c + 1}{3c + 2}$$

$$\therefore \quad \text{limit when } c \to 1 \text{ gives } x = 2/5 \text{ and hence }$$

$y = -1/25$.

$$\therefore \quad \text{Centre } (-g, -f) \text{ is } (2/5, -1/25).$$

$$\therefore \quad \text{Circle is }$$

$$x^2 + y^2 - (4/5)x + (2/25)y + k = 0.$$

It passes through $(2, 0) \quad \therefore \quad k = -(12/5)$

Hence the required circle is

$$25(x^2 + y^2) - 20x + 2y - 60 = 0.$$

(b) Tangent to parabola $y = x^2$ at $(2, 4)$ is

$$\frac{1}{2}(y + 4) = x \cdot 2 \quad \text{or} \quad 4x - y - 4 = 0$$

It is also a tangent to the circle so that the centre lies on the normal through (2, 4) whose equation is $x + 4y = \lambda$ where $2 + 16 = \lambda$

$\therefore$ $x + 4y = 18$ is the normal on which lies (h, k).

$\therefore$ $h + 4k = 18$ ...(1)

Again distance of centre (h, k) from (2, 4) and (0, 1) the points on the circle are equal

$\therefore$ $(h - 2)^2 + (k - 4)^2 = h^2 + (k - 1)^2$

$\therefore$ $4h + 6k = 19$ ...(2)

Solving (1) and (2), we get the centre $(-16/5, 53/10)$.

13. (a) Since the circle touches x-axis therefore its equation is $(x - h)^2 + (y - k)^2 = k^2$ ...(1)

(Rule (c), P. 850)

It passes through the given points.

$\therefore$ $(1 - h)^2 + (-2 - k)^2 = k^2$ ...(2)

$(3 - h)^2 + (-4 - k)^2 = k^2$ ...(3)

Subtracting (2) and (3), we get $h = k + 5$

Putting in (2), we get $k^2 + 12k + 20 = 0$

$\therefore$ $k = -10, -2$ and hence $h = -5, 3$

$\therefore$ Centres are $(-5, -10)$ or $(3, -2)$

$\therefore$ Circles are $(x + 5)^2 + (y + 10)^2 = 10^2$

and $(x - 3)^2 + (y + 2)^2 = 2^2$

(b) Proceed as in part (a) above. The required circle is $(h, k), h$

or $A\left(\dfrac{5}{2}a, 3a\right), \dfrac{5}{2}a$ and $B\left(\dfrac{205}{3}a, \dfrac{29}{3}a\right), \dfrac{205}{3}a$.

Now angle between tangents is the same as angle between normals i.e. radii. So find slopes m_1, m_2 of the radii AP and BP where P is any of the given points $(4a, a)$ or $(a, 5a)$ etc.

(c) Proceed as in part (a); here $f^2 = c$ as the circle touches the y-axis. The equation of the circles are

$x^2 + y^2 - 20x - 22y + 121 = 0$

and $x^2 + y^2 - 4x - 6y + 9 = 0$

2nd part : A question of Maxima. Now let the point on y-axis be $P(0, \lambda)$ and suppose $\angle APB = \theta$.

m_1 of $PB = \dfrac{5 - \lambda}{2 - 0} = \dfrac{5 - \lambda}{2}$

and m_2 of $PA = \dfrac{3 - \lambda}{4 - 0} = \dfrac{3 - \lambda}{4}$

$\tan \theta = \dfrac{\left(\dfrac{5 - \lambda}{2}\right) - \left(\dfrac{3 - \lambda}{4}\right)}{1 + \dfrac{(5 - \lambda)(3 - \lambda)}{8}}$

or $y = \tan \theta = \dfrac{2(7 - \lambda)}{\lambda^2 - 8\lambda + 23}$ ...(1)

Clearly θ will be greatest when $\tan \theta$ is greatest.

Now $\dfrac{dy}{d\lambda} = 2 \cdot \dfrac{(-1)(\lambda^2 - 8\lambda + 23) - (2\lambda - 8)(7 - \lambda)}{(\lambda^2 - 8\lambda + 23)^2}$

or $\dfrac{dy}{d\lambda} = \dfrac{2(\lambda^2 - 14\lambda + 33)}{(\lambda^2 - 8\lambda + 23)^2} = \dfrac{2(\lambda - 3)(\lambda - 11)}{+ \text{ive}}$

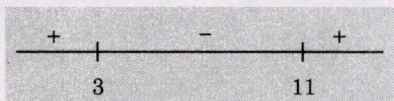

Fig. 21

For max. and min. of y, we must have $\dfrac{dy}{d\lambda} = 0$.

$\therefore$ $\lambda = 11$ or 3.

From the figure above $dy/d\lambda$ changes sign from + ive to − ive while passing through 3 and hence y is maximum when $\lambda = 3$ and it changes sign from − ive to + ive while passing through 11 and hence minimum at $\lambda = 11$.

$\therefore$ Max. $y = $ Max. $\tan \theta = \dfrac{2(7 - 3)}{9 - 24 + 23} = 1$, by (1)

$\therefore$ $\theta = 45°$

$\therefore$ The greatest value of $\angle APB$ is 45°.

(d) From the figure $\cos \theta = 3/5$ and $\sin \theta = 4/5$. If the third vertex of the square be $C(x, y)$, then

$y = CL = 5 \sin (90° - \theta) = 5 \cos \theta = 5 \times \dfrac{3}{5} = 3$

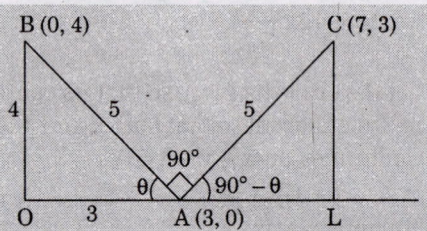

Fig. 22

$x = OL = OA + AL = 3 + 5 \cos (90° - \theta)$

$= 3 + 5 \sin \theta$

$= 3 + 5 \times \dfrac{4}{5} = 3 + 4 = 7$

The point C is $(7, 3)$. Hence, the equation of the circle having centre at $(7, 3)$ and touching x-axis is

$(x - h)^2 + (y - k)^2 = k^2$

or $(x - 7)^2 + (y - 3)^2 = 3^2$

or $x^2 + y^2 - 14x - 6y + 49 = 0$

14. (a) From the figure it is clear that centre of such a circle will lie in 1st and 4th quadrant and as it touches both the axes it is of the form $(h, \pm h), h$ where $2h = c$ or $h = c/2$.

Therefore its equation is

$(x - c/2)^2 + (y \pm c/2)^2 = (c/2)^2$

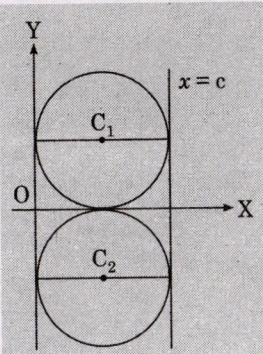

Fig. 23

(b) Circle touching both axes is $(h, h), h$ i.e.

$$(x - h)^2 + (y - h)^2 = h^2 \qquad ...(1)$$

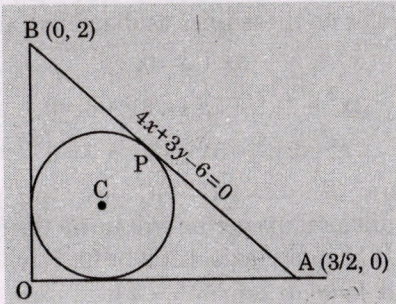

Fig. 24

The condition of tangency with given line gives

$$\frac{4h + 3h - 6}{\pm 5} = h \quad \text{or} \quad 7h - 6 = \pm 5h$$

$\therefore \quad h = 3, 1/2.$

Since the circle is to lie below the line, the value of h cannot exceed 3/2 hence $h = 3$ is rejected.

$\therefore \quad h = 1/2.$ Putting in (1) we get the answer.

(c) Centre (h, h) and radius h as in (a) as it touches co-ordinate axes on + ive sides. Again it touches the line $3x + 2y - 6 = 0$.

$$\therefore \quad \frac{3h + 2h - 6}{\pm \sqrt{(13)}} = h \quad \text{or} \quad (5h - 6)^2 = 13h^2$$

$$\text{or} \quad 12h^2 - 60h + 36 = 0 \quad \text{or} \quad h^2 - 5h + 3 = 0.$$

$$\therefore \quad h = \frac{5 \pm \sqrt{13}}{2} \text{ (both + ive)}$$

Here there will be two circles, one on either side of the line $3x + 2y - 6 = 0$ and touching both the axes. In part (b) similar to above we had found two circles but taken only one as the circle was to lie below the line.

15. (a) The given circle is $(-3, 3), 3$. Hence it touches both the axes in IInd quadrant. The lines which make equal intercepts $(m = \pm 1)$ on the axes are of the form $x - y = a$ or $x + y = b$. ...(1)
The condition of tangency $p = r$ with lines (1) gives $a = -6 \pm 3\sqrt{2}$ and $b = \pm 3\sqrt{2}$.

(b) The pair of lines is $x^2 - (y - 1)^2 = 0$

or $x + y - 1 = 0$ and $x - y + 1 = 0$

If (h, k) be the centre, then it will lie on the bisectors of these

$$\therefore \quad \frac{h + k - 1}{\sqrt{2}} = \pm \frac{h - k + 1}{\sqrt{2}} = r$$

$\therefore$ either $k = 1$ or $h = 0$

when $k = 1$ then $h = \pm \sqrt{2}r$

when $h = 0$ then $k = 1 \pm \sqrt{2}r$

Hence the circles are

$$(x \pm \sqrt{2}r)^2 + (y - 1)^2 = r^2$$

or $(x - 0)^2 + (y - 1 \mp \sqrt{2}r)^2 = r^2$

Above give the required families of circles, r being the parameter.

We call the above as family of circles because of parameter r. Here we are given only two conditions whereas a circle is completely determined if three conditions are given to find three unknowns g, f, c or h, k, r.

(c) Let the sides AB and AD be chosen along the axes and hence the circle touches the axes so that it is $(h, h), h$.

$$(x - h)^2 + (y - h)^2 = h^2 \qquad ...(1)$$

Also equation of PQ by intercepts form is

$$\frac{x}{h} + \frac{y}{h} = 1 \quad \text{or} \quad x + y = h. \qquad ...(2)$$

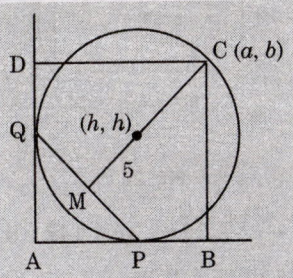

Fig. 25

as $AP = AQ = h$

Let the vertex C be (a, b) whose distance from PQ is 5, given

$$\therefore \quad \frac{a + b - h}{\sqrt{2}} = 5$$

$$\therefore \quad a + b = 5\sqrt{2} + h \qquad ...(3)$$

We have to find the area of rectangle, i.e., ab

Again (a, b) lies on circle (1)

$$\therefore \quad (a - h)^2 + (b - h)^2 = h^2$$

$$a^2 + b^2 - 2h(a + b) + h^2 = 0$$

Putting the value of h from (3),

$$(a^2 + b^2) - 2(a + b)[a + b - 5\sqrt{2}]$$
$$+ (a + b - 5\sqrt{2})^2 = 0$$

or $\quad (a+b)^2 - 2ab - 2(a+b)^2 + 10\sqrt{2}(a+b)$
$\qquad\qquad +(a+b)^2 - 10\sqrt{2}(a+b) + 50 = 0$

or $\quad -2ab + 50 = 0$

$\therefore \quad ab = 25 = $ area of rectangle.

16. (a) The required circle by **Rule (i) P. 851** is
$\qquad (x+4)(x-12) + (y-3)(y+1) = 0$

or $\quad x^2 + y^2 - 8x - 2y - 51 = 0$.

$\therefore \quad g = -4,\ f = -1,\ c = -51$.

Intercept on y-axis

$\qquad 2\sqrt{f^2 - c} = 2\sqrt{(1+51)} = 2\sqrt{52} = 4\sqrt{13}$

Rule (g), P. 851.

(b) $x(x-2) + (y+1)(y-3) = 0$

or $\quad x^2 + y^2 - 2x - 2y - 3 = 0$;

$\therefore \quad g = -1,\ f = -1,\ c = -3$.

Intercept on x-axis $= 2\sqrt{(g^2 - c)} = 2\sqrt{1+3} = 4$.

Rule (g), P. 851.

(c) Let the given lines be AB, BC, CD and DA respectively which enclose a rectangle $ABCD$. Solving them we get the points B and D as $(7, 1)$ and $(20, 2)$. Now write the equation of circle on BD as diameter.

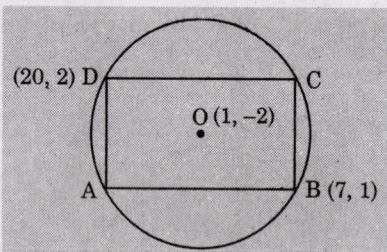

Fig. 26

Ans. $\quad x^2 + y^2 - 27x - 3y + 142 = 0$

(d) The four lines are $x = 2, x = 6, y = 5, y = 9$. Hence the vetices of the square are $(2, 5), (2, 9), (6, 5), (6, 9)$. The centre of the circle in the square is mid-point of AC or BD, i.e., $(4, 7)$.

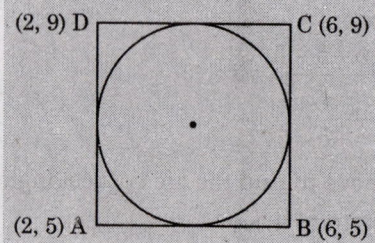

Fig. 27

17. (a) The given side of length 1 lies along x-axis and the third vertex will lie on a line perpendicular to x-axis and passing through mid-point $(3/2, 0)$ of given side. If it be $(3/2, k)$, then

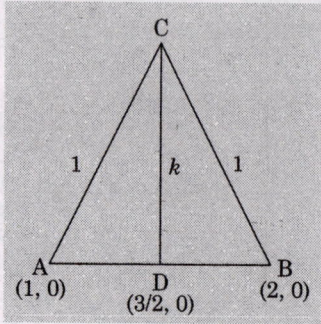

Fig. 28

$k = CD = 1 . \sin 60° = \dfrac{\sqrt{3}}{2}$

$\therefore \quad A(1,0), B(2,0), C(3/2, \sqrt{3}/2)$. The required circles on these lines as diameters are

$\qquad x^2 + y^2 - 3x + 2 = 0,$

$\qquad 2x^2 + 2y^2 - 7x + \sqrt{3}y + 6 = 0$

$\qquad 2x^2 + 2y^2 - 5x - \sqrt{3}y + 3 = 0$

(b) Here $\quad BC = 2 = AB = AC$ as the triangle is equilateral. Its vertex will lie on the right bisector of BC i.e. on y-axis. Let it be $(0, k)$ where k is + ive and equal to $2 \sin 60° = \sqrt{3}$.

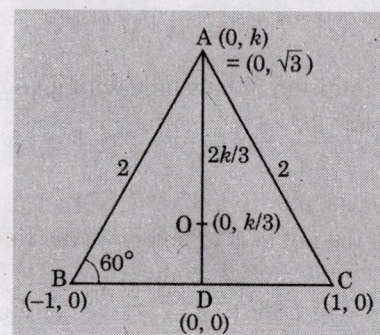

Fig. 29

Its centre O will coincide with centroid $G\left(0, \dfrac{k}{3}\right)$ i.e. $\left(0, \dfrac{1}{\sqrt{3}}\right)$ and radius $r = OA = \dfrac{2k}{3} = \dfrac{2}{\sqrt{3}}$.

Circle is $x^2 + \left(y - \dfrac{1}{\sqrt{3}}\right)^2 = \left(\dfrac{2}{\sqrt{3}}\right)^2$

or $\quad x^2 + y^2 - \dfrac{2y}{\sqrt{3}} - 1 = 0$

(c) Ans. $x^2 + y^2 = 4a^2$. In an equilateral triangle the circumcentre and centroid coincide so the centre is $(0, 0)$. Also centroid divides the median in the ratio $2 : 1$. Hence radius is $\dfrac{2}{3}(3a) = 2a$.

$\therefore \quad$ Circle is $x^2 + y^2 = 4a^2$.

(d) Ans. $x^2 + (y-2)^2 = 4^2$.

Here two lines each makes an angle of 60° with $y = 0$ (x-axis) and hence triangle is equilateral each side being $\sqrt{48} = 4\sqrt{3}$. The median as before lies along altitude and is $4\sqrt{3}\sin 60° = 6$.

∴ The centroid coincides with circumcentre and divides it in the ratio $2:1$.

∴ $r = \dfrac{2}{3}(6) = 4$ and centre is at $(0,2)$.

18. (a) Let OC be the common chord of the circles drawn on OA and OB as diameters. Then angle in a semi-circle being a right angle

$$\angle OCA = \angle OCB = 90°$$

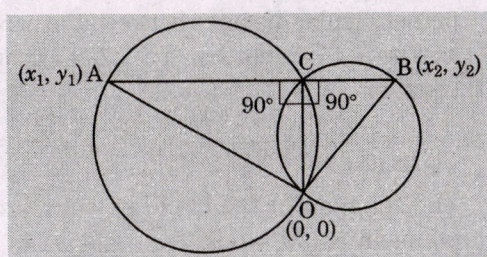

Fig. 30

∴ ACB is a straight line.

$$\Delta OAB = \frac{1}{2}(x_1 y_2 - x_2 y_1) = \frac{1}{2}OC \cdot AB$$

∴ $OC = $ length of c.c. $= \dfrac{x_1 y_2 - x_2 y_1}{AB}$

(b) Ans. (a).

The tangents PQ and RS meet at X.

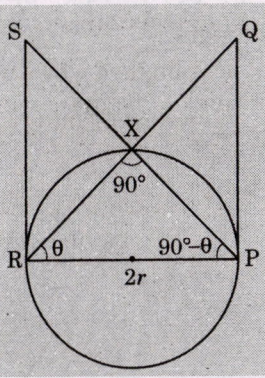

Fig. 31

The point X lies on the circumference and we know that any diameter subtends a rt. angle at any point on the circumference

∴ $\tan\theta = \dfrac{PQ}{2r}$ and $\tan(90° - \theta) = \dfrac{RS}{2r}$

∴ $\tan\theta \cot\theta = \dfrac{PQ \cdot RS}{(2r)^2}$

or $d = 2r = \sqrt{PQ \cdot RS}$

(c) Ans. (c) $S_1 = x^2 + y^2 - 2x - 6y + 6 = 0$

or $(1,3), 2$

$S_2 = (x-2)^2 + (y-1)^2 = r^2$ (say)

or $x^2 + y^2 - 4x - 2y + (5 - r^2) = 0$

Their common chord is $S_1 - S_2 = 0$

$2x - 4y + (1 + r^2) = 0$

This chord being diameter of S_1, passes through the centre $(1, 3)$ of S_1

∴ $2 - 12 + 1 + r^2 = 0$

∴ $r^2 = 9$ or $r = 3$

19. (a) **First Method :**

$$x^2 + y^2 + 2gx + 2fy + c = 0.$$

It passes through the points $(3,0), (1,-6)$ and $(4,-1)$.

∴ $6g + 0f + 9 + c = 0$ ...(1)

$2g - 12f + 37 + c = 0$ ...(2)

$8g - 2f + 17 + c = 0.$ ...(3)

Subtracting (2) from both (1) and (3) thereby eliminating c,

$4g + 12f - 28 = 0$

or $g + 3f - 7 = 0$ ...(4)

$6g + 10f - 20 = 0$

or $3g + 5f - 10 = 0$ ...(5)

Solving (4) and (5), we get

$f = 11/4, \quad g = -5/4$

and hence from (1), $c = -3/2$.

Putting for g, f and c the required circle is

$$2x^2 + 2y^2 - 5x + 11y - 3 = 0.$$

Second Method : When three points A, B, C are given, we write the equation of a circle on AB as diameter, say $S = 0$ and also the equation of AB, say $u = 0$. Then any circle through A, B will be of the form $S + \lambda u = 0$. Then λ is determined by the condition that it passes through C. Here A, B, C are $(3,0), (1,-6)$ and $(4,-1)$ respectively. The circle on AB as diameter is

$S = (x-3)(x-1) + (y-0)(y+6) = 0$

or $S = x^2 + y^2 - 4x + 6y + 3 = 0$

And equation of the line AB is

$$y - 0 = \frac{-6-0}{1-3}(x-3)$$

or $u = 3x - y - 9 = 0$

∴ Any circle through A, B is $S + \lambda u = 0$

i.e. $x^2 + y^2 - 4x + 6y + 3 + \lambda(3x - y - 9) = 0$

It passes through $(4, -1)$ so that

$16 + 1 - 16 - 6 + 3 + \lambda(12 + 1 - 9) = 0$

∴ $\lambda = \dfrac{2}{4} = \dfrac{1}{2}$

Hence the required equation of the circle is

$$x^2 + y^2 - 4x + 6y + 3 + \frac{1}{2}(3x - y - 9) = 0$$

or $2x^2 + 2y^2 - 5x + 11y - 3 = 0$

(b) We can determine the equation of a circle passing through three points as its equation involves three unknowns g, f and c. However, if only two points A and B are given, we can find the family of circles given by

$$S + \lambda L = 0 \quad \text{[(n) , P. 858]} \qquad \text{...(1)}$$

where S is circle on AB as diameter and L is the line AB.

$$S_1 = 0 \qquad \text{...(2)}$$

is another fixed circle.

Common chords of (1) and (2) are given by

Rule : $S_1 - S_2 = 0$ *i.e.*, $(S + \lambda L) - S_1 = 0$

or $(S - S_1) + \lambda L = 0$ or $U + \lambda L = 0$,

where U is common chord of S and S_1 which is fixed. But $U + \lambda L = 0$ represents a family of straight lines (*i.e.*, common chords) which pass through the intersection of fixed lines $U = 0$ and $L = 0$ and hence a fixed point.

20. (a) Refer particular case **Circle OAB** as $x^2 + y^2 - ax - by = 0$ **(P. 851)**. Here $O(0,0)$, $A(4,0), B(0,3)$.

Ans. $x^2 + y^2 - 4x - 3y = 0$.

(b) Take one vertex as origin and two sides along axes. The required circle will be on join of $(0, 0)$ and (a, a) as diameter, *i.e.*

$$(x - 0)(x - a) + (y - 0)(y - a) = 0$$

or $x^2 + y^2 - ax - ay = 0$

21. (a) $x^2 + y^2 - ax - by = 0$ is the circle OAB,

whose centre is $(a/2, b/2)$. The line AB $\dfrac{x}{a} + \dfrac{y}{b} = 1$

passes through (p, q)

$\therefore \quad \dfrac{p}{a} + \dfrac{q}{b} = 1$. Put $\dfrac{a}{2} = x, \dfrac{b}{2} = y$

$\therefore \quad \dfrac{p}{x} + \dfrac{q}{y} = 2$ is the required locus.

(b) Circle OAB is $x^2 + y^2 - ax - by = 0$

where $\dfrac{a^2}{4} + \dfrac{b^2}{4} - 0 = r^2 = 9k^2$

If (x, y) be centroid of OAB, then $x = \dfrac{a}{3}, y = \dfrac{b}{3}$.

Eliminate a and b and you get the result.

(c) Circle OAB as usual is

$x^2 + y^2 - \left(\dfrac{1}{l}\right)x - \left(\dfrac{1}{m}\right)y = 0$ whose centre is

$(x, y) = \left(\dfrac{1}{2l}, \dfrac{1}{2m}\right)$. The given condition can be

written as $\dfrac{1}{l^2} + \dfrac{1}{m^2} = 4$.

$\therefore$ Locus is $(2x)^2 + (2y)^2 = 4$ or $x^2 + y^2 = 1$.

(d) Let $A(a, 0)$, $B(0, b)$ be the points on the axes then $\angle AOB = \pi/2$ therefore circle OAB is on AB as diameter whose equation is

$(x - a)(x - 0) + (y - 0)(y - b) = 0$

or $x^2 + y^2 - ax - by = 0$.

If (h, k) be the centre then $h = a/2$, $k = b/2$.

Since $AB = c$ $\therefore$ $a^2 + b^2 = c^2$

or $4h^2 + 4k^2 = c^2$.

$\therefore$ Locus of centre is $x^2 + y^2 = c^2/4$.

22. (a) Ans. True. Since the centre $(3, -1)$ of the circle lies on the line $x + 3y = 0$

(b) Ans. $3/4$. The diameter of the circle is the perpendicular distance between the parallel lines $3x - 4y + 4 = 0$ and $3x - 4y - (7/2) = 0$ and so it is equal to

$$\dfrac{4}{\sqrt{(9 + 16)}} - \dfrac{-7/2}{\sqrt{(9 + 16)}} = \dfrac{3}{2}. \quad \therefore \quad r = \dfrac{3}{4}$$

23. (a) The equation of the circle passing through two points by $S + \lambda P = 0$ is

$x(x - a) + y(y - a) + \lambda(x + y - a) = 0$

or $x^2 + y^2 - (a - \lambda)x - (a - \lambda)y - \lambda a = 0$.

We have to choose λ such that its radius is least

$$r^2 = \left(\dfrac{a - \lambda}{2}\right)^2 + \left(\dfrac{a - \lambda}{2}\right)^2 + \lambda a = 0$$

$$\dfrac{1}{2}(a^2 + \lambda^2 - 2a\lambda + 2a\lambda) = \dfrac{1}{2}(a^2 + \lambda^2)$$

It will be least when $\lambda = 0$ and hence the required circle is $x^2 + y^2 - ax - by = 0$ which passes through origin.

(b) Centre is obtained by using the formula $\left(\dfrac{\Sigma ax_1}{\Sigma a}, \dfrac{\Sigma ay_1}{\Sigma a}\right)$ for incentre

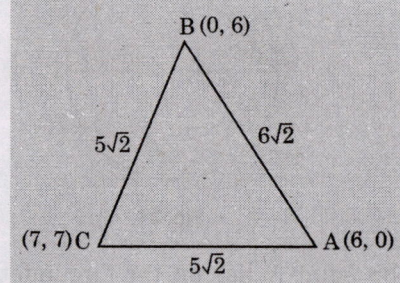

Fig. 32

$\left(\dfrac{72\sqrt{2}}{16\sqrt{2}}, \dfrac{72\sqrt{2}}{16\sqrt{2}}\right)$ or $\left(\dfrac{9}{2}, \dfrac{9}{2}\right)$

Radius is distance of centre from any side say AB whose equation by intercepts form is

$$\dfrac{x}{6} + \dfrac{y}{6} = 1 \quad \text{or} \quad x + y - 6 = 0$$

$\therefore \quad r = \dfrac{\dfrac{9}{2} + \dfrac{9}{2} - 6}{\sqrt{2}} = \dfrac{3}{\sqrt{2}}$

$\therefore$ Circle is $\left(x - \dfrac{9}{2}\right)^2 + \left(y - \dfrac{9}{2}\right)^2 = \left(\dfrac{3}{\sqrt{2}}\right)^2$

or $x^2 + y^2 - 9x - 9y + 36 = 0$

24. (a) See (j) three methods P. 851.

Solving the sides of the triangle in pairs the required vertices are $(3, -4), (0, 5)$ and $(6, -7)$. Now proceeding as in **Q. 19 P. 856-870** the circle is
$x^2 + y^2 - 30x - 10y + 25 = 0$.

Alternative : Without finding the points of intersection, let the equation of the circle through the points of intersection of given lines be

$l_1 l_2 + \lambda (l_2 l_3) + \mu (l_3 l_1) = 0$ ...(1)

Apply the condition that the above equation represents a circle i.e. coeff. of x^2 = coeff. of y^2 and coeff. of $xy = 0$. This will give two equations in λ and μ. Solve and put in (1). All this is explained with a numerical example given in part (b) below.

(b) Let the equation of the lines be $P = 0, Q = 0, R = 0$. Consider the equation $QR + \lambda RP + \mu PQ = 0$

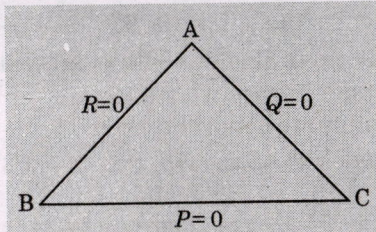

Fig. 33

$(3x - y - 7)(x - 2y + 1) + \lambda (x - 2y + 1)(2x + y - 3)$
$\qquad + \mu (2x + y - 3)(3x - y - 7) = 0$ ...(1)

The above equation is satisfied by $Q = 0, R = 0$ i.e. point A and similarly by points B and C. Hence the curve whatsoever it may be passes through the points A, B and C. Since it is to be a circle.

$\therefore$ Coeff. of x^2 = Coeff. of y^2 and

Coeff. of $xy = 0$ in (1)

$\therefore$ $3 + 2\lambda + 6\mu = 2 - 2\lambda - \mu$

and $-7 + \lambda(-3) + \mu(1) = 0$

or $4\lambda + 7\mu = -1$ and $3\lambda - \mu = -7$

Solving the above, we get $\lambda = -2, \mu = 1$.

Putting the values of λ and μ in (1), we get the result as given.

(d) Proceed as in part (a).

$5(x^2 + y^2) - 18x - 44y + 9 = 0$

25. (a) It is exactly the same as last part

$u_2 u_3 + \lambda u_3 u_1 + \mu u_1 u_2 = 0$ ...(1)

$(a_2 x + b_2 y + c_2)(a_3 x + b_3 y + c_3)$
$\qquad + \lambda (a_3 x + b_3 y + c_3)(a_1 x + b_1 y + c_1)$
$\qquad + \mu (a_1 x + b_1 y + c_1)(a_2 x + b_2 y + c_2) = 0$

Apply the condition that it represents a circle

$a_2 a_3 + \lambda a_3 a_1 + \mu a_1 a_2 = b_2 b_3 + \lambda b_3 b_1 + \mu b_1 b_2$

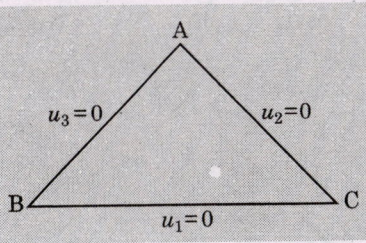

Fig. 34

or $(a_2 a_3 - b_2 b_3) + \lambda (\ ) + \mu (\ ) = 0$ ...(2)
and $(a_2 b_3 + a_3 b_2) + \lambda (\ ) + \mu (\ ) = 0$ ...(3)

Eliminating λ, μ between (1), (2), (3), we get the result in determinant form. Divide R_1 by $u_1 u_2 u_3$ etc.

Another form : Expanding above, the coefficient of $\dfrac{1}{u_1}$ is

$(a_3 a_1 - b_3 b_1)(a_1 b_2 + a_2 b_1) - (a_3 b_1 + a_1 b_3).$
$\qquad\qquad\qquad\qquad\qquad (a_1 a_2 - b_1 b_2).$

There will be eight terms in the above out of which four will cancel and the remaining four are

$a_3 b_2 (a_1^2 + b_1^2) - a_2 b_3 (a_1^2 + b_1^2)$

$= (a_1^2 + b_1^2)(a_3 b_2 - a_2 b_3)$

$= (a_1^2 + b_1^2)\begin{vmatrix} a_2 & a_3 \\ b_2 & b_3 \end{vmatrix}$ etc.

(b) As in other parts the equation of the curve which passes through the vertices of the triangle formed by the given lines is

$(bx + cy + a)(cx + ay + b) + \lambda (cx + ay + b)$
$(ax + by + c) + \mu (ax + by + c)(bx + cy + a) = 0$ ...(1)

If it represents circumcircle of the triangle then coeff. of x^2 = coeff. of y^2 and coeff. of $xy = 0$

$bc + \lambda ca + \mu ab = ca + \lambda ab + \mu bc$

or $c(a - b) + \lambda a(b - c) + \mu b(c - a)$ ...(2)

and $(c^2 + ab) + \lambda (a^2 + bc) + \mu (b^2 + ca) = 0$ ...(3)

If (1) passes through $(0, 0)$, then

$ab + \lambda bc + \mu ca = 0$ ...(4)

Eliminating λ, μ from (2), (3) and (4), we get

$\begin{vmatrix} ca - bc & ab - ca & bc - ab \\ c^2 + ab & a^2 + bc & b^2 + ca \\ ab & bc & ca \end{vmatrix} = 0$

Apply $R_2 - R_3$

$\begin{vmatrix} ac - bc & ab - ca & bc - ab \\ c^2 & a^2 & b^2 \\ ab & bc & ca \end{vmatrix} = 0$

$\begin{vmatrix} ac & ab & bc \\ c^2 & a^2 & b^2 \\ ab & bc & ca \end{vmatrix} = \begin{vmatrix} bc & ca & ab \\ c^2 & a^2 & b^2 \\ ab & bc & ca \end{vmatrix}$

Now interchange R_1 and R_2 and then make C_3 cross over two columns to get the required form.

(c) L_1 is $x \cos \alpha_1 + y \sin \alpha_1 - p_1 = 0$ etc.

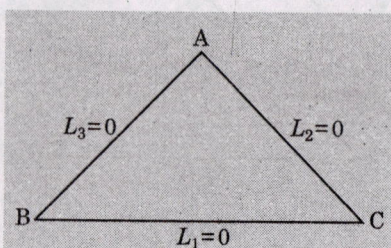

Fig. 35

Now as in other parts the circumcircle of $\triangle ABC$ is

$$L_2 L_3 + \lambda L_3 L_1 + \mu L_1 L_2 = 0 \qquad \ldots(1)$$
$(x \cos \alpha_2 + y \sin \alpha_2 - p_2)$
$(x \cos \alpha_3 + y \sin \alpha_3 - p_3) + \lambda (\ ) + \mu (\ ) = 0$

It will represent a circle if coeff. of x^2 = coeff. of y^2 and coeff. of xy is zero.

$\cos \alpha_2 \cos \alpha_3 + \lambda \cos \alpha_3 \cos \alpha_1 + \mu \cos \alpha_1 \cos \alpha_2$
$= \sin \alpha_2 \sin \alpha_3 + \lambda \sin \alpha_3 \sin \alpha_1 + \mu \sin \alpha_1 \sin \alpha_2$

or $\cos (\alpha_2 + \alpha_3) + \lambda \cos (\alpha_3 + \alpha_1)$
$\qquad + \mu \cos (\alpha_1 + \alpha_2) = 0 \qquad \ldots(2)$

Again equating to zero the coefficient of xy, we get

$\sin (\alpha_2 + \alpha_3) + \lambda \sin (\alpha_3 + \alpha_1)$
$\qquad + \mu \sin (\alpha_1 + \alpha_2) = 0 \qquad \ldots(3)$

Eliminating λ, μ from (1), (2) and (3) the equation of circle is

$$\begin{vmatrix} L_2 L_3 & L_3 L_1 & L_1 L_2 \\ \cos (\alpha_2 + \alpha_3) & \cos (\alpha_3 + \alpha_1) & \cos (\alpha_1 + \alpha_2) \\ \sin (\alpha_2 + \alpha_3) & \sin (\alpha_3 + \alpha_1) & \sin (\alpha_1 + \alpha_2) \end{vmatrix} = 0$$

Above is the required equation of the circle. In case it passes through $(0, 0)$, then putting $x = 0$, $y = 0$ in L_1, L_2, L_3 the above reduces to

$$\begin{vmatrix} p_2 p_3 & p_3 p_1 & p_1 p_2 \\ \cos (\alpha_2 + \alpha_3) & \cos (\alpha_3 + \alpha_1) & \cos (\alpha_1 + \alpha_2) \\ \sin (\alpha_2 + \alpha_3) & \sin (\alpha_3 + \alpha_1) & \sin (\alpha_1 + \alpha_2) \end{vmatrix} = 0$$

or $\Sigma p_2 p_3 \sin (\alpha_1 + \alpha_2 - \alpha_3 - \alpha_1) = 0$
or $p_2 p_3 \sin (\alpha_2 - \alpha_3) + p_3 p_1 \sin (\alpha_3 - \alpha_1)$
$\qquad + p_1 p_2 \sin (\alpha_1 - \alpha_2) = 0$

26. (a) As in **Q. 19 P. 856-870** , $g = 0, f = -3, c = -76$

$$x^2 + y^2 - 6y - 76 = 0$$

and it passes through $(6, 10)$ also.

(b) $3(x^2 + y^2) - 13x - 17y + 14 = 0$. It passes through $(0, c)$.

$\therefore \quad 3c^2 - 17c + 14 = 0 \qquad \therefore \quad c = 1, \ 14/3$.

$\therefore \quad c = 14/3$ as $c = 1$ is already there for point $(0, 1)$.

(c) Solving, the vertices are

$$A\left(\frac{3}{2}, \frac{1}{2}\right), B(0, 0), C\left(-\frac{2}{9}, -\frac{4}{9}\right), D\left(\frac{42}{17}, -\frac{19}{17}\right).$$

The equation of the circle is

$$x^2 + y^2 + 2gx + 2fy = 0$$

as it passes through $B(0, 0)$.

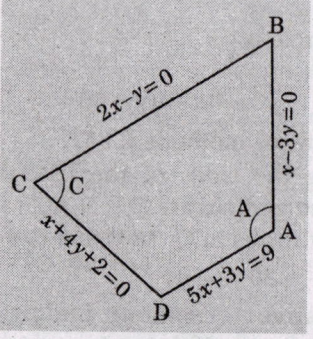

Fig. 36

It passes through A and C

$\therefore \quad \frac{9}{4} + \frac{1}{4} + 3g + f = 0$

or $10 + 12g + 4f = 0$

$\frac{4}{81} + \frac{16}{81} - \frac{4g}{9} - \frac{8f}{9} = 0$

or $20 - 36g - 72f = 0$

Solving for f and g, we get $g = -\frac{10}{9}$, $f = \frac{5}{6}$

Hence the circle is $9(x^2 + y^2) - 20x + 15y = 0$. The co-ordinates of 4th point D also satisfy it.

Note : In case we are to show only that the four points are concyclic, then

slopes of AD and AB are $-5/3, 1/3$

$\therefore \quad \tan A = \frac{-5/3 - 1/3}{1 - 5/9} = -\frac{9}{2}$

slopes of CB and CD are $2, -1/4$

$\therefore \quad \tan C = \frac{2 + 1/4}{1 - 2.1/4} = \frac{9}{2}$

$\therefore \quad \tan A = -\tan C = \tan (\pi - C)$

$\therefore \quad A = \pi - C$ or $A + C = \pi$

Hence $B + D = \pi$

Therefore $ABCD$ is a cyclic quadrilateral.

(d) If the quadrilateral be cyclic, then $\theta + \phi = \pi$

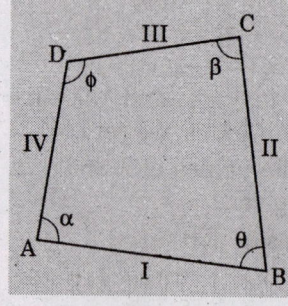

Fig. 37

or $\tan \theta = -\tan \phi$

or $\dfrac{A_1 B_2 - A_2 B_1}{A_1 A_2 + B_1 B_2} = -\dfrac{A_3 B_4 - A_4 B_3}{A_3 A_4 + B_3 B_4}$ see rule

or $(A_1 B_2 - A_2 B_1)(A_3 A_4 + B_3 B_4)$
$\qquad + (A_1 A_2 + B_1 B_2)(A_3 B_4 - A_4 B_3) = 0$

For Another Form :

Multiplying and combining keeping in view the desired result. Combine the terms of $A_1 A_3$, $B_1 B_3$ and $A_2 A_4$ and $B_2 B_4$ and you get the result.

(e) Ans. (c).

We know that if $ABCD$ be a cyclic quadrilateral then $\alpha + \gamma = \pi$ and $\beta + \delta = \pi$

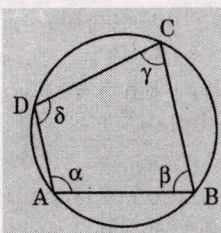

Fig. 38

or $\cos \alpha = \cos (\pi - \gamma) = -\cos \gamma$

$\therefore \quad \cos \alpha + \cos \gamma = 0$ ...(1)

and $\cos \beta + \cos \delta = 0$ ...(2)

$\therefore \quad \cos \alpha + \cos \beta + \cos \gamma + \cos \delta = 0$

Square.

$\cos^2 \alpha + \cos^2 \beta + \cos^2 \gamma + \cos^2 \delta$
$$+ 2\Sigma \cos \alpha \cos \beta = 0$$

or $2(\cos^2 \alpha + \cos^2 \delta) + 2\Sigma \cos \alpha \cos \beta = 0$

$$\text{by (1), (2)}$$

$(1 - \sin^2 \alpha) + (1 - \sin^2 \delta) + \Sigma \cos \alpha \cos \beta = 0$

$\therefore \quad 2 + \Sigma \cos \alpha \cos \beta = \sin^2 \alpha + \sin^2 \delta \Rightarrow (c).$

27. (a) The lines $y = x$ and $y = -x$ are at right angles to each other and the circle passes through origin.

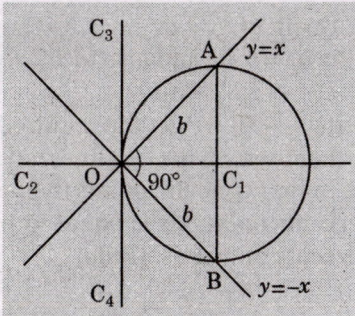

Fig. 39

Also $OA = OB = b$.

and $\angle AOB = \pi/2$

and hence AB is a diameter of length

$$\sqrt{(b^2 + b^2)} = b\sqrt{2}.$$

$\therefore \quad r = \dfrac{b\sqrt{2}}{2} = \dfrac{b}{\sqrt{(2)}} = OC_1.$

Clearly C_1 is centre on x-axis with co-ordinates $(b/\sqrt{2}, 0)$.

Similarly the other centres could be

$C_2 (-b/\sqrt{2}, 0)$ or $C_3 (0, b/\sqrt{2})$

or $C_4 (0, -b/\sqrt{2})$.

Hence the circles are

$$\left(x \pm \frac{b}{\sqrt{(2)}}\right)^2 + y^2 = \left(\frac{b}{\sqrt{(2)}}\right)^2$$

or $x^2 + y^2 \pm \sqrt{2}\, bx = 0$

or $(x - 0)^2 + \left(y \pm \dfrac{b}{\sqrt{(2)}}\right)^2 = \left(\dfrac{b}{\sqrt{(2)}}\right)^2$

or $x^2 + y^2 \pm \sqrt{2}\, by = 0$.

(b) The given circle $(x - 1)^2 + y^2 = 1$ whose centre is $(1, 0)$ and radius 1. It passes through origin O. Let OP be any chord through origin whose equation is $y = mx$ where $m = \tan \theta$. Solving with circle $x^2 + y^2 - 2x = 0$, we get

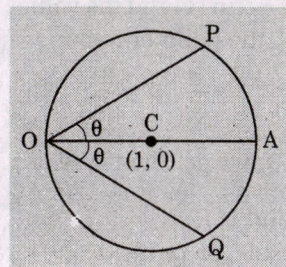

Fig. 40

$$x = 0, \quad x = \frac{2}{1 + m^2}$$

$\therefore \quad P$ is $\left(\dfrac{2}{1 + m^2}, \dfrac{2m}{1 + m^2}\right)$

Since OQ is equally inclined to x-axis

$\therefore \quad \tan(-\theta) = -\tan \theta = -m$

Hence point Q is $\left(\dfrac{2}{1 + m^2}, \dfrac{-2m}{1 + m^2}\right)$.

If (h, k) be the mid-point of PQ, then $2k = 0$

$\therefore \quad$ Locus of mid-point is $y = 0$ i.e., x-axis.

28. (a) $x = 2 + 4 \cos \theta$, $y = -1 + 4 \sin \theta$.

Clearly $(x - 2)^2 + (y + 1)^2$

$$= 16(\cos^2 \theta + \sin^2 \theta) = 16.$$

Above represents a circle with centre $(2, -1)$ and radius 4.

(b) The given circle is $\left(-\dfrac{1}{2}, -\dfrac{\sqrt{3}}{2}\right), 1$

or $\left(x + \dfrac{1}{2}\right)^2 + \left(y + \dfrac{\sqrt{3}}{2}\right)^2 = r^2 = 1^2$

Its parametric equations are given by

$$x + \frac{1}{2} = r \cos \theta = \cos \theta,$$

$$y + \frac{\sqrt{3}}{2} = r \sin \theta = \sin \theta.$$

(c) $(x-1)^2 + (y-2)^2 = 4^2$

Any point on this circle can be taken as

$(1 + 4\cos\theta, 2 + 4\sin\theta)$ (parametric) ...(1)

If d be the distance from origin, then

$d^2 = (1 + 4\cos\theta)^2 + (2 + 4\sin\theta)^2$

$d^2 = 5 + 16 + 8(\cos\theta + 2\sin\theta)$

$d^2 = 21 + 8\sqrt{5}\left(\dfrac{1}{\sqrt{5}}\cos\theta + \dfrac{2}{\sqrt{5}}\sin\theta\right)$

$d^2 = 21 + 8\sqrt{5}\cos(\theta - \alpha)$

where $\cos\alpha = \dfrac{1}{\sqrt{5}}, \sin\alpha = \dfrac{2}{\sqrt{5}}$ ...(2)

It will be maximum when $\cos(\theta - \alpha)$ is maximum and equal to 1.

In this case $\theta - \alpha = 0$ or $\theta = \alpha$

Puting $\theta = \alpha$ in (1) and the values of $\cos\alpha$ and $\sin\alpha$ from (2), the point becomes

$\left(1 + \dfrac{4}{\sqrt{5}}, 2 + \dfrac{8}{\sqrt{5}}\right)$.

29. Dividing by 3, we get the circle as $C\left(\dfrac{5}{6}, 1\right), r = \dfrac{1}{6}\sqrt{13}$

and given point is P.

P will be outside, on or inside the circle according as

$CP^2 >, =$ or $< r^2$. But $CP^2 = \dfrac{12}{36} < \dfrac{13}{36} = r^2$.

Since $CP^2 < r^2$, the point P is inside the circle.

30. (a) $S \equiv x^2 + y^2 - 6x - 10y + k = 0$.

Centre $C(3, 5), r^2 = 9 + 25 - k = 34 - k$.

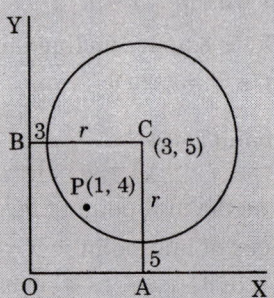

Fig. 41

Point $P(1, 4)$ lies inside the circle therefore

$\therefore \quad S' = -$ive $\Rightarrow -29 + k < 0$ or $k < 29$ ...(1)

Since the circle neither touches nor intersects the axes of co-ordinates, therefore from the figure it is clear that $r < 3$ (x co-ordinate of centre) and $r < 5$ (y co-ordinate of centre).

Hence, $r < 3 \Rightarrow r^2 < 9$

or $34 - k < 9$ or $25 < k$ ...(2)

From (1) and (2), we have $25 < k < 29$.

(b) Since the line does not intersect the given circle, $p > r$ where p is perpendicular from centre $(-10, -10)$ on the line $y = mx$.

$\therefore \quad \dfrac{-10(m-1)}{\sqrt{m^2 + 1}} > 6\sqrt{5}$

or $5(m-1)^2 > 9(m^2 + 1)$

or $0 > 4m^2 + 10m + 4$ or $2m^2 + 5m + 2 < 0$

or $(2m+1)(m+2) < 0 \quad \therefore \quad -2 < m < -1/2$

2nd Method : Eliminate y and find a quadratic in x and apply the condition that its roots are imaginary *i.e.*, $\Delta < 0$.

(c) Let the line $px + qy + r = 0$ ...(1)

touch the circle $x^2 + y^2 = a^2$ ...(2)

at the point (h, k).

Now the equation of tangent at (h, k) is

$xh + yk - a^2 = 0$ ...(3)

Comparing (1) and (3), we get $\dfrac{h}{p} = \dfrac{k}{q} = \dfrac{-a^2}{r}$

whence $h = -a^2 p/r$ and $k = -a^2 q/r$

Since (h, k) lies on the given circle $\therefore$ from (2)

$a^4 p^2/r^2 + a^4 q^2/r^2 = a^2$

or $r^2 = a^2(p^2 + q^2)$

which is the required condition and the point of contact is $(-a^2 p/r, -a^2 q/r)$.

31. (a) The curve through the four points of intersection of the given lines and axes whose equation is $xy = 0$ is

$(a_1 x + b_1 y + c_1)(a_2 x + b_2 y + c_2) + \lambda xy = 0$ ...(1)

It represents a circle as the four points are concyclic.

Coeff. of $x^2 =$ Coeff. of y^2

and Coeff. of $xy = 0$

$\therefore \quad a_1 a_2 = b_1 b_2$ and also $(a_1 b_2 + a_2 b_1) + \lambda = 0$

$\therefore \quad \lambda = -(a_1 b_2 + a_2 b_1)$

Putting in (1), we get the required circle.

Another form : If the two lines cut the co-ordinate axes in four concylic points then **product of their intercepts on x-axis is equal to product of their intercepts on y-axis. (Rule)**

$\therefore \quad -\dfrac{c_1}{a_1} \cdot -\dfrac{c_2}{a_2} = -\dfrac{c_1}{b_1} \cdot -\dfrac{c_2}{b_2} \quad \therefore \quad \mathbf{a_1 a_2 = b_1 b_2}$

(b) As in part (a) the equation of the circle passing through the intersection of the given lines and axes $xy = 0$ is

$(\lambda x - y + 1)(x - 2y + 3) + kxy = 0$

Condition for circle $a = b$, $h = 0$

$\lambda = 2$ and $-1 - 2\lambda + k = 0$

$\therefore \quad k = 5$ as $\lambda = 2$

$\therefore \quad (2x - y + 1)(x - 2y + 3) + 5xy = 0$

or $2x^2 + 2y^2 + 7x - 5y + 3 = 0$ ...(1)

It passes through all the four points of intersection of the given lines with co-ordinate axes, one of which is $\left(-\dfrac{1}{\lambda}, 0\right)$, it will satisfy (1).

or $\dfrac{2}{\lambda^2} - \dfrac{7}{\lambda} + 3 = 0$ or $3\lambda^2 - 7\lambda + 2 = 0$

or $(\lambda - 2)(3\lambda - 1) = 0$ $\therefore$ $\lambda = 2, \dfrac{1}{3}$

(c) On dividing by ab the equation of lines can be re-written as $\dfrac{x}{b} + \dfrac{y}{a} = 1$ and $\dfrac{x}{a} + \dfrac{y}{b} = 1$. Clearly product of intercepts on x-axis = product of inercepts on y-axis each equal to ab. Hence P, Q, R, S are concylic.

32. Let the two rods be AB (along x-axis) and CD along y-axis so that four points A, B, C, D are on a circle whose centre is (h, k), say. If r be radius then from the figure we have

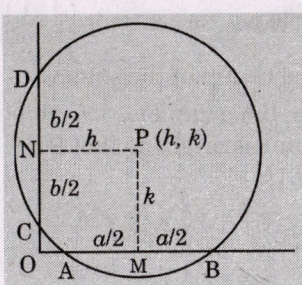

Fig. 42

$r^2 = PA^2 = k^2 + a^2/4$,
$r^2 = PD^2 = h^2 + b^2/4$

Eliminating r by subtracting, we get

$h^2 - k^2 = \dfrac{a^2}{4} - \dfrac{b^2}{4}$

or $4(x^2 - y^2) = a^2 - b^2$ is the required locus.

Alternative Method : Let the centre of the circle be (h, k), its equation is

$x^2 + y^2 - 2hx - 2ky + \lambda = 0$

$AB = a$ = Intercept on x-axis

$= 2\sqrt{g^2 - c} = 2\sqrt{h^2 - \lambda}$

$CD = b$ = Intercept on y-axis

$= 2\sqrt{f^2 - c} = 2\sqrt{k^2 - \lambda}$

$\therefore$ $a^2 = 4(h^2 - \lambda)$, $b^2 = 4(k^2 - \lambda)$.

Eliminating the variable λ we get on subtracting

$(a^2 - b^2) = 4(h^2 - k^2)$

Hence locus of centre is $4(x^2 - y^2) = a^2 - b^2$

33. (a) In order to find the locus of the point of intersection we have to eliminate the variable α between the lines for which we square and add.

$\therefore$ $x^2(\sin^2\alpha + \cos^2\alpha) + y^2(\sin^2\alpha + \cos^2\alpha)$
$= a^2 + b^2$

or $x^2 + y^2 = a^2 + b^2$ which represents a circle.

(b) Any tangent to first circle is

$x\cos\alpha + y\sin\alpha = a$

as its distance from centre $(0, 0)$ is equal to radius a. Any tangent to $x^2 + y^2 = b^2$ but perpendicular to above is obtained by replacing α by $\alpha - 90°$ and its equation is

$x\cos(\alpha - 90°) + y\sin(\alpha - 90°) = b$

or $x\cos(90° - \alpha) - y\sin(90° - \alpha) = b$

or $x\sin\alpha - y\cos\alpha = b$.

Locus of the point of intersection of these tangents as in part (a) is $x^2 + y^2 = a^2 + b^2$ which is a circle concentric with the given circles.

(c) Let the circle be $x^2 + y^2 = a^2$ and any tangent to it is $x\cos\alpha + y\sin\alpha = a$ and a perpendicular tangent to it is $x\sin\alpha - y\cos\alpha = k$, where $k = a$ by condition of tangency *i.e.* $p = r$. Hence it is $x\sin\alpha - y\cos\alpha = a$. Locus of their point of intersection is obtained by eliminating α for which we square and add. $x^2 + y^2 = 2a^2$ is the required locus.

(d) The given circle is

$x^2 \cdot 1 + y^2 \cdot 1 - 2x(a\cos\theta + b\sin\theta)$
$- 2y(a\sin\theta - b\cos\theta) + (a^2 + b^2 - k^2) = 0$

Above equation represents a circle whose centre is the point

$x = a\cos\theta + b\sin\theta$
$y = a\sin\theta - b\cos\theta$ where θ varies.

The locus of centre is obtained by eliminating the variable θ. Squaring and adding, the required locus is $x^2 + y^2 = a^2 + b^2$.

Also radius of given circle is

$\sqrt{g^2 + f^2 - c} = \sqrt{k^2} = k$.

34. The given circle is $(-8, 12), 5$

The given line is $4x + 7y + 13 = 0$

The required circle will be $(h, k), 5$ where (h, k) is the reflection of centre $(-8, 12)$ in the line

$4x + 7y + 13 = 0$

$\therefore$ $\dfrac{h - \alpha}{a} = \dfrac{k - \beta}{b} = -\dfrac{2l'}{a^2 + b^2}$

or $\dfrac{h + 8}{4} = \dfrac{k - 12}{7} = -2$ $\therefore$ $h = -16, k = -2$

$\therefore$ Required circle is $(x + 16)^2 + (y + 2)^2 = 5^2$

or $x^2 + y^2 + 32x + 4y + 235 = 0$

35. (a) Let the given points be chosen along x-axis and the distance between them be $2a$ and their mid-point as origin.

Hence their co-ordinates are

$A(a, 0)$, $B(-a, 0)$.

Let P be any point (x, y) such that $\dfrac{PA}{PB} = k$.

$\therefore$ $PA^2 = k^2 PB^2$

or $(x - a)^2 + y^2 = k^2 [(x + a)^2 + y^2]$

or $(x^2 + y^2 + a^2)(1 - k^2) - 2\bar{a}x(1 + k^2) = 0$

or $x^2 + y^2 + a^2 - 2ax \cdot \dfrac{1 + k^2}{1 - k^2} = 0$

which is a circle.

It will pass through $(a, 0)$ if

$$2a^2 - 2a^2 \cdot \dfrac{1 + k^2}{1 - k^2} = 0 \quad \text{or} \quad -4a^2 k^2 = 0.$$

Above is not possible as $a \neq 0$, $k \neq 0$.

Therefore the point A does not lie on the circle.

Now putting $(-a, 0)$, we get

$$2a^2 + 2a^2 \dfrac{1 + k^2}{1 - k^2} = 0 \quad \text{or} \quad 4a^2 = 0 .$$

Above is also not possible as $a \neq 0$.

Hence B also does not lie on the circle.

(b)   Same as above.

36. (a)   Take the side $BC = 2a$ along x-axis and its mid-point as origin.

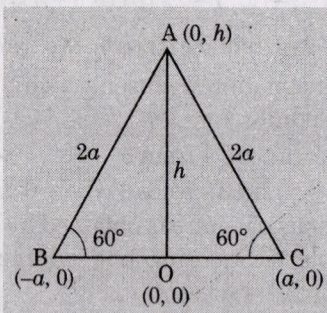

Fig. 43

∴ B is $(-a, 0)$ and C is $(a, 0)$. Δ being equilateral, vertex A will lie on y-axis, say it is $(0, h)$.

∴ $h = 2a \sin 60° = a\sqrt{3}$.

Hence the sides are $y = 0$, $y = \sqrt{3}(x + a)$

and $y = -\sqrt{3}(x - a)$

or $\sqrt{3}x - y + a\sqrt{3} = 0$, $\sqrt{3}x + y - a\sqrt{3} = 0$, $y = 0$

$p_1^2 + p_2^2 + p_3^2 = \lambda^2$

∴ $\left(\dfrac{\sqrt{3}x - y + a\sqrt{3}}{2}\right)^2 + \left(\dfrac{\sqrt{3}x + y - a\sqrt{3}}{2}\right)^2 + y^2 = \lambda^2$

or $[2\{3x^2 + (y - a\sqrt{3})^2\}] + 4y^2 = 4\lambda^2$

or $6x^2 + 6y^2 - 4ya\sqrt{3} + 6a^2 = 4\lambda^2$

or $x^2 + y^2 - \dfrac{2a}{\sqrt{3}}y + a^2 - \dfrac{2}{3}\lambda^2 = 0$

Above represents a circle.

(b)   Let $P(x, y)$ be any point then by the given conditions the sum of the squares of its distances from the four sides of the square is 9.

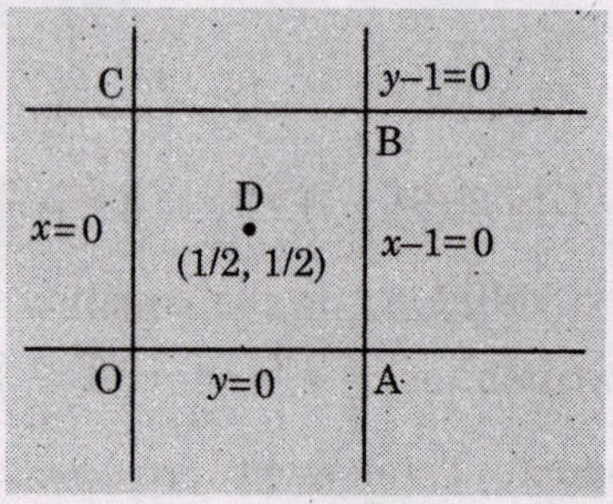

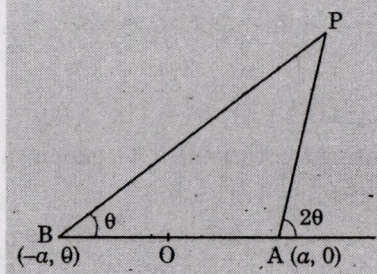

Fig. 44

∴ $x^2 + y^2 + (x - 1)^2 + (y - 1)^2 = 9$

$2(x^2 + y^2) - 2x - 2y - 7 = 0$

or $x^2 + y^2 - x - y - 7/2 = 0$

is a circle whose centre is $\left(\dfrac{1}{2}, \dfrac{1}{2}\right)$ which coincides with the centre of the square.

(c)   Choose the side $BC = 2a$ along x-axis and its mid-point as origin so that B is $(-a, 0)$, $C(a, 0)$ and let A be (h, k).

∴ $(x - a)^2 + y^2 + (x + a)^2 + y^2 + (x - h)^2$

$\qquad\qquad\qquad + (y - k)^2 = 3\lambda^2$ (say)

∴ $3x^2 + 3y^2 - 2hx - 2ky$

$\qquad\qquad + 2a^2 + h^2 + k^2 - 3\lambda^2 = 0.$

Clearly its centre on dividing by 3 is the point $\left(\dfrac{h}{3}, \dfrac{k}{3}\right)$ which is the centroid of $\Delta\,ABC$.

37. (a)   As usual we take the fixed points A and B to be at a distance $2a$ apart along x-axis and their mid-point be chosen as origin so that $A(a, 0)$ and $B(-a, 0)$. Initially they coincided along this line AB. These lines now rotate so that BP makes an angle θ and AP makes an angle 2θ and both these meet at P, whose locus we have to find. If $\tan\theta = m$ then

$$\tan 2\theta = \dfrac{2m}{1 - m^2}.$$

Fig. 45

Eq. of BP is $y = m(x + a)$ ∴ $m = \dfrac{y}{x + a}$ ...(1)

Eq. of AP is $y = \dfrac{2m}{1 - m^2}(x - a)$ ...(2)

In order to find the locus of their point of intersection, eliminate m between (1) and (2)

$$\left[1 - \frac{y^2}{(x+a)^2}\right] y = 2 \cdot \frac{y}{x+a}(x-a)$$

$$(x+a)^2 - y^2 = 2(x+a)(x-a)$$

or $x^2 + 2ax + a^2 - y^2 = 2x^2 - 2a^2$

or $x^2 + y^2 - 2ax - 3a^2 = 0$

(b) Circle is $(5, 3), 2$

AB being parallel to $y = x + 3$ makes $45°$ with x-axis so that AC will make $45° + 45° = 90°$ with x-axis.

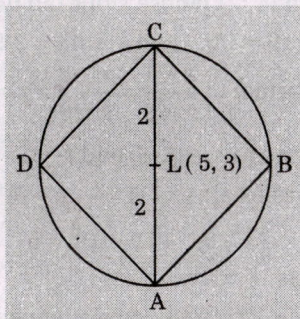

Fig. 46

$\therefore \quad \dfrac{x-5}{\cos 90°} = \dfrac{y-3}{\sin 90°} = 2, -2$ for C, A

$\therefore \quad x = 5, y = 3+2$ or $3-2$

$\therefore$ $(5, 5)$ and $(5, 1)$ are the two vertices C and A. DB will make an angle of $0°$ with x-axis.

$\therefore \quad \dfrac{x-5}{\cos 0°} = \dfrac{y-3}{\sin 0°} = 2, -2$ for B, D

$\therefore \quad x = 5+2, 5-2, y = 3$

$\therefore$ $(7, 3), (3, 3)$ are the vertices B and D.

38. (a) Ans. (b), (d).

Since $\angle B = \angle C = 75°$

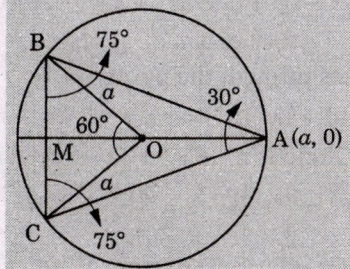

Fig. 47

$\therefore \quad \angle A = 30°$. Hence angle at centre O is $60°$.

Since $OB = OC =$ radius $\therefore$ Isosceles $\triangle OBC$ is an equilateral triangle.

$\therefore \quad OB = OC = BC = a$

or $\quad BM = MC = \dfrac{a}{2}$

$\therefore \quad OM^2 = OB^2 - BM^2 = a^2 - \dfrac{a^2}{4}$

$\therefore \quad OM = \pm \dfrac{a\sqrt{3}}{2} = -\dfrac{a\sqrt{3}}{2}$

$\therefore$ B is $\left(-\dfrac{a\sqrt{3}}{2}, \dfrac{a}{2}\right)$ and C is $\left(-\dfrac{a\sqrt{3}}{2}, -\dfrac{a}{2}\right)$

(b) Ans. (d). The centre of the given circle is $(1, -2)$ and sides of the inscribed square are parallel to the co-ordinate axes. Hence no vertex of the square can have its x-co-ordinate equal to 1 and no vertex can have its y-co-ordinate equal to -2.

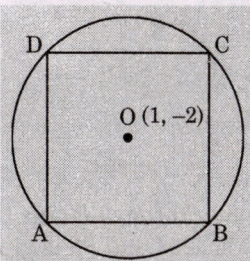

Fig. 48

Hence none of the points given in (a), (b), (c) can be the vertex of the square.

39. (a) Eliminating θ the circle is $x^2 + y^2 = 25$ ...(1)

The line through $(-\sqrt{8}, \sqrt{8})$

and having slope $\tan 135° = -1$ is

$y - \sqrt{8} = -1(x + \sqrt{8})$ or $y = -x$.

The line $y + x = 0$ passes through the centre $(0, 0)$ of the circle $x^2 + y^2 = 25$. Hence it is a diameter, say AB, whose length is $2r = 10$.

(b) The given circle is with centre at $\left(-1, \dfrac{1}{4}\right)$ and radius $\dfrac{1}{4}\sqrt{67}$. The point on the line

$y = 2x + 11$ or $2x - y + 11 = 0$ ...(1)

which is nearest to the circle, will lie on the diameter which is perpendicular to (1). The line does not intersect the circle as

$p = \dfrac{35}{4\sqrt{5}} = \dfrac{7\sqrt{5}}{4} > r = \dfrac{1}{4}\sqrt{67}$.

Its equation is given by

$(x+1) + 2\left(y - \dfrac{1}{4}\right) = 0$.

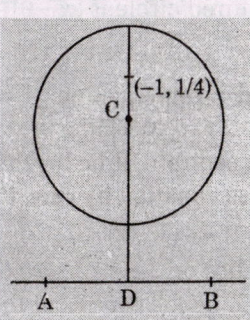

Fig. 49

or $x + 2y + \dfrac{1}{2} = 0$ or $2x + 4y + 1 = 0$ ...(2)

Solving (1) and (2), we get the point $\left(-\dfrac{9}{2}, 2\right)$.

40. (a) Ans. True. C is $(2, 1)$, $P(10, 7)$ and $r = 5$
$\therefore$ $PC = 10$.

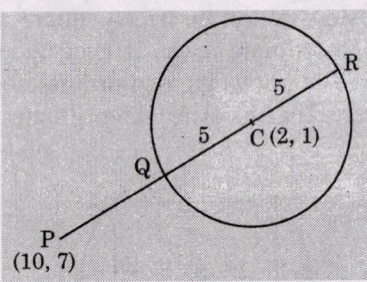

Fig. 50

If the diameter through P cuts the circle in Q and R, then PQ is least and PR is greatest
$\therefore$ $PQ = PC - r = 10 - 5 = 5$
and $PR = PC + r = 10 + 5 = 15$

(b) **Hint** : First note that shortest distance from the circle is the distance from its centre minus the radius. Hence the required locus is
$\sqrt{[(x-1)^2 + (y+3)^2]} - 4 = x - 3$
or $(x-1)^2 + (y+3)^2 = (x+1)^2$
or $y^2 + 6y - 4x + 9 = 0$

41. (a) $x^2 + y^2 - 2x - 4y - 20 = 0$.
Centre $A(1, 2)$ and radius $= 5$.

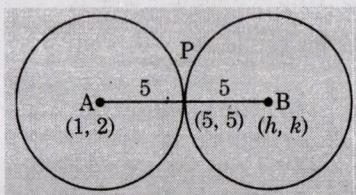

Fig. 51

Point of contact P is $(5, 5)$. If $B(h, k)$ be the centre of the required circle of radius 5 then from the figure P is mid-point of AB.
$\therefore$ $5 = \dfrac{h+1}{2}$ and $5 = \dfrac{k+2}{2}$, $\therefore h = 9, k = 8$

Hence required circle is $(x-9)^2 + (y-8)^2 = 5^2$
or $x^2 + y^2 - 18x - 16y + 120 = 0$.

(b) **Ist Method** : The equation of the tangent at the point $(1, 2)$ is $4x + 3y - 10 = 0$.
Hence the centre will lie on the normal through $(1, 2)$ whose equation by **rule 15** is
$3(x-1) - 4(y-2) = 0$
$\therefore$ Centre lies on $3x - 4y - 5 = 0$
If C_1 and C_2 be the centres of the required circles which touch at $P(1, 2)$ then $PC_1 = 5$ and $PC_2 = -5$

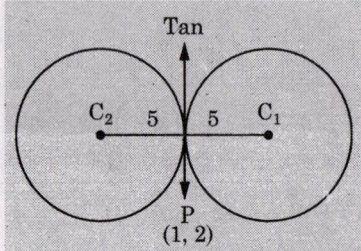

Fig. 52

$PC_2 = -5$ where C_1 and C_2' lie on the normal through $(1, 2)$ whose slope $\tan \theta = 3/4$
$\therefore$ $\cos \theta = 4/5$ and $\sin \theta = 3/5$
$\therefore$ Normal is $\dfrac{x-1}{\cos \theta} = \dfrac{y-2}{\sin \theta} = r = 5$ or -5
$\therefore$ Centres are $(5, 5)$ and $(-3, -1)$
$\therefore$ Circles are $(x-5)^2 + (y-5)^2 = 5^2$
and $(x+3)^2 + (y+1)^2 = 5^2$.

2nd Method :
Since $4x + 3y - 10 = 0$ is a tangent to the circle at $(1, 2)$, its equation can be taken as
$\underset{\text{Pt. circle}}{(x-1)^2 + (y-2)^2} + \lambda \underset{\text{Tangent}}{(4x + 3y - 10)} = 0$ **(n₁, P. 853)**
or $x^2 + y^2 + (4\lambda - 2)x + (3\lambda - 4)y + (5 - 10\lambda) = 0$
Its radius is 5.
$\therefore$ $g^2 + f^2 - c = 25$
This implies that $25\lambda^2 = 100$ $\therefore \lambda = 2, -2$
Hence the required circles are
$x^2 + y^2 + 6x + 2y - 15 = 0$
and $x^2 + y^2 - 10x - 10y + 25 = 0$

(c) Ans. (c).
The equation of the circle is
$\underset{\text{Point circle}}{(x-1)^2 + (y-1)^2} + \lambda \underset{\text{Tan.}}{(y-2)} = 0$
It passes through the point $(-1, 7)$
$\therefore$ $40 + 8\lambda = 0 \Rightarrow \lambda = -5$
$\therefore$ Circle is $x^2 + y^2 + 3x - 7y + 2 = 0$
$\therefore$ $r^2 = \dfrac{9}{4} + \dfrac{49}{4} - 2 = \dfrac{50}{4}$
$\therefore$ $4r^2 = (2r)^2 = 50$ $\therefore$ $2r = 5\sqrt{2}$ $\Rightarrow$ (c)

(d) The given normals are $x - 3y = 0$, $x - 3 = 0$ which intersect at centre whose co-ordinates are $(3, 1)$.
The given circle is $C_1(3, -3)$, $r_1 = 1$, C_2 is $(3, 1)$ and $r_2 = (?)$. If the two circles touch externally, then
$C_1 C_2 = r_1 + r_2$
$\therefore$ $4 = 1 + r_2$ $\therefore$ $r_2 = 3$.
$\therefore$ $(x-3)^2 + (y-1)^2 = 3^2$
or $x^2 + y^2 - 6x - 2y + 1 = 0$

42. (a) $x^2 + y^2 - 4x - 6y - 12 = 0$.

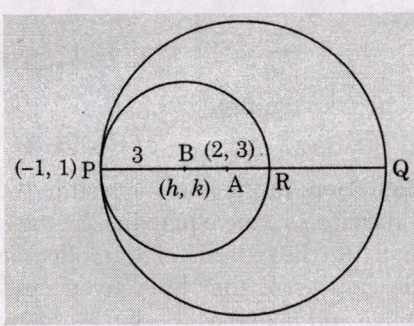

Fig. 53

Centre A is $(2, 3)$ and radius $= 5 = PA$, $B(h, k)$ is the centre of the required circle of radius $BP = 3$ which touches the given circle internally at $P(-1, -1)$

$\therefore \quad BA = PA - PB = 5 - 3 = 2.$

Thus B divides PA in the ratio $3 : 2$.

$\therefore \quad h = \dfrac{3 \cdot 2 + 2(-1)}{3 + 2} = \dfrac{4}{5}, \quad k = \dfrac{3 \cdot 3 + 2 \cdot (-1)}{3 + 2} = \dfrac{7}{5}.$

Hence the required circle is

$(x - 4/5)^2 + (y - 7/5)^2 = 3^2$

or $\quad 5x^2 + 5y^2 - 8x - 14y - 32 = 0.$

(b) Centre A is $(-1, -1)$ and radius $= 1$
Centre B is $(2, 3)$ and radius $= 4$
Distance between the centres

$= AB = \sqrt{3^2 + 4^2} = 5 = r_1 + r_2 = 4 + 1$

Hence the two circles touch each other externally. If $P(h, k)$ be the point of contact then it will divide $A(-1, -1)$, $B(2, 3)$ in the ratio of the radii $1 : 4$.

$\therefore \quad P$ is $\left(-\dfrac{2}{5}, -\dfrac{1}{5}\right).$

(c) Let the circle be $x^2 + y^2 = a^2$ and the diameter AB be chosen along x-axis so that A is $(a, 0)$ and B is $(-a, 0)$.

Since CD is parallel to AB and half of its length therefore x-co-ordinate of C will be $a/2$ and that of D will be $-a/2$.

$\therefore \quad C$ is $\left(\dfrac{a}{2}, -\dfrac{\sqrt{3}}{2}a\right).$

Equation of AC is $y - 0 = \sqrt{3}(x - a).$ ...(1)

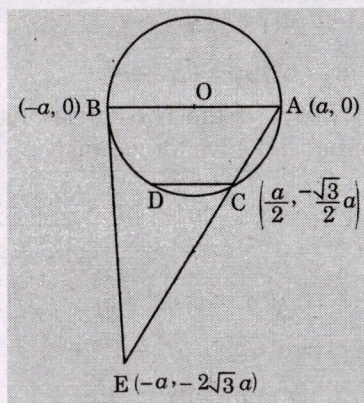

Fig. 54

Tangent at B is $x = -a.$ ...(2)

(1) and (2) meet at E whose co-ordinates are $(-a, -2\sqrt{3}a)$

$\therefore \quad AE^2 = (a + a)^2 + (2\sqrt{3}a)^2 = 4a^2 + 12a^2 = 16a^2$

$\therefore \quad AE = 4a = 2AB.$

43. (a) $C_1(2, 1), r_1 = 3, C_2(6, 4), r_2 = 8, C_1C_2 = 5 = r_2 - r_1.$

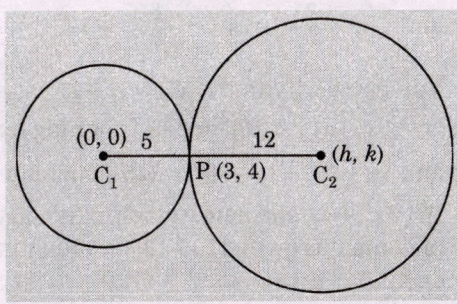

Fig. 55

Hence the circles touch internally. The common tangent being

$S_1 - S_2 = 0 \quad$ or $\quad 4x + 3y + 4 = 0$

and common normal C_1C_2 is $3x - 4y - 2 = 0.$

Solving these, the point of contact is $\left(-\dfrac{2}{5}, -\dfrac{4}{5}\right).$

The point of contact can also be found by ratio formula. Since the circles touch internally there will be no direct common tangents.

(b) Circle touching y-axis is

$(x - h)^2 + (y - k)^2 = h^2.$ Also centre of other circle is $(3, 3)$ and $r_1 = 2$. Since the two circles touch externally

$\therefore \quad C_1C_2 = r_1 + r_2$

$\therefore \quad (h - 3)^2 + (k - 3)^2 = (2 + h)^2$

or $\quad k^2 - 10h - 6k + 14 = 0$

$\therefore \quad$ Locus is $y^2 - 10x - 6y + 14 = 0.$

(c) I. **Touching externally** at $P(3, 4)$ which divides C_1C_2 in the ratio $5 : 12.$

$\dfrac{5h + 0}{5 + 12} = 3, \quad \dfrac{5k + 0}{5 + 12} = 4$

$\therefore \quad (h, k)$ is $\left(\dfrac{51}{5}, \dfrac{68}{5}\right).$

II. **Touching internally** at $P(3, 4).$

$\therefore \quad C_1$ divides PC_2 in the ratio $5 : 7.$

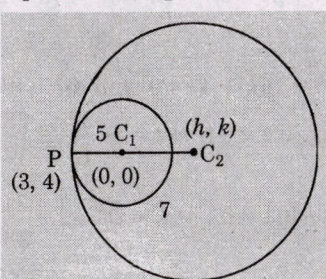

Fig. 56

$$0 = \frac{5h + 21}{12}, \quad 0 = \frac{5k + 28}{12}$$

$\therefore \quad (h, k)$ is $\left(-\frac{21}{5}, -\frac{28}{5}\right)$

Circles are : $\left(x - \frac{51}{5}\right)^2 + \left(y - \frac{68}{5}\right)^2 = 12^2$

and $\left(x + \frac{21}{5}\right)^2 + \left(y + \frac{28}{5}\right)^2 = 12^2$

You can verify that $C_1C_2 = r_1 + r_2$ or $r_1 - r_2$

(d) $(x - 15)^2 + (y + 20)^2 = 225$ Touching externally

and $(x + 3)^2 + (y - 4)^2 = 225$ Touching internally

44. (a) $AB = r_1 + r_2$, and hence touch externally and point of contact is $(-19/13, 9/13)$ by ratio formula as in Q. 42.

The common tangent is given by $S_1 - S_2 = 0$ or $12x - 5y + 21 = 0$ where S_1 and S_2 are the equations of the circles in standard form.

(b) Show that $C_1C_2 = r_1 + r_2$ or $r_1 - r_2$.

The points of contact are to be found by ratio formula. Common tangents are given by

$S_1 - S_2 = 0, \quad S_2 - S_3 = 0, \quad S_3 - S_1 = 0$

which can be shown to be concurrent at $(-3, -3)$.

(c) The given circles are $S_1(0, 2), 3; S_2(-6, -2), 3$ and $S_3(-3, -6), 3$. In other words all the three circles

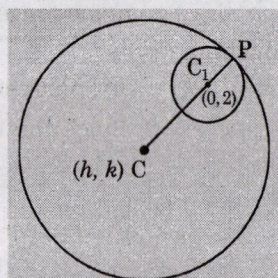

Fig. 57

are of same radius. Let the required circle be $(h, k), r$. The circle is to contain the three given circles and should be of minimum radius. Hence the given circles should touch the required circle internally so that the distance between the centres is equal to difference of radii, i.e., $r - 3, r - 3, r - 3$ as all circles are of equal radius.

$\therefore \quad h^2 + (k - 2)^2 = (h + 6)^2 + (k + 2)^2$

$= (h + 3)^2 + (k + 6)^2 = (r - 3)^2$

$\therefore \quad 6h + 16k + 41 = 0$ and $6h - 8k - 5 = 0$

Solving, we get $(h, k) = \left(-\frac{31}{18}, -\frac{23}{12}\right)$

and $(r - 3)^2 = h^2 + (k - 2)^2 = \left(-\frac{31}{18}\right)^2 + \left(-\frac{47}{12}\right)^2$

$= \frac{1}{(36)^2}(23725) = \frac{25 \times 949}{(36)^2}$

$\therefore \quad r - 3 = \frac{5}{36}\sqrt{949}$ or $r = 3 + \frac{5}{36}\sqrt{949}$

Hence the required circle is

$(x - h)^2 + (y - k)^2 = r^2$

Note. Here in the above question the radii of the three circles were equal. In case they be different, then find the radius R of the circle passing through the centres of the three given circles as found above and take it as $(r - \text{largest of given radii})$

$\therefore \quad r = R + \text{largest radius}$.

(d) Since the circles touch $\therefore \quad C_1C_2 = r_1 \pm r_2$

$(g_1 - g_2)^2 + (f_1 - f_2)^2$

$= [\sqrt{g_1^2 + f_1^2 - c_1} \pm \sqrt{g_2^2 + f_2^2 - c_2}]$

Squaring and cancelling, we get

$-2g_1g_2 - 2f_1f_2 = -c_1 - c_2 \pm 2r_1r_2$

$\therefore \quad [2g_1g_2 + 2f_1f_2 - (c_1 + c_2)]^2 = 4r_1^2r_2^2$

45. (a) $C_1(2, 2), 2$ and $C_2(6, 5), r$

Both touch externally $\therefore \quad C_1C_2 = 2 + r$

or $5 = 2 + r \therefore r = 3$.

Hence its equation is $(x - 6)^2 + (y - 5)^2 = 3^2$.

(b) Let the circle C_1 be $(h, k), r$ which touches $C_2(0, 0), a$ and $C_3(2a, 0), 2a$ externally. Applying $C_1C_2 = r_1 + r_2$, we have

$\sqrt{h^2 + k^2} = r + a$ ...(1)

$\sqrt{(h - 2a)^2 + k^2} = r + 2a$ ...(2)

In order to find the locus, eliminate the variable r by subtracting (1) from (2).

$\therefore \quad \sqrt{(h - 2a)^2 + k^2} - \sqrt{h^2 + k^2} = a$.

Now proceeding as in **Q. 14** by using L-M method the locus of the centre is

$12x^2 - 4y^2 - 24ax + 9a^2 = 0$.

46. (a) $C_1(-a, -2a), 2\sqrt{2}a, \quad C_2(4a, 3a), 3\sqrt{2}a$

Clearly $C_1C_2 = 5\sqrt{2}a = r_1 + r_2$. Hence they touch. The point of contact will divide C_1C_2 in the ratio of radii i.e. $2 : 3$. Hence by ratio formula it is $(a, 0)$.

(b) A is $(-a, 0), \quad r_1 = \sqrt{a^2 - c}$

B is $(0, -b), \quad r_2 = \sqrt{b^2 - c}$

$AB = r_1 \pm r_2$ if the two circles touch, + ive for external and − ive for internal

$\therefore \quad \sqrt{a^2 + b^2} = \sqrt{a^2 - c} \pm \sqrt{b^2 - c}$. Square

$a^2 + b^2 = a^2 - c + b^2 - c \pm 2\sqrt{(a^2 - c)(b^2 - c)}$

or $c = \pm\sqrt{(a^2 - c)(b^2 - c)}$

or $c^2 = a^2b^2 - c(a^2 + b^2) + c^2$

or $\frac{1}{c} = \frac{a^2 + b^2}{a^2b^2} = \frac{1}{a^2} + \frac{1}{b^2}$.

Alternative : If the two circles touch then their common chord $S_1 - S_2 = 0$ i.e. $ax - by = 0$ should be a tangent to either. Hence perpendicular from centre $(-a, 0)$ is equal to radius $\sqrt{a^2 - c}$.

$$\therefore \quad \frac{-a^2}{\sqrt{(a^2 + b^2)}} = \sqrt{a^2 - c} \text{ . Square}$$

$$a^4 = (a^2 - c)(a^2 + b^2) = a^4 + a^2 b^2 - c(a^2 + b^2)$$

or $\quad \dfrac{1}{c} = \dfrac{a^2 + b^2}{a^2 b^2} = \dfrac{1}{a^2} + \dfrac{1}{b^2}$

(c) Apply $S_1 - S_2 = 0$ is a tangent to either.

47. (a) We know that the two circles touch if

$\qquad C_1 C_2 = r_1 + r_2$ [Externally]

$\qquad C_1 C_2 = r_1 - r_2$ [Internally]

In case they intersect in real points, then

$\qquad C_1 C_2 < r_1 + r_2$ and $C_1 C_2 > r_1 - r_2$ ...(1)

$\qquad C_1 = (0, 0), \ C_2 = (5, 0), \ r_1 = r, \ r_2 = 3$

$\therefore \quad 5 < r + 3$ and $5 > r - 3$

or $\quad 2 < r$ and $8 > r$ i.e. $r < 8$

Hence the required condition is $2 < r < 8$.

(b) Proceed as in part (a).

(c) For intersection we have as in last part.

$\qquad C_1 C_2 < r_1 + r_2, \quad C_1 C_2 > r_1 - r_2$ ...(1)

where $C_1 C_2 = \sqrt{10} = 3 \cdot 16$,

$\qquad r_1 = \sqrt{21} = 4 \cdot 58, r_2 = 2$.

Both the conditions in (1) are satisfied by these values.

48. (a) Circle through $(0, 0)$ and $(1, 0)$ is

$$x^2 + y^2 - x + 2fy = 0 \quad \because \ c = 0, 2g = -1$$

$$C_1 \left(1/2, -f \right), r_1 = \sqrt{\left(\frac{1}{4} + f^2 \right)},$$

$$C_2 (0, 0), \ r_2 = 3.$$

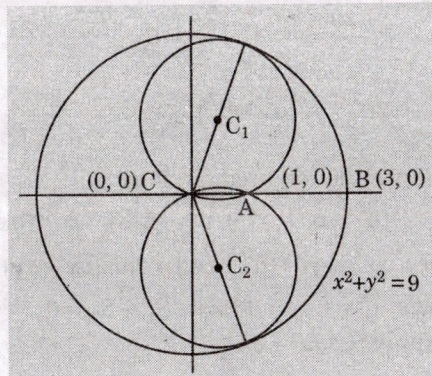

Fig. 58

If the two circles touch, then

$\qquad C_1 C_2 = r_2 - r_1$ or $r_2 + r_1$

$$\therefore \quad \sqrt{\left(\frac{1}{4} + f^2 \right)} = 3 \pm \sqrt{\left(\frac{1}{4} + f^2 \right)}$$

$$\therefore \quad \sqrt{\left(\frac{1}{4} + f^2 \right)} = \frac{3}{2} \quad \text{or} \quad 0 = 3 \text{ (rejected)}$$

$$\therefore \quad f^2 + 1/4 = 9/4 \quad \therefore \ f = \sqrt{2}, -\sqrt{2}$$

$$\therefore \quad (1/2, \pm \sqrt{2})$$

(b) If the two circles C_1 and C_2 touch internally then $C_1 C_2 = r_1 - r_2$. But if C_2 lies inside the circle C_1 then $C_1 C_2 < r_1 - r_2$.

Here $C_1 \left(\frac{1}{2}, 0 \right), r_1 = \frac{1}{2}\sqrt{105}, C_2 = (0, 1), r_2 = 4$

$$C_1 C_2 = \sqrt{1/4 + 1} = \frac{1}{2}\sqrt{5}$$

and $r_1 - r_2 = \dfrac{1}{2}\sqrt{105} - 4$

Clearly $C_1 C_2 < r_1 - r_2$. Hence circle C_2 lies completely inside circle C_1.

(c) Let r_1 and r_2 be the radii of the circles with centres C_1 and C_2 where $r_1 > r_2$ as C_2 lies within C_1. Let C be the centre of circle C of radius say r. Since C touches C_2 externally and $[CC_2]$ stands for distance between their centres, then

$$[CC_2] = r + r_2 \qquad \qquad \text{...(1)}$$

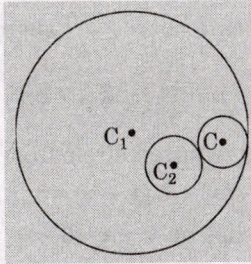

Fig. 59

Again C touches C_1 internally.

$$\therefore \qquad [C_1 C] = r_1 - r \qquad \qquad \text{...(2)}$$

$$\therefore \qquad [CC_2] + [C_1 C] = r_1 + r_2 = \text{constant}$$

Thus the sum of the distances of centre of C from the centres of circles C_1 and C_2 is constant $= 2a$ say. Hence the locus of centre of C is an ellipse whose foci are at the centre of the given circles and major axis is equal to sum of the radii of given circles. See another def. of ellipse.

(d) The equation $x^2 + 2xy + 3x + 6y = 0$ can be written on factorizing the L.H.S. as

$$(x + 3)(x + 2y) = 0.$$

Thus the equations of the two normals to the required circle are :

$$x + 3 = 0 \quad \text{and} \quad x + 2y = 0.$$

Solving these, we get the co-ordinates of the centre as $(-3, 3/2)$. Again as the required circle just contains the circle $x(x - 4) + y(y - 3) = 0$, that is,

$$x^2 + y^2 - 4x - 3y = 0.$$

This means that the required circle will touch the circle (1) internally. Let r be the radius of required circle. Also the radius of the circle (1) is $\sqrt{2^2 + (3/2)^2 - 0} = 5/2$ and its centre is $(2, 3/2)$.

Now the required circle will touch the circle (1) internally, if the distance between their centres is equal to the difference of their radii, that is,

$$\sqrt{[(-3-2)^2 + (3/2 - 3/2)^2]} = r - 5/2$$

or $5 = r - 5/2$, giving $r = 15/2$.

Hence the equation of the required circle is

$$(x+3)^2 + (y - 3/2)^2 = (15/2)^2$$

or $x^2 + y^2 + 6x - 3y - 45 = 0$.

49. (a) The required circle by $S + \lambda P = 0$ is

$$\therefore \quad (x^2 + y^2 - a^2) + \lambda (x \cos \alpha + y \sin \alpha - p) = 0$$

...(1)

or $x^2 + y^2 + x(\lambda \cos \alpha) + y(\lambda \sin \alpha)$

$$- (a^2 + \lambda p) = 0.$$

Its centre is $\left(\dfrac{-\lambda}{2} \cos \alpha, \dfrac{-\lambda}{2} \sin \alpha \right)$.

Since the line MN is a diameter of the required circle and hence its centre will lie on $P = 0$.

$$\therefore \quad \dfrac{-\lambda}{2} \cos \alpha . \cos \alpha + \dfrac{-\lambda}{2} \sin \alpha . \sin \alpha - p = 0.$$

$$\dfrac{\lambda}{2} . 1 + p = 0 \therefore \lambda = -2p.$$

Hence the required circle from (1) is as given.

(b) $(x^2 + y^2 - 2x) + \lambda (y - x) = 0$

Its centre lies on $y - x = 0$

$$\therefore \quad \lambda = -1 \therefore x^2 + y^2 - x - y = 0$$

(c) $(S + \lambda P = 0)$. Its centre lies on $P = 0$.

$$\therefore \quad \lambda = -1.$$

Ans. $x^2 + y^2 - x - y - 3 = 0$.

50. (a) Since the diameter is along x-axis and the chord $y = mx$ passes through the origin therefore centre is $(a, 0)$ where a is the given radius of the circle. Hence its equation is

$$S = (x - a)^2 + y^2 = a^2$$

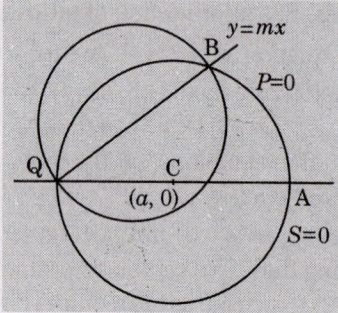

Fig. 60

or $x^2 + y^2 - 2ax = 0$

P is $y = mx$ (m is variable). Circle through the intersection of

$S = 0$ and $P = 0$ is

$S + \lambda P = 0$ or $(x^2 + y^2 - 2ax) + \lambda (y - mx) = 0$

or $x^2 + y^2 - x(2a + m\lambda) + \lambda y = 0$

Centre is $\left(\dfrac{2a + m\lambda}{2}, \dfrac{-\lambda}{2} \right)$.

Since the chord $y = mx$ is a diameter of the required circle therefore its centre lies on it

$$\therefore \quad \dfrac{-\lambda}{2} = m . \dfrac{2a + m\lambda}{2}$$

or $\lambda (1 + m^2) = -2am \therefore \lambda = \dfrac{-2am}{1 + m^2}$.

Putting for λ, the required circle is

$$(1 + m^2)(x^2 + y^2 - 2ax) - 2am(y - mx) = 0$$

$$(1 + m^2)(x^2 + y^2) - 2a(x + my) = 0.$$

If (h, k) be the co-ordinates of its centre, then

$$h = \dfrac{a}{1 + m^2}, \quad k = \dfrac{am}{1 + m^2}.$$

In order to find its locus we have to eliminate m.

Dividing $\dfrac{k}{h} = m$ and putting in $h(1 + m^2) = a$,

we get $h \left(1 + \dfrac{k^2}{h^2} \right) = a$ or $h^2 + k^2 = ah$.

Generalising, the required locus is

$$x^2 + y^2 - ax = 0, \text{ which is a circle.}$$

(b) Proceed as in part (a).

Ans. $5(x^2 + y^2) - 8x - 16y = 0$

51. (a) The equation of the common chord by

$S - S' = 0$ is $ax - by = 0$.

The required circle by $S + \lambda P = 0$

is $(x^2 + y^2 - 2ax) + \lambda (ax - by) = 0$.

Its centre is $\left(\dfrac{2a - \lambda a}{2}, \dfrac{\lambda b}{2} \right)$ and since the common

chord $ax - by = 0$ is a diameter it will lie on it

$$a . \dfrac{2a - \lambda a}{2} - b . \dfrac{\lambda b}{2} = 0.$$

$$\therefore \quad 2a^2 = \lambda (a^2 + b^2) \text{ or } \lambda = \dfrac{2a^2}{a^2 + b^2}.$$

Hence the required circle is

$$(a^2 + b^2)(x^2 + y^2 - 2ax) + 2a^2 (ax - by) = 0$$

or $(x^2 + y^2)(a^2 + b^2) = 2ab(bx + ay)$

(b) Ans. $10x - 3y - 18 = 0. S_1 - S_2 = 0.$

(c) Apply $S + \lambda P = 0$

$$\left(x^2 + y^2 - \dfrac{2c^2}{a^2 + b^2} \right) + \lambda (ax + by + c) = 0$$

Its centre $\left(-\dfrac{\lambda a}{2}, -\dfrac{\lambda b}{2} \right)$ lies on the diameter

$ax + by + c = 0 \quad \therefore \lambda = \dfrac{2c}{a^2 + b^2}$ etc.

52. (a) Let (a, b) and $(b, -a)$ be the co-ordinates of the points A and B respectively and let (h, k) be any point P on the required circle. The slopes of the lines AP and BP are respectively $(k-b)/(h-a)$ and $(k+a)/(h-b)$.

As given, the angle $APB = 45°$ so that the angle between the lines AP and BP is $45°$.

$$\therefore \quad 1 = \tan 45° = \frac{m_1 - m_2}{1 + m_1 m_2}$$

$$= \frac{[(k-b)/(h-a)] - [(k+a)/(h-b)]}{1 + [(k-b)/(h-a)][(k+a)/)h-b)]}$$

or $\quad (k-b)(h-b) - (k+a)(h-a)$
$$= (h-a)(h-b) - (k-b)(k+a)$$

or $\quad h^2 + k^2 = a^2 + b^2$

$\therefore$ The locus of the point (h, k), that is, the equation of the required circle is $x^2 + y^2 = a^2 + b^2$.

Note : For another method, see next part.

(b) Any circle through two points A, B by **(n), P. 853** is
$$(x+1)(x-5) + (y-1)(y-5) + \lambda(2x-3y+5) = 0$$
$\quad$ Circle on AB as diameter $\qquad$ Line AB

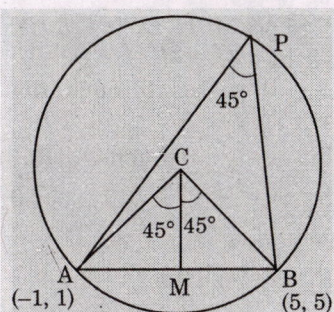

Fig. 61

or $\quad x^2 + y^2 - 4x - 6y + \lambda(2x - 3y + 5) = 0$ ...(1)

or $\quad x^2 + y^2 + x(2\lambda - 4) + y(-3\lambda - 6) + 5\lambda = 0$

Since AB subtends $45°$ at any point P, hence angle subtended by AB at centre C is $90°$.

Clearly CM is right bisector of AB.

$\therefore \quad AM = CM = BM = \dfrac{1}{2} AB = \sqrt{13}$

$\therefore \quad r = AC = \sqrt{13 + 13} = \sqrt{26}$

$\therefore \quad 26 = r^2 = g^2 + f^2 - c$

$$\left(\frac{2\lambda - 4}{2}\right)^2 + \left(\frac{-3\lambda - 6}{2}\right)^2 - 5\lambda = 26$$

or $\quad 4(\lambda^2 - 4\lambda + 4) + 9(\lambda^2 + 4\lambda + 4) - 20\lambda = 104$

or $\quad 13\lambda^2 - 52 = 0 \quad \therefore \quad \lambda = \pm 2$

Putting the values of λ in (1), the required circles are $\quad x^2 + y^2 - 12y + 10 = 0$

and $\quad x^2 + y^2 - 8x - 10 = 0$.

53. (a) Any circle through the intersection of given circles is $S_1 + \lambda S_2 = 0$

or $\quad (x^2 + y^2 - 2x - 4y - 4) + \lambda(x^2 + y^2$
$$- 10x - 12y + 40) = 0$$

or $\quad (x^2 + y^2) - 2\dfrac{(1+5\lambda)}{1+\lambda} x - 2\dfrac{(2+6\lambda)}{1+\lambda} y$
$$+ \frac{40\lambda - 4}{1 + \lambda} = 0 \quad ...(1)$$

$r = \sqrt{g^2 + f^2 - c} = 4$, given.

$$\therefore \quad 16 = \frac{(1+5\lambda)^2}{(1+\lambda)^2} + \frac{(2+6\lambda)^2}{(1+\lambda)^2} - \frac{40\lambda - 4}{1 + \lambda}$$

$$16(1 + 2\lambda + \lambda^2) = 1 + 10\lambda + 25\lambda^2 + 4 + 24\lambda$$
$$+ 36\lambda^2 - 40\lambda^2 - 40\lambda + 4 + 4\lambda$$

or $\quad 16 + 32\lambda + 16\lambda^2 = 21\lambda^2 - 2\lambda + 9$

or $\quad 5\lambda^2 - 34\lambda - 7 = 0$

$\therefore \quad (\lambda - 7)(5\lambda + 1) = 0 \quad \therefore \quad \lambda = 7, -1/5$

Putting the values of λ in (1), the required circles are

$$2x^2 + 2y^2 - 18x - 22y + 69 = 0$$

and $x^2 + y^2 - 2y - 15 = 0$.

(b) $S + \lambda S_2 = 0, \lambda = 4/3,$
$$7(x^2 + y^2) - 10x - 10y - 12 = 0.$$

(c) Ans (a). $\quad S_1 + \lambda S_2 = 0, \quad \lambda = -2$

54. (a) The required circle by $S + \lambda P = 0$ is
$$x^2 + y^2 - 2x + 1 + \lambda(x + 2y - 1) = 0$$

or $\quad x^2 + y^2 - x(2 - \lambda) + 2\lambda y + (1 - \lambda) = 0$

Centre $(-g, -f)$ is $[(2 - \lambda)/2, -\lambda]$
$$r = \sqrt{g^2 + f^2 - c} = \sqrt{(2 - \lambda)^2/4 + \lambda^2 - (1 - \lambda)}$$
$$= \frac{1}{2}\sqrt{5\lambda^2} = (\lambda/2)\sqrt{5}.$$

Since the circle touches the line $2x - y + 3 = 0$ therefore perpendicular from centre is equal to radius

$$\frac{2 \cdot [(2 - \lambda)/2] - (-\lambda) + 3}{\pm\sqrt{5}} = \frac{\lambda}{2}\sqrt{5}$$

or $\quad 5 = \pm\dfrac{\lambda}{2} \cdot 5 \quad \therefore \quad \lambda = \pm 2$

Putting the values of λ in (1), the required circles are

$$x^2 + y^2 + 4y - 1 = 0,$$
$$x^2 + y^2 - 4x - 4y + 3 = 0.$$

(b) The required circle will be
$$(x-3)^2 + (y+1)^2 + \lambda(x + 2y - 1) = 0 \quad ...(1)$$
$\quad$ Point circle $\qquad\qquad$ Tangent

It passes through $(2, 1)$

$$5 + 3\lambda = 0 \quad \therefore \quad \lambda = -5/3$$

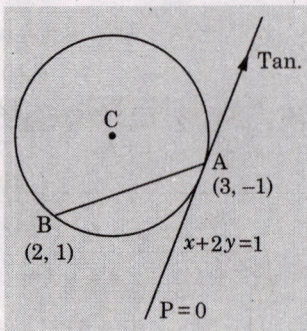

Fig. 62

Putting in (1), the required circle is
$$3(x^2 + y^2) - 23x - 4y + 35 = 0$$

(c) $S + \lambda S' = 0$.

Centre $\left(\dfrac{1}{1+\lambda}, \dfrac{2}{1+\lambda}\right)$ and $r = \dfrac{1}{1+\lambda}\sqrt{1 + 4\lambda^2}$.

Applying the condition of tangency, we get
$$\lambda = \pm 1,$$
For $\lambda = 1$, $x^2 + y^2 - x - 2y = 0$.

Note that $\lambda = -1$ gives $x + 2y - 4 = 0$
which is the common chord of the two circles.

Alt. $S + \lambda S' = 0$, gives
$$(x^2 + y^2 - 4) + \lambda(x^2 + y^2 - 2x - 4y + 4) = 0$$

It touches the line $x + 2y = 0$. Hence its intersection with the line will give equal roots. Putting $x = -2y$, we get
$$(5y^2 - 4) + \lambda(5y^2 + 4) = 0$$
or $\quad 5(1+\lambda)y^2 + 0y - 4(1-\lambda) = 0$

For equal roots $\Delta = B^2 - 4AC = 0$

$\therefore \quad 0 + 80(1+\lambda)(1-\lambda) = 0$

$\therefore \quad \lambda = \pm 1$ as found above.

(d) Let $S \equiv x^2 + y^2 + 2gx + 2fy + c = 0 \qquad \dots(1)$

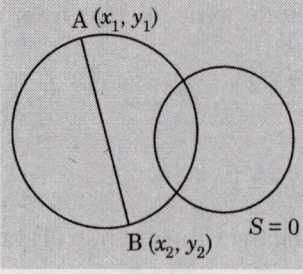

Fig. 63

The equation of any circle passing through two fixed points A and B is **(See (n), P. 853)** $S + \lambda P = 0$
i.e., Circle on AB as diameter $+ \lambda$ (line AB) $= 0$
or $\quad (x - x_1)(x - x_2) + (y - y_1)(y - y_2)$
$$+ \lambda \begin{vmatrix} x & y & 1 \\ x_1 & y_1 & 1 \\ x_2 & y_2 & 1 \end{vmatrix} = 0 \qquad \dots(2)$$

Common chord of circles (1) and (2) is given by
$S_1 - S_2 = 0$
or $\quad (x^2 + y^2 + 2gx + 2fy + c) - \{(x^2 + y^2)$
$$- x(x_1 + x_2) - y(y_1 + y_2) + x_1 x_2 + y_1 y_2 + \lambda$$
$$(\text{Det})\} = 0$$
or $\quad x\{(x_1 + x_2) + 2g\} + y\{(y_1 + y_2) + 2f\}$
$$- x_1 x_2 - y_1 y_2 - \lambda \, \text{Det} = 0$$
Above is of the form $P - \lambda Q = 0$ which represents a family of lines passing through the intersection of two fixed lines which is a fixed point.

55. (a) $S + \lambda S' = 0$ and passes through $(1, 1)$
$$x^2 + y^2 - 3x + 1 = 0.$$

(b) Proceed as above $\lambda = \dfrac{1}{2}$ etc.

56. (a) Their common chord is
$$2x(g - g') + 2y(f - f') + c - c' = 0.$$
If the first circle bisects the circumference of the second circle then their common chord must pass through the centre $(-g', -f')$ of the second circle. i.e. it must be diameter of second. Hence the required condition is
$$-2g'(g - g') - 2f'(f - f') + c - c' = 0.$$
or $\quad 2g'(g - g') + 2f'(f - f') = c - c'$.

(b) $S_1 - S_2 = 0$ passes through the centre of first circle.

(c) The line $x - y = 0$ touches at $(0, 0)$.
$$S_1 \Rightarrow x^2 + y^2 + \lambda(x - y) = 0 \qquad \dots(1)$$
$$\text{Pt. Circle} \qquad \text{Tan}$$
$$S_2 \Rightarrow x^2 + y^2 + 2y - 3 = 0 \qquad \dots(2)$$
S_1 bisects the circumference of S_2.
Common chord $S_1 - S_2 = 0$ passes through the centre $(0, -1)$ of S_2.
$$\therefore \quad \lambda(x - y) - 2y + 3 = 0$$
$$\lambda + 2 + 3 = 0 \Rightarrow \lambda = -5 \quad \therefore \text{ Put in (1)}$$
$$x^2 + y^2 - 5x + 5y = 0$$

(d) Let the given circles be denoted by S_1, S_2, S_3 respectively whose centres are $(0, 0)$, $(3, 4)$ and $(-1, 2)$. If the required circle be
$$x^2 + y^2 + 2gx + 2fy + c = 0,$$
then it cuts each of the given circles at the extremities of a diameter. This, in other words, means that their common chords $S - S_1 = 0$, $S - S_2 = 0, S - S_3 = 0$ pass through the centres of S_1, S_2, S_3 respectively.
$$\therefore \quad c = -4, 3g + 4f + 18 = 0, \quad g - 2f - 4 = 0$$
Solving, we get $g = -2$ and $f = -3$
Required circle is $x^2 + y^2 - 4x - 6y - 4 = 0$.

57. (a) By $S_1 - S_2 = 0$ the equation of common chord AB is $x - y = 0$. Its length is $2\sqrt{r^2 - p^2}$ by **(m)**, **P. 853**.
Consider the circle $(a, b), c$.

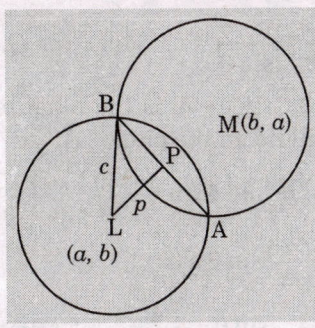

Fig. 64

$$\therefore \quad p = \frac{a-b}{\sqrt{2}}, r = c.$$

$$\therefore \quad \text{Length } AB = 2\sqrt{c^2 - (a-b)^2/2}$$

$$= \sqrt{4c^2 - 2(a-b)^2}$$

If the two circles touch each other, then length of common chord is zero and hence

$$4c^2 - 2(a-b)^2 = 0 \quad \text{or} \quad (a-b)^2 = 2c^2$$

(b) $C_1 : x^2 + y^2 = 16,$

$C_2 : (x-h)^2 + (y-k)^2 = 25.$

Common chord by $S_1 - S_2 = 0$ is

$$2hx + 2ky = (h^2 + k^2 - 9)$$

$$\therefore \quad \text{Its slope} = -h/k = 3/4, \text{ given} \qquad \ldots(1)$$

If p be the length of $\perp$ on it from the centre $(0, 0)$ of C_1 of radius 4 then $p = \dfrac{h^2 + k^2 - 9}{\sqrt{(4h^2 + 4k^2)}}$. Also the

length of the chord is $2\sqrt{r^2 - p^2} = 2\sqrt{4^2 - p^2}$.

The chord will be of maximum length if

$$p = 0 \text{ or } h^2 + k^2 - 9 = 0 \text{ or } h^2 + (16/9)\,h^2 = 9$$

$$\text{by (1)}$$

$$\text{or} \quad 25h^2 = 81 \quad \therefore \quad h = \pm(9/5)$$

$$\therefore \quad k = \mp(12/5) \qquad \qquad \text{by (1)}$$

Centres are $\left(\dfrac{9}{5}, -\dfrac{12}{5}\right)$ and $\left(-\dfrac{9}{5}, \dfrac{12}{5}\right)$.

(c) Ans. (b), (c). Length of chord on line

$L_2 \quad x + y - 1 = 0$ by circle $\left(\dfrac{1}{2}, -\dfrac{3}{2}\right), \dfrac{\sqrt{5}}{2}$ is

$$2\sqrt{r^2 - p^2} = 2\sqrt{\dfrac{5}{2} - \left(\dfrac{4}{2\sqrt{2}}\right)^2} = \sqrt{2}.$$

Let L_1 any line through origin be $y = mx$

or $mx - y = 0$

$$\therefore \quad \text{Length of chord on } L_1 = \sqrt{2} \text{ as given}$$

$$\therefore \quad 2\sqrt{r^2 - p^2} = \sqrt{2} \quad \text{or} \quad 2(r^2 - p^2) = 1$$

$$\text{or} \quad 2\left(\dfrac{5}{2}\right) - 2\left[\dfrac{m+3}{2\sqrt{(1+m^2)}}\right]^2 = 1$$

$$\text{or} \quad 4 = \dfrac{(m+3)^2}{2(1+m^2)} \quad \text{or} \quad 8m^2 + 8 = m^2 + 6m + 9,$$

$$7m^2 - 6m - 1 = 0 \quad \therefore \quad m = 1, -1/7$$

L_2 is $x - y = 0$ or $x + 7y = 0.$

58. (a) Here also common chord is $x - y = 0.$

$$C\left(-\dfrac{a}{2}, -\dfrac{b}{2}\right) \text{ and } r = \dfrac{1}{2}\sqrt{a^2 + b^2 - 4c}$$

$$p = \dfrac{(-a/2) - (-b/2)}{\sqrt{(2)}} = \dfrac{b-a}{2\sqrt{(2)}}$$

$$\text{Length } AB = 2\sqrt{r^2 - p^2} = \sqrt{4r^2 - 4p^2}$$

$$\therefore \quad AB = \sqrt{(a^2 + b^2 - 4c) - \left(\dfrac{b-a}{\sqrt{2}}\right)^2}$$

$$= \sqrt{\dfrac{(a+b)^2 - 8c}{2}}$$

(b) Do yourself.

(c) $2\sqrt{r^2 - p^2} = 2\sqrt{3} \Rightarrow r^2 - p^2 = 3 \qquad \ldots(1)$

Circle is $(1, -1), r = 4 \quad \therefore \quad p^2 = r^2 - 3 = 13 \quad \ldots(2)$

Line is $(1 - \lambda)\,x + (5 + 8\lambda)\,y - (22 + 30\lambda) = 0$

$$\therefore \quad p = \dfrac{(1 - \lambda).1 - (5 + 8\lambda) - (22 + 30\lambda)}{\sqrt{[(1 - \lambda)^2 + (5 + 8\lambda)^2]}}$$

Squaring and simplifying, we get

$$(5\lambda^2 + 6\lambda + 2).13^2 = 13^2\,(2 + 3\lambda)^2$$

or $2\lambda^2 + 3\lambda + 1 = 0 \quad \therefore \quad \lambda = -1, -1/2$

Ans. $2x - 3y + 8 = 0, \ 3x + 2y - 14 = 0$

(d) C is $(3, -1)$, AB is $2x - 5y + 18 = 0.$

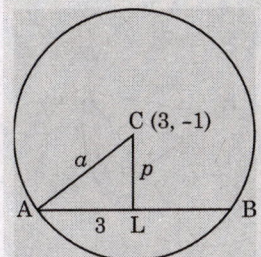

Fig. 65

$$\therefore \quad p = CL = \dfrac{6 + 5 + 18}{\sqrt{(29)}} = \sqrt{29}$$

Also $AL = \dfrac{1}{2} AB = 3.$

$$\therefore \quad a^2 = AL^2 + CL^2 = 9 + 29 = 38.$$

$$\therefore \quad \text{Circle is } (x - 3)^2 + (y + 1)^2 = 38.$$

(e) Let AB be the chord, the $AB = 3PQ = 3 \cdot \dfrac{7}{3}\sqrt{2} = 7\sqrt{2}$

The equation of PQ and hence of AB is $y = x$. If CL be perpendicular from $C(2, 1)$ to the chord AB,

$y = x$, then $CL = \dfrac{2 - 1}{\sqrt{2}} = \dfrac{1}{\sqrt{2}}$

$$\therefore \quad \text{radius of circle is given by } CA^2 = CL^2 + AL^2$$

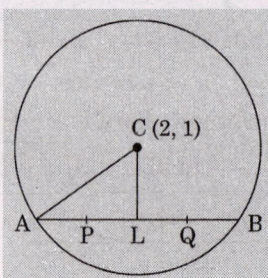

Fig. 66

or $r^2 = \frac{1}{2} + \left[\frac{1}{2}(7\sqrt{2})\right]^2 = \frac{1}{2} + \frac{49}{2} = 25$

$\therefore \quad r = 5$

Also $\quad r^2 = 25 = g^2 + f^2 - c$

$\qquad 25 = 2^2 + 1^2 + c \quad \therefore \quad c = 20$

59. Let the chord be $y - 4 = m(x - 3)$

or $\quad mx - y + (4 - 3m) = 0$ ...(1)

$\qquad AP = AQ = 5$

$\therefore \quad 5 = 2\sqrt{(r^2 - p^2)}$

Circle is $x^2 + y^2 - 6x - \frac{7}{4}y = 0$

C is $\left(3, \frac{7}{8}\right)$ and $r = \frac{25}{8}$

$\therefore \quad p = \dfrac{3m - \frac{7}{8} + 4 - 3m}{\sqrt{1 + m^2}} = \dfrac{25}{8\sqrt{1 + m^2}}$

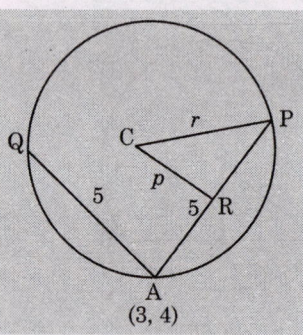

Fig. 67

Hence from (1), we get

$\dfrac{25}{4} = \left(\dfrac{25}{8}\right)^2 - \left(\dfrac{25}{8}\right)^2 \cdot \dfrac{1}{(1 + m^2)}$

or $\quad 16(m^2 + 1) = 25 m^2 \quad \therefore \quad m = \pm 4/3$

Hence from (1) the lines are $4x - 3y = 0$ and $4x + 3y - 24 = 0$.

Alternative Method :

On dividing by 4, the circle is

$(x - 3)^2 + \left(y - \frac{7}{8}\right)^2 = \left(\dfrac{25}{8}\right)^2$ ...(1)

Any line through (3, 4) is

$y - 4 = \tan\theta (x - 3)$ ...(2)

or $\quad \dfrac{x - 3}{\cos\theta} = \dfrac{y - 4}{\sin\theta} = r = 5$ for P or Q.

$(5\cos\theta + 3, 5\sin\theta + 4)$ is the other extremity of chord which will lie on the circle (1).

$\therefore \quad (5\cos\theta)^2 + \left(5\sin\theta + \dfrac{25}{8}\right)^2 = \left(\dfrac{25}{8}\right)^2$

or $\quad 25 + \dfrac{125}{4}\sin\theta = 0$

This gives $\quad \sin\theta = -\dfrac{4}{5} \quad \therefore \quad \cos\theta = \pm\dfrac{3}{5}$.

Hence $\quad \tan\theta = \pm\dfrac{4}{3} = m$

Putting for $\tan\theta$ in (2), the required lines are $4x = 3y$ and $4x + 3y - 24 = 0$.

60. (a) Solve the two equations; the points are $(4, 2)$ and $(-2, -6)$.

(b) Eliminating y,

$\qquad 25x^2 - 2(3\lambda + 80)x + (\lambda^2 + 32\lambda - 80) = 0$

For real points

$\qquad B^2 - 4AC > 0 \quad \therefore \quad \lambda^2 + 20\lambda - 525 < 0$

or $\quad (\lambda + 35)(\lambda - 15) < 0 \quad \Rightarrow \quad -35 < \lambda < 15$.

61. (a) Let α, β and γ, δ be the roots of the first and second of the given equations. Then

$\qquad \alpha + \beta = -2a, \quad \alpha\beta = -b^2$

$\qquad \gamma + \delta = -2p, \quad \gamma\delta = -q^2$.

Now co-ordinates of A and B are (α, γ) and (β, δ) respectively.

$\therefore$ The equation of the circle on AB as diameter is

$\qquad (x - \alpha)(x - \beta) + (y - \gamma)(y - \delta) = 0$

or $\quad x^2 + y^2 - (\alpha + \beta)x - (\gamma + \delta)y + \alpha\beta + \gamma\delta = 0$

or $\quad x^2 + y^2 + 2ax + 2py - b^2 - q^2 = 0$.

Its radius $= \sqrt{a^2 + p^2 + b^2 + q^2}$.

(b) Ans. $\quad x^2 + y^2 + 2x + 4y - a^2 - b^2 = 0$

Centre $(-1, -2)$ and radius $\sqrt{a^2 + b^2 + 5}$

62. The equation of the circle is

$\qquad x^2 + y^2 + 4x - 6y - 12 = 0$

and equation of tangent at the point $A(2, 0)$ is

$\qquad x.2 + y.0 + 2(x + 2) - 3(y + 0) - 12 = 0$

or $\quad 4x - 3y - 8 = 0$.

Now the lines through $A(2, 0)$ inclined at an angle of $45°$ to line (1) are found as in **Q. 26** to be

$\qquad m = 4/3, \quad t = \tan 45° = 1$

$\qquad m_1 = \dfrac{m - t}{1 + m.t} = \dfrac{1}{7},$

$\qquad m_2 = \dfrac{m + t}{1 - m.t} = -7$

$\qquad y - 0 = -7(x - 2)$ and $y - 0 = \dfrac{1}{7}(x - 2)$

or $\dfrac{x-2}{-1} = \dfrac{y}{7} = r$ and $\dfrac{x-2}{7} = \dfrac{y}{1} = r$

Writing them in the form $\dfrac{x - x_1}{\cos\theta} = \dfrac{y - y_1}{\sin\theta} = r$

or $\dfrac{(x-2)}{-1/\sqrt{(50)}} = \dfrac{(y-0)}{7/\sqrt{(50)}} = \pm 5\sqrt{2}$

$\dfrac{(x-2)}{7/\sqrt{(50)}} = \dfrac{y-0}{1/\sqrt{(50)}} = \pm 5\sqrt{2}$

The centres of the required circles are given to be at a distance of $5\sqrt{2}$ from $A(2,0)$

$x - 2 = -1, +1, 7, -7 \quad \therefore \quad x = 1, 3, 9, -5$

$y - 0 = 7, -7, 1, -1 \quad \therefore \quad y = 7, -7, 1, -1$

Hence the centres of the circles are $(1,7)$, $(3,-7)$, $(9,1)$ and $(-5,-1)$.

Since radius of each is 3, their equations are

$(x-1)^2 + (y-7)^2 = 3^2$,

$(x-3)^2 + (y+7)^2 = 3^2$,

$(x-9)^2 + (y-1)^2 = 3^2$

and $(x+5)^2 + (y+1)^2 = 3^2$.

63. Let the equation of the circle be

$x^2 + y^2 + 2gx + 2fy + c = 0$.

Since $(m_i, 1/m_i)$ lies on it, we have

$m_i^2 + \dfrac{1}{m_i^2} + 2gm_i + \dfrac{2f}{m_i} + c = 0$

or $m_i^4 + 2gm_i^3 + cm_i^2 + 2fm_i + 1 = 0$.

Since roots of this equation in m_i are m_1, m_2, m_3, m_4 we have

$m_1 m_2 m_3 m_4 = \dfrac{\text{constant term}}{\text{coeff. of } m_i^4} = \dfrac{1}{1} = 1$.

64. (a) The required circle will be a circle on the join of $(-4,4)$ and $(6,-1)$ as diameter whose equation is clearly

$(x+4)(x-6) + (y-4)(y+1) = 0$.

or $x^2 + y^2 - 2x - 3y - 28 = 0$ ...(1)

Intercept on y-axis

$= 2\sqrt{(f^2 - c)} = 2\sqrt{\left(\dfrac{9}{4} + 28\right)} = 11 = AB$.

Putting $x = 0$ in (1) the points A and B are given by

$y^2 - 3y - 28 = 0$ or $(y-7)(y+4) = 0$

$\therefore \quad A(0,7), B(0,-4)$

$T_A = 2x - 11y + 77 = 0$

$T_B = 2x + 11y + 44 = 0$.

If they meet at C then C is $\left(\dfrac{-121}{4}, \dfrac{3}{2}\right)$. Now we know the vertices of the triangle ABC and its area can be easily found out to be $\left(\dfrac{11}{2}\right)^3$. Since the points A, B are y-axis and $AB = 11$

$\therefore \quad \Delta = \dfrac{1}{2} b \times h = \dfrac{1}{2} \cdot 11 \times \left(\dfrac{-121}{4}\right) = \left(\dfrac{11}{2}\right)^3$

numerically.

(b) None of the points A, B satisfies the equation of diameter and hence given diameter is not along the diagonals AC or BD. If the centre be (h, k), then

$2h - k + 4 = 0$ ...(1)

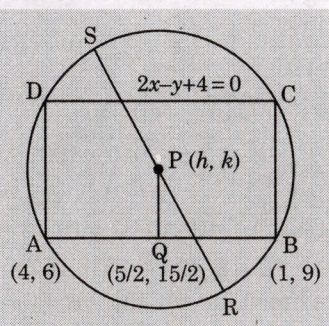

Fig. 68

If $Q(5/2, 15/2)$ be mid-point of AB, then PQ is perpendicular to AB.

$\therefore \quad m_1 m_2 = -1$ gives $k = h + 5$ ...(2)

Solving (1) and (2), we get $P(1,6)$.

Now $AB = 3\sqrt{2}, PQ = 3/\sqrt{2} \quad \therefore \quad AD = 2PQ = 3\sqrt{2}$

$\therefore$ Rectangle is a square of side $3\sqrt{2}$ so that its area $(3\sqrt{2})^2 = 18$.

(c) Refer figure part (b).

The given diameter $4y = x + 7$ is not satisfied by any of the points $A(-3,4)$ and $B(5,4)$ whose mid-point Q is $(1,4)$. If RS be the diameter through the centre (h, k), then

$4k = h + 7$ ...(1)

Slope of $AB = 0 \quad \therefore \quad$ Slope of $PQ = \infty$

or $\dfrac{k-4}{h-1} = \infty$ or $h - 1 = 0$

$\therefore \quad h = 1$ and hence $k = 2$

$\therefore$ Centre P is $(1,2)$ and Q is $(1,4)$

$\therefore \quad PQ = 2 \quad \therefore \quad BC = 2PQ = 4$.

Also $AB = 8$,

Area of rectangle $= 8 \times 4 = 32$ sq. units

65. (a) The two lines meet at $B(3,3)$. Slopes of AB and BC are 3 and 1.

$\therefore \quad \tan 2\theta = \dfrac{3-1}{1+3} = \dfrac{1}{2}$

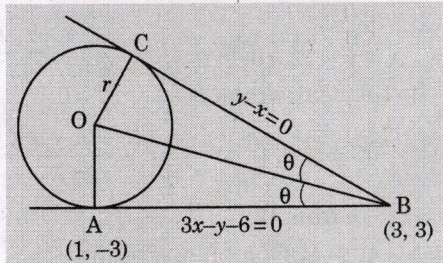

Fig. 69

Also from the figure,

$$\tan \theta = \frac{r}{AB} = \frac{r}{2\sqrt{(10)}} \quad \therefore \quad AB^2 = 40$$

Now

$$\frac{2\tan\theta}{1-\tan^2\theta} = \frac{1}{2}$$

or $\quad 4\tan\theta = 1 - \tan^2\theta$

Putting the value of $\tan\theta$, we get

$$\frac{2r}{\sqrt{(10)}} = 1 - \frac{r^2}{40}$$

$\therefore \quad r^2 + 8\sqrt{10}\, r - 40 = 0$

$\therefore \quad r = \dfrac{-8\sqrt{10} \pm \sqrt{640 + 160}}{2}$

$\quad = -4\sqrt{10} \pm 10\sqrt{2} = 10\sqrt{2} - 4\sqrt{10}$

$\quad = 10 \times 1.414 - 4 \times 3.162 = 1.49 = 1.5$

(b) Centre must lie on the bisectors of the angles between the lines which are found to be

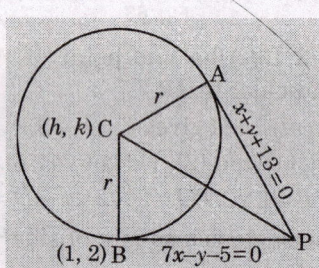

Fig. 70

$$x - 3y = 35 \quad \text{and} \quad 3x + y = -15$$

If (h, k) be the centre, then

$$h - 3k = 35 \qquad \qquad ...(1)$$

and $\quad 3h + k = -15 \qquad \qquad ...(2)$

$$CB \perp BP \Rightarrow \frac{k-2}{h-1} \times 7 = -1$$

or $\quad h + 7k - 15 = 0 \qquad \qquad ...(3)$

Solving (1), (3) and (2), (3), we get the centres as $C_1\,(-6, 3)$ and $C_2\,(29, -2)$.

$$r_1^2 = 50 \quad \text{and} \quad r_2^2 = 800$$

$\therefore \quad$ Circles are $(x+6)^2 + (y-3)^2 = 50$

and $\qquad (x-29)^2 + (y+2)^2 = 800$

66. Draw a diagram of the lines and plot the point $(4, -1)$. You will observe that centre lies on the bisector of obtuse angle whose equation can be found as usual to be

$$x + y - 12 = 0 \qquad \qquad ...(1)$$

If (h, k) be the centre then $h + k - 12 = 0 \quad ...(2)$

Again $(h-4)^2 + (k+1)^2 = r^2 = \left(\dfrac{h - 2k + 4}{\sqrt{5}}\right)^2$

Put $\; k = 12 - h$ from (2)

or $\quad 5\,[(h-4)^2 + (13 - h)^2] = (3h - 20)^2$

or $\quad h^2 - 50h + 525 = 0$

or $\quad (h - 15)(h - 35) = 0$

$\therefore \quad h = 15, k = -3$ or $h = 35, k = -23$

$\therefore \quad$ Centres are $(15, -3)$ and $r^2 = 125$

or $\quad (35, -23)$ and $r^2 = 1445$

Above gives the data of the two circles.

67. (a) The equation of a circle through the given points $A\,(3, 7)$ and $B\,(6, 5)$ is $S + \lambda P = 0$ where $S = 0$ is equation of circle on AB as diameter and $P = 0$ is the equation of line AB.

$(x-3)(x-6) + (y-7)(y-5) + \lambda\,(2x+3y-27) = 0$

$S = x^2 + y^2 + (2\lambda - 9)\,x + (3\lambda - 12)\,y + 53 - 27\lambda = 0$

$S_1 = x^2 + y^2 - 4x - 6y - 3 = 0$

Common chord is given by $S_1 - S_2 = 0$

$$(2\lambda - 5)\,x + (3\lambda - 6)\,y + (56 - 27\lambda) = 0$$

or $\quad (-5x - 6y + 56) + \lambda\,(2x + 3y - 27) = 0$

It is of the form $P + \lambda Q = 0$ which represents a family of lines passing through the intersection of $P = 0$ and $Q = 0$ *i.e.* the point $\left(2, \dfrac{23}{3}\right)$.

(b) The equation of circle through A and B as in part (a) is $S + \lambda P = 0$

or $\quad (x+1)(x-1) + (y-4)(y-2)$
$$\qquad\qquad\qquad + \lambda\,(x+y-3) = 0$$

or $\quad x^2 + y^2 + \lambda x + (\lambda - 6)\,y + (7 - 3\lambda) = 0$

The circle touches the line $3x - y - 3 = 0$. We may apply the condition of tangency *i.e.* $p = r$ and find two values of λ yourself.

Another method is that if the line is a tangent then it will cut the circle in two coincident points.

Putting $y = 3\,(x - 1)$ in the equation of circle, we get

$x^2 + 9\,(x-1)^2 + \lambda x + 3\,(x-1)\,(\lambda - 6) + 7 - 3\lambda = 0$

or $\quad 10x^2 + (-36 + 4\lambda)\,x + (34 - 6\lambda) = 0$

The roots of the above quadratic should be equal

$\therefore \qquad \Delta = 0$

$$\lambda^2 - 18\lambda + 81 - 5\,(17 - 3\lambda) = 0$$

$$\lambda^2 - 3\lambda - 4 = 0 \quad \text{or} \quad \lambda = 4, -1$$

Hence the circles are :

$$x^2 + y^2 + 4x - 2y - 5 = 0$$

and $x^2 + y^2 - x - 7y + 10 = 0$

68. Let the chord be $lx + my = 1$, and it subtends a right angle at the origin. Making the curve $3x^2 - y^2 - 2x + 4y = 0$ homogeneous by the help of the chord, we get

$$3x^2 - y^2 - 2(x - 2y) \cdot (lx + my) = 0$$

or $\quad (3 - 2l)\,x^2 - 2xy\,(m - 2l) + (4m - 1)\,y^2 = 0$

Since the above equation represents a pair of perpendicular lines, we have $A + B = 0$

$\therefore \quad 3 - 2l + 4m - 1 = 0 \quad \text{or} \quad 2l - 4m - 2 = 0$

or $\quad l - 2m = 1$

Above shows that the line $lx + my = 1$ passes through the point $(1, -2)$. Now if the curve be a circle

$$3x^2 + 3y^2 - 2x + 4y = 0$$

or $\quad x^2 + y^2 - \dfrac{2}{3}x + \dfrac{4}{3}y = 0$

whose centre is $\left(\dfrac{1}{3}, -\dfrac{2}{3}\right)$.

All the chords of this circle which subtend a rt. angle at the origin a point on the circumference must be diameters of the circle which must pass through the centre $(1/3, -2/3)$. Thus the result holds in the case of circles and the point of concurrency in this case is the centre of the circle.

69. (a) The two circles meet at $P(0, c), Q(0, -c)$. Any line through P is

$$y = mx + c \qquad \ldots(1)$$

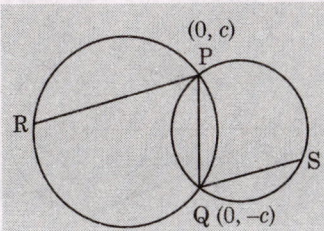

Fig. 71

where m is variable and c is intercept on y-axis and parallel line through Q is

$$y = mx - c \qquad \ldots(2)$$

(1) meets S_1 in point R

$$R \text{ is } \left[\dfrac{-2(a + mc)}{1 + m^2}, \dfrac{-2m(a + mc)}{1 + m^2} + c\right]$$

(2) meets S_2 in point S, $c \to -c$, m remains same, $a \to b$.

$$\therefore \quad S \text{ is } \left[\dfrac{-2(b - mc)}{1 + m^2}, \dfrac{-2m(b - mc)}{1 + m^2} - c\right]$$

If (x, y) be the mid-point of RS, then

$$2x = \dfrac{-2(a + b)}{1 + m^2}, 2y = \dfrac{-m(a + b)}{1 + m^2}$$

In order to find the locus we have to eliminate the variable m. Dividing we get $m = y/x$. Putting in any, we get

$$2x\left(1 + \dfrac{y^2}{x^2}\right) = -2(a + b)$$

or $\quad x^2 + y^2 + (a + b)x = 0$

(b) Ans. (b).

Let $CD = \alpha$ so that $AB = 2\alpha$ be two parallel lines. Taking A as origin the co-ordinates are $A(0, 0)$, $B(2\alpha, 0)$, $D(0, 2r)$ and $C(\alpha, 2r)$. Since the circle is touching the axes of co-ordinates it is of form

$$(x - r)^2 + (y - r)^2 = r^2 \quad i.e. \quad (r, r), r \qquad \ldots(1)$$

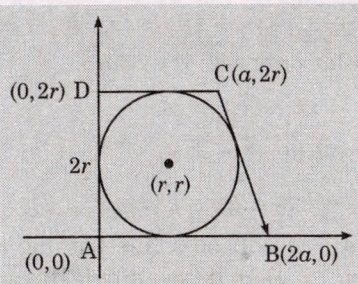

Fig. 72

Equation of BC is $y - 0 = -\dfrac{2r}{\alpha}(x - 2\alpha)$

or $\quad \alpha y + 2rx = 4r\alpha \qquad \ldots(2)$

The above line (2) is a tangent to circle (1). Apply the condition of tangency i.e., $p = r$ we have

$$= \dfrac{\alpha r + 2r^2 - 4r\alpha}{\sqrt{(\alpha^2 + 4r^2)}} = r$$

or $\quad (2r - 3\alpha)^2 = \alpha^2 + 4r^2$

$$8\alpha^2 - 12r\alpha = 0 \quad \therefore \quad 2\alpha = 3r \qquad \ldots(3)$$

Area of quadrilateral i.e. trapezium $ABCD$ is

$$\dfrac{1}{2}(\alpha + 2\alpha) \cdot 2r = 18 \quad \therefore \quad \alpha r = 6 \qquad \ldots(4)$$

or $\quad \dfrac{3}{2}r^2 = 6$ by (3) $\quad \therefore \quad r^2 = 4 \quad$ or $\quad r = 2$

70. Let the circle be $x^2 + (y - \sqrt{2})^2 = r^2$

or $\quad x^2 + y^2 - 2\sqrt{2}y = \lambda$ say,

where λ is either rational or irrational. Now let (h, k) be any rational point on it, then

$$h^2 + k^2 - 2\sqrt{2}k = \lambda \qquad \ldots(1)$$

Case I. (λ rational) :

Equating rational and irrational parts

$$h^2 + k^2 = \lambda, \quad k = 0 \quad \therefore \quad h = \pm\sqrt{\lambda} \quad \therefore \quad (\pm\sqrt{\lambda}, 0)$$

If λ is a perfect square, then h will be rational. Thus there will be two rational points on it. But if λ is not perfect square, then these two points will be irrational.

Case II. (λ irrational) :

Comparing rational and irrational in (1), we get

$$h^2 + k^2 = 0 \quad \text{and} \quad -2\sqrt{2}k = \lambda$$

$\therefore \quad h = 0, k = 0$ and hence $\lambda = 0$ which is a contradiction as λ is irrational. Thus by case I there will be only two rational points on it.

§5 Tangent, Normal, Chord of Contact, Polar, Chord with a given middle point, length of tangent, Radical axis, Orthogonal intersection of two circles.

(a) **Tangent to the circle**

$$x^2 + y^2 + 2gx + 2fy + c = 0$$

at any point (x_1, y_1) is

$$xx_1 + yy_1 + g(x + x_1) + f(y + y_1) + c = 0$$

or $x(x_1 + g) + y(y_1 + f) + (gx_1 + fy_1 + c) = 0$ ...(1)

Particular case : $x^2 + y^2 = a^2$

$$xx_1 + yy_1 = a^2.$$ ...(2)

Rule : Write $x^2 = x \cdot x_1$,

$y^2 = y \cdot y_1, 2gx = g(x + x_1), 2fy = f(y + y_1)$.

(b) **Normal :** It will be a line passing through the point (x_1, y_1) and perpendicular to tangent found above. It also passes through the centre of the circle.

(c) Normal at (x_1, y_1) to $x^2 + y^2 = a^2$ is $\dfrac{x}{x_1} = \dfrac{y}{y_1}$

Normal at (x_1, y_1) to $x^2 + y^2 + 2gx + 2fy + c = 0$ is

$$\frac{x - x_1}{x_1 + g} = \frac{y - y_1}{y_1 + f}$$

Ex. If the circle be $(x - 4)^2 + (y - 7)^2 = 20$ and P is $(2, 3)$ then T_p is $x + 2y = 8$ and normal at $P(2, 3)$ will be $2(x - 2) - 1(y - 3) = 0$

or $2x - y - 1 = 0$ **(Note the method)**

It will pass through the centre $(4, 7)$ of the circle.

Another method to write tangent at (2, 3) to the given circle :

Let the circle be $X^2 + Y^2 = 20$

and $P(x, y) = (2, 3)$

where $X = x - 4 = (2 - 4) = -2$

$Y = y - 7 = (3 - 7) = -4$

∴ Tangent at $P(x, y)$ to given circle is same as tangent at $(X, Y) = (-2, -4)$ to $X^2 + Y^2 = 20$

whose equation is $X(-2) + Y(-4) = 20$

or $X + 2Y = -10$

or $(x - 4) + 2(y - 7) = -10$

or $x + 2y - 8 = 0$

(c) **Tangent in terms of slope m.**

Let the circle be $x^2 + y^2 = a^2$.

Any line whose slope is m is $y = mx + c$

or $mx - y + c = 0$.

If it is a tangent then perpendicular from the centre $(0, 0)$ is equal to the radius a.

∴ $\pm \dfrac{c}{\sqrt{(1 + m^2)}} = a$ or $c = \pm a\sqrt{1 + m^2}$.

*Hence the line $y = mx \pm a\sqrt{1 + m^2}$.   ...(3)

is always a tangent to the circle. Corresponding to a given line there will be two tangents parallel to it.

Similarly, if the equation of the circle be $(x - h)^2 + (y - k)^2 = a^2$, then the line

$y - k = m(x - h) \pm a\sqrt{1 + m^2}$ is always a tangent to it.   ...(4)

Note. Corresponding to a given direction, *i.e.*, given value of m, there will be two parallel tangents to the circle as shown in (3) and (4).

General Method for equation of tangent applicable to circle, parabola, ellipse, hyperbola and to any other curve :

If the line $y = mx + c$ is a tangent to any curve then it will cut it in two coincident points. Solving the equation of line and curve by eliminating x or y you have a quadratic equation whose roots should be equal *i.e.*, $\Delta = B^2 - 4AC = 0$.

This will give the condition and also the point at which the line is a tangent.

(c_1) **Tangents from a given point (h, k)**

Any line through (h, k) is $y - k = m(x - h)$

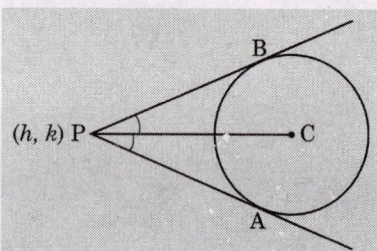

Fig. 73

In order to find the value of m apply the condition of tangency, $p = r$ and we shall get two values of m. Hence we will have two tangents that can be drawn to a given circle from a given point (h, k), outside the circle and the centre will lie on the bisector of the angle between these tangents.

Note : If the point be on the circle then there will be only one tangent in case the point is inside the circle then no tangent can be drawn from it.

*Centre C will lie on the bisectors of the angle between the tangents.

The combined equation of two tangents from $P(h, k)$ to a given circle is also given by $SS_1 = T^2$

where T is tangent at (h, k) and S_1 is the value of S for (h, k).

General method for finding the tangents drawn from any point (h, k) to a given conic *i.e.* circle, parabola, ellipse and hyperbola.

Any tangent to the circle $x^2 + y^2 = a^2$ is $y = mx + a\sqrt{1 + m^2}$. If it passes through (h, k), then

$(k - mh)^2 = a^2 (1 + m^2)$

or $m^2(h^2 - a^2) - 2mhk + (b^2 - a^2) = 0$ ...(1)

Above is a quadratic eqn. in m and will give two values of m and hence there will be two tangents passing through (h, k).

Director Circle. In case the two tangents drawn from (h, k) be perpendicular, then $m_1 m_2 = -1$.

$$\therefore \quad \frac{k^2 - a^2}{h^2 - a^2} = -1 \quad \text{or} \quad h^2 + k^2 = 2a^2$$

Hence the locus of the point (h, k) is $x^2 + y^2 = 2a^2$. This is called 'director circle'.

For other curves we will choose a tangent in terms of slope and proceed exactly as above.

(d) Chord of contact of tangents drawn from a point (x_1, y_1).

Let the points of contact of tangents from any point $T(x_1, y_1)$ be $A(p, q), B(h, k)$ on the circle $x^2 + y^2 = a^2$.

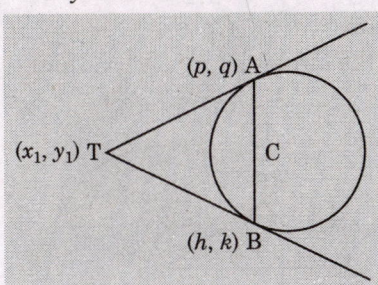

Fig. 74

$$T_A = px + qy = a^2$$
$$T_B = hx + ky = a^2.$$

Both these tangents pass through $T(x_1, y_1)$.

$$\therefore \quad px_1 + qy_1 = a^2$$

and $hx_1 + ky_1 = a^2$. ...(A)

Now consider the equation $xx_1 + yy_1 = a^2$.

Above is an equation of first degree in x, y and as such it represents a straight line and by virtue of relations in A it passes through $A(p, q)$ and $B(h, k)$.

Hence the equation $xx_1 + yy_1 = a^2$ ...(4)

represents the equation of the line AB, and is called the chord of contact of the point (x_1, y_1).

Note : The equation of the chord of contact of a point (x_1, y_1) (outside the circle) is of the same form as the equation of tangent to the circle at the point (x_1, y_1).

(e) Polar of a given point (x_1, y_1) w.r.t. the circle $x^2 + y^2 = a^2$.

Definition : If through any fixed point $P(x_1, y_1)$ chords of the circle be drawn then the locus of the points of intersection of tangents at the extremities of these chords is called the polar of the point P and the point P is called the pole.

Equation of polar.

Let QR be the chord passing through the point $P(x_1, y_1)$ tangents at the extremities of which

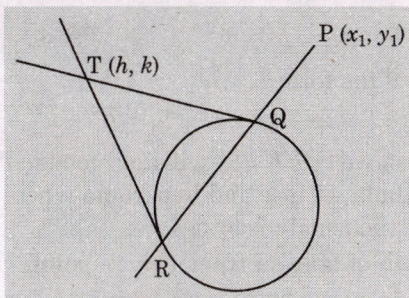

Fig. 75

intersect at the point $T(h, k)$ whose locus we are to find.

Now QR is the chord of contact of the point (h, k) and hence its equation is

$$hx + ky = a^2.$$ ...(A)

But QR passes through $P(x_1, y_1)$.

$$\therefore \quad hx_1 + ky_1 = a^2$$

Hence from (a) the locus of the point (h, k) is

$$xx_1 + yy_1 = a^2$$ ...(5)

Above is the equation of the polar of the point (x_1, y_1).

Note : The form of the equation of the polar of any point (x_1, y_1) is the same as the equation of tangent at the point (x_1, y_1) or the chord of contact of tangents drawn from the point (x_1, y_1).

Conjugate points and Conjugate lines.

Two points A and B are said to be conjugate w.r.t. a circle if the polar of either passes through the other.

Similarly any two lines $l_1 = 0$ and $l_2 = 0$ are said to be conjugate w.r.t. a circle if the pole of either lies on the other.

(f)**Chord with a given middle point : Let L be the middle point of the chord AB and C be the centre of the circle $x^2 + y^2 = a^2$, then CL is perpendicular to AB.

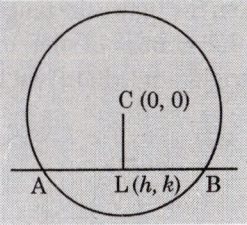

Fig. 76

Slope of $CL = \dfrac{k - 0}{h - 0} = \dfrac{k}{h}$

$\therefore$ Slope of $AB = -h/k$ $[\because m_1 m_2 = -1]$

Equation to AB which passes through $L(h, k)$ and whose slope is $-h/k$.

$$\therefore \quad y - k = \frac{-h}{k}(x - h)$$

or $hx + ky = h^2 + k^2$ ...(6)

It is of the form $T = S_1$

where $T = hx + ky - a^2$, $S_1 = h^2 + k^2 - a^2$.

The above rule $T = S_1$ will hold good in the case of **parabola, ellipse** and **hyperbola** where T and S_1 have the usual meanings.

(g) Length of tangent from a given point.

Let the circle be $x^2 + y^2 + 2gx + 2fy + c = 0$

and the given point P be (x_1, y_1) and PT be the tangent drawn from P.

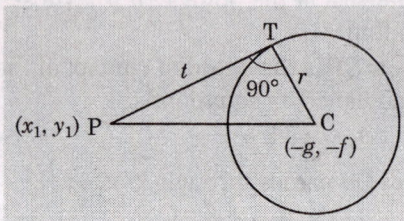

Fig. 77

Now if $C(-g, -f)$ be the centre then CT is perpendicular to PT

$\therefore$ $CP^2 = PT^2 + CT^2$

or $(x_1 + g)^2 + (y_1 + f)^2 = PT^2 + [\sqrt{g^2 + f^2 - c}]^2$

$$x_1^2 + y_1^2 + 2gx_1 + 2fy_1 + c = PT^2 = S_1 \quad ...(7)$$

*__Rule :__ Put down the co-ordinates of the point $P(x_1, y_1)$ in the equation of the circle and you get the square of the length of tangent drawn from P.

Note : The equation of the circle should be in standard form *i.e.*, coefficient of x^2 and y^2 should be each unity. If they be not unity then first make them unity and then apply the above rule.

(h) Orthogonal intersection of two circles. Two circles are said to intersect orthogonally if the angle between the tangents to them at their common point of intersection is a right angle. Clearly from the figure the tangent to one will pass through the centre of the other. Hence from ΔPC_1C_2 right angled at P we have

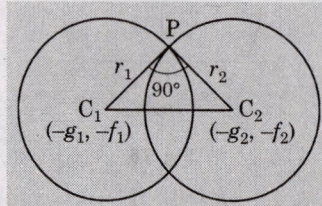

Fig. 78

$C_1C_2^2 = C_1P^2 + C_2P^2$

or $(g_1 - g_2)^2 + (f_1 - f_2)^2 = (g_1^2 + f_1^2 - c_1)$

                        $+ (g_2^2 + f_2^2 - c_2)$

*or $2g_1g_2 + 2f_1f_2 = c_1 + c_2$.   ...(8)

Another method for orthogonal intersection.

$C_1P =$ length of tangent from the centre of first circle to 2nd and it is equal to r_1 the radius of the first circle *i.e.*

             $C_1P = r_1$.

Similarly $C_2P = r_2$.

Now, apply $C_1C_2^2 = r_1^2 + r_2^2$ $\Rightarrow$ result (8)

Angle of Intersection of two circles.

In case the circles intersect at an angle θ, then from triangle C_1PC_2 by cosine formula, we have

$$\cos\theta = \frac{r_1^2 + r_2^2 - d^2}{2r_1r_2}$$

where $d = C_1C_2$

Ex. 1. If the circles be $x^2 + y^2 = 4$ and

         $x^2 + y^2 - 2x - 2y = 0$,

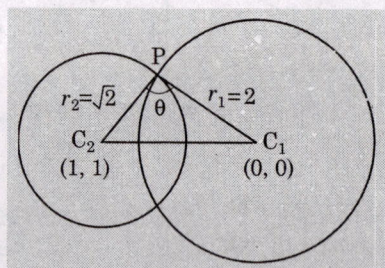

Fig. 79

   $C_1(0,0)$, $r_1 = 2$, $C_2(1,1)$, $r_2 = \sqrt{2}$

and $d = C_1C_2 = \sqrt{2}$.

$$\cos\theta = \frac{4 + 2 - 2}{2.2\sqrt{2}} = \frac{1}{\sqrt{2}} \quad \therefore \quad \theta = 45°.$$

Ex. 2. Two circles $x^2 + y^2 + 2g_1x + 2f_1y + c_1 = 0$ and $x^2 + y^2 + 2g_2x + 2f_2y + c_2 = 0$ intersect at an angle of $120°$ then prove that

$(2g_1g_2 + 2f_1f_2 - c_1 - c_2)^2$

                $= (g_1^2 + f_1^2 - c_1)(g_2^2 + f_2^2 - c_2).$

Sol. $\cos\theta = \dfrac{r_1^2 + r_2^2 - d^2}{2r_1r_2}$

Put $\cos\theta = \cos 120° = -\dfrac{1}{2}$ and the values of r_1^2, r_2^2 and

$d^2 = C_1C_2^2 = (g_1 - g_2)^2 + (f_1 - f_2)^2$

$\therefore$ $(r_1r_2)^2 = (r_1^2 + r_2^2 - d^2)^2$. Now put the values.

(i) Radical axis.

Definition : The radical axis of two circles $S_1 = 0$ and $S_2 = 0$ (in standard form *i.e.* coefficient of x^2 and y^2 is each unity) is the locus of a point which moves so that the lengths of the tangents drawn from it to the two circles are equal. If $P(h, k)$ be the point, then by definition

       $PT^2 = PT'^2$

or $h^2 + k^2 + 2g_1 h + 2f_1 k + c_1$
$= h^2 + k^2 + 2g_2 h + 2f_2 k + c_2$ by (g)

∴ $2h(g_1 - g_2) + 2k(f_1 - f_2) + c_1 - c_2 = 0$.

Hence the locus of the point (h, k) is

* $2x(g_1 - g_2) + 2y(f_1 - f_2) + c_1 - c_2 = 0$

or $S_1 - S_2 = 0$ ...(9)

In case the circles touch, then the radical axis $S_1 - S_2 = 0$ becomes the common tangent and in case they intersect then it becomes the equation of their common chord.

Slope of radical axis $= -\dfrac{2(g_1 - g_2)}{2(f_1 - f_2)} = m_1$

Slope of $C_1 C_2 = \dfrac{f_1 - f_2}{(g_1 - g_2)} = m_2$.

Clearly $m_1 m_2 = -1$.

Hence radical axis is perpendicular to the line joining the centres of the two circles.

(j)   **Coaxial Family of circles.** A system of circles is said to be co-axial if every pair of the system has the same radical axis.

The equation of a family of co-axial circles in the simplest form is

$x^2 + y^2 + 2gx + c = 0$,   **(See Q. 47 P. 900-24)**

where g is a parameter and c is a constant.

Here radical axis of the above system of circles is $x = 0$, that is, y-axis. For if we take any two different values g_1, g_2 of g then the two circles $x^2 + y^2 + 2g_1 x + c = 0$ and $x^2 + y^2 + 2g_2 x + c = 0$ have the radical axis $2(g_1 - g_2)x = 0$, that is, $x = 0$.

The centres of all circles lie on x-axis.

Another family of co-axial circles in the simplest form is $x^2 + y^2 + 2fy + c = 0$,

where c is a constant and f is a parameter.

Here the common radical axis is x-axis, i.e. $y = 0$. The centres of the circles of this family lie on y-axis.

Circles coaxial with two circles.

The equation of the family of circles coaxial with the circles $S_1 = 0$ and $S_2 = 0$ is

$S_1 + \lambda S_2 = 0$ or $S_1 + \mu v = 0$

where $v = S_1 - S_2$, λ, μ being parameters.

Limiting points of a system of coaxial circles are members of the system which are of zero radius.

Ex. Find the equation of a circle through the origin and belonging to the coaxial system of which the limiting points are $(1, 2), (4, 3)$.

$S_1 = (x - 1)^2 + (y - 2)^2 = 0$

$S_2 = (x - 4)^2 + (y - 3)^2 = 0$

The system of circles coaxial with S_1 and S_2 is $S_1 + \lambda S_2 = 0$. It passes through origin.

∴ $S_1 + \lambda S_2 = 0 \Rightarrow (1 + 4) + \lambda(16 + 9) = 0$

∴ $\lambda = -\dfrac{1}{5}$

Hence, the required circle is $S_1 - \dfrac{1}{5} S_2 = 0$

or $5S_1 - S_2 = 0$

or $5[x^2 + y^2 - 2x - 4y + 5]$
$\qquad\qquad - [x^2 + y^2 - 8x - 6y + 25 = 0]$

or $4(x^2 + y^2) - 2x - 14y = 0$

or $2(x^2 + y^2) - x - 7y = 0$

(k)*   **Common tangents to two circles.**

The following propositions can be easily proved :

(i)   *The direct common tangents to two circles meet on the line of centres and divide it externally in the ratio of the radii. (This follows from the similar Δ^s CBM and CAL in the following diagram).*

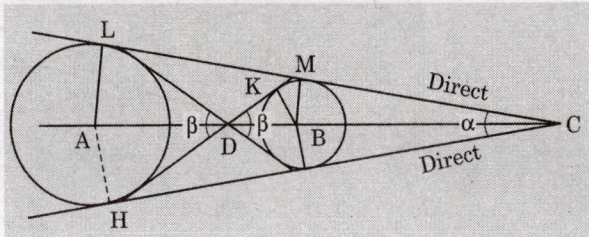

Fig. 80

(ii)   *The transverse common tangents also meet on the line of centres and divide it internally in the ratio of radii. (This follows from the similarity of the Δ^s BKD and AHD).*

Hence we obtain the following rule to obtain the equations of common tangents to the two circles.

Let A and B be the centres and a, b the radii of two given circles. Find the points C and D say, which respectively divide AB externally and internally in the ratio $a:b$. Then for the direct common tangents find the straight lines through C which are at a distance a from centre A and for the transverse common tangents find the straight lines through D at a distance a from A.

Note 1 : The points C and D which divide the line of centres AB internally and externally in the ratio of the radii are called the **centres of similitude** of the two circles.

Note 2 : Both the circles subtend equal angles α at C and β at D.

Note 3 : The direct common tangents of two circles are bisected by their radical axis. In the figure LM and HB will be bisected by the radical axis of the two circles. Further, their combined equation can also be obtained by the formula $SS_1 = T^2$ where S is any of the circles and T the tangent (at the point C) and S_1 is the value of that circle S for point C.

*Number of Common Tangents

If the circles are **touching internally** i.e. $C_1C_2 = r_1 - r_2$ there will be only **one** common tangent as in **figure 91**. If **they are intersecting** i.e.

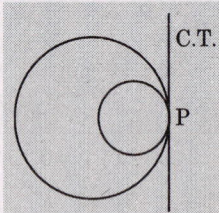

Fig. 81

$r_1 - r_2 < C_1C_2 < r_1 + r_2$ there will be **two** common tangents as in **figure 82**. In case they are **touching**

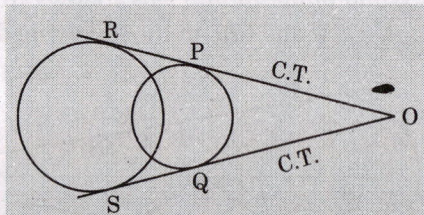

Fig. 82

externally i.e. $C_1C_2 = r_1 + r_2$ then there will be **three** common tangents as in **figure 83**. In case they are neither touching nor intersecting i.e. $C_1C_2 > r_1 + r_2$ then there will be **four** common tangents as in **figure 80**. If one circle is **completely**

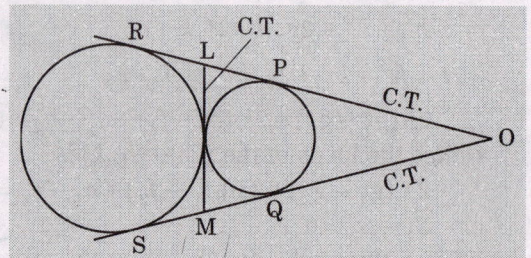

Fig. 83

within the other i.e. $C_1C_2 < r_1 - r_2$ then there will be **no common tangent** as in **fig. 84**.

Ex. Circle C_1 is $(0,0)$, r and circle C_2 is $(3r,0)$, $2r$. The

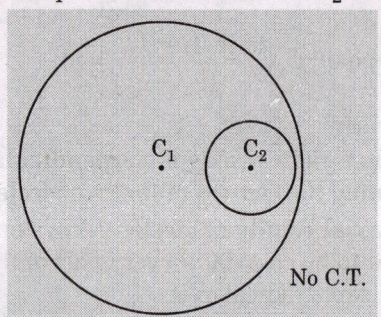

No C.T.

Fig. 84

number of common tangents to these circles is

(a) 1   (b) 2   (c) 3   (d) 4

Sol. Ans. (c).

$C_1C_2 = 3r = 2r + r$ = sum of radii.

Hence, the circles touch externally. Hence, as is shown in **Fig. 83**, there will be three common tangents.

Problem Set (2)

**Condition of tangency. Tangents from a point. Circles touching each other internally or externally.
Common tangents to two circles. Chord with a given middle point. Chord of contact,
Pole and polar. Length of tangent from a point. Radical axis and radical centre.
Coaxial circles. Orthogonal intersection of two circles.**

1. (a) Prove that the line $y = mx + c$ will be a tangent to the circle $(x-a)^2 + (y-b)^2 = r^2$ if
$m^2(a^2 - r^2) + 2ma(c-b) + (c-b)^2 = r^2$.

(b)* The circle OAB where O is origin and A, B are points on the co-ordinate axes is drawn such that the distances of points A and B from the tangent to the circle at origin are p and q respectively. Prove that the diameter of the circle is $p+q$ and its centre is $\left[\frac{1}{2}\sqrt{p(p+q)}, \frac{1}{2}\sqrt{q(p+q)}\right]$.

(c) If $a > 2b > 0$ then the positive value of m for which $y = mx - b\sqrt{1+m^2}$ is a common tangent to $x^2 + y^2 = b^2$ and $(x-a)^2 + y^2 = b^2$ is

(a) $\dfrac{2b}{\sqrt{a^2 - 4b^2}}$ (b) $\dfrac{\sqrt{a^2 - 4b^2}}{2b}$

(c) $\dfrac{2b}{a - 2b}$ (d) $\dfrac{b}{a - 2b}$ (I.I.T. Sc. 2002)

2. (a)* Show that the straight line $7y - x = 5$ touches the circle $x^2 + y^2 - 5x + 5y = 0$ and find the co-ordinates of the point of contact. Show that the other parallel tangent is $7y - x = -45$.

(b) Find the equation of those tangents to the circle $x^2 + y^2 - 6x + 4y - 12 = 0$ which are parallel to the line $4x + 3y + 5 = 0$.

(c) Prove that the tangent to the circle $x^2 + y^2 = 5$ at the point $(1, -2)$ also touches the circle $x^2 + y^2 - 8x + 6y + 20 = 0$ and find its point of contact.

3. (a)* A circle passes through $(-1, 1)$, $(0, 6)$ and $(5, 5)$. Find the points on this circle at which the tangents are parallel to the line joining the origin to its centre.

(b) Extremities of a diagonal of a rectangle are $(0,0)$ and $(4,3)$. Find the equations of the tangents to the circumcircle of the rectangle which are parallel to this diagonal. **(Roorkee 2000)**

(c) Show that the area of the triangle formed by the positive x-axis and the normal and the tangent to the circle $x^2 + y^2 = 4$ at $(1, \sqrt{3})$ is $2\sqrt{3}$.

4. (a) Find the equation of the tangents to the circle $x^2 + y^2 - 2x - 4y - 20 = 0$ which pass through the point $(8, 1)$.

(b) Find the equation of the two tangents from the point $(0, 1)$ to the circle $x^2 + y^2 - 2x + 4y = 0$.

(c) The equation of tangents drawn from the origin to the circle $x^2 + y^2 - 2rx - 2hy + h^2 = 0$ are $x = 0$ and $(h^2 - r^2) x - 2rhy = 0$

(d) Find the equations of tangents to the circle $x^2 + y^2 + 20 (x + y) + 20 = 0$ which pass through the origin.

5. (a)* Prove that the angle between two tangents from the origin to the circle $(x - 7)^2 + (y + 1)^2 = 25$ is $\pi/2$. **(M.N.R. 1990)**

(b)* A tangent drawn from the point $(4, 0)$ to the circle $x^2 + y^2 = 8$ touches it at a point A in the first quadrant. Find the co-ordinates of another point B on the circle such that $AB = 4$. **(Roorkee 1996)**

(c)* If $3x + y = 0$ is a tangent to the circle which has its centre at the point $(2, -1)$, then find the equation of the other tangent to the circle from the origin. **(M.N.R. 1996)**

(d) Find the equation of circle passing through $(4, -3)$ and touching the lines $x + y = 2$ and $x - y = 2$.

6. (a) Show that the angle at which the circle $x^2 + y^2 = 16$ can be seen from the point $(8, 0)$ is $\pi/3$.

(b) Tangents are drawn from the point (a, a) to the circle $x^2 + y^2 - 2x - 2y - 6 = 0$. If the angle between the tangents lies in the range $\left(\dfrac{\pi}{3}, \pi\right)$, then the exhaustive range of values of a is :
(a) $(1, \infty)$
(b) $(-5, -3) \cup (3, 5)$
(c) $(-\infty, 2\sqrt{2}) \cup (2\sqrt{2}, \infty)$
(d) $(-3, -1) \cup (3, 5)$

7. (a) Find the equation of the tangent line to the circle $(x + 2)^2 + (y - 3)^2 = 25$ at the point $A(-5, 7)$.

(b) Show that the equation to the tangent at A where $\theta = \alpha$ to the circle $(x - a)^2 + (y - b)^2 = r^2$ is $(x - a)\cos\alpha + (y - b)\sin\alpha = r$.

8. (a)* The centres and radii of two given circles are $A(a, 0), b$ and $B(-a, 0), c$. Show that the points of contact of their common tangents lie on the circle $x^2 + y^2 = a^2 \pm bc$, it being given that $a > b > c$.

(b) Find the co-ordinates of the point of intersection of the tangents drawn to the circle $x^2 + y^2 = a^2$ at the points whose parametric angles are α and β.

9. (a) The chord of the circle $x^2 + y^2 = 32$ makes equal intercepts of length l on the co-ordinate axes then $|l| < 8$.

(b) Any tangent to the circle $x^2 + y^2 = a^2$ meets the axes of co-ordinates in A and B respectively. The rectangle $OACB$ is completed. The locus of the vertex of the rectangle $OACB$ is the curve $x^{-2} + y^{-2} = a^{-2}$.

10. (a)* Find the locus of the feet of the normals drawn to the family of cricles $x^2 + y^2 - 2\lambda x = 0$ from any point (α, β).

(b) Tangents are drawn to the circle $x^2 + y^2 = 25$ from the point $(13, 0)$. Prove that the angle between them is $2 \tan^{-1} (5/12)$ and their equations are $12y + 5x + 65 = 0$ and $12y - 5x - 65 = 0$.

11. (a)* Find the equation of the circle which passes through the point $(1, 1)$ and which touches the circle $x^2 + y^2 + 4x - 6y - 3 = 0$ at the point $(2, 3)$ on it.

(b) What is the equation of the family of circles tangent to $3x - y = 6$ at $P(1, -3)$? Select the member or members of the family with radius equal to $2\sqrt{10}$.

(c) Which passes through the point $(2, 3)$ and touches the line $2x - 3y - 13 = 0$ at the point $(2, -3)$.

(d) Find the equation of the circle passing through the points $(4, 3)$ and $(3, 2)$ and touching the line $3x - y - 17 = 0$.

12. (a) Prove that the equation of the circle which passes through the point $(-2, 1)$ and is tangent to the line $3x - 2y - 6 = 0$ at the point $(4, 3)$ is $7(x^2 + y^2) + 4x - 82y + 55 = 0$.

(b)* A circle touches the hypotenuse of a right-angled triangle at its middle point and passes through the mid-point of the shorter side. If a and b $(a < b)$ be the length of the sides, then prove that the radius is $\dfrac{b}{4a}\sqrt{a^2 + b^2}$.

(c) If the circle $x^2 + y^2 + 2gx + 2fy + c = 0$ is touched by $y = x$ at P such that $OP = 6\sqrt{2}$, then prove that $c = 72$.

13. (a)* Find the locus of the point of intersection of tangents to the circle $x = a\cos\theta, y = a\sin\theta$ at the point whose parametric angles differ (i) by $\pi/3$, (ii) by $\pi/2$.

(b) Find the equation of tangents to the circle $x^2 + y^2 = a^2$ which makes with axes a triangle of area a^2.

(c) The extremities of a diameter of a circle are $(1, 2)$ and $(3, 4)$. Find its equation. Also determine the equations of tangents which are parallel to this diameter.

14. (a) Two parallel tangents to a given circle are cut by a third tangent in the points R and Q. Show that the lines from R and Q to the centre of the circle are mutually perpendicular.

(b) If the line $lx + my = 1$ be a tangent to the circle $x^2 + y^2 = a^2$, prove that the point (l, m) lies on a circle.

(c)* A point $P(h, k)$ of the circle $x^2 + y^2 = a^2$ is at a constant distance d from the extremities of the chord AB. Prove that the equation of the chord is

$$hx + ky = \left(\frac{d^2}{2} - a^2 \right).$$

Common Tangents. Read (k), P. 893-894.

15. (a)* Find all the common tangents to the circles

$$x^2 + y^2 - 2x - 6y + 9 = 0$$

and $x^2 + y^2 + 6x - 2y + 1 = 0$.

(b) Let T_1, T_2 be two tangents drawn from $(-2, 0)$ onto the circle $C : x^2 + y^2 = 1$. Determine the circles touching C and having T_1, T_2 as their pair of tangents. Further, find the equations of all possible common tangents to these circles, when taken two at a time. **(I.I.T. 1999)**

(c) Find the equation of circle passing through the points where the circles

$$x^2 + y^2 + 6x - 8y - 11 = 0 \text{ and}$$

$x^2 + y^2 - 8x + 14y + 56 = 0$ subtend equal angles and cut the first of these circles orthogonally.

16. (a) Find the equation to the four common tangents to the circles $x^2 + y^2 = 25$ and $(x - 12)^2 + y^2 = 9$.

(b)* A straight line AB is divided at C so that $AC = 3 CB$. Circles are described on AC and CB as diameters and a common tangent meets AB produced at D. Show that BD is equal to the radius of the smaller circle.

17. (a) Find the number of common tangents to the circles $x^2 + y^2 + 2x + 8y - 23 = 0$ and

$$x^2 + y^2 - 4x - 10y + 19 = 0.$$

(b)* The number of common tangents to the circles $x^2 + y^2 = 4$ and $x^2 + y^2 - 6x - 8y = 24$ is

(a) 0   (b) 1
(c) 3   (d) 4   **(I.I.T. 1998)**

(c) For the two circles $x^2 + y^2 = 16$ and

$$x^2 + y^2 - 2y = 0$$

(i) there are two pairs of common tangents.
(ii) there are no common tangents.
(iii) there are three common tangents.

(iv) there is one pair of common tangents.

(d)* How many common tangents can be drawn to the circles $x^2 + y^2 - 6x = 0$ and $x^2 + y^2 + 2x = 0$. What is the nature of the figure formed by these tangents ?

18. A circle of radius 2 units rolls on the outerside of the circle $x^2 + y^2 + 4x = 0$, touching it externally. Find the locus of the centre of this outer circle. Also find the equations of the common tangents of the two circles when the line joining the centres of the two circles makes an angle of $60°$ with x-axis.

(IIT 2007; Roorkee 2000)

Chord with a given mid-point [(f), P. 891-892].

19. (a) Find the locus of the middle points of the chords of the circle $x^2 + y^2 = a^2$ which subtend a right angle at the centre.

(b)* The equation of the locus of the mid-points of the chords of the circle $4x^2 + 4y^2 - 12x + 4y + 1 = 0$ that subtend an angle of $2\pi/3$ at its centre is ....

(I.I.T. 1993)

(c) Show that the locus of the mid-points of the chords of the circle $x^2 + y^2 - 2x - 2y - 2 = 0$ which make an angle of $120°$ at the centre is $x^2 + y^2 - 2x - 2y + 1 = 0$. **(M.N.R. 1994)**

(d)* Prove that the locus of the mid-points of the chords of circle $x^2 + y^2 = 4$ such that the segment intercepted by the chord on the curve $x^2 = 2(x + y)$ subtends a right angle at the origin is $x^2 + y^2 - 2x - 2y = 0$.

20. (a) Find the locus of the middle points of the chords of the circle $x^2 + y^2 - 2x - 6y - 10 = 0$ which pass through the origin.

(b) Through a fixed point (x_1, y_1) secants are drawn to the circle $x^2 + y^2 = a^2$. Show that locus of mid-points of the secants intercepted by the given circle is $x^2 + y^2 = xx_1 + yy_1$. **(M.N.R. 1992)**

(c) From the origin chords are drawn to the circle $(x - 1)^2 + y^2 = 1$.

Find the equation of the locus of the middle points of these chords.

21. (a)* Let a circle be given by

$2x(x - a) + y(2y - b) = 0 \quad (a \neq 0, \ b \neq 0)$

Find the conditition on a and b if two chords each bisected by the x-axis, can be drawn to the circle from $(a, b/2)$. **(I.I.T. 1992)**

(b) If two distinct chords, drawn from the point (p, q) on the circle $x^2 + y^2 = px + qy$ (where $pq \neq 0$) are bisected by the x-axis, then

(a) $p^2 = q^2$ (b) $p^2 = 8q^2$
(c) $p^2 < 8q^2$ (d) $p^2 > 8q^2$.   **(I.I.T. 1999)**

(c) A pair of tangents are drawn from a point P to the circle $x^2 + y^2 = 1$. If the tangents make an intercept of 2 on the line $x = 1$, the locus of P is
(a) straight line
(b) pair of lines
(c) circle
(d) parabola

22. (a) From points on a given circle tangents are drawn to another circle. Prove that the locus of the mid-points of the chord of contact is also a circle.

(b)* Find the locus of the mid-points of the chords of the circle $x^2 + y^2 = a^2$ which subtend a right angle at any point (α, β).

(c)* The mid-point of the chord AB of the circle $x^2 + y^2 - 6x - 4y + 3 = 0$ is the point $(1, 1)$. Determine the co-ordinates of the point of intersection of tangents to the circle at its extremities.

23.* Find the intervals of values of a for which the line $y + x = 0$ bisects two chords drawn from a point $\left(\dfrac{1 + \sqrt{2}a}{2}, \dfrac{1 - \sqrt{2}a}{2} \right)$ to the circle $2x^2 + 2y^2 - (1 + \sqrt{2}a) x - (1 - \sqrt{2}a) y = 0$ (I.I.T. 1996)

Chord of Contact and Polar (P. 891).

24. (a) If tangents be drawn to the circle $x^2 + y^2 = 12$ at its points of intersection with the circle $x^2 + y^2 - 5x + 3y - 2 = 0$, find the co-ordinates of their point of intersection.

(b) Prove that the pole of the straight line $9x + y - 28 = 0$ with respect to the circle $2x^2 + 2y^2 - 3x + 5y - 7 = 0$ is $(3, -1)$.

(c)* Prove that the locus of the point of intersection of tangents at the extremities of a chord of the circle $x^2 + y^2 = a^2$ which touch the circle $x^2 + y^2 - 2ax = 0$ is the parabola
$$y^2 = -2a (x - a/2).$$

(d) Find the co-ordinates of the point from which tangents are drawn to the circle $x^2 + y^2 - 6x - 4y + 3 = 0$ such that mid-point of its chord of contact is $(1, 1)$.

25. (a) The chords of contact of the pair of tangents drawn from each point on the line $2x + y = 4$ to the circle $x^2 + y^2 = 1$ pass through the point ....
(I.I.T. 1997)

(b)* C_1 and C_2 are two concentric circles, the radius of C_2 being twice that of C_1. From a point P on C_2, tangents PA and PB are drawn to C_1. Prove that the centroid of the triangle PAB lies on C_1. (I.I.T. 1998)

(c)* Prove that the equation $x^2 + y^2 - 2x - 2ay - 8 = 0$ represents a family of circles passing through two

fixed points, say P and Q. Choose the member of the family tangents to which at P and Q intersect on the line $x + 2y + 5 = 0$.

(d) Tangents are drawn to the circle $x^2 + y^2 + 6x + 4y - 12 = 0$ from origin. Determine the equation of the circle passing through the points of contact of the tangents and the origin.

(e) From the focus of the parabola $y^2 = 8x$, tangents are drawn to the circle $(x - 6)^2 + y^2 = 4$. The equation of the circle through the focus and points of contact of the tangents is :
(a) $x^2 + y^2 + 8x - 12 = 0$
(b) $x^2 + y^2 - 8x + 12 = 0$
(c) $x^2 + y^2 + 6x - 12 = 0$
(d) $x^2 + y^2 - 6x + 12 = 0$

(f) The line $9x + y - 28 = 0$ is the chord of contact of the point $P(h, k)$ w.r.t. the circle $2x^2 + 2y^2 - 3x + 5y - 7 = 0$, then the point P is
(a) $(3, -1)$
(b) $(3, 1)$
(c) $(-3, 1)$
(d) none

(g) Tangents drawn from the point $P(1, 8)$ to the circle $x^2 + y^2 - 6x - 4y - 11 = 0$ touch the circle at the points A and B. The equation of the circumcircle of the triangle PAB is
(a) $x^2 + y^2 + 4x - 6y + 19 = 0$
(b) $x^2 + y^2 - 4x - 10y + 19 = 0$
(c) $x^2 + y^2 - 2x + 6y - 29 = 0$
(d) $x^2 + y^2 - 6x - 4y + 19 = 0$ (I.I.T. 2009)

26. (a)* Find the area of the triangle formed by the tangents from the point (h, k) to the circle $x^2 + y^2 = a^2$ and their chord of contact.

(b) The area of the triangle formed by tangents from the point $(4, 3)$ to the circle $x^2 + y^2 = 9$ and the length of the line joining their points of contact is $7\dfrac{17}{25}$ units.

(c)* The chords of contact of tangents drawn from a variable point to two fixed circles are perpendicular to each other. Prove that its locus is a circle whose centre is at the mid-point of the line joining the centres of two given circles.

(d) The chord of contact of tangents drawn from any point on the circle $x^2 + y^2 = a^2$ to the circle $x^2 + y^2 = b^2$ touches the circle $x^2 + y^2 = c^2$. Show that a, b, c are in G.P. $(a > b)$.

27. (a) If the pole of any line with respect to the circle $x^2 + y^2 = c^2$ lies on the circle $x^2 + y^2 = 9c^2$, then the line will be a tangent to the circle $x^2 + y^2 = c^2/9$.

(b) If the polar of the point (x_1, y_1) with respect to the circle $x^2 + y^2 = a^2$ touches the circle $(x-a)^2 + y^2 = a^2$, prove that the locus of the point (x_1, y_1) is $y^2 + 2ax - a^2 = 0$.

(c)* Find the pole of the straight line $9x + y - 28 = 0$ with respect to the circle $2x^2 + 2y^2 - 3x + 5y - 7 = 0$.

(d) Prove that the ratio of the distances of any two points from the centre of a circle is the same as the distance of each from the polar of the other.

Orthogonal Intersection of two circles [(h), P. 892].

28. (a) Find the equation of the circle which cuts the circles
$$x^2 + y^2 - 9x + 14 = 0$$
and $$x^2 + y^2 + 15x + 14 = 0$$
orthogonally and passes through the point $(2, 5)$.

(b) Obtain the equation of the circle orthogonal to both the circles
$$x^2 + y^2 + 3x - 5y + 6 = 0$$
and $$4x^2 + 4y^2 - 28x + 29 = 0$$
and whose centre lies on the line
$$3x + 4y + 1 = 0.$$

(c) Find the equation of a circle passing through the origin and cutting the circles
$$x^2 + y^2 + 2g_1 x + 2fy_1 + c_1 = 0$$
and $x^2 + y^2 + 2g_2 x + 2f_2 y + c_2 = 0$ orthogonally.

29. (a) If the circles $x^2 + y^2 + 2x + 2ky + 6 = 0$ and $x^2 + y^2 + 2ky + k = 0$ intersect orthogonally, then k is

(a) 2 or $-\dfrac{3}{2}$ (b) -2 or $-\dfrac{3}{2}$

(c) 2 or $\dfrac{3}{2}$ (d) -2 or $\dfrac{3}{2}$ **(I.I.T. Sc. 2000)**

(b) Find the equation of the circle which passes through the points of intersection of circles
$$x^2 + y^2 - 2x - 6y + 6 = 0$$
and $x^2 + y^2 + 2x - 6y + 6 = 0$
and intersects the circle
$$x^2 + y^2 + 4x + 6y + 4 = 0$$ orthogonally.
    (Roorkee 2001)

(c) Show that the locus of the centres of the circles which cut the circles
$$x^2 + y^2 + 4x - 6y + 9 = 0$$
and $$x^2 + y^2 - 4x + 6y + 4 = 0$$
orthogonally is $8x - 12y + 5 = 0$.

(d) If a circle passes through the point $(1, 2)$ and cuts the circle $x^2 + y^2 = 4$ orthogonally then equation of the locus of its centre is the straight line $2x + 4y + 9 = 0$.   **(M.N.R. 1992)**

30. (a) Find the locus of the centre of a circle which touches the x-axis and cuts
$$x^2 + y^2 - 20x - 10y + 100 = 0$$
orthogonally. What curve does it represent and determine its data.

(b)* Find the equation of a circle which touches the line $x + y = 5$ at the point $(-2, 7)$ and cuts the circle $x^2 + y^2 + 4x - 6y + 9 = 0$ orthogonally.
    (Roorkee 1998)

(c) A circle passes through the origin and has its centre on $y = x$. If it cuts $x^2 + y^2 - 4x - 6y + 10 = 0$ orthogonally, then show that the equation of the circle is $x^2 + y^2 - 2x - 2y = 0$.
    (EAMCET 1994)

(d) Let $px + qy + r = 0$ where p, q, r are in A.P. be normal to the family of circles. The equation of the circle of the family which intersects the circle $x^2 + y^2 - 4x - 4y - 1 = 0$ orthogonally is :

(a) $x^2 + y^2 - 2x + 4y - 3 = 0$

(b) $x^2 + y^2 + 2x - 4y - 3 = 0$

(c) $x^2 + y^2 - 2x + 4y - 5 = 0$

(d) $x^2 + y^2 - 2x - 4y + 3 = 0$

31. (a)* Prove that the two circles which pass through the points $(0, a)$ and $(0, -a)$ and touch the line $y = mx + c$ will cut orthogonally if $c^2 = a^2 (2 + m^2)$.

(b)* The centre of circle S lies on the line $2x - 2y + 9 = 0$ and S cuts at right angles the circle $x^2 + y^2 = 4$, show that S passes through each of two fixed points and find their co-ordinates.

(c) A circle touches the line $2x + 3y + 1 = 0$ at the point $(1, -1)$ and is orthogonal to the circle which has the line segment having end points $(0, -1)$ and $(-2, 3)$ as the diameter.

(d) Two circles of radii r_1, r_2 intersect orthogonally. The length of their common chord is

(a) $\dfrac{2r_1 r_2}{\sqrt{r_1^2 + r_2^2}}$ (b) $\dfrac{r_1 r_2}{\sqrt{r_1^2 + r_2^2}}$

(c) $\dfrac{2r_1^2 r_2}{\sqrt{r_1^2 + r_2^2}}$ (d) $\dfrac{2r_2^2 r_1}{\sqrt{r_1^2 + r_2^2}}$ **(I.I.T. 2004)**

32. (a)* From a point $A (0, 3)$ on the circle $x^2 + 4x + (y-3)^2 = 0$, a chord AB is drawn and extended to a point M such that $AM = 2AB$. Find the equation of the locus of M.

(b) The line joining the points $A(3, 4), B(1, 0)$ cuts the circle $x^2 + y^2 = 4$ in points P and Q. If $\dfrac{AP}{PQ} = \lambda$ and

$\dfrac{AQ}{QB}=\mu$, then prove that λ and μ are the roots of

$3y^2 + 2y - 21 = 0$.

33.* Let A be the centre of the circle

$$x^2 + y^2 - 2x - 4y - 20 = 0.$$

Suppose that the tangent at the point $B(1,7)$ and $D(4,-2)$ on the circle meet at the point C. Find the area of the quadrilateral $ABCD$.

34. (a)* Find the equations of the circles passing through $(-4,3)$ and touching the lines $x+y=2$ and $x-y=2$.

(b) The lines $x-2y+4=0$ and $2x-y-8=0$ are tangents to a circle. Find the equation of that circle if it passes through the point $(4,-1)$.

(c)* Find the equation of circles passing through the point $(2,8)$, touching the lines

$$4x - 3y - 24 = 0 \text{ and } 4x + 3y - 42 = 0$$

and having x-co-ordinate of the centre of the circle less than or equal to 8.

35. (a) Find the equation of the circle which touches the straight lines $x+y=2, x-y=2$ and also touches the circle $x^2 + y^2 = 1$.

(b)* Lines $5x+12y-10=0$ and

$5x-12y-40=0$

touch circle C_1 of diameter 6. If the centre of C_1 lies in the first quadrant, find the equation of the circle C_2 which is concentric with C_1 and cuts intercept of length 8 on these lines.

(c)* The lines $7x-y-5=0$ and $x+y+13=0$ are tangents to a circle and $(1,2)$ is the point of contact of one of the lines. Determine the equations of the circles.

36. (a)* OAB is any chord of a circle which passes through O a point in the plane of the circle and meets it in points A and B. A point P is taken on this chord such that OP is (a) A.M. (b) G.M. of OA and OB. Prove that the locus of P in either case is a circle whose equation you have to determine.

(b)* Find the equation of tangent to the circle $x^2 + y^2 - 4x - 8y + 16 = 0$ at the point $(2+\sqrt3,3)$. If the circle rolls up along this tangent by 2 units then find its equation in the new position.

37. (a)* A triangle has two of its sides along the axes, its third side touches the circle $x^2 + y^2 - 2ax - 2ay + a^2 = 0$.

Prove that the locus of the circum-centre of the triangle is $a^2 - 2a(x+y) + 2xy = 0$.

(b)* The circle $x^2 + y^2 - 4x - 4y + 4 = 0$ is inscribed in a triangle which has two of the sides along the co-ordinate axes. The locus of the circumcentre of the triangle is $x + y - xy + k\sqrt{(x^2+y^2)} = 0$, find k.

(c)* If $4l^2 - 5m^2 + 6l + 1 = 0$, prove that the line, $lx + my + 1 = 0$ touches a fixed circle.

Radical axis and Coaxial circles. P. 893.

38. (a) Prove that the radical axis of three circles taken in pairs are concurrent. What is the point of concurrency called ?

(b)* The line $Ax + By + C = 0$ cuts the circle $x^2 + y^2 + ax + by + c = 0$ in P and Q.

The line $A'x + B'y + C' = 0$ cuts the circle $x^2 + y^2 + a'x + b'y + c' = 0$ in R and S.

If P,Q,R,S are concyclic, then show that

$$\begin{vmatrix} a-a' & b-b' & c-c' \\ A & B & C \\ A' & B' & C' \end{vmatrix} = 0.$$

(c) Circles are drawn on the three sides of a triangle as diameters. Prove that their radical centre is the orthocentre of the triangle.

39. (a) Find the co-ordinates of the point from which the lengths of tangents to the following three circles be equal

$$3x^2 + 3y^2 + 4x - 6y - 1 = 0,$$
$$2x^2 + 2y^2 - 3x - 2y - 4 = 0,$$
$$2x^2 + 2y^2 - x + y - 1 = 0.$$

(b) The equations of three circles are given

$$x^2 + y^2 = 1, \quad x^2 + y^2 + 8x + 15 = 0,$$
$$x^2 + y^2 + 10y + 24 = 0.$$

Determine the co-ordinates of the point such that the tangents drawn from it to three circles are equal in length.

(c) Distance from the origin to the centres of the three circles $x^2 + y^2 - 2\lambda x = c^2$ (where c is constant and λ is variable) are in G.P. Prove that the lengths of tangents drawn from any point on the circle $x^2 + y^2 = c^2$ to the three circles are also in G.P.

40. (a)* From a point P tangents drawn to the circles

$$x^2 + y^2 + x - 3 = 0,$$
$$3x^2 + 3y^2 - 5x + 3y = 0 \text{ and }$$
$$4x^2 + 4y^2 + 8x + 7y + 9 = 0$$

are of equal length. Find the equation of the circle through P which touches the line $x+y=5$ at the point $(6,-1)$. **(Roorkee 1992)**

(b) A and B are two points $(0,0)$ and $(3a,0)$ respectively. Points P and Q are taken on this line such that $AP = PQ = QB$. Circles are drawn on AP, PQ and QB as diameters. If T be the point from where the sum of the squares of the lengths of tangents to these three circles be b^2 then locus of T is the circle $3(x^2+y^2) - 9ax + 8a^2 - b^2 = 0$.

41. (a) Find the general equation of all circles, so that the radical axis of any two of them is the same as those of the circles
$$x^2 + y^2 = 4 \text{ and } x^2 + y^2 + 2x + 4y - 6 = 0.$$

(b)* Find the equation of the circle which passes through the point $(2a, 0)$ and whose radical axis w.r.t. the circle $x^2 + y^2 = a^2$ is the line $x = a/2$.

(c) If the tangent at the point P on the circle $x^2 + y^2 + 6x + 6y = 2$ meets the straight line $5x - 2y + 6 = 0$ at a point Q on the y-axis, then the length of PQ is

(a) 4   (b) $2\sqrt{5}$

(c) 5   (d) $3\sqrt{5}$ **(I.I.T. Sc. 2002)**

42. (a) The lengths of the tangents from any point on the circle $15x^2 + 15y^2 - 48x + 64y = 0$ to the two circles $5x^2 + 5y^2 - 48x + 64y + 300 = 0$ and $5x^2 + 5y^2 - 24x + 32y + 75 = 0$ are in the ratio $2:1$. Is this true or false ?

(b) Tangents are drawn to the circles $x^2 + y^2 + 4x + 6y - 19 = 0$ and $x^2 + y^2 = 9$ from any point on the line $2x + 3y = 5$. Prove that their lengths are equal.

(c) A point moves in such a way that square of the tangent drawn from it to the circle $x^2 + y^2 = 25$ is five times its distance from the line $3x + 4y - 8 = 0$. Determine the equation or equations to the locus of this moving point.

(d) If $b > a$ then prove that the length of the tangent drawn from any point on the circle $x^2 + y^2 + 2gx + 2fy + a = 0$ to the circle $x^2 + y^2 + 2gx + 2fy + b = 0$ is $b - a$.

43. (a) The circle $S \equiv x^2 + y^2 + 2gx + 2fy + c = 0$ subtends an angle θ at any point $P(x_1, y_1)$ then prove that $\tan\dfrac{\theta}{2} = \dfrac{r}{t} = \dfrac{r}{\sqrt{S'}}$ where t is the length of the tangent drawn from P to the circle S.

(b) Find the locus of a point at which the two circles S_1 and S_2 of radii r_1 and r_2 respectively subtend equal angles.

(c) Tangents are drawn one to each of the concentric circles $x^2 + y^2 = 4$ and $x^2 + y^2 = 9$. They include an angle of $60°$. Find the locus of the point of intersection of these tangents.

(d) Let $2x^2 + y^2 - 3xy = 0$ be the equation of a pair of tangents drawn from the origin O to a circle of radius 3 with centre in the first quadrant. If A is one of the points of contact, find the length of OA.   **(I.I.T. 2001)**

44. (a) Prove that the locus of a point which moves such that the difference of the squares of the lengths of tangents drawn from it to two given circles is

constant is a line parallel to the radical axis of the given circles.

(b) A point P moves so that the length of the tangent from P to the circle $x^2 + y^2 - 2x - 4y + 1 = 0$ is three times the distance of P from the point $(1, -2)$. Then the locus of P is a straight line. Is this statement true ?

45. (a)* Through a given point $P(h, k)$ secants are drawn to cut the circle $x^2 + y^2 = a^2$ at the points $A_1, B_1; A_2, B_2; ....; A_n, B_n$.
Prove that
$$(PA_1 \cdot PB_1) = (PA_2 \cdot PB_2) .... = (PA_n \cdot PB_n) = PQ^2$$
where PQ is the length of tangent from P to the given circle.

(b)* What is the general equation of a circle passing through two given points (x_1, y_1) and (x_2, y_2) ? If S_1, S_2, S_3 be three members of this family and t_2, t_3 be the lengths of tangents from any point on S_1 to circles S_2 and S_3, then show that t_2/t_3 is constant.

46. (a) If two circles cut a third circle orthogonally then prove that their radical axis or their common chord will pass through the centre of the third circle.

(b)* The radical axis of the circles
$$x^2 + y^2 + 2gx + 2fy + c = 0$$
and $2x^2 + 2y^2 + 3x + 8y + 2c = 0$
touches the circle $x^2 + y^2 + 2x + 2y + 1 = 0$;
show that either $g = \dfrac{3}{4}$ or $f = 2$.

47. (a) Define coaxial circles and deduce their equation in simplest form.

(b)* Prove that the equation of given circles can always be put in the form $x^2 + y^2 + ax + b = 0$, $x^2 + y^2 + a'x + b = 0$ and that one of the circles will be within the other if aa' and b are both +ive.

48. (a) If $S_1 = 0$, $S_2 = 0$ be the equations of two circles and $P = 0$ be the equation of a line then interpret the equations $S_1 + \lambda S_2 = 0$ and $S_1 + \lambda P = 0$.

(b)* Prove that as λ varies the circles
$$x^2 + y^2 + 2ax + 2by + 2\lambda (ax - by) = 0$$
form a coaxial system. Find the equation of radical axis and also the equation of the circle which are orthogonal to the circles of the above system.

(c) A variable circle passes through the point of intersection of any two fixed straight lines and cuts off from them portions OA and OB such that $pOA + qOB = 1$. Show that this circle always passes through a fixed point.

49. (a) Find the equation of a circle which is coaxial with the circles $2x^2 + 2y^2 - 2x + 6y - 3 = 0$
and $x^2 + y^2 + 4x + 2y + 1 = 0$.
It is given that the centre of the circle to be determined lies on the radical axis of these circles.

(b)* Find the equation of the system of coaxial circles that are tangent at $(\sqrt{2}, 4)$ to the locus of the point of intersection of two mutually perpendicular tangents to the circle $x^2 + y^2 = 9$. **(Roorkee 1993)**

50. (a)* If from any point on the circle $x^2 + y^2 + 2gx + 2fy + c = 0$ tangents are drawn to the circle
$$x^2 + y^2 + 2gx + 2fy + c\sin^2\alpha$$
$$+ (g^2 + f^2)\cos^2\alpha = 0,$$
show that angle between the tangents is 2α.

(b)* The angle between a pair of tangents drawn from a point T to the circle
$x^2 + y^2 + 4x - 6y + 9\sin^2\alpha + 13\cos^2\alpha = 0$ is 2α.
The equation of the locus of the point T is
(a) $x^2 + y^2 + 4x - 6y + 4 = 0$
(b) $x^2 + y^2 + 4x - 6y - 9 = 0$
(c) $x^2 + y^2 + 4x - 6y - 4 = 0$
(d) $x^2 + y^2 + 4x - 6y + 9 = 0$ **(I.I.T. 1996)**

(c)* Show that the locus of the point the tangents from which to the circle $x^2 + y^2 = a^2$ include a constant angle α is
$(x^2 + y^2 - 2a^2)^2 \tan^2\alpha = 4a^2(x^2 + y^2 - a^2)$.

51. (a) Tangents PQ, PR are drawn to the circle $x^2 + y^2 = a^2$ from a given point P. Find the equation of the circum-circle of the triangle PQR.

(b) Let $S_1 = g_1, f_1, c_1 = 0$, $S_2 = g_2, f_2, c_2 = 0$ be the equations of two circles of radii r_1 and r_2 respectively. Prove that the locus of the point P at which these circles subtend equal angles is given by $r_2^2 S_1 - r_1^2 S_2 = 0$.

(c) Tangents OP and OQ are drawn from origin O to the circle $x^2 + y^2 + 2gx + 2fy + c = 0$ with centre C. Prove that the centre of circle circumscribing $\triangle OPQ$ is $(-g/2, -f/2)$ and the area of quadrilateral $OPCQ$ is $\sqrt{c(g^2 + f^2 - c)}$.

(d) Tangents TP and TQ are drawn from a point T to the circle $x^2 + y^2 = a^2$. If the point T lies on the line $px + qy = r$, find the locus of centre of the circum-circle of triangle TPQ. **(Roorkee 2001)**

52. (a) If two curves whose equations are
$$ax^2 + 2hxy + by^2 + 2gx + 2fy + c = 0$$
and $d'x^2 + 2h'xy + b'y^2 + 2g'x + 2f'y + c' = 0$
intersect in four concyclic points, prove that

$$\frac{a-b}{h} = \frac{d'-b'}{h'}.$$

(b) If the four points of intersection of the lines $(2x - y + 1)(x - 2y + 3) = 0$ with the axes lies on a circle, then find its centre.

53. (a)* If the equations of the circles whose radii are r and R be respectively $S = 0$ and $S' = 0$, then prove that the circles $\dfrac{S}{r} \pm \dfrac{S'}{R} = 0$ will cut orthogonally.

(b) If a circle passes through the point (a, b) and cuts the circle $x^2 + y^2 = k^2$ orthogonally, then the locus of its centre is
$$2ax + 2by - (a^2 + b^2 + k^2) = 0.$$

54. (a)* Prove that the circle through the origin and cutting the circles
$x^2 + y^2 + 2g_1 x + 2f_1 y + c_1 = 0$ and
$x^2 + y^2 + 2g_2 x + 2f_2 y + c_2 = 0$
orthogonally is
$$\begin{vmatrix} x^2 + y^2 & -x & -y \\ c_1 & g_1 & f_1 \\ c_2 & g_2 & f_2 \end{vmatrix} = 0$$

(b) Prove that the equation of the circle cutting the three circles $x^2 + y^2 + 2g_i x + 2f_i y + c_i = 0$ $(i = 1, 2, 3)$ orthogonally is
$$\begin{vmatrix} x^2 + y^2 & x & y & 1 \\ -c_1 & g_1 & f_1 & -1 \\ -c_2 & g_2 & f_2 & -1 \\ -c_3 & g_3 & f_3 & -1 \end{vmatrix} = 0$$

(c)* P, Q, R, S are the centres of the four circles each of which is cut by a fixed circle orthogonally. If $t_1^2, t_2^2, t_3^2, t_4^2$ be the squares of the lengths of tangents to the four circles from a point in their plane, then prove that
$$t_1^2 \, \triangle QRS + t_2^2 \, \triangle RSP + t_3^2 \, \triangle SPQ + t_4^2 \, \triangle PQR = 0$$

55. (a)* The lengths of tangents from a fixed point to three circles of a co-axial system are t_1, t_2, t_3 respectively. If P, Q, R be the centres of the three circles, show that $QR t_1^2 + RP t_2^2 + PQ t_3^2 = 0$.

(b)* P, Q, R are the centres and r_1, r_2, r_3 are the radii respectively of three coaxial circles, show that
$$r_1^2 \, QR + r_2^2 \, RP + r_3^2 \, PQ = -PQ \cdot QR \cdot RP$$

56.* Show that general equation of a circle which passes through the points (x_1, y_1) and (x_2, y_2) may be written as
$$(x - x_1)(x - x_2) + (y - y_1)(y - y_2)$$
$$+ \lambda \begin{vmatrix} x & y & 1 \\ x_1 & y_1 & 1 \\ x_2 & y_2 & 1 \end{vmatrix} = 0$$
and hence deduce the diameter form of the equation of a circle.

57. (a)* Let $S = x^2 + y^2 + 2gx + 2fy + c = 0$ be a given circle. Find the locus of the foot of the perpendicular drawn from the origin upon any chord which subtends a right angle at the origin.

(b)* A circle of constant radius r passes through origin O and cuts the axes of co-ordinates in points A and B. Prove that the locus of the foot of perpendicular from O to AB is

$$(x^2 + y^2)^2 \left(\frac{1}{x^2} + \frac{1}{y^2} \right) = 4r^2.$$

58.* The line $y = x$ touches a circle at P so that $OP = 4\sqrt{2}$, where O is the origin. The point $(-10, 2)$ is inside the circle and the length of the chord on the line $x + y = 0$ is $6\sqrt{2}$. Find the equation of the circle.

(I.I.T. 1990)

59.* From a point on the line $4x - 3y = 6$ tangents are drawn to the circle $x^2 + y^2 - 6x - 4y + 4 = 0$ which make an angle of $\tan^{-1} \dfrac{24}{7}$ between them. Find the co-ordinates of all such points and the equations of tangents.

(Roorkee 1995)

60. P is a variable point on the line $y = 4$. Tangents are drawn to the circle $x^2 + y^2 = 4$ from P to touch it at A and B. The parallelogram $PAQB$ is completed. Prove that the locus of the point Q is $(y + 4)(x^2 + y^2) = 2y^2$.

Solutions to Problem Set (2)

1. (a) Perpendicular from the centre (a, b) to the tangent $mx - y + c = 0$ should be equal to radius r

$$\frac{ma - b + c}{\sqrt{(m^2 + 1)}} = r. \text{ Square}$$

$$m^2 a^2 + (c - b)^2 + 2ma(c - b) = r^2(m^2 + 1)$$

or $m^2(a^2 - r^2) + 2ma(c - b) + (c - b)^2 = r^2$.

(b) **Refer (j) particular case P. 851.**

Circle OAB is $x^2 + y^2 - ax - by = 0$

Tangent at $(0, 0)$ is $ax + by = 0$

$$\therefore \quad p = \frac{a^2}{\sqrt{(a^2 + b^2)}}, q = \frac{b^2}{\sqrt{(a^2 + b^2)}}$$

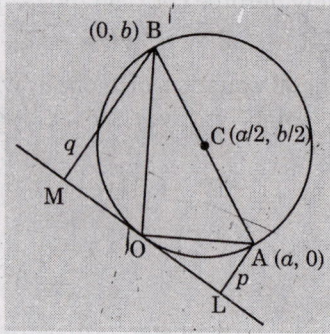

Fig. 85

$$\therefore \quad p + q = \sqrt{(a^2 + b^2)} = \text{diameter } AB$$

$$\therefore \quad a^2 = p\sqrt{(a^2 + b^2)} = p(p + q),$$

$$b^2 = q(p + q)$$

$$\therefore \quad \text{Centre is } \left(\frac{1}{2}a, \frac{1}{2}b \right) \text{ etc.}$$

(c) **Ans. (a).** The given line is a tangent to 1st circle $[y = mx \pm a\sqrt{1 + m^2}]$. If it is to be a tangent to 2nd circle $(a, 0), b$ then apply $p = r$.

$$\therefore \quad \frac{ma - b\sqrt{1 + m^2}}{\pm\sqrt{1 + m^2}} = b$$

or $ma = 0$ or $2b\sqrt{1 + m^2}$

$$\therefore \quad m = 0 \text{ (rej.)} \quad \text{or} \quad m^2 a^2 = 4b^2 + 4m^2 b^2$$

or $m^2(a^2 - 4b^2) = 4b^2$ $\therefore$ $m = \dfrac{2b}{\sqrt{a^2 - 4b^2}}$

2. (a) Circle is $\left(\dfrac{5}{2}, \dfrac{-5}{2} \right), \dfrac{5}{2}\sqrt{2}$

Line is $7y - x - 5 = 0$.

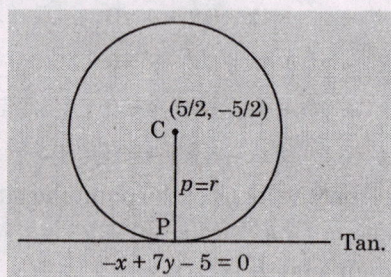

Fig. 86

Condition of tangency $p = r$

$$p = \frac{-50}{2\sqrt{(50)}} = \frac{5\sqrt{2}}{2} = r$$

Parallel tangent : Any line parallel to $7y - x - 5 = 0$ is $7y - x + \lambda = 0$.

Condition of tangency

$$\frac{7(-5/2) - 5/2 + \lambda}{\sqrt{(50)}} = \frac{5\sqrt{2}}{2}$$

$$\lambda - 20 = \pm 5\sqrt{2} \cdot 5\sqrt{2}/2 = \pm 25.$$

$$\therefore \quad \lambda = -5 \quad \text{or} \quad +45.$$

Hence the other parallel tangent is

$$7y - x + 45 = 0 \quad \text{as} \quad 7y - x - 5 = 0$$

is already a tangent.

Point of contact P is foot of perpendicular from centre C on the tangent at P. If its co-ordinates be (h, k), then

$$\frac{h - 5/2}{-1} = \frac{k + 5/2}{7} = -\frac{r}{a^2 + b^2} \quad \textbf{(Cor.)}$$

$$= -\frac{(-5/2) + 7 \cdot (-5/2) - 5}{1^2 + 7^2} = \frac{25}{50} = \frac{1}{2}$$

$\therefore$ $h = \dfrac{5}{2} - \dfrac{1}{2}, k = -\dfrac{5}{2} + \dfrac{7}{2} = 1$

$\therefore$ P is $(2, 1)$.

Follow this method for point of contact.

2nd Method : Solve the tangent with the circle by eliminating one variable say y and you will have a quadratic in x having equal roots as the line is a tangent giving $x = 2$ and hence $y = 1$.

$\therefore$ Point is $(2, 1)$.

(b) Proceed as in part (a).

$4x + 3y + 19 = 0, 4x + 3y - 31 = 0$.

(c) $T_{(1, -2)} = x - 2y - 5 = 0$

Apply $p = r$ with $(4, -3), \sqrt{5}$. It is satisfied. Point of contact as in part (a) is $(3, -1)$.

3. (a) The required circle $x^2 + y^2 - 4x - 6y = 0$ whose centre is $C(2, 3)$. If (h, k) be any point on this circle, then

$h^2 + k^2 - 4h - 6k = 0$ ...(1)

Tangent at (h, k) is

$x \cdot h + y \cdot k - 2(x + h) - 3(y + k) = 0$

Its slope is $-\dfrac{h - 2}{k - 2} = \dfrac{3}{2}$ as it is parallel to join of O

and C.

$\therefore$ $2h + 3k = 13$ ...(2)

Solving (1) and (2), we get the points $(5, 1)$ and $(-1, 5)$.

Alt. Method : $(x - 2)^2 + (y - 3)^2 = 13$

or $X^2 + Y^2 = 13$

Any tangent whose slope is $\dfrac{3}{2}$ *i.e.* of OC is

$Y = mX \pm a\sqrt{1 + m^2}$

or $y - 3 = \dfrac{3}{2}(x - 2) \pm \sqrt{13}\sqrt{1 + \dfrac{9}{4}}$

or $3x - 2y + 13 = 0$ or $3x - 2y - 13 = 0$

are two parallel tangents.

The points of contact are feet of perpendiculars from centre $(2, 3)$ on these tangents. If it be (h, k), then

$\dfrac{h - 2}{3} = \dfrac{k - 3}{-2}$

$= -\dfrac{3(2) - 2(3) \pm 13}{3^2 + 2^2} = 1$ or -1

$\therefore$ (h, k) is $(5, 1)$ or $(-1, 5)$.

(b) Circumcircle of rectangle will be a circle on AC as diameter $x(x - 4) + y(y - 3) = 0$

or $x^2 + y^2 - 4x - 3y = 0$

Centre $(2, 3/2)$ and radius $5/2$

Equation of AC is $3x - 4y = 0$

Any line parallel to it is $3x - 4y + \lambda = 0$

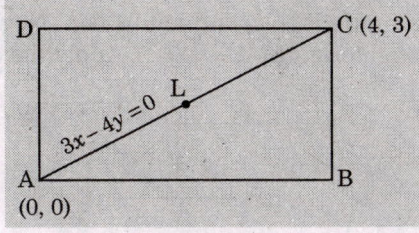

Fig. 87

If it is a tangent, then $p = r$ gives

$\dfrac{6 - 6 + \lambda}{5} = \pm \dfrac{5}{2}$ $\therefore$ $\lambda = \pm \dfrac{25}{2}$

$\therefore$ $3x - 4y \pm \dfrac{25}{2} = 0$ are the required tangents.

(c) Ans. $2\sqrt{3}$.

The tangent at $P(1, \sqrt{3})$ is $x + y\sqrt{3} = 4$ and normal is $\sqrt{3}x - y = 0$. They form a ΔOPA with the x-axis.

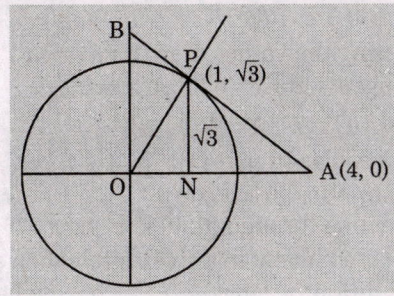

Fig. 88

Clearly $OA = 4$ and $PN = \sqrt{3}$ so that the area of

$\Delta OPA = \dfrac{1}{2}OA \cdot PN = \dfrac{1}{2} \cdot 4 \cdot \sqrt{3} = 2\sqrt{3}$.

4. (a) Any line through the point $(8, 1)$ is

$y - 1 = m(x - 8)$

or $mx - y + (1 - 8m) = 0$.   ...(1)

If it is a tangent then perpendicular from centre $(1, 2)$ is equal to radius $\sqrt{1 + 4 + 20} = 5$

$\therefore$ $\dfrac{m - 2 + (1 - 8m)}{\sqrt{(m^2 + 1)}} = 5$

or $(-7m - 1)^2 = 25(m^2 + 1)$

or $49m^2 + 14m + 1 = 25m^2 + 25$

or $24m^2 + 14m - 24 = 0$

or $12m^2 + 7m - 12 = 0$

or $12m^2 + 16m - 9m - 12 = 0$

$(3m + 4)(4m - 3) = 0$

$\therefore$ $m = -4/3, 3/4$.

Putting the values of m in (1), the required tangents are

$4x + 3y - 35 = 0$

and $3x - 4y - 20 = 0$.

(b) Proceed as above.

$m = 2, -\dfrac{1}{2}, 2x - y + 1 = 0, \quad x + 2y - 2 = 0$.

(c) The centre is (r, h) and radius is r. Now any line through origin is $y - mx = 0$. Apply the condition

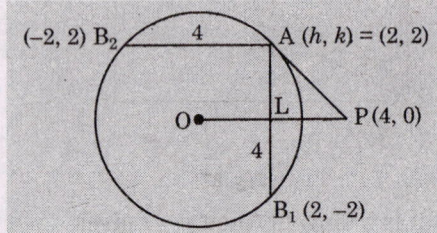

Fig. 89

of tangency, i.e., $p = r$

$$\frac{h - mr}{\sqrt{(1 + m^2)}} = r$$

or $h^2 + m^2 r^2 - 2mhr = r^2 + m^2 r^2$

or $0m^2 + 2mhr + (r^2 - h^2) = 0$

∴ $m = \infty, \ m = (h^2 - r^2)/2hr$.

Putting the values of m in $y/x = m$

Tangents are $x = 0$ for $m = \infty$,

and $(h^2 - r^2) x - 2rhy = 0$

(d) Proceed as in part (a).

$x + 2y = 0, \quad 2x + y = 0$.

5. (a) Any line through $(0, 0)$ is $y - mx = 0$

If it is a tangent to a given circle then applying the condition of tangency, i.e., $p = r$ where centre is $(7, -1)$ and $r = 5$, we get

∴ $\dfrac{-1 - 7m}{\sqrt{(m^2 + 1)}} = 5$

or $(1 + 7m)^2 = 25(1 + m^2)$

or $24m^2 + 14m - 24 = 0$

Above gives us the slopes of the two tangents drawn from $(0, 0)$:

Since $m_1 m_2 = -\dfrac{24}{24} = -1$

Hence the tangents are perpendicular.

(b) Let A be (h, k) tangent at which is $hx + ky = 8$. It passes through $(4, 0)$.

∴ $4h = 8$ or $h = 2$

Also $h^2 + k^2 = 8$ ∴ $k^2 = 4$

∴ $k = 2$ (only) in Ist quadrant.

∴ $A(2, 2)$. Now let B be (p, q)

∴ $p^2 + q^2 = 8$ ...(1)

Also $AB = 4 \Rightarrow (p - 2)^2 + (q - 2)^2 = 16$

or $p^2 + q^2 - 4(p + q) + 8 = 16$

or $p + q = 0$, by (1) ...(2)

Solving (1) and (2), we get $(2, -2)$ or $(-2, 2)$.

(c) Using $p = r$, we get $r = \sqrt{(5/2)}$.

Any line through origin is $y = mx$.

If it is a tangent to $(2, -1), \sqrt{(5/2)}$, then using $p = r$, we get

$$\frac{2m + 1}{\sqrt{(m^2 + 1)}} = \sqrt{\frac{5}{2}}. \text{ Square}$$

$2(4m^2 + 4m + 1) = 5(m^2 + 1)$

or $3m^2 + 8m - 3 = 0$

or $(m + 3)(3m - 1) = 0$

∴ $m = -3, 1/3$ where -3 corresponds to given tangent.

Hence the other tangent is $y = \dfrac{1}{3} x$ or $x - 3y = 0$.

(d) If (h, k) be the centre, then $p = r$ gives

$$\frac{h + k - 2}{\sqrt{2}} = \pm \frac{h - k - 2}{\sqrt{2}} = \sqrt{(h - 4)^2 + (k + 3)^2}$$

Taking +ive sign, we have $k = 0$

and $\left(\dfrac{h - 2}{\sqrt{2}}\right)^2 = (h - 4)^2 + 9$

∴ $h^2 + 20h + 46 = 0$

∴ $h = -10 \pm 3\sqrt{6}$

and $r^2 = (h - 4)^2 + 9 = \dfrac{(-12 \pm 3\sqrt{6})^2}{2}$

Taking –ive sign, we have $h = 2$

∴ $\left(\dfrac{k}{12}\right)^2 = 36 + (k - 3)^2$

or $k^2 - 12k + 90 = 0$

Its roots are imaginary.

Hence the required circle is

$(x - h)^2 + (y - 0)^2 = r^2$ etc.

6. (a) Any tangent to given circle is

$$y = mx \pm 4\sqrt{1 + m^2}$$

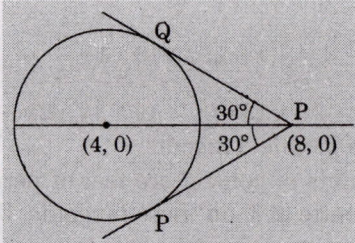

Fig. 90

It passes through $(8, 0)$

∴ $8m \pm 4\sqrt{1 + m^2} = 0$

or $4m^2 = 1 + m^2$ ∴ $m = \pm \dfrac{1}{\sqrt{3}}$.

Hence the two tangents are equally inclined to x-axis at an angle of $30°$. Hence the circle can be seen at an angle of $60°$ i.e. $\pi/3$.

(b) Ans. (d).

The point (a, a) lies outside the circle $(1, 1), 2\sqrt{2}$

∴ $S' > 0$

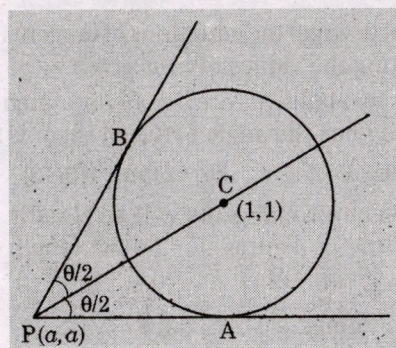

Fig. 91

or $2a^2 - 4a - 6 > 0$ or $a^2 - 2a - 3 > 0$

$(a+1)(a-3) > 0$

∴ $a < -1$ or $a > 3$ ...(1)

If θ be the angle between the tangents then from the figure

$$\tan\frac{\theta}{2} = \frac{r}{\sqrt{S'}} = \frac{2\sqrt{2}}{\sqrt{2a^2 - 4a - 6}}$$ **(g) P. 892** ...(2)

Since $\dfrac{\pi}{3} < \theta < \pi \Rightarrow \dfrac{\pi}{6} < \dfrac{\theta}{2} < \dfrac{\pi}{2}$

$\tan\dfrac{\pi}{6} < \tan\dfrac{\theta}{2} < \tan\dfrac{\pi}{2}$

∴ $\tan\dfrac{\theta}{2}$ lies in $\left(\dfrac{1}{\sqrt{3}}, \infty\right)$

∴ $\dfrac{2\sqrt{2}}{\sqrt{2a^2 - 4a - 6}} > \dfrac{1}{\sqrt{3}}$ by (2)

or $a^2 - 2a - 15 < 0$ or $(a+3)(a-5) < 0$

∴ $-3 < a < 5$ ...(3)

Hence from (1) and (3), we get

$a \in (-3, -1) \cup (3, 5)$.

7. **(a)** The given circle is

$x^2 + y^2 + 4x - 6y - 12 = 0$.

Tangent at $(-5, 7)$ is

$x(-5) + y(7) + 2(x-5) - 3(y+7) - 12 = 0$

or $-3x + 4y - 43 = 0$

or $3x - 4y + 43 = 0$.

Alternative method :

The given circle is

$X^2 + Y^2 = 25$, point is $(-5, 7)$

$X = x + 2 = -5 + 2 = -3$,

$Y = y - 3 = 7 - 3 = 4$ ∴ point is $(-3, 4)$

∴ Tangent is $X(-3) + Y(4) = 25$

or $(x+2)(-3) + (y-3)\,4 = 25$

or $3x - 4y + 43 = 0$

(b) Shift the origin to the point (a, b) by writing $x + a$ for x and $y + b$ for y so that the equation of the circle becomes

$x^2 + y^2 = r^2$.

Tangent at $\theta = \alpha$ i.e. $(r\cos\alpha, r\sin\alpha)$ is

$x(r\cos\alpha) + y(r\sin\alpha) = r^2$

or $x\cos\alpha + y\sin\alpha = r$.

Shift the origin back to (a, b) by writing $x - a$ for x and $y - b$ for y.

∴ $(x-a)\cos\alpha + (y-b)\sin\alpha = r$

is the required tangent.

8. **(a)** The given circles are

$(x-a)^2 + y^2 = b^2$ ...(1)

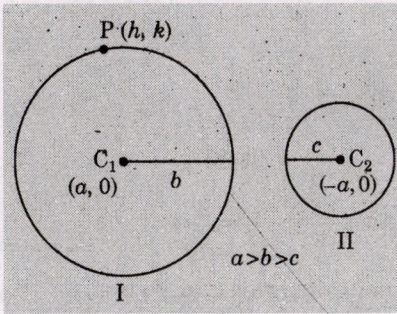

Fig. 92

$(x+a)^2 + y^2 = c^2$ ...(2)

$C_1 C_2 = 2a = a + a > b + c$

∵ $a > b > c$

Hence the circles are non-intersecting.

Let (h, k) be any point on (1).

∴ $(h-a)^2 + k^2 = b^2$ ...(A)

or $h^2 + k^2 - 2ah + a^2 = b^2$

Tangent at any point (h, k) to (1)

$(h-a)x + ky - ah + a^2 - b^2 = 0$

If it is a tangent to 2nd circle, then applying the condition of tangency with 2nd circle, we get

$$\frac{-a(h-a) - ah + a^2 - b^2}{\sqrt{[(h-a)^2 + k^2]} = b} = c$$ by (A)

$-2ah + 2a^2 - b^2 = \pm bc$

Putting for $-2ah$ from (A)

$(b^2 - k^2 - h^2 - a^2) + 2a^2 - b^2 = \pm bc$ by (A)

or $h^2 + k^2 = a^2 \pm bc$

∴   Locus of (h, k) is $x^2 + y^2 = a^2 \pm bc$

(b) Solve $x\cos\alpha + y\sin\alpha - a = 0$

and $x\cos\beta + y\sin\beta - a = 0$

by the method of cross-multiplication.

Ans. $\left(\dfrac{a\cos\dfrac{\alpha+\beta}{2}}{\cos\dfrac{\alpha-\beta}{2}}, \dfrac{a\sin\dfrac{\alpha+\beta}{2}}{\cos\dfrac{\alpha-\beta}{2}}\right)$

9. **(a)** Any chord making equal intercepts on co-ordinate axes is $x \pm y = \pm l$. Since it is a chord hence perpendicular from centre $(0, 0)$ must be less than the radius $4\sqrt{2}$.

$\therefore \quad \left| \pm \dfrac{l}{\sqrt{2}} \right| < 4\sqrt{2} \quad \therefore \quad |l| < 8$

(b) Let tangent AB be $\dfrac{x}{\alpha} + \dfrac{y}{\beta} = 1$.

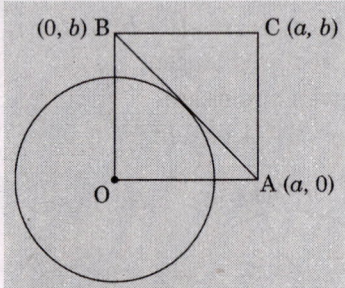

Fig. 93

$p = r$ gives $\dfrac{1}{\alpha^2} + \dfrac{1}{\beta^2} = \dfrac{1}{a^2}$

$\therefore \quad$ Locus of vertex $C(\alpha, \beta)$ is
$x^{-2} + y^{-2} = a^{-2}$

10. (a) Let $L(h, k)$ be the foot of normal CL which is drawn from the point (α, β). Its equation is

$y - k = \dfrac{k}{h - \lambda}(x - h)$

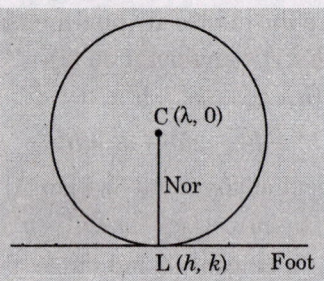

Fig. 94

It passes through the point (α, β)

$\therefore \quad (\beta - k)(h - \lambda) = k(\alpha - h)$

or $\quad h - \dfrac{k(\alpha - h)}{\beta - k} = \lambda \quad$ or $\quad \dfrac{h\beta - k\alpha}{\beta - k} = \lambda \quad \ldots(1)$

But (h, k) lies on the circle $h^2 + k^2 = 2\lambda h \quad \ldots(2)$

Eliminating the variable λ from (1) and (2), we get

$\dfrac{h\beta - k\alpha}{\beta - k} = \dfrac{h^2 + k^2}{2h}$

$\therefore \quad$ Locus of (h, k) is
$2x(x\beta - y\alpha) = (x^2 + y^2)(\beta - y)$

(b) Any line through $(13, 0)$ is

$y - 0 = m(x - 13) \quad \ldots(1)$

or $\quad mx - y - 13m = 0$

The condition of tangency $p = r$ gives

$\dfrac{-13m}{\sqrt{(m^2 + 1)}} = 5 \quad$ or $\quad 169m^2 = 25m^2 + 25$

$\therefore \quad m = \pm 5/12.$

Hence we get the equations of tangents from (1) on putting the values of m as given.

The two tangents are equally inclined to the axes and hence the angle between them is 2θ where

$\tan\theta = 5/12. \quad \therefore \quad 2\theta = 2\tan^{-1}(5/12)$

Alt. The two tangents will be equally inclined to the line of centres. If t be the length of tangent, then $t^2 = S' = 144. \quad \therefore \quad t = 12$

Also radius is 5 $\quad \therefore \quad \tan\theta = 5/12.$

Hence $\quad 2\theta = 2\tan^{-1}(5/12).$

11. (a) **1st Method :** Tangent at $(2, 3)$ to given circle $S = 0$ is easily found to be $P \equiv x - 2 = 0$.

The required circle is $S + \lambda P = 0$

Since it passes through $(1, 1) \quad \therefore \quad \lambda = -3$

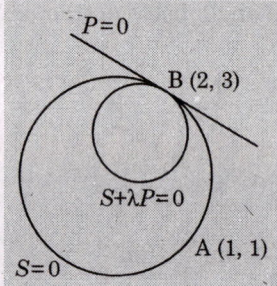

Fig. 95

Hence $x^2 + y^2 + x - 6y + 3 = 0$

2nd Method : $S + \lambda P = 0$ where S is point circle at $(2, 3)$ and P is tangent at P.

$\therefore \quad (x - 2)^2 + (y - 3)^2 + \lambda(x - 2) = 0$

$\qquad$ pt. circle $\qquad\qquad$ tangent **(By (n$_1$) P. 853)**

It passes through $(1, 1) \quad \therefore \quad \lambda = 5.$

$\therefore \quad x^2 + y^2 + x - 6y + 3 = 0$

Note : In Ist method, S is given circle and in IInd method, S is the point circle and hence the values of λ are different.

(b) Here tangent at $(1, -3)$ is $3x - y - 6 = 0$. Hence the required family of circles is

$(x - 1)^2 + (y + 3)^2 + \lambda(3x - y - 6) = 0 \qquad \ldots(1)$

pt. circle $\qquad\qquad$ tangent $\qquad$ **[By (n$_1$) P. 853]**

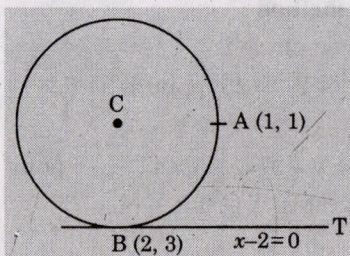

Fig. 96

We have to choose the member of the family whose radius is $2\sqrt{10}$.

$x^2 + y^2 + x(3\lambda - 2) + y(6 - \lambda) + 10 - 6\lambda = 0 \ ,\ldots(2)$

Its radius $= \sqrt{g^2 + f^2 - c} = 2\sqrt{10}$

or $\left(\dfrac{3\lambda - 2}{2}\right)^2 + \left(\dfrac{6-\lambda}{2}\right)^2 - 4(10 - 6\lambda) = 40$

or $10\lambda^2 = 160$ ∴ $\lambda = 4, -4$.

Putting in (2), the required circles are

$x^2 + y^2 + 10x + 2y - 14 = 0$

or $x^2 + y^2 - 14x + 10y + 34 = 0$

Radius of each of the above two circles is $\sqrt{40}$ i.e. $2\sqrt{10}$.

(c) Proceed as in parts (a) and (b).

∴ Required circle is $x^2 + y^2 - 13 = 0$

(d) Chord through $A(4, 3)$ and $B(3, 2)$ is

$x - y - 1 = 0$.

The required circle **[by (n) P. 853]** is

$\underbrace{(x - 4)(x - 3) + (y - 3)(y - 2)}_{\text{circle on } AB \text{ as diameter}} + \lambda \underbrace{(x - y - 1)}_{\text{chord } AB} = 0$

or $x^2 + y^2 - 7x - 5y + 18 + \lambda(x - y - 1) = 0$

...(1)

$x^2 + y^2 + (\lambda - 7)x - (\lambda + 5)y - (\lambda - 18) = 0$

centre is $\left(-\dfrac{\lambda - 7}{2}, \dfrac{\lambda + 5}{2}\right)$

and $r^2 = \left(\dfrac{\lambda - 7}{2}\right)^2 + \left(\dfrac{\lambda + 5}{2}\right)^2 + (\lambda - 18) = \dfrac{\lambda^2 + 1}{2}$

If the line $3x - y - 17 = 0$ is a tangent then $p = r$ gives

$\dfrac{-3\left(\dfrac{\lambda - 7}{2}\right) - \dfrac{\lambda + 5}{2} - 17}{\sqrt{9 + 1}} = r$

or $(-2\lambda - 9)^2 = 10 r^2$

or $4\lambda^2 + 36\lambda + 81 = 10\left[\dfrac{\lambda^2 + 1}{2}\right]$

or $\lambda^2 - 36\lambda - 76 = 0$

or $(\lambda - 38)(\lambda + 2) = 0$

or $\lambda = -2, 38$

Putting the value of λ in (1) the required circles are

$x^2 + y^2 - 9x - 3y + 20 = 0$

and $x^2 + y^2 + 31x - 43y - 20 = 0$

12. (a) Do yourself.

(b) Choose the perpendicular sides along axes of co-ordinates so that the hypotenuse is $\dfrac{x}{a} + \dfrac{y}{b} = 1$

which is a tangent at mid-point $(a/2, b/2)$.

The equation of the circle by **(n₁) P. 853** is

$\underbrace{\left(x - \dfrac{a}{2}\right)^2 + \left(y - \dfrac{b}{2}\right)^2}_{\text{Point circle}} + \lambda \underbrace{\left(\dfrac{x}{a} + \dfrac{y}{b} - 1\right)}_{\text{Tangent}} = 0$

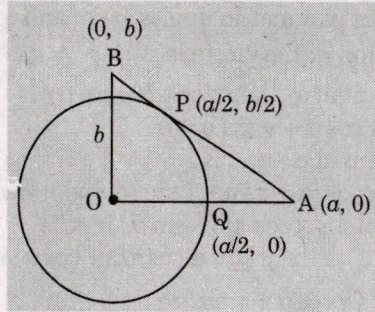

Fig. 97

It passes through mid-point Q of OA i.e. $\left(\dfrac{a}{2}, 0\right)$

∴ $\dfrac{b^2}{4} - \dfrac{\lambda}{2} = 0$ or $\lambda = \dfrac{b^2}{2}$

Required circle is

$\left(x - \dfrac{a}{2}\right)^2 + \left(y - \dfrac{b}{2}\right)^2 + \dfrac{b^2}{2}\left(\dfrac{x}{a} + \dfrac{y}{b} - 1\right) = 0$

or $x^2 + y^2 + x\left(-a + \dfrac{b^2}{2a}\right) + y\left(-b + \dfrac{b}{2}\right)$

$\qquad\qquad + \dfrac{a^2 + b^2}{4} - \dfrac{b^2}{2} = 0$

or $x^2 + y^2 + \dfrac{b^2 - 2a^2}{2a}x - \dfrac{b}{2}y + \dfrac{a^2 - b^2}{4} = 0$

∴ $r^2 = g^2 + f^2 - c$

$= \left(\dfrac{b^2 - 2a^2}{4a}\right)^2 + \left(\dfrac{b}{4}\right)^2 - \dfrac{(a^2 - b^2)}{4}$

$= \dfrac{b^4}{16a^2} + \dfrac{a^2}{4} - \dfrac{b^2}{4} + \dfrac{b^2}{16} - \dfrac{a^2}{4} + \dfrac{b^2}{4}$

$= \dfrac{b^4 + a^2 b^2}{16a^2}$ ∴ $r = \dfrac{b}{4a}\sqrt{a^2 + b^2}$.

(c) The point P lies on $x - y = 0$

or $\dfrac{x - 0}{\cos 45°} = \dfrac{y - 0}{\sin 45°} = r = OP = 6\sqrt{2}$

P is $(6, 6)$. It also lies on circle

$72 + 12(g + f) + c = 0$ ...(1)

Since $y = x$ touches the given circle, its intersection with given circle will have equal roots.

∴ $2x^2 + 2x(g + f) + c = 0$ has equal roots.

∴ $(g + f)^2 = 2c$ ...(2)

Note : You will get the same result if you apply $p = r$.

Eliminating $(g + f)$ between (1) and (2), we get

$\dfrac{[-(c + 72)]^2}{144} = 2c$

or $(c + 72)^2 - 4 \times 72 \times c = 0$ or $(c - 72)^2 = 0$

∴ $c = 72$ $\quad [\because (x + y)^2 - 4xy = (x - y)^2]$

13. (a) Let the parametric angles be α and $\alpha + \pi/3$ and equation of the circle is $x^2 + y^2 = a^2$.

Tangent at α, *i.e.* $(a\cos\alpha, a\sin\alpha)$ is

$$x\cos\alpha + y\sin\alpha = a. \qquad \ldots(1)$$

Tangent at $\alpha + \pi/3$ is

$$x\cos(\alpha + \pi/3) + y\sin(\alpha + \pi/3) = a.$$

or $x(\cos\alpha\cos\pi/3 - \sin\alpha\sin\pi/3)$
$$+ y(\sin\alpha\cos\pi/3 + \cos\alpha\sin\pi/3) = a.$$

or $\dfrac{1}{2}(x\cos\alpha + y\sin\alpha)$

$$- (\sqrt{3}/2)(x\sin\alpha - y\cos\alpha) = a$$

or $\dfrac{1}{2}a - \dfrac{\sqrt{3}}{2}(x\sin\alpha - y\cos\alpha) = a$ by (1)

or $x\sin\alpha - y\cos\alpha = -a/\sqrt{3}$ $\qquad \ldots(2)$

In order to find the locus of the point of intersection we have to eliminate the parameter α for which we square and add (1) and (2).

$\therefore \quad x^2(\cos^2\alpha + \sin^2\alpha) + y^2(\sin^2\alpha + \cos^2\alpha)$
$$= a^2 + a^2/3 = 4a^2/3$$

or $3x^2 + 3y^2 = 4a^2$.

When the parametric angles differ by $\pi/2$, then the 2nd tangent at $\left(\alpha + \dfrac{\pi}{2}\right)$ is

$$-x\sin\alpha + y\cos\alpha = a \qquad \ldots(3)$$

The locus is found by squaring and adding (1) and (3) as $x^2 + y^2 = 2a^2$.

(b) Any tangent to the circle $x^2 + y^2 = a^2$ is

$$y = mx \pm a\sqrt{1 + m^2}.$$

Its intercepts on the axes are

$$OA = h = \pm(a/m)\sqrt{1 + m^2}$$

and $k = \pm a\sqrt{(1 + m^2)}$.

Area of the triangle formed by the tangent and the axes will be $\dfrac{1}{2}hk = a^2$ given.

$\therefore \quad \pm\dfrac{1}{2}\cdot\dfrac{a}{m}\sqrt{1 + m^2}\cdot a\sqrt{1 + m^2} = a^2$

or $(1 + m^2) = \pm 2m$ or $1 + m^2 \pm 2m = 0$

or $(1 \pm m)^2 = 0$ $\therefore$ $m = \pm 1$.

Hence the required tangents are $y = \pm x \pm a\sqrt{2}$.

(c) The slope of given line is 1 and circle on this line as diameter is

$$x^2 + y^2 - 4x - 6y + 11 = 0 \quad \text{or} \quad (2, 3), \sqrt{2}.$$

Any line parallel to given diameter is $y = x + c$ or $x - y + c = 0$. The condition of tangency $p = r$ gives $c = 3, -1$.

$\therefore \quad x - y + 3 = 0$ and $x - y - 1 = 0$ are tangents.

14. (a) Let the circle be $x^2 + y^2 = a^2$ and two parallel tangents be drawn at $A(0, a)$ and at $B(0, -a)$ whose equations are $y = a$ and $y = -a$.

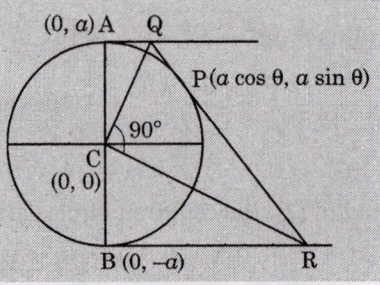

Fig. 98

Let $P(a\cos\theta, a\sin\theta)$ be any point on the circle tangent at which is $x\cos\theta + y\sin\theta = a$. Solving with the tangents $y = a$ and $y = -a$, we get the points

$$Q\left(a\dfrac{1 - \sin\theta}{\cos\theta}, a\right) \quad \text{and} \quad R\left(a\dfrac{1 + \sin\theta}{\cos\theta}, -a\right)$$

and C is $(0, 0)$.

$$m_1 = \text{slope of } CQ = \dfrac{a\cos\theta}{a(1 - \sin\theta)} = \dfrac{\cos\theta}{1 - \sin\theta}$$

$$m_2 = \text{slope of } CR = \dfrac{-a\cos\theta}{a(1 + \sin\theta)} = \dfrac{-\cos\theta}{1 + \sin\theta}$$

Clearly $m_1 m_2 = -1$ as $1 - \sin^2\theta = \cos^2\theta$

Hence the lines CQ and CR are perpendicular.

(b) Condition of tangency gives $l^2 + m^2 = 1/a^2$ and hence the point (l, m) lies on the circle $x^2 + y^2 = 1/a^2$.

(c) $P(h, k)$ lies on circle $\therefore$ $h^2 + k^2 = a^2$ $\qquad \ldots(1)$

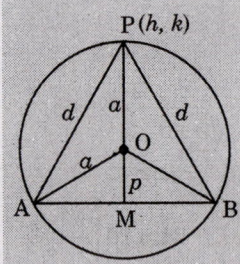

Fig. 99

ΔPAB is isosceles hence AB is $\perp$ to OP whose slope is k/h $\therefore$ Slope of AB is $-h/k$ and hence its equation can be taken as $hx + ky = \lambda$ $\qquad \ldots(2)$

If p be perpendicular from $O(0, 0)$ to AB, then

$$p = \dfrac{\lambda}{\sqrt{(h^2 + k^2)}} = \dfrac{\lambda}{a} \qquad \ldots(3)$$

Now we have to find the value of λ in terms of known quantities a and d. From rt. angled triangles AMO and AMP,

$$AM^2 = a^2 - p^2 = d^2 - (a + p)^2$$

or $2a^2 = d^2 - 2ap = d^2 - 2\lambda$, by (3)

$\therefore \quad \lambda = \dfrac{d^2}{2} - a^2$. Put in (2) etc.

15. **(a)** The centres and radii of the circles are
$$C_1 (1,3) \text{ and } r_1 = \sqrt{1+9-9} = 1.$$
$$C_2 (-3,1) \text{ and } r_2 = \sqrt{9+1-1} = 3.$$
$$C_1 C_2 = \sqrt{20}, r_1 + r_2 = 4 = \sqrt{16}$$
$\therefore$ $C_1 C_2 > r_1 + r_2$. Hence the circles are non-intersecting. Thus there will be four common tangents.

Transverse common tangents are tangents drawn from the point P which divides $C_1 C_2$ internally in the ratio of radii $1:3$.

Co-ordinates of P are
$$\left(\frac{1(-3)+3.1}{1+3}, \frac{1.1+3.3}{1+3} \right) \text{ i.e. } \left(0, \frac{5}{2}\right).$$

Direct common tangents are tangents drawn from the point Q which divides $C_1 C_2$ externally in the ratio $1:3$.

Co-ordinates of Q are
$$\left(\frac{1(-3)-3(1)}{1-3}, \frac{1.1-3(3)}{1-3} \right) \text{ i.e. } (3,4).$$

Transverse tangents are tangents through the point $P(0,5/2)$.

Any line through $(0,5/2)$ is
$$y - 5/2 = mx \qquad \ldots(1)$$
or $mx - y + 5/2 = 0$.

Apply the usual condition of tangency to any of the circle
$$\therefore \quad \frac{m.1 - 3 + 5/2}{\sqrt{(m^2+1)}} = 1$$

or $\left(m - \frac{1}{2} \right)^2 = m^2 + 1$

or $-m - 3/4 = 0$ or $0m^2 - m - 3/4 = 0$.

Hence $m = -3/4$ and ∞ as coeff. of m^2 is zero.

Therefore from (1),
$$\frac{y - 5/2}{x} = m = \infty \text{ and } -3/4.$$

$\therefore$ $x = 0$ is a tangent and $y - 5/2 = -3x/4$
or $3x + 4y - 10 = 0$ is another tangent.

Direct tangents are tangents drawn from the point $Q(3,4)$.

Now proceeding as for transverse tangents their equations are
$$y = 4, \ 4x - 3y = 0.$$

(b) Any line through $(-2,0)$ is $y = m(x+2)$
Condition of tangency $p = r$ gives $3m^2 = 1$

$\therefore$ $m = \pm 1/\sqrt{3}$ etc.

$\therefore$ T_1 $x - y\sqrt{3} + 2 = 0$,
T_2 $x + y\sqrt{3} + 2 = 0$

Any circle through C and T_1 is
$$(x^2 + y^2 - 1) + \lambda(x - y\sqrt{3} + 2) = 0$$

Condition of tangency with T_2 i.e. $p = r$ gives
$$\lambda - 1 = \pm 1 \quad \therefore \quad \lambda = 2 \text{ (0 rejected)}$$
$$C_1 \equiv x^2 + y^2 + 2x - 2\sqrt{3}y + 3 = 0$$
or $(-1, \sqrt{3}), 1$

Similarly any circle through C and T_2 and touching T_1 is $C_2 \equiv x^2 + y^2 + 4x + 4\sqrt{3}y + 7 = 0$

or $(-2, -2\sqrt{3}), 1$

Now there will be four common tangents of C_1 and C_2, as $C_1 C_2 > r_1 + r_2$ i.e. $\sqrt{28} > 1 + 3$

These can be found as in **Q. 15 (a)** above.

(c) The given circles are
$$C_1 (-3,4), r_1 = 6$$
$$C_2 (4,-7), r_2 = 3$$
The circles subtend equal angles at the points from where common tangents are drawn. **(See Note 2, P. 893)** These points divide the line of centres in the ratio of the radii internally and externally. These are easily found to be $A(11, -18), B\left(\frac{5}{3}, -\frac{10}{3}\right)$.

If the required circle be
$$x^2 + y^2 + 2gx + 2fy + c = 0.$$
Since it passes through the points A and B, we have
$$22g - 36f + c = -445 \qquad \ldots(1)$$
$$\frac{10}{3}g - \frac{20}{3}f + c = -\frac{125}{9} \qquad \ldots(2)$$

Also condition of orthogonality with the first gives
$$6g - 8f - c = -11 \qquad \ldots(3)$$
Adding (1) and (3) and then (2) and (3) thus eliminating c, we get
$$7g - 11f = -114 \quad \text{and} \quad 7g - 11f = -\frac{56}{3}$$

These are inconsistent. Hence no such circle exists.

16. **(a)** The centres of similitude from where the common tangents pass are easily found to be the points $(15/2, 0)$ and $(30, 0)$.

Ans. $\sqrt{5}\,y = 2x - 15, \sqrt{5}\,y = -2x + 15,$
$$\sqrt{35}\,y = x - 30, \sqrt{35}\,y = -x + 30$$

(b) We take the co-ordinates of A and B as $(-a, 0)$ and $(a, 0)$ respectively so that the mid-point of AB is the origin and AB the x-axis. If $(h, 0)$ are the co-ordinates of C, then since $AC = 3CB$, we have
$$h = \frac{3.a + 1.(-a)}{3+1} = \frac{1}{2}a.$$

On AC and CB as diameters we draw two circles so that they touch each other at $C\left(\frac{1}{2}a, 0\right)$. Their

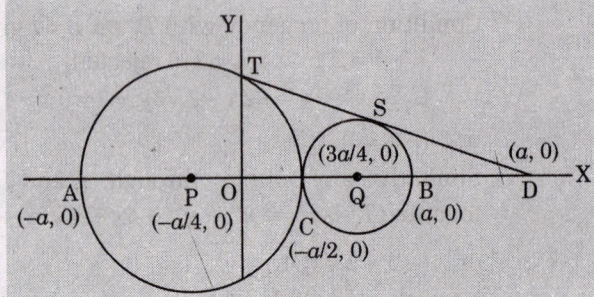

Fig. 100

centres are $P\left(-\dfrac{1}{4}a, 0\right)$ and $Q\left(\dfrac{3}{4}a, 0\right)$ and radii

are $\dfrac{3}{4}a$ and $\dfrac{1}{4}a$ respectively. Let a common

tangent RS meet AB produced in D. Let $(\alpha, 0)$ be the co-ordinates of D. Then since D divides PQ externally in the ratio of the radii $\dfrac{3}{4}a : \dfrac{1}{4}a$

i.e. $3 : 1$ [See § 2 (j)], we have

$$\alpha = \dfrac{3 \cdot \left(\dfrac{3}{4}a\right) - 1 \cdot \left(-\dfrac{1}{4}a\right)}{3 - 1} = \dfrac{5}{4}a.$$

∴ $OD = \dfrac{5}{4}a$ and $OB = a$ so that

$$BD = \dfrac{5}{4}a - a = \dfrac{1}{4}a.$$

Hence BD is equal to the radius of the smaller circle.

17. (a) Ans. 3. Here $C_1C_2 = 3\sqrt{10} = r_1 + r_2$.

Therefore the two circles touch externally and have one common tangent. There will also be two direct common tangents. Hence 3 in all.

(b) **Refer note P. 853 and part (d) below.**

Ans. (b). $C_1C_2 = r_1 - r_2$ *i.e.* touching internally.

(c) Ans. (ii). $C_1(0, 0)$, $C_2(0, 1)$ $r_1 = 4$, $r_2 = 1$

$C_1C_2 = 1$ and $r_1 - r_2 = 3 \therefore C_1C_2 < r_1 - r_2$ and hence 2nd circle is completely within the 1st. Therefore there are no common tangents.

(d) $C_1(3, 0)$, $r_1 = 3$; $C_2(-1, 0)$, $r_2 = 1$

Distance between centres is $4 = r_1 + r_2$. Hence they touch and common tangent by $S_1 - S_2 = 0$ is

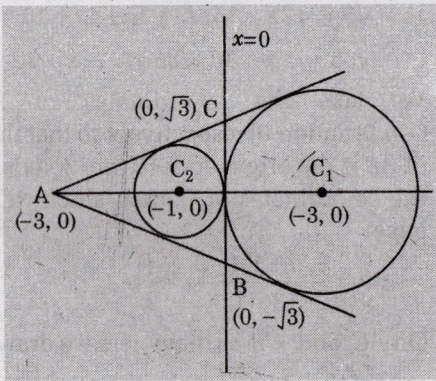

Fig. 101

$x = 0$ *i.e.* y-axis. Other two direct common tangents are found as in **part (a)** to be $x - \sqrt{3}y + 3 = 0$ and $x + \sqrt{3}y + 3 = 0$ being drawn from the point $(-3, 0)$. These two tangents meet the common tangent $x = 0$ at $B(0, \sqrt{3})$ and $C(0, -\sqrt{3})$. Clearly ABC is equilateral as each side $= 2\sqrt{3}$. Hence the figure formed by these tangents is an equilateral triangle.

18. $CP^2 = 4^2 \implies (h+2)^2 + k^2 = 16$

∴ Locus is $(x+2)^2 + y^2 = 16$

Since the two circles touch externally there will be only three common tangents.

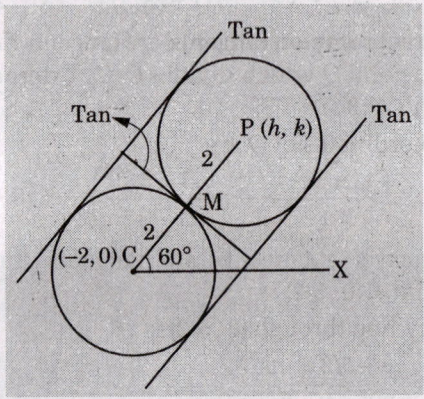

Fig. 102

One will be perpendicular to line of centres and other two will be parallel to the line of centres as the circles are of equal radius. The centre P is given by

$$\dfrac{x+2}{\cos 60°} = \dfrac{y-0}{\sin 60°} = \dfrac{4}{P}, \dfrac{2}{M}$$

∴ $P(0, 2\sqrt{3})$, $M(-1, \sqrt{3})$

Clearly M is mid-point of CP.

Slope of CP is $\tan 60° = \sqrt{3}$

∴ Slope of line perp. to CP is $-\dfrac{1}{\sqrt{3}}$.

Its equation $x + \sqrt{3}\,y + \lambda = 0$

It will pass through $M(-1, \sqrt{3})$ ∴ $\lambda = 2$

Hence $x + \sqrt{3}\,y + 2 = 0$ is one common tangent. The other two will be parallel to CP.

∴ $\sqrt{3}\,x - y + \lambda = 0$. Apply $p = r$ for λ from any centre C or P.

$$\dfrac{0 - 2\sqrt{3} + \lambda}{2} = \pm 2$$

∴ $\lambda = 2\sqrt{3} \pm 4$

Other common tangents are

$$\sqrt{3}x - y \pm 4 + 2\sqrt{3} = 0$$

19. (a) Equation of the chord AB of the circle

$$x^2 + y^2 = a^2$$

whose mid-point is (h, k) is $hx + ky = h^2 + k^2$.

Rule (f) P, 891

$\angle ACB = 90°$ (given), $D(h, k)$ is the mid-point of AB

$\therefore \quad \angle ACD = \angle BCD = 45°$

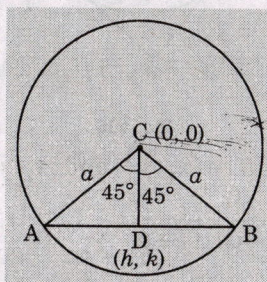

Fig. 103

$$CD = a \cos 45° = \frac{a}{\sqrt{2}} \quad \text{or} \quad CD^2 = \frac{a^2}{2}$$

or $h^2 + k^2 = \frac{a^2}{2}$ or $x^2 + y^2 = \frac{a^2}{2}$

(b) The centre of the given circle is $(3/2, -1/2)$ and its radius is $3/2$. From the figure if $M(h, k)$ be the middle point of chord AB subtending an angle $2\pi/3$ at C, then

$$\frac{CM}{AC} = \cos \frac{\pi}{3} = \frac{1}{2} \quad \text{or} \quad 4CM^2 = AC^2$$

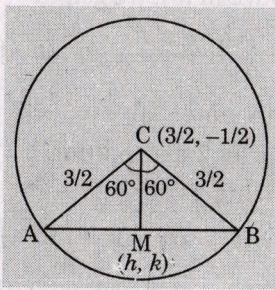

Fig. 104

or $4[(h - 3/2)^2 + (k + 1/2)^2] = 9/4$

$\therefore$ Locus is $4x^2 + 4y^2 - 12x + 4y + (31/4) = 0$

(c) Proceed as in part (b).

(d) If (h, k) be mid-point, then $T = S_1$

or $hx + ky = h^2 + k^2$ ...(1)

Now make the curve $x^2 = 2(x + y)$ homogeneous by the help of (1)

$\therefore \quad x^2 = 2(x + y) \cdot \dfrac{hx + ky}{h^2 + k^2}$

or $x^2(h^2 + k^2) - 2(hx + ky)(x + y) = 0$

It represents a pair of perpendicular lines through origin $\therefore$ $A + B = 0$

or $(h^2 + k^2 - 2h) - 2k = 0$

Now generalize (h, k).

20. (a) **1st Method :** The centre of circle is $(1, 3)$ and $L(h, k)$ is the mid-point of the chord which passes through origin $(0, 0)$.

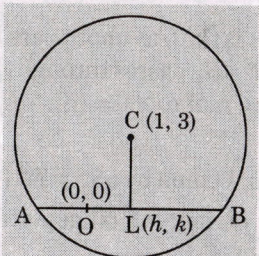

Fig. 105

Clearly $CL \perp AB$ $\therefore$ $m_1 m_2 = -1$.

$\therefore \quad \dfrac{k - 3}{h - 1} \cdot \dfrac{k}{h} = -1$

or $h(h - 1) + k(k - 3) = 0$.

Hence the locus of the mid-point (h, k), is

$$x^2 + y^2 - x - 3y = 0.$$

Alt. Method : (by $T = S_1$)

If (h, k) be the mid-point, then equation of chord by rule $T = S_1$ [[f) P. 891]] is

$x \cdot h + y \cdot k - (x + h) - 3(y + k) - 10 = h^2$
$\qquad\qquad\qquad + k^2 - 2h - 6k - 10$

It passes through origin.

$\therefore \quad -h - 3k - 10 = h^2 + k^2 - 2h - 6k - 10$

Locus of mid-point (h, k) is $x^2 + y^2 - x - 3y = 0$

(b) If the chord passes through a fixed point (x_1, y_1), then $hx_1 + ky_1 = h^2 + k^2$.

Hence the locus of the mid-point in this case is

$xx_1 + yy_1 = x^2 + y^2$ or $x^2 + y^2 - xx_1 - yy_1 = 0$

Above respresents a circle whose centre is $\left(\dfrac{1}{2} x, \dfrac{1}{2} y\right)$.

(c) Ans. $x^2 + y^2 - x = 0$. $T = S_1$ passes through $(0, 0)$.

21. (a) The given circle is $S = x^2 + y^2 - ax - \dfrac{b}{2} y = 0$.

Since the two chords are bisected by x-axis so let $(h, 0)$ be the mid-point where h has two real values. Equation of the chord by $T = S_1$ is

$$x \cdot h + y \cdot 0 - \frac{a}{2}(x + h) - \frac{b}{4}(y + 0) = h^2 - ah.$$

It passes through $(a, b/2)$.

$\therefore \quad ah - \dfrac{a}{2}(a + h) - \dfrac{b}{4}\left(\dfrac{b}{2}\right) = h^2 - ah.$

or $h^2 - \dfrac{3}{2} ah + \left(\dfrac{a^2}{2} + \dfrac{b^2}{8}\right) = 0$

Since the values of h are real and distinct we must have $B^2 - 4AC > 0$

$$\therefore \quad \frac{9}{4}a^2 - 4\left(\frac{a^2}{2}\frac{b^2}{8}\right) > 0 \quad \text{or} \quad a^2 > 2b^2$$

(b) Ans. (d).

Mid-point is $(h, 0)$ as chords are being bisected by axis of x. $T = S_1$ passes through (p, q). Quadratic in h will have real roots $\Rightarrow$ (d).

(c) Ans. (d).

Let P be (h, k) then by $SS_1 = T^2$ **(§3 (c$_1$) P. 891)** the equation of pair of tangents drawn from P to $x^2 + y^2 = 1$ is

$$(h^2 + k^2 - 1)(x^2 + y^2 - 1) = (hx + ky - 1)^2$$

Its intersection with the line $x = 1$ is given by

$$y^2 (h^2 + k^2 - 1) = (ky + h - 1)^2$$

or $\quad y^2 (h^2 - 1) - 2yk (h - 1) - (h - 1)^2 = 0$ ...(1)

It is a quadratic in y and we are given that length of intercept is 1 $\therefore y_1 - y_2 = 2$

or $\quad (y_1 + y_2)^2 - 4 y_1 y_2 = 1$

or $\quad \left[\dfrac{2k (h - 1)}{h^2 - 1}\right]^2 + 4\dfrac{(h - 1)^2}{h^2 - 1} = 4$

or $\quad \dfrac{4k^2}{(h + 1)^2} + \dfrac{4(h - 1)}{h + 1} = 4$

or $\quad k^2 = (h + 1)^2 - (h^2 - 1) = 2h + 2$

Hence the locus of (h, k) is $y^2 = 2(x + 1)$ which represents a parabola.

22. (a) Let (p, q) be a point on a given circle.

$$x^2 + y^2 + 2gx + 2fy + c = 0 \text{ so that}$$

$$p^2 + q^2 + 2gp + 2fq + c = 0 \qquad \text{...(1)}$$

Let tangents be drawn to the circle $x^2 + y^2 = a^2$ from P and mid-point of chord of contact AB be (h, k).

AB is $\quad px + qy = a^2$ as chord of contact.

AB is $\quad hx + ky = h^2 + k^2$, by $T = S_1$

Comparing,

$$\frac{p}{h} = \frac{q}{k} = \frac{a^2}{h^2 + k^2}$$

$$\therefore \quad p = \frac{a^2 h}{h^2 + k^2}, q = \frac{a^2 k}{h^2 + k^2}$$

Put these values of p and q in (1) and generalize (p, q) and you get a circle.

(b) $x^2 + y^2 = a^2$ ...(1)

$hx + ky = h^2 + k^2$ ...(2)

where (h, k) is middle point of chord AB, by $T = S_1$.

AP and PB are perpendiculars as AB subtends an angle of $90°$ at $P (\alpha, \beta)$.

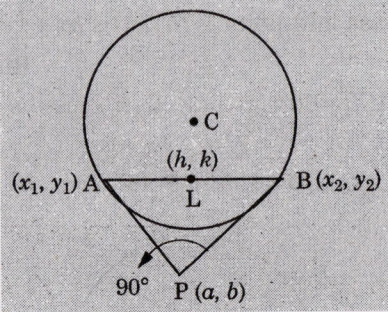

Fig. 106

If A and B be (x_1, y_1) and (x_2, y_2) respectively

$$\frac{y_1 - \beta}{x_1 - \alpha} \cdot \frac{y_2 - \beta}{x_2 - \alpha} = -1$$

or $\quad (x_1 - \alpha)(x_2 - \alpha) + (y_1 - \beta)(y_2 - \beta) = 0$

or $\quad (x_1 x_2 + y_1 y_2) - \alpha (x_1 + x_2) - \beta (y_1 + y_2)$
$\quad\quad\quad\quad\quad\quad\quad\quad\quad\quad + \alpha^2 + \beta^2 = 0$ ...(3)

Eliminating y between (1) and (2), we will get a quadratic

$$x^2 + \left(\frac{\lambda - hx}{k}\right)^2 = a^2, \text{ where } \lambda = h^2 + k^2$$

or $\quad x^2 (h^2 + k^2) - 2\lambda hx + \lambda^2 - a^2 k^2 = 0$

$$\lambda x^2 - 2\lambda hx + \lambda^2 - a^2 k^2 = 0$$

Similarly $\quad \lambda y^2 - 2\lambda ky + \lambda^2 - a^2 h^2 = 0$

Putting the values of $x_1 x_2, y_1 y_2, x_1 + x_2, y_1 + y_2$ from above in (3), we get

$$\frac{\lambda^2 - a^2 k^2 + \lambda^2 - a^2 h^2}{\lambda} - \alpha . 2h - \beta . 2k + \alpha^2 + \beta^2 = 0$$

or $\quad 2(\lambda - h\alpha - k\beta) + (\alpha^2 + \beta^2) - a^2 = 0$

Dividing by 2 and putting $\lambda = h^2 + k^2$ and then generalizing

$$x^2 + y^2 - \alpha x - \beta y + \frac{1}{2}(\alpha^2 + \beta^2 - a^2) = 0$$

(c) If (h, k) be the required point, then AB is chord of contact of (h, k) and its equation is also given by $T = S_1$ as $(1, 1)$ is its mid-point :

$2x + y = 3 \quad\quad$ by $T = S_1$
$x . h + y . k - 3 (x + h) - 2 (y + k) + 3 = 0$

or $\quad x (h - 3) + y (k - 2) = 3h + 2k - 3$ as C.C.

Comparing, we get

$$\frac{h - 3}{2} = \frac{k - 2}{1} = \frac{3h + 2k - 3}{3}$$

Above will give two equations which when solved give $h = -1, k = 0$.

23. Let the given point be $(p, \bar{p}) = \left(\dfrac{1 + \sqrt{2}a}{2}, \dfrac{1 - \sqrt{2}a}{2}\right)$ and

the equation of the circle becomes

$$x^2 + y^2 - px - \bar{p}y = 0$$

Since the chord is bisected by the line $x + y = 0$, its mid-point can be chosen as $(k, -k)$ on this line. Hence the equation of the chord by $T = S_1$ is

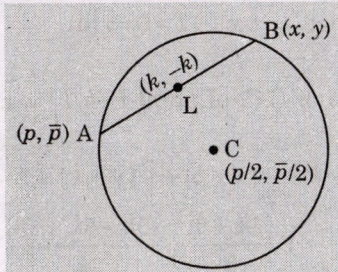

Fig. 107

$$kx - ky - \frac{p}{2}(x+k) - \frac{\bar{p}}{2}(y-k) = k^2 + k^2 - pk + \bar{p}k$$

It passes through $A(p, \bar{p})$.

$$\therefore \quad kp - k\bar{p} - \frac{p}{2}(p+k) - \frac{\bar{p}}{2}(\bar{p}-k) = 2k^2 - pk + \bar{p}k$$

or $3k(p - \bar{p}) = 4k^2 + (p^2 + \bar{p}^2)$ ...(1)

Put $p - \bar{p} = a\sqrt{2}$,

$$p^2 + \bar{p}^2 = 2 \cdot \frac{(1 + 2a^2)}{4} = \frac{1 + 2a^2}{2} \qquad ...(2)$$

Hence from (1) by the help of (2), we get

$$4k^2 - 3\sqrt{2}\, ak + \frac{1}{2}(1 + 2a^2) = 0 \qquad ...(3)$$

Since there are two chords which are bisected by $x + y = 0$, we must have two real values of k from (3)

$$\Delta > 0 \quad \text{or} \quad 18a^2 - 8(1 + 2a^2) > 0$$

or $a^2 - 4 > 0$ or $(a + 2)(a - 2) > 0$

$\therefore \quad a < -2$ or > 2 $\therefore a \in (-\infty, -2) \cup (2, \infty)$

or $a \in\,]-\infty, -2[\cup]2, \infty[$.

24. (a) $S = x^2 + y^2 - 12 = 0$,

$S' = x^2 + y^2 - 5x + 3y - 2 = 0$.

Equation of the common chord is $S - S' = 0$.

or $5x - 3y = 10$. ...(1)

If the tangents to the circle $x^2 + y^2 = 12$ at the extremities of the chord (1) intersect at the point (h, k) then this chord is the chord of contact of the point (h, k) w.r.t. the circle $x^2 + y^2 = 12$ is

$$hx + ky = 12. \qquad ...(2)$$

Comparing (1) and (2), we get

$$\frac{h}{5} = \frac{k}{-3} = \frac{12}{10} \quad \text{or} \quad (h, k) = \left(6, -\frac{18}{5}\right)$$

(b) Do yourself.

Compare polar of (h, k) with given line.

(c) Let $P(h, k)$ be the point of intersection. Its chord of contact w.r.t. $x^2 + y^2 = a^2$ is $hx + ky - a^2 = 0$. It touches the circle $x^2 + y^2 - 2ax = 0$ i.e. $C(a, 0)$, a.

Apply $p = r$. $\therefore \quad \dfrac{ah - a^2}{\sqrt{(h^2 + k^2)}} = a$

Now square and generalize h, k.

(d) If the required point be (α, β), then equation of C.C. is

$$\alpha x + \beta y - 3(x + \alpha) - 2(y + \beta) + 3 = 0$$

or $x(\alpha - 3) + y(\beta - 2) + (-3\alpha - 2\beta + 3) = 0$ ...(1)

Since (1, 1) is its mid-point then $T = S_1$.

Its equation is

$$1 \cdot x + 1 \cdot y - 3(x + 1) - 2(y + 1) + 3 = S_1 = -5$$

or $2x + y - 3 = 0$ ...(2)

Comparing (1) and (2),

$$\frac{\alpha - 3}{2} = \frac{\beta - 2}{1} = \frac{3\alpha + 2\beta - 3}{3}$$

$\therefore \quad \alpha - 2\beta = -1$ and $3\alpha - \beta = -3$

Solving, we get $\alpha = -1, \beta = 0$

25. (a) Ans. $\left(\dfrac{1}{2}, \dfrac{1}{4}\right)$

Let (h, k) be any point on the given line

$\therefore \quad 2h + k = 4$ and C.C. is $hx + ky = 1$

or $hx + (4 - 2h) y = 1$ $\because k = 4 - 2h$

or $(4y - 1) + h(x - 2y) = 0$

It is of the form $P + \lambda Q = 0$. It passes through the intersection of $P = 0$ and $Q = 0$ or $\left(\dfrac{1}{2}, \dfrac{1}{4}\right)$

(b) Let $P(h, k)$ be on C_2 $\therefore \quad h^2 + k^2 = 4r^2$ ...(1)

C.C. of P w.r.t. C_1 is $hx + ky = r^2$

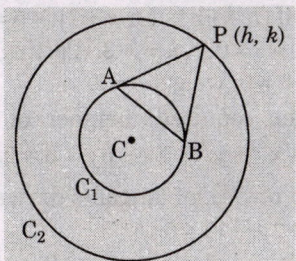

Fig. 108

It intersects C_1, $x^2 + y^2 = a^2$ in A and B.

Eliminating y, we get

$$x^2 + \left(\frac{r^2 - hx}{k}\right)^2 = r^2$$

or $x^2(h^2 + k^2) - 2r^2 hx + r^4 - r^2 k^2 = 0$

or $x^2 \cdot 4r^2 - 2r^2 hx + r^2(r^2 - k^2) = 0$

$\therefore \quad x_1 + x_2 = \dfrac{2r^2 h}{4r^2} = \dfrac{h}{2}, y_1 + y_2 = \dfrac{k}{2}$

If (x, y) be the centroid of $\triangle PAB$, then

$$3x = x_1 + x_2 + h = \frac{h}{2} + h = \frac{3h}{2}$$

$\therefore \quad x = h/2$ or $h = 2x$ and similarly $k = 2y$.

Putting in (1) we get $4x^2 + 4y^2 = 4r^2$

$\therefore \quad$ Locus is $x^2 + y^2 = r^2$ i.e. C_1.

(c) The given circle is

$$(x^2 + y^2 - 2x - 8) - 2ay = 0 \qquad ...(1)$$

It is of the form $S + \lambda P = 0$ and hence represents a family of circles passing through the points of intersection $S = 0$ and $P = 0$ **[(n), P. 853]** *i.e.* $x^2 + y^2 - 2x - 8 = 0$ and $y = 0$.

∴ P and Q are $(-2, 0)$ and $(4, 0)$.

Equation of PQ is $y = 0$ ...(2)

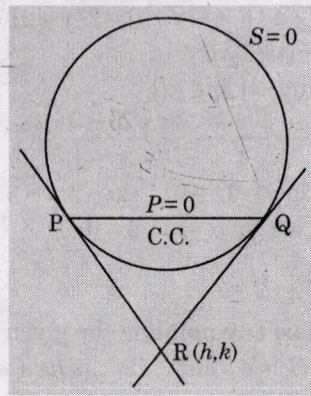

Fig. 109

If tangents at P and Q intersect at $R(h, k)$ then PQ is chord of contact of (h, k) whose equation is

$$x.h + y.k - (x + h) - a(y + k) - 8 = 0$$

or $x(h - 1) + y(k - a) - (h + ak + 8) = 0$ ...(3)

Comparing (3) and (2), $h - 1 = 0$, $h + ak + 8 = 0$,

$k - a =$ any constant,

∴ $h = 1$. If (h, k) lies on $x + 2y + 5 = 0$

∴ $h + 2k + 5 = 0$ ∴ $k = -3$. Putting for (h, k) in $h + ak + 8 = 0$, we get $a = 3$.

Hence the required member of the family of circles is $x^2 + y^2 - 2x - 6y - 8 = 0$. by (1)

(d) Equation of C.C. of tangents drawn from $(0, 0)$ is

$$3x + 2y - 12 = 0$$

∴ Required circle by $S + \lambda P = 0$ is

$$(x^2 + y^2 + 6x + 4y - 12) + \lambda(3x + 2y - 12) = 0$$

Since it passes through $(0, 0)$ ∴ $\lambda = -1$.

∴ Circle is $x^2 + y^2 + 3x + 2y = 0$

(e) **Ans. (b).**

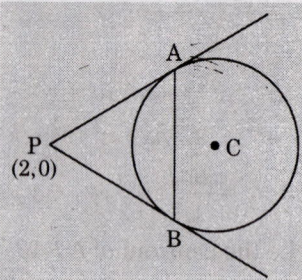

Fig. 110

AB is chord of contact of tangents drawn from focus $P(2, 0)$ to the circle $x^2 + y^2 - 12x + 32 = 0$.

Its equation is

$$x.2 + y.0 - 6(x + 2) + 32 = 0$$

or $x - 5 = 0$.

Then by $S + \lambda P = 0$ the equation of circle is

$(x^2 + y^2 - 12x + 32) + \lambda(x - 5) = 0$. It passes through $P(2, 0)$ ∴ $12 - 3\lambda = 0$ or $\lambda = 4$.

∴ $x^2 + y^2 - 8x + 12 = 0 \Rightarrow$ (b).

(f) **Ans. (d).**

Equation of C.C. of point $P(h, k)$ w.r.t. the given circle is

$$2xh + 2yk - \frac{3}{2}(x + h) + \frac{5}{2}(y + k) - 7 = 0$$

or $x\dfrac{(4h - 3)}{2} + y\dfrac{(4k + 5)}{2} - \dfrac{(3h - 5k + 14)}{2} = 0$

Comparing with $9x + y - 28 = 0$, we have

$$\frac{4h - 3}{9 \times 2} = \frac{4k + 5}{1 \times 2} = \frac{3h - 5k + 14}{28 \times 2}$$

∴ $4h - 36k = 48$ or $h - 9k = 12$

and $3h - 117k = 126$.

Solving for (h, k), we get $h = 3$, $k = -1$

∴ P is $(3, -1)$.

But S' for $(3, -1)$ is $20 - 21 = -1$ *i.e.*, $-$ive

∴ $P(3, -1)$ lies inside the circle. Hence, the given line cannot be chord of contact for any point P.

(g) **Ans. (b).**

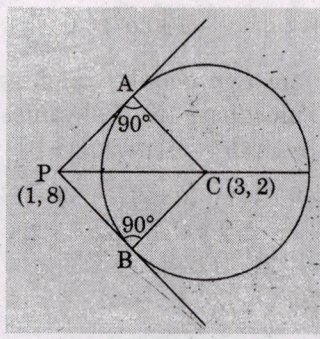

Fig. 111

Given $P(1, 8)$ and $C(3, 2)$ is the centre of the circle.

∴ Radii CA and CB both are perpendicular to tangents PA and PB drawn from the point $P(1, 8)$.

Now we know that diameter of a circle subtends a right angle at any point on the circumference. Hence the circumcircle of $\triangle PAB$ is a circle on PC as diameter whose equation is

$$(x - 1)(x - 3) + (y - 8)(y - 2) = 0$$

or $x^2 + y^2 - 4x - 10y + 19 = 0$

26. (a) Equation of the chord of contact AB of tangents drawn from the point $P(h, k)$ to the given circle is

$$hx + ky - a^2 = 0.$$

$OM =$ perp. distance of $(0, 0)$ from AB.

∴ $OM = \dfrac{-a^2}{\sqrt{(h^2 + k^2)}}$.

∴ $AM^2 = OA^2 - OM^2 = a^2 - \dfrac{a^4}{h^2 + k^2}$

$$= \frac{a^2(h^2 + k^2 - a^2)}{(h^2 + k^2)}$$

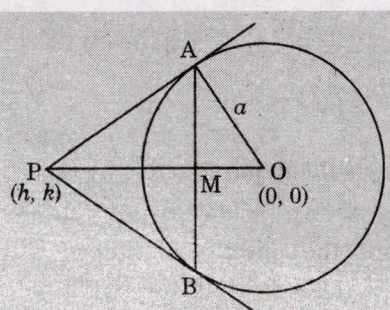

Fig. 112

$\therefore \quad AB = 2AM = 2a\sqrt{\left(\dfrac{h^2 + k^2 - a^2}{h^2 + k^2}\right)}$

$PM = $ perp. distance of (h, k) from AB

$\therefore \quad PM = \dfrac{h^2 + k^2 - a^2}{\sqrt{(h^2 + k^2)}}$

$\Delta\, PAB = \dfrac{1}{2}\, PM \cdot AB$

$= \dfrac{1}{2} \cdot \dfrac{h^2 + k^2 - a^2}{\sqrt{(h^2 + k^2)}} \cdot 2a\sqrt{\left(\dfrac{h^2 + k^2 - a^2}{h^2 + k^2}\right)}$

$= a\,\dfrac{(h^2 + k^2 - a^2)^{3/2}}{h^2 + k^2}$ \qquad ....(2)

(b) Do yourself.

(c) Let the circles be $x^2 + y^2 = a^2$ and

$x^2 + y^2 + 2gx + 2fy + c = 0$

If the variable point P be (h, k), then its chord of contact w.r.t. to given circles are

$hx + ky - a^2 = 0$ \qquad ...(1)

$hx + ky + g(x + h) + f(y + k) + c = 0$ \qquad ...(2)

The lines (1) and (2) are perpendicular

$\therefore \quad a_1 a_2 + b_1 b_2 = 0$

or $\quad h(h + g) + k(k + f) = 0$

$\therefore \quad$ locus of (h, k) is

$x(x + g) + y(y + f) = 0$

Above represents a circle whose diameter is $(0, 0)$ and $(-g, -f)$ and hence its centre is $(-g/2, -f/2)$ i.e. the mid-point of centres of given circles.

(d) $(a\cos\theta, a\sin\theta)$ is on $x^2 + y^2 = a^2$.

$\therefore \quad$ Chord of contact is $ax\cos\theta + ay\sin\theta = b^2$

It touches $x^2 + y^2 = c^2$

$\dfrac{b^2}{a\sqrt{(\cos^2\theta + \sin^2\theta)}} = c$ or $b^2 = ac$

$\therefore \quad a, b, c$ are in G.P.

27. (a) Suppose the co-ordinates of the pole are (x_1, y_1) and as it lies on

$x^2 + y^2 = 9c^2 \quad \therefore \quad x_1^2 + y_1^2 = 9c^2.$ \qquad ...(1)

The polar of this point w.r.t. the circle $x^2 + y^2 = c^2$ is $xx_1 + yy_1 = c^2$.

If this polar touches the circle $x^2 + y^2 = c^2/9$ then perpendicular from centre $(0, 0)$ should be equal to radius $c/3$.

$\therefore \quad \dfrac{0 + 0 - c^2}{\sqrt{(x_1^2 + y_1^2)}} = \dfrac{c}{3}$

or $\quad 9c^2 = x_1^2 + y_1^2.$

Above is true by the help of (1).

(b) The polar of the point (x_1, y_1) with respect to the circle $x^2 + y^2 - a^2 = 0$ is

$xx_1 + yy_1 - a^2 = 0$ \qquad ...(1)

Since (1) touches the circle $(x - a)^2 + y^2 = a^2$, we must have distance from the centre $(a, 0)$ equal to radius a, i.e. $p = r$

$\dfrac{ax_1 + 0 \cdot y_1 - a^2}{\sqrt{(x_1^2 + y_1^2)}} = \pm a$

or $\quad x_1^2 + y_1^2 = (x_1 - a)^2$

or $\quad y_1^2 + 2ax_1 - a^2 = 0.$

The locus of (x_1, y_1) is $y^2 + 2ax - a^2 = 0.$

(c) Let (h, k) be the required pole. Then its polar with respect to the circle $2x^2 + 2y^2 - 3x + 5y - 7 = 0$ is

$2xh + 2yk - (3/2)(x + h) + (5/2)(y + k) - 7 = 0$

or $\quad (4h - 3)x + (4k + 5)y - 3h + 5k - 14 = 0$ \quad ...(1)

Comparing (1) with $9x + y - 28 = 0$, we get

$\dfrac{4h - 3}{9} = \dfrac{4k + 5}{1} = \dfrac{-3h + 5k - 14}{-28}$

From first two ratios, we get

$h - 9k - 12 = 0.$ \qquad ...(2)

and second and third ratios give

$h - 39k - 42 = 0.$ \qquad ...(3)

Solving (2) and (3), we get $h = 3$, $k = -1$

Hence the required pole is $(3, -1)$.

(d) Let the equation of the circle be $x^2 + y^2 = a^2$ and the co-ordinates of any two points are $P(x_1, y_1)$ and $Q(x_2, y_2)$. The centre of the circle is $(0, 0)$.

$\therefore \quad \dfrac{OP}{OQ} = \dfrac{\sqrt{x_1^2 + y_1^2}}{\sqrt{(x_2^2 + y_2^2)}}$ \qquad ...(1)

Polar of $P(x_1, y_1)$ is $xx_1 + yy_1 - a^2 = 0.$

Its distance from $Q(x_2, y_2)$ is

$\dfrac{x_1 x_2 + y_1 y_2 - a^2}{\sqrt{(x_1^2 + y_1^2)}}.$ \qquad ...(2)

Polar of $Q(x_2, y_2)$ is $xx_2 + yy_2 - a^2 = 0.$

Its distance from $P(x_1, y_1)$ is

$$\frac{x_1 x_2 + y_1 y_2 - a^2}{\sqrt{(x_2^2 + y_2^2)}}. \qquad ...(3)$$

Ratio of these distances

$$= \frac{\sqrt{x_2^2 + y_2^2}}{\sqrt{(x_1^2 + y_1^2)}} = \frac{OQ}{OP}, \text{ by } (1)$$

28. (a) Let the equation of the circle be

$$x^2 + y^2 + 2gx + 2fy + c = 0.$$

Since it passes through the point $(2, 5)$

$$\therefore \quad 4g + 10f + c = 29. \qquad ...(1)$$

Also it cuts the two given circles orthogonally and hence applying the condition

$$2g_1 g_2 + 2f_1 f_2 = c_1 + c_2, \text{ we get}$$
$$2g(-9/2) + 2f(0) = c + 14 \qquad ...(2)$$
$$2g(15/2) + 2f(0) = c + 14 \qquad ...(3)$$

Subtracting (2) and (3), we get

$$2g(12) = 0 \quad \therefore \quad g = 0.$$

Hence from (2),

$$c + 14 = 0 \quad \text{or} \quad c = -14.$$

Therefore from (1) on putting for g and c, we get

$$10f = -15 \quad \text{or} \quad f = -3/2.$$

The required circle is $x^2 + y^2 - 3y - 14 = 0$.

(b) Ans. $x^2 + y^2 + \dfrac{1}{2} y - \dfrac{29}{4} = 0$.

(c) Let the required circle through origin be

$$x^2 + y^2 + 2gx + 2fy = 0 \qquad ...(1)$$

Condition of orthogonality gives

$$2gg_1 + 2ff_1 = c_1 \qquad ...(2)$$
$$2gg_2 + 2ff_2 = c_2 \qquad ...(3)$$

Eliminating the unknowns $2g$ and $2f$ from (1), (2) and (3), we get

$$\begin{vmatrix} x & y & x^2 + y^2 \\ g_1 & f_1 & -c_1 \\ g_2 & f_2 & -c_2 \end{vmatrix} = 0$$

Above is the required equation of circle.

29. (a) Ans. (a).

Apply $2g_1 g_2 + 2f_1 f_2 = c_1 + c_2$

$$2(0) + 2k \cdot k = 6 + k \quad \text{or} \quad 2k^2 - k - 6 = 0$$

$$\text{or} \quad (k-2)(2k+3) = 0 \quad \therefore \quad k = 2, -3/2.$$

(b) By $S_1 + \lambda S_2$ the required circle is

$$(x^2 + y^2 - 2x - 6y + 6)$$
$$+ \lambda(x^2 + y^2 + 2x - 6y + 6) = 0$$

$$\text{or} \quad (x^2 + y^2 - 6y + 6)(1 + \lambda) + 2x(\lambda - 1) = 0$$

$$\text{or} \quad x^2 + y^2 + 2x\frac{\lambda - 1}{\lambda + 1} - 6y + 6 = 0 \qquad ...(1)$$

It cuts $x^2 + y^2 + 4x + 6y + 4 = 0$ orthogonally.

Hence $2g_1 g_2 + 2f_1 f_2 = c_1 + c_2$

i.e. $2\dfrac{\lambda - 1}{\lambda + 1} \cdot 2 - 2 \cdot 3 \cdot 3 = 6 + 4$

$$\text{or} \quad 4(\lambda - 1) = 28(\lambda + 1)$$
$$\lambda - 1 = 7\lambda + 7 \quad \therefore \quad \lambda = -4/3$$

Hence the required circle by (1) is

$$x^2 + y^2 + 14x - 6y + 6 = 0.$$

(c) Apply the condition of orthogonality with each of the circles and subtract. Replace

$$-g \text{ by } x \text{ and } -f \text{ by } y.$$

(d) Proceed as in (b).

30. (a) Let the circle touching the x-axis be

$$(x - h)^2 + (y - k)^2 = k^2$$

$$\text{or} \quad x^2 + y^2 - 2hx - 2ky + k^2 = 0 \qquad ...(1)$$

It cuts $x^2 + y^2 - 20x - 10y + 100 = 0$ orthogonally.

$$\therefore \quad 2h(10) + 2k(5) = h^2 + 100$$

$$\therefore \quad \text{Locus of centre } (h, k) \text{ is}$$

$$x^2 - 20x + 100 = 10y$$

$$\text{or} \quad (x - 10)^2 = 10y$$

Above equation represents a parabola with vertex at $(10, 0)$ and L.R. $= 10$ and axis is along the line $x - 10 = 0$ and tangent at vertex being x-axis *i.e.* $y = 0$

(b) The required circle by **Rule (n_1), P. 853** is

$$(x + 2)^2 + (y - 7)^2 + \lambda(x + y - 5) = 0$$

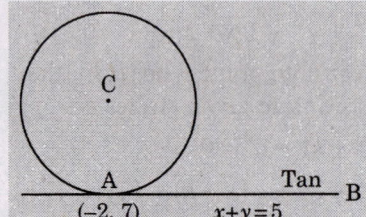

pt. circle   tangent

Fig. 113

$$\text{or} \quad x^2 + y^2 + x(4 + \lambda) + y(-14 + \lambda) + (53 - 5\lambda) = 0$$

It cuts orthogonally the circle

$$x^2 + y^2 + 4x - 6y + 9 = 0$$

$$2 \cdot \frac{4 + \lambda}{2} \cdot 2 + 2\frac{(-14 + \lambda)}{2}(-3) = 9 + 53 - 5\lambda$$

$$\text{or} \quad \lambda(2 - 3 + 5) = 62 - 42 - 8$$

$$\text{or} \quad 4\lambda = 12 \Rightarrow \lambda = 3$$

Hence the required circle is

$$x^2 + y^2 + 7x - 11y + 38 = 0$$

(c) Ans. (c).

Since the circle passes through origin $c = 0$, its centre lies on $y = x$ $\therefore$ $g = f$. It cuts orthogonally the given circle

$$\therefore \quad 2g(-2) + 2f(-3) = 10 + 0 \quad \text{But } g = f$$

$$\therefore \quad g = -1 = f \quad \text{and} \quad c = 0.$$

(d) Ans. (a).

$$2q = p + r \quad \therefore \quad px + \left(\frac{p+r}{2}\right)y + r = 0$$

or $\left(x + \frac{y}{2}\right) + \frac{r}{q}\left(1 + \frac{y}{2}\right) = 0$

Above is of the form $P + \lambda Q = 0$ which represents a family of lines passing through the point of intersection of $P = 0$ and $Q = 0$,

i.e., $x + \frac{y}{2} = 0, 1 + \frac{y}{2} = 0$

$\therefore \quad y = -2, x = 1$

$\therefore$ $(1, -2)$ is the point through which all lines (normals given) pass. Hence $(1, -2)$ is centre of the family of circles whose equation is $x^2 + y^2 - 2x + 4y + c = 0$.

It cuts $x^2 + y^2 - 4x - 4y - 1 = 0$ orthogonally.

$\therefore \quad 2g_1g_2 + 2f_1f_2 = c_1 + c_2$ gives

$2(-1)(-2) + 2(2)(-2) = c - 1$

$4 - 8 = c - 1 \quad \therefore \quad c = -3$

$\therefore \quad x^2 + y^2 - 2x + 4y - 3 = 0 \Rightarrow$ (a).

31. (a) Let the equation of the circle be

$$x^2 + y^2 + 2gx + 2fy + \lambda = 0.$$

Since it passes through $(0, a)$ and $(0, -a)$.

$\therefore \quad a^2 + 2fa + \lambda = 0,$

$a^2 - 2fa + \lambda = 0.$

Subtracting, we get $4fa = 0, \therefore f = 0$; and $\lambda = -a^2$.

Hence the circle becomes

$$x^2 + y^2 + 2gx - a^2 = 0.$$

Centre is $(-g, 0)$

and radius $= \sqrt{g^2 - \lambda} = \sqrt{g^2 + a^2}$.

It is given that the circle touches the line

$y = mx + c$ or $mx - y + c = 0$.

Hence perpendicular from centre should be equal to radius

$$\frac{-mg + c}{\sqrt{(m^2 + 1)}} = \sqrt{g^2 + a^2}.$$

Square $(c - mg)^2 = (g^2 + a^2)(m^2 + 1)$

or $g^2 + 2gmc + \{a^2(1 + m^2) - c^2\} = 0.$

$\therefore \quad g_1g_2 = a^2(1 + m^2) - c^2.$ ...(1)

Above is a quadratic in g and gives us two values of g showing that there will be two circles which satisfy the given conditions. If the two values of g be g_1 and g_2 then the two circles are

$$x^2 + y^2 + 2g_1x - a^2 = 0$$

and $x^2 + y^2 + 2g_2x - a^2 = 0.$

These two will intersect orthogonally if

$2g_1g_2 + 2f_1f_2 = c_1 + c_2$

$2\{a^2(1 + m^2) - c^2\} + 0 = -a^2 - a^2 = -2a^2$

or $a^2(1 + m^2) - c^2 = -a^2$

or $a^2(2 + m^2) = c^2$

is the required condition.

(b) Let the circle be

$$x^2 + y^2 + 2gx + 2fy + c = 0.$$

Its centre $(-g, -f)$ lies on $2x - 2y + 9 = 0$.

$\therefore \quad -2g + 2f + 9 = 0.$ ...(1)

It cuts orthogonally the circle $x^2 + y^2 - 4 = 0$.

$\therefore \quad 2g_1g_2 + 2f_1f_2 = c_1 + c_2$

or $0 + 0 = c - 4 \quad \therefore \quad c = 4$

and from (1), $2g = 9 + 2f$.

Putting the values of c and g we get the equation of the circle as

$$x^2 + y^2 + (9 + 2f)x + 2fy + 4 = 0.$$

or $(x^2 + y^2 + 9x + 4) + 2f(x + y) = 0.$

Above is of the form $S + \lambda P = 0$.

Above represents a family of circles which passes through the points of intersection of $S = 0$ and $P = 0$.

Solving $x^2 + y^2 + 9x + 4 = 0$ and $x + y = 0$ we get the fixed points as $(-1/2, 1/2)$ and $(-4, 4)$.

(c) **Refer (n_1) P. 853.**

The equation of the circle is

$$S_1 = (x - 1)^2 + (y + 1)^2 + \lambda(2x + 3y + 1) = 0$$

Pt. Circle   Tangent

S_2 = The circle on the join of $(0, -1)$ and $(-2, 3)$ as diameter i.e., $x(x + 2) + (y + 1)(y - 3) = 0$

The above equations can be re-written as

$$S_1 = x^2 + y^2 + 2x(\lambda - 1) + 2y\left(1 + \frac{3\lambda}{2}\right) + (2 + \lambda) = 0$$

...(1)

$S_2 = x^2 + y^2 + 2x - 2y - 3 = 0$

Apply the condition $2g_1g_2 + 2f_1f_2 = c_1 + c_2$ for orthogonal intersection of S_1 and S_2.

$$2(\lambda - 1) \cdot 1 + 2\left(1 + \frac{3\lambda}{2}\right)(-1) = 2 + \lambda - 3$$

or $-\lambda - 4 = \lambda - 1$ or $-3 = 2\lambda$

or $\lambda = -3/2$

Putting the value of λ in (1), the required circle is $2x^2 + 2y^2 - 10x - 5y + 1 = 0.$

(d) Ans. (a).

Common chord $= AB = 2AL$.

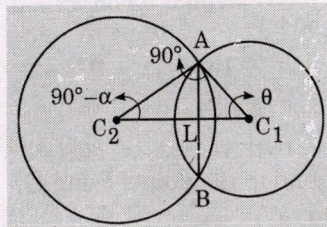

Fig. 114

Since the circles cut orthogonally $\angle A = 90°$

$\therefore \quad AL = r_1 \sin\theta = r_2 \sin(90° - \theta)$

$\therefore \quad \sin\theta = \dfrac{AL}{r_1}, \cos\theta = \dfrac{AL}{r_2}$

Square and add $1 = AL^2 \left(\dfrac{1}{r_1^2} + \dfrac{1}{r_2^2} \right)$

$\therefore \quad AL = \dfrac{r_1 r_2}{\sqrt{r_1^2 + r_2^2}} \quad \therefore \quad AB = 2AL$

32. (a) Since $AM = 2AB$, we have $AB = \dfrac{1}{2} AM$.

It follows that B is the mid-point of AM. If M is the point (h, k), then B is $\left[\dfrac{1}{2}(h+0), \dfrac{1}{2}(k+3) \right]$ i.e. $\left[\dfrac{1}{2} h, \dfrac{1}{2}(k+3) \right]$. But AB is a chord of the circle $x^2 + 4x + (y-3)^2 = 0$, and hence the point B lies on the circle.

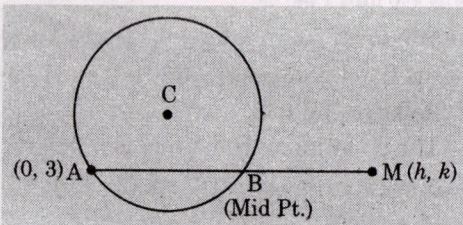

Fig. 115

$\therefore \quad \left(\dfrac{1}{2} h \right)^2 + 4\left(\dfrac{1}{2} h \right) + \left[\dfrac{1}{2}(k+3) - 3 \right]^2 = 0$

or $\quad h^2 + k^2 + 8h - 6k + 9 = 0$.

$\therefore \quad$ The locus of M is the circle

$$x^2 + y^2 + 8x - 6y + 9 = 0.$$

(b) Let P or Q divide AB in the ratio $k : 1$ then the co-ordinates of P or Q are

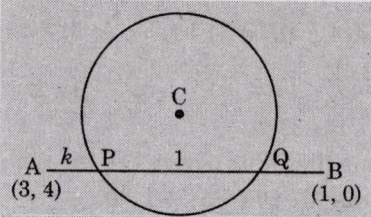

Fig. 116

$\left(\dfrac{k+3}{k+1}, \dfrac{4}{k+1} \right)$ which lie on $x^2 + y^2 = 4$

$\therefore \quad (k+3)^2 + 16 = 4(k+4)^2$

or $\quad 3k^2 + 2k - 21 = 0$

It gives two values of k, i.e. λ and μ which correspond to the points P and Q.

33. Circle is $(1, 2), 5$

T_A is $3x - 4y - 20 = 0$, T_B is $y - 7 = 0$

Both meet at $C(16, 7) \quad \therefore \quad CB = CD = 15$ by distance formula

or $\quad CB = CD = t = \sqrt{S'} = \sqrt{225} = 15$

Area of quadrilateral

$= 2\,\Delta\,ABC = 2 \cdot \dfrac{1}{2} \cdot r \cdot t = 5 \times 15 = 75$ sq. units.

34. (a) Let the circle be $(x-h)^2 + (y-k)^2 = r^2$.

Centre lies on either of bisectors of angle between the tangents which are

$\dfrac{x+y-2}{\sqrt{2}} = \pm \dfrac{x-y-2}{\sqrt{2}}$ or $y = 0$ or $x = 2$

$\therefore \quad k = 0$ or $h = 2$

Again by applying $p = r$ with any tangent

$\dfrac{h+k-2}{\sqrt{2}} = r$. Put $k = 0$ $\therefore$ $(h-2)^2 = 2r^2$ ...(1)

Again the circle passes through $(-4, 3)$.

$\therefore \quad (4+h)^2 + (3-k)^2 = r^2$ Put $k = 0$

$h^2 + 8h + 25 = \dfrac{(h-2)^2}{2}$

or $\quad h^2 + 20h + 46 = 0$ $\therefore$ $h = -10 \pm 3\sqrt{6}$

and $r^2 = \dfrac{1}{2}(h-2)^2 = \dfrac{1}{2}(-12 \pm 3\sqrt{6})^2 = 99 \pm 36\sqrt{6}$

$\therefore \quad$ Circle is $(x + 10 \pm 3\sqrt{6})^2 + y^2 = 99 \pm 36\sqrt{6}$

Note : If we take the other bisector, then $h = 2$ and as above the quadratic in k will be $k^2 - 12k + 96 = 0$. Its roots are imaginary.

(b) Let (h, k) be the centre and r the radius. The point (h, k) lies on either of the two bisectors of the angle between tangents, i.e.

$x + y - 12 = 0$ and $3x - 3y - 4 = 0$

$\therefore \quad h + k - 12 = 0$ ...(1)

and $h - k = 4/3$ ...(2)

It passes through $(4, -1)$

$\therefore \quad (h-4)^2 + (k+1)^2 = r^2$

Again $p = r$ gives

$\therefore \quad \left(\dfrac{h - 2k + 4}{\sqrt{5}} \right)^2 = (h-4)^2 + (k+1)^2$ ...(3)

Now put $k = 12 - h$ from (1)

$\therefore \quad (h - 24 + 2h + 4)^2 = 5[(h-4)^2 + (13-h)^2]$

$\therefore \quad (3h - 20)^2 = 5(2h^2 - 34h + 177)$

or $\quad h^2 - 50h + 525 = 0$

$\therefore \quad h = 15, 35$ and $k = -3, -23$

$r^2 = 125$ or 1445

Hence the circles are

$(x - 15)^2 + (y + 3)^2 = 125$

or $\quad (x - 35)^2 + (y + 23)^2 = 1445$

Again if you put $k = h - 4/3$ from (2) and proceed as above you will not find real values of h and k etc.

(c) The bisectors of the given tangents are $y = 3$ and $x = 66/8$ on which will lie the centre of the circle. Since $x \leq 8$,

∴ $x = \dfrac{66}{8}$ is rejected. Hence let the centre be $(h, 3)$ and radius be taken as a. The circle passes through $(2, 8)$.

∴ $(h - 2)^2 + (3 - 8)^2 = a^2$

or $(h - 2)^2 + 25 = a^2$.   ...(1)

The given condition of tangency $p = r$ for any tangent gives

$4h - 33 = \pm 5a$.   ...(2)

Eliminating a between (1) and (2), we get

$9h^2 + 164h - 364 = 0$

or $(h - 2)(9h + 182) = 0$.

∴ $h = 2$ and from (2) $a = 5$.

∴ $(x - 2)^2 + (y - 3)^2 = 25$

or $x^2 + y^2 - 4x - 6y - 12 = 0$

35. (a) $l_1 = 0$, $l_2 = 0$ are tangents to required circle which intersect at $A(2, 0)$. The centre of the required circle will lie on bisector of acute angle between these tangents i.e. on

$\dfrac{x + y - 2}{\sqrt{2}} = \dfrac{x - y - 2}{\sqrt{2}}$ i.e. $y = 0$

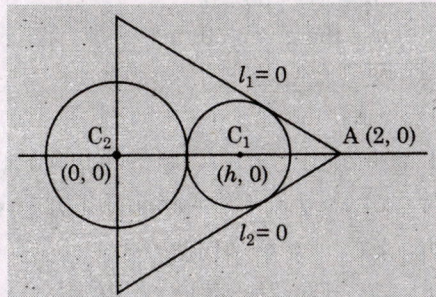

Fig. 117

Let it be $(h, 0)$ where h is + ive and if r be the radius then it touches $x^2 + y^2 = 1$ externally

$C_1 C_2 = r_1 + r_2$ or $h = 1 + r$ ...(1)

$p = r$ with any tangent gives $\dfrac{h - 2}{\sqrt{2}} = r$

∴ $h = 2 \pm \sqrt{2} r = 1 + r$, by (1)

$1 = (1 + \sqrt{2}) r$ ∴ $r = \dfrac{1}{1 + \sqrt{2}} = \sqrt{2} - 1$

only as $r = +$ ive

∴ $h = 2 \pm \sqrt{2}(\sqrt{2} - 1) = 4 - \sqrt{2}, \sqrt{2}$

Hence the circles are $(4 - \sqrt{2}, 0), (\sqrt{2} - 1)$ and $(\sqrt{2}, 0), (\sqrt{2} - 1)$

(b) If C be the centre of the circle C_1 then it lies on the bisectors of the given lines which are

$\dfrac{5x + 12y - 10}{13} = \pm \dfrac{5x - 12y - 40}{13}$

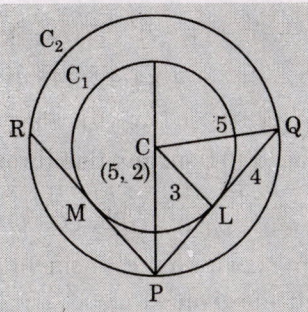

Fig. 118

These give $x = 5$ and $y = -5/4$. Since centre lies in 1st quadrant therefore $y = -5/4$ is ruled out. Let the centre be $(5, k)$ then its perpendicular distance from each of lines will be 3,

i.e. $p = r$.

∴ $\dfrac{25 + 12k - 10}{13} = 3$ and $\dfrac{25 - 12k - 40}{13} = 3$

∴ $k = 2$ or $k = -\dfrac{54}{12} = -\dfrac{9}{2}$

The value $-9/2$ of k is ruled out as centre C lies in 1st quadrant ∴ C is $(5, 2)$.

Now the circle C_2 cuts off intercepts 8 from these lines and if its radius be r, then

$r^2 = 3^2 + 4^2 = 25$ or $r = 5$

∴ Circle C_2 is $(x - 5)^2 + (y - 2)^2 = 5^2$

or $x^2 + y^2 - 10x - 4y + 4 = 0$

(c) $(1, 2)$ lies on $7x - y - 5 = 0$. The equation of the circle is

$\underbrace{(x - 1)^2 + (y - 2)^2}_{\text{Point circle}} + \lambda \underbrace{(7x - y - 5)}_{\text{Tangent}} = 0$ ...(1)

(See Rule (n_1), P. 853)

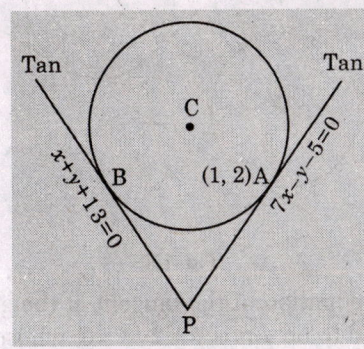

Fig. 119

Its centre is $(-g, -f)$

or $\left[-\left(\dfrac{7\lambda - 2}{2}\right), \left(\dfrac{\lambda + 4}{2}\right)\right]$, it will lie on the bisectors of the angle between the tangents whose equations are

$x - 3y = 35$ and $3x + y + 15 = 0$ ...(2)

Putting in (2), we get the values of λ as -8 or 2.

Hence from (1) the required circles are

$(x - 1)^2 + (y - 2)^2 - 8(7x - y - 5) = 0$

and $(x-1)^2 + (y-2)^2 + 2(7x-y-5) = 0$

or $x^2 + y^2 - 58x + 4y + 45 = 0$
and $x^2 + y^2 + 12x - 6y - 5 = 0$ $\Bigg\}$

36. (a) Let O be (α, β) then any line through O is
$$\frac{x-\alpha}{\cos\theta} = \frac{y-\beta}{\sin\theta} = \frac{r}{OP} \left(= \frac{r_1}{OA}, \frac{r_2}{OB}\right)$$
$\therefore$ $x = r\cos\theta + \alpha$, $y = r\sin\theta + \beta$ ...(1)
It meets the given circle $x^2 + y^2 = a^2$ in A and B
$\therefore$ $(r\cos\theta + \alpha)^2 + (r\sin\theta + \beta)^2 = a^2$
or $r^2 + 2r(\alpha\cos\theta + \beta\sin\theta) + (\alpha^2 + \beta^2 - a^2) = 0$
...(2)

Above is a quadratic in r and its roots are $OA = r_1$, $OB = r_2$

(i)   Given OP is A.M. of OA and OB
$\therefore$ $2r = r_1 + r_2$
$2r = -2(\alpha\cos\theta + \beta\sin\theta)$, by (2)
Cancel 2 and multiply by r
$\therefore$ $r^2 + (\alpha r\cos\theta + \beta r\sin\theta) = 0$
or $(x-\alpha)^2 + (y-\beta)^2 + \alpha(x-\alpha) + \beta(y-\beta) = 0$,
by (1)
It represents a circle.

(ii)   Given OP is G.M. of OA and OB
$\therefore$ $r^2 = r_1 r_2 = \alpha^2 + \beta^2 - a^2$ by (2)
or $(x-\alpha)^2 + (y-\beta)^2 = \alpha^2 + \beta^2 - a^2$ by (1)
Above is also a circle.

(b) The given circle is $(2, 4)$, 2

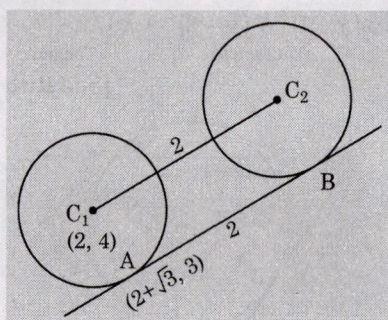

Fig. 120

The equation of the tangent at the given point is found to be $\sqrt{3}x - y - 2\sqrt{3} = 0$, whose slope is $\sqrt{3}$ *i.e.* it makes an angle $60°$ with x-axis. After the circle rolls up along the tangent through a distance 2, its centre will move from C_1 to C_2 whose co-ordinates we have to find. Now $C_1 C_2$ makes an angle of $60°$ and passes through C_1 $(2, 4)$ and C_2 is at a distance of 2 units from C_1
$\therefore$ $\frac{x-2}{\cos 60°} = \frac{y-4}{\sin 60°} = r = 2$ for C_2
$\therefore$ $C_2 = \left(2 + 2 \cdot \frac{1}{2}, 4 + 2 \cdot \frac{\sqrt{3}}{2}\right) = (3, 4 + \sqrt{3})$

Hence the equation of circle in new position is
$$(x-3)^2 + (y-4-\sqrt{3})^2 = 2^2$$

37. (a) The given circle has its centre (a, a) and radius a so that this circle touches both the axes along which lie the two sides of the triangle.

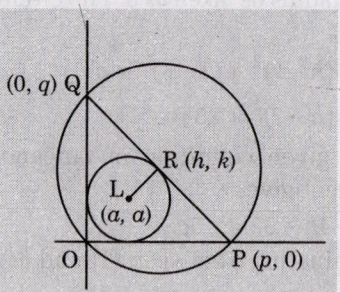

Fig. 121

Let the third side be $x/p + y/q = 1$, so that P is $(p, 0)$ and Q is $(0, q)$. The line PQ touches the given circle at the point R.
Since $\angle POQ$ is a right angle therefore PQ is diameter of the circle passing through the points O, P and Q and its centre is mid-point R of PQ.
$\therefore$ R is $(p/2, q/2) = (h, k)$, say.
$p = 2h$, $q = 2k$
Now the line PQ is $x/p + y/q = 1$
or $qx + py - pq = 0$
touches the given circle. $\therefore$ $p = r$
or $\frac{qa + pa - pq}{\sqrt{(p^2 + q^2)}} = a$. Square

$a^2(p+q)^2 + p^2 q^2 - 2pqa(p+q) = a^2(p^2 + q^2)$
or $a^2 \cdot 2pq + p^2 q^2 - 2pqa(p+q) = 0$ cancel pq
or $2a^2 - 2a(p+q) + pq = 0$
or $2a^2 - 2a(2h + 2k) + 2h \cdot 2k = 0$
$\therefore$ Locus of centre (h, k) is
$$a^2 - 2a(x+y) + 2xy = 0$$

(b) It is same question as part (a) if we choose $a = 2$. The condition of tangency gives
$$\frac{qa + pa - pq}{\pm\sqrt{(p^2 + q^2)}} = a,$$
put $a = 2$, $p = 2h$ and $q = 2k$
$$(2k)2 + (2h)2 - 4hk = \pm 2\sqrt{4h^2 + 4k^2}$$
or $h + k - hk \pm \sqrt{h^2 + k^2} = 0$.
Locus is $x + y - xy \pm \sqrt{x^2 + y^2} = 0$ $\therefore$ $k = \pm 1$.

(c) Let the circle be $(x-a)^2 + (y-b)^2 = r^2$.
Condition of tangency gives
$$\frac{(al + bm + 1)}{\sqrt{(l^2 + m^2)}} = r$$
or $(al + bm)^2 + 1 + 2(al + bm) = r^2(l^2 + m^2)$

or $l^2(a^2-r^2)+m^2(b^2-r^2)+2ablm+2al$
$$+2bm+1=0. \quad ...(1)$$

Compare with $4l^2-5m^2+6l+1=0$

$\therefore \quad a^2-r^2=4,\ b^2-r^2=-5,\ ab=0,$

$2a=6,\ 2b=0$

$\therefore \quad a=3,\ b=0,\ \therefore \quad r^2=5$

Hence the circle is $(x-3)^2+y^2=5$

or $x^2+y^2-6x+4=0.$

38. (a) Let in usual notations the three circles be

$S_1=0,\ S_2=0,\ S_3=0$

Their radical axes taken in pairs are given by

$S_1-S_2=0,\ S_2-S_3=0$ and $S_3-S_1=0$

i.e. $2x(g_1-g_2)+2y(f_1-f_2)+c_1-c_2=0 \quad ...(1)$
$2x(g_2-g_3)+2y(f_2-f_3)+c_2-c_3=0 \quad ...(2)$
$2x(g_3-g_1)+2y(f_3-f_1)+c_3-c_1=0 \quad ...(3)$

Adding (1), (2) and (3), we get $0x+0y+0=0.$

Hence the three radical axes are concurrent by **Rule 18 or Q. 16 (a).**

The point of concurrency is called the radical centre of the three circles and the length of the tangents drawn from this point to the three circles are equal in length.

(b) Let the given circles be denoted by $S_1=0$ and $S_2=0$ and the points P,Q,R,S lie on the circle say $S_3=0.$ PQ intersects both S_1 and S_3 and RS intersects both S_2 and $S_3.$

$\therefore \quad PQ$ is radical axis of S_1 and S_3 and RS is radical axis of S_2 and S_3

$\therefore \quad Ax+By+C=0$ is

radical axis of S_1 and S_3 and

$A'x+B'y+C'=0$ is

radical axis of S_2 and $S_3.$

Also radical axis of S_1 and S_2 is given by

$S_1-S_2=0$

or $(a-a')x+(b-b')y+(c-c')=0.$

Again from part (a) we know that the radical axis of three circles taken in pairs are concurrent. Hence by **rule 19**, we have

$$\begin{vmatrix} a-a' & b-b' & c-c' \\ A & B & C \\ A' & B' & C' \end{vmatrix}=0$$

(c) Choose the side $BC=2a$ along x-axis and its mid-point be taken as origin so that B and C are as marked. Let A be $(h,k).$ Circles on sides as diameters are

$S_1=x^2+y^2-a^2=0$

$S_2=(x-h)(x-a)+(y-k)y=0$

or $x^2+y^2-x(h+a)-ky+ah=0$

Replacing a by $-a$

$S_3=x^2+y^2-x(h-a)-ky-ah=0$

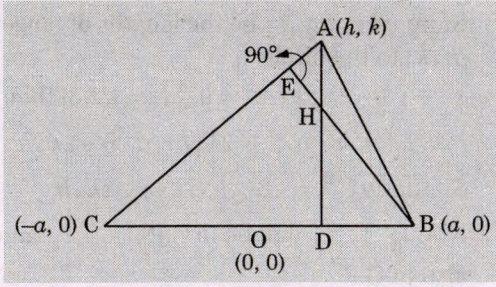

Fig. 122

Radical axis of S_1 and S_2 is $S_1-S_2=0$

$x(h+a)+ky-ah-a^2=0$

Replacing a by $-a$ radical axis of S_1 and S_3 is

$x(h-a)+ky+ah-a^2=0$

Solving the above two we get the radical centre as

$\left(h,\dfrac{a^2-h^2}{k}\right).$

Now in order to find orthocentre we have to find the equation of altitudes AD and $BE.$

AD is $x=h$

$\therefore \quad BE:y-0=-\dfrac{h+a}{k}(x-a) \quad \because \quad BE\perp AC$

Solving we get the orthocentre as $\left(h,\dfrac{a^2-h^2}{k}\right)$

which is same as radical centre.

39. (a) Here we have to find the radical centre of the three circles. First reduce them to standard form in which coefficients of x^2 and y^2 be each unity. Subtracting in pairs the three radical axes are

$\dfrac{17}{6}x-y+\dfrac{5}{3}=0;\ -x-\dfrac{3}{2}y-\dfrac{3}{2}=0$

$-\dfrac{11}{6}x+\dfrac{5}{2}y-\dfrac{1}{6}=0.$

Solving any two, we get the point $\left(\dfrac{-16}{21},\dfrac{-31}{63}\right)$

which satisfies the third also. This point is called the radical centre and by definition the length of the tangents from it to the three circles are equal.

(b) Let the point be (h,k) then by the given condition

$t^2=h^2+k^2-1=h^2+k^2+8h+15$

$=h^2+k^2+10k+24.$

From 1st and 2nd, we get $h=-2.$

From 1st and 3rd, we get $k=-5/2.$

Hence the required point is

$(-2,-5/2)$ and $t^2=37/4.$

(c) If $\lambda_1,\lambda_2,\lambda_3$ be the three values of $\lambda,$ then

$\lambda_2^2=\lambda_1\lambda_3. \quad ...(1)$

If $(h,k),$ be any point on the circle $x^2+y^2=c^2$

then $h^2+k^2=c^2. \quad ...(2)$

Suppose t_1, t_2, t_3 be the lengths of tangents from (h, k) to the circle

$$x^2 + y^2 - 2\lambda_r x - c^2 = 0, \quad (r = 1, 2, 3) \text{ then}$$

$$t_1{}^2 = h^2 + k^2 - 2\lambda_1 h - c^2 = -2\lambda_1 h \quad \text{by (2)}.$$

Similarly $t_2{}^2 = -2\lambda_2 h$, $t_3{}^2 = -2\lambda_3 h$.

Now t_1, t_2, t_3 will be in G.P. if $t_1{}^2, t_2{}^2$ and $t_3{}^2$ are also in G.P.

or $(-2\lambda_2 h)^2 = (-2\lambda_1 h)(-2\lambda_3 h)$.

or $\lambda_2{}^2 = \lambda_1 \lambda_3$ which is true by (1).

40. (a) Proceeding as in part (a) the co-ordinates of the radical centre are found to be $P(0, -3)$. Now we have to find a circle which passes through $P(0, -3)$ and touches the line $x + y = 5$ at $(6, -1)$. The required circle by **rule (n_1) P. 853** is

$$(x - 6)^2 + (y + 1)^2 + \lambda (x + y - 5) = 0$$

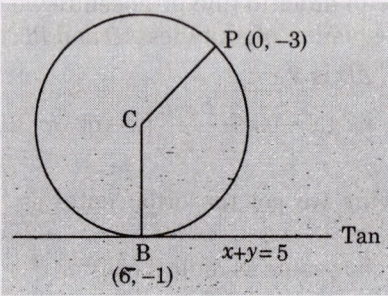

pt. circle   tangent

P (0, –3)

C

B (6, –1)   x+y=5   Tan

Fig. 123

It passes through $P(0, -3)$.

$\therefore \quad 36 + 4 + \lambda (-8) = 0 \quad \therefore \quad \lambda = 5$

Putting in (1), the required circle is

$$x^2 + y^2 - 7x + 7y + 12 = 0.$$

(b) $A(0, 0), P(a, 0), Q(2a, 0), B(3a, 0)$ as $AP = PQ = QB$.

$$S_1 = x(x - a) + y^2 = 0$$

or $x^2 + y^2 - ax = 0$

$$S_2 = (x - a)(x - 2a) + y^2 = 0$$

or $x^2 + y^2 - 3ax + 2a^2 = 0$

$$S_3 = (x - 2a)(x - 3a) + y^2 = 0$$

or $x^2 + y^2 - 5ax + 6a^2 = 0$

If T be (h, k) from where tangents are drawn, then

$$t_1^2 + t_2^2 + t_3^2 = b^2$$

$$3(h^2 + k^2) - 9ah + 8a^2 = b^2$$

$\therefore$ Locus of (h, k) is

$$3(x^2 + y^2) - 9ax + 8a^2 - b^2 = 0.$$

41. (a) If the two circles intersect at P and Q, then PQ will be their radical axis. Now of all those circles which pass through the points P and Q, any pair have its radical axis the line PQ. Hence the general equation of the circles are the circles

which pass through the intersection of the given circles and their equation will be $S_1 + \lambda S_2 = 0$.

or $(x^2 + y^2 - 4) + \lambda (x^2 + y^2 + 2x + 4y - 6) = 0$

Such a system is called coaxial system of circles as their common chord or radical axis is the line PQ.

2nd form : The common chord PQ is given by

$$S_1 - S_2 = 0 \quad \text{or} \quad P = 0 \quad \therefore \quad S_1 + \lambda P = 0$$

also represents a family of circles each of which passes through the point of intersection of

$S_1 = 0$ and $S_2 = 0$ or $S_1 = 0$ and $P = 0$

$P = 0$ is $S_1 - S_2 = 0$ or $-2x - 4y + 2 = 0$

or $x + 2y - 1 = 0$.

$\therefore$ Required family is given by $S_1 + \lambda P = 0$

i.e. $(x^2 + y^2 - 4) + \lambda (x + 2y - 1) = 0$.

(b) Radical axis PQ is $x - a/2 = 0$ which cuts the circle $x^2 + y^2 = a^2$ in P and Q. Now any circle which passes through the points P and Q will have radical axis the line PQ with respect to $x^2 + y^2 - a^2 = 0$. Hence its equation is the equation of the circle through the points of intersection of the circle $x^2 + y^2 - a^2 = 0$ and the line $x - a/2 = 0$ and is given by $S + \lambda P = 0$

i.e. $(x^2 + y^2 - a^2) + \lambda (x - a/2) = 0$.

As it passes through the point $(2a, 0)$,

$\therefore \quad (4a^2 - a^2) + \lambda (2a - a/2) = 0 \quad \text{or} \quad \lambda = -2a$.

Hence the required circle is

$$(x^2 + y^2 - a^2) - 2a(x - a/2) = 0$$

or $x^2 + y^2 - 2ax = 0$.

Alt. : You may take the circle as g, f, c and it passes through $(2a, 0)$.

$\therefore \quad 4a^2 + 4ag + c = 0 \quad \quad \dots(1)$

Find the radical axis by $S_1 - S_2 = 0$ and then compare with $x - a/2 = 0$. This will give $g = -a$, $f = 0, c = 0$, by the help of (1).

$\therefore \quad x^2 + y^2 - 2ax = 0$.

(c) Ans. (c). Tangent at P is drawn from Q (on y-axis) and the line $5x - 2y + 6 = 0$ $\therefore$ Q is $(0, 3)$. Hence QP is the length of tangent from $(0, 3)$ to the circle.

$\therefore \quad PQ^2 = S' = 0 + 9 + 0 + 18 - 2 = 25$

$\therefore \quad PQ = 5$.

42. (a) True. Reduce the circles to standard form by making the coefficients of x^2 and y^2 each unity. If (p, q) be any point on S_1, then

$$p^2 + q^2 - \frac{48}{15} p + \frac{64}{15} q = 0 \quad \dots(1)$$

$$\therefore \quad \frac{t_1^2}{t_2^2} = \frac{p^2 + q^2 - \dfrac{48}{5} p + \dfrac{64}{5} q + 60}{p^2 + q^2 - \dfrac{24}{5} p + \dfrac{32}{5} q + 15} = \frac{S_2'}{S_3'}$$

Now putting the value of $p^2 + q^2$ from (1) in the above, we get $t_1^2/t_2^2 = 4/1$ etc.

(b) The given line $2x + 3y - 5 = 0$ is $S_1 - S_2 = 0$ *i.e.* radical axis. Hence by definition the length of tangents drawn from any point on it are equal.

(c) $t^2 = p \Rightarrow x^2 + y^2 - 25 = 5\dfrac{3x + 4y - 8}{\pm 5}$

$\therefore \quad x^2 + y^2 - 3x - 4y - 17 = 0$

or $\quad x^2 + y^2 + 3x + 4y - 33 = 0$

(d) If P be (h, k) on 1st, then

$\qquad h^2 + k^2 + 2gh + 2fy + a = 0 \qquad \dots(1)$

$\therefore \quad t^2 = S' = h^2 + k^2 + 2gh + 2fy + b = b - a$ by (1)

43. (a) $\angle POQ = \theta$ given $\qquad \therefore \quad \angle COP = \theta/2$

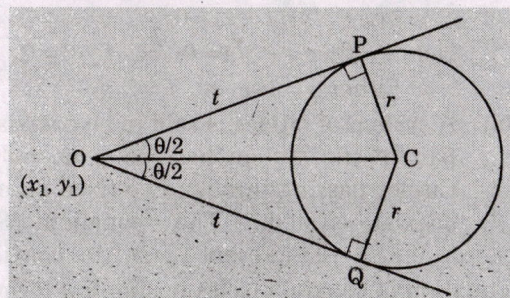

Fig. 124

$\therefore \quad \tan\dfrac{\theta}{2} = \dfrac{r}{t} = \dfrac{r}{\sqrt{S'}} \quad \because \quad t^2 = S'$

(b) By angle subtended by a circle at a point we mean the angle between the tangents drawn to the circle from that point.

Clearly PA is the length of tangent t_1 drawn from P

$\therefore \quad PA = \sqrt{S_1'}$

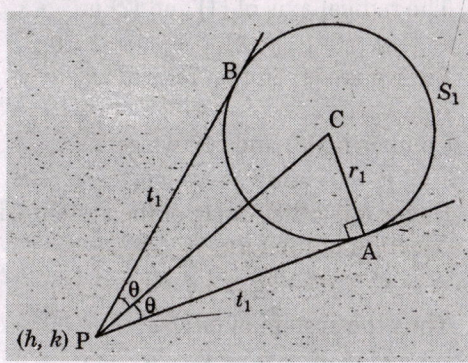

Fig. 125

where S_1' is the value of S_1 for the point P.

$\therefore \quad \tan\theta = \dfrac{r_1}{\sqrt{S_1'}} \quad$ Similarly $\tan\theta = \dfrac{r_2}{\sqrt{S_2'}}$

$\therefore \quad \dfrac{r_1^2}{S_1'} = \dfrac{r_2^2}{S_2'}$

Generalize *i.e.* S_1' becomes S_1 and S_2' becomes S_2.

$\therefore \quad$ Locus of P is $r_1^2 S_2 - r_2^2 S_1 = 0$

(c) Let tangents at A and B meet at $P(h, k)$ and include an angle $60°$.

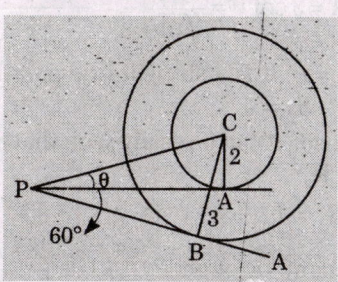

Fig. 126

If $\angle CPA = \theta$ then $\angle CPB = \theta + 60°$

$\therefore \quad \sin\theta = \dfrac{2}{CP}, \sin(\theta + 60°) = \dfrac{3}{CP}$

$\therefore \quad \dfrac{\sin(\theta + 60°)}{\sin\theta} = \dfrac{3}{2}$

or $\quad -2\left(\dfrac{1}{2}\sin\theta + \dfrac{\sqrt{3}}{2}\cos\theta\right) = 3\sin\theta$

or $\quad 2\sin\theta = \sqrt{3}\cos\theta \quad$ or $\quad \tan\theta = \dfrac{\sqrt{3}}{2}$

But $\tan\theta = \dfrac{CA}{PA} = \dfrac{2}{\sqrt{S'}} = \dfrac{2}{\sqrt{h^2 + k^2 - 4}}$

$\therefore \quad \dfrac{\sqrt{3}}{2} = \dfrac{2}{\sqrt{h^2 + k^2 - 4}}$. Square and generalize.

$\qquad 3(x^2 + y^2 - 4) = 16$

or $\quad 3(x^2 + y^2) = 28$

It is again a concentric circle.

(d) $\tan 2\theta = \dfrac{2\sqrt{h^2 - ab}}{a + b} = \dfrac{1}{3}$

where $a = 2$, $b = 1$, $h = -3/2$

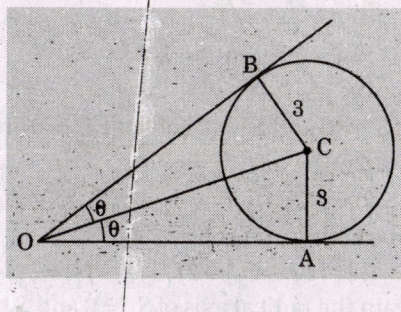

Fig. 127

or $\quad \dfrac{2t}{1 - t^2} = \dfrac{1}{3} \qquad$ where $t = \tan\theta$

or $\quad t^2 + 6t + 1 = 0$

$\therefore \quad \tan\theta = -3 \pm \sqrt{10}$

Since $\theta < 90° \quad \therefore \quad \tan\theta = +$ ive and hence we choose $\tan\theta = -3 + \sqrt{10}$ (+ ive)

Now from the figure

$$OA = 3 \cot \theta = \frac{3}{\sqrt{10} - 3} = \frac{3(\sqrt{10} + 3)}{1}$$

44. (a) $S_1 - S_2 = k$. It is a straight line parallel to radical axis $S_1 - S_2 = 0$

(b) **Ans. False.** It can be easily seen that the locus of P is a circle.

45. (a) $PQ^2 = S_1 = h^2 + k^2 - a^2$ ...(1)

Any secant through $P(h, k)$ is $\dfrac{x-h}{\cos\theta} = \dfrac{y-k}{\sin\theta} = r$

where r is the distance of P from any point on the line.

$(r\cos\theta + h, r\sin\theta + k)$ is any point on the line.

If it lies on the circle, then

$$(r\cos\theta + h)^2 + (r\sin\theta + k)^2 = a^2$$

or $r^2 + 2r(h\cos\theta + k\sin\theta) + (h^2 + k^2 - a^2) = 0$

It gives two values of r say PA and PB.

$$PA \cdot PB = r_1 r_2 = h^2 + k^2 - a^2 = S_1$$

$$= PQ^2 = \text{constant}, \qquad \text{by (1)}$$

as it is independent of θ. Hence all the products are equal and each equals to PQ^2.

(b) $S + \lambda P = 0$ is the required equation where $S = 0$ is a circle on given points as diameters and $P = 0$ is the line joining these two points.

Let S_1, S_2, S_3 be the three members of this family corresponding to $\lambda_1, \lambda_2, \lambda_3$.

Let $P(h, k)$ be any point on S_1

$$\therefore \quad S' + \lambda_1 P' = 0 \qquad \text{...(1)}$$

Now $\dfrac{t_2^2}{t_3^2} = \dfrac{S' + \lambda_2 P'}{S' + \lambda_3 P'} = \dfrac{-\lambda_1 P' + \lambda_2 P'}{-\lambda_1 P' + \lambda_3 P'}$ by (1)

$$= \dfrac{\lambda_2 - \lambda_1}{\lambda_3 - \lambda_1} = \text{constant}$$

$$\therefore \quad \dfrac{t_2}{t_3} = \text{constant.}$$

46. (a) Let $S_1 = 0$ and $S_2 = 0$ both cut $S_3 = 0$ orthogonally.

$$\therefore \quad 2g_1 g_3 + 2f_1 f_3 = c_1 + c_3$$
$$2g_2 g_3 + 2f_2 f_3 = c_2 + c_3$$

Subtracting, we get

$$2g_3(g_1 - g_2) + 2f_3(f_1 - f_2) = c_1 - c_2 \quad \text{...(1)}$$

Again the radical axis of $S_1 = 0$ and $S_2 = 0$ is given by $S_1 - S_2 = 0$

$$\therefore \quad 2x(g_1 - g_2) + 2y(f_1 - f_2) + c_1 - c_2 = 0.$$

It will pass through the centre $(-g_3, -f_3)$ of $S_3 = 0$

if $-2g_3(g_1 - g_2) - 2f_3(f_1 - f_2) = -(c_1 - c_2)$

or $2g_3(g_1 - g_2) + 2f_3(f_1 - f_2) = c_1 - c_2$.

Above is true by (1).

(b) The second circle can be reduced to standard form on dividing by 2 so that its equation is

$$S_2 = x^2 + y^2 + \frac{3}{2}x + 4y + c = 0.$$

The radical axis of circles $S_1 = 0$ and $S_2 = 0$ is given by $S_1 - S_2 = 0$

or $2x(g - 3/4) + 2y(f - 2) = 0$

or $x(g - 3/4) + y(f - 2) = 0$

It touches the circle $S_3 = 0$ whose centre is $(-1, -1)$ and radius 1. The condition of tangency i.e. $p = r$ gives

$$\frac{-1 \cdot (g - 3/4) - (f - 2)1}{\sqrt{[(g - 3/4)^2 + (f - 2)^2]}} = 1.$$

Squaring, we get

$$(g - 3/4)^2 + (f - 2)^2 + 2(g - 3/4)(f - 2)$$
$$= (g - 3/4)^2 + (f - 2)^2$$

$$\therefore \quad 2(g - 3/4)(f - 2) = 0.$$

Hence either $g - 3/4 = 0$ or $f - 2 = 0$.

$$\therefore \quad \text{Either } g = 3/4 \text{ or } f = 2.$$

47. (a) A system of circles is said to be co-axial if every pair of the system has the same radical axis. Circles passing through two fixed points form a coaxial system. The equation $S + \lambda P = 0$, $S_1 + \lambda S_2 = 0$ represent a family of coaxial circles.

Equation of coaxial circles in simplest form :

Let the common radical axis be chosen along y-axis and the line of centres which will be perpendicular to radical axis be along x-axis. Hence the equation of any circle will be

$$x^2 + y^2 + 2gx + c = 0. \qquad \text{...(1)}$$

as y-co-ordinate of centre is zero.

Let any other circle of the system be

$$x^2 + y^2 + 2g_1 x + 2f_1 y + c_1 = 0. \qquad \text{...(2)}$$

The radical axis of (1) and (2) is

$$2x(g - g_1) - 2f_1 y + (c - c_1) = 0. \qquad \text{...(3)}$$

But we are given that radical axis is y-axis

i.e. $x = 0$. ...(4)

Comparing (3) and (4), we get

$$f_1 = 0 \text{ and } c - c_1 = 0 \therefore c_1 = c.$$

Hence any other circle of the system will have its equation of the form

$$x^2 + y^2 + 2g_1 x + c = 0.$$

Thus the system of circles

$$x^2 + y^2 + 2g_r x + c = 0,$$

where c is constant and g_r a parameter represents a family of coaxial circles whose common radical axis is y-axis, i.e. $x = 0$.

(b) For the first part **see part (a)**.

One circle will be within the other if

$$C_1 C_2 < r_1 - r_2$$

$$\therefore \quad \left\{ -\frac{a}{2} - \left(-\frac{d}{2} \right) \right\}^2 < \left[\sqrt{\frac{a^2}{4} - b} - \sqrt{\frac{d^2}{4} - b} \right]^2$$

or $\quad a^2 + a'^2 - 2aa' < (a^2 - 4b) + (a'^2 - 4b)$
$$- 2\sqrt{(\ )}\sqrt{(\ )}$$
or $\quad -aa' + 4b < -\sqrt{a^2 - 4b}\sqrt{a'^2 - 4b}$

Multiply both sides by – sign and change the sign of inequality and then square
$$(aa' - 4b)^2 \geq (a^2 - 4b)(a'^2 - 4b)$$
$$- 8aa'b \geq -4b(a^2 + a'^2)$$

or $\quad 4b(a^2 + a'^2 - 2aa') \geq 0$

or $\quad 4b(a - a')^2 \geq 0$

Now $(a - a')^2$ is + ive $\therefore$ b must also be +ive.

Now $\dfrac{a^2}{4} - b = +$ ive being radius

$\therefore \quad a > 2\sqrt{b}$

Similarly $a' > 2\sqrt{b}$ $\therefore$ $aa' > 4b$

$\therefore \quad aa'$ is also +ive as b is +ive

Hence both aa' and b are +ive.

48. (a) Refer Q. 41.

(b) $S + \lambda P = 0$ forms a coaxial system, the radical axis being $P = 0$ for all values of λ. Let g, f, c be the circle orthogonal to $S + \lambda P = 0$. Applying the condition of orthogonality, we get
$$2a(1 + \lambda)g + 2b(1 - \lambda)f = 0 + c$$
or $\quad 2(ag - bf)\lambda + 2(ag + bf) - c = 0$

Above relation holds for all values of λ and hence
$$2(ag - bf) = 0, 2(ag + bf) - c = 0$$
$\therefore \quad g = c/4a, f = c/4b.$

Ans. $x^2 + y^2 + (c/2a)x + (c/2b)y + c = 0$

(c) Choose one fixed line along x-axis and the other through origin as $y = mx$ where $m = \tan\theta$ (θ fixed as lines are fixed)

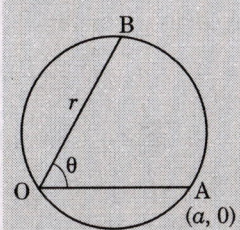

Fig. 128

Let $OA = a$ $\therefore$ A is $(a, 0)$ and $OB = r$

$\therefore \quad B$ is $(r\cos\theta, r\sin\theta)$

We are given that
$$p \cdot OA + q \cdot OB = 1$$
or $\quad pa + qr = 1$ ...(1)

where a and r are variables

Now let the circle OAB be chosen as
$$x^2 + y^2 + 2gx + 2fy = 0$$ ...(2)

(**Mind** $c = 0$ as it passes through $O(0, 0)$. Note that A is on x-axis but not B). It passes through $A(a, 0)$.

$\therefore \quad a^2 + 2ga = 0$ $\therefore$ $2g = -a$

The point B is $(r\cos\theta, r\sin\theta)$ which lies on the circle.

$\therefore \quad r^2 + 2r(g\cos\theta + f\sin\theta) = 0$

$\therefore \quad r = -2(g\cos\theta + f\sin\theta)$

$\therefore \quad r = a\cos\theta - 2f\sin\theta$ $\because$ $2g = -a$

Putting in (1), we get
$$pa + q(a\cos\theta - 2f\sin\theta) = 1$$
$\therefore \quad (p + q\cos\theta)a - 1 = 2fq\sin\theta$

Putting the values of g and f in (2) the equation of circle becomes
$$x^2 + y^2 - ax + \frac{[(p + q\cos\theta)a - 1]}{q\sin\theta}y = 0$$

Collect the terms of variable a.
$$\left(x^2 + y^2 - \frac{y}{q\sin\theta}\right) + a\left(\frac{p + q\cos\theta}{q\sin\theta}y - x\right)$$

It is of the form $S + \lambda P = 0$, where $S = 0$ is a circle and $P = 0$ is the equation of line. It clearly passes through the points of intersection of S and P which are fixed as their equations contain all constants.

49. (a) The two given circles in standard form are
$$S_1 = 0 \text{ or } x^2 + y^2 - x + 3y - \frac{3}{2} = 0$$
$$S_2 = 0 \text{ or } x^2 + y^2 + 4x + 2y + 1 = 0$$

Radical axis is given by $S_1 - S_2 = 0$.

$\therefore \quad -5x + y - \dfrac{5}{2} = 0$

or $\quad 10x - 2y + 5 = 0$ ...(1)

Circle coaxial with the given circles is
$$S_1 + \lambda S_2 = 0.$$
$$\left(x^2 + y^2 - x + 3y - \frac{3}{2}\right) + \lambda(x^2 + y^2$$
$$+ 4x + 2y + 1) = 0$$

or $\quad (x^2 + y^2)(1 + \lambda) - (1 - 4\lambda)x + (3 + 2\lambda)y$
$$- \frac{3}{2} + \lambda = 0$$

or $\quad x^2 + y^2 - \dfrac{1 - 4\lambda}{1 + \lambda}x + \dfrac{3 + 2\lambda}{1 + \lambda}y + \dfrac{\lambda - \dfrac{3}{2}}{1 + \lambda} = 0,$ ...(2)

Its centre $\left(\dfrac{1}{2} \cdot \dfrac{1 - 4\lambda}{1 + \lambda}, -\dfrac{1}{2} \cdot \dfrac{3 + 2\lambda}{1 + \lambda}\right)$

$i.e. (-g, -f)$ lies on (1)

$\therefore \quad \dfrac{5(1 - 4\lambda)}{1 + \lambda} + \dfrac{3 + 2\lambda}{1 + \lambda} + 5 = 0.$

or $\quad 5 - 20\lambda + 3 + 2\lambda + 5 + 5\lambda = 0$

or $\quad 13 - 13\lambda = 0$ $\therefore$ $\lambda = 1$

Putting in (2), the required circle is
$$x^2 + y^2 + \frac{3}{2}x + \frac{5}{2}y - \frac{1}{4} = 0$$

or $\quad 4x^2 + 4y^2 + 6x + 10y - 1 = 0.$

(b) Required locus is $x^2 + y^2 = 2a^2 = 18$ *i.e.* director circle **(See P. 891)**. Tangent at $(\sqrt{2}, 4)$ is $\sqrt{2}\, x + 4y - 18 = 0$.

Coaxial circle is given by $S + \lambda P = 0$.

50. (a) Centre of the first circle is $(-g, -f)$ and its radius

$$CT = r_1 = \sqrt{g^2 + f^2 - c}$$

The centre of the second circle is also $(-g, -f)$ but its radius is

$$CP = r_2 = \sqrt{g^2 + f^2 - c \sin^2 \alpha - (g^2 + f^2)\cos^2 \alpha}$$

or $r_2 = \sqrt{g^2 + f^2 - c} \cdot \sin \alpha$

$$= r_1 \sin \alpha \qquad \qquad ...(1)$$

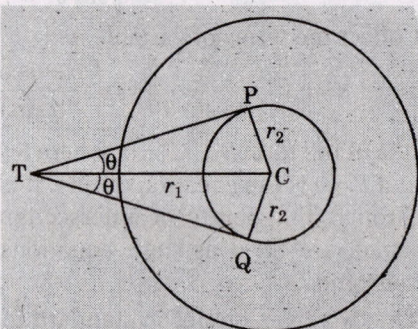

Fig. 129

Since $\sin \alpha$ is less than 1 therefore $r_2 < r_1$ and as such the second circle is inner circle concentric with outer circle. Now if θ be the angle PTC, then from right angled triangle

$$\sin \theta = \frac{r_2}{r_1} = \frac{r_1 \sin \alpha}{r_1} = \sin \alpha$$

$\therefore \quad \theta = \alpha \quad \therefore \quad \angle PTQ = 2\theta = 2\alpha.$

(b) Ans. **(d).** Refer figure part (a). C is $(-2, 3)$.

and $r_2^2 = 4 + 9 - 9\sin^2 \alpha - 13\cos^2 \alpha$

$$= 4 - 4\cos^2 \alpha = 4\sin^2 \alpha$$

$\therefore \quad \dfrac{CP}{CT} = \sin \alpha = \dfrac{2 \sin \alpha}{CT}$

$\therefore \quad CT = 2 = \text{constant}$

Thus the point T is at a constant distance 2 from $C(-2, 3)$.

Hence locus of T is $(x + 2)^2 + (y - 3)^2 = 2^2$

or $x^2 + y^2 - 4x + 6y + 9 = 0$

(c) Refer figure **Q. 50 (a)**, above. $\angle PTC = \alpha/2$ where T is (h, k) and where

$$\tan \frac{\alpha}{2} = \frac{CP}{PT} = \frac{a}{\sqrt{(h^2 + k^2 - a^2)}} \qquad ...(1)$$

$$\tan \alpha = \frac{2 \tan (\alpha/2)}{1 - \tan^2 (\alpha/2)} = \frac{2a\sqrt{(h^2 + k^2 - a^2)}}{h^2 + k^2 - a^2 - a^2}$$

Squaring both sides, we get

$(h^2 + k^2 - 2a^2)^2 \tan^2 \alpha = 4a^2 (h^2 + k^2 - a^2).$

Hence the required locus of the point is

$$(x^2 + y^2 - 2a^2)^2 \tan^2 \alpha = 4a^2 (x^2 + y^2 - a^2)$$

Particular case : If the tangents be at right angles then $\alpha = 90° \therefore \alpha/2 = 45°$

Hence from (1) we get $\sqrt{(h^2 + k^2 - a^2)} = a$

or $h^2 + k^2 = 2a^2$

$\therefore \quad$ Required locus is $x^2 + y^2 = 2a^2$.

51. (a) Let P be (x_1, y_1) so that QR is chord of contact whose equation is $xx_1 + yy_1 - a^2 = 0$. The circle PQR thus passes through the intersection of given circle and chord QR and hence by $S - \lambda P = 0$ its equation is

$$(x^2 + y^2 - a^2) - \lambda (xx_1 + yy_1 - a^2) = 0 \quad ...(1)$$

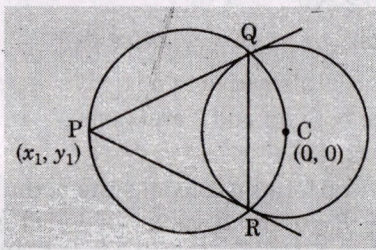

Fig. 130

As it passes through $P(x_1, y_1)$

$\therefore \quad (x_1^2 + y_1^2 - a^2)$

$\quad - \lambda (x_1^2 + y_1^2 - a^2) = 0. \quad \therefore \quad \lambda = 1$

Putting the value of λ in (1) the required circle is $x^2 + y^2 - xx_1 - yy_1 = 0$ which clearly passes through the centre $(0, 0)$ of the given circle.

Another form : The equation of the circle can also be written as

$$(x - 0)(x - x_1) + (y - 0)(y - y_1) = 0$$

i.e., it is on CP as diameter.

(b) $\tan \theta = \dfrac{r_1}{t_1} = \dfrac{r_2}{t_2} \quad \therefore \quad t_2^2 \cdot r_1^2 = t_1^2 \cdot r_2^2$

or $S_2' r_1^2 = S_1' r_2^2 = 0$. Generalising the required locus is $r_2^2 S_1 - r_1^2 S_2 = 0$.

(c) Circumcircle of $\triangle OPQ$ is $S + \lambda P = 0$ where P is chord of contact of $O(0, 0)$.

$$(x^2 + y^2 + 2gx + 2fy + c) + \lambda (gx + fy + c) = 0$$

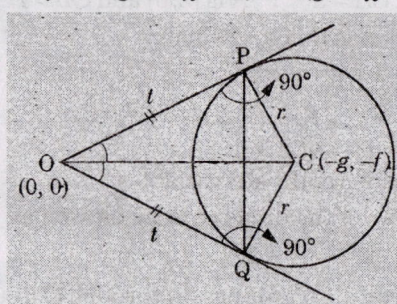

Fig. 131

It passes through $O(0,0)$

$\therefore \quad c + \lambda c = 0 \quad$ or $\quad \lambda = -1$

$\therefore \quad x^2 + y^2 + gx + fy = 0$ is the circumcircle of $\triangle OPQ$

whose centre is $(-g/2, -f/2)$.

Area of Quadrilateral $= 2\triangle OCP = 2 \cdot \dfrac{1}{2} \cdot r \cdot t$

$= \sqrt{(g^2 + f^2 - c)} \sqrt{c} = \sqrt{c(g^2 + f^2 - c)}$

$\because \quad t = \sqrt{S'} = \sqrt{c}$ where t is length of tangent drawn from $(0, 0)$.

(d) Circle TPQ is $S + \lambda P = 0$ where P is chord of contact of $T(h, k)$.

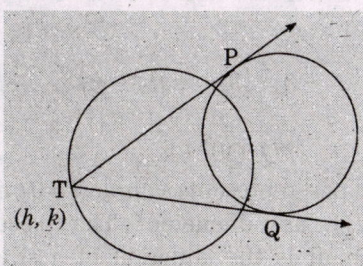

Fig. 132

Circumcircle is $(x^2 + y^2 - a^2) + \lambda (hx + ky - a^2)$

It passes through $T(h, k)$

$\therefore \quad (h^2 + k^2 - a^2) + \lambda (h^2 + k^2 - a^2) = 0$

or $\quad \lambda = -1$

Circle is $x^2 + y^2 - hx - ky = 0$

Its centre $x = \dfrac{h}{2}$, $y = \dfrac{k}{2}$. But (h, k) lies on

$px + qy + r = 0$, $\therefore \quad ph + qk + r = 0$.

Eliminating h, k we get the locus as

$\qquad p \cdot 2x + q \cdot 2y + r = 0$.

52. (a) The equation of the conic through the four points of intersection of $S_1 = 0$ and $S_2 = 0$ is given by $S_1 - \lambda S_2 = 0$.

If it be a circle, then

coeff. of x^2 = coeff. of y^2 $\therefore \quad a - \lambda a' = b - \lambda b'$

or $\quad a - b = \lambda (a' - b')$ ...(1)

Coeff. of $xy = 0$ $\therefore \quad 2h - \lambda \cdot 2h' = 0$.

$\qquad h = \lambda h'$. ...(2)

Eliminating λ, we get $\dfrac{a - b}{h} = \dfrac{a' - b'}{h'}$.

(b) Apply the condition that $S - \lambda xy = 0$ represents a circle where $xy = 0$ represents the equation of axes. $\therefore \quad \lambda = -5$.

Ans. $2x^2 + 2y^2 + 7x - 5y + 3 = 0$, centre $(-7/4, 5/4)$.

Note : See. Q. 31 (b) P. 857.

53. (a) For the sake of convenience let the line of centres be chosen as axis of x and distance between them be $2a$ and mid-point of the centres be chosen as

origin so that the centres are $(a, 0)$, radius r for S and $(-a, 0)$, radius R for S'.

$\therefore \quad S = (x - a)^2 + y^2 = r^2$

or $\quad x^2 + y^2 - 2ax + a^2 - r^2 = 0$

$\qquad S' = (x + a)^2 + y^2 = R^2$

or $\quad x^2 + y^2 + 2ax + a^2 - R^2 = 0$.

The two circles are

$\dfrac{S}{r} \pm \dfrac{S'}{R} = 0 \quad$ or $\quad RS \pm rS' = 0$

Circle $RS + rS' = 0$ becomes

$(R + r)(x^2 + y^2 + a^2) - 2ax(R - r) - rR(r + R) = 0$

or $\quad x^2 + y^2 - 2a\dfrac{R - r}{R + r}x + (a^2 - rR) = 0$. ...(1)

Replacing r by $-r$ the circle $RS - rS' = 0$ becomes

$\qquad x^2 + y^2 - 2a\dfrac{R + r}{R - r}x + (a^2 + rR) = 0$. ...(2)

The circles (1) and (2) will cut orthogonally if

$\qquad 2g_1 g_2 + 2f_1 f_2 = c_1 + c_2$

i.e. $2\left\{-a\dfrac{R - r}{R + r}\right\}\left\{-a\dfrac{R + r}{R - r}\right\} + 0$

$\qquad\qquad = (a^2 - rR) + (a^2 + rR)$

or $\quad 2a^2 = 2a^2$ which is true.

Hence the circles $\dfrac{S}{r} \pm \dfrac{S'}{R}$ cut each other orthogonally.

(b) Let the circle be $x^2 + y^2 + 2gx + 2fy + c = 0$.

Since it cuts $x^2 + y^2 - k^2 = 0$ orthogonally therefore

$\qquad 2g(0) + 2f(0) = c - k^2 = 0 \therefore c = k^2$

Again the circle C_2 passes through (a, b)

$\therefore \quad a^2 + b^2 + 2ga + 2fb + k^2 = 0 \because c = k^2$

$\therefore \quad$ Locus of centre $(-g, -f)$ is

$\qquad a^2 + b^2 + 2a(-x) + 2b(-y) + k^2 = 0$

or $\quad 2ax + 2by - (a^2 + b^2 + k^2) = 0$

54. (a) Let the circle through origin be

$\qquad x^2 + y^2 + 2gx + 2fy = 0$

Condition of orthogonality gives

$\qquad 2gg_1 + 2ff_1 = 0 + c_1$ ...(1)

$\qquad 2gg_2 + 2ff_2 = 0 + c_2$ ...(2)

The given circle can be written as

$\qquad 2gx + 2fy = -(x^2 + y^2)$ ...(3)

Eliminating the unknown quantities g and f from (1), (2) and (3), we get the result in determinant form.

(b) Let the circle be $x^2 + y^2 + 2gx + 2fy + c = 0$ ...(1)

where g, f, c are unknown. Apply the condition of orthogonality with given three circles

$$2gg_1 + 2ff_1 - (c + c_1) = 0$$

or $-c_1 + 2gg_1 + 2ff_1 - c = 0$ ...(2)

$$-c_2 + 2gg_2 + 2ff_2 - c = 0 \quad ...(3)$$
$$-c_3 + 2gg_3 + 2ff_3 - c = 0 \quad ...(4)$$

Eliminate the unknown g, f, c between the above four relations and you get the equation of circle as given.

(c) P, Q, R, S are centres of circles
$$x^2 + y^2 + 2g_r x + 2f_r y + c_r = 0,$$
where $r = 1, 2, 3, 4$ ∴ P is $(-g_1, -f_1)$

Now choose any fixed point in the plane of the circles as $(0, 0)$, then $t^2 = S'$
$$\therefore \quad t_1^2 = c_1, t_2^2 = c_2, t_3^2 = c_3, t_4^2 = c_4$$

Let the circle which cuts each of them orthogonally be
$$x^2 + y^2 + 2gx + 2fy + c = 0$$
$$\therefore \quad 2gg_1 + 2ff_1 = c + c_1 = c + t_1^2$$

or $2gg_1 + 2ff_1 - c - t_1^2 = 0$ ...(1)

There will be four such relations as (1) and we have to eliminate the three unknowns g, f and c between these four.

$$\therefore \quad \begin{vmatrix} 2g_1 & 2f_1 & -1 & -t_1^2 \\ 2g_2 & 2f_2 & -1 & -t_2^2 \\ 2g_3 & 2f_3 & -1 & -t_3^2 \\ 2g_4 & 2f_4 & -1 & -t_4^2 \end{vmatrix} = 0$$

$$\begin{vmatrix} t_1^2 & g_1 & f_1 & 1 \\ t_2^2 & g_2 & f_2 & 1 \\ t_3^2 & g_3 & f_3 & 1 \\ t_4^2 & g_4 & f_4 & 1 \end{vmatrix} = 0$$

$$t_1^2 |D_1| - t_2^2 |D_2| + t_3^2 |D_3| - t_4^2 |D_4| = 0 \quad ...(2)$$

The first determinant D_1 is
$$\begin{vmatrix} g_2 & f_2 & 1 \\ g_3 & f_3 & 1 \\ g_4 & f_4 & 1 \end{vmatrix} = 2\Delta\, QRS$$

$$\therefore \quad \Delta\, QRS = \frac{1}{2} \begin{vmatrix} -g_2 & -f_2 & 1 \\ -g_3 & -f_3 & 1 \\ -g_4 & -f_4 & 1 \end{vmatrix} = \frac{1}{2} \begin{vmatrix} g_2 & f_2 & 1 \\ g_3 & f_3 & 1 \\ g_4 & f_4 & 1 \end{vmatrix}$$

Hence from (2) we prove the required result.

55. (a) By special choice of axes the equation of coaxial system of circles can be put in the form
$$x^2 + y^2 + 2g_r x + c = 0 \text{ where } r = 1, 2, 3.$$
The co-ordinates of the centres of the three circles are
$$P(-g_1, 0), \quad Q(-g_2, 0), \quad R(-g_3, 0)$$
$$\therefore \quad QR = (-g_3) - (-g_2) = g_2 - g_3$$
$$RP = g_3 - g_1 \text{ and } PQ = g_1 - g_2.$$

If the fixed point from where the tangents be drawn be (h, k), then
$$t_1^2 = h^2 + k^2 + 2g_1 h + c \text{ etc.}$$
$$\therefore \quad QRt_1^2 + RPt_2^2 + PQt_3^2$$
$$= (g_2 - g_3)\{h^2 + k^2 + c + 2g_1 h\} + \cdots + \cdots = 0$$
or $(h^2 + k^2 + c)\Sigma(g_2 - g_3)$
$$+ 2h\,\Sigma g_2(g_1 - g_3) = 0$$
$$\therefore \quad \Sigma(g_2 - g_3) = 0 \text{ and } \Sigma g_1(g_2 - g_3) = 0.$$

(b) From part (a), $r_1^2 = (g_1)^2 - c$ etc.
$$\therefore \quad r_1^2 \cdot QR + r_2^2 \cdot RP + r_3^2 \cdot PQ$$
$$= (g_1^2 - c)(g_2 - g_3) + (g_2^2 - c)(g_3 - g_1)$$
$$+ (g_3^2 - c)(g_1 - g_2)$$
$$= \Sigma g_1^2(g_2 - g_3) - c\,\Sigma(g_2 - g_3)$$
$$= -(g_1 - g_2)(g_2 - g_3)(g_3 - g_1) - c \cdot 0$$
$$= -PQ \cdot QR \cdot RP.$$

56. The first part represents a circle $S = 0$ on $P(x_1, y_1)$ and $Q(x_2, y_2)$ as diameter. The second part i.e. determinant is the equation of a straight line $u = 0$ which passes through the points P and Q. The given equation is now of the form $S + \lambda u = 0$ which represents a circle passing through the intersection of $S = 0$ and $u = 0$ i.e. the points P and Q. In case PQ is a diameter then the centre $\left(\dfrac{x_1 + x_2}{2}, \dfrac{y_1 + y_2}{2}\right)$ will lie on the line PQ and hence the determinant becomes

$$\begin{vmatrix} \dfrac{x_1 + x_2}{2} & \dfrac{y_1 + y_2}{2} & 1 \\ x_1 & y_1 & 1 \\ x_2 & y_2 & 1 \end{vmatrix} \text{ becomes zero,}$$

because $\dfrac{1}{2}(R_2 + R_3)$ becomes identical with R_1. The equation $S + \lambda u = 0$ in this case reduces to $S = 0$ which therefore represents the circle described on PQ as diameter.

57. (a) Any chord of the circle be $lx + my = 1$ ...(1)

It subtends a right angle at the origin. In other words the lines joining origin to the points of intersection of chord and circle are at right angles. Making the equation of circle homogeneous by the help of line (1) and applying the condition $a + b = 0$ of perpendicularity, we get
$$c(l^2 + m^2) + 2(gl + fm) + 2 = 0 \quad ...(2)$$

Any line through origin ⊥ to (1) is
$$mx - ly = 0 \quad ...(3)$$

Both (1) and (3) give the foot of perpendicular whose locus is obtained by eliminating the variables l, m between (1), (2) and (3). Solving (1) and (3) for l and m we have $m = \dfrac{ly}{x}$.

Putting in (1), we get

$$lx + \frac{ly}{x} y = 1$$

$$\therefore \quad l = \frac{x}{x^2 + y^2}, m = \frac{y}{x^2 + y^2}$$

Putting the values of l and m from above in (2), we get the required locus.

$$c \cdot \frac{1}{(x^2 + y^2)} + 2 \frac{(gx + fy)}{(x^2 + y^2)} + 2 = 0$$

or $\quad x^2 + y^2 + gx + fy + \frac{1}{2}c = 0$.

(b) The circle OAB is $x^2 + y^2 - ax - by = 0$

where $\quad \frac{a^2}{4} + \frac{b^2}{4} = r^2$ ...(1)

Equation of AB is $\frac{x}{a} + \frac{y}{b} = 1$ ...(2)

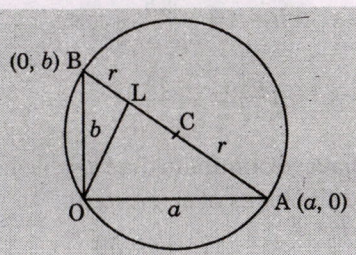

Fig. 133

Any line through $(0, 0)$, perpendicular to it

$$\frac{x}{b} - \frac{y}{a} = 0$$ ...(3)

Both (2) and (3) give the foot of perpendicular. We have to eliminate the variables a and b from the three relations (1), (2) and (3).

Solving (2) and (3) for a and b, we have $b = \frac{ax}{y}$.

Putting in (1), we get

$$\frac{x}{a} + \frac{y \cdot y}{ax} = 1 \quad \therefore \quad x^2 + y^2 = ax$$

$$\therefore \quad a = \frac{x^2 + y^2}{x} \quad \therefore \quad b = \frac{x^2 + y^2}{y}.$$

Putting in (1), we get

$$(x^2 + y^2)^2 \left[\frac{1}{x^2} + \frac{1}{y^2} \right] = 4r^2 \text{ is the required locus.}$$

58. $OPCL$ is a rectangle in which $OP = 4\sqrt{2} = CL$. Also $RQ = 6\sqrt{2}$. Hence

$$r^2 = (4\sqrt{2})^2 + (3\sqrt{2})^2 = 50$$

If the centre be (h, k), then the circle is

$$(x - h)^2 + (y - k)^2 = 50$$ ...(1)

$y - x = 0$ is a tangent $\quad \therefore \quad p = r$

or $\quad \frac{k - h}{\pm\sqrt{2}} = 5\sqrt{2} \quad \therefore \quad k - h = \pm 10$ ...(2)

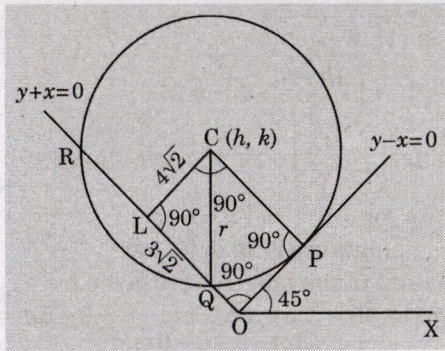

Fig. 134

The distance of $C(h, k)$ from $y + x = 0$ is $4\sqrt{2}$.

$$\therefore \quad \frac{k + h}{\pm\sqrt{2}} = 4\sqrt{2} \quad \therefore \quad k + h = \pm 8$$ ...(3)

Eq. (2) and (3) will make four sets of equations which when solved will give the centres as $(9, -1), (1, -9), (-1, 9), (-9, 1)$.

Hence the equations of all the possible circles are

$$(x - 9)^2 + (y + 1)^2 - 50 = 0$$ ...(1)

$$(x - 1)^2 + (y + 9)^2 - 50 = 0$$ ...(2)

$$(x + 1)^2 + (y - 9)^2 - 50 = 0$$ ...(3)

and $(x + 9)^2 + (y - 1)^2 - 50 = 0$ ...(4)

Since the point $(-10, 2)$ lies inside the circle, its co-ordinates must make the left hand side of the required circle negative. This condition is satisfied by (4) only. Hence the equation of the required circle is $x^2 + y^2 + 18x - 2y + 32 = 0$.

59. $2\alpha = \tan^{-1} \frac{24}{7} \quad \therefore \quad \frac{2t}{1 - t^2} = \frac{24}{7}$

or $\quad 24t^2 + 14t - 24 = 0$

or $\quad (8t - 6)(3t + 4) = 0$

$$\therefore \quad t = \tan \alpha = \frac{6}{8} = \frac{3}{4} = \frac{3}{PQ}$$

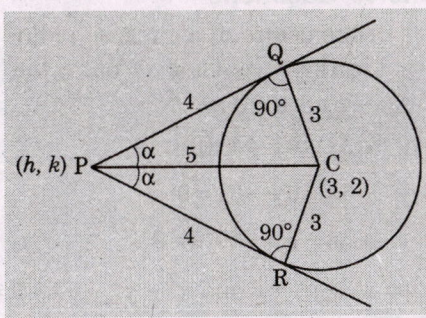

Fig. 135

$$\therefore \quad PQ = 4, \ CQ = 3 \quad \therefore \quad PC = 5.$$

If the co-ordinates of P be (h, k), then

$$(h - 3)^2 + (k - 2)^2 = 25$$ ...(1)

The point (h, k) lies on $4x - 3y = 6$

$$\therefore \quad 4h - 3k = 6 \quad \therefore \quad \frac{4h - 6}{3} = k$$ ...(2)

Putting in (1), we get

$$(h-3)^2 + \left(\frac{4h-6}{3} - 2\right)^2 = 25$$

or $(h-3)^2\left[1 + \frac{16}{9}\right] = 25$ ∴ $(h-3) = \pm 3$

∴ $h = 6$ or 0 ∴ $k = 6$ or -2

Hence the points are $(6, 6)$ or $(0, -2)$.

The equation of the tangents are given by

$y - 6 = m(x - 6)$ or $mx - y + 6 - 6m = 0$

Apply $p = r$ we get $\dfrac{3m - 2 + 6 - 6m}{\sqrt{(m^2 + 1)}} = 3$

∴ $(4 - 3m)^2 = 9(m^2 + 1)$

or $0 \cdot m^2 + 24m - 7 = 0$

∴ $m = \infty$ or $\dfrac{7}{24}$ ∴ $x - 6 = 0$

or $7x - 24y + 102 = 0$

Similarly, we can find the tangents passing through $(0, -2)$ as $\dfrac{y+2}{x} = \infty$ or $\dfrac{7}{24}$ i.e. $x = 0$ or $7x - 24y - 48 = 0$

Note : The tangents from a point can also be obtained by using $SS_1 = T^2$.

60. P lies on $y = 4$ and hence its co-ordinates be taken as $(h, 4)$, then AB is the chord of contact with respect to circle $x^2 + y^2 = 4$ whose equation is

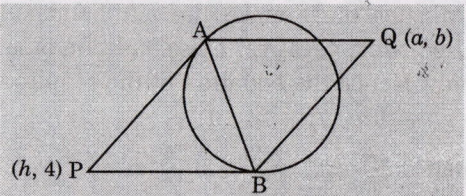

Fig. 136

$$hx + 4y = 4 \qquad \text{...(1)}$$

Solving with circle, we get

$$x^2 + \left(\frac{4 - hx}{4}\right)^2 = 4$$

or $x^2(16 + h^2) - 8hx - 48 = 0$

Above gives abscissas of the points A and B.

∴ $x_1 + x_2 = \dfrac{8h}{16 + h^2}$.

Also the points A and B lie on (1)

∴ $4(y_1 + y_2) = 8 - \dfrac{h \cdot 8h}{16 + h^2}$

∴ $y_1 + y_2 = \dfrac{32}{16 + h^2}$

Now if the point Q be (α, β), then the figure $PAQB$ being a parallelogram its diagonals bisect

∴ $x_1 + x_2 = h + \alpha = \dfrac{8h}{16 + h^2}$ ...(2)

$y_1 + y_2 = 4 + \beta = \dfrac{32}{16 + h^2}$ ...(3)

Now we have to eliminate the variable between (2) and (3) to find the locus of Q, i.e. (α, β).

Dividing $\dfrac{h + \alpha}{4 + \beta} = \dfrac{h}{4}$ ∴ $4\alpha = h\beta$

or $h = \dfrac{4\alpha}{\beta}$. Put in (3) and we get

$$(4 + \beta)\left(16 + \frac{16\alpha^2}{\beta^2}\right) = 32$$

∴ Locus is $(y + 4)(x^2 + y^2) = 2y^2$

Problem Set (3)

▶ Multiple Choice Questions

1.* The locus of the centre of a circle of radius 2 which rolls on the outside of the circle $x^2 + y^2 + 3x - 6y - 9 = 0$ is

(a) $x^2 + y^2 + 3x - 6y + 5 = 0$

(b) $x^2 + y^2 + 3x - 6y - 31 = 0$

(c) $x^2 + y^2 + 3x - 6y + 29/4 = 0$

2. Two circles $x^2 + y^2 = 6$ and $x^2 + y^2 - 6x + 8 = 0$ are given. Then the equation of the circle through their point of intersection and the point $(1, 1)$ is

(a) $x^2 + y^2 - 6x + 4 = 0$ (b) $x^2 + y^2 - 3x + 1 = 0$

(c) $x^2 + y^2 - 4y + 2 = 0$ (d) None of these

3. The area of circle centred at $(1, 2)$ and passing through $(4, 6)$ is

(a) 5π (b) 10π

(c) 25π (d) None of these

4. Given the circles $x^2 + y^2 - 4x - 5 = 0$

and $x^2 + y^2 + 6x - 2y + 6 = 0$

Let P be a point (α, β) such that the tangents from P to both the circles are equal. Then

(a) $2\alpha + 10\beta + 11 = 0$ (b) $2\alpha - 10\beta + 11 = 0$

(c) $10\alpha - 2\beta + 11 = 0$ (d) $10\alpha + 2\beta + 11 = 0$.

5. The length of tangent from $(5, 1)$ to the circle $x^2 + y^2 + 6x - 4y - 3 = 0$ is

(a) 81 (b) 29 (c) 7 (d) 21

6. If the equation $ax^2 + by^2 + 2hxy + 2gx + 2fy + c = 0$ represents a circle, the condition will be

(a) $a = b$ and $c = 0$ (b) $f = g$ and $h = 0$

(c) $a = b$ and $h = 0$ (d) $f = g$ and $c = 0$

7. (i)* Given the equation of two circles $x^2 + y^2 = r^2$ and $x^2 + y^2 - 10x + 16 = 0$, the value of r such that they intersect in real and distinct points is given by

(a) $2 < r < 8$ (b) $r = 2$ or $r = 8$

(c) $r < 2$ or $r > 8$ (d) None of the above

(ii)* The two circles $x^2 + y^2 - 2x - 3 = 0$ and

$x^2 + y^2 - 4x - 6y - 8 = 0$ are such that

(a) they touch each other

(b) they intersect each other

(c) one lies inside the other

(d) each lies outside the other   **(M.N.R. 1995)**

8. The equation of the circle passing through the origin is $x^2 + y^2 - 6x + 2y = 0$. The equation of one of its diameters is

(a) $x + 3y = 0$ (b) $x + y = 0$

(c) $x = y$ (d) $3x + y = 0$

9. The circle $x^2 + y^2 + 4x - 7y + 12 = 0$ cuts an intercept on y-axis equal to

(a) 1   (b) 3   (c) 4   (d) 7

10. AB is a diameter of a circle and C is any point on the circumference of the circle. Then

(a) the area of $\triangle ABC$ is maximum when it is isosceles.

(b) the area of $\triangle ABC$ is minimum when it is isosceles.

(c) the perimeter of $\triangle ABC$ is maximum when it is isosceles.

(d) none of these

11. The centre of a circle passing through the point $(0, 1)$ and touching the curve $y = x^2$ at $(2, 4)$ is

(a) $\left(\dfrac{-16}{5}, \dfrac{27}{10}\right)$ (b) $\left(\dfrac{-16}{7}, \dfrac{5}{10}\right)$

(c) $\left(\dfrac{-16}{5}, \dfrac{53}{10}\right)$ (d) None of these

12. The locus of the mid-points of a chord of the circle $x^2 + y^2 = 4$ which subtends a right angle at the origin is

(a) $x + y = 2$ (b) $x^2 + y^2 = 1$

(c) $x^2 + y^2 = 2$ (d) $x + y = 1$

13. The pole of the straight line $9x + y - 28 = 0$ with respect to the circle $2x^2 + 2y^2 - 3x + 5y - 7 = 0$ is

(a) $(3, 1)$ (b) $(1, 3)$

(c) $(3, -1)$ (d) $(-3, 1)$

14. The equation of the circle passing through $(4, 5)$ having the centre at $(2, 2)$ is

(a) $x^2 + y^2 + 4x + 4y - 5 = 0$

(b) $x^2 + y^2 - 4x - 4y - 5 = 0$

(c) $x^2 + y^2 - 4x = 13$

(d) $x^2 + y^2 - 4x - 4y + 5 = 0$

15. (i)* The equation of tangents drawn from the origin to the circle $x^2 + y^2 - 2rx - 2hy + h^2 = 0$ are

(a) $x = 0$

(b) $y = 0$

(c) $(h^2 - r^2)x - 2rhy = 0$

(d) $(h^2 - r^2)x + 2rhy = 0$

(ii) The angle between two tangents from the origin to the circle $(x - 7)^2 + (y + 1)^2 = 25$ is

(a) $\pi/3$ (b) $\pi/6$

(c) $\pi/2$ (d) 0 **(M.N.R. 1990)**

16. (i) If the two circles $(x - 1)^2 + (y - 3)^2 = r^2$ and $x^2 + y^2 - 8x + 2y + 8 = 0$ intersect in two distinct points, then

(a) $2 < r < 8$ (b) $r = 2$,

(c) $r < 2$ (d) $r > 2$

(ii) The number of common tangents to the circles $x^2 + y^2 + 2x + 8y - 23 = 0$ and $x^2 + y^2 - 4x - 10y + 19 = 0$ are

(a) 1   (b) 2

(c) 3   (d) 4

17. If $(x, 3)$ and $(3, 5)$ are extremities of a diameter of a circle with centre at $(2, y)$, then the value of (x, y) is

(a) $(1, 4)$ (b) $(4, 1)$ (c) $(8, 2)$ (d) none

18. The lines $2x - 3y = 5$ and $3x - 4y = 7$ are the diameters of a circle of area 154 square units. The equation of the circle is

(a) $x^2 + y^2 + 2x - 2y = 62$ (b) $x^2 + y^2 - 2x + 2y = 47$

(c) $x^2 + y^2 + 2x - 2y = 47$ (d) $x^2 + y^2 - 2x + 2y = 62$

                  (AIEEE 2003, 06; IIT 1989)

19. The point diametrically opposite to the point $P(1, 0)$ on the circle $x^2 + y^2 + 2x + 4y - 3 = 0$

(a) $(-3, 4)$ (b) $(-3, -4)$ (c) $(3, 4)$ (d) $(3, -4)$

                  (AIEEE 2008)

20. The centre of circle inscribed in a square formed by the lines $x^2 - 8x + 12 = 0$ and $y^2 - 14y + 45 = 0$ is

(a) $(4, 7)$ (b) $(7, 4)$ (c) $(9, 4)$ (d) $(4, 9)$

                  (IIT Screening 2003)

21. If the lines $2x + 3y + 1 = 0$ and $3x - y - 4 = 0$ lie along diameters of a circle of circumference 10π, then the equation of the circle is

(a) $x^2 + y^2 + 2x - 2y - 23 = 0$

(b) $x^2 + y^2 - 2x - 2y - 23 = 0$

(c) $x^2 + y^2 + 2x + 2y - 23 = 0$

(d) $x^2 + y^2 - 2x + 2y - 23 = 0$ **(AIEEE 2004)**

22. Tangents drawn from the point $P(1, 8)$ to the circle $x^2 + y^2 - 6x - 4y - 11 = 0$ touch the circle at the points A and B. The equation of the circucircle of the triangle PAB is

(a) $x^2 + y^2 + 4x - 6y + 19 = 0$

(b) $x^2 + y^2 - 4x - 10y + 19 = 0$

(c) $x^2 + y^2 - 2x + 6y - 29 = 0$

(d) $x^2 + y^2 - 6x - 4y + 19 = 0$

23. The radius of the circle, having centre at (2, 1) whose one of the chord is a diameter of the circle $x^2 + y^2 - 2x - 6y + 6 = 0$ is

(a) 1   (b) 2   (c) 3   (d) $\sqrt{3}$

(IIT Screening 2004)

24. The intercept on the line $y = x$ by the circle $x^2 + y^2 - 2x = 0$ is AB equation of the circle on AB as a diameter is

(a) $x^2 + y^2 - x + y = 0$ (b) $x^2 + y^2 - x + y = 0$

(c) $x^2 + y^2 + x + y = 0$ (d) $x^2 + y^2 - x - y = 0$

(AIEEE 2004, IIT 1996)

25. The locus of centre of circle passing through (a, b) and cuts orthogonally to circle $x^2 + y^2 = p^2$ is

(a) $2ax + 2by - (a^2 + b^2 + p^2) = 0$

(b) $2ax + 2by - (a^2 - b^2 + p^2) = 0$

(c) $x^2 + y^2 - 3ax - 4by + (a^2 + b^2 - p^2) = 0$

(d) $x^2 + y^2 - 2ax + 3by + (a^2 - b^2 + p^2) = 0$

(IIT 1988; AIEEE 2005)

26. The tangent to the curve $y = e^x$ drawn at the point (c, e^c) intersects the line joining the points $(c - 1, e^{c-1})$ and $(c + 1, e^{c+1})$

(a) on the left of $x = c$ (b) on the right of $x = c$

(c) at no point   (d) at all points

(IIT-JEE 2007)

27. If a circle passes through the point (a, b) and cuts the circle $x^2 + y^2 = 4$ orthogonally, then locus of its centre is

(a) $2ax - 2by - (a^2 + b^2 + 4) = 0$

(b) $2ax + 2by - (a^2 + b^2 + 4) = 0$

(c) $2ax - 2by + (a^2 + b^2 + 4) = 0$

(d) $2ax + 2by + (a^2 + b^2 + 4) = 0$

(AIEEE 2004)

28. The locus of centre of the circle which touches the circle $x^2 + (y - 1)^2 = 1$ externally and also touches x-axis is

(a) $\{(x, y) : x^2 + (y - 1)^2 = 4\} \cup \{(x, y) : y > 0\}$

(b) $\{(x, y) : x^2 = 4y\} \cup \{(0, y) : (y < 0)\}$

(c) $\{(x, y) : x^2 = y\} \cup \{(0, y) : y < 0)\}$

(d) $\{(x, y) : x^2 = 4y\} \cup \{(x, y) : y < 0\}$

(IIT-sc. 2005)

Integer Type Questions

29. Two parallel chords of a circle of radius 2 are at a distance $\sqrt{3} + 1$ apart. If the chords subtend at the centre angle of $\dfrac{\pi}{k}$ and $\dfrac{2\pi}{k}$ where $k > 0$. Then the value of $[k]$ is

(IIT JEE 2010)

30. The straight line $2x - 3y = 1$ divides the circular region $x^2 + y^2 \leq 6$ into two parts

It $S = \left[\left(2, \dfrac{3}{3}\right), \left(\dfrac{5}{2}, \dfrac{3}{4}\right), \left(\dfrac{1}{4}, \dfrac{1}{4}\right), \left(\dfrac{1}{8}, \dfrac{1}{4}\right) \right]$

Then the number of points lying inside the smaller part is

(IIT JEE 2011)

True and False Type Questions

State whether the following statements are true or false.

31. The point $(1, 2)$ lies inside the circle

$x^2 + y^2 - 2x + 6y + 1 = 0$

32. The line $3x + 5y + 9 = 0$ is a diameter of the circle $x^2 + y^2 - 4x + 6y + 5 = 0$.

33. The equation $x^2 + y^2 + 2x - 10y + 30 = 0$ represents the equation of a circle.

34.* Two distinct tangents can be drawn from the point $(8, 6)$ to the circle $x^2 + y^2 - 100 = 0$.

Fill in the blanks

35. The length of the tangent from the point $(1, 2)$ to the circle $2x^2 + 2y^2 + 6x - 8y + 3 = 0$ is ....

36. (i) The equation of the circle through $M(5, 4)$ and touching the x-axis at $L(2, 0)$ is ....

(ii) Circles are drawn through the point $(2, 0)$ to cut intercept of length 5 units on the x-axis. If their centres lie in the first quadrant, then their equation is ....

37. The equation of the circle of radius 5 in the first quadrant which touches the x-axis and the line $4y = 3x$ is ....

38. The equation of the circle through the origin and cutting intercepts of lengths 2 and 3 from the positive sides of x and y axes is ....

39.* A and B are points in the plane such that $PA / PB = k$ (constant) for all points P on a circle, then the value of k cannot be equal to ....

40.* The equation $x^2 + y^2 + 2gx + c = 0$, where g is a parameter and c is a constant represents a co-axial family of circles any two members of which have the radical axis ....

41.* The centre of the circle passing through the points $(0, 0), (1, 0)$ and touching the circle $x^2 + y^2 = 9$ is

(a) $(3/2, 1/2)$ (b) $(1/2, 3/2)$

(c) $(1/2, 1/2)$ (d) $(1/2, -2^{1/2})$

(I.I.T. 1992)

42. Three distinct points A, B and C are given in the 2-dimensional coordinate plane such that the ratio of the distance of any one of them from the point $(1, 0)$ to the distance from the point $(-1, 0)$ is equal to $\dfrac{1}{3}$. Then the circumcentre of the triangle ABC is at the point

(a) $\left(\dfrac{5}{3},0\right)$ (b) $(0,0)$

(c) $\left(\dfrac{5}{4},0\right)$ (d) $\left(\dfrac{5}{2},0\right)$

(AIEEE 2009)

Solutions to Problem Set (3)

1. **Ans. (b).** Let (h,k) be the centre of the circle which rolls on the outside of the given circle. The centre of the given circle is

$\left(-\dfrac{3}{2},3\right)$ and its radius $=\sqrt{\left[\dfrac{9}{4}+9+9\right]}=\dfrac{9}{2}$.

Clearly (h,k) is always at a distance equal to the sum $\left(\dfrac{9}{2}+2\right)=\dfrac{13}{2}$ of the radii of two circles.

∴ $\left(h+\dfrac{3}{2}\right)^2+(k-3)^2=\left(\dfrac{13}{2}\right)^2$

∴ $h^2+k^2+3h-6k+\dfrac{9}{4}+9-\dfrac{169}{4}=0$

∴ Locus of (h,k) is

$x^2+y^2+3x-6y-31=0$.

2. **Ans. (b).** See Q. 55 (a) P. 860-884.
3. **Ans. (c).**
4. **Ans. (c).**
5. **Ans. (c).**
6. **Ans. (c).**
7. (i) Ans. (a).
   (ii) Ans. (b)
   See Q. 47 (a, b) P. 865-881.
8. **Ans. (a).**
   The line which passes through centre $(3,-1)$.
9. **Ans. (a).**

$2\sqrt{f^2-c}=\sqrt{4f^2-4c}=\sqrt{\left(4\times\dfrac{49}{4}-4\times12\right)}=1$.

10. **Ans. (a).**
11. **Ans. (c).** See Q. 12 (b) P. 865-881.
12. **Ans. (c).**
13. **Ans. (c).**
14. **Ans. (b).** Clearly (b) or (d) have centre $(2,2)$ but only (b) is satisfied by the points $(4,5)$ and hence it is correct.
15. (i) Ans. (a) and (c). **See Q. 4 (c) P. 895-904.**
    (ii) Ans. (c). **See Q. 5 (a) P. 895-904.**
16. (i) Ans. (a). **See Q. 47 (b) P. 860-881.**
    (ii) Ans. (c). **See Q. 17 (b) P. 896-910.**
17. **Ans. (a).**
    The mid-point of diameter is centre.
18. **Ans. (b).**
    Centre of circle = Point of intersection of diameters $=(1,-1)$
    Area $=154\Rightarrow\pi r^2=154\Rightarrow r=7$
    ∴ required equation of the circle is

$(x-1)^2+(y+1)^2=7^2\Rightarrow x^2+y^2-2x+2y=47$

19. **Ans. (b).** Point $(1,0)$ lie on the circle $x^2+y^2+2x+4y-3=0$

centre $(-1,-2)$

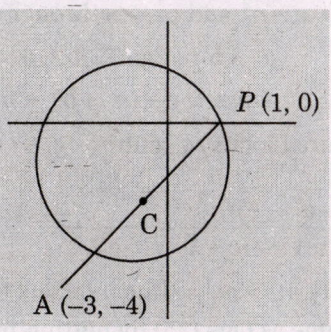

Fig. 137

C is the mid point of AP

∴ required point must be $(-3,-4)$

20. **Ans. (a).** Centre is $(4,7)$

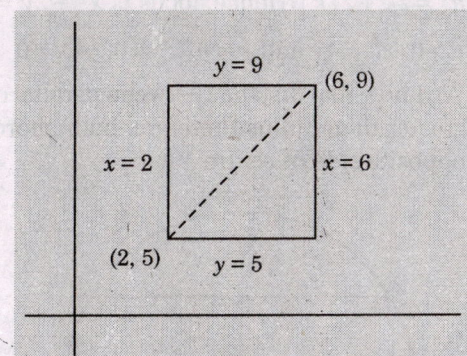

Fig. 138

21. **Ans. (d).** Solving both the given equation, we get $x=1$, $y=-1$

∴ centre of the circle is $(1,-1)$

∴ $2\pi r=10\pi\Rightarrow r=5$

∴ required circle is $(x-1)^2+(y+1)^2=5^2$

⇒ $x^2+y^2-2x+2y-23=0$

22. **Ans. (b).** $(x-1)(x-3)+(y-8)(y-2)=0$

(∵ For required circle $P(1,8)$ and $O(3,2)$ will be the end points)

⇒ $x^2+y^2-4x-10y+19=0$

23. **Ans. (c).** The centre of the given circle is $(1,3)$ and radius is 2, therefore AB is a diameter of the given circle and its mid points is $(1,3)$. The radius of the required circle is 3.

24. **Ans. (d).** Given $x^2+y^2-2x=0$ ...(1)
    and $y=x$ ...(2)
    Using (2) in (1), we get $x=0,1$
    Let $A=(0,0)$ $B=(1,1)$ Then equation of required circle is $(x-0)(x-1)+(y-0)(y-1)=0$

$\Rightarrow \quad x^2 + y^2 - x - y = 0$

25. (a) Let equation of circle be

$$x^2 + y^2 + 2gx + 2fy + c = 0$$

with $x^2 + y^2 = p^2$ cutting orthogonoally we get

$0 + 0 = c - p^2$ and passes through (a, b) we get

$$a^2 + b^2 + 2ga + 2fb + p^2 = 0$$

$$\Rightarrow \quad 2ax + 2by - (a^2 + b^2 + p^2) = 0$$

Required locus as centre $(-g, -f) = (x, y)$

26. (a) $m_2 = \dfrac{e^{c+1} - e^{c-1}}{c+1-(c-1)} = \dfrac{e^c \left(e - \dfrac{1}{e}\right)}{2} \quad m_1 = e^c$

clearly $m_2 > m_1 \Rightarrow$ line intersect to left of C

27. (b) do same as Qus (25) by putting $p = 2$.

28. (b) As per given $C_1 C_2 = r_1 + r_2$

$\therefore \quad \sqrt{(h-0)^2 + (k-1)^2} = 1 + |k|$

$\Rightarrow \quad h^2 + (k-1)^2 = (1 + 1 + 1)^2$

$\Rightarrow \quad h^2 = 2k + 2|k|$. Hence, locus is $x^2 + 2y = 2|y|$

$y > 0$, $x^2 = 4y$ and $y < 0$, $x^2 = 0$, $\Rightarrow x = 0$

29. (c) We know that distance between parallel chords is greater than radius therefore, both chords lie on opposite side of centre

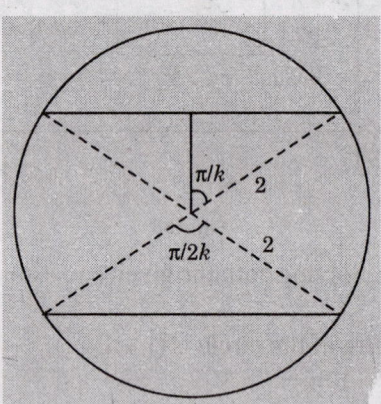

Fig. 139

$$2\cos\frac{\pi}{2k} + 2\cos\frac{\pi}{k} = \sqrt{3} + 1$$

If we take $\dfrac{\pi}{2k} = \theta$

Then $\quad 2\cos\theta + 2\cos 2\theta = \sqrt{3} + 1$

$\Rightarrow \quad 2\cos\theta + 2(2\cos^2\theta - 1) = \sqrt{3} + 1$

$\Rightarrow \quad 4\cos^2\theta + 2\cos\theta - (3 + \sqrt{3}) = 0$

Solving for $\cos\theta$, we get

$$\cos\theta = \frac{-1 \pm (2\sqrt{3} + 1)}{4}$$

$$\cos\lambda \frac{\pi}{2k} = \frac{\sqrt{3}}{2}, \frac{-(\sqrt{3}+1)}{2} \quad \text{rejected}$$

$\therefore \quad \dfrac{\pi}{2k} = \dfrac{\pi}{6} \quad \Rightarrow \quad k = 3 \quad \Rightarrow [k] = 3$

30. Ans. 2.

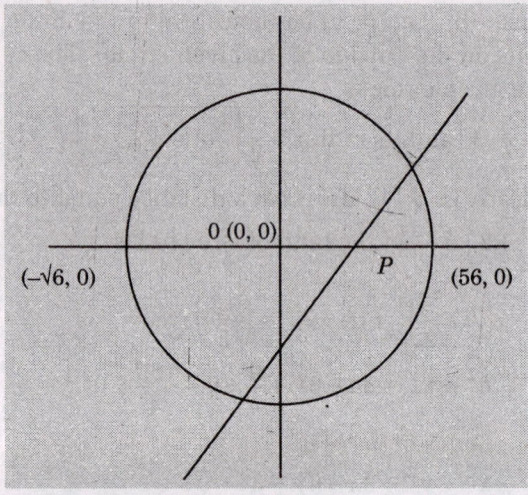

Fig. 140

$2x - 3y = 1$; $x^2 + y^2 \le 6$

$$S = \left\{ \underset{\text{(i)}}{\left(2, \frac{3}{4}\right)}, \underset{\text{(ii)}}{\left(\frac{5}{2}, \frac{3}{4}\right)}, \underset{\text{(iii)}}{\left(\frac{1}{4}, \frac{-1}{4}\right)}, \underset{\text{(iv)}}{\left(\frac{1}{8}, \frac{1}{4}\right)} \right\}$$

Plot the two curves (ii), (iii), (iv) will lie inside the circle and the point (I, III, IV) will lie on P of $(0, 0)$ and the given point will lie opposite to the line $2x - 3y + 1 = 0$

$P(0, 0) = $ negative, $P\left(2, \dfrac{3}{4}\right) = $ positive

$P\left(\dfrac{1}{4}, -\dfrac{1}{4}\right) = $ positive, $P\left(\dfrac{1}{8}, \dfrac{1}{4}\right) = $ negative

$P\left(\dfrac{5}{2}, -\dfrac{3}{4}\right) = $ positive, but it will not lie in the given circle, therefore point $\left(2, \dfrac{3}{4}\right)$ and $\left(\dfrac{1}{4}, -\dfrac{1}{4}\right)$ will lie on the opposite side of the line, their two point $\left(2, \dfrac{3}{4}\right)$ and $\left(\dfrac{1}{4}, -\dfrac{1}{4}\right)$. Further $\left(2, \dfrac{3}{4}\right)$ and $\left(\dfrac{1}{4}, -\dfrac{1}{4}\right)$ satisfy $S_1 < 0$.

31. Ans. False.

32. Ans. True.

33. Ans. False.

The radius of this circle $= \sqrt{1^2 + (-5)^2 - 30} = \sqrt{(-4)}$ which is imaginary.

34. Ans. False.

The point $(8, 6)$ lies on the circle $x^2 + y^2 - 100 = 0$ and so only one tangent can be drawn to the circle.

35. Ans. $\sqrt{3/2}$.

36. (i) Ans. $4x^2 + 4y^2 - 16x - 25y + 16 = 0$.

(ii) Ans. $x^2 + y^2 - 9x + 2fy + 14 = 0$,

$2\sqrt{g^2 - c} = 5$ and $4 + 2g + c = 0$.

37. Ans. $x^2 + y^2 - 30x - 10y + 225 = 0$

38. Ans. $x^2 + y^2 - 2x - 3y = 0$. Circle OAB

39. Ans. 1.   **40.** Ans. $x = 0$.

41. Ans. (d).

See Q. 48 (a) P. 865-881.

42. Ans. (a).

Let M be $(1, 0)$ and N be $(-1, 0)$. If $P(x, y)$ be any point then by given condition,

$$\frac{PM}{PN} = \frac{1}{3} \quad \text{or} \quad 9PM^2 = PN^2$$

or $9[(x - 1)^2 + y^2] = [(x + 1)^2 + y^2]$

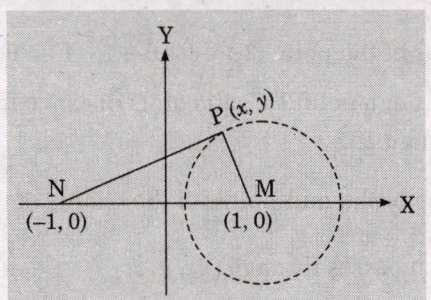

Fig. 141

$8x^2 + 8y^2 - 20x + 8 = 0$

or $x^2 + y^2 - \dfrac{5}{2}x + 1 = 0$

Hence the locus is a circle with centre at $\left(\dfrac{5}{4}, 0\right)$. The point A, B, C lie on this circle, hence circumcentre of $\triangle ABC$ is $\left(\dfrac{5}{4}, 0\right)$.

MISCELLANEOUS EXERCISE

Matching Entries

♦ *Match the entries of List-A and List-B.*

1.   **List-A (Equation of Circles)**   **List-B (Equations)**

(a) OAB where O is origin and $A(3, 0)$ and $B(0, 5)$ (i) $x^2 + y^2 - 4x - 6y + 11 = 0$

(b) $P(3, 4)$, $Q(1, 2)$ is diameter   (ii) $x^2 + y^2 - 4x - 4y - 5 = 0$

(c) Touches x-axis at $(3, 0)$ and makes an intercept of 8 on y-axis.   (iii) $x^2 + y^2 - 3x - 5y = 0$

(d) Passes through $(4, 5)$ and centre is $(2, 2)$ (iv) $x^2 + y^2 - 6x \pm 10y + 9 = 0$

2.   **List-A (Lines)**   **List-B (Equations)**

(a) Tangent to $x^2 + y^2 - 6x + 4y - 12 = 0$ which is parallel to $4x + 3y + 5 = 0$ (i) $2x + 3y - 13 = 0$

(b) Common chord of the circles $x^2 + y^2 - 6x + 2y + 4 = 0$ and   (ii) $4x + 3y + 19 = 0$

$x^2 + y^2 - 10x - 12y + 40 = 0$ $4x + 3y - 31 = 0$

(c) Chord of the circle $x^2 + y^2 = 25$ whose mid-point is $(2, 3)$ (iii) $3x + 2y = 13$

(d) Tangent at $(3, 2)$ to the circle $x^2 + y^2 + 6x + 4y - 39 = 0$ (iv) $4x + 7y - 18 = 0$

3.   **List-A (Length)**   **List-B**

(a) Length of common chord of the circles $x^2 + y^2 + 4x - 6y - 4 = 0$ (i) 15

and $x^2 + y^2 - x + 6y + 2 = 0$

(b) Length of the tangent drawn from $(16, 7)$ to circle   (ii) 6

$x^2 + y^2 - 2x - 4y - 20 = 0$

(c) Length of intercept on x-axis by the circle $x^2 + y^2 + 10x - 6y + 9 = 0$ (iii) 2

(d) Length of intercept on the line $2x - 5y + 18 = 0$ by the circle   (iv) 8

$x^2 + y^2 - 6x + 2y - 28 = 0$

4.   **List-A (Locus)**   **List-B (Equations)**

(a) Locus of the point of intersection of two mutually $\perp$ tangents to   (i) $(x - 2)^2 + (y - 1)^2 = 16$

circle $x^2 + y^2 = a^2$

(b) Locus of the point $(2 + 4\cos\theta, -1 + 4\sin\theta)$ (ii) $x^2 + y^2 - xx_1 - yy_1 = 0$

(c) Locus of a point s.t. ratio of its distance from two given points is constant k (iii) $x^2 + y^2 = 2a^2$

(d) Locus of the mid-points of the chords of the circle $x^2 + y^2 = a^2$ (iv) $x^2 + y^2 - 2ax\dfrac{(1 + k^2)}{1 - k^2} + a^2 = 0$

which passes through (x_1, y_1) where $2a$ is distance along given points.

5.   **List-A**   **List-B**

(a) Tangent to $(x - 2)^2 + (y + 1)^2 = 1$ (i) $8x + 7y + 5$

(b) Chord of contact of point $(6, 4)$ w.r.t. $x^2 + y^2 + 4x + 6y - 19 = 0$ (ii) $3x + 4y - 2$

(c) Diameter of circle given in (a)   (iii) $x^2 + y^2 - cx \pm cy + \dfrac{c^2}{4}$

(d) Circle touching both axes and the line $x = c$ (iv) $y = 0$

6.   **List-A**   **List-B**

(a) If a circle passes through the points $(5, 2)$ and $(7, -4)$ and its centre lies on y-axis, then its radius is ...   1. $x^2 + y^2 - 4x - 3y = 0$

(b) Two diameters of a circle passing through the point $(6, 2)$ are $x + y = 0$ and $x + 2y = 4$, then its radius is ...   2. $(16, 13), (-4, -11)$

(c) The line $3x + 4y = 12$ meets the axes in the points A and B, and O is origin then the circle OAB is ...   3. $\pi/3$

(d) The centres of the two equal circles of radius 13 units and having a common tangent at the point $(1, 1)$ are ...   4. $2\sqrt{5}$

(e) The equation $x^2 + y^2 + 4x + 6y + 13 = 0$ represents ...   5. Point $(-2, -3)$

(f) The angle at which the circle $x^2 + y^2 = 16$ is seen from the point $(8, 0)$ is ...   6. $2\sqrt{5}$

7.   **List-A**   **List-B**

(a) The slopes of the tangents drawn to the circle $x^2 + y^2 - 2x - 4y - 4 = 0$ from the point $(1, 7)$ are ...   1. $7(x^2 + y^2) - 10x - 10y - 12 = 0$

(b) Equation of a circle which cuts an intercept of length 8 units on x-axis and touches y-axis at $(0, 3)$ is ...   2. 3

(c) The equation of the circle passing through the intersection of the circles $x^2 + y^2 - 6x + 2y + 4 = 0$, $x^2 + y^2 + 2x - 4y - 6 = 0$ and having its centre on the line $y = x$ is ...   3. $\pm\dfrac{4}{3}$

(d) The equation of the circle described on the common chord of the circles $x^2 + y^2 + 2x = 0$ and $x^2 + y^2 + 2y = 0$ as diameter is ...   4. $x^2 + y^2 \pm 10x - 6y + 9 = 0$

(e) If the circles $x^2 + y^2 - 2ax + c^2 = 0$ and $x^2 + y^2 - 2by + c^2 = 0$ touch each other externally, then the required condition is ...   5. $x^2 + y^2 + x + y = 0$

(f) If the circles of same radius a and centres at $(2, 3)$ and $(5, 6)$ cut orthogonally then $a = ...$ 6. $\dfrac{1}{a^2} + \dfrac{1}{b^2} = \dfrac{1}{c^2}$

8. Consider the circle $S = x^2 + y^2 + 4x + 6y - 19 = 0$ and the point $P(6, 4)$ outside the circle

   Column-I   **Column-II**

(a) Distance of P from centre of the circle   (p) $\dfrac{72\sqrt{226}}{113}$

(b) Length of tangent from P to the circle

(c) Length of chord of contact of P to the circle

(d) Shortest distance of P from the circle

(q) 9

(r) $\sqrt{113} - \sqrt{32}$

(s) $\sqrt{113}$

9.   **Column-I**

(a) The circles $x^2 + y^2 + 2x + 3y + c^2 = 0$ and
$x^2 + y^2 - x + 2y + c^2 = 0$ intersect orthogonally

(b) The circle $x^2 + y^2 = 9$ contains the circle $x^2 + y^2 - 2x + 1 - c^2 = 0$

(c) The circle $x^2 + y^2 = 9$ is contained in the circle
$x^2 + y^2 - 6x - 8y + 25 - c^2 = 0$

(d) The circle $x^2 + y^2 + 2x + c = 0$ and $x^2 + y^2 + 2y + c = 0$ touch each other

Column-II

(p) $c = 1$

(q) $c = -1$

(r) $c = \dfrac{1}{2}$

(s) $c > 8$

10. The circle $x^2 + y^2 - 14x - 10y + 24 = 0$ makes an

Column-I

(a) intercept on x-axis

(b) intercept on y-axis

(c) intercept on $y = x$

(d) intercept on $7x + y - 4 = 0$

Column-II

(p) 0

(q) 2

(r) $8\sqrt{3}$

(s) 10

11.   **Column-I**

(a) Two intersecting circles

(b) Two mutually external circtes

(c) Two circles one strictly inside the other

(d) Two branches of a hyperbola

Column-II

(p) Have a common tangent

(q) Have a coon normal

(r) do not have a common tangent

(s) do not have a common normal

12. Let (x, y) be such that that $\sin^{-1} ax + \cos^{-1} y + \cos^{-1} (bxy) = \dfrac{\pi}{2}$

Column-I

(a) If $a = 1$, and $b = 0$ then (x, y)

(b) If $a = 1$ and $b - 1$ then (x, y)

(c) If $a = 1$ and $b = 2$ then (x, y)

(d) If $a = 2$ and $b = 2$ then (x, y)

Column-II

(p) lies on the circle $x^2 + y^2 = 1$

(q) lies on $(x^2 - 1)(y^2 - 1) = 0$

(r) lies on $y = x$

(s) lies on $(4x^2 - 1)(y^2 - 1) = 0$

(IIT-JEE 2007)

Answers

1. (a) → (iii), (b) → (i), (c) → (iv), (d) → (ii)
2. (a) → (ii), (b) → (iv), (c) → (i), (d) → (iii)
3. (a) → (iii), (b) → (i), (c) → (iv), (d) → (ii)
4. (a) → (iii), (b) → (i), (c) → (iv), (d) → (ii)
5. (a) → (iv), (b) → (i), (c) → (ii), (d) → (iii)
6. (a) → (4), (b) → (6), (c) → (1), (d) → (2),
    (e) → 5, (f) → (3)

7. (a) → (3), (b) → (4), (c) → (1), (d) → (5),
    (e) → 6, (f) → (2).
8. (a) → (s), (b) → (q), (c) → (p), (d) → (r)
9. (a) → (p, q) , (b) → (p, q, r), (c) → (s), (d) → (r)
10. (a) → (s), (b) → (q), (c) → (r), (d) → (p)
11. (a) → (p, q), (b) → (p, q), (c) → (q, r), (d) → (q, r)
12. (a) → (r), (b) → (q), (c) → (p), (d) → (s)

Hints/Solutions

1. (a) $A(a, 0)$, $B(0, b)$ will be diameter.

(c) $x^2 + 2gx + c = (x - 3)^2$ and $2\sqrt{f^2 - c} = 8$

2. (a) Apply $p = r$ (b) $S_1 - S_2 = 0$

(c) $T = S_1$

3. (a) $2\sqrt{r^2 - p^2}$ (b) $\sqrt{S_1}$

(c) $2\sqrt{g^2 - c}$ (d) $2\sqrt{r^2 - p^2}$

4. (a) Two mutually ⊥ tangents are
$x \cos \alpha + y \sin \alpha = a$
and $x \sin \alpha - y \cos \alpha = a$
Square and add.

(b) Eliminate θ by using $\cos^2 \theta + \sin^2 \theta = 1$

(c) Choose $AB = 2a$ along x-axis and its mid- point as origin

5. (a) The point at which tangent is drawn is not given. The line $y = 0$ cuts the circle when $(x - 2)^2 = 0$ i.e. at coincident point $(2, 0)$ and $(2, 0)$ and hence it is a tangent.

(c) $3x + 4y - 2 = 0$ is satisfied by centre $(2, -1)$

(d) Its centre will $(c/2, \pm c/2)$ and radius $c/2$.

6. (a) $x^2 + y^2 + 2gx + c = 0$, centre being on y-axis $f = 0$.

Put the points and solve for g and c

$\therefore \quad g = -9, \quad c = 61$.

(b) Centre is point of intersection of the two diameters i.e. the point $C(8, -2)$

$\therefore \quad r = CP = \sqrt{(4 + 16)} = 2\sqrt{5}$

(c) **Q. 20 (a) P. 856-870.**

(d) Normal at $(1, 1)$ is $12x - 5y - 7 = 0$ on which will lie the centres at distances of $13, -13$ from the point $(1, 1)$.

$\therefore \quad \tan\theta = \dfrac{12}{5}$

$\therefore \quad \cos\theta = \dfrac{5}{13}, \quad \sin\theta = \dfrac{12}{13}$

$\dfrac{x - 1}{\cos\theta} = \dfrac{y - 1}{\sin\theta} = 13, -13$

or $\quad (16, 13)$ and $(-4, -11)$.

(e) $r = 0.$ $(x + 2)^2 + (y + 3)^2 = 0$ implies $x + 2 = 0,$ $y + 3 = 0.$ Hence the point $(-2, -3)$.

(f) **Q. 6 P. 895-896.**

7. (a) Any line through $(1, 7)$ is

$y - 7 = m(x - 1)$ or $mx - y + (7 - m) = 0$.

Circle is $(1, 2), 3$. Apply $p = r$ for tangency.

$\dfrac{m - 2 + 7 - m}{\sqrt{1 + m^2}} = 3$

or $\quad 25 = 9 + 9m^2 \quad \therefore \quad m = \pm\dfrac{4}{3}$

(b) **Q. 2 (a) P. 854-862.**

(c) $S_1 + \lambda S_2 = 0$. Reduce to standard form and find its centre which lies on $y = x \implies \lambda = 4/3$.

(d) $S_1 - S_2 = 0 \implies x - y = 0$ is a diameter.

$\therefore \quad$ Circle is $S + \lambda P = 0$

$(x^2 + y^2 + 2x) + \lambda (x - y) = 0$

Its centre $\left(-\dfrac{2 + \lambda}{2}, \dfrac{\lambda}{2}\right)$ lies on diameter $x - y = 0$

$\therefore \quad \lambda = -1.$

(e) Common tangent is given by $S_1 - S_2 = 0$ or $ax - by = 0$. The condition of tangency $p = r$ from $(a, 0), \sqrt{a^2 - c^2}$ or $(0, b), \sqrt{b^2 - c^2}$ gives

$\dfrac{a^2}{\sqrt{a^2 + b^2}} = \sqrt{a^2 - c^2}$

or $\quad a^4 = (a^2 + b^2)(a^2 - c^2)$

or $\quad a^2 b^2 = c^2 (a^2 + b^2)$ or $\dfrac{1}{a^2} + \dfrac{1}{b^2} = \dfrac{1}{c^2}$

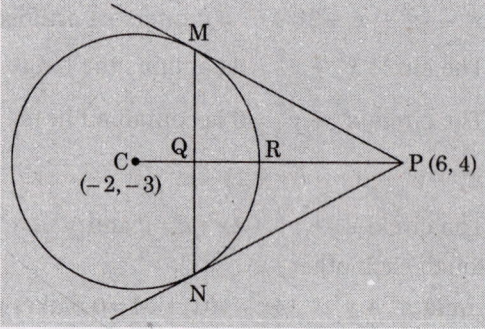

Fig. 142

(f) $(C_1 C_2)^2 = r_1^2 + r_2^2$ or $18 = a^2 + a^2$

8. Ans. (a) $\to$ (s), (b) $\to$ (q), (c) $\to$ (p), (d) $\to$ (r)

(a) $PC = \sqrt{64 + 49} = \sqrt{113}$

$\therefore \quad$ (a) $\to$ (s)

(b) $PM = PN = \sqrt{S'}$ for $(6, 4)$

$= \sqrt{36 + 16 + 24 + 24 - 19} = \sqrt{81} = 9$

$\therefore \quad$ (b) $\to$ (q)

(c) Eq. of C.C.of point $(6, 4)$ is $8x + 7y + 5 = 0$

PQ is perpendicular distance of P from C.C.

$= \dfrac{8.6 + 7.4 + 5}{\sqrt{64 + 49}} = \dfrac{81}{\sqrt{113}}$

and $PM = 9$ by part (b)

$\therefore \quad MQ = \sqrt{PM^2 - PQ^2} = \sqrt{81 - \dfrac{(81)^2}{113}} = 9\sqrt{\dfrac{113 - 81}{113}}$

$MN = 2MQ = \dfrac{18\sqrt{32}}{\sqrt{113}} = \dfrac{72\sqrt{2}}{\sqrt{113}} = \dfrac{72\sqrt{226}}{113}$

$\therefore \quad$ (c) $\to$ (p)

(d) Shortest distance of P from the circle is $PR = CP - CR$

$= \sqrt{113} - \sqrt{32} \quad \because \quad CR = r = \sqrt{g^2 + f^2 - c} = \sqrt{32}$

$\therefore \quad$ (d) $\to$ (r).

9. Ans. (a) $\to$ (p, q) , (b) $\to$ (p, q, r), (c) $\to$ (s), (d) $\to$ (r)

(a) $2g_1 g_2 + 2f_1 f_2 = c_1 + c_2$

$\implies \quad 2 (1)\left(-\dfrac{1}{2}\right) + 2\left(\dfrac{3}{2}\right)(1) = c^2 + c^2$

or $\quad 2 = 2c^2 \quad \therefore \quad c = 1, -1 \quad \therefore \quad$ (a) $\to$ (p, q)

(b) $S_1 = (0, 0), 3$ and $S_2 = (1, 0), c$

S_1 contains S_2 if $C_1 C_2 < r_1 - r_2$

$1 < 3 - c$ or $c < 2$

(b) $\to$ (p, q, r)

(c) $S_1 = (0, 0), 3$ and $S_2 = (3, 4), \sqrt{25 - (25 - c^2)}$

or $S_1 = (0, 0), 3$ $S_2 = (3, 4), c$

Here S_2 contains S_1 $\therefore$ $C_2 C_1 < r_2 - r_1$

$5 < c - 3$ or $8 < c$ $\therefore$ $c > 8$

(d) In this case, $C_1 C_2 = r_1 \pm r_2$

$C_1 (-1, 0), r_1 = \sqrt{1 - c}$

$C_2 (0, -1), r_2 = \sqrt{1 - c}$

$C_1 C_2 = \sqrt{1 + 1} = \sqrt{2} = r_1 - r_2$ or $r_1 + r_2$

or $\sqrt{2} = 0$ or $2\sqrt{1 - c}$ $\therefore 2 = 4(1 - c)$ or $\dfrac{1}{2} = 1 - c$

$\therefore$ $c = 1 - \dfrac{1}{2} = \dfrac{1}{2}$ $\therefore$ (d) $\to$ (r)

10. Ans. (a) $\to$ (s), (b) $\to$ (q), (c) $\to$ (r), (d) $\to$ (p)

Putting $y = 0$, we have $x^2 - 14x + 24 = 0$ $\therefore$ $x = 12, 2$

$\therefore$ Intercept $= x_1 - x_2 = 12 - 2 = 10$

$\therefore$ (a) $\to$ (s)

(b) Putting $x = 0$, $y^2 - 10y + 24 = 0$ $\therefore$ $y = 6, 4$

$\therefore$ Intercept $= y_1 - y_2 = 6 - 4 = 2$

$\therefore$ (b) $\to$ (q)

(c) Putting $y = x$, we have $2x^2 - 24x + 24 = 0$

$x^2 - 12x + 12 = 0$ $\therefore$ $x = y = 6 \pm 2\sqrt{6}$

$x_1 - x_2 = y_1 - y_2 = 4\sqrt{6}$

$\therefore$ $I = (I_x^2 + I_y^2)^{1/2} = 4\sqrt{6}\sqrt{1 + 1} = 4\sqrt{12} = 8\sqrt{3}$

(d) Solving the line $y = 4 - 7x$ with the circle, we have $x^2 + (4 - 7x)^2 - 14x - 10(4 - 7x) + 24 = 0$

or $50x^2 + x(-56 - 14 + 70) + (16 - 40 + 24) = 0$

$\therefore$ $x = 0, 0$ $\therefore$ $y = 4, 4$ i.e., points $(0, 4), (0, 4)$

Distance between these coincident points is zero.

$\therefore$ (d) $\to$ (p).

11. Use the following results

(i) Two intersecting circles have common tangents as well as common normal

(ii) Two mutually external circles have common tangents as well as common normal

(iii) If one circle is strictly inside the other then they can not have a common tangent but they can have common normal

(iv) Two branches of hyperbola can have a common normal the line joining the vertices but have no common tangent.

12. Ans. (a).

If $a = 1, b = 0$ then $\sin^{-1} x + \cos^{-1} y = \dfrac{\pi}{2}$

$\Rightarrow$ $\sin^{-1} x = \dfrac{\pi}{2} - \cot^{-1} y = \sin^{-1} y \Rightarrow x = y$

(b) $a = 1, b = 1 \Rightarrow \sin^{-1} x + \cos^{-1} y + \cos^{-1} xy = \dfrac{\pi}{2}$

$\Rightarrow$ $\cos^{-1}(yxy - \sqrt{1 - y^2}\sqrt{1 - x^2 y^2})$

$= \dfrac{\pi}{2} - \sin^{-1} x = \cos^{-1} x$

$\Rightarrow$ $(yxy - \sqrt{1 - y^2}\sqrt{1 - x^2 y^2}) = x$

on solving we get $(x^2 - 1)(y^2 - 1) = 0$

(c) $a = 1, b = 2$ then $\sin^{-1} x + \cos^{-1} y + \cos^{-1} 2xy = \dfrac{\pi}{2}$

$\Rightarrow$ $\cos^{-1}\left[2xy^2 - \sqrt{1 - y^2}\sqrt{1 - 4x^2 y^2}\right] = \cos^{-1} x$

$\Rightarrow$ $2xy^2 - \sqrt{1 - y^2} \cdot \sqrt{1 - 4x^2 y^2} = x$

$\Rightarrow$ $x^2 (2y^2 - 1)^2 = (1 - y^2)(1 - 4x^2 y^2)$

$\Rightarrow$ $x^2 + y^2 = 1$

(d) If $a = 2, b = 2$, then

$2xy^2 - \sqrt{1 - y^2}\sqrt{1 - 4x^2 y^2} = 2x$

On solving we get

$(4x^2 - 1)(y^2 - 1) = 0$

Assertion / Reason

1. Tangents are drawn from the point $(17, 7)$ to the circle $x^2 + y^2 = 169$.

STATEMENT-1 : The tangents are mutually perpendicular.

because

STATEMENT-2 : The locus of the points from which mutually perpendicular tangents can be drawn to the given circle is $x^2 + y^2 = 338$.   **(I.I.T. 2007)**

Sol. Ans. (a).

Any line through the point $(17, 7)$ is

$y - 7 = m(x - 17)$ or $mx - y = 17m - 7$.

The condition of tangency to the circle $x^2 + y^2 = 169$

i.e., $p = r$ gives $\dfrac{17m - 7}{\sqrt{(m^2 + 1)}} = 13$. Square

$(17m - 7)^2 = 169(m^2 + 1)$

or $120m^2 - 238m - 120 = 0$

Hence there will be two tangents

$\therefore$ $m_1 m_2 = \dfrac{-120}{120} = -1$.

Hence they are perpendicular $\Rightarrow$ statement (1) is true. The locus of the point of intersection of two perpendicular tangents to a circle $x^2 + y^2 = a^2$ is $x^2 + y^2 = 2a^2$ and $169 \times 2 = 338$.

2. Consider

$$L_1 : 2x + 3y + p - 3 = 0$$
$$L_2 : 2x + 3y + p + 3 = 0,$$

where p is a real number, and

$$C : x^2 + y^2 + 6x - 10y + 30 = 0 \qquad \text{(IIT-JEE 2008)}$$

STATEMENT-1 : If line L_1 is a chord of circle C, then line L_2 is not always a diameter of circle C. and

STATEMENT-2 : If line L_1 is a diameter of circle C, then line L_2 is not a chord of circle C.

Sol. Ans. (c). $L_1 : 2x + 3y + p - 3 = 0,$
$\qquad\qquad L_2 : 2x + 3y + p + 3 = 0$

Circle : Centre is $(-3, 5)$, radius 2.

Distance between L_1 and L_2 is

$$\frac{(p+3) - (p-3)}{\sqrt{13}} = \frac{6}{\sqrt{13}} = \sqrt{\frac{36}{13}} < \sqrt{\frac{52}{13}} = \sqrt{4} = 2$$

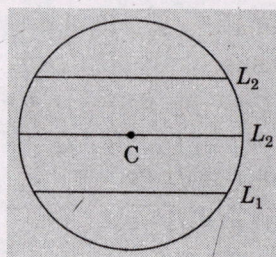

Fig. 143

$\therefore \quad p_1 - p_2 <$ radius 2 of the circle. Distance between parallel lines L_1 and L_2 is less than radius of circle. Hence, if L_1 is a chord then L_2 may be or may not be a diameter. On the other, if one of them is a diameter then the other parallel line must be a chord. Hence statement 1 is true but statement 2 is false.

Comprehension

1. **Passage 1.** Consider the equation of circle $x^2 + y^2 - 2x - 2\lambda y - 8 = 0$ where λ is variable then answer the following :

(a) The given equation represents a family of circles passing through two fixed points.
Find the coordinates of the fixed points.

Sol. Ans. $A(-2, 0), (B(4, 0).$

The given equation is of the form $S + \lambda P = 0$ i.e., $(x^2 + y^2 - 2x - 8) - 2\lambda y = 0$ which represents a family of circles passing through the intersection of $S = 0$ and $P = 0$.

Putting $y = 0$, we get $x^2 - 2x - 8 = 0$

or $(x - 4)(x + 2) = 0 \therefore x = 4, -2.$

Hence, the points are $(-2, 0)$ and $(4, 0)$.

(b) Find the equation of a circle of this family tangents to which at these fixed points A and B of part (a) meet on the line $x + 2y + 5 = 0$

Sol. Ans. $x^2 + y^2 - 2x - 6y - 8 = 0$

Let the tangents at A and B to this circle intersect at (h, k) then AB (i.e., $y = 0$) is the chord of contact of the point (h, k) whose equation is

$$xh + yk - (x + h) - \lambda (y + k) - 8 = 0$$

or $x(h - 1) + y(k - \lambda) - (h + \lambda k + 8) = 0$

If it represents $y = 0$, then

$$h - 1 = 0 \quad \text{and} \quad h + \lambda k + 8 = 0$$

$\therefore \quad h = 1 \quad \text{and} \quad \lambda k + 9 = 0$

But (h, k) lies on $x + 2y + 5 = 0$

$$h + 2k + 5 = 0 \quad \text{or} \quad 2k + 6 = 0 \quad \therefore \quad k = -3$$

and hence, $\lambda = 3$ from $\lambda k + 9 = 0$

Putting $\lambda = 3$, the required member of the family is

$$x^2 + y^2 - 2x - 6y - 8 = 0.$$

(c) If the chord joining the fixed points subtends an angle α at the centre of the circle, then $\alpha = \pi / 2$.

Slope of $AC = \dfrac{3 - 0}{1 + 2} = 1 = m_1$

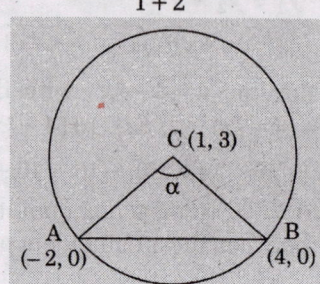

Fig. 144

Slope of $BC = \dfrac{3 - 0}{1 - 4} = -1 = m_2$

Since $m_1 m_2 = -1$, hence AC and BC are perpendicular,

$\therefore \quad \angle ACB = \pi / 2$

2. **Passage 2 :** A tangent PT is drawn to the circle $x^2 + y^2 = 4$ at the point $P(\sqrt{3}, 1)$. A straight line L, perpendicular to PT is a tangent to the circle $(x - 3)^2 + y^2 = 1$

(i) a common tangent of the two circles is

(a) $x = 4$ (b) $y = 2$

(c) $x + \sqrt{3}y = 4$ (d) $x + 2\sqrt{2}y = 6$

(ii) A possible solution of L is

(a) $x - \sqrt{3}y = 1$ (ii) $x + \sqrt{3}y = 1$

(c) $x - \sqrt{3}y = -1$ (d) $x + \sqrt{3}y = 5$ (IIT-JEE 2012)

Sol. Ans. (d).

B divides C_1, C_2 in 2 : 1 externally $\Rightarrow B (6, 0)$

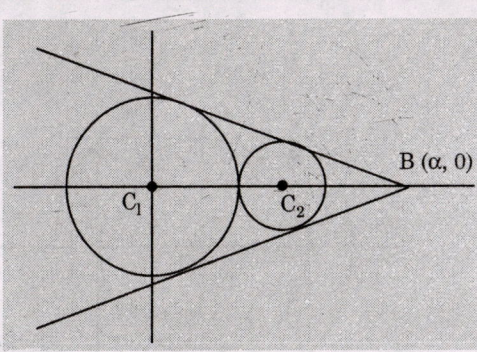

Fig. 145

∴ Equation of the common tangent is

$y - 0 = m(x - 6)$

⇒ $mx - y - 6m = 0$

∴ Length of the perpendicular from centre $(0, 0)$

= radius = $\left|\dfrac{6m}{\sqrt{1+m^2}}\right| = 2 \Rightarrow m = \dfrac{\pm 1}{2\sqrt{2}}$

Hence, the required equation is $x + 2\sqrt{2}y = 6$ or $x - 2\sqrt{2}y = -6$

(ii) Ans. (a). Equation of tangent at $(\sqrt{3}, 1)$

$\sqrt{3}x + y = 4$

equation of L is $x - y\sqrt{3} = c$

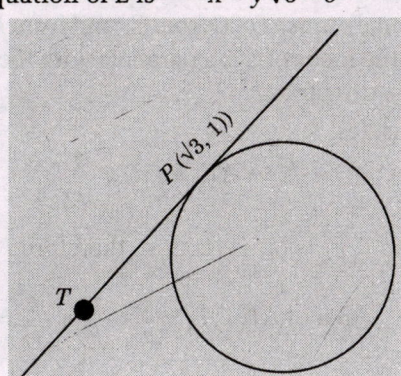

Fig. 146

∴ Length of perpendicular from centre = radius of the circle

∴ $\left|\dfrac{3+c}{2}\right| = 1 \Rightarrow c = -1, -5$

Hence, required equation is $x - \sqrt{3}y = 1$ or $x - \sqrt{3}y = 5$

3 **Passage 3.** A circle of radius 1 is inscribed in an equilateral triangle PQR. The points of contact of C with the sides PQ, QR and RP are D, E, F, respectively. The line PQ is given by the equation $\sqrt{3}x + y - 6 = 0$ and the point D is $\left(\dfrac{3\sqrt{3}}{2}, \dfrac{3}{2}\right)$. Further, it is given that the origin and the centre of C are on the same side of the line PQ.

(i)   The equation of circle C is

(a) $(x - 2\sqrt{3})^2 + (y + 1)^2 = 1$

(b) $(x - 2\sqrt{3})^2 + \left(y + \dfrac{1}{2}\right)^2 = 1$

(c) $(x - \sqrt{3})^2 + (y + 1)^2 = 1$

(d) $(x - \sqrt{3})^2 + (y - 1)^2 = 1$

(ii) Points E and F are given by

(a) $\left(\dfrac{\sqrt{3}}{2}, \dfrac{3}{2}\right), (\sqrt{3}, 0)$ (b) $\left(\dfrac{\sqrt{3}}{2}, \dfrac{1}{2}\right), (\sqrt{3}, 0)$

(c) $\left(\dfrac{\sqrt{3}}{2}, \dfrac{3}{2}\right), \left(\dfrac{\sqrt{3}}{2}, \dfrac{1}{2}\right)$ (d) $\left(\dfrac{3}{2}, \dfrac{\sqrt{3}}{2}\right), \left(\dfrac{\sqrt{3}}{2}, \dfrac{1}{2}\right)$

(iii) Equations of the sides QR, RP are

(a) $y = \dfrac{2}{\sqrt{3}}x + 1, y = \dfrac{-2}{\sqrt{3}}x - 1$

(b) $y = \dfrac{1}{\sqrt{3}}x, y = 0$

(c) $y = \dfrac{\sqrt{3}}{2}x + 1, y = -\dfrac{\sqrt{3}}{2}x - 1$

(d) $y = \sqrt{3}x, y = 0$

(IIT-JEE 2008)

Sol. (i) Ans. (d) $\alpha = \dfrac{3\sqrt{3}}{2} - 1 \cdot \cos 30° = \sqrt{3}$

$\beta = \dfrac{3}{2} - 1 \cdot \sin 30° = 1$

∴ Required equation is $(x - \sqrt{3})^2 + (y - 1)^2 = 1$

(ii) Ans. (a). $\angle FGD = \angle DGE = 120°$

⇒ $F = (\sqrt{3}, 0)$ and $GF = GE = GD = 1$

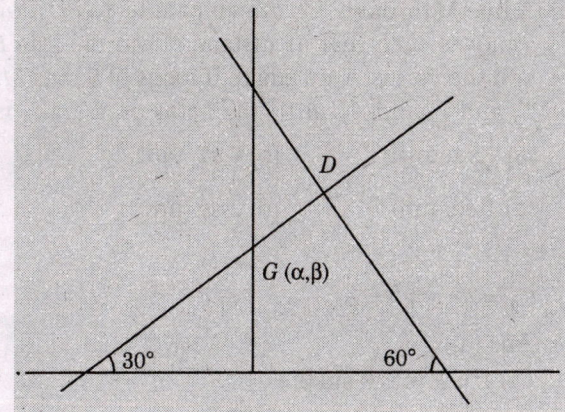

Fig. 147

∴ $E \equiv \left(\dfrac{\sqrt{3}}{2}, \dfrac{3}{2}\right)$

(iii) Ans. (d). Slope of $QR = \sqrt{3}$

∴ equation of QR is $y - \dfrac{3}{2} = \sqrt{3}\left(x - \dfrac{\sqrt{3}}{2}\right)$

⇒ $y = \sqrt{3}x$

and slope of $RP = 0 \Rightarrow$ Equation of RP is $y = 0$

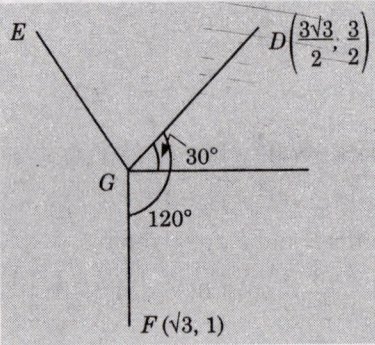

Fig. 148

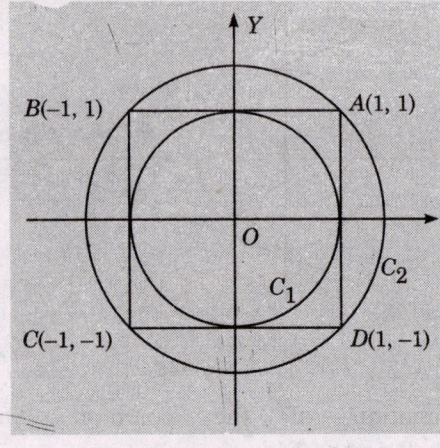

Fig. 149

4. **Passage 4** Let $ABCD$ be a square of side length 2 unit, C_2 is the circle through vertices A, B, C, D and C_1 is the circle touching all the sides of the square $ABCD$. L is a line through A　　　　　　　　**(IIT-JEE 2006)**

(i) If P is a point on C_1 and Q is another point on C_2, then

$$\frac{PA^2 + PB^2 + DC^2 + PD^2}{QA^2 + QB^2 + QC^2 + QD^2} \text{ equal to}$$

(a) 0.75　　　　　(b) 1.25
(c) 1　　　　　　(d) 0.5

(ii) A circle touches the line L and the circle C_1 externally such that both the circles arc on the same side of the line, then the locus of the centre of the circle is

(a) ellipse　　　　(b) hyperbola
(c) parabola　　　(d) pair of straight line

(iii) A line M through A is drawn parallel to BD. Point S moves such that its distance from the line BD and the vertex A are equal. If locus of S cuts M at T_2 and T_3 and AC at T_1, then area of $\Delta T_1 T_2 T_3$ is

(a) $\frac{1}{2}$ sq. unit　　　(b) $\frac{2}{3}$ sq. unit
(c) 1 sq. unit　　　　(d) 2 sg. unit

Sol. Here $C_1 : x^2 + y^2 = 1$

$C_2 = x^2 + y^2 = 2$

(i) **Ans.(a).**

Let $P = P(\cos\theta, \sin\theta)$
then $PA^2 + PB^2 + PC^2 + PD^2$

$= (\cos\theta - 1)^2 + (\sin\theta - 1)^2 + (\cos\theta + 1)^2$
$\qquad + (\sin\theta - 1)^2 + (\cos\theta + 1)^2 + (\sin\theta + 1)^2$
$\qquad\qquad + (\cos\theta - 1)^2 + (\sin\theta + 1)^2$

$= 12$

Let　　$Q = Q(\sqrt{2}\cos\phi, \sqrt{2}\sin\phi)$ then

$$QA^2 + QB^2 + QC^2 + QD^2 = 16$$

$$\Rightarrow \frac{PA^2 + PB^2 + PC^2 + PD^2}{QA^2 + QB^2 + QC^2 + QD^2} = \frac{12}{16} = 0.75$$

(ii) **Ans. (c).**

Consider a line L_1 parallel to L and at a distance 1 unit from L in the direction opposite to the sides where C_1 and C_2 lie. Since, L is given therefore, L_1 is also fixed. If C be the centre of variable circle then distances of C from C_1 and from L_1 are equal, so the locus of C is a parabola with focus at C_1 and L as directrix.

(iii) **Ans. (c).**

$$AG = \sqrt{2} \Rightarrow AT_1 = T_1G = \frac{1}{\sqrt{2}}$$

also T_1T_2 is latus rectum, therefore $T_2T_3 = 4 \times \frac{1}{\sqrt{2}}$

$\therefore$　Area of $\Delta T_1 T_2 T_3 = \frac{1}{2} \times \frac{1}{\sqrt{2}} \times \frac{4}{\sqrt{2}} = 1$

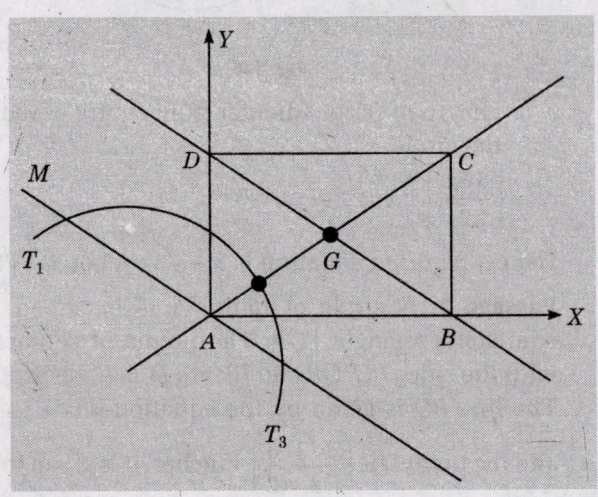

Fig. 150

Fascinating Facts

- The equation of the circle with centre at (h, k) and radius r is $(x - h)^2 + (y - k)^2 = r^2$. This form is called central form of the circle.

- The equation of every circle can be written as $x^2 + y^2 + 2gx + 2fy + c = 0$ where $g^2 + f^2 - c^2 \geq 0$. Its centre is $(-g, -f)$ and radius $= \sqrt{g^2 + f^2 - c}$

- The locus of the equation $x^2 + y^2 + 2gx + 2fy + c = 0$ is
  (i) an empty set if $g^2 + f^2 - c < 0$
  (ii) a point circle $(-g, -f)$ if $g^2 + f^2 - c = 0$
  (iii) a circle if $g^2 + f^2 - c > 0$

- If the line $y = mx + c$ is normal to the circle with radius r and centre at (a, b) then $b = ma + c$

- The line $ax + by + c = 0$ is a tangent to the circle $x^2 + y^2 = r^2$ if and only if $c^2 = r^2(a^2 + b^2)$

- If the tangent to the circle $x^2 + y^2 = r^2$ at the point (a, b) meets the co-ordinate axes at the point A and B and 0 is the origin, then the area of the triangle OAB is $\dfrac{r^4}{2ab}$.

- The radius of the given circle $x^2 + y^2 + 2gx + 2fy + c = 0$ be r and it touches both the axes then $|g| = |f| = \sqrt{c} = r$

- The angle between the tangents from (α, β) to the circle $x^2 + y^2 = a^2$ is $2\tan^{-1}\left(\dfrac{a}{\sqrt{\alpha^2 + \beta^2 - a^2}}\right)$

- If the points where the lines $a_1 x + b_1 y + c_1 = 0$ and $a_2 x + b_2 y + c_2 = 0$ meet the coordinate axes are concyclic then $a_1 a_2 = b_1 b_2$

- Equation of pair of tangents drawn from the origin to $x^2 + y^2 + 2gx + 2fy + c = 0$ is $(gx + fy)^2 = c(x^2 + y^2)$

- The condition that the line $lx + my + n = 0$ touches the circle $x^2 + y^2 + 2gx + 2fy + c = 0$ is
  $$(lg + mf - n)^2 = (l^2 + m^2)(g^2 + f^2 - c)$$

❑

Pair of Straight Lines

§1. The straight lines

(a) To find the angle between the straight lines represented by the equation
$$ax^2 + 2hxy + by^2 = 0.$$

$ax^2 + 2hxy + by^2 = 0$ is a homogeneous equation of 2nd degree and will represent two straight lines passing through the origin. Suppose that these lines are

$$y - m_1 x = 0 \text{ and } y - m_2 x = 0$$

$$\therefore \quad (y - m_1 x)(y - m_2 x) = 0$$

or $\quad y^2 - xy(m_1 + m_2) + m_1 m_2 x^2 = 0 \quad ....(1)$

Dividing the given equation by b, we get

$$y^2 + \frac{2h}{b} xy + \frac{a}{b} x^2 = 0 \qquad ...(2)$$

Comparing the coefficients in (1) and (2),

$$\boldsymbol{m_1 + m_2 = -\frac{2h}{b} \text{ and } m_1 m_2 = \frac{a}{b}.} \qquad ...(3)$$

If the angle between the lines be θ, then

$$\tan \theta = \frac{m_1 - m_2}{1 + m_1 m_2} = \frac{\sqrt{[(m_1 + m_2)^2 - 4m_1 m_2]}}{(1 + m_1 m_2)}$$

or $\quad \tan \theta = \dfrac{\sqrt{\left(\dfrac{4h^2}{b^2} - \dfrac{4a}{b}\right)}}{1 + \dfrac{a}{b}} = 2 \cdot \dfrac{\sqrt{(h^2 - ab)}}{a + b}$

$$\therefore \quad \theta = \tan^{-1} 2 \frac{\sqrt{(h^2 - ab)}}{a + b} \qquad ....(4)$$

(b) Condition for the lines to be perpendicular.
If the lines be perpendicular, then

$$\theta = 90^\circ \text{ and } \tan 90^\circ = \infty; \quad \therefore \ a + b = 0$$

Hence **coefficient of x^2 + coefficient of $y^2 = 0$.**
[by (4)]

(c) Condition for the lines to be parallel or coincident.
In this case, $\theta = 0$

$$\therefore \quad \tan \theta = 0 \quad \therefore \ h^2 = ab$$

Note : In this case the lines will be coincident only as both pass through origin.

(d) Equation of any two perpendicular lines through the origin.
If the lines represented by $ax^2 + 2hxy + by^2 = 0$ be perpendicular, then $a + b = 0$ or $b = -a$.
Hence the equation becomes

$$ax^2 + 2hxy - ay^2 = 0$$

or $\quad x^2 + \dfrac{2h}{a} xy - y^2 = 0$

or $\quad x^2 + pxy - y^2 = 0$

where p is any constant. (**Note and remember**).

§2 Equation of Bisectors

Find the equation of the bisectors of the angles between the lines given by the equation
$$ax^2 + 2hxy + by^2 = 0$$

If the lines represented by the given equation be

$$y - m_1 x = 0 \text{ and } y - m_2 x = 0,$$

then $\qquad m_1 + m_2 = -\dfrac{2h}{b}$

and $\qquad m_1 m_2 = \dfrac{a}{b}.$

Equations of their bisectors are

$$\frac{y - m_1 x}{\sqrt{(1 + m_1^2)}} = \pm \frac{y - m_2 x}{\sqrt{(1 + m_2^2)}}$$

or $\quad \left[\dfrac{y - m_1 x}{\sqrt{(1 + m_1^2)}} + \dfrac{y - m_2 x}{\sqrt{(1 + m_2^2)}} \right]$

$$\left[\frac{y - m_1 x}{\sqrt{(1 + m_1^2)}} - \frac{y - m_2 x}{\sqrt{(1 + m_2^2)}} \right] = 0$$

or $\quad \dfrac{(y - m_1 x)^2}{(1 + m_1^2)} - \dfrac{(y - m_2 x)^2}{(1 + m_2^2)} = 0$

or $\quad (1 + m_2^2)(y^2 - 2xym_1 + m_1^2 x^2)$
$$- (1 + m_1^2)(y^2 - 2xym_2 + m_2^2 x^2) = 0$$

or $\quad y^2 (m_2^2 - m_1^2) + x^2 (m_1^2 - m_2^2)$
$$- 2xy \{(m_1 - m_2) + m_1 m_2 (m_2 - m_1)\} = 0$$

or $\quad - y^2 (m_1 + m_2) + x^2 (m_1 + m_2)$
$$- 2xy (1 - m_1 m_2) = 0$$

or $(x^2 - y^2)\left(-\dfrac{2h}{b}\right) = 2xy\left(1 - \dfrac{a}{b}\right)$

or $\dfrac{x^2 - y^2}{a - b} = \dfrac{xy}{h}$

or $\dfrac{x^2 - y^2}{\text{coeff. of } x^2 - \text{coeff. of } y^2} = \dfrac{xy}{\text{half the coeff. of } xy}$

Since sum of the coefficient of x^2 and y^2 in the above equation is zero, *i.e.* $a + b = 1 - 1 = 0$, hence the bisectors are perpendicular.

§3 General Equation of Second Degree

$$ax^2 + 2hxy + by^2 + 2gx + 2fy + c = 0 \qquad \ldots(1)$$

To find the condition that the above equation may represent a pair of straight lines.

If the equation (1) represents a pair of straight lines, it should be possible for us to decompose (1) into product of two linear factors

$$\left.\begin{array}{l} l_1 x + m_1 y + n_1 = 0 \\ \text{and} \quad l_2 x + m_2 y + n_2 = 0, \end{array}\right\} \qquad \ldots(A)$$

each representing a straight line.

$\therefore \quad ax^2 + 2hxy + by^2 + 2gx + 2fy + c$

$\equiv (l_1 x + m_1 y + n_1)(l_2 x + m_2 y + n_2).$

Comparing the coefficients, we get

$$\left.\begin{array}{l} l_1 l_2 = a, \, m_1 m_2 = b, \, n_1 n_2 = c, \\ l_1 m_2 + l_2 m_1 = 2h, \, m_1 n_2 + m_2 n_1 = 2f, \\ n_1 l_2 + n_2 l_1 = 2g \end{array}\right\} \qquad \ldots(B)$$

Now $\begin{vmatrix} l_1 & l_2 & 0 \\ m_1 & m_2 & 0 \\ n_1 & n_2 & 0 \end{vmatrix} \begin{vmatrix} l_2 & l_1 & 0 \\ m_2 & m_1 & 0 \\ n_2 & n_1 & 0 \end{vmatrix} = 0$

$\because$ Each determinant is zero.

$\therefore \begin{vmatrix} 2l_1 l_2 & l_1 m_2 + l_2 m_1 & l_1 n_2 + l_2 n_1 \\ l_1 m_2 + l_2 m_1 & 2m_1 m_2 & m_1 n_2 + m_2 n_1 \\ n_1 l_2 + n_2 l_1 & m_1 n_2 + m_2 n_1 & 2n_1 n_2 \end{vmatrix} = 0$

or $\begin{vmatrix} 2a & 2h & 2g \\ 2h & 2b & 2f \\ 2g & 2f & 2c \end{vmatrix} = 0$ or $\begin{vmatrix} a & h & g \\ h & b & f \\ g & f & c \end{vmatrix} = 0$

or $a(bc - f^2) - h(hc - fg) + g(hf - bg) = 0$

or $abc + 2fgh - af^2 - bg^2 - ch^2 = 0 \qquad \ldots(2)$

Above is the required condition.

Remember that a, b, c stand for coefficients of x^2, y^2 and constant term respectively and f, g, h stand for half the coefficients of x, y and xy.

Point of intersection of the two lines.

Solving equations in (A), we get

$$\dfrac{x}{m_1 n_2 - m_2 n_1} = \dfrac{y}{n_1 l_2 - n_2 l_1} = \dfrac{1}{l_1 m_2 - l_2 m_1}$$

Now

$$(m_1 n_2 - m_2 n_1)^2 = (m_1 n_2 + m_2 n_1)^2 - 4 m_1 m_2 n_1 n_2$$

$$= 4(f^2 - bc) \text{ from (B)}$$

$$\dfrac{x}{2\sqrt{(f^2 - bc)}} = \dfrac{y}{2\sqrt{(g^2 - ca)}} = \dfrac{1}{2\sqrt{(h^2 - ab)}}$$

Hence the point of intersection is

$$\left[\sqrt{\dfrac{f^2 - bc}{h^2 - ab}}, \ \sqrt{\dfrac{g^2 - ca}{h^2 - ab}}\right].$$

§4 Explain the method of finding the equations of straight lines joining the origin to the points of

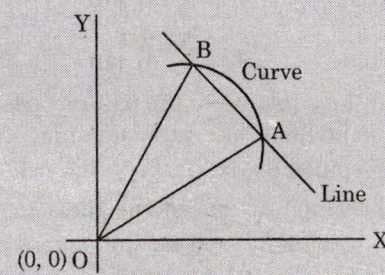

Fig. 1

intersection of a given straight line and a given curve. Illustrate the same with a suitable example.

Suppose that the line $px + qy + r = 0$ cuts the curve whose equation is

$$ax^2 + 2hxy + by^2 + 2gx + 2fy + c = 0$$

in the points P and Q. In order to find the equations to the lines joining origin to the points **P and Q, make the equation of the curve homogeneous with the help of the equation** of the straight line, because we know that the combined equation of the lines through the origin is homogeneous.

Rule : Find the value of 1 from the equation of the line in terms of x and y, e.g.

$$px + qy = -r \quad \text{or} \quad \left(\dfrac{px + qy}{-r}\right) = 1.$$

Now multiply the first degree terms of the equation of the curve by 1, *i.e.* $\left(\dfrac{px + qy}{-r}\right)$ and the constant term by

1^2 *i.e.* $\left(\dfrac{px + qy}{-r}\right)^2$. On simplification we shall obtain an equation which will be homogeneous and will represent the required lines OP and OQ. **Remember that if these lines be perpendicular, then**

coeff. of x^2 + coeff. of $y^2 = 0$, *i.e.* $a + b = 0$

[§ 1 (b), P. 944]

Note : If the line be $2x - 3y = 7$ then do not write $\dfrac{7 + 3y}{2x} = 1$ or $\dfrac{2x - 7}{3y} = 1$. We should write $\dfrac{2x - 3y}{7} = 1$ *i.e.* the value of 1 is to be found in terms of x and y.

Problem Set (1)

Lines represented by homogeneous equation $ax^2 + 2hxy + by^2 = 0$ and angle between them and their bisectors.

1. (i) What curve (or curves) does the equation $x^2 - 5xy + 4y^2 = 0$ represent ?

   (ii) The angle between the pair of straight lines $x^2 + 4y^2 - 7xy = 0$ is

   (a) $\tan^{-1}\left(\dfrac{1}{3}\right)$ (b) $\tan^{-1}\left(\dfrac{1}{2}\right)$

   (c) $\tan^{-1}\{\sqrt{(33)}/5\}$ (d) $\tan^{-1}\{5/\sqrt{(33)}\}$

2. (a) Find the equation to the pair of lines through the origin which are perpendicular to the lines represented by $ax^2 + 2hxy + by^2 = 0$.

   (b) If the slope of one of the lines represented by $ax^2 + 2hxy + by^2 = 0$ be the square of the other, then prove that $\dfrac{a+b}{h} + \dfrac{8h^2}{ab} = 6$.

   (c) Find the combined equation of the images of the pair of lines represented by $ax^2 + 2hxy + by^2 = 0$ in the line mirror $y = 0$.

3. (a) Find the equation to the pair of lines through the origin which are perpendicular to the lines represented by $2x^2 - 5xy + y^2 = 0$.

   (b) From a point $A(1, 1)$ straight lines AL and AM are drawn at right angles to the pair of straight lines $3x^2 + 7xy - 2y^2 = 0$. Find the equation of pair of straight lines AL and AM. Also find the area of the quadrilateral $ALOM$ where O is the origin of co-ordinates.   **(D.C.E. 1998)**

4.* Prove that the product of the perpendiculars drawn from the point (x_1, y_1) on the lines represented by $ax^2 + 2hxy + by^2 = 0$ is $\dfrac{ax_1^2 + 2hx_1y_1 + by_1^2}{[(a-b)^2 + 4h^2]^{1/2}}$.

5.* (a) Prove that two of the lines represented by the equation $ax^3 + 3bx^2y + 3cxy^2 + dy^3 = 0$ will be perpendicular if $a^2 + 3ac + 3bd + d^2 = 0$

   (b) Equation $ax^3 - 9yx^2 - y^2x + 4y^3 = 0$ represents three straight lines. If two of the lines are perpendicular, then $a = \ldots\ldots$

6.* Prove that two of the lines represented by the equation $ay^4 + bxy^3 + cx^2y^2 + dx^3y + ex^4 = 0$

   will be perpendicular if
   $(b + d)(ad + be) + (e - a)^2 (a + c + e) = 0$

7. Show that the difference of the tangents of the angles which the lines
   $(\tan^2 \alpha + \cos^2 \alpha) x^2 - 2xy \tan \alpha + \sin^2 \alpha \, y^2 = 0$
   make with the axis of x is 2.

8.* Prove that the angle between the straight lines represented by

   $(x^2 + y^2)\sin^2 \alpha = (x\cos\theta - y\sin\theta)^2$ is 2α.

9. (a) Find the condition that one of the lines given by the equation $ax^2 + 2hxy + by^2 = 0$ coincides with one of those given by $a'x^2 + 2h'xy + b'y^2 = 0$.

   (b)* Find the condition that one of the lines given by the equation $ax^2 + 2hxy + by^2 = 0$ be perpendicular to one of those given by $a'x^2 + 2h'xy + b'y^2 = 0$.

10. If the pair of lines $x^2 + 2xy + ay^2 = 0$ and $ax^2 + 2xy + y^2 = 0$ have exactly one line in common, then prove that joint equation of the other two lines is given by $3x^2 + 10xy + 3y^2 = 0$.

11. Prove that each of the lines given by the equation $(x_1 y - xy_1)^2 = a^2 (x^2 + y^2)$ is at a distance a from the point (x_1, y_1).

12.* Show that the straight lines
   $(A^2 - 3B^2) x^2 + 8AB \, xy + (B^2 - 3A^2) y^2 = 0$
   form with the line $Ax + By + C = 0$ an equilateral triangle of area $\dfrac{C^2}{\sqrt{3}.(A^2 + B^2)}$.

13. Prove that the equation $3x^2 - 8xy - 3y^2 = 0$ and $x + 2y = 3$ represent the sides of an isosceles right angled triangle.

14. (a) A pair of perpendicular straight lines is drawn through the origin forming with the line $2x + 3y = 6$ an isosceles triangle right angled at the origin. Find the equation of pair of lines and the area of the triangle.

   (b) Let ABC be a right angled triangle with angle at $A(2, 1)$ being $90°$. If the equation of the line BC be $2x + y = 3$ then the joint equation of the lines AB and AC is $3x^2 - 3y^2 + 8xy - 20x - 10y + 25 = 0$

15. Prove that the equation
   $x - y = 3$ and $x^2 + 4xy + y^2 = 0$
   represent the sides of an equilateral triangle.

16.* (i) Find the angle between the lines given by the equation $\lambda y^2 + (1 - \lambda^2) xy - \lambda x^2 = 0$ is

   (a) $45°$ (b) $60°$

   (c) $90°$ (d) $15°$

   (ii) The angle between the pair of straight lines $y^2 \sin^2 \theta - xy \sin^2 \theta + x^2 (\cos^2 \theta - 1) = 0$ is

   (a) $\pi/3$ (b) $\pi/4$

   (c) $2\pi/3$ (d) none of these

   (iii) The angle between the pair of lines given by the equation $x^2 + 2xy - y^2 = 0$ is

(a) $\pi/3$ (b) $\pi/6$

(c) $\pi/2$ (d) 0   **(M.N.R. 1990)**

17. Find the area of the triangle formed by the lines
$y^2 - 9xy + 18x^2 = 0$ and $y = 9$

18. Find the internal angles of the triangle formed by the pair of straight lines $x^2 - 4xy + y^2 = 0$ and the straight line $x + y + 4\sqrt{6} = 0$. Give the co-ordinates of the vertices of the triangle so formed and also the area of the triangle.

19.* Find the area of the triangle formed by the lines $ax^2 + 2hxy + by^2 = 0$ and $lx + my + n = 0$.

20.* (a) If the lines $ax^2 + 2hxy + by^2 = 0$ be two sides of a parallelogram and the line $lx + my = 1$ be one of its diagonals, show that the equation of the other diagonal is $y(bl - hm) = x(am - hl)$.

(b) Find the equation of the circle on the straight line joining the points of intersection of $ax^2 + 2hxy + by^2 = 0$ and $lx + my = 1$ as diameter.

21.* Show that the orthocentre of the triangle formed by the lines $ax^2 + 2h\overline{x}y + by^2 = 0$ and $lx + my = 1$ is given by
$$\frac{x}{l} = \frac{y}{m} = \frac{a+b}{am^2 - 2hlm + bl^2}.$$

22. A triangle has the lines $y = m_1 x$ and $y = m_2 x$ as two of its sides, where m_1, m_2 are the roots of the equation $bx^2 + 2hx + a = 0$. If $P(a,b)$ is the orthocentre of the triangle then prove that the equation of its third side is $(a+b)(ax + ay) = ab(a+b-2h)$.

23. If one of the lines given by the equation $2x^2 + axy + 3y^2 = 0$ coincides with one of the lines given by $2x^2 + bxy - 3y^2 = 0$ and the other lines represented by them be perpendicular, then prove that $a/b = 5$.

Solutions to Problem Set (1)

1. (i) $(x-4y)(x-y)=0$ represents two straight lines through the origin given by $x-4y=0, x-y=0$.

(ii) Ans. (c). ∵ $\theta = \tan^{-1}\dfrac{2\sqrt{(h^2-ab)}}{(a+b)}$,

$a=1, b=4, h=-7/2$.

2. (a) If the lines represented by $ax^2 + 2hxy + by^2 = 0$, be $y - m_1 x = 0$ and $y - m_2 x = 0$ then
$m_1 + m_2 = -\dfrac{2h}{b}$ and $m_1 m_2 = \dfrac{a}{b}$ by § 1 (a), P. 944

The lines perpendicular to them and passing through origin will be
$$y = -\frac{1}{m_1}x \text{ and } y = -\frac{1}{m_2}x.$$
Their combined equation is
$$(m_1 y + x)(m_2 y + x) = 0$$
or $m_1 m_2 y^2 + xy(m_1 + m_2) + x^2 = 0$

or $\dfrac{a}{b}\cdot y^2 + xy\left(-\dfrac{2h}{b}\right) + x^2 = 0$

or $bx^2 - 2hxy + ay^2 = 0$

Rule : Interchange the coefficients of x^2 and y^2 and change the sign of the term of xy.

(b) If the slope of the two lines be m, m^2 then
$m + m^2 = -\dfrac{2h}{b}$ and $m.m^2 = \dfrac{a}{b}$

Cubing first relation, we have
$$m^3 + m^6 + 3m.m^2(m+m^2) = -\frac{8h^3}{b^3}$$
∴ $\dfrac{a}{b} + \dfrac{a^2}{b^2} + \dfrac{3a}{b}\left(-\dfrac{2h}{b}\right) = -\dfrac{8h^3}{b^3}$

or $\dfrac{a(a+b)}{b^2} - \dfrac{6ah}{b^2} = -\dfrac{8h^3}{b^3}$

Multiply throughout by $\dfrac{b^2}{ah}$

$\dfrac{a+b}{h} + \dfrac{8h^2}{ab} = 6.$

(c) Let the given lines be $y = m_1 x, y = m_2 x$ where $m_1 = \tan\theta_1, m_2 = \tan\theta_2$
The image of $y = m_1 x$ about $y = 0$ i.e., axis of x will make an angle $-\theta_1$ with x-axis and hence its equation is $y = \tan(-\theta_1)x$
or $y = -\tan\theta_1 x$ or $y + m_1 x = 0$
∴ Combined equation is
$$(y + m_1 x)(y + m_2 x) = 0$$
or $y^2 + xy(m_1 + m_2) + m_1 m_2 x^2 = 0$
or $by^2 - 2hxy + ay^2 = 0$

3. (a) $x^2 + 5xy + 2y^2 = 0$ **by Rule Q. 2 above.**

(b) Lines through origin perpendicular to given lines $3x^2 + 7xy - 2y^2 = 0$ is
$$-2x^2 - 7xy + 3y^2 = 0$$
or $2x^2 + 7xy - 3y^2 = 0$.

Hence lines through $A(1,1)$ perpendicular to given lines are
$$2(x-1)^2 + 7(x-1)(y-1) - 3(y-1)^2 = 0$$
or $2x^2 + 7xy - 3y^2 - 11x - y + 6 = 0$.

Above gives the equation of lines AL and AM.

4. If the lines represented by the given equation be
$y - m_1 x = 0$ and $y - m_2 x = 0$,
then by **§ 1, P. 944.**
$m_1 + m_2 = -\dfrac{2h}{b}$ and $m_1 m_2 = \dfrac{a}{b}$

If p_1 and p_2 be the perpendiculars to them from the point (x_1, y_1), then
$$p_1 \times p_2 = \frac{y_1 - m_1 x_1}{\sqrt{(1+m_1^2)}} \cdot \frac{y_1 - m_2 x_1}{\sqrt{(1+m_2^2)}}$$

$$= \frac{y_1^2 - x_1 y_1 (m_1 + m_2) + m_1 m_2 x_1^2}{\sqrt{(1 + m_1^2 + m_2^2 + m_1^2 m_2^2)}}$$

$$= \frac{y_1^2 - x_1 y_1 \left(-\dfrac{2h}{b}\right) + \dfrac{a}{b} x_1^2}{[1 + (m_1 + m_2)^2 - 2m_1 m_2 + m_1^2 m_2^2]^{1/2}}$$

$$= \frac{b y_1^2 + 2h x_1 y_1 + a x_1^2}{b \left[1 + \dfrac{4h^2}{b^2} - 2\dfrac{a}{b} + \dfrac{a^2}{b^2}\right]^{1/2}} = \frac{a x_1^2 + 2h x_1 y_1 + b y_1^2}{\sqrt{[(a-b)^2 + 4h^2]}}.$$

5. **(a)** The given equation being homogeneous of 3rd degree represents three straight lines through the origin. Since two of these lines are to be at right angles, as such one factor giving these two lines will be of the form

$$x^2 + pxy - y^2 = 0 \qquad \textbf{[1 (c), P. 944]} \quad ...(1)$$

The other factor will be linear homogeneous and let it be

$$ax - dy = 0 \qquad ...(2)$$

We have taken the 2nd factor keeping in view that in the product of (1) and (2) coefficients of x^3 and y^3 may be a and d respectively as are in the equation whose factors are these.

$$\therefore \quad ax^3 + 3bx^2 y + 3cxy^2 + dy^3$$
$$= (x^2 + pxy - y^2)(ax - dy).$$

Comparing the coefficients of similar terms, we get

$$3b = ap - d \qquad ...(3)$$
$$\text{and} \quad 3c = -a - pd \qquad ...(4)$$

Required condition is obtained by eliminating the unknown quantity p from (3) and (4).

$$\therefore \quad \frac{3b + d}{a} = -\frac{3c + a}{d}$$

$$\text{or} \quad d(3b + d) + a(3c + a) = 0,$$
$$\text{or} \quad a^2 + 3ac + 3bd + d^2 = 0.$$

(b) The given equation being homogeneous equation of third degree represents three straight lines through the origin. Since two of them are perpendicular, they are given by

$$x^2 + pxy - y^2 = 0$$

Hence the given equation is

$$(ax - 4y)(x^2 + pxy - y^2) = 0$$

Comparing coefficients, we get

$$ap - 4 = -9, \quad -a - 4p = -1.$$

$$\therefore \quad p = -\frac{5}{a} = \frac{a-1}{-4}$$

$$\text{or} \quad a^2 - a - 20 = 0 \Rightarrow (a-5)(a+4) = 0$$

$$\therefore \quad a = 5, -4$$

6. Arguing as in **Q. 5** above one of the factors of the given equation will be $x^2 + pxy - y^2 = 0$. **[by § 1 (c), P. 944]**.

Now keeping in view the coefficients of x^4 and y^4 the other factor will be

$$ex^2 + qxy - ay^2 = 0$$

$$\therefore \quad ay^4 + bxy^3 + cx^2 y^2 + dx^3 y + ex^4$$
$$= (x^2 + pxy - y^2)(ex^2 + qxy - ay^2).$$

Comparing the coefficients,

$b = -ap - q$	(by xy^3)	...(1)
$d = ep + q$	(by $x^3 y$)	...(2)
$c = -a - e + pq$	(by $x^2 y^2$)	...(3)

Solving (1) and (2) for p and q,

$$p = \frac{b+d}{e-a} \quad \text{and} \quad q = -\frac{ad + be}{e-a}.$$

On putting the values of p and q in (3), we get

$$(c + a + e) = -\frac{(b+d)(ad+be)}{(e-a)^2}$$

or $(a + c + e)(e-a)^2 + (b+d)(ad + be) = 0.$

7. If the lines be $y - m_1 x = 0$ and $y - m_2 x = 0$, then

$$m_1 + m_2 = -\frac{2h}{b} = \frac{2\tan\alpha}{\sin^2\alpha} = \frac{2}{\sin\alpha\cos\alpha}$$

$$m_1 m_2 = \frac{a}{b} = \frac{\tan^2\alpha + \cos^2\alpha}{\sin^2\alpha}$$

If the lines make angles θ and ϕ respectively with axis of x, then $\tan\theta = m_1$ and $\tan\phi = m_2$.

$$\therefore \quad (\tan\theta - \tan\phi)^2 = (m_1 - m_2)^2$$

$$= (m_1 + m_2)^2 - 4m_1 m_2$$

$$\text{or} \quad (\tan\theta - \tan\phi)^2$$

$$= \frac{4}{\sin^2\alpha\cos^2\alpha} - 4\left(\frac{\tan^2\alpha + \cos^2\alpha}{\sin^2\alpha}\right)$$

$$= \frac{4}{\sin^2\alpha\cos^2\alpha}[1 - \sin^2\alpha - \cos^4\alpha]$$

$$= \frac{4}{\sin^2\alpha\cos^2\alpha}[\cos^2\alpha - \cos^4\alpha]$$

$$= \frac{4}{\sin^2\alpha\cos^2\alpha}\cos^2\alpha(1 - \cos^2\alpha)$$

$$= \frac{4}{\sin^2\alpha\cos^2\alpha}\sin^2\alpha\cos^2\alpha = 4$$

$$\therefore \quad \tan\theta - \tan\phi = 2.$$

8. The given equation can be written as

$$x^2(\sin^2\alpha - \cos^2\theta) + 2xy\sin\theta\cos\theta$$
$$+ y^2(\sin^2\alpha - \sin^2\theta) = 0$$

It is of the form $ax^2 + 2hxy + by^2 = 0$ and hence if ϕ be the angle between them, then

$$\tan\phi = 2\frac{\sqrt{(h^2 - ab)}}{a+b}$$

$$2\sqrt{(h^2 - ab)} = 2[\sin^2\theta\cos^2\theta$$
$$- (\sin^2\alpha - \cos^2\theta)(\sin^2\alpha - \sin^2\theta)]^{1/2}$$

$$= 2[-\sin^4\alpha + \sin^2\alpha(\sin^2\theta + \cos^2\theta)]^{1/2}$$

$$= 2 \sin \alpha \, [1 - \sin^2 \alpha]^{1/2}$$
$$= 2 \sin \alpha \cos \alpha = \sin 2\alpha.$$
$$a + b = \sin^2 \alpha - \cos^2 \theta + \sin^2 \alpha - \sin^2 \theta$$
$$= 2 \sin^2 \alpha - 1$$
$$= -(1 - 2 \sin^2 \alpha) = -\cos 2\alpha$$
$$\therefore \quad \tan \phi = \frac{\sin 2\alpha}{-\cos 2\alpha} = -\tan 2\alpha. \quad \therefore \quad \phi = \pi - 2\alpha$$

or $\phi = 2\alpha$

9. (a) If the line $y = mx$ be common to both the pairs then putting mx for y in the two equations, we get
$$ax^2 + 2hmx^2 + bx^2 m^2 = 0$$

or $bm^2 + 2hm + a = 0$ ...(1)
$$a'x^2 + 2h'mx^2 + b'x^2 m^2 = 0$$

or $b'm^2 + 2h'm + a' = 0$ ...(2)

$$\therefore \quad \frac{m^2}{(a'h - ah')} = \frac{2m}{ab' - a'b} = \frac{1}{bh' - b'h} \text{ by (1), (2)}$$

$$\therefore \quad m = \frac{2(a'h - ah')}{(ab' - a'b)} \quad \text{(from 1st and 2nd)}$$

and $m = \frac{(ab' - a'b)}{2(bh' - b'h)}$. (from 2nd and 3rd)

$$\therefore \quad \frac{2(a'h - ah')}{(ab' - a'b)} = \frac{(ab' - a'b)}{2(bh' - b'h)}$$

or $(ab' - a'b)^2 - 4(a'h - ah')(bh' - b'h) = 0$

is the required condition.

(b) If one of the lines given by the first pair be $y = mx$, then by the given condition one of the lines given by the 2nd pair should be
$y = -(1/m) x.$

$$\therefore \quad bm^2 + 2hm + a = 0$$

and $b'(-1/m)^2 + 2h'(-1/m) + a' = 0$

or $a'm^2 - 2h'm + b' = 0$ **Rest as in Q. 9.**

Ans. $(aa' - bb')^2 - 4(hb' + h'a)(bh' + ha') = 0.$

10. Let $y = mx$ be a line common to both
$$\therefore \quad am^2 + 2m + 1 = 0 \text{ and } m^2 + 2m + a = 0$$

$$\therefore \quad \frac{m^2}{2(1-a)} = \frac{m}{a^2 - 1} = \frac{1}{2(1-a)}$$

$$\therefore \quad m^2 = 1 \text{ and } m = -\frac{1}{2}(a+1)$$

$$\therefore \quad \frac{1}{4}(a+1)^2 = m^2 = 1 \text{ or } (a+1)^2 - (2)^2 = 0$$

or $(a+3)(a-1) = 0 \quad \therefore \quad a = -3, 1$

For $a = 1$, the equations become identical so that both the equations are common. Since only one equation is common, we choose $a = -3$.
The two pairs are $x^2 + 2xy - 3y^2 = 0$
and $-3x^2 + 2xy + y^2 = 0$
or $(x + 3y)(x - y) = 0$ and $-(x - y)(3x + y) = 0$
$x - y = 0$ is the common line and the other lines are given by $x + 3y = 0$, $3x + y = 0$.

Their joint equation is $(x + 3y)(3x + y) = 0$
or $3x^2 + 10xy + 3y^2 = 0$ **Proved.**

11. Suppose that any of the straight lines represented by homogeneous equation is $y - mx = 0$.
$$\therefore \quad m = y/x. \quad ....(1)$$
By the given condition $\dfrac{y_1 - mx_1}{\sqrt{(1+m^2)}} = a$

or $(y_1 - mx_1)^2 = a^2(1+m^2)$ ...(2)

Since (2) is quadratic in m, hence there will be two straight lines which will satisfy the given condition. In order to find their equation we will eliminate m between (1) and (2).

$$\therefore \quad \left(y_1 - \frac{y}{x} \cdot x_1\right)^2 = a^2\left(1 + \frac{y^2}{x^2}\right)$$

or $(xy_1 - yx_1)^2 = a^2(x^2 + y^2).$

12. Let m be the slope of the line AB or AC which passes through $A(0, 0)$ and hence their equations will be of the type $y = mx$ and for both of them
$$m = y/x. \quad ....(1)$$

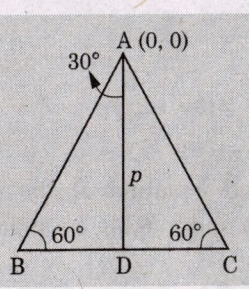

Fig. 2

If the triangle is to be equilateral, then
$\angle B = \angle C = 60°$. Slope of line $Ax + By + C = 0$ is $-A/B$.
Now AB and AC make angles of $60°$ and $-60°$ respectively with BC.

$$\therefore \quad \tan(\pm 60°) = \frac{m + A/B}{1 - m \cdot A/B} \text{ or } \pm\sqrt{3} = \frac{mB + A}{B - mA}$$

$$\therefore \quad 3(B - mA)^2 = (mB + A)^2.$$

The combined equation of the lines AB and AC is obtained by putting
$m = y/x,$ from (1)

$$\therefore \quad 3\left(B - \frac{y}{x} A\right)^2 = \left(B \cdot \frac{y}{x} + A\right)^2$$

or $3(Bx - Ay)^2 = (By + Ax)^2$ which on simplification reduces to the given equation and hence proved.
Now if p be perpendicular from A on BC, then
$$p = \frac{C}{\sqrt{(A^2 + B^2)}} \quad ...(1)$$

Area of $\Delta = \frac{1}{2} BC \cdot AD$
$$= \frac{1}{2} \cdot (2BD) . AD$$

$$= (p \tan 30^\circ)\, p = \frac{1}{\sqrt{3}} \cdot p^2$$

$$= \frac{C^2}{\sqrt{3}.(A^2 + B^2)} \text{ by (1)}$$

13. Since $a + b = 3 - 3 = 0$ therefore the equation $3x^2 - 8xy - 3y^2 = 0$ represents a pair of perpendicular straight lines. Now as in **Q. 12** we can prove that it is the combined equation of that pair of lines each of which is inclined at an angle of 45° to the line $x + 2y = 3$. Hence rt. angled isosceles triangle.

14. (a) Let any line through origin be $y = mx$. It makes an angle of $\pm 45^\circ$ with $2x + 3y = 6$ whose slope is $-2/3$

$$\therefore \quad \tan(\pm 45^\circ) = \frac{m - \left(-\frac{2}{3}\right)}{1 + m\left(-\frac{2}{3}\right)} = \frac{3m + 2}{3 - 2m}$$

$$\therefore \quad (3 - 2m)^2 = (3m + 2)^2.$$

Now put $m = \frac{y}{x}$

$$\therefore \quad \left(3 - 2\frac{y}{x}\right)^2 = \left(3\frac{y}{x} + 2\right)^2$$

or $(3x - 2y)^2 = (3y + 2x)^2$

or $5x^2 - 24xy - 5y^2 = 0$

is the required equation of the pair of lines through origin and making an angle of 45° with the given line.

Area of $\Delta = \frac{1}{2} BC \cdot p = BD.p.$ **(Refer Fig. Q. 12)**

But $p = BD \tan 45^\circ = BD$

$\therefore$ Area $= p^2$, p is perpendicular from origin on the line $2x + 3y = 6$

$$\therefore \quad p = \frac{6}{\sqrt{(4 + 9)}} = \frac{6}{\sqrt{13}}.$$

$\therefore$ Area $= \frac{36}{13}$ sq. units.

(b) Let m be the slope of any of the lines AB and BC each inclined at 45° to $2x + y = 3$ (slope -2).

$$\therefore \quad \tan(\pm 45^\circ) = \frac{m + 2}{1 - 2m} = \pm 1$$

$\therefore$ $m + 2 = 1 - 2m$
and $m + 2 = -(1 - 2m)$

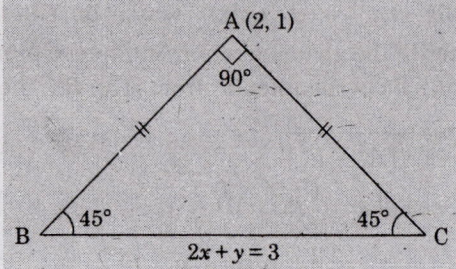

Fig. 3

$\therefore$ $m = -1/3, m = 3$
Hence, the two lines are

$$y - 1 = 3(x - 2) \text{ and } y - 1 = -\frac{1}{3}(x - 2)$$

or $3x - y - 5 = 0$ and $x + 3y - 5 = 0$
Their combined equation is
$(3x - y - 5)(x + 3y - 5) = 0$
or $3x^2 - 3y^2 + 8xy - 20x - 10y + 25 = 0$

15. Proceed as in **Q. 13 or 14.**

$$\tan(\pm 60^\circ) = \frac{m - 1}{1 + m} = \pm\sqrt{3}$$

$$\therefore \quad (m - 1)^2 = 3(1 + m)^2$$

or $\left(\frac{y}{x} - 1\right)^2 = 3\left(1 + \frac{y}{x}\right)^2$

or $(y - x)^2 = 3(x + y)^2$

or $2x^2 + 8xy + 2y^2 = 0$

or $x^2 + 4xy + y^2 = 0$

16. (i) Since $a + b = \lambda - \lambda = 0$ $\therefore$ 90°.
(ii) As in part (i)
$a + b = \sin^2\theta + \cos^2\theta - 1 = 0.$
The lines are $\perp$. Hence (d) is correct.
(iii) Ans. (c).

17. The sides of the triangle are $y - 3x = 0$ and $y - 6x = 0$ and $y = 9$.
Solving in pairs, its vertices are
$(0,0)$; $\left(\frac{3}{2}, 9\right)$; $(3,9)$

or $\Delta = \frac{1}{2}(x_1 y_2 - x_2 y_1) = \frac{27}{4}$ sq. units.

18. $x^2 - 4xy + y^2 = 0$
or $y^2 - 4xy + 4x^2 = 3x^2$
or $(y - 2x)^2 = (x\sqrt{3})^2$
$\therefore$ $y - 2x = \pm x\sqrt{3}$
or $y = (2 + \sqrt{3})x$, and $y = (2 - \sqrt{3})x$, are the two lines, the third line is $x + y + 4\sqrt{6} = 0$.

Now $\tan\theta = \frac{2\sqrt{(h^2 - ab)}}{a + b}$,

$a = b = 1, h = -2$

$\therefore$ $\tan\theta = 2\frac{\sqrt{(4-1)}}{1+1} = \sqrt{3}.$

$\therefore$ $\theta = 60^\circ$ and the corresponding vertex is clearly $(0, 0)$.
Again if β be the angle between the lines
$x + y + \sqrt{6} = 0$ and $y = (2 + \sqrt{3})x$
whose slopes are -1 and $2 + \sqrt{3}$ respectively, then

$$\tan\beta = \frac{(-1) - (2 + \sqrt{3})}{1 + (2 + \sqrt{3})(-1)} = \frac{-3 - \sqrt{3}}{-1 - \sqrt{3}} = \sqrt{3}$$

$\therefore$ $\beta = 60^\circ$

Since two angles are $60°$ each therefore the third angle is also $60°$. Hence the triangle is equilateral. Area of Δ as in **Q. 12**.

$$p^2 \tan 30° = \frac{1}{\sqrt 3} p^2 = \frac{1}{\sqrt 3} \cdot \left(\frac{4\sqrt 6}{\sqrt{(1+1)}} \right)^2$$
$$= 16\sqrt 3 \text{ sq. units.}$$

as p is perpendicular from origin to the line
$$x + y + 4\sqrt 6 = 0.$$

19. Let the lines represented by the given pair be $y = m_1 x$ and $y = m_2 x$, so that
$$m_1 + m_2 = -2h/b \quad \text{and} \quad m_1 m_2 = a/b \quad \text{...(1)}$$
These lines will meet the third line in points
$$\left(\frac{-n}{l + mm_1}, \frac{-nm_1}{l + mm_1} \right) \text{ and } \left(\frac{-n}{l + mm_2}, \frac{-nm_2}{l + mm_2} \right)$$
which will be two vertices of the triangle and the third vertex is clearly $(0, 0)$; hence the area of the triangle when one vertex is at the origin is
$$\frac{1}{2} (x_1 y_2 - x_2 y_1) = \frac{1}{2} \frac{n^2 (m_1 - m_2)}{(l + mm_1)(l + mm_2)}$$
$$= \frac{1}{2} n^2 \frac{[(m_1 + m_2)^2 - 4m_1 m_2]^{1/2}}{l^2 + lm(m_1 + m_2) + m^2 \cdot m_1 m_2}$$
$$= \frac{n^2 \sqrt{(h^2 - ab)}}{am^2 - 2hlm + bl^2}, \text{ from (1).}$$

20. (a) Let the equation $ax^2 + 2hxy + by^2 = 0$ represent $y = m_1 x$ and $y = m_2 x$ intersecting at $A(0, 0)$ so that
$$m_1 + m_2 = -2h/b \quad \text{and} \quad m_1 m_2 = a/b \quad \text{...(1)}$$

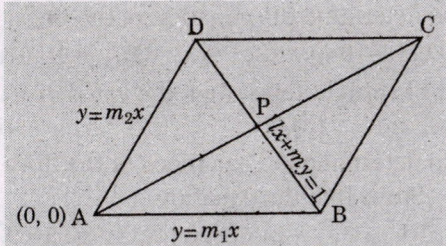

Fig. 4

then the diagonal $lx + my = 1$ is BD. We cannot take this equation for the diagonal AC as $lx + my = 1$ does not pass through origin. The co-ordinates of B and D are found by solving $y = m_1 x$ and $y = m_2 x$ with $lx + my = 1$ and are
$$\left(\frac{1}{l + mm_1}, \frac{m_1}{l + mm_1} \right) \text{ and } \left(\frac{1}{l + mm_2}, \frac{m_2}{l + mm_2} \right)$$
If E be the middle point of BD, whose co-ordinates are (h, k). Then
$$2h = \frac{2l + m(m_1 + m_2)}{(l + mm_1)(l + mm_2)}$$
$$\text{and } 2k = \frac{l(m_1 + m_2) + 2mm_1 m_2}{(l + mm_1)(l + mm_2)}$$

or $\quad h = \dfrac{bl - hm}{b(l + mm_1)(l + mm_2)}$

and $\quad k = \dfrac{am - hl}{b(l + mm_1)(l + mm_2)}, \quad$ from (1).

Now equation of the other diagonal which passes through $(0, 0)$ and (h, k) is
$$y = \frac{k}{h} x = \frac{am - hl}{bl - hm} x$$
or $\quad y (bl - hm) = x(am - hl)$.

(b) The points of intersection are as given in last question. The required circle is
$$(x - x_1)(x - x_2) + (y - y_1)(y - y_2) = 0$$
or $\quad x^2 + y^2 - x(x_1 + x_2) - y(y_1 + y_2) + x_1 x_2 + y_1 y_2 = 0$
where,
$$x_1 + x_2 = \frac{2l + m(m_1 + m_2)}{(l + mm_1)(l + mm_2)} = \frac{bl - hm}{am^2 - 2hlm + bl^2}$$
$$x_1 x_2 = \frac{b}{am^2 - 2hlm + bl^2}$$
Similarly $y_1 + y_2$ and $y_1 y_2$. Hence the required circle is
$$(x^2 + y^2)(am^2 - 2hlm + bl^2) - 2x(bl - hm) - 2y(am - hl) + (a + b) = 0.$$

21. Let AB, AC and BC be $y = m_1 x$, $y = m_2 x$ and $lx + my = 1$. Equation of AD which is perp. to BC and passes through $A(0, 0)$ is
$$mx - ly = 0 \quad \text{or} \quad \frac{x}{l} = \frac{y}{m} = k \text{ (say).}$$

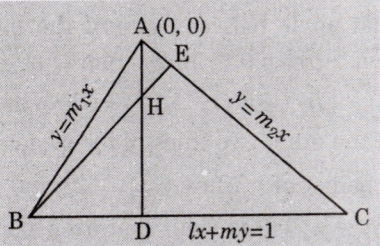

Fig. 5

Orthocentre will be some point on this line and its co-ordinates are (kl, km) for such suitable value of k so that the point may also lie on the line BE which is perpendicular to $y = m_2 x$, i.e., AC and passes through B whose co-ordinates on solving AB and BC are
$$\left(\frac{1}{l + mm_1}, \frac{m_1}{l + mm_1} \right).$$

∴ Equation to BE is
$$\left(y - \frac{m_1}{l + mm_1} \right) = -\frac{1}{m_2} \left(x - \frac{1}{l + mm_1} \right)$$
or $\quad m_2 y + x = \dfrac{1 + m_1 m_2}{l + mm_1}$

If (kl, km) is orthocentre, then it lies on above.

$$\therefore \quad k(l+mm_2) = \frac{1+m_1m_2}{l+mm_1}$$

or $\quad k = \dfrac{1+m_1m_2}{(l+mm_1)(l+mm_2)}$

$\qquad = \dfrac{a+b}{am^2 - 2hlm + bl^2}$. **See Q. 19, P. 947-951**

Hence the orthocentre is given by

$$\frac{x}{l} = \frac{y}{m} = \frac{a+b}{am^2 - 2hlm + bl^2} \qquad \dots(2)$$

22. Proceed as in last question.

23. Let $y = mx$ be a line common to both, and their lines perpendicular to each other be $y = m'x$ and $y = -\dfrac{x}{m'}$

$$\therefore \quad m+m' = -\frac{2h}{b} = \frac{-a}{3}, mm' = \frac{a}{b} = \frac{2}{3}$$

$$m - \frac{1}{m'} = -\frac{2h}{b} = \frac{b}{3}, m\left(-\frac{1}{m'}\right) = \frac{a}{b} = -\frac{2}{3}$$

Multiplying, we get $m^2 = \dfrac{4}{9}$ $\therefore$ $m = \dfrac{2}{3}, -\dfrac{2}{3}$

If $m = \dfrac{2}{3}, m' = 1$ and if $m = -\dfrac{2}{3}, m' = -1$

$$m+m' = -\frac{a}{3} \Rightarrow \frac{2}{3}+1 = -\frac{a}{3} \Rightarrow a = -5$$

$$m - \frac{1}{m'} = \frac{b}{3} \Rightarrow \frac{2}{3}-1 = \frac{b}{3} \Rightarrow b = -1$$

If $m = -\dfrac{2}{3}, m' = -1$, then $a = 5$, $b = 1$

In each case $\dfrac{a}{b} = \dfrac{5}{1}$.

Problem Set (2)

Lines represented by general equation of second degree $ax^2 + 2hxy + by^2 + 2gx + 2fy + c = 0$.

1. Determine the equation of bisectors of the angle between the lines $4x^2 - 16xy - 7y^2 = 0$

2. If $(a+b)^2 = 4h^2$ prove that one of the lines given by the equation $ax^2 + 2hxy + by^2 = 0$ will bisect the angle between the co-ordinate axes.

3. Show that the line $y = mx$ bisects the angle between the lines $ax^2 + 2hxy + by^2 = 0$ if $h(1 - m^2) - m(a-b) = 0$.

4. Prove that the straight lines $ax^2 + 2hxy + by^2 = 0$ have the same pair of bisectors as those of the lines given by
$$a^2x^2 + 2h(a+b)xy + b^2y^2 = 0.$$

5.* Prove that angle between one of the lines given by $ax^2 + 2hxy + by^2 = 0$ and one of the lines $ax^2 + 2hxy + by^2 + \lambda(x^2 + y^2) = 0$ is equal to the angle between the other two lines of the system.

6. If a pair of lines $x^2 - 2pxy - y^2 = 0$ and $x^2 - 2qxy - y^2 = 0$ is such that each pair bisects the angle between the other pair, prove that $pq = -1$.

7. (a) Prove that the equation
$$6x^2 + 17xy + 12y^2 + 22x + 31y + 20 = 0$$
represents a pair of straight lines and find their equations.

(b)* Show that the four straight lines given by the equations $12x^2 + 7xy - 12y^2 = 0$

and $\qquad 12x^2 + 7xy - 12y^2 - x + 7y - 1 = 0$

lie along the sides of a square.

8. Prove that the point of intersection of the lines given by the equation $x^2 - 5xy + 4y^2 + x + 2y - 2 = 0$ is (2, 1).

9.* (a) For what value of λ does the equation
$$12x^2 - 10xy + 2y^2 + 11x - 5y + \lambda = 0$$
represent a pair of straight lines ? Find their equations.

(b) For what real value of λ, the equation $2x^2 + 3y^2 - 8x - 6y + 11 - \lambda = 0$ represents a pair of straight lines ?

10. Prove that the equation
$$6x^2 - xy - 12y^2 - 8x + 29y - 14 = 0$$
represents a pair of lines and angle between them is $\tan^{-1}(17/6)$.

11. If $x^2 - 3xy + \lambda y^2 + 3x - 5y + 2 = 0$ represents a pair of straight lines, then the value of λ is
(i) 1 (ii) 4 (iii) 3 (iv) 2
Also determine the equation of the lines.

12.* If $\lambda x^2 - 10xy + 12y^2 + 5x - 16y - 3 = 0$ represents a pair of straight lines, then the value of λ is
(i) 4 (ii) 3 (iii) 2 (iv) 1
Also determine the equations of the lines.

13. (i) Prove that the equation
$$8x^2 + 8xy + 2y^2 + 26x + 13y + 15 = 0,$$
represents two parallel straight lines and find the distance between them.

(ii) The equation of second degree
$$x^2 + 2\sqrt{2}xy + 2y^2 + 4x + 4\sqrt{2}y + 1 = 0$$
represents a pair of parallel straight lines, the distance between them is
(a) 4 (b) $4/\sqrt{3}$
(c) 2 (d) $2\sqrt{3}$

14.* Prove that the general equation
$$ax^2 + 2hxy + by^2 + 2gx + 2fy + c = 0$$
will represent two parallel straight lines if $h^2 = ab$ and $bg^2 = af^2$. Also prove that the distance between them is $2\sqrt{\left\{\dfrac{g^2 - ac}{a(a+b)}\right\}}$.

Also prove that $\dfrac{a}{h} = \dfrac{h}{b} = \dfrac{g}{f}$.

15. (a) Prove that the straight lines joining origin to the points of intersection of the straight line $3x - y - 2 = 0$ and the curve $7x^2 - 4xy + 8y^2 + 2x - 4y - 8 = 0$ are at right angles to each other.

(b)* Find the equation of the lines joining the origin to the points of intersection of the line $4x - 3y = 10$ with the circle $x^2 + y^2 + 3x - 6y - 20 = 0$ and show that they are perpendicular.

(c)* Find the equations of the straight lines joining the origin to the points of intersection of the line $x - y = 2$ and the curve
$$5x^2 + 12xy - 8y^2 + 8x - 4y + 12 = 0$$
and find the angle between them. Also show that these lines are equally inclined to the axes.

16. Prove that the lines joining the origin to the points of intersection of circle $(x - h)^2 + (y - k)^2 = k^2$ with the line $\dfrac{x}{h} + \dfrac{y}{k} = 2$ will be perpendicular if (h, k) lies on the circle $x^2 + y^2 = r^2$.

17. (a) Find the equations of the lines joining the origin to the points of intersection of the lines $y = mx + c$ with the circle $x^2 + y^2 = a^2$ and find the condition for these lines to be perpendicular.

(b)* The portion of the line $lx + my = 1$ intercepted by the circle $x^2 + y^2 = a^2$ subtends an angle of $45°$ at the centre of the circle. Prove that $4[a^2(l^2 + m^2) - 1] = [a^2(l^2 + m^2) - 2]^2$

18.* Find the condition that the lines joining the origin to the points of intersection of the curves
$$ax^2 + 2hxy + by^2 + 2gx = 0 \text{ and}$$
$$a_1x^2 + 2h_1xy + b_1y^2 + 2g_1x = 0$$
be perpendicular.

19. (i) The angle between the straight lines
$$x^2 - y^2 - 2y - 1 = 0 \text{ is}$$

    (a) $90°$ (b) $60°$

    (c) $75°$ (d) $36°$ **(M.N.R. 1991)**

(ii) If the angle between the two lines represented by $2x^2 + 5xy + 3y^2 + 6x + 7y + 4 = 0$ is $\tan^{-1} m$ then m is ....   **(M.N.R. 1993)**

20. The equation $y^2 - x^2 + 2x - 1 = 0$ represents

    (a) a pair of straight lines   (b) a circle

    (c) a parabola   (d) an ellipse **(M.N.R. 1991)**

21. The equation
$$x^2y^2 - 2xy^2 - 3y^2 - 4x^2y + 8xy + 12y = 0$$
represents

    (a) a pair of lines

    (b) pair of lines and a circle

    (c) a pair of lines and a parabola

    (d) four lines forming a square

22. If by rotating the axes through an angle θ the general equation of second degree
$$ax^2 + 2hxy + by^2 + 2gx + 2fy + c = 0$$
is free from the term of xy, then prove that $\tan 2\theta$ is $\dfrac{2h}{a - b}$

23. $3x^2 + 8xy - 3y^2 = 0$ represents a pair of lines AB and BC, whereas the equation
$$3x^2 + 8xy - 3y^2 + 2x - 4y - 1 = 0$$
represents two lines CD and DA.

Answer the following :

    (a) The equation of CD is ...

    (b) The nature of the quadrilateral $ABCD$ is ...

    (c) Area of quadrilateral is ...

    (d) The co-ordinates of point D are ...

24. Let a and b be non-zero real numbers. Then, the equation
$$(ax^2 + by^2 + c)(x^2 - 5xy + 6y^2) = 0 \text{ represents}$$

    (a) four straight lines, when $c = 0$ and a, b are of the same sign

    (b) two straight lines and a circle, when $a = b$, and c is of sign opposite to that of a

    (c) two straight lines and a hyperbola, when a and b are of the same sign and c is of sign opposite to that of a

    (d) a circle and an ellipse, when a and b are of the same sign and c is of a sign opposite to that of a

                                      (I.I.T. 2008)

Solutions to Problem Set (2)

1. $a = 4, b = -7, h = -8$

    Bisectors are $\dfrac{x^2 - y^2}{a - b} = \dfrac{xy}{h}$ or $\dfrac{x^2 - y^2}{11} = \dfrac{xy}{-8}$.

2. The bisectors of the angle between the co-ordinate axes will make an angle of $45°$ or $135°$ with the +ive direction of x-axis and hence their equations are $y = x$ or $y = -x$.

If $y = x$ belongs to $ax^2 + 2hxy + by^2 = 0$, then
$$ax^2 + 2hx(x) + b(x)^2 \quad \therefore \quad a + b = -2h.$$

Similarly if $y = -x$ belongs to
$$ax^2 + 2hxy + by^2 = 0, \text{ then}$$
$$a + b = 2h \quad \therefore \quad a + b = \pm 2h$$

Squaring, we get $(a + b)^2 = 4h^2$.

3. Bisectors of the given pair of lines is $\dfrac{x^2 - y^2}{a - b} = \dfrac{xy}{h}$. If $y = mx$ be one of the bisectors, then it will satisfy above.

$$\therefore \quad \dfrac{x^2 - m^2x^2}{a - b} = \dfrac{x.mx}{h}$$

or $h(1-m^2) - m(a-b) = 0$.

4. The bisectors of the pair of lines
$a^2 x^2 + 2h(a+b)xy + b^2 y^2 = 0$ is given by

$$\frac{x^2 - y^2}{\text{coeff. of } x^2 - \text{coeff. of } y^2} = \frac{xy}{\text{half the coeff. of } xy}$$

or $\dfrac{x^2 - y^2}{a^2 - b^2} = \dfrac{xy}{h(a+b)}$ or $\dfrac{x^2 - y^2}{a-b} = \dfrac{xy}{h}$

But these are also the bisectors of the lines given by first pair.

5. Prove as above that the two pairs have the same bisectors

$$\frac{x^2 - y^2}{(a+\lambda) - (b+\lambda)} = \frac{xy}{h} \quad \text{or} \quad \frac{x^2 - y^2}{a-b} = \frac{xy}{h}$$

and these are also the bisectors of 1st pair.

6. Equations of the bisectors of $x^2 - 2pxy - y^2 = 0$ are

$$\frac{x^2 - y^2}{1 - (-1)} = \frac{xy}{-p} \quad \text{or} \quad x^2 - y^2 = \frac{-2xy}{p}. \qquad \dots(1)$$

But the bisectors of first pair of lines are given by the 2nd pair, *i.e.* by

$$x^2 - y^2 = 2qxy \qquad \dots(2)$$

Comparing (1) and (2), we get

$-1/p = q$ or $pq = -1$

or $pq + 1 = 0$.

7. **(a)** **Method to find the two factors of the given equation.**

Rule : First factorize the second degree terms of the given equation and then add p and q to each of these factors respectively. Now multiply these two factors, compare the coefficients of x, y and constant in this product with the corresponding coefficients in the given equation. Thus you will find the values of p and q.

$6x^2 + 17xy + 12y^2 = 6x^2 + 8xy + 9xy + 12y^2$

$\qquad\qquad = 2x(3x+4y) + 3y(3x+4y)$

$\qquad\qquad = (2x+3y)(3x+4y)$.

Hence the factors of the given equation are

$(2x + 3y + p)(3x + 4y + q) \qquad \dots(1)$

Comparing the coefficients of x, y and constant in the product of (1) with the corresponding coefficients in the given equation, we get

$3p + 2q = 22 \qquad \dots(2)$

$4p + 3q = 31 \qquad \dots(3)$

and $pq = 20 \qquad \dots(4)$

On solving (2) and (3), we find that $p = 4$ and $q = 5$ and these values of p and q satisfy (4) as well. Hence the given equation represents a pair of straight lines whose separate equations are

$2x + 3y + 4 = 0$ and $3x + 4y + 5 = 0$

(b) The first pair gives the two lines as $3x + 4y = 0$ and $4x - 3y = 0$ which are perpendicular. The second

pair as in part (a) gives the lines as $3x + 4y - 1 = 0$ and $4x - 3y + 1 = 0$.

Since the distance between each set of parallel lines is same 1/2 and hence these lines enclose a square.

8. Do yourself.

9. **(a)** Here $a = 12, b = 2, c = \lambda, f = -\dfrac{5}{2}, g = \dfrac{11}{2}, h = -5$.

Putting these values in the condition

$$abc + 2fgh - af^2 - bg^2 - ch^2 = 0$$

we get $24\lambda + \dfrac{275}{2} - 75 - \dfrac{121}{2} - 25\lambda = 0$

$\therefore \qquad \lambda = 2$

$\therefore \qquad 12x^2 - 10xy + 2y^2 + 11x - 5y + 2 = 0$

represents a pair of straight lines and proceeding as in part (a), their equations are

$4x - 2y + 1 = 0$ and $3x - y + 2 = 0$.

Alt. The factors of 2nd degree terms are $(2x - y)(6x - 2y)$. Hence the two lines are $(2x - y + p)(6x - 2y + q)$. Comparing the coefficients

$6p + 2q = 11, \; -2p - q = -5$ and $pq = \lambda$

The first two give $p = \dfrac{1}{2}, q = 4 \; \therefore \; pq = 2 = \lambda$

and the lines are $2x - y + \dfrac{1}{2} = 0$

and $\qquad 6x - 2y + 4 = 0$

(b) The second degree terms cannot be factorized into two linear factors or else $h^2 - ab = 0 - 6 = -$ive.

Hence the given equation does not represent a pair of lines whatever λ may be.

10. Ans. $2x - 3y + 2 = 0$ and $3x + 4y - 7 = 0$.

11. Clearly for $\lambda = 2$ the second degree terms become $x^2 - 3xy + 2y^2$ which can be factorized as $(x - 2y)(x - y)$ and as in **Q. 7** the two lines are $(x - 2y + 1) = 0$ and $(x - y + 2) = 0$. You may apply the condition as in **Q. 9**.

12. Clearly for $\lambda = 2$ the second degree terms become

$2x^2 - 10xy + 12y^2 = 2x^2 - 4xy - 6xy + 12y^2$

$\qquad\qquad = (x - 2y)(2x - 6y)$

and as in **Q. 7** the two lines are

$(x - 2y + p)(2x - 6y + q) = 0$

where $p = 3$ and $q = -1$.

Hence the two lines are $x - 2y + 3 = 0, \; 2x - 6y - 1 = 0$.

13. **(i)** Here $h^2 - ab = (4)^2 - 2 \times 8 = 0$.

$\therefore$ the lines are parallel.

On dividing by 2,

$$4x^2 + 4xy + y^2 + 13x + \frac{13}{2}y + \frac{15}{2} = 0$$

Suppose its factors are $(2x + y + p)(2x + y + q)$.

On comparing the coefficients, we get

$2(p + q) = 13, \; p + q = \dfrac{13}{2}$ and $pq = \dfrac{15}{2}$, or $\quad p\left(\dfrac{13}{2}-p\right)=\dfrac{15}{2}\quad$ or $\quad 2p^2-13p+15=0$

$\therefore\quad (p-5)(2p-3)=0$

or $\quad p=5,\dfrac{3}{2};\quad \therefore\quad q=\dfrac{3}{2},5$

$\therefore\quad 2x+y+5=0,\quad 2x+y+\dfrac{3}{2}=0$

are the required lines.

If p_1 and p_2 be their distances from origin, then the distance between them is

$$p=p_1\sim p_2=\dfrac{5}{\sqrt{(4+1)}}\sim\dfrac{3/2}{\sqrt{(4+1)}}=\dfrac{7}{2\sqrt5}$$

(ii) As in part (a) the two parallel lines are
$$(x+\sqrt2 y+p)(x+\sqrt2 y+q)=0$$
where $p+q=4$ and $pq=1$

$\therefore\quad p-q=\sqrt{(16-4)}=2\sqrt3$

$\therefore\quad$ Req. distance $=\dfrac{p}{\sqrt3}-\dfrac{q}{\sqrt3}=\dfrac{1}{\sqrt3}(2\sqrt3)=2$

$\therefore\quad$ **(c)** is correct.

14. As on **P. 944** result **§ 1 (c)** we can show that the general equation of second degree will represent a pair of parallel straight lines if $h^2=ab$ or $h=\sqrt{(ab)}$. In order to find the second condition, put the value of h in the equation.

$\therefore\quad ax^2+2\sqrt{(ab)}\,xy+by^2+2gx+2fy+c=0$

or $\quad [\sqrt{(ax)}+\sqrt{(by)}]^2+2gx+2fy+c=0.$

Now suppose that above is equal to
$$[\sqrt{(ax)}+\sqrt{(by)}+p]\,[\sqrt{(ax)}+\sqrt{(by)}+q]=0$$
Comparing the coefficients,

$p\sqrt a+q\sqrt a=2g\quad$ or $\quad (p+q)=\dfrac{2g}{\sqrt a}\qquad$ ...(1)

$p\sqrt b+q\sqrt b=2f\quad$ or $\quad p+q=\dfrac{2f}{\sqrt b}\qquad$ ...(2)

$pq=c\qquad\qquad$ ...(3)

Now from (1) and (2),

$\dfrac{2g}{\sqrt a}=\dfrac{2f}{\sqrt b}\quad$ or $\quad bg^2=af^2$

Distance between the lines as in **R. 21, P. 8.**

$=\dfrac{0+0+p}{\sqrt{(a+b)}}-\dfrac{0+0+q}{\sqrt{(a+b)}}=\dfrac{p-q}{\sqrt{(a+b)}}$

$=\dfrac{\{(p+q)^2-4pq\}^{1/2}}{\sqrt{(a+b)}}=\left\{\dfrac{\dfrac{4g^2}{a}-4.c}{(a+b)}\right\}^{1/2}$

[by (1) and (3)]

$=2\sqrt{\left\{\dfrac{g^2-ac}{a(a+b)}\right\}}.$

Now from above, we have $h^2=ab$ and $bg^2=af^2$.

$\dfrac{a}{h}=\dfrac{h}{b}=k$ say,

$\therefore\quad a=hk$ and $b=\dfrac{h}{k}$;

$\therefore\quad$ from the condition $bg^2=af^2$,

$\dfrac{h}{k}g^2=hk\,.\,f^2$;

$\therefore\quad \dfrac{g^2}{f^2}=k^2\qquad$ or $\qquad \dfrac{g}{f}=k$;

$\therefore\quad \dfrac{a}{h}=\dfrac{h}{b}=\dfrac{g}{f}$ as each is equal to k.

15. **(a)** $\quad 3x-y-2=0\quad$ or $\quad \dfrac{3x-y}{2}=1.$

Making the equation of the curve homogeneous, we get

$7x^2-4xy+8y^2+2(x-2y)\dfrac{(3x-y)}{2}$

$\qquad\qquad\qquad -8\cdot\left(\dfrac{3x-y}{2}\right)^2=0$

or $\quad (7x^2-4xy+8y^2)+(3x^2-7xy+2y^2)$

$\qquad\qquad\qquad -2(9x^2-6xy+y^2)=0$

or $-8x^2+xy+8y^2=0$ is the required equation to the lines.

Since $a+b=-8+8=0$, and hence the lines are perpendicular.

(b) Proceed as in part (a).

(c) From the equation of the line we have $x-y=2$

or $\quad \dfrac{x-y}{2}=1.\qquad\qquad$ ...(1)

Equation of the curve

$5x^2+12xy-8y^2+4(2x-y)+12=0$

$5x^2+12xy-8y^2+4(2x-y)\cdot1+12\cdot1^2=0$

[Make it homogeneous]

Equation of the required lines is

$5x^2+12xy-8y^2+4(2x-y)\left(\dfrac{x-y}{2}\right)$

$\qquad\qquad +12\left(\dfrac{x-y}{2}\right)^2=0\quad$ [by (1)]

or $\quad (5x^2+12xy-8y^2)+2(2x^2-3xy+y^2)$

$\qquad\qquad\qquad +3(x^2-2xy+y^2)=0$

or $\quad 12x^2+0xy-3y^2=0\qquad$ or $\qquad y=\pm2x.$

If $\tan\theta=2$, then $-2=-\tan\theta=\tan(\pi-\theta).$

They are clearly equally inclined to axes.

Angle between them is $\pi-2\theta=\pi-2\tan^{-1}2.$

16. Making the equation of circle homogeneous,

$x^2+y^2-2(hx+ky)\cdot\dfrac{1}{2}\left(\dfrac{x}{h}+\dfrac{y}{k}\right)$

$\qquad\qquad =(h^2+k^2-r^2)\cdot\dfrac{1}{4}\left(\dfrac{x}{h}+\dfrac{y}{k}\right)^2$

$A + B = 0 \implies \left(\dfrac{h^2 + k^2 - r^2}{4}\right)\left(\dfrac{1}{h^2} + \dfrac{1}{k^2}\right) = 0$

$\therefore \quad h^2 + k^2 - r^2 = 0$, as $\dfrac{1}{h^2} + \dfrac{1}{k^2} \neq 0$

$\therefore$ Locus of (h, k) is $x^2 + y^2 = r^2$.

17. (a) From the equation $\dfrac{y - mx}{c} = 1$.

$\therefore \quad x^2 + y^2 = a^2 \cdot 1^2$,

or $\quad x^2 + y^2 = a^2 \dfrac{(y - mx)^2}{c^2}$

Ans. $(c^2 - a^2 m^2) x^2 + 2am^2 xy + (c^2 - a^2) y^2 = 0$.

If it represents two perpendicular straight lines, then

coeff. of x^2 + coeff. of $y^2 = 0$.

$c^2 - a^2 m^2 + c^2 - a^2 = 0$

$2c^2 = a^2 (1 + m^2)$ is the required condition.

(b) The centre of the circle is origin. The equations of the lines joining origin to the points of intersection of the line and circle are

$x^2 + y^2 = a^2 (lx + my)^2$

or $\quad x^2 (a^2 l^2 - 1) + 2 lm a^2 xy + y^2 (a^2 m^2 - 1) = 0$

$Ax^2 + 2Hxy + By^2 = 0$

$\tan 45° = 1 = \dfrac{2 \sqrt{H^2 - AB}}{A + B}$

$(A + B)^2 = 4 [H^2 - AB]$

$[a^2 (l^2 + m^2) - 2]^2 = 4 [a^2 (l^2 + m^2) - 1]$

18. We know that the combined equation of the lines through the origin is homogeneous. Hence eliminating the first degree terms of x between the given equations we shall obtain homogeneous equation which will represent the required lines. Multiplying the first equation by g_1 and 2nd by g and subtracting, we get

$g_1 (ax^2 + 2hxy + by^2 + 2gx)$

$\qquad - g (a_1 x^2 + 2h_1 xy + b_1 y^2 + 2g_1 x) = 0$

or $\quad (g_1 a - a_1 g) x^2 + 2xy (hg_1 - h_1 g)$

$\qquad\qquad + (g_1 b - b_1 g) y^2 = 0$

If the above equation represents two perpendicular lines, then

coeff. of x^2 + coeff. of $y^2 = 0$.

$\therefore \quad g_1 a - a_1 g + g_1 b - b_1 g = 0$

$\therefore \quad (a + b) g_1 = (a_1 + b_1) g$ is the required condition.

19. (i) Ans. [a].

(ii) Ans. $\dfrac{1}{5}$.

$\tan \theta = \dfrac{2 \sqrt{(h^2 - ab)}}{a + b} = \dfrac{1}{5} \quad \therefore \quad \theta = \tan^{-1} \dfrac{1}{5}$.

20. Ans. (a).

21. Ans. (d).

Collecting the terms y^2 and y the given equation can be written as

$y^2 (x^2 - 2x - 3) - 4y (x^2 - 2x - 3) = 0$

or $\quad (x - 3)(x + 1) y (y - 4) = 0$

It represents four lines $x = -1$, $x = 3$, $y = 0$ and $y = 4$. These two sets of parallel lines form a square of side four.

22. Let the axes be rotated through an angle θ so that $\left. \begin{array}{l} x \to x \cos \theta - y \sin \theta \\ y \to x \sin \theta + y \cos \theta \end{array} \right\}$ by **(d) P. 17**

$a (x \cos \theta - y \sin \theta)^2 + 2h (x \cos \theta - y \sin \theta)$

$(x \sin \theta + y \cos \theta) + b (x \sin \theta + y \cos \theta)^2$

$\qquad\qquad + 2g (x \cos \theta - y \sin \theta)$

$\qquad\qquad\qquad + 2f (x \sin \theta + y \cos \theta) + c = 0$

Collect the coefficients of xy and put it equal to zero

$(- a \sin 2\theta + b \sin 2\theta) + 2h (\cos^2 \theta - \sin^2 \theta) = 0$

$\dfrac{\sin 2\theta}{\cos 2\theta} = \dfrac{2h}{a - b} \implies \tan 2\theta = \dfrac{2h}{a - b}$

23. (a) $AB \equiv x + 3y = 0$, $BC = 3x - y = 0$ represent two perpendicular lines passing through the point $B (0, 0)$. The other two lines are $(x + 3y + 1)(3x - y - 1) = 0$

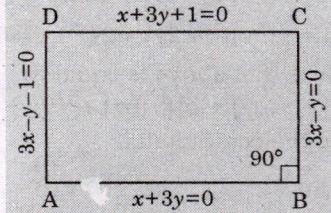

Fig. 6

$\therefore$ These are parallel to AB and BC respectively.

$\therefore$ Equation of CD is $x + 3y + 1 = 0$.

(b) Since $a + b = 0$, the two pairs represent pair of perpendicular straight lines. Hence the quadrilateral is a square or a rectangle. But distance between parallel sides $= \dfrac{1}{\sqrt{10}}$ each and hence it is a square.

(c) Area $p^2 = \dfrac{1}{10}$.

(d) Solving CD and AD, the point D is $\left(\dfrac{1}{5}, -\dfrac{2}{5}\right)$.

24. Ans. (b).

$x^2 - 5xy + 6y^2 = 0 \implies (x - 3y)(x - 2y) = 0$

Above represents two straight lines through $(0, 0)$.

$ax^2 + by^2 + c = 0 \implies x^2 + y^2 = -\dfrac{c}{a}$ ...(1)

where, $c = 0$ and a and b are of same sign *i.e.*, of the form $5x^2 + 9y^2 = 0$. This is not possible.

When $a = b$ and c is of sign opposite to that of a then from (1), 2nd factor is $x^2 + y^2 = +ive = k^2$. Hence a circle $\Rightarrow$ (b) is correct.

Both (c) and (d) are obviously incorrect.

MISCELLANEOUS EXERCISE

Matching Entries

♦ *Match the entries of List-A and List-B.*

1.   **List-A**   **List-B**

(a) The lines joining the origin to the points of intersection of the line
    $4x - 3y = 10$ with the circle $x^2 + y^2 + 3x - 6y - 20 = 0$ include an angle   1. $h = \pm \dfrac{2}{3}\sqrt{ab}$

(b) The two lines given by $a^2 x^2 + 2hxy + b^2 y^2 = 0$ are such that slope of
    one is three times of the other, then h is equal to   2. 2

(c) If the equation $12x^2 - 10xy + 2y^2 + 11x - 5y + \lambda = 0$ represents a pair
    of straight lines then $\lambda =$ 3. 10

(d) If $x^2 - 3xy + \lambda y^2 + 3x - 5y + 2 = 0$ represents a pair of lines which
    include an angle θ, then $\csc^2 \theta =$ 4. $\pi / 2$

2.   Match the entries of col. I with those of col. II.
    The lines given by left hand side in col. I have the property mentioned in col. II.

     Column I   **Column II**

(a) $6x^2 + 5xy - 6y^2 - x + 5y - 1 = 0$ (p) parallel

(b) $30x^2 + 36xy + 6y^2 - 35x - 11y + 5 = 0$ (q) perpendicular

(c) $30x^2 + 41xy + 6y^2 - 35x - 11y + 5 = 0$ (r) $I_x = 5/6$

(d) $6x^2 + 12xy + 6y^2 - 7x - 7y + 1 = 0$ (s) $I_y = 1/6$

Answers

1.   (a) $\to$ (4), (b) $\to$ (1), (c) $\to$ (2), (d) $\to$ (3)
2.   (a) $\to$ (q, r, s), (b) $\to$ (r, s), (c) $\to$ (r, s), (d) $\to$ (p, r)

Hints/Solutions

1.   (a) $2x^2 - 3xy - 2y^2 = 0$, $\pi/2$

(b) $m + 3m = -\dfrac{2h}{b^2}$, $m \cdot 3m = \dfrac{a^2}{b^2}$

$\therefore \quad 2m = -\dfrac{h}{b^2} \Rightarrow m = -\dfrac{h}{2b^2}$

$\therefore \quad 3\left(-\dfrac{h}{2b^2}\right)^2 = \dfrac{a^2}{b^2} \quad \therefore \quad h^2 = \dfrac{4}{3} a^2 b^2$

$\therefore \quad h = \pm \dfrac{2}{\sqrt{3}} ab$

(c) **See Q. 9, P. 952-95**
(d) **See Q. 11, P. 952-954**
    $m_1 = 2, m_2 = 1$
    $\therefore \quad \tan \theta = 1/3 \quad \therefore \quad \csc^2 \theta = 1 + \cot^2 \theta = 10$

2.   (a) $\to$ (q) as $a + b = 0$. Its intersection with x-axis ($y = 0$)
    is given by
    $6x^2 - x - 1 = 0$ or $(3x + 1)(2x - 1) = 0 \quad \therefore \quad x = \dfrac{1}{2}, -\dfrac{1}{3}$

$\therefore \quad I_x = x_1 - x_2 = \dfrac{1}{2} + \dfrac{1}{3} = \dfrac{5}{6} \quad \therefore \text{(a)} \to \text{(r)}$

Its intersection with y-axis ($x = 0$) is given by
$-6y^2 + 5y - 1 = 0$ or $6y^2 - 5y + 1 = 0$

or $(3y - 1)(2y - 1) = 0 \quad \therefore \quad y = \dfrac{1}{2}, \dfrac{1}{3}$.

$I_y = y_1 - y_2 = \dfrac{1}{2} - \dfrac{1}{3} = \dfrac{1}{6} \quad \therefore \text{(a)} \to \text{(s)}$

$\therefore \quad$ (a) $\to$ (q, r, s)
(b) $\to$ (r, s), (c) $\to$ (r, s). Proceed as in (a).

(d) $6(x + y)^2 - 7(x + y) + 1 = 0$ or $6t^2 - 7t + 1 = 0$

$\therefore \quad (t - 1)(6t - 1) = 0$

$\therefore \quad x + y - 1 = 0$ or $x + y - \dfrac{1}{6} = 0$

$\therefore \quad$ Parallel lines (d) $\to$ (p)

$y = 0, x = 1, \dfrac{1}{6} \quad \therefore \quad I_x = 1 - \dfrac{1}{6} = \dfrac{5}{6} \quad \therefore \text{(d)} \to \text{(r)}$

$x = 0, y = 1, \dfrac{1}{6} \quad \therefore \quad I_y = 1 - \dfrac{1}{6} = \dfrac{5}{6} \quad \therefore \text{(d)} \to \text{(p, r)}$

Fascinating Facts

- Two points (x_1, y_1) and (x_2, y_2) not lying on the line $ax + by + c = 0$ lie on the same side or on opposite sides of $ax + by + c = 0$ according as $ax_1 + by_1 + c$ and $ax_2 + by_2 + c$ are of the same sign or of opposite sign.

- The point of concurrence of the altitudes of a triangle is called its orthocentre and the point of concurrence of the right bisectors of the sides of a triangle is called its circumcentre.

- If two linear equations represent the same line, then their corresponding coefficients are proportional.

- A system of two equations in which one equation can be obtained from the other by multiplying by an appropriate (non-zero) real number is called a system of dependent equations.

- The equation $ax + by + c = 0$, where k is a parameter, represents a family of straight lines parallel to the line $ax + by + c = 0$

- The equation $bx - ay + k = 0$, k is a parameter, represents a family of straight lines perpendicular to the line $ax + by + c = 0$.

- The equation $x = a, a \in \mathbf{R}$ represents the family of lines which are parallel to y-axis.

- The equation $y = b, b \in \mathbf{R}$ represents the family of lines which are parallel to x-axis.

- If the lines represented by the general equation $ax^2 + 2hxy + by^2 + 2gx + 2fy + c = 0$ are perpendicular, then the square of the distance between the points of intersection and origin is $\dfrac{f^2 + g^2}{h^2 + b^2}$ or $\dfrac{f^2 + g^2}{h^2 + a^2}$

- The two pairs of straight lines
$$ax^2 + 2hxy + by^2 + 2gx + 2fy + c = 0 \text{ forms a}$$
(i) square if $(a - b)\, fg + h\,(f^2 - g^2) = 0$, $a + b = 0$
(ii) rectangle if $(a - b)\, fg + h\,(f^2 - g^2) \neq 0$, $a + b = 0$
(iii) rhombus if $(a - b)\, fg + h\,(f^2 - g^2) = 0$, $a + b \neq 0$
(iv) parallelogram if $(a - b)\, fg + h\,(f^2 - g^2) \neq 0$, $a + b \neq 0$

- The square of the distance between the points of intersection of the lines represented by the equation $ax^2 + 2hxy + by^2 + 2gx + 2fy + c = 0$ and origin is $\dfrac{c(a + b) - f^2 - g^2}{ab - h^2}$

❑